W9-CJQ-867

COMMUNISM IN AFRICA

COMMUNISM IN AFRICA

By

FRITZ SCHATTEN

FREDERICK A. PRAEGER, *Publishers*

NEW YORK · WASHINGTON

BOOKS THAT MATTER

Published in the United States of America in 1966
by Frederick A. Praeger, Inc., Publishers
111 Fourth Avenue, New York 3, N.Y.

Second printing, 1966

Library of Congress Catalog Card Number: 65-14187

This book is Number 174 in the series of
Praeger Publications in Russian History and World Communism

Printed in the United States of America

CONTENTS

Chapter I

THE AFRICAN REVOLUTION

THE twentieth century is witnessing yet another revolution. A gigantic, elementary upheaval beyond anything previously known: the emancipation of a whole continent from historical darkness and political formlessness. This new eruption is changing not only the face of Africa but that of the whole world. Since the beginning of the modern era the history of the world has been dominated by fewer and fewer powers, and at first it seemed that a 'monopoly' had been established. From time to time the balance may have shifted slightly between the big Powers and their groups of alliances, and the pattern of individual loyalties may have changed a little, but the basic structure always remained the same. Even after the Second World War, which led to the development of great Powers with their allies and satellites, nothing changed fundamentally; instead, as Robert Strausz-Hupé wrote in 1948:[1] 'this balance of power lost none of its validity and merely took on a more subtle significance.' The tension between the two international poles after the Second World War determined world political development after 1945, and led to the establishment of a *status quo* which appeared to be permanent and unalterable.

Since 1960, however, we can see the beginning of a fundamental and decisive change in world affairs: the revolutionary upheaval in Africa, the emancipation of the African continent, and its emergence from the status of a mere passive object of the great European Powers to that of a potential individual actor on the world stage, constitute a development that has suddenly enhanced the importance of these States. Previously they had swung indecisively this way and that between the Eastern and Western blocs, while never being really strong enough to act effectively as a 'third force'. If this group of neutral or non-aligned Powers, now being tremendously reinforced by the new African countries, is ever in a position to act independently and with determination, and is able to maintain its independence and to strengthen internal solidarity, then a completely new international situation will develop. It can, for example, operate as a 'new majority' in the United Nations and the specialized agencies and even out-vote the 'old Powers' in matters exclusively concerning them—a possibility underlined by events at the United Nations since the autumn of 1960, and especially demonstrated during the sessions in 1962 and 1963. It was not incidental that the presidents of the General Assembly's 17th, 18th and 19th sessions came from the three 'emergent' continents: from Asia (1962), Latin America (1963) and Africa (1964).

Again, if either the West or the East should succeed in influencing this process and win even some of the Afro-Asian Powers over to its side, the consequences would be equally far-reaching. Such a shift in Power relationships would automatically change the *status quo*—as the Cuban example demonstrated for Latin America—and the struggle between liberty and totalitarianism would enter a new, more dynamic phase. As events in recent years have clearly shown, such a shift in the balance of power in Asia could be brought about only by military means and with great difficulties. Both East and West are thus concentrating their efforts to a far greater extent on Africa, a continent whose spiritual and political liability, vacillation and vehemence seem to offer ideal conditions for the exercise of both ideological and practical influence on the part of the great Powers.

Thus practically overnight Africa has become an area of international importance; quite suddenly a vast continent, which only yesterday seemed an out-of-the-way region, has acquired enormous political significance. As far as Europe and America were concerned, Africa was until very recently regarded as a sort of primeval, heathen, mysterious and magical nature reserve. It was a favourite area for the investigations of zealous archaeologists, anthropologists and ethnologists; a promising field of endeavour for missionaries of all denominations; an ideal background for big-game hunters, globe-trotters, adventurers, charlatans, reformers and ordinary business men. This vast continent, the last to be explored and to be carved into colonies (a process which ended only at the beginning of the twentieth century) seemed like an unchanging *terra incognita*, an unformed world patiently awaiting the arrival and civilizing influence of the White Man, who alone could rescue it from primitive backwardness. During the last two thousand years the traditional European picture of Africa hardly changed; the Dark Continent was still, as in the days of the Roman Empire, regarded as just the southern coast of the Mediterranean. And as such it represented both an exclusion of, and a task for Europe.

An Africa against, or even without, Europe, was unthinkable. The only alterations permitted in this picture were carefully calculated to create a future European–African partnership within the framework of an enormous, compact 'Eurafrica'. The very name of this artificial construction, which has frequently come up for discussion during the past twenty years, reflects the idea of European primacy. That this is no accident can be seen from the views expressed by Dietrich Westermann, who might be described as the Nestor of international Africanism. Referring to the Eurafrican ideal he declared:

> 'That is the decisive factor today: the lives of individuals and communities flow together, but in every case inevitably along lines marked out by whites, and people's destinies depend on how they come to terms with this experience.'[2]

This assumption of superiority, this demand for white domination, which up to a few years ago determined European colonial policy, is the chief factor for understanding European–African relationships right down to the present. This attitude emerged unaltered from the chaos of the Second World War and still dominated the European outlook as late as January 1944. At the Brazzaville conference, which took place under the aegis of de Gaulle, it was solemnly declared that 'the aims of French colonial policy exclude any idea of autonomy and any possible future self-government for the colonies'.[3] And in the same year Arthur Creech-Jones, the British Colonial Secretary in the Labour Government, announced:

> 'Great Britain stands firmly in her colonies and cannot withdraw. And I for one do not think she should withdraw. We have obliga-

tions towards these colonial areas and we must continue our policy of constructive trusteeship.'[4]

Thus the provision of the Atlantic Charter, promising self-determination to the dependent colonial areas, remained a dead letter, although the various Powers continued to pay lip-service to it. The African policy of the Western Powers remained conservative, even reactionary. During the Second World War hundreds of thousands of Africans fought and many of them died on the battle-fields of Europe and North Africa for the ideas of democracy and liberty; in return for their efforts they were not, however, given independence, but 'practical equality'. 'Assimilation' became the keyword of colonial policy; the colonial areas were to be integrated into the Motherland. London talked of 'partnership' and Paris talked of 'one hundred million Frenchmen'. The *Lex Caracalla* of 7 May 1946 assured all 'French peoples' that

'From 1 January 1946 onwards all the peoples of French overseas territories, including Algeria, will enjoy exactly the same rights, as citizens, as Frenchmen living in the Motherland.'[5]

Referring to this period, Maurice Violette, former Governor-General of Algeria, later declared:

'I am still in favour of the policy of assimilation . . . I feel that it would be possible to bring the whole population (of Algeria) in great swathes into a French unity, and that in this way France would become the greatest *Mohammedan* Power in the world. It was a grand dream—and one I thought worthy of my country—to desire one heart beating for France from the North Sea to the Congo'.[6]

Ideas such as these led to the formation of the *Union Française*, established by proclamation of the Fourth Republic on 27 October 1947 and France still clung to this dream long after Tunisia and Morocco were lost and even after the *loi-cadre* of 1956, which granted 'internal autonomy' in order to counteract the danger of a coloured African movement for external independence. During the first Constituent Assembly of the Fourth Republic, Pierre Cot, presenting the draft of the new Constitution to the Assembly, announced: 'The Colonial Empire is dead!' But in 1959 there were still official posters from Paris on walls in the French Ivory Coast territory, lyrically praising the idea of French hegemony:

'Africa! We have devoted the energy and inventiveness of so many generations to her, and we have carried the idea of our power and grandeur to her so that now she bears our indelible stamp! Under our protection and our leadership her advance in the coming years and the coming centuries will be steady, prosperous and profound!'[7]

However, the death-knell of colonialism had already tolled in Africa and it was to the accompaniment of such grandiloquent phrases that the French colonial empire, with all its 'power and grandeur', slid into liquidation. The first phase of this process of dissolution began in the Maghreb. Libya attained independence in 1951, and Morocco, Tunisia and the former Anglo-Egyptian Sudan followed suit in 1956. Then, only a few months later nationalism began to spread over the Dark Continent. On 6 March 1957, a date of historic importance, the British colony formerly known as the Gold Coast became Ghana, the first independent black African nation of the twentieth century—110 years after the foundation of the West African State of Liberia. And with Ghana—synonym for a great pre-colonial Negro State—came a programme for the liberation of the whole African continent, a programme which Europe could not ignore.

De Gaulle came to power as 'the Saviour of France', and of African France too, after the chaos of the Algerian revolt of May 1958. He immediately recognized the challenge of Ghana and realized that her influence was spreading throughout West Africa. His response was the far-reaching plan for a 'Communauté Française', which provided that the French African possessions should remain 'with limited sovereignty' in a community with the Motherland. However sensible and attractive the proposal appeared, it was too late for half-measures. On 28 September 1958 Guinea rejected the Constitution of the Fifth Republic and thus the 'Communauté Française'. Sékou Touré, 'the elephant of African nationalism', had successfully canvassed for an overwhelming 'No!' vote in de Gaulle's referendum. On hearing the dismayed comments from Paris, Dakar, Bamako, Abidjan, and other capitals of the French Community, the rebel of Conakry proudly and mockingly answered:

'If they say in the Ivory Coast, in the Sudan or in Senegal that Guinea is lost because she chose liberty, then let them say it. I promise you that within two months we shall be showing the others the way . . .'[8]

Touré, and not de Gaulle, was proved right. Guinea exercised a magnetic attraction: within a few weeks Conakry, the capital of Guinea, developed into a new centre of anti-colonial agitation even outdoing Accra, the capital of Ghana. Within a few months Conakry became the new secular Mecca to which radical nationalists from all over Africa flocked and listened in quasi-religious ecstasy to the gospel of 'secession from Europe' which they carried back to their native lands. Even the moderates in the *Communauté* were soon gazing with fascination at Guinea. In his Conakry residence Touré received delegations and ambassadors from all over the world. During his first journey abroad as president he was received in Washington, at the UNO headquarters, and in London, Bonn, Moscow and Prague. Meanwhile the African leaders of the French Community had to content themselves with their role of administrators in what was still, in fact if not in name, colonial territory. Their position deteriorated as the stirring slogans from Conakry and Accra strengthened opposition within their own territories and at the same time their own ambitions and desire for independence remained unsatisfied. If they wanted to save face they would have to allow the dynamic propaganda to carry them along too. It is characteristic of the psychological dilemma which this created for the *Communauté* that it was 'the best African friends of France' who were the first to demand that the *Communauté* should 'adapt itself to the new situation'. Speaking in Abidjan on behalf of Houphouet-Boigny, the president of the Ivory Coast Republic, Mamadou Coulibaly, the Speaker in Parliament, declared:

'The formula of the "reformed Communauté" will no longer deceive anyone overseas. It's just another veneer stuck over the old one, but the old worm-eaten timber is still underneath . . . The "reformed Communauté" which is supposed to meet the requirements of the new world situation appears to have just about as much chance of survival as the old one . . .'[9]

Two years after the establishment of the *Communauté Française*, which had been planned to give colonialism a breathing space in

Africa, the constitutional scaffolding collapsed. In order to prevent 'an all-African Guinea' or perhaps even a Dien Bien Phu in the desert and the torrid jungle of the Dark Continent, Paris gave member-states their freedom. A new framework was drawn up and a 'modified Communauté' on the lines of the British Commonwealth was planned; but no one was deceived, it was a very ephemeral structure, a phantasmagoria without a solid basis.

Thus 1960 became, as the extremists had prophesied, Africa's Year: within a few months seventeen African countries—the Cameroons, Togoland, Senegal, the Sudan, Mali, Madagascar, the Belgian Congo, the French Congo, Somalia, Upper Volta, the Ivory Coast, Dahomey, Niger, Chad, the Central African Republic, Gabon, Mauritania—became independent. In London the Colonial Office hastened to keep up with the breakneck pace and hurriedly announced the dates on which Sierra Leone, Nigeria, and Tanganyika were to achieve their independence. Leaders of other African territories were urgently invited to confer with the Colonial Secretary at Lancaster House to work out a time-table for the independence of their countries and by now Great Britain has granted independence to all her African territories with the exceptions of Southern Rhodesia, Basutoland, Bechuanaland and Barotseland.

Thus, at a date far earlier than even the most enthusiastic supporters of African nationalism would have dared to prophesy, the end of white colonial dominance over the Dark Continent became a certainty. Portugal and Spain may try to ignore the writing on the wall, but it can only be question of time before they are compelled to bow before the inevitable. A series of revolutionary factors precipitated the whole process, as history develops its own dynamic. Nothing can now hold it up: neither reason nor moderation, nor the dream of a *grande nation* embracing the continents, nor any humanitarian ideal of a multiracial partnership and brotherhood. Such things are nothing but shifting sands on which the last bastions of white colonialism in Africa hope to rest.

Belgium, in particular, has been given good reason to know this. Belgium was guilty of terrible cruelties and atrocities in the Congo (Roger Casement described them in detail in 1903), but gradually she adopted a policy of enlightened paternalism, which was supported by the Church and by business interests. Planning was very long-term indeed. Belgium carefully graded her economic and educational reforms. Nothing was to be hurried, there was time, plenty of time, and above all there were no political or educational ambitions among the natives which had to be considered.

While Britain and France steadily furthered educational schemes in their colonial territories and established a narrow pyramid of educated Africans fairly quickly, and while more and more coloured students were to be seen at the Sorbonne and the London School of Economics, the Belgian authorities stuck rigidly to their old horizontal plan: all the 'primitive children of the Congo' were to be taught the three R's at once and anything that went further was rejected as premature and likely to endanger the grand plan. The idea of encouraging the development of a native élite who could take over the administration was not a matter of practical politics—it was no more than a theoretical possibility for the far-distant future.

Certainly up to the early 1950s Belgian calculations met with a good deal of approval in Europe. British and French travellers to the Belgian Congo usually found more to praise than to blame and, in particular, were inclined to regard the educational and social policy of the Belgians as eminently sensible. Some urged their own governments to regard Belgian policy as a prime example of enlightened colonial policy.

Faced with such unsolicited admiration, the Belgian Government certainly saw no reason to worry or to revise its tried and trusted Congo policy—particularly as young King Baudouin was welcomed by his African subjects in the Congo with tremendous enthusiasm. Though the waves of nationalism were beating high in other parts of Africa, they seemed at a low ebb in the Belgian Congo. In the summer of 1958 a Belgian official in Leopoldville declared smugly to the author:

> 'In many parts of Africa anti-white and anti-European passions are rising, but there is no danger of any such thing in the Congo. And we shall certainly not make the mistakes that other colonial powers have made. Belgium has no plans for meeting the demands of native politicians. But the future prospects are all the more promising.'[10]

How far away that future was thought to be can be judged from discussions that took place in Brussels on the African policy of the Belgian Government. Deeply impressed by what was happening in the Maghreb and in Ghana, anti-colonial intellectuals and left-wing politicians in Paris and London gave colonialism a life-span of ten, or at a maximum fifteen, years in Africa. That was in 1955. But the Belgian opposition was far more optimistic in its estimate of the remaining life-span of colonialism. For example, in 1955 the Belgian colonial historian, van Bilsen, a critic of his country's colonial policy, drafted a '*Plan de trente ans pour l'Emancipation de l'Afrique Belge*'. In other words, even the opponents of Belgium's colonial policy in the Congo assumed that any radical change in the immediate future was out of the question. It would take thirty years to establish a basis for Congolese autonomy: 1985—not a moment earlier!

In fact, the life-span of Belgian colonialism in the Congo was just three, and not thirty, years from that date. The picture of 'the sleeping Congo', painted by both white and black, proved to be false. In January 1959 the first and only violent insurrection of the natives took place in Leopoldville; from then on '*Uhuru!*' (Swahili for 'freedom')—the battle cry of African nationalism—resounded throughout the Congo. Incredulous horror seized the Belgian settlers, technicians and officials in the Congo, while the politicians in Brussels were overcome with dismay, although the first news of the revolt had actually been joked about as 'the false report of the year'. Belgian smugness, not to say frivolity, about colonial affairs disappeared. A panic ensued and paternalist illusions were abandoned overnight. Until then Belgians had regarded the Congo as 'the most secure investment for our future', but now they found themselves sharing the opinion of Disraeli that 'the wretched colonies are a millstone round our neck'. The sooner that millstone was jettisoned the better and without previous warning King Baudouin used the fateful word 'independence'. Once this was done Belgium herself advanced the date again and again and a year later—on 24 January 1960—the Brussels Round-Table Conference fixed the date for lowering the Belgian flag in Africa as 30 June 1960, less than six months later. African nationalism had won a lightning victory and Brussels dropped the Congo—as one Belgian publicist put it—'like a hot brick'. We all know the result.

The speed at which Africa won its liberty, and at which Europe retreated from the African continent, is unequalled in history. How very different was the evolution in Asia. The withdrawal of European colonialism from Asia was also accompanied by violent and protracted upheavals, but there had been warnings of the coming struggle. As early as 1835 Lord Macaulay prophesied that it would not be long before India would be lost to the British Crown. The final phase of the struggle for independence in India lasted for forty years if we take 1909, the year in which the radical wing of the Congress Party put forward the demand for complete independence, as its beginning. Mahatma Gandhi started *Satyagraha*, the movement for 'passive resistance until victory', in 1919. From 1927 the Congress Party demanded independence with growing insistence. Britain felt compelled to grant home rule to Ceylon as early as 1931, but it was only in 1947 that the island attained dominion status. The national-revolutionary movement in Indo-China goes back to the days of the Chinese revolution of 1911, but it was not until 1954 that it was finally successful, after various changes of front and repeated partition of the Secession States. The Philippines were first shaken by a nationalist revolt as early as 1898 when the United States took over the islands from Spain. From 1916, the national-revolutionary movement harassed the United States forces by protracted guerilla warfare. Resistance flared up again in 1932 and only in 1946 were the islands able to celebrate the attainment of their independence. Reformist groups first put forward a nationalist programme for Indonesia in 1908; they increased their activity during the First World War and consolidated their position with the foundation of Sukarno's National Party in 1927. However it was not until 1945 that they approached their objective and after Dutch and British intervention their triumph came in 1950.

The modern Asian nationalist movement thus has a long and impressive tradition and its ultimate victory was the result of a struggle waged over a long period of time. The African nationalist movement, on the other hand, has no such tradition: it drew up its demands virtually out of nothing and gained them in an incredibly short time. The fact is that everything went too fast for them. Men who are now determined opponents of 'half-solutions' and who look with contempt on those who still think in terms of assimilation and integration only yesterday thought in that way themselves and rejected the path of nationalism. Ferhat Abbas, former head of the provisional government of the Republic of Algeria, is a case in point. In 1937, in his book *Beyond Nationalism*, he wrote:

'If I had created the Algerian nation I would be a nationalist, and I should see no reason to blush for that . . . But I did not create it. I turned to history, to the living and the dead. I visited the cemeteries. You cannot build on dust and wind. We have got rid of the mist and spectres once and for all, and we are determined to throw in our lot irrevocably with the great work of French construction in our country. Six million Mohammedans live in a territory that has been French for a hundred years. They live in holes, go barefoot and in rags, and they have not enough to eat. Our aim is to turn this mass of starvelings into a modern society . . . We want to educate them to human dignity so that they will become worthy of being called Frenchmen.'[11]

You can find statements by many African native leaders who had similar ideas regarding their own people.

The reasons for this sudden change in the African situation and for the African upheaval itself are extremely complicated. African and non-African factors merge into each other and it often seems impossible to separate the important from the subsidiary. But again and again we shall be brought back to the fact that the westernization of Africa, the awakening of the continent, and its colonization—as distinct from its colonial conquest—did not start until the beginning of this century and did not become really effective until after the First World War. Apart from one or two early attempts the same is true of the missionary work to convert Africa to Christianity. As against this, a French Jesuit, Alexandre de Rhodes, was in Indo-China at the beginning of the seventeenth century. Within a few years an Annamite Catechism was available and by 1660 there were French bishops in Siam, Cochin-China and Tonkin. Moreover, Asiatic religions gradually adapted themselves to the general process of spiritual and intellectual enlightenment. In Africa the situation was very different; as the Nigerian leader Doctor Nnamdi Azikiwe suggests in his book, *Renascent Africa*, published in London in 1937, that until quite recently African society was culturally stagnant (apart from the period of classical antiquity in Ethiopia and 'the immortal achievements of our ancestors in Negro Africa', for example, during the Middle Ages when Songhai flourished).

Azikiwe is himself a Methodist and he feels that the Christian mission is an important factor in the advance of Africa.

It can, of course, be argued that only one out of seven of the 220 million native inhabitants of Africa is a Christian, but this reliance on statistics is deceptive. Whoever reads the biographies of the leaders of present-day Africa will constantly come across Christian influences.

In their political writings many African leaders have stressed the liberating and encouraging effect of the Christian message, which they compared favourably with the fatalism of the primitive religions of Africa.

There is, of course, something else in the Christian message which is of great importance to Africans: 'All men are children of God, and all men are equal before God, whether black or white'. This is the teaching of Christianity and the missionaries took it with them to Africa, where the newly converted natives took it up with religious fervour. It was not long before they discovered that in practice this equality operated only within their own community, while many ostensibly Christian whites refused to recognize them as Christian brothers.

From here it is only a short step to the sectarian adaptations of Christianity which arise in Africa from time to time and in which Christian influences merge with survivals of old African nature religions. Soon after the First World War a movement known as Kimbanguism arose in the Congo and developed into the *Mission des Noires*. After the Second World War it came to the fore again and played quite an important role in the tragic events in the Congo in 1960 as well as in 1964. Its founder, Simon Kimbangu, was born in 1889, became a Baptist and in 1921, 'thanks to the grace of God', was, so he claims, 'entrusted with the divine mission' of freeing his black brothers. He adopted the title of Ngunza, which means Messiah. The sect he founded grew rapidly and even won supporters from African missionaries, partly because Kimbangu was clever enough to use the traditional deep respect of Africans for their ancestors as a cornerstone of his creed. Kimbangu frequently had 'revelations' from his own ancestors and finally announced that he had been instructed to sever all connections with the white man's Church and to establish 'the Kingdom of the Black Saviour' on earth. With this the white man, and particularly the white missionary, became superfluous. To Kimbangu and his followers the white man was comparable to the Egyptians and Philistines who had threatened Israel, the Jews who crucified Jesus, and the Romans. The white man was now 'the instrument of Satan' and it was the duty of the black man to destroy him. The Belgian authorities put Kimbangu under lock and key, but if they had hoped that this would destroy his political influence they were mistaken. Kimbangu was regarded as a martyr and even worshipped as the Messiah who would return to drive out the white heathen and liberate his faithful black followers: 'God has sent us Simon Kimbangu. He is to us what Moses was to the Jews, Jesus to the Gentiles and Mohammed to the Arabs.'

Kimbanguism has now developed into a militant, aggressive religion of salvation. The 'Ngunzaists' aimed at establishing a strongly centralized and liberated Congo. One of their prophets advocated that 'when the Divine seizure of power takes place' the followers of the movement should treat the 'femmes-madames' of the whites like whores. It is not difficult to imagine the effect of such an Africanization of Christianity in these troubled days. Incidentally quite a number of the more radical Congo leaders have in recent years expressed their support for Kimbanguism.

The majority of African Christians, of course, regard Kimbanguism or Ngunzaism as a distortion of Christianity; however we must not lose sight of the cause of this new movement: the obvious contradiction between the idea of the equality of all men before God, preached by the Christian missionaries, and the constant discrimination practised by white against black men. The result has been an inversion of beliefs. The *Mission des Noires* now declares that the black man, and not the European, is in 'a state of Grace', that he is the vessel of God's will and is called upon to perform God's mission on earth. This mission is to wrench the mask from the face of 'the white hypocrite', to expose him as the 'instrument of the Devil', and to drive him out of 'the promised land'.[12] We are faced here with one of the negative aspects of negritude—the overcompensation of an inferiority complex that has developed, understandably enough, among many Africans, particularly among the intellectuals. At the same time, even the more moderate forms of negritude—the awakening of the national consciousness of African Negroes—represent a reaction against European colonization.

It was not only Christian missionaries who proclaimed the principle of equality; before long, equality before God was supplemented by the cry for equality before the law, while books written by white men advocated social equality as well. Students at Makerere College eagerly studied English and American history; by the age of twelve the child in the British missionary school was learning about the democratic institutions of Britain. In French missionary schools the strains of the Marseillaise were heard and the 14th of July, the day of the storming of the Bastille, was as much a national holiday in French Africa as in France. The children learnt the three great principles of the French Revolution 'Liberty, Equality, Fraternity!' in their earliest primers. These were later translated into African languages and in this way their influence spread even further. However, wrenched out of their historical context, these great political principles were often reduced to the level of propaganda slogans.

The clash which was to come was therefore inevitable: sooner or later the African arrived at the point where he could see the contradiction between the officially proclaimed principles of 1789 and the failure, or even refusal, to put them into practice which, naturally, he found intolerable. Even the *evolués*, the more educated Africans, who were willing to accept the 'ifs' and 'buts' and supported the evolutionary programmes of the colonial Powers found it difficult to get round this contradiction. For example, in a lecture delivered in November 1959 to the Royal Institute of International Affairs in London, Sékou Touré declared:

'At first many of us accepted the assimilation programme because it seemed to open up new horizons. But these horizons came no closer. The original objective was the equality of the rulers and the ruled. But only too often those Africans who, for example, got into the *Assemblée*, found their own problems farther away than ever from a solution.'[13]

It is understandable that those who were disappointed with the slow progress made in realizing this original objective began to turn to more radical measures when they discovered that all they had to do was to increase nationalist agitation and build up pressure from below and the Colonial Office would recognize that the areas in question had arrived at the necessary degree of maturity.

The upheaval in Africa can be divided into three phases. The ideological basis for emancipation was laid during the first period, which ended with the Second World War. African intellectuals came together at Lincoln University in the United States and at various European universities. In an investigation into the political awakening of the coloured people, Bernard Fonlon writes:

'The coming together of coloured students in European and American centres became of far-reaching significance. Africans who came to London, Paris and New York from the Antilles, Africa and America found each other . . . From their meeting developed a joint consciousness, a feeling of racial solidarity, and an irresistible and steadily growing force.'[14]

Such political demands as were put forward did not seek the exclusion of the colonial Powers from Africa. In those days African intellectuals were not so much interested in political independence as in the questions of domestic freedom and the political rights of the individual.

The second period was dominated by the war-time experience of Africans. In addition to the large force raised in the Maghreb (Tunisia, Morocco and Algeria), many thousands of Africans fought on the various fronts of 'the European civil war'.[15] They were mobilized to fight for democracy and liberty against a system which trampled on the fundamental rights of man. Further, they were mobilized against a régime which was waging a brutal campaign of extermination against a whole race—the Jews. This gave Africans food for thought. The demands of the African élite became more political and more radical in an atmosphere of growing bitterness. Various organizations, once mainly educational and social, quickly developed into political associations and in October 1946 African leaders in French West Africa met in Bamako and founded the *Rassemblement Démocratique Africain*. It was the first big political party on the African continent. A few months later, on 27 March 1947, an anti-colonial revolt broke out in Madagascar. Together with the Mau-Mau insurrection, this explosion shattered the hope of the European Powers that colonial unrest could be confined to Asia. The wind 'bloweth where it listeth', particularly the wind of change, and road blocks are no good against ideas. The influence of events in Asia sparked off trouble in Africa much sooner than had been expected and the slogan of equality and liberty was taken up throughout the continent.

Nevertheless, in that phase it was still possible for the colonial Powers to suppress the Madagascar revolt and to crush the Mau-Mau terror by a white counter-terror that was only gradually decreased. This brings us to the third stage of the African upheaval, which began in the mid-fifties. In this period (apart from exceptions such as South Africa and Angola) force ceased to play its former role in the defence of colonial interests; in fact it became the practice of colonial Powers to forestall threatened outbreaks of violence by making concessions—even at the ultimate price of colonial self-liquidation. The most remarkable example of this is the Congo. In other words, colonialism ceased to exist as a naked power system.

Two factors determined this change. The first, one could term 'the Dien Bien Phu experience': the catastrophic defeat suffered by the French in Indo-China, coupled with the subsequent realization that it could have been avoided by more adroit tactics, was a great shock for Europe. The military retreat of colonialism in Asia, of which Dien Bien Phu was a symbol, revealed the inability of conventional military and political measures to deal with a psychological force such as the movement for political independence by the non-white peoples. Colonialism was compelled to recognize that the time had come when force could achieve nothing. Force only led to ever more violent counter-measures and ultimately destroyed the economic basis of colonialism itself. Dien Bien Phu demonstrated that the strategic concepts of Sandhurst and St Cyr had lost their validity in colonial policy.

The second factor arose in the West itself: after the Second World War the question of liberty was given a new and even more extreme formulation and made into one of the main instruments of Western foreign policy, and one cannot condemn Nazism and Bolshevism as systems hostile to human liberty while maintaining old-style colonial policies. One cannot condemn Hitler, Stalin and Khrushchev for refusing liberty to their satellites while at the same time refusing liberty to the people of Africa and Asia: not, at least, without being accused of double standards and hypocrisy. You cannot cancel out Uganda with Hungary, or Tanganyika with Tibet.

With this we have arrived at a point which is of fundamental importance; the independence of the African peoples is not the result of an examination of conscience in the West, it is not the result of a voluntary act of repentance and a determination to follow the straight and narrow path in the future—let there be no illusions about that. It is mainly the East-West conflict that has forced the West to repair some of its errors and cure some of its own moral sores.

NOTES

[1] 'The Great Powers and the New World Order', *The Annals of the American Academy of Political and Social Science*, CCLVII (May 1958), p. 52.

[2] Dietrich Westermann, *Africans Tell of Their Lives*, quoted in Rolf Italiaander, *The New Leaders of Africa* (New York, 1961), p. v.

[3] *Conférence africaine française* (Paris, ?), p. 35. Cf. also Charles de Gaulle, *Mémoires de Guerre* (Paris, ?), II: *L'Unité*, pp. 555 ff. For English translation, see *War Memoirs of Charles de Gaulle* (New York, 1958-60), II: *Unity 1942-1944*.

[4] Quoted in T. Walter Wallbank, 'Britain's New Programme for the Colonies', *Current History*, XV (August 1948), p. 84.

[5] Quoted in Herbert Lüthy, 'Ein Kolonialreich in der Krise', *Der Monat* (Berlin), No. 14 (November 1949), p. 184.

[6] Ibid.

[7] Observed by the author during a visit to the Ivory Coast.

[8] From a speech delivered by Sékou Touré at the Cinema Vox, Conakry, 2 October 1958. Cyclostyled publication of the Government of Guinea.

[9] *Fraternité* (Abidjan), 3 June 1960.

[10] In an interview with the author, Leopoldville, 1958.

[11] Quoted in Lüthy, op. cit., p. 182.

[12] Georges Balandier, *Sociologie actuelle de l'Afrique Noire* (Paris, 1945); E. Andersson, *Messianic Popular Movements in the Lower Congo* (Uppsala, 1958).

[13] Cyclostyled text issued by the Government of Guinea (December 1959).

[14] *Afrika* (Munich), 11 November 1960, p. 439.

[15] More than 120,000 Africans in French-speaking West and Equatorial Africa were called up for war service. Cf. 'Chronique de la Communauté', *Documentation Française* (Paris), March 1960, p. 11.

Chapter II

AFRICAN CONTRASTS

LÉOPOLD SÉDAR SENGHOR, one of the leading intellectuals of the new Africa, has described 'the nation' as 'the primary reality of the twentieth century' and 'the historical inevitability of our continent'.[1] Sékou Touré, for some time the exponent of political radicalism in Africa, supplements this by saying: 'Europe can afford to abandon the idea of sovereign nationhood today because it has outgrown the national stage of its history. We have not done that yet. This is the tragedy of our situation.'[2]

The second observation is particularly interesting, partly because of the undertone of resignation and regret and partly because it is in such strong contrast to the enthusiasm with which Touré usually speaks of African nationhood. The tragedy of Africa lies in the fact that so far this idea of nationhood has dominated the thoughts of a small élite only; it has still to be turned into a concrete fact for the masses of the African people and the conditions under which this has to be done are desperately unfavourable. Even the early stages of nationhood in Africa are providing more painful than similar experiences elsewhere.

According to Ernest Renan: 'What makes a nation is not merely speaking the same language or belonging to the same ethnic group, but the fact that in the past its members have done great deeds together and aspire to do them again in the future.'[3] Writing in 1928, Salvador de Madariaga went further and argued that 'not even history, geography, religion, language and a common will are enough to constitute a nation. A nation is a psychological fact.'[4] And Cedric Dover declares:

'The solidarity of a community depends on whether there is

sufficient acknowledgement in its ranks of a certain number of essential values. Certain beliefs, certain patterns of behaviour and certain patterns of action must be common to all if social life is to function without friction.'[5]

If we look at African reality from this angle the difficulty becomes obvious. The common acceptance of a certain number of essential values, the great deeds done together in the past, the aspiration to do them again in the future, and the psychological fact of which de Madariaga speaks—where are they in Africa? According to Nkrumah, 'The African nation has formed itself in the struggle against colonialism', and at first sight there would seem to be something in his contention. In only a few of the African countries was there a short period prior to independence in which the nationalist slogans of the élite were taken up by the masses. This was the case in Guinea where, on 28 September 1958, a referendum showed that over ninety-five per cent of the population were opposed to de Gaulle's proposal for a 'Communauté Française'. It was also true in Ghana in 1955, when Nkrumah began the final phase of his struggle for independence, and it was also the case in Leopoldville during the January uprising of 1959. But in most of the other countries of Africa the movement for independence rested on small groups of leaders who were active, not on the masses. In the new 'model' African nations there is now, even *after* independence, very little evidence of any national solidarity. On the contrary, it would appear that the new élite have prematurely hitched their wagon to the star of the future; for the traditional leaders of African society, the tribal and paramount chiefs, have no use for such a future, while the masses of the people have little notion of what it is all about. The fact is that there is a gap of centuries between the dream of the few and the force of inertia of the many.

In the spring of 1964 a young Kenyan politician explained the internal quarrels in his country by saying:

'We had set such high hopes on our independence, but instead things only got worse, much worse. At one time there really was something like a single, united Kenya, but that's all past. The question of how best to govern, and the question of with whom we should line up in foreign affairs, has divided once more. The

Kenyans? Every tribe, every group appeals to Kenya, and each means something different. It's terrible.'

The situation in Kenya reflects the situation in Africa as a whole. The Congolese could find these words applicable to their country in exactly the same way. After its 'liberation' the former Belgian Congo was also divided 'a dozen times over'.

Even the strong African States on the west coast, such as Ghana and Guinea, are not immune to this tendency. Has Nkrumah really created an African nation in his country as he repeatedly claims? Has Touré's energetic leadership in Guinea really overcome the racial and tribal separatism formerly blamed on colonialism? During his travels in Africa the author found frequent evidence (particularly in Guinea and Ghana) of the fact that rivalries between the various ethnic groups are still as strong as ever. In Ghana the Ashanti complain of the predominance of the coastal tribes and of their own inadequate representation in the central political organizations. In Guinea the Fulani complain that they are being placed at a disadvantage by the Malinke and the Susu. And the unrest of April 1960 and the revolt of November 1961 as well as the tensions late in 1964 were really caused by tribal rivalries, although they were later exacerbated by slogans of an ideological character. Despite these things, Nkrumah and Touré are already talking of 'the United States of Africa'. The deplorable experience of the Mali Federation, proclaimed in the summer of 1960 by the leaders in Dakar and Bamako, seems to contain no warning for them. Yet the swift and inglorious collapse of the federation came as a surprise only to those who knew nothing whatever about the situation. If you ask a Senegalese taxi-driver in Dakar whether he's Sudanese or, conversely, ask a Sudanese whether he comes from Senegal, the answer will always be the same: 'Sir, do you really take me for one of that Sudanese (or Senegalese) lot?'

The gigantic artificial structure erected in the Congo fell to pieces even more quickly than the Mali Federation. Only a few days after the removal of the corset of colonialism, the whole 'Heartland of Africa', as Patrice Lumumba called it, broke into a chaos of races and tribes. Katanga, the richest province of the old Belgian Congo, refused for years to submit to the central government, rejecting the idea of national unity, while in the Kasai province the

Balubas and Luluas reverted to their old tribal enmity and terrible slaughter ensued.

The politicians of the new Africa may aim as high as they like in their dreams and projects, but at their feet are the ball and chain of the past. The pre-colonial and colonial heritage has left a crushing mortgage which is a severe burden, as is the rapid dissolution of the old social structure.

First there is the difficult question of frontiers: the present frontiers were drawn at a time when the whole continent was viewed exclusively in terms of imperial, colonial and strategic interests. The Powers taking part in the Berlin Conference of 1884, and the subsequent conference in 1885, had no idea of the ethnographic conditions of the continent whose map they light-heartedly carved up with the help of ruler and drawing-board. Races and tribes were arbitrarily joined together or torn apart. Today, seventy years later, those on whom this heritage devolves ask themselves in despair how national unity will ever develop in the face of the elementary antagonisms of race and religion.

It is not, however, merely a question of tribal disputes and racial and religious resentments and rivalries—suppressed with difficulty in the latter-day phase of colonialism—now bursting out all the more violently in the wake of de-colonization and liberation. The problem is more complicated than this. Present-day Africa is experiencing not only a political, but also a profound social, economic, and cultural revolution, and in the process traditional values are being called into question before new ones have been evolved. The fact that this process is historically inevitable and necessary does not make it any the less painful.

The actual process involved is only partially described by the terms 'liberation' or 'emancipation'. Parallel with liberation there has been general disintegration, a total dissolution of the inner structure of African society. It began when the white man seized the African continent and it was accelerated when the phase of exploration, subjugation and mere domination developed into the purer form of colonialism, that is, the imposition of European educational, social, and economic ideas on African society. With this, traditional African societies found themselves faced with systems they were unable to compete with, and the more rational European methods of dominating man and nature proved their superiority. Up to this time the African had just taken things as they came, but now, as the African publicist, Thomas Diop, points out, 'he began to ask questions'[6] and to have doubts about his traditional values.

These values related to the narrow world of the family hierarchy, the clan and the tribe, the natural community in which the African lived. In distant, out-of-the-way places such communities may still be intact and functioning effectively. All the same, large family and clan groups—usually based on the patriarchate, with a council of elders, a strict hierarchy of chiefs and medicine men, and associations of young men and girls, with their plethora of ritual instructions, exercises and obligations—this traditional structure finds itself condemned to disappear in the face of economic development, the growth of communications, the conquest of illiteracy, the increasing prestige of the African élite who have broken away from the old traditions, and the democratization of the African State.

Naturally, the old order is not giving up without a struggle. Shortly before Nigeria achieved independence the Sardauna and the Emirs in Northern Nigeria bitterly opposed the introduction of school attendance for boys and girls; they resisted the orders for Nigerianization issued from Lagos and deliberately delayed the date for their country's self-government. There have been a number of revolts by tribal chiefs in Ghana, Guinea, Uganda, Tanganyika and other countries during recent years and the new rulers had to demonstrate their power forcefully before they could be repressed.

In the Cameroons, partly as a revolt of the agricultural population against the domination of the chiefs, the so-called *Chefferie*, the peasants and artisans, small traders and merchants of the Bamileke tribe refused to pay the traditional, and often high tributes to the chiefs, something that would have been unthinkable as recently as 1950. The chiefs allied themselves with the Ahidjo Government, which is supported by the feudal North. But in the long run the upshot of this struggle, here as elsewhere, is not in doubt. More and more Africans are coming to regard the *Chefferie* as an anachronism and even the chiefs are beginning to feel that the days of their power are numbered.

The new centres in Africa are the factories, the large-scale plantations, and the industrial giants: Fria in Guinea, Edea in Cameroon, others in Katanga and Rhodesia, and above all in the towns. These centres exercise an enormous attraction which reaches into the most distant reserves of the hinterland. New values have been set up, primarily the value of money. By observing their white masters the Africans realized that money could achieve what formerly only birthright offered; money makes all men equal; and nothing can be so quickly squeezed out of the misery of the dependent, the enslaved, and the oppressed. Money makes it possible for the African to dress like the European and nowhere in the world are top hats, morning coats, patent-leather shoes, even spats, more highly thought of than among the new African élite. For money you can drink foaming beer—the turnover and profits of African breweries and of European beer exporters have risen to fantastic heights—and money affords the chance of better education (until recently some missionary schools charged fees for their pupils).

Until recently all this was to be had only by direct connection with the whites, so the flow of people into the towns and European colonial centres was increasing rapidly. *Bidonvilles*, the colonies of shacks made of petrol tins and corrugated iron, have shot up like mushrooms around the white towns. Johannesburg, Leopoldville, Douala, Lagos, Abidjan, Dakar, Salisbury and other capitals now have more than twice as many inhabitants today as twenty years ago, and the process continues in a mad, uncontrolled rush. Dilapidated, jerry-built huts of tin cans and wood spring up in the drainless streets and alleyways of these *Bidonvilles*—mud, clay, unhewn stones, ragged sacks, any kind of material goes into their making. They collapse, are rebuilt, collapse, and are rebuilt yet again. 'Fascinating Africa!', a favourite expression of the advertisements of tourist agencies and shipping lines, but one look at the grim reality of these chaotic, squalid settlements is enough to destroy all these illusions about 'the untouched land', 'virgin soil', etc. Women with swollen bellies and flaccid, hanging breasts pound their maize monotonously and squat among old packing cases and cardboard boxes, offering trifling articles for sale. Three paces away others squat for a different purpose. Scruffy, scabby children whine and bombard passers-by with demands for *cadeau* or dash, meaning alms. The great plagues of the pre-colonial era have been mastered but more civilized scourges, infectious diseases, particularly syphilis and tuberculosis, still claim large numbers of victims. Prostitution is rampant; according to conservative calculations in 1960, seven per cent of the women in the New Bell native quarter of Douala prostituted themselves. Grinding poverty and proletarianization represent the fate of the many thousands who flock to the market-places of a foreign civilization from their own savannahs and the bush, and all are drawn and fascinated by the new totem—money.

As there is not enough work for everyone, and as the training of Africans for the more complicated industrial jobs is still deficient, social tensions increase with the arrival of every person who leaves the security of his village to brave the hazards of urban life. Unemployment is steadily increasing; today those unemployed number between twenty and twenty-five per cent of the total of employable persons almost everywhere. The first African regional conference of the International Labour Organization, which took place in December 1960 in Lagos, declared that 'rural poverty and under-employment is now developing into urban unemployment and frustration.'[7]

The situation is aggravated by the fact that when an African comes into a town he is immediately confronted with both the sunny and the seamy sides of the imported European civilization; and—as a Nigerian study points out—he accepts both naïvely 'without being able to tell what is good and what is bad'. In this connection there are three things which have a particularly unfavourable influence on urban Africans: alcohol, the cinema, and pulp literature.

Alcohol has always been a companion of colonialism. According to German sources (for example, the minutes of the Reichstag of 13 March 1896) the imports of spirits into what was then the German Cameroons rose from a value of 550,000 marks in 1892 to 981,000 marks in 1894, although in that period the value of the mark remained stable. The importation of alcoholic liquor represented fifteen per cent of the total imports of the Cameroons, and thirty per cent of the total imports of Togoland.[8] In 1953, Madagascar paid twenty times more for imports of wines and spirits than for the importation of agricultural machinery. Similarly, the Ivory Coast Republic paid twice as much for imports of spirits in 1958 as for the importation of artificial fertilizers. The consequences of this excessive importation of alcohol can be seen any evening in the *Bidonvilles* of modern Africa. Beer or raw spirits can be bought at almost every corner of the slum quarters. It has been calculated that the inhabitants of the native quarter of New Bell in Douala spend up to twenty-five per cent of their income on beer and spirits. It certainly did not take Africans long to discover what an effective narcotic alcohol is for the poor. . . .

Western films are hardly a less demoralizing influence. There are many flea-pit cinemas where the programme is changed daily. They rarely if ever show anything of any real value, usually just the dregs of the American and European film markets. These films, with their strip-tease, love scenes, vice and crime, adultery, and lynchings, have a deplorable impact on a public whose ethical and social standards are even less firmly grounded than those of audiences in the West. As seen from the angle of this spurious cinematic world, which he takes for real, the naïve African cannot but regard the commandments of Christianity, which he too is called upon to keep, as plain hypocrisy. The result is that the already low moral authority of the white man is understandably being further undermined. How do the guiding principles of Christian education and training compare with this 'other reality' that Africans can see evening after evening on the cinema screen?

The situation is very much the same when one examines most of the literary imports available. If you visit African bookshops in Lagos or Salisbury in order to discover what kind of books are favoured, everywhere the answer will be the same: apart from teach-yourself manuals on English, arithmetic and geography, they are paper-backs of love and adventure, and other more or less undesirable literature besides. The windows are largely filled with trash whose coloured covers depict either half-naked women or scenes of violence and leave no doubt as to the literary level of the book. In addition, many of these bookshops have a special collection of pornographic publications imported from overseas.

This is another aspect of the Westernization of Africa, continuing at a break-neck pace, breaking down old standards, and replacing old ideals by new, and often inferior ones. It is true that modern African nationalism calls loudly for the development of a *personalité africaine*, an African consciously drawing on his own cultural and historical past and resisting foreign and outside influences. But the fact is that the true sources of African history and culture are being destroyed and buried—the imported attractions of the European world are too strong.

Even the leaders of the new élite who were the first to inscribe the slogan 'Back to Africa!' on their banners do not seem to think so. If one expected to find their loudly proclaimed adherence to their own African tradition reflected in the style, decoration, and furnishing of their houses, one would be disappointed. A visitor to the homes of the leaders of young Africa will seldom find examples of African art, collected with pride in the creative achievements of Africa past and present for their admiration. Instead, the interiors, reception and drawing rooms owe everything to London, Paris or Brussels and the various articles of furnishing have been culled from the catalogues of European firms or from the advertisement columns of European newspapers.

This is symptomatic of the deep hiatus which exists between the Africa of yesterday and of today, though to some extent the two still exist side by side. The great mass of the people and the old feudal ruling class are still closely attached to the old traditions and ignore modern innovations, but in the towns the restless, rootless, unattached proletariat and the young élite are groping their way forward into strange, extra-African spheres. The result is a split in African society and the cultural secession of the élite, a tragedy illustrated by the frank admission of President Sékou Touré of Guinea that he feels more at home with his French friends, for example, than he does with 'my older brother who has never been to school.'[9]

What kind of people belong to this new élite? Hugh and Mabel Smythe of the Department of Sociology and Anthropology of Brooklyn College, New York, went to Nigeria in 1960 to investigate the problem. Their analysis is influenced by American behaviourism and in some ways is unsatisfactory, but it declares: 'A certain number of Nigerians have studied abroad, particularly in Great Britain and the United States, and they have accumulated a wealth of first-class professional experience. Every year more and more coloured people follow their example. These are the men and women who form the new upper stratum, and very little is known about them outside Africa. The typical representative of the present-day élite is between twenty-five and forty-five years old. He came from the rural areas into the town in search of opportunities for education and work. As nationalism and politics in general are most highly developed in the towns he also took up party politics. He may very well be a member of one or other of the various chief religions of his country, animism, Christianity (chiefly in the south) or Mohammedanism (chiefly in the north), but any such religious differences will not bring him into conflict with the other members of the élite. Language is also not a factor making for separation. There are over ninety languages and dialects in Nigeria, and the essential condition for belonging to the élite is that he should be able to speak English.'[10]

The authors also provided certain illuminating figures regarding the rapid growth of this élite. For example, between the years 1938 and 1948 only 177 Nigerians had the opportunity of being educated abroad. During the next four years the number increased to 665 and by the end of 1952 there were no fewer than 2,028 Nigerians studying in Great Britain and another 334 in the United States. The authorities in Lagos calculate that the corresponding figures for 1958 were 3,000 in Great Britain and 300–400 in the United States. But in 1964 there were at least 15,000 Nigerians studying abroad.

If one takes these figures in relation to the population of Nigeria as a whole (which, as the census results of 1964 show, is 55 million) we see that by now one person out of 3,500 has received some sort of higher education, or approximately 0·030 per cent of the population; and it must be remembered that not all of these completed their studies.

In this respect Nigeria is in an exceptionally favourable position. When the former Belgian Congo became independent fewer than one hundred Congolese had had the advantage of some form of higher education. In other African States the situation will be somewhere between these two extremes, with the exception of the Portuguese colonial territories, where higher education is still difficult to attain for Africans. However, the élite does not consist exclusively of those who have had some sort of higher education. The élites include employees of the administration, particularly teachers and trade-union leaders. The size of this group in Nigeria, including university graduates, was estimated in 1963 to be 70,000, and in view of the great progress being made in this, the biggest African country, in the campaign against ignorance and illiteracy, we may assume a rapid growth in the future.

It is naturally very difficult to lay down hard and fast rules for this young élite, beyond saying that it is sharply separated from the old élite. Origins, social background, and, in particular, intellectual and professional interests, and political affiliations, all these and other factors are producing a progressive differentiation in the ranks of the new élite of Africa. The fundamental differences between British and French colonial policy have also played an important role.

However, there are similarities between the two groups: the new élite is marked by a common ideological disposition, a consciousness of its historical task, the shared experience of colonial subjugation, and racial discrimination. Thus the present-day élite in Africa, which is, of course, closely connected with the national upheaval and serves, indeed, as its fermenting yeast, could hardly be conservative. This élite is constantly brought face to face with the dire consequences of colonialism: the misery and impoverishment of the masses, the startling contradiction between the vast economic resources of the African continent and the little that has been done to exploit them, the bitter heritage of the African past and the cruel economic and social dilemma of the present. This situation is so unusual and exceptional that they are literally forced to the conclusion that it cannot be remedied by ordinary means.

But what traditional examples and methods are there to solve their problems? What models, technological methods, were actually created to transform Africa into a continent of economic, social, and intellectual progress?

A liberal, moderate intellectual East African speaking in a discussion at the Second All-African Peoples' Conference declared:

'Your present-day African is a man without prejudices, without ideological ballast and without the burden of a historical past. He is of our own day and he refuses to look for the solution of his problems along the old, well-worn paths. He is not hemmed in; he is free. And this means that he is able to examine anything anywhere in the world completely without prejudice and solely from the standpoint of its usefulness to him.'[11]

But this judgement requires some modification. Most of the members of this young African élite are certainly not without prejudices, particularly where the West, democracy and capitalism are concerned. In a description of the new social strata in Africa, Jean D. Merlo, a young French sociologist who became closely acquainted with African problems as a student-priest in Paris, has the following to say about the attitude of African intellectuals:

'They reject imperialism and colonial capitalism. But first of all they distort it in order to be able to reject it. This is 'the healthy method' . . . In the same way they reject a democratic system that is simply transplanted from Europe to Africa. In their opinion liberal democracy is no use in Africa because the general political education of the population is not sufficiently advanced to allow them to give the voting paper its proper political significance.'[12]

Merlo does not examine the reasons for this attitude, but they are obvious enough. The nationally conscious, educated African sees the Western economic system primarily as an instrument of political colonialism. Such contact as he has had with it has been confined to Africa. It was at home in the colonial territories that he first heard the names of Esso, Shell, Unilever, UTC, UAC, Firestone, and so on. In his mind these concerns—and others as well—have made gigantic profits at the cost of the Africans. He compares the social standards of European directors, managers and technicians with the wages of the African workers and commercial employees, and comes to the conclusion that the whites were able to get rich because they kept the Africans in poverty. And it is, of course, a fact that for the same work performed under the same conditions, a European often receives much higher wages than an African worker. Even in the Congo where (according to a study of the International Labour Office, 30 August 1960) wages were on the whole more favourable to Africans than elsewhere, the minimum wage for European-born workers was from seven to twenty-seven times greater than the corresponding minimum wages for Africans.

In the eyes of many an African intellectual, capitalism destroys that harmony of society for which a social being must strive. At the same time he believes that such harmony existed in Africa before colonialism destroyed it. He believes that capitalism automatically produces inequality and causes social tension, and where it finds social tensions already in existence it exacerbates them. At the same time capitalism results in the formation of intensely antagonistic classes and opens the door to a reckless, anti-social rush for individual profits and power.

There is clearly an element of paradox in this. On the whole, the enlightened African rejects the old Africa with its rigid social structure, its unproductive use of labour, and its lack of efficient methods. But at the same time he makes no attempt to conceal his inner attachment to a society based essentially on the common use of the land by the tribe, the clan, and the family, and on the division of property; a society in which, in the most ideal sense, there was a 'communism', an actual communal rule. He would like to maintain or re-create this integrated, egalitarian society despite the economic revolution, which he recognizes as necessary and inevitable. His problem is whether Africa, while maintaining its communal solidarity, can achieve such economic and technological progress that it can, in fact, overcome its backwardness (by comparison with the highly industrialized countries). It is thus hardly surprising that Africans arrive at a completely different assessment of socialism and communism from that of West Europeans. The African regards the social theories of Proudhon, St Simon, Marx, Lenin, and Mao Tse-tung as promising remedies for his country, particularly as on the face of it they appeal to the communal spirit of Africans.

At this point it is not our intention to offer an analysis of the attitude this same African intellectual adopts towards the West, as distinct from the East, but it must be pointed out that the African élite find the way to socialism or communism made easy for them by a number of factors. Unlike the Europeans, and to a certain extent the Asians, Africans have come to know communism during a phase in which Russia, having left the worst barbarisms of Stalinism behind, has entered a slightly more liberal period. The uninitiated African, who has not witnessed forty-five years of communist dictatorship, but only a short and relatively peaceful phase and therefore knows little or nothing about the atrocities and mass terrorism of the twenties and the thirties in Russia, or of the days of Stalinist imperialist expansion in Central Europe, is misled by the results of 'the intensified class struggle'. In particular, he is more inclined to see the result than the methods by which it was obtained. For him the tangible result is a world power created, apparently, out of nothing, a power now able to shoot *luniks* and *sputniks* into the air, a power with a tremendous industrial potential, powerful armaments, and international prestige. To reinforce this favourable picture, he is influenced by communist propaganda that seeks to convince him that Soviet success was attained by the methods of 'real socialism' and collectivism, to the exclusion of parasitic individualism and individualistic groups.

Perhaps he is also strongly impressed by the example of the Chinese People's Republic. Here too the African is more inclined to see the end result than the methods by which it was achieved, atrocities and hecatombs of victims. And even though the achievements of the Chinese People's Republic are not yet as great as those of the Soviet Union, nevertheless they are, from his point of view, already considerable. Communist China has emancipated itself, both economically and politically, from an allegedly colonial and a preponderantly agrarian condition, despite the fact that it was hampered by the legacy of long years of civil war. At the same time Chinese communist propaganda suggests that 'real socialism' and true collectivism are even more to the fore in China than in the Soviet Union.

The effect of this can be seen from the case of Barry Diawadou, former Minister of Education in Guinea. After a visit to China he declared:

'Since my return I am quite convinced of the efficacy of Chinese methods. I was greatly impressed by the similarity of the economic problems that China has succeeded in solving and those that are now facing the peoples of Africa. In China I saw what can be done if you mobilize the vital forces of a nation. With all due regard to the difference in magnitude we now propose to do the same thing.'[13]

One can readily think of many examples that must seem like striking parallels to Africans when they compare the starting points of the economic revolutions in the Soviet Union and in Communist China with the present situation in Africa. Even those African intellectuals who are under no illusions about the seamy side of the communist world are not entirely immune to such ideas. Léopold Sédar Senghor, the Senegalese friend of France, demands, in his *Rapport sur la Doctrine et le Programme du Parti de la Fédération Africaine*, as well as in other writings and speeches, that Africans should bear 'the positive achievements of Marx' in mind. He also pleads for the application of 'the dialectical method and a comprehensive planning of the economic, social, political, and cultural process'. Although Senghor himself rejects the materialist philosophy of Marxism-Leninism, what about his less intelligent followers? Are they able to distinguish between 'the positive achievements' and the negative features? And where is the line to be drawn between what is acceptable and what is not?

Apart from the general attraction which certain orthodox, socialist economic theories hold for Africans, communism exercises one special fascination. This is the achievement of discipline, the apparent ability of the communists to give everyone his task within the general process of development, to place him where he is required, even if by force. From the standpoint of the African it looks as though everyone behind the Iron Curtain is given his own function in a sharply defined framework and that the people work together for the ultimate objective of a classless society.

Compare this admirable discipline and efficient organization of communist society with the apparent waste of manpower and material in the West! Intellectual, artistic, and creative talents are allowed to run to seed uselessly instead of being suitably employed for the benefit of society. Five, six, and even more firms compete with each other for industrial orders, whereas in the East a whole undertaking will be planned from the start by one (and of course the best one) while a staff of technicians work out a programme for executing projects in the most economical way. Thus Africans come to the conclusion that the wasteful methods of the West are not the best for their continent. We have to take this into consideration.

NOTES

[1] Report to the Constitutive Congress of the Party of African Federation (PFA), Dakar, 1 July 1959. Congress Record, p. 51.

[2] Lecture by Sékou Touré to the Royal Institute of International Affairs, London, in November 1959. Cyclostyled report issued by the Government of Guinea (December 1959).

[3] Quoted in W. R. Sharp and G. Kirk, *Contemporary International Politics* (New York, 1940), p. 113.

[4] Salvador de Madariaga, *Englishmen, Frenchmen and Spaniards* (London, 1928), p. xi.

[5] Quoted by Thomas Diop, 'Wesenszüge des Afrikaners', *Afrika* (Munich), November 1960, p. 425.

[6] Ibid., p. 424.

[7] Stenographic Minutes of the First African Regional Conference of the International Labour Organization, Lagos, December 1960.

[8] Stenographic Report of the Proceedings of the German Reichstag, 1896, II, pp. 1424-7, 1505.

[9] Lecture by Sékou Touré to the Royal Institute of International Affairs, London, in November 1959.

[10] *Afrika-heute* (Cologne, 1960), pp. 44 ff.

[11] Notes made by the author at the Second All-African Peoples' Conference, Tunis, January 1960.

[12] Jean D. Merlo, 'Probleme der jungen Elite Schwarzafrikas', *Afrika* (Munich), January 1961, p. 19.

[13] J. Jacquet-Francillon, 'En Afrique–la Chine arrive', *Le Figaro*, 25 December 1959.

Chapter III

THE AFRICAN CRISIS

So far two generations have been responsible for the African revolution. Initially, at least, both were guided by high ideals and it is only now that the third generation, which is beginning to come forward, finds itself forced to face the harsh realities of the situation. This third generation will determine which way the continent will go, what path the States will follow in their development and what economic and social ideas, doctrines and programmes will get the upper hand in this part of the world.

The first generation consisted of the prophets and dreamers. They did not and could not have had much to offer beyond splendid but rather vague ideals. At first it was little more than an appeal for the 'rise of the coloured people', and it was only later that more concrete aims emerged. Often they appealed to symbols of the past, and in this phase conceptions such as Ghana, Mali, Songhai, Malawi, Zambia and Zimbabwe developed into propaganda myths. The first signs of all this appeared in the United States in the early part of the nineteenth century when a consciousness of their origins began to grow among the slaves.

With the support of philanthropic whites, Negroes whose freedom had been purchased began to return to the land of their fathers. However, the Liberian experiment, which began on 7 January 1822 with the landing of black Pilgrim Fathers on the Pepper Coast, proved a failure. These high-minded Negroes, who felt they were returning to their ancestral home, were not always accepted by the natives as brothers; on the contrary, they were regarded as strangers and even enemies, and it was only after long and bloody struggles that they managed to establish themselves. The aftermath of this conflict is still noticeable today. Far from finding their way back to an original culture in the Land of the Free, the descendants of the Negro slaves of the United States have set themselves up as a master-caste known as the Americo-Liberians and they tend to remain aloof from the natives of the hinterland. Although President Tubman, who has been uninterruptedly at the helm since 1944, has tried to reduce some of the worst inequalities under the pressure of radical changes beyond the frontiers of Liberia, the gap between the two groups remains very deep. The majority of the original native tribes still live in near-archaic conditions, while the living conditions and behaviour of the small group of Americo-Liberians resemble a caricature of life in the southern States of the United States around 1880. In fact this 'first modern African State' has nothing in common with present-day Africa and modern African statesmen and politicians cannot make use of the Liberian experiment. Kwame Nkrumah, who visited Monrovia, the capital of Liberia, in 1947 felt repelled rather than attracted by this country.

Unfortunately however, there are few useful models anywhere for the guidance of modern Africans. The first generation of African *homines novi* concentrated on the fight for independence. They assumed that this was the most difficult task. The second generation, educated, guided and enthused by the prophets and dreamers of the first, carried out this task with astonishing speed, especially once they became aware of the weakness and demoralization of colonialism, and then set about creating modern political organizations for their countries. The international situation, exacerbated by the East-West conflict, did the rest. In consequence, what had looked like the task of decades was carried out almost throughout Africa within the space of a few years. But then Africans were faced with a much harder task: the consolidation of their gains. They had to cope as well as they could with the legacy of colonialism, and to work out practical programmes for the first phase of independence—indeed, even to find half-way passable tracks through the jungle of difficulties which faced them.

The current problems demanding a solution are vast. In many, even most, parts of Africa the twentieth century and the Middle Ages rub shoulders. Fanatical enlightenment amongst the so-called *evolués* finds itself up against a no less fanatical traditionalism. As we have seen, for example, in the Congo in 1964 the deepest ignorance and obscurantism contrast directly with determined intellectualism; narrow-minded tribalism clashes with national demands; a general unwillingness to work hard takes no account of the urgent need for economic progress; mass misery mocks the pomp of feudal chiefs and the arrogance of young upstarts. In such circumstances it is not really surprising that some of the leaders of this new generation think, for the moment, only of power (and generally speaking this means personal power) and its consolidation. History offers numerous examples of the tendency of even serious, honest revolutionaries to call a halt once they have managed to seize power. For the first time they are enjoying the taste of power and it is understandable that it tends to go to their heads. Their policies veer away from their earlier promises and ideals; urgent, difficult social problems are pushed into the background, until such time as the revolution is considered to be securely safeguarded against any internal or external threats.

In Africa the temptation to behave in this way is perhaps greater because of the enormous complexity of the problems and the limited means available for their solution. The majority of the African population does not bother much about the future and certainly not about 'the nation'. There is little desire for hard work, and even less for hard work in the interest of the general welfare. Even in Guinea, where Sékou Touré managed to get the masses to start working on a voluntary construction programme (*investissement humain*), enthusiasm, self-sacrifice, and thought for the common welfare soon faded. From the standpoint of political organization Guinea is the most advanced country in Africa, but the 1963 congress of Sékou Touré's *Parti Démocratique* ended with a flood of bitter complaints about the low labour morale of the people, the lack of mass initiative, and the declining popularity of the party and its aims among the population: and this is typical. Black marketeering and corruption are flourishing, discontent and even veiled rebellion are growing.

What is a threat in Guinea is already a fact in other African countries. The victorious leaders of the second generation set out to establish absolute power, but their dictatorial and usually autocratic régimes are not particularly strong and stable. In some of the young States the writ of the government hardly extends beyond the area served by the main roads, sometimes not much beyond the government buildings in the capital. Behind the petty bureaucracy, the smug pretentiousness and arrogance of the Ministers, there is frequently uncertainty, incompetence and ignorance. Take the former Belgian Congo: after five years of independence it has still not emerged from the anarchy which marked its birth as an independent State. Unemployment figures are rising steadily, the national income, even after reunification with Katanga, is falling alarmingly. Despite currency reform the Congolese franc is still without proper backing and has no real purchasing power. Regionalism is strong and if the writ of the central government extends beyond the Boulevard de 30 Juin, it is only thanks to the support of the Casques Bleues and the United Nations civilian operations in the Congo. Trade unions, students' organizations, and the followers of the late Lumumba are constantly plotting new revolts, issuing grandiloquent manifestos and proposing new panaceas. Meanwhile the various régimes appear unconcerned. Corrupt and incompetent, they rely completely on outside help and enjoy the record of having the largest administration of any African State, absorbing ninety-two per cent of the national income.

The Congo may be an extreme case, but elsewhere in Africa similarly deplorable conditions often exist. Three factors are primarily responsible for this depressing situation. First of all the leaders of the independence movements and the mass of their followers hoped for too much from their victory over colonialism. Anyone who witnessed the final phase before 'Uhuru Day' anywhere in Africa knows that the hope and belief that a radical change would come about as soon as independence was won was deliberately and artificially inflated. Secondly, the elementary conditions needed for the formation of capital are lacking, particularly when capital is taken to include the sum of accumulated labour. This lack naturally results in a regrettable dependence on foreign capital; in fact, those African countries which were formerly under French rule have to look abroad for no less than ninety per cent of the capital they need, while other African countries need between fifty and seventy-five per cent before they can make any investments at all. Thirdly, the immediate effect of the new slogans and plans is to accelerate the breakdown of existing social structures, aggravating the explosive processes of social change.

The older generation of African nationalists are largely aware of these fundamental facts, and they know how easily a single spark could result in an explosion. But a third generation is growing up, educated not only in Africa but also in schools and universities as far apart as the United States and Red China. They are already putting forward their demands. Here and there they have already succeeded in enforcing them elsewhere, and they do not hesitate to use force if necessary.

Unlike their predecessors, this third generation were not brought up amidst dreams of sovereignty, nor were they involved in the struggle to attain it. They grew up after independence had been won, and are only interested in rapid progress. Their minimum demand is for a share of responsibility, which means a share of political power. So far this demand has been refused, sometimes quite ruthlessly, but here and there individuals or groups have succeeded in worming their way into the ruling strata thanks chiefly to nepotism or the influence of cliques. They sometimes find that the established régime is prepared to go a long way towards weakening and neutralizing their radicalism by corrupting them with material temptations. This tactic has been used very successfully in Addis Ababa where, during the past few years, intriguing and troublesome young intellectuals have been promoted from their coffee bars to lucrative administrative posts and given pompous-sounding titles with no real influence or opportunities for development. But this has been relatively easier in Ethiopia than in other African countries. In Nigeria, for example, it was calculated at the end of 1963 that the coming four years would see the return of 15,000–17,000 students after the completion of their studies and training at universities and high schools abroad. At least 3,000 of these will return to Nigeria from the countries of the Soviet bloc. But no matter where they come from, or what social ideas they bring with them, the really important question is whether suitable jobs can be found for them. Even worse, if the educational system develops at its present rate, by 1966 only sixty per cent of those who complete secondary school will have a chance of finding suitable jobs, or be able to go on to high educational institutions in Nigeria or elsewhere. Taken together with the growing mass unemployment in the towns this is producing a problem which looks insoluble.

There are already examples of difficulties created if those in power ignore these, and other, sources of tension, and occupy themselves with propaganda and power politics instead of taking the drastic measures needed. The ostensible motives may vary from case to case, but one thing runs like a red thread through all the attempts at revolt, the assassination attempts and the *coups d'état* which, in 1963 alone, took place in Tunisia, Senegal, Ghana, Mali, Somalia, Algeria, the two Congos, Togo, the Ivory Coast Republic, Chad and Dahomey, as well as the revolts in Zanzibar and Gabon, and the mutinies in Tanganyika, Kenya and Uganda early in 1964.

In all these tense situations, there is one fundamental cause which is always present: the introduction of the one-party State and one-man rule.

The theoretical justification for this state of affairs is given in negative terms. By Léopold Senghor to Modibo Keita, Kwame Nkrumah, Julius Nyerere, and Felix Houphouet-Boigny, democracy is unanimously rejected as being irreconcilable with African needs and with the given African situation. It is certainly true that the difficulties in the way of establishing a democratic society in Africa are enormous. Even in Europe and in the United States democracy is an extraordinarily complicated system which is very difficult to manage; so much so that in many instances it is only a working hypothesis. How much more difficult and complicated is it to establish in a continent where social differences are so enormous, where people live mainly in small, isolated communities, where there are hundreds of languages and dialects, where there is widespread illiteracy and no solidly established middle class, and where the inexperienced élite are desperately trying to solve the urgent tasks facing them. Furthermore, democracy as a political system is discredited owing to the fact that the oldest and greatest European democracies, Great Britain and France, were the chief representatives of colonialism in Africa.

Nevertheless, the almost wholesale condemnation of democracy in Africa is still astonishing. It is equated with anarchy and 'a struggle of all against all'. At best it is described as a luxury that young countries cannot afford. Africans claim that as it is a system in which many political parties fight each other, its adoption would rapidly lead to 'the disruption of the nation'.

I do not propose to question the cogency of many of the arguments and over-simplifications advanced against democracy. No one suggests that a political structure which allowed each little group or tribe to express itself by forming a political party would be suitable for Africa. No one wants to see the creation of dozens of political parties whose endless struggles would lead to political paralysis. But what can be, and in fact is being, more and more impatiently demanded by the people is that governments show some respect for certain elementary, democratic principles, such as freedom of speech, of the Press, and of religion, and the adoption of a system which neither excludes all traditional bodies nor ignores all regional and tribal interests in favour of unrestricted centralization and modernization.

However, this is precisely the opposite of what the second generation of élites is attempting to do in most African countries. Even in Nigeria, where a federal system of originally three (now four) regions was established, and where democracy seemed to be working, the régime has not always adhered to these elementary principles as the circumstances of the General Elections at the end of 1964 demonstrated. And the situation is, of course, worse in those countries where, right from the start, little or no attention was paid to traditional or regional interests.

Very soon after independence the rulers of Ghana, Tanganyika, Dahomey, and other countries proclaimed that the traditional social structure was 'incompatible' with the political structure of a modern State. Under the slogan of 'national concentration', chiefs and headmen were deprived of their social functions and often of their dignity and refused any representation, while differences between regions and tribes were ignored. Once in power, the leading men of the New Guard centralized the administration down to the last detail. They turned the trade unions into state organizations, and declared all opposition treasonable. They introduced, or are on the way to introducing, legislation such as the Preventive Detention Act of Ghana, which allows political rivals to be disposed of without the formality of a trial. All this is being done for the sake of 'national unity' and 'national construction'.

However, to short-circuit history is not an easy task and ironically the result of these 'unification processes' has been the opposite of what was intended. Opposition to such régimes is growing, even among former sympathizers. Trade unions which started with a keen desire to co-operate with the Government have, since being nationalized and placed under government control, suddenly become hotbeds, not only of trade-union opposition but of party-political conspiracies, as was illustrated by the Tanganyika crisis in January 1964. In the same way the gagged Press frequently manages to make its views known, while tame opposition politicians are developing from obedient yes-men into awkward opponents.

The most crucial fact for all these opposition groups is that the existing constitutions do not allow them the right of opposition. Legality is the exclusive privilege of one party and the one man. This means that the opposition is forced to conduct an illegal struggle. The lesson this teaches, as more than one African leader has had to learn, is written in blood. Regrettable as this is, it would be too easy merely to condemn those who are forced to adopt these tactics. The guilty ones are those who have hidden behind a barrier of smug decrees and savage laws, who have closed their eyes to current political realities, and who blindly devote themselves to the cult of their own personalities and power.

No matter how clever their tactics or how firm their conviction that they hold an endless lease of power, the ultimate result will always be the same. It will end, as in Togo, with the murder of the president, a man who started off with everything on his side but ignored the interests of a small, important group. It will end with the sudden overthrow of the leader, as in the former French Congo, where the Abbé Foulbert Youlou, a politician who considered himself the Lord's Anointed, wandered around in a cassock but ignored the most elementary canons of Christianity. It will end, as it did in Dahomey, with the dismissal of a president who thought himself powerful enough to act like a French governor and play off groups, tribes and politicians against each other. Or it will end, as in Ghana, with a president too scared to appear among his people for months on end and forced to live cooped up in a colonial fort behind security cordons. Everywhere the radicalization of the opposition and the adoption of extreme, sometimes violent measures is the inevitable result of authoritarianism and dictatorship practised in the name of national unity. No nation, however young and poor, is so lacking in spiritual, social and political resources that it does not wish to share in the government of the country or to criticize and think for itself. Such wishes cannot be repressed indefinitely. If these elementary human and political desires and needs are blocked, and even suppressed by violence, they will one day crystallize into demands which will finally break the restrictive structure of a one-party State. The inevitable result of a system which concentrates all power in the hands of a few, often even of one man, under the cloak of a struggle against national disunity, will be the disruption of that self-same national unity.

This will come about sooner if, in addition, the upholders of the one-party State fail to produce any stirring ideas likely to appeal to the nation, and are not able to persuade them that they really do hold out some promise for the future. But the situation is particularly unfortunate in this respect. We have already pointed out that the first and second generations in Africa concentrated their attention on gaining independence. However, the fact that this independence fell into their laps with unexpected suddenness, giving them no time to develop any broad practical plans, cannot be accepted as a valid excuse for their present attitude of despair and resignation, or for the ingenuous belief that they have completely exhausted all the possibilities open to them, so that now they concentrate exclusively on staying in power, using ideas only as a means of camouflage.

But that is the situation today and in the last resort expressions like 'African unity' and 'African socialism' are frequently empty words. African unity, in particular, is likely to remain unattainable for a very long time. Firstly, because those who proclaim its desirability regard it in terms of power politics. Men like Nasser and Nkrumah have always aimed at unity that would be in their own interests rather than in the interests of the continent. That is why the Casablanca Group (founded in 1961) rapidly degenerated into a farce. It collapsed because of the conflicting ambitions within it and because African unity is hardly possible while large areas of the continent remain in neo-colonialist dependence on France—an economic, political and military dependence planned on a long-term basis. Finally the Casablanca Group collapsed because the colonial heritage of arbitrarily divided, or united, tribes and peoples proved so burdensome that even with the best will in the world, the new rulers could do very little about it. The conflicts between Morocco and Mauritania and between Ghana and Togo, the frontier clash between Morocco and Algeria in the autumn of 1963 and the ever-present threat of open war over the Ogaden district between Ethiopia and Somalia in 1964 are not exceptional; they are merely the local symptoms of an explosive danger which exists throughout the continent and which could come to the surface at any time. The decision of the Congress for African Unity in Addis Ababa in May 1963 that existing frontiers should be recognized—a decision that was confirmed once and for all by a second congress in Addis Ababa in the following November—has never had anything but rhetorical significance. It will be called more and more into question as various régimes find it necessary to distract the attention of their people from domestic problems to higher national tasks. Algeria carried out such a manoeuvre in the autumn of 1963 when the frontier dispute with Morocco was a gift from heaven for Ben Bella's hard-pressed régime.

'Pan-Africa' and 'African unity' are no more than slogans. The noble feelings that find expression in such ideals are destroyed by egoistic dreams of power and precedence. Pan-Africa is not pursued as a practical aim requiring long, hard, solid work, but has become a fetish and a cover for very different aims.

The terms 'socialism'—and in particular, 'African socialism'—also have their ambiguities. In Tanganyika, Julius Nyerere wants to develop a kind of family organism which he calls 'Ujamaa', a Swahili term which combines the family and socialism. What Ujamaa would mean in practice is not clear. In his book, *I Speak of Freedom: a Statement of African Ideology*, Kwame Nkrumah discusses 'Ghanaian socialism' at great length, and talks of the political ideology which, according to him, inspires his Convention People's Party. He says that the CPP is both a dynamic and a socialist party, but does not explain what these terms mean. At *Parti Démocratique de Guinée* congresses, Sékou Touré eloquently defends ideas such as 'democratic centralism', 'criticism and self-criticism', 'planned economy', 'collective leadership', and 'the unity of all the toilers', but one is reminded of a juggler constantly producing rabbits out of a hat—and only imitation rabbits anyway. There is a good deal of talk about the necessity for tight governmental control 'in the first phase of socialist transformation', about the role of the one united party as the motive power in the historical process towards socialism, and about 'the special role of leading personalities' in the initial phase of that process. Words, words, words, but without any real meaning, without anything tangible or concrete to give us any idea of what is really intended.

At first the communists, keepers of the Holy Grail of 'scientific socialism', were startled and dismayed by the woolly ideas of African socialists, but they seem to have given up worrying. They entertain the well-founded hope that this African socialism will soon expose itself as a mere rhetorical façade erected by the men who hold power in Africa and that the African masses will soon see for themselves how little substance there is in the ideology of the leaders of the second generation. When this happens, they hope the masses (and in particular the up-and-coming élite of the third generation) will turn to 'real' socialism, socialism in its most logical, radical form, namely communism. Meanwhile the communists seem content to let the present rulers stew in their own juice while urgent problems of Africa pile up menacingly.

Is their calculation realistic? Has communism a good chance of gaining influence in, or even winning over, parts of this continent?

We shall examine this important question in detail.

Chapter IV

COMMUNISM, COLONIALISM, AND WORLD REVOLUTION

THE Africa policy of the communists developed rather late, and as a reaction to the genuine success of the movement for independence. The communists had no traditional, practical experience to fall back on, apart from some improvised attempts to exercise influence on the chiefly literary awakening of the coloured peoples in the twenties.[1] Against their lack of practical experience, however, they had a long tradition of theory, ready-made explanations of the phenomenon of 'colonial revolution', and theoretical solutions for it. The African problem was part and parcel of this theory. For our purposes, it is essential to take a closer look at the original communist theory of 'colonial revolution', because many of the practical steps now being taken as part of their African policy are understandable only in terms of these earlier ideological assumptions. Fortunately it is not necessary to go right back to the classic representatives of scientific socialism, Marx and Engels, since they confined their theories almost entirely to capitalism in the highly developed countries (although there are one or two chapters in Marx's *Das Kapital* that touch upon the colonial problem). The series of articles on China and India, written by Marx in 1863 for the *New York Tribune* also touch upon the subject, but only rather superficially. As far as the orthodox fathers of scientific socialism were concerned, 'the actual history of mankind' began in the industrialized countries. Industrialization produces capitalism and capitalism produces its own grave-diggers in the shape of the impoverished proletariat, who have nothing to lose but the chains which they finally cast off in a revolutionary upheaval. The famous communist manifesto of 1848 ends with the words 'Workers of the world, unite!' But although they said the world, Marx and Engels were thinking primarily of central and western Europe.

If Lenin had tried to uphold this theory inflexibly he would have found himself in an impossible dilemma, because Russia was the largest agricultural power in Europe and industrialization was only in its preliminary stages. There was no accumulation of capital and no strong proletariat. Particularly after the failure of the revolution of 1905 however, the will to power triumphed over strict loyalty to dogma. Although in his book, *Two Tactics for Social Democracy in the Democratic Revolution*, Lenin condemns 'the reactionary idea' of looking for 'the salvation of the working class in anything but the further development of capitalism', at the same time he recommends a 'tactical opening on the right', that is, a strengthening of the proletarian forces by turning to the peasantry.[2] This extension of the original sphere of communist action is of fundamental importance. By politically rehabilitating the peasantry and allowing them into an alliance with the proletariat, Lenin introduced a new basic factor into communist revolutionary movements in countries which were not sufficiently developed, economically and structurally, to comply with the original Marxist conditions for a socialist upheaval. This new departure applied not only to Tzarist Russia, but also to China, where it took on increasing importance. In fact, Mao Tse-tung's doctrine of anti-imperialist action and of 'the New Democracy' is based on the position Lenin adopted in 1905. Today, when the communists adopt similar tactics in their efforts to win over Asia and Africa, they are acting in complete accord with Lenin's own ideology.

This early solution of the central dilemma of communism was developed further during the First World War. In a discussion with Rosa Luxemburg and in his book, *Imperialism, the Highest Stage of Capitalism*, Lenin stressed the value of colonial territories for monopoly capitalism and discussed the likely political effects of the disintegration of the colonial system. He insisted that the ruling strata of the industrial States of the West were being increasingly compelled to go in for colonial expansion in order to create new markets for their goods and to obtain the raw materials they needed. In his view, the struggle for these markets and for the control of the colonial and semi-colonial peoples had become a fundamental law of monopoly capitalism.[3]

Following on this, Lenin seized on the implication that there were other ways, apart from the classic way of revolution, in which socialism could be victorious: to prise the colonies out of the capitalist economic structure, for example, would deal capitalism a fatal blow and would indirectly assist in a communist victory.[4]

With the victory of the Bolsheviks in the November Revolution of 1917 these ideas became of great practical significance. It is well known, of course, that in the first flush of victory the communists thought a chain reaction of socialist upheavals would be set up in the highly industrialized countries of the West. Their plans for extending the national into an international revolution included the East, and although at first this meant only Asiatic Russia, it was soon extended to the whole colonial and semi-colonial sphere, including Latin America and, finally, Africa; as time went on, this aspect of the world revolution began to play an increasingly important role. On 7 December 1917 Lenin, as the first Chairman of the Council of People's Commissars, and Stalin, as People's Commissar for Nationalities, issued an appeal 'to all toiling Muslims in the East' (including Africa it should be remembered). After referring to the explosive upheaval in Russia the appeal went on:

'But Russia does not stand alone in this holy cause . . . The workers and soldiers of the West are already flocking to the banner of socialism and shaking the bastions of imperialism to their foundation. And far-away India, which has been enslaved for centuries by the modern robbers of Europe, has already raised the standard of revolt, is organizing her Soviets, throwing off the hated chains of slavery and calling on the peoples of the East to fight for their freedom . . . You are not threatened with oppression by Russia and her revolutionary Government, but by robber imperialism, which has turned your countries into impoverished and exploited colonies . . . Lose no time in shaking off the chains of oppression in your countries!'[5]

Clearly the references to India were more in accordance with Bolshevik wishes than with reality, but although at the time this appeal represented little more than empty words it nevertheless documented a significant change in communist policy: the Bolsheviks were no longer pinning their hopes exclusively on the proletarian masses of the West, they were trying to draw the impoverished peasant masses of the East into the hoped-for world revolution. The theoretical importance of this appeal is that it built for the first time a strategic bridge between Europe and the Afro-Asian world and established a new connection between revolutionary forces in the West and the East.

A year later Stalin wrote in the same spirit in his book, *The October Revolution and the National Question*, declaring that

'The great world-wide significance of the October Revolution chiefly consists in the fact that it has widened the scope of the national question and converted it from the particular question of combating national oppression in Europe into the general question of emancipating the oppressed peoples, colonies and semi-colonies from imperialism.

'It has thereby erected a bridge between the socialist West and the enslaved East, having created a new front of revolutions *against* [Stalin's italics] world imperialism, extending from the proletarians of the West, through the Russian Revolution, to the oppressed peoples of the East.'[6]

At the same time, in October 1918, communists and crypto-communists from Asia, the Levant, and North Africa were meeting in Moscow to discuss the practical problems of a 'unification of the revolutionary forces of the East'. Under Soviet auspices they founded a League for the Emancipation of the East, though for the time being its operations were confined to the peoples of Asiatic Russia and the Levant. The chief interest of this league is that it was the first communist front organization for the colonial areas and its programme contained *in nuce* all the essential communist demands for an economic, social and political transformation of the under-developed countries. Particular attention should be paid to one point which has been repeated since then in innumerable communist declarations and which represents one of the main arguments of communist anti-colonial propaganda: despite cultural and technical backwardness, Afro-Asia can 'go forward over the heads of both feudalists and capitalists and advance from its pre-capitalist system to socialism without first going through the painful stage of capitalism'.[7] This formula did much to give new life and vigour to the theories first worked out by Lenin in 1905, and extended in 1916, for a 'communist theory' of colonial emancipation and it is no accident that Peking, in particular, is still working in the underdeveloped countries according to the programme of the early League for the Emancipation of the East.

These theories, however, remained on paper, as did the stirring appeals addressed to the West. The revolution in Germany for which Moscow hoped and worked did not take place. Likewise the longed-for upheavals in India, China and other Eastern countries failed to materialize, or were damp squibs. Thus for the time being there was no question of the much desired 'united and effective front against Western imperialism'. In this disappointing situation Lenin made a general reassessment of the world situation and of communist chances in both the West and the East. With his eye on the forthcoming Second Congress of the Communist International, he wrote his famous book, *Left-Wing Communism*, perhaps better known by its sub-title *An Infantile Disorder*.[8] The Congress met in July-August 1920 and duly adopted the new thesis laid down in this book. Henceforth it was the tactical bible of world communism.

The important questions discussed at this congress were questions of tactics, including discussions about the most profitable areas for political action. Lenin's book had settled the general question of communist tactics. He opposed dogmatic, rigid methods and he insisted on the adoption of elastic tactics. However, there was still little hope of success in the West, where capitalism was gradually re-establishing its hold, so the Second World Congress of the Comintern decided that, for the time being, there were greater prospects of success in the East. It was therefore in the East that Lenin's new tactics were to be given their first trial. The theoretical basis for this tactical experiment was provided by an original 'Draft Thesis on the National and Colonial Question' drawn up by Lenin for the World Congress and put forward by the Indian communist, Manabendra Nath Roy. Later on Roy was expelled from the Comintern as a heretic, but the Second World Congress adopted his analysis if not all his conclusions. His second and third points are particularly interesting:

'2. European capitalism draws its strength mainly not from the European industrial countries but from its colonial possessions. To keep itself in existence it needs control over the extensive colonial markets and a wide field for exploitation. Britain, the bulwark of imperialism, has been suffering for a century from over-production. Without her extensive colonial possessions, which are necessary for the sale of her goods and which at the same time represent her raw-material basis, the capitalist order in Britain would long ago have collapsed under its own weight. In turning millions of the inhabitants of Asia and Africa into slaves, British imperialism at the same time keeps the British proletariat under the dominance of the bourgeoisie.

'3. The extra profits obtained in the colonies represent one of the chief sources from which the strength of contemporary capitalism is drawn. The European working class will be able to overthrow the capitalist order only when this source is finally cut off.'[9]

Hardly any opposition was voiced at the World Congress to this thesis which placed the fulcrum of the world revolution, for the time being, not in the West but in the colonies. In fact the delegates seemed enthusiastic at the prospect of finding a way out of the blind alley in which communism found itself in the West. But even their enthusiasm could not prevent them from recognizing the enormous gap that existed between desire and reality. There were either no communist parties at all in the colonial countries, or they were very weak indeed. Manabendra Roy and a number of extremely doctrinaire communists called for the gingering-up of these groups and insisted that they be given freedom to enter into alliances with non-communist groups. Roy did not fail to point out that 'at first . . . the revolution in the colonies will not be a communist revolution', but he consoled the congress with the assurance that provided the communist advance guard put itself at the head of the colonial revolution at once it would soon be able to lead the masses along 'the correct path'. Even on the (for him) all-important agrarian question Roy was in favour of adopting cautious tactics, and the ninth point of his theses declares that it would be an error 'to try to carry out the agrarian revolution according to communist principles immediately'. At the same time he insisted that at no time should the leadership in the colonies be left 'in the hands of the bourgeois democrats'. Indeed, 'the proletarian parties' were to carry on intensive propaganda for communist ideas and form 'workers' and peasants' soviets' at the first opportunity. These soviets were to work 'in the same way as in the Soviet Republics of the more advanced capitalist countries in order to bring about the final overthrow of the capitalist régime all over the world.'[10]

Lenin, and therefore the majority of the Congress, had other views, however. Lenin was well aware that the communists in the colonial countries were not strong enough to form such workers' and peasants' soviets, and that there would consequently have to be a long transitional period leading from colonial exploitation to the 'national democratic' phase of liberation, to the seizure of power by the communists. However, even Lenin demanded that in the colonial question communist propaganda should not adopt the usual formulae in the question of national self-determination and the equality of nations.[11]

Instead of 'an empty slogan for recognition and self-determination', Lenin declared in the original draft theses that it must be made clear to the oppressed peoples that there was no salvation for them 'except through the victory of the Soviet power' and that 'only a Soviet system of society is in a position to give the nations real equality'.[12]

However, more important for the future of communist policy in the colonial and semi-colonial countries is what Lenin had to say about the co-operation of the communists with other elements. In *Left-Wing Communism: an Infantile Disorder* he had condemned as obstinate the refusals to make compromises with other, even with hostile, groups. He insisted that communists must be prepared 'to agree to all and every sacrifice, and even—if need be—to resort to various stratagems, artifices, illegal methods, to evasions and subterfuges'[13] in order to gain their ends. Lenin recommended the use of such methods for the colonial struggle too. Addressing the Second World Congress he declared:

'With regard to the backward states and nations, in which feudal or patriarchal and patriarchal-peasant relations predominate, it is particularly important to bear in mind:

First, that all Communist Parties must assist the bourgeois-democratic liberation movement in these countries;

Second, that it is necessary to wage a fight against the clergy and other influential reactionary and mediaeval elements in backward countries;

Third, that it is necessary to combat Pan-Islamism and similar trends which strive to combine the liberation movement against European and American imperialism with the attempt to strengthen the positions of the khans, the landlords, mullahs, etc;
Fourth, that it is necessary in the backward countries to give special support to the peasant movement against the landlords, against large landownership, and against all manifestations or survivals of feudalism, and strive to lend the peasant movement the most revolutionary character and to establish the closest possible alliance between the West-European communist proletariat and the revolutionary peasant movement in the East, in the colonies, and in the backward countries generally.'[14]

Now come the decisive passages which unmistakably reveal the real purpose of all these and similar manoeuvres:

'The Communist International must support the bourgeois-democratic national movements in colonial and backward countries *only on condition* [italics added] that in all backward countries the elements of future proletarian parties which are communists not only in name shall be grouped together and trained to appreciate their special tasks, viz. to fight the bourgeois-democratic movements within their own nations; the Communist International must enter into a temporary alliance with bourgeois-democracy in colonial and backward countries, but must not merge with it and must under all circumstances preserve the independence of the proletarian movement, even if in its most rudimentary form.'[15]

The delegates to the Second World Congress of the Communist International approved these plans and accepted the report of the Commission for National and Colonial Questions presented by Lenin. This document developed the existing ideological preliminaries into an integral theory governing communist penetration of the colonial world. This was what Lenin meant when he declared that the Communist International needed a *scientifically based plan* to bring the backward countries into the Soviet system 'with the aid of the proletariat of the advanced countries'. Once this was achieved then, after they had passed through a certain stage of development, they could be brought to the Soviet system 'without having to pass through the capitalist stage.'[16]

To sum up: proceeding from Lenin's theses of 1905 and 1916 and from the discussions that took place from 1917 to 1920, the Second Congress of the Communist International adopted a uniform, power-political conception of the communist colonial revolution, which is still valid today. It embraces the following points:

1. In view of the lack of communist success in the progressive countries the colonial areas offer possibilities for world-revolutionary expansion.

2. However, the proletarian forces in these areas are not yet strong enough to take independent revolutionary action. The national-revolutionary movements are under bourgeois-democratic dominance. Therefore, in this situation the communists must, *temporarily*, support the bourgeois-democratic forces, enter into an alliance with them and adopt their slogans.

3. This policy does not mean the abandonment of the ultimate communist objectives, which are the transformation of the bourgeois-democratic phase of the national-revolutionary movement into a socialist phase; and, after that, the gradual establishment of a Soviet system followed by a *direct transition to Communism.*

4. In order to extend their power and influence, the communists must maintain complete (ideological) independence within the framework of their alliance with the bourgeois-democratic forces and, at the same time, must systematically train the future elements of the proletarian parties in the spirit of Marxism-Leninism. It is the duty of all existing communist parties to give this process their full support.

If at the same time we remember that at Lenin's suggestion the Second Congress of the Communist International, for propaganda purposes, replaced the expression 'bourgeois-democratic movement' by 'national-revolutionary movement', we can see that the leading communists of our own day have contributed few new ideas to the communist theory of colonial revolution and that they are quite right when they identify their Eastern policy of the sixties with the theories of Lenin. The controversy now going on between Moscow and Peking with regard to this Eastern policy is also nothing new; it is, in fact, typical of the permanent communist dispute about methods and, in this case, the Chinese communists have taken over the more rigid views of men like Manabendra Nath Roy, who failed to recognize the value of Lenin's supple elastic tactics, ran the danger of isolating themselves by their ultra-left attitude, and robbed themselves of all influence.

A few months later, the anti-colonial principles of the Second Congress of the Communist International were taken up, for propaganda purposes, by a specifically Afro-Asian body, the First Congress of the Peoples of the East, which met in Baku in September 1920 and was attended by 1,891 delegates from thirty-two 'nations of the East', ranging from Manchuria to Morocco to South Africa. According to the report subsequently submitted to the Executive Committee of the Communist International (ECCI) by Zinoviev on 20 September 1920, only two-thirds of those present at the congress could be called communists. The others were representatives of those national-revolutionary groups—chiefly members of the intelligentsia—that were now to be deliberately wooed and won for an alliance with communism. Despite revolutionary harangues by Radek and Bela Kun, who apparently had not toed the line completely, the congress followed the intended policy. Zinoviev said frankly that in the Soviet view communism could not yet be realized in Asia and Africa. However, the time for national revolts against imperialism was at hand and the Soviet Government was ready and willing to co-operate with all the national, democratic and revolutionary forces in the colonial countries. The congress decided to form a Council of Propaganda and Action for the Peoples of the East. Its activities were largely propagandistic and it founded and published the periodical *People of the East* in Russian, Turkish, Persian and Arabic.[17]

Lenin died on 21 January 1924, long before it was possible to discover whether the colonial policy laid down by the Second Congress of the Communist International at his behest was likely to be effective. His last article, published posthumously in *Pravda*, painted the national and international position of Soviet communism in sombre rather than cheerful colours. It talked about 'the confusion in our camp' and recorded the general 'recovery of capitalism'. World revolution seemed to have drifted into a blind alley. Significantly, Lenin pinned what hope he had onto the 'unusual speed' with which the thickly peopled colonial continents were 'being dragged into the fight for emancipation', so that, '*in this respect* there cannot be the slightest shadow of doubt what the final outcome of the world struggle will be. *In this sense*, the complete victory of socialism is fully and absolutely assured.'[18]

A number of knowledgeable people regard these words as the real testament of Lenin and it is impossible not to agree with them. In any case, his successors, and in particular Stalin, have always understood the last article of the founder of Soviet socialism in this sense. The Fifth Congress of the Communist International in 1924 drew up marching orders for the world revolution 'in the East' and Stalin, who for some time had presented himself as the ideological successor of Lenin, underlined the theoretical consequences in a series of lectures delivered in April and May 1924, 'The Foundations of Leninism'. He dismissed 'the former idea' that a victory of the proletariat in Europe could take place without *a direct alliance with the liberation movement in the colonies*, denouncing it as an 'anti-revolutionary standpoint' which must be 'exposed'. He went on,

'Leninism has proved . . . that the national question can be solved only in connection with and on the basis of the proletarian revolution and that the road to victory of the revolution in the West lies through the revolutionary alliance with the liberation movements of the colonies, and dependent countries against imperialism . . . Leninism . . . recognizes the existence of revolutionary capacities in the national liberation movements of the oppressed countries, and the possibility of using these for overthrowing the common enemy, for overthrowing imperialism.'[19]

Stalin qualified his contention, however, by saying that only national-revolutionary movements whose interests did not 'clash with the interests of the proletarian movement' were to be supported in this way. Even the struggle of the Emir of Afghanistan for the independence of his country from imperialism could be regarded as a contribution to the revolutionary movement

'despite the monarchist views of the Emir and his associates, for it weakens, disintegrates and undermines imperialism . . . For the same reason, the struggle that the Egyptian merchants and bourgeois intellectuals are waging for the independence of Egypt is *objectively* [italics added] a *revolutionary* [Stalin's italics] struggle, despite the bourgeois title of the leaders of the Egyptian national movement, despite the fact that they are opposed to socialism; whereas the struggle that the British 'Labour' Government is waging to preserve Egypt's dependent position is for the same reason a *reactionary* [Stalin's italics] struggle despite the proletarian origin and the proletarian title of the members of that government.'[20]

Such words clearly show that Khrushchev's co-existence policy towards Ethiopia, Liberia, Morocco or Tunisia was not in conflict with communist tradition, but was firmly based on history and theory, and was completely in conformity with the communist strategy and tactics laid down in the twenties.

One year later Stalin introduced a new differentiation into the colonial debate. On 18 May 1925, at the fourth anniversary of the foundation of the 'Communist University of the Toilers of the East' in Tashkent, he addressed students 'from no less than fifty nations and national groups in the East' and told them that 'there are no fewer than three categories of colonial and semi-colonial countries' and that therefore specific tactics must be developed for each of them. For the first time the expression 'national bourgeoisie' was used; thenceforth it squeezed out expressions such as 'bourgeois democrats' and became a key-word of communist anti-colonialism. Stalin defined and classified the three categories according to 'the degree of consciousness of the national bourgeoisie or the proletariat', and this degree determined the communist approach.

In countries such as Morocco (Category 1) 'where the national bourgeoisie has, as yet, no grounds for splitting up into a revolutionary party . . . the task of the communist elements is to take all measures to create a united national front against imperialism'. The situation in Egypt and China (Category 2) was regarded as different: the national bourgeoisie here was already split and one wing was inclined towards 'reactionary tendencies'. Here the communists could co-operate only with the petty bourgeoisie. Finally, in countries such as India (Category 3) the compromising bourgeoisie had already gone over completely to the side of imperialism, therefore the communists must go in for independent action and an alliance with the revolutionary bourgeoisie could serve only to prepare the proletariat 'to take the leading role in the movement for freedom'. The 'hegemony of the proletariat' must be clearly safeguarded and so, too, must the alliance of the movement for freedom with the 'proletarian movement of the advanced countries'.[21]

The co-operation between the communists and the national

bourgeoisie in the first category soon became of increasing practical importance. In order to establish a broad, anti-imperialist united front the communists were even prepared to keep their manoeuvres in the background and, outwardly, to play second fiddle to bourgeois scholars, authors and politicians. This was the case in the various anti-colonial and anti-imperialist leagues, committees, etc., founded in many Western countries, which came together at the Congress against Colonial Oppression and Imperialism, held at the Palais Egmont in Brussels in February 1927, where the chief organizer and wire-puller was the German communist, Willi Münzenberg, and the finance came from the Communist International. Incidentally, the significance of this congress is exaggerated today by people who are inclined to see 'a red conspiracy' behind every move towards co-operation between communists and non-communists. A number of well-known people were present at that meeting including Jawaharlal Nehru, Messalij Hadj, Paul-Henri Spaak, Henri Barbusse, Theodor Lessing and Madame Sun Yat-sen, and it developed into a great protest against the colonial policy of the Western powers, while by way of contrast the anti-colonialist attitude of the Soviet Union was lavishly praised.[22]

A year later the Sixth Congress of the Communist International opened in Moscow to discuss communist and anti-colonial strategy and tactics in greater detail, and Stalin's recommendations were officially adopted. The catastrophic failure of communist action in China in 1927, which was primarily the result of Stalin's policy of alliance with the national bourgeoisie, giving the Kuomintang the opportunity to crush the communist party of China for the time being, did nothing to hamper the Eastern orientation of the Comintern. On the contrary, in accordance with Stalin's thesis that irrespective of dogma, communism should seek out 'the weakest links in the imperialist chain' and apply to these the lever of revolution, the main weight of communist activity was now increasingly concentrated on the East, where the colonial countries were described as the most vulnerable sector of the imperialist front. As there could be no question of any strong proletariat or of any 'revolutionary mass consciousness' in these areas, the Congress instructed communists to support *local bourgeois movements* everywhere and to identify themselves with the developing forms of nationalism and the slogan of self-determination.[23] Ultimately, of course, the 'movements for national-revolutionary freedom' would be persuaded that there was no salvation for them, except in 'an alliance with the revolutionary proletariat and as a result of the victory of the proletarian world revolution over world imperialism.'[24] The national factor must, however, always be taken into account and special attention paid to the peasantry as well as the intelligentsia—in fact, permission was expressly given to the intelligentsia in the colonies to form the *chief cadre.*[25] The Sixth Congress again appealed to the communist parties of the metropolitan States to be active in their colonial territories, particularly as there had been no progress in this field since the Fifth Congress of the Communist International. Then, in a report presented to the congress on 30 June 1924, Manuilsky had indignantly declared, 'A year ago the Communist International issued an appeal to the colonial slaves to rise in revolt against their masters, but when this revolutionary appeal came to the notice of a local branch of the French Communist Party in Sidi-Bel-Abbes in Algeria, it adopted a resolution condemning this Communist International appeal . . . I should like to ask our French comrades what public pronouncements their Communist Party has made demanding freedom for the colonies . . . Our English comrades are no less deserving of blame. Not one of the official statements on the attitude of the British Communist Party contains any clear and unambiguous demand for the separation of the colonies from the British Empire.'[26] In the period between the two congresses the communist parties of France and Great Britain had failed to become more resolute and vigorous, so they had once again to be called to order. The Negro problem in the United States also came up for closer attention. The theses of the Sixth Congress classified Negroes into the following main groups: those in Central Africa; in the colonial and semi-colonial countries, such as Haiti; in the Union of South Africa; in North America; and in Central and South America. In future these groups should be linked and the coloured people of the United States were called upon to pay special attention to their brothers in Africa.[27] All the measures decided upon by the congress and its tactical and strategic proposals were summed up in the programme of the Sixth World Congress, which declared:

'The international proletarian revolution represents a combination of processes which differ in character and in point of time. There are purely proletarian revolutions; bourgeois-democratic revolutions developing into proletarian revolutions; national-revolutionary wars; and colonial revolutions. The world dictatorship of the proletariat comes only as the result of the (total) revolutionary process.'[28]

Although the Sixth Congress of the Communist International dealt with the colonial problem in great detail and all the delegates solemnly promised that in the future they would 'support the struggle of the colonial and semi-colonial peoples more and more effectively', all the talk and the resolutions came to nothing.

The reason for this was not entirely due to the impotence of international communism, but was rather the result of the anti-international shift that took place in the Kremlin as a result of Stalin's final victory over Trotsky, the rejection of Trotsky's programme of permanent revolution and the adoption of Stalin's thesis of '*the building up of socialism in one country alone*' (the Soviet Union). Thus the Sixth Congress of the Communist International cannot be regarded as having drawn up a new programme for regenerating communism; what it did was to provide the epilogue to a ten-year period of world revolutionary activity. From now on, communist propaganda organs everywhere were to trumpet about the 'gigantic' successes of Soviet industrialization and collectivization; finally, when the great party purge of the late thirties gutted the Comintern too, the egoistic, imperialistic Soviet-Russian interests personified by Stalin celebrated their full triumph over the interests of the world-wide proletarian revolution.

For the next twenty years, from 1928 to 1948, the colonial problem disappeared almost completely from the theoretical debates of communism. Apart from the problem of China, Stalinist foreign policy touched on Afro-Asian themes in a very pragmatic fashion and without in the least bothering about dogma or principles. The Seventh (and last) Congress of the Communist International, which took place in 1936, was completely dominated by the anti-fascist struggle (to the exclusion of the old anti-imperialism) and by the effort of forming United Fronts, People's Fronts, and other front organizations in the capitalist States. The congress dismissed the colonial problem by saying that the formation of People's Fronts was the chief task of communists. In practice these coalition manoeuvres were not based on profound ideas or principles and amounted to little more than a readiness to work together with any and every ally. A good example of United Front policy in practice is offered by the relations between the communists and Hadj Amin al Husseini, the ex-Mufti of Jerusalem, who was extremely right-wing rather than liberal. During the uprisings of 1929 and 1936, Husseini was vigorously supported by the Bolsheviks and in 1937 two communist Middle Eastern leaders, Fuad Nasr[29] and Nimr Oda, acted as his liaison officers and advisers. The attitude of the Soviet Government in the Italo-Abyssinian war was no less ambiguous. The reports of Soviet oil deliveries to Mussolini shortly before the invasion of Abyssinia have never been officially denied by the Kremlin. Finally the Russians showed little or no interest when the French authorities launched an attack on the Algerian Communist Party in 1937, a time when the communists were co-operating closely with the French socialists in the People's Front. In other words, there was no longer a clear, definite communist policy in Afro-Asian matters. The great alliance between the Soviets and the Western Powers between 1941 and 1945 resulted in the complete neglect of colonial problems by the communists; clearly, consideration for their new allies forbade any intervention in colonial affairs. It was not until Mao's success in China, the rising of the post-war anti-colonial wave in Asia and the Near East, and the gradual formation of nationalist groups in Africa, that the attention of the Russians was again—twenty years after the Sixth Congress of the Comintern—irresistibly turned towards developments in Asia and Africa. And then they found—with growing misgivings—that matters were proceeding almost completely according to their own laws and along their own channels. With this, the largely platonic premises and assumptions of the communists' Afro-Asian policy from 1918 to 1928 took on a new significance.

Zinoviev's name had been erased from all Soviet history books, but his words to the Congress of the Eastern Peoples at Baku in 1920 now became topical: 'The real revolution will develop only when the eight hundred million inhabitants of Asia are united with us, when the African continent is united with us, when we see that hundreds of millions of people are on the move'.[30] And it was just as long since Stalin had written in one of the most important declarations on Eastern strategy:

'If Europe and America may be called the front or the arena of the major battles between socialism and imperialism, the unequal nations and the colonies with their raw materials, fuel, food and vast store of manpower must be regarded as the rear, the reserve of imperialism. To win a war it is necessary not only to triumph at the front, but also to revolutionize the enemy's rear, his reserves. Hence the victory of the world proletarian revolution may be regarded as assured only if the proletariat is able to combine its own revolutionary struggle with the liberation movement of the labouring masses of the unequal nations and the colonies against the rule of the imperialists and for the dictatorship of the proletariat.'[31]

The period after the Second World War was more than ever the time for communists to put these words into action.

NOTES

[1] Cf. George Padmore, *Pan-Africanism or Communism?* (London and New York, 1956).

[2] V. I. Lenin, 'Two Tactics of Social Democracy in the Democratic Revolution', *Selected Works* (2 vols, London, 1947).

[3] In an article entitled 'Revolution in China and in Europe', published in the *New York Tribune*, 14 June 1853, Marx wrote that the day must come 'when the extension of the [colonial] markets is unable to keep pace with the extension of British manufactures, and this disproportion must bring about a new crisis with the same certainty as it has done in the past. But if one of the great markets suddenly becomes contracted, the arrival of the crisis is necessarily accelerated thereby.' (*Marx on China 1853-1860: Articles from The New York Daily Tribune* [London, 1951], p. 4.) As so often with Marx, his desire to see this happen was stronger than his understanding of the realities and possibilities of modern industrial economics.

[4] Lenin, *Collected Works.*

[5] *Izvestia*, 22 November 1917 (old Russian calendar).

[6] J. V. Stalin, *Works* (Moscow, 1952-55), IV, pp. 169-70.

[7] Quoted by K. Troyanovsky, *Moskau und der Orient* (Berlin, 1922), p. 10.

[8] Lenin, 'Left-Wing Communism, An Infantile Disorder', *Selected Works* (3 vols, Moscow, 1961), III.

[9] Ibid. (annotated by Troyanovsky).

[10] Ibid. (annotated by Troyanovsky).

[11] Speaking on this point at the Eighth Congress of the Russian Communist Party (Bolsheviks) on 18 March 1919, Bukharin declared cynically: 'Let us by all means proclaim self-determination for the European colonies, for Hottentots, Bushmen, Negroes, Indians, and the rest. It won't cost us anything.' And Piatakov, the leader of the Ukrainian Communist Party, was equally frank: 'All this talk about self-determination isn't worth a tinker's damn. It's either a diplomatic game we sometimes have to play, or—much worse—it's a game we are wrong to take seriously.' Lenin, *Selected Works* (? vols; London, ?), VIII, p. 26.

[12] Ibid., p. 14.

[13] Lenin, *Selected Works* (Moscow, 1961), III, p. 404.

[14] Lenin, *Selected Works* (London, 1947), II, p. 657.

[15] Ibid., pp. 657-8.

[16] Lenin, *Selected Works* (Moscow, 1961), III, p. 501.

[17] *Syezd Narodov Vostoka*, the stenographic minutes of the Congress of the Peoples of the East, Baku, 1-8 September 1920 (Petrograd-Moscow, 1920).

[18] Lenin, *Selected Works* (London, 1947), II, p. 854.

[19] Stalin, *Works*, VI, p. 146.

[20] Ibid., pp. 148-9.

[21] Ibid., VII, pp. 149, 151.

[22] *Das Flammenzeichen vom Palais Egmont*, the official minutes of the Brussels Congress Against Colonial Oppression and Imperialism.

[23] 'Theses and Resolutions of the Sixth World Congress of the Communist International', *International Press Correspondence* (Vienna), VIII, No. 28, p. 1670.

[24] Ibid., p. 1661.

[25] Ibid., p. 1670.

[26] 'Protokoll des V. Kongresses der Kommunistischen Internationale' (Hamburg, ?), p. 630.

[27] 'Theses and Resolutions of the Sixth Congress of the Communist International,' p. 1672.

[28] Ibid, p. 1661.

[29] Fuad Nasr was appointed General Secretary to the Communist Party of the Kingdom of Jordan, although in 1941 he had collaborated with the Nazis and broadcast over Athens Radio as the mouthpiece of Nazi Arab propaganda. Although the Mufti also collaborated closely with Hitler and Ribbentrop, he was always treated with great consideration in Soviet Middle Eastern propaganda.

[30] *Syezd Narodov Vostoka*, p. 45.

[31] Stalin, *Works*, V, p. 57.

Chapter V

STALIN—KHRUSHCHEV—MAO

The Three Paths of the 'Colonial Revolution' after 1945

THE Soviet Union emerged from the Second World War as a Great Power and as a result of the post-war communist operations in Europe communism enlarged its geo-political basis into a Socialist Camp. When the victory of Mao in China added vastly to the area under communist domination, a Socialist World System was pronounced. However, this enormous extension of communist power resulted far less from the application of original Marxist theorems than from the ruthless use of imperialist Machiavellian principles and techniques. By this time, the original communist ideology had mostly degenerated into terminology and its main function was to provide *ex post facto* ideological trimmings to give the results Marxist respectability.

Power breeds a desire for more power; the next phase of communist policy, not only in Europe, but also in Asia and the Near East, was carried out to the accompaniment of sabre-rattling and the roll of minatory drums. As the conventional methods of power politics—which have nothing to do with ideology—had produced such unexpected successes, the communists were naturally tempted to try them out on a world scale. In consequence this whole period, which reached its peak in 1950 and persisted until 1955, was remarkable for the abandonment of the usual methods of propagandist infiltration and dexterous manoeuvring, the formation of alliances, and all the other tricks and devices of communist penetration and conquest. Soon after the war, in September 1947, Zhdanov, who up to Stalin's death in 1953 was his close confidant, addressed the inaugural conference of what was dubbed the

Communist Information Bureau (Cominform) and summed up the guiding principle of communist post-war operations in the 'Two Camp' slogan: on the one hand there was the camp of the imperialist bloc under the leadership of Washington, and on the other the anti-imperialist camp under the leadership of Moscow. These two camps were declared to be in irreconcilable opposition and the rest of the world was told that it would have to choose between them. There was no middle way, no possibility of *positive neutrality*, or of any other halfway solution.[1]

This new policy had two related consequences: firstly, the bourgeois leaders of the movements for colonial independence and all bourgeois national-revolutionary groups were contemptuously dismissed, and disqualified as allies. Instead of co-operation with such people there was now to be revolutionary—that is to say primarily military or para-military—action in the colonial countries and even in those former colonies which had already attained their independence. But as the working class was still too weak to conduct independent political operations and as it was now forbidden to pursue a policy of alliance with the 'national bourgeoisie', all that remained was a policy of *military force*. The result was the armed insurrections of 1946 and 1948 in Indo-China, Burma, Malaya, the Philippines and Indonesia and in the Telengana area of India. The theoretical explanation provided for these complex processes was that the working class had now 'taken over the leading role in the struggle for national independence', pushing aside 'the treacherous bourgeoisie' and at the same time establishing the 'natural connection between the anti-imperialist struggle and the class struggle'.

The relative failure of this kind of revolution did not dismay the communists. Those responsible for communist policy refused to consider the realities of the situation and their activities were still obstinately directed towards an 'independent communist policy', which involved a *war on two fronts*, against both foreign imperialists and national imperialists. Not even the real anti-Western developments in the colonial and former colonial countries were sufficient to persuade the communists to abandon their independent tactics or, at least, to adapt them to the situation. Some years later the Persian communist Eskandari admitted:

'We have experienced great difficulties in our activities, and have made no few mistakes . . . For example, we did not support Mossadegh, who undoubtedly represented the interests of the national bourgeoisie . . . thereby isolating ourselves from the masses who followed the bourgeoisie, and not our Party.'[2]

In India, Gandhi was declared to be a 'traitor' and 'demagogue' who never had been serious in his professed intention of liberating India and abolishing the caste system. The founders of the first Indian trade unions were denounced as 'mercenaries of capitalism'. And what communists dismissed as the 'pseudo-left wing' of the Congress Party, (which was after all under the leadership of Pandit Nehru) had to put up with the reproach that it made 'revolutionary and anti-imperialist gestures' only in order to put pressure on the British imperialists and thus obtain better conditions for the collaborators.[3] A similar attitude was taken towards the Egyptian 'Wafd' movement and when King Farouk was finally deposed an official Soviet source made the following comment: 'In the night of July 22nd a reactionary group of officers in alliance with the United States seized power.'[4] In the same way the African national movement was denigrated and abused. Except for the orthodox leaders of the *Rassemblement Démocratique Africain* (Sékou Touré, Ruben Um Nyobe and Modibo Keita) they were, according to Soviet accounts, merely 'lickspittles' and 'lackeys of colonialism and imperialism'. For example, a book published in the Soviet Union in December 1954 entitled *Narody Afriki* (*The Peoples of Africa*) described Kwame Nkrumah's Convention People's Party and the first government formed by Nkrumah as 'shields behind which the reality of British imperialist dominance conceals itself'.

The tactics recommended by Lenin, Stalin, and the Comintern from the twenties onwards seemed to have been forgotten. In those days communists had been advised to aim at tactical co-operation with the national revolutionary movements, but now the line was: 'History has proved that the national bourgeoisie of the colonial and semi-colonial countries, which are attached by a thousand bonds to the feudal classes and to foreign imperialism, can never lead the national-revolutionary movement to victory. The anti-imperialist and anti-feudal revolution can be victorious only *under the leadership of the communists* and on the basis of an alliance between the workers and peasants.'[5]

In the meantime however, the colonial system was rapidly deteriorating. In Asia, North Africa, and later in the whole of Africa, the leaders of the national bourgeoisie showed very clearly that they were, in fact, quite capable of leading the national-revolutionary movement to victory on their own, without communist assistance, while the communists found themselves in increasing danger of being excluded from an important historical process and of being left behind. Peking was the first of the communist régimes to take steps to win friends in the colonial and ex-colonial countries. Even during the Korean war the leaders of the Chinese Communist Party had come to the conclusion that quite a number of the allegedly pro-imperialist governments of Asia were by no means in the pockets of the British and the Americans and that they were honestly seeking an independent line between the two big political blocs. Consequently the Chinese communists set out to woo India and the Indian Ambassador in Peking was showered with attention. A further consequence was the drawing-up of the famous 'Five Principles' of non-intervention and co-existence between the Chinese and Indian governments.

It was not until the first half of 1955 that Moscow began to revise its policy. At the time of the Bandung Conference, Russia was compelled to recognize that the statesmen of almost all the existing African and Asian States had come together (in the presence of representatives from Red China and North Vietnam, but in the absence of North Korea, the Mongolian People's Republic and the Soviet Union!) to form an oriental Third Force and to constitute themselves as an independent Power of a politico-moral nature. The 'spirit of Bandung' radiated a magic attraction amongst Afro-Asians, and threatened to drive Moscow's 'Spirit of the November Revolution' from the minds of the Afro-Asian élite. It was obviously necessary and urgent for Moscow to have second thoughts about its own anti-colonial policy.

What guiding principles have since emerged? What official declarations are available summarizing the new policy? First of all there are the policy lines drawn up in 1955 and confirmed at the Twentieth Congress of the Communist Party of the Soviet Union and at the Moscow conferences of 1957 and 1960. Among a profusion of official declarations, perhaps what was said by Idris Cox, a leading member of the British Communist Party, best sums up the reasons for the change of policy. During a discussion at the Leipzig Historical Institute of the Karl Marx University in East Germany at the end of May 1949, which was attended by representatives from the Soviet Union, the satellite countries, Africa, and Asia, Idris Cox examined the role of the bourgeoisie in the national-revolutionary movement and declared that

'At the Sixth Congress of the Comintern in 1928 the perspective was that the colonies would achieve political independence only after the working class (in alliance with the peasants, petty bourgeoisie, and progressive sections of the national bourgeoisie) was in the leadership of the national-liberation movement. In practice it has been revealed since the Second World War that political independence has been achieved in India, Indonesia, Ghana and other countries under the leadership of the national bourgeoisie.'[6]

This is a frank and self-critical presentation of the dilemma in which the communists now find themselves. They cannot get out of it by saying that it was due to 'the growth of the socialist world' that imperialism was compelled to abandon its old methods of oppression, so that therefore, indirectly, it was communism after all which helped the national-revolutionary movement to victory. Communism did not, as Cox freely admitted, trigger off the national-revolutionary movement in very large areas of Asia and Africa; in reality the much-abused national bourgeoisie proved itself a stronger force than the communists. Incidentally, the negative attitude now adopted towards the decisions of the Sixth Congress of the Communist International requires no comment. Tactically, the slogans of this congress were—from the communist point of view—more cleverly formulated than most of the official communist declarations from 1945 to 1955; nowadays there is a tendency to present the ideas of this congress as the root of all evil; this is merely one of the many attempts now being made by men in the Kremlin, who were themselves responsible for the rigid, unsuccessful communist anti-colonial policy of the post-war decade, to shift the burden of responsibility from their own shoulders.

This tendency first became evident at the Twentieth Congress of the Communist Party of the Soviet Union in February 1956, when Khrushchev, Otto Kuusinen, and Shepilov (who was Soviet Foreign Minister at the time) proposed the revision of the communist programme for colonial revolution. Kuusinen, an old Finnish communist and member of the Praesidium of the Central Committee, was put up to draw attention to 'the sectarian errors' of certain Soviet orientalists and publicists—though not, of course, to the errors of the communist leaders themselves. 'Under the changed conditions of the present day and now that the prestige of the Soviet Union has greatly increased,' as Kuusinen put it, there must in particular be a re-examination of the character and role of the national bourgeoisie in the colonial and semi-colonial countries.[7] Shepilov, the first speaker to refer to the special situation in Africa, struck a somewhat different note when he declared:

'Communists are in principle opponents of sectarian narrowness. They advocate that the efforts of all kinds and varieties of mass movements of the present day must be merged into an anti-imperialist stream. The great aspirations of all the downtrodden peoples of the Arab, Asian or Latin American countries, of all working people, whether they be Catholics, Protestants, followers of Buddhism or Islam, will find their realization in the struggle against social oppression, against colonialism, in the struggle for peace and democracy. Never before has the great slogan of *unity* had such active and comprehensive purport.'[8]

This statement, and the admission of Khrushchev that there was now 'an extensive zone of peace' in Asia and Africa, mark the re-opening of a protracted inter-Marxist discussion on the necessity, usefulness, and objectives of a communist policy of alliance with the national forces of the colonial and former colonial countries—on both an international and a national level.

The stages of this discussion became public on four occasions, at the two publicity meetings in the spring of 1959 devoted to an analysis of the situation and at the two Moscow conferences in 1957 and 1960.

The first two meetings took place in Moscow and Leipzig respectively. In Moscow the editorial boards of the Moscow *Mezhdunarodnaya Zhisn* (*International Life*) and of the Peking *Shi Chi Shi* (*World Culture*) held a joint meeting to discuss 'the particular characteristics of the national-revolutionary movement in the colonial and dependent countries of the East'. Specialists and journalists from the Soviet Union, from the satellite States and from the West, from Africa, and Asia took part in the meeting at the Karl Marx University in Leipzig. Chinese representatives were not present on this occasion. The subject was 'The Role of the Bourgeoisie in the National-Revolutionary Liberation Movement'. The result of these deliberations was that the national bourgeoisie was rehabilitated and declared worthy of being an ally of the communists. It was at the conference in Moscow that this was stated most clearly. The Leipzig meeting had adopted an almost defeatist attitude towards the national bourgeoisie, but the Moscow conference emphasized the practical nature of any alliances with it. Two quotations will suffice to make clear the difference of tone and attitude:

'In the present conditions of revolutionary struggle for national independence and democracy (in Africa) the social and economic development of the national bourgeoisie can be neither halted nor retarded . . . In our days imperialist plans will, in the final analysis, merely aggravate the contradictions between the oppressed peoples on the one hand, and imperialism on the other, between the national bourgeoisie in the oppressed countries and the big capitalists in the oppressor countries.'[9]

The above is a quotation from Leipzig; the tone at Moscow was different:

'The working class of the oppressed countries . . . regards the achievement of national independence merely as a stage and a necessary pre-condition for social transformations and for the subsequent development of the national and colonial revolution into the socialist revolution. As far as the national bourgeoisie is concerned, the achievement of national independence is its ultimate aim, and it consists in the establishment of their undivided rule in a sovereign State.'[10]

However, the Moscow conference, which was largely dominated by the radical theses of the Chinese, was also compelled to recognize the actual strength of the national bourgeoisie in the underdeveloped countries and even to grant it 'revolutionary possibilities' for the future. The point was made that this situation called for 'very elastic tactics but at the same time firm principles' on the part of the communist parties and the crypto-communist groups. The declaration then went on to say: 'The struggle of the working class for a *People's Democratic* solution in those countries that have already achieved their political independence does not exclude the determined exploitation of every revolutionary possibility afforded by the national bourgeoisie and the anti-imperialist movement—on the contrary, it presupposes it. The struggle demands the maximum extension and intensification of all such possibilities, and must lend the whole movement a far-reaching democratic character'.[11] For 'democratic' one must read 'communist'.

This was a clear extension of the decisions of the first Moscow conference, in November 1957, which declared:

'1. Communism recognizes the objective advantage of the Afro-Asian movement for independence because, although the existence of new, independent States does not *subjectively* facilitate the victory of communism, it *objectively* weakens imperialism;

'2. The socialist camp, as the natural partner of the new States of Asia and Africa, desires to consolidate the independence of these new States by means of improved diplomatic, economic and cultural relations, and thus free them from the pressure of Western imperialism and of Western capital;

'3. The struggle of many peoples for their national independence against colonial aggression and feudal oppression makes it necessary to form an anti-imperialist and anti-feudalist united front of the workers and peasants, the urban petty bourgeoisie, the national bourgeoisie and other patriotic and democratic forces.'[12]

These were very vague formulations and revealed the abandonment of any attempt at either an ideological analysis or a formulated strategic-tactical point of view. On the one hand this was because the examination of the situation had led to no very clear conclusions and on the other because the intention was to appeal to every possible ally in the colonial and ex-colonial countries and to avoid offending them.

Three years later, at the second conference in Moscow in November 1960, the communists formulated their objectives and intentions more clearly. They recorded that the national-revolutionary movement in the East, which had triggered off the dissolution of the system of colonial slavery, was in its historic significance 'the most important phenomenon after the rise of the socialist world system'. They went on to say:

1. The urgent tasks of national re-birth in the freed countries can be carried out 'only if a determined struggle is waged against imperialism and the remnants of feudalism and if all the patriotic forces of the nation come together in a national, democratic united front'.

2. The following measures in particular were declared necessary:

'the consolidation of political independence, agrarian reform in the interests of the peasantry, the abolition of the last vestiges of feudalism, the abolition of the economic roots of imperialist rule, the restriction and elimination of foreign monopoly undertakings in the national economy, the creation and development of national industry, the raising of living standards for the people, the democratization of public life, a peace-loving foreign policy, and the development of economic and cultural relations with the socialist countries.'

The national bourgeoisie was still reproached for a strong tendency to vacillate and for various 'undemocratic' actions, but on the whole it was highly commended. For the first time since the twenties it was very definitely laid down for the communist movement as a whole that 'the national bourgeoisie in the colonial and dependent countries is objectively interested—in so far as it is not connected with imperialist circles—in carrying out the chief tasks of the anti-imperialist, anti-feudalist revolution'. This being so it is regarded as worthy of 'taking part in the revolutionary struggle against imperialism and feudalism and to be given a clean bill of health for the purposes of alliance.'[13]

This statement, as other passages indicate, did not involve any compromise in principle with the national bourgeoisie, but the intention was unmistakable: the ruling strata in the non-communist countries in Africa and Asia were, for the time being, to be treated with respect, granted far-reaching recognition on account of their 'progressive' behaviour, and considered worthy of both internal and external support by communism. That policy was especially applied to India in the Himalaya crisis in October 1962, but could also be observed in the Soviet wooing of Nasser and other Arab leaders in recent years. This attitude was clearly illustrated by the new description of the progressive national States as 'national democracies'. Boris Ponomarov, member of the Central Committee of the C.P.S.U. and in charge of the communist and crypto-communist parties outside the 'socialist camp', explained the specific characteristics of each 'independent national democratic State' in an article published in *Communist*, an official organ of the Party, in December 1960:

'First of all, it should most vigorously and determinedly defend its political and economic independence against the imperialists and the war bloc, and object most strongly to the establishment of military bases on its territory. Secondly, it should fight against new forms of colonialism and against the penetration of the country by imperialist capital. In particular the nation which is united in such a State must be filled with an abiding hatred of the imperialist exploiters and carry on a relentless struggle against all imperialist attempts to undermine the full independence of its own domestic and foreign policy and of its own independent path of development. Thirdly, this State must reject all dictatorial and despotic methods of government. The most widespread democratic rights and liberties will be secure in such a State, including the freedom of speech, the freedom to meet and to demonstrate, and the freedom to form political parties and other organizations. And fourthly, such a State will safeguard the possibility of introducing agrarian and other reforms, and in general measures instituting democratic and social changes, including the right of the masses of the people to take part in the formation of public policy, and so on. In such a country the broad masses of the people will be drawn into the process of building up its economy, since it will spurn foreign patronage whilst at the same time its people will be filled with a desire to overcome centuries-old backwardness, misery and lack of culture.'[14]

The first thing that strikes one about this list of ideal qualifications for a National Democracy is that it does not even mention the word 'socialist', much less 'communist', and everything is judged by *democratic* and *anti-imperialist* criteria. But is there any country anywhere that conforms to this ideal picture and fulfils all the conditions laid down by Ponomarov? Do Morocco, Ethiopia, Liberia and the United Arab Republic conform? And how far do the communists extend their 'specific characteristics'? What about Ghana and Guinea? Can they be included amongst Ponomarov's independent national democratic States? It is not easy to find clear answers to these important questions. However, the Moscow conference of 1960 did, strange to relate, inform the world that Iraq had 'successfully concluded its anti-imperialist revolt'—this at a time when Kassem was engaged in the liquidation of the communist party in Iraq! If necessary communism is apparently prepared to tolerate such behaviour. An official communist publication has this to say on the subject:

'It often happens that when the representatives of the national bourgeoisie are in power . . . they launch violent attacks against the communist parties. But even in such cases the communists continue to let their relations with such governments be guided primarily by the basic criterion of the role such governments play in the struggle against imperialism.'

In such cases the representatives of these 'anti-imperialist bourgeois governments' have to be left 'to learn by experience that they are not threatened by "the communist danger" but by the inner and outer reaction.'[15]

In the meantime—and even before Kassem was killed—Iraq has disappeared from the ranks of the national democratic States. On the other hand, in December 1961 Ivan Potekhin, the leading Soviet specialist on Africa, listed Ghana, Guinea and Mali as States entitled to be referred to as national democracies.[16] The East German publication *Einheit* lays it down that 'an important step on the way to the national democratic State is the formation of broad democratic fronts'. Indonesia is mentioned as one of the States in which such a broad united front has been formed. The article then goes on, 'a similar development towards the formation of strong national democratic fronts is taking place in Ceylon, Guinea, Ghana and Mali'.[17] The unwillingness of communist publicists to be specific in this matter, as displayed here and in other communist publications, is obviously caused by the fact that the expression 'national democracy' represents an ideal state of affairs. They dare not be specific because if they were it would in all cases restrict and reduce the significance of the term. In all probability this is why the expression is used only very rarely in the programme of the Communist Party of the Soviet Union as adopted by the Twenty-second Congress of the party in October 1961. Chapter VI of this programme is entirely devoted to the national-revolutionary liberation movement, which the congress declared to be the most important international phenomenon since the establishment and consolidation of the socialist camp. At the same time it warns this movement not to be content with the achievement of political independence, but to 'end economic dependence on imperialism', build up national industry, liquidate the vestiges of feudalism, carry out a radical agrarian reform, pursue 'an independent and peace-loving foreign policy', 'democratize social life', and pursue a policy of alliance with 'all the patriotic and progressive forces of the nation'. The 'fundamental condition for the solution of all national tasks' is defined as 'a thoroughgoing struggle against imperialism' and its chief bulwark, US imperialism. The young national States are warned that they can expect only 'an intensification of social inequality' from 'a capitalist path of development', whereas socialism would open up brilliant future prospects for them.

Regretfully it is admitted that most of these young States have not yet found the way to socialism, and that difficult sociological problems, due primarily to the weakness of the working class, still exist. For the time being, therefore, the working class in these countries must seek alliances with the peasantry, *and with the national bourgeoisie* which, under the circumstances, is 'objectively interested in carrying out the fundamental tasks of the anti-imperialist and anti-feudal revolution'. The programme goes on to say that 'in consequence the progressive role of the national bourgeoisie and its ability to take part in the carrying out of the urgent general national tasks are not yet exhausted'. Despite this ambiguity, neither the programme nor the other documents of the Twenty-second Party Congress show any tendency to write off the national bourgeoisie. Indeed, as the leading strata of the former colonial States they are conceded to have the ability to play an influential part in the international field—above all in 'the solution of the central problem of our time, the prevention of a new world war'.[18] The section of the party congress resolution which enumerates the 'fundamental' problems of world politics returns to this aspect of the problem. The 'final liquidation of all forms and phenomena of colonial oppression, and the provision of real and effective help for those peoples who have recently achieved their independence' is listed immediately after the demand for general and complete disarmament. In this connection it is interesting to note that such hotly disputed and important matters as the German and Chinese questions and the reorganization of the United Nations come only after the references to the under-developed countries.[19]

Despite a great profusion of words, the Twenty-second Congress of the Communist Party of the Soviet Union did nothing to alter the fundamental Soviet line. As various statements after the congress show, Soviet communists are still in favour of eliminating ideological considerations from their relations with the under-developed countries. Generally speaking they are prepared to do without the immediate inauguration of a people's democratic, socialist policy and to aim for the time being at casting off or loosening economic and political bonds with the West and, as far as possible, at drawing the new States into an anti-imperialist front. This new attitude makes sense only if we recognize the transformation of the Soviet Union itself into a neo-bourgeois social system far removed from any communist programme and engaged in pursuing imperialist power policies—disguised perhaps by the slogan of *co-existence* but conducted essentially in the style of the bourgeois imperialist States of the nineteenth and twentieth centuries. From this standpoint, Afro-Asian States are regarded less as areas for communist infiltration than as areas to be removed, economically and politically, from the sphere of influence of the West. It is logical therefore that the Soviets pay special attention to the Congo, demanding vociferously that the colonial system be completely liquidated, because it is the biggest producer of cobalt and uranium in the world. This, too, is the reason for the friendly words to Morocco, Ethiopia, and Liberia. Although reactionary feudal conditions prevail in all these States they nevertheless enjoy at least the goodwill of the Soviet Press.

This opportunist attitude towards the Third World was certainly not adopted without internal communist opposition. The gradual abandonment by Moscow of Zhdanov's ideas of the rehabilitation of the national bourgeoisie, and the policy of co-existence and alliance with partners not really qualified for the purpose have—as numerous references and documents show—aroused the growing mistrust and undisguised opposition of Peking. In fact the Chinese Communist Party did formally append its signature to the declarations of the Moscow conferences of 1957 and 1960. It was formerly in favour of a more elastic attitude to the question of co-operation with other classes and during the period 1952 to 1957 (during which they took part in the Bandung Conference) the Chinese operated no less opportunistically towards the existing national-bourgeois régimes.

The orthodox attitude of the Chinese Communist Party, based on strict revolutionary principles, is chiefly due to the Chinese claim—in competition with Moscow—for a monopoly role in the liberation of the colonial and semi-colonial countries. Even before (and certainly after) their own seizure of power, the Chinese communists disputed the claim of the Russians that the November Revolution and the socialism of the Soviet Union represented an obligatory model for the rest of the world in the matter of emancipation and social revolution. As early as November 1949 Liu Shao-chi, in a speech to the Trade-Union Conference of Asian and Australasian countries, declared that China was the model for the colonial countries to follow. Eighteen months later Lu Ting-yi, one of Peking's leading men, went even further: the following quotations were printed in a Cominform publication; according to this source Liu Shao-chi declared unmistakably:

'The path taken by the Chinese people to defeat imperialism and its lackeys and to found the People's Republic of China should now be followed by other countries in order to achieve their national independence and allow them to establish a people's democratic régime.'[20]

The decisive passage in Lu Ting-yi's speech reads:

'The November Revolution is the classic type of a revolution in imperialist (that is to say, capitalistically developed) countries. *The Chinese revolution is the classic type of a revolution in colonial and semi-colonial countries*, and its experience is of incalculable value to the peoples of such countries.'[21]

On 16 June 1950 *Jen Min Jih Pao*, the official organ of the Communist Party of China, referring to 'Lessons of the Chinese Revolution', the joint work of Mao Tse-tung and Liu Shao-chi, wrote in the same strain:

'The experiences of the revolutionary victory of China are of great significance for the peoples of all countries who are still groaning under the dominance of imperialism and their own reactionaries. In other words, the chief characteristic of the Chinese revolution, the armed struggle, can under certain historical conditions become the common characteristic of the revolutionary development in all colonial and semi-colonial countries.'[22]

This view has been repeated in innumerable variations since then, particularly since 1959, and the speech of Liu Shao-chi to the Seventh Congress of the Communist Party of China is frequently quoted to justify the Chinese claim for a monopoly in colonial affairs. In fact, this speech, 'On the Party', is one of the fundamental documents of Chinese communism, one with which it stakes its claim to independence. In this speech Liu Shao-chi declared:

'The proletarian programme and the policy of the Chinese Communist Party differ from those of *all other parties*. It was on the basis of this programme and this policy that our party ***independently*** organized and carried out the anti-imperialist and anti-feudalist new democratic revolution of the Chinese people and carried out the tasks of the Chinese proletariat in the present bourgeois-democratic revolution in the widest possible sense, and secured for itself the leadership of the people's revolution, whose ultimate aim is socialism and communism.'[23]

This speech is particularly interesting because *expressis verbis*—it sets out why the Chinese communists claim the right to be the only 'true' model for the colonial and semi-colonial countries to follow. Liu stressed that the Chinese revolution took place in a 'colonial, semi-colonial and semi-feudal country' and he pointed out that 'the chief forces of our party' were concentrated in the rural areas.[24] He went on to say: 'the broad masses of the peasants represented the chief strength of our revolution'.[25] And in another passage 'the present revolution in China is essentially a peasant revolution'.[26] He also pointed out that the working class acted more as a vehicle than as an active participant, and declared:

'the lessons of Mao Tse-tung on the Chinese revolution united the Marxist-Leninist theory with the present practice of the Chinese revolution. It is communism and Marxism adapted to China. The lessons of Mao Tse-tung on the Chinese revolution represent *the further development of Marxism in the national-democratic revolution in a colonial and semi-feudal country . . .*[27] These lessons represent a great and useful contribution to the struggle for liberation of the peoples of all countries in general and the peoples of the East in particular.'[28]

After the victory of the Chinese communists in 1949 this 'specific character' of the Chinese revolution was intensified by a number of exclusively Chinese 'achievements'. Peking claims originality for the Chinese *organization of the people* (in the People's Communes for example), for the Chinese *organization of labour* (in the mass application of labour power and in the 'individual iron smelting works') and above all in *the revolutionary organization of all forces in the struggle against imperialism.* The last point is of particular importance: it refers to the Chinese thesis that complete liberation from colonialism and victory over world imperialism can be won *only by force of arms.* In his speech to the Trade-Union Conference of Asian and Australasian countries in November 1949 Liu Shao-chi made a special point of this:

'If the people of a colonial or semi-colonial country have no arms to defend themselves they have nothing at all. The existence and development of proletarian organizations and the existence and development of a national united front are *closely linked* to the existence and development of such an armed struggle. For many colonial and semi-colonial peoples this is *the only way* in their struggle for independence and liberation.'[29]

Two recent Western publications, *Problems of Communism* and the *China Quarterly*, are right to draw attention in this and other Chinese statements to the necessity of an armed struggle. Arthur A. Cohen draws attention to a study published in Peking in 1951 by Ch'en Po-ta under the somewhat cumbersome title, 'Mao Tse-tung's Theory of the Chinese Revolution and the Integration of Marxism-Leninism with the Practice of the Chinese Revolution'. Ch'en Po-ta also mentions *guerilla warfare* as a characteristic feature of the Maoist strategy of revolution.[30] The official Chinese communist writings, which recommend waging a prolonged revolutionary struggle from self-supporting communist bases in the countryside and using guerilla warfare tactics, aroused great interest after the victory of communism in China. In recent years this interest has noticeably revived and the question has received a new significance. For example, in the new edition of Mao's book, *How can China's Red Political Power Exist?*, originally written in 1928 and published as the first volume of his *Selected Works* in 1951, there is an added footnote emphasizing the applicability of the Chinese revolutionary experience to other countries in the East. The key passage in the voluminous footnote reads:

'Thus—just as the Chinese people did—all, or at least some, of the colonial peoples of the East can hold big or small base areas and maintain revolutionary régimes for a protracted period, and wage permanent revolutionary war to encircle the towns from the countryside and thus proceed gradually to take over the towns and win nation-wide victory in their respective countries.'[31]

As we shall show in connection with Chinese policy in the Cameroons, these recommendations have not fallen on deaf ears in Africa and the tactics suggested have actually been adopted, while in its controversy with Moscow the Chinese Communist Party has returned to its contention that 'all political power goes back to the barrel of a gun',[32] and stressed this revolutionary axiom in its propaganda in Africa and Asia.

We do not propose to analyse the Sino-Soviet controversy as such. It has been going on for a long time though it first came to public notice only in the preparatory phase of the second Moscow conference of November 1960. However, in order to understand Chinese policy in Africa we must at least deal with that aspect of the dispute which has arisen over communist strategy and tactics in the colonial and semi-colonial countries.

Sino-Soviet disagreement on this question first came into the open in a leading article in *Pravda* on 26 August 1960 by Yevgeni Zhukov, a member of the Soviet Academy. His arguments were clearly directed against Peking and it was obviously the Chinese communists he had in mind when he said reproachfully that there were comrades who failed to understand the role of the national bourgeoisie in the colonial and semi-colonial countries in the struggle for liberation from colonialism. He went on, 'Dogmatists and sectarians, who understand nothing of the laws of social development, suggest that the application of the Leninist principles of peaceful co-existence hampers the development of the movement for national liberation and condemns it to stagnation—a thoroughly false point of view!'

As against the Chinese Communist Party, which regards the yoke of colonialism as having been shaken off only if political as well as economic independence has been won and which therefore regards mere political sovereignty as a sham, Zhukov said: 'Only petty-bourgeois left-wingers and hopeless dogmatists can deny the importance of the fact that sovereign States have been formed in Asia and Africa, even though some of them have not yet achieved economic independence.' Zhukov grants, of course, that the proletariat represents the great counterweight to imperialism, but he points out that Lenin regarded it as quite natural that at the beginning of every national movement the (national) bourgeoisie should play a leading role and Lenin called for support of the revolutionary elements in the bourgeois-democratic national liberation movements. Zhukov made a clear distinction between the national and the social (socialist) revolution when he pointed out that the front of the 'anti-imperialist liberation movement' was much broader than that of the 'social revolution'.[33]

This article represented a clear warning to the Chinese communists not to stake everything, in sectarian fashion, on the extreme left wing but rather to pursue an elastic policy *in the present phase*, supporting the bourgeois forces 'in so far as they work for liberation from colonialism' because they represent the leading force in the anti-colonial movement.

The answer of the comrades in Peking was not long delayed: 'If we were to agree to regard the movement led by the bourgeoisie in the colonial countries as the main stream of the national-revolutionary liberation movement, and keep silent about the anti-imperialist struggle of the masses, or even treat it with contempt [the reference is, of course, to the left-wing revolutionaries], this would represent in practice an adoption of the bourgeois standpoint and run counter to Lenin's views.'[34]

In an article published on 2 November 1960 *Hung Ch'i* (*The Red Flag*), the theoretical organ of the Communist Party of China, launched a frontal attack on the Soviet standpoint. Just before the departure of the Chinese delegation led by Liu Shao-chi to the second Moscow conference, an editorial entitled 'Fundamental

Summary of the Experiences of the Victory of the Chinese People's Revolution' appeared, ostensibly in connection with the publication of the fourth volume of Mao Tse-tung's works. Four points in this editorial are of particular importance:

1. The Chinese communists reject every form of united front in the colonial and semi-colonial countries. That is to say they are opposed to the tactic forced on the communists of Iraq on Khrushchev's orders. This tactic aimed at establishing a 'united front' with General Kassem and the bourgeois and military forces behind him, and after temporary successes it ended in the defeat and destruction of the Communist Party of Iraq. In February 1961 even the international communist periodical *Problems of Peace and Socialism* was compelled to admit that the Communist Party of Iraq had suffered a defeat. In the view of the Chinese Communist Party 'united fronts' are permissible only if they guarantee 'the independence of the proletarian movement' and allow the communists independent control of their own *armed* forces, thus placing them in a position to extend their power.

2. Alliances with the imperialists (and this term includes the reactionary forces in the Afro-Asian countries) are of extremely limited value. To place any trust in the promises of the imperialists must, as the Chinese experience with Chiang Kai-shek in the twenties and in 1945–6 shows, create a dangerous situation for the revolutionary forces.

3. As the victory of the Chinese communists in 'a great Eastern country' proves, it is necessary to form 'innumerable small revolutionary bases (cells) . . . in the rural areas' and arm the people's forces. 'The existence and development of revolutionary armed forces and revolutionary bases (cells) will inevitably strengthen the revolutionary consciousness of the masses'.

4. The 'people's democratic dictatorship' in China had two phases of development:

'Before the founding of the People's Republic the people's democratic dictatorship in our country was in effect a dictatorship of a democratic revolution, the dictatorship of several revolutionary classes led by the proletariat and based on an alliance of the workers and peasants, a dictatorship of the Chinese people over the jackals of imperialism, the *compradore* class and the feudal class. After the founding of the Chinese People's Republic in 1949 the people's democratic dictatorship took on a new quality—it became a dictatorship of the socialist revolution, a real dictatorship of the proletariat. *But no dictatorship can be effective or even continue to exist unless it is based on force.* What is force? It is based on the armed forces, the police, the People's Courts, the prisons, etc.'[35]

In a direct attack on the thesis put forward by Khrushchev (and adopted by the Moscow conference in 1957), according to which there is in certain countries a non-violent, parliamentary way of taking over power, *Hung Ch'i* wrote, 'China found herself in a totally different situation. As comrade Mao Tse-tung said, there was no possibility in a semi-colonial, semi-feudal country like China of using the parliamentary way.' Only 'left-wing opportunists' in the Chinese C.P. had ignored this fact. In China the main way (to socialism) had consisted in 'the struggle of the communist armed forces in alliance with the peasants as the main contingent'.[36]

There can be no doubt about the great importance of this editorial, particularly because the quotations and ideas are all taken from volume IV of the works of Mao Tse-tung. To clinch the matter, since its appearance in October 1960 the Chinese communists have repeatedly informed the world that the book is not to be regarded merely as a collection of reminiscences but as 'a guide to action' for all revolutionary groups in the colonial and semi-colonial countries. 'Abandon your illusions and prepare yourselves for battle!' and 'In our actions we relied on our brains and on our rifles' are the two most important axioms of Mao's book; there is no doubt that today these axioms are directed at the left wing of the Afro-Asian liberation movement which, in the view of Peking, finds itself in a situation similar to that of the Chinese 'liberation movement, before its victory over Chiang Kai-shek and his colonialist wire-pullers'. This was made very clear during a number of open Sino-Soviet clashes. One took place in December 1961 at a meeting of the World Peace Council in Stockholm, which was being run by the Russians exclusively on the subject of disarmament. The Chinese representatives strongly opposed the view of the Soviet and other delegates that negotiation was essential for the maintenance of world peace, and the chief Chinese delegate, Liao Cheng-chi, insisted: 'The idea that we can come to an understanding with the imperialists and attain peaceful co-existence by negotiation merely demoralizes the fighting spirit of the people and damages the cause of world peace. We must stress that the struggle between the oppressed peoples and imperialism and colonialism is a life and death struggle.'[37] Another Chinese delegate, Liu Ning-yi, spoke even more plainly:

'Today disarmament is certainly not the most important problem for oppressed countries such as Laos, Algeria, Angola and the Cameroons. The important thing for them is the strengthening and building up of their armed forces. Neither Cuba nor any of the other young independent countries can be in favour of a reduction of the armed forces they have only just formed. On the contrary, in order to defend their independence they must strengthen their armies.'[38]

The dispute was continued at the conference of Afro-Asian authors held in Cairo from 12 to 15 February 1962:

'A proposal that the writers' conference should send a message to the World Peace Council and adopt a resolution on disarmament was opposed by the Chinese delegation, which was the largest at the conference. In his speech the leader of the Chinese group, Mao tun, Minister of Culture, stressed the difference between "unconditional" and what he called "principled" peaceful co-existence, adding that "sheep and wolves can never co-exist peacefully". He claimed that it was the struggle for national independence above all that helped "to create the necessary conditions for principled peaceful co-existence".[39] Mirzo Tursun-Zade, leader of the Soviet delegation, answered the following day with a plea for disarmament and peaceful co-existence, saying: "Only madmen and those who want a new world war do not, or are unwilling to, understand the enormous losses which could be inflicted on mankind by hydrogen warfare". Unlike the Stockholm conference, at which the Chinese were in the minority, the majority of the delegates to the Cairo meeting seem to have voted in support of the Chinese line.'[40]

It is significant that this clash was immediately made public by the Albanian friends of Peking; in a long, detailed statement Tirana accused the Kremlin of 'sinking ever deeper into the morass of anti-Marxism' particularly where the national liberation struggle was concerned, and of regarding the struggle against various forms of imperialism and colonialism as of secondary importance, while supporting 'bourgeois pacifist ideas'.[41]

The supporters of Moscow now came out into the open and at the beginning of 1962 the leading theorist of the Belgian Communist Party, Jean Terfve, published a series of articles in *Le Drapeau Rouge*, the official organ of the Belgian party, in which he accused the Chinese of making an idol of military might in the struggle against imperialism and colonialism. At the same time he drew the attention of the Chinese to a number of objective factors which still hampered the advance of communism in Africa, Asia and Latin America. Terfve charged the Chinese delegates at the Stockholm World Peace Conference with having tried to play off the idea of 'the arming of the colonial and dependent peoples against the communist aim of disarmament'. Between the lines, Terfve also condemned Peking's attempts to 'adjust' the national liberation movement to suit itself and to take over the leadership.[42]

Once again Peking returned to the charge, particularly over the question of disarmament or rearmament of the dependent and colonial peoples. *Jen Min Jih Pao* published an article again stressing the need for more militant policies in the colonial and dependent countries and for the use of methods derived from the Chinese revolution:

> 'Chairman Mao's writings are carrying more and more weight, and in very many countries people are eagerly studying them in the hope of finding something they can use in their own struggle for liberation . . . To put it bluntly, all oppressed nations and peoples will sooner or later rise in revolt and this is precisely why revolutionary experience and theories will naturally gain currency among such nations and peoples . . . That is why *pamphlets about guerilla warfare in China* enjoy such a wide circulation in Africa, Latin America and Asia, and are looked upon as precious documents, even after they are worn and tattered.'[43]

The main points of dispute in the 'colonial question' had already been clearly indicated and the statements which were published by the Russians and the Chinese later, in particular in the summer of 1963, were no more than a repetition. Nevertheless it is relevant to quote a few passages from one of the more recent documents in which Peking brands the Russians as 'apologists of neo-colonialism'. In the *Fourth Comment on the Open Letter of the Central Committee of the CPSU* by the editorial departments of *Jen Min Jih Pao* and *Hung Ch'i*, published on 22 October 1963, the following statements appear:

'In their words, the leaders of the CPSU dare not completely discard the slogans of support for the national-liberation movement, and at times, for the sake of their own interests, they even take certain measures which create the appearance of support. But if we probe to the essence and consider their views and policies over a number of years, we see clearly that their attitude towards the liberation struggles of the oppressed nations of Asia, Africa and Latin America is a passive or scornful or negative one, and that they serve as apologists for neo-colonialism.

'The leaders of the CPSU have also created the theory that the national-liberation movement has entered upon a "new stage" having economic tasks as its core. Their argument is that, whereas "formerly, the struggle was carried on mainly in the political sphere", today the economic question has become the "central task" and "the basic link in the further development of the revolution".

'The national-liberation movement has entered a new stage. But this is by no means the kind of "new stage" described by the leadership of the CPSU. In the new stage, the level of political consciousness of the Asian, African and Latin American peoples has risen higher than ever and the revolutionary movement is surging forward with unprecedented intensity. They urgently demand the thorough elimination of the forces of imperialism and its lackeys in their own countries and strive for complete political and economic independence. The primary and most urgent task facing these countries is still the further development of the struggle against imperialism, old and new colonialism and their lackeys. This struggle is still being waged fiercely in the political, economic, military, cultural, ideological and other spheres. And the struggles in all these spheres still find their most concentrated expression in political struggle, which often unavoidably develops into armed struggle when the imperialists resort to direct or indirect armed suppression.

'According to this theory of theirs, the fight against imperialism, old and new colonialism and their lackeys is, of course, no longer necessary, for colonialism is disappearing and economic development has become the central task of the national-liberation movement. Does it not follow that the national-liberation movement can be done away with altogether? Therefore the kind of "new stage" described by the leaders of the CPSU, in which economic tasks are in the centre of the picture, is clearly nothing but one of no opposition to imperialism, old and new colonialism, and their lackeys, a stage in which the national-liberation movement is no longer desired.'

The *Fourth Comment* then deals with Moscow's 'nostrums for all the ills of the oppressed nations'. Moscow's theory of 'peaceful co-existence' is attacked and Soviet economic aid to Asia and Africa is belittled; referring to Soviet disarmament proposals the Chinese comment says: 'This is not just the fostering of illusions, it is opium for the people'.

Even more serious are the following accusations:

'Although they talk about supporting the movements and wars of national liberation, the leaders of the CPSU have been trying by every means to make the people of Asia, Africa and Latin America abandon their revolutionary struggle, because they themselves are sorely afraid of the revolutionary storm.

'The leaders of the CPSU have the famous "theory that even a tiny spark can cause a world conflagration" and that a world war must necessarily be a thermonuclear war, which means the annihilation of mankind. Therefore, Khrushchev roars that " 'local wars' in our time are very dangerous", and that "we will work hard . . . to put out the sparks that may set off the flames of war". Here Khrushchev makes no distinction between just and unjust wars and betrays the communist stand of supporting just wars.

'The history of the eighteen years since World War II has shown that wars of national liberation are unavoidable so long as the imperialists and their lackeys try to maintain their brute rule by bayonets and use force to suppress the revolution of oppressed nations. These large-scale and small-scale revolutionary wars against the imperialists and their lackeys, which have never ceased, have hit hard at the imperialist forces of war, strengthened the forces defending world peace and effectively prevented the imperialists from realizing their plan of launching a world war. Frankly speaking, Khrushchev's clamour about the need to "put out" the sparks of revolution for the sake of peace is an attempt to oppose revolution in the name of safeguarding peace.'

Some concrete examples follow to strengthen the Chinese argument and the Soviet attitude to the Algerian war and Russia's policy in the Congo are particularly severely criticized:

'Take the example of the Algerian people's war of national liberation. The leadership of the CPSU not only withheld support for a long period but actually took the side of French imperialism. Khrushchev used to treat Algeria's national independence as an "internal affair" of France. Speaking on the Algerian question on 3 October 1955, he said, "I had and have in view, first of all, that the USSR does not interfere in the internal affairs of other States." Receiving a correspondent of *Le Figaro* on 27 March 1958 he said, "We do not want France to grow weaker, we want her to become still greater".

'To curry favour with the French imperialists, the leaders of the CPSU did not dare to recognize the Provisional Government of the Republic of Algeria for a long time; not until the victory of the Algerian people's war of resistance against French aggression was a foregone conclusion and France was compelled to agree to Algerian independence did they hurriedly recognize the Republic of Algeria. This unseemly attitude brought shame on the socialist countries. Yet the leaders of the CPSU glory in their shame and assert that the victory of the Algerian people paid for with their blood should also be credited to the policy of "peaceful co-existence".

'Again, let us examine the part played by the leaders of the CPSU in the Congo question. Not only did they refuse to give active support to the Congolese people's armed struggle against colonialism, but they were anxious to "co-operate" with US imperialism in putting out the spark in the Congo.

'On 13 July 1960, the Soviet Union joined with the United States in voting for the UN Security Council resolution on the dispatch of UN forces to the Congo; thus it helped the US imperialists to use the flag of the United Nations in their armed intervention in the Congo. The Soviet Union also provided the UN forces with means of transportation. In a cable to Kasavubu and Lumumba on 15 July, Khrushchev said that "the United Nations Security Council has done a useful thing". Thereafter, the Soviet press kept up a stream of praise for the United Nations for "helping the Government of the Congolese Republic to defend the independence and sovereignty of the country", and expressed the hope that the United Nations would adopt "resolute measures". In its statements of 21 August and 10 September, the Soviet Government continued to praise the United Nations, which was suppressing the Congolese people.

'In 1961 the leaders of the CPSU persuaded Gizenga to attend the Congolese parliament, which had been convened under the "protection" of UN troops, and to join the puppet government. The leadership of the CPSU falsely alleged that the convocation of the Congolese parliament was "an important event in the life of the young republic" and "a success of the national forces".

'Clearly these wrong policies of the leadership of the CPSU rendered US imperialism a great service in its aggression against the Congo. Lumumba was murdered, Gizenga was imprisoned, many other patriots were persecuted, and the Congolese struggle for national independence suffered a setback. Does the leadership of the CPSU feel no responsibility for all this?'

The Chinese point of view is then summarized, pointing out that 'the centre of the world contradictions of world political struggles' has shifted; 'Today the national liberation revolutions in Asia, Africa and Latin America are the most important forces dealing imperialism direct blows. The contradictions of the world are concentrated in Asia, Africa and Latin America'.[44]

There is detailed information in the following chapters on the practical policies of the USSR and China and to show that the attitudes of Moscow and Peking to the Third World are very different. It is important to note that what separates the two big communist Powers are irreconcilable differences of principle, but not of the ultimate aims of communist policy, in the under-developed countries. Neither Moscow nor Peking has abandoned the Messianic idea of world revolution and, now as before, both centres of communism relate their practical manoeuvres and operations to their profound eschatological beliefs. However, in the world of political reality, particularly in the world of communist reality, working methods can sometimes, even for long periods, take on a greater importance than objectives governed by matters of principle.

Soviet policy in Asia and Africa reflects the profound transformation of outlook and of the social system that has taken place in the Soviet Union. The result of these changes is that ideology counts for less in Soviet politics and in the behaviour of Soviet politicians. After forty years of a pragmatic domestic and foreign policy, the revolutionary core of the November Revolution has crumbled. The extension of Soviet imperialist power and the tremendous economic accumulation that has taken place in the Soviet Union have given rise to new strata of bureaucrats, technicians, skilled workmen, etc., and have led to the increasing adoption of 'bourgeois' ways of life; a state of affairs that is also reflected in the foreign policy of the Soviet Government. To pursue any kind of revolutionary (that is orthodox Marxist) policy at the moment would involve the risk of losing everything that has been gained, as it would provoke counteraction by the enemy. In the present stage of military development this risk would exist even if revolutionary policies were confined to peripheral zones. Even a local conflict, in Laos, in the Congo, or in any of the other trouble spots in Asia or Africa, could rapidly escalate into a global catastrophe.[45]

Secondly, because of this danger and because of the changed attitude of its rulers, the policy of the Soviet Union *vis-à-vis* the under-developed countries is, for the time being, not conditioned by any fundamental or specifically communist doctrine of social and national liberation, but seeks only to exploit the national-revolutionary movement empirically and opportunistically for its own ends. The domestic interests of the workers and peasants in these countries, who are allegedly represented by the communists, are secondary to the interests of the Soviet Union. At present the Soviet Union wants allies rather than proselytes and in this way hopes, for example, to weaken the West and strengthen the communist front in the United Nations. Such allies would take up a pro-Soviet (but not necessarily pro-communist) attitude. Soviet policy therefore seeks co-operation not so much with the embryonic communist movements in these countries as with their ruling classes, and the Russians seek to woo the existing régimes in Asia and Africa by giving them economic assistance. This new policy is clearly reflected in the Soviet attitude towards Iraq, India, Indonesia, the

United Arab Republic, Morocco, Ethiopia, Liberia and other independent countries. However, two qualifications are necessary: (a) this new line does not change the ultimate Soviet aim, which is still world communism; the young intelligentsia in the new countries, the third generation of the liberation movement, are still to be won over ideologically; (b) where régimes with left-wing tendencies exist, the Soviet Union naturally does not try to slow down the less social-revolutionary process. On the contrary, it invariably does its utmost to give it new impulse and to guide it into the desired revolutionary channels. Ghana, Guinea and Zanzibar are the best examples of this policy.

Thirdly, the Chinese communists, unlike their Soviet colleagues, are still unconditionally wedded to a revolutionary policy and to revolutionary tactics. Unlike the Soviet Union, China is not highly industrialized, and there is no comfortable neo-bourgeois stratum likely to inquire anxiously about the risks involved in important decisions. For twenty-eight years before coming to power the Chinese communists had to wage a constant war against both internal and external enemies. On two occasions during those years, from 1923 to 1927 and again in 1936, the Soviet Government exercised intense pressure on the Chinese communists to persuade them to enter into an alliance with Chiang Kai-shek, the leader of the Chinese bourgeoisie. The tangible result of this policy imposed by the Soviet communists was political disaster for the Chinese Communist Party, and its recovery was slow and difficult. It is understandable therefore that Mao Tse-tung is not greatly enamoured of strategy and tactics which in the past brought him to the verge of total destruction on two separate occasions.

In accordance with Maoism, China therefore prefers to support and encourage the communist forces, the predestined instruments of the revolutionary process, in the under-developed countries. The Chinese Communist Party is firmly convinced that its policy is correct because it believes it can see fundamental similarities between the social and economic situation of Africa and of pre-communist China. From this it concludes that complete decolonization is the first stage towards the establishment of a revolutionary socialist system in Africa and that this can be achieved only with the same *methods of violence* that proved so successful in China.

Finally, because of this Peking has developed a completely original programme of its own for 'the Eastern peoples'. This programme differs radically from Moscow's long-term proposals and seeks to bring about the eventual communist seizure of power in Africa and the establishment of a society of the Chinese communist pattern.

NOTES

[1] Pravda, 22 October 1947.

[2] *World Marxist Review*, II, No. 9 (September 1959), p. 72.

[3] Cf. *Bolshaya Sovietskaya Entsiklopaediya* (2nd ed.; Moscow, 1952), X, p. 203.

[4] Ibid., XV, p. 460.

[5] *Sovietskoye vostokovodenye*, Nos 5-6 (1955).

[6] *World Marxist Review*, II, No. 8 (August 1959), p. 66.

[7] Proceedings of the Twentieth Congress of the Communist Party of the Soviet Union, *Current Digest of the Soviet Press*, VIII, No. 10 (18 April 1956), p. 24.

[8] Ibid., VIII, No. 7 (28 March 1956), p. 20.

[9] *World Marxist Review*, II, No. 9 (September 1959), p. 68.

[10] Report of the conference in *Mezhdunarodnaya Zhisn* (Moscow), No. 3 (1959).

[11] Ibid.

[12] *Pravda*, 22 January 1957.

[13] Ibid., 6 December 1960.

[14] *Kommunist* (Moscow), No. 12 (1960).

[15] *Mezhdunarodnaya Zhisn*, No. 3 (1959).

[16] *Asiya i Africa segodniya* (Moscow), No. 9 (1961).

[17] *Einheit* ([East] Berlin), No. 11/12 (1961).

[18] *Izvestia*, 2 November 1961.

[19] *Pravda*, 1 November 1961.

[20] 'For A Lasting Peace. For A People's Democracy!' Bucharest, 27 January 1950.

[21] Ibid. Cf. *Politika* (Belgrade), 5 August 1951.

[22] Quoted from Mao Tse-tung and Liu Shao-chi, *Lessons of the Chinese Revolution* (Bombay, 1950).

[23] Liu Shao-chi, *On the Party* (Peking, 1954), p. 15.

[24] Ibid.

[25] Ibid.

[26] Ibid.

[27] Ibid.

[28] Ibid.

[29] Originally published in the Cominform journal; quoted here from A. M. Halpern, 'The Foreign Policy Uses of the Chinese Revolutionary Model', *The China Quarterly*, No. 7 (July-September 1961).

[30] Arthur A. Cohen, 'How Original is "Maoism"?', *Problems of Communism*, x, No. 6 (November-December 1961).

[31] Mao Tse-tung, *Selected Works* (New York, 1954), I, p. 304, n. 7.

[32] *Yen-min Yih-pao*, 10 December 1961.

[33] *Pravda*, 8 August 1960.

[34] *Daily Telegraph* (London), 31 August 1960.

[35] New China News Agency, 2 November 1960.

[36] Ibid.

[37] *Peking Review*, No. 51 (1961).

[38] Ibid., No. 52 (1961).

[39] 'Chinese Influence in the AAPSO', *The Interpreter* (London), March 1962.

[40] Ibid.

[41] *Zeri i Popullit*, 9 January 1962; quoted in *Ostprobleme* (Bonn), XIV, No. 6.

[42] *Le Drapeau Rouge* (Brussels), 5-17 January 1962.

[43] *Yen-min Yih-pao*, 10 December 1961.

[44] *Peking Review*, No. 43 (25 October 1963).

[45] Referring to this situation, the prominent Russian military expert Major General Talensky wrote in October 1960 in *Mezhdunarodnaya Zhisn* that even local wars had now become 'impossible' because there was always a dangerous tendency for them to escalate into world catastrophes. In consequence, the dictum of Clausewitz that 'war is the continuation of politics by other means' had lost its validity; modern warfare had become suicidal and therefore nonsensical.

Chapter VI

THE POLITICAL USES OF AFRICAN STUDIES

IN the summer of 1920, at the Second Congress of the Communist International 'the colonial question' was for the first time discussed in principle, theoretically analysed and linked up with the world-revolutionary ideas and aims of Moscow. However zealously the delegates sought to clarify their standpoint and to arrive at a general practical plan of operations for Asia and Africa, they invariably found themselves grappling with a serious weakness in their position: their inadequate and inaccurate knowledge of the history, conditions and possibilities of Africa and Asia, while the little they did know was strongly coloured by wishful thinking.

That kind of vagueness and confusion in the communist camp no longer exists today. On the contrary, if the West were to try to understand and judge Soviet African policy today by the criteria of the early 1920s, when it was a highly theoretical affair based largely on illusions and ignorance, they would be guilty of short-sighted optimism and fatal smugness. The truth is that the Soviet offensive in Africa today is the most powerful attempt of any non-African power to secure a dominating influence over the development of the awakening black continent and to determine its future economic, political, social and cultural pattern. The ideological framework of communist actions in Africa is more than the general colonial-revolutionary theory worked out from 1918 to 1928 and further developed since 1955. It is based on very thorough research and analysis of the essential factors of African politics, economics, society, linguistics and culture. For years now hundreds of Soviet experts, working together with agents in the satellite countries, have been intensively engaged in exploring the political topography and in keeping up to date with the changes taking place. The results of their labours are harnessed to political aims and used for communist purposes. Soviet African studies play a special role in this general framework: they provide the basic material on which Soviet plans in Africa rest.

The decisive point in Soviet Africa policy was reached at the Twentieth Congress of the Communist Party of the Soviet Union which met in February 1956. In a self-critical mood, this congress recognized that a tremendous amount of energy was being generated and dissipated in the colonial and former colonial territories, particularly in Africa. Furthermore, it was realized that this energy was directed towards an independent process of emancipation over which communism exercised only marginal influence. Characteristically, the leading politicians were exonerated from all blame for Soviet errors and failures. Otto Kuusinen, the Finn, and Anastas Mikoyan, the Armenian, blamed the experts for the failure to intervene in this process earlier. Mikoyan declared mockingly: 'The Academy of Sciences does have an institute that studies the problems of the East, but all that can be said of it is that although in our day the whole East has awakened, this institute is still dozing. Isn't it time for it to rise to the level of current requirements?'[1]

Up to this time Soviet African studies certainly had been rather isolated from practical politics. The number of original works published was very small. Although a centre of African studies, under the direction of Professor Olderogge, had existed at the Ethnographical Institute of the University of Leningrad since 1946 and although there had been a joint research programme with the Moscow Africanist Professor Ivan Potekhin since 1949, the activities of the few experts on Africa were dull and academic—not that they differed greatly from their Western colleagues in this respect! However, after the Twentieth Party Congress there was a change: men from other branches of research were brought in while still others were newly trained in this field. The rather generalized view of Africa was now rapidly consolidated by increasing specialization. For example, North Africa was handed over to special oriental institutes, whilst black or Negro Africa became the sphere of the ethnographical departments of the Academy of Sciences; for special political aspects there was now a special Moscow Institute for Oriental Studies. Finally, in 1959, an independent Africa Institute was founded at the Academy of Sciences under the directorship of Professor Potekhin, so that Moscow now has a sound organizational framework for intensive study of African subjects. In February 1957 the first big research programme was drawn up. This programme had three main objectives:

1. An objective analysis of economic, social, ethnographical, cultural and linguistic problems relating to Africa with a view to providing the appropriate party and government departments with reliable, unbiased material on which to base their decisions;

2. A Marxist-Leninist interpretation of both the historical and present-day problems of Africa in order to allow the development of general communist theory and in particular of communist propaganda in Africa on a 'scientific' plane;

3. The drafting of Marxist-Leninist solutions to offer to the African élite in a way calculated to convince them of their logic and effectiveness.

The programme thus represents an intimate combination of objective scientific ideas with politically determined objectives and demonstrates graphically the important *political* role now being played by Soviet African studies in the formulation of foreign policies. Unlike African studies in the West, Soviet African studies are centrally controlled and governed by a uniform political approach (and, as we shall show later, this is so not only in the Soviet Union but also in the other countries of the Soviet bloc). Although there is good reason to doubt the scientific objectivity of some aspects of these studies, there can certainly be no doubt about the enormous advantages of this concentration of effort; the West would be well advised to take these activities very seriously indeed.

The Kremlin has never attempted to deny that the real aim of their African studies is political. Professor Gafurov, Director of the Moscow Oriental Institute, points out in an article[2] that in view of the 'growing political and world economic importance of Africa' the aim of his institute is 'to publish works of importance for the educational institutions and *government departments* engaged in the practical tasks in the East'. A little later another Russian publication stated: 'Our Orientalists regard it as a distinction to publish collections, monographs, pamphlets, articles, etc., whose content can be creatively utilized by *Soviet foreign policy* in its operations in the Eastern countries.'[3]

Similar statements have been repeatedly made by the late Professor Potekhin; what he said is particularly worthy of note as there was no one who personified the double task of communist African studies better than he. Professor Potekhin was not only director of the Moscow Africa Institute, he was also chairman of the Soviet Society for the Furtherance of Friendship with the Peoples of Africa, a member of the Soviet Committee for Solidarity with the Afro-Asian Peoples, and chief adviser to the Soviet Foreign Ministry on all African affairs. In an English-language broadcast to Africa, Potekhin, who died in 1964, declared:

'[Soviet] scientists concern themselves closely with all the new phenomena of the African historical process, such as the collapse of the colonial system, the rise of new States, the growing importance of Africa in world economics and world politics, the development of national [African] economic systems and a national African culture in those countries which have freed themselves from colonial oppression.'

Writing in *Izvestia*, Potekhin declared that his Africa Institute would

'deal with a wide range of problems directly connected with the struggle of the African peoples for independence, for emancipation from the chains of imperialism, and for the formation of sovereign independent States . . . The activity of the institute will support the extension and consolidation of friendly relations between the Soviet Union and the countries of Africa, while at the same time acquainting the Soviet people more closely with the history and culture of the African continent, which is now advancing vigorously towards complete emancipation from the yoke of the imperialist colonialists.'[5]

Such a frank and outspoken admission of Soviet aims and motives should not, however, deceive the West into regarding Soviet African studies as a mere adjunct of Soviet political activities. Since the death of Stalin, it has progressively emancipated itself from this subordinate role and although it is true that even today Soviet science can hardly be separated from Soviet political objectives, nevertheless in recent years a reciprocal relationship has developed between science and politics in the Soviet Union. To give an example: the gradual rehabilitation of the national bourgeoisie and the more moderate and objective view now held of the embryonic working class in Africa were both to a large extent due to the recommendation of African specialists. A number of studies made it clear to the Soviet political leadership how weak the actual proletariat was, and still is, in Africa, whereas already after the Second World War Stalin was banking on their support. When Professor Potekhin wrote his contribution on Africa in the *Great Soviet Encyclopaedia* of 1950, he was still hamstrung by the stereotyped sterile formulae of classic Stalinism which permitted no deviation. As late as 1953 the essential Stalinist theses were formally repeated in a general work on 'The Imperialist Struggle for Africa, and the National-Revolutionary Emancipation Movement of the African Peoples'. But even this work pointed out that the national bourgeoisie, and even some tribal chiefs, were supporting the anti-imperialist united front. Earlier still, in October 1952, a Soviet periodical[6] published a devastating criticism by A. Orlova of S. Datlin's book, *Afrika podigom imperialisma* (*Africa under the Yoke of Imperialism*) a Stalinist work which had previously always been described as 'a masterpiece of Soviet African studies'. A typical passage of this criticism reads:

'It is also questionable whether the author has judged the role of the working class accurately. He is quite right when he says that the importance of the working class for the liberation movement of the African peoples is steadily growing, but it must not be forgotten that numerically the working class in Africa is *very weak* by comparison with the population as a whole, and that it is *very poorly organized*. Communist parties exist only in the French North-African colonies. Only a very small percentage of the proletariat is organized in trade unions. For example, in Madagascar, where the proletariat numbers 230,000, including 48,000 industrial workers, only 12,000 are members of trade unions.'

Writings of this kind contain an indirect but clear warning to the Soviet political leaders, and to those in charge of propaganda, not to rely exclusively on class conflicts nor to concentrate excessively on the class situation in Africa and to reconsider the role of the non-proletarian, anti-colonial forces. This warning was repeated after Stalin's death and in February 1955 was couched, for the first time, in quite unmistakable terms when the Soviet periodical *Sovietskoya*

Vostokovedenia analysed 'the anti-imperialist movement on the Gold Coast' (Ghana). Writing in the same periodical in January 1956, shortly before the Twentieth Congress of the Communist Party of the Soviet Union, Professor Potekhin frankly admitted the existence of a vigorous, all-national, liberation movement in Africa. For the first time he stressed the role of the African middle classes, and he no longer used the usual barren Stalinist formulae. He pointed out that the colonialists were seeking to win over the middle classes in the hope of creating a stabilizing factor which would preserve their own power; but he went on to say that the political aims of the national bourgeoisie drove them, willy-nilly, to the side of the people and that this transformed them objectively into an anti-imperialist force. This was the prologue to the astonishing change of tactics introduced at the Twentieth Party Congress. It was the cue for the new, more discriminating and elastic policy Moscow now put into operation in Africa.

In a number of ethnographical, linguistic and historical studies published in recent years similar, perhaps even greater, independence has been noticeable. Olderogge's work *The West Sudan from the Fifteenth to the Nineteenth Century*, which finally appeared in 1960, though it had been publicized a long time in advance, is said by Western experts to be, in many respects, highly expert and scientifically sound. The book is well documented, contains a number of facsimiles of ancient documents, some of them previously unknown, translations from the Hausa language, and so on. There are also a number of detailed and largely objective ethnographical maps of Africa, collections from Arab sources on the history of black Africa and, of course, from dictionaries and grammars of a number of the more modern African languages. Many Soviet works in this field cannot be denied their scientific seriousness. A number of works by Olderogge and (with some qualifications) Potekhin are of interest and value to Western students of Africa.

On the other hand, when they set out to provide an interpretation of social phenomena such works are completely subordinated to the general political objectives of communism. Even linguistic problems cannot always be treated with complete objectivity. For example, the Soviet periodical *Problemy vostokovedenia* writes: 'Our linguists must always remember that though their research work might at first glance seem to be quite abstract it should nevertheless aim to facilitate the struggle of the Eastern peoples against colonialism and its ideology.'

A case in point is the attitude of Soviet experts to the multi-language problem of Africa. According to them this is not a natural development, but was created artificially by (guess who?) 'the imperialists and colonialists'. With their policy of *divide et impera* and their colonial ideology, the imperialists, 'for obvious reasons', first created these great cultural divisions, isolation and language difficulties between the individual tribes.[7]

We have now arrived at a subject which is exercising the minds of Soviet Africanists, namely the rewriting of African history. Potekhin dealt with this problem in an interview published in *Izvestia*:

'Progressive scholars now have a very complicated but valuable task to perform, namely the writing of the *real* history of the century-old struggle of the African peoples . . . This is all the more important because the history of the African peoples has been distorted to the point of unrecognizability by bourgeois historians. In the works of the majority of the bourgeois historians the development of the African peoples is represented as a very small section of the histories of Great Britain, France, Belgium and other Western European powers. You will look in vain in such histories for any description of the obstinate and protracted struggle of the African peoples against the colonialists.'

In another contribution (the Moscow radio broadcast of 14 November 1959) Potekhin gave some idea of Soviet motives in these efforts to rewrite African history:

'The names of countries which existed in the Middle Ages are now beginning to reappear on the political maps of Africa. Gold Coast Colony, only a little while ago under British rule, is now Ghana, having adopted the name of one of these States. The Mali Federation was named after another. All this indicates that the peoples of Africa are becoming much more interested in their own history. They are properly proud of their own past and are anxious to know more about it . . . Up to the present, it is true that almost nothing has been done to study the history of the former mediaeval States of Ghana and Mali . . . There is, therefore, all the more reason why we should now make a serious study of the mediaeval epoch in Africa.'

Thus it is clear that the Russians are interested in rather more than a Marxist-Leninist interpretation of ancient Africa, because if its inquiries in this respect were strictly circumscribed by the canons of historical materialism they would arrive at a devastating denigration of the mediaeval epoch, whose social structure, being feudal, was (according to Marxist ideas), uncompromisingly hostile to progress. The real purpose of the new interpretation, as pointed out in a number of leading Soviet periodicals, is to serve the needs of Soviet foreign policy, which is anxious to exploit the historical consciousness of the nationalist élite. Hence the attempts to persuade this élite to accept the results of Soviet research. Similar motives are behind the demands of Potekhin, and other Soviet experts, for the rewriting of nineteenth-century African history. The first conference of Soviet African experts, which took place in February 1957, established two principles to facilitate this task:

1. The general heinousness of 'imperialist conquest, division and rule in Africa' must be constantly exposed in all its details and it must also be stressed that the so-called civilizing work of colonization was more apparent than real.

2. The revolts and insurrections against the colonists must be closely studied, presented *in extenso* and 'in harmony with the present-day national liberation movement'.

In 1957 certain subjects were chosen for full treatment. They included the Berlin Conference of 1894–5, Anglo-German rivalry in East Africa, the struggle of the Zulus and the Xhosas against British and Boer colonization, the struggle of the Matabele and the Mashona against the subjugation of Rhodesia. Some of these studies have since appeared and they have been supplemented by descriptions of the revolts in Tanganyika, Dahomey, Ghana, the Cameroons and other parts of Africa. Here too, as the texts indicate, the authors have been guided by the same motives that led to Soviet attempts to rewrite the history of Africa in the Middle Ages: Africans are to be persuaded that they have a glorious past characterized in particular by a ceaseless, heroic struggle first against feudalism and then against colonialism and, what is more important from the Soviet point of view, they are to be persuaded that only progressive Soviet scholars are able and willing to reveal this history to them.

The 1957 conference also planned a third group of research tasks under the heading, 'Africa's ethnic composition'. Two special problems were underlined:

1. African frontiers as they exist today were arbitrarily drawn by the colonial powers and are in contradiction to the natural settlement areas of the African peoples. Present-day African States are therefore multi- or part-national States which must be reorganized. These results of Soviet African studies comply to a remarkable degree with the demands of the Africans themselves, for example, with a resolution of the First All-Africa People's Conference in Accra in December 1958. Section 3 of that resolution on frontiers and federations declares:

'the artificial barriers and frontiers created by imperialism in order to carve up the African peoples must be abolished and re-examined . . . Frontiers which cut through the settlement area of any particular ethnic group, or which separate people of the same origin, are unnatural, and their maintenance can never lead to peace and stable conditions'.

The magazine *Sovietskaya etnografia* seized on this resolution to point out triumphantly that Soviet ethnographical scholars had already paid special attention to this problem, and that in order to show how ethnic groups had been separated by unnatural frontiers, the frontier demarcation in a number of areas had been especially studied—for example, in Kenya, Tanganyika, the Belgian Congo, South-West Africa, the Central African Federation, Angola, Mozambique and Nigeria. The periodical concluded that Soviet research offered a reliable basis for discussion of the more complex problems relating to the formation of African nations.

The *Bulletin of the Institute for the Study of the USSR* published an article by G. A. von Stackelberg on this point:

'The contention that the colonial frontiers of present-day Africa were arbitrarily drawn is of great practical importance to the Soviets. The obvious discrepancies between present-day political frontiers and ethnic lines of demarcation in Africa allow the Soviets to put forward the slogan of the unification of Africa on an ethnographical basis and thus to intervene in the internal affairs of the African countries. Present-day Soviet policy is to encourage the ex-colonial countries to unite within the framework of larger State structures. The formation of such bigger States with a central government could make it easier for pro-communist elements to take over and thus strengthen Soviet influence in Africa.'[9]

On the other hand, the formation of smaller States must necessarily, in Moscow's view, hamper the activity of pro-Soviet parties and trade unions and favour anti-communist elements. The Soviet periodical *Problemy vostokovedenia* also takes this view: 'The existence of a large number of single parties and the lack of unity between them weakens the anti-colonial front and prevents the establishment of a united front.'[10]

In contradiction to the classic maxim *divide et impera* the maxim of Soviet communist imperialism today is *unifica et impera*—unite and rule. Soviet foreign policy has sought to realize this conception both in the Congo, where from the start the Soviets backed the centralist group, and in the Cameroons, where—in the hope that in this way the extremist *Union des Populations du Cameroun* would be strengthened by amalgamation with the Cameroun Party—they came out in favour of a unification of the British and French mandate territories. All this despite the fact that even the *Great Soviet Encyclopaedia* had previously admitted the very great ethnic differences which still exist in the Congo territory today. The 1953 edition declared: 'The independent development of nationalities and States in the Congo area was violently interrupted in the fifteenth century by the arrival of European colonists.' If Soviet politicians see advantages in the large, centralized State, then quite clearly history must be rewritten to give support to this view. Potekhin and other Soviet experts carried out this task with great aplomb. Their present 'nationalities' ideology for Africa includes a theory of the development of the tribes (*plemeni*) into peoples (*narody*) and of peoples into nations (*natsii*). This last stage, it is pointed out, has not yet been reached everywhere, but it is an historical necessity which the African peoples will be unable to prevent. They once again argue that a linguistically united nation is a *sine qua non* for the political consciousness necessary for such supra-States. The areas involved in these calculations are indicated by Potekhin's reference to the

Nilotic peoples, whose settlement area extends from the Sudan over the former Belgian Congo, Uganda, and Kenya. It is not claimed that these groups already represent a united people, but it is pointed out that the Nilotic languages form a single stock of words and that three of them have an identical grammatical structure. This is apparently sufficient reason for Potekhin to conclude: 'it is by no means impossible that, given favourable circumstances, the Nilotic peoples will be in a position to form themselves into one united national people.'[11] For similar reasons the philological department has devoted itself for years now to the more widespread African languages such as Swahili, which is at least a trading and bartering medium for millions of people in East and Central Africa, and to Hausa, which is widespread in parts of West Africa. Treatment of the tribal problem has been guided by the same *arrière pensée*, with the result that the structure and behaviour of African tribal society has come in for some severe criticism. The campaign against tribalism began with the publication of a monograph, *The Peoples of Africa* (*Narody Afriki*), in Moscow in 1954. Since then there has been a systematic, pseudo-scientific campaign to denigrate the idea of tribalism while the colonial powers are accused of having deliberately preserved tribal structures, tribal consciousness and tribal rituals 'in order to prevent the awakening of the African masses' or, at least, to delay and hamper it. A Moscow radio broadcast in English,[12] prepared by Soviet African experts, declared:

'One of the [negative] phenomena is tribalism, which stands in no relationship to the present stage of development of African society, and hampers natural progress. With the rise of the struggle for liberation the interest of the African in his past has naturally increased, but certain African leaders are now taking up a wrong attitude in this respect: they talk of a particular "African way of life", and say that it has developed on the basis of tribalism and the leadership of the tribal chiefs. In fact, they go even further, and declare that the tribes, the tribal chiefs, and tribal relations in general are an integral part of this "African way of life". This conclusion is due to a lack of insight into the laws of social development . . . Tribalism plays into the hands of colonialism . . . The tribal structure is so conservative and reactionary that it serves only anti-popular objectives.'

The frequent quoting of remarks by young, progressive Africans, who have allegedly recognized the hampering effect of tribalism and condemned it as 'a hindrance to social, economic and technical progress', clearly reveals the objectives of this 'scientific' propaganda. By attempting to establish a direct connection between tribalism and reactionary colonialism, it is hoped to awaken the resentment of young Africans and persuade them to destroy the integrating factors of African community life. The violent breaking-up of the existing social order in Africa and the social anarchy which results (a process which has already reached an explosive stage in the towns of West and Central Africa) favour those extremist tendencies in Africa which make for communism. How far this 'scientific' propaganda campaign against 'the remnants of feudalism and colonialism' has already gone can be seen from the growing number of Soviet attempts to denigrate Christianity as a non-African ideology. A symposium, entitled 'Problems of the History of Religions and Atheism' ('Voprossy istorii religii i ateisma'), and the Soviet periodicals *Sovietskaya etnografia* and *Voprossy vostokovedenia*, as well as Radio Moscow in its broadcasts to Africa, all deal exhaustively with the role of the Christian missions in Africa, and everything possible is done to create the impression that 'the chains of religion' fasten Africa 'to imperialism and backwardness'.

This investigation of certain aspects of the aims and methods of Soviet African studies leads to the following conclusions:

1. Soviet African studies are part of Moscow's political-propaganda programme for Africa. Its task is to provide an ideological and scientific-theoretical basis for Soviet policy in Africa.

2. At the same time it has a practical objective: by interpreting the past and present structure and consciousness of African society in the spirit of extreme African nationalism, to demonstrate the identity of its own views with those of the African élite—unlike similar studies in the West, which try to maintain high standards of objectivity.

3. It is intended to achieve the gradual indoctrination of the African élite with the ideas, formulations, and assumptions of dialectical and historical materialism, thus securing their ideological commitment to communism. As they are well aware of the importance of history and national aspirations as integrating factors in the development of political consciousness and national feeling, the

communists hope that this 'thorough, basic and scientific, cultural offensive' will sooner or later have the desired political effect.

NOTES

[1] *Current Digest of the Soviet Press*, VIII, No. 8 (4 April 1956), p. 10.

[2] In *Voprossi istorii*, No. 5 (1958).

[3] *Problemy vostokovedenia*, No. 1 (1959).

[4] Radio Moscow broadcast, 14 November 1959.

[5] *Izvestia*, 24 January 1960.

[6] *Sovietskaya etnografia*, No. 10 (1952).

[7] *Problemy vostokovodenia*, No. 1 (1959).

[8] *Izvestia*, 24 January 1960.

[9] *Bulletin of the Institute for the Study of the USSR* (Munich), No. 9 (1960).

[10] *Problemy vostokovodenia*, No.

[11] *Sovietskaya etnografia*, No. 4 (1957).

[12] Radio Moscow broadcast, 2 July 1960.

Chapter VII

THE OVERTURE: FRIENDSHIP AND CO-EXISTENCE

The ideological foundations of Soviet African policy of the Soviet Government were laid quite early and a systematic study of African affairs in the Soviet Union also began some time ago, but practical action, including political activity, diplomacy, propaganda, infiltration, economic and cultural contacts have a comparatively short history. There were certainly tentative attempts to infiltrate and form cadres as early as the twenties. The organizational instruments for this early Soviet activity were chiefly the Communist Party of Great Britain, the Communist Party of France, and one or two front organizations such as the International Union of Seamen and Dockers. But as both the Comintern and Profintern (the communist international trade union organization) repeatedly admitted, these attempts were very patchy; and in the last resort met with little success. The first efforts made after the Second World War were no more successful. The French Communist Party had proved itself incapable of exploiting the really big opportunity for successful communist activity and propaganda that existed in French-speaking Africa; the collapse of the *Rassemblement Démocratique Africain*, which was temporarily connected with the French Communist Party, and the spectacular defection of such prominent party supporters as Félix Houphouet-Boigny and Gabriel d'Arboussier spelt the collapse of the high hopes which Moscow had cherished with regard to French-speaking Africa. In the year of Stalin's death such vague Soviet hopes as still existed were pinned chiefly on a racial clash in the Union of South Africa and on the Mau-Mau movement in Kenya.[1]

Unconfirmed reports, zealously spread by some Western correspondents concerning 'communist intrigues' and 'powerful Soviet influence' in these areas turned out on closer examination to be little more than propaganda designed to compromise the independence movement of the coloured peoples by presenting it as a communist conspiracy. In the two or three years following the death of Stalin the men in the Kremlin were chiefly exercised by the ferment in the Near and Middle East, and it was not until Ghana and Guinea achieved their independence that Soviet interest in African nationalism was fully aroused. In fact it is only from this period onwards that one can talk of any really large-scale communist operations south of the Sahara. But it was only in 1959–60, on the eve of the radical changes in the political map of Africa, that after careful consideration and after studying the methods most likely to lead to success and making tentative approaches to the new Powers on the African continent, the Soviet Union really launched its African policy. The new departure was accompanied by a flood of pro-African declarations and publications and by personnel changes in two important Soviet diplomatic posts in Africa. On 12 October 1959 A. V. Budakov, who until then had been chief of the African Department of the Soviet Foreign Ministry, was appointed Ambassador Extraordinary to the Court at Addis Ababa, and on 2 January 1960, D. S. Solod, one of the best-known Orientalists of the Soviet Foreign Ministry, was appointed Soviet Ambassador to the new Republic of Guinea.

These appointments clearly indicated the scope of the forthcoming Soviet political offensive in Africa and demonstrated the special interest in Ethiopia and Guinea, two States fundamentally different in history, social structure, political outlook, and background. In fact, one might almost have been forgiven for supposing that co-operation and friendly relationships with one would have ruled out similar relations with the other. Soviet engagement in Ethiopia, for example, would be bound to call the honesty of Moscow's ambitions in Guinea into question. The dilemma was obvious and more than one naïve observer of the Soviet Union's African policy underlined this fact, questioning how the Soviet Government could, on the one hand, woo the feudalist ruler of a backward country and, on the other, make advances to the progressive leader of a quasi-socialist State. But obviously what the Soviet Government had in mind, with the appointment of two such prominent diplomats as Budakov and Solod, was an attempt to reconcile the apparently irreconcilable, to look both right and left, and to seek success in both directions. From the beginning, therefore, the Soviet Government was determined to allow no dogmatic rigidity to hamper its African policy. The friendly relationships with both Guinea and Ethiopia were intended to demonstrate the earnestness of the Soviet efforts to establish friendly relations with all the countries of Africa, whatever their social structures.

Neither Ethiopia nor Guinea offered ideal conditions for *direct* revolutionary activity. However, for the time being Soviet policy in Africa had to take three important negative factors into account, and the Soviet failure in the Congo underlined this:

1. The upheaval in Africa and its transformation from a mere object of colonial exploitation to a world-political force, particularly its scope and its speed, took the communists by surprise. As a result they were unprepared and not able to take advantage of the situation to obtain a firm foothold from the start.

2. Whereas most of the Asiatic countries had professional revolutionary élites or cadres trained in various countries of the Soviet bloc, and communism had become a traditional element in the political life of many such countries, Africa almost completely lacked organized communists. (Apart from Basutoland, where a communist party was founded in 1962, and Nigeria where a communist party was founded in November 1963, there were no communist parties in tropical Africa till the end of 1964, though in Senegal there is, for what it was worth, the crypto-communist PAI, whose influence has been confined to a small number of young intellectuals and in Cameroon the UPC.)

3. The infiltration by communists from outside, whether as diplomats or 'experts', their intervention in internal affairs, as in the Congo, or their support of guerilla groups, as in Cameroon, involved the risk of revealing to the Africans the real power-political objectives of the Soviet Union and rightly being regarded by them as a *direct* threat.

This review of the situation persuaded the Kremlin to adopt a different line, though one hardly less menacing to Africa in the long run. Guinea and Ethiopia were chosen as experimental fields for this, a long-term programme of infiltration and a demonstration of co-existence. In the first phase of this new policy (up to the middle of 1961), Soviet activity in Guinea was not greatly different from Soviet activity in Ethiopia. In Guinea, where communists found the ruling group and a great part of the youth psychologically and ideologically receptive to socialism, and where there were also very favourable opportunities for contacts with other extremist groups in Africa (especially of Cameroon and Angola), it was possible to eliminate the *first stage* of Soviet operations and aim more directly at the ultimate objective. Before long similar opportunities emerged in Ghana and Mali but on the whole they were, nevertheless, still very restricted, and the Kremlin therefore had to recognize that ideologically, Africa as a whole was still not ready to accept communism. This meant going through a *preliminary stage*. Ethiopia is a classic example of the strategy and tactics of this stage. It is an example of a grotesquely involved dialectical performance such as only Marxist-Leninists can put up when called upon to provide the theoretical justification for a policy which does not remotely fit into the pattern of their revolutionary ideas and principles. The party line first appeared in the controlled Press of the Soviet Union and the satellites. To take communist newspaper articles at their face value one might have supposed that ideal social and political conditions existed under Haile Selassie, 'The Lion of Judah', in a State which first arose in the early days of Christianity and which established Christianity as the State religion three hundred years later under the legendary King Azana. This State flourished until it broke up in the eighteenth century and was reconstituted on two occasions, after British pacification and after Italian occupation under Mussolini. Even the attempt to overthrow the régime in December 1960 did not stop the Press in the communist countries from continuing to praise the deeds of the Negus, while deliberately ignoring everything that did not fit in with their image. The fact that 'the progressive ruler' (Moscow Radio's description of the Negus) was doing little or nothing to encourage the development of his people, that one third of the arable land of Ethiopia was owned by the Coptic Church, while other big estates were still administered by the *Gultenya*, the Amharic landlords, 'under the auspices of the Crown'; that apart from 3–4 million Amharic tribesmen all the rest of Ethiopia's about twenty million people were without rights—all these and many other evils hardly existed for the communist Press, which was too busy criticizing evils in 'the reactionary West' to waste time on the evils in the 'progressive East'.

In the circumstances this paradoxical situation deserves more than summary treatment. In June 1960 an East German correspondent travelled through Ethiopia. The fruits of this journalistic visit were not, however, published until January 1961, a time when the events which had led to the serious political crisis and *putsch* against Haile Selassie in December 1960 were causing very frank discussion in the Western world about the deplorable aspects of his feudal policy. In a series of five articles entitled 'Journey into the Legendary Land of Ethiopia', the correspondent painted quite a different picture for his readers. As his reports enable us to draw certain conclusions about the domestic situation in Ethiopia and are an illustration of the methods of communist propaganda in Africa, a few quotations will not be out of place.

'Present-day Ethiopia is certainly a feudal State. It is ruled by the Negus Haile Selassie I, who, according to State tradition, is the 255th ruler of the Salomonic line, the "Lions of Judah". However, in forming a judgement on African social structure, caution is to be recommended. First of all, we must remember that many African republics have no more than a narrow bourgeois strip along the coast while their hinterlands are still way back in the feudal and even pre-feudal ages. For example, the Nigerians are ruled by the party of the Sultan of Sokoto (one of the biggest Fullani emirs to the south of the Sahara). And secondly, the Negus was not only one of the first anti-imperialist fighters and leaders of Africa, and one of the first victims of fascist preparations for war, but he is also a man who, despite tradition and dynastic outlook, is determined to lead his country out of the feudal middle ages into a bourgeois Africa of our own day.'

The following passages are even more interesting, completely ignoring the difference which existed between the wording of the constitution and its application in practice. The communist journalist describes what he regards as five 'particular advantages' of Haile Selassie's policy and administration.

'1. When he came to the throne in 1930 he introduced a constitution, and its provisions were extended in 1955 to include the general franchise for all men and women over the age of twenty-one.' (It should be pointed out here that no opposition party is permitted in Ethiopia, where the only political organization is Haile Selassie's own party of yes-men. Furthermore, all candidates are chosen by the Throne according to property and educational qualifications.) 'He (Haile Selassie) voluntarily restricts his own power as an absolute monarch in the following important aspect: war can be declared only with the approval of Parliament.' (This, by the way, is worth just about as much as a similar provision which existed in Hohenzollern Germany.) 'All territorial changes and all financial imposts on his subjects have first to be approved by both Houses of Parliament before they can be ratified by the Head of the State.' (All very fine, but in view of the composition of these two Houses of Parliament, an empty pretence.)

'2. The whole imperial family possesses bourgeois property: commercial undertakings, workshops, factories and shares in foreign-owned concerns . . . Against the opposition of the temporal and spiritual princes the Negus has introduced legislation to protect capitalist property.'[2]

Amazing though it may seem, no misunderstanding is possible: here is an official communist publication recording approvingly the interlocking of the economic interests of the imperial family with those of domestic and foreign capital and the extension of imperial family property (including estates, factories, mines, etc.) and representing all this as progressive; and this without the slightest criticism of the extension of the feudal property structure or the identification of the ruling stratum with the development of early capitalist profit-making enterprises.

It is the same with regard to the other two points the correspondent puts forward as indications of progressive development in Ethiopia: 'the head of the Ethiopian State is also in favour of land reform . . . the Negus is the inspiration behind a Five-Year Plan for the country and favours the investment of industrial capital.'[3]

People who read only the communist Press cannot discover that, in practice, Haile Selassie's 'land reform' is as useless to the people as the extension of the industrial sector on the basis of foreign-capital investment. However, readers are told why this feudal State should enjoy such considerate treatment:

'Ethiopia's foreign policy is developing rapidly, and the visit of Haile Selassie to Prague in 1959 gave a practical framework to the "alliance" policy on which it is admittedly based . . . The visit was an indication of political and economic far-sightedness . . . The fact that Ethiopia can now rely on the great and unfailing aid of the Soviet Union backed by its tremendous economic resources indicates a new orientation of Ethiopia's foreign policy and suggests a proper understanding of the changed power relationships in the world today.'[4]

This form of reporting, of which there are many other examples in Soviet journalism, is particularly interesting for its omissions. For example, the reader behind the Iron Curtain rarely if ever hears anything about the unusually high level of illiteracy in Ethiopia, nor about the impoverishment and misery of the masses of the people, particularly among the non-Amharic tribes. And of course the communist Press made no mention of the disagreeable incident in Dilla (in the Galla area) at the beginning of December 1960 when over two hundred natives were killed by a punitive imperial expedition. Nor have there been any reports about the 'mopping-up' operations carried out by Haile Selassie's imperial forces against the Somalis in the summer of 1960–1. The unsuccessful *putsch* which took place in Addis Ababa in December 1960 was widely reported in the Western Press. Obvious comparisons were drawn between early Tibet and contemporary Ethiopia and the archaic conditions existing in Ethiopia came in for a good deal of criticism. But the communist Press exaggerates the progressive aspects of Ethiopia while deliberately ignoring what might disturb the agreeable picture required by communist political interests. For more than once Ethiopia was heralded in the Soviet Press for the 'important role' it is playing in liberating and modernizing Africa. (See for instance *Yezhegodnik Bolshoy Sovietskoy Entsiklopedii*, 1962 [p. 405] or the book *Strany mira* [Moscow, 1962], p. 287.

This was not always the case. As late as 1955 the Soviet Press was denouncing the Negus as a 'reactionary autocrat' and feudal ruler, and the relations between Ethiopia and the West, particularly with the United States, were cited as a proof of an 'alliance between imperialism and colonialism'. Then came the Bandung conference and Moscow looked again at the role of Ethiopia. As a result the

Kremlin discovered that Haile Selassie's empire stood in good repute (despite certain reservations), with the young élite of Africa who were agitating for independence and sovereignty in British and French territories, because of its resistance to Italian fascist imperialism. One need only look at what Nkrumah has to say in his autobiography.[5] It was now remembered that friendly relations between Russia and Ethiopia had been traditional, and even though this had been in Tzarist Russia they saw no reason for not exploiting it now. Ethiopia was, in fact, the one country in Africa to which Tzarist Russia had paid particular attention, primarily because the Russian Orthodox Church felt it had common ground with the Coptic Church of Abyssinia and was in favour of union with its Abyssinian brothers in Christ. From 1888 onwards Russian visitors travelled to 'the roof of Africa' with the blessing of both the Russian government and the Orthodox Church: adventurers like the Cossack Ashinov, emissaries like the officer Mashkov, geographers like Yelisayev and Leontiev, the Archimandrite Yefrem, diplomats, and doctors who founded a hospital in Addis Ababa. Many of these Russians actually entered the service of the Emperor. Diplomatic relations established between Russia and Abyssinia in 1902 under the Tzars were renewed in 1943 by the Soviets and the present emissaries of Moscow in Addis Ababa never tire of stressing the 'friendly relationship' which, they say, 'has always existed' between the Emperor's palace in Addis Ababa and the Kremlin in Moscow. They prefer to ignore the fact that there are very different rulers in the Kremlin today from those in the old St Petersburg palace of the Tzar. Here, as elsewhere, the Soviet Union is acting as the legitimate successor to Tzarist Russia. In other words, Haile Selassie, Emperor of Abyssinia, is invited to look upon the Soviet Union not as a world revolutionary centre threatening all non-communist rulers with destruction, but as a loyal partner offering valuable economic benefits as the country which covers one-sixth of the world's surface, shoots *sputniks* and *luniks* into the sky and is the friend of all friendly people, in particular the friend of all Africans.

This was the atmosphere in which Haile Selassie's state visit to the Soviet Union took place in the summer of 1959. The Emperor was received by the Soviet leaders with unequalled pomp and accorded all the honours due to his high rank. In addition, he was presented with a splendidly equipped plane for his personal use by

Mr Khrushchev and Ethiopia was granted credits of 400 million old roubles (the equivalent of one hundred million dollars), the largest credit until then granted by the Soviet Union to any African country. On this state occasion very little was said about socialism, but a good deal about the traditional friendship between the two countries and the necessity for world-wide co-existence. The Negus was suitably impressed, and on his return to his capital declared:

'From the moment of Our arrival in the Soviet Union, the warm and wonderful reception accorded to Us by the people and their leaders, whose hospitality is well known, was beyond Our expectation . . . during Our fortnight's stay We were most impressed to see how the peoples of the Soviet Union have succeeded in recovering from the aftermath of a devastating war, have carried out full reconstruction within a very short period of time, and have at the same time achieved remarkable progress in the economic, industrial, scientific and social fields, thus establishing themselves, within the span of forty years, as one of the Great Powers of our time . . . We were able to make the personal acquaintance of Mr Voroshilov, the President of the Supreme Soviet, and Mr Khrushchev, the Prime Minister of the Soviet Union. A frank and friendly exchange of views on various matters resulted in full agreement being reached on all of them.'[6]

The naïve reader might imagine he was reading about a state occasion between the representatives of countries sharing a common ideology, something along the lines of the conventional state visits of monarchs in the nineteenth century.

Indeed, the representatives of the Soviet Union have referred as little as possible to the cardinal ideological differences between the two countries. This attitude inspires all the exhibitions arranged by the Soviet House of Culture in Addis Ababa and all the Soviet propaganda carried out in the interior. Some out-of-the-way village, consisting of tumbledown huts by the side of a road, will receive a visit from these Soviet cultural propagandists. The next village is perhaps twenty-five miles away and the capital, Addis Ababa, one hundred and thirty miles away. In the village there is no electric light, no telephone and no school; in fact nothing at all that could make the place worthy of notice by white men. Nevertheless the inhabitants of the village find themselves invited to an evening's entertainment. A film van parks in the small village square, a portable dynamo provides the projector with light, and a portable film screen is set up between two poles. On the screen every villager can see for himself just how warm and friendly are the feelings of the people of the Soviet Union for the subjects of Haile Selassie. Each stage of the state visit of the Negus to the Soviet Union in 1959 is recorded: there is the historic meeting between Haile Selassie and Nikita Khrushchev; the usual gala evening in the Bolshoi Opera House with *Swan Lake*; the Emperor talking to ordinary Soviet men and women; and, of course, a tremendous amount about the great achievements of the Soviet Union: huge tractors working on collective farms, hydraulic power stations, engineering works, schools, laboratories, universities, great blocks of flats in Moscow, Kiev and Leningrad, the special Ilyushin 14 plane, a personal gift from Mr Khrushchev to the Emperor. The presents from the Soviet Union to Ethiopia: a secondary school in Addis Ababa for 1,000 pupils, with a gymnasium, kitchen and dining hall; instruments and drugs for the old Russian hospital in Addis Ababa; and finally, the 400 million roubles of credit—the crowning proof of Soviet friendship. The effect of this unique confrontation on the dark-skinned audience is, of course, profound. Henceforth people up and down the country who have seen such films will automatically equate all ideas of higher civilization, greater economic strength, and unselfish friendship with the Soviet Union.

The only reference to socialism on such occasions is the phrase: 'The Great Union of Socialist Soviet Republics'. Little or nothing is said about communism and then only *sotto voce*. Soviet propaganda in Ethiopia is not interested in spreading an ideology; it is not intended to convert the Ethiopians to communism or used in order to form the usual communist cells. In fact it is quite different from the attitude of the Soviet Union to Western Europe, where behind a screen of normal diplomatic relations communist and crypto-communist groups are encouraged in every possible way to disturb or, if possible, undermine the social order in the host countries. Where Ethiopia is concerned the Soviet motto is 'honest co-existence whilst recognizing and even supporting the given domestic political order'.

What is going on here is a policy of long-term political speculation. Its aim is to dissipate psychological inhibitions and political reservations towards the Soviet Union, while at the same time gaining influence by force of example. So far the results of this policy have been highly satisfactory. It is true that Soviet-Ethiopian relations deteriorated temporarily when Moscow arranged to deliver arms to Somalia in 1963. But the Soviet arms deal with Somalia never materialized on its original scale, and as soon as the Soviet Union realized the increased continental importance of Addis Ababa as the capital in which the Organization of African Unity had been formed in May 1963, and that Addis Ababa had become the headquarters of the OAU, the Soviet campaign of friendship and co-existence towards Ethiopia was stepped up again.

NOTES

[1] See for instance Cyril Bryner, 'Russian Interest in Africa', *Current History*, July 1953.

[2] *Neues Deutschland* ([East] Berlin), 12-30 January 1961.

[3] Ibid.

[4] Ibid.

[5] *Ghana: The Autobiography of Kwame Nkrumah* (2nd ed.; Edinburgh, 1960), p. 22.

[6] *Speeches Delivered by His Imperial Majesty Haile Selassie I, Emperor of Ethiopia, on Various Occasions, May 1957 to December 1959* (Addis Ababa, 1960), p. 145.

Chapter VIII

REVOLUTIONARY UNITY AND NATIONAL RESERVATIONS: THE CASE OF GUINEA

So far the most favourable conditions for communism in Africa were to be found in Guinea, the country on the west coast which contemptuously rejected de Gaulle's *Communauté Française*. In September 1958, under the vigorous leadership of Sékou Touré, the people of Guinea dramatically defied de Gaulle and chose independence. Since the end of the Second World War there had been some contacts between communists and nationalists in Guinea. These contacts were zealously exploited and the countries of the Soviet bloc systematically extended and consolidated them. In addition, the spread of communist ideas was favoured by the extremely critical situation in which the young State found itself at that time. As Guinea was dropped by France and ignored by the West both economically and politically, the communist bloc was given an opportunity of breaking the international isolation in which Guinea thus found itself. The communist countries promptly signed trade agreements, granted credits, and sent technicians to save Guinea from ruin. From the spring of 1959 the communists were able to claim one success after another and it seemed only a question of time before Sékou Touré's country would be a mere satellite, bound hand and foot to communism. But at the last moment a dramatic change took place in Guinea and the triumph of communism was frustrated. In the late autumn of 1961 Touré uncovered a communist conspiracy, and as a result the Soviet Ambassador was compelled to leave Guinea rather hurriedly. Although it is not easy to unravel all the truth about events in this *état pilote* of

West Africa, it is necessary to examine the case of Guinea as closely as available information allows.

Guinea is a dictatorial State, the first and the most fully developed in Africa, with all the monotonous features of complete totalitarianism. The security forces, the police, the army, the officials of the party and the State exercise 'revolutionary vigilance' at all times and in a way familiar to anyone who has experienced the practices of fascist and communist countries. The model followed by the officials who lord it over the villages and rural areas is obviously a caricature of the behaviour of subordinate white colonial officials around 1898. The fact that all this is in contradiction to the much-lauded *Communaucratie* and the alleged 'complete solidarity of the people, the party, and the government' seems to disturb no one. If you want to be someone in Guinea you have to exercise whatever power you may possess as ostentatiously and blatantly as possible.

If this disagreeable aspect of 'the permanent revolution' is mentioned to anyone in authority in Guinea, he just shrugs his shoulders: 'What can we do about it? We can't control every subordinate official to make sure that he behaves himself.' That significant word 'control' is not used accidentally. Whoever glances at the decisions of the Political Bureau, or at the minutes of the congresses of the *Parti Démocratique de Guinée* (PDG), will repeatedly come across words like 'control', 'authority' and 'organization'. There is a great deal of talk about 'a merciless struggle against individualism, opportunism and egoism in all their forms'.[1] 'In what position would the Government or the Party be', demanded Sékou Touré at the Fifth Congress, 'if the leadership of the country had no authority? Wouldn't the country soon collapse in uproar and anarchy, and thus very soon lose its independence? When it is a question of authority there is no single problem, everything interlocks to form a whole.'[2]

The logical conclusion arrived at by Sékou Touré was that democratic centralism must be strengthened. In Guinea, as in the communist countries, this is the name for the process which safeguards the power of the bureaucracy and of the cadres. It replaces 'the revolution from below' by the guided and controlled 'revolution from above'. Sékou Touré constantly demanded that these cadres should be better trained, strengthened, and better prepared for leadership within the organization.[3] 'Organization' is the magic word in Guinea. It means 4,000 village cells of the *Parti Démo-*

cratique, thousands of subordinate part-time officials and a few hundred full-time officials in the main centres. It means not only a totalitarian party but a State trade union led and controlled by the party. Despite constitutionally guaranteed free trade unions this body jealously defends its monopolist position and has squeezed out the small group of Christian trade unionists, forcing them underground.

A big role is played by the *Jeunesse RDA*, also known as the Young Pioneers. The visitor will realize what power this organization possesses only when he comes across it in places far away from the urban centres; for example in one of the impoverished villages out in the bush where civilization has not yet penetrated. Among dilapidated, broken-down huts thatched with straw, he will find one newly whitewashed, barrack-style hut, above its entrance the green, yellow and red cockade in the shape of an elephant, the symbol of the new Guinea. (Sékou Touré's native title is 'Tilly' or 'big elephant'.) On the doors will be the initials PDG–JRDA. Inside the hall, under a picture of Sékou Touré, an official will be instructing the village youth. They will all be there sitting at his feet. Everything is highly disciplined and no one dares to complain. Instructions are issued briskly and smartly. The national programme known as *l'Investissement humain* is in full swing. On a Sunday the group may start building a permanent path to the capital—'voluntarily', of course, and without pay, encouraged only by the dull rhythmic thumping of the tom-tom and the new songs of the nation; it may well be '*Avant l'indépendance nous étions dans l'obscurité tels des aveugles cherchant leur chemin et, c'est pourquoi dans cette incompréhension, ses incidents sanglants nous divisaient*', or '*Salut à toi indépendance de la Guinée qui nous a ouvert definitivement la voie de la fraternité*'.

First we build the path, then a road, later a local schoolhouse, and after that a hospital; then perhaps a new market square—everything will come in good time. 'The party rightly demands', bellows the official, 'that we should not wait until progress comes to us. We must make it ourselves.' There is a good deal of talk about competitions between neighbouring villages and there are great national contests for the Gold Medal of the party. Everyone must feel responsible for everyone else, just as the organization is there for everyone—'Everything depends on organization . . .'

There are only a few men at the head of the organization; they are all members of the National Political Bureau of the party and most of them are also members of the Cabinet or leading officials. But the whole organization was created by one man, Sékou Touré, leader of the new Guinea, whose upright figure resembles that of an athlete rather than a politician. He is a passionate nationalist, a brilliant speaker and a persuasive agitator. But—particularly in African conditions—he is something more than that: he is a great, painstaking organizer. Under the noses of the French administrators, he built up a political machine which lends force to his nationalist slogans.

'You can't make politics with hopes alone,' he is once said to have exclaimed. When General de Gaulle presented his referendum in September 1958, this axiom was seen to be doubly true, both in Guinea and in France's other overseas territories. In the Niger territory, for example, all the leaders were firmly determined to reject de Gaulle's proposals, and yet two-thirds of the population voted 'yes' at the referendum.

The situation in Guinea was different. When de Gaulle arrived in Conakry shortly before the referendum in order to get support for the *Communauté Française*, Sékou Touré met him, not merely as the head of the administration, as a man filled with wishes, hopes and longings, but as the confident leader of a disciplined, efficient group of cadres, whose influence already extended into the farthest corners of the country. He did not allow himself to be intimidated either by the programme or the prestige of the general, still less by his pathos. 'Guinea prefers freedom in poverty to slavery in riches', he told de Gaulle bluntly. 'Then you will have to vote "no",' de Gaulle told him and, according to reports, he was more amused than angry. Sékou Touré saw to it that his people did, in fact, vote 'no'. He organized the referendum so efficiently that ninety-six per cent of the electors voted 'no', and Guinea was the only one of France's overseas territories to reject the *Communauté*. On 2 October 1958, Sékou Touré proclaimed the independence of Guinea, and the National Political Bureau of the PDG took power in the name of the people and for the people. Sékou Touré became President, Prime Minister, Defence Minister and, temporarily, Foreign Minister. In January 1961, when the first presidential elections were held, it appeared that the power of the party had not declined. There was only one candidate, and that was of course Sékou Touré, who won a victory which was overwhelming even if compared with what the Nazis and communists have been known to claim in similar circumstances: 1,576,747 votes were cast and of these 1,576,580, or 99·999 per cent, were for Touré. Of the million and a half people entitled to vote only ten thousand abstained.

Sékou Touré comes from an old clan of what is known as the sword nobility. When the whites first penetrated into Guinea in the 1880s, Touré's grandfather led his tribe against them and resisted vigorously, but their primitive weapons were useless against the firearms of the invaders and they were defeated and subjugated. Touré himself grew up in poverty and without social advantages. He eventually had some higher education, but was not able to complete his studies. Others, like him, remained dispossessed, but in Touré there was something of the fierce pride of his forefathers. As he was unable to complete his formal studies he taught himself and after a while managed to become a post office official. It was then that he began to show an interest in politics. At first he is reported to have veered first one way and then the other like a weathercock, but this ceased when he came into closer contact with Marxist ideas. He read the most important writings of Marx, Engels, Lenin and other communist theoreticians and towards the end of the Second World War, when the communist trade unions in France went in for missionary work in French West and Central Africa, he joined the *Confédération Générale des Travailleurs* (CGT), which was under communist control. Before long Touré was the leader of the CGT in Conakry. He also attended a number of courses run by the French CGT, and some at training-centres of the communist World Federation of Trade Unions (WFTU) on the other side of the Iron Curtain, though today the President of Guinea is disinclined to discuss these experiences and evades all questions on that subject. The evidence, including a report published in a Prague newspaper cannot, however, be disputed. This newspaper wrote: 'One day a young Negro came to our country to study . . . Since then twelve years—at least many years—have passed, and that young Negro has become the Prime Minister of his newly liberated country. A progressive Prime Minister, of course . . . He is Sékou Touré, the leader of the new African State of Guinea.'[4]

During the next stages of his career he held various official positions in the *Rassemblement Démocratique Africain* (RDA), founded in 1947, and the first mass organization to extend over the whole of French West Africa. Sékou Touré was one of its founders. Until the first split in 1950 the RDA followed a pro-communist line and provided the African representatives to the World Peace Movement and other front organizations run by the communists. Touré's own organization, the *Parti Démocratique de Guinée*, of which he is President, was first formed as a national section of the RDA. He first came to Conakry as mayor and in January 1956 he was elected deputy for Guinea in the French National Assembly.

During this period he engaged in a bitter struggle against what is known in Africa as the *chefferie*. He had long propagated the view that there was no hope of progress unless the chains of the past were broken and the country was liberated from the sterile traditionalism of tribal life. The rule of the old chiefs was, he declared, 'a totally unsuited instrument for bringing about the emancipation of Guinea'. Unlike most African politicians, Touré did not concentrate his attentions exclusively on the urban population and the officials. While mayor of Conakry and during the short period when he was a member of the French National Assembly he spent more time in the interior of Guinea than in Conakry or in Paris. He organized people everywhere, systematically and with unflagging vigour. He formed cadres in all areas and among all tribes and wherever he went he won supporters: the unemployed in Conakry, taxi-drivers, ex-soldiers, students, and above all women and peasants. He encouraged the peasants in their resistance to the feudal domination of the chiefs, who sought to reintroduce tribute and forced labour, and he promised the abolition of the worst social abuses.

The form and objectives of Sékou Touré's policy differed fundamentally from the organization and methods adopted elsewhere in Africa, but their success was not entirely due to his personality and undoubted ability. His movement and rise would have been inconceivable if the French had not first introduced various administrative reforms: labour legislation, the general franchise, municipal administration, and the *loi-cadre* introducing a measure of political and administrative autonomy. It was these French innovations that gave Touré his chance and prepared the way for his success. In particular his movement was never subjected to any particularly repressive measures on the part of the French colonial administration, which could easily have hampered, if not prevented, the growth of the PDG. If they had intervened, it would certainly have afforded Sékou Touré's enemies the opportunity of splitting the movement.

Of course, nowadays—and despite some reconciliation between Guinea and France in 1963—no one in Guinea mentions the tolerance shown by the French administration; no one has a good word to say for the civilizing achievements of the colonial era. In fact the legend is accepted that Touré was victorious only as the result of a hard, bitter struggle against colonial oppression, not to say terrorism. The truth is that he was strongly supported in his struggle against the *chefferie* by the French High Commissioner, Jean Ramadier, and the independence of Guinea is due solely to the fact that de Gaulle himself offered immediate and absolute independence as an alternative to the *Communauté Française* which he would have favoured. But Touré's propaganda goes very much farther than merely concealing these facts, and the people of Guinea are solemnly assured in numerous speeches and appeals that colonial bandits and imperialist agents are for ever threatening the independence of their country and that such plans and intrigues demand that they should 'intensify their revolutionary vigilance against foreign machinations', while at the same time waging 'a relentless struggle against the remnants of colonial behaviour and the colonial outlook' that have allegedly been left behind among the people.

As a government professing such an outlook could hardly continue to maintain friendly relations with 'the biggest and most ruthless colonial power in Africa' (which is France, of course), on 1 March 1960 Guinea withdrew from the French franc area. By this time, thanks to the intrigues of certain circles both in Conakry and in the French capital, relations between Conakry and Paris had sunk to a low level, although officially the step was explained by Conakry as 'an attempt to resolve the numerous economic difficulties facing Guinea since her independence'. The introduction of the Guinea franc was 'to make Guinea into one single economic area, a house open to all'. But the exact opposite occurred; the Guinea franc is up to now Touré's private currency and is unquoted outside Guinea; even banks in Liberia and other 'friendly countries' will not handle it. As the new Guinea franc is accepted only in Guinea and as the National Bank of Guinea has little or no foreign currency, and has to be very careful with any it has, the export and import trade has practically ceased since 1960. Another result of the currency change was an acute shortage of commodities; there are only empty shelves in the few shops still open in the capital, while the few remaining Europeans look back on the rationing period during the war as a relative paradise.

Far worse is the fact that, apart from the officials of the PDG, the people of Guinea are suffering from an acute shortage of staple goods. Gifts of rice from the United States and Red China have not gone very far and bad harvests have aggravated food shortages. Rigorous austerity measures, including close control of private trading in villages and areas, have done very little to remedy matters. The attempt to give local leaders of the PDG the responsibility for the distribution of foodstuffs in particularly short supply has merely resulted in a flourishing black market and caused nepotism and corruption.

Guinea's first Three-Year Plan, adopted in April 1960, was heralded as a guarantee of decisive changes in this situation. But this plan was mostly based on Soviet aid and on the then intimate relationship between Guinea and the communist countries. This relationship provides a typical example of communist policy—and failure—in the under-developed areas. In the case of Guinea, the troubles started in the late summer of 1959, when Saifoulaye Diallo, President of the Parliament of Guinea, went to the Soviet Union at the head of a government and party delegation on the first official visit to the Soviet Union. It was during this visit that negotiations between Anastas Mikoyan and Saifoulaye Diallo led to a credit of 140 million roubles being granted to Guinea.

On its return to Conakry the delegation was greeted with tremendous enthusiasm, but this soon gave way to depression when the expectations aroused by promises made in Moscow were not satisfied. Tension developed and discussions between Sékou Touré and Rashidov, then the Uzbekistan Prime Minister, and other members of the Soviet delegation at the Fifth National Congress of the PDG in Conakry, did nothing to clear up the situation. The countries of the Soviet bloc did at least take up the agreed banana and coffee quotas and, in return, modest supplies of sugar and grain arrived in Guinea; but the promised credits did not transpire.

The situation was not cleared up until November 1959, when

Touré paid his first state visit to Moscow. In an interview with Mr Khrushchev the Soviet Premier suggested that Soviet experts should visit Guinea to study, on the spot, the best way of utilizing the promised Soviet credits. Similar offers also came, either directly or through their Moscow embassies, from the People's Republic of China and from various Soviet satellite States. As Guinea's economic situation was deteriorating and as the extreme left wing of the Political Bureau of the PDG approved the communist proposals with enthusiasm, Sékou Touré had little alternative but to accept Mr Khrushchev's offer. With this the Soviet bloc secured the technical basis it required for exercising an even more powerful influence over developments in Guinea, which in any case were proceeding in its favour.

In 1960 there was a veritable invasion of Guinea by communist 'advisers' and 'experts', delegations from the Soviet Union, Czechoslovakia, Roumania, Poland, North Vietnam and Mao's China soon turned the only available hotel in Conakry, the Hôtel de France, into a dependency of the Savoy Hotel in Moscow. Experts on fisheries, soil erosion, veterinary science, broadcasting, and sport, bobbed up all over the place and in the background there were trade-union officials and military experts. In the spring of 1960 a 'trade delegation' of no fewer than seventy members arrived from Czechoslovakia to put the finishing touches to the Three-Year Plan. In the second half of the year, Chinese agricultural experts arrived from Peking; as a result of their investigations they proposed the formation of agricultural collectives along Chinese lines. The Political Bureau of the PDG had previously sent a delegation to Red China and it now declared itself in agreement with the Chinese proposals. However, the first attempts to found these collectives led to great unrest in the Kekedou-Kissidou area where the local agricultural population objected violently to the scheme. But the PDG leadership had gone too far in its enthusiastic acceptance of the Chinese proposals to draw back immediately and so, egged on by the Chinese guests, they used force against the restive peasants—announcing first that imperialist agents had stirred up the people and carried on anti-revolutionary agitation in the troubled areas. The troops sent in to 'pacify' the disaffected districted were able, for the first time, to make use of the weapons Guinea had obtained as a result of the military-aid agreement signed in Prague. Another result of this agreement was that groups of officers and NCOs from Guinea were to be sent to Czechoslovakia for training at communist military academies.

The evidence of large-scale political and propagandist infiltration was even more significant. Officials of the Soviet bloc countries delivered lectures in the State schools on DIAMAT (the communist abbreviation for 'dialectical materialism'), and on the principles and practice of current Soviet policy in Africa. Instructors of the communist-dominated World Federation of Trade Unions were active at the so-called trade-union university of Conakry and at the trade-union school in Dalaba. A sport exchange had also been organized with the countries of Eastern Europe and under the guidance of Hungarian trainers this increasingly took on the form of political support for the activist youth of Guinea. The bookshops and book depots run by the Youth League and the PDG were becoming centres for the distribution of vast quantities of communist literature. The works of Mao Tse-tung, Khrushchev's speeches, the works of Lenin, and the 'classics of socialist realism' were all to be had at low prices, and often even free. In the same way the *World Communist Review*, *Humanité*, and the various periodicals and publications of the WFTU were easily obtainable. The formulae and slogans of communist agitation were becoming more and more strongly impressed on public opinion in Guinea. Even the show trials that followed the suppression of unrest in April 1960 and led to a number of death sentences were held according to the same grotesque horror ritual with which Soviet Russia and its satellites have made us familiar. Guinea thus became a perfect replica: the counter-revolutionary agents, and the alleged discovery of imperialists in the background, invented evidence and forged exhibits.

Finally we must not omit to mention the furtive anti-clerical campaign conducted by the PDG against religion, with the ultimate aim of enthroning Marxist materialism in the minds of the people. Instructions issued by the PDG as part of this campaign had the illuminating title 'Pray less, work more!' In the summer of 1960, the Christian Working Youth, the Christian Country Youth, and the Scout organization were ordered to end their activities. On applying for an exit permit Catholics from Guinea who wished to take part in the Vatican Council found, to their surprise, that this Catholic religious assembly was, in reality, 'aimed at spiritually preparing neo-colonialism' and that therefore they could not attend it.

Guinea's foreign policy developed along much the same pro-communist lines as its domestic policy. At the time of the acute Congo crisis its attitude was hardly distinguishable from that of the Soviet Union. While even Ghana and the United Arab Republic both expressly supported the Lumumba and Gizenga régime, showed a certain reserve and discretion, deliberately delayed the withdrawal of their troops and, up to a point, even adopted a mediatory role in the United Nations between West and East, Guinea never shifted from its extreme anti-Western attitude. At first Guinea sent a contingent of its troops to form part of the UN force (as Lumumba had requested) and supported the policy of the United Nations, but later it changed its Congo policy in close accordance with the changes in Moscow's attitude. The culmination was reached with Sékou Touré's second visit to Moscow, in September 1960, shortly before Khrushchev's rowdy performance at the UN in New York. Khrushchev and Touré issued a joint communiqué stressing their 'complete agreement' on the Congo question and a little later, at the plenary session of the United Nations on 9 October 1960, Touré supported to the hilt the Soviet attack upon Hammerskjöld and the 'Western imperialists', declaring:

'It is impossible not to make the United Nations responsible for the dangerous situation in the Congo . . . The confusion that developed in the wake of Belgian aggression threatens everyone in the world today. Political oppression and economic exploitation still exist in all forms and every possible guise . . . Africa plays a dominating role in the expansionist ambitions of the imperialist powers, and they are co-ordinating their plans to secure the military bases (in Africa) that are essential for their expansionist lusts.'[5]

It was not surprising, therefore, that Guinea should withdraw its contingent (of 740 men) from the United Nations force in the Congo. Thereafter accusations and diplomatic protests synchronized completely with the attacks of the Soviet Union, whether against the late Secretary-General, Dag Hammerskjöld, the UN commanders and representatives in the Congo, the federalist Congo politicians, the Belgians, the Americans, the French, or 'the whole imperialist bloc'. Touré's Congo emissary, Tunkara, declared: 'The

UN command in Leopoldville has flagrantly interfered in the domestic affairs of the Congolese Republic and acted as an occupation force.'[6] It is not surprising to find that exactly the same things were being said in Moscow: 'The troops of the United Nations have become an occupation power robbing the Congolese population of their freedom.'[7] In connection with the alleged flight of a German plane carrying arms to Katanga, a Conakry radio broadcast declared: 'The coalition of the imperialist powers against the Congo is very obvious here, as also is the role of the German Federal Republic. The composition of Tshombe's forces is typical: West-German mercenaries, both officers and NCOs, and former SS men.'[8] No one could therefore have been surprised to discover that the All-African People's Conference in Cairo accorded the German Federal Republic the honour of second place after the United States in the list of neo-colonialist powers.

Whoever examines the details of Guinea's development between 1958 and 1961 is forced to the conclusion (after making allowances for the claim of 'positive neutrality between the two blocs' of the Government and the PDG) that this neutrality really meant neutrality, if not hostility, towards the West only, and close, cordial relations with the East.

There is certainly no doubt that this was the conclusion drawn by the Soviet Government about the political situation in Guinea. It could not but feel confident; it was impossible to doubt that Sékou Touré's party had gone over whole-heartedly to its side and that this could soon be triumphantly confirmed in public.

From the beginning of 1960 the Soviet Government had a very clever operator at the head of its mission in Conakry: Daniel Semyonovitch Solod, a man whose diplomatic career had been a series of successes. This Ukrainian had been attached for a long time to the foreign-political department of the Soviet Foreign Office and he had occupied one post after another in the East. In 1944 Stalin sent him to the newly founded and already troubled States of Lebanon and Syria. In the six years that followed, Solod developed his mission so that it held a key communist position in the Levant and he won the reputation of being the most skilful communist representative in the Middle East. Speaking fluent Arabic, French and English, he persuasively put forward what appeared to be unconventional and undoctrinaire arguments and gradually succeeded in lessening resentment against the Soviet Union and intensifying resentments against the Western Powers. By the time Solod was recalled to Moscow in 1950, his work was done and Syrian representatives were negotiating with the Soviet Foreign Minister, Vyshinsky, for the conclusion of trade and military agreements. At the same time the Syrian Minister for National Economy, Maaruf al-Davalibi, a close personal friend of Solod, was saying openly that he would 'sooner see the Arab Republics become Soviet Republics than victims of Zionism'. When Solod finally left Damascus to take up a leading position in the Middle East Department in Moscow's Foreign Ministry, he was accorded an honour that no Soviet representative before him had ever enjoyed in the Arab world: hundreds of Syrian notables assembled to give him a warm ovation.[9]

Three years later, after the triumph of the revolutionary junta over the corrupt but pro-Western régime of King Farouk in Egypt, Solod appeared again outside the Soviet Union, this time as Ambassador in Cairo, where he repeated his successful Damascus and Beirut performance. It was not long before he succeeded in improving the traditionally frosty relations between Moscow and Cairo and in creating a warm and friendly atmosphere. When Nasser came to the fore, Moscow's chances increased and Solod was actually assisted at the birth of the policy of 'positive neutrality' formulated in Cairo. Incidentally Western correspondents always referred to him amongst themselves as 'Mr Troublemaker'. It was also Solod who launched the large-scale trading deals between Egypt and the Soviet Union and, as Nasser has told us, it was Solod who first broached the possibility of Soviet arms deliveries to Egypt. In an interview granted to an Egyptian newspaper, Nasser described Solod's approach. It appears that at a diplomatic reception Solod took him into a corner and asked him point-blank whether the Egyptian Government would be prepared to consider buying arms from the Soviet Union. Should Nasser's Government feel so inclined he, Solod, would see that this interesting information reached the appropriate quarter. Nasser went on to say: 'I answered him in the same tone, saying that I found his offer extremely interesting and that I should be prepared to enter into negotiations in that sense.'[10]

By February 1956, when Solod returned to Moscow to become Deputy-Chief (for a while even Acting-Chief) of the Middle East

Department of the Foreign Office, the basis of the new relationship between Egypt and the Soviet Union had been well established. He was now in charge of Soviet operations in the United Republic, Iraq, the Lebanon, Jordan, the Sudan, Ethiopia, Libya, Tunisia, and Morocco, and he made use of his Cairo experiences in his dealings with the whole Arab world. But Solod's value to the Soviet Government was even greater: he had a keen eye for African developments and for the advance of African nationalism and in this capacity he was now invaluable to the Soviet Foreign Ministry, especially if one bears in mind the role played by Cairo in the extremist African nationalist movement. After the victory of the ambitious Nasser over the more moderate and conservative Neguib, Cairo became the centre for almost all the radical anti-colonial elements throughout Africa, and to some extent it still is. Jomo Kenyatta's successor party to Mau-Mau, the liberation groups in Angola, Mozambique, the Congo, and Tanganyika, the Uganda National Congress, and the terrorist *Union des Populations du Cameroun*, all established action centres in exile in Cairo. Their lack of money, arms, and tactical experience and their ardent longing for violent action drove these various groups into the arms of the Soviet representatives who were, of course, only too willing to assist them. Solod's close contact with such groups was clearly demonstrated at the second Afro-Asian Solidarity Conference in April 1960 at Conakry. Although he had no official connection with the conference it enabled him to renew his acquaintance with many African politicians and to make new friends, particularly amongst the Congolese and Angolan 'Friends of Peace'.

As Ambassador to Conakry, Solod's sphere of operations was by no means confined to Guinea. In fact his mission was a double one: first, to consolidate and extend the 'friendship between the Soviet Union and Guinea', and to guide the left-wing course of the Government of Guinea in the direction most favourable to the Kremlin. Second, in Moscow's interests he was to turn Conakry into the key West African centre for communist ideas and intrigues.

At first, as we have already shown, this policy was largely successful. Guinea's dependence on the Soviet bloc increased visibly and Soviet confidence grew to such an extent that in Soviet publicity Guinea was already regarded as a 'People's Democracy'.[11] In other words, in Soviet eyes Guinea had already reached the penultimate stage before the final transition to a fully developed socialist State. The award of the Lenin Prize of 1961 to Sékou Touré was therefore not surprising and it was followed by an invitation to the PDG to send a delegation to the Twenty-second Congress of the Communist Party of the Soviet Union—an honour shared by the totalitarian parties of Ghana and Mali. This congress took place in October 1961 and the guests from Guinea were invariably referred to as Tovarishchi, or Comrades. On 23 October, Saifoulaye Diallo, Political Secretary of the PDG and President of the Parliament of Guinea, addressed the congress as follows:

'The historic Twenty-second Congress of the Communist Party of the Soviet Union is of importance not only to the Communist Party of the Soviet Union, to all socialist countries, to the socialist or communist parties of those countries that are still under the dominance of capitalism, and to the progressive and anti-imperialist parties of the colonial and dependent territories, but also to the newly independent and under-developed countries of Africa, where neo-colonialism—a new aspect of transoceanic imperialism—is doing everything possible to stifle the proper efforts of our peoples to win freedom, justice, democracy, peace and happiness. The *Parti Démocratique de Guinée* fights unwaveringly on the basis of positive neutralism for peace and democracy and against colonialism and imperialism . . . In this way our positive neutralism does not mean indifference to the problems of peace and war, colonialism and the true independence of the peoples . . . In what circumstances could the *Parti Démocratique de Guinée* adopt the same attitude towards those who exploit and torment Africa as it adopts towards those who help Africa to free herself? Those who fight in a common cause against the same evil and for the victory of the same ideals are naturally in the same camp. Therefore we declare that co-operation between the socialist countries and the young countries of Africa is a perfectly natural thing. It cannot be weakened by any blackmail on the part of neo-colonialism . . . The socialist countries and the communist and working-class parties lend wings of hope to the peoples of Africa fighting for their independence and for the development of their countries; and, indeed, to the whole world . . . They (the delegates to the Party Congress) would understand better than others what significance Africa, exploited, colonialized and humiliated, must rightly attach to the glorious Revolution of 1917; and what hopes are raised among the peoples of Africa by your successes in the political, economic and social as well as technological spheres . . . Revolutionary Africa knows that it can rely on the socialist countries.'[12]

This last assurance must have been given with tongue in cheek, because during the months before the congress met it had become very clear to Guinea that it could not, in fact, rely on the 'selfless socialist support' promised. After the original priming operations and the grandiloquent promises of economic assistance, the Soviet-bloc countries did less and less for Guinea. The impoverished country and its one-party State staggered from crisis to crisis, while the Soviets and their satellites deliberately marked time instead of helping—obviously on the assumption that a worsening of the economic crisis in Guinea, having burnt its bridges to the West, would soon pitch the country completely into the arms of communism.

Promised supplies of foodstuffs either did not arrive, or when they reached Conakry they were rotten and no longer fit for human consumption. By the time a shipload of grain from Soviet Army stocks was unloaded in Conakry it was fermenting. And as though to make a mockery of their poor dupes, the Soviets sent consignments of snow-ploughs and large supplies of lavatory seats. At the same time Soviet and Czech technicians in Guinea were unable to make the water- and power-supply systems work satisfactorily, and the technical personnel sent to extend and improve the organization of the airfield at Conakry did no better. After violent disputes they were ultimately withdrawn and replaced by Egyptian technicians. A large printing plant financed and built by the East German Government, and which was intended to provide a technological basis for the propaganda infiltration of West Africa, had to suspend some of its operations shortly after it opened in the summer of 1961, because of constructional defects. Other important projects due to be carried out in accordance with Soviet plans for utilizing the credits granted in 1959 were repeatedly delayed and postponed.

While these and other defects and failures of Soviet aid were making themselves painfully felt, the unfortunate country also became aware of the drawbacks attached to the other less tangible forms of communist support. The hoped-for stream of foodstuffs, consumer goods, factory equipment and machine-tools from the Soviet bloc did not materialize, but the unflagging stream of communist propaganda continued unabated. It became such a problem that the authorities felt compelled to intervene, though only very cautiously. But the delegations still came, the instructors, the 'friendship groups', and the numbers of films, pamphlets, books and newspapers continued to grow bigger. As a result of this growing ideological infiltration, which was tolerated, if not actually encouraged, by the authorities, it is not surprising that an increasing number of party officials, particularly the younger men and youth offlcials, adopted the ideas pumped out from behind the Iron Curtain and that in consequence they decided optimistically that the acute difficulties affecting their country were 'natural crises of growth', brought about by the continued existence of 'class contradictions'—a situation aggravated, they decided, by a lack of ideological firmness on the part of the government. Obviously, if this were true, no improvement could be hoped for until the government abandoned its half-hearted attitude towards scientific socialism and went over whole-heartedly to orthodox socialism.

The trial which ended on 24 November 1961 with the conviction of five leading officials of the Teachers' Union of Guinea revealed the influence of these ideas. It also served as a signal for certain radical groups to launch a political offensive. In the capital and in a number of other towns throughout the country, students and young trade unionists marched through the streets demonstrating against the government. At first the slogans were confined to demands for the release of the convicted teachers, but before long they turned into general demands for socialism and communism. The government, which was being accused of indecisiveness, certainly reacted swiftly and vigorously to this offensive. It closed down all the schools and arrested a large number of the ringleaders, but two weeks passed before a sensational statement was made. Issued on 11 December 1961, it attributed the whole affair to 'a communist-inspired conspiracy'.[13] These were startling words for the Guinean public to hear. Meanwhile, Diallo Alpha, a Minister of State, was sent to Moscow with a special message from Sékou Touré. Received by Khrushchev and Gromyko on 18 December, he firmly demanded no less than the recall of the Soviet Ambassador to Guinea, the highly-prized Solod. Mr Khrushchev recalled him at once.

What had Solod done to give such offence? Not surpringly, the Soviet Government had nothing to say about this and the Government of Guinea only made vague statements. In fact, Radio Conakry repeated the Moscow story, according to which Solod was recalled in order to take up 'another important post'. The only occasions on which the disagreeable word 'expulsion' was mentioned were during two speeches made by Sékou Touré in Susu, the native tongue. The reason given then was that the ambassador had interfered in the internal affairs of Guinea and his embassy had co-operated with the conspirators.[14]

But this charge was so general that it came to be widely assumed that there was no real evidence against Solod and that, in all probability, he had been made a scapegoat for the attitude of the Soviet Government towards Guinea and that he had been sacrificed to appease the Government of Guinea, which was understandably irritated by the many breakdowns, delays and postponements in the economic and credit agreements. According to information available in Conakry, Touré had made demarches on several occasions in the second half of 1961, and Solod is said to have lacked diplomatic finesse on these occasions, insisting bluntly that the responsibility for the delays and misunderstandings lay with the Government of Guinea and not with the Soviet Union. According to other reports, Sékou Touré had for several months refused to receive Solod, who finally expressed his annoyance in blunt, offensive terms. He is also alleged to have said that the trouble was that Guineans 'didn't want to work, and that they were ruining good Soviet equipment', and that in general it was difficult to take them seriously.[15]

The reaction of the Soviet Government to the Solod affair is an indication of the dismay it caused. If a Western State had dared to bundle out a Soviet Ambassador in this fashion, there is no doubt that the Soviet Government would have reacted in a no less dramatic fashion, but in the Solod affair Moscow adopted a policy of appeasement. Solod's expulsion was swallowed with as good a grace as possible and the Soviet Vice-Premier, Anastas Mikoyan, was sent off post-haste to Guinea. But when he arrived in Conakry his reception was anything but friendly, and Sékou Touré kept Mr Mikoyan kicking his heels in waiting-rooms on several occasions.[16] Mikoyan tried desperately to persuade the Government of Guinea that it was all a misunderstanding. At the opening of a Soviet exhibition in the capital he made the only public speech of his visit, though he was in Guinea for almost a week, from 5 to 10 January. He made a particular point of stressing that 'Soviet policy respects the sovereignty and independence of all peoples and does not interfere in their internal affairs', after which he turned with relief to the old story and put all the blame on the imperialists who had, it appeared, 'employed all sorts of devices . . . to sow doubts . . . on the various fields of our co-operation'. He concluded by assuring his hearers that 'our friendship is solidly based on equality and non-interference'.[17] But Touré was not so easily appeased and replied coldly and pointedly that other nations should not try to export revolutions to his country. He also told Mikoyan bluntly that Guinea would not tolerate interference in its internal affairs, even from countries lending it economic aid.[18]

Did this mean that communist hopes for a triumph in Guinea were illusory? Did it perhaps mean that this young West African State might turn towards the West? Despite the extraordinary events which provoked this question, the latter was too much to hope for. It is significant that in his statement of 11 December 1961, Touré included 'elements in Paris and Dakar' in the 'anti-Guinea conspiracy' in his attack, and declared that the French Mission in Conakry had played the role of a 'go-between' in what he described as an attempted *putsch*. There is, as the last years show, little room for much optimism in the West; even after this shake-up there are still prominent supporters of an orthodox socialist policy in the leading circles of the party and government and nothing has been done to get rid of them or to curb their political activities. Furthermore, during 1962 and 1963 both Guinea and the Soviet Union made some efforts to restore friendly relations, particularly in the economic field. It is also interesting to note that the relatively good relations between Guinea and the satellites survived the critical period at the end of 1961 and the beginning of 1962. When a Bulgarian government delegation arrived in Guinea in March 1962, Sékou Touré spoke of 'our joint socialist ideals'.[19] Finally, relations between Guinea and Mao's China (which we shall deal with later in connection with China's African policy) improved during this period. In fact, during conversations the author had with a number of politicians in Guinea, it was even suggested that the disputes in the communist world, and in particular the clash between the Soviet Union and Mao's China, had an important influence on the conflict between Guinea and the Soviet Union, and it is reported that in the period immediately preceding the Twenty-second Congress of the Communist Party of the Soviet Union, the PDG (Guinea's totalitarian party) made several attempts to interfere in the discussion in favour of the Chinese and Albanian standpoint. It is also reported to have been opposed to the Soviet policy of granting credits to non-socialist African States, to have expressed disapproval of the disarmament policy of the Soviet Union and to have declared itself in favour of the Chinese policy of supporting all revolutionary groups in African territories which are still in colonial hands. The ambiguous Soviet attitudes over the Cameroons rebellion, the Gizenga affair and the Angolan question, are said to have led to further disillusionment in Conakry over Soviet policy in the under-developed countries.

From any standpoint, the crisis in relations between Moscow and Conakry is significant. It clearly indicates two things:

1. Soviet African policy is by no means as successful as was hoped. In fact it is, to an astonishing extent, failing to exploit the very real chance for communism that exists in Africa; in particular it has failed to take immediate advantage of the situation in a country where, psychologically, conditions were unquestionably favourable. Confused by the great diversity and complexity of conditions in Africa and by the necessity of adopting different tactics towards each of the many groups, parties and régimes to be dealt with, hampered by the multifarious defects inherent in an over-centralized foreign trade structure, and relatively unpractised in the art of exploiting economic aid for the under-developed countries, Soviet African policy has persistently made the kind of blunders that have usually been ascribed exclusively to the legendary 'ugly Americans'.

2. Left-wing African socialism, even of Sékou Touré's variety, while ready and willing to co-operate with Marxist-Leninists and anxious to be recognized by the international communist movement as an equal partner, still has many reservations. These are due partly to nationalist fervour and partly to the personal vanity of its leaders (particularly Touré) who, like Tito, are keenly conscious that they too have accomplished something on their own. Like Yugoslav

Titoism, Guinean socialism is very proud of having won independence by its own efforts and of having created the organizational basis for its victory. Of course a parallel between Tito and Touré must not be pushed too far, but nevertheless it is quite clear that Yugoslavia and Guinea have certain things in common. And as in the case of Yugoslavia it is quite certain that there will be many ups and downs and unexpected changes before the position of Guinea becomes quite clear.

NOTES

1 Cyclostyled Minutes of the Fifth National Congress of the *Parti Démocratique de Guinée* (PDG), 14–17 September 1959.

2 Ibid.

3 See, for instance, the cyclostyled Minutes of the Ninth National Congress of the *Parti Démocratique de Guinée*, September 1963.

4 *Zemedelske Noviny* (Prague), 11 April 1959.

5 United Press International, 9 October 1960.

6 At a Press conference in Leopoldville, attended by the author.

7 Radio Moscow, English-language broadcast for Africa, 23 September 1960.

8 Radio Conakry broadcast, 14 April 1961.

9 CRU (London), 20 October 1955.

10 Quoted in Jean and Simone Lacouture, *L'Egypte au Mouvement* (Paris, 1956), p. 214.

11 A. Arzumanyan, in *Pravda*, 17 December 1961.

12 Report in *Pravda*, 26 October 1961.

13 Radio Conakry broadcast, 11 December 1961.

14 Information given in a private report to the author.

15 Reported in *Le Soir* (Paris), 26 October 1961.

16 Reported in the *New York Herald Tribune* (Paris ed.), 19 January 1962.

17 Radio Conakry broadcasts, 6 and 10 January 1962.

18 Reported in the *New York Herald Tribune* (Paris ed.), 19 January 1962.

19 Radio Conakry broadcast, 23 March 1962.

Chapter IX

IN SEARCH OF PROSELYTES: GHANA AND MALI

SOME observers have suggested, especially after the Soviet-Guinean crisis, that Ghana or Mali might ultimately play the role which Russia originally had in mind for Guinea, i.e. the role of a Soviet bridgehead distribution-centre for agitation and propaganda and of a base for infiltration in West Africa. Taking the long view, such fears, though they may seem exaggerated at the moment, are by no means without foundation. This somewhat pessimistic view is based, particularly where Ghana is concerned, not so much on the magnitude of communist successes so far achieved as on the internal ideological and constitutional crises.

The most surprising and alarming thing about Ghana is the extraordinary speed with which the old Gold Coast Colony (called by the name of the historic Ghana Empire since 7 March 1957) has been moving away from its original programme and the initial moderation of its leadership. The small group that made up the national élite of Ghana has suffered a steady process of erosion and disintegration, and in consequence the most intelligent and liberal personalities have gradually disappeared; they are now, as The *Guardian* stated in February 1964, 'in prison, in exile or muttering gloomily and doing nothing'.[1] The national life of the country also suffers: there is widespread and alarming corruption among members of the upper strata; State-run business and commerce is entangled in bureaucratic red tape; there is no effective opposition and such rival groups as existed originally, including the trade unions and the youth and women's associations have been swallowed up by the Convention People's Party (CPP). All healthy public opinion has been suppressed and individual, regional, tribal and ethnic differences are being flattened out.

These disturbing features unfortunately coincide with the increasing self-assertion and vanity of Kwame Nkrumah, the man who secured Ghana's independence from the British and has since been in control of the fate of its 6,300,000 people. The rather modest and likable young man who wrote the autobiography published in 1956 has since become 'Osagyefo' (which means Great Man, Redeemer, or All-powerful *Führer*), His Highness the President, 'Kukurundi' or Brave Hero, 'Kasapreko', He who has the Last Word, 'Nufeno' or Immortal Ruler over Life and Death, to quote a few of the obsequious titles showered upon him.

Wherever one goes in Ghana it is impossible to get away from his name—as it was with that of Stalin in the Soviet Union in the old days. There are Kwame Nkrumah roads, streets and avenues, Kwame Nkrumah training centres, schools and institutions—and everywhere there are his statues and pictures, many of them larger than life. True believers throughout the country learn the litanies of Nkrumahism by heart. For example:

> 'I believe in Kwame Nkrumah, the Creator of Ghana, the Founder and Benefactor of Ghana's schools and colleges; I believe in the revolutionary Convention People's Party, his imperishable organization and our salvation, granted to us by the inspiration of History, born of the masses, humbled, persecuted and repressed with harsh laws until they arose from their despair in the Third Month . . .'[2]

The religious parallel is obvious and as though to dissipate any lingering doubts Nkrumah is lauded in the nationalist Press and party publications and in the government as 'Saviour', 'Messiah' and 'Transfigurer'. Objections by the Christian Churches to the use of such terms were rejected as hypocrisy and phrases were picked from the Oxford English Dictionary to show that, 'despite the arrogant clerical claim for a monopoly of sacred concepts', it is right and proper to praise Kwame Nkrumah as the 'Re-born' and the 'Saviour'.[3] The Young Pioneers of the Convention People's Party even pester visitors to buy picture postcards showing the President of the West African Republic of Ghana standing side by side with Jesus Christ.

This personality cult reached a first peak in the spring of 1960. Up to that time Ghana was still a member of the British Commonwealth of Nations under the Queen of Great Britain. This was, of course, only a matter of form, but Nkrumah and his followers attached great importance to formalities. They therefore staged a referendum to decide whether Ghana should continue to remain under the British Crown or adopt a new status in the British Commonwealth of Nations as a republic. The nominee for President of Ghana was, of course, Kwame Nkrumah.

There was not the slightest doubt about the outcome of this referendum, although the oppositional United Party did put up Doctor J. B. Danquah, the grand old man of Ghanaian politics, as a rival candidate. But just as it organizes everything else in Ghana, Nkrumah's State party, the Convention People's Party, organized the referendum, and did so very painstakingly and systematically. For weeks before the great day the population was steam-rollered into meetings, processions and mass demonstrations; special propaganda commandos of party members and youths flooded the countryside to make certain that every inhabitant of even the most remote villages was suitably housed and also to ensure that the local chiefs and headmen accepted the patronage of the campaign for Nkrumah in their localities. Leaflets bearing the picture of the 'Messiah' were distributed all over the country and anyone suspected of opposition to the campaign was persecuted with the African equivalent of 'rough music', personal insults, and baseless accusations in order to shame them in the eyes of their fellows. 'Who is it that in these great days does not stand behind our Government and our powerful Party, to which we owe everything, and behind our leader and protector Kwame Nkrumah? If there be such a one who stands aside, he can only be a traitor—a bought tool of Imperialism!'[4] But the Convention People's Party organizers did not rely exclusively on these methods; they announced that free food and drinks would be provided at meetings, adding that if anyone of goodwill were sick 'the gifts of the Saviour' would be brought to his bedside. Just before the referendum the government announced that 'in order to ensure a tranquil poll' voting would not take place simultaneously throughout the country, but with several days' pause between three separate voting areas. The idea behind this arrangement was obviously to give the CPP an opportunity of clinching the final victory by concentrating all its forces on each voting area in turn and, to be doubly certain, all opposition meetings were prohibited in order not to 'endanger public order and security'. Another reason advanced for this suppression of all opposition was that otherwise 'the lives of members of the opposition would be endangered'. The result was that on the days fixed for the polling only Nkrumah's men were on the streets, even in places known to be anti-Nkrumah, such as the stronghold of the opposition Ashanti tribe. Cars and lorries plastered with 'Yes' placards and with pictures of Nkrumah drove from village to village, their loudspeakers alternately cajoling and threatening and, as prophesied, the culmination of the campaign became 'a triumphal vote even before the poll'.

Similar methods of intimidation, cajoling and manipulation were used and even improved four years later, when a second referendum asked the Ghanaians to vote for a one-party State—at a time when only one party existed anyway in Ghana—Nkrumah's Convention People's Party. Again, the people voted as they were forced to vote; according to official figures released in Accra, over 2,500,000 people voted in support of one-party government; less than three thousand voted against it. *The Economist* commented on this result:

'President Nkrumah's one-man-one-vote-one-party State has been legitimized . . . Whom does the Osagyefo think he is fooling? Not the West: it has learned what to think about results like that. Not the East: it knows too well how such results are obtained. Not those of Ghana's people who oppose the régime: they know best of all why they felt it the better part of valour to acquiesce. Surely the answer is not Dr Nkrumah himself? A more hard-headed answer is probably this: in spite of Ghana's admirable economic, educational and technical progress since independence in 1957, the majority of the people have been left untouched by what can only be called the European mode of life. Dr Nkrumah, it ncw seems, intends to clutch his people by the lapels (or the kente cloths) and shake them once again, in the hope that they will sweat to create black Africa's first truly modern society in Ghana. This aim cannot be carped at: it is what all under-developed countries want. But the method—driving, deceiving, and regimenting the people—might turn out to be self-defeating.'[5]

But did the voters really have any idea of what was at stake—in 1960 as well as in 1964? The simple fact is that the great majority of the people of Ghana are neither able nor willing to take part in a rational political discussion, and in consequence the objections of the opposition to Nkrumah's proposed constitutional changes in 1960 and in 1964 came to nothing, for want of an audience capable of understanding them. The urban proletariat, the timber workers, plantation workers, fishermen and cattle drovers of the interior did not care whether according to the constitution of 1960 the President is at the same time the Prime Minister and has the power to veto any legislation of which he disapproves, or whether, if he thinks fit, he has power to prorogue parliament altogether, to quash any verdict of the Supreme Court of Ghana[6] and even to appoint its judges. For most Ghanaians Accra is so far away it might as well be on the moon, and in any case, had things not always been done that way in Accra and not merely since the CPP came to power?

As Peter Preston reported in The *Guardian* in February 1964:

'The men in the street selling gold watches, hairpins, and English chewing-gum don't care much about what happens in Flagstaff House . . . As one Ghanaian admitted: "We don't think much about politics really, as long as there is food and sunshine!" Few had much time for the delirious cant of the party Press. Dr Nkrumah's paternalistic image was tarnished still further by the pointlessness and stench of it all; only in the remoter regions, where new schools and water supplies are minor miracles, is his lustre undiminished.'[7]

The April 1960 referendum was synonymous with the complete emasculation of the people of Ghana. The 1964 referendum meant the complete emasculation of the last remnants of political individuality and opposition.

One of the few former leaders of the United Party who still dared to talk openly to foreigners told me bluntly in 1960:

'At the moment Ghana is ruled by fascism. Tomorrow it may be communism; and it will certainly be communism when Nkrumah leaves the stage—by natural causes or otherwise—because the left-wing leaders in the government camp are even worse than he is. They already have control of all the most important posts in the country. Nkrumah calls himself an "undogmatic Marxist," but the others—make no mistake about it—are orthodox Marxists.'[8]

By now this man is a detainee, his party is banned and the treatment meted out for the opposition by the leaders of the CPP has certainly demonstrated a thoroughly fascist outlook. Or should we rather say that the communist training of a number of its leading officials has borne fruit? Their methods are summed up in the Act which has become so well known today, the Preventive Detention Act, a symbol of repression in Ghana. This Act allows the authorities to take anyone into 'preventive custody' under mere suspicion of any act likely 'to endanger the security or authority of the State', or any 'predatory act', or any 'unworthy and criminal conduct'. The vague terminology gives the government a completely free hand to use the Act at any time to intimidate or hamstring active or potential opponents.

For a long time the government and its supporters tried to play down the implications of the Preventive Detention Act, but its operations were finally publicly admitted in an article published on 25 April 1960, by the official *Ghanaian Times*, which recorded that from the end of October 1958 no less than forty-nine leaders of the opposition, including the whole urban élite of the United Party, had been arrested and thrown into detention centres. In December 1960 the government arrested and imprisoned 118 people. According to information given by the leader of the United Party, Joseph Appiah, who was among those arrested, there were at least eighty members and officials of his party under arrest who, according to the provisions of the Preventive Detention Act, can be held in prison without trial for five years.[9] That Appiah was left at liberty for so long was perhaps due to the fact that he is the husband of the daughter of the late Sir Stafford Cripps, former Labour Chancellor of the Exchequer in Great Britain, and it was not possible to spirit him away without international public opinion showing some interest in his fate. However, in October 1960 Nkrumah abandoned these reservations and Appiah was arrested, together with forty-eight other members of the opposition, including J. B. Danquah. With this blow, the legal opposition (the United Party) ceased its *de facto* existence.[10] The *coup de grâce* was delivered a little later: on 13 November 1961 the parliamentary leader of the United Party, Diedjo Dombo, courageously informed the Press that within the past few days many hundreds of Nkrumah's opponents had been arrested, including 250 people in Kumasi, where the prisons were so overcrowded that the prisoners were unable to lie down at night. Among those arrested in this new wave of persecution were certain opposition elements within the Convention People's Party itself. A number of prospective victims escaped arrest by fleeing from the country. Meanwhile another decree lengthened the period during which a prisoner may be held without trial to twenty years. Among those lucky enough to make their escape in the spring of 1962 was Nkrumah's old confidant, K. A. Gbedemah, whose last post was that of Finance Minister. According to official calculations there were already, by the autumn of 1961, no fewer than 6,000 fugitives from Ghana in the neighbouring States of Togo and the Ivory Coast Republic.[11] In October 1961 a further law was passed introducing the crime of *lèse-majesté* for the person of Nkrumah and on 23 December 1961 the process was rounded off by a new State Security Law. The Nkrumah régime thus guarded itself by every possible legal device against any contingencies that might threaten to unseat it.

Despite this, there are still optimists in Ghana who have not altogether given up hope of a better future. They feel that the youth and the intelligentsia may still save Ghana and it is true that nowhere else in Africa are young people so politically wideawake and democratic in outlook as in Ghana. There is a sharp opposition at the University of Ghana in Legon, which is on the outskirts of Accra, and in the many colleges in the interior and even in the Ministry of Information and Education. The atmosphere around Nkrumah, the blatant political nepotism and patronage, the corruption in leading circles and the attempt to enforce complete political conformism are regarded with suspicion, disappointment and anger by many young intellectuals. The repressive actions taken by Nkrumah early in 1964 led to startling scenes of violence which caused considerable damage. Large crowds taken out to the university in CPP buses demonstrated against the students, whom they called 'saboteur intellectuals'. The students had earlier protested at the forced interruption of their studies for a seventeen-day period during the January 1964 referendum, and were discontented by the summary expulsion of six of their Western lecturers. Moreover, at a congress of the National Union of Ghana Students at Legon, resolutions were passed criticizing the attack on the judiciary, Sir Arku Korsah's dismissal, and 'creeping racial discrimination' against African students in Eastern Europe.[12] But Nkrumah's Convention People's Party had the upper hand. The *Ghanaian Times* published a formal warning that 'other nations have had to adopt sterner action . . . in order to obtain a reorientation of the élite',[13] and as most students are living on government grants, the intimidations of the CPP were not without effect. 'In the long run anyone in Ghana who tries to oppose Nkrumah is in a hopeless position,' a missionary told me in September 1964.

'Such a man is psychologically isolated, put under systematic pressure, and forced to confess his sins. If he does, and only then, he is allowed back into the community again. It must be remembered that these young intellectuals object mainly to Nkrumah's domestic policy; the opposition youth does not disapprove of his Pan-Africanism and certainly shares his favourable attitude towards the Soviet bloc.'

Extreme left-wing or radical socialism exercises a very strong attraction for the young intellectual élite of Ghana. Many discussions with students in Ghana have shown me that while they uncompromisingly reject colonialism—which they associate with the West—they regard socialism as a 'sensible solution' and accept it as a suitable 'third path' for Africa. At the same time their knowledge of communism and their ideas about it are usually based on the reading of one or two Marxist–Leninist books, reinforced by an uncritical acceptance of communist propaganda.

Broadcasts from Moscow and Peking can be quite well received along the whole of the West African coast and the Soviet Embassy in Accra, with its large staff, does its utmost to supplement these broadcasts with printed communist propaganda illustrating the happy life under socialism. In addition, the newspapers of the CPP are very susceptible to advertising pressure and the Soviet Embassy and representatives of other Soviet-bloc countries frequently pay for whole pages of the *Ghanaian Times*, the *Daily Graphic* and the *Evening News* in order to publish propaganda articles for the Ghanaian reader.

However it would be wrong to dismiss this paid propaganda as due exclusively to the corruptibility of newspapers, editors and advertising departments. The fact is that all means of influencing public opinion in Ghana are closely controlled by the government and the CPP and therefore such things could not happen without the toleration, if not encouragement, by official quarters. This is particularly true of radio broadcasts and these facilities are liberally placed at the disposal of Soviet representatives and of visitors from the Soviet bloc. As official exchanges of cultural groups, sports delegations, and scientific parties between Ghana and Eastern Europe are steadily growing there is nearly always some industrial or cultural exhibition in progress. It is quite clear that these matters are not arranged merely between minor communist officials and their Ghanaian counterparts, but are decided at government level with the blessing of the highest authorities in Ghana.

This may seem surprising because in the first phase of Ghana's independence it had not been greatly helped by the countries of the Soviet bloc. In accordance with rigid Stalinist doctrine, Nkrumah was automatically regarded as 'a marionette of neo-colonialism', quaintly abused as 'a representative of the compradore bourgeoisie' and considered unworthy of support or co-operation.[14] A change came about partly as a result of changes in Khrushchev's policy and partly as a result of the policy Nkrumah began to pursue both at home and abroad.

The essentials of Nkrumah's policy are Pan-Africanism and 'positive neutrality', the neutrality being reserved for the West and the positive side for the East. Nkrumah's relationship with the Soviet bloc has improved primarily because Pan-Africanism is now vigorously supported by Moscow, though (as we shall show elsewhere) Moscow was at first very cautious about this. However, Soviet Russia has now come to recognize that the Pan-African policy initiated in Accra is an excellent means of influencing African circles.

The dream of Pan-Africanism is older than the present clamour by African nationalists for independence. Like many similar movements it grew out of educational and cultural organizations, which were formed in London, Paris, and the United States in the early twenties, by African and American Negro students and writers. Although during his stay in London Nkrumah was for a time the secretary of an all-African students' group, he did not have much contact with these early idealistic endeavours.[15] His form of Pan-

Africanism is more elementary and political, and to some of his opponents and critics it appears to be nothing more than a cloak for egocentric dreams of African power.

So far very little has been done to put Nkrumah's political ideas into practice. In recent years the ostensible aim of Pan-Africanism—the establishment of an All-African Federation of States, or even of a United States of Africa—has not moved nearer to realization. The largest African State, Nigeria, without which there can be no united Africa, has firmly rejected the plans formulated in Accra. Even Ghana's immediate neighbours, Togo and the Ivory Coast Republic, are not enamoured of the idea of union with Kwame Nkrumah's State—particularly as Ghana has lodged territorial claims against both and, since 1957, there has been constant tension between Togo and Ghana over the problem of uniting the Ewe tribe. The tension was increased when Accra chose the very moment of Togo's declaration of independence to reveal its annexationist tendencies.

The only step towards the far-reaching ideal was the union with Guinea which Nkrumah brought about on 23 November 1958. The presidents of both countries made the following joint declaration:

> 'Inspired by the example of the thirteen American colonies that ultimately led to the formation of the United States of America, inspired by the efforts of the peoples of Europe, Asia and the Near East to come together on a rational basis, and, finally, inspired by the declaration of the Conference of Accra on African personality, we agree . . . that our two States shall form the core of the United States of West Africa.'[16]

This declaration has remained purely rhetorical, and an agreement signed by Nkrumah and Sékou Touré on 1 May 1959 materially restricted its scope. This second agreement did no more than refer to a 'co-ordination' of political, economic, military, and diplomatic measures. The union was to have a common anthem, a common flag and a common motto (Independence and Unity) but it was to have no supranational authority.[17]

Although no practical steps towards closer association were taken, both countries maintained the fiction of their 'union'. When the Sudan–Senegal Federation broke up in August 1960, both Conakry and Accra put out feelers in the hope of winning the left-wing, pro-Marxist politicians of Bamako (the former French Sudan is now known as Mali) for the idea of union. Nkrumah welcomed the first meeting with Modibo Keita of Mali, which took place in Bamako in November 1960, with the same exaggerated optimism which he had shown concerning his alliance with Touré two years previously. On his return he declared that their discussions had brought nearer the day when Mali and Ghana would have a 'common parliament'—the start of a new Pan-African Federation.

In fact the politicians of Bamako were more interested in Conakry than in distant Accra. Traditional attachments exist between Mali and Guinea, dating from the days of the *Rassemblement Démocratique Africain*, the first big supranational party in West Africa. (This organization sailed in the wake of communism until it was broken up by the defection of the Ivory Coast leader, Houphouet-Boigny.) In order not to be left out, Nkrumah immediately changed his ground: instead of a united Ghana-Mali he now urged a revival of the alliance with Conakry and the extension of the old union by the establishment of an Accra-Conakry-Bamako axis. In December 1960 the three national leaders met in Conakry and signed a declaration in favour of 'closely co-ordinating' their policies. Expressions like 'co-ordination' still meant no more than the fact that each party would be willing to surrender national sovereignty in order to establish a United States of West Africa, and this was not saying a great deal. In reality, their solidarity was already then being undermined by the jealousies and the mutual mistrust of the three leading men of the 'Union'.

To a certain extent this was also true of the relations of the Casablanca States, Egypt, Algeria, Morocco, Guinea, Mali and Ghana, whose governments were all associated. This union, established in Casablanca in January 1961, soon gave rise to the well-founded suspicion that it had been established chiefly in order to further the personal power aspirations of the various leaders. From the start both Nasser and Sékou Touré—with Nkrumah, who was not going to be outdone—did their utmost to put their own stamp on the Casablanca group and to exploit the propagandist declarations of the various sessions in their own national and Pan-African interests. Just how seriously the participants took their obligations could be seen from the obvious inconsistency between the voluble anti-Israeli declarations (forced through by Nasser) and the far-reaching economic co-operation between Israel and both Ghana and Mali. The oft-repeated announcement about their intention of forming a joint military command was also to be regarded as primarily propagandist, even though at its meeting in June 1961 the Casablanca group did adopt 'a definitive decision' to establish such a supreme command in Accra.

The unbridgeable gulf between the idea and the reality of a United States of Africa was soon recognized in Accra, but Nkrumah did not allow this to prevent him from taking advantage of the wave of nationalist enthusiasm throughout Africa. To increase Ghana's prestige, Nkrumah played yet another card: Accra was to be turned into a centre for all so-called liberation movements and all nationalist and anti-colonial forces throughout the African continent just as Cairo had been a centre for the Arab world until the trouble with Tunis and Baghdad, and was again striving to become such a centre.

How keen Nkrumah was on this can be seen from his invitation to Félix-Roland Moumié, exiled President of the *Union des Populations du Cameroun* (UPC), at the end of 1957, to move his headquarters from Cairo to Accra where he would be better placed to direct and organize the partisan war in the Cameroons. At that time Moumié was already receiving financial and 'technical' assistance from the Soviet bloc. Subsequently—first from Accra, then from Conakry—he broadcast spirited appeals to his guerilla units. It was also Moumié who persuaded the Government of Ghana of the advantage of establishing close relations with the Chinese People's Republic, which had been the chief source of support for the rebels in the latter phase of the civil war in the Cameroons. The successors of Moumié still have their headquarters in Accra, where they are praising Chinese revolutionary propaganda as well as Ghana's support for their 'anti-imperialist struggle'.[18]

Gradually more and more of the exiled extreme left-wing leaders of the African liberation movements in the Portuguese territories, East Africa, and some of the West and Central African Republics, had established their main headquarters in Accra, where, encouraged and financially supported by Nkrumah, they represented the hard core of the two organizations which had intensified the anti-colonial struggle in recent years: the Afro-Asian Solidarity Conference, which is definitely under communist leadership, and the All-African

People's Conference, whose leadership was controlled by Nkrumah, Touré and Nasser. For various reasons, the Solidarity Council, the executive of the Afro-Asian Solidarity Conference, stayed in Cairo, but the executive of the All-African People's Conference established itself in Accra and it was here, in December 1958, that the First All-African People's Conference took place and adopted a resolution condemning NATO and its 'economic auxiliary', the Organization for European Economic Co-operation (OEEC) and the European Common Market, as manifestations of 'military and economic colonialism'. Naturally no reference was made to the neo-colonialist intrigues and operations of the Soviet bloc.

It was during this conference that a friendship began which was soon to have a disastrous effect on developments in Africa—the friendship between Nkrumah and Patrice Lumumba, the nationalist Congo leader, who had founded his *Mouvement National Congolais* two months previously and was eagerly casting around abroad for advice and assistance. Nkrumah found a willing pupil for his Pan-African ideas in Lumumba, who assured him at once that as soon as he was head of an independent Congolese State, he would forthwith institute discussions with 'the already existing Union of West African States [Ghana and Guinea] in order to bring about a speedy unification of the three countries and thus lay the basis for a permanent edifice of the All-African State'. Even more sinister was the fact that Nkrumah confirmed and encouraged his Congolese pupil in the conviction that the way to power in the final phase of the struggle for liberation must necessarily be through spectacular, demonstrative actions. He assured Lumumba of 'every conceivable moral and practical support' when the time came for action.

It was not long before Lumumba was badly in need of the promised support. In January 1959—only a few weeks after his meeting with Nkrumah—a revolt broke out in Leopoldville, and in the following months, while independence for the Congo was drawing near, Lumumba had to ward off the attacks of numerous domestic opponents who resisted the ideas that he, the leader of the *Mouvement National Congolais*, had borrowed from Nkrumah—in particular, the idea that the coming, independent Congo State must be strictly centralist (along Ghanaian lines). Immediately prior to the declaration of independence, Nkrumah persuaded Lumumba that, in order to seize power and get his centralized State over its first hurdle, he must co-operate with his political opponent, Kasavubu, the 'king' of the Bakongo—although, of course, with the ulterior motive of getting rid of the awkward ruler of the Lower Congo at a later, more convenient stage. This, in any case, was the plan revealed in documents found at the time of Lumumba's arrest and made public by the Congolese military commander, Joseph Mobutu.[19]

In the spring of 1960 Nkrumah had reacted with cautious reserve to a Soviet offer of credits, but before long his attitude changed. In August 1960 a delegation from Accra travelled to the Soviet Union and an agreement was signed in Moscow for a 'far-reaching exchange' of scientific experience and of cultural delegations. In addition, the Soviet Union agreed to grant the West African State long-term credits to the tune of 160 million roubles. This was to finance the 'fraternal assistance' the Soviet Union proposed to give Ghana to help it exploit its natural resources, develop its industry, build hydraulic power stations and train technicians. The Soviet Union agreed to accept cocoa beans, coffee, rubber and fruit from Ghana in return.[20]

Towards the end of 1960 Nkrumah announced that over the next few years Ghana would send 3,000 students to the countries of the Soviet bloc for specialist training—a number far greater than in any previous agreements of this kind between Russia and African and Asian countries. More serious were the reports, which cropped up regularly from the middle of 1961, that Ghana intended to have the greater part of its officers and NCOs trained at Soviet military academies. The belief that there was to be close military co-operation between Ghana and the Eastern European countries was underlined, towards the end of June 1962, by the arrival of a Soviet military delegation in Accra. It was announced that the visit of the delegation, led by General Komarov, deputy-commander of Soviet land forces, was in return for the visit of Ghanaian military leaders to the Soviet Union; in fact, these military leaders had already made frequent visits to Eastern Europe, in particular in the spring of 1962.[21]

This close contact—particularly the military co-operation—was the result of talks between Nkrumah and representatives of the Soviet Government during his visits to the Soviet Union in July and September 1961. Nkrumah's first visit extended to other countries of the Soviet bloc as well and lasted several weeks, during which time he made dozens of pro-Soviet declarations in Moscow, Prague, East Berlin, Budapest and Bucharest. In a speech delivered at a banquet in his honour at the Kremlin on 11 July 1961 Nkrumah said that the future of Ghana was 'closely connected with the future of the Soviet Union'. After praising Lenin he concluded by saying: 'The new ideas of your country in this new era will, I am convinced, defeat the forces of reaction.'[22]

In East Berlin (which Nkrumah was the first representative of an African government to visit) and in Sofia and Budapest, the Ghanaian leader expressed approval of Soviet intentions towards Germany, stressing in particular the need for a peace treaty with 'the two German States' as set out in the proposals of the Soviet Government of 10 January 1959.[23]

Nkrumah's attitude at the Belgrade Conference of uncommitted nations, in September 1961, was no less clear. Of all the statesmen present he was the one who most staunchly supported the policy of the Soviet Government towards Germany and the one who, in the private sessions, called most vigorously for a joint recognition of the East German régime and the establishment of diplomatic relationships with its government.[24]

This attitude was further underlined during Nkrumah's subsequent visit to the Soviet Union and during the visit of Anastas Mikoyan to Accra in 1962. According to the reports of communist journalists, 'Ghanaian-Soviet harmony' was given 'overwhelming expression' during visits by the Soviet delegation to the house of the President of the Executive Bureau of the Convention People's Party and to the headquarters of the Ghanaian Trade-Union Federation. Everywhere the Soviet guests were greeted with the strains of the 'International'. The Secretary of the CPP declared: 'Nkrumah says that the aim of our party is socialism; and this is what binds us together.'[25] To clinch matters, Ghanaian leaders pointed out that like the ruling parties of Cuba, Guinea, and Mali, the CPP of Ghana had been treated as an equal at the Twenty-second Congress of the Communist Party of the Soviet Union, while its representatives had been made to feel 'the co-operation and friendship' that marked the relationship between the Communist Party of the Soviet Union and the CPP.[26]

This harmony between Soviet communism and Ghanaian socialism, though neither complete nor without friction, naturally began to influence the day-to-day policy of Ghana, both at home and abroad. The language used by the leaders of Ghana was gradually becoming identical with communist phraseology. Eric Mettler, who as the London correspondent of the *Neue Zürcher Zeitung* has visited Ghana on several occasions, was quite right when he pointed out in December 1961:

'The new men who now wield influence with Nkrumah, the men who have been put in to replace his old comrades since he returned from his visits to the countries of the Soviet bloc [in 1961], talk in a pseudo-Marxist jargon, but they have digested the new ideas no better than they had previously assimilated the libertarian ideas of the West. They are impelled by an almost obsessive urge to shake off "Western tutelage".'

But Mettler exaggerated the practical effects of the American decision to finance the building of the Volta dam. The offer of American aid did not hamper pro-Soviet developments in Ghana. For example, the mere announcement of any proposed aid from the communist Powers was enough to send the controlled Press and Radio of Ghana into ecstasies of admiration and gratitude, but the late President Kennedy's decision to finance the Volta project with American dollars was coldly received and cynically denigrated. The *Evening News* of Accra, the official organ of the CPP, had only one thing to say about Kennedy's decision: 'Dollar Boss! Better late than never'—After which it immediately went on to publish a detailed report 'exposing the hostile policy of the United States' over the question of Red China's membership of the United Nations. The text of this article, incidentally, was provided by the Chinese embassy in Accra.[27] A Western correspondent in Accra aptly summed up the situation: 'The West pays, the East increases its influence.' The correspondent went on to say:

'Ghana already has a source from which it can obtain all the industrial plants it needs for making use of the surplus Volta power and making the whole Volta project viable. This source is the £38·1 million credits granted by various countries of the Soviet bloc. As a result of these credits Ghana is to receive an iron ore plant, a steel works, boot and shoe and textile factories, several shipbuilding yards, assembly works for Soviet tractors, sugar, rubber and yarn factories, a glass works, and so on. It will all be industrial plant that Ghana badly needs, and some of it will consume a great deal of power. Without the Volta project this power would simply not be available, so in the last resort, by financing the Volta project the United States is creating the basis on which the Soviet bloc can industrialize Ghana and dig itself in with its technical (and political) advisers, its experts, and all its usual methods . . .'[28]

In short, the Volta project will do nothing to dissuade Ghana from proceeding with economic measures designed to bring about fundamental social changes towards socialism. For some time now there has been a plan calculated to secure immediate economic benefits; it is based on a report drawn up at the beginning of 1962 by the communist Joseph Bognar, a Budapest professor of economics, and it lays down details for the stage-by-stage collectivization of Ghanaian agriculture. Ghanaian peasant farmers would, it was rightly assumed, oppose the plan, and an appropriate tax policy had been worked out to compel them to surrender their holdings. As a preliminary, they were warned in the summer of 1962 not to extend their activities, though they had been called upon to do just that the previous year.[29] The cocoa-bean growers were in any case in a precarious position; from the beginning of January 1961, when they were first compelled to sell half their production (Ghana is the world's biggest supplier of cocoa) through the state-controlled United Ghana Farmers' Council, which was in a position to depress prices and which is taking full advantage of this power. There was also the decree of July 1961, by which they are 'voluntarily' compelled to invest ten per cent of the guaranteed producer price in government bonds.

These measures stem from an economic policy directed against private initiative and property and in favour of collectivization and the establishment of a state economic sector; a policy vigorously supported by the propaganda of the CPP, which vociferously praises the communist economic system while bitterly attacking the European Economic Community. In 1962 Nkrumah joined in personally, in a vehement speech to an Accra conference of African

Freedom Fighters (most of whom have been subsidized by Ghana for years):

'The EEC serves the profit lust of the imperialists and is hostile to the independent and neutralist policy of the African States . . . The EEC represents an attempt to replace the old system of colonial exploitation by a new system of collective colonialism which will be stronger and more dangerous than the old evil from which we are seeking to liberate our continent.'[30]

But as an African Common Market had no hope of success, the only course left open to Nkrumah was still greater reliance on the economic system of the Soviet bloc.

With this we come to Ghana's cardinal difficulty, which is exacerbated by the rejection of all other possibilities and by the hasty adoption of measures decided upon in a highly emotional state. Constitutionally there is no longer any system of checks and balances that could help the country to maintain an even keel. On the one hand, the power of the old, conservative, traditionalist elements has been undermined; on the other hand, the new liberal forces have been hamstrung. A group of wild pseudo-Marxists is in control, though they still protest publicly that they have no intention of binding the country to either power bloc, but to Pan-Africanism and to a powerful Third Force based on a policy of non-alignment. It is possible that at first their assurances were honest, but today they are nothing but a camouflage for the truth. As neither Pan-Africanism nor a Third Force has hope of immediate success, the contradiction between words and deeds is becoming more obvious, and the way to a more moderate policy (and perhaps even to co-operation with the West) has been barred. The real beneficiary of this confused situation is the Soviet Union. *Not that communism has won the final victory in Ghana; far from it.* In fact, its practical successes and scope are not as great as they were in Guinea during 1960 and the first half of 1961. But public opinion in Ghana is being more and more bewildered and dominated by communist agitation and propaganda. The right to express unorthodox opinions is restricted and often suppressed. A thin stratum of pro-communists, entrenched in the various ministries and political organizations, is facilitating the infiltration of communist ideology and propaganda into the various groups and institutions.

The time is past when Ghana propagated 'African socialism', in contrast to 'Scientific socialism'. Early in 1963 *Spark*—the journal of the government-subsidized Bureau of African Affairs—came out in sharp contradiction to one of the basic tenets of African socialism, as expressed by Sékou Touré of Guinea, that 'the class struggle here is impossible for there are no classes but only social strata'. This *Spark* denied: 'Socialist parties in Africa must clearly realize their class struggle'.[31] At the beginning of January, 1964, the official *Ghanaian Times* wrote:

'Some of our political scientists have served us with the false doctrine that Ghana is fortunate to be starting its socialist revolution without basic class anatagonism. This is a dangerous fallacy . . . we underestimated the nature of the growing capitalist class and opened our ranks wide for them to infiltrate and subvert our revolution'.[32]

At the same time, CPP headquarters instructed party members that 'a real education in Nkrumahism must be preceded by an understanding of the principles of Marxism'. The staff of the Kwame Nkrumah Ideological Institute in Accra, most of them communist sympathizers and lecturers from bloc countries, has repeatedly made it clear that Marxism is to be understood as 'Marxism-Leninism'. Commenting on the January 1964 referendum in Ghana, Peter Preston wrote in *The Guardian*:

'Observers in Accra hold that the régime's current swing leftward eclipses all others . . . They either hold that the President, hidden perpetually in his white castle on the coast, ringed by militia and armoured cars, has lost all touch with reality, and dismiss him and his new batch of party advisers as "crackpots", or they find a pattern, tracing the sudden change of course to the conference of African leaders in Addis Ababa last year (May 1963). There, the argument goes, Nkrumah, who had not travelled abroad for a long time, found that his influence was negligible . . . He then decided that the only way to remain a power on the continent was to appeal to the extreme but influential minorities which exist in every African country . . . The belief is that communism is the Redeemer's means to his own ideological end.'[33]

Similar tendencies are present in Mali, the former French Sudan.

This State was established in August 1960 under the leadership of Modibo Keita, who proudly traces his origin back to the famous Keita dynasty which reigned in the early Middle Ages. After the break-up of the Mali Federation, which consisted of the former French Sudan and Senegal, the former adopted the name which had been given to the federation. The federation failed for a number of reasons: structural inadequacies, French intrigues and, in the last resort, the incompatible temperaments of the two partners, Léopold Sédar Senghor of Senegal and Modibo Keita. To put it bluntly, one might say that the Mali Federation broke up because it set out to reconcile the irreconcilable: a democratic spirit and constitution in Senegal, an authoritarian temperament and totalitarian conditions in the Sudan.

The constitution of the Sudan, headed by the Sudanese section of the old RDA under Modibo and Madeira Keita, revealed definite left-wing tendencies. Like Touré's *Parti Démocratique de Guinée* (PDG), the Sudanese State party still upholds the pro-communist ideas on which the RDA was originally based—not surprising when we recall that many of its leaders and officials were trained at various communist centres in the 1940s and 1950s.

In accordance with their communist training, the Sudanese leaders demanded all the decisive powers when the Mali Federation was officially founded in July 1960. They occupied the Ministries of the Interior and of Defence and opposed the election of Senghor as President of the Federation. When the Senegalese vigorously objected to such methods, Modibo Keita put the first phase of his 'seizure of power' campaign into action. It was his bad luck however that he had to operate in Dakar—the Senegalese city which had been chosen as the capital—because this meant that the slightest miscalculation spelt failure. Details of the planned *coup* became known, the attempt to arrest various leading personalities was a failure, and the broadcasting station remained in Senegalese hands. Possession of the radio station enabled the Senegalese, led by Senghor and Mamadou Dia, to organize successful counter-action. The Sudanese were packed off to Bamako. They broke off relations with Dakar and proclaimed the Republic of Mali, which was now confined to the Sudan.

Since then, Sudanese Mali has become a staunch partner of Ghana and, in particular, of Guinea. Nkrumah, Touré and Keita established the three-State union of West Africa; at the beginning of 1961 the three, together with the United Arab Republic, Morocco and the Algerian GPRA, joined to form the Casablanca group. In a series of conferences a joint policy, particularly on the Congo, was worked out among Casablanca, Accra, Conakry and Cairo. This was chiefly characterized by wild attacks on Western colonial imperialism, full support for Lumumba, and later for the rebel movement in the Congo and in general the encouragement of communist agitation and propaganda. It was obvious, of course, that this alliance of the three West African States with the three North African States was a marriage of political convenience. The United Arab Republic was following its own interests and so were Ghana and Guinea, while Mali had unmistakably taken up its position alongside its two African brothers.

The nature of the policy pursued by Mali was first visible in the attitude of the Bamako representatives at the fifteenth session of the United Nations in the autumn of 1960. After Keita had established diplomatic relations with Peking in August 1960 Mali's demand for the admission of Red China as a member of the UN did not come as a surprise, particularly as most of the African States had taken a stand against the United States either by supporting the Soviet proposals or by withholding their votes. But on the Tibetan question, Mali and Guinea were the only two African States to support the Soviet Union when it angrily opposed a discussion of the tragic events in Tibet at the United Nations. Tunisia, Libya and Nigeria voted with the United States for a discussion of the Tibetan question, while the other African States (with the exception of Mali and Guinea) abstained. When voting took place on the proposal to put the Hungarian question on the agenda for discussion Mali was the only African State to vote with the Soviet Union against it. Tunisia and Liberia voted for the West, while the other African States abstained.

Mali's behaviour in the UN showed that the communists had a new potential ally in Africa. It is true that discussions are still going on within the Mali State Party concerning the particular degree of co-operation with communism, but the fact is that communist theses, arguments and propaganda are already playing a big role in Bamako, while various ministries, high party and trade union offices, and posts in the youth and women's organizations are (as in Ghana) already in the hands of orthodox Marxist elements, who have not only embraced communist ideology but have adopted communist methods and unscrupulousness and the communist technique of seizing and wielding political power. There is no doubt that the pro-communist elements in Mali have grown in strength since independence. In fact, as Soviet influence has tended to decline in Guinea, so it has increased in Mali; though Mali (particularly in economic matters, for example, on the question of co-operation with the EEC) has not yet burnt all its bridges to the West. On the other hand the representatives of the Mali State Party at the Twenty-second Congress of the Communist Party of the Soviet Union certainly outdid their colleagues from Ghana and Guinea in their pro-communist attitude.

Tidjani Traoré, a member of the Political Bureau of the *Union Soudanaise* and a deputy of the Mali National Assembly, declared at the Moscow Congress:

'Comrade Members of the Praesidium, Comrade guests, Comrade delegates to the Party Congress! Today with enthusiasm we observe the picture of the great prophecies of Lenin, who, because he presented the peoples with the methods of analysis and unexampled, practical guidance to conscious, creative action, enriched Marxism and developed it into Marxist-Leninism, whose correctness and effectiveness is being confirmed every day by the successes of the Soviet Union in the scientific and technological sphere . . . Imperialism is digging its own grave. Yesterday, today, and at all times when peace-loving people anywhere throw off their chains, the colonialists immediately begin to whine: "Beware, this is the hand of Moscow, the hand of communism!" But this means that *communism has become synonymous with freedom*. Each time when an organization arises and does its best to abolish inequality and to secure a just distribution of the material goods of this world, the colonialists begin to shout: "Beware, this is the hand of Moscow, the hand of communism!" But this means that *communism is synonymous with justice*, *synonymous with equality*. Whenever any party exposes discrimination the imperialists and the colonialists start to rage: "Beware, they are agents of Moscow; they are communists!" But this means that *communism is synonymous with fraternity!* The peoples of Africa . . . know who their real friends are. And it is quite natural that the Soviet Union and the countries of the Socialist camp are amongst those friends, and that they give unlimited support to the powerful national revolutionary movements.'[34]

A few months later Modibo Keita himself talked in exactly the same tone. Speaking in the Lomonossov Institute in Moscow, the President of Mali declared:

'Unfortunately at the present time the experiment of neo-colonialism is being carried out in Africa, and its aim is to perpetuate capitalism under cover of talk about socialism. This is a great fraud, and we must fight against it unless we want to see the people of Africa deceived by such lies. How can one talk of socialism when foreign military bases are in one's country, and when the economic oppression of capitalism continues unchanged?'[35]

At a dinner given by Leonid Breshnev, then President of the Supreme Soviet, to the guest from Mali, Keita spoke even more clearly: 'You and we are both convinced of the victory of socialism. Precisely for this reason it was our desire to travel to the source of this idea, to see the life in your country with our own eyes and to witness your successes.'[36]

Nikita Khrushchev naturally welcomed talk of this kind and, at a demonstration of Soviet-Mali friendship held in the Kremlin he declared: 'Some of these countries [in Africa] have actually won their independence, and they can decide for themselves what they do. Others have for the time being won only a fictitious independence.' He went on to say that the peoples of these latter countries still had a hard fight ahead before they could win through to real independence, and in a number of cases this fight could take on 'very intense forms, including even armed struggle in conditions of existing national independence.'[37]

With these words Khrushchev was unmistakably laying down the guiding principle of Soviet policy in Africa: the Kremlin is to determine the nature of independence and thus the methods and the forms of the struggle—that is, by implication, the Soviet-communist form of action. Where forces favourable to communism are at work, as in Ghana and Mali, the Kremlin will wait for them to develop of their own accord. Nevertheless, there is a possibility, even in Ghana and Mali, that the ruling élite may still realize the dangers and penalties of co-operating with communism—as happened in Guinea in the late autumn of 1961. No prophetic vision is required to see that sooner or later a conflict will break out between the pro-communist nationalist forces and the pro-communist internationalist forces.

NOTES

[1] The *Guardian* (Manchester), 4 February 1964.

[2] Pamphlet issued by the Government of Ghana in early 1961; translated from the Twi.

[3] Editorial in the *Ghanaian Times* (Accra), 23 April 1960.

[4] Radio Accra broadcast, 18 April 1960.

[5] The *Economist* (London), 8 February 1964.

[6] As Dr Nkrumah did in February 1964 when he ordered the dismissal from office of the Chief Justice, Sir Arku Korsah.

[7] The *Guardian*, 4 February 1964.

[8] In conversation with the author, 26 April 1960.

[9] Information given in a conversation with the author, 24 April 1960.

[10] Reuters, 4 October 1961. Joseph Appiah and Dr Danquah were later released.

[11] *Neue Zürcher Zeitung*, 9 November 1961.

[12] *African Review* (London), March 1964, p. 5.

[13] Ibid.

[14] Cf. for example *Narody Afriki* (Moscow), 1954; *Neue Zeit* (Moscow), 14 February 1951.

[15] Cf. Nkrumah, op. cit., in particular, the remarks on Du Bois and Garvey.

[16] Radio Accra broadcast, 24 November 1958.

[17] Undated cyclostyled publication issued by the Government of Guinea (May 1959).

[18] See for instance the statement by Kingue Abel, Vice-President of the UPC, reported by (North) Korean News Agency (KCNA), 19 February 1964.

[19] *Neue Zürcher Zeitung*, 30 September 1960.

[20] *Vedemosti vershovnogo Soviets*, No. 51 (1960), pp. 1169-71.

[21] *Neue Zürcher Zeitung*, 1 July 1962.

[22] AFP (Moscow), 12 July 1961.

[23] *Neues Deutschland*, 13 August 1961.

[24] Cyclostyled reports of the Belgrade Conference.

[25] *Neues Deutschland*, 13 January 1962.

[26] Cf. the speech of E. Tsefas at the Twenty-second Congress of the CPSU, reported in *Pravda*, 25 October 1961.

[27] *Frankfurter Allgemeine Zeitung*, 27 December 1961.
[28] Ibid.
[29] *Neue Zürcher Zeitung*, 4 July 1962.
[30] *Neues Deutschland*, 17 June 1961.
[31] Cited in *African Review* (London), March 1964, p. 4.
[32] Ibid., p. 5.
[33] The *Guardian*, 4 February 1964.
[34] *Pravda*, 26 October 1961.
[35] Tass, 22 May 1962.
[36] Cf. *Neues Deutschland*, 24 May 1962.
[37] Tass, 30 May 1962.

Chapter X

THE ECONOMIC APPROACH

ECONOMIC factors play an important part in Soviet calculations concerning Africa. This is hardly surprising when we remember that Marxism is a 'science' based essentially on the determining role of the productive forces and the means of production in social life. Lenin even went so far as to describe politics as 'concentrated economics', thus underlining the dominant role of economics, its potentials and processes. Addressing the Twenty-first Congress of the Communist Party of the Soviet Union in January 1959, Mr Khrushchev described economics as 'the main sphere in which the peaceful competition between socialism and capitalism develops' and added: 'Our interest is to win this competition in the shortest possible historical space of time.'[1] The Soviet leader knew very well, of course, that in some respects the result of this competition will largely depend on whether capitalism or socialism can dominate the enormous natural resources and economic potential of Africa and harness them in its own interests. According to Lenin's theory capitalism must collapse when it loses its 'last reserves'—the colonial and semi-colonial countries—and it is therefore a significant indication of communist thinking that the political studies and propaganda writings of the Eastern bloc on Africa deal extensively with economic questions. For example, the February 1961 number of the international communist publication *Problems of Peace and Socialism* published a survey entitled 'Africa—Continent of the Future: Facts and Documents'. The survey noted that the natural resources of Africa included the biggest known deposits of uranium, 34·4 per cent of the iron-ore deposits, 74·9 per cent of the chromium, 51·4 per cent of the cobalt, 90·2 per cent of the diamonds, and

47·3 per cent of the copper in the capitalist world, in addition to vast oil deposits. The survey went on to say:

'According to a United Nations report, most of the minerals extracted in Africa (92 per cent) are still exported, and only eight per cent are left for internal consumption . . . Thus, though direct colonial rule has been abolished on the greater part of the continent, colonialism still exists. It relies mainly on *the economic positions of the imperialist powers* in Africa.'[2]

The Africans themselves had also realized this, the survey continued, and it quoted the President of Guinea, Sékou Touré, as follows:

'We have no grounds for saying that the imperialist States intend to relinquish voluntarily their economic, political and military power. Africa, despised and deprived of rights, now occupies the main place in their expansionist plans . . . Colonialism tends to acquire an international form which permits the banners and anthems of African nationalism but forbids any infringement of colonial interests. Political independence does not in itself signify complete national liberation. It is, of course, an important and decisive stage. Nevertheless, we must recognize that national independence presupposes not only political liberation but, and this is the main thing, economic liberation. Social progress is impossible without these two essential factors.'[3]

The ideas of Sékou Touré are shared by many African nationalists. The young African élite almost unanimously regards the traditionally one-sided economic relationships between the newly-independent countries and the West as a new form of colonialism that prevents full freedom of political decision and makes the welfare of the new African States dependent on the capitalist world market, with all its fluctuations, including the steady drop in prices of raw materials while prices of investment goods and technical apparatus are rising. There is a large measure of agreement between the Russians and many Africans when they regard the Soviet Union as an alternative to the West, and above all as an economic alternative, thus facilitating Russian attempts to influence the trading and industrialization policies of the African States. Communist propaganda tries to camouflage the imperialist core of this Soviet economico-political offensive, though it could be clearly detected in the Congo policy of the Soviet Union, which aimed at ending American and European exploitation of Katanga's enormous resources and thus depriving the West of its uranium and cobalt supplies.

But the ultimate aims of communist economic policy go much further: in practice, the balance of trade between most of the under-developed countries and the West is unfavourable to the former. Egypt is the best example of this. In 1959 the United States exported goods to the value of 30 million Egyptian pounds to Egypt and imported goods from Egypt to the value of only two million Egyptian pounds. On the other hand, the Soviet Union was prepared to accept an unfavourable balance in its 1959 trade with the United Arab Republic. The Soviet Union exported goods to the value of 26·8 million Egyptian pounds to the United Arab Republic and imported goods to the value of 28·3 million Egyptian pounds from the UAR.[4]

In other words, the commercial interests of the West are allowed to dominate its economic relations with the under-developed countries. This means that in African eyes the economic policy of the West bears a heavy psychological burden because it prevents the under-developed countries from balancing their imports by a corresponding volume of exports. A striking example of this situation is afforded by the trading relations between France and Guinea. When Sékou Touré defiantly led his country to political independence in 1958, France answered with draconian sanctions by immediately cancelling Guinea's exports of bananas to France, exports that were a matter of economic life and death for Guinea. This action of the French Government proved to be a grave error. The Soviet bloc (particularly East Germany) stepped in at once and offered to take Guinea's entire banana crop, though at a reduced price. Since then—and in spite of the Solod crisis and the following period of deterioration of the political relations—most of the countries of the Soviet bloc have concluded long-term trading agreements with Guinea, relieving it of its most immediate export problems.

Communist trade with Egypt and Guinea, as well as with Ghana, illustrates the political implications of economic relations with the new African States. Here was the beginning of a communist commercial offensive that would inevitably have political repercussions affecting both the internal order and the foreign policy of the underdeveloped countries. At the moment (and also it had been intensified in the early 1960s) this offensive is only in its preliminary stages, but it is already impossible to shut one's eyes to its inner dynamism and ultimate objectives. As early as 1959–60 the countries of the Soviet bloc were trying to do business with those African countries which were not yet independent. The Soviet Union, Czechoslovakia, China and East Germany all tried to establish relations with East Africa before independence; once sovereignty was achieved such relations could easily be extended. As late as 1958 the Soviet Union had no commercial relations with the three East African countries, Kenya, Uganda, and Tanganyika, but in 1959 the Russians imported goods from Uganda to the value of £2·48 million sterling.[5] In 1960 China and Czechoslovakia followed the example of the Soviet Union. The Soviet bloc also succeeded in increasing its trade turn-over with the former Rhodesian Federation and with Nyasaland. In 1959, African imports from these countries reached a total value of £482,000 sterling, and exports £4·86 million sterling, while the respective figures for the first half of 1960 were already £411,000 and £3·838 million respectively. Commercial relations with independent African States have developed in much the same proportions over the past seven years. The exports of Togo, only a small sum in 1959, had already risen to 19 million new francs in the first half of 1960, when Eastern Europe temporarily imported more goods from Togo than the West.[6] There had been no trade between Mali and the Soviet Union before 1960. By the end of September 1962, the Soviet Union was second only to France as an import market for Mali. Soviet shipments amounted to $8,844,000 against $15,136,000 for France.[7] In 1961 alone the Soviet Union expanded its trade (as compared with 1960) with Guinea by 293 per cent; with Algeria by 771 per cent; Sudan by 76 per cent, and Soviet exports to Ghana increased by 178 per cent.[8]

From the long-term point of view this development of commercial relations between Africa and the communist countries seems more important than Soviet technical aid and credits for Africa. Unlike the West, the communists are not, for the moment, attaching great importance to the sale of their own commodities on the African market, but are aiming primarily at 'liquidating the export difficulties' of the African countries. The communists' acceptance of an unusually unfavourable balance of trade is thus a political move which the national bourgeoisie of certain African countries approve since it enables them to consolidate their position as agents for foreign (mainly Western) goods within their own countries. This one-sided Soviet trade is facilitated by the favourable terms of payment which the Soviet-bloc countries are prepared to grant to their African trading partners. Unlike the West, which often demands payment for its goods in hard currencies, the communists will accept payment in any currency and pay for their imports from Africa in any desired form. The advantages for the Africans are so very great that the threat of dependence involved is often ignored.

It is hardly necessary to point out that African economic dependence on the Soviet bloc enables the communists to make political demands and to carry on political activity in the countries with which they have trading relations.

Another factor of inestimable importance enters into these commercial transactions and into the granting of credits and the placing of investments: the Soviet economic approach to Africa is essentially 'anti-capitalist'. Economic activities are conducted entirely through governmental channels, whereas those of the Western countries are primarily of a private capitalist and non-governmental nature. The Western businessman does not look for his business partners in government departments, but in the sphere of private enterprise. The Soviet-bloc countries have no private importers or exporters, no representatives of individual firms or concerns, but exclusively *officials* of a monolithic communist state economy. They are not interested in talking to, or doing business with private businessmen, but only with governments and government departments with whom they negotiate down to the last detail, and they encourage their African trading partners to implement their agreements. In this way they exert pressure on them to *organize* and plan their imports and exports.

The credit policy of the communist countries has the same aim. Credits are regarded as political instruments with which Africa's ties with the West can be disrupted, and economic measures introduced which will, in the long run, strengthen communism. Though the intentions of the Soviet bloc are perfectly clear, its activities do not, so far, appear to represent any real danger.

Firstly, the credits granted until now to African countries south of the Sahara have been on quite a small scale.

Secondly, although they are offered on very favourable terms (including low rates of interest), Soviet aid is often less attractive than Western aid. In a study in *Problems of Communism*, David L. Morrison deals with 'Moscow's first steps' (in Africa) and correctly points out that Soviet loans and credits are intended to be repaid, whereas this is by no means the case with all Western credits. In fact, when the West makes money available to the underdeveloped countries this is often not in the form of loans, but of direct grants.

For example, in the period 1 July 1957–30 June 1959, Western countries, independently and through the International Bank for Reconstruction and Development and other UN agencies, granted loans totalling \$114·7 million to Africa, while in the same period non-repayable grants amounted to \$296·3 million.[9] In their negotiations with Western finance agencies, African governments often proceed on the assumption that the 'credits' they are being granted will in the long run not be repayable. So far no major case of similar generosity is known on the part of the Soviet-bloc countries. It is well known that in 1961 the Soviet Union was pressing for the first repayment of credits granted to Guinea in 1959, although the credits had not yet been completely taken up.

The third factor of great importance in this matter is that Soviet credit grants are greatly inflated by propaganda. The formal declaration that a credit is to be granted is invariably made into a major item of publicity. During the negotiations, and above all when the agreement is signed, the Africans are given the most generous assurances concerning the rapidity and efficiency with which the arrangements will be implemented. (Invariably they include the construction of plants with the assistance of Soviet technicians.) Expectations are therefore very high and the African beneficiary visualizes gigantic factories, imposing sports stadiums and splendid school buildings literally shooting out of the ground like mushrooms. Before long, however, they face a reality which is usually less impressive. Many months, sometimes even years, pass before the projects for which Soviet aid has been promised emerge from the planning stage. Apart from one or two prestige buildings, it takes even longer before the various projects are actually completed. The result is subsequent disappointment and a loss of faith in the selflessness of Soviet aid.

Guinea provides the best example of all this. During a visit to Moscow in August 1959, a delegation of the *Parti Démocratique de Guinée* were promised credits of 140 million roubles, or roughly the equivalent of $35 million. Announcements on 1 March and 8 September 1960 provided information as to how these credits were to be used. The first joint Soviet-Guinean announcement declared that the Soviet Union had promised technical assistance 'for the building of a cement works, a saw-mill for the production of railway sleepers, a combined leather and shoe factory, a canning factory for fruit and vegetables, refrigeration plant, a Polytechnic Institute for 1,500 students and a sports stadium in Conakry to seat 25,000 people'.[10] The communiqué also mentioned geological surveys for diamond and gold prospecting, the supply of machinery and equipment for diamond mining, the delivery of complete agricultural technical equipment, technical assistance for the development of Conakry airport, and for the building of the Conakry–Mamou railway line.[11] In the second announcement the Soviet Union promised technical assistance to help to build an industrial centre on the Konkouré river.

Up to the end of 1963 only a fraction of these and many other smaller projects had been realized. According to a statement made to the author by a highly-placed Guinean, by the beginning of 1963 various projects were at the planning stage and not one of them had been implemented. Dozens of projects had been allowed to fade out, particularly after the second half of 1961 when the crisis in the relations between Guinea and the Soviet Union was at its height. According to the same source, in the thirty-six months following the Soviet blanket assurances of August 1959 the Government of Guinea had been able to make use of, or had had placed at its disposal, only fifteen per cent of the promised Soviet credits. The 'generous and selfless assistance' offered by the Soviet Union, accompanied by widespread propaganda and publicity, turned out to be something of a fiasco—and was made more painful by the fact that, for a long period, the Government of Guinea had had to meet the expenses of innumerable Soviet experts, advisers, members of the planning staffs, and so on.

Taking into account such disappointing experiences and other disadvantages, the spectre of the 'rouble offensive' in Africa, which has been painted in such grisly colours by the Western Press, begins to look less menacing, even if we include the assistance provided by the other countries of the Soviet bloc.[12]

The following survey of communist credit policy towards some African States provides details of credits offered and credits actually made available. Up to the end of 1963 only six States had been offered any credits: Ethiopia, Guinea, Ghana, Mali, Somalia and Nigeria. When the communist Press publishes figures relating to Soviet aid, it departs from its usual custom of differentiating between North Africa and Black Africa. Thus when communists talk of 'Soviet aid to Africa' this includes, for example, all the arrangements between the Soviet Union and Egypt. In consequence the statement of the official Soviet foreign-trade publication that no less than 28·8 per cent of all foreign aid granted by the Soviet Union up to 15 March 1961[13] had gone to Africa appears much less impressive when one realizes that Soviet aid to Egypt, which represented a total of over $U.S. 600 million till then, is included in this amount When the details of Soviet aid to individual African countries south of the Sahara are examined they prove to be far less significant.

1. *Ethiopia*: The Empire of Haile Selassie was the first country in non-Arab Africa on the Soviet credit list. On 12 July 1959, during the visit of the Negus to the Soviet Union, the Kremlin granted Ethiopia credits totalling 400 million (old) roubles, representing a value of $U.S. 102 million. A joint statement published on 25 March 1960 recorded that the credits were to be used for building an oil refinery in Assab with a capacity for refining 500,000 tons per annum, and for geological prospecting, the construction of a caustic-soda factory in Massowa, gold mining and ore-dressing plant, and a small smelting works.[14] In addition, the Soviet Union promised to build a hospital and a technical high school for 1,200 students.

2. *Guinea*: We have already given details concerning the use of the credit of 140 million (old) roubles credit granted to Guinea in 1959. In addition, other communist countries also granted Guinea credits: the Chinese People's Republic ($U.S. 25 million), Czechoslovakia (commodity credits to the value of $U.S. 10 million), Poland ($U.S. 5 million), and Hungary ($U.S. 2·56 million). The grants and the financial and commodity credits made available by the

East German Government are not known in detail, but they are believed to amount to a total of about $U.S. 10 million. Part of this sum is known to have been spent on building a large printing works in Conakry. This was inaugurated in the summer of 1961, but within a few weeks it had to be partly closed because of grave technical defects.

3. *Ghana*: The first agreement for economic and technical co-operation between the Soviet Union and Ghana was signed on 4 August 1960.[15] Under this agreement Moscow granted Accra a first credit of 160 million (old) roubles, (about $U.S. 40 million), at 2½ per cent interest per annum over an amortization period of twelve years. A programme for the use of this aid was published on 23 December 1960. Soviet aid was concentrated mainly on the following ten projects: the building of an hydraulic power station at Bui on the Black Volta (a project not to be confused with the other Volta River building operations financed by the West and about 60 miles away from the Soviet venture), the laying of about 150 miles of overland pipe lines, geological surveys, the building of a number of factories for the fishing industry, the establishment of three State farms, the experimental planting of cotton with a view to establishing a State cotton farm and a cotton mill, the building of domestic housing estates in Accra and Tema, a study of the practicability of building a smelting works, an iron-ore and manganese works, and a tractor-assembly plant.[16]

Between 1961 and 1963 there were reported negotiations concerning these credits, and the details were revised several times. It was not until 22 September 1961, that a definite agreement was arrived at for the building of the power station at Bui on the Black Volta river. And in June 1962 Ghana's Deputy Minister for Industry had to inform parliament that certain projects had been 'postponed' because it had been found that they were not in accordance with 'the present stage of Ghana's development'. This referred in particular to a project for a steel works, for which the Soviet Union had been pressing since 1959. A project to build a railway line from Kumasi to Ouagadougou in the Upper Volta Republic, which had been enthusiastically welcomed in the Ghanaian Press, was said by the Deputy Minister of Transport to exist solely in the imagination of Ghanaian editors influenced by the whispers of Soviet propaganda.[17]

There were long delays in Ghana before the agreed Soviet credits were made available. However, a correspondent in Accra[18] reported that by the middle of 1962 a good third of the credits granted to Ghana by the Soviet countries had been made available. But the doubt which still surrounded a second Soviet credit, said to have been promised to Nkrumah in 1961, has not been dissipated to this day. So far neither Soviet sources nor official sources in Ghana have said anything definite about the amount involved, or about the individual projects which the credit is to serve. The original announcement spoke only in general terms about institutions designed to train the 'national technical forces' of Ghana.[19] Apart from the Soviet Union the following communist States have also granted credits to Ghana so far:

Hungary	21 April 1961	£2·5 million
Czechoslovakia	22 May 1961	£5 million
Poland	25 May 1961	£1 million
People's Republic of China	8 August 1961	£7 million (free of interest)

The various credits granted by the East European States are to be used, among other things, for building a pharmaceutical works, an aluminium cable works, an electric-bulb factory (Hungary), a cane-sugar factory, a car-tyre factory (Czechoslovakia), an iron foundry, a machine-tool factory and a shipbuilding yard (Poland).[20] It has not yet been possible to discover whether the construction of various industrial enterprises (including furniture factories, mass-tailoring workshops, and technical-equipment factories) promised by Poland in an agreement signed on 18 December 1961, and representing an investment of £10 million in Ghanaian currency, is to be carried out on a credit basis.[21] On 20 April 1961 Poland had already signed an agreement with Ghana granting it commodity credits to the value of £5 million sterling.[22] However, a number of the projects promised by Poland, like some of the Soviet projects already mentioned, have been either deferred or abandoned altogether.[23]

4. *Mali*: On 18 March 1961 representatives of the Soviet Union and of Mali met in the Kremlin to sign agreements for economic and technical co-operation and for commercial and cultural exchanges. At the same time Mali was granted credits for 40 million new roubles (approximately $U.S. 44·5 million) at 2½ per cent per annum. The programme of Soviet projects for Mali included (1) geological

survey and prospecting operations, (2) the improvement of transport on the Niger, (3) the building of a sports stadium in Bamako to seat 25,000, (4) the building of a railway line between Bamako and Conakry (Guinea), (5) the building of a cement works with capacity for an annual production of 100,000 tons, and (6) the building of an educational institute for 300 students. The Soviet Union was also to provide Mali, as it did Guinea and Ghana, with planes to build a national air service.[24]

5. *Nigeria*: Nigeria, the biggest of the new African States and with pro-Western rather than neutralist policies, received a promise of Soviet credits (in June 1961) to a total of 40 million new roubles (approximately $U.S. 44·5 million), at 2½ per cent per annum. Up to the end of 1964 there were still no details available as to how this credit was to be used. In a joint communiqué issued by representatives of the Soviet Union and Nigeria, there was only a general reference to Soviet assistance in the founding of certain agricultural undertakings, factories for the preparation of agricultural produce, and the establishment of centres for training technical personnel for industry and agriculture.[25] Poland also agreed to advance credits to finance certain industrial projects,[26] and Czechoslovakia promised some credits but without a firm commitment.

6. *Somalia*: The Somali Government took advantage of a Soviet 'goodwill' mission to Somali in April 1961 to ask the Soviet Union for long-term credits.[27] During the visit of Premier Abdirashid Shermake to Moscow, the Soviet Government granted Somalia a credit of 40 million new roubles (approximately $U.S. 44·5 million), together with a five-year commodity credit of 7 million new roubles (approximately $U.S. 7·78 million). The Soviet Government also promised to provide assistance for the building of two hospitals, a high school, a broadcasting station, and a printing works. It also agreed to provide Soviet medical and teaching personnel and to train Somali doctors in the Soviet Union.

In granting these credits the Soviet Union intends to pave the way for Africa's greater dependence on the Soviet bloc. At the third session of the UN Economic Commission for Africa, held in Addis Ababa in February 1961, Soviet Minister V. S. Semenov declared that if the present expenditure on armaments could be diverted to the development of Africa it could catch up with Europe industrially in a very short time. He also declared that by 1965 the Soviet Union and the other socialist countries would together account for half the world's industrial production. He went on: 'Mr Khrushchev has pointed out that with the development of our own economy we shall progressively expand our co-operation with the African countries.'[28] This association of Soviet economic aid to Africa with the rising graph of Soviet economic development means conversely that any difficulties experienced by the Soviet economic system is bound to have an unfavourable effect on Soviet aid to Africa. This was already noticeable from the autumn of 1961 to the beginning of 1965 when the Soviet authorities closed their ears to African requests for financial and commodity credits, except the requests for military aid from Somalia.

Irrespective of the fluctuations of Soviet credit facilities and commodity deliveries, communist economic propaganda in Africa continues at high pressure. More than a third of the African broadcasts of Radio Moscow deal with socio-economic questions. The West and the motives of Western capital exports to, and investment in, Africa are played down, while the value of Soviet State aid is inflated. Thousands of communist publications, from weighty tomes to ephemeral pamphlets, sound the same note. In a study by Dr Ismailova Fruck, *State Capitalism in the Young African States*, published by the Institute for Economic Science in Moscow (a department of the Soviet Academy of Sciences) the young African States are strongly recommended to introduce nationalization measures, since this is the only way in which a State sector of the economic system can be created. At the same time the élite in the under-developed countries are urged to reject every form of industrialization by private enterprise. The study declares:

> 'The accumulation of capital in the hands of the national bourgeoisie is insufficient, and the still-powerful foreign monopolies often refuse to invest their capital in the national industries. In consequence the State *must* play an active role in the process of industrialization. In this respect the rise of State capitalism is of increasing importance.'

The study further points out that the recommended policy would be anti-imperialist, for a State sector in the economic system would automatically restrict the sphere of operations open to private capitalists. Moreover, the creation of State capitalism would have repercussions on the political structure of the country. In other words the advantage of State capitalism, in the eyes of the communists, is that it encourages the development of a socialist economic structure in the young national States and thus facilitates the transition to communism.[29]

This point of view is also reflected in an article written in 1962 by Jack Woddis, a member of the British Communist Party and a specialist on African affairs. For a symposium on 'Paths of Development of Newly Emergent Countries', Woddis wrote: 'The creation of a State sector of the economy is extremely important for the newly independent African countries where little industry exists and where the commanding heights of the economy are in the hands of foreign monopolies.'[30] He also points out that the creation of a State economic sector will greatly facilitate the direct transition of Africa from a colonial to a socialist State.

In May 1962 the Soviet Government began a special economic propaganda campaign for Africa. Launched on an unusually wide scale, it was directed chiefly against the EEC and the idea of the Common Market and it opposed any association between the EEC and the sixteen African States with European connections. Mr Khrushchev himself fired the first shot in the campaign at a reception on 30 May 1962, given in Moscow in honour of the President of Mali, Modibo Keita.

'Of late,' he declared, 'the imperialist monopolies have set great hopes on the so-called Common Market. This Common Market represents no danger to us, but the situation is different where the young States of Asia, Africa and Latin America are concerned, because they have only recently obtained their political independence and they do not yet enjoy economic independence. One of the main aims of the Common Market is to chain those countries which have obtained their political freedom to the economy of the imperialist States.'

Mr Khrushchev went on to say that everything possible should be done 'to free international trade from arrangements by which the stronger are enabled to enrich themselves at the expense of the weaker'. He described the EEC, or Common Market, as 'a State monopoly agreement of the Western European finance oligarchy' and declared that it threatened the vital interests of the people and of peace 'because aggressive imperialist circles are using it to strengthen NATO and to intensify the arms race'. The antidote he recommended—particularly to the African countries—was that they should create State monopolies for foreign trade and support the Soviet plan for holding an international conference under the auspices of the United Nations with a view to creating a world-wide trading organization.[31] The same line was adopted in an article by V. Tcherpakov in *Communist* of May 1962. In defiance of the practical experience of the EEC's African associates, Tcherpakov argued that any association with the Common Market 'will inevitably slow down their economic development . . . will to a great extent impede the solution of social problems and the introduction of socio-economic measures'.[32] The campaign was given further impetus at a Comecon conference in Moscow in June 1962, at which it was decided to revise the statutes of the Council for Mutual Economic Aid (COMECON), so that in future 'non-European countries' could become members. It is interesting to note that it did not say 'Asiatic countries', which would have included Mongolia and the other communist Asiatic States.

The Soviet Union's economic activity in Africa is only beginning, but its ultimate objectives are already quite clear. Despite all the propaganda to the contrary, the Soviet Government is much less interested in affording 'unselfish aid' to African countries than it is in creating a favourable atmosphere, or psychological climate, in which it would be easier to introduce communist economic principles. The Soviet call for complete economic independence from the West, the creation of a State-controlled economy and a collectivized agriculture falls on many sympathetic ears among the African political élite who believe in a socialist solution for their countries.

NOTES

[1] *Pravda*, 28 January 1959.

[2] *Probleme des Friedens und des Sozialismus*, IV/2 (30) (February 1961), pp. 139 ff.

[3] Ibid.

[4] *UAR Statistics* (Cairo, 1961).

[5] Trade and Revenue Report for Kenya, Uganda and Tanganyika for the month of August 1960, published by the East Africa High Commission.

[6] *Bulletin Mensuel du Togo*, July 1960.

[7] The *New York Times* (European ed.), 27 January 1964.

[8] *Neue Zürcher Zeitung*, 27 November 1962.

[9] *Problems of Communism*, x, No. 6 (November-December 1961), p. 12.

[10] Cf. 'Der Ostblock und die Entwicklungsländer', *Vierteljahresbericht der Friedrich-Ebert-Stiftung* (Hanover), No. 6 (December 1961), p. 10.

[11] *Pravda*, 3 March 1960.

[12] Soviet, East European Credits to Africa from 1958 to the end of 1962 (in million US dollars)

	Soviet aid	Bloc countries	USA
Ethiopia	102	12	117·8
Ghana	109	87	156·5
Guinea	78	47	14·3
Mali	44	54	5·1
Morocco	17	—	352·0
Somalia	57	6	26·4
Sudan	23	—	65·0
Tunisia	28	18	293·3

Source: *Hinter dem Eisernen Vorhang* (Munich), x, No. 1 (January 1964).

[13] *Vnezhnaya Torgovlia*, No. 4 (1961), p. 20.

[14] *Pravda*, 27 March 1960.

[15] *Vedomosti Verkhovnogo Sovieta SSSR*, No. 51 (1960), pp. 1169 ff.

[16] Ibid., No. 30 (1961), pp. 715 ff.

[17] *Neue Zürcher Zeitung*, 1 July 1962.

[18] Ibid.

[19] *Pravda*, 27 July 1962.

[20] Cf. 'Der Ostblock und die Entwicklungsländer', p. 10.

[21] Radio Accra broadcast, 18 December 1961; New China News Agency, 19 December 1961.

[22] *Neue Zürcher Zeitung*, 21 April 1961.

[23] Ibid., 1 July 1962.

[24] 'Der Ostblock und die Entwicklungsländer', p. 10.

[25] *Pravda*, 10 June 1961.

[26] Radio Warsaw broadcast, 13 June 1961.

[27] *Pravda*, 24 March 1961.

[28] *Problems of Communism*, x, No. 6 (November-December 1961), p. 12.

[29] *Neues Deutschland*, 7 February 1961.

[30] *Probleme des Friedens und des Sozialismus*, IV (44) (April 1962), pp. 348 ff.

[31] *Neues Deutschland*, 31 May 1962.

[32] *Neue Zürcher Zeitung*, 17 June 1962.

Chapter XI

THE CHINESE IN AFRICA

After a decade dominated largely by the need to consolidate power at home, during which military and subversive ventures were confined to immediately adjoining areas, Mao Tse-tung's régime has in recent years embarked upon large-scale diplomatic offensives and attempts at infiltration in all the under-developed countries. As Chou En-lai's tour of ten African countries in December 1963 and January 1964 demonstrated, this continent is one of the main targets of the Chinese political 'leap forward'. As the Chinese prime minister said in Mogadishu at the end of his seven-week journey, 'revolutionary prospects are excellent throughout Africa.'[1] The continent is, in fact, in a state of great unrest and upheaval, and offers innumerable opportunities to the messianic world-political ambitions of Peking. The old-fashioned colonialism and paternalism of the white man is beating a precipitate retreat before the tumultuous advance of a nationalism based mainly on emotion and, on the whole, without clear-cut aims on all those decisive questions which will determine the future political, social, and economic shape of the continent. The young African élite lacks experience and there are no familiar models close at hand on which to base its strivings. It is equally opposed to traditionalism and to European liberalism. So far, their encounter with orthodox Marxism has not opened the eyes of many African leaders and men like Félix Houphouet-Boigny, President of the Ivory Coast Republic, are denounced by their more radical colleagues as reactionaries seeking conciliation with the colonialist régime.

In such a situation communism naturally exerts a strong attraction. In the view of some radical African leaders it has led to the social and economic development of backward countries despite the opposition of local reactionaries, and without foreign aid. Most Africans are not aware of the fact that these successes were bought at the price of tremendous suffering, including loss of life on a vast scale. When Westerners point this out they are regarded with mistrust, because many Africans are inclined to reject anything that comes from the West. And of course communist propaganda does its utmost to sustain them in this attitude by telling them that although many people did indeed lose their lives in this salutary process, it was entirely their own fault for opposing 'the march of history'. It would not be fair, however, to say that this propaganda has always been uncritically accepted in Africa. The Kremlin's version of the Hungarian tragedy of 1956 was regarded with great misgiving. On the other hand, Chinese communist aggression in Tibet is generally accepted and Westerners will be told by Africans that Peking was absolutely right in behaving as it did, since its action was obviously part of the general struggle against the same reactionary, entrenched feudal forces which are also seeking to stem the tide of progress in Africa and that they have to be defeated everywhere, whether in Africa or in Tibet.

These arguments reveal the many opportunities open to communism in Africa, opportunities which Peking has either created or which, if they existed, it has cleverly exploited. In this respect China has a great advantage over the Soviet Union in Africa, where Moscow's strength is at the same time its weakness. When the Russians boast about their *luniks*, *sputniks*, rockets and industrial achievements they are, in the eyes of many Africans, equating their country with the industrialized Western countries. Such boasting suggests that the Soviet Union has already achieved a stage of economic and industrial development far ahead of the underdeveloped countries—so far ahead as to be out of reach for all practical purposes. Its great achievements offer Africans no examples which they can follow now. An African visiting Moscow will undoubtedly be deeply impressed by the skyscrapers, the modern underground railway and the giant industrial plants, but they will also make him aware of the vast, the infinite, gulf that separates his own country from the Soviet Union.

If the same man visited communist China, he would experience something very different. Although, like the Russians, the Chinese take care in choosing what they show to foreign visitors, no member of any of the numerous delegations that have visited Mao's empire can have failed to notice the evidence that much is still unfinished and rudimentary.[2] The poverty of the Chinese people is as obvious as the primitive nature of many of their methods of work; in fact the reports of African visitors to China suggest that their Chinese guides made no attempt to conceal these things—on the contrary, they used them cleverly to impress their African visitors with alleged similarities between China's economic condition in 1950 and that of large parts of Africa today. A polite European may conceal a tolerant smile at the sight of China's 'back-yard' furnaces, but an African's reaction is different: he is filled with enthusiasm because this is something he could apply in his own country. He may be impressed, but he is much less stirred by ultra-modern, fully automatic blast furnaces and rolling mills, since this complicated industrial equipment is altogether out of reach for him and his fellow-countrymen and is likely to remain so for a long time. But China's back-yard furnaces can be constructed and manned by unskilled labourers in Guinea or in the Congo. In addition, and especially since the Moshi Conference in February 1963, Mao's propagandists set out to persuade their African visitors (with some success) that the Chinese and the Africans are 'brother races', as distinct from the Russians who are 'white'. Soviet propagandists do their best to counter this and try to curry favour with the Africans by pushing the representatives of their Asian minorities into the foreground. Nevertheless, the Soviet régime as such remains 'European' in African eyes, and at the end of the Geneva World Trade Conference in June 1964, for example, they did not succeed in persuading the Afro-Asians that the Soviet Union is a European and not an Asian country.

On the diplomatic level Peking found a uniquely favourable situation in Africa which still operates in China's favour. When the new African States emerged, Red China had already existed for about eight years. There were, of course, two Chinas, but for States which had just emerged from colonial tutelage, the choice between the island State of Formosa (or Taiwan, to give it its Chinese name) and the vast mainland empire under Mao's domination was not difficult. Moreover, at the Bandung Conference, communist China had already appeared as a potential ally of the African States, and the appeal of a communist State which had managed to free itself 'entirely by its own efforts and without foreign aid' from feudalism and semi-colonialism was much more powerful than the appeal of Chiang Kai-shek's régime in Formosa, which obviously relied for its existence on American support and patronage. From the beginning many Africans regarded 'People's China' as a possible model and example: 'I am convinced', said Ahmed Balafrej, a former premier of Morocco, 'that China's revolution has awakened the Africans.'[3]

Such views are by no means confined to extremist groups and can be found among the African bourgeoisie as well. In such cir- circumstances therefore, it is not surprising that Mao's China found little difficulty in establishing friendly diplomatic relations with the new African States. Official relationships were established with the Egyptian Government on 30 May 1956, and a Chinese embassy was established in Cairo. This embassy is responsible for maintaining contacts throughout the Arab world and it also influenced exiled African groups and politicians who had established themselves in the Egyptian capital. An exchange of ambassadors was subsequently arranged with the Sudan (1 November 1958), with the new Algerian provisional government (20 December 1958), with Guinea (4 October 1959), and with Ghana (5 July 1960). At the end of 1965, full diplomatic relations between the Chinese People's Republic and the following African countries had been established: Algeria, Burundi, Central African Republic, Congo-Brazzaville, Dahomey, Ghana, Guinea, Kenya, Mali, Mauritania, Morocco, Somalia, Sudan, Tanzania, Tunisia, Uganda, the UAR and Zambia. Burundi suspended diplomatic relations with China in February 1965. This means that there were seventeen African countries at the end of 1965 with which Red China maintained official relationships, and this number is likely to increase. Only Madagascar, the ex-Belgian Congo, Liberia and the Ivory Coast Republic recognized the Formosa Government at that time. By comparison Red China was officially recognized by nine-non-communist States in Asia, and Chiang Kai-shek's Government by an equal number. For Europe (not including the countries of the Soviet bloc) the ratio was 7 : 8. In Latin America, Cuba was the only country which recognized the Peking Government.

THE FIRST STAGE

Those who regard the Chinese as the guardians of Marxist-Leninist orthodoxy will have to adjust their views where Africa is concerned. Peking's representatives there are quite prepared to let dogmatism go by the board whenever it suits them. They obviously attach considerable importance to persuading Africans to forget, at least in the beginning, that they are dealing with communists. This flexibility first paid dividends in Morocco, for example. When the Moroccan Communist Party was proscribed in September 1959 (a measure subsequently confirmed by the Moroccan Supreme Court) the Chinese Embassy in Rabat immediately severed all relations with members of the prohibited organization. It is also significant to note that neither Peking's African broadcasts nor the Chinese publications distributed in Morocco contain even a breath of criticism of the anti-communist measures taken by the Moroccan Government. Chinese wooing is now concentrated on the *Union Nationale des Forces Populaires*, the leader of which, Mahdi Ben Barka, former President of the Moroccan Consultative Assembly, visited China and on his return expressed warm sympathy for the Chinese People's Republic. The Moroccan Government has also repeatedly emphasized the importance of friendly relations with Peking and the desirability of increasing trade between the two countries. In fact, Red China has moved into fifth place in the list of Morocco's trading partners. The increasing importance of China in Morocco's trade was reflected at the industrial fair in Casablanca in 1964, where Peking had the largest pavilion of all the exhibitors. A good deal of literature was made available informing African visitors of the considerable amount of aid granted by Peking to the under-developed countries and drawing their attention to the bright prospects for all African countries which maintain good relations with China.

But there is, of course, more to all this than the mere desire to promote trade. Some attempt at indoctrination is made. The writings of Mao Tse-tung and other Chinese leaders are on sale in Casablanca, Rabat and Meknes. Special attention is given to the young Moroccan intelligentsia, and books and other publications are being distributed free to students.

Other African States are treated with a similar absence of dogmatism. While Moscow is constantly attacked for supporting the feudal, bourgeois and unprogressive elements, Peking does not hesitate to canvass the friendship of Ethiopian courtiers, Tanzanian businessmen, and Muslim dignitaries in Somalia and the Sudan. In fact Peking goes even further by establishing trading relations with countries with such governments as Rhodesia and Malawi, and even with the Union of South Africa.

It is interesting to see that Red China has made efforts to include Muslims in its friendship delegations and, through them, to get into touch with Muslims in Africa. The Russians have made one or two attempt to do the same, but without much success. The Chinese have been more successful and even Africans who are otherwise disillusioned with communism are convinced that Red China is friendly to Islam.

A China–Islam Association was officially formed in May 1953, and one of its main aims was to persuade Muslims outside China that the interests of their co-religionists in China are carefully safeguarded. This is, of course, completely dishonest, because at various times in the past Muslim communities have been so dissatisfied with their treatment at the hands of the communist régime in China that they have actually risen in revolt. In 1958 for example, even the Chinese Press printed reports of riots and uprisings by Muslim communities.

Since then however the Chinese communist Government has relaxed restrictions on Muslims, who are now given facilities to obtain the special supplies of food and oil they need to celebrate Id al-Fitr, the Festival of Bairam, which traditionally concludes the Ramadan fast.

In 1956, when a number of Islamic delegates were in Peking as guests at the May Day celebrations, the Chinese Government marked the event by organizing particularly elaborate festivities for that year's Id al-Fitr, and on 12 May a hundred Chinese Muslims celebrated the festival with co-religionists from Syria, Egypt, the Sudan and Indonesia. Later they attended a special dinner given by the China-Islam Association. Pakistani and Sudanese Muslims celebrated Id al-Fitr at the famous Nan Kuan mosque in Urumchi. The Chinese Government had good reason to be pleased with the results of its efforts; the delegates were enthusiastic about the special hospitality given to them as Muslims and assured their hosts that on their return to their own countries they would let everyone know of 'the free and happy life' led by their Muslim co-religionists in Red China.[4]

A similar show, accompanied by a good deal of publicity, was put on during the celebration of the Qurban festival by the Muslim community in China in May 1961. Chinese Muslims, diplomatic representatives from Muslim countries, and Muslim students joined in a special service in a mosque in the eastern part of Peking, and a special reception to celebrate the feast was given on 28 May by Burhan Shahidi, the chairman of the China–Islam Association. Once again diplomatic envoys were present from Islamic Asian and African countries. Addressing his guests, Burhan Shahidi observed that the friendship between the Muslims of China and those of other Asian and African countries had grown rapidly alongside the struggle of the peoples of Asia and Africa to attain and maintain their national independence; he assured them that Chinese Muslims laid great store by this friendship.[5]

In the following year the festivals of Qurban and Id al-Fitr were once again accompanied by a great deal of official publicity, and Peking Radio broadcast a message in Swahili from Mohammed Ali Chang, vice-chairman of the China–Islam Association, to the Muslims of Africa and the whole world on the occasion of the feast of Id al-Fitr. Ali Chang assured his listeners that Muslims in China enjoyed full political rights as citizens and were left perfectly free to practise their religion. They were, he declared, particularly gratified that Islamic peoples in various African and Asian countries had 'hoisted the banner of resistance to imperialism and colonialism'. This, he added with satisfaction, was a great blow to the imperialists and would help to bring about the promise of the prophet Muhammad that 'God will punish those who persecute others in this world'. He concluded by assuring his listeners that 'every passing day' would see the bonds of friendship and co-operation between the Muslims of China and those of Asia and Africa strengthened.[6]

Chinese Muslims celebrated the feast of Qurban on 15 May and there were religious services and celebrations in Peking and other parts of China. The celebrations in Peking were attended by diplomatic representatives from Guinea, the United Arab Republic, Pakistan, Afghanistan and Mali and by representatives of various other Muslim communities. In addition, according to the New China News Agency, the mosques in Yinchuan, the capital of the Ninghsia Hui Autonomous Region, were 'packed with Muslims' for the occasion.

Since 1955 Chinese Muslims have been allowed to make the annual pilgrimage to Mecca, but those who have taken part in the pilgrimages from Red China have impressed observers as being more interested in the opportunity of assuring everyone that China allows her Muslims freedom of worship than in the unique opportunity of practising their religion. Since 1960 Chinese Muslims on their way to and from Mecca have been breaking their journeys in the United Arab Republic, Morocco, Guinea, Mali, Somalia and other countries, for similar propaganda purposes.

Further evidence of Red China's efforts to establish contact with Muslims in Africa and the Middle East was provided in a Peking broadcast on 4 November 1960, which informed the world that two of the teachers at the Peking mosque had been seconded from the United Arab Republic.

Burhan Shahidi, chairman of the China-Islam Association, is also the deputy chairman of the Afro-Asian Society of China, vice-president of the Chinese-African People's Friendship Association (founded on 12 April 1960) and president of the joint Friendship Association of China and the United Arab Republic. Those Africans who have made his acquaintance would probably indignantly reject the suggestion that Burhan Shahidi is a communist and they do not realize that the China-Islam Association is just another communist-front organization.

THE SECOND STAGE

For some time many of Red China's African activities have been concentrated on Guinea, and Guinea has been Peking's first spearhead in Africa. Following the conclusion of a technical aid agreement in October 1959, the dispatch of a Chargé d'Affaires and the arrival of the first Chinese ambassador in Conakry, Mao's representatives had gained increasing influence on Guinea's political and economic life, in particular on the development of Guinea's agriculture—so much so, that in April 1960 the Three-Year plan adopted by Guinea embodied plans for the wide-scale collectivization of agriculture. After discussions which took place at the second Afro-Asian Solidarity Conference at Conakry, in April 1960, it was reported that Guinea had decided to take full advantage of 'the experiences of the great agrarian revolution in the People's Republic of China'. Following this, a large group of Chinese agrarian experts arrived in Conakry in the early summer of 1960. There were also unsubstantiated reports that several hundred Chinese rice-growers were to go to the West-African Republic to reorganize its rice production.

The climax of relations between Guinea and Red China was the visit of Sékou Touré to Peking in September 1960. Until then, no neutral Head of State had ever been received in the Chinese capital with as much pomp and ceremony. Liu Shao-chi, Chou En-lai and Mao Tse-tung had long discussions with their African guest. Enormous mass demonstrations formed an impressive background to the visit. To quote his own words, Sékou Touré was 'quite overwhelmed'. The two countries signed a number of friendship and trade agreements and Mao offered his guest credits amounting to 100 million roubles on terms which were more favourable than the 140-million-roubles credit granted to Guinea by the Moscow Government in 1959. China had previously granted similar credits, on very favourable terms, to other countries, including Indonesia, Ceylon and North Vietnam. These were at rates of interest of 1 to 1·5 per cent per annum. The Moscow credits bear interest at 2·5 per cent per annum but the Chinese credits to Guinea were free of interest. A second important concession made to Sékou Touré was that repayments were not to begin until 1970 and need not be completed before 1980. In addition it was agreed that Chinese experts sent to assist Guinea in its economic development should be paid at a rate not higher than that enjoyed by officials of equal standing in the service of the Republic of Guinea. The psychological importance of this provision can hardly be exaggerated. The Government of Guinea had usually had to foot the bill for the maintenance of Soviet, Czechoslovak and other Soviet-bloc experts and whoever knows anything about the style of living of these communist experts knows that it is at least as lavish as that enjoyed formerly by colonialists.

Sékou Touré's visit to China was not only an occasion for Chinese concessions. In his speeches and toasts the President of the Republic of Guinea dissipated all remaining doubts about his ideological and political allegiance. At a banquet given in his honour by Liu Shao-chi on 10 September, he declared: 'In the struggle between justice and injustice we have taken our place beside those who wage a just struggle for the well-being of all men and peoples', and he left no doubt in the minds of his hearers as to their identity. On another occasion he turned to his host and declared: 'We can assure you that we Africans know where truth is to be found, for Africans know that you had to fight against the same foes they are now fighting. They know that the great victory you have won is their victory too. Africans are also well able to learn the lessons your victory has taught them . . .' Speaking as official leader of an African State, Touré supported Peking's demand for the 'liberation' of Formosa and echoed the anti-American spirit of his hosts by referring to the 'imperialist States led by the USA', which had, he said, already been encircled by the 'people's forces' of the world and whose days were therefore numbered.[7]

Sékou Touré's remarks on so public an occasion made it clear that relations between the two countries were based on certain ideological affinities. A minor incident which took place towards the end of 1959 clearly indicated the pro-Chinese attitude of Guinea's leadership at that time: a lively clash of views took place in the Cairo Secretariat of the Afro-Asian Solidarity Committee over the exact formulation of a message of greeting to the forthcoming All-African People's Conference, which was to take place in Tunis from 25 to 31 January 1961. Some members of the secretariat proposed an uncontroversial text which did not attack the role of the national bourgeoisie in the movement for national liberation, referring to the programme of the Solidarity Committee in moderate terms in order to avoid giving offence. All the countries represented in the secretariat, including the Soviet Union but with the exception of China and Guinea, were in favour of the proposal. China and Guinea alone voted against it, and their representatives declared in concert that the attitude adopted by the majority was in contradiction to 'the revolutionary objectives' of the solidarity movement and would therefore do more harm than good.

It was also no coincidence that at the meeting of the World Peace Council in Stockholm in December 1961 Guinea's representative,

Diallo Seydou, sided with the Chinese communists against the Soviet Union on the question of disarmament and on the granting of active support to the armed national liberation struggle. (This incident has already been described in Chapter V.) In this connection it is also interesting to record that at the time of the Solod crisis in Conakry the Chinese Embassy was the only communist embassy allowed to continue distributing information and propaganda as before.

However, in my opinion, it would be an exaggeration to regard these incidents as proof that Maoism dominated ideology and politics in Guinea, or to regard the Solod affair—as some observers are apt to do—as another incident in the Sino-Soviet clash. It is certain, however, that irrespective of the question of communism as such, there is a large measure of agreement between Red China and Guinea on anti-colonialist policy. Inevitably this has its practical consequences, but it does not necessarily make Guinea a satellite of Red China. This is also true of the much-improved relationship between Ghana and China, particularly since 1961. In both these countries the Chinese have obtained a foothold which enables them to contact and influence the exiled leaders of various African extremist groups, now living in these countries, and in one or two cases they have succeeded in winning them over. This applies, in particular, to exiled politicians from the Ivory Coast Republic, the Portuguese territories, and some of the leaders of the terrorist wing of the UPC of Cameroon.

The promotion of co-existence with the Moroccan Government, the exploitation of China's apparent tolerance of Islam, the encouragement of trade relations with bourgeois régimes and the close contacts established with the leaders of Guinea and Ghana, all these can be properly understood only if seen as tactics preparing the way for the ultimate policy the Chinese communists envisage for Africa, as elsewhere, or as stages on the way to the armed struggles which, they believe, will end in the reorganization of Africa along Chinese lines. In three cases Peking has already tried to act in accordance with these ideas; in Algeria, Cameroon, and the Congo. As far as can be seen at present, Mao has not met with a great deal of success in any of these ventures. Algeria is now independent and, officially, is not in the least interested in introducing Chinese communism economically, culturally, or politically. The civil war in Cameroon has died down, though it could flare up again if the leaders of the terrorist UPC manage to gather their forces together, while in the Congo the Chinese and their African supporters have been excluded from any effective influence on events and their chances of a come-back are very slender. However, these three examples of Chinese communist influence in Africa are typical and what happened yesterday in Algeria, Cameroon, and the Congo could happen again in other parts of Africa if the circumstances were appropriate.

Let us return briefly to the Chinese-Moroccan relationship, which many observers regard as unusual. In my opinion, China was more interested in Algeria than Morocco. After a temporary clash with Cairo in 1959 (the Syrian communist leader, Bakdash, had made a sharp protest in Peking against the suppression of the Communist Party in the United Arab Republic and launched wild accusations against Nasser), and in view of the coolness of Tunisia, Morocco remained the only State in North Africa which offered Peking any chance of exerting influence on the Algerian war. In these circumstances it was hardly accidental that Chinese diplomatic activity was concentrated largely in the strategically placed Peking consulates in Tangiers, and in Oujda on the Moroccan-Algerian border.

Peking regarded the Algerian *Front de la Libération Nationale* (FLN) as an avant-garde anti-colonialist movement and sought to shape it, along the lines of the Viet-Minh movement in Indo-china, into an instrument of revolutionary strategy against France and against the West generally. When the Algerian Provisional Government was formed by Ferhat Abbas in the autumn of 1958, Red China was the first communist country to offer to establish official diplomatic relations with it, and in the following December the first Algerian delegation was received in Peking by the leaders of Red China. This delegation, led by Armaments Minister Sherif, and Social Minister Ben Chedda, had a number of discussions with prominent generals of the Peking Defence Ministry. Before long a second FLN delegation arrived in Peking. This time there were soldiers among its members, and it was led by the Secretary of State Amar U-Seddick, an experienced guerilla fighter who operated in the neighbourhood of Algiers. Two Algerian ministers then visited Peking during the tenth anniversary celebrations of the communist victory in China and after a visit by Krim Belkacem in the spring of 1960, Ferhat Abbas himself followed in August.

This visit of Ferhat Abbas, for which the Chinese communists had been pressing for some time, was repeatedly postponed as a result of the Algerian Government's indecision. The Government was divided into two camps and was unable to come to a decision. Those who favoured closer relationships between the FLN and the Chinese Communist Party insisted that the visit was absolutely necessary if the military aid promised by China towards the end of 1959 were to materialize, while others opposed it on the ground that communist influence on the FLN might grow too strong. Peking offered to send volunteers trained in guerilla warfare to North Africa to assist the FLN, and to provide 20 or 25 fighter-bombers, together with pilots and ground staff, large quantities of heavy and automatic weapons and munitions. For the time being, Abbas used this offer as a means of exerting pressure on de Gaulle, threatening to accept it unless Paris would agree to a solution of the conflict acceptable to the FLN. This attempted blackmail was successful and in the summer of 1960, under pressure from the other Western powers, (which were becoming alarmed at the possible consequences of Chinese intervention) France was compelled to back down on its conditions for a settlement, abandon the slogan *Algérie française*, and consider the alternative of *Algérie algérienne*. Discussions between representatives of the French Government and the Provisional Government of Ferhat Abbas began in Mélun. When these came to nothing the Algerian Provisional Government immediately sought closer contact with Red China; the long-delayed appointment of a Chinese ambassador took place, and the visit of Ferhat Abbas to China was decided upon. Although the tactics of Ferhat Abbas in this matter were designed to secure a political end, military aid from Peking ('its scope is a military secret'—Ferhat Abbas) began to take on more practical forms and the threat of direct Chinese military intervention in the Franco-Algerian war now became a possibility; in fact it was ultimately prevented only by de Gaulle's acceptance of *Algérie algérienne*, the referendum of January 1961 and the reopening of direct contacts between the French Government and the FLN in the spring of 1961.

There can be no doubt whatever about the intentions of the Chinese communists. They were not in the least interested in securing a peaceable solution of the Algerian problem, no matter how favourable the conditions. They did their utmost, by a vast flood of propaganda (including the holding of 'Algeria days' and even 'weeks') and by exerting all possible pressure on Algerian groups and leading personalities, to obtain the acceptance of their own revolutionary ideas. It is interesting to examine the difference between Moscow and Peking on the Algerian question. Moscow, of course, was not averse to making propaganda declarations of support for the FLN. During the meeting of the United Nations in New York in the autumn of 1960 Khrushchev ostentatiously received representatives of the Algerian Provisional Government and subsequently referred to these talks as 'an expression of our *de facto* recognition of the Algerian Provisional Government'. However, on several occasions, from the autumn of 1959 onwards, the Kremlin made it clear that it was interested in securing a *peaceable* understanding between de Gaulle and the Algerian insurrectionists. Addressing the Supreme Soviet on 31 October 1959, Khrushchev declared: 'The recent proposal of President de Gaulle for a solution of the Algerian question on the basis of self-determination and a people's referendum in Algeria can play an important role . . .' He also went out of his way to make it clear that there were, in fact, 'close historical ties between France and Algeria' and that if in the future these ties could be strengthened 'on the basis of a mutually acceptable arrangement voluntarily entered into and on a basis of equality' this could lead to the pacification of Algeria. The Soviet premier went on to make the idea of a peaceable settlement of the Algerian conflict more attractive to the French by a little flattery: 'It is not difficult to see that a peaceable solution of the Algerian question would greatly heighten the international prestige of France as a great power.'[8]

What had the Chinese to say on this point? On 17 October 1959, in a commentary issued by the Hsinhua Agency and broadcast by Radio Peking, they declared: 'French imperialism is now engaged in a dark conspiracy . . . The plan for "cease fire" negotiations and for a "people's referendum" in Algeria, proposed by President de Gaulle a month ago, is nothing but a *sugared poison draught* . . . There is merely a tactical difference in the situation: France is now trying to obtain by a trick what it has not been able to attain by force of arms.'[9]

The differing attitudes of the two communist powers were underlined by a number of irreconcilable statements issued by Peking and Moscow, particularly in connection with the talks between de Gaulle and Bourguiba, the Tunisian president. Khrushchev had come to the conclusion that there was no chance of influencing the Algerian movement for liberation or of turning the 'revolution of arms' into a 'socialist revolution'. He therefore preferred to bide his time and hope for a future phase of internal conflict in Algeria, which would, he felt, inevitably arise out of structural problems. In the meantime, if he pleaded for 'the exclusion of war as a solution' in Algeria too, this attitude was calculated to increase his prestige as a 'prince of peace' and a prophet of peaceful co-existence.

On the other hand, the Chinese communists regarded war as inevitable for communism. Only so long as the armed conflict in Algeria continued could they have any hope of transforming an 'ideologically barren' fight into a real revolutionary struggle for a socialist revolution. In their eyes any other attitude to the Algerian conflict was an opportunistic deviation from the revolutionary strategy of Marxism-Leninism which, they maintain, implies effective, powerful intervention in any smouldering international conflict as the *conditio sine qua non* of ultimate communist victory.

It is not surprising therefore that when the final settlement was arrived at between de Gaulle and the Algerian Provisional Government, leading to the proclamation of independence on 1 July 1961, the Chinese reaction was very cool. At first the Evian Agreement was ignored altogether in the Chinese popular Press; finally it was reported without comment. An editorial on the subject in the Chinese newspaper *Jenmin Jih Pao* was typical of the Chinese attitude.[10] It admitted that if the agreement could be carried out without being sabotaged by the French colonialists, then peace and independence would be assured in Algeria. However, the cease-fire declaration did not mean the end of the struggle of the Algerian people, but rather the beginning of a new one—to make sure that France honoured its pledges. De Gaulle's government had connived at the OAS terror against the Algerian people and the OAS had been supported by the United States imperialists. There was also 'a new grave danger posed by the US neo-colonialists in Algeria'.

Evidence of continuing influence of Chinese propaganda, (particularly on guerilla warfare) on events in Algeria has come with the publication of a report by a New China News Agency (NCNA) correspondent writing from Algiers. The report, dated 22 December 1963, was prepared after the correspondent had toured Algeria for over a year and described how he had been left with the impression that Mao's works enjoyed wide popularity among the people.

This popularity developed during the years of the 'revolutionary war', when, though banned, Mao's writings 'circulated underground often at the risk of lives, breaking through the blockade of the enemy'. According to an Algerian who was imprisoned at that time: 'All my fellow inmates read his works in prison. I read much of Mao Tse-tung's writings, which steeled my will to fight, and strengthened my confidence in Algeria's independence'.

Mao's works also circulated among guerillas in the Aures area. The officer commanding the insurgent troops in the Kabylia Mountains 'repeatedly quoted the theories of Mao Tse-tung to show how to arouse the peasants to fight the guerilla war'.

This account was said to have reminded the NCNA reporter of talks he had himself had with many officers of the Algerian National Liberation Army, who had testified, 'often with faces glowing with admiration', to the way they had been inspired by Mao's military theories to beat back the attacks of better-equipped troops. He also recalled how he had found four well-worn volumes of Mao's *Selected Works* in French and a copy of *Problems of Strategy in China's Revolutionary War*, copiously annotated in Arabic, in the political commissar's office in a barracks near the Moroccan border. On another tour he had been told that the experience of the Chinese revolution was 'a special course given in Algerian military training'.

These tributes to the inspiration and practical advice which Algerians found in Mao's writings during the years preceding the country's independence were echoed by the Algerian Minister of State Ammar Wizgan, who arrived in Peking on 29 September 1963 at the head of a delegation invited to join China's National Day celebrations. At a rally the following day Wizgan stated that liberty from 'French imperialism' had been won 'through people's struggle', and that Algerian officers and men fed themselves on Chairman Mao Tse-tung's works relating to the revolutionary strategy of guerilla warfare. But there is no proof of that from other sources. And at the end of 1965 one has to consider a remarkable deterioration of Chinese-Algerian relations, first because of the banning of the Algerian Communist Party only shortly after the country became independent; in contrast to the Soviet Union, Chinese propaganda did not hesitate to condemn this suppression. Secondly the relations cooled down necessarily after the overthrowing of Ben Bella by Colonel Boumedienne; the Chinese recognized the new government immediately, but only during the first weeks of Boumedienne's rule could one find friendly reactions to Algerian measures in the Chinese Press. How much the relations between Peking and Algiers had deteriorated was demonstrated later in 1965, when the Chinese government virtually boycotted the second Bandung Conference due to begin on 5 November 1965; the Chinese did not even consider Boumedienne's appeal to 'friendly governments' to act in favour of the meeting. They only had in mind their own ambitions and when they found out that a second Bandung Conference would not favour the Chinese position they took a firm stand against the meeting, which was then cancelled. No one can say now how and if China will be enabled to realize one of her ambitions—the still wider spread of Chinese influence in Africa by using Algerian help or Algerian proselytes.

This ambition is even more in evidence over the Cameroon question. Since 1955 this equatorial gateway to the African continent has been paralysed by chaos similar to that which disrupted Algeria, though perhaps not on the same scale. The Cameroon Government, under the leadership of Ahmadou Ahidjo (who asked the French to leave troops in the country even after the declaration of independence and for years depended heavily on this military assistance) soon found itself faced with increasing opposition from the insurrectionary *Union des Populations du Cameroun* (UPC) and with unpolitical banditry and powerful social discontent. This heterogeneous front against Paris and the Francophile administration was at first centred around Ruben Um Nyobé, who lost his life in the guerilla fighting in the autumn of 1958, and then around Félix-Roland Moumié, who died of poisoning in Switzerland in November 1960. Moumié was even more responsible than Um Nyobé for innumerable atrocities, massacres, banditry, arson, attacks on mission stations, government institutions and peaceful villages, and, unlike many other members of the UPC, he made no secret of his communist affiliations. In fact, he was the first *professional communist revolutionary* in Africa. As he told me, he was the son of a poor peasant of the Bamoun tribe in North Cameroon. He went to high school in Brazzaville and studied medicine in Dakar. While a student, he came into contact with the communist movement and from Dakar went as the vice-president of the students' organization of the *Rassemblement Démocratique Africain* on a visit to the East European countries in 1948. From the beginning he belonged to the extreme left wing of the UPC and the process of radicalization in this party was marked by his election as vice-president in 1949 and as president in 1952. In 1955 the movement went underground; as general secretary of the UPC Um Nyobé refused to emigrate, but Moumié wandered restlessly from country to country: first to the British Cameroons, then to Cairo, to Accra and finally, in 1958, to Conakry, the capital of Guinea, where he won admiration as 'the leader of the new anti-colonial Cameroon' and established a centre for Cameroon political exiles. In his last years he was present at all the important Pan-African conferences—and he visited Prague, Moscow and Peking. For a while he was a friend of Nasser's and he remained the personal friend of Kwame Nkrumah and Sékou Touré till the end of his days. He was received by Khrushchev and wooed by Mao Tse-tung—and not only wooed, but financed. He supplied his supporters in Cameroon with arms (chiefly Czech) and with increasingly violent slogans, and although he always described himself as a Cameroon nationalist, he began to play a more important international role. The red connecting threads to all radical and pro-communist groups in West Africa were gathered together in his UPC office in Conakry, which significantly was housed in the building of the National Assembly of Guinea. When the former Belgian Congo achieved its independence, Moumié went to the Congo as Lumumba's unofficial adviser. When the unrest began he founded a school for guerilla fighters, with Lumumba's approval and support, in the neighbourhood of Leopoldville, where young Congolese and Angolans were trained in the practice of guerilla warfare.[11] Powerful outside intervention and the victory of Mobutu in Leopoldville finally put a stop to this activity.

Who instigated and financed Moumié's actions? He seemed to have astonishing resources at his disposal. After his death, according to an official statement of the Cameroon Government, it was found that his bank account in Switzerland showed a credit of 771 million CFA francs (a sum equivalent to about a million pounds sterling!). Inquiries instituted by the Cameroon Government and other bodies cast some light on the question. As the result of a discussion with Sékou Touré on the Moumié affair, Cameroon's Foreign Minister, Charles Okala, informed the Yaoundé parliament on 9 December 1960 that Guinea had obviously supported the illegal UPC and was still doing so. It is also significant that Moumié was travelling on a passport issued to him by the Government of Guinea and that when he died his body was flown from Switzerland in a Guinean charter plane to Conakry, where he was given a state burial. President Nkrumah's attitude was also illuminating: on hearing of Moumié's assassination he announced publicly, 'Now the torch of freedom in Africa must be raised still higher'. On the other hand, President Nasser assured the Cameroon Government that his country had 'long since' ceased giving active support to the UPC—particularly as Moumié had tried to denigrate the Egyptian President in Pan-African circles. It is interesting that Cameroon's Foreign Minister, Okala, even discussed the Moumié affair with Khrushchev while they were both at the plenary meeting of the United Nations in New York. Reporting this interview to the Yaoundé parliament, Okala declared that Khrushchev had said: 'I told M. Moumié that revolutions cannot be organized from without . . . Go back to Cameroon to suffer with your fellow-countrymen, and win power *legally* by elections.'[12]

These statements and this circumstantial evidence expose the existence of a considerable international system of common interests extending far beyond the narrow sphere of Cameroon's problems—a system in which Moscow, Conakry and Accra appeared as the wire-pullers of an extreme political radicalism uninhibited by any moral scruples, and this compromises them in the eyes of the genuinely democratic forces in Africa. Incidentally Khrushchev's statement to Cameroon's Foreign Minister should be taken with a pinch of salt: the former Soviet Premier admitted that he had had talks with Moumié and had given him advice. Obviously he could not admit to Okala that he had encouraged Moumié to persist in his extremist policies. Apart from this question, however, Khrushchev's statement was in accordance with the Soviet thesis, adopted at the

Twentieth Congress of the Communist Party of the Soviet Union and reaffirmed at the two Moscow meetings in November 1957 and 1960, which accepts the parliamentary method as one of two ways in which the still unfree peoples of Asia and Africa can achieve their independence. It is this alternative which is given weight by the Soviet policy of co-operation with the national bourgeoisie.

There is little doubt that, up to a certain point, the Kremlin gave more than mere propaganda support to the operations of the UPC in Cameroon. On the eve of the independence celebrations in Garoua on 3 January 1960, Ahidjo, then the Premier of Cameroon, gave a reception to local and foreign guests in the former Governor's palace. On this occasion he had a discussion lasting an hour with the Soviet representative at the celebrations, Nikolai Pavlovitch Firyubin. Up to this point the Soviet Government had not followed its usual practice of immediately offering to establish diplomatic relations with any new African State; indeed, because of the support the Soviets had given to the UPC they had been disavowed at all banquets and receptions. The long discussion between Ahidjo and Firyubin was therefore all the more remarkable, and the next day an official close to Ahidjo informed the author that this first official contact with the Soviet Government had been brought to a 'satisfactory conclusion' for Cameroon. According to later information from UPC circles, there seems little doubt that this 'satisfactory conclusion' involved an undertaking by the Soviet Government to cease its one-sided encouragement of the UPC and to use its influence to persuade the rebel leaders not to reject out of hand any proposals the Yaoundé Government might make for negotiations.

In any case, it is interesting to note that during an interview with the author, in Conakry in April 1960, Moumié very definitely changed his ground. During this interview, which lasted two hours, he did not even mention Moscow and the Russian communists to whom, up till then, he had always referred with great enthusiasm. Instead he spoke in great detail about his experiences during his stay in China, from which he had then just returned. With this we come to the decisive point of the Moumié affair. He frankly admitted that he had had personal talks with various Chinese communist leaders, including a discussion with Mao Tse-tung on Matworthy's classic book *Questions of Guerilla Strategy*, which appeared for the first time in 1938.[13] Almost triumphantly Moumié produced a

French edition of this book with a personal dedication written by Mao, saying: 'In this book you can read everything which is now going to happen in the Cameroons.'

After this there were further indications of Peking's keen interest in the civil war in Cameroon. These suggest that the Chinese communists were gaining increasing influence over the UPC, whose chief protector they now are. In the summer of 1960, Moumié again visited the Chinese People's Republic and his visit was followed by that of his deputy Ouandié and by at least three groups of alleged trade unionists from Cameroon. A special department for contacts with the UPC was then established in the Chinese Embassy on Conakry, and in addition to Chinese communist officials, there were two 'diplomats' from North Vietnam as advisers to the UPC centre in Conakry.

Further evidence was afforded by Byiavue Nicanor, the permanent representative of the UPC in Rabat, in an interview with the Morocco correspondent of the Chinese Hsinhua Agency. According to the account published in the English-language edition of *New China*, Nicanor declared: 'The Chinese people have never hesitated to support our struggle.' The tone suggests that he felt that this was not the case with other communist peoples:

'The daily growing interest of the Chinese people in our struggle is tangible proof of their attachment to the principle of the anti-imperialist struggle and of proletarian solidarity. *The great Chinese contribution* encourages the people of Cameroon to continue and intensify their revolutionary struggle. The rich experience of China amassed during twenty-eight years of victorious battle against imperialism and its lackeys, and China's great economic successes with "the great leap forward", and with the establishment of the People's Communes, add up to a valuable example for the peoples of Africa, particularly as the conditions of life and struggle in Africa do not differ greatly from those which existed in pre-revolutionary China.'[14]

There was thus complete adoption of Marxist phraseology, the unmistakable confirmation of the close relationship between the UPC and the Chinese people, the reference to the Chinese People's Communes, and finally a condemnation not quoted here of 'US and West German support for France in its aggression against the

Algerian and the Cameroon peoples'. All these already then spoke for themselves. The angry reaction of the Chinese Press and the Chinese Radio to the news of Moumié's death, a reaction which was very much more vehement than the treatment accorded to it in the non-Chinese communist Press, provided new evidence that the UPC owed its continued existence and ability to carry on to the Chinese, whose propaganda urged them to continue 'the war in Cameroon'.

How far it will prove possible for the UPC to carry out the Chinese plans is a matter of grave doubt. There was violent fighting in various parts of Cameroon in 1961, during which something like eighty per cent of all church and mission property was destroyed. In 1962 there was guerilla activity in various parts of the country, and in the following year the trials of captured terrorists suggested that the struggle was still smouldering, though the Cameroon authorities did their best to prevent news from leaking abroad. In the meantime, however, relations between the Ahidjo régime and some former UPC backers in Africa improved noticeably. Cairo, Accra and Conakry practically stopped their support for the exiled leaders of the UPC. The countries of the Soviet bloc also began to adopt a more friendly attitude to Ahidjo. The Soviet Union established diplomatic relations with Yaoundé in 1964 and only China, Albania, and the two Asian communist powers still support the UPC. In 1962 an official Cameroon Government delegation visited several Soviet-bloc countries, and between 19 and 30 September, Victor Kanga, the Cameroon National Economy Minister, had discussions with various prominent communist politicians in Warsaw, Prague and Moscow. In the Soviet capital he was demonstratively welcomed by Khrushchev.[15] At the same time, while Kanga was still behind the Iron Curtain, a delegation of the terrorist UPC, under the leadership of its vice-president, Abel Kingue, was being no less heartily welcomed in Peking by the Chinese Premier, Chou En-lai.[16] The presence of this delegation brought forth great praise in the Chinese Press and on the Chinese Radio for 'the battle-tested Cameroon National Liberation Army'.[17] Numerous reports from disillusioned trainees show that the programme organized by the Chinese for training Africans in guerilla warfare is still going on. In mid-summer 1961 details were given of the experiences of six men from Cameroon who had undergone a ten-week course in China in 1960, during which the 'theory and practice of guerilla warfare' and combat tactics were well drilled into them both in the class room and during a battle course. During their stay in China they were taught how to make and use explosives, how to blow up bridges, houses, rails, tanks and lorries; how to sabotage airfields and telephone communications and how to destroy power stations and wireless stations. They were taught how to set ambushes, fortify villages, and deal with unsympathetic villagers and with sentries. They were taught that puppet agents and traitors should be killed off and that terrorist activities must be carried on. They were instructed in the ways in which to infiltrate vital concerns and organizations in order to reach positions from which their activities would have the maximum effect. On their return to the Cameroon Republic the six men carried documents giving detailed instructions for terrorist and guerilla activities and political action, together with binoculars, cameras, and transistor radio sets. These six men were arrested on their return to Africa. Another group of thirty 'students' came back to Cameroon after they had been expelled from China in August 1962. The students blamed this on racial discrimination by the Chinese. In the following months the leadership of the UPC became more and more subjected to pressures and manipulation by both the Russians and the Chinese, so that it seems to have reached a a point of almost complete disintegration. One of the first indications occurred in March 1964 when rival delegates, one supporting the Soviet Union, the other China, arrived at an Afro-Asian Solidarity meeting in Algiers. A couple of months later, in June 1964, the death in Cairo of Abel Kingue brought a stream of condolences from China and her sympathizers, but not from the Soviet Union. Then in September 1964 the UPC Revolutionary Committee declared after a meeting in Accra that the Chinese had 'assumed a hostile attitude towards them, had grossly interfered in the UPC's internal affairs and had supported opportunist elements which opposed its leadership'. This was followed by the news that Aloys-Marie Ndjog, former publicity and propaganda secretary of the UPC, had returned to Yaounde to make peace with President Ahidjo's government. Ndjog had been in exile for seven years, mostly in Cairo. His 'defection' from the exiles at this time suggested complete disillusionment with the present situation inside the Cameroon as well as in the UPC leadership. In 1965 the position of Ahidjo's government was stronger than ever before since independence was declared on 1 January 1960. The UPC is apparently split into several factions. But there is still a state of unrest in some parts of the country. And in September 1965 President Ahidjo told a Press conference in Paris that 'China has not completely stopped' interfering in Cameroon's internal affairs.[18]

In January 1959, when the insurrection took place in Leopoldville and the Congo limped painfully forward to national sovereignty in a confused welter of personal, political, and tribal conflicts, the Chinese gleefully indicated that similar chances were opening up for them here as in Algeria and in Cameroon. At the end of January 1960, at a time when Independence Day for the Congo was being fixed at a round-table conference in Brussels, Congolese politicians and Chinese agents were meeting for important discussions against the background of the second All-Africa People's Congress in Tunis. Lumumba's representatives came to an agreement with the General Secretary of the Peking Afro-Asian Solidarity Committee, Chou Tzu-chi, on 'practical measures to support the Congolese people in their struggle against colonialism'. According to local information Peking then decided against one-sided support for the Congolese Socialist Party and provided Lumumba's party, the *Mouvement Nationale Congolais*, with large sums of money for its election campaign. Shortly before the declaration of independence several groups of Congolese politicians were in China, and on Independence Day Theodore Bengila, the General Secretary of the African Solidarity Party of the Congo, declared that China had given the peoples of Africa 'a shining example'. True independence, he declared (and he made it clear that this meant the complete exclusion of all Western, including economic, influences) could be attained in Africa only if the people took 'the Chinese lessons' to heart. Bengila also declared that 'the American imperialists' were planning 'a conspiracy against the independence of the Congo'. With this he gave the signal for an outburst of propaganda from Peking laced with violent threats. It was launched at the time of the *Force Publique* mutiny, and has not ceased since.[19]

Lumumba never visited China and neither did his deputy Antoine Gizenga. As a leading member of the *Parti Solidaire Africaine* (which, unlike Lumumba's MNC, openly proclaimed its extremist policy) Gizenga was always a potential ally of the communists. On 8 September 1960 he wrote a letter to the Peking Government:

'The Government of the Congo Republic would be very much obliged to learn to what extent your government would be in a position to support us in the following matters: personnel (volunteers); arms (various weapons with ammunition, fighter-planes, helicopters, artillery, tanks, armoured reconnaissance cars); finances (the sums necessary for certain urgent expenditure); and foodstuffs (rice, flour and tinned food). This urgently needed assistance would make it possible for the Government of the Congo to ensure the independence of its country, which is at the moment dangerously threatened. Signed on behalf of the Premier by the Deputy Premier, Antoine Gizenga.'[20]

Before long the friends of China in the Congo were compelled to realize that 'present conditions' were not favourable to their activities and that there was, for the moment, little hope of extending Chinese influence—as admitted by Mandungo, the Vice-President of the Congo-China Association in a Peking broadcast on 9 December 1960. The arrest of Lumumba, the vigorous action of Mobutu's troops, and the intervention of the United Nations force greatly diminished communist influence, and in October President Kasavubu closed down all the Soviet-bloc consulates in Leopoldville. China's Congo propaganda now became shriller, and Radio Peking, which is clearly received in the Congo, did its best to exacerbate the situation. With the murder of Lumumba it reached new heights. The Communist Party of China organized mass protest demonstrations; 500,000 people went on to the streets in Peking, 400,000 in Shanghai, 350,000 in Tientsin, and 200,000 in Canton, to protest against 'the imperialistic murder of Lumumba'. Addressing the demonstrators in the Chinese capital, Liao Chen-chi, Chairman of the Peking Afro-Asian Solidarity Committee, declared: 'The murder of Prime Minister Lumumba proves once more that the imperialists and the colonialists will never leave the stage of history of their own accord.' In other words, they must be driven from the stage by force in accordance with Chinese tactics; Soviet tactics won't do!

'The murder of Lumumba', Liao went on, 'teaches the Congolese people, all the peoples of Africa, and oppressed peoples everywhere that the imperialist bloc led by America must be regarded as a group of cannibalistic monsters who will never voluntarily grant the colonial peoples the boon of independence. True independence must therefore be won by a *people's struggle*. There is no other and less costly way.'

Referring to Moscow, he concluded:

'Many who have previously harboured illusions about the true character of imperialism because they have not faced all the facts are now being compelled by the crimes of imperialism to recognize the real situation . . . This is the logic of revolution. All the peoples of the Congo, of Africa and the whole world are now taking action. This is exactly what happened years ago in China.'[21]

These words raise once more the central problem in the dispute between Moscow and Peking. In Peking's view all attempts to come to any arrangement with the imperialists are just as hopeless as the chances of peaceful co-existence; no kind of conciliation is possible. The only alternative to the imperialism of Washington is that of an irreconcilable armed struggle, as exemplified by the case of China. There is no denying the fact that the murder of Lumumba greatly strengthened the hand of the Chinese communists and they lost no opportunity of reproaching Moscow with the 'hopelessness' of their 'soft' tactics in the under-developed countries. Incidentally Peking was the first of all the communist governments to recognize the Gizenga 'government' in Stanleyville as 'the only legal government of the Congo', and on 19 February 1961 it proposed the establishment of diplomatic relations. Even before that—on 16 January 1961—Gizenga's Foreign Minister, André Mendi, announced that Peking had promised 'all material assistance necessary for the victorious struggle of the Congolese people'. However, differences of opinion in the new capital, Stanleyville, delayed any effective Chinese intervention, as had similar differences of opinion in the Provisional Government in Algeria. Moreover, the practical basis of communist power in the Congo is weak; unlike the situation in Cameroon, there is very little of what might be termed virulent communism. Nevertheless together with Cameroon and Algeria, the Congo is still the main target of China's Africa policy and many reports refer to massive support by China for Pierre Mulele's movement (the *Jeunesse Mulele*), which terrorized several Congolese provinces in 1964.

Apart from these three areas, Algeria, Cameroon, and the Congo, which are receiving detailed attention, and Guinea and Ghana, Peking's efforts in Africa during recent years were largely concentrated on seeking to influence certain movements and groups in East Africa. Reports of infiltration in the ranks of the 'liberating elements' in Portuguese territory cannot be verified. On the other hand, reports from British sources concerning Chinese communist attempts to influence individual groups and publications in Uganda and Kenya seem to have some basis in fact. Incidentally Peking's embassy in Dar es Salaam is apparently being used more for representational purposes than for involved and devious underground machinations. The centre of Chinese communist activity in East Africa was Zanzibar and here Peking was banking on the Zanzibar Nationalist Party and its active general secretary, Abdul Rahman Mohamed, known as 'Babu'. Closely connected with his headquarters was *Zanews*, a cyclostyled publication completely taken up with Chinese agitation and propaganda and unquestionably controlled and financed by the New-China News Agency, some of its issues have contained only material provided by this agency. Numerous other publishing ventures were closely connected with *Zanews* and the objective behind this organization was to keep East Africa steadily supplied with Chinese communist propaganda material.

Babu's big moment came on 12 January 1964, when an armed group of anti-Arab nationalists succeeded in overthrowing the Sultan on the island. A new government was formed and declared the country a 'people's republic'. Shayk Abeid Karumé, quite neutral, was made President, and Hanga, who was known for having good contacts with the Soviet Union, became Vice-President. Abdul Rahman Mohamed 'Babu' took over the all-important Ministry of Foreign Affairs. He achieved rapid recognition for his country by the communist States, first and foremost by the Chinese People's Republic, for which he expressed particular sympathy in an official telegram. China immediately promised economic aid, and in a broadcast on 19 February 1964 Babu was able to announce the first fruits of this promise in the form of a grant of some

$U.S. 500,000.[22] While in the following weeks alarming reports circulated about the development of Zanzibar into an 'African Cuba' and Babu's name was linked with all these, President Julius Nyerere of Tanganyika was preparing the decisive neutralization of this danger. On 22 April 1964 he surprised Africa and the world with the announcement of political and economic fusion of Tanganyika and Zanzibar, which became a reality when it was accepted by both parliaments on 24 April 1964. Colin Legum commented on this sensational development in the London *Observer*, and with particular reference to Babu's position wrote as follows:[23]

'The decision by President Nyerere and President Karumé to merge Tanganyika and Zanzibar into a new union is as revolutionary an act as last January's *coup* which brought the Zanzibar Revolutionary Council to power.

'Everything now depends on the ability of these two leaders to hold their disparate countries together against the challenge of the extreme leftists.

'The struggle is not between moderates and militants, but between two sets of militants—the one committed to genuine non-alignment, the other using non-alignment as a façade to orientate Zanzibar in a communist direction.

'This conflict has been at the heart of the power struggle inside Zanzibar from the start of the revolution.'

And pointing to Babu's position, Legum wrote:

'Babu's strength came in large measure from his own superb abilities as an effective revolutionary leader. This gave him a clear advantage over the slow, unsure, defensive Karumé.

'But his natural capacity for leadership was heavily reinforced by two other circumstances. The first was the financial and moral support given to the revolution after its success by the communist countries: by the Russians no less than the Chinese. Chinese finance went not only to the Government but to Babu's group in a separate account. This gave him both prestige and financial resources.

'The second circumstance was the equivocal attitudes shown by the Western countries to the revolution. Babu exploited this fully to represent the British and the Americans as the enemies of the revolution.'

Only the future can tell how this fusion of the two countries will evolve and whether Western fears that it will open up new opportunities on the mainland for the communist elements in Zanzibar will materialize. Be that as it may: the role which Babu played during the short period of Zanzibar's revolutionary régime up to January 1964 is an indication of the close connections between China and some radical Africans, and of the effectiveness of the impact which Chinese radical policies have on certain strata of African society. A similar development could be observed in the former French Congo after the right-wing régime of Abbé Youlou was overthrown in a *coup d'état* in August 1963. Since the establishment of diplomatic relations in February 1954, the Chinese embassy in Brazzaville grew rapidly and Chinese influence was noted to be extraordinary, especially in the youth wing of the ruling *Mouvement National de la Révolution* (MNR). In its June 1965 issue the *African Review*, published in London, wrote:

'If the Chinese have been disappointed in the rebellion in Congo (Léopoldville), they are persisting in their attempts to gain a firm hold over Congo (Brazzaville). There are now more than 200 Chinese in Congo (Brazzaville). The Embassy has a staff of thirty and the rest are technical or military advisers, including some of their leading "experts". Colonel Kan Mei, the Embassy Counsellor, is an authority on subversive warfare, who has already figured as the main Chinese adviser to the Congolese rebels, while Kao Liang, head of the *New-China News Agency* arrived in Brazzaville from Dar es Salaam, where he had made contact with exiled African politicians and prepared the ground for the establishment of the Chinese Embassy in Burundi. Now the Chinese are concentrating on building up the army and the *Jeunesse* movement in Brazzaville with the help of other Communist and Arab States.

'The Chinese military mission consists of twenty officers, and liaison officers have been attached to every command of the new "People's Army", one of whose chief officers, Felix Mouzoubakani, has been sent to the Congo (Brazzaville) Embassy in Peking as military attaché.

'The Communists probably envisage Brazzaville as a model "Socialist" State with a one-party system, a policy of "scientific Socialism", a single trade union, and women's and youth movements closely tied to the ruling party on the Communist pattern. Thus the appointment of a number of young Communist-trained officials to Cabinet positions and the removal of the moderates is, as *Jeune Afrique* says, "a victory for those who are considered to be under the influence of the Chinese Communists".'

THE CHINESE RADIO OFFENSIVE

As a propaganda vehicle for reaching the illiterate, broadcasting has unlimited possibilities and the Chinese communists are taking full advantage of them. For one thing, the presence of Chinese communities overseas provides a ready-made audience for broadcasts in Kuoyu and Cantonese. The first available record of Chinese communist broadcasts to Africa dates from 1956, when broadcasts totalling three and a half hours a week were beamed to Egypt and Central Africa. Since then, and especially since 1958, Chinese broadcasts to Africa have steadily increased. But the following list gives some idea of the great expansion that has taken place since 1956:

Broadcasts in English

1956 Radio Peking inaugurated broadcasts in English to Egypt and Central Africa. Broadcasting time: $3\frac{1}{2}$ hours weekly.

1958 A list of broadcasts in English published in December contained no mention of specific broadcasts to Africa.

1959 Peking broadcasts in English to South and East Africa. Total broadcasting time: 7 hours weekly.

1960 Peking broadcasts to South and East Africa. Broadcasting time: 7 hours weekly.

Peking broadcasts to West, Central and North-east Africa. Broadcasting time: 14 hours weekly.

Peking broadcasts to East Africa. Broadcasting time: 14 hours weekly.

1961 According to a list published in the *Peking Review* in October, broadcasts showed no increase.

1962 (January) Peking broadcasts to Africa (regions unspecified). Broadcasting time: 14 hours weekly.

West Africa: Broadcasting time totalled 7 hours weekly.

South-east Africa: Broadcasting time totalled 21 hours weekly.

1963 (April) Broadcasts to the whole of Africa totalled 63 hours weekly.

1964 (June) Peking broadcasts in English to Africa totalled 71 hours weekly.

Broadcasts in French

1961 Broadcasts in French totalled 12·50 hours weekly. In April 1963 they totalled 27 hours weekly. Prior to September 1961, broadcasts in French were increased to 21 hours weekly by the end of 1959, and to 28 hours weekly by the end of 1960. They were not designed specifically for African audiences but were transmitted on wave-lengths that could be heard in Africa. However, in September 1961 the broadcasting service was rearranged and there were two transmissions for Africa and two for Europe. From that date Peking catered specifically for African audiences and although previously there had been a greater number of broadcast hours the broadcasts themselves had been directed primarily at European listeners.

Broadcasts in Portuguese

1960 Peking broadcasts totalled 7 hours weekly. More recent information suggests that this time is divided equally into 3½ hours for South Africa and 3½ hours for West Africa.

Broadcasts in Kuoyu

1959 Peking broadcasts to North Africa totalled 7 hours weekly.

1961 Peking broadcasts to North Africa totalled 14 hours weekly. More recent information suggests that this time is divided equally into 7 hours for sub-Saharan Africa (regions unspecified) and 7 hours to North Africa.

Broadcasts in Cantonese

1958 Peking broadcasts to South-east Africa totalled 7 hours weekly.

1959 Peking broadcasts to South-east Africa totalled 3½ hours weekly.

1960 Peking broadcasts to South-east Africa totalled 7 hours weekly.

Broadcasts in Swahili

1961 Peking broadcasts to East Africa totalled 7 hours weekly. These broadcasts were started on 1 September. On 20 October it was announced that as from 30 October two additional wave-lengths would be used when broadcasting each of the 2½-hour-daily transmissions. However, it has not been possible to trace such broadcasts on any new wave-lengths and there is some doubt as to whether they are, in fact, being used.

Broadcasts in Arabic

1957 Peking broadcasts to North Africa totalled 7 hours weekly.

1958 Peking broadcasts to North Africa totalled 10½ hours weekly.
1959 Peking Radio broadcasts to North Africa totalled 14 hours weekly.

The following list shows the weekly number of broadcast-hours devoted by Peking Radio to transmissions beamed to one or more parts of Africa (according to information available in January 1965)

English	82	Cantonese	7	French	38
Swahili	24·5	Portuguese	7	Arabic	24
Kuoyu	14				

making a total of 206·5 hours[24] as compared with about 150 broadcasting-hours devoted to Africa by Moscow Radio.

The three main themes in these Chinese broadcasts are: 1. China as an example: the methods by which China was freed from the semi-colonialism of Chiang Kai-shek and the subsequent developments (economic, social, and cultural) in Mao's empire since 1949. These are presented as a model for Africa to follow in its struggle for freedom. 2. Decolonization: Africans are told that their liberation from Western domination must be quicker and more thorough; and to this end it is most important that they should liquidate Western capital possessions and reject all offers of aid from the West as these are attempts to gain neo-colonial influence. Pride of place is given to the exposure of American imperialism as 'the chief wire-puller' behind all colonialist undertakings in Africa. In the summer of 1960 Peking Radio began a special series of broadcasts designed 'to expose the criminal intentions of US imperialism' and to warn Africans against 'the fatal consequences' likely to ensue if they accepted 'so-called aid' from the United States. These propaganda broadcasts were transmitted in several African languages. 3. The complete identification of China with any and every form of African emancipation: according to a Peking broadcast on 30 May 1960, Hu Yu-chi, a member of the Political Bureau of the Chinese Communist Party, declared at a reception for Congolese politicians: 'The Chinese people, who won their victory in a long struggle against imperialism and colonialism, regard the struggle of the Congolese people as their own struggle, and the victory of the Congolese people as their own victory.'

These three themes recur constantly in Chinese propaganda

material for Africa and in all Chinese demonstrations, etc., devoted to African questions, such as 'Kenya Day', 'Uganda Day', 'Help Algeria Week', 'Cameroon Solidarity Day', and so on. The unmistakable aim of Chinese propaganda in Africa is to present communist China as 'the natural ally of the awakening continent of Africa'. At the same time Africans are to be persuaded that by virtue of China's 'special experience' in the anti-colonial struggle for freedom and its subsequent economic reconstruction and class reorganization, that country is entitled to be the senior partner in the alliance. As such, it is called upon to lead the revolutionary forces and to protect Africa from all imperialist intervention. Denouncing alleged internal and external conspiracies against his government in a speech in Conakry on 10 May 1960, Sékou Touré declared that China, in particular among the Afro-Asian nations, had given an assurance that in the event of an imperialist attack on Guinea, it would mobilize its forces 'within forty-eight hours'. It is thus clear that Peking is not only anxious to present communist China as the protector of Africa, but also that these pretentions are being accepted in certain African circles.

THE ORGANIZATION

The strict centralization of China's Africa policy is intended to facilitate a more rapid and effective achievement of Peking's political ambitions in the future. At first the Peking branch of the Afro-Asian Solidarity Organization played an important part in the execution of China's Africa policy, but in the summer of 1960 a special Society for Chinese-African Friendship was founded. The next step came in December 1960 when Mao Tse-tung instituted a 'Special Committee for Africa' as part of the Political Bureau of the Chinese Communist Party, and appointed Li Keh-nu, former secretary of the Party Bureau for Social Affairs and an extreme member of the party leadership, to run it.

All relations with overseas friendship and cultural organizations are now under the joint supervision of the International Liaison and Organization Departments of the Central Committee of the Communist Party of China, and the State Council's Commission for Cultural Relations with Foriegn Countries. This body is responsible for the Association for Cultural Relations with Foreign

Countries together with the appropriate departments of the Ministry of Foreign Affairs, and wherever relevant the Chinese Institute for International Relations and the Chinese People's Institute for Foreign Affairs.

The following organizations are also concerned with African matters:

The Chinese People's Association for Cultural Relations with Foreign Countries. This association 'was founded in May 1954, with the aim of fostering friendly relations between the Chinese people and the peoples of other lands by increasing cultural contacts between them. It sponsors the exchange of cultural delegations, and the visits of writers, artists and scientists, the holding of exhibitions and commemoration meetings of outstanding cultural figures of different ages and different countries, and the staging of theatrical performances. Through these and other channels Chinese cultural achievements are introduced to the peoples of other countries whilst those of other peoples are introduced to China'.[25]

The Chinese People's Institute for Foreign Affairs. This institute 'was established in December 1949 as a people's organization devoted to the study of international affairs. It extends invitations to foreign political leaders to visit this country, and through personal contacts helps to promote international understanding and friendship.'[26]

The Chinese-African People's Friendship Association was founded in Peking on 12 April 1960 on the initiative of seventeen national people's organizations. On 17 April a rally was held to celebrate jointly the fifth anniversary of the Bandung Conference and the founding of the association.

Department of the State Council. The Friendship Association is one of the four departments set up under the aegis of the State Office of the Government of the Chinese People's Republic:

(a) *The Africa Office.* This department, which is also known as the General Africa Directorate, unlike the other three, is under the direction of the Ministry for Foreign Affairs.

(b) *The Research Commission for African Subjects*, which is responsible for the study and financial control of operations in African countries. It is in contact with the State Office, and controls the work of the other sections.

(c) *The Chinese-African People's Friendship Association*, whose most important undertaking to date has been the extensive four-month tour (from March 1961) of a Friendship Delegation led by the President of the Association, Liu Chang-sheng, to eight West-African countries. On his return Liu's comprehensive report on this tour was broadcast in Swahili in ten instalments.

(d) *The Commission for Social Relations with the Peoples of Africa*, which operates directly under the State Office and controls Chinese communists working in the various countries of Africa.

The China-Egypt Friendship Association was founded in Peking on 11 November 1956. In February 1958 it was amalgamated with the China-Syria Friendship Association to form the China and United Arab Republic Friendship Association. However in September 1959, the Syrian Minister for Social Affairs ordered the dissolution of certain organizations, including the China-Syria Friendship Association, and it is probable that the amalgamated organization now concerns itself only with Egypt, particularly as Syria and Egypt have since parted company.

The Asia-Africa Society. This is the latest organization formed in Peking for the promotion of interest in Africa and the propagation of communism. The society was founded on 19 April 1962 to promote academic research in China into the political, economic, religious, and cultural development of the Asian and African countries, and to intensify and extend China's contacts with these countries. The society, whose president is Chou Yang, has over five hundred members, most of whom are research workers and college professors.

Friendship Organizations in Africa: The Congo-China Association was founded in September 1960, with Alphonse Makwanbela as president; a Tunisia-China Association has been in existence since November 1960, and a Nigeria-China Friendship Society was founded in 1961, with C. Anozie as president.

Together with the very active Afro-Asian Solidarity Council (see the special chapter devoted to this organization) these bodies form a close network in Africa and in China dedicated to the propagation of communism. With them, communist China undoubtedly controls the strongest and most widespread organizational basis for African operations, far greater than anything set up by any other communist country.

NOTES

[1] Radio Mogadishu broadcast, 4 February 1964.

[2] In 1960 no less than 800 delegations from foreign countries visited Mao's China; of these, 270 were from Africa. For later years the figures from various sources disagree; cf. Ho Wei-yang, 'Communist China's Policy in Africa', *Aussenpolitik* (Stuttgart), XII, No. 3 (March 1961).

[3] C. Garratee, 'Peking's Star in Africa', *Far Eastern Economic Review*, 25 August 1960.

[4] New-China News Agency (hereinafter cited as NCNA), 12 and 13 May 1956.

[5] NCNA, 28 May 1961.

[6] Radio Peking, Swahili-language broadcast, 8 March 1962.

[7] NCNA, 10 September 1959.

[8] Radio Moscow broadcast, 31 October 1959.

[9] Two other quotations from different sources: on 15 July 1959 the Chinese newspaper *Ta Kung Pao* wrote: 'The Algerian people are simply compelled to continue their just war to a victorious end.' On 15 September 1959, the Moscow labour-union organ, *Trud*, wrote: 'The only realistic way to solve the Algerian problem is by the opening up of direct negotiations', i.e., between Paris and the leaders of the FLN.

[10] NCNA, 20 March 1961.

[11] Radio Yaoundé broadcast, 9 December 1960.

[12] Ibid.

[13] This book had a great influence on the strategy and tactics of the communist guerilla and liberation armies in Indo-China and was regarded as a textbook in Ho Chi-minh's movement.

[14] NCNA, 11 September 1960.

[15] Tass, 19 and 24 September 1962.

[16] NCNA, 3 October 1962.

[17] Radio Peking broadcast, 5 October 1962.

[18] Radio Yaoundé, 14 September 1965

[19] NCNA, 30 June 1960. See also the report by Radio Brazzaville on 23 October 1963 stating that during a Press conference on that day, M. Amany, Centre Defence Minister and Commissioner General Extraordinary for Leopoldville, referred to 'copies of Mao Tse-tung on guerilla warfare' which he said had been found in the abandoned hideouts of the followers of the Gizenga faction in Kwilu province.

[20] *Die Weltwoche* (Zurich), 11 November 1960.

[21] NCNA, 2 March 1961.

[22] Cf. *Newsweek*, 2 March 1964.

[23] The *Observer* (London), 26 April 1964.

[24] Monitoring reports of the Voice of America, the BBC, and the *Deutsche Welle* (Cologne).

[25] *China Handbook* (Peking), April 1957.

[26] Ibid.

Chapter XII

THE FRONT ORGANIZATIONS (I)

WHOEVER regards communism in action merely as a gigantic State machine and international party organization is overlooking one of the most important reasons for its success. Unlike conventional imperial systems and world political movements, communism breaks through the customary structure of organization and creates an additional sphere of activity on an international pattern—a third dimension of attack. This assumes decisive importance when traditional methods fail: when the communist parties are still embryonic or prohibited, when overt agitation is dangerous and any idea of penetrating into the State or sharing power is out of the question. Operations are then directed not so much at the converted as at the innocent, the undecided, the politically naïve. The snares in which they are caught and finally transformed into supporters differ according to circumstances and requirements: associations for the rights of mothers, trade unions, professional associations of lawyers, teachers, and artists; youth leagues and student groups, sports associations and peace committees—all these organizations offer excellent possibilities for camouflage. As front organizations, i.e. façades, they allow the communists to conceal their real intentions. In this way the true aims of communism are kept in the background, and potentially hostile reactions are forestalled.

Even in Lenin's day communism recognized the great value of these transmission belts, but it was not until after the Second World War that this political 'third dimension' offensive was organized on a big scale. Then communists everywhere set out to exploit the longing for peace and human solidarity, and finding supporters in the West, they founded the World Trade Union

Federation, the World League of Democratic Youth, the International Union of Students and innumerable auxiliary organizations, in which a variety of honest, if politically naïve people, reputable intellectuals, enthusiastic youngsters, dogged world reformers, empty-headed babblers, people in dire need of sympathy and comfort, came together to demonstrate 'the essential unity of the world' and to work for the realization of 'high ideals'. Although these organizations and associations rapidly lost much of their usefulness because of splits and exposures, they remained valuable to the communists in those areas where they were still weak and where people failed to recognize the front organizations for what they were. Particularly was this true in Africa and Asia. In Africa, front organizations are enjoying rapid growth and winning new adherents. Today not a single African country is without at least one of these 'humanitarian', 'pacifist', 'anti-imperialist' associations and, as time goes on, Africa is being increasingly covered with a network of the pink auxiliary organizations of communism. There is no shortage of African representatives at the various communist-organized and -controlled (though usually cleverly camouflaged) trade-union, peace, teachers, recreational, legal, and youth congresses; in fact their organizers always seem anxious for coloured faces to be prominent on the various praesidiums and special committees, and in particular at Press conferences. In this way Africans are used by these front organizations as a guarantee of 'neutrality' and as proof that they are 'non-party' and above board. They also serve to demonstrate the world-wide scope and 'growing support' the front organizations are receiving 'among the masses.'

The motives and objectives of this activity are as simple as they are effective:

1. The front organizations operate as a great dredger, scooping up neutral forces and gradually converting them into sympathizers, fellow-travellers or puppets. At first the intellectual bait seems relatively harmless and consists of very general ideas and conceptions, behind which one would not immediately suspect specifically communist ideas. But once the outlook of the victims has been focused in the desired direction, more sharply formulated slogans are introduced.

2. Contacts with like-minded people, who are also peace-loving and decent, even if they are in the communist camp, are intended to

persuade the approached people that they are not alone and can count on real friends in the socialist countries. In all this the communists are seeking to counteract a general unwillingness to enter into engagements and alliances with them, to dissipate coolness and distrust and to persuade the representatives of the national bourgeoisie and intelligentsia of the harmlessness and usefulness of the national people's fronts and unity programmes.

3. As long as there are only a few communist parties in Africa the front organizations serve as the disseminators of communist ideas and opinions and make the public familiar with them.

In different circumstances it might be possible to regard such efforts with indifference, but in Africa today there is a strong tendency, a psychological willingness, to enter into associations with all 'well-meaning' people, in fact, with almost anyone who is prepared to identify himself with the current slogans of African nationalism, provided (an essential condition this) that he is not 'in the camp of imperialism and colonialism'. Many Africans are prepared to risk the definite disadvantages to themselves of co-operation with, or membership of, such front organizations, provided it gives them a platform and a chance to address a sympathetic audience. To arrange this is simple for the communists; they can easily organize mass demonstrations and processions with bands and banners, and arrange appeals, resolutions, and so on. This ability is, in fact, the fundamental strength of communism, its tools for creating and exercising mass psychological influence, for keeping its followers in constant movement and in repeated emotional tension. It uses half the old recipe of 'bread and circuses', and the circuses happen to be the more important half.

Perhaps all this is only superficial and temporary. Even so, the founders of the science of mass psychology, particularly Tarde, Le Bon, and Sighele, have pointed out the profound emotional effect of even short-lived mass tension, and as far as our own particular problem is concerned it can hardly be denied. What satisfies the participant in such affairs, with their fanfares and drum-rolls, is an almost indefinable need for sympathy and contact. They help him to feel that he is no longer alone and on the fringe. He is now one of an applauding, cheering mass of people, all of whom obviously feel as he does and want the same things: national independence, freedom for the whole of Africa, the distribution of the best land among the coloured people instead of among the white exploiters, condemnation of Verwoerd's *apartheid* in South Africa, the right of Africans to a say in all important international affairs—and so on. It made a tremendous impression on Africans when, at the People's Congress for Peace in Vienna in December 1952, 2,000 delegates from a hundred countries sprang to their feet to cheer 23 delegations with 203 African members for their 'heroic struggle for freedom from the yoke of colonialism'; and when, on the communist Day of Colonial Youth, celebrated at every communist world youth festival, boys and girls from the 'free' countries of the world presented bouquets of flowers to their 'friends from Africa' in token of their 'heroic struggle for national independence'. And when, to quote another example, a subordinate official of a tiny break-away trade union in, say, Sierra Leone, finds himself a guest at a World Trade-Union Congress. Perhaps he is at first perplexed to hear himself introduced as 'an important African trade-union leader', but his doubts are dissipated quickly when he is invited to take his place among 'the guests of honour' on the platform and he hears the thunderous applause with which he is welcomed as 'a representative of the new Africa'. They seem almost to be vying for his favours. People from Czechoslovakian, Bulgarian, Russian, French and Italian brother-unions—people he has never seen before—surround him enthusiastically, shaking his hand and clapping him on the shoulder. Every evening he is the guest of this or that trade-union delegation. He is invited to report on his own country, his friends and comrades, and his struggle for freedom. Whatever he says is listened to attentively and received enthusiastically. He also discovers (how heart-warming and stimulating) that these strangers know a great deal about his troubles and what he should do about them. When the congress is over he finds that he now has innumerable 'real friends' and is warmly invited to accompany them forthwith to their own countries in order to get an objective picture of their many social achievements. Within a few weeks he has visited two or three socialist countries, shaken thousands of friendly hands and been shown all their 'socialist achievements': the exemplary health services, the people's factories and industrial undertakings, the 'fantastic social performance' of the collective farms, and the wonderful opportunities for youth. When he gets back to his own country he will babble enthusiastically about all he has seen in 'the lands of socialism'. When the next congress takes place he will not again go alone, but with a whole delegation from his union.

There is another bond that henceforth binds him to his new companions. The congress in which he took part adopted a resolution calling for the total economic independence of Sierra Leone from the West; and as everyone in the hall enthusiastically lifted his hand in favour, our African delegate could hardly refuse to raise his when his new-found friends put other resolutions to the vote, such as a demand for the 'liquidation of the West Berlin espionage network' and the transformation of West Berlin, about which he knows little or nothing, into a 'free, de-militarized' city. There were also other resolutions of a similar tenor: against American spy flights, against the treacherous plans of the imperialists in Vietnam, in Japan, or wherever else the heat was being turned on at that moment, and also resolutions thanking the leading men of the Kremlin for their peace policy. By this time he finds himself voting automatically for everything, no matter what. During his subsequent tour of the Soviet-bloc countries he will find himself surrounded by communist journalists anxious to hear what he thinks of the tremendous achievements of socialism. Next day their newspapers will contain a report (somewhat embellished if necessary) of his remarks under the headline 'Sierra Leone Trade-Union Leader enthusiastic about Socialist Construction in our Country'. On having it read to him he will find that he has said 'Your deeds and achievements open up new perspectives for us'. There are quite a number of cases in which newspapers containing such reports have then found their way to Africa (or the communists have used such statements in their African propaganda broadcasts and publications) with the result that the unfortunate spokesman is called to account by his friends and fellow-workers at home. But that is his worry, and really not very important; the point is that once the man has made such statements and taken up this position he is psychologically branded and has a halter round his neck that is very difficult to get rid of. Thus an almost casual meeting has developed into an engagement. The next step takes place with inevitable logic: he becomes an agent, in the strict sense of the word. He is asked to collect signatures for this or that new communist peace appeal, for an anti-imperialist protest resolution, for the acceptance of Red China into the United Nations, and so on. Or perhaps he is asked to organize a 'solidarity demonstration' to give moral support to the Castro régime in Cuba. Before long he is on his way to attend a six-month training course at a World Federation of Trade Unions centre in East Europe.

This is not just a hypothetic example: one could quote many similar cases. I could mention the names of half a dozen Africans who have had similar experiences. The organizations in the background are not always big, well known, or easily identifiable, and the wire-pullers are well camouflaged. There is (one example among many) an organization known as the *Fédération Internationale Syndicale de l'Enseignement* (FISE). It sounds harmless: an international trade-union organization for teachers. Every year its members hold a World Teachers' Conference, and in 1960 its conference took place for the first time on African soil: from 27 July to 1 August at Conakry. The preliminary material and the invitations were not issued by a Soviet or Chinese vice-president, but by a French trade-union official named Paul Delanoue. No one was told anything about him; he is in fact a member of the French Communist Party and a leading official of the French communist *Confédération Générale du Travail* (CGT). Adroitly FISE persuaded the Federation of Coloured African Teachers, with which it has maintained close fraternal relations for a long time, to ask the African *governments* to choose the national delegations—a gesture that did not fail to please. In consequence, the President of Guinea, Sékou Touré, officially opened the conference and became a member of its præsidium, where he found himself hob-nobbing with the Soviet educational expert, Ivan Grivkov, with Alfred Wilke of East Germany, Fang Ming of Red China, Soebandri of Vietnam, old fellow-travellers and 'new friends', with Delanoue himself, with Oshilak of Denmark, Ballantini of Italy, Miss Azango of Liberia, and Leslie Rodriguez of Cuba. The mask, already slipping, was dropped completely when it came to drawing up the agenda and electing committees to work out 'a common attitude' to the following problems: 1. the development of culture, education and international solidarity; 2. international recreation and peace; 3. social security. In each case the communists and their supporters set the tone of the resolutions on these subjects. Not surprisingly, all the resolutions denounced Western principles and methods and Western 'imperialist educational aggression', while opting for 'socialist pedagogy'. However, although it was a teachers' conference, educational problems as such played a subordinate role; the political standpoint was what mattered and the correct standpoint was made clear in the first resolution adopted by the conference. It was entitled 'the participation of teachers in the struggle for full national independence' and declared: 'We vigorously condemn all the actions of the imperialists because they are leading to an intensification of international tension. We demand the immediate abandonment of atomic tests. We condemn the violation of the air space of sovereign national States and all other espionage.'[1] Another resolution called for support for the struggle of the Soviet Union against the 'provocative' policy of the United States.

The technique is always the same: first comes an invitation that looks harmless and seems to be without strings; then a programme is drawn up in such general terms that almost anyone could accept it. The programme is read at the opening session and various committees are formed in an outwardly democratic fashion to draw up the resolutions for the conference. In between, there are one or two public demonstrations to secure an emotional response from 'the masses', then the conference gets down to a guided discussion; finally, in addition to the generalized, non-binding formulations used as an introduction, deliberate and unmistakable pro-communist resolutions are pushed through. The success of such methods requires that the communists control the show from start to finish, and as they are invariably the only well-organized group with definite objectives (whereas the others are an amorphous mass with multifarious opinions) they find this easy enough. So the same trick succeeds again and again. Usually only a quite minor subterfuge is necessary in order to jockey a meeting or conference in the desired direction. In most cases it is enough to 'cook' the list of speakers who are to take part in the discussions, and to see that the right people are chosen as members of the various committees and commissions which deal with individual subjects behind the scenes. The results of their discussions are then presented to the full session of the conference for endorsement. To give two examples of how this gerrymandering works in practice: at the FISE conference in Conakry, the communist wire-pullers shunted off unreliable candidates into the unimportant committee dealing with social questions. The result was that the communists and their friends had complete control of the two political commissions in which the really important resolutions were drafted. At the Tashkent Conference of Afro-Asian Writers in October 1958 the delegates, who came from almost fifty countries, were asked to submit the text of their speeches and contributions to the præsidium of the conference as soon as possible, the ostensible reason being that this would allow time to supply accurate translations into the various languages. The præsidium also laid down the order in which the speakers were to address the conference, and its tactics ensured that any unreliable speaker was immediately followed by two or three committed men who would efface the effect of anything unfortunate the first speaker might have said. When these safe speakers had had their say, another 'doubtful' could be allowed to take the floor again . . . and so on. In order to deceive public opinion, and even the delegates themselves, as to the number of communists present, and to make it difficult to identify them, these front organization congresses never mention to what party a speaker belongs. In consequence the innocent delegates do not know who is addressing them or what his background is.

The conference of Afro-Asian writers in Tashkent (which has been followed by a number of similar ones arranged by a permanent organizing bureau) and the FISE Congress in Conakry, both clearly revealed what the communists are aiming at in their struggle on 'the cultural front'. The organizers of the conference in Tashkent, capital of the Uzbek S.S.R., naturally did not present the 196 delegates and the 22 guests at the conference with a cut-and-dried communist programme. The main principle, a relatively modest one, put forward by the conference was that the writer must not 'lock himself up in an ivory tower' and behave as an individualist. Instead, he must take an active part in the 'everyday life of the people' and in 'the struggle of the people'. The important passages in the appeal adopted by the conference read: 'The Tashkent Conference stresses the very important mutual interactions of creative literature and the struggle of the peoples. As writers we fully recognize that the great and joyful cause of literary and cultural creation can thrive only in freedom. We also know that our lives are indissolubly connected with the lives of our peoples. Their aims are our aims, their struggle is our struggle, and we fight determinedly by their side against the remains of colonial dominance and against the threat of nuclear war, for freedom, unity and friendship between the peoples.'[2] In an article on the Afro-Asian Writers' Association, which was founded after the Tashkent Conference, the Soviet African official, Sharaf Rashidov, took as his motto the words of the Cameroonian writer, Benjamin Matip: 'The African writer is at once a sort of doctor who prescribes for the people a remedy against colonialism and a soldier who fights for national independence.'[3] Rashidov developed this idea further in writing on the Tashkent Conference:

'Perhaps the most widely discussed question at the conference was that of *the writer's place in the social struggles of his people.* Some writers tend to be suspicious of appeals to participate in such struggles and in public life generally. They still believe that art can be divorced from politics . . . Such prejudices, the reasons for which are quite clear, should be countered by thoughtful, convincing and tactful argument. The ideologists of imperialism seek to divert the Afro-Asian writers from the vital and urgent issues of our time and from participation in nation-wide movements for freedom and peace by trotting out the old argument that the writer is an artist not a politician. But no artist can be an indifferent bystander. The true artist is one whose art expresses the life of his people . . . In the course of informal talks and discussions, the writers who believe in the active, social significance of art succeeded as a rule in convincing the doubters.'[4]

The Afro-Asian Congress of the International Association of Democratic Jurists in Beirut in 1960, and the Twentieth Congress of the International Democratic Women's Federation in Cairo were held under similar auspices and with similar slogans.

Not to be overlooked were the efforts of the International Journalists' Organization (IJO) to get a foothold in Africa and to influence public opinion with the usual methods of communist Press policy. In pursuance of these efforts the IJO held a first African Regional Conference at the end of May 1961 in Bamako, the capital of Mali. Outwardly it was, supposedly, completely independent of the IJO, and its organizers had high hopes of an outstanding success, reckoning on the presence of about 600 deluded African journalists. The author was present as correspondent of the *Neue Zürcher Zeitung*, and was the only representative of the

Western Press. The gathering was not as successful as had been hoped and was attended by only thirty journalists and official government representatives. They came from Ghana, Guinea, Upper Volta, Mali, the United Arab Republic, and Algeria, and from certain left-wing opposition elements in Cameroon, Togo and Madagascar. The whole affair was organized and operated by the secretariat of the communist-controlled International Journalists' Organization, which had brought translators, interpreters and simultaneous translation apparatus from its headquarters in Prague.

The idea of the conference was first publicly mooted at an International Journalists' Day, organized by the IJO in Baden, near Vienna, in October 1960, at which a number of African guests were present. At the beginning of March 1961 the Ministries of Information of Ghana, Guinea and Mali held a preliminary meeting in Accra at which a secretariat was formed to organize the conference and send out invitations to African journalists throughout the continent. Doudou Guèye, a political adviser to Modibo Keita, the President of Mali, was put in charge of this secretariat. Guèye was no newcomer; he had been the vice-president of the IJO and had held various posts in the Senegalese movement for independence until the authorities in Dakar expelled him and sent him back to Bamako. Thereafter, he visited several Soviet-bloc countries. Thus the organizing arrangements for the African Regional Conference in Bamako were in safe hands. The few African visitors who did attend found themselves faced with a group of IJO representatives almost as numerous as themselves, culled from the various national organizations affiliated to the IJO and from the communist journalist organizations of the Soviet bloc. No journalist organizations in the West were represented; either they were not invited or their invitations were sent out too late for them to send even observers.

Under these circumstances the conference was completely controlled by pro-communists and so-called neutralists, and in any case, anti-Western elements. All the delegations from the countries of the Soviet bloc adopted declarations of solidarity for their coloured colleagues' struggle for freedom. There was, of course, no shortage of violent attacks on the colonial and neo-colonial policies of the West, which was said to be using its news agencies, Press services and 'monopoly position' in the African Press and Radio to wage an 'anti-African cultural offensive'. Representatives from the IJO, the International Radio Organization (IRO) (which is also, significantly, domiciled in Prague) and of various associations from other East European countries promised their 'unconditional aid' to the Africans to help them ward off this 'attack of intellectual colonialism' as quickly as possible. It was also announced that various measures had already been taken to this end: the participants were informed that East Germany had established in Conakry the biggest printing works in the whole of Africa, and had built radio studios in various African countries. It was stated that a solidarity meeting, held a short while earlier in East Germany, had collected 700,000 marks. In addition, the Polish Journalists' Association contributed 2·5 million zloty, which would be used to assist the publicity efforts of the young African national States. The Czechoslovak Journalists' Association was reported to be helping to establish Press facilities in Mali. Finally it was announced that the IJO and the IRO had generously contributed 'millions of roubles' in aid, and the leader of the IJO delegation, a Russian named Yefremov, assured his listeners that this was only a beginning and reminded them that the Soviet bloc had unlimited potential.

This undisguised propaganda by the Soviet representatives met with only an indirect response. The representatives of the United Arab Republic sought to persuade Africans to avail themselves of the services of the Cairo News Agency, and Ofori, a delegate from Ghana, announced that all facilities for establishing a Pan-African news agency were already in existence in Ghana, or could be set up immediately by the Nkrumah Government and placed at the disposal of the Pan-African scheme. However, these suggestions were turned down by the conference controllers, who also rejected certain timid attempts to tone down the vehemently anti-Western resolutions placed before the conference. These resolutions were largely the work of a committee including Jean Dean, from Guinea, Doudou Guèye, the Mali representative, and certain extreme left-wing delegates from Cameroon and Madagascar. Finally Dean was elected president, and Guèye general secretary of the Pan-African Journalists' Association in Bamako.

The note sounded by the Mali conference was, on the whole, discordant. The absence of both journalists and government representatives from the greater part of Africa clearly expressed a growing dislike of both violent language and communist influence; on the other hand, it revealed the extent to which the Press and publicity of some African countries were already under communist influence. In the circumstances it was not surprising that the newly formed association of journalists should proclaim its eagerness to co-operate actively with the IJO. In any case, the IJO had secured an instrument of its own for infiltration in Africa.[5]

In the meantime several declarations issued by the secretariat of this Pan-African journalists' organization, in connection with various international and African questions, have provided repeated confirmation of the real set-up.[6] This kind of activity by the secretariat of various communist-front organizations represents the follow-up and the conferences are only one aspect of the activities and efforts of the communist-front organizations. All the auxiliary organizations that they establish have their own executive committees and secretariats which carry out on a large scale pro-communist propaganda almost independently. Apart from the big World Peace Congresses, the World Peace Council (founded in 1948) has the following organizations at its disposal: a council, consisting of 400 representatives of all the individual organizations, trades, professions, and so on, affiliated to the council. As the countries of the Soviet bloc are not in the majority on this council, an executive bureau is necessary. This has only 60 members and is much easier to control. Outwardly it is represented by various Lenin-prize winners and it meets more often than the council, whose effective control it ensures. This is the case to an even greater extent with the decisive body, the secretariat, which consists of eight members only and is permanently established in Prague. The situation in other international organizations (for instance, the World Trade Union Federation; the World League of Democratic Youth; the International Union of Students; and the International Democratic Women's Federation) is the same. The secretariats of these various bodies are responsible for the editing and issuing of the various official publications, which appear in many languages. They are responsible for the ceaseless flood of resolutions and declarations on all possible questions. No opportunity for communist propaganda is ever lost by the World Peace Council, the Afro-Asian Solidarity Conference, the IDFF, the World Federation of Trade Unions, the IUS and so on—that is to say, in each case the communist-controlled secretariat of these bodies issues manifestos, decisions and appeals to world public opinion in the name of 'all friends of peace', 'all trade unionists', 'all peoples', and so on. The demands they put forward represent the comprehensive communist bag, from general disarmament and the admittance of Red China to the United Nations, to the condemnation of the imperialists over Suez, the Congo, Laos, Cuba, and the military bases in Africa. In a world so prone to propaganda, particularly in continents such as Asia and Africa, where ordinary people know little or nothing about the activity behind the scenes, this permanent propaganda cataract, which serves the communists and is, to put it mildly, anti-Western, must be taken very seriously, particularly as communism spares neither money nor effort to spread these manifestations into the farthest corners of Africa. At the same time it is disturbing to note that very rarely indeed do any of the great number of members or fellow-travellers of these communist-front organizations object to the misuse of their names in all the appeals, demands, etc. issued by the tiny minority of communists in control.

NOTES

[1] Cyclostyled report of the proceedings of the conference, issued at Conakry, 1 August 1960.

[2] *Die Presse der Sowjetunion* (Soviet German-language publication), No. 126 (1958).

[3] *World Marxist Review: Problems of Peace and Socialism*, IV, No. 3 (March 1961), p. 33.

[4] Ibid., p. 37.

[5] *Neue Zürcher Zeitung*, 2 June 1961.

[6] Special arrangements have been made between 1961 and 1965 to provide African newspapers and news agencies with material from East European sources. Africans are attending special journalist-training courses in East Europe. In his speech to the steering committee meeting of the Pan-African Union of Journalists held in Bamako on 10–11 April 1965, Sepp Fischer, IOJ Secretary, said that in the last six months alone the IOJ had organized or participated in eighty campaigns in support of the interests of the African nations. The International Solidarity Fund had given 10,000 dollars' worth of support in the first quarter of this year to journalists and their families persecuted by reaction. He recalled that many African journalists were studying in the various IOJ schools of journalism in East Europe and that in 1965 courses would be held in Africa itself. Four teachers, including Professor Treffkorn, the director of the School for African Journalists in East Berlin, would be sent to Accra. All this was part of the IOJ's Three-Year Plan. (*The Democratic Journalist* No. 6/7, July 1965.)

Chapter XIII

THE FRONT ORGANIZATIONS (II)

THERE are three front organizations that the communists find particularly valuable and all three are extremely active in Africa. These organizations are the World Federation of Democratic Youth (WFDY) the World Federation of Trade Unions (WFTU) and the Afro-Asian Solidarity Organization. The World Federation of Democratic Youth is the central communist instrument for selecting, consolidating and utilizing the future cadres of the West, and particularly of the colonial and former colonial countries. The organization was founded in November 1945 in London, and had its origins in the various international youth conferences held from 1941 onwards, when anti-fascism bound together the young people of the East and West. From its inception this organization, which was more vehemently anti-colonial than any of the other auxiliary communist organizations, aimed at being a reservoir of the 'progressive youth' of Asia and Africa. Afro-Asian students and young workers took part in the preliminary conferences which led to its formation; they were present, for example, at a conference in London in November 1941. A resolution adopted by the 1945 inaugural conference expressly declared: 'This conference supports the just struggle of the colonial and semi-colonial peoples for freedom and self-determination.'[1] A Western study devoted to the World Federation of Democratic Youth records: 'Subsequently the federation carried on widespread and successful activity in Asian, African and South-American countries. It was in these countries that it successfully broke into the ranks of the non-communist youth organizations.'[2] Elsewhere, referring to 'the basic rights' tabulated by the league, the study states: 'The basic rights proclaimed by the federation, the right to employment, education, recreation and medical attention, the right to organize, the right to belong to trade unions, and equality between the sexes, apply exclusively to the Western and *colonial* countries. All these rights are regarded as already firmly established in the countries of the Eastern bloc. The delegates of the communist unity organizations glorify political and social conditions in their countries, and invariably present them as exemplary. This means, of course, that the activity of the federation is exclusively directed to the West and to the colonial countries.'[3] However, the secession (from the federation) of many of the youth organizations in the West between 1948 and 1950 narrowed its activity in Europe and America. With the general emancipation of the colonial territories, the organizers and wire-pullers of the federation concentrated their activities more on Asia, Latin America and, of late, particularly on Africa. In the summer of 1964, the World Federation of Democratic Youth numbered the following affiliated organizations in Africa: *Fédération des Etudiants d'Afrique Noire en France* (FEANF); West African Students' Union (London); *Union Générale des Etudiants d'Afrique Occidentale*; *Union Générale des Etudiants Musulmans Algériens* (UGEMA); *Union de la Jeunesse de Dahomey*; *Ligue de la Jeunesse Africaine* (Ivory Coast); *Union de la Jeunesse Démocratique Gabonaise* (Gabon); Wasa Youth Association (Ghana); Takoradi Youth Association (Ghana); *Jeunesse Démocratique du Cameroun*; *Union Nationale des Etudiants Kamerunais* (UNEK, Paris); *Union de la Jeunesse du Congo*; *Jeunesse Populaire Africaine* (Leopoldville); *Alliance de la Jeunesse du Congo* (Leopoldville); *Union de la Jeunesse Congolaise* (Brazzaville); *Fikambanan 'my Tanora Demokration i Madagasikara*; *Association des Etudiants d'Origine Malgache* (AEOM, Paris); *Union Démocratique de la Jeunesse Marocaine*; *Union Démocratique de la Jeunesse Nigérienne* (Niger); Nigerian Youth Congress; Afro-Shirazi Youth League (Zanzibar); Youth's Own Union (Zanzibar); Somali Union of Democratic Youth; *Rassemblement des Jeunesses Démocratiques d'Afrique* (Senegal); Youth Action Committee (South Africa); *Ittihad al Shabab al Sudani* (Sudan); *Jeunesse Libre Togolaise*; *Union de la Jeunesse Tchadienne* (Chad); and the *Jeunesse Travailleuse Oubanguienne* (Central African Republic, formerly Oubangi-Chari).[4]

Apart from these directly affiliated organizations there are also a number of associated organizations which work closely with the federation, for example, the left-wing Council of African Youth, which has about 900 youth groups throughout the territories of former French West Africa. Close links also exist between the federation and the Pan-Africa Youth Conference. The idea of this particular organization was first mooted at a meeting of the non-communist World Assembly of Youth (WAY) at Bamako in August 1959. At a meeting in Conakry in March 1960 the Executive Committee of the World Federation of Democratic Youth decided to nominate a preparatory committee for such a conference, ostensibly in collaboration with Africans who had supported the idea at the WAY meeting. At a bureau meeting of the federation in Sofia, from 28 October to 2 November 1960, resolutions adopted on Africa included one supporting the establishment of an African Youth Congress as an 'autonomous organization' and a centre in Guinea to co-operate with all African youth organizations.

A preparatory meeting in Accra on 13–14 October 1961 was attended by Diallo Abdoulaye and 25 delegates from Ghana, Guinea, Mali, Niger, both Congos, Nigeria, Gambia, Tunisia, Angola, Basutoland, the Algerian revolutionary movement (FLN) and the exiled wing of the *Union des Populations du Cameroun* (UPC). The conference was scheduled to take place in January 1962, but it opened on 26 April. It was attended by delegates from 25 African States, extremist groups being well represented. Representatives from the two communist youth organizations, the World Federation of Democratic Youth and the International Union of Students (IUS), were present as observers. The conference adopted a number of resolutions condemning Western colonialism and neo-colonialism in Africa and supporting the struggle for liberation in Angola, Mozambique, and South Africa. Like other Pan-African organizations, this youth movement will ostensibly remain independent of other international organizations. This proviso will also apply to its affiliated organizations, though they will be entitled 'to maintain relations' with any international organizations they please. Soviet and Chinese Afro-Asian Solidarity committees and other youth organizations sent messages of greeting to the conference and stressed its value in uniting youth 'against Western imperialism'.

The headquarters of the new Pan-Africa Youth Movement (PAYM) are in Conakry and there are secretariats in Lagos and

Cairo. The general secretary of the PAYM is Kanfory Bangoura, who is also *directeur du cabinet* of the Guinean Ministry of Labour.

It is interesting to note that the first meeting of the executive committee of the World Federation of Democratic Youth, in March 1960, was held in Guinea, a country whose youth association was not formally affiliated to the federation. However, close links existed between the federation and the JRDA in Guinea, especially since the federation and the JRDA sections co-operated with other groups to organize the first Festival of African Youth in Bamako; for years Conakry served the federation as a distribution centre for its intensive propaganda in Africa, including such periodicals and bulletins as *Jeunesse du Monde*; *Nouvelles de la Fédération Mondiale Jeunesse Démocratique*; *Jeune Sportif*; *Jeunesse Travailleuse*; *Culture et Jeunesse*; *Bulletin d'Information*, etc.

Like all the propaganda publications of communist camouflage organizations, those of the WFDY take cover behind apparently harmless and innocent material, from sport to the 'Basic Rights of Youth', the announcement of meetings, and so on. Nevertheless, they do put forward a more specifically communist point of view than the publications of the teachers' organization, FISE, or the Democratic Association of Jurists. On the front pages of a pamphlet intended for distribution in Africa there is a representation of the famous Picasso dove of peace, while in the text readers are exhorted to take up arms in the struggle against the imperialists, and to drive the enemy out of Africa by force of arms. A typical example of the aggressive attitude adopted by the WFDY is a book published in 1960 in East Berlin and now being distributed in Africa, *United with Eighty-Seven Millions*. Among other things it contains a list of exemplary organizations and officials. There are 'the heroic youth of the Chinese People's Republic' and 'the young guerilla units in Vietnam'. It goes on to say: 'Among the most prominent fighters for the freedom and independence of Africa, from Algeria to the Cape of Good Hope, are the youth of Cameroon—the *Jeunesse Démocratique du Cameroun*. Every hour of their existence is filled with a struggle for the unity and the national independence of their country.' Cameroon is, of course, already independent. 'Its members [of the *Jeunesse Démocratique du Cameroun*] are fighters and commanders in the guerilla struggle in the jungle. They go from plantation to plantation to organize the young workers. Thousands of them have paid the supreme sacrifice for their burning love of freedom. In the long years of the underground struggle against the French colonial masters and under Ahidjo, the President of the independent Republic of Cameroon, the *Jeunesse Démocratique du Cameroun* has grown to be a powerful organization of 50,000 members.'[5] Side by side with the Budapest officers of the Hungarian communist security police, who fought 'heroically' against 'the Hungarian counter-revolutionaries', Paul Momo, a Cameroon WFDY official, is praised as 'a hero of the international youth movement'. Paul Momo, who is said to be 'a member of the National Council of the Cameroon Democratic Youth and Commander of the National Liberation Army in the Bamileke area' must be something of a 'scarlet pimpernel'. There is, we are told, a reward of 700,000 francs (CFA) on his head and 'gendarmes and five companies of French soldiers are searching for him; but although a whole company of soldiers is near his headquarters, two or three miles away he sits in a hut, the red flag with the black crab of free Cameroon on the wall, and discusses the next action with his fighters. For 400,000 out of the 500,000 inhabitants of the Bamileke area, Paul Momo's word is law.'[6]

With this, the conciliatory talk about peace, the mask of democracy and democratic methods is dropped and the ideological core comes nakedly into view: all the decent youth of Africa who love freedom are exhorted to think and act like Paul Momo and his friends of the Democratic Youth of Cameroon and to take up arms and achieve a revolutionary, rather than an evolutionary, solution. The same tone predominates at the 'world-wide' 'solidarity days' and 'solidarity weeks' organized by the WFDY and the International Union of Students every year; 21 February, Solidarity Day for the Fighters against Colonialism; 21–29 March, World Youth Week; 24 April, World Youth Day against Colonialism and for Peaceful Co-existence; 17 November, International Students' Day. A special Africa Commission attached to the secretariat of the WFDY in Budapest issues the appropriate slogans and instructions for these affairs and for the organization of demonstrations, mass meetings, and so on. The material issued in this connection is full of militant, aggressive exhortations to the youth in Africa and elsewhere about 'the struggle of youth against colonialism and neo-colonialism'.

The climax of communist efforts to win over the youth of Africa,

Asia, and Latin America is always the World Festival of Youth and Students which has been held every two years since 1947. Far too little attention has been paid to the fact that since 1955, at least, these affairs represent the biggest communist cadre-recruiting drive for the under-developed countries, and that the maintenance of 'friendly contacts' between the communist youth associations of the various Soviet-bloc countries with the communist-dominated youth organizations in Western Europe is a purely secondary matter. An unpublished study by a number of West German observers at the Vienna World Youth Festival in 1959 concludes: 'The political accent of the festival was undoubtedly on the under-developed countries, and the delegations present from these countries were generally stronger than they had been at the previous festival in Moscow in 1957. The "anti-colonialist" theme dominated the discussions and the various gatherings in connection with the festival. The coloured delegates were pushed into the forefront everywhere, and they were often appointed chairmen of the discussions and meetings. Some of the coloured delegations were communist, but the majority were not. The main objective of the festival was to get these non-communists interested in communism and to win them over to communism if possible. This intention was made perfectly clear in the preparatory phase, particularly in the matter of finance. As it would have been impossible for delegations coming from far-distant countries to pay their own expenses, the various youth associations in the Soviet-bloc countries sponsored the journeys of groups from Africa, Asia and Latin America. For example, in preparation for this Vienna Festival, the Free German Youth (the communist youth organization in East Germany) collected solidarity contributions on behalf of the Algerian, Iraqi and Sudanese delegations. Naturally these collections and the sums collected in the sponsor countries were utilized for intensive propaganda. A few weeks before the festival special friendship delegations from the Soviet-bloc countries visited the partner countries in order to bring them formal invitations and the cash necessary to comply with them. At the same time, of course, they made as much propaganda as possible for the World Youth Festival.'[7]

There are no accurate figures on the participation of Africans in these festivals. It was announced that 52 per cent of all the delegates present at the Budapest Festival of Youth in 1949 (a total of 10,371 delegates from 82 countries) came from 'capitalist and colonial countries'. It was reported that 2,592 delegates (out of a total of 34,000) at the Sixth Festival of Youth in Moscow in 1957 came from Africa and the Middle East. Some 18,000 delegates were present at the Vienna Festival of Youth in 1959, and 528 of them were said to be African (not including those from the United Arab Republic). The strongest delegations came from the Sudan (108 members); Algeria (55); Morocco (80); Ghana (39); Guinea (39); Senegal (41); Tunis (34); and Madagascar (25). Participation in the Helsinki Festival in August, 1962, was limited by the organizers, but most of the African countries were represented there. There were the following delegations: Algeria (157 participants); Angola (15); Ethiopia (2); Basutoland (2); Dahomey (7); Ivory Coast (4); Gabon (1); Gambia (3); Ghana (13); Guinea (78); Portuguese Guinea (4); Cameroon (7); Kenya (10); Congo–Leopoldville (9); Congo–Brazzaville (4); Liberia (4); Madagascar (17); Mali (68); Mauritania (26); Mauritius (3); Mozambique (2); Nigeria (24); Réunion (4); Rhodesia (1); Rwanda (1); Senegal (124); Sierra Leone (3); Somalia (14); Sudan (85); South Africa (17); Tanganyika (5); Togo (9); Chad (2); Tunisia (80); Uganda (11); Zanzibar (7).[8]

The opportunity afforded by these Festivals of Youth to influence the Afro-Asian delegates in favour of communism is described in the study on the Vienna Festival already quoted: 'The Free German Youth, which took part in the festival from East Germany, arranged friendship get-togethers with South American, British, Japanese and French delegates and delegates from the English-speaking parts of Africa. The well-appointed camp of the German delegates certainly made a good impression, and the generous hospitality extended to the visitors obviously had its effect too. In a discussion between an Algerian delegate and a student from East Germany, the Algerian (a nationalist, not a communist) asked about living conditions in East Germany, including grants for students and so on. He was particularly interested, he said, because he was thinking of studying in Germany. The East German student eagerly answered his questions and offered to help him. The Algerian student was obviously unacquainted with the political geography of modern Germany, and mentioned Marburg as a small university at which he would like to study. Whereupon the German student, who came from Leipzig in East Germany, informed the Algerian that Marburg was in West Germany and that West Germany supported the colonial powers, including de Gaulle. The East German then took advantage of the opportunity to persuade the Algerian to study in East Germany. In the special student gatherings at the festival the delegates from East Germany repeatedly stressed that the universities and high schools of their part of Germany would be glad to have students from the under-developed countries, and that grants were available to assist them to study there. A student from Jordan announced that he had studied for two and a half years in West Germany but was now studying in East Germany. He contrasted his experiences in the two Germanies and assured his listeners that he had found things better in East Germany, where, he said, both officialdom and the ordinary people were more frank and friendly than in the Federal Republic. The delegates from East Germany naturally exploited his remarks to the utmost in the subsequent discussion and did their best to influence the non-communists present... They sought to create the impression that by comparison with conditions in the Federal Republic the greatest possible freedom existed in their zone, while according to them the Federal Republic directly or indirectly suppressed freedom in its own territory and supported the last of the colonial powers.'[9]

This, it must be pointed out, is just one example of general communist tactics towards Afro-Asian delegations. The aim is to create a feeling of solidarity between the coloured delegates and the communists. There are friendship get-togethers in the various national camps, musical evenings and exhibitions, and coloured delegates are particularly favoured in the elections for presidents and members of the various committees formed in connection with the festival. In addition, the regular Colonial Youth Day ends in a celebration of friendship and solidarity with the youth from the colonial countries and from those States which have recently won their independence. There are also endless discussions and constant acts of friendly consideration towards the coloured delegates. Experience shows that this sort of thing is not without its effect, especially as the end of the festival is not the end of these high-pressure communist friendships. During the festival individual and group invitations to visit the countries of the Soviet bloc are freely distributed and many of the coloured delegates are taken in by these flatteries.

All these communist efforts to impress the youth of the developing countries, particularly at the World Youth Festivals, must be judged from a much broader angle. For one thing, only qualified (i.e. tried and trusted) members and officials of the Youth Leagues in the Soviet bloc are ever sent to these world festivals. Before they go they are specially trained for their job and their meetings and contacts with the young people from the West and the under-developed world are prepared in advance and carefully stage-managed. This activity has two main aims: the first is to create an impression of solidarity in favour of the East, to make propaganda for its 'socialist achievements' and at the same time to denigrate Western values and achievements. The second aim is to select likely young adherents both from the West and from the under-developed countries. Those considered 'capable of development' are invited to visit the countries of the Soviet bloc, where a more intensive attempt is made to win them over by grants, training and indoctrination.

These had also been the main aims for the proposed 9th Youth Festival scheduled for July 1965 in Algiers. About 25,000 people had been expected to take part in the first attempt to hold such a festival outside Europe. But after the *coup d'état* of Colonel Boumedienne against Ben Bella, the Soviet and East European members of the International Preparatory Committee, who had been living in Algiers for some time, hastily left, and on 10 July 1965 decided at a meeting in Tampere, Finland, to postpone the Algiers festival. The WFDY thus suffered a serious setback in Africa.

NOTES

[1] *World Youth and Peace* (Prague, 1945), pp. 27 ff.

[2] 'Aus Politik und Zeitgeschichte', supplement to the weekly *Das Parlament* (Bonn), 31 July 1957.

[3] Ibid.

[4] From various sources, especially World Federation of Democratic Youth publications.

[5] *Vereint mit 87 Millionen* ([East] Berlin), (1960), pp. 14 ff.

[6] Ibid., p. 102.

[7] This study is in the author's possession.

[8] *Frieden und Freundschaft? Weltjugendfestspiele, Funktion und Wirkung* (Bonn, 1964), pp. 50–6.

[9] Ibid.

Chapter XIV

COMMUNISM AND THE TRADE UNIONS

THE most important of the communist front organization is undoubtedly the World Federation of Trade Unions (WFTU). It was founded after the Second World War, ostensibly as an uncommitted and non-party international organization of trade and labour unions from both East and West, but despite the fact that the Western affiliated organizations were represented in the præsidium and the secretariat, it was not long before it degenerated into a mere tool of the Kremlin and became the successor of the Profintern, the international communist trade union federation of the Comintern era. In 1949, when the cold war was at its height, disappointed and embittered democratic trade unionists from the West turned their backs on it and founded the International Confederation of Free Trade Unions (ICFTU). This new organization quickly gained the upper hand in the West and in the neutral countries and former colonial territories, but despite impressive successes it has never gained the upper hand in Africa. Attempts to draw trade-union organizations in the European-dominated areas of Africa to the ICFTU have not been successful and the communist WFTU has even managed to worm its way into sections of the ICFTU in Africa.

This development was facilitated by a number of psychological and tactical errors on the part of the ICFTU, which the WFTU, with its clearer political and strategic objectives and more elastic tactics, was able to exploit to the full. To begin with, the choice of Brussels as the seat of the ICFTU Executive was a handicap as far as Africa was concerned, because for the politically-conscious élite of Africa Brussels was a centre of colonialism. Furthermore, the fact that when socialist and labour parties were in power in the metropolitan countries, white trade-union leaders in Belgium and Britain, directly or indirectly, supported the policies of their governments and took no decisive steps to end the colonial régimes and abolish discrimination greatly damaged their credit in the eyes of their African colleagues. Moreover, the ICFTU hesitated for a long time before it appointed Africans to any responsible posts in its secretariat and executive organs, or before it gave any signs of taking Africans seriously. Initially, the ICFTU rarely made public condemnations of colonialism in general or of the Algerian policy of France and the racial terror in South Africa in particular; when it did so, its phraseology was felt by Africans to be tortuous and too generalized.

The facts show that the ICFTU lacked understanding of the symbiosis that exists between nationalism and trade unionism in Africa. The absence of a widespread industrial working class in Africa was regarded as an obstacle to serious trade-union activity. In other words, the ICFTU made the mistake of approaching African reality with European ideas; when in consequence it achieved nothing, it preferred to ignore a reality that refused to fit in with its preconceived notions. The situation was aggravated by sectarian ideas about the 'non-political' nature of trade-union tasks. For a while the West simply refused to co-operate with Africans who regarded trade unions as a spring-board for a political career, and under pressure of circumstances organized trade unions as a substitute for political parties, because the colonial authorities prohibited or hampered direct party-political activities.

On the other hand, the communists, with their keen eye for cadre policy and tactical manoeuvres, immediately recognized the favourable opportunities for infiltration offered by the African trade unions and realized that important political forces were crystallizing in these bodies. In all the independent governments in Africa today there are cabinet ministers who, at one time or another, were active in the trade unions—perhaps even founded them and certainly used them as a platform for the anti-colonial struggle. To mention only a few prominent personalities with trade-union backgrounds: Tom Mboya in Kenya, Sékou Touré in Guinea, and Cyrille Adoula in the Congo. As all these men harnessed the power of the trade unions into political channels during their anti-colonial struggle it is quite natural that now, in the post-colonial era, they should realize that the trade unions can fulfil important functions and carry out certain ideas on behalf of the government outside the socio-economic sphere. They are, in fact, using the trade unions as a 'transmission belt' and it is no coincidence that Nkrumah, the ambitious President of Ghana, makes a special point of using the trade unions in his campaign to achieve his Pan-African objectives. In a speech delivered on 14 March 1960 he declared:

'If the unity of our continent is to become a reality . . . the working class must take its place as the advance guard in the struggle against poverty, ignorance and sickness. A most important aspect of the establishment of African unity is the achievement of unity in the trade-union sphere by the formation of an All-Africa trade union federation.'[1]

Sékou Touré has declared: 'The path that Africa will take depends in no small measure on the African trade unions. Their decisions will be of decisive importance for the whole continent.'[2] Walter Ulbricht, the East German communist leader, has expressed similar ideas. Speaking at a reception to mark the twenty-second meeting of the executive committee of the communist WFTU on 3 February 1961 in East Berlin, he said: 'The time has come to give very active support to the free anti-imperialist trade-union movement, particularly in Africa. A strong, free trade-union movement in the African States is the most important guarantee of a democratic development.'[3]

This is not the first time that such ideas have influenced the African policy of the communists. As early as 1928 the Profintern established an International Committee of Coloured Workers, whose chief backing came from the Communist Party of South Africa, which was then a legal party.

From 1944 onwards, taking advantage of their position as partners in the French Popular Front Government, the French communists established branches of their *Confédération Générale du Travail* (CGT) in French West and Central Africa and in Madagascar. Some of these groups were still in existence in 1949. But at first it was the democratic ICFTU that made rapid progress, particularly in the English-speaking areas of Africa, partly because the various colonial administrations, particularly in East Africa, answered every attempt to affiliate to the communist WFTU by suppressing the groups in question. However, one way or the other, in the space of seven years the membership of the African sections affiliated to the ICFTU rose from 58,000 (in 1952) to 1·7 million (in 1959). Today the ICFTU in Africa is being seriously threatened from several directions. Pan-African, neutralist, and openly communist tendencies are growing, even in some organizations affiliated to the ICFTU, which had recently declared the Brussels executive to be a bulwark of free trade unionism.

Developments in Nigeria are typical: as recently as 1960 the Trade Union Congress of Nigeria (TUCN) was thought to be relatively immune to neutralist and left-wing influence, but since 1961 this body, which (with over 200,000 members) is easily the strongest affiliated organization of the ICFTU in Africa, has been hopelessly disrupted, and there is reason to fear that the rump organization—all that is left in the ICFTU and now known as the Nigerian Labour Congress (NLC)—will decline still further. The leaders of this rump, Adebola and Borha, insist that the majority of the Nigerian workers are behind them, but this can no more be proved than can the contrary contention of their opponents.

The first cracks in the TUCN edifice appeared in the autumn of 1959, when Imoudu, President of the TUCN and an active, popular personality, was invited to visit East Germany, the Soviet Union and Red China. Imoudu accepted without consulting his colleagues, and for several weeks he was passed from one Iron-Curtain host to another. He reported that he had been shown 'many impressive things' and given 'many proofs of sincere solidarity'. The result was that Imoudu allowed himself to be persuaded that only the Communist WFTU could offer African workers 'a future, and selfless assistance in their struggle for freedom'.[4]

When Imoudu returned to Lagos he made no attempt to deny holding views which the communists had, in the meantime, ascribed to him. He began to agitate at once for the withdrawal of the TUCN from the ICFTU, whereupon its general secretary, Borha, dismissed him from office. With this a split became unavoidable. The TUCN elected Adebola its new president and Imoudu and his friends founded the Nigerian Trade Union Congress (NTUC). However, this new body did not, as had been announced, formally affiliate itself to the communist WFTU. Instead Imoudu began to campaign vigorously for the affiliation of his organization to an 'independent All-African Trade Union Federation', whose initiators were the government-sponsored trade unions of Ghana and Guinea.

Borha and Adebola immediately took him up on this point. Although they were still loyal to the ICFTU they declared that they, too, were in favour of establishing an All-African Trade Union Federation, but that the affiliated bodies would have to decide whether to continue their association with the ICFTU or the WFTU. There would have to be firm guarantees that the federation would not be controlled by Ghana, Guinea or the WFTU. In particular the leaders of the TUCN accused the break-away leader, Imoudu, of having accepted at least £5,500 from John Tettegah, president of Ghana's government-sponsored trade union; these funds demonstrably came from the Government of Ghana and the WFTU. They also alleged that a Czechoslovak official of the WFTU had come from Ghana to Nigeria to give the Imoudu group practical instructions and that during the course of the previous year a number of Imoudu's followers had been sent, via Accra and Conakry, to training schools behind the Iron Curtain to take special courses for African trade-union leaders. Moreover, they declared, the WFTU had offered Imoudu 500 grants, through the Ghana and Guinea unions, to train his followers at various centres in the Soviet-bloc countries.[5]

Imoudu did not deny all these charges. He announced, for example, that in accordance with its declared neutrality his organization was prepared to accept training grants from both camps, from Britain as well as from Russia, from the United States as well as from East Germany. But he could hardly be blamed, he added, if the only grants that had been offered had been from the Soviet-bloc countries. Instead of blaming him, his detractors should complain to the 'neglectful' Western countries. Imoudu answered the charge that he had entered into close relations with the WFTU, although such a thing was clearly at odds with his expressed intention 'to build up a trade-union movement completely independent of the government, the employers, or foreign tutelage', by saying that the WFTU was not opposed to his programme, which was 'a completely autonomous matter'. He declared that he was not under the tutelage of Moscow or Peking, whereas the ICFTU was certainly subject to pressure from Washington and London.[6]

Unfortunately, as was proved during the strike in 1964, such attitudes meet with a good deal of approval from trade unionists in Nigeria. Talks with Nigerian working men indicate that the more radical attitude of Imoudu is often closer to their idea of what trade-union policy ought to be than the more cautious, prudent policy of Borha and Adebola. At a trade-union meeting in Lagos the audience booed every time Imoudu's speakers mentioned Washington, London or Brussels, and cheered whenever they talked about 'the peaceful policy' of Moscow, or 'the solidarity aid of the East-European working class'. There is another psychological factor which must be reckoned with: the cold, reserved and 'bourgeois' attitude of certain European and American trade-union leaders, their conventional habits, their constant appeals for moderation. To African workers this seems to suggest that Imoudu is right when he denounces the representatives of the ICFTU as 'disguised capitalists, bought and paid for by Western colonialism and neo-colonialism' in order to keep the bridle on the African workers.

Nevertheless, the democratic forces in the Nigerian trade-union movement succeeded in calling a general congress on 5 May 1962 in Ibadan, when 659 delegates supported their proposal for continued affiliation to the ICFTU. But no fewer than 407 delegates dissented, withdrew their previous consent to the organization of all the trade-union groups in the Nigerian Labour Congress and continued their old line in the NTUC, which, according to reports in the Lagos Press, is still based on close co-operation with the communist WFTU. The NTUC also sent a delegation to the Fifth Congress of the WFTU, which took place from 4 to 15 December 1961 in Moscow. Imoudu himself, and Ibrahim Nok, general secretary of the NTUC, were members of this delegation, and at the congress they both sharply attacked the ICFTU. Imoudu, chairman of the NTUC, called for international trade-union unity within the socialist camp and the victory of socialism throughout the world. It is interesting to note that at the beginning of 1963 the NTUC was conducting vigorous propaganda against the Common Market and Nigeria's association with it, in accordance with the line laid down in December 1962 at a conference on the consequences of the Common Market held by the WFTU in Leipzig.[7]

The leaders of the ICFTU might feel easier if developments in Nigeria were exceptional, but this is not the case: there are officials like Imoudu in almost all the African trade-union bodies affiliated to the ICFTU. Their slogan is 'Break with Brussels', and they make life very difficult for the moderate trade-union leaders by their demagogic, anti-colonial and class-struggle slogans. Not all of them betray their sympathy for the WFTU as openly as Imoudu. Many are just drifting along in the wake of the Pan-African ideas propagated by Accra and Conakry, and few are dismayed by the close relationship between some of the African and communist trade unions. However, it is precisely this relationship which provides the key to an understanding of recent events in African trade unions. The relationship has its history in the rise and decline of the first supranational trade-union link-up in the *Union Générale des Travailleurs de l'Afrique Noire* (UGTAN).

After a preliminary conference in 1957 in Cotonou, Dahomey, UGTAN was officially founded in Conakry in January 1959. It embraced trade-union groups in Guinea, Senegal, Mali, Nigeria, Togo, the Ivory Coast, Upper Volta, Dahomey, Cameroon, Congo–Brazzaville, Gabon, the Central African Republic and Mauritania. Most of these groups had been founded from 1944 onwards by French communists of the CGT, and their leading members had all been trained in communist trade-union schools in France, some even in training centres behind the Iron Curtain. Sékou Touré, who was elected president of UGTAN, had been a delegate to the third congress of the WFTU in Moscow. The second prominent man in UGTAN was Diallo Abdoulaye, later Guinea's Minister Resident in Accra. Until the formation of UGTAN, he was vice-president of the WFTU, and as late as the WFTU council meeting in Sofia in September 1956 it was he who presented the official report on 'the struggle against colonialism'. Diallo Seydou, who was elected general secretary of UGTAN, was frequently seen at meetings of the WFTU. He was present as an observer at its council meeting in June 1960 in Peking. Radio Peking and the New-China Agency both reported that he had 'extremely useful discussions with various highly-placed communist leaders'. Another prominent UGTAN official who was present at this council meeting was Yao Ngo Blaise, leader of the now illegal UGTAN organization in the Ivory Coast Republic. After his expulsion by Houphouet-Boigny he went to Conakry, where he is now active in the UGTAN central organization. It is interesting to note that at the meeting in Peking, Blaise was not thinly disguised as an observer (as was his general secretary) but was openly a delegate. Thus we have the odd situation that one of the UGTAN groups directed from Conakry is allowed to maintain its membership of the communist WFTU, whereas the central UGTAN organization in the same town is declared to be 'a completely independent body'.

This is by no means the only anomaly. After a short phase in which UGTAN sought to establish friendly relations with the West, it has now practically no contact at all with the democratic ICFTU and its affiliated organizations. On the other hand, 'mutual consultations' are constantly taking place between UGTAN and the labour organizations in the Soviet-bloc countries. The communist Press, from East Berlin to Peking, is continually publishing reports of the visits of UGTAN representatives to the communist countries and of return visits by representatives of the labour organizations in these countries to Conakry. The WFTU runs its liberal programme of grants through the UGTAN central organization and its subordinate body in Accra, where John Tettegah is one of the three UGTAN vice-presidents. It woos African trade unionists of all shades, including even the Christian organizations. The WFTU also uses Conakry for the distribution of books, pamphlets, films, technical equipment and money from the Solidarity Fund. The WFTU financed UGTAN's Central Training School in Dalaba (Guinea) and the African Workers' University in Conakry, where communist officials from the Soviet Union, Red China, Czechoslovakia and East Germany dominated the scene. No secret was made of this, for example, 'at a ceremony in Conakry on 4 November 1962 in connection with the opening of the sixth trade-union course run by the WFTU-sponsored African Workers' University, when Maurice Gastand, the director, thanked the WFTU and its member-organizations for their continued support'.[8]

However, after the inaugural congress in January 1959, this obvious link-up between UGTAN and the WFTU, and the use of UGTAN by the Guinea Government for its own purposes, resulted in much resentment outside Guinea. The UGTAN central organization in Conakry rather obviously ignored the 'national characteristics' and programmes of the affiliated West and Equatorial African sections. The differing tendencies in the States of the former *Communauté*, the growing independence of the African partners, and increasing resentment against Guinea resulted in 1959–61 in a crisis within UGTAN. UGTAN in Senegal split into three parts, an orthodox and two autonomous sections, under Cissé Alioune and Guèye Abbas respectively. The affiliated organization in the Ivory Coast Republic has no longer any legal standing. In these territories, and elsewhere throughout the West and Central African countries, the *Confédération Africaine des Syndicats Libres* (an organization founded by the French *Force Ouvrière*) made considerable progress until the new African governments began to force through their own preference for government-sponsored organizations. It proved impossible to check the decline of UGTAN, even by closer co-operation with the Ghana TUC, which had discontinued its original affiliation with the ICFTU, or even as a result of the break-up of the Mali Federation and the consequent re-establishment of closer relations between the Sudanese UNTS (now the *Confédération Nationale des Syndicats du Mali*—CNSM) and Conakry. In consequence, it became clear as early as the spring of 1960 that the old UGTAN was no longer viable. The hopes of the extreme Marxist initiators of UGTAN to establish a permanent, left-wing, anti-Western trade-union monolith in what had once been French West and Equatorial Africa were only partly fulfilled.

The left-wing forces now transferred their activities from regional bloc-building to the idea of Pan-African trade unionism. Even during UGTAN's inaugural congress in January 1959, discussions took place between representatives of UGTAN and trade-union officials from Ghana, Tunis, Morocco and Algeria; and these discussions resulted in a joint appeal for the speedy formation of an All-Africa Trade Union Federation. At Nkrumah's suggestion the central committee of the All-Africa People's Conference held a preparatory trade-union conference in Accra on 6 November 1959. A special commission under the leadership of Mahjoub Ben Seddik, general secretary of the Moroccan UMT, got in touch with trade-union organizations throughout Africa. Further discussions took place at the Second All-African People's Conference in Tunis at the end of January 1960. May 1960 was fixed as the provisional date and Casablanca the provisional venue for the proposed inaugural congress of the All-Africa Trade Union Federation.

However, this Tunis conference revealed considerable differences of opinion, and a number of organizations affiliated to the democratic ICFTU firmly rejected the proposed statutes of the new organization because they excluded the continued affiliation of any of the member-organizations to the ICFTU—or to the WFTU. Incidentally the WFTU had already instructed its African groups to bank completely on the Pan-Africa card and to oppose any form of double affiliation. In other words, the WFTU adopted a tactic completely in accord with Lenin's instructions: 'In order to get into the trade unions, to stay in them and be able under all circumstances to carry on communist work in them, we must be prepared to adopt all possible tricks, to use guile and illegal methods, to keep quiet if necessary and conceal the truth.'[9]

Still more vehement clashes between the 'neutralist' (i.e. pro-communist) elements and the democratic trade unionists took place at various meetings in the spring of 1960. This was particularly evident at a Seminar for African Youth, held in Tunis in April. There was a battle between the two leaders of the opposing factions, Diallo Seydou and Ahmed Tlili (UGTT, Tunisia). Tlili accused Diallo of being a tool of Moscow and Diallo accused Tlili of being a tool of 'international monopoly capitalism and Western colonialism'. Despite the pressure brought to bear on him, Tlili insisted that he and his followers would join the proposed Pan-African trade-union federation only if it were possible for their organization (the UGTT) to remain affiliated to the ICFTU. It proved impossible to come to any agreement. Some of the trade unions vacillated, adopting first one position then the other. The Casablanca inaugural congress had to be postponed, first until the following August, then for a whole year.

The most important of these vacillating trade-union organizations was the Moroccan Federation (UNT), with 600,000 members, and the Algerian *Union Générale des Travailleurs Algériens* (UGTA) with 110,000 members. Since the spring of 1960 both sides—the so-called neutralist, pro-communist organizations and the pro-Western organizations—have been doing their utmost to win them over. After tough negotiations the ICFTU succeeded in persuading UGTA, which sympathized with the FLN, to abandon its original position favouring the radical programme of Ghana and Guinea. Negotiations with the Moroccan representatives, in particular with Ben Seddik, were more difficult. Ben Seddik had meanwhile come into conflict with his own government and gone over to the opposition *Union Nationale des Forces Populaires* led by Mehdi Ben Barka.

Ben Seddik's zigzag policy is understandable in view of the fact that no other African trade-union organization is being so ardently wooed by the Soviet bloc as the UMT; and since the autumn of 1959 the East German, government-sponsored trade-union organization has concentrated its efforts on its Moroccan colleagues. At one time the Moroccans were regarded as being completely immune to communist influence, but the situation changed when Ben Seddik visited East Berlin in October 1959 as a guest at the celebration of the tenth anniversary of the foundation of the East German Republic. While in East Berlin he had discussions with members of the præsidium and secretariat of the FDGB, the East German trade-union organization, including its chairman, Herbert Warnke. Ben Seddik revisited East Berlin in July 1960 as the leader of a twelve-man 'students' delegation'. On this occasion, after further discussions with East German trade-union leaders, a decision was made to 'intensify trade-union co-operation' between the UMT and the FDGB. After this it was hardly surprising to learn that the UMT was sending 'an observer' to the council meeting of the WFTU in Peking, or to hear more anti-Western statements from its leaders.

The International Confederation of Arab Trade Unions (ICATU) is affiliated neither to the ICFTU nor to the WFTU, and on Nasser's instructions is steering a neutralist course. But for a long time after its formation in March 1956 it was under strong communist influence; in fact, its general secretary, Fathy Kamal, was present at the fourth congress of the communist WFTU in Leipzig in October 1957, where he delivered a fierce attack on the West and in particular on the ICFTU. In this situation Louis Saillant, general secretary of the WFTU, was able to report with satisfaction to the executive meeting in Prague in July 1958 that relations between the WFTU and the ICATU had developed into 'close co-operation'. He even assured the executive that from then on co-operation between the two organizations would be 'permanent and fruitful, and serve as a visible and exemplary instance of the development of that community of action which the WFTU has been striving for since its foundation.' However, things did not go so smoothly, and a few months later the communists had to moderate their hopes, when in April 1959 the ICATU replaced general secretary Kamal by Mohammed Assad Rejeh, who is much more moderate and less subject to left-wing extremism.

Meanwhile the ICFTU had not been idle. Alarmed by the way things were going, it began to work of a re-alignment of its African forces, and in November 1959 a conference in Lagos adopted statutes for a new African regional organization. In June 1960 these were accepted with only minor alterations by the executive committee of the ICFTU. That summer a trade-union mission, of which the Tunisian, Ben Azzedine, was a member, toured several African countries to win the support of trade-union organizations for the inaugural congress of the new regional organization, which finally took place in Tunis from 7 to 11 November. Delegations from the following organizations were present: *Union Générale des Travailleurs Algériens*; Gambia Labour Union; *Confédération Congolaise des Syndicats Libres* (Brazzaville); *Union Nationale du Cameroun* (CASL); *Union des Syndicats Autonomes du Cameroun*; *Union Nationale Côte d'Ivoire* (CASL); Kenya Federation of Labour; Congress of Industrial Organizations of Liberia; Libyan General Workers' Union; *Confédération des Travailleurs de Madagascar*; the Mauritanian UNT; Mauritius Trade Union Congress; *Union Marocaine du Travail*; Trade Union of Nigeria; Northern Rhodesia Trade Union Congress; Nyasaland Trade Union Congress; Sierra Leone Council of Labour; *Confederazione Somala de Lavoratori*; Tanganyika Federation of Labour; *Union Générale Tunisienne du Travail;* Uganda Trade Union Congress; and Zanzibar and Pemba Federation of Labour.

The following organizations sent observers: Egyptian Confederation of Labour; Gambia Workers' Union; *Union des Travailleurs du Sénégal*; South African Trade Union Council; Southern Rhodesia African Trade Union Congress and *Union Nationale Travailleurs du Togo*.

Apart from the absence of the trade unions of Ghana and Guinea from this observer group, it is interesting to note that most trade-union groups in former French West and Equatorial Africa were also missing. In consequence, there was a clear preponderance of English-speaking organizations at the congress and this generally stamped its proceedings, a circumstance which led to some dissension by the French-speaking delegates, who at one time threatened to boycott the sessions.

More important was the attitude of Tom Mboya and Ben Seddik. In order to show his disapproval of the congress' not having taken place sooner, and his annoyance at not having been promised the office of general secretary of the African regional organization in advance, Mboya (who was then perhaps the most outstanding representative of free trade unionism in Africa) did not attend the congress at all. Ben Seddik was present, but for one day only; and he was then careful not to take an open part in the proceedings. In fact, his behaviour as the leader of the largest African trade union suggested cautious reserve rather than approval.

The delegates did not hesitate to voice criticism and the executive of the ICFTU was bombarded with reproaches. It was accused of being lukewarm towards the principle of self-determination for Africa, of not having done enough to secure the release of arrested African trade unionists and of hampering initiative by its bureaucratic methods. At the same time there was an undercurrent of misgiving at the American preponderance in the ICFTU and some resentment at the rather brusque methods of its representatives, in particular of Irving Brown, the representative of the American Federation of Labor in Europe.

The success of the congress remained in the balance till the last moment, and the Africans repeatedly threatened to form their own independent regional organization. In the end, however, the ICFTU managed to attain its objective, but only because it agreed to accept an uncompromising African resolution on the colonial question and because a number of important questions were deliberately left vague. Ahmed Tlili, who was chairman of the congress, underlined the lack of positive obligations entered into when he described the congress as having 'put out feelers'. No working programme for the new organization was agreed to, and no budget was adopted. It was left to organizations which wished to remain in the ICFTU to affiliate to the proposed All-Africa Trade Union Federation if they so desired.

Subsequent discussions between representatives of the non-aligned African trade union organizations in December 1960 and again after the first African regional conference of the International Labour Organization (ILO) in Lagos, ended just as indecisively. Discussions with them did not give the impression that the Tunis congress and the discussions in Lagos had done much to consolidate the position of the ICFTU in Africa, or to create a clear understanding of the danger of a left-wing African trade union federation.

In the meantime, a different kind of activity was being carried on in Lagos by the so-called neutralists led by Diallo Seydou. They repeatedly met in separate conclave, and they did their best to win over the pro-Western trade unionists for the third All-African People's Conference, which was to be followed by a trade-union conference. All the ILO delegates and guests received a strongly anti-Western pamphlet in which the ICFTU was accused of 'neo-colonial' ideas and actions. The introduction to this pamphlet came from the pen of Gogo Chu Nzeribe, who took part in the council meeting of the WFTU in Peking in June 1960 as general secretary of the new left-wing Nigerian trade union, and who seems to have been thoroughly indoctrinated during his stay in Red China.

This pamphlet fulminated at length against 'the great conspiracy' which, it alleged, was directed by the West, with the assistance of the ICFTU, against Africa, in order to subjugate the continent once more. Naturally, there was no word about the communist conspiracy, with the assistance of African agents, to turn African trade unions into 'transmission belts' for revolutionary propaganda and action. This assistance is all the more important for communism in view of the fact that, at the moment, there are no communist parties working effectively anywhere in Africa, although communist publicists claim that while there were fewer than 3,000 communists in the whole of Africa in 1939, there were about 50,000 in 1959.[10]

Following the reconstruction of the executive committee of the WFTU at its Berlin meeting in 1951, the organizational centre of this conspiracy is now in the hands of a special section of the executive committee known as the Colonial Bureau. An African, Ibrahim Zakaria, is ostensibly in charge of this body. He comes from the Sudan Federation of Trade Unions and was present at the session of the WFTU Council in Peking in June 1960, when he made bitter attacks on the 'colonial and neo-colonial forces in Africa'. In reality, this Colonial Bureau is ultimately dependent on instructions from the Secretariat for African Affairs in the Soviet labour union, which is staffed primarily by officials from the Asian Soviet Republics. This was clearly seen in October 1960, at the first conference of the Afro-Asian Solidarity Committee of the Soviet Union, in Stalinabad, where the leading role was played by Salimgerei Toktamisov, a member of the Kazakhstan Labour Union Council and of the præsidium of the Central Labour Union Council of the Soviet Union.

From Peking to East Berlin the work of this body is furthered by the various 'national' African committees of the respective government-sponsored unions. In addition to Peking and Prague, a key role is played by East Berlin. From East Berlin alone African trade unions have received support, in cash and kind, out of solidarity and other funds, totalling ten million marks.

No less remarkable are the contributions of the WFTU and the individual labour-union organizations of the Soviet bloc for the indoctrination of African trade unionists at training centres behind the Iron Curtain. Since June 1960 a Seminary for Trade Unionists from Africa and the Arab World has been established in Leipzig as an annex to the Institute for Foreign Studies attached to the Karl Marx University. Special courses for Africans are held regularly at the Fritz Heckert East German Trade-Union High School in Berlin-Bernau.

Among the 70 trade-union officials from 18 countries attending the first course in Leipzig were officials from Ghana, Guinea, Nigeria, the Congo, Togo, Cameroon, Somalia, Angola, the Ivory Coast Republic, Senegal, Sierra Leone, Morocco, Mauritius, Zanzibar, and the Central African Republic. The curriculum of these eight-month courses, held in English and French, includes problems of international trade-union solidarity and problems of the political mass and youth work, etc. At the founding of this institution on 22 September 1960 the chairman of the East German State labour organization, Herbert Warnke, was perfectly clear about the objectives of the course of study laid down in the curriculum: 'The young African working-class movement needs cadres which are acquainted with the problems of trade-union work *and with the scientific outlook of the working class.*'[11]

The 'World Trade Union Movement' of November-December 1961 carried a detailed description of the trade-union school for trainees from Africa and certain Asian countries organized by the Central Council of Czechoslovak Labour Unions at its school near Prague the previous summer. The director of the course was Yaroslav Tehle, head of the Central School of the Czechoslovak revolutionary labour movement. He revealed that the East German FDGB High School at Bernau (which had already had a good deal of experience in the running of trade-union courses for Africans) had assisted in the preparations, which had lasted a year. 'We also took advantage of the wide experience gained by the international seminars organized by UNESCO, in which Czechoslovak trade unionists took part.' In consequence it proved possible for the Czechoslovak Labour Union Central School to prepare 30 specialized lectures six months in advance, to translate the texts of the basic lectures into French and English, and to provide two speakers for each lecture—one for the French-speaking and the other for the English-speaking group.

Twenty-five trade unionists from ten African and two Asian countries took part in the course; some from countries which had already achieved more or less complete independence, others from countries which were still dependent. Most of the students were between 20 and 30 years of age.

'The basic teaching consisted of 16 lectures on the following subjects: an outline of the development, experience and present problems of the Czech Republic; an outline of the development of human society; an analysis of imperialism; a description of the origin, present position, and significance of the world socialist system in international politics; and finally, a comparison of the fundamental principles of capitalist and socialist economics.

'A second series of lectures dealt with the following subjects: the origin and role of trade-union organizations under capitalism in the struggle for socio-economic rights, for social progress, and for peace; the origin and development, and the role of the WFTU and other international trade-union organizations (relating in particular to the need for trade-union unity in Africa); the development of the struggle for national liberation and the disintegration of the world colonial system; the world socialist system and the nature of the assistance it has granted to the economically less-developed countries; the problems of agriculture in Africa, and the role and tasks of the trade unions in close liaison with the peasantry in the efforts to solve these problems; and an analysis of class forces and their role in the national liberation movement.

'The following problems were dealt with in the final part of the course: the position and the role of the trade unions in the period of the building-up of socialism; the basic principles of the structure of the national economy, and the role of the trade unions in organizing the participation of the workers in the management of production; the participation and the role of the trade unions in raising living standards; and finally, the work of the trade unions in the field of culture and education.'

A central training school for the countries of the Soviet bloc was opened in Budapest in 1959 specially for the training of African trade unionists. The lecturers and instructors were provided by Czechoslovakia, Hungary, East Germany, the Soviet Union, and the communist trade unions of France and Belgium. At the end of the first course, the Secretary General of the WFTU, Louis Saillant, addressed the Africans who had taken part in it:

'See that you do not lose the ground under your feet when you return home. In your tremendous continent, where the young proletariat is rising and building up a young trade-union movement ... the bourgeoisie is anxious to spread obscurantism in certain vital questions, to intensify the contradictions and then to cloak these contradictions. Do not forget that the most important school for the working-class official is the *class struggle*, which he will wage side by side with his class brothers ... In the fire of the great anti-imperialist struggle, in which we join with all other sections of the people in all countries, we must always think of the necessity of *strengthening our own special class forces*.'[12]

These words unmistakably reveal the methods used and the aims pursued by the communists among the African trade unions. They are out to infiltrate the African trade-union cadres and create communists whose task will be to transform the national revolution in Africa into a socialist revolution and turn the anti-colonial, national struggle into a revolutionary class struggle. This intention was also clearly expressed at the twenty-second meeting of the executive committee of the WFTU which took place in East Berlin in February 1961, when Louis Saillant demanded that 'still greater attention' should be paid to developments in Africa. Thanks to its solidarity actions, he declared, the WFTU had succeeded in strengthening its influence in Africa.

At this meeting the executive committee also set out some of the aims which are to be propagated in Africa and form the basis for propaganda in the trade unions:

'Abolition of imperialist military bases throughout the whole world [a demand directed especially against Nigeria and one or two members of the *Communauté Française*, which had agreements with Britain and France for the use of African airfields and harbours]; the prohibition of nuclear armaments and a halt to the arms race carried on by the imperialist camp; general and complete disarmament; peaceful co-existence; the conclusion of peace treaties with both German States and thus the abolition of the most dangerous war flashpoint created and maintained by the aggressive NATO bloc under the leadership of the ruling circles of the United States; and the abolition of the American-Japanese Security Treaty.'

In conclusion Saillant declared:

'The movement for national independence has become a part of the movement for the defence of world peace. The working class and the trade unions must therefore give the peoples who have already won their independence constant and vigorous political, military and economic support.'[13]

Characteristically, nothing was said about the social problems of Africa, raising the living standards of African workers, social security, labour protection measures, agreements on working hours, and so on. Instead, as the executive meeting demonstrated, the WFTU has clearly put forward an aggressive programme with power-political aims. In the words of Victor Grischin, 'the friendly masses in the liberated countries must be enlisted in the tremendous and invincible front of the forces of peace'.[14]

The communist trade-union leaders believe they have come nearer to this aim since the long-prepared Pan-African concentration was achieved at the Casablanca congress in May 1961 by the foundation of the All-African Trade Union Federation (AATUF). For the moment the foundation of the AATUF has intensified the split between the various tendencies, particularly since January 1962, when, as an answer to Casablanca, those groups that remained loyal to the ICFTU came together in Dakar and founded the African Trade Union Confederation (ATUC).

The Casablanca congress which led to the foundation of the AATUF was a model example of a rigged meeting. The sponsors showed bias in extending invitations, and at the congress itself they pursued such undemocratic methods as voting by acclamation in order to get their way. Finally the wire-pullers gerrymandered the adoption—also by acclamation—of a charter embodying their ideas, but only after a number of important delegates, Tom Mboya among them, had left. The key clause of this charter prevents any member-union of the AATUF from affiliating to any other international trade-union organization and is, of course, aimed against affiliation to the ICFTU.

The ICFTU still claims that the great majority of the trade-union organizations throughout Africa are behind it. At first glance this would seem to be true, but the fact is that the connection of these African trade unions with the ICFTU is usually very loose and often involves no sort of obligation. Prominent trade unionists who are members of organizations formally affiliated to the ICFTU do not hesitate to take advantage of the propaganda and material support of the WFTU (for example, the Kenya Trade Union Congress, if one is to believe a report in the Nairobi *Daily Nation*)[15] or to send delegations to the Soviet-bloc countries and to receive the delegates of communist trade-unions in their own countries. The list of African countries whose trade unions were represented at the Fifth World Trade Union Congress in Moscow, in December 1961, is interesting. Amongst them were groups from the following African territories: Angola, Basutoland, Cameroon, Congo (Leopoldville), Dahomey, French Somaliland, Guinea, Kenya, Madagascar, Mali, Mauritania, Mauritius, Morocco, Niger, Nigeria, Portuguese Guinea, Senegal, South Africa, the Sudan, and Tanganyika.

Ibrahim Zakaria (Sudan), the WFTU secretary, delivered a lengthy report to the congress on 'The Development of Trade-Union Activities and Solidarity to aid Peoples Fighting to end Colonialism'. He stated that in the preceding four years '215 trade unionists from Asia, Africa, and Latin America have received trade-union education in schools organized by the WFTU and in some of its national centres. For two years now a permanent trade-union school has been run with the co-operation of UGTAN and the WFTU.'[16] Zakaria repeated the assurance of the WFTU that it 'considers the creation of the All-Africa Trade Union Federation to be a great success for the forces fighting for the unity of the trade-union movement in Africa . . . The AATUF and the African workers have . . . a sincere friend—the WFTU—which extends a helping hand to them.'[17]

There is nothing new in all this. As the communists themselves worked for the formation of the AATUF they can hardly regard it as a rival organization and so the propaganda put out by the countries of the Soviet bloc is full of approving references to the AATUF and its activities. For this reason, an article by the leader of the illegal Moroccan Communist Party, Ali Yata, in the *World Marxist Review*, December 1961, which expresses certain misgivings about the AATUF is particularly interesting. After a lengthy tribute to the federation's support for the struggle of the African workers against 'imperialism . . . neo-colonialism . . . and feudalism', the article goes on to say that this new anti-colonial 'weapon' was not without its faults. For example, it had not laid sufficient emphasis on the 'expansion of trade-union rights', on the need to 'end foreign monopoly domination' by urging nationalization, or on condemning those neutralist trade-union leaders who 'indiscriminately place the socialist and imperialist countries in the same category'. Ali Yata made his objective clear when he urged that the neutrality of such an organization as the AATUF should not preclude 'fraternal ties' with the international working-class movement, specifically with the World Federation of Trade Unions (WFTU).

Even more interesting from the standpoint of future communist tactics in Africa was Ali Yata's insistence that the trade unions alone could not lead 'the struggle for national and social liberation': such a role could be played only by 'the vanguard of the working class . . . the communist parties'. It was logical, therefore, to strengthen the existing communist parties and to form new parties where necessary. Meanwhile communists everywhere were enjoined to link up with the workers in the AATUF and support the federation.

At least the executive bodies of the AATUF are acting in this respect and trying to use AATUF as an organization through which communist ideas and intentions can be channelled. Three officers in the original executive of AATUF had close links with WFTU: Seydou Diallo (Guinea), Wahab Goodluck (Nigeria) and Abdoulaya Guèye (Senegal). A former WFTU vice-president, Abdoulaye Diallo, also from Guinea, was instrumental in AATUF's formation. Membership of the committee formed at AATUF's second congress at Bamako (Mali) in June 1964 provides further evidence of communist penetration. Of the newly-elected vice-presidents, Goodluck, Kaba Mamady (Guinea), Mamadou Sissoko (Mali) and Thauley Ganga (Congo-Brazzaville) have had dealings with WFTU, some dating back to the late 1950s. The treasurer is Lazare Coulibaly (Mali), a former committee member of a WFTU trade department (TUI). The extent of AATUF's financial commitments clearly shows that WFTU channels money through AATUF.

The Bamako conference decided to establish a permanent secretariat in Ghana. It is headed by John Tettegah, a Ghanaian, and six secretaries, three of whom are newcomers to Pan-African trade unionism. They are Amlon (Dahomey), Kawambwa (Zambia), and Madia Diop (Senegal). Two other secretaries, who reflect AATUF's desire to influence and take over union activities in Central and East Africa, are John Reich of the Federation of Uganda Trade Unions, and O.O. Mak'anyengo of the Kenyan African Workers' Union. Both have communist connections and have formed splinter unions in their own countries. Mak'anyengo has publicly declared himself a supporter of the Marxist theory of class warfare, which he considers applicable to African conditions.

Since AATUF's earliest days, communist sympathizers in the federation's executive have aimed at strengthening their links with WFTU but without formal affiliation. The chief means of achieving closer co-operation have been through TUI. In addition to the significant number of TUI contacts on the AATUF Executive Committee, specifically African 'trade groupings' on the lines of WFTU, two trade departments have been formed in Accra, for agricultural, forestry and plantation workers, and for commercial, industrial, technical and clerical workers. The two groupings established after WFTU representatives had visited Accra, are closely supervised by WFTU officials and organize joint conferences, seminars, study courses and other group activities which provide opportunities for communist contact.

AATUF is a rich and well-organized federation. One wonders what will happen if and when the Organization of African Unity succeeds in sponsoring the formation of one Pan-African trade union organization to replace the AATUF and ATUC. At the beginning of 1960, AATUF's Executive Committee was already preparing for that moment and publicly declaring that AATUF could easily provide the infra-structure for the new organization.

NOTES

[1] Radio Accra broadcast, 14 March 1960.

[2] At the Fifth Congress of the *Parti Démocratique de Guinée*, September 1959.

[3] *Neues Deutschland*, 4 February 1961.

[4] In a discussion with the author in Lagos, December 1960.

[5] Information given to the author by Nigerian trade-union officials in Lagos, December 1960.

[6] Ibid.

[7] Cf. *Lagos Morning Post* and *Nigerian Tribune* of 1 March 1962; *Lagos Daily Telegraph*, 2 March 1962.

[8] *Horoya* (Conakry), 7 November 1962.

[9] Cf. Lenin, 'Left-Wing Communism, An Infantile Disorder', *Selected Works* (12 vols; New York, 1943), x, pp. 95-6.

[10] *World Marxist Review: Problems of Peace and Socialism*, II, No. 10 (October 1959), p. 51.

[11] *Tribune* ([East] Berlin), 23 September 1960.

[12] *Die Weltgewerkschaftsbewegung* ([East] Berlin), November 1959; quoted in *Ostprobleme* (Bonn), XII (1960), p. 101. Cf. also *Nepszava* (Budapest), 1 September 1959.

[13] Minutes of the executive meeting.

[14] Ibid.

[15] *Daily Nation* (Nairobi), 31 August 1962.

[16] *For the Abolition of Colonialism*, publication of the World Federation of Trade Unions (London, 1962), p. 16.

[17] Ibid., p. 37.

Chapter XV

THE AFRO-ASIAN SOLIDARITY ORGANIZATION

ONLY a decade has passed since the historic Bandung Conference, but there are already many legends, fables and contradictory interpretations about this meeting at which the Heads of State and leading politicians of 24 African and Asian countries were present. Bandung has become a symbol and 'the spirit of Bandung' a shibboleth from Djakarta to Dakar. Nowadays even people and groups outside the Afro-Asian world claim to be legatees of the Bandung Conference and appeal to its principles.

The communists were not slow to realize the tremendous, almost magical attraction of Bandung. When the President of Senegal, Léopold Sédar Senghor, declared that 'no event of such historical importance' as the meeting at Java, in the spring of 1955, had taken place since the Renaissance, we may be sure that his remarks were carefully noted and soberly analysed, particularly in the Soviet countries.

This is understandable; the claim, first made by the coloured world at Bandung, that it should be able to go its own way independently of either of the great power blocs shocked not only the West, which up the late 1950s still cherished the delusion that anyone not definitely on its side must be against it. The communists also clung obstinately to the same idea in reverse and have never seen any reason to qualify it. For communism, which is less accustomed to ideological competition than the West, 'ideological coexistence', even after Stalin, is regarded as 'irreconcilable with the spirit of Marxist-Leninism', and a great deal depends (particularly in Asia and Africa) on whether it can succeed in forcing through the ideological, social, and economic model of its own radical socialism, thereby securing a dominating role in the new community.

Leaving Africa out of consideration for the moment it can be said that until the Bandung Conference communism's chances of success in Asia were good. A systematic extension of the communist sphere of influence in Asia followed hard on the heels of Mao's triumph in China, but with the Korean War and the powerful intervention of the United States, the *status quo* was only maintained with difficulty, though the victory over the French at Dien Bien Phu in Vietnam clearly demonstrated the sinister power of a revolutionary movement over a great colonial empire. Throughout Asia the classic front organizations were active—from the World Peace Council to the World Youth League—busily infiltrating the ranks of the local élite and gaining influence over neutral governments. A number of spectacular propaganda congresses held under communist auspices drew the attention of the Asian intelligentsia to the communist programme and its slogans, which were made more acceptable by peaceable assurances.

The bare announcement by the five Colombo States—India, Pakistan, Ceylon, Indonesia and Burma—of their intention to meet at Bandung was in itself enough to arouse anxiety and fears in the communist camp, though the participation of the Chinese People's Republic and of North Vietnam seemed to offer some compensation. But when it came to the point, the ten principles laid down at the conference showed that it was the two communist delegations, not the neutrals, which had to make compromises under pressure.

It was not difficult to anticipate this, so before the Bandung Conference, which took place in April 1955, the communists used the Asian branches of their World Peace Movement to launch a rival conference in New Delhi, with the intention of prejudicing the results of the Bandung Conference and exerting pressure on those who were to attend it, or as the communists put it, of 'making the voice of the people heard'. This was given the ponderous name of Conference for the Relaxation of International Tensions and it, (and not, as the communists are so fond of saying, the Bandung Conference) was the origin of what became known as the Afro-Asian Solidarity Movement.

All the future characteristics of this 'solidarity organization' were clearly visible at the New Delhi Conference. Representation was limited to 'the true representatives of the peoples' and to 'the dedicated forces of peace and progress'—that is to say, exclusively to parties and groups of a decided 'left-wing neutralist' character. The communist countries of Asia had representatives at the conference, and the representatives of Soviet Asia were there too. Finally the initiators, stage managers, and wire-pullers of the conference were, beyond all question, either communists or thoroughly reliable fellow-travellers. Incidentally, one of the latter was Mrs Rameshvari Nehru, who was appointed chairman of the organizing committee and later played a leading role in the Afro-Asian Solidarity Organization.

The ideological background of this organization is obvious from the list of requirements put forward at the Conference for the Relaxation of International Tensions for work in the colonial and dependent countries. These included: the calling of a conference to solve the problems of Taiwan (Formosa) and Korea; the withdrawal of all United States forces from Formosa and Formosan waters; the ending of Portuguese rule in Goa, of Dutch rule in New Guinea, and of British rule in Malaya; the prohibition of all nuclear weapons; the admission of the Chinese People's Republic to the Security Council of the United Nations; the diplomatic recognition of the Chinese People's Republic by all other nations; and the removal of the trade embargo imposed on China by the Western Powers. It is interesting to note that the Chinese demand for membership of the United Nations was not even mentioned at the Bandung Conference.

Despite these and other slogans, the Conference for the Relaxation of International Tensions in New Delhi was a signal failure, particularly in comparison with the Bandung Conference.

There were two main reasons for this. First, the scope of the conference in New Delhi was extremely narrow in comparison with Bandung, which was attended by delegations from African countries, including Egypt, Ethiopia, Ghana, Liberia, Libya and the Sudan, in addition to the Asian delegations, and this meant that the importance and influence of Bandung extended far beyond the confines of Asia.

Secondly, as a protest against the obvious communist manipulation of the New Delhi Conference, numerous political representatives who really were neutral ostentatiously left the conference hall. One or two of the delegations so obviously lacked proper credentials that the organizers of the conference had reluctantly to refuse them. In addition, the Indian and Indonesian Governments went out of their way to make it quite clear that in no circumstances were they prepared to recognize the New Delhi meeting as 'a preliminary conference for Bandung' and that they were not prepared to allow any direct organizational, or other, relation between the two conferences. It was therefore not surprising that at the Bandung Conference there were one or two contemptuous references to 'the fictitious character' of the Conference for the Relaxation of International Tensions.

Even the communists were reluctantly compelled to recognize the difference in the quality and importance of the two conferences. The lack of influence secured by the New Delhi Conference was only too obvious, and the communist efforts at Bandung, which had a tremendous import throughout 'the Third World', were relatively unsuccessful. The communists were not slow to draw the conclusions. With one accord their publicists began to take the Bandung Conference very seriously (although they had at first adopted a reserved attitude towards it, being uncertain which way it would develop). From now on almost no reference was made to the Conference for the Relaxation of International Tensions. The old, stirring, and crude radical talk was toned down and communist propaganda in Afro-Asia took on more honeyed accents, with the hope of establishing friendly relations with the national bourgeoisie. The rigid Stalinist line became more flexible and in February 1954 the Twentieth Congress of the Communist Party of the Soviet Union inscribed the slogan 'co-operation with the broad masses of the people' on the communist banner for the anti-colonial struggle instead of, as previously, co-operation only with communist or crypto-communist organizations and groups. Gradually a new line emerged and this was certainly, to some extent, due to Bandung and its consequences. One result was the decision to wind up the Communist Information Bureau, better known as the Cominform.

In Asia and Africa this meant the tightening up of front organizations and determined efforts to create a special, unexceptionable front organization for all the African countries, in addition to the existing, compromised organizations and groups. For this purpose three conditions were laid down:

1. The new organization must exploit 'the Bandung image' and

extend the Bandung scope, without relying exclusively, as Bandung had done, on established governments, and without allowing itself to be restricted by the Bandung programme.

2. The new organization must be founded as 'the people's representation' of the two 'Eastern contingents' and embrace bourgeois as well as pro-communist groups—this in order that it should not be suspected of being a Soviet cat's paw.

3. The new organization must, from the beginning, recognize the right of the Soviet Union, as a member of the Asian people's community, to belong to it and enjoy equal rights within it.

The New Delhi Conference had already gone some way towards fulfilling this third condition by unconditionally accepting the representatives of the Soviet Asian republics as partners with equal rights. Later it constituted itself, with the inclusion of the Soviet representatives, as a preparatory Asian Solidarity Committee. The Soviet Union took the final step on 16 August 1956, when Mirzo Tursun-Zade, a Tadjik writer and president of a Peace Committee for the Asian Soviet Republics, formed a National Asian Solidarity Committee of the Soviet Union. This new body was immediately welcomed by the national committees that had in the meantime been formed in one or two Asian countries.

It was not long before the next step, and at the end of December 1956 the delegates to the New Delhi Conference decided to organize an inaugural conference of the new regional front organizations 'at an early date' in Cairo. This city was chosen as the venue because on account of the Suez affair (November 1956) it exercised a certain attraction. It was also decided to make an immediate start with the preparations. An Asian Writers' Conference, which took place in New Delhi in December 1956, and an Afro-Asian Jurists' Conference, held in Damascus in November 1957, afforded an opportunity of making close contact with various personalities and political groups from both continents, discussing which delegations should be sent, and drawing up the agenda of the proposed inaugural conference. Incidentally the so-called preparatory conferences in the Indian and Syrian capitals were naturally attended not only by writers and jurists. Both in New Delhi and in Damascus there were numerous officials of the Afro-Asian peace movement and the pro-communist labour and youth organizations. Indeed, political questions of a general nature clearly dominated the discussions and the resolutions despite the specialized subjects on the agendas. The resolutions adopted at Damascus were sharply directed against the 'imperialist-bloc policies' of NATO, SEATO, and the Baghdad Pact. Needless to say, Soviet military policy was not even mentioned, neither was the Hungarian question.

Despite the fact that all the preparations made it unmistakably clear that the future organization would be ideologically linked to communism and hostile to the West, in the last days of 1957, 39 delegations arrived in Cairo from almost all the African and Asian countries, to take part in the First Afro-Asian Solidarity Conference (AASC). Apart from the usual delegations from the communist countries of Asia (including the Soviet Union), there were official delegations from Egypt, Morocco and Tunis, semi-official delegations from other countries, and a number of groups (whose status would be difficult to describe) from the colonial areas of Africa. Although the Egyptian Government (through the Solidarity Council of the United Arab Republic) arranged the conference, the communist delegations ran it from the start. Rashidov, the chief Soviet delegate, who was President of the Supreme Soviet of Uzbekistan at the time and a leading official in charge of Soviet Eastern policy, lost no time in making the aims of the Kremlin clear when he promised all the delegations generous Soviet economic aid, assuring them that this would afford them an opportunity of breaking 'the grip of neo-colonial exploitation' and escaping from 'economic slavery at the hands of Western colonial capitalism'. He went on to declare: 'It would hardly be possible to exaggerate the importance of this conference, in which more than 40 Afro-Asian countries are taking part. At the Bandung Conference 29 countries condemned colonialism and proclaimed the principles of peaceful co-existence. These principles have since been adopted as the foreign policy of numerous countries all over the world, and they are fully supported by the Soviet Union. This Afro-Asian Solidarity Conference, its spirit, and its ideas are supported by all honest men throughout the world, because it is *anti-imperialist*, *anti-colonial and anti-militarist* and thus at the same time *just*, *progressive and humane*. The Soviet people support this consolidation of those forces in the Afro-Asian countries that will henceforth play an important role by *extending the zone of peace* in the struggle against the rotten system and piracy of imperialism.' Rashidov observed unblushingly that the oppression of other peoples and interference in their internal affairs 'are foreign to the true nature of the Soviet socialist state'. He described the Soviet Union as 'a tireless pioneer in the struggle for peace and an irreconcilable enemy of imperialism and colonialism'. He enumerated in detail the actions of the Soviet Union which, he declared, 'supported the struggle of the colonialized peoples for their freedom'. He concluded emphatically with the appeal: 'Brothers, comrades and friends, lift up your heads, the end of your enslavement is at hand!'[1]

Representatives of North Korea, North Vietnam, the Mongolian People's Republic and Red China sounded the same note and there was a good deal of talk about 'the unswerving solidarity of all African and Asian peoples', the 'glorious example' of the Asian people's democracies in the struggle 'to overcome the remnants of colonialist thought', and about the alleged attempts of the West ('the imperialist powers') to undermine the unity of the Eastern countries by intrigues, murderous weapons and provocations, and to keep the oppressed peoples in slavery for ever. To trained Western observers, the conference was clearly a communist set-up and its aims were manifestly communist, but what about the uncommitted groups and personalities present? John Kale, the general secretary of the Uganda National Congress (a man of goodwill and good faith who was elected a leading member of the permanent solidarity secretariat and was later killed in mysterious circumstances when the plane in which he was travelling crashed in the Soviet Union) told the author in a private conversation a few months before his death: 'For those of us who were taking part in such an important international conference for the first time and rubbing shoulders with cabinet ministers, presidents and prominent trade unionists, scientists, artists and writers from countries all over the world, Cairo was a tremendous experience. For the first time we felt that we were being taken seriously. They all treated us as equals, whether they had won their own independence 40 years ago or perhaps only a couple of years back. It seemed to us that a new force was coming together here, a force based on true solidarity and a common consciousness of a struggle against the old colonial order and against the obsolete social and economic system of our own countries in favour of something new and revolutionary. Although many of us instinctively, and some of us even consciously, rejected Soviet-communist interference in our work, and although many of us distrusted the communists, this mistrust was outweighed by a feeling of real gratitude that a great world Power should support our demands.'[2]

Kale's words illustrate the ideological and emotional trust of many of those who took part in the Cairo Conference and demonstrate the psychological success of communist initiative. It would be too easy to try to dismiss men like John Kale as communists, crypto-communists or fellow-travellers. Now that he is dead it is possible to reveal that during the second Afro-Asian Solidarity Conference he gave the author valuable information about communist manœuvres in the secretariat, although he knew perfectly well that his information would be used as proof that the communists had succeeded in infiltrating the Afro-Asian solidarity movement on a massive scale. As the representative of Uganda in the permanent secretariat, Kale constantly opposed communist efforts to gain complete control of the movement, and we may be sure that he did not stand alone in this.

His impressions of the activities of the communists in Cairo are therefore all the more valuable. They show how cunningly the communists take the political naïveté of their non-communist collaborators into account and how little even their crudest abuse of the West diminishes the willingness of these people to co-operate with them. It was therefore relatively easy for the communists to whip up anti-Western and anti-colonial resentment among the delegates by numerous emotional appeals, and subsequently to make them the basis of a completely anti-imperialist standpoint. The concluding declaration of the conference called upon the Western Powers to accept the Soviet proposal for the immediate abolition of nuclear tests; then followed a condemnation of 'imperialism in all its forms and manifestations', including all political pacts (not the Warsaw Pact, of course), military aid, economic aid 'with political strings', and 'the establishment of foreign military bases in Asia and Africa'. Great Britain was fiercely attacked for its 'innumerable brutalities' against the people of the Yemen and for its 'crimes in Kenya'; France was accused of pursuing a policy of 'cruelty and extermination' in Algeria; the United States was generally accused of continual interference in the internal affairs of the Arab countries. The conference demanded immediate and complete independence for all colonial countries and protectorates, the abolition of United

Nations trusteeships and the cession of West Guinea to Indonesia, of Portuguese Goa to India, and Okinawa to Japan. Finally it appealed for support on behalf of nationalist movements in Cameroon, Kenya, Uganda, Madagascar, Bahrein, Cyprus and Somaliland.[3]

This catalogue of aims, which was later endorsed by the permanent secretariat in innumerable declarations, was nothing but a rehash of the demands put forward by communist propaganda for Asia and Africa. The organizational work carried on in Cairo by the communists has been more important than these declarations—on the traditional communist principle that *propaganda is useless unless it is backed up by effective organization to give strength to the forces behind it*. And this is what the Cairo Conference was all about: a resolution put forward by the Committee for Organizational Questions which was, of course, dominated by the communists, called for the immediate establishment of two permanent organs, a solidarity council and a permanent secretariat. The resolution, unanimously adopted, declared that the task of these bodies would be to act as a liaison between the plenary sessions of the solidarity organization and to ensure the implementation of the decisions and recommendations of the conference. Representatives from the following countries were elected to this permanent secretariat: the Soviet Union, the Chinese People's Republic, Cameroon, Ghana, the Sudan, India, Japan, Indonesia, Iraq and Syria. Youssef el Sebay, an Egyptian, was elected general secretary.[4]

Superficially the secretariat has a preponderance of non-communist representatives, but in reality the situation is very different. For example, the Sudanese delegate elected to the secretariat was not a representative of the Sudanese Government but a member of the outlawed communist party, while the Cameroonian delegate represented only the terrorist *Union des Populations du Cameroun*. Further, the Indian, Japanese, Indonesian and Iraqi representatives in the secretariat were without exception left-wing politicians if not actually Communist Party members. This left only three neutrals in the secretariat: the members for Syria and Ghana were actually representatives of their governments, and the secretary general is an official of the 'peace movement' tolerated by both Nasser and Khrushchev. Thus, even when John Kale was made a member of the secretariat as the representative of the Uganda National Congress, there was still a preponderance of communists and crypto-communists in the executive body of the solidarity movement. This has remained the case. In my conversation with John Kale, he declared that these communist and pro-communist officials 'quite definitely dictated the work of the secretariat', though they had to show some outward consideration to the neutrals, and though the fear of secessions, which would have blunted the edge of the solidarity movement, caused them to steer 'a very careful course'.

It was in the nature of things—and altogether in the interests of the Soviet Union and its allies—that this Afro-Asian Solidarity Organization should occupy itself more with African problems. Apart from Indonesia, developments in Asia had lost their original revolutionary impetus, whereas the revolutionary upheaval in Africa was only just starting. It is not surprising therefore that in this situation the members of the secretariat felt it right to devote the greater part of their attention to Africa, as was pointed out in the joint declaration of the Guinean leaders and the general secretary, signed on 29 January 1960 in Tunis, announcing the convening of the second Solidarity Conference for April 1960 in Conakry, the capital of Guinea. In another passage the joint declaration states this even more plainly: 'Since it started its activities following the first Solidarity Conference, the secretariat has concerned itself primarily with African affairs. A review of the individual activities of the secretariat during the past two years shows very clearly what a vigorous part it has played in the struggle for African independence and unity.'[5]

This paraphrase hardly reflects the real situation accurately, and the truth is that during the 28 months between the conferences of Cairo and Conakry the problems of Asia hardly existed for the secretariat. *In fact it soon became very clear that the Asian interest was never intended to be anything but a platform which the Asian communist groups could exploit—'in the spirit of the fraternal solidarity of the masses of the peoples of the two continents'—in order to intervene in the process of African emancipation, in communist interests, and to influence and win over the neutral forces in Africa.*

This aim can be seen more clearly when we examine the three planes on which the Afro-Asian Solidarity movement operates—that is, the three planes on which communist infiltration is taking place:

1. *Propaganda infiltration*: From the beginning the communist States have emphasized three fundamental themes through the permanent secretariat and its subordinate national committees. The first was the demand for 'the unleashing of a continental struggle against the colonialists and imperialists'. At the same time all attempts to secure a peaceable settlement of outstanding issues with 'the colonial masters' were denounced as 'the manœuvres of collaborating and reactionary African politicians', while all revolutionary attempts at 'de-colonialization' were highly praised. This tendency was clearly seen in the attitude of the secretariat to the referendum organized by de Gaulle on 28 September 1958. All those who supported his proposed *Communauté Française* were denounced as unworthy 'to bear the honourable title of African', while the opposition to the *Communauté Française* led by Sékou Touré (and his subsequent success at the referendum) were acclaimed as 'a pledge of real African patriotism'.[6] In the case of Cameroon, the secretariat joined with the underground *Union des Populations du Cameroun* to denigrate the intention of the United Nations to grant independence to the trusteeship area from 1 January 1960. At the same time all attempts by the moderate elements in Cameroon to bring the rebellion to an end on the basis of a compromise and by negotiations before sovereignty was granted were vigorously rejected by the solidarity movement and denounced in fierce counter-propaganda.

The second theme advanced by the secretariat in its published propaganda was that after achieving political independence the African peoples must attain independence in all other fields as well, in particular economic independence. This campaign, which is conducted throughout the African continent was, and is still, directed against any and every form of Western economic aid, in particular against the continued existence of Western firms and undertakings in the politically sovereign African lands. Individual Western economic undertakings and Western economic activity in Africa in general are attacked in leaflets and pamphlets—'The Infiltration of Franco-American Economic Undertakings and Their Role in the Exploitation of Africa'; 'West-German Capital to support French Colonialism!'; 'Belgian Colonial Policy in the Congo—The Shareholders of the *Union Minière du Haut Katanga* in Action'; and so on. These propaganda tracts all finish with the same slogan: the African countries will not be 'really free' until they end the economic dominance of colonialism in their territories. Needless to say, all these publications advocate the economic principles of the communist countries as the proper model for 'a really independent economic development of the new Africa'.

The third theme in this propaganda infiltration is the defamation of the United States. America is constantly under attack in all the publications of the solidarity movement as 'the chief whipper-in of colonialist policy'. More recently a great deal of attention has been paid to 'Fidelism' in Cuba. Examples of 'America's interventionist policy' in Latin America are quoted in order to persuade the Africans that any dealings with the US imperialists will inevitably develop into 'a crushing and fatal embrace'. On this point the influence of Peking on the propaganda activity of the solidarity secretariat has noticeably increased.

2. *Solidarity actions and solidarity propaganda*: This is chiefly a matter of demonstrations and collections intended to attract general attention and is intended primarily for external consumption. Certain standard themes are worked out each time. The secretariat has fixed 1 December of each year as 'Quit-Africa Day' and this is celebrated with demonstrations in all communist countries 'to draw the attention of world public opinion to the colonial shame' in Africa and to stir the conscience of the world in order to compel the imperialists to liquidate their colonial bases in Africa. The solidarity secretariat has also fixed special Angola, Congo, and South Africa Days. The National Solidarity Committees in the Soviet Union, China, and other countries issue appropriate propaganda material for use in the Press and for broadcasting in connection with the special themes to be stressed on these various 'Days'. Throughout Soviet-controlled territory from Vladivostok to East Berlin any African who can be mobilized is pressed into service to persuade public opinion of the necessity for 'determined action against Africa's colonial masters'.

Often special solidarity collections are arranged in connection with these Days. For example, on Algeria Day members of the official labour organization in East Germany had to contribute a proportion of their pay to the Algerian Solidarity Fund. The use to which such money is put can be seen from the fact that the underground activity of the *Union des Populations du Cameroun* has been financed in part by the solidarity contributions of the various national solidarity committees—in this case chiefly the Chinese committee—channelled through the secretariat of the movement in Cairo.

Part of this activity was the communist attempt to obtain support for the formation of an International Algerian Brigade and to persuade the solidarity secretariat and the second Solidarity Conference in Conakry to adopt a decision to this end. If this communist manœuvre had succeeded, Asian volunteers (including, of course, volunteers from the Soviet Union, Red China and North Vietnam) would have arrived in North Africa to take an active part in the Algerian struggle on the side of the FLN. In fact the inner councils of the FLN were divided and it proved impossible to reach an agreement which would, in any case, have gone no further than calling for the establishment of an African Brigade. In consequence the communist manœuvre failed.

3. *Cadre formation and cadre training*: The Solidarity Council and the organizations affiliated to it represent the formal channels for a large-scale communist programme for Africa and fifty per cent of all African visitors to China during the past few years went at the invitation of the National Chinese Afro-Asian Solidarity Secretariat, though of late (outwardly at least) the special Chinese Solidarity Committee for Africa has been playing a more prominent role. Not that this really matters, because in fact it is the same institution under different names and both are controlled by the Chinese Communist Party. Grants to African students for courses in the Soviet Union and its satellite countries are distributed through the solidarity council and its subordinate bodies. The real aim of this activity is to recruit proselytes. The idea is to seed valuable and effective cadres for training at one or another of the various communist labour-union, youth, and women's schools, or universities, in order that they may return to their own countries and form communist or pro-communist cells (often in completely non-communist organizations) and generally act as a revolutionary yeast. In other words, the real purpose of the Solidarity Council is to serve as a central communist recruiting agency in Africa. An example of how this activity is carried out in practice can be seen from the behaviour of the delegations from the Soviet Union, the satellite States and Red China at the second Afro-Asian Solidarity Conference in Conakry, in April 1960. They not only distributed

propaganda pamphlets on behalf of the Moscow University of People's Friendship and the various Chinese training centres, but also issued personal invitations to dozens of African delegates to visit their countries and in many cases the airline ticket was handed over with the invitation. The same tactic was followed by the Soviet and Chinese delegations to the third Afro-Asian Solidarity Conference in February 1963, in Moshi, Tanganyika.

Communist solidarity propaganda and the communist cadre policy in the solidarity movement, with communist activity in the African branch organizations, are not universally welcomed. During the few months before the second Solidarity Conference there was a good deal of trouble in the leading bodies, some of it quite serious; and a number of African members handed in their resignations rather than continue to tolerate communist tactics. In the preparatory phase of the Conakry Conference there was similar trouble in the secretariat. This arose out of the temporary deterioration of relations between Peking and the United Arab Republic, the Sino-Indian border clash, and the obvious intention of the communist members to fix the conference venue and the future seat of the executive bodies in their own interests. However, the conflict between the Indian and Chinese representatives over the Sino-Indian clash was diminished by the announcement that there were to be direct talks between the Chinese Prime Minister, Chou En-lai, and Nehru. Moscow and Peking proposed Baghdad as the conference venue, and the final choice of Conakry was a compromise. The fact that Cairo is still the seat of the permanent secretariat—despite the protests of the communist and Iraqi delegations—was then regarded by the more moderate politicians of the Solidarity Movement as a clear victory for them. Some even went so far as to regard it as proof that the movement was freeing itself from communist entanglements and was on the way to becoming a completely neutral organization independent of communist control.

Thirty-nine groups were represented in Cairo, but at the Conakry Conference delegates attended from 68 African and Asian parties, associations, committees and trade unions, though some of them led an ambiguous and precarious political existence. A good many of the East African and South African delegates had been living for years in exile in Cairo, cut off from any real contact with their home countries. The only Cameroonian representatives were the extremist leaders of the *Union des Populations du Cameroun* headed by their late president, Félix-Roland Moumié. These men were permanently resident in Conakry. They had previously prevented Liberia from issuing an official invitation to a legal delegation from Cameroon. The Ivory Coast was represented by a so-called liberation committee which had no real following. A group from Cairo was accepted, without cavil, as representing Palestine. During the conference this group distributed violently anti-Semitic leaflets in the style of the notorious Nazi publication *Der Stürmer*. Together with other Arab delegates they also persuaded the conference to eject the Israeli ambassador, who was present as an unofficial observer.

The agenda of the Conakry Conference contained four familiar and characteristic points: 1. The complete liquidation of colonialism in Asia and Africa (sub-sections: independence, unity, co-existence, and disarmament). 2. The economic development of Asia and Africa. 3. Questions of cultural and social development. 4. The extension of the Afro-Asian Solidarity Movement. The delegation leaders were almost permanently in session and the main body of delegates was presented with a number of reports, of which only one—that drawn up by John Kale—broke away from the usual communist-inspired generalities so typical of all communist-controlled conferences. In his report Kale frankly admitted that the work of the Solidarity Movement was making no progress in a number of countries and was meeting with opposition from other political organizations. He recorded that the support which the movement was receiving from the various governments concerned was negligible. Since the last conference a number of areas had not even formed national solidarity committees in accordance with the decision of the Cairo Conference. Although there was a good deal of vehement discussion in the various commissions on these and other questions, the plenary sessions presented, on all five days, a completely harmonious picture of Afro-Asian solidarity and full agreement on all important questions. The denunciation of colonialism, Western imperialism, French nuclear tests in the Sahara and white racial policy in South Africa poured out monotonously, interrupted only by the equally stereotyped phraseology in praise of the Soviet disarmament plan and the principles of peaceful co-existence.[7]

Resolutions and proposals relating to cultural, social, and

economic problems in Africa and Asia, however, were of rather greater importance. The conference expressed itself whole-heartedly in favour of 'learning from socialist experiences' in the economic development of the individual countries concerned, and it was repeatedly stressed that 'the next stage of the struggle against colonialism' must achieve 'economic decolonization'. At the same time, it was proposed that historians, writers, sociologists and scientists from all Afro-Asian countries be invited to co-operate on various commissions, which would meet regularly. This programme for increasing co-operation in the intellectual sphere was initiated by the leader of the Soviet delegation, the Tadjik writer, Mirzo Tursun-Zade, a veteran organizer of many 'friendship conferences'.

One or two organizational changes made at the Conakry Conference were of some importance. In accordance with the growing interest in the development of Africa the permanent secretariat was extended by co-opting representatives of Algeria, Guinea and the former Belgian Congo. Apart from the general secretary, an Afro-Asian parity in the secretariat was established, with representatives of the Soviet Union, Red China, Japan, India, Indonesia, Iraq, Algeria, Ghana, Guinea, the former Belgian Congo, Cameroon (the illegal *Union des Populations du Cameroun*), and Uganda. In order to improve the political leadership and control of this instrument, a 27-member steering committee was established and was to meet twice a year. The committee was made completely responsible to a *conseil de l'organisation*, consisting of the leaders of all affiliated groups, which was to meet once after each conference. Finally it was decided to change the name of the Solidarity Movement, henceforth to be known as the *Organisation de Solidarité des Peuples Afro-Asiatiques.*

The subjects on the agenda of this second Afro-Asian Solidarity Conference indicated once again how directly the movement is communist-controlled and inspired. Since then further proof has been provided, if any were still necessary, that this solidarity movement is a front organization. An economic conference, held in May 1960 in Cairo, achieved little or nothing, but several measures on the part of the secretariat, particularly on the Congo question, underlined the complete ideological identity of the movement with the attitudes and actions of communist parties and governments. The list of resolutions adopted by the Afro-Asian Women's Conference, which took place in January 1961 in Cairo, obediently listed all the current propaganda themes of communism, from the denunciation of the neo-colonialism of the *Communauté Française* to approval of the rebels in Cameroon and Laos.

All communist-front organizations suffer from the same weakness: even before their methods and their objectives have been completely exposed, they begin to lose their attraction, become useless for the purpose for which they were formed, and have to be replaced by new organizations. The Afro-Asian Solidarity Movement is already facing this situation in Asia, but not yet in Africa. Discussions with African politicians show that many of them still do not realize that the solidarity movement is communist-controlled, while others either deny this or try to make light of it. Generally speaking, many Africans of goodwill still share the views of John Kale, which he expressed to the author shortly before his death. The experienced and cunning communist officials operating in the secretariat and its subordinate executive bodies are still able to deceive many well-meaning Africans, who are unaware of the real situation and are greatly impressed by the demonstrations of solidarity for their cause. In their innocence they are fair game and they become cat's paws of communism.

This situation obviously still existed when the third of these Afro-Asian solidarity conferences took place. After a number of postponements, it was held from 4 to 11 February 1963 in Moshi. The choice of Tanganyika as the host-country was no less premeditated than the previous choice of Egypt for the first conference and of Guinea for the second. In 1957 Cairo was an obvious choice on account of the recent events in Suez, which made it the ideal venue for an anti-imperialist and anti-colonialist demonstration. At that time Cairo was an excellent centre for making contacts throughout the Arab and African world. Three years later, in 1960, Conakry offered the wire-pullers of the Afro-Asian Solidarity Movement similar advantageous opportunities in West Africa, an area which at the time was in the decisive phase of its anti-colonial struggle. Now, at the beginning of 1963, conditions in the Arab countries and in West Africa had been consolidated—and not entirely in favour of communism. The main sphere of communist action had shifted to South Africa and East Africa, where Somalia, Uganda and Tanganyika had achieved full political independence. In

Zanzibar and Kenya the compass had been set for independence, but a critical phase within the disrupted African front was about to begin and there were, in consequence, many favourable opportunities for communist initiative. The collapse of the Central African Federation was obviously a matter of time, and of only a short time, and the likelihood of clashes between black and white in Southern Rhodesia was imminent. Finally the anti-Portuguese forces were massing in and around Mozambique for more determined action, while in South Africa antagonism between the white racial fanatics and African nationalism was assuming new intensity and bitterness. Tanganyika lies in the centre of this tremendous field of tension and Julius Nyerere had deliberately aligned his country in the vanguard of African nationalism. Since Tanganyika's independence, Dar es Salaam has become for East Africa and South Africa what Accra and Conakry were for West Africa—a centre of anti-colonial propaganda, a meeting place for groups of exiles from surrounding countries and a base of operations for the liberation of the neighbouring areas.

International communism therefore set out to make useful contacts, to play a role in the coming struggle against colonialism, obtain an influence on forces likely to be of importance in the future, win friends by making gestures of solidarity, and (this is true in particular of the Chinese communists) influence the nature and tactics of the coming struggle by advice, instructions and a supply of arms.

There were, and still are, many factors favourable to these communist aims and objectives. As in West Africa from 1958 to 1961, the anti-communist propaganda of the existing colonial administrations is often so gauche that it actually strengthens the communists. For a long time the British colonial authorities clung obstinately to the convenient axiom that all the followers of Mau-Mau could automatically be regarded as communists. At the same time the colonialist Press never loses an opportunity to denounce awkward African politicians and groups as communists or as paid agents of communism, as soon as it is able to point out the slightest similarity between their slogans and arguments and those used by the communists. The statements and charges given publicity on every conceivable occasion by the authorities in South Africa, Southern Rhodesia and Mozambique are even wilder and more extreme.

Anyone who is opposed to the dominance of the white race in Africa is automatically dubbed a communist. It is obvious that this stupid attitude must lead to exactly the opposite of what its propagandists hope to attain. The communists are denounced as the arch-enemies of colonialism, and in consequence Africans are automatically inclined to regard them as friends. And since no one in these areas has any practical experience of what communism is like in reality, and as the support by third groupings and elements is not particularly effective, communism finds almost ideal conditions ready-made for its operations. This is particularly the case when it is able to present itself to the ordinary African in the mask of well-meaning, helpful friend—as at the third Afro-Asian Solidarity Conference in Moshi in 1963. The situation becomes even more favourable when the wire-pullers of the various manœuvres succeed in keeping themselves in the background.

The Tanganyikan Government obviously hesitated for quite a while before it finally gave permission for the third Afro-Asian Solidarity Conference to be held on its territory. As a result of warnings of communist intrigues, received from various West African politicians, it attempted to delay the calling of the conference, and finally, when it did agree, it put forward various transparent pretexts for shifting the venue from Dar es Salaam to the more remote Moshi (which lies directly beneath Kilimanjaro) where public impact would be much less than in the capital. In fact, the 14,000 inhabitants of Moshi took hardly any notice of the conference. The posters and other propaganda put up in the streets and the squares of the town were already defaced by the second day of the conference and soon completely washed away by one or two heavy downpours. The conference itself was held in the building of a secondary school some distance from the town centre.

Thus the outward circumstances in which the conference was held were not impressive. The same was true of its composition, though the secretariat proudly announced that the conference was being attended by delegates from 58 affiliated organizations and by 40 other delegations as observers. Julius Nyerere and Jomo Kenyatta delivered the opening and closing speeches and the Russians and the Chinese attended in force. But neighbouring Kenya sent only a ten-man delegation, consisting entirely of officials of only one of the three main political parties, and even they were 'political unknowns, hand-picked by that communist-financed capitalist Oginga Odinga.'[8]

The biggest African country, Nigeria, was represented by only one delegate and he was there on behalf of the Youth Congress. Some comment was aroused by the fact that this 'youth delegate' had a grey beard. Exiles from Cameroon and delegates from Mali and Guinea were the only representatives of the French-speaking territories of West Africa. Ghana, which sent an enormous delegation to the second Afro-Asian Solidarity Conference, was represented at the third by only one politician, and he did not attend all the sessions and manifested a marked lack of interest in the proceedings. The group from Uganda consisted entirely of youthful unknowns. The head of the delegation, as he found himself called, was so astonished at this honour he thought they were playing a joke on him. There were the usual delegations from Palestine, Cameroon, and other parts of Africa, whose members as usual represented only themselves—little groups kept alive artificially by communist or Arab subsidies. There was at least one representative delegation, that from Malaysia, but in accordance with the anti-Malaysia line of the Russians and the Chinese, the credentials committee refused to accept it and it was unable to take part in the proceedings.

Two serious conflicts between members of the Afro-Asian Solidarity Movement formed the main background to the Moshi Conference. First, there was the question of the smouldering Sino-Indian frontier clash, the effects of which are still being felt throughout Asia and Africa. Secondly, there was the ideological dispute between Moscow and Peking, which was then reaching new heights with the Chinese denunciation of the 'Revisionists'. The Sino-Indian conflict was threatening to flare up at the second Afro-Asian Solidarity Conference in Conakry, but the fires were dampened by conciliatory gestures from both Peking and New Delhi, only to burst out with renewed vehemence two years later. The Sino-Soviet dispute echoed repeatedly through the Afro-Asian secretariat and at various meetings of the affiliated organs—for example, at the Gaza meeting in the spring of 1962. Unlike the Russians, the Chinese, in the period between Conakry and Moshi, had succeeded in extending and consolidating their influence over the various Afro-Asian solidarity organizations—for example, in the

Afro-Asian Solidarity Fund Organization, whose dominating committee member was Chu Tzu-chi, formerly chief Chinese delegate to the permanent secretariat of the movement, and in the permanent bureau of the Afro-Asian Writers' Association. Strong pro-Chinese tendencies also made themselves noticeable at an Economic Seminar held in Ceylon in October 1962, which was at first boycotted by Moscow. In view of the repeatedly sharp attacks by Peking against the allegedly soft attitude of Moscow on the question of intensifying the 'national liberation struggle', it was to be expected that Moshi would be the scene of more or less open Sino-Soviet controversy.

In fact, nothing of the kind took place, and this was perhaps the outstanding, though negative, feature of Moshi and the one and only success the Russians attained at the conference. At the preliminary meetings of the permanent secretariat they succeeded in persuading the Chinese, who arrived spoiling for a fight, that any open conflict at the conference between the hostile communist brothers would damage the general plans of communism, which both supported, and would have an unfavourable effect on their joint front organization in Africa.[9] An appeal issued by the World Peace Council not to debate differences of opinion in public and instead 'to stress the things all had in common' was handed, as a sort of address of welcome, to all the delegations arriving in Tanganyika.

But even this appeal could not prevent the Sino-Soviet conflict from expressing itself in Moshi in other ways. For example, the conference documents issued by the Russians stressed the urgent necessity for general disarmament and co-existence, while those issued by the Chinese pointedly made no reference either to disarmament or to co-existence; for the knowledgeable, the existence of the differences in the background was unmistakable. Behind the scenes both the Soviet and the Chinese delegations pursued what was described as tactics of 'fierce lobbying and currying for favour'. The author was present at smaller gatherings in which the Chinese did their utmost to persuade the African and Asian politicians that Khrushchev's attitude in the Cuban affair was proof that the Russians could not be relied on and that reliance could be placed only on 'really revolutionary countries', such as People's China. In addition, the Chinese never lost an opportunity of emphasizing that the Russians were 'whites' and not members of the 'Asian brother-race'. So the prophecy of the Nairobi *Daily Nation* on the opening day of the conference was borne out: many delegates did indeed find themselves 'dissipating their energies in a three-way stretch among the non-aligned, the Moscow-aligned, and the Peking-aligned.'[10] And in view of the struggle which was clearly going on behind the scenes, it can only be described as a breath-taking performance when, on the third day of the conference, Oginga Odinga rose and declared that the Sino-Soviet conflict was nothing but an invention of the Western imperialists.

Unfortunately for him, the facts made it impossible for him to adopt the same attitude towards the Sino-Indian conflict and so everything possible was done to bury this damaging dispute between two Asian countries under a welter of appeals for compromise and restraint. At the opening session of the conference the general secretary of the permanent secretariat, Yussuf El Sabai, urged the delegates not to give public expression to opinions which might lead to tension and disruption, and added: 'The delegations from India and China have agreed to treat their border dispute in the spirit of Bandung.' Awkwardly, however, Nehru's telegram of greeting to the conference contained the provocative word 'aggression', in referring to the action of the Chinese and therefore the least the Indian delegation could do was to ask the conference to include 'a special reference to the dispute in the final resolution'. The leader of the Indian delegation, Chaman Lal, declared that 'despite our adherence to the principles of peaceful co-existence a grave conflict has been thrust on India, and this conflict has endangered the very basis of Afro-Asian solidarity, the principles of non-alignment and world peace'. With a further indirect tilt at the Chinese, he declared: 'The dangerous world we live in is the *raison d'être* for the policy of peaceful co-existence. Let this be a warning to those who in their folly or arrogance persist in denying in word or action this policy of peaceful co-existence.'[11]

However, the Indian protests found little echo at the conference and the Chinese continued to blame India for the Himalayan frontier clash. The Indians even had to walk out of a meeting of the political committee of the conference on 7 February when they failed in their attempt to get a resolution accepted on the proposal of the Colombo States for the opening of negotiations on the Sino-Indian border dispute. This particular clash between the Indians and the Chinese was so heated that the committee chairman, Bhoke

Munanka, had to intervene repeatedly. Chaman Lal demanded that the Chinese accept the recommendation of the Colombo States without reservation, and when he was unable to get his point accepted he left the hall, declaring bluntly: 'The organization is killed, destroyed, ended. Without India there is no organization.'[12] Tremendous efforts were made to persuade the Indians to return, and after four days' absence the Indian delegation reappeared to endorse a compromise recommendation from which the words 'without reservation' had been deleted.

But that was not the end of the conference's troubles. Many of the delegates were more concerned with their own local problems than with world affairs and this opened up cracks in the façade of solidarity. The delegates from Kenya staged a walk-out of their own when the Somali delegates laid claim to the Northern Frontier District of Kenya. There were also bitter complaints by the delegates from Zanzibar that neither India nor Indonesia was buying their cloves. A heated altercation took place between the delegates from Aden and the Yemen. However, the much-vaunted feelings of 'solidarity' were able to express themselves happily in denouncing the West and 'neo-colonialism' in the usual stereotyped jargon. Even so, one of the Liberian delegates soberly pointed out: 'Talk about neo-colonialism, and the shouting of other disparaging slogans are merely abstract shibboleths to many minds. They are mere words, and their meaning has not yet been clearly defined.'[13] The Tanganyikan Minister of National Culture, acting as the leader of his delegation, also complained that the conference had heard 'too many words meaning too little in the way of practical action.'[14]

There was a good deal of substance to this; indeed, one got the impression that the work of the conference consisted of little more than the constant repetition of meaningless clichés. Most of the speeches sounded as though they had been run off the same gramophone record; grateful thanks to the host; references to the growing achievements of awakening nationalism in recent years; pledges of unswerving solidarity; attacks against colonialism, neo-colonialism, and imperialism; references to local problems in the homeland of the respective speaker; further denunciations of Western colonialism; grateful thanks to 'the real friends of the peoples of Africa and Asia', meaning, of course, the communist States, and so on.

Apart from all this talk there were ludicrous changes of front.

For example, after having conducted the friendliest talks with Golda Meir, Israel's Foreign Minister, and having agreed on close co-operation, the Tanganyikan and Ugandan delegates expressed their unqualified approval of the Arab attacks on Zionism and finally they all voted for an anti-Israel resolution. When Press representatives buttonholed Oscar Kambona, chairman of the conference and afterwards Tanganyika's first Foreign Minister, and pointed out the lack of logic in his attitude, he wriggled out of it by saying that there would be plenty of time 'later on' to discuss how this or that resolution adopted by the conference was to be put into practice. Delegates from member-States of the Pan-African organization PAFMECSA, which had invariably supported the legal authorities in the Congo, now unanimously applauded speeches and resolutions denouncing Cyrille Adoula, the Congolese Prime Minister, though as recently as December 1962 they had adopted a resolution expressing satisfaction at 'the clear policy the United States Government had recently adopted in the Congo'. Now they saw no harm or lack of logic in voting for a resolution which denounced the Congo policy of the selfsame government as devilish imperialist manœuvre.

After listening to this sort of thing for a few days the objective observer began to wonder whether he ought to take the conference seriously at all. The whole performance had little or nothing to do with solidarity. It was impossible to reconcile it either with the principle of strict neutrality and non-alignment or with the earnestly stressed dignity of representatives of the people of Asia and Africa. All in all, it is not surprising to record that the Moshi Conference achieved little if any practical significance: the Chinese distributed invitations to various African politicians to visit China; a special committee was formed to examine the advantages of a planning system for the economies of the former colonial countries; a good deal was said about the necessity for increasing the material assistance granted to the liberation movements in Asia and Africa; a list of denunciations was reeled off against Western colonialism; and once more the solidarity organization was given *carte blanche* to carry on endless propaganda activity between the conferences in the name of 'the peoples of Asia and Africa'.

The original communist plan (put forward chiefly by the Chinese) to extend the organization to Latin America had to be abandoned, probably because the only delegation from that part of the world came from Castro's Cuba. The conference did not succeed in persuading objective observers that it was either representative or powerful. Perhaps the most significant comment, and by no means an unfair one, was made by Ronald Ngala, former Chief Minister for Kenya, who declared forthrightly that the conference had been a failure. That opinion was undoubtedly shared by many other delegates.

This laconic judgement even found some support in the summary handed to the delegates by the general secretary, Yussuf El Sabai. His report confirmed that the chief activity of the permanent secretariat between the conferences consisted almost exclusively of propaganda, Press releases, denunciations, solidarity gestures and the issue of pamphlets. But even this propaganda campaign suffered, it appeared, not only from lack of support by the affiliated organizations, but also from an indifferent reception. The following passages from the report of the general secretary will show that this conclusion is not unfair:

'A circular letter was sent to the national solidarity committee calling on them to contribute material for these publications [a monthly bulletin, a quarterly publication, and various pamphlets on important questions], to make any proposals of their own to further the work and to help in the distribution. Unfortunately there was no response at all.'[15]

'The Quarterly was not published at all owing to lack of response on the part of the national committees to our appeal.[16]

'The efficiency of the Contacts Section reached a remarkably high level . . . Nevertheless, the fact remains that the response of the national committees and other organizations to our appeals and our letters is still irregular.'[17]

'The Research Section still stands in need of improvement. Unfortunately the critical financial situation of the secretariat constitutes the main obstacle to the establishment of a sound basis for the work of this section. The sub-sections for political, economic, social, and cultural research are similarly hampered in carrying out their tasks for the same reason: namely, lack of finance and the lack of response on the part of the committees and organizations to our appeals.'[18]

What are we to say to all this? How are we to sum up the significance of the whole movement? How effective is it as a channel for communist ideas and propaganda? How effectively does it further practical communist activities? It is not easy to give a satisfactory answer. Even at the second conference in Conakry I was still inclined to regard the movement as being of some importance—even indeed, as a threatening factor in African developments. But in Moshi, and before Moshi, I began to have doubts about the effectiveness of the organization as a communist instrument. Its original impetus seems to be largely exhausted. Apart from dramatic gestures and declarations which really do not mean very much, it seems to be finding no response. The fact that certain delegates took part in the conference does not even tell one much about their real political attitudes. Indeed, most of them seem to be using such platforms as an opportunity for putting forward their own egoistical wishes and plans, though there is always a point at which these coincide with the wishes and plans of the communist wire-pullers. This was certainly true of some of the delegations from still-subject areas in East, South, and Central Africa. Finally it must not be forgotten that in these days mere propaganda often has as much weight as practical action where Africa is concerned.

In the future we shall have to pay closer attention to the various branches and special organizations affiliated to the movement, most of which have not been long in existence. This is especially true of bodies such as the Afro-Asian Legal Consultative Committee; the Afro-Asian Organization for Economic Co-operation; the Afro-Asian Students' Organization; the Afro-Asian Reconstruction Organization; the Afro-Asian Youth Office; the Afro-Asian Sports Committee (which organized an Afro-Asian Table-Tennis Conference in December 1961); the International Committee for Aid to the Congo; the Afro-Asian Writers' Organization; and the Afro-Asian Solidarity Fund (with its seat in Conakry). It is beginning to look as though, in future, the communist wire-pullers behind the Afro-Asian Solidarity Movement intend to concentrate on the activities of such organizations, especially since the fourth conference of the AAPSO, held in Ghana from 9 to 16 May 1965, failed to attract prominent African and Asian politicians and became yet again an arena for the Sino-Soviet dispute, despite a ruling by AAPSO's permanent secretariat that ideological quarrels should be kept out of future meetings. Host for the meeting at the Winneba Ideological Institute was the Ghana Convention People's Party with President Nkrumah opening the conference. Moscow Radio commented that the conference's most important result was that the 'idea of unity of nations triumphed once more'. The Chinese, however, directly attacked the Russians—an editorial in the *Peking People's Daily* said that a 'struggle between two lines ran through the whole conference'. Lagos Radio said that the most surprising feature of the conference was its 'reluctance to address itself to certain practical problems facing African and Asian politics today'. It suggested that the delegates might have contributed 'their widow's mite' to the coffers of the OAU Liberation Fund, which 'could have been a more concrete and more convincing expression of solidarity than shouting anti-imperialist speeches'. Abidjan Radio (Ivory Coast) said that all that had been achieved was 'the customary verbiage of international communist dialectics which masks its active imperialism from those who do not share its devouring taste for domination'.[19]

However, the ultimate success or failure of the Afro-Asian Solidarity Movement and its various subordinate bodies depends largely on factors other than the activity of the communists themselves. Often the mistakes of the West unintentionally assist the communists to achieve their aims; and often, too, intransigent action on the part of the Western States where Africa is concerned drive the African nationalists to make common cause with the communists.

The stirring appeals of the Solidarity Council in the Lumumba case, its repeated protests against French nuclear tests in the Sahara, its constant condemnation of racialism in South Africa and of the reactionary policy of the white settlers in Rhodesia, its repeated exposure of co-operation between the democratic Western States and Portugal in Angola and Mozambique, the exposure of foolish neo-colonialist manœuvres on the part of capitalist undertakings in Africa, and many other such activities—which are taken very seriously by Africans—appeal to Africans, help to obscure the activity and aims of the communist wire-pullers and prevent African politicians from taking the movement into their own hands and turning it into a real instrument for the realization of their own ideas and aims.

NOTES

[1] Cyclostyled minutes of the First Afro-Asian People's Solidarity Conference, Cairo, January 1958.

[2] In Conakry, April 1960.

[3] Cyclostyled minutes of the First Afro-Asian People's Solidarity Conference.

[4] Ibid.

[5] Cyclostyled publication (Tunis, 29 January 1960).

[6] Declaration of the Permanent Secretariat of the AAPSO, Cairo, 4 October 1958.

[7] Based on the author's notes during the Conakry Conference.

[8] The *Daily Nation*, 4 February 1963.

[9] A year later, the Chinese and the Soviets clashed at an AAPSO secretariat meeting in Algiers.

[10] The *Daily Nation*, 4 February 1963.

[11] Cyclostyled minutes of the Moshi Conference.

[12] Witnessed by the author.

[13] Ibid.

[14] Ibid.

[15] Political-Organizational Report of the Permanent Secretariat for Afro-Asian People's Solidarity to the Third Afro-Asian People's Solidarity Conference.

[16] Ibid.

[17] Ibid.

[18] Ibid., p. 42.

[19] *African Review*, June 1965.

Chapter XVI

IT'S THE CADRES THAT COUNT

Almost every great political movement ultimately turns its back on reality and, always with the same arguments, seeks salvation in myths and legends. In the same way, African nationalism claims that the dissolution of the colonial system was its own achievement and ascribes it to the effects of 'the people' and 'the masses'. Yet the truth is clearly quite different. In Africa political emancipation was ***primarily*** the result of the emancipation of small élites—not of the masses. It was the élite who prepared the way for the upheaval, which was accelerated by a number of non-African factors. Trained and educated against a European background and at European universities in the spirit of liberalism and humanism, this intellectual minority succeeded in carrying through its programme, despite—and not because of—the masses, which remained largely lethargic.

The upheaval in Africa thus fits into the general historical tendency discussed and defined by Vilfredo Pareto and Gaetano Mosca. Their political sociology compares the fascination of the masses concept with the outstanding importance of the choice and distribution of the élite; and the validity of their theory has been confirmed by the history of both Soviet and Chinese communism.

There is thus a marked parallel between communism and African nationalism, and this is an important starting-point for communist infiltration into Africa, since the intellectual and organizational development of the leading strata of present-day Africa has been moulded on lines similar to that of the communist cadres in late-Tzarist Russia and revolutionary China. In each case the ideas that caused the revolutionary ferment were brought in as a mental pabulum from outside. Unlike Africa however, where the import was accidental rather than centrally organized, Leninism and Maoism systematically set about selecting and training their cadres, sending them abroad and giving them a uniform ideology. This created the essential condition for the communist seizure of power. It came about primarily as a result of the conscious, deliberate fashion in which communists treated the cadre problem, which as early as 1902 it regarded as decisive for defeat or victory.

For Marx, revolution was the task of a chosen 'class', the historic mission of *all* proletarians who, he was convinced, would organize themselves into this class and into a corresponding political party. The Communist Manifesto of 1848 declared: 'All previous historical movements were movements of minorities, or in the interests of minorities. The proletarian movement is the self-conscious, independent movement of the immense majority.'[1] In Russia at least this prophecy was not fulfilled. Tzarist Russia was a backward agricultural country, and the proletariat developed only late and as a minority class. In 1913 only 2,552,000 persons were engaged in Russian industry (and even that number included handicraft and home-workers), and this naturally represented an exceptionally weak basis for a class struggle.[2] Further, very few of these proletarians felt inclined to act, or were sufficiently knowledgeable to think, 'according to their class situation'; at the beginning of the great revolutionary year, 1917, the Russian Social Democratic Workers' Party, from which the Communist Party of the Soviet Union developed, had only 23,000 members.[3] In such circumstances, and on account of proscription and illegality, Lenin gave up all idea of leading the revolution to victory by winning over the 'proletarian masses' and making them politically active: and in his programmatic statement 'What is to be done?', written in 1902, he dismissed all thought of an 'appeal to the masses' as 'an attempt to drag us backwards'. If it tried to start from the basis of 'a large-scale working-class organization allegedly open to the masses' the Social Democratic Party would achieve nothing. Lenin's idea was very different: 'Let us begin with a sound organization of [professional] revolutionaries . . . A firm, small core of reliable, experienced and steeled workers . . . can, with the far-reaching co-operation of the masses, and without taking on any fixed form, carry out all functions a Social Democracy would wish.'[4]

These words, which sum up the communist cadre principle *in nuce* deserve to stand as a motto for the whole history of modern communism. They form the basic formula of the communist struggle for power and the secret of communist successes. However, they require an important addition. For Lenin the formula 'a firm small core' of professional revolutionaries implied a sound, uniform, dogmatic training according to centralized basic principles. As the conditions for this were very unfavourable in Tzarist Russia at the time, particularly after the failure of the Russian Revolution of 1905, he ordered the establishment of party schools abroad. The result was the formation of Bolshevist 'cadre smithies' in Longjumeau near Paris and on the island of Capri. Among other teachers, Lenin and Maxim Gorki lectured at these schools in which the 'advance guard of the Revolution' was trained for the decisive clash with Tzarism. In addition to these there were also itinerant schools, both in Russia and abroad, at which small groups worked according to a uniform curriculum on the basis of party ideological and practical themes.

As this method proved extraordinarily successful, it was a foregone conclusion that after the triumph of Bolshevism the idea would be mooted of trying the same method on a larger scale with foreign communists. Before long, special training centres for foreign communists were set up in the Soviet Union. The first of these started in Tashkent in May 1921, as the University of the Eastern Toilers. Then, as now, the Soviet concept of 'the East' was not confined solely to Asia, but included all colonial and semi-colonial countries, including Africa and Latin America. Thus as far back as 1921, not long after the victorious Bolshevik Revolution, Moscow began to select and train revolutionary cadres systematically for the whole sphere of communist colonial activity.

The enormous importance of this technique of 'exporting revolution' was first demonstrated in China and Korea. The Sun Yat-sen University was founded in Moscow in the early 1920s specially for the Chinese comrades, and up to 1949 most of the Chinese communist leaders and officials, the 'cadres', were trained there. Stefan Possony writes: 'The fact remains that when the time came for China, the communist midwives were prepared for it. They had thousands of trained experts experienced in the arts of revolutionary warfare and fully versed in Chinese affairs.'[5]

Between 1929 and 1939 about 800,000 Koreans were transferred from Outer Mongolia and the Amur district and settled in Turkestan, and every year between 600 and 700 reliable candidates were sent to the University of the Eastern Toilers in Tashkent to be trained for revolutionary activity. A special Korean Institute was subsequently founded in Fergana (Turkestan) and an additional 1,200 Koreans were trained there every year. Finally, about 700 selected Koreans received special training in the NKVD training centre in Tashkent. All men capable of bearing arms were called up for military service with the Red Army. When the Soviets took over North Korea after the Second World War, the élite of the Turkestan Koreans were resettled in their own country and entrusted with the establishment of "people's democratic rule". For example, the present Premier of North Korea, Kim Il-sung, who was also Commander-in-Chief of the North Korean Army during the Korean War, is known to have been one of those North Koreans who was trained in the Soviet Union for unspecified 'tasks in his own country'.[6]

Of course, this systematic organization and training of Korean cadres cannot be compared with the efforts of the communists to form and train an élite in Africa. Most of the students at the University of the Eastern Toilers were Asians and communists from the Near East. From Africa there were only Moroccans, Tunisians and Sudanese in any number, and in the 1920s only members of the communist groups and trade unions from South Africa, Senegal and Madagascar. However, the African ambitions of the Soviets were not forgotten at the fourth anniversary celebrations of the university in 1925. Stalin declared: 'There are about ten different groups of students at the Eastern University and they have come to us from colonial and semi-colonial countries . . . The task of the Eastern University is to forge them into *real revolutionaries*, equip them with the theory of Leninism and with practical experience of Leninism and thus enable them to carry out effectively the immediate tasks in the struggle for the liberation of the colonial and semi-colonial countries.'[7] Stalin gave the university students five tasks to accomplish on their return to their own countries: '1. To win the best elements of the working class for the revolutionary movement and found independent communist parties. 2. To form a national-revolutionary block of the workers, peasants and revolutionary intellectuals to oppose the alliance of the national bourgeoisie with imperialism. 3. To establish the hegemony of the proletariat in the national-revolutionary movement. 4. To wage a struggle to free the urban and rural petite-bourgeoisie from the influence of the national bourgeoisie and its ally imperialism. 5. To work for an alliance between the national-revolutionary movement and the proletarian movements in the progressive countries.'[8] Stalin appealed to his Asian and African listeners: 'The mission of the peoples of the East where the colonial and semi-colonial countries are concerned . . . is to take all the special features of the revolutionary development of these countries into account, and to guide the education and training of the cadres from these countries towards the fulfilment of the various immediate tasks I have enumerated.'[9]

The curriculum of the University of the Eastern Toilers was fashioned with these tasks in view; among the subjects taught were: the history of the Communist Party of the Soviet Union; the history of the Soviet Union; the history of the colonial peoples; the methods used in the revolutionary upheavals among the peoples of the East; historical and dialectical materialism; individual psychology and the psychology of the peoples of the East, and so on. In September 1955 the periodical *Ostprobleme* reported that all nationalities and groups of peoples—*including North, Central and South Africa*—had their own department in the faculties of Tashkent University—the university that developed from the original University of the Eastern Toilers—and that the curricula were specially adapted to the particular circumstances of their countries. 'For example, the history and dogma of Islam is an important subject for students from the Islamic countries. The course of study until the final examinations usually lasts from four to five years. Quite recently arrangements have been made to establish *special faculties for African questions* in order to train native Africans to become communist agents, at first chiefly for operations in North Africa, Nigeria, and the Gold Coast.'[10]

This development is obviously very closely connected with the increased activity of the communist-front organizations, particularly the World League of Democratic Youth, in selecting cadre candidates. Since the end of the Second World War thousands of Africans—often without realizing it—have been sifted by the central communist seeding apparatus in connection with international trade-union, women's, teachers' and youth congresses and world youth celebrations under communist auspices. The total number of

Africans who have been trained at the University of the Eastern Toilers or in Soviet or people's democratic youth and trade-union schools during the past ten years must now run into many thousands. They are still being trained according to the principles Stalin laid down in his Tashkent speech in May 1925; the revolutionary African advance guard are being schooled to become officials of the revolutionary class struggle, deeply versed in the spirit of communist Machiavellianism. An African course held at the high school of the Communist Youth League of the German Soviet Zone at Bogensee in central Germany in 1960, and run by officials of the Communist Youth League (FDJ) and the WFDY, included the following subjects in its curriculum: Marxist-Leninism, the formation of active youth cells at universities and schools in the colonial and semi-colonial countries, practical questions for active youth workers (including how to organize protest demonstrations, etc.), and the provision and distribution of literature (for 'literature' read propaganda material).[11] It is obvious that such a programme of training aims very definitely at communist objectives, as was made clear in a speech delivered by Louis Saillant at the Central Communist Trade Union School for African cadres in Budapest and reported in greater detail elsewhere in this book. The speaker left no room for doubt about the aims of the school when he stated: 'Do not forget that the most important school for working-class officials is the class struggle itself.'[12]

There are many training schools for coloured students (and in particular African students) in the countries of the Soviet bloc today and the situation is complicated by a flood of tendentious reports concerning 'thousands of African agents' who are alleged to be receiving training at the present time in those countries. The Paris newspaper *Le Monde* is probably right to describe the so-called Institute for Economic Studies, founded in Prague in 1958, as 'literally a military academy'. In the same report *Le Monde* mentions a number of special institutes for the training of coloured communist cadres in the Soviet Union, as well as others in Albania, Bulgaria, and East Germany. In addition there are said to be two such schools in the Chinese People's Republic.[13] There are also a number of military training centres in various countries behind the Iron Curtain; for example, in a private talk with the author in April 1960, a member of the Czech Embassy in Conakry confirmed the fact that NCOs of the Guinean Army are being trained at the

Prague Military Academy. In October 1961 the Ghanaian Government also decided to make use of military training schools in the countries of the Soviet bloc and announced that, for the time being, some 400 trainees would go to Iron Curtain countries to take part in communist officers' training courses.[14] According to a broadcast on Radio Accra the first 71 trainees left there in October 1961, on their way to Moscow to undergo such training.[15] Even where the training is frankly military there is little doubt that ideological indoctrination will be an important feature of the course.

Since 1955 communist cadre policy has undergone a noticeable change. In accordance with general Soviet policy towards Africa, which includes both revolutionary action and co-existentialist agreements and alliances, the Kremlin is laying less stress on the revolutionary aspect. Today cadre recruitment among the African élite pursues two distinct lines: there is the training of African professional revolutionaries completely devoted to communist doctrines and aims which is going on as usual, but at the same time Africans are being offered a supposedly academic and technological training, ostensibly without ideological strings. The large-scale programme of scholarship grants organized by the communist countries for Africa and in particular by the new Friendship University, founded in 1960 in Moscow, is aimed primarily at members of the bourgeoisie and intelligentsia who are not, or not yet, committed communists. In this connection the following aims are paramount: the dissipation of anti-communist feelings; the formation of influential groups of people who are at least amiably disposed to the Soviet Union and its satellites; and the exploitation of such persons later, when they return to their countries, as propagandists for a policy of co-existence, if not alliance, with the Soviet bloc.

Up to 1960 such students were recruited primarily on the basis of mutual agreement between the Soviet Union and the various African countries concerned or by means of scholarship grants to the United Nations through the (communist) International Students League or the Afro-Asian Solidarity Committee. Apart from free education, students were offered 900 roubles a month to live on plus a grant of 3,000 roubles for the purchase of winter clothing, fares to and from the Soviet Union, and specially arranged tours. What the student does not learn beforehand is that he will have to pay 90 roubles a month for his place in a common dormitory and over 500 roubles a month for food, books and fares. African students returning from the Soviet Union have also mentioned more important disadvantages: the continuous surveillance, the isolation from the Russian people and the constant if indirect indoctrination. Typical of these complaints is the account given by Andrew Richard Amar of Uganda, who in the autumn of 1960 left the Soviet Union in disgust and returned to his own country:

'Four students shared a room. Two of them were always Russians and they were in control. The students from Iraq were the only ones treated differently; sometimes they were left to themselves, or there was only one Russian in with them. To make this surveillance appear casual and not deliberate the Russian students were usually in residence before the foreign students arrived. Very often, but not always, these Russian students were in the uniform of the Soviet military security service. There were at least two such uniformed men to each floor. At first I, too, had to sleep in a room with one of these policemen, because that was really what these Russian students were. Soon after I arrived and before I had had much experience I asked the management of the institute why these men were present. I was told that they really had nothing to do with the institute at all and that they were there simply because there was a shortage of accommodation. The longer I stayed in Moscow the more I began to doubt this explanation, because, for one thing, these uniformed police-soldiers took part in all the activities of a university to which they allegedly did not belong.

'The surveillance system in Moscow covers all university students. It is quite effective and is being tightened up from year to year. The fact that it is obligatory to attend the various lectures is no cause for complaint, but the limitation of personal freedom is very onerous. I have already mentioned these uniformed policemen, or militiamen, who are always around in the main university buildings and whose presence is a source of resentment. There are two of the militiamen to each floor. The main building consists of six sectors, known as "zona", and these usually consist of nine floors. This means that there are a hundred policemen always around, and perhaps more, and the students can never get out of their sight. But these are only the external indications of power.

Each of us students had to suffer, in addition, from the attentions of Komsomol activists and spies, and this was true in particular of non-Russian and above all, African, students, who are practically put away in an institutional ghetto. There is a system of university passes, known as *propusks*, and this also greatly restricts the freedom of movement of all students. But worst of all was perhaps the interference and unfriendliness we had to suffer from our Russian fellow-students and room-mates. No one doubted that they were only there to spy on us, and in reality they were nothing but "student security police". On at least one occasion they were used by the university authorities to enforce discipline, and I witnessed at least one arrest . . .'[16]

Amar also describes the constant surveillance and the restriction of movement outside the university. Conducted tours were organized for the students in and around Moscow, but they were shown 'only the typical tourist attractions, and it was expressly forbidden to leave the party and go around on one's own. Whole days were often devoted to receptions and meetings with various organizations, such as the Communist Party, the Communist Youth and the Young Pioneers.' But even more important is what Amar has to say about the ideological indoctrination of the foreign students, and in particular the obligatory Russian lessons.

Amar writes:

'The first two or three months were devoted entirely to language lessons, and there were four full lessons every day, and, in addition, homework—as far as we were able to work at all in the inadequately heated and overcrowded rooms. Subsequently these language lessons were reduced to two a day. At first they were all given in the institute itself, later we went into the main building for courses and lectures. The Soviet authorities attach particular importance to the introductory lessons. When I was there all the language teachers were women. I was put into a class with students from Iraq. Right at the start our teacher told us: "Forget everything you ever learned before you came to Russia". Our first exercises were all to do with Russian popular heroes and people's leaders. Comparisons were made and parallels drawn with our own countries. Finally we were asked whether we would not wish such heroes and revolutionary leaders for our own countries, and it was made quite clear to us what reply was expected. This method of instruction was intended not only to indoctrinate and mould us, but also to discover our own ideas and tendencies. If we started to discuss things or to ask awkward questions, we were told that we were wasting valuable time and ought to apply for a transfer. The students were sifted according to political, not intellectual, criteria. All my friends experienced the same sort of thing. The teachers deliberately dragged out their lessons and never lost an opportunity to slip in little political homilies, at the same time studying our reactions in order to be able to sift and classify us. Once I realized this I pretended to be naïve. When I was asked a particularly provocative question I would answer innocently: "I haven't any idea" or "I really don't know much about the history of my country". After a month we were presented with carefully chosen extracts from the newspapers, all of which, of course, severely criticized and denounced the capitalist countries. One of our teachers, Valeria Dmitrievna, was particularly cunning: she admitted openly that our lessons were intended to educate us politically, and by her apparent frankness she hoped to win our confidence. She also assured us that the British, French and Americans did not want us to be educated and become free, whereas, on the other hand, all Russians were eager to help the Africans.'[17]

Similar stories were told at a Press conference in Frankfort-on-Main on 21 September 1960, at which three African students who had broken with Moscow vigorously denounced the establishment of a Soviet Friendship University specially for Africans, Asians and Latin Americans. They insisted that the founding of such an institution would be an insult to the peoples concerned, and that the idea violated the traditional concept of the university as an institution of learning open to all, irrespective of race, religion, or origin.[18]

Recently, and especially in 1963, Africans who have studied at institutions in the communist satellite States have reported similarly disappointing experiences on a par with those related by Richard Amar about the Soviet Union. Six Somalis who came from Prague in December 1961 had a particularly dramatic story to tell. They had been inveigled into Czechoslovakia with glittering promises and at first they found themselves treated in friendly fashion. The unpleasantness started when it came to buying some urgently needed winter clothing. Although they had been promised 'an adquate sum' for such purchases, all they were handed when they arrived in Prague was 500 crowns, and with clothing prices as high as they are behind the Iron Curtain this did not go far. Each of them had to 'borrow' from other grants to make up the deficiency, with the result that most of them spent their book allowance of 400 crowns on clothes. When they refused to join a very obviously communist-controlled Union of Somali Students in the socialist camp, the secretary of this organization warned them that if they persisted in their refusal it might entail 'disagreeable consequences', and buttressed his arguments by declaring that their 'socialist hosts' were entitled to demand 'a friendly attitude' on their part. After this, especially on arrival at a language school in Dobruska, the Somalis found themselves under suspicion and many irritating restrictions were placed on their personal freedom. Letters from home were opened and read before being handed to them and telegrams were often kept back for days before they received them—already opened. It was impossible for them to acquire any objective sources of information. The only newspapers they were allowed to see were those published behind the Iron Curtain or by communist parties abroad. All other Press material was confiscated before it reached them. Outside the institute, the students became aware of various forms of restriction and discrimination, all in flagrant contradiction to communist propaganda. They were not allowed to leave the Dobruska district without special permission. They also found that ordinary Czechs tended to avoid them, doubtless fearing the attentions of the secret police if they established contact with the Somalis. Even in dance halls and restaurants they found themselves cold-shouldered. Finally, they were made to suffer for their religious beliefs. They were ridiculed for upholding their religious observances and sometimes they were deliberately served with pork, although other kinds of meat were available and those responsible were well aware that Muslims are forbidden to eat pork. In the end, things got so bad that they decided to leave the country, but this they found far from easy and they had to suffer protracted and tiresome delays before they were finally able to obtain their exit permits. They stayed in Prague during this time and were kept under constant surveillance by relays of plain-clothes police. They were also made to endure continual chicanery: for example, they were unable to get hotel rooms and they had to spend the bitterly cold nights in the open.[19]

To what extent are such experiences typical? And do those who nevertheless persist to the end in their training behind the Iron Curtain—perhaps despite misgivings—share the disappointment of those who abandoned their studies, returned home and broke with communism? Or are these students who have returned home disappointed and discontented exceptions compared with the majority of coloured students behind the Iron Curtain? And are the latter content with their lot and perhaps even enthusiastic about their hosts? There are, of course, a few malcontents among the coloured students at Western universities too, though we know that they are exceptions.

Thus caution is advisable before coming to any final conclusions. In almost all cases where coloured students left, or were compelled to leave, training centres in Soviet-bloc countries, the associations of coloured students studying there adopted resolutions criticizing and denouncing them. This was the case with Richard Amar and with the six Somali students and with those who left Bulgaria in 1963 or the Soviet Union after the heavy clashes in December 1963. They were approached by other Africans, who sought to influence them and dissuade them from returning home prematurely.

Despite the mass demonstrations of African students in Moscow in December 1963, it seems that those Africans who go behind the Iron Curtain to study and are disappointed with what they find are in the minority, and there is much evidence to suggest that most of the African students behind the Iron Curtain are inclined—at least at first—to see advantages in the communist system. In fact, they are often fascinated by communism. The scale of the communist scholarship-grants programme and the intense propaganda that accompanies it have not failed to make a profound impression.

In particular, it would be foolish not to acknowledge the favourable reception given to Khrushchev's announcement, on 21 February 1960, that the Soviet Government intended to establish a great Friendship University (now named after Patrice Lumumba) and that after a short period it would be open to 4,000 coloured students. As soon as it was announced that the first 750 places were ready to be filled, no fewer than 43,500 applications poured in.[20] In short, the revelations of Amar and his friends have clearly not affected the flood of applicants, most of them from Africa, according to Moscow Press reports. Indeed, the Soviet authorities seem to attach particular importance to wooing coloured students, and during the first year 190 students were accepted from Africa, 145 from Asia and 130 from Latin America, so that Africa provides the biggest contingent.[21]

A number of points in connection with the founding of this new university deserve close attention:

1. Although Khrushchev and the Soviet Government were the first to announce the establishment of the new university (*Pravda*, 28 March 1960), Moscow still maintains the fiction that it is not a government institution and that it is being run primarily by the Afro-Asian Solidarity Committee, the Soviet labour unions, the Communist Committee, and the Communist Youth. These organizations, and not the Soviet Government, are said to have appointed the first Rector (S.W. Rumyantzev, formerly Deputy Minister for Soviet High Schools), chosen the university council and laid down arrangements for accepting students. *Pravda* has repeatedly stressed that the authorities will restrict their role in connection with the new university to providing quarters for the students, building laboratories and so on. This unusual—and patently hypocritical—attitude is intended to disguise the real state of affairs. Although Moscow Radio and Soviet propaganda publications instruct candidates to make their applications through their local Soviet embassies, the Russian authorities are able to disclaim all responsibility to the governments of the countries from which the students come. In this way they are able to side-step those governments with which they have cultural and educational agreements, and which would otherwise have a say in the choice of the students accepted for training.

2. The university has another important object in view, according to A. Sofronov, the Russian secretary of the Afro-Asian Solidarity Committee. It appears from his article that most of the students are to be recruited from strata of society from which youngsters would ordinarily find it impossible to attend 'capitalist high schools' abroad. This means an extension to other countries of the class educational monopoly as it exists in the countries of the Soviet bloc and the establishment of a monopoly for the education of the so-called 'workers' and peasants' children'. The communists hope that

when such students have completed their studies they will 'remain loyal to their class'. Thus Moscow intends to accept only applicants who are likely to serve the cause of communism in the African 'class struggle', as a result of their Soviet training and indoctrination.

3. The Russians have repeatedly sought to discount misgivings expressed in neutral countries that a course of study in the Soviet Union must automatically result in ideological indoctrination. At the opening of the university Khrushchev made a point of rejecting all responsibility for any 'cases of infection with that fashionable disease communism'. But it is quite clear that the spread of this disease is precisely what he and the university are aiming at. The students have to spend the whole period of their study in the Soviet Union—from three to four years. In addition there is the preliminary language instruction, and this takes a year. Furthermore, the university has not restricted applications to students who have already had a high-school education and are therefore ready for university training: it also takes younger students who need a period of 'preparatory training', and this will take another year or two. So that when one remembers that each student will spend between four and six years in the Soviet Union, out of touch with the non-communist world except by mail, and constantly influenced by Soviet newspapers, broadcasts and films, it is not difficult to imagine the ultimate effect of such surroundings and their direct and indirect indoctrination. It would be an illusion to suppose that all the graduates of the Friendship University will return to their own countries as diehard anti-communists, or disappointed and sobered. It is hardly to be expected that the Russians will abandon their practice of personal regimentation for the sake of a few thousand coloured students who may be embarrassed by it.

However, we can learn all we need to know from the Rector of the Friendship University himself. Writing in *Problems of Peace and Socialism*, Professor Rumyantsev says that there are six faculties in his university: economics, engineering, agriculture, medicine, history and philosophy, and international law. This sounds harmless enough, but he then goes on to stress the essential connection between study and 'social life' and quotes Lenin as having said that the under-developed countries must be helped in three ways: 'to go over to the use of machines, to lighten their labour, and to go forward to democracy and socialism.'[22]

Meanwhile, the many reports on the progress of the Friendship University all indicate the great importance the Soviet Government attaches to this educational institution. When the preliminary stage was completed the Rector had a staff of almost a thousand at his disposal, including 250 teachers of Russian. In addition there were a large number of full-time professors and over 700 younger lecturers; thus at the end of its first stage, the university had about 1,500 students, and there were two professors, lecturers or teachers for every three students—a proportion likely to be maintained as the university develops.[23]

Since its foundation the Friendship University has served as an example for similar foundations in a number of other countries of the Soviet bloc. In 1961 the University of 17 November was founded in Prague with four faculties: teachers' training, engineering, agronomy, and building.[24] In the following year 654 new students were enrolled.[25] The Polish Government also plans to concentrate all students from Asia, Africa, and Latin America in a single university. At the beginning of 1962 there were no fewer than 900 Africans studying in Poland on Patrice Lumumba scholarships.[26] And for a long time Leipzig has been the East German centre for training Asian and African students.

Since 1961 this cadre training has been supplemented by a new form of 'cadre export' to Africa from the countries of the Soviet bloc: one of the provisions of the so-called cultural agreements between many African States and the communist countries is that teachers should be sent to Africa from behind the Iron Curtain. As a case in point, the cultural agreement signed between the Soviet and Mali Governments in Bamako in February 1962 expressly provides for teachers from the Soviet Union to be sent to Mali. These Soviet educationalists will lecture on the Soviet system of higher and secondary education and the Bauman Higher Technical School in Moscow will assist the Technical Lycée in Bamako to arrange its curriculum.[27] From another source we learn that Czech experts have drafted a plan for a network of general and specialized schools in Mali and Somalia and that Czechoslovakia will provide the necessary text-books and help with the buildings and the supply of teachers.[28] These are only a few of many examples illustrating increased activity in the training of pro-communist cadres in Africa. For the sake of completeness we should not omit to mention communist broadcast propaganda which, where Africa is concerned, is concentrating more on educational and pseudo-educational 'lessons'—broadcasts for teaching Russian with illustrations taken from Soviet educational procedure, broadcasts from East Germany, and so on—not forgetting the broadcasts from Red China.

Naturally, these ambitious Soviet plans have not passed unnoticed in the West, but the general view is that it would be foolish to exaggerate either the extent or effect of these operations. After all, year after year thousands of Asians and Africans still come to the West for both university education and technological training. There are more Africans studying in France than in all the countries of the Soviet bloc together. But these reassuring arguments miss the core of the problem and they reveal a disturbing ignorance of communist propaganda techniques. All the West offers these Asian and African students is objective education and scientific training, and it does not make this easier for them by providing adequate grants. Apart from such education and training, the young student from Asia or Africa is left largely to his own devices. At best, he will strive to fit himself into the individualistic pattern of Western society and come to adopt similarly individualistic ideas and behaviour patterns. But in the Western world ideological factors play a minor role, and generally speaking there will be no specific attempt to mould his views in any particular direction—though admittedly the general environment of bourgeois democracy may be regarded as a factor tending to inculcate a certain ideology in the student. Socially and politically, the whole Western high-school system and environment tend in the last resort to result in intense individualism. The African who studies medicine at Oxford or Harvard will probably become a good doctor, but very little will be done to encourage him to take any particular social and political line outside his practice. On the other hand, the activity of communist student groups in Paris, which have many African members, suggests that the African student is inclined to counter the threat of excessive individualization and satisfy his instinctive objection to the anti-social environment of the West by turning to left-wing radical groups. At least they offer him an attachment and a 'solution'.

In the countries of the Soviet bloc, the communists do their best to persuade the student to regard his scientific training and his work as only one side of his 'service to the community'; and they often succeed. According to communist calculations, when the African doctor trained in Moscow or Prague returns to his own country he will be something more than a doctor; he will be an 'agent' (in the strictest sense of the word). He will not regard it as his task merely to heal his patients physically, he will also try to heal them ideologically. At best, from the communist standpoint, foreign students who have been trained in the Soviet bloc will return to their own countries as 'missionaries' and agents of a world-wide ideological movement with a 'historical task' to perform. Whether they know it or not they will have become communist cadres in their own countries.

This picture is, of course, over-simplified. The reality, both in the West and in the East, is far more complicated—as shown by the example of many Africans who fled from Eastern Europe. However, the really dangerous omission at the moment is the lack of any systematic élite programme by the West in an effort to give its Afro-Asian students something more than an objective education or scientific training, in order to counterbalance the systematic, large-scale and effective programme being operated behind the Iron Curtain. The plans of the communist universities in Tashkent, Moscow, Prague and Budapest are a clear warning. They may differ slightly in detail, but they are at one in their fundamental objective based on the Stalin principle, 'It's the cadres that count!'

NOTES

[1] Karl Marx and Frederick Engels, *Communist Manifesto* (London, 1934).

[2] B. Gukhman, *The Size of the Proletariat and Wages in the USSR* (Moscow, 1926); cited by Solomon M. Schwartz in *Labor in the Soviet Union* (New York, 1951), p. 6.

[3] According to a statistical table drawn by A. Bubnov for the *Great Soviet Encyclopaedia* (Moscow, 1930); cited by Merle Fainsod in *How Russia Is Ruled* (Cambridge, Mass., 1953), p. 60.

[4] Lenin, '*Chto delat?*' Sochineniya IV, p. 452.

[5] Stefan T. Possony, *A Century of Conflict: Communist Techniques of World Revolution* (Chicago, 1953), pp. 350-1.

[6] *Ostprobleme*, II, No. 50 (December 1950).

[7] *Pravda*, 22 May 1925.

[8] Ibid.

[9] Ibid.

[10] *Ostprobleme*, VII, No. 39 (September 1955), p. 1505.

[11] Information given to the author by a communist official who fled from East Germany.

[12] *Die Weltgewerkschaftsbewegung*, November 1959.

[13] *Le Monde*, 18 July 1960.

[14] The *Guardian*, 11 October 1961.

[15] Radio Accra broadcast, 10 October 1961.

[16] *Neue Zürcher Zeitung*, 6 and 12 December 1960.

[17] Ibid.

[18] *East Europe*, IX, No. 12 (December 1960), p. 48.

[19] *Forum Service* (London), No. 461 (February 1962).

[20] *Pravda*, 17 November 1960.

[21] *Politika*, 5 November 1960.

[22] *World Marxist Review: Problems of Peace and Socialism*, III, No. 8 (August 1960), p. 86.

[23] *Neue Zürcher Zeitung*, 23 January 1962.

[24] The *Ethiopian Herald*, 23 January 1961.

[25] CTK, 16 and 19 February 1962.

[26] Warsaw Radio broadcast, 21 February 1962.

[27] Tass, 16 February 1962.

[28] The *Ethiopian Herald*, 23 January 1962.

Chapter XVII

SOME CONCLUSIONS

HARDLY a month goes by without newspaper headlines proclaiming some dramatic new event in Africa. The revolution of this continent has, in fact, become one of the main themes of our time and is likely to remain so for many years to come. But although the West is unamimous in agreeing on the importance of this revolution, views differ widely when it comes to judging the motives behind it and the results which are likely to emerge. Has the West any chance in Africa? Can African nationalism take its place as an independent force in a new system of international relationships between West and East? How far does communist influence in Africa already extend? Is communism a real danger in Africa today, is it likely to engulf the African continent and turn it into a new geo-political base for its struggle for world power? Western views on these and other points are often diametrically opposed and it is difficult to arrive at any objective conclusion because the debate is so often dominated by two extreme attitudes.

One group declares that African nationalism is nothing but a cover for communism and that one should look for the real wire-pullers not in Cairo, Accra or Leopoldville, but in Moscow, Peking, and Prague. This group would have us believe that the Red dominion over the black thrones has already taken place. The conclusion we are asked to draw from this presents us with dangerous alternatives: either the West should defend its remaining positions in Africa to the bitter end and with all possible means, including the use of brute force, or it should leave the field to the 'Bolshies and the Niggers'. The main upholders of this stark, unimaginative attitude are the former Algerian ultras, the colonial officers of Portugal, and the *apartheid* fanatics of Pretoria and Salisbury—people who are anxious to force the West into 'colonial solidarity' with them, thus buttressing their own weak positions.

The other extreme group consists of the one-eyed or politically blind, who have long assured us that 'communist aggression' is largely an invention of the West to discredit and halt 'progress'. They regard warnings against communist activities as political hysteria and attempt to examine this running sore of our times and diagnose the creeping communist infection as McCarthyism and a conspiracy on the part of 'the right' to destroy 'progress'. The gist of their argument is that the West should regard the hostile policy of radical African nationalism as a 'natural reaction' to its own centuries-long system of colonial oppression and make no attempt to counter it. Instead of examining colonial history objectively and acknowledging the long tale of slave-trading, slaughter and repression, they prefer to accept the anti-Western outbursts of black extremists—a mixture of practical calculation and emotion—at face value. The bad conscience from which these intellectual worshippers of progress suffer at the thought that they themselves are part of the 'gang of exploiters' (part of the West, which has in their view been 'poisoned by colonialism') leads them to over-compensate for their feelings by a rather touching but pathological Negrophilia which draws sustenance from artificial pictures of both the 'wicked white' and the 'good Negro'. And they do just as much damage as the other extremists with their Negrophobia.

The psychological interaction between these two extremist groups goes even further: the louder the one shouts 'Hosannah!', the louder the other shouts 'Crucify him!'. The more incredible the arguments of one side, the more credible—temporarily at least—become the arguments of the other. All this would not matter very much but for the fact that the whole discussion on Africa in the West is being constantly distorted by these radical and ultra-radical poles. If only we could free our minds from the whirlpool of prejudices, self-deception, ideologies and baseless illusions and analyse the situation objectively, instead of allowing ourselves to be sidetracked by wishful thinking and a self-destructive '*peccavi*'.

Before this can be done, the West will have to eschew these isolated notions of the situation and make an objective analysis of African nationalism, of the success achieved by the communists and of its own present and future role in Africa. It is the interrelation of these three factors which determines the present and will determine the future of Africa. The fate of the continent does not lie entirely in the hands of the Africans themselves; to a great extent it will be determined by the East and the West. In the same way, the successes of communism are not exclusively due to communist activity and initiative, but to the willingness of Africans to adopt communist slogans, plus the failures and mistakes of the West. Finally the strength or weakness of the West in Africa will depend on whether it is able to overcome its own failings and find a constructive answer to the challenge of present-day Africa and to the destructive provocation of communism, which will not be defeated in Africa by conventional means.

African nationalism, communist activities, and the position of the West—let us consider once again the interaction and some specific characteristics of these three factors before drawing conclusions.

First, African nationalism: its present strength derives primarily from the fact that it has succeeded in attaining its original aim—the liquidation of colonialism and the achievement of political independence—in an extraordinarily short time, so short that historically it is hardly measurable. But here lies its innate weakness and the source of its enormous difficulties and present complicated disputes. Africans were prepared for a long struggle to attain sovereignty; instead, victory fell into their laps before they had a chance to consider, even theoretically, the complicated internal and external problems of government. It was not difficult to mobilize the African élite *against* something and occasionally it was even possible to mobilize the lethargic African masses against colonialism. But what now? What constructive slogans and objectives are best calculated to attract them after independence has been won? What constructive programme is best calculated to hold the élite together? But before these questions can be answered, others are piling up and they all demand a speedy answer. The nationalist leadership of the new African States finds itself faced with a disrupting and disintegrating social and economic situation. For the first time the African leaders are beginning to realize the full magnitude of the problems they are up against: lack of an internal market, of capital, and of industrial plant. They are saddled with the single-crop cultivation that was in the best interests of colonialism but which does not accord with their present interests and involves them in the growing raw-material crisis on the world market. This crisis hits Africa particularly hard because it occasions a constant fluctuation of raw-material prices. And this is only a part of the urgent economic problems facing them. Even more dangerous is the social unrest which is spreading over the whole continent. The ancient harmony and integration of African tribal society has been violently disrupted, and in some places destroyed, by the break-through of European standards and values, the emergence of an anti-traditionalist élite, and the general and increasing Westernization of African life. The more profoundly this process of dissolution affects African society the more rapid becomes the process of social differentiation. Once homogeneous groups and associations begin to split up, minority groups aggressively press forward their own special interests; and radical and ultra-radical slogans are adopted. During the era of colonialism it was relatively easy for the young nationalist movement to place the responsibility for growing economic and social conflict on the broad shoulders of whatever foreign régime was involved; and in so doing it greatly strengthened its own psychological basis and appeal. But now Africans must tackle these problems for themselves. It is no longer colonialism but African nationalism which has the task of working out solutions and making them acceptable to those directly concerned.

But the fact is, whoever talks to leading African nationalists, or reads their speeches and writings, soon discovers that they are in deep perplexity and do not know what to do. Most of them have some general ideas about the difficulties and the requirements of their countries, but their plans do not add up to a coherent programme based on any specifically African conceptions. To say this is not to reproach them or to gloat over their condition. Their perplexity is general, even a man like Sékou Touré, a leading apologist of black nationalism, has little more than a collection of slogans and generalities to offer—which is not much good when it comes to dealing with harsh realities. Time is pressing! In almost all the independent States opposition groups are forming, recruited from among the sullen and dissatisfied people who expected too much from their leaders, people who were passed over in the distribution of privileges and are now disappointed. In Ghana, opposition liberals are putting every possible pressure on Kwame Nkrumah to adopt a programme of European liberalism; the conservatives would like to see the power and authority of the tribal chiefs restored; while the National Association of Socialist Student Organizations (NASSO), or the weekly *Spark*, whose influence is steadily increasing, demand the complete nationalization of the economy and a total, Marxist-inspired, over-all plan for economic and social development. A similar process, different only in degree and local conditions, is taking place in other African States. In East Africa, arguments about economic and social ideas were vehement even before independence was achieved, as internal dissensions in Kenya, Uganda, and Tanzania clearly showed. The crisis in January 1964 did not come as a surprise. Almost everywhere, the leaders of the anti-colonial struggle are now beginning to find their prestige and power seriously threatened; in some African countries there is a masked antipathy to deliberation and discussion and this contributes to the progressive poisoning of the political atmosphere. (In 1963 alone, no fewer than seven of the twelve countries belonging to the *Union Africaine et Malgache* (now OCAM) were involved in serious internal upheavals.)

The way of escape from this situation which the new masters of the African continent are choosing is one which is tragic for Africa and a threat to the West. Freedom from outside rule has been won, but now the African leaders are, almost without exception, turning against the internal freedom of the African people, while simultaneously inveighing in a new emotional outburst against the alleged neo-colonialism of the West. Many reasons are being put forward to explain this rejection of democracy and the establishment of dictatorial or semi-authoritarian régimes, and they cannot all be dismissed as being groundless. It is, of course, perfectly true that early African society knew little about democratic forms and techniques and the undemocratic ways of the various colonial administrations were hardly calculated to create confidence in the democratic principles of the West. However, the contention of many Africans that the short history of African independence has already exposed democracy as a destructive system rings hollow and suspect. With smug indignation, the new African dictators justify this attitude by pointing to the Congo. But the Congo exposes the falsity of this attitude; the confusion and chaos there were due not only to a failure of democracy, but to the fact that the party of Patrice

Lumumba (which certainly secured no mandate at the elections) sought to impose its policy on the country in defiance of the most elementary democratic principles.

Unlike his allies in Ghana, Guinea, and Mali, Lumumba let his real intentions be seen only incidentally and fortuitously. For example, in March 1960, Madeira Keita, Bamako's Minister of the Interior, wrote in the periodical *Présence Africaine* that in the circumstances a strong central administration was necessary because regional and tribal dissensions had to be suppressed with a firm hand. Authoritarianism was therefore preferable to Western-type democracy. Keita went on to argue that differences over the functions and tasks of the administration, which would justify the existence of opposition groups, were simply unthinkable in the young African States. Everyone, he insisted, had the same high aims and ideals, and, as time was pressing and the great problems which faced them had to be swiftly settled, the new African States could not afford 'a ministerial crisis every six months or so'.

No one can expect the young African States to become carbon copies of Western democracies, which are not in any case always ideal themselves. No one expects the new African rulers not to govern firmly in a difficult situation, or to undermine their own position by showing excessive consideration to every opposition tendency—provided, however, that their régime is amenable to reasonable influence in tackling its problems and that freedom of discussion is constitutionally safeguarded. Certainly one can readily imagine moments of crisis when it might become necessary to introduce moderate and reasonable restrictions on democratic liberties. Despite misgivings, one could hardly deny President Olympio of Togo (who was murdered in 1963) the right to introduce a one-party régime in April 1961 and to establish certain special presidential rights, as his small country was under heavy pressure from its more powerful neighbour Ghana, an expansionist State. But the situation is very different when Kwame Nkrumah, relying on his all-powerful State party, arrests the last minor leaders and supporters of the crushed and impotent opposition party and thrusts them into concentration camps for an indefinite period without trial. Or where they are tortured to death as happened to the 'Grand Old Man' of Ghanaian nationalism, J. B. Danquah, in February 1965.

In each case the suppression of the opposition, the restriction of fundamental human rights, and the general advance towards authoritarianism represent the disruption of the national unity achieved in the anti-colonialist struggle—although those responsible still praise this national unity *ad nauseam*. The techniques of dictatorial rule poison the political atmosphere, arouse resentment, and lead to a strengthening of extremist forces. In this connection one should remember and be clear about two things: (1) communism unquestionably has a highly developed technique of opposition and underground struggle at its disposal and the means to infiltrate. If the communists succeed in influencing and winning over the opposition groups in the right-wing African States, then sooner or later we shall see the formation of a pro-communist united front reaching from the left-wing ruling groups in some West African countries to the opposition forces of large sections of the liberal and right-wing elements in Africa. (2) The right-wing dictatorial régimes in Africa have no really effective power behind them, as was demonstrated by the revolt against Abbé Youlou in Brazzaville in August 1963. There is hardly a single African State today which has a numerically strong, well-trained, well-equipped and efficient army on which the régime could rely with confidence in times of acute trouble. The successor States of the French *Communauté*, which have military arrangements with France, could call on Paris to aid them in times of trouble, but what happened in Gabon in February 1964, when French troops intervened in a *coup d'état* in favour of the régime, shows the serious psychological difficulties involved in such appeals to the former colonial power for military assistance. The presence of French troops on Gabon territory has driven into opposition even those groups who were formerly loyal to the Government. At the same time, the civil service, which has been the last bulwark against anarchy and chaos for many countries in Asia, the Near East, and Latin America, is still too weak, inexperienced and heterogeneous, to play that saving role in Africa, and in consequence it is no more reliable than the army.

One or two of the right-wing African dictatorships already have some conception of the difficulties and dangers involved in the political structure they have adopted. The radical agitation of their oppositions (all more or less violently repressed) is carried on with all the standard theses of communist propaganda, and this results in growing popular unrest, which is constantly intensified by attacks from extreme nationalist and left-wing countries outside. The reproaches and attacks culminate in the argument that although political independence has been won there has been no fundamental change in the economic and social policy of the new State. The situation of the masses of the people has not improved; on the contrary, owing to the absence of foreign capital investments and credits, constant fluctuations on the raw-material markets, and the increase in prices and taxation that these involve, it has grown steadily worse. Further, the 'reactionary' governments of Africa still have as their foreign advisers the very same men who before independence played the role of colonial masters; and finally, the economic power of colonialism is still unbroken. These governments are accused of being 'puppet governments' and every new economic agreement with the former colonial power is taken as further evidence in support of the opposition charge that the change of administration has been more apparent than real, and that the sovereignty of the new African States under such reactionary government is a sham. The opposition loudly insists that such decolonization is nothing more than an 'imperialist trick'. At the same time any delay by a government in establishing diplomatic relations with the Soviet bloc, the failure to encourage trading relations with the countries of the socialist camp and the absence of any cultural agreements with the Kremlin are all cited by the opposition as evidence of an un-African foreign policy serving the interests of the imperialist camp. These accusations are not confined to the pro-communist opponents of such African governments.

What is the result? 1. A political minority denigrates the new régime, denounces it as 'dishonest', 'treacherous' and 'incompetent', and claims for itself alone the true custodianship of sincere and uncompromising nationalism. 2. Naturally when attacked in this way governments do their best to defend themselves, and a number of right-wing African régimes have endeavoured to increase their popularity by outdoing the opposition with even more radical nationalistic slogans. Cautiously, some of these régimes are taking up certain demands of the opposition and trying to satisfy them. The best example of this can be seen in Nigeria where, especially since the electoral farce in 1964, the régime is constantly under attack from its radical opposition, trade unions, and various youth and student organizations. In order to reduce this pressure, the Lagos régime established diplomatic relations with nearly all the communist countries including Red China. Furthermore, the Nigerian Government was the only African administration that responded to the third French nuclear test in the Sahara by breaking off diplomatic relations with France. The premier saw no other way of rebutting the charge that his cabinet was deliberately delaying the 'Nigerianization' of the administration than by making concessions to the opposition, and it is a fact that since then the agitation of the opposition (which is supported by Ghana and the countries of the Soviet bloc) has lost a good deal of its sting. On the other hand, even the Nigerian Government is now gradually adopting a policy of 'neutrality' and professing to struggle against 'neo-colonialist intrigues'—the sort of thing which in practice favours the left. Developments in this direction have already gone so far that one wonders what further concessions the Nigerian Government will make to the opposition if its internal and external enemies put on the pressure again.

The communists are observing this trend with unconcealed satisfaction, as their Africa propaganda quite clearly reveals. The helplessness and perplexity of the Africans in the face of their economic and social difficulties, and the growing tendency towards disruption in the nationalist movement itself, confirms the communists in their belief that African nationalism is essentially a transitional phase, a part of the inevitable historical process which must finally lead to socialism. The communist position in Africa is greatly strengthened by a number of other factors, and in particular by the psychologically important fact that communism had nothing to do with the clash between black and white which led to the present upheaval in Africa. Communism has always, in its propaganda at least, been on the side of the black élite. In the Trusteeship Commission of the United Nations, for example, the Soviet Union exceeded all other Powers in the vigour of its demands for the release of the mandated areas from European control. Another great advantage for the communists is that Africans came into touch with communism relatively late and at a time when Stalinism, with its terrorism, had already undergone modifications. Apart from the Arab Northern region and South Africa, which were in any case always isolated from the rest of Africa, there was not a communist party anywhere south of the Sahara until the early 1960s. In consequence, the Africans never had the salutary experience of witnessing the wrigglings of a political body completely dependent on Kremlin orders and subject to brutal purges and fierce campaigns of 'self-criticism', initiated and controlled from outside. Today communism is able to present itself in Africa as the opposite of its old traditional image of a bloodthirsty, oppressive and fanatical organization, bent on securing power at all costs. For Africans, Soviet-communism is first of all a mighty international bloc led by the Soviet Union, which is the biggest counterblast to the highly industrialized West. Furthermore, in an extraordinarily short space of time the Soviet Union has performed economic and technical miracles, including sending up the first *sputnik*, the first *lunik*, and the first manned space-ship. In African eyes, the mere existence of this powerful State did much to force the West to abandon its colonial policy and give Africa its independence. *This* is the communism the Africans know—a tremendous concentration of power, progress and moral force.

Naturally the communist countries do their utmost to consolidate and strengthen this favourable interpretation, using all the powerful propaganda at their disposal—broadcasts, written propaganda, invitations, cultural festivals, and so on—to underline their self-styled role as unselfish friends and helpers of all Africans. The never-ending spate of pro-African declarations, which are an essential part of this propaganda, seek to persuade the Africans that communism has no expansionist plans in Africa, since it has sufficient room for expansion within its own frontiers, and that—unlike the West—it does not depend on Africa's great natural resources, since the Soviet bloc has its own enormous deposits of uranium, cobalt, ores and so on. Moreover, it claims to be in favour of total and unconditional international disarmament and the political neutralization of Africa, whereas the West still maintains a large number of military establishments and bases on African soil and has concluded defence and military-aid agreements with a number of African countries. Communism also claims, though with rather less cogency, that it upholds the right of self-determination for all peoples everywhere in the world, whereas the United States organized and financed the invasion of Cuba, France and Great

Britain went to war over Suez, and Portugal, a NATO member, carries on a ruthless campaign of extermination in Angola against a people longing for its liberty.

The economic, social and political techniques of communism are particularly attractive to Africans. The solutions proposed by the West for Africa's difficulties are rejected by many Africans either instinctively, as 'colonial' or 'neo-colonial' deceptions, or as impracticable, whereas communism appears to them as the practical and useful model to overcome their acute economic and social misery. After all, forty years ago Russia itself was as little developed as are many African States today. While after their victory over 'the feudal régime of the Chiang Kai-shek clique and the camouflaged colonialism of the United States', the Chinese had found themselves faced with difficulties similar to those the Africans are facing today. And how quickly and progressively the Russians and the Chinese developed their countries and consolidated the power of the revolutionary groups!

This is the glowing picture presented by communist propaganda in hours of daily broadcasting in English, French, Portuguese, Arabic, and Swahili. Meanwhile most of the naïve African visitors to the countries of the Soviet bloc come back confirming much of this and (since no other solution promises rapid success and any attempt to co-operate with the imperialist West would compromise them) they are prepared to use communist know-how and to try communist methods to tackle the economic, social, and political problems of Africa. This means, in effect, the establishment of an authoritarian, one-party State with a hierarchic structure of command and obedience, the quickest possible methods of industrialization based on concentration of labour, and the complete control of labour for 'collective social uses'. The Africans do not realize how great the risk is, because not only do the Chinese, the Russians, the Czechs, and the leaders of all the other communist States promise them material and personnel assistance, but they guarantee the automatic success of the experiment. The proposition is made even more attractive because certain of the communist assumptions are in complete harmony with the ideas and the desires of the African élite.

We know that communism is something more, and something very much more dangerous, than the idealized and harmless image cooked up by communists for the benefit of Africans and accepted by many at its face value. *We* know, but they do not, that communism is a highly developed compound of promises, of dogmatic interpretation of the past and the present, and the incarnation of Machiavellianism: a gigantic power-political compound that subordinates all its measures, pronouncements, and plans to the one aim of securing total dominance of the whole world. The proclamation of the policy of co-existence with ideological infiltration, the support of feudal régime and the creation of a revolutionary élite to overthrow it; Peking's open and aggressive attitude to the national bourgeoisie and Moscow's readiness to conclude a temporary fraternal alliance with this same group; the granting of credits and the acceptance of an unfavourable balance of trade with the new States of Africa; the game of hide-and-seek in the front organizations and at the same time the arming, equipping and training of cadre troops for jungle warfare in Cameroon, the Congo, and Angola —all these are but variations on the same basic theme—power. For communism in Africa, the greatest advantage, which it does its best to consolidate and extend, lies in the fact that this power complex and the imminent danger it represents to the whole African continent is as yet hardly discerned. Almost without exception African nationalists harbour the illusion that the negative and unfavourable phenomena they do recognize can be readily dealt with as long as there are no official communist parties in existence.

Fortunately there are limits to what the communists can realistically hope for in Africa. In the first phase of their operations, the Russians, in particular, made glaring mistakes: (a) They overestimated their strength and popularity among the Africans and relied too much on the widespread but superficial identity of their slogans with those of the Africans. (b) They underestimated the Africans, misjudged them and often found themselves backing the wrong horse. The difficulties in which they became entangled were especially obvious in Guinea and the Congo. I am of the opinion that the Russians had such a flying start in Guinea in 1959–60 that with a little adroitness, tact, and economic aid on a really effective scale, they could have turned Sékou Touré into an African Castro and Guinea into an African Cuba. They failed because they omitted to make proper allowance for the natural dignity of a man like Sékou Touré, (which, to some extent, they also did with Castro), because they talked about aid instead of giving it effectively, and because what they really wanted was an African satellite, not an African ally. If they had treated Touré as a real comrade on an equal footing and had conceded him the right to make his own national way towards socialism they would be in a much better position in Guinea than they are today.

They behaved even more foolishly in the Congo. Thanks to their clumsy tactics—which might not have mattered had well-trained communist cadres existed in the territory—they played right into the hands of the United Nations and the United States. Thus the whole edifice of their Congolese propaganda collapsed like a pack of cards as soon as Americans and the United Nations seriously tackled the problem of Katanga separation. In February 1963 the communists did secure the adoption of a resolution by the third Afro-Asian Solidarity Conference criticizing the Congo policy of the United States and the United Nations. But by that time it was too late to remedy the situation and the fiasco of Russia's Congo policy was obvious to everyone in Africa.

It was certainly clear by this time that the communists erred in thinking that nationalism in the new Africa would be easy game for them. One of the chief reasons for their error is the egocentricity, common to communist leaders, who draw conclusions from themselves to others and firmly believe that they have a theory which will explain anything anywhere in the world. They fail to realize that the Africans they are wooing, including those who appear to be willing to come to terms with them, are people with a variety of different mentalities. Instead of trying to understand this, they too readily assume that the obvious willingness of many Africans to go part of the way with them means that they are ready to go all the way and take over orthodox Marxist-Leninist philosophy *in toto*.

This misconception dates back to the early 1920s, when the first contacts were established between African nationalists and communists. Even in those days African students were privileged guests at communist meetings and demonstrations in France, Britain and the United States. They served to underline the internationalism of the communist parties of those countries. In the meantime, however, the communist parties of Great Britain and France, who had been given the task of carrying out the instructions on Africa of the Second Congress of the Communist International, made little or no progress and finally landed in a blind alley, because of the natural contradiction between communism and British and French nationalism. The attitude of the communist parties of Great Britain and France to the colonies' struggle for liberation was far from clear. Speaking at the Fifth Congress of the Communist International on 30 June 1924, Manuilski observed reproachfully:

'About a year ago the Communist International directed an appeal to the colonial slaves to rise in revolt against their masters. When a copy of this appeal got as far as one of the branches of the French Communist Party—Sidi bel Abbès in Algeria—the branch actually adopted a resolution condemning the attitude of the Communist International . . . I will also take the liberty of asking the French comrades what documents they can produce to show that the French Communist Party has very clearly demanded in the hearing of the whole world that the colonial countries should be given their freedom . . . Our British comrades have earned just as serious a reproach for their passivity in this same matter . . . In none of the documents that have come to our notice concerning the British Communist Party's attitude to the colonies do we find one single clear and definite statement that our British comrades are uncomprisingly in favour of the separation of the colonies from the British Empire.'[1]

Even in 1947, Maurice Thorez was talking at the Eleventh Congress of the French Communist Party in ambiguous terms about the policy of the French communists towards the colonies; both he and Etienne Fajon described the *Union Française*—the policy of a French assimilation of the colonial peoples—as 'the most favourable framework' for the activities of the overseas territories.[2]

In such circumstances even those Africans who had at first felt drawn towards communism were repulsed instead of being won over. The result was evident in French-speaking Africa in the collapse of the *Rassemblement Démocratique Africain* in 1950, though there were certainly other, deeper-lying reasons for what happened in the RDA. All in all, one can say that the secession of such prominent party men as Félix Houphouet-Boigny in the Ivory Coast and Gabriel d'Arboussier in Senegal was the result of profound emotional and psychological misgiving. Communism expected its African followers to rally unconditionally round the aims and actions of the metropolitan parties, but it refused to take into consideration the particular conditions, requirements, desires and longings of the Africans. Blindly the traditional class pattern of communism was transferred quite arbitrarily to African conditions. In strict logic, though in crass stupidity, all 'non-proletarian' Africans were condemned as 'secret lackeys of colonialism', even when they were clearly engaged in fighting against colonialism. Evidence of this is provided in *Narody Afriki* (*The Peoples of Africa*), published in Moscow in 1954. It roundly denounced Kwame Nkrumah and his Convention People's Party as 'a screen behind which the reality of British imperialist dominance is hidden'. Even as late as 1955 an official Soviet publication[3] declared: 'the anti-imperialist and anti-feudal revolution in Africa' can never be carried out in alliance with the national bourgeoisie 'but only on the basis of an alliance of the workers and peasants led by the communists'. Four years later the British communist, Idris Cox, finally had to admit that after the Second World War political independence has been won by India, Indonesia, Ghana and other countries under the leadership of their national bourgeoisies.[4] Thus, at first, communism largely ignored the genuine national movement in Africa, though it was obviously growing rapidly. The communist leaders also failed to understand that most of the Africans who were co-operating with them (especially those in the *Rassemblement Démocratique Africain*) were seeking association with them, not full commitment; they had their own ideas and were pursuing their own interests.

This attitude involved, and still involves, a very important reservation, a matter of principle which precludes any total commitment. In the past, many African politicians in close touch with radical continental socialism have drawn attention to this particular point, which is primarily of an ideological-religious nature. Sékou Touré put it pertinently to Fernand Gigon:

'In my view Marxism offers us important ideas concerning the history of mankind. Dialectical and philosophical materialism offers us a possibility of interpreting social and economic reality, but it involves the denial of the existence of God. Now nowhere in any African country, and particularly not in Guinea, will you find a single man or woman who does not believe in the existence of God.

Even if you find someone who tells you that he is a fetishist, or that he hasn't any religion, nevertheless he is a believer.'[5]

In a lecture entitled 'Ghana's Conception of Socialism', the Ghanaian politician, Kofi Baako, said much the same thing:

'I should like to draw your attention to the religious feelings of our people. No native of Ghana, or of any other African country, is an atheist. Deep down within him there are hidden spiritual forces which move him to honour the gods of his ancestors . . . No matter how educated or intelligent he may be, his whole being instinctively rejects the idea that the beginning and end of all life is in this world alone . . . It would therefore be well to bear in mind that no political ideology that fails to take these basic facts into account can be regarded as acceptable, and that if it is nevertheless imposed on the people it will lead to nothing but trouble and social revolt. You will therefore understand that the type of society we are trying to build in Ghana will be permanent and bring peace only if it takes the given conditions and traditions into account.'[6]

With this it is clear that the all-embracing monopoly claimed by communist ideology is breached at a most decisive point, and this often gives rise to serious conflict between orthodox communists and their African comrades. Students who have broken off their studies in the countries of the Soviet bloc and returned home are a living proof of this. Most of these men were Africans who were officials in communist groups or front organizations before going behind the Iron Curtain. One of them, who may serve as a typical example, is Mahdi Ismael of Somalia. He studied in Soviet-bloc countries for four years and for a while represented a radical Somali trade union there. At one time he was even a member of the Communist Party of Great Britain. One of the reasons for his breach with communism was, he explained, that 'communist officials think coldly and abstractly, and are quite unable to satisfy the spiritual needs of African students.' In Ismael's opinion, their contempt for religious feelings and their cold, calculated reasoning put them on a level with 'the representatives of the capitalist West, who are just as cold and unspiritual in their hunt for profits and who worship God without believing in Him.'[7]

Walter Kolarz, who has also analysed this phenomenon,[8] draws a parallel with certain forms of Asian communism when he writes: 'Like the Buddhist Marxist in Burma, the Afro-Asian Marxist has no use for Marxism as a universal materialist ideology dominating all aspects of life, as it is usually understood in Europe.'

Another and no less important factor is the quite different attitude of African socialists to the world situation. The upheaval brought about by the African struggle for liberation has not carried the African socialist beyond the confines of his own continent. He is interested only in Africa: Africa is the scene of his desires and the aim of his struggles and he is not particularly interested in an abstract world proletariat, which means very little to him; in fact he is completely in agreement with Kwame Nkrumah, who has replaced the slogan 'Workers of the World Unite!' by the slogan 'Peoples of Africa Unite!' This slogan embraces the peoples of all colonial territories and more often than not has a definitely racial tendency. For the African the world is not so much divided into capitalists and proletarians as into rich whites and poor blacks. Similarly, the ideal of many Africans is not an 'international of the toilers', but an 'international of the coloured peoples'. The Soviet leaders have now recognized this phenomenon and are doing their best to take it into account by making use of officials and experts from their own Asian republics in their African policy. Often, however, this has had much the same effect as the similar tactics of the US State Department in appointing coloured US citizens to diplomatic posts in Asia and Africa. The manœuvre met with little success because the motive behind it was too transparent.

Despite all this however, Africans are susceptible to the fascination of communism. Its attraction is powerful when there are obvious parallels with the situation in Africa—which means that it is less powerful where the Soviet Union and its European satellites are concerned and more powerful where China and Yugoslavia are concerned. It is obvious that Africans see very distinct differences between these three models and this approach to communism is taking place at a time when 'the Third Rome' has already lost a great deal of its prestige as the exclusive centre of world communism. One might say that the modern African has been born, politically, into a polycentric communist world which no longer offers only one way, but a number of quite different ways of socialist development.

The success of communism in Africa depends on the extent to which it can take these fundamental facts into consideration in its plans, thus giving itself the opportunity to operate unconventionally and we have given a number of examples that suggest that it now understands the situation, which it exploits with suppleness.

It will succeed all the more rapidly if the West persists in its failure to recognize the changed face of Africa and in harbouring illusions about its own potential there. The West has already suffered a heavy defeat in Africa and by this I do not mean the fact that it has abandoned, or been compelled to abandon, its former colonial territories. This was inevitable and foreseeable and was in any case welcome on moral grounds. The real defeat of the West lies in the fact that it did not encourage this development from the beginning, guiding it harmoniously and without violence or bloodshed; it lies also in the fact that the departure of the white man from Africa coincided with a profound shattering of confidence in him and in his way of life.

It is not the task of this book to write the history of colonialism and to list the benefits it brought to Africa and the crimes it committed in the name of Europe. Perhaps one day the science of history will be in a position to provide a sober, objective picture of the part-contact, part-collision which has taken place between Europe and Africa. But what must be exposed and explained here are the direct causes which led to the weakening of the Western position in Africa and facilitated the rise of extremists, radical, anti-European and anti-white movements, and which made communist infiltration so easy. We cannot afford to hide our heads in the sand and refuse to recognize that the popular attitude in present-day Africa is sharply anti-Western, and that many Africans regard communism as an attractive alternative to the political, economic, social, and moral principles of the Western world. This is a situation that must be faced.

The errors, omissions and failures of the African policy of the West can be summed up in five points:

1. Despite the repeatedly proclaimed moral principles of Western policy, the ultimate recognition of Africa's right to self-determination was not, in fact, a matter of moral principle but primarily a matter of political expediency. Even then, recognition was granted reluctantly and only under increasing pressure from black national-

ism, when the West was increasingly harassed by actual or threatened risings and when its position had become untenable in the face of a hostile public opinion. The demand for the right of self-determination for the nations of Eastern Europe and the refusal or restriction of this same right for the peoples of Africa made the representatives of the West appear as hypocrites and demagogues in African eyes. The tactics, adopted by the West, of making concessions only in answer to nationalist pressures, attacks and reproaches, instead of forestalling them by voluntary concessions in the first place, meant the surrender of the *moral initiative* to the African liberation movement and thus indirectly to the hypocritical forces, particularly communism, that supported it. The surrender, when it came, was the result of precipitate, panic-stricken decisions—as in the Belgian Congo, which was surrendered without a reasonable period of transition and planning and was abandoned to a sovereignty shaped by the centralist ideas of the local radicals.

2. The moral and material support granted by the West—though not uniformly—to France in the Algerian war, to the South African racial fanatics in their policy of *apartheid* and to the small, obstinate groups of white settlers in Kenya, Rhodesia and Nyasaland, grievously compromised the cause of the West as a whole, particularly since African nationalism, inspired and encouraged by the communists, deliberately exploited this attitude as a cardinal issue. Declarations by certain Western politicians that the fate of the Western world was at stake in Algeria, the invitation extended to South African Premier Verwoerd to visit the West, and the official and officious expressions of sympathy for Spain and Portugal, all contributed to discredit the West in Africa. Until Kennedy took office, in January 1961, the African policy of the United States, which for years supported the most reactionary régimes in Africa (those in Liberia and Ethiopia) vacillated first one way and then the other, without any firm, guiding policy. The still unresolved racial problem in the United States represents an extra burden in Africa. When African delegates to the United Nations find it almost impossible to obtain accommodation in New York and discover that because they are coloured they have to pay much more than the normal price for houses and leases, the consequences can hardly be overestimated. This sort of thing makes Africans wonder whether United States African policy really is unprejudiced after all.

Even worse for the prestige of the West in Africa was its policy of material self-interest in the Congo, where Belgium, South Africa and one or two other countries intervened—against the decisions and behind the back of the United Nations—in support of a separatist Katanga (the President of which, Tshombe, was regarded, probably rightly, as a mere puppet of the Belgian *Union Minière du Haut Katanga*), and where a year passed after the creation of the Congo State before the 'Belgian advisers' could be moved out of Elisabethville—and then only under strong United Nations pressure. Making allowances for the responsibility borne by such men as Lumumba and Gizenga, fairness demands that the destructive, un-African role of Tshombe and his supporters should not be forgotten. In view of the fact that the Katanga group did not enjoy the slightest respect, even among the friends of the West in Africa, whereas Lumumba (allowing for misgivings on account of his demagogy and indolence) was and is regarded as a typical representative of the young, dynamic, fighting Africa, the consequences of such blantantly selfish, behind-the-scenes intrigues can readily be imagined.

3. Another important disadvantage of the West is that Africans are accustomed (and encouraged by communist propaganda) to regard the actions and behaviour of individual Western countries as reflecting the general attitude of the West, although, of course, this assumption that there is a general solidarity and co-ordination of the African policies of the various Western Powers is quite unfounded. The ambiguity and the conflicts of Western policy in Africa have a long history. Europe always exported to Africa not only those things it had in common but also those things which divided it: Flemings and Walloons did not cease to rub each other the wrong way in the Congo just because 'Belgium's black children' were looking on at the spectacle; Catholics and Protestants, Baptists and Anglicans, blindly carried their religious differences into the colonies and there were the power-political struggles of the European governments and the intense economic competition of the European countries. Today in the United Nations the characteristic features of the Western policy towards Africa are disunity, antagonism, disharmony, and the absence of any will to solidarity. This has its effect in frequent, almost grotesque changes of front, which do further damage to the image of the West in Africa. For example, the United States votes with the Soviet Union for a programme of

complete de-colonization, while at the same time some of the NATO allies of the United States (such as France, Portugal and Spain) either abstain from voting or vote against the United States.

This lack of co-ordination and co-operation is particularly obvious in connection with the discussions, planning and execution of Western aid programmes for Africa. The damaging dividing line between the Common Market (EEC) countries and the countries of the European Free Trade Association (EFTA) extends into Africa. France and Belgium have secured the association of their former African territories in the Common Market, with the consequent benefits for them of preferences and import facilities and with consequent disadvantages for the non-associated African countries. Apart from this there are at least seven different Western aid programmes for Africa (apart from the aid programmes of the United Nations, the World Bank, the International Monetary Fund, and many private institutions). This confusion, which is rendered worse by selfish interests and rivalries, is all the more harmful at a time when concentrated aid is so necessary. But so far, neither on a national nor an inter-allied scale has the West any central, co-ordinating bodies which could give its Africa policy a uniform front and create the impression that there really is some effective control and understanding of the immense problems of the under-developed countries. On the contrary, new rivalries have lately developed which make for further confusion and conflict and their aim is obviously to secure a market monopoly in Africa for the former colonial Powers while keeping out 'foreign' countries and competitors.

4. The aid policy of the West in Africa lacks clear, cogent, long-term, productive ideas. Even today, the initiative for individual projects is usually taken by the Africans themselves. They approach their bi-lateral and multi-lateral partners in the West with proposals which their Western partners proceed to examine, discuss and eventually approve. But there are two important disadvantages in this process: the investigation is restricted to the individual project concerned and delay and procrastination are an inevitable part of the system. According to information given by Schleswig-Holstein's Premier, von Hassel, it usually takes eighteen months before a decision can be arrived at on any proposal made to the Federal Government. A French Deputy to the Council of Europe at

Strasbourg reports that it can take two years before a request from one of the African States associated with the Common Market for an aid project can be dealt with in the general framework of the aid programme and advanced to the point where instructions can be given to start the job. President Olympio of Togo, during a visit in May 1961, stated that he had been waiting for months for the arrival of a hydrographical commission from the German Federal Republic which was to make a preliminary survey before work on an all-important harbour for Togo could be started. Olympio, who has since been murdered, was a friend of the West, but he hinted that 'certain promises' made by Tito while he was in Lomé had received much prompter attention from the Yugoslav communists. In many cases the requests reflect the prestige requirements of the ruling élite rather than the real needs of the country. Thus certain African régimes have a passion for large-scale industrial projects, including atomic reactors and fully automatic steel works. Such projects incidentally favour the State economic sector, and further centralist ideas of State economic control. But according to the unanimous opinion of most economic experts, what Africa really needs is economic aid which will encourage not only the infrastructure but also intensive labour forms, a network of small industries and handicrafts, and above all, agricultural units producing for market needs. In this way a large section of the population could be painlessly introduced to sound economic principles (based on a market economy rather than on self-sufficiency) and educated to sensible economic thinking. As a result there would be a wider and fairer distribution of the national income, coupled with social amelioration for a broad section of the population.

But two fundamental requirements must be fulfilled: the West must always bear in mind that the best possible results from economic aid will be secured only if the social and economic conditions of the country being helped are largely accepted and if no attempt is made to encourage any particular development merely because it happens to favour the current social and economic interests of the country providing the aid. In other words, a free capitalist economic policy for Africa is not possible today, and any attempt to impose it would only do damage because it would force the Africans to abandon the traditional communal and co-operative principles by which they have always lived and worked. One must take into account the fact that for hundreds of years agriculture, trade, and handicraft in Africa have been carried on collectively and that large areas of the continent have never known anything but communal ownership of land. Traditionally, social and economic thought in Africa has been directed at the communal satisfaction of needs; and the West will ignore this at its peril. In such matters, the Israelis are far ahead of the Europeans and Americans in Africa, because with their *kibbutzim* they go a long way towards meeting traditional African ideas and desires. They are thus in a position to offer Africans an effective way of adapting their centuries-old social and economic institutions to modern requirements, without in any way encroaching on the voluntary principle which is so deplorably lacking in Soviet and Chinese collectivism. If Israel were not a small country wrestling desperately with tremendous problems of its own and if its every initiative did not automatically provoke counter-measures on the part of Cairo, it would be in a position to make a valuable contribution to the development of Africa which would have an effect far beyond the African continent. With certain provisos this is also true of Yugoslavia, which first established close contact with Africa when Tito made his West-African journey in the spring of 1961. Yugoslav 'national communism' is respected and admired among the native élite of Africa, primarily because the Yugoslav forms of property and economic activity, with their relative liberalism and collectivist trend, are more in accordance with African social feeling.

But the possibilities at the disposal of Israel and Yugoslavia are limited, and in consequence African eyes are still chiefly directed at the great models offered by West and East. Unfortunately, Africans are soon compelled to recognize by experience that whereas the East *is* prepared to compromise and adapt itself to African ideas, the West is seldom willing to do so. The first condition Western countries usually make when Africans apply for credits and technical assistance is that there should be some sort of investment and credit guarantee; immediately afterwards comes the demand that the preliminary investigations before the investment of the proposed credits, and then the actual investment itself, should be carried out by private investors and producers. This automatically makes Africans suspect that the motive behind this is not an unselfish desire to assist an under-developed country but an attempt to use economic aid as a lever to secure profits and returns from the African market. Yet the countries of the West are not without economic models and solutions which could appeal to Africans and arouse their enthusiasm. Throughout Western Europe there are co-operative organizations in trade and handicraft, and particularly in agriculture, with a long tradition of strict voluntarism. The West should mobilize these experiences and adapt them to African needs and desires. But as long as it fails to do this, it must not wonder and complain when Africans gaze in fascination at the Potemkin villages of communist collectives.

5. More important than economic or technical aid is generous educational assistance. A large-scale programme to develop broad educated strata in Africa is necessary. The worst omissions of the West lie here. Nine-tenths of all Africans are still illiterate and for a long time Africa will be short of skilled workers, agricultural experts, doctors, elementary school teachers, businessmen, trade-union officials, civil servants, mechanics and technicians. One of the first requirements for a large-scale educational programme for Africa is the abandonment of the unsatisfactory practice of sending Africans to Europe for their studies, since this makes their training more difficult by erecting artificial barriers of language, customs, and ideas, while forcing Africans to adapt themselves to Western habits. Secondary training schools, training workshops, trade schools, technical schools and universities must grow up in Africa itself. Europeans must go to Africa as teachers instead of making Africans come to Europe to be educated and trained in an atmosphere which is completely foreign and inhibiting to them and inevitably leads to unnecessary conflicts. In this respect, there is a further disadvantage under which the West labours; the personal and professional inadequacy of too many of the political, diplomatic, technical and teaching personnel that the West sends out to Africa. In general, they lack a sense of mission, which their sometimes clumsy communist rivals have in abundance. What most hampers the work of these Western representatives is that, almost to a man, they feel a sense of superiority towards Africans, whose language, culture and customs they despise. Africa must no longer be regarded as a place to which the second-best can safely be sent, a backwater for personnel not good enough to be used elsewhere. Africa must become the field for a new altruistic idealism on the part of our young people,

who should be made to realize the enormously important fact that the struggle for the real emancipation and the liberation of Africa will be decided by the 'third generation' of African nationalists now growing up in Africa. This is the generation which will pass judgement, and a great deal indeed will depend on their decision—not only for Africa but for the whole world. It would mean nothing less than total surrender if the West failed to recognize and meet the constructive appeal and challenge of Africa, and refused to mobilize its spiritual and material forces for a great and altruistic programme of development. Failure would clear the way for communism.

There is no point in indulging in a fruitless discussion of our errors, especially as there is now increasing recognition of the European-Atlantic obligation towards Africa, and the policy of the West is beginning to show signs of a real change.

An important factor is the immense psychological and political progress made in Africa by the United States under President Kennedy. This resulted not only from his inspiring plan to set up a Peace Corps, but also from the spirit of the New Frontier, which now determines America's relationship with the Third World. Where Africa is concerned, this culminates in the unqualified recognition of the right of its new States to go their own way between the great power blocs in a spirit of real political neutrality. Under Kennedy's leadership the US administration broke with the dangerous tendency to blame communism for any and every trouble anywhere in the world—an attitude which involved granting aid only where it would seem to reinforce the basic principle of American strategy, namely, a sterile anti-communism. In all this, the constitutional structure and political tendency of the country receiving aid was largely ignored. At first this policy paid no attention whatever to the political constitution or moral attitude of the régime concerned: any régime was automatically worthy of aid if it had the power and the will to crush any incipient social revolts. In consequence, men like Trujillo, Batista, and one or two reactionary African potentates were able to enjoy American support for a long time without any pressure being exerted to persuade them to introduce just and civilized measures in their countries. Mere anti-communism frequently triumphed over the principle of liberty, and it was therefore a very good thing when, on 6 June 1961, after his Vienna meeting with Khrushchev, President Kennedy told the

American people that he proposed to discontinue this policy and that henceforth aid to the under-developed countries would not be granted merely on the grounds of anti-communism. 'Aid', Kennedy declared, 'represents the recognition of both our opportunity and our duty to help these people to live in freedom.' In another speech he referred to a remark Khrushchev had made to him, to the effect that communism should not be held responsible for *all* the unrest in the world, and he frankly admitted that this was quite right. He added that it was too easy to dismiss every anti-governmental or anti-American movement, every revolt against a corrupt régime, and every mass protest against misery and despair, as being communist-inspired. The communists certainly exploited events for their own purposes, but they had not created the conditions which had led to the events. With this, President Kennedy decisively broke through a taboo which, until then, had been carefully preserved in Washington and the West. The first consideration of the West, particularly in Africa, should not be the struggle against communism. The communists should not necessarily be suspected of being behind every anti-Western move. The West should aim at an improvement of the objective conditions and *at changing the existing circumstances in such a way that they no longer favour the growth and spread of communism.*

The progress which has already been achieved in the analysis of the African situation, and in the West's practical African policy is not enough in itself. The fact is that the West finds itself, particularly in Africa, still in the position of merely reacting to the attacks of an active and virulent communism. The result is that many of the measures taken by the West are triggered off in the first place by actions taken by the communists and their followers. As things stand, a summary of the whole situation, dealing with the interaction of all the various relevant factors (and in particular with the interrelations of black nationalism, communism and Western policy in Africa) can hardly prove favourable to the West. In the continuing economic, social, and political upheaval on the African continent, African nationalism is obviously divided. It is unstable and it is particularly subject to crises. Above all, it has no clearly formulated ideas of its own. In this situation the communists are waging a determined offensive behind a grinning mask of friendship, and making attractive offers of assistance. Unfortunately the

West still lacks the necessary moral force and a clear and convincing programme adapted to African conditions and requirements; in fact, it often seems to have no real idea of the direct threat to the idea of freedom represented by the co-operation of Africans and communists.

Over and above this, the West lacks a clear insight into what it can and should do in Africa. A similar problem has already existed for some time in Asia and Latin America, and it is therefore of great importance that it should be solved now. The basic question is whether the alternative to communism should be a political, economic and even military alliance with the West and the adoption of strictly Western ideas, customs and standards in these areas, or whether there is not a 'third way' which could be permitted to these countries and peoples on their own responsibility. At least as far as Africa is concerned, it is already clear that in view of the continuing upheaval there, the alternatives cannot be East or West; there is indeed a third possibility, the establishment of a stable African power, an independent and free Africa as the best answer to communist attempts at infiltration and domination. In reality, the West has no alternative but to do its utmost to see that the slogan of African nationalism—'Africa for the Africans!'—becomes a reality in the shortest possible time and that the new Africa develops into a respected factor in the world political situation. The West hesitated and procrastinated before allowing Africa to plunge into the insecurity of political sovereignty, but it should not hesitate to encourage Africa to attain its complete political, economic, and spiritual independence. This is the only way in which communism and the extreme, brutally anti-libertarian wing of African nationalism can be thwarted, and in which the resistance of the African continent to totalitarian solutions and practices can be built up.

No one who thinks in terms of practical politics can imagine that it is possible for all this to be carried out swiftly and smoothly. But since Africa and the whole of the free world is faced with great dangers, the West will finally have to recognize that desperate diseases require desperate remedies, that it must come forward with new and original ideas, make new and greater efforts, and even take considerable risks. Meanwhile, communists will do their utmost to denigrate and sabotage any pro-African policy on the part of the

West and it will not be easy to convince the suspicious Africans that such a policy is, in fact, pro-African.

It is not the aim of this book to provide detailed solutions to these problems or to reshape the West's African policy. But the material we have examined and the objective comments we have made do, of themselves, suggest a number of possibilities and we propose to summarize them under five headings.

1. The West should solemnly and convincingly proclaim that it aims at the abolition of all colonial and semi-colonial survivals anywhere in the world and it should not hesitate to exert really strong pressure on any members of the Western alliance if they attempt to flout this proclaimed intention. At the same time the West should stress that its own pro-African attitude is not influenced by any form of political self-interest or *arrière pensée*, but is based solely on the categoric imperatives of liberty, social justice, and democracy.

2. A uniform programme of African development should be worked out—one that could be followed by the West as a whole. It should be determined and implemented largely by Africans themselves. The first matter requiring attention is the establishment of a world-wide raw-materials fund from which the steady losses incurred by the under-developed countries through the creeping depreciation of raw-material prices on the world market can be made good. The greatest importance should be attached to the programme for training and educating wide sections of the population. The degree of aid offered to the individual under-developed countries should not be made dependent on the régime's attitude to the West but on the degree to which they are clearly striving to establish liberty and social justice in their countries.

3. The West should solemnly proclaim that it will oppose any attempt, no matter from what quarter, to intervene in the internal affairs of Africa and that with a view to reducing international tensions it will make no attempt to involve any African State in any military alliance provided the East will agree to exercise similar restraint. This would mean the evacuation of its military bases in Africa, but they are in any case of limited strategic importance.

4. The West should make it unmistakably clear that in order to keep the cold war out of the African continent it will reject any ideological propaganda rivalry between communism and Western

libertarian ideas there, but that if there is a continuation of communist agitation and propaganda it will take measures to counteract such activities. In this event the West should ascertain that Africans realize from the start that, in such circumstances, the West will not be acting on its own initiative, but simply reacting to communist provocation; that it will be defending itself and not launching an attack.

5. Even in African countries the constitutions of which conflict with Western principles or which already co-operate with the communists, the West should not lose heart or allow itself to be forced out completely despite its weak position, nor must it hold itself aloof, as so often in the past, from left-wing Pan-African or regional projects, or allow itself to be excluded from them. On the other hand, it must also make it quite clear that it will evince the greatest respect and sympathy for such countries, groups and elements as acknowledge the basic principles of human liberty.

The West must now try to recover the moral initiative in Africa and turn the whole continent into a demonstrating theatre for its ethical, spiritual, social, and economic values and abilities, though its aim should not and cannot be to bind Africa to Europe again, or to make Africa dependent on Europe, or turn it into a satellite. On the contrary, the West must help Africa to attain its own independent and free existence.

NOTES

[1] *Protokoll des V. Kongresses des Kommunistischen Internationale* (Hamburg, n.d.), pp. 630-2.

[2] *L'Humanité* (Paris), 26 and 27 June 1947.

[3] *Sovietskoya Vostokovodenie* (Moscow), Nos 5 and 6 (1955).

[4] 'New Features of the National-Liberation Movement', *World Marxist Review: Problems of Peace and Socialism*, II, No. 9 (September 1959), pp. 77-8. A discussion of the role of the bourgeoisie in the national struggle for liberation.

[5] Fernand Gigon, *Guinée Etat-pilote*; quoted in Franz Ansprenger, *Politik im Schwarzen Afrika* (Cologne, 1961), p. 292.

[6] Kofi Baako, 'Ghana's Conception of Socialism', lecture to an international seminar of Christian students in Accra, 19 August 1961. Typescript in the possession of the author.

[7] Statement made in a conversation with the author, in Bonn, 30 December 1961.

[8] Walter Kolarz, 'Communism in Africa—The West African Scene', *Problems of Communism*, No. 6 (1961).

INDEX

THE OVARY

Second Edition

PETER C. K. LEUNG
Department of Obstetrics and Gynecology
University of British Columbia
British Columbia Children and Women's Hospital
Vancouver, British Columbia
Canada

Eli Y. Adashi
Department of Obstetrics and Gynecology
University of Utah
Salt Lake City, Utah

ELSEVIER
ACADEMIC
PRESS

AMSTERDAM BOSTON HEIDELBERG LONDON NEW YORK OXFORD PARIS
SAN DIEGO SAN FRANCISCO SINGAPORE SYDNEY TOKYO

Elsevier Academic Press
525 B Street, Suite 1900, San Diego, California 92101-4495, USA
84 Theobald's Road, London WC1X 8RR, UK

This book is printed on acid-free paper. 

Library of Congress Cataloging-in-Publication Data
Application submitted

British Library Cataloguing in Publication Data
A catalogue record for this book is available from the British Library

ISBN: 0-12-444562-4

For all information on all Academic Press publications
visit our website at www.academicpress.com

Printed in the United States of America
03 04 05 06 07 08 9 8 7 6 5 4 3 2 1

International Standard Book Number: 0-12-444562-4
PRINTED IN THE UNITED STATES OF AMERICA
03 04 05 06 07 7 6 5 4 3 2 1

Contents

PART III

The Corpus Luteum

PART IV

Intraovarian Regulators

PART V
Cyclic Ovarian Cell Death

CHAPTER 19
Apoptosis in Ovarian Development, Function, and Failure
Jonathan L. Tilly, James K. Pru, and Bo R. Rueda

CHAPTER 20
Reactive Oxygen Species and Ovarian Function
Jessica A. Bertout, Neal G. Mahutte, Sandra L. Preston, and Harold R. Behrman

CHAPTER 21
Follicle Selection in Mammalian Ovaries: Regulatory Mechanisms of Granulosa Cell Apoptosis during Follicular Atresia
Noboru Manabe, Naoke Inoue, Takashi Miyano, Kazuhiro Sakamaki, Miki Sugimoto, and Hajime Miyamoto

PART VI
Novel Experimental Models

CHAPTER 22
Generation and Application of Ovarian Steroidogenic Cell Lines
Abraham Amsterdam and R. Sasson

CHAPTER 23

The Application of Gene Ablation and Related Technologies to the Study of Ovarian Function

Kathleen H. Burns and Martin M. Matzuk

CHAPTER 24

Bioinformatic Analysis of Ovarian Genes Using an Ovary-Specific Database

Izhar Ben-Shlomo and Aaron J. W. Hsueh

PART VII

Human Ovarian Pathophysiology: Select Aspects

CHAPTER 25

Gonadotropin Ovulation Induction

Nick S. Macklon and Bart C. J. M. Fauser

CHAPTER 26

The Role of Gn-RH Antagonists in Supporting Ovarian Hyperstimulation Protocols

Nathalie Chabbert-Buffet, F. Olivennes, Bart C. J. M. Fauser, Philippe Bouchard, and René Frydman

CHAPTER 27

The Ovarian Factor in Assisted Reproductive Technology

Laurel Stadtmauer, Estella Jones, and Roger Gosden

CHAPTER 28

Ovarian Function in Assisted Reproduction

Carole Gilling-Smith and Stephen Franks

CHAPTER 29

Polycystic Ovarian Syndrome

Richard S. Legro

CHAPTER 30

The Role of the Ovary in the Genesis of Hyperandrogenism

Denis A. Magoffin

CHAPTER 31

Luteal Dysfunction

Rebecca S. Usadi and Marc A. Fritz

CHAPTER 32
Germ Cell Failure and Ovarian Resistance: Human Genes and Disorders
Joe Leigh Simpson and Aleksandar Rajkovic

CHAPTER 33
Ovarian Function and Survival of Patients with Cervical Carcinoma Treated with Radical Hysterectomy and Ovarian Transposition
Kazuhira Okamoto, Noriaki Sakuragi, and Seiichiro Fujimoto

CHAPTER 34
The Role of Mitochondria in the Aging Ovary
Rong-Hong Hsieh, Heng-Kien Au, Ruey-Sheng Wang, Peng-Sheng Yang, and Chii-Ruey Tzeng

Part VIII
Human Ovarian Surface Epithelium and Neoplasia

CHAPTER 35
Development and Differentiation of Ovarian Surface Epithelium: Cues for the Basis of its Malignant Potential
Nelly Auersperg and Michelle M. M. Woo

CHAPTER 36

Ovarian Carcinogenesis

Barbara C. Vanderhyden, Tanya J. Shaw, Kenneth Garson, and Angela M. Tonary

CHAPTER 37

The Role of X-Linked Inhibitor of Apoptosis Protein in Chemoresistant Ovarian Cancer

Michael Fraser and Benjamin K. Tsang

CHAPTER 38

Molecular Mechanisms of Pathogenesis and Progression of Epithelial Ovarian Cancer

Robert C. Bast, Jr., and Gordon B. Mills

Contributors

Abraham Amsterdam, Ph.D., *Department of Molecular Cell Biology, Weizmann Institute of Science, Rehovot 76100, Israel*

Heng-Kien Au, M.D., *Department of Obstetrics and Gynecology, Taipei Medical University Hospital, 252 Wu Hsing Street, Taipei, Taiwan 110*

Nelly Auersperg, M.D., Ph.D., *Department of Obstetrics and Gynecology, University of British Columbia, British Columbia Children and Women's Hospital, Room 2H30, 4490 Oak Street, Vancouver, British Columbia V6H 3V5, Canada*

Robert C. Bast, Jr., M.D., *Department of Experimental Therapeutics, University of Texas M.D. Anderson Cancer Center, Box 355, 1515 Holcombe Boulevard, Houston, Texas 77030-4009*

Harold R. Behrman, Ph.D., *Department of Obstetrics, Gynecology, and Reproductive Sciences, Yale University School of Medicine, 333 Cedar Street, New Haven, Connecticut 06520*

Adam S. Bellinger, B.S., *Department of Medicine, University of Texas Health Science Center at San Antonio, 7703 Floyd Curl Drive, San Antonio, TX 78284*

Izhar Ben-Shlomo, M.D., *Department of Obstetrics and Gynecology, HaEmek Medical Center, Afula and the Rappaport Faculty of Medicine, Technion-Israel Institute of Technology, Haifa, Israel*

Jessica A. Bertout, *Department of Obstetrics, Gynecology, and Reproductive Sciences, Yale University School of Medicine, 333 Cedar Street, New Haven, Connecticut 06520*

Derek Boerboom, D.V.M., Ph.D., *Centre de Recherche en Reproduction Animale and Département de Biomédecine Vétérinaire, Faculté de Médecine Vétérinaire, Université de Montréal, 3200 Sicotte, Saint-Hyacinthe, Québec J2S 7C6, Canada*

Philippe Bouchard, M.D., *Endocrinology Unit, Hospital Saint Antoine APHP and EA1533 Genetics of Human Reproduction, UFR Saint Antoine, 184 Rue du Fg. St. Antoine, 75012 Paris, France*

Jennifer M. Bowen-Shauver, Ph.D., *Department of Physiology and Biophysics, University of Illinois at Chicago, 835 South Wolcott Avenue, MC 901, Chicago, Illinois 60612*

Mats Brännström, M.D., Ph.D., *Department of Obstetrics and Gynecology, The Sahlgrenska Academy at Göteborg University, S-413 45 Göteborg, Sweden*

Kathleen H. Burns, *Department of Pathology, Department of Molecular and Human Genetics, Baylor College of Medicine, One Baylor Plaza, Houston, Texas 77030*

Antonella Camaioni, Ph.D., *Department of Public Health and Cell Biology, Faculty of Medicine, University of Rome Tor Vergata, Building E Nord, First Floor, Room 160, via Montpellier 1, 00133 Rome, Italy*

Nathalie Chabbert-Buffet, M.D., *Internal Medicine Unit, Hospital Tenon APHP, 4 Rue de la Chine, 75020 Paris France, and EA1533 Genetics of Human Reproduction, UFR Saint Antoine, 184 Rue du Fg. St. Antoine, 75012 Paris France*

Stacey C. Chapman, Ph.D., *Department of Neuropbiology and Physiology, Northwestern University, 2205 Tech Drive, Hogan 4-150 Evanston, Illinois 60208*

C. K. Cheng, Ph.D., *Department of Obstetrics and Gynecology, University of British Columbia, British Columbia Children and Women's Hospital, 4490 Oak Street Vancouver, British Columbia, Canada V6H 3V5*

Lane K. Christenson, Ph.D., *University of Pennsylvania Center for Research on Reproduction and Women's Health, 1355 Biomedical Research Building II/III, 421 Curie Boulevard, Philadelphia, Pennsylvania 19104-6142*

W. Les Dees, Ph.D., *Department of Veterinary Anatomy and Public Health, Texas A&M University, VMA Building, Room 104, University Drive, College Station, Texas 77843*

Rabindranath de la Fuente, D.V.M., Ph.D., *Center for Animal Transgenesis and Germ Cell Research, University of Pennsylvania School of Veterinary Medicine, New Bolton Center, 382 West Street Road, Kennett Square, Pennsylvania 19348-1692, and The Jackson Laboratory, 600 Main Street, Bar Harbor, Maine 04609*

Gregory A. Dissen, Ph.D., *Division of Neuroscience, Oregon National Primate Research Center, Oregon Health and Science University, 505 NW 185th Avenue, Beaverton, OR 97006*

John J. Eppig, Ph.D., *The Jackson Laboratory, 600 Main Street, Bar Harbor, Maine 04609*

Lawrence L. Espey, Ph.D., *Department of Biology, Trinity University, One Trinity Place, San Antonio, Texas 78212*

Bart C. J. M. Fauser, M.D., Ph.D., *Center for Reproductive Medicine, Department of Obstetrics and Gynecology, Erasmus Medical Center, Rotterdam 3015 GD, The Netherlands*

Stephen Franks, *Department of Reproductive Science and Medicine, Institute of Reproductive and Developmental Biology, Imperial College, Hammersmith Hospital, London, England W12 0NN*

Michael Fraser, *Reproductive Biology Unit, Department of Obstetrics and Gynaecology and Cellular and Molecular Medicine, University of Ottawa Hormones, Growth, and Development Program, Ottawa Health Research Institute, 725 Parkdale Avenue, Ottawa, Ontario, Canada K1Y 4E9*

Marc A. Fritz, M.D., *Division of Reproductive Endocrinology and Fertility, Department of Obstetrics and Gynecology, University of North Carolina at Chapel Hill, CB# 7570, Chapel Hill, North Carolina 27599*

René Frydman, M.D., *Gynecology Unit, Hospital Antoine Béclère APHP, 157 Rue de la Porte de Trivaux, 92141 Clamart, France*

Seiichiro Fujimoto, M.D., *Department of Obstetrics and Gynecology, Hokkaido University Graduate School of Medicine, N15, W7, Kitaku, Sapporo 060-8638, Japan*

Csaba Fulop, Ph.D., *Department of Biomedical Engineering, ND20, The Cleveland Clinic Foundation, 9500 Euclid Avenue, Cleveland, Ohio 44195*

Kenneth Garson, Ph.D., *Centre for Cancer Therapeutics, Ottawa Regional Cancer Centre, 503 Smyth Road, Third Floor, Ottawa, Ontario, Canada K1H 1C4*

Eli Geva, *Department of Obstetrics, Gynecology, and Reproductive Sciences, Center for Reproductive Sciences, University of California, San Francisco, California 94143-0556*

Geula Gibori, Ph.D., *Department of Physiology and Biophysics, University of Illinois at Chicago, 835 South Wolcott Avenue, MC 901, Chicago, Illinois 60612*

Carole Gilling-Smith, M.A., M.R.C.O.G., Ph.D., *Assisted Conception Unit, Chelsea and Westminster Hospital, 369 Fulham Road, London SW10 9NH, England*

Roger Gosden, *Jones Institute for Reproductive Medicine, Department of Obstetrics and Gynecology, Eastern Virginia Medical School, Norfolk, Virginia 23507*

Alain Gougeon, Dr.Sci., *Interactions Cellulaires en Biologie de la Reproduction, INSERM U-407, Faculté de Médecine Lyon-Sud, BP 12, 69 921 Oullins Cedex, France*

Vincent C. Hascall, Ph.D., *Department of Biomedical Engineering, ND20, The Cleveland Clinic Foundation, 9500 Euclid Avenue, Cleveland, Ohio 44195*

Jane A. Healy, B.S., M.D./Ph.D. student, *Duke University School of Medicine, Durham, North Carolina 27710*

Clement K. M. Ho, M.B.B.S., Ph.D., *University of Pennsylvania Center for Research on Reproduction and Women's Health, 1355 Biomedical Research Building II/III, 421 Curie Boulevard, Philadelphia, Pennsylvania 19104-6142*

Rong-Hong Hsieh, Ph.D., *Department of Nutrition and Health Sciences, Taipei Medical University, 252 Wu Hsing Street, Taipei, Taiwan 110*

Aaron J. W. Hsueh, Ph.D., *Division of Reproductive Biology, Department of Gynecology and Obstetrics, Stanford University Medical Center, 300 Pasteur Drive, Room A-344, Stanford, California 94305-5317*

Ilpo Huhtaniemi, M.D., Ph.D., *Institute of Reproductive and Developmental Biology, Imperial College London, Hammersmith Campus, Du Cane Road, London W12 0NN, England*

Naoke Inoue, Ph.D., *Unit of Anatomy and Cell Biology, Department of Animal Sciences, Kyoto University, Kyoto 606-8502, Japan*

Robert B. Jaffe, *Department of Obstetrics, Gynecology, and Reproductive Sciences, Center for Reproductive Sciences, University of California, San Francisco, California 94143-0556*

Estella Jones, *Jones Institute for Reproductive Medicine, Department of Obstetrics and Gynecology, Eastern Virginia Medical School, Norfolk, Virginia 23507*

Hilary A. Kenny, *Department of Neuropbiology and Physiology, Northwestern University, 2205 Tech Drive, Hogan 4-150, Evanston, Illinois 60208*

Richard S. Legro, M.D., *Department of Obstetrics and Gynecology, H103, Penn State University College of Medicine, 500 University Drive, M.S. Hershey Medical Center, Hershey, Pennsylvania 17033*

Peter C. K. Leung, Ph.D., *Department of Obstetrics and Gynecology, University of British Columbia, British Columbia Children and Women's Hospital, 4490 Oak Street, Vancouver, British Columbia, Canada V6H 3V5*

Nick S. Macklon, M.R.C.O.G., M.D., Ph.D., *Center for Reproductive Medicine, Department of Obstetrics and Gynecology, Erasmus Medical Center, Rotterdam 3015 GD, The Netherlands*

Denis A. Magoffin, Ph.D., *Department of Obstetrics and Gynecology, Cedars-Sinai Medical Center, 8700 Beverly Boulevard, Davis 2066, Los Angeles, California 90048*

Neal G. Mahutte, M.D., *Department of Obstetrics, Gynecology, and Reproductive Sciences, Yale University School of Medicine, 333 Cedar Street, New Haven, Connecticut 06520*

Noboru Manabe, Ph.D., *Unit of Anatomy and Cell Biology, Department of Animal Sciences, Kyoto University, Kyoto 606-8502, Japan*

Carrie Marin-Bivens, Ph.D., *The Jackson Laboratory, 600 Main Street, Bar Harbor, Manie 04609*

Martin M. Matzuk, Ph.D., *Departments of Pathology, Molecular and Human Genetics, and Molecular and Cellular Biology, Baylor College of Medicine, One Baylor Plaza, Houston, Texas 77030*

Gordon B. Mills, M.D., Ph.D., *Department of Molecular Therapeutics, University of Texas M.D. Anderson Cancer Center, 1515 Holcombe Boulevard, Houston, Texas 77030*

Takashi Minegishi, M.D., Ph.D., *Department of Gynecology and Reproductive Medicine, Graduate School of Medicine, Gunma University, 3-39-22 Showa-Machi, Maebashi, Gunma 371-8511, Japan*

Hajime Miyamoto, Ph.D., *Unit of Anatomy and Cell Biology, Department of Animal Sciences, Kyoto University, Kyoto 606-8502, Japan*

Takashi Miyano, Ph.D., *Laboratory of Animal Reproduction, Department of Animal Sciences, Kobe University, Kobe 657-850, Japan*

Bruce D. Murphy, Ph.D., *Centre de Recherche en Reproduction Animale, Faculté de Médecine Vétérinaire, Université de Montréal, 3200 Sicotte, Saint-Hyacinthe, Québec, Canada J2S 7C6*

Sekar Natesampillai, Ph.D., *Professional Associate in Research, Mayo Clinic College of Medicine, 200 First Street SW, Room 5-228 Joseph Rochester, Minnesota 55905*

Sergio R. Ojeda, D.V.M., *Division of Neuroscience, Oregon National Brimate Research Center, Oregon Health and Science University, 505 NW 185th Avenue, Beaverton, OR*

Kazuhira Okamoto, M.D., *Department of Obstetrics and Gynecology, Hokkaido University Graduate School of Medicine, N15, W7, Kitaku, Sapporo 060-8638, Japan*

F. Olivennes, M.D., Ph.D., *Reproductive Medicine Unit, Hospital Chochin APHP, 27 Rue du Fg. St. Jacques, 75014 Paris, France*

Alfonso Paredes, Ph.D., *Departamento Bioquimica y Biologia Molecular, Facultad de Ciencias Quimicas y Farmaceuticas, Universidad de Chile, Olivos 1007, Comuna de Independencia, Santiago, Chile*

Sandra L. Preston, *Reproductive Biology Section, Department of Obstetrics, Gynecology, and Pharmacology, Yale University School of Medicine, New Haven, Connecticut 06520*

James K. Pru, Ph.D., *Vincent Center for Reproductive Biology, Massachusetts General Hospital-East, 149 13th Street, Room 6613, Charlestown, Massachusetts 02129*

Aleksandar Rajkovic, M.D., Ph.D., *Department of Obstetrics and Gynecology, Division of Reproductive Genetics, Baylor College of Medicine, 6550 Fannin, Suite 901A, Houston, Texas 77030*

Carmen Romero, Ph.D., *Department of Obstetrics and Gynecology, Facultad de Medicino, Hospital Clinico, Universidad de Chile, Santos Dumont 999, Santiago, Chile*

Bo R. Rueda, Ph.D., *Vincent Center for Reproductive Biology, Massachusetts General Hospital-East, 149 13th Street, Room 6604C, Charlestown, Massachusetts 02129*

Kazuhiro Sakamaki, Ph.D., *Laboratory of Tmore Cell Biology, Department of Life Sciences, Kyoto University, Kyoto 606-8502, Japan*

Noriaki Sakuragi, M.D., *Department of Obstetrics and Gynecology, Hokkaido University Graduate School of Medicine, N15, W7, Kitaku, Sapporo 060-8638, Japan*

Antonietta Salustri, *Department of Public Health and Cell Biology, Faculty of Medicine, University of Rome Tor Vergata, Building E Nord, First Floor, Room 168, via Montpellier 1, 00133 Rome–Italy*

R. Sasson, *Department of Molecular Cell Biology, Weizmann Institute of Science, Rehovot 76100, Israel*

Khampoune Sayasith, Ph.D., *Centre de Recherche en Reproduction Animale and Département de Biomédecine Vétérinaire, Faculté de Médecine Vétérinaire, Université de Montréal, 3200 Sicotte, Saint-Hyacinthe, Québec J2S 7C6, Canada*

Tanya J. Shaw, B.S., *Department of Cellular and Molecular Medicine, University of Ottawa and Centre for Cancer Therapeutics, Ottawa Regional Cancer Centre, 503 Smyth Road, Third Floor, Ottawa, Ontario, Canada K1H 1C4*

Joe Leigh Simpson, M.D., *Department of Obstetrics and Gynecology and Department of Molecular and Human Genetics, Baylor College of Medicine, 6550 Fannin, Suite 901A, Houston, Texas 77030*

Jean Sirois D.V.M., Ph.D., *Centre de Recherche en Reproduction Animale and Département de Biomédecine Vétérinaire, Faculté de Médecine Vétérinaire, Université de Montréal, 3200 Sicotte, Saint-Hyacinthe, Québec J2S 7C6, Canada*

Laurel Stadtmauer, *Jones Institute for Reproductive Medicine, Department of Obstetrics and Gynecology, Eastern Virginia Medical School, Norfolk, Virginia 23507*

Richard L. Stouffer, Ph.D., *Division of Reproductive Sciences and Department of Biochemistry and Molecular Biology, Oregon National Primate Research Center, Oregon Health and Science University, 505 NW 185th Avenue, Beaverton, Oregon 97006*

Jerome F. Strauss III, M.D., Ph.D., *University of Pennsylvania Center for Research on Reproduction and Women's Health, 1355 Biomedical Research Building II/III, 421 Curie Boulevard, Philadelphia, Pennsylvania 19104-6142*

Miki Sugimoto, Ph.D., *Unit of Anatomy and Cell Biology, Department of Animal Sciences, Kyoto University, Kyoto 606-8502, Japan*

Jonathan L. Tilly, Ph.D., *Vincent Center for Reproductive Biology, Massachusetts General Hospital-East, VBK137C-GYN, 55 Fruit Street, Charlestown, Massachusetts 02129*

Angela M. Tonary, Ph.D., *Chemical Biology Group, Steacie Institute for Molecular Sciences, National Research Council Canada, 100 Sussex Drive, Room 2108, Ottawa, Ontario, Canada K1A 0R6*

Benjamin K Tsang, Ph.D., *Reproductive Biology Unit, Department of Obstetrics and Gynaecology and Cellular and Molecular Medicine, University of Ottawa Hormones, Growth and Development Program, Ottawa Health Research Institute, 725 Parkdale Avenue, Ottawa, Ontario, Canada K1Y 4E9*

Chii-Ruey Tzeng, M.D., *Center for Reproductive Medicine and Sciences and Department of Obstetrics and Gynecology, Taipei Medical University Hospital, 252 Wu Hsing Street, Taipei, Taiwan 110*

Rebecca S. Usadi, M.D., *Division of Reproductive Endocrinology and Fertility, Department of Obstetrics and Gynecology, University of North Carolina at Chapel Hill, CB# 7570, Chapel Hill, North Carolina 27599*

Barbara C. Vanderhyden, Ph.D., *Department of Cellular and Molecular Medicine, University of Ottawa and Centre for Cancer Therapeutics, Ottawa Regional Cancer Centre, 503 Smyth Road, Third Floor, Ottawa, Ontario, Canada K1H 1C4*

Johannes D. Veldhuis, M.D., *Professor of Internal Medicine, Consultant, Clinical Investigator, Endocrine Research Unit, Mayo Clinic College of Medicine, 200 First Street SW, Room 5-194 Joseph, Rochester, Minnesota 55905*

Maria M. Viveiros, Ph.D., *Department of Animal Biology, University of Pennsylvania School of Veterinary Medicine, 382 West Street Road, Kennett Square, Pennsylvania 19348-1692*

Ruey-Sheng Wang, M.D., *Department of Obstetrics and Gynecology, Taipei Medical University Hospital, 252 Wu Hsing Street, Taipei, Taiwan 110*

Michelle M. M. Woo, B.Sc., M.Phil., *Department of Obstetrics and Gynecology, British Columbia Children's and Women's Hospital, University of British Columbia, 2H30-4490 Oak Street, Vancouver, British Columbia, Canada V6H 3V5*

Teresa K. Woodruff, Ph.D., *Department of Neuropbiology and Physiology and Robert H. Lurie Comprehensive Cancer Center, Northwestern University, 2205 Tech Drive, Hogan 4-150, Evanston, Illinois 60208*

Peng-Sheng Yang, M.D., *Department of Obstetrics and Gynecology, Taipei Medical University Hospital, 252 Wu Hsing Street, Taipei, Taiwan 110*

Anthony J. Zeleznik, Ph.D., *Department of Cell Biology and Physiology, University of Pittsburgh School of Medicine, Scaife Hall, Room 830, 3550 Terrace Street, Pittsburgh, Pennsylvania 15261*

Preface

It is with great pleasure that the co-editors present this second edition of *The Ovary*. It is difficult to believe that it has been only ten years since the first edition of this contribution went to press. The readers may recall that at that time, much ground had to be covered in that prior editions of a related tome were significantly dated. Although only ten years have transpired since the co-editors embarked on this journey, much progress has been made that requires further update. It is good to recall that the last several years were witness to the "genomic revolution" with its multiple implications now leading to the age of "proteomics." Indeed, the pace has picked up substantially with the introduction of high throughput technologies and the streamlining of ablational approaches such as homologous recombination. These developments along with the startling discovery of the multifaceted roles of RNA, especially the RNAi phenom, have markedly changed the ground rules not to mention the pace of discovery.

It is against this backdrop that the co-editors have undertaken to revise, update, and enhance the first edition of *The Ovary*. Although the general organization of the book, as exemplified by its table of contents, remains largely unaltered, the subject matter has been brought up to date. In that context the co-editors are delighted to welcome both veteran contributors alongside first time contributors thereby creating the dynamic ever-changing format that is so essential to timely contributions.

It is the sincere hope of the co-editors that the readers of this text will find it useful in their own studies, in their teaching obligations and in their investigative pursuits. Stated differently, it is the hope of the co-editors that this contribution will prove useful not only to graduate students pursuing studies in the reproductive sciences, but also to the teaching and investigator faculty. Finally, it is the conviction of the co-editors, that this edition will be of value to students of Reproductive Medicine and their faculty in the context of the relevant curriculum.

Best wishes,
Peter C. K. Leung and Eli Y. Adashi, Co-Editors

PART I

The Ovarian Follicular Apparatus: Operational Characteristics

CHAPTER 1

Neural and Neurotrophic Control of Ovarian Development

GREGORY A. DISSEN, ALFONSO PAREDES, CARMEN ROMERO, W. LES DEES, AND SERGIO R. OJEDA

INTRODUCTION

The mammalian ovary is a prominent terminal field for sympathetic and sensory neurons. The neurons projecting to the ovary innervate the different structural components of the gland, including the vasculature, interstitial tissue, and developing follicles, with various degrees of complexity. Before the 1990s several reports appeared documenting the distribution of intraovarian nerve fibers, their presence in different species, and their neurotransmitter identity. During the early 1990s the availability of simplified culture procedures and new biochemical and molecular techniques provided insights into the specific contribution that ovarian nerves may have to the regulation of ovarian function. Thus a number of reports appeared indicating an involvement of neurotransmitters contained in ovarian nerves, such as norepinephrine (NE) and vasoactive intestinal peptide (VIP), in the control of follicular steroidogenesis (for reviews, see [1, 2]) and suggesting the facilitatory participation of the sympathetic innervation in follicular development [3, 4]. More intriguingly, evidence was provided for the unsuspected participation of a neurotrophic complex, intimately linked to the innervation, in the control of follicular development.

Key components of this complex are a family of polypeptide growth factors, called *neurotrophins (NTs)*, and their cell membrane–spanning receptors. The presence of NTs is required for the establishment and maintenance of the ovarian innervation. They are secreted by ovarian cells targeted by the innervation and act via specific receptors expressed on the innervating fibers. In addition, the receptors are also present in nonneuronal cells of the ovary, indicating that NTs not only support the innervation of the gland but perhaps, more importantly, can directly influence specific ovarian functions. Thus the ovarian innervation and neurotrophic factors may act in coordinated yet independent manners to control diverse aspects of ovarian physiology such as follicular development, steroid production, and ovulation. In the first edition of this chapter published 10 years ago [5], we proposed the concept that these two components of ovarian regulation represent an example of a distinct class of neuroendocrinotrophic regulatory systems that, when operating in the interphase between the nervous and the endocrine system, act as molecular links for neuroendocrine interaction. This class of neuroendocrinotrophic regulatory systems appears to be active in diverse tissues such as the heart [6], pancreas [7], skin [8, 9], and the ovary [5, 10]. As it will become evident later, a growing body of experimental evidence now supports the overall validity of this concept. In addition to data gathered by traditional neuroendocrine approaches, the genetic ablation of NTs or their receptors has unveiled unsuspected functions for this family of neurotrophic factors during ovarian development, suggesting that some of its members may play a fundamental role in the control of early follicular growth.

It is our purpose to discuss, in the context of findings made since publication of the first edition of this book, the involvement of the ovarian innervation and neurotrophic factors in the control of follicular development and ovulation. In discussing these issues, we will first provide a succinct account of relevant aspects of early follicular development, the distribution of ovarian nerves, and some of the important features that define the NT family and its receptors.

Early Ovarian Development

The ovary develops as a thickening along the ventral cranial mesonephros, called the *genital ridge*. The germ cells, which originate in the yolk sac of the embryo, migrate to the ovary (for review, see [11]), first arriving at the genital ridge during early gestation in humans (6 weeks, [12]) or by midgestation in other species, such as the mouse (embryonic days 11 or 12, [13, 14]).

After the germ cells colonize the indifferent gonad, the germ cells and the somatic cells undergo mitotic proliferation. As the mitotic division of the germ cells is completed, meiosis begins. The first meiotic prophase consists of five stages: leptonema, zygonema, pachynema, diplonema, and diakinesis [15]. The germ cells arrest during, diplonema, the stage at which germ cells become enclosed within follicles.

Before completion of germ cell mitosis, the mesonephric tubules (wolffian duct) become discontinuous, and the resulting clumps of epithelial cells form the rete ovary [11]. This occurs at about embryonic day 15 in the rat [16] or the fifteenth week of gestation in the human [17]. By embryonic day 17, the rete ovary of the rat consists of three portions: (1) extraovarian, (2) connecting, and (3) intraovarian. A continuum of cell cords and tubes that extend into the ovary form the rete [18, 19]. The intraovarian rete consists of a network of cell cords and tubules that occupies most of the ovarian medulla and reaches into the cortex enveloping the oocytes, which at this time are either isolated or arranged in clusters. Although it appears that granulosa cells enclosing the oocytes differentiate from epithelial cells, some controversy exists about their origin. Some authors believe that they originate exclusively from the surface epithelium, but others [16, 18] have concluded that granulosa cells derive from the rete ovary instead (for reviews, see [11, 20]).

Development of the mesenchymal component of the ovary represents another event of importance for follicular formation. Although a precise period has not been established, it appears that mesonephric mesenchymal cells begin an outward migration from the innermost portion of the primordial ovary at a time that antedates the formation of the rete cell-oocyte relationship [17]. As they proliferate, they intercalate between the epithelial cells of the gland to form stromal "pockets" that contain epithelial cells and one or more oocytes. As this process continues, the mesenchymal cells further disrupt the developing epithelial cords into isolated groups of presumptive granulosa cells that now surround single oocytes. In the rat the "packaging" process is completed by the end of the first day of postnatal life resulting in an explosive phase of follicular formation [21, 22]. A primordial follicle is recognized when the single layer of flattened granulosa cells surrounding the oocyte is enclosed by a basement membrane [20]. The theca then develops from the intercalating mesenchymal cells [17].

As indicated earlier, folliculogenesis in the rat is initiated neonatally [22, 23] and is characterized by rapid follicle formation between 24 and 72 hours after birth (Figure 1.1). Although no follicles are seen at 24 hours after birth, almost 500 develop in the next 12 hours, and this number doubles during the subsequent 12 hours. Follicular assembly in the mouse ovary also occurs postnatally ([24, 25], and our own observations), although in some strains of mice, assembly is initiated on the day of birth [24]. In the human, follicular formation occurs after 11 or 12 weeks of gestation [12].

Once follicular development begins, it continues throughout postnatal life (for review, see [26]). During this time the oocyte enlarges while the granulosa and thecal cells proliferate, increasing the layers of cells surrounding the oocyte. This proliferative phase ends as follicular fluid begins to accumulate and the antral cavity forms [20, 26]. During the juvenile period, there are waves of follicular development [26]; however, most of these follicles undergo atresia before puberty. It is only at puberty that follicular growth progresses further toward formation of large antral, Graafian follicles that ovulate in response to the preovulatory surge of gonadotropins.

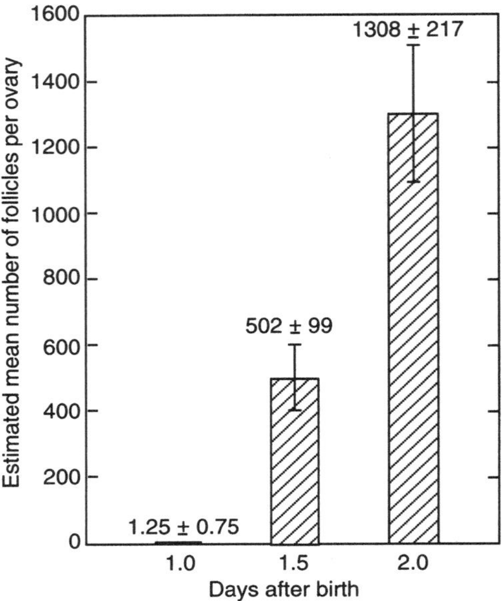

FIGURE 1.1 Development of primordial follicles in the neonatal rat ovary. Columns represent mean values. Vertical lines indicate standard errors of the means. N = 4 for each column. (From Ref. [22], with permission.)

Extrinsic Ovarian Innervation

Through anatomical descriptions mostly derived from rodent studies, we know that the extrinsic innervation of the ovary is primarily provided by sympathetic and sensory nerves, as well as a small contingency of parasympathetic nerves [27]. These nerves originate from neurons located either in specific brain or spinal cord nuclei or from peripheral ganglia (for references and further description, see [28–30]. The sympathetic innervation of the gland is represented by catecholaminergic and neuropeptide Y (NPY)-containing nerve fibers [3, 31–33]. The sensory innervation is provided by substance P (SP) and calcitonin-gene related peptide (CGRP)-containing nerves [28, 32, 34, 35]. VIP-containing fibers of both sympathetic and sensory nature [28, 36] also innervate the ovary [32, 37]. These extrinsic nerves reach the ovary via two main routes: (1) the ovarian plexus nerve (OPN), which travels along the ovarian artery; and (2) the superior ovarian nerve (SON), which is associated with the suspensory ligament of the ovary [27, 38, 39]. The parasympathetic innervation is provided by postganglionic cholinergic neurons, which presumably reach the ovary via vagal efferents [40] and/or branches of the hypogastric plexus that contribute to the OPN [29, 40]. However, recent observations have questioned some of these earlier conclusions. Using antibodies specific for choline-acetyltransferase, Mayerhofer and his colleagues found no evidence of cholinergic fibers in rat and rhesus monkey ovaries [41, 42] and concluded that the source of ovarian acetylcholine is nonneuronal (see later discussion).

Although the time in development when the ovary becomes innervated has not been precisely established, it now is clear that innervation of the gland is an early event that precedes the initiation of folliculogenesis [22]. Experiments with perinatal rat ovaries have identified some of the early fibers as sympathetic because they contain tyrosine hydroxylase (TH), the rate-limiting enzyme in catecholamine synthesis, and have shown that at this time most, if not all, of the developing innervation is limited to the medullary portion of the ovary. This initial distribution, observed before the first postnatal day of life, suggests that any influence that the developing innervation may have on the prefollicular ovary must be exerted on events taking place within this region of the gland. This may be a developmental feature of physiological significance, because the medullary region of the ovary is precisely where the rete ovary enters the gland and follicular formation begins [11, 18, 20].

Human [35] and rhesus macaque [43] ovaries are also innervated by the same types of nerve fibers present in other species, with the exception of SP-ergic nerves, which have not been detected. A remarkable feature observed in monkey ovaries was the innervation of a subpopulation of primordial follicles by VIP-ergic fibers, which appeared to target selected follicles and enclose them almost completely, while leaving neighboring follicles uninnervated [43]. This peculiar distribution appeared to be specific for VIP-ergic fibers, because it was not observed with CGRP, NPY, or TH fibers. Because of its uniqueness, it raises the possibility that the ovarian VIP-ergic innervation of higher primates contributes to the process of follicular selection by singling out follicles at early stages of development.

The ability of neurotransmitters contained in ovarian nerves to stimulate steroidogenesis in rat ovaries led to the hypothesis that ovarian nerves may facilitate prepubertal ovarian development (for reviews, see [2, 44]). Semiquantitative evaluation of the changes in nerve fiber density during postnatal development of the rhesus monkey ovary provided further credence to this notion, because it demonstrated a significant increase in the density of sympathetic and VIP-ergic nerve fibers between the neonatal period and the expected time of puberty (approximately 3 years of life) (Figure 1.2). No further changes were noted during adulthood and no developmental changes in the density of the sensory innervation were detected, suggesting that the changes observed are specific for nerve fibers containing neurotransmitters able to affect ovarian steroid output.

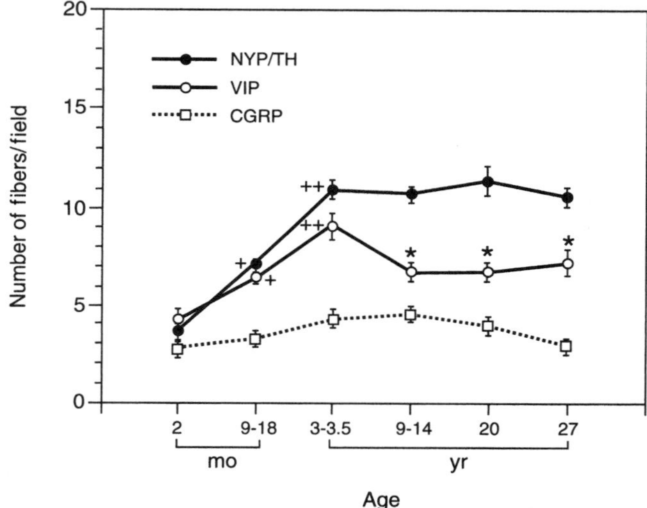

FIGURE 1.2 Developmental changes in the density of sympathetic, VIP-ergic, and CGRP sensory innervation of rhesus monkey ovaries. Note the significant increase in sympathetic (both NPY/TH) and VIP fibers between 2 and 9 to 18 months of age, and then again between this time and the expected time of puberty (3 to 3.5 years). Thereafter, the number of NPY/TH fibers did not change, whereas the number of VIP fibers decreased significantly by adulthood (9 to 14 years of age), without changing during senescence. No significant developmental changes were detected in the number of CGRP sensory fibers. Each point represents the mean number of fibers counted in 8 to 12 fields of view/age/immunoreactive substance. Vertical lines are standard error of the mean (SEM). $^{+}$ = $P < 0.01$ vs the number of fibers at 2 months; $^{++}$ = $P < 0.01$ vs the number of fibers at 9 to 18 months; * = $P < 0.05$ vs the number of VIP fibers at 3 to 3.5 years of age. (From Ref. [43], with permission.)

Intrinsic Ovarian Neurons

Besides the extrinsic innervation the ovary also contains an intrinsic innervation. We first demonstrated, using both rhesus and Japanese macaque monkeys, that the intrinsic nerves originate from neurons within the gland itself [45, 46]. Initially, using an antiserum to the human low affinity nerve growth factor (NGF) receptor (now known as *p75 NT receptor [p75^{NTR}]* because it recognizes all NTs with similar affinity), we described the presence of cells with a neuronal-like appearance, having a soma of approximately 20 μm in diameter and well-developed unipolar, bipolar, and multipolar processes. In addition to their morphological appearance, the expression of neuron specific enolase and neurofilament immunoreactivity further demonstrated their neuronal phenotype. Some of these p75^{NTR}-positive cells were also immunoreactive to antibodies to TH,

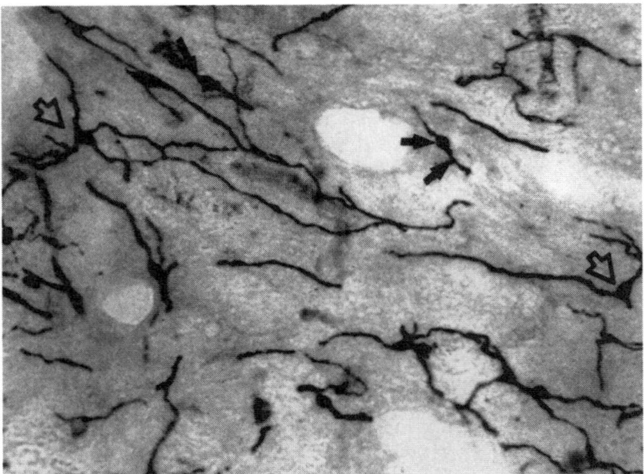

FIGURE 1.3 p75^{NTR} immunopositive cells in a 9-year-old rhesus macaque. Note the neuronal-like appearance of these cells in the interstitial area, as depicted by the well-developed unipolar (*single arrow*), bipolar (*double arrow*), and multipolar (*open arrows*) processes extending from their respective soma. Also note that the processes from numerous cells appear interconnected and therefore form a rather dense network. Magnification: ×300. (From Ref. [46], with permission.)

demonstrating that they are catecholaminergic [46]. A subsequent study revealed that ovarian neurons also express the gene encoding dopamine-β hydroxylase [47], the enzyme that metabolizes dopamine to norepinephrine. Ovarian neurons and their processes are found in the cortex and medullary regions of the monkey ovary. In the cortex they were seen in the interstitial region with their processes appearing densely interconnected with each other (Figure 1.3). Processes were also observed within the thecal cell layer of the growing follicles and occasionally appeared to innervate primordial follicles. In the medulla, neurons were often observed associated with the blood vasculature, with their processes joining other processes and contributing to the innervation of blood vessels. Occasionally, neurons in both the cortex and medulla were clustered into ganglia, with medullary ganglia observed more often.

Neuronlike cells, clustered into a ganglion in the medulla of the human ovary, were described more than a century ago using a potassium bichromate–osmium tetroxide–silver nitrate stain [48]. However, a study conducted 40 years later could not confirm these initial findings [49]. Thus the immunocytochemical localization and definitive description of neurons intrinsic to the nonhuman primate ovary [45–47] reopened a line of inquiry that had been closed for almost 60 years. More recently, the presence of neurons in ovaries of Wistar rats [50, 51] and in fetoneonatal human ovaries [52] was described. The size of these neurons, their localization within the ovary either in isolation or clustered into ganglia within cortical and/or medullary regions of the gland, and the fact that some are catecholaminergic indicate the ovarian neurons in the rat and human are similar to those previously described in monkeys. More recently, we have observed intraovarian neurons in the domestic pig and found that they presumably migrate from the neural crest to the genital ridge during embryonic development [52a].

There are a few species differences with regard to the localization, morphology, or chemical phenotype of the intraovarian neurons. However, two striking differences between primates and rats should be noted. First, the neurons have been observed in the ovaries of all human and nonhuman primates examined thus far but were seen in only one strain of rats. Although the neurons are present in the ovary of Wistar rats [50], they are absent in Sprague-Dawley and Long Evans rats [51]. The second major difference is the number of ovarian neurons observed. In the Wistar rat the mean number of neurons was reported to be approximately 15 per ovary [51], whereas in the rhesus monkey, for example, it is not uncommon to observe as many as 80 to 100 isolated neurons per tissue section [52a]. In the fetoneonatal human ovaries, most of the neurons were found isolated, and perhaps as a result of the small sample size analyzed, none was seen in ganglia [52]. In the rhesus monkey, although the unquestionable majority of neurons were isolated, ganglia were also observed in adult [46] and fetal ovaries. In addition, the human ovarian neurons were mostly observed in the medulla, with fewer in the cortex, at least up to 10 months of age. Conversely, a dense network of interconnecting cortical neurons was observed by 8 months of age in the rhesus monkey [52a]. These differences could represent a species variation or perhaps reflect the existence of an earlier outward migration of the neurons or an earlier development of the ovarian cortex in nonhuman primates.

The function of ovarian neurons is not yet known; however, several lines of evidence suggest they may play one or more roles in controlling intraovarian physiological events. The fact that some of these neurons produce catecholamines [46, 51, 52] suggests they may influence steroidogenesis [53, 54]. In rhesus monkeys the number of catecholaminergic neurons increases significantly at puberty and remains elevated throughout the reproductive life span [52a]. In the rat, some of the intraovarian neurons also produce NPY [51], a peptide that extensively innervates the ovarian vasculature [33], suggesting a role in control of blood flow. It is important to note that only a small percentage of the ovarian neuronal population is catecholaminergic or NPY-ergic; hence, it would appear that other neuronal phenotypes exist as well. In rhesus monkey ovaries, we have observed that the total number of p75^{NTR}-positive neurons per ovary decreases dramatically from the time of reproductive competence through menopause and into the senescent period [52a]. This further suggests that these neurons have a role in ovarian physiology and that the decline in ovarian function with age is associated with the loss of these neurons. Interestingly, the selective presence of neurons in the ovary of Wistar rats correlates with the longer reproductive life span in this strain than other strains of rats (for reviews, see [51]). These observations, along with the anatomical complexity of the ovarian neuronal network in primates, suggest a role for these neurons as an independent, intrinsic regulatory component capable of acting together with the extrinsic innervation to modify ovarian function. Determining the actual function(s) of these intraovarian neurons remains not only important for understanding more about the control of normal ovarian physiology but may also provide insights to understanding certain pathologies of ovarian function.

Ovarian Nerves and Follicular Steroidogenesis

The noradrenergic nerves reach the ovary via the SON and OPN [39]. Although the fibers originating from the OPN have a predominantly perivascular distribution, the majority of those derived from the SON innervate the secretory compartments of the gland (i.e., interstitial cells, the thecal layer of follicles, and the corpus luteum) [3, 39, 55, 56]. Catecholamines have been shown to affect ovarian steroidogenesis via activation of β_2-adrenergic receptors [53, 54]. Catecholamines stimulate release of progesterone (P) from granulosa and luteal cells [53, 57, 58] and androgens from thecal cells [59, 60]. More importantly, they also facilitate the steroidogenic response of ovarian cells to low concentrations of gonadotropins, suggesting that under physiological circumstances the catecholaminergic sympathetic nerves contribute to amplify the effects of circulating gonadotropins on ovarian steroidogenesis (for reviews, see [1, 44]).

Vasoactive intestinal peptide is contained in nerve fibers that reach the ovary via the SON [28, 61]. As in the case of catecholaminergic nerves, VIP-ergic fibers innervate all three main compartments of the prepubertal ovary (i.e., interstitial tissue, follicles, and ovarian vasculature). VIP is a potent stimulus of P, estradiol (E_2), and androgen (A) secretion [37, 62]. The molecular mechanisms underlying these effects involve an enhanced synthesis of all three components of the side-chain cleavage-enzyme complex, the rate-limiting enzyme in steroid biosynthesis [63, 64], and stimulation of aromatase activity [62, 65]. It appears that VIP targets a population of immature granulosa cells that is unresponsive to follicle-stimulating hormone (FSH) [66], implying a role for the neuropeptide in early granulosa cell function. Such a role for VIP in granulosa cell differentiation is suggested because the actions of the neuropeptide are exerted via activation of cyclic adenosine monophosphate (cAMP) synthesis and cAMP itself induces granulosa cell differentiation [67]. The participation of VIP in the control of early ovarian development is further suggested by the observation that VIP can induce aromatase activity in fetal ovaries, before the formation of follicles and before the ovary acquires responsiveness to gonadotropins [65].

The ovary of many species is innervated by a network of sympathetic fibers containing NPY immunoreactive material (see [32, 33]). As shown in other sympathetic neurons, many of the ovarian fibers containing NPY also contain NE [31, 56]. However, noradrenergic fibers reach the ovary via both the SON and OPN whereas NPY-ergic nerves are restricted to the OPN [33, 68]. The rather profuse NPY-ergic innervation of the ovarian vasculature suggests a role for NPY in the control of blood flow. Although NPY does not appear to be involved in the control of ovulation [56], inhibitory effects of the neuropeptide on human chorionic gonadotropin (hCG)-induced P release from pig granulosa cells [69] and on NE release from ovarian nerve terminals [70] have been reported.

With regard to the sensory innervation of the ovary, SP and CGRP fibers have been shown to reach the ovary via the OPN [28, 61, 71] and innervate all ovarian compartments but have no discernible effect on ovarian steroidogenesis. Because of this and their prominent perivascular localization, SP-ergic and CGRP-ergic fibers are thought to be predominantly involved in regulation of blood flow [61, 71, 72]. As in other terminal fields of the peripheral nervous system, SP and CGRP coexist in ovarian nerves [71]. Both neurotransmitters are thought to provide the sensory afferents from the ovary [28, 32, 34–36, 71].

Intrinsic Sources of Ovarian Neurotransmitters

Although there is no doubt that various neurotransmitters arrive at the ovary via the extrinsic innervation, it is now also evident that some neurotransmitters are produced by intrinsic neurons and nonneural cells of the gland. A prominent example is provided by the detection of catecholaminergic and NPY-containing neurons in the monkey and human ovary (see earlier) and by the demonstration that the monkey ovary expresses the genes encoding the catecholamine synthesizing enzymes, TH and dopamine-β hydroxylase [47]. In this latter study, evidence showed that monkey oocytes can uptake dopamine via a specific dopamine transporter and metabolize the catecholamine to norepinephrine via dopamine-β hydroxylase. Isolated follicles containing their oocytes, but not follicles devoid of oocytes, respond to dopamine with a β-adrenergic receptor-mediated elevation in cAMP levels, suggesting the existence of a functional, catecholamine-mediated link between granulosa cells and oocytes in antral follicles [47]. Based on these findings, the concept has been proposed [47] that oocytes and granulosa cells are linked by a neuroendocrine loop consisting of norepinephrine synthesized in oocytes from actively transported dopamine and cAMP produced by granulosa cells in response to norepinephrine-induced β-adrenoreceptor activation. The dopamine is presumably produced in granulosa cells (or derived from the innervation and/or ovarian neurons).

Recently, it was demonstrated that granulosa cells of antral follicles in the rhesus monkey and human ovary contain choline acetyl transferase and produce acetylcholine [41] and thus represent an intrinsic source of cholinergic influence on ovarian function. The intraovarian effects of acetylcholine appear to be mediated by muscarinic receptors of the M3R subtype, expressed in oocytes, and M1R and M5R subtypes, expressed in granulosa cells. Two functions of this endogenously produced acetylcholine have been described. One is the stimulation of granulosa cell proliferation [73]; the other is a stimulatory effect on the synthesis of steroid acute regulatory protein [74]. Because of this latter effect, the response of granulosa cells to hCG is increased. In addition to acetylcholine, the ovary has been shown to contain other putative neurotransmitters/neuromodulators such as gamma-aminobutyric acid (GABA) [75, 76], gastrin-releasing peptide [35, 72], peptide histidine isoleucine [35], enkephalin [77], somatostatin, and cholecystokinin [31, 68]. Although the function of most of these peptides is unknown, some evidence exists that GABA may increase ovarian blood flow, stimulate E_2 secretion, and decrease P secretion [78]. The physiological significance of these findings remains to be determined.

Ovarian Nerves and Follicular Development

A variety of experiments have been conducted over the years to determine if the ovarian nerves influence follicular development. Although in most cases the changes observed were transient or of small magnitude (for a review, see [3]), they have consistently supported the notion that the ovarian sympathetic innervation exerts a facilitatory influence on follicular growth. We have used the approaches of passive and active immunosympathectomy during neonatal life to demonstrate that permanent loss of the sympathetic innervation results in delayed follicular development, reduced ovarian steroid output, and marked irregularities of the rat estrous cycle [4, 79]. Of particular interest are the studies in which the animals were passively immunosympathectomized via administration of antibodies to NGF during neonatal life. This approach was chosen based on the finding that the developing ovary synthesizes NGF [80], which is known to be essential for the survival of peripheral sympathetic neurons [81]. In designing these experiments, we reasoned that if the ovary is a target organ for sympathetic neurons, blockade of NGF action during the early phases of neuronal-target cell encounter should effectively prevent development of the innervation. Indeed the treatment nearly eliminated the sympathetic nerves of the ovary, as assessed by immunohistochemistry in late juvenile animals, and resulted in a significant reduction in large antral follicles as compared with the normally innervated ovaries of control animals. The simplest explanation for these findings is that the loss of the innervation abolishes the sympathetic input to developing follicles and hence deprives them of a facilitatory influence. Although this is tenable, the subsequent finding that follicular thecal cells express one of the receptors involved in mediating NGF actions [82] raised the intriguing possibility that NGF itself and/or a member of the NGF family contributes directly to regulating follicular development and function.

Neurotrophins and Their Receptors in the Ovary

NTs are a family of target-derived trophic factors required for the survival and differentiation of neuronal populations in the central and peripheral nervous systems. Five NTs have been identified to date, including NGF [81], brain-derived neurotrophic factor (BDNF) [83], neurotrophin-3 (NT-3) [84–86], neurotrophin-4/5 (NT-4/5) [87, 88], and neurotrophin-6 (NT-6) [89]. The NTs initiate their biological actions by binding to high-affinity transmembrane tyrosine kinase receptors encoded by members of the *trk* proto-oncogene family [90–92]. There are three members of the trk receptor family: *trkA* that binds NGF, *trkB* that binds BDNF and NT-4/5, and *trkC* that binds NT-3 [91, 92]. In addition, all NTs (and perhaps also NT-6) are recognized with similar low affinity by a more abundantly expressed receptor, a member of the tumor necrosis receptor family [93] known as the *low-affinity neurotrophin receptor (NTR)* or $p75^{NTR}$ [94, 95]. The actions of the $p75^{NTR}$ are complex; whereas NGF binding results in the death of glial cells and some neurons that express $p75^{NTR}$, but not trkA [96], the presence of $p75^{NTR}$ in sensory neurons and PC12 cells (which also contain trkA receptors) causes cell death even in the absence of NGF [96]. Ectopic expression of $p75^{NTR}$ in NIH-3T3 fibroblasts demonstrated that NGF uses the receptor to activate sphingomyelin hydrolysis, resulting in the production of ceramide, which is thought to initiate an apoptotic signaling cascade [96, 97]. Co-expression of trkA with the $p75^{NTR}$ in these cells blocked the hydrolysis of sphingomyelin, suggesting that this is a mechanism by which trkA receptors may counteract the death signal conveyed by the binding of NGF to $p75^{NTR}$ [96]. In addition to the direct signaling mediated by $p75^{NTR}$, NGF binding to $p75^{NTR}$ leads to either amplification [98] or inhibition [99] of trkA-mediated biological responses. These interactions are especially evident in the case of NGF and BDNF, which have been shown to exert antagonistic effects on the growth of sympathetic neurons and the ability of these neurons to innervate their target tissues, via alternative binding to $p75^{NTR}$ [99] (for a review, see [100]). The ovary not only contains four of the known NTs (NGF, BDNF, NT-3, and NT-4/5) [80, 87, 101–104] but also expresses the receptors for each of them ($p75^{NTR}$, trkA, trkB, and trkC) [82, 104–107].

Expression of Neurotrophins during Ovarian Development

The Time of Folliculogenesis

The NTs and their respective receptors were originally detected in the feto-neonatal rat ovary before formation of the first primordial follicles [104] and subsequently in fetal human ovaries, also before the time of follicular assembly [108]. Studies using rat ovaries showed that the expression of some NTs, including their receptors, changes around the time of definitive ovarian histogenesis and initiation of follicular growth [104]. For instance, the cellular localization of $p75^{NTR}$ in perinatal rat ovaries using a specific monoclonal antibody demonstrated that the receptor is predominantly expressed in mesenchymal cells [104]. By gestational day 18, these cells begin to infiltrate the adjacent epithelium forming "pocketlike" structures, which as gestation approaches term, separate the epithelial, presumptive pregranulosa cells into groups surrounding individual oocytes. This enclosure continues postnatally resulting in the organization of the three cell types (oocytes, epithelial cells, mesenchymal cells) into primordial follicles between 24 and 72 hours after birth. As predicted by these immunohistochemical studies, the content of $p75^{NTR}$ messenger ribonucleic acid (mRNA), measured by ribonuclease (RNase) protection assay, increases after birth to become maximally elevated at the time of follicular assembly. Resembling this cellular pattern of expression, $p75^{NTR}$ in the human fetal ovary is exclusively expressed in mesenchymal cells of the ovarian stroma [108].

In contrast to this increase in $p75^{NTR}$, the ovarian content of NGF mRNA and trkA mRNA, also measured by RNase protection assay, appears to decrease at the time of folliculogenesis [104]. This decrease is selective for NGF and its trkA receptor; because the levels of NT-4/5 mRNA (detected by semiquantitative PCR) and those of the mRNA encoding trkB, the NT-4/5 high-affinity receptor (detected by RNase protection assay), increase at this time. In situ hybridization showed that the main increase in NT-4/5 mRNA expression occurred in a subpopulation of oocytes between 24 to 48 hours after birth and that low levels of trkB mRNA were present at this time in epithelial, pregranulosa cells [104]. In contrast to NT-4/5, expression of the gene encoding BDNF, the other trkB ligand, remained at low levels throughout the period studied (fetal day 18 to neonatal day 4), which suggests that, at this phase of ovarian development, NT-4/5 initiates most trkB-dependent signaling. In agreement with these results, NT-4/5 and BDNF mRNA transcripts have also been found in the human fetal ovary [108] during the midtrimester of gestation (13 to 21 weeks of gestation).

No major changes in either NT-3 mRNA or trkC mRNA, which encodes the high-affinity receptor for NT-3, were detected at the time of follicular assembly in the rat ovary [104]. Of particular significance, both mRNAs were unambiguously expressed in the ovary by 18 days of fetal life, the earliest fetal age studied, a finding consistent with the detection of a seemingly unchanging content of NT-3 and trkC mRNAs reported in the human fetal ovary [108].

In a subsequent study that used mouse ovaries, we found that after completion of follicular assembly—when the growth of primary and secondary follicles is already under way (7 days of age)—trkA receptor immunoreactivity can be detected in prethecal-interstitial cells but in a much more restricted pattern of expression than the $p75^{NTR}$ receptor (Figure 1.4). Unexpectedly, trkA immunostaining was also detected in granulosa cells and oocytes (see Figure 1.4, *A*, *B*, *D*, *E*). The abundance of trkA immunoreactivity in granulosa cells varied between follicles, appearing to be greater in primary follicles (see Figure 1.4, *B*, *E*) than in follicles with more than one layer of granulosa cells (see Figure 1.4, *A*, *D*). Likewise, trkA immunoreactivity in oocytes appeared more abundant in oocytes of a subpopulation of primordial follicles (see Figure 1.4, *E*) than in oocytes of follicles in more advanced stages of development (see Figure 1.4, *A*, *D*). In a recent study, we performed an immunohistochemical analysis of 7-day-old mouse ovaries [109] to identify the cell types expressing the ligands BDNF and NT-4/5 and their trkB receptor. As predicted by our previous ribonucleic acid (RNA) measurements, we found low levels of immunoreactive BDNF in the gland. Although some of this immunoreactivity was found in oocytes of primordial, primary, and secondary follicles, the appearance of BDNF in the apical domain of granulosa cells of primary and secondary follicles was a noticeable feature. On the other hand, NT-4/5 immunoreactivity was initially present in the oocytes of primordial follicles but switched to granulosa cells when the follicles reached the primary and secondary stages. A recent report showed an identical developmental pattern of NT-4/5 expression in the human fetal ovary [108].

Antibodies that recognize the full-length trkB receptor demonstrated low levels of immunoreactive material in oocytes of primordial follicles, nongrowing primary follicles, and growing primary and secondary follicles [109]. In all cases, only a fraction of the receptors appeared to be associated with the cell membrane. In agreement with our previous observations [104], full-length trkB receptors were also detected, albeit at low levels, in granulosa cells of growing primary and secondary follicles. Besides the full-length trkB receptor, alternative splicing of the trkB pre-mRNAs also generates two truncated protein isoforms [110, 111]. These isoforms, called *T1* and *T2* [111], lack the tyrosine kinase domain and have distinct short intracellular domains. We used an antibody that specifically

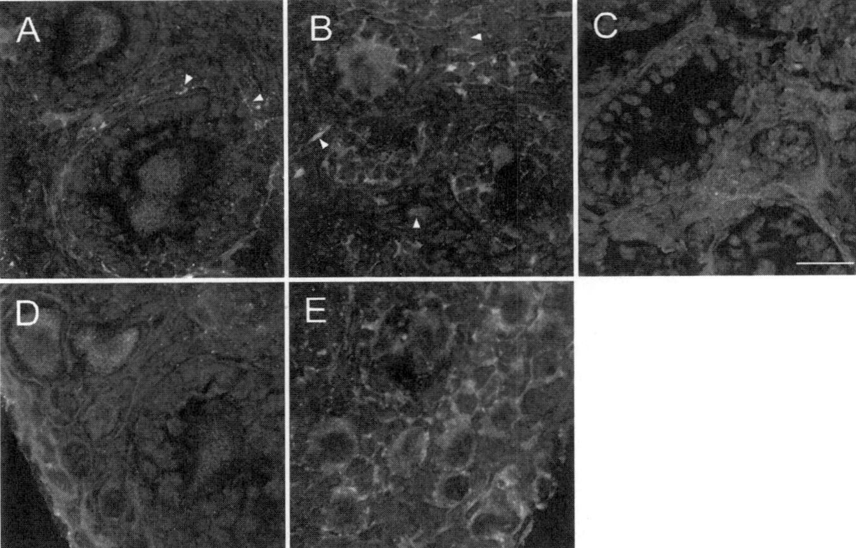

FIGURE 1.4 Detection of trkA (*green label*) and $p75^{NTR}$ (*red label*) immunoreactive material in infantile (7-day-old) ovaries from wild-type and NGF–/– mice by immunohistofluorescence-confocal microscopy. Cell nuclei stained with the vital dye Hoechst are shown in blue. **A,** Detection of trkA positive cells in interstitial cells, prethecal cells of secondary follicles (*arrowheads*), and in subsets of granulosa cells in the same follicles (ovary from a wild-type animal). $p75^{NTR}$-positive cells are mostly confined to the interstitial-prethecal compartments of the ovary. **B,** Abundant trkA immunoreactivity in granulosa cells of growing primary follicles and discrete localization in subsets of interstitial cells (*arrowheads*) (ovary from an NGF–/– mouse). **C,** Control section incubated without the trkA antibody but in the presence of the $p75^{NTR}$ antibody (ovary from a wild-type mouse). **D,** Example of different levels of trkA immunoreactivity in oocytes in different phases of development and of a discrete content of trkA-like material in granulosa cells of a secondary follicle (ovary from a wild-type mouse). **E,** Example of a subset of primordial follicles containing oocytes strongly immunoreactive for trkA (ovary from an NGF–/– mouse). Bar in *C* = 25 µm. (From Ref. [118], with permission.) (See color plate.)

recognizes T1, the predominant truncated receptor expressed in various tissues [112], to determine if this form is expressed in the mouse ovary. In contrast to the low levels of full-length trkB receptor detected in growing follicles, the T1 receptor was abundantly expressed in oocytes of growing primary follicles and secondary follicles. In all cases the T1 receptor was strongly associated with the cell membrane of the oocyte. The oocytes from primordial follicles showed a much lower level of T1 expression, but the receptor was not targeted to the cell membrane.

The presence of NTs and their receptors in somatic and germ cells of developing follicles suggests their involvement in the control of either follicular assembly or early follicular growth. As discussed later, the use of mutant mice lacking either the NTs or their receptors has begun to more precisely define the role played by NTs in these early developmental processes.

The Time of First Ovulation

After the completion of follicle formation the bulk of newly formed follicles remain in a state of quiescence. Selected cohorts are, however, recruited into waves of gonadotropin-dependent proliferative pools from which one or more follicles are selected for ovulation. These gonadotropin-responsive follicles undergo many biochemical and morphological changes during and after the preovulatory surge of gonadotropins (for reviews, see [113, 114]). Both trkA and NGF gene expression increase following the gonadotropin surge and preceding the ovulatory rupture of the follicle [103]. The fugacious nature and magnitude of the NGF/trkA gene activation suggests that NGF-initiated, trkA-mediated responses are integral components of the ovulatory process; whereas virtually no trkA mRNA can be detected either shortly before the preovulatory luteinizing hormone (LH) surge (morning of proestrus) or a few hours after ovulation (i.e., on the morning of the first estrus, more than a 100-fold increase in mRNA levels occurs shortly after the LH surge). Immunohistochemistry and hybridization histochemistry showed that NGF and trkA are produced by thecal cells of large antral follicles and interstitial cells [103]. The activation of the trkA gene in nonneural cells of the ovarian follicle at a time when the follicle is becoming biochemically and cytologically differentiated into a new structure, the corpus luteum, suggests that ligand-mediated activation of trkA receptors contributes to these acute differentiating events.

In contrast to the NGF/trkA signaling complex that is located in thecal/stromal cells of the preovulatory follicle, recent studies of human periovulatory follicles have shown that BDNF is secreted by granulosa cells of the cumulus oophorus in response to cAMP stimulation and that exposing mouse oocytes to BDNF induces polar body extrusion [115]. These findings suggest that BDNF-initiated, trkB-mediated signaling in oocytes accelerates the meiotic maturation of oocytes at the time of ovulation [115]. More recently, the same authors extended their findings by showing that NT-4/5 is also present in the follicular fluid of periovulatory human follicles, and like BDNF, can induce first polar body extrusion from mouse oocytes in vitro [116].

Functions of Neurotrophins in the Developing Ovary

Functions around the Time of Folliculogenesis

The NGF-trkA Signaling Module. As indicated earlier, the abundance of the mRNAs encoding NGF and its high-affinity trkA receptors decreases in the rat ovary by 24 hours after birth (i.e., antedating the onset of follicular assembly). Such a pattern of expression suggested a role for NGF in developmental events antedating the organization of primordial follicles [104]. We recently used mice lacking the NGF gene [117] to address this issue. The results indicated that NGF is not necessary for follicular assembly, because the number of primordial follicles is similar in the ovaries of NGF Knockout (KO) mice as compared with wild type controls. In contrast, we found that NGF is required for the differentiation of newly formed primordial follicles (one single layer of flattened pregranulosa cells) into primary follicles (one single layer of cuboidal epithelial cells) [118]. Presumably as a consequence of this deficiency, there is also a reduction in the number of secondary follicles (two or more layers of granulosa cells) (Figure 1.5). A much less severe, but still detectable, phenotype is an increase in the number of naked oocytes (i.e., those that fail to become organized with somatic cells into a follicular structure) (see Figure 1.5). The decreased number of primary and secondary follicles seen in NGF-deficient mice does not appear to be caused by a gonadotropin deficiency, because serum follical-stimulating hormone (FSH) and LH levels are similar in wild-type animals and those carrying either one disrupted NGF allele or the homozygotic mutation.

In view of the finding that NGF is a potent mitogen in nonneuronal cell lines of mesenchymal origin and endocrine neoplasms [98, 119], we considered the possibility that the delayed initiation of follicular growth seen in NGF-deficient mice may be related to a deficiency in somatic cell proliferation. At birth (i.e., preceding the organization of primordial follicles) only mesenchymal cells are actively proliferating in the rodent ovary, because epithelial cells leave the cell cycle before birth and resume proliferation only as they become incorporated into follicles after postnatal day 1 [120]. In turn the proliferative activity of mesenchymal cells decreases markedly at the time of follicular assembly [120], probably reflecting a switch from a predominantly proliferative condition to the differentiation mode required for the organization of primordial follicles. The ovaries from NGF KO mice analyzed at the time of birth show a dramatic decrease in the number of mesenchymal cells labeled with antibodies to

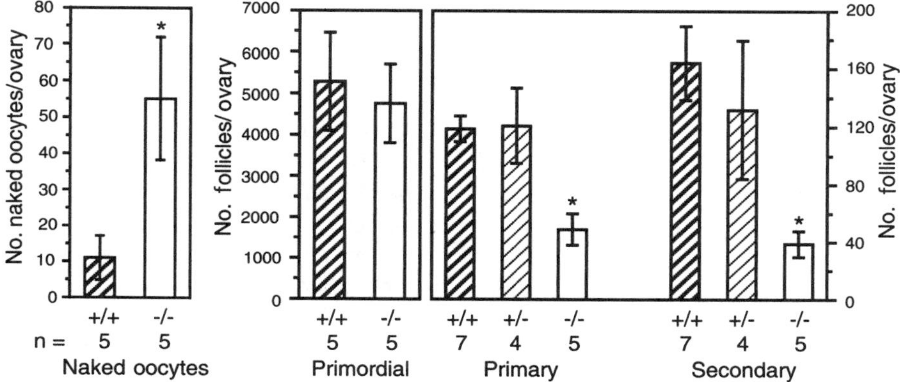

FIGURE 1.5 Number of primordial and growing follicles present in the ovary of 7-day-old NGF–/–, NGF+/–, and NGF+/+ mice. The number of primordial, primary, and secondary follicles, in addition to the number of naked oocytes, was determined in every third section of a series of 6μm paraffin-embedded, hematoxylin picric acid–methyl blue–stained sections covering the entire ovary, as described in Ref. [118]. Oocytes were considered naked when they were adjacent to epithelial cells not surrounded by a basal lamina and not apposed by stromal cells [23]. Follicles were classified in different stages of development as recommended [151]. Bars are means and vertical lines represent SEM. Numbers below bars are number of ovaries per group. * = $p < 0.01$ vs NGF+/+ or NGF+/– ovaries. (From Ref. [118], with permission.)

proliferating cell nuclear antigen (PCNA) [118], a nuclear protein associated with the cell cycle [121, 122]. PCNA accumulates during the transition between the G_1 and S phases of the cell cycle, reaches a plateau during the G_2 phase, and decreases to much lower levels during the M phase, to disappear during G_0. Thus its presence in a cell can be used as an index of proliferation. Because PCNA expression may not always be associated with cell proliferation [123], we performed additional experiments in which the ovaries of newborn mice were exposed in vitro to bromodeoxyuridine (BrdU) and the ovaries were collected 24 hours later for immunohistochemical analysis of the cells that incorporated the nucleotide analog. The results confirmed the findings with PCNA by showing that the rate of proliferation of mesenchymal cells in the ovaries from NGF KO animals was about half of that detected in wild-type littermates [118]. Although the proliferation rate detected in newborn NGF+/+ ovaries was identical to that previously described for normal neonatal rat ovaries before follicular assembly [120], cell proliferation in NGF–/– ovaries was as low as that seen in normal ovaries at the time of follicular organization [120], indicating that the absence of NGF results in a premature, and inappropriately sustained, reduction in ovarian mitogenic activity. Thus the decrease in trkA and NGF mRNA abundance observed in the normal rat ovary at the time of definitive ovarian histogenesis [104] is in keeping with the notion that a temporally restricted reduction in NGF-initiated signals may be a physiological component of the decrease in mitogenic activity that occurs in the ovary during this developmental stage.

The mechanisms underlying the supportive effect of NGF on follicular growth include not only a proliferative signal on mesenchymal cells but also the induction of FSH receptors (FSHR). This effect manifests after a relatively short time (8 hours) and appears to be mediated by intracellular pathways independent of cAMP [124]. Previous studies in neuronal systems have shown that although NGF on its own does not induce cAMP accumulation, it effectively facilitates the effect of adenylate cyclase-stimulating agents on cellular responses [125, 126], suggesting that a cAMP-mediated pathway and NGF may act in collaboration to induce cellular differentiation [126]. Consistent with this concept, our results show that, in the neonatal ovary, NGF potentiates the effect of cAMP accumulation on FSHR mRNA levels without affecting the cAMP response to activation of adenylate cyclase by other activators [124]. That NGF is, indeed, required for formation of FSHR during early ovarian development demonstrated by the reduced content of FSHR mRNA seen in mice lacking the NGF gene when compared with wild-type controls [124]. Furthermore, an 8-hour exposure of infantile rat ovaries to NGF not only increased FSHR mRNA content but also resulted in the formation of biologically active FSH receptors, as assessed by the ability of FSH to

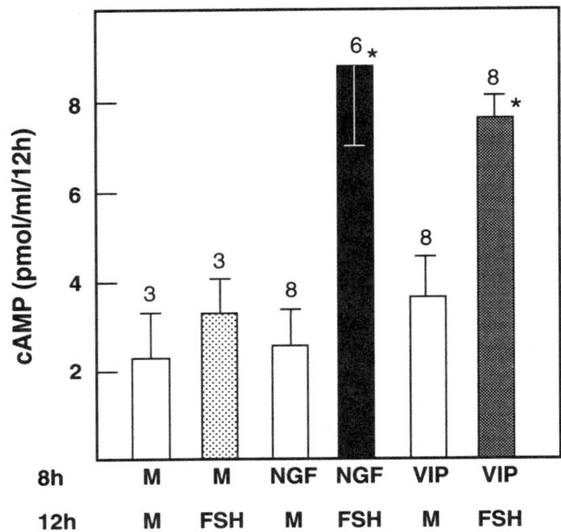

FIGURE 1.6 NGF, like VIP, induces the appearance of functional FSH receptors in neonatal 2-day-old rat ovaries, as determined by the ability of FSH to stimulate cAMP formation. After an 8-hour pretreatment with NGF (100 ng/ml) or VIP (2 μM), the medium was replaced with fresh medium containing purified FSH (500 ng/ml). After 2 hours the medium was collected for cAMP radioimmunoassay (RIA). * = $p < 0.025$ vs groups cultured in medium alone (M) and groups not exposed to FSH regardless of pretreatment. Vertical lines are SEM, and numbers above bars are number of ovaries per group. (From Ref. [124], with permission.)

induce cAMP formation (Figure 1.6) and initiate follicular growth (Figure 1.7).

Thus NGF not only contributes to facilitating the growth of primordial follicles but also promotes the initial biochemical differentiation of growing follicles into gonadotropin-responsive structures [124]. The mechanisms underlying these effects of NGF remain to be determined, but they may result from direct actions of the NT on granulosa cells and indirect actions on mesenchymal (prethecal) cells associated with the growing follicle. Figure 1.8 illustrates our current concept of how NGF contributes to facilitating early follicular growth.

The NT-4/5–BDNF–trkB Signaling Module. As indicated earlier, NT-4/5 mRNA levels increase in oocytes at the time of follicular assembly. A more sustained increase in the abundance of the mRNA encoding the NT-4/5 receptor, trkB, was also observed at this time, encompassing the first 4 days after birth [104]. The developmental pattern and cellular sites of NT-4/5 expression in the neonatal ovary suggested the possibility that the NT may be a signaling molecule used by the oocyte to communicate with pregranulosa cells at the time of follicular formation. According to this concept, NT-4/5 would contribute to the organization of primordial follicles, so that in its absence a deficiency in follicular formation would occur. Contrary to this expectation, the ovaries from mice carrying a null mutation of the trkB gene (which eliminates the expression of

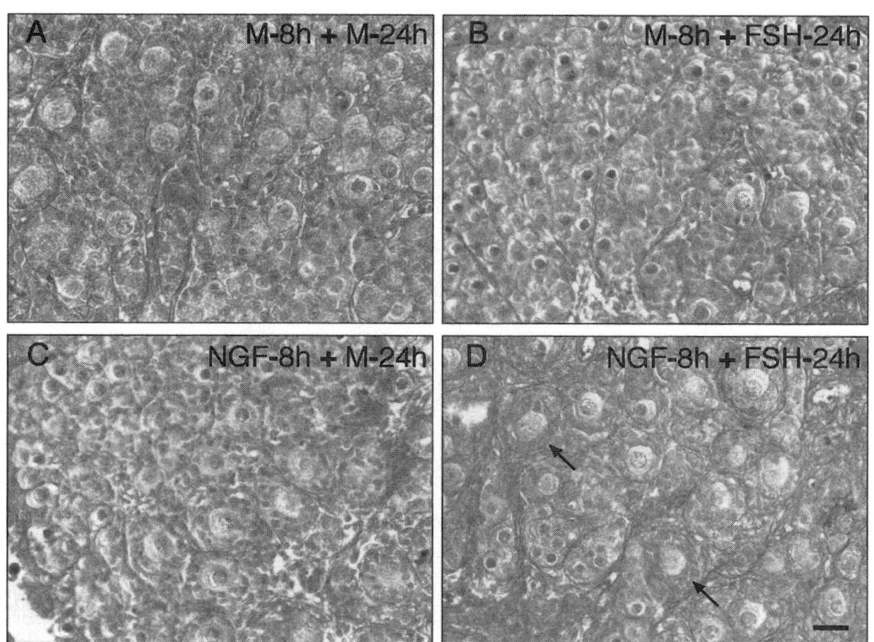

FIGURE 1.7 **A**, Histological aspect of 2-day-old rat ovaries cultured for 32 hours in medium alone. **B**, Cultured for 8 hours in medium alone followed by a 24-hour treatment with FSH (500 ng/ml). **C**, Cultured for 8 hours in medium containing NGF (100 ng/ml) followed by 24 hours in medium alone. **D**, Treated with NGF for 8 hours and then with FSH for 24 hours. Arrows = Growing follicles with three or more layers of granulosa cells; bar = 20 μm. (From Ref. [124], with permission.) (See color plate.)

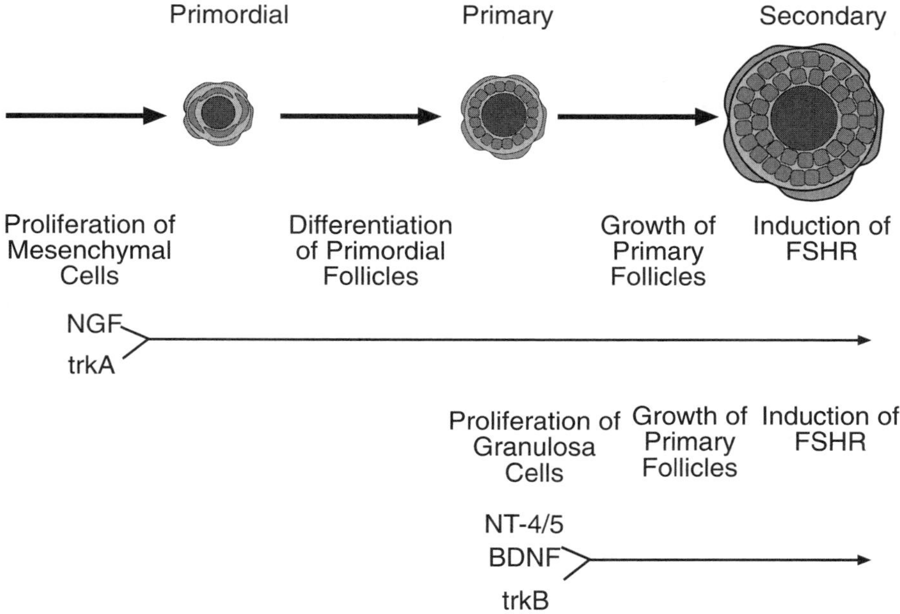

FIGURE 1.8 Postulated roles of the NTs (NGF, NT-4/5, and BDNF) and their respective receptors (trkA and trkB in early follicular development). NGF acting via trkA receptors facilitates the differentiation of newly formed primordial follicles (one complete or incomplete layer of flattened granulosa cells) into primary follicles (one cuboidal layer of granulosa cells) and the subsequent growth of these follicles into secondary follicles (two or more layers of granulosa cells). NGF may exert this effect by acting on trkA receptors located on granulosa cells and indirectly via trkA receptors expressed in mesenchymal cells. Proliferation of these cells is prominent before follicular assembly and appears to require the presence of the NT. In addition to promoting follicle growth, NGF also induces the formation of FSH receptors in secondary follicles, an effect likely to be mediated by trkA receptors located on granulosa and mesenchymal cells. NT-4/5 and BDNF acting via trkB receptors appear to be required for the growth of primary follicles into secondary follicles. It is unclear if this effect is exerted via activation of full-length trkB receptors present at low levels in granulosa cells and oocytes, or via truncated trkB receptors, which are highly expressed in growing oocytes. TrkB receptor signaling is also required for formation of FSH receptors, because trkB-deficient mice have a reduced expression of FSH receptor mRNA. (Modified from Ref. [152], with permission.)

full-length and truncated trkB receptors) show no defects in follicular formation [109]. The ovaries, analyzed after completion of ovarian histogenesis, exhibited a normal number of primordial and primary follicles but had a gonadotropin-independent deficiency in early follicular growth, demonstrated by a selective reduction in the formation of secondary follicles. Mitogenic activity of follicular granulosa cells, which is required for the growth of primary into secondary follicles, is markedly reduced in trkB KO mice. In contrast, no evidence for an increase in apoptotic cell death was detected in trkB-deficient ovaries [109].

Previous studies had shown that, like trkB-dependent signaling, the oocyte-derived growth factor GDF-9 and the granulosa cell product kit ligand (KL) do not influence follicular formation but are required for the initiation of follicle growth [127–129]. The genetic deletion of GDF-9 [127] and natural mutations in the steel panda gene encoding KL [128, 130] result in arrest of follicle development at the primary stage (i.e., at the same stage where follicles become arrested in trkB–/– mice.) In addition, as with trkB-deficient mice, GDF-9 null mutants show a defect in granulosa cell proliferation but no increase in apoptotic cell death [131]. Furthermore, the oocyte expression of truncated trkB receptors (our results) and GDF-9 [132] becomes first evident in primary follicles, increasing markedly thereafter. It does not appear, however, that the two systems are functionally or hierarchically related, because neither GDF-9 mRNA expression nor that of its putative granulosa cell receptor BMPRII [133] were decreased in trkB KO ovaries.

The distribution of NT-4/5 and BDNF in granulosa cells and trkB receptors in oocytes is similar to the KL/c-kit signaling system, in which KL is produced by granulosa cells [134, 135] and binds to c-kit receptors expressed in the oocyte [136]. The ovaries of trkB null mice showed no changes in either KL or c-kit mRNA levels, indicating that trkB-mediated signaling does not require an increased expression of the KL/c-kit signaling complex. It thus appears that activation of ovarian trkB receptors regulates follicle growth via unidentified pathways that function in parallel to those activated by GDF-9 in granulosa cells and KL in the oocyte. These two systems are also relatively independent from each other, because animals lacking GDF-9 have elevated KL mRNA levels but a normal c-kit expression [131]. Lastly, early follicular growth has been shown to be under the inhibitory control of antimüllerian hormone (AMH) [25, 137]. Whether trkB signaling plays a role in the control of AMH production remains to be determined.

Overall, these results indicate that NT-4/5 and BDNF contribute to regulating mammalian ovarian development by providing a proliferative signal transduced by trkB receptors to granulosa cells of growing follicles. Because NGF-deficient mice also show a defect in ovarian cell proliferation during early postnatal life, it would appear that facilitation of cell proliferation may represent a general mechanism used by NTs to regulate nonneural cell function during development. Our current concept concerning the involvement of NT-4/5 and BDNF in the control of early follicular growth is illustrated in Figure 1.8. A more detailed discussion of non-NT factors involved in the control of follicular assembly and early follicle growth can be found in Refs. [138, 139].

A question that arises now concerns the role that the innervation may play in the overall process of early follicular growth. It is well established that arrival of the innervating axons to a target organ of the peripheral nervous system results in up-regulation of the gene expression of NGF and the $p75^{NTR}$ [8, 140]. It has also been shown that VIP will induce the formation of functional FSHR, based on the ability of ovaries in culture to produce cAMP in response to FSH, following pretreatment with VIP (see Figure 1.6 and Ref. [67]). Because either stimulation of cAMP formation or exposure to norepinephrine or isoproterenol increases NGF mRNA levels in cultured Schwann cells [141], the possibility exists that the ovarian innervation contributes to regulating the process of early follicular growth indirectly via a neurotransmitter-induced increase in NT and FSH receptor gene expression. That the early innervation of the ovary is circumscribed to the innermost portion of the gland [22], where follicular growth is initiated [11], inferentially supports this possibility. Because NGF itself can enhance $p75^{NTR}$ gene expression [142], a similar mechanism may operate in the developing ovary to amplify the stimulatory effects of the incoming innervation.

Overall, these results support the emerging concept that NTs play important roles in the development of nonneuronal systems [143]. The factors involved in regulating the expression of NTs and their receptors in the ovary remain to be elucidated, but they might be similar (or related) to the Wnt factors recently shown to regulate NT expression in a nonneuronal system in which ectodermal/mesenchymal interactions are prominent [9].

Potential Functions at the Time of Ovulation

The NGF-trkA Signaling Module. Ovulation is another major cytodifferentiation phase of ovarian development in which NGF appears to play a role. Mammalian ovulation resembles an inflammatory process that, instead of being initiated by injury, is set in motion by hormonal stimulation. The inflammatory-like changes that occur in the preovulatory follicle because of LH stimulation result in the dissolution of the follicular wall and ovulatory rupture. A number of substances involved in inflammation, such as interleukins, prostaglandins, and vasoactive factors, have been found in periovulatory follicles [144]. Injury of

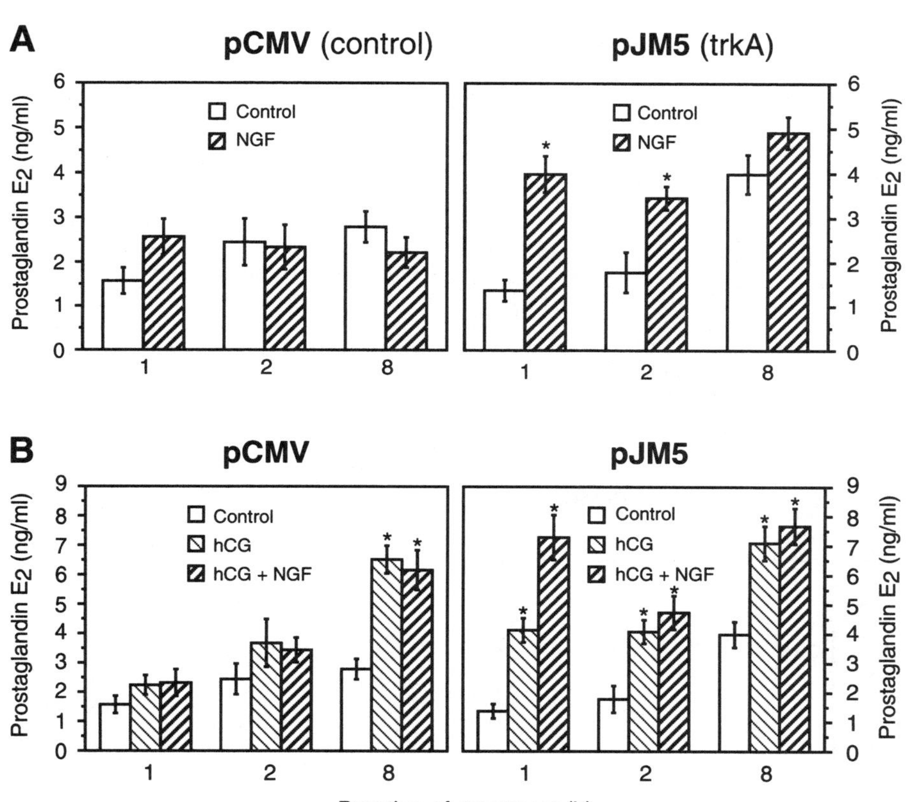

FIGURE 1.9 NGF stimulates PGE_2 release from thecal cells isolated from small, medium, and large follicles, expressing the trkA receptor. Thecal cells (plated at 500,000 cells/well in six-well plates) were transfected with either pCMV (control plasmid) or with an expression vector (pJM5) containing the trkA coding region under the control of the CMV promoter. After 24 hours the cells were treated with **(A)** 100 ng/ml NGF, or **(B)** hCG (1 μg/ml), or hCG in combination with NGF. In both **A** and **B**, PGE_2 levels were determined in the medium collected at 1, 2, or 8 hours. * = $p < 0.05$ vs control for that time period (n = 6 for all groups). (From Ref. [148], with permission.)

the peripheral nervous system results in rapid activation of NGF synthesis and NGF-dependent processes (see [145]). The ovary behaves similarly, as shown by the dramatic increase in ovarian trkA gene expression and the simultaneous elevation in NGF mRNA levels that accompanies and follows the first preovulatory surge of gonadotropins [103]. The increase in trkA mRNA content is striking (> 100-fold); it lasts for at least 8 hours, is mainly observed in cells of the follicular wall and interstitial gland, and is accompanied by a corresponding increase in immunoreactive trkA protein. In vitro and in vivo experiments demonstrated that this preovulatory increase in trkA expression is an LH-dependent phenomenon.

The proestrus LH surge stimulates ovarian synthesis of the cytokinin interleukin-1β (IL-1β) [146], which appears to play a role in the preovulatory increase of prostaglandin release [147]. Our studies showed that IL-1β enhances trkA and NGF gene expression in ovarian cells and that the natural IL-1β receptor antagonist, IL-1ra, prevented this effect [103]. The increase in prostaglandin E_2 (PGE_2) elicited by IL-1β was reduced by immunoneutralization of NGF actions and by the pharmacological blockade of trk receptors with the tyrosine kinase inhibitor K-252a [103]. NGF stimulated PGE_2 release from ovarian cells in culture, and NGF antibodies administered in vivo reduced the preovulatory increase in ovarian PGE_2 synthesis, further suggesting that part of the preovulatory increase in ovarian PGE_2 release is, at least in part, an NGF-dependent event [148] (Figure 1.9). That activation of the ovarian NGF–trkA ligand/receptor complex is a required component of the ovulatory cascade was suggested by experiments in which PMSG-induced ovulation was inhibited by the intrabursal administration of NGF antibodies or a blocker of trk tyrosine kinase activity [103].

Hints to the mechanism by which NGF may affect the ovulatory process were first provided by the cellular distribution of NGF and its receptor. The localization of NGF and its trkA high-affinity receptor in thecal cells of periovulatory follicles suggested that the neurotrophic factor may play a role in follicular rupture, instead of the intrafollicular processes governing granulosa cell and/or oocyte physiology at the time of ovulation. As indicated before, activation of trkA receptors ectopically expressed in fibroblasts results in proliferative responses [98, 119]. This would suggest that acquisition of NT receptors by mesenchymal cells engaged in specialized functions, such as thecal cells, may lead to a similar response. In fact, evidence exists that during the hours preceding ovulation, fibroblast-like thecal cells switch from a quiescent to an active, proliferative condition [149]. The marked increase in trkA and NGF gene expression detected in the follicular wall at this time suggests that an NGF-dependent

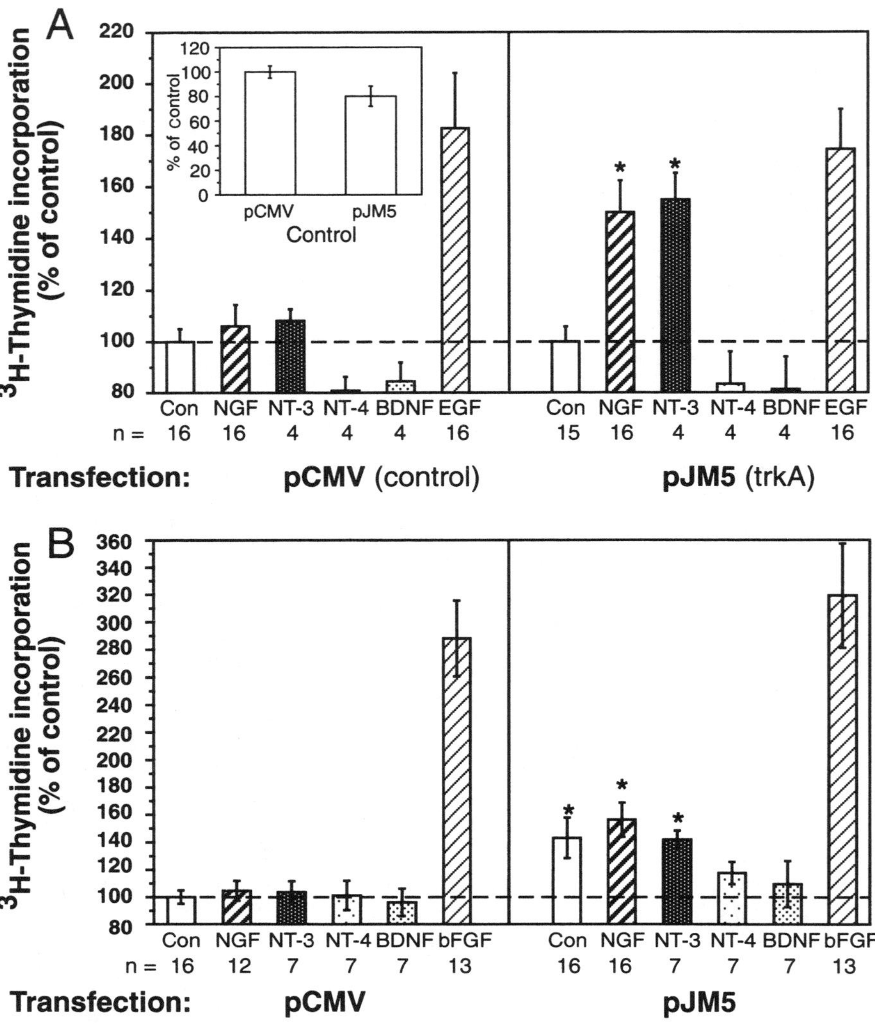

FIGURE 1.10 NGF induces proliferation in isolated thecal cells, isolated from small, medium, and large follicles, expressing trkA receptors. Thecal cells (plated at 10,000 cells/well in 24-well plates) were transiently transfected with either the pCMV control plasmid or the trkA-expressing plasmid pJM5 and immediately treated with the growth factors shown in the figure. Measuring ^{3}H-thymidine incorporation assessed proliferation. EGF and bFGF, two known mitogenic growth factors, were used as positive controls. **A,** Summary of four experiments in which transient expression of trkA receptors in the absence of NTs did not result in increased proliferation (*inset*). To emphasize this result the values obtained in cells transfected and treated with the different growth factors were expressed as percent of the basal mitogenic activity detected in cells transfected with either pCMV or pJM5 but otherwise left untreated. **B,** Summary of four experiments in which transient expression of trkA receptors resulted in an increased incorporation of ^{3}H-thymidine in the absence of exogenous growth factor treatment. To better demonstrate this observation, all experimental values are expressed as percent of the values detected in cells transfected with the control pCMV plasmid. * = $p < 0.05$ vs pCMV control. (From Ref. [148], with permission.)

activation of trkA receptors may contribute to the preovulatory proliferation of thecal cells. In fact, we have observed that purified bovine thecal cells engineered to transiently express trkA receptors in culture do proliferate in response to NGF stimulation [148] (Figure 1.10). In another study [150], we used a similar preparation of purified bovine thecal cells transfected with a trkA expression vector to gain insight into some of the cytodifferentiation processes affected by NGF in the follicular wall during the preovulatory period. The results showed that activation of trkA receptors by NGF results in serine phosphorylation of connexin-43, the main protein constituent of gap junctions in thecal cells of preovulatory follicles. The phosphorylating effect of NGF is rapid (10–30 minutes) and is followed by a disruption in cell-cell communication, as indicated by a reduction in the ability of thecal cells exposed to NGF to transfer fluorescent dye via gap junctions. Thus NGF-dependent activation of trkA receptors in periovulatory thecal cells appears to represent a signal for the loss of cell adhesion that occurs in the follicular wall before ovulation (Figure 1.11).

The BDNF–NT-4/5 Signaling Module. The recent findings of Seifer et al. showing that, in the human periovulatory ovary, both BDNF and NT-4/5 are produced by granulosa cells of the cumulus oophorus and can induce oocyte maturation [115, 116] provided evidence that, in addition to the NGF-trkA module, the ovulatory process is also under the regulatory influence of a BDNF–NT-4/5–trkB signaling complex. In considering these observations, one may conclude that mammalian ovulation is a process influenced by different NTs acting coordinately at different anatomical sites of the periovulatory follicle. Whereas NGF-dependent activation of trkA receptors on the follicular wall appear to contribute to the cascade of events leading to follicular rupture, activation of trkB receptors in oocytes by BDNF–NT-4/5 produced in cumulus cells may facilitate oocyte maturation (Figure 1.12). See Ref. [139] for an account of all other factors thus

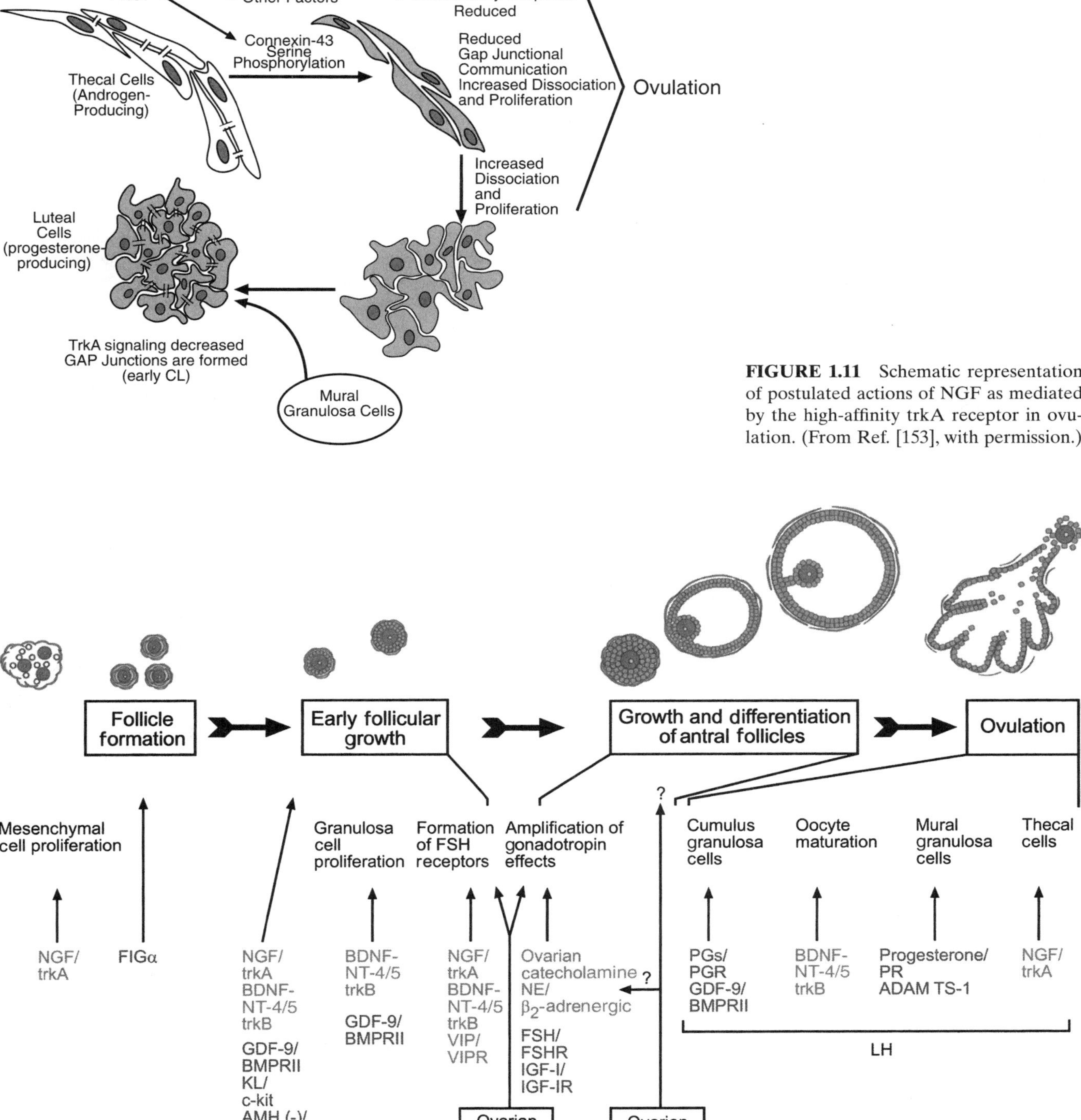

FIGURE 1.11 Schematic representation of postulated actions of NGF as mediated by the high-affinity trkA receptor in ovulation. (From Ref. [153], with permission.)

FIGURE 1.12 Postulated role of different components of the ovarian neuroendocrinotrophic complex (NTs, nerves and local sources of neurotransmitters) in follicular growth and ovulation. Components of the ovarian neuroendocrinotrophic complex are shown in red. Depicted in blue are select factors other than NTs shown to be involved in follicular development and ovulation. *ADAM TS1*, A disintegrin and matrix metalloproteinase with thrombospondin-like repeats; *AMHR*, antimüllerian hormone receptor; *FIGα*, factor in the germline α; *IGF-I*, insulin-like growth factor-I; *IGF-IR*, insulin-like growth factor-I receptor; *PGs*, prostaglandins; *PGR*, prostaglandin receptor; *PR*, progesterone receptor; *VIPR*, vasoactive intestinal peptide receptor. For a detailed account of all factors involved, see Refs. [138, 139]. (Modified from Ref. [154], with permission.) (See color plate.)

far found to participate in the events leading to the ovulatory rupture.

CONCLUSION

During the last 10 years, experimental evidence has been provided supporting the view that NTs are not neural cell-specific but are also physiological components of regulatory events that affect the development of the reproductive endocrine system. Studies conducted by several groups, including ours, have led credence to the concept that some key aspects of ovarian function, including early follicular growth, ovulation, and oocyte maturation, are regulated by a neuroendocrinotrophic complex that includes neurotransmitters produced in situ by nonneural cells (and intrinsic neurons) of the ovary, neurotransmitters arriving at the gland via the extrinsic innervation, and NTs and their receptors expressed in nonneural cells of the gonad (see Figure 1.12). A major goal for future research is the identification of both the primary genes that activate the cell-specific expression of NTs and their receptors in ovarian cells and the identification of target genes affected by the activation of ovarian neurotrophic receptors.

ACKNOWLEDGMENTS

We appreciate the collaboration of Drs. Artur Mayerhofer (Anatomisches Institut, Universitat Munchen, Germany); Sasha Malamed (Department of Neurosciences and Cell Biology, Robert Wood Johnson Medical School, University of Medicine and Dentistry of New Jersey, Piscataway, NJ); Anne Newman Hirshfield (Department of Anatomy, University of Maryland School of Medicine, Baltimore); and Michael Skinner (Washington State University, Pullman) in some of the studies discussed in this article. We thank Janie Gliessman for editorial and typing assistance and Maria Costa, Pablo Ojeda, Leela Goodspeed, Summer Johnson, and Jill Hiney for technical assistance. This work was supported by National Institutes of Health Grants HD07438, HD24870, RR00163, AA07216, AA00104, and HD18185.

References

1. Hsueh, A. J. W., Adashi, E. Y., Jones, P. B. C., and Welsh, T. H. J. (1984). Hormonal regulation of the differentiation of cultured ovarian granulosa cells. *Endocr. Rev.* 5, 76–127.
2. Ojeda, S. R., Lara, H., and Ahmed, C. E. (1989). Potential relevance of vasoactive intestinal peptide to ovarian physiology. *Semin. Reprod. Endocrinol.* 7, 52–60.
3. Burden, H. W. (1985). The adrenergic innervation of mammalian ovaries. In *Catecholamines as Hormone Regulators*, eds. N. Ben-Jonathan, J. M. Bahr, and R. I. Weiner, 261–278. New York: Raven Press.
4. Lara, H. E., McDonald, J. K., Ahmed, C. E., and Ojeda, S. R. (1990). Guanethidine-mediated destruction of ovarian sympathetic nerves disrupts ovarian development and function in rats. *Endocrinology* 127, 2199–2209.
5. Dissen, G. A., Dees, W. L., and Ojeda, S. R. (1993). Neural and neurotrophic control of ovarian development. In *The Ovary*, eds. E. Y. Adashi and P. C. K. Leung, 1–19. New York: Raven Press.
6. Huang, M.-H., Friend, D. S., Sunday, M. E., Singh, K., Haley, K., Austen, K. F., and Kelly, R. A. (1996). An intrinsic adrenergic system in mammalian heart. *J. Clin. Invest.* 98, 1298–1303.
7. Mezey, E., Eisenhofer, G., Harta, G., Hansson, S., Gould, L., Hunyady, B., and Hoffman, B. J. (1996). A novel nonneuronal catecholaminergic system: Exocrine pancreas synthesizes and releases dopamine. *Proc. Natl. Acad. Sci. USA* 93, 10377–10382.
8. Davies, A. M., Bandtlow, C., Heumann, R., Korsching, S., Rohrer, H., and Thoenen, H. (1987). Timing and site of nerve growth factor synthesis in developing skin in relation to innervation and expression of the receptor. *Nature* 326, 353–358.
9. Patapoutain, A., Backus, C., Kispert, A., and Reichardt, L. F. (1999). Regulation of neurotrophin-3 expression by epithelial-mesenchymal interactions: The role of Wnt factors. *Science* 283, 1180–1183.
10. Tessarollo, L. (1998). Pleiotrophic functions of neurotrophins in development. *Cytokine Growth Factor Rev.* 9, 125–137.
11. Byskov, A. G., and Hoyer, P. E. (1988). Embryology of mammalian gonads and ducts. In *The Physiology of Reproduction*, eds. E. Knobil and J. Neill, 265–302. New York: Raven Press.
12. Kurilo, L. F. (1981). Oogenesis in antenatal development in man. *Hum. Genet.* 57, 86–92.
13. Everett, N. B. (1943). Observational and experimental evidences relating to the origin and differentiation of the definitive germ cells in mice. *J. Exp. Zool.* 92, 49–91.
14. Snow, M. H. L., and Monk, M. (1983). Emergence and migration of mouse primordial germ cells. In *Current Problems in Germ Cell Differentiation*, eds. A. McLaren and C. C. Wylie, 115–135. Cambridge: Cambridge University Press.
15. Goodenough, V., and Levine, R. P. (1974). *Genetics.* New York: Holt, Rinehart & Winston.
16. Stein, L. E., and Anderson, C. H. (1979). A qualitative and quantitative study of rete ovarii development in the fetal rat: Correlation with the onset of meiosis and follicle cell appearance. *Anat. Rec.* 193, 197–212.
17. Konishi, I., Fujii, S., Okamura, H., Parmley, T., and Mori, T. (1986). Development of interstitial cells and ovigerous cords in the human fetal ovary: an ultrastructural study. *J. Anat.* 148, 121–135.
18. Byskov, A. G., and Lintern-Moore, S. (1973). Follicle formation in the immature mouse ovary: The role of the rete ovarii. *J. Anat.* 116, 207–217.
19. Byskov, A. G. (1986). Differentiation of mammalian embryonic gonad. *Physiol. Rev.* 66, 71–117.
20. Hirshfield, A. N. (1991). Development of follicles in the mammalian ovary. *Int. Rev. Cytol.* 124, 43–101.

21. Rajah, R., and Hirshfield, A. N. (1991). The changing architecture of the rat ovary during the immediate postpartum period: A three-dimensional reconstruction. *Biol. Reprod.* 44, 152.
22. Malamed, S., Gibney, J. A., and Ojeda, S. R. (1992). Ovarian innervation develops before initiation of folliculogenesis in the rat. *Cell Tissue Res.* 270, 87–93.
23. Rajah, R., Glaser, E. M., and Hirshfield, A. N. (1992). The changing architecture of the neonatal rat ovary during histogenesis. *Dev. Dyn.* 194, 177–192.
24. Eppig, J. J., and O'Brien, M. J. (1996). Development in vitro of mouse oocytes from primordial follicles. *Biol. Reprod.* 54, 197–207.
25. Durlinger, A. L. L., Gruijters, M. J. G., Kramer, P., Karels, B., Ingraham, H. A., Nachtigal, M. W., Uilenbroek, J. Th. J., Grootegoed, J. A., and Themmen, A. P. N. (2002). Anti-müllerian hormone inhibits initiation of primordial follicle growth in the mouse ovary. *Endocrinology* 143, 1076–1084.
26. Peters, H. (1969). The development of the mouse ovary from birth to maturity. *Acta Endocrinol.* 62, 98–116.
27. Burden, H. W. (1978). Ovarian innervation. In *The Vertebrate Ovary: Comparative Biology and Evolution*, ed. R. E. Jones, 615–638. New York: Plenum Press.
28. Klein, C. M., and Burden, H. W. (1988). Substance P- and vasoactive intestinal polypeptide (VIP)-immunoreactive nerve fibers in relation to ovarian postganglionic perikarya in para- and prevertebral ganglia: Evidence from combined retrograde tracing and immunocytochemistry. *Cell Tissue Res.* 252, 403–410.
29. Burden, H. W., Leonard, M., Smith, C. P., and Lawrence, I. E. J. (1983). The sensory innervation of the ovary: A horseradish peroxidase study in the rat. *Anat. Rec.* 207, 623–627.
30. Gerendai, I., Toth, I. E., Boldogkoi, Z., Medvecxky, I., and Halasz, B. (1998). Neuronal labeling in the rat brain and spinal cord from the ovary using viral transneuronal tracing technique. *Neuroendocrinology* 68, 244–256.
31. McNeill, D. L., and Burden, H. W. (1986). Neuropeptide Y and somatostatin immunoreactive perikarya in preaortic ganglia projecting to the rat ovary. *J. Reprod. Fertil.* 78, 727–732.
32. Papka, R. E., Cotton, J. P., and Traurig, H. H. (1985). Comparative distribution of neuropeptide tyrosine-, vasoactive intestinal polypeptide-, substance P-immunoreactive, acetylcholinesterase-positive and noradrenergic nerves in the reproductive tract of the female rat. *Cell Tissue Res.* 242, 475–490.
33. McDonald, J. K., Dees, W. L., Ahmed, C. E., Noe, B. D., and Ojeda, S. R. (1987). Biochemical and immunocytochemical characterization of neuropeptide Y in the immature rat ovary. *Endocrinology* 120, 1703–1710.
34. Dees, W. L., Kozlowski, G. P., Dey, R., and Ojeda, S. R. (1985). Evidence for the existence of substance P in the prepubertal rat ovary. II. Immunocytochemical localization. *Biol. Reprod.* 33, 471–476.
35. Kannisto, P., Ekblad, E., Helm, G., Owman, Ch., Sjöberg, N.-O., Stjernquist, M., Sundler, F., and Walles, B. (1986). Existence and coexistence of peptides in nerves of the mammalian ovary and oviduct demonstrated by immunocytochemistry. *Histochemistry* 86, 25–34.
36. McNeill, D. L., and Burden, H. W. (1987). Neuropeptides in sensory perikarya projecting to the rat ovary. *Am. J. Anat.* 179, 269–276.
37. Ahmed, C. E., Dees, W. L., and Ojeda, S. R. (1986). The immature rat ovary is innervated by vasoactive intestinal peptide (VIP)-containing fibers and responds to VIP with steroid secretion. *Endocrinology* 118, 1682–1689.
38. Baljet, B., and Drukker, J. (1980). The extrinsic innervation of the pelvic organs in the female rat. *Acta Anat.* 107, 241–267.
39. Lawrence, I. E., Jr., and Burden, H. W. (1980). The origin of the extrinsic adrenergic innervation to the rat ovary. *Anat. Rec.* 196, 51–59.
40. Burden, H. W., and Lawrence, I. E. J. (1978). Experimental studies on the acetylcholinesterase-positive nerves in the ovary of the rat. *Anat. Rec.* 190, 233–241.
41. Fritz, S., Wessler, I., Breitling, W., Rossmanith, W., Ojeda, S. R., Dissen, G. A., Amsterdam, A., and Mayerhofer, A. (2001). Expression of muscarinic receptor types in the primate ovary and evidence for nonneuronal acetylcholine synthesis. *J. Clin. Endocrinol. Metab.* 86, 349–354.
42. Mayerhofer, A., and Fritz, S. (2002). Ovarian acetylcholine and muscarinic receptors—hints to a novel intrinsic ovarian regulatory system. *Microsc. Res. Tech.* 59, 503–508.
43. Schultea, T. D., Dees, W. L., and Ojeda, S. R. (1992). Postnatal development of sympathetic and sensory innervation of the rhesus monkey ovary. *Biol. Reprod.* 47, 760–767.
44. Ojeda, S. R., and Lara, H. E. (1989). Role of the sympathetic nervous system in the regulation of ovarian function. In *The Menstrual Cycle and Its Disorders*, ed. K. M. Pirke, W. Wuttke, and U. Schweiger, 26–32. Berlin: Springer-Verlag.
45. Dees, W. L., Schultea, T. D., Hiney, J. K., Dissen, G., and Ojeda, S. R. (1992). The rhesus monkey ovary contains a developmentally regulated network of nerve growth factor receptor immunoreactive neurons in addition to its extrinsic innervation. *Prog. 74th Ann. Mtg. Endocrine Soc.*, p 59.
46. Dees, W. L., Hiney, J. K., Schultea, T. D., Mayerhofer, A., Danilchik, M., Dissen, G. A., and Ojeda, S. R. (1995). The primate ovary contains a population of catecholaminergic neuronlike cells expressing nerve growth factor receptors. *Endocrinology* 136, 5760–5768.
47. Mayerhofer, A., Smith, G. D., Danilchik, M., Levine, J. E., Wolf, D. P., Dissen, G. A., and Ojeda, S. R. (1998). Oocytes are a source of catecholamines in the primate ovary: Evidence for a cell-cell regulatory loop. *Proc. Natl. Acad. Sci. USA* 95, 10990–10995.
48. Winterhalter, E. H. (1896). Ein sympathisches ganglion im menschlichen ovarium. *Arch. Gynäkol.* 51, 49–55.
49. Dahl, W., and Flaskamp, W. (1937). Innervation der weiblichen geschlechtsorgane. In *Vegatative Nervensystem*, ed. L. R. Muller, 719–736. Madrid: Labor.
50. D'Albora, H., and Barcia, J. J. (1996). Intrinsic neuronal cell bodies in the rat ovary. *Neurosci. Lett.* 205, 65–67.
51. D'Albora, H., Lombide, P., and Ojeda, S. R. (2000). Intrinsic neurons in the rat ovary: An immunohistochemical study. *Cell Tissue Res.* 300, 47–56.
52. Anesetti, G., Lombide, P., D'Albora, H., and Ojeda, S. R. (2001). Intrinsic neurons in the human ovary. *Cell Tissue Res.* 306, 231–237.

53. Adashi, E. Y., and Hsueh, A. J. W. (1981). Stimulation of β_2-adrenergic responsiveness by follicle-stimulating hormone in rat granulosa cells *in vitro* and *in vivo*. *Endocrinology* 108, 2170–2178.
54. Aguado, L. I., Petrovic, S. L., and Ojeda, S. R. (1982). Ovarian β_2-adrenergic receptors during the onset of puberty: Characterization, distribution, and coupling to steroidogenic responses. *Endocrinology* 110, 1124–1132.
55. Flerko, B. (1977). Sympathetic nerve function in the ovary. In *Endocrinology, Vol. 1: Proceedings of the V International Congress of Endocrinology*, ed. V. H. T. James, 210–214. Amsterdam: Excerpta Medica.
56. Jorgensen, J. C., Kannisto, P., Liedberg, F., Ottesen, B., Owman, C., and Schmidt, G. (1991). The influence of neuropeptide Y and norepinephrine on ovulation in the rat ovary. *Peptides* 12, 975–982.
57. Aguado, L. I., and Ojeda, S. R. (1984). Ovarian adrenergic nerves play a role in maintaining preovulatory steroid secretion. *Endocrinology* 114, 1944–1946.
58. Weiss, G. K., Dail, W. G., and Ratner, A. (1982). Evidence for direct neural control of ovarian steroidogenesis in rats. *J. Reprod. Fertil.* 65, 507–511.
59. Dyer, C. A., and Erickson, G. F. (1985). Norepinephrine amplifies human chorionic gonadotropin-stimulated androgen biosynthesis by ovarian theca-interstitial cells. *Endocrinology* 116, 1645–1652.
60. Hernandez, E. R., Jimenez, J. L., Payne, D. W., and Adashi, E. Y. (1988). Adrenergic regulation of ovarian androgen biosynthesis is mediated via β_2-adrenergic theca-interstitial cell recognition sites. *Endocrinology* 122, 1592–1602.
61. Dees, W. L., Ahmed, C. E., and Ojeda, S. R. (1986). Substance P- and vasoactive intestinal peptide-containing fibers reach the ovary by independent routes. *Endocrinology* 119, 638–641.
62. Davoren, J. B., and Hsueh, A. J. W. (1985). Vasoactive intestinal peptide: A novel stimulator of steroidogenesis by cultured rat granulosa cells. *Biol. Reprod.* 33, 37–52.
63. Trzeciak, W. H., Ahmed, C. E., Simpson, E. R., and Ojeda, S. R. (1986). Vasoactive intestinal peptide induces the synthesis of the cholesterol side-chain cleavage enzyme complex in cultured rat ovarian granulosa cells. *Proc. Natl. Acad. Sci. USA* 83, 7490–7494.
64. Trzeciak, W. H., Waterman, M. R., Simpson, E. R., and Ojeda, S. R. (1987). Vasoactive intestinal peptide regulates cholesterol side-chain cleavage cytochrome P-450 (P-450scc) gene expression in granulosa cells from immature rat ovaries. *Mol. Endocrinol.* 1, 500–504.
65. George, F. W., and Ojeda, S. R. (1987). Vasoactive intestinal peptide enhances aromatase activity in the neonatal rat ovary before development of primary follicles or responsiveness to follicle-stimulating hormone. *Proc. Natl. Acad. Sci. USA* 84, 5803–5807.
66. Kasson, B. G., Meidan, R., Davoren, J. B., and Hsueh, A. J. W. (1985). Identification of subpopulations of rat granulosa cells: Sedimentation properties and hormonal responsiveness. *Endocrinology* 117, 1027–1034.
67. Ranta, T., Knecht, M., Darbon, J.-M., Baukal, A. J., and Catt, K. J. (1984). Induction of granulosa cell differentiation by forskolin: Stimulation of adenosine 3′,5′-monophosphate production, progesterone synthesis, and luteinizing hormone receptor expression. *Endocrinology* 114, 845–850.
68. McNeill, D. L., and Burden, H. W. (1987). Peripheral pathways for neuropeptide Y- and cholecystokinin-8-immunoreactive nerves innervating the rat ovary. *Neurosci. Lett.* 80, 27–32.
69. Pitzel, L., Jarry, H., and Wuttke, W. (1991). Effects of substance-P and neuropeptide-Y on *in vitro* steroid release by porcine granulosa and luteal cells. *Endocrinology* 129, 1059–1065.
70. Ferruz, J., Ahmed, C. E., Ojeda, S. R., and Lara, H. E. (1992). Norepinephrine release in the immature ovary is regulated by autoreceptors and neuropeptide-Y. *Endocrinology* 130, 1345–1351.
71. Calka, J., McDonald, J. K., and Ojeda, S. R. (1988). The innervation of the immature rat ovary by calcitonin gene-related peptide. *Biol. Reprod.* 39, 1215–1223.
72. Häppölä, O., and Lakomy, M. (1989). Immunohistochemical localization of calcitonin gene-related peptide and bombesin/gastrin-releasing peptide in nerve fibers of the rat, guinea pig, and pig female genital organs. *Histochemistry* 92, 211–218.
73. Fritz, S., Föhr, K. J., Boddien, U., Berg, U., Brucker, C., and Mayerhofer, A. (1999). Functional and molecular characterization of a muscarinic receptor type and evidence for expression of choline-acetyltranferase and vesicular acetylcholine transporter in human granulosa-luteal cells. *J. Clin. Endocrinol. Metab.* 84, 1744–1750.
74. Fritz, S., Grünert, R., Stocco, D. M., Hales, D. B., and Mayerhofer, A. (2001). StAR protein is increased by muscarinic receptor activation in human luteinized granulosa cells. *Mol. Cell. Endocrinol.* 171, 49–51.
75. Erdö, S. L. (1985). Peripheral GABAergic mechanisms. *Trends Pharmacol. Sci.* 6, 205–208.
76. Laszlo, A., Villanyi, P., Zsolnai, B., and Erdö, S. L. (1989). Gamma-aminobutyric acid, its related enzymes and receptor-binding sites in the human ovary and fallopian tube. *Gynecol. Obstet. Invest.* 28, 94–97.
77. Häppölä, O., Lakomy, M., and Yanaihara, N. (1989). Met^5-enkephalin- and Met^5-enkephalin-Arg^6-Gly^7-Leu^8-immunoreactive nerve fibers in the pig female reproductive system. *Neurosci. Lett.* 101, 156–162.
78. Erdö, S. L., Varga, B., and Horvath, E. (1985). Effect of local GABA administration on rat ovarian blood flow, and on progesterone and estradiol secretion. *Eur. J. Pharmacol.* 111, 397–400.
79. Lara, H. E., McDonald, J. K., and Ojeda, S. R. (1990). Involvement of nerve growth factor in female sexual development. *Endocrinology* 126, 364–375.
80. Lara, H. E., Hill, D. F., Katz, K. H., and Ojeda, S. R. (1990). The gene encoding nerve growth factor is expressed in the immature rat ovary: Effect of denervation and hormonal treatment. *Endocrinology* 126, 357–363.
81. Levi-Montalcini, R. (1987). The nerve growth factor 35 years later. *Science* 237, 1154–1162.
82. Dissen, G. A., Hill, D. F., Costa, M. E., Ma, Y. J., and Ojeda, S. R. (1991). Nerve growth factor receptors in the peripubertal rat ovary. *Mol. Endocrinol.* 5, 1642–1650.

83. Leibrock, J., Lottspeich, F., Hohn, A., Hofer, M., Hengerer, B., Masiakowski, P., Thoenen, H., and Barde, Y.-A. (1989). Molecular cloning and expression of brain-derived neurotrophic factor. *Nature* 341, 149–152.
84. Maisonpierre, P. C., Belluscio, L., Squinto, S., Ip, N. Y., Furth, M. E., Lindsay, R. M., and Yancopoulos, G. D. (1990). Neurotrophin-3: A neurotrophic factor related to NGF and BDNF. *Science* 247, 1446–1451.
85. Hohn, A., Leibrock, J., Bailey, K., and Barde, Y.-A. (1990). Identification and characterization of a novel member of the nerve growth factor/brain-derived neurotrophic factor family. *Nature* 344, 339–341.
86. Rosenthal, A., Goeddel, D. V., Nguyen, T., Lewis, M., Shih, A., Laramee, G. R., Nikolics, K., and Winslow, J. W. (1990). Primary structure and biological activity of a novel human neurotrophic factor. *Neuron* 4, 767–773.
87. Berkemeier, L. R., Winslow, J. W., Kaplan, D. R., Nikolics, K., Goeddel, D. V., and Rosenthal, A. (1991). Neurotrophin-5: A novel neurotrophic factor that activates trk and trkB. *Neuron* 7, 857–866.
88. Ip, N. Y., Ibañez, C. F., Nye, S. H., McClain, J., Jones, P. F., Gies, D. R., Belluscio, L., Le Beau, M. M., Espinosa, R., III, Squinto, S. P., Persson, H., and Yancopoulos, G. D. (1992). Mammalian neurotrophin-4: Structure, chromosomal localization, tissue distribution, and receptor specificity. *Proc. Natl. Acad. Sci. USA* 89, 3060–3064.
89. Götz, R., Köster, R., Lottspeich, F., Schartl, M., and Thoenen, H. (1994). Neurotrophin-6 is a new member of the nerve growth factor family. *Nature* 372, 266–269.
90. Barbacid, M., Lamballe, F., Pulido, D., and Klein, R. (1991). The *trk* family of tyrosine protein kinase receptors. *Biochim. Biophys. Acta* 1072, 115–127.
91. Yancopoulos, G. D., Maisonpierre, P. C., Ip, N. Y., Aldrich, T. H., Belluscio, L., Boulton, T. G., Cobb, M. H., Squinto, S. P., and Furth, M. E. (1990). Neurotrophic factors, their receptors, and the signal transduction pathways they activate. In *Cold Spring Harbor Symposia on Quantitative Biology, Vol. LV*, 371–379. Plainview, N.Y.: Cold Spring Harbor Laboratory Press.
92. Raffioni, S., Bradshaw, R. A., and Buxser, S. E. (1993). The receptors for nerve growth factor and other neurotrophins. *Annu. Rev. Biochem.* 62, 823–850.
93. Dechant, G., and Barde, Y.-A. (1997). Signaling through the neurotrophin receptor $p75^{NTR}$. *Curr. Opin. Neurobiol.* 7, 413–418.
94. Bothwell, M. (1991). Keeping track of neurotrophin receptors. *Cell* 65, 915–918.
95. Chao, M. V., Bothwell, M. A., Ross, A. H., Koprowski, H., Lanahan, A. A., Buck, C. R., and Sehgal, A. (1986). Gene transfer and molecular cloning of the human NGF receptor. *Science* 232, 518–521.
96. Barrett, G. L. (2000). The p75 neurotrophin receptor and neuronal apoptosis. *Prog. Neurobiol.* 61, 205–229.
97. Dobrowsky, R. T., Jenkins, G. M., and Hannun, Y. A. (1995). Neurotrophins induce sphingomyelin hydrolysis. *J. Biol. Chem.* 270, 22135–22142.
98. Hantzopoulos, P. A., Suri, C., Glass, D. J., Goldfard, M. P., and Yancopoulos, G. D. (1994). The low-affinity NGF receptor, p75, can collaborate with each of the trks to potentiate functional responses to the neurotrophins. *Neuron* 13, 187–201.
99. Kohn, J., Aloyz, R. S., Toma, J. G., Haak-Frendscho, M., and Miller, F. D. (1999). Functionally antagonistic interactions between the trkA and p75 neurotrophin receptors regulate sympathetic neuron growth and target innervation. *J. Neurosci.* 19, 5393–5408.
100. Dechant, G. (2001). Molecular interactions between neurotrophin receptors. *Cell Tissue Res.* 305, 229–238.
101. Ernfors, P., Wetmore, C., Olson, L., and Persson, H. (1990). Identification of cells in rat brain and peripheral tissues expressing mRNA for members of the nerve growth factor family. *Neuron* 5, 511–526.
102. Hallböök, F., Ibañez, C. F., and Persson, H. (1991). Evolutionary studies of the nerve growth factor family reveal a novel member abundantly expressed in Xenopus ovary. *Neuron* 6, 845–858.
103. Dissen, G. A., Hill, D. F., Costa, M. E., Dees, W. L., Lara, H. E., and Ojeda, S. R. (1996). A role for *trk*A nerve growth factor receptors in mammalian ovulation. *Endocrinology* 137, 198–209.
104. Dissen, G. A., Newman Hirshfield, A., Malamed, S., and Ojeda, S. R. (1995). Expression of neurotrophins and their receptors in the mammalian ovary is developmentally regulated: Changes at the time of folliculogenesis. *Endocrinology* 136, 4681–4692.
105. Klein, R., Parada, L. F., Coulier, F., and Barbacid, M. (1989). *trk*B, a novel tyrosine protein kinase receptor expressed during mouse neural development. *EMBO J.* 8, 3701–3709.
106. Amano, O., Abe, H., and Kondo, H. (1991). Ultrastructural study on a variety of nonneural cells immunoreactive for nerve growth factor receptor in developing rats. *Acta Anat.* 141, 212–219.
107. Lamballe, F., Klein, R., and Barbacid, M. (1991). *trk*C, a new member of the *trk* family of tyrosine protein kinases, is a receptor for neurotrophin-3. *Cell* 66, 967–979.
108. Anderson, R. A., Robnson, L. L. L., Brooks, J., and Spears, N. (2002). Neurotropins and their receptors are expressed in the human fetal ovary. *J. Clin. Endocrinol. Metab.* 87, 890–897.
109. Paredes, A., Romero, C., Dissen, G. A., DeChiara, T., Reichardt, L., Ojeda, S. R., and Xu, B. (2003). trkB receptors are essential for early follicular growth in the mammalian ovary. *Dev. Biol.* (submitted).
110. Klein, R., Conway, D., Parada, L. F., and Barbacid, M. (1990). The *trk*B tyrosine protein kinase gene codes for a second neurogenic receptor that lacks the catalytic kinase domain. *Cell* 61, 647–656.
111. Middlemas, D. S., Lindberg, R. A., and Hunter, T. (1991). *trk*B, a neural receptor protein kinase: Evidence for a full-length and two truncated receptors. *Mol. Cell. Biol.* 11, 143–153.
112. Shelton, D. L., Sutherland, J., Gripp, J., Camerato, T., Armanini, M. P., Phillips, H. S., Carroll, K., Spencer, S. D., and Levinson, A. D. (1995). Human trks: Molecular cloning, tissue distribution, and expression of extracellular domain immunoadhesions. *J. Neurosci.* 15, 477–491.
113. Richards, J. S., Russell, D. L., Robker, R. L., Dajee, M., and Alliston, T. N. (1998). Molecular mechanisms of ovulation and luteinization. *Mol. Cell. Endocrinol.* 145, 47–54.
114. Robker, R. L., Russell, D. L., Yoshioka, S., Sharma, S. C., Lydon, J. P., O'Malley, B. W., Espey, L. L., and Richards,

J. S. (2000). Ovulation: A multigene, multistep process. *Steroids* 65, 559–570.

115. Seifer, D. B., Feng, B., Shelden, R. M., Chen, S., and Dreyfus, C. F. (2002). Brain-derived neurotrophic factor: A novel human ovarian follicular protein. *J. Clin. Endocrinol. Metab.* 87, 655–659.

116. Seifer, D. B., Feng, B., Shelden, R. M., Chen, S., and Dreyfus, C. F. (2002). Neurotrophin-4/5 and neurotrophin-3 are present within the human ovarian follicle but appear to have different paracrine/autocrine functions. *J. Clin. Endocrinol. Metab.* 87, 4569–4571.

117. Crowley, C., Spencer, S. D., Nishimura, M. C., Chen, K. S., Pitts-Meek, S., Armanini, M. P., Ling, L. H., McMahon, S. B., Shelton, D. L., Levinson, A. D., and Phillips, H. S. (1994). Mice lacking nerve growth factor display perinatal loss of sensory and sympathetic neurons yet develop basal forebrain cholinergic neurons. *Cell* 76, 1001–1011.

118. Dissen, G. A., Romero, C., Newman Hirshfield, A., and Ojeda, S. R. (2001). Nerve growth factor is required for early follicular development in the mammalian ovary. *Endocrinology* 142, 2078–2086.

119. Cordon-Cardo, C., Tapley, P., Jing, S., Nanduri, V., O'Rourke, E., Lamballe, F., Kovary, K., Jones, K., Reichardt, L. F., and Barbacid, M. (1991). The *trk* tyrosine protein kinase mediates the mitogenic properties of nerve growth factor and neurotrophin-3. *Cell* 66, 173–183.

120. Hirshfield, A. N., and DeSanti, A. M. (1995). Patterns of ovarian cell proliferation in rats during the embryonic period and the first three weeks postpartum. *Biol. Reprod.* 53, 1208–1221.

121. Xiong, Y., Zhang, H., and Beach, D. (1992). D-type cyclins associate with multiple protein kinases and the DNA replication and repair factor PCNA. *Cell* 71, 505–514.

122. Liu, Y., Marraccino, R. I., and Keng, P. C. (1989). Requirement for proliferating cell nuclear antigen expression during stages of the Chinese hamster ovary cell cycle. *Biochemistry* 28, 2967–2974.

123. Hall, P. A., Levison, D. A., Woods, A. L., Yu, C. C. W., Kellock, D. B., Watkins, J. A., Barnes, D. M., Gillett, C. E., Camplejohn, R., Dover, R., Waseem, N. H., and Lane, D. P. (1990). Proliferating cell nuclear antigen (PCNA) immunolocalization in paraffin sections: An index of cell proliferation with evidence of deregulated expression in some neoplasms. *J. Pathol.* 162, 285–294.

124. Romero, C., Paredes, A., Dissen, G. A., and Ojeda, S. R. (2002). Nerve growth factor induces the expression of functional FSH receptors in newly formed follicles of the rat ovary. *Endocrinology* 143, 1485–1494.

125. Berg, K. A., Maayani, S., McKay, R., and Clarke, W. P. (1995). Nerve growth factor amplifies cyclic AMP production in the HT4 neuronal cell line. *J. Neurochem.* 64, 220–228.

126. Heidemann, S. R., Joshi, H. C., Schechter, A., Fletcher, J. R., and Bothwell, M. (1985). Synergistic effects of cyclic AMP and nerve growth factor on neurite outgrowth and microtubule stability of PC12 cells. *J. Cell Biol.* 100, 916–927.

127. Dong, J., Albertini, D. F., Nishimori, K., Kumar, T. R., Lu, N., and Matzuk, M. M. (1996). Growth differentiation factor-9 is required during early ovarian folliculogenesis. *Nature* 383, 531–535.

128. Huang, E. J., Manova, K., Packer, A. I., Sanchez, S., Bachvarova, R. F., and Besmer, P. (1993). The murine steel panda mutation affects kit ligand expression and growth of early ovarian follicles. *Dev. Biol.* 157, 100–109.

129. Yoshida, H., Takakura, N., Kataoka, H., Kunisada, T., Okamura, H., and Nishikawa, S.-I. (1997). Stepwise requirement of *c*-kit tyrosine kinase in mouse ovarian follicle development. *Dev. Biol.* 184, 122–137.

130. Kuroda, H., Terada, N., Nakayama, H., Matsumoto, K., and Kitamura, Y. (1988). Infertility due to growth arrest of ovarian follicles in *Sl/Sl^t* micde. *Dev. Biol.* 126, 71–79.

131. Elvin, J. A., Yan, C., Wang, P., Nishimori, K., and Matzuk, M. M. (1999). Molecular characterization of the follicle defects in the growth differentiation factor 9-deficient ovary. *Mol. Endocrinol.* 13, 1018–1034.

132. Elvin, J. A., Clark, A. T., Wang, P., Wolfman, N. M., and Matzuk, M. M. (1999). Paracrine actions of growth differentiation factor-9 in the mammalian ovary. *Mol. Endocrinol.* 13, 1035–1048.

133. Vitt, U. A., Mazerbourg, S., Klein, C., and Hsueh, A. J. W. (2002). Bone morphogenetic protein receptor type II is a receptor for growth differentiation factor-9. *Biol. Reprod.* 67, 473–480.

134. Manova, K., Huang, E. J., Angeles, M., De Leon, V., Sanchez, S., Pronovost, S. M., Besmer, P., and Bachvarova, R. F. (1993). The expression pattern of the c-*kit* ligand in gonads of mice supports a role for the c-*kit* receptor in oocyte growth and in proliferation of spermatogonia. *Dev. Biol.* 157, 85–99.

135. Joyce, I. M., Pendola, F. L., Wigglesworth, K., and Eppig, J. J. (1999). Oocyte regulation of kit ligand expression in mouse ovarian follicles. *Dev. Biol.* 214, 342–353.

136. Manova, K., Nocka, K., Besmer, P., and Bachvarova, R. F. (1990). Gonadal expression of c-*kit* encoded at the *W* locus of the mouse. *Development* 110, 1057–1069.

137. Durlinger, A. L. L., Kramer, P., Karels, B., de Jong, F. H., Uilenbroek, J. Th. J., Grootegoed, J. A., and Themmen, A. P. N. (1999). Control of primordial follicle recruitment by anti-müllerian hormone in the mouse ovary. *Endocrinology* 140, 5789–5796.

138. Matzuk, M. M., Burns, K. H., Viveiros, M. M., and Eppig, J. J. (2002). Intercellular communication in the mammalian ovary: Oocytes carry the conversation. *Science* 296, 2178–2180.

139. Richards, J. S. (2001). Perspective: The ovarian follicle—A perspective in 2001. *Endocrinology* 142, 2184–2193.

140. Wyatt, S., Shooter, E. M., and Davies, A. M. (1990). Expression of the NGF receptor gene in sensory neurons and their cutaneous targets prior to and during innervation. *Neuron* 2, 421–427.

141. Matsuoka, I., Meyer, M., and Thoenen, H. (1991). Cell-type-specific regulation of nerve growth factor (NGF) synthesis in nonneuronal cells: Comparison of Schwann cells with other cell types. *J. Neurosci.* 11, 3165–3177.

142. Miller, F. D., Mathew, T. C., and Toma, J. G. (1991). Regulation of nerve growth factor receptor gene expression by nerve growth factor in the developing peripheral nervous system. *J. Cell Biol.* 112, 303–312.

143. Donovan, M. J., Hahn, R., Tessarollo, L., and Hempstead, B. L. (1996). Identification of an essential nonneuronal

function of neurotrophin 3 in mammalian cardiac development. *Nat. Genet.* 14, 210–213.

144. Espey, L. L. (1994). Current status of the hypothesis that mammalian ovulation is comparable to an inflammatory reaction. *Biol. Reprod.* 50, 233–238.
145. Lindholm, D., Heumann, R., Meyer, M., and Thoenen, H. (1987). Interleukin-1 regulates synthesis of nerve growth factor in non-neuronal cells of rat sciatic nerve. *Nature* 330, 658–659.
146. Hurwitz, A., Ricciarelli, E., Botero, L., Rohan, R. M., Hernandez, E. R., and Adashi, E. Y. (1991). Endocrine- and autocrine-mediated regulation of rat ovarian (theca-interstitial) interleukin-1β gene expression: Gonadotropin-dependent preovulatory acquisition. *Endocrinology* 129, 3427–3429.
147. Kokia, E., Hurwitz, A., Ricciarelli, E., Tedeschi, C., Resnick, C. E., Mitchell, M. D., and Adashi, E. Y. (1992). Interleukin-1 stimulates ovarian prostaglandin biosynthesis: Evidence for heterologous contact-independent cell-cell interaction. *Endocrinology* 130, 3095–3097.
148. Dissen, G. A., Parrott, J. A., Skinner, M. K., Hill, D. F., Costa, M. E., and Ojeda, S. R. (2000). Direct effects of nerve growth factor on thecal cells from antral ovarian follicles. *Endocrinology* 141, 4736–4750.
149. Espey, L. L., and Lipner, H. (1994). Ovulation. In *Physiology of Reproduction*, 2d ed., eds. E. Knobil and J. D. Neill, 725–780. New York: Raven Press.
150. Mayerhofer, A., Dissen, G. A., Parrott, J. A., Hill, D. F., Mayerhofer, D., Garfield, R. E., Costa, M. E., Skinner, M. K., and Ojeda, S. R. (1996). Involvement of nerve growth factor in the ovulatory cascade: *Trk*A receptor activation inhibits gap-junctional communication between thecal cells. *Endocrinology* 137, 5662–5670.
151. Wandji, S.-A., Srsen, V., Voss, A. K., Eppig, J. J., and Fortune, J. E. (1996). Initiation in vitro of growth of bovine primordial follicles. *Biol. Reprod.* 55, 942–948.
152. Dissen, G. A., Romero, C., Paredes, A., and Ojeda, S. R. (2002). Neurotrophic control of ovarian development. *Microsc. Res. Tech.* 59, 509–515.
153. Dissen, G. A., Mayerhofer, A., and Ojeda, S. R. (2000). Neurotrophins and the ovulatory process: A role for NGF and trkA? In *Ovulation: Evolving Scientific and Clinical Concepts*, eds. E. Y. Adashi and A. J. W. Hsueh, 167–174. Norwell, Mass./New York: Springer.
154. Ojeda, S. R., and Dissen, G. A. (1994). Developmental regulation of the ovary via growth factor tyrosine kinase receptors. *Trends Endocrinol. Metab.* 5, 317–323.

CHAPTER **2**

Dynamics of Human Follicular Growth: Morphologic, Dynamic, and Functional Aspects

ALAIN GOUGEON

ABSTRACT

By integrating morphometrical and endocrinological data, as well as biological effects of various peptides synthesized by the primate follicle, this chapter proposes a dynamic view of the follicle growth within the human ovary. Folliculogenesis starts with the entry of nongrowing follicles into the growth phase, a process that results from a balance between inhibitory and activating factors. Early follicle growth is a long process because several months are required for a new growing follicle to reach the preantral stage (0.15 mm), then 70 additional days are needed to reach the size of 2 mm. Early growing follicle growth is regulated by subtle interactions between gonadotropins and local factors. From the time they enter the selectable stage during the late luteal phase, follicles become sensitive to cyclic changes of follicle-stimulating hormone (FSH) in terms of granulosa cell proliferation but not in terms of steroidogenesis because they do not synthesize estrogens. During the early follicular phase the selected follicle grows quickly and aromatase is expressed in its granulosa cells as indicated by the presence of estradiol in the follicular fluid. However, the total steroid production remains moderate. From the midfollicular phase, the preovulatory follicle synthesizes high quantities of estradiol; then after the midcycle gonadotropin surge, it synthesizes large amounts of progesterone. Thus as the follicle develops, its responsiveness to gonadotropins progressively increases. In vitro studies suggest that the progressive acquisition of follicular cell responsiveness to gonadotropins is under the control of local factors that act in an autocrine/paracrine fashion within the follicle.

INTRODUCTION

In humans, folliculogenesis starts when nongrowing follicles leave the ovarian reserve and culminates with the production of a single dominant follicle during each menstrual cycle. This process can be divided into three main steps: (1) initiation, (2) early follicle growth, and (3) selection and maturation of the preovulatory follicle (Figure 2.1). Although morphological and dynamic aspects of the human follicular growth did not substantially change during the past 10 years, significant progress in the knowledge of ovarian function has been made not only through generation of knockout mice models but also through phenotypic analyses of subjects bearing spontaneous mutations that affect fertility in various species, including humans. One of the most exciting facts that has emerged during the past few years is that local factors, especially those produced by the oocyte, play a critical role in folliculogenesis, including activation of resting follicles, early growth, and terminal maturation. For example, Eppig et al. [1] recently demonstrated that midgrowth oocytes accelerate follicular development, which strongly suggests that the oocyte may be operating as a "folliculogenesis clock." However, despite these new insights, our comprehension of ovarian function is still limited and many questions remain unanswered. Thus this chapter attempts through the use of a chronological perspective to (1) describe morphological changes that affect the follicular tissues during growth, (2) describe regulations that may operate inside the follicle at the different stages of folliculogenesis, and finally, (3) point out some poorly understood issues that migh be relevant for future researches to improve fertility in humans.

ANATOMY OF THE HUMAN OVARY

The human ovary is a paired intra-abdominal organ, amygdaloid in shape, whose primary roles are to release, during each menstrual cycle, an egg that is fully competent for fertilization and embryonic development (gametogenic function) and to prepare the accessory reproductive organs for the pregnancy and birth of a healthy baby by producing steroid hormones (endocrine function).

When the mature human ovary is observed in midsagittal section (Figure 2.2), it consists of an outer zone, the *cortex,* and an inner zone, the *medulla.* The cortex is covered by a specialized mesothelium called the *surface epithelium;* it contains an outer strip of connective tissue,

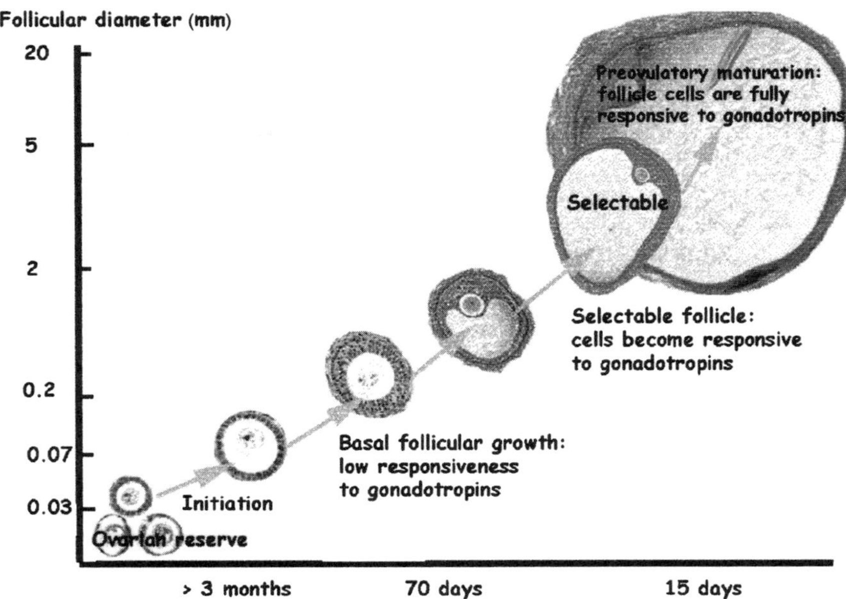

FIGURE 2.1 Schematic description of human follicular growth including initiation, basal follicular growth, and selection/maturation of the follicle destined to ovulate.

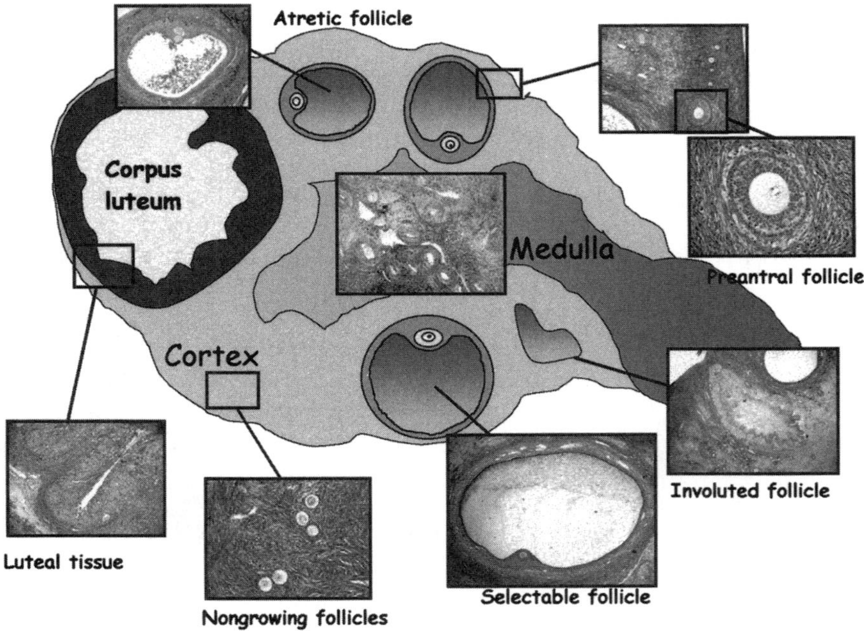

FIGURE 2.2 Schematic representation of an adult human ovary during the luteal phase that shows the main follicular and luteal structures that can be observed in a histological section.

the *tunica albuginea,* and an inner zone that contains the follicles. The resting follicles are located in a relatively avascular layer in the ovarian cortex beneath the *tunica albuginea*. In contrast, growing and atretic follicles and involuting *corpora lutea* are found in the cortical medullary border, which is richly vascularized. Follicles are closely surrounded by a complex and dynamic milieu of ovarian stromal cells and branches of the vasculature and autonomic nervous system. The medulla contains a variably dense connective tissue that enmeshes stromal cells, blood vessels, lymphatics, and embryological remnants such as the rete ovarii.

INITIATION OF THE FOLLICULAR GROWTH

Oogenesis and Composition of the Ovarian Reserve

In humans, at the beginning of the fourth week of embryonic development the primordial germ cells (PGC) migrate to the coelomic epithelium of the gonadal ridges. When sexual differentiation occurs, the PGC continue to proliferate in the embryonic ovary and become oogonia. By the twentieth week of pregnancy, about 7 million oogonia are present [2]; thereafter oogonia enter meiotic prophase, which marks the end of germ cell production. Around the twenty-fourth week of gestation, almost all these germ cells, now called *oocytes,* have passed through the first four stages of meiosis I and are arrested at the diplotene stage. The oocytes are surrounded by a layer of epithelial pregranulosa cells to form primordial follicles. Although some of these follicles start to grow almost immediately, most remain in a resting stage until they either degenerate or enter the growth phase. After birth the pool of follicles at the resting stage constitutes the ovarian reserve, including primordial follicles in which the oocyte is surrounded by flattened granulosa cells (GC) (Figure 2.3, *A*), transitory follicles in which the oocyte is surrounded by a mixture of flattened and cuboidal GC (Figure 2.3, *B*), and small primary follicles in which the oocyte is surrounded by a single layer of cuboidal GC (Figure 2.3, *C*).

Aging Changes

In humans, as in other mammals, the size of the ovarian reserve decreases drastically with age (Table 2.1). Attrition of the ovarian reserve has started during fetal life, as soon as the twenty-fourth week of pregnancy when the number of oocytes began to reduce dramatically. At birth the size of the ovarian reserve varies among individuals. Although follicular counts have been performed in a small number of newborn ovaries, it can be proposed from direct counts [2, 3] and mathematical extrapolation [4] that each ovary contains between 250,000 and 500,000 resting follicles. In humans the rate of follicular depletion might vary among subjects and accelerates from approximately 38 years of age onward, leading to a stock at menopause estimated between less than 100 [4] and 1000 [5] resting follicles per ovary.

Given the age range, comprised between 40 and 60 years, for menopause occurence it takes 50% more time for some women to exhaust their follicle pool than it does for others. This may be related to variable depletion rates, differences in the initial number of resting follicles, or both. The menopausal age of a given woman is correlated with the timing of menopause in her mother and sisters, which strongly suggests a genetic component in factors that regulate depletion of the follicle pool. Parity and environmental factors such as nutrition, race, and socioeconomic status also influence the age at which menopause occurs [6]. Among these factors, lifestyle exposures—especially smoking—can hasten menopause occurence [7].

In all mammalian species, follicles leave the stock of resting follicles in a continuous stream, either by apoptosis or by entry into the growth phase. By taking into account the number of growing follicles within the ovaries throughout life [4], it can be estimated that more than 90% of the ovarian reserve escapes by apoptosis mainly during infancy and early adulthood.

Depletion of the Pool by Atresia

It is now widely accepted that apoptosis, an active energy-consuming process controlled by a number of intracellular proteins, is mainly responsible for attrition of the ovarian reserve (see Part V for a detailed discussion of follicular apoptosis). Two comments can be made concerning apoptosis of nongrowing follicles in humans. Firstly, atresia of these follicles is difficult to appreciate. Careful examinations of the ovarian reserve show that the oocyte is the first cell to disappear, which leads to follicles exhibiting an irregular ring of transformed GC

TABLE 2.1 Total number ($\times 10^{-3}$) of different types of small follicles from human ovaries in various age groups. Values are mean ± SEM; number of ovaries is indicated in parentheses.

	Age groups (years)				
Follicular types	**19–30 (5)**	**31–35 (9)**	**36–40 (13)**	**41–45 (28)**	**≥46 (26)**
Primordial	51.9 ± 9.0	19.5 ± 2.8	9.7 ± 1.1	4.9 ± 1.5	1.3 ± 0.2
Transitory	21.8 ± 2.7	10.6 ± 1.7	6.0 ± 1.3	3.1 ± 0.7	0.9 ± 0.1
Primary	4.9 ± 0.6	2.3 ± 0.3	1.5 ± 0.4	0.7 ± 0.1	0.3 ± 0.1
Total	79.6 ± 12.4	33.3 ± 4.0	20.6 ± 3.7	8.9 ± 2.1	2.7 ± 0.4

SEM, standard error to the mean.

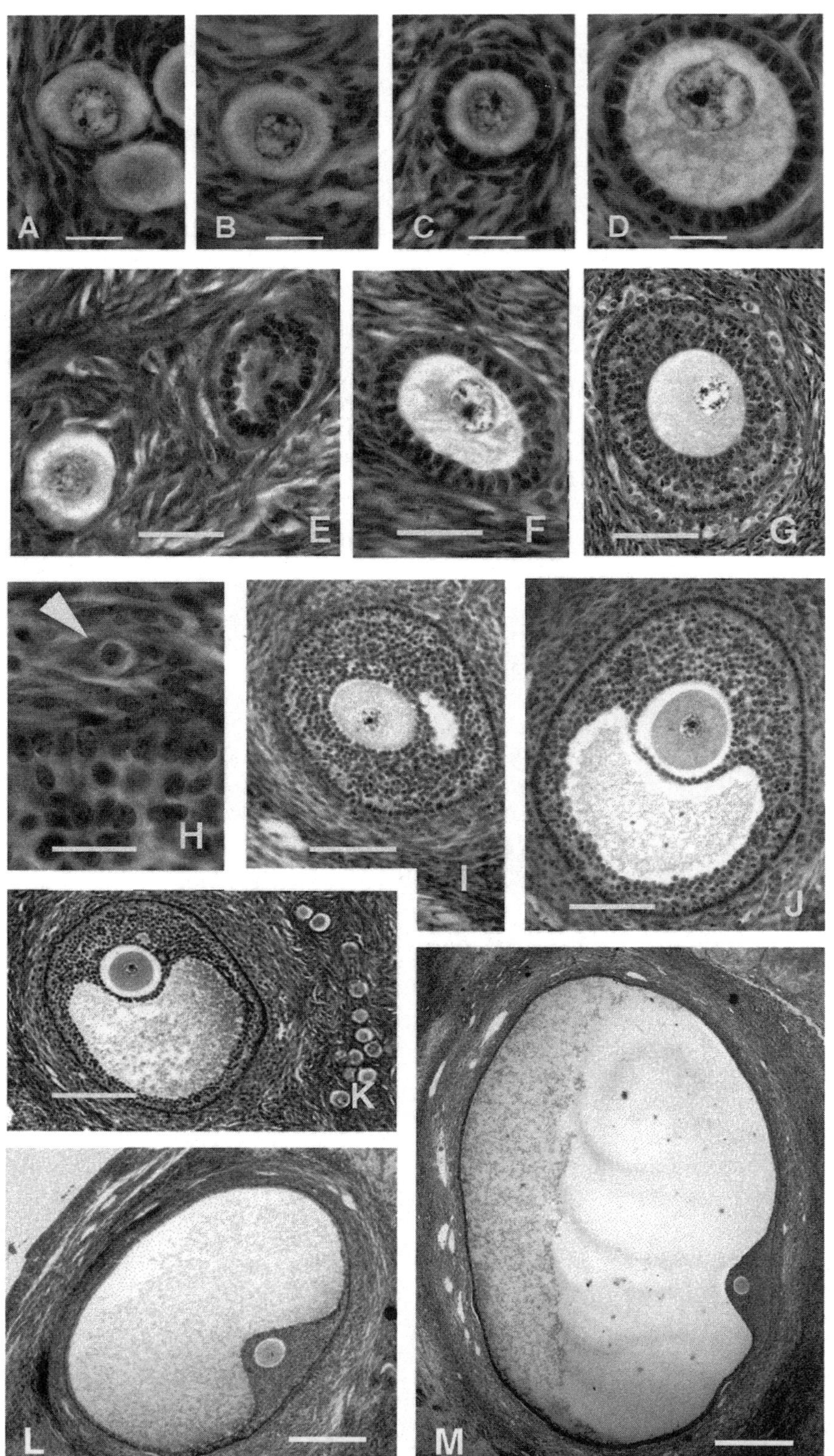

FIGURE 2.3 Classification of human follicles. **A,** Primordial follicle. **B,** Intermediary follicle. **C,** Small primary follicle. (*A, B, C* scale bar = 18 μm.) **D,** Large primary follicle (scale bar = 20 μm). **E,** Atretic primary follicle (*top right*) in which the oocyte has disappeared; a normal primordial follicle (*left*) is present (scale bar = 30 μm). **F,** Secondary follicle (scale bar = 40 μm). **G,** Preantral follicle (class 1, 0.15–0.2 mm) (scale bar = 75 μm). **H,** High-power micrograph of epithelioid theca cells (*white arrow*) from a preantral follicle (scale bar = 18 μm). **I,** Follicle with a small antrum (class 2, 0.2–0.4 mm) (scale bar = 100 μm). **J,** Early antral follicle; the GC surounding the oocyte constitute the *cumulus oophorus* (class 2) (scale bar = 90 μm). **K,** Small antral follicle (class 3, 0.5–0.9 mm); nongrowing follicles are on right (scale bar = 160 μm). **L,** Small antral follicle (class 4, 1–2 mm) (scale bar = 300 μm). **M,** Selectable follicle (class 5, 2–5 mm) (scale bar = 530 μm).

TABLE 2.2 Morphometric characteristics of primordial, transitory, and primary follicles in the adult human ovary. Data expressed as mean ± s.d. for the n° of follicles given in parentheses.

Type of follicle		Follicular diameter (μm)	Oocyte diameter (μm)	Oocyte nuclear diameter (μm)	Granulosa cells	
					Mean n°	Range
Primordial	(408)	35.4 ± 6.2	32.1 ± 6.0	16.1 ± 6.1	13 ± 6	7–23
Transitory	(409)	37.8 ± 8.2	31.7 ± 8.0	16.3 ± 4.0	28 ± 6	9–50
Primary	(153)	46.0 ± 6.2	32.6 ± 4.9	16.7 ± 2.5	76 ± 27	23–223

(Figure 2.3, *E*). This is likely caused by a quick disappearance of apoptotic oocytes, which suggests that the oocyte may have an intrinsic mechanism for apoptosis activation. Secondly, in most cases, survival or apoptosis results from a balance between expression of survival (antiapoptotic) and proapoptotic factors. Among these factors, the proteins bcl-2 and bax likely play a critical role. On one hand, in bcl-2–deficient mice, decreased numbers of follicles are present after birth [9], whereas overexpression of bcl-2 leads to decreased follicular apoptosis [10]. On the other hand, bax deficiency leads to prolongation of ovarian life span [11]. Taken together, available data show that even if bax and bcl-2 proteins are involved in nongrowing follicle apoptosis, the factors that initiate the apoptotic cascade in physiologic conditions remain unknown.

Depletion of the Pool by Initiation of Follicular Growth

Follicles continuously enter the growth phase from fetal life to menopause. The mechanism(s) regulating this process remain(s) poorly understood. It is still unclear which follicles are growing follicles and whether activation of primordial follicles is regulated by an inhibitor, a stimulator, or a balance between inhibitory and stimulatory factors. Consequently, the following questions can be adressed concerning initiation of follicular growth.

Can We Differentiate Growing from Nongrowing Follicles?

Our limited understanding of the precise mechanisms controlling the initiation of follicular growth can be attributed to the difficulty of distinguishing early growing follicles from resting follicles. Whether transitory follicles, which possess at least one cuboidal GC, are or are not quiescent follicles has been debated for a long time. Whereas transitory and primary follicles in rodent ovaries were considered growing follicles by some investigators [12], they were considered quiescent follicles by others in rats [13], cattle [14], and humans [15]. In humans, primordial, transitory, and small primary follicles differ in their diameter because of differences in the number and size of GC but do not differ in the mean diameter of their oocyte and its nucleus (Table 2.2), which is about 16 μm in diameter, a size largely below that of 19 μm observed when active follicular growth starts [15]. In addition, van Wezel and Rodgers [14] observed that in cattle more than 82.5% resting follicles contain at least one cuboidal GC and assumed that "this proportion is so high that if all these follicles were growing, the ovary could be expected to become devoid of oocytes, and the cow sterile, within a matter of months."

In rats, several authors observed the presence of at least one proliferating GC, either flattened or cuboidal, within primordial, transitory, and primary follicles [16–18], and therefore assumed that when GC proliferate, the follicles are no longer quiescent and have entered the growth phase. However, the occasional presence of a dividing cell does not necessarily signify that the follicle has entered the growth phase. Indeed, in a recent experiment in rats consisting of BrDU infusion, more than half of the transitory follicles were labelled even 150 days after the removal of the BrDU source thus demonstrating that, despite the presence of cuboidal GC and at least one proliferating GC, these follicles had to be considered as nongrowing follicles [13].

Which Factors May Be Involved in Activation of Resting Follicles?

The kit system seems to play a pivotal role in the initiation of follicular growth because in mice displaying various more or less inactivating mutations of *steel* (the cyclic adenosine monophosphate [cAMP]-responsive [19] gene coding for the kit ligand [KL, also called *SCF*]), follicular growth is more or less blocked at the primary stage [20]. By using either antibodies against c-kit, the receptor for KL [21, 22] or in vitro techniques [22, 23], this critical role of the kit system in nongrowing follicle activation has been recently demonstrated. By using similar in vitro techniques in rats, basic fibroblast growth factor (bFGF) has also been demonstrated to play a role in initiating follicular growth [24]. However, although KL and c-kit have been detected in primate nongrowing follicles [25, 26], bFGF was not detected in human follicles before the preantral stage [27]. In cynomolgus monkeys, transforming growth factor-alpha (TGF-α) is absent in GC from resting follicles and is present in GC from growing follicles [25]. Because TGF-α stimulate GC proliferation [28], it could be tempting to speculate that TGF-α may play a role in the initiation of follicular growth via induction of GC proliferation.

In primates, nongrowing follicles can be blocked at the resting stage for a long time—up to 50 years in humans. Consequently, one question can be adressed: Is the resting stage caused by the action of a molecule(s) preventing nongrowing follicles from activation? Several molecules are attractive candidates to play this role. Anti-Müllerian hormone (AMH) has been recently demonstrated to inhibit, at least partly, initiation of follicular growth in neonate rat ovaries [29]. Since in the primate ovary AMH is only produced by GC from growing follicles (Figure 2.4), it cannot be excluded that AMH produced by these follicles can block the follicles at the resting stage. Somatostatin and its receptors (mRNA and proteins) have been detected in the human ovary [29a]. Somatostatin is a potent inhibitor of cAMP generation in most epithelial cells [30] and is able to inhibit activation of the kit system in the testis [31]. In cynomolgus monkeys, transforming growth factor-β2 (TGF-β2) is present in GC from resting follicles, whereas both TβRI and RII are present in their oocytes [25]. Because TGF-β1 inhibits marrow stromal cell expression of KL and hematopoietic progenitor cell expression of c-kit [32] and TGF-β stimulates SST2A (the ovarian receptor for somatostatin) expression in the mouse [33], it can be suggested that TGF-βs and/or somatostain might operate together in the nongrowing follicle to inhibit the kit system and subsequently follicle growth initiation.

If nongrowing follicles may be maintained at the resting stage through the action of an inhibitor(s) repressing cAMP generation, a positive signal, acting through activation of cAMP production, must be operating to initiate follicular growth. Some neuropeptides such as the vasoactive intestinal peptides (VIP) and the pituitary adenylate cyclase activating peptide (PACAP), which are produced in the ovary and are potent inducers of cAMP generation, are attractive candidates. In addition, several experiments and analyses of transgenic mice models argue in favor of a role for neurotrophins, a group of molecules including nerve growth factor (NGF), brain-derived neurotrophic factor (BDNF), and neutrophin-4 (NT-4) in initiation of follicular growth (see Chapter 1 [34]). However, to date, a role for neuropeptides and neurotrophins in the primate ovary has not been demonstrated.

In conclusion, available data suggest that initiation of ovarian follicular growth may depend on a balance between inhibitory and activating factors, either produced by nongrowing follicles themselves or present in their ovarian microenvironment.

Are Gonadotropins Involved in Initiation of Follicular Growth?

Whether FSH is or is not involved in initiation of follicular growth is still debated. In rats, early studies suggested that gonadotropins might be involved in the initiation of follicular growth observed at days 5 to 7 of life (for review, see [35]). In hypogonadal (hpg) mice suffering from a deletion of the gonadotropin-releasing hormone (Gn-RH) gene, the number of early growing follicles is reduced; it can be restored to its normal number by treatment with FSH [36]. Hypophysectomy slows the loss of resting follicles in rats [37], whereas in transgenic mice that maintain a chronically elevated luteinizing hormone (LH) level, the ovarian reserve is depleted faster than in normal controls [38]. In aged rats, unilateral ovariectomy increases concentration of FSH and is associated with increased loss of primordial follicles [39], a situation that can be related to the observation in humans where increasing serum FSH levels [40] are observed at the time of accelerated depletion of the ovarian reserve [4]. Taken together, these data suggest that gonadotropins may be involved in activation of resting follicles. However, several pieces of evidence suggest that gonadotropins are not the primary motor of

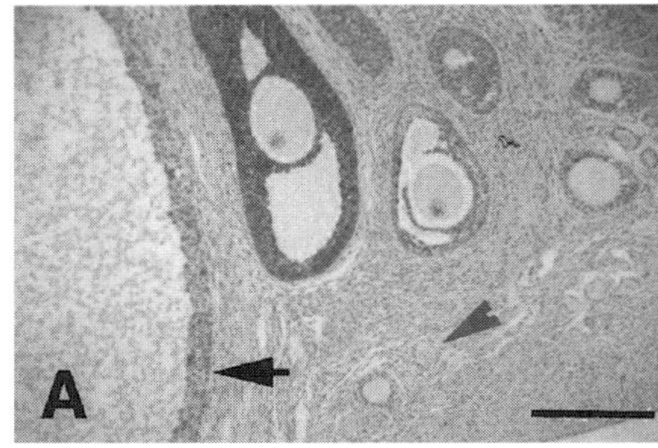

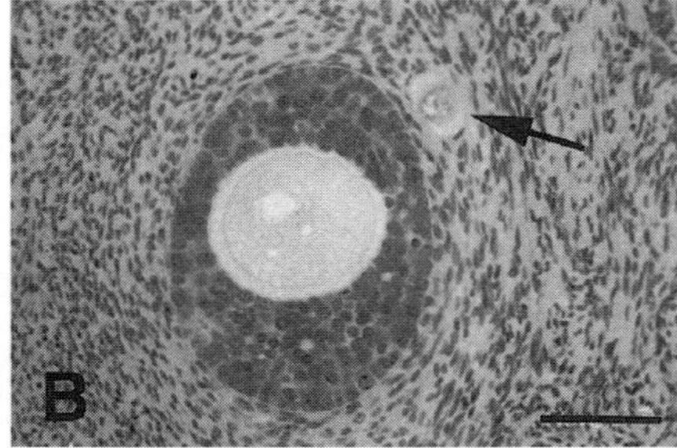

FIGURE 2.4 Immunodetection of AMH in the primate ovary. **A,** AMH immunostaining in the macaca ovary. Nongrowing follicles (*red arrow*) are not immunostained. On the contrary to small follicles that display a strong immunostaining in their GC, both early growing and large antral (*black arrow*) follicles display a low staining in the presence of the antibody for AMH (scale bar = 170 μm). **B,** AMH immunostaining in the human ovary. The GC of a preantral follicle stain positively for AMH, whereas those of a primordial follicle (*black arrow*) stain negatively (scale bar = 65 μm). (The AMH antibody was a gift from Dr. Nathalie Josso.) (See color plate.)

this process. In humans, primordial follicles do not express FSH receptor messenger ribonucleic acid (mRNA) [41], and although FSH receptors are present in transitory and primary follicles, FSH receptors in bovine primary follicles are not coupled to the adenylate cyclase second messenger system [42]. In mice, rats, cattle, and baboons, initiation of follicular growth can occur in vitro in the absence of FSH (for review, see [25]). When grafted in female mice homozygous for severe combined immunodeficiency (SCID) and hpg, human resting follicles can be activated despite the absence of FSH [43]. In FSH β subunit–[44] and FSH receptor–[45] null female mice, activation of resting follicles can occur and preantral follicles can be seen. Similarly, in women with a mutated FSH β subunit, follicles can grow up to the selectable stage [46].

Thus, there are conflicting data concerning a possible role for gonadotropins in the process of resting follicle activation. Nevertheless, it can be hypothesized that these data may be conflicting only in appearance. Some local factors, either produced by nongrowing follicles themselves or by neighbor growing follicles, could activate resting follicles, explaining why activation can occur in gonadotropin-deprived situations. However, gonadotropins might increase production of these local factors by growing follicles, which explains the accelerated depletion of the ovarian reserve when circulating levels of gonadotropins are increased. In conclusion, whereas the exact pattern by which gonadotropins and local factors control resting follicle activation remains poorly understood, this process may be envisioned as a multiphased process regulated by biological molecules acting either at the oocyte or at the GC level.

FOLLICLE GROWTH

Early Follicle Growth

Morphological Aspects

When follicles enter the growth phase, they enlarge by proliferation of GC and by increase in size of the oocyte. The first stage of follicular growth in humans is the large primary follicle (Figure 2.3, *D*). Ultrastructural studies show that the immature GC contain mainly rough endoplasmic reticulum, which reflects the preponderance of protein synthesis for proliferation [47]. In addition, these GC become metabolically coupled with each other by adherent junctions that are associations of filamentous dense material on the intercellular sides of the plasma membrane, and by gap junctions that are aggregates of transmembrane channels, which are composed of six identical subunits of connexins arranged to form a central pore. The metabolic syncitium so formed is important for follicular development because in mice lacking connexin-43, a protein associated with gap junctions between GC, folliculogenesis can proceed to the primary stage but subsequent development is impaired [48]. A zona pellucida, composed of three glycoproteins (ZP 1, ZP 2, ZP 3), is laid down around the oocyte shortly after initiation of follicular growth [49]. In each follicle from the primordial stage, the granulosa is enveloped by a *basal lamina* that separates the surrounding stromal/thecal elements from GC and excludes capillary, blood cells, and nerves from the granulosa layers [50].

Progressively, follicles become secondary follicles (i.e., follicles with two or more complete layers of GC surrounding the oocyte) (Figure 2.3, *F*). The smallest early growing follicles lack an independent blood supply, but secondary follicles 80 to 100 μm in diameter are served by one or two arterioles, terminating in an anastomotic network just outside the basal lamina [12]. The physiological importance of this event is emphasized by the fact that the follicle becomes directly exposed to factors circulating in the blood. At this stage of development, some stroma cells near the basal lamina become aligned parallel to each other and constitue the theca layer. As the follicle enlarges, this theca stratifies and differentiates in two parts. The outer part, the *theca externa,* consists of cells that do not differ in any respect from the cells of the undifferentiated theca. In the inner part, the *theca interna,* some fibroblast-like precursor cells assume the appearance of typical steroid-secreting cells (also called *epithelioid cells*) (Figure 2.3, *H*). Morphological studies have shown that definitive theca layers appear only when follicles contain three to six layers of GC (follicle diameter = 103–163 μm in women) [51]. From the time of appearance of epithelioid cells, the secondary follicle is defined as a preantral follicle (Figure 2.3, *G*) and constitutes the first class of growing follicles in a classification based on morphological aspect and total number of GC in each individual follicle [51]. In humans the number of preantral follicles is the highest during the early luteal phase. Whether this can be related to endocrine periovulatory (LH) or to microenvironmental changes (local factors produced by the preovulatory follicle) remains to be determined. It has been assumed that these follicles, which constitute a group growing at the same time and at a similar rate as if in a wave, start to develop during the early luteal phase and culminate, almost three cycles later, in ovulation of only one of them (Figure 2.5).

When small fluid-filled cavities aggregate to form the antrum, the follicle becomes early antral (Figure 2.3, *I*). From this time, the GC surrounding the oocyte constitute the *cumulus oophorus* (Figure 2.3, *J*). These GC form heterologous gap junctions with the oocyte via processes passing through the zona pellucida to contact the *oolemma* [52]. These GC-oocyte contacts play a critical role during terminal follicular maturation as demonstrated by the lack of preovulatory follicles in connexin-37 null mice [53]. In primates, as in most mammals, shortly after the follicle acquires a single antral cavity, the GC that border the

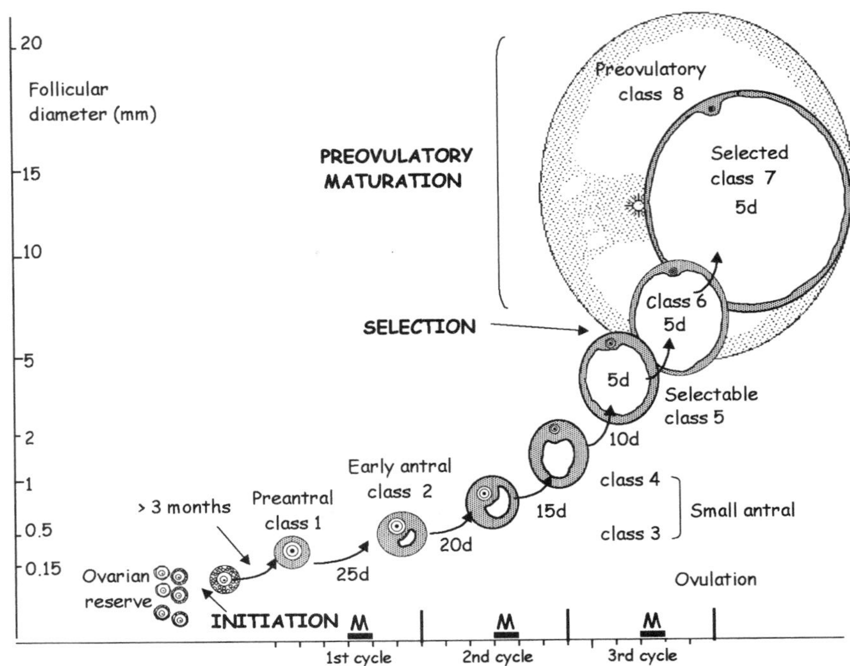

FIGURE 2.5 Chronology of follicle growth during the human menstrual cycle. Growth starts when small primary follicles become large primary follicles. More than 3 months are required for these follicles to reach the preantral stage (class 1). Follicles preferentially enter into class 1 during the early luteal phase. An entry of follicles into class 2 can be seen 25 days later during the late follicular phase of the following cycle. Twenty days later, follicles pass into class 3 during the late luteal phase. Fifteen days later, follicles pass into class 4 during the late follicular phase of the subsequent cycle. Ten days later, follicles enter into class 5 during the late luteal phase; they constitute the follicle population from which the follicle destined to ovulate during the subsequent cycle will be selected. Selection occurs 5 days later and the selected follicle (class 6, 6–10 mm) can be identified during the early follicular phase of the ovulatory cycle. Five days later, during the mid-follicular phase, the dominant follicle is 10 to 16 mm in diameter; it will ovulate within the 5 subsequent days in response to the LH surge.

TABLE 2.3 Evolution of morphometric characteristics of granulosa cells in healthy growing follicles (numbers in parentheses) during folliculogenesis (values are expressed as mean ± SEM).

Class	Number of GC	Mitotic index (%)	n° GC ($\times 10^{-5}$) per cubic mm of tissue	Thickness of GC layer (μm)
1 (742)	2100 ± 100	0.384 ± 0.008	12.13 ± 0.17	NA
2 (565)	7600 ± 100	0.440 ± 0.008	11.08 ± 0.08	35.9 ± 1.0
3 (342)	33,300 ± 1300	0.532 ± 0.011	10.45 ± 0.12	36.0 ± 0.5
4 (143)	176,800 ± 7500	0.875 ± 0.031	9.82 ± 0.19	27.6 ± 0.8
5 (133)	933,500 ± 44,900	0.981 ± 0.040	8.53 ± 0.27	27.1 ± 0.9
6 (31)	3,400,000 ± 300,000	1.191 ± 0.125	7.46 ± 0.23	77.5 ± 4.2
7 (16)	24,140,000 ± 2,970,000	0.930 ± 0.170	6.29 ± 0.25	81.2 ± 3.2
8 (22)*	54,760,000 ± 4,610,000	0.639 ± 0.070	6.24 ± 0.13	97.8 ± 3.3
8 (16)†	59,070,000 ± 5,510,000	0.027 ± 0.007	4.59 ± 0.20	99.1 ± 3.2

*Before the midcycle gonadotropin surge.
†After the midcycle gonadotropin surge.

basement membrane loose their cuboidal shape and assume a columnar appearance, whereas the remaining GC remain cuboidal. In humans and monkeys, follicles pass from the preantral (class 1) to the early antral stage (class 2) at a follicular diameter comprised between 180 and 250 μm [51, 54]. Through accumulation of fluid in the antral cavity and proliferation of GC and theca interna cells, the follicle progresses at an increasing rate (see Figure 2.5 and Table 2.3) through subsequent stages of development (Figures 2.3, *K* and *L*) until it reaches a size between 2 and 5 mm and becomes a selectable follicle (Figure 2.3, *M*). Thus at the beginning of the follicle growth, the oocyte enlarges, theca interna cells proliferate, and differentiate, and GC proliferate.

Oocyte Growth

Despite the apparent nuclear quiescence, oocytes are transcriptionally active and display high levels of synthetic activity, as indicated by the presence of one or more nucleoli [55], ribonucleic acid (RNA) polymerase activity, and a continuous uptake of amino acids and ribonucleosides. As the oocyte increases in volume, its cytoplasm assumes a more complex organization. For example, mitochondriae become more vacuolated and the Golgi apparatus expands and migrates nearer the periphery [55]. It is during the early follicular growth that the oocyte grows at the quickest rate; indeed in humans, its diameter increases from approximatly 30 μm in primary follicles to approximately

100 μm in early antral follicles. Beyond this stage of development, the increase in size of the oocyte occurs at a slow rate because its diameter will reach approximately 140 μm in the preovulatory follicle.

Although KL alone is involved in oocyte growth occurring at the time of initiation of follicle growth, it is efficient in sustaining oocyte growth of early growing follicles up to the preantral stage only in the presence of contact communication with GC [23]. The KL-induced oocyte growth could be controlled by the growth differentiation factor 9 (GDF-9), because in GDF-9 null mice follicles beyond the primary stage display morphologically abnormal GC and oocytes [56]. This abnormal oocyte growth could be caused by an overexpression of KL in the absence of GDF-9 [57].

Theca Cell Proliferation and Differentiation

By attracting stroma cells around the follicle, then stimulating their proliferation and their differentiation, KL [58] and epidermal growth factor (EGF) [59] have been postulated to act as "granulosa-derived theca cell organizers." The mechanisms leading to organization of the theca and differentiation of stroma cells surrounding primary and secondary follicles into theca cells remain unclear, but they may involve the action of GDF-9 on production of the extracellular matrix on which theca cells can attach [60]. LH has been considered the primary hormone regulating the differentiation of theca interna cells [61], and in primates, epithelioid theca cells specifically bind LH at all stages from the preantral stage [62, 63]. However, various peptides including GDF-9 [56] and insulin-like growth factor-I [64] may be acting as differentiation factors for theca cells in inducing either LH receptors [64] or steroidogenic enzymes [56]. In humans, steroidogenic enzymes controlling androgen biosynthesis are present, although at a low level, in the theca interna of early antral follicles (Figure 2.6, *A*).

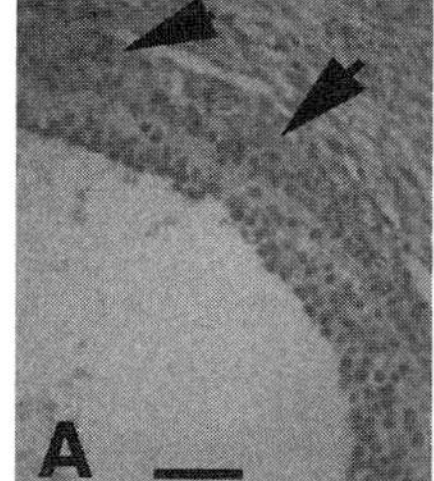

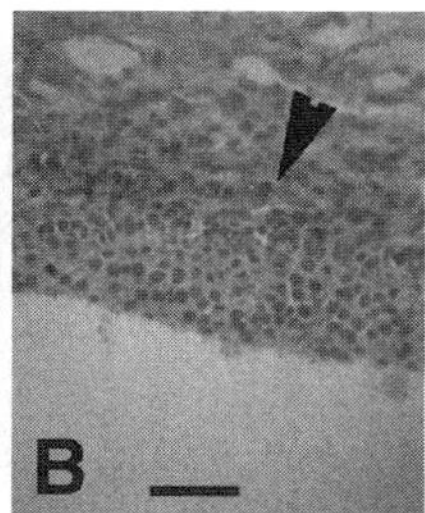

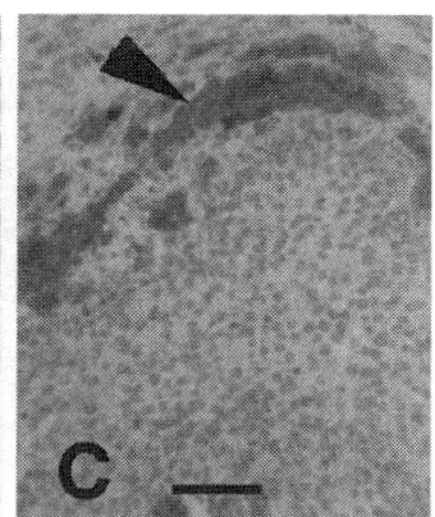

FIGURE 2.6 Thecal steroidogenesis, immunohistochemical detection of $P450_{c17\alpha/lyase}$ (*black arrows*), during human folliculogenesis (scale bar = 50 μm). **A,** Weak immunostaining in the theca interna of a class 3 follicle. **B,** Moderate immunostaining in the theca interna of a selectable follicle. **C,** Strong immunostaining in the theca interna of a preovulatory follicle. (The $P450_{c17\alpha/lyase}$ antibody was a gift from Dr. Shiro Kominami.) (See color plate.)

Granulosa Cell Proliferation: What Role Does FSH Play during This Process?

When early growing follicles become vascularized, they are directly exposed to factors circulating in the blood, especially gonadotropins. These hormones, particularly FSH, are the primary pituitary regulators of ovarian folliculogenesis, although its action on GC and its interactions with local factors appear to be complex [65]. However, similar to the situation observed for activation of resting follicles, the role of FSH in sustaining early follicular growth remains unclear.

It has been proposed that early growing follicles are FSH-independent because they can reach the selectable stage (large preantral follicles in rodents) in the absence of either bioactive FSH [44, 46] or FSH receptor [45]. However, because of the absence of morphometrical studies concerning ovaries of mice null for FSH-β and for the FSH receptor, one can wonder if these ovaries would not be similar to those observed in hypophysectomized [66] and hpg [36] mice and in Gn-RH antagonist-treated juvenile rats [67]. In these ovaries, healthy preantral follicles are present but in lower numbers than in controls and/or with structural abnormalities. In these situations, although ovulation cannot occur, early follicular growth is not abolished but impaired and, in all these cases, exogenous FSH restores the normal aspect of early growing follicles and increases their number [36, 67–69]. These situations can also be compared with various pathological (hypogonadotropic hypogonadism, hypophysectomy) situations in humans where, despite low levels of gonadotropin, transvaginal sonographies indicate the presence of many selectable follicles (for reviews, see [51, 70]). In patients displaying a partial inactivation of the FSH receptor (FSHR) gene, follicles can grow up to a size of several mm [71, 72]; however, when stimulated with human menopausal gonadotropins (hMG), these patients cannot ovulate.

Taken together, these observations indicate that FSH levels required to support the preovulatory growth are largely higher than those supporting growth of small follicles. More surprising is that in the absence of FSH, folliculogenesis can proceed up to the selectable stage, although it is not known if, in these conditions, folliculogenesis is quantitatively and qualitatively normal.

Many local factors such as activin A [73], EGF [74], TGF-β [75], bFGF [76], keratinocyte growth factor (KGF), and hepatocyte growth factor (HGF) [76], as well as peptides produced by the oocyte (e.g., GDF-9 [77] and bone morphogenetic protein [BMP]-15 [78]), have been shown to stimulate GC proliferation in the absence of FSH. Although the role of estrogens remains to be determined during follicular growth in primates (for review, see [70]), recent data show that androgens sustain early follicular development in monkeys. Yet, a 3- to 10-day treatment of monkeys with either dihydro-testosterone or testosterone [79] strongly increased the number of early growing follicles. This effect of androgens, acting through their receptors present in follicles [80], can be caused by their ability to stimulate GC proliferation in follicles at all stages of development [81]. Consequently, it can be assumed that in the absence of FSH, local factors can support early follicle growth. However, many experiments have demonstrated that FSH acts in synergy with local factors to enhance follicle growth. Growth of preantral follicles isolated from immature rats is enhanced by KGF and GDF-9 acting in synergy with FSH [82]. In adult hamsters, EGF and TGF-β2 synergize with FSH to stimulate GC proliferation from preantral follicles [74]. Although activin A alone can induce the FSH receptors in cultured rat GC in the absence of FSH, this effect is enhanced by FSH [83]. Finally, TGF-β1 can induce the FSH responsiveness of preantral follicles from 11-day-old juvenile mice, although neither FSH nor TGF-β1 alone have a significant effect when administered separately [75].

Taken together, these observations indicate that in experimental conditions leading to gonadotropin deprivation, the development of early growing follicles can be sustained by local factors; however, it appears likely that these factors are less efficient to sustain growth than they are when they act in synergy with gonadotropins.

Early Growing Follicles Are Poorly Responsive to Gonadotropins

In humans, secondary follicles require several months to reach the selectable stage [51]. Therefore, despite the positive role played by FSH and local factors on their development, early growing follicles grow slowly and do not display any change of their GC mitotic index in relation to the cyclic changes of gonadotropin circulating levels [84]. Various factors produced by the follicles themselves may counteract FSH- and growth factor–induced GC proliferation. In rats, activin A, produced by large preantral/early antral follicles, has been shown to inhibit the FSH-induced growth of secondary/small preantral follicles (100–120 μm) [85]. It has also been proposed [86] that WT1, a protein that is highly expressed in monkey preantral follicles, may delay follicle growth by repressing the transcriptional activity of genes encoding gonadotropin-receptors and intraovarian growth factors. Finally, it has recently been demonstrated that in the mouse ovary, AMH inhibits the FSH-stimulated follicle growth [87], suggesting that this molecule, which has the same pattern of expression in the primate ovary (Figure 2.4, *A*), may partly inhibit GC proliferation in humans.

Another characteristic of early growing follicles is that their GC are undifferentiated; they express neither aromatase nor enzymes for synthesis of progestins nor LH receptors [62, 88, 89]. Whereas some local factors act, either alone or in synergy with FSH to promote GC proliferation, these factors also can inhibit the FSH-induced differentiation of GC. In rats, EGF and bFGF inhibit the FSH-induced FSHR mRNA expression [90]. In humans, TGF-α from theca cells rather than EGF might operate inside the growing follicle to inhibit FSH-induced GC differentiation [91]. HGF and KGF inhibit basal or hormone-stimulated GC differentiation [92]. It has also been suggested that GDF-9 and BMP-15 may repress GC differentiation during early follicular growth [57, 78, 93]. The high expression of certain IGF binding proteins decreases the bioavailability of IGFs, which stimulates GC proliferation and differentiation and could be partly responsible for the slow growth rate of these follicles and their poor GC differentiation (for review, see [94]).

Taken together, these data show that early growing follicles produce factors that not only can sustain their growth, either in the absence or in the presence of FSH, but that also can inhibit, at least partly, FSH-induced GC proliferation and differentiation.

The Selectable Follicle and Selection of the Follicle Destined to Ovulate

Healthy follicles measuring 2 to 5 mm, called *selectable follicles,* are observed at all stages of the menstrual cycle [95]. During the late luteal phase, their number and quality rise in humans [96] as in monkeys [97] in response to increasing peripheral FSH levels following the demise of the cyclic *corpus luteum*. At this time, their number is between 3 and 11 per ovary in 24- to 33-year-old women [98], but the number strongly decreases with aging. It is among these follicles that the follicle destined to ovulate during the subsequent cycle is selected [95, 96]. Whereas early growing follicles are unsensitive to cyclic hormonal changes, selectable follicles are more receptive to these alterations. Their GC mitotic index strongly increases from the mid- to the late luteal phase [84] and they are highly responsive to exogenous gonadotropins in terms of GC proliferation [99]. However, the intrafollicular concentration of estradiol in selectable follicles is low when compared with that of androgens (Table 2.4). The follicular fluid of selectable follicles contains high levels of factors [100, 101] that possess the ability to inhibit FSH-induced aromatase [102] and thecal production of androgens [103]. Nonetheless, these negative effects on the production of aromatizable androgens could be counteracted, at least partly, by an increasing number of LH receptors [63], an increasing LH pulse frequency during the early follicular phase [104], and the positive effect of GDF-9 on androgen production by theca cells [105], leading to a moderate activity of enzymes involved in androgen production (Figure 2.6, *B*).

In conclusion, it appears that when follicles reach the selectable stage, their GC become responsive to FSH in terms of proliferation but not in terms of estrogen production.

Every mammalian species is characterized by a fixed number of follicle(s) that ovulate at each cycle (ovulatory quota). The term *selection* has been used by Goodman and Hodgen [106] to indicate the final adjustment of the cohort

TABLE 2.4 Changes in follicular fluid mean (± SEM) concentrations (ng/ml) of steroids from the selectable to the preovulatory stage.

Follicle type	E2	A + T + DHT	17α-OHP	Progesterone	Total
Atretic (1–5 mm)	20 ± 5	794 ± 90	NA	73 ± 13	887
Selectable	15 ± 5	638 ± 113	NA	130 ± 45	783
Newly selected (EF)	658 ± 38	487 ± 128	713 ± 318	417 ± 120	2275
Preovulatory (MF)	1270 ± 161	542 ± 176	460 ± 112	440 ± 74	2712
Preovulatory (LF : E2 peak)	2396 ± 348	203 ± 37	1002 ± 212	1228 ± 228	4829
Preovulatory (LF: E2 << LH surge)	2583 ± 22	287 ± 44	1812 ± 142	2464 ± 226	6146
Preovulatory (after the LH surge)	1109 ± 142	79 ± 21	2034 ± 326	7773 ± 643	10,995

17α-OHP, 17α-hydroxy-progesterone; *A*, androstenedione; *DHT*, dihydrotestosterone; *E2*, estradiol; *EF*, early follicular phase; *LF*, late follicular phase; *MF*, midfollicular phase; *T*, testosterone.

of growing follicles to this ovulatory quota. To be stimulated by circulating FSH, each growing follicle possesses a threshold requirement that should be surpassed to ensure ongoing preovulatory development [107]. It has been suggested that the selected follicle is the one that grows most rapidly in response to the intercycle rise in FSH (i.e., the one with the lowest FSH "threshold" [96]). At the beginning of the follicular phase the largest healthy follicle appears to be the selected follicle. It grows at a faster rate than do other subordinate follicles [108], contains a detectable level of FSH [109], and differs substantially from selectable follicles by its estradiol concentration in the follicular fluid (see Table 2.4). Taken together, these data strongly suggest that in the selected follicle, stimulators of GC proliferation and differentiation operate. Because IGFs promote human GC proliferation and differentiation [110] as well as production of androgens by theca cells [101], the importance of the IGF system in regulating FSH action has become increasingly apparent during the past decade [111]. Briefly, the IGF binding protein, IGFBP4, a potent inhibitor of FSH-induced steroid production by human GC [112], can neutralize the IGF bioactivity. By stimulating an IGFBP4 protease, the pregnancy-associated plasma protein-A (PAPP-A) in humans [113], FSH eliminates the inhibitory activity of IGFBP4 [114] and indirectly stimulates its own effect on GC proliferation and steroidogenesis via IGF action. In conclusion, it can be proposed that the follicle with the lowest FSH threshold will be the first to exhibit an increased bioactivity of its IGFs, which leads to an enhanced growth and differentiation of its GC. Being the first to produce estradiol, to differentiate LH receptors on its GC, to grow despite decreasing levels of FSH, and to inhibit growth of less developed follicles, it will be the first to ovulate.

Morphologic and Dynamic Aspects of Follicular Atresia in Humans

In humans, only one follicle is selected during each menstrual cycle. Nonselected follicles disappear at the term of a process called *atresia,* an apoptotic process [8] that variably affects follicles during their growth. Thus the fate for each individual follicle is to degenerate, allowing the ovary to produce cyclically the ovulatory quota. It is generally assumed that follicular atresia in the adult ovary consists of an underlying tonic component that mainly affects the ovarian reserve and early growing follicles, reflecting a lifelong process on which cyclic losses are superimposed [51].

Morphological Characterization of Atresia

In early histological studies, morphological criteria have been used to assess the health status of individual follicles (i.e., whether actively growing or degenerating). Oocyte involution, irregular shape of the follicle and/or of the oocyte, and, above all, nuclear pyknosis in granulosa layers resulting from GC apoptosis are criteria that have been most commonly used to describe early atresia. In follicles less than approximately 1 mm, atresia is characterized by a fast and early oocyte degeneration and hypertrophy of theca interna cells (Figure 2.7, *A*), suggesting that theca interna differentiation is partly repressed by either GC or the oocyte in the growing healthy follicle. On the contrary, the oocyte persists long after GC have disappeared in follicles larger than 1 mm and displays cyclic meiosis-like alteration (including germinal vesicle breakdown, alignment of chromosomes in metaphase, and expulsion of a polar body) that rises sharply during the periovulatory period [115]. Atretic human follicles larger than 1 mm have been arranged into four successive stages of degeneration (Figures 2.7, *B* to *E*).

Follicular Atresia in the Human Ovary during the Menstrual Cycle

In primates, atresia affects early growing follicles only slightly [54]. The mean rate of atresia is moderate and does not exhibit substantial cyclic changes for the smallest growing follicles; it is similar for preantral (class 1) and early antral follicles (class 2), 30% and 32% respectively, and for 0.5 to 0.9 mm (class 3) and 1 to 2 mm (class 4) follicles, 15% and 16% respectively. In contrast, atresia of the largest follicles varies significantly throughout the cycle

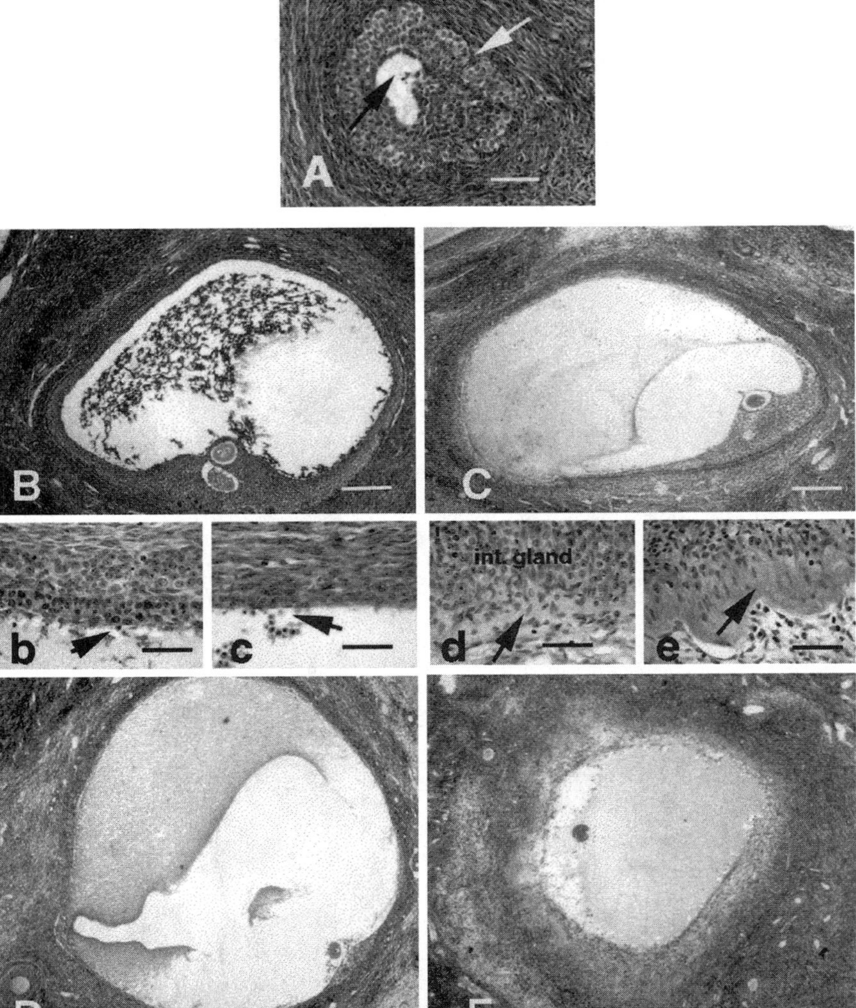

FIGURE 2.7 Follicular atresia in human follicles. **A,** Preantral or early antral follicle. The oocyte is the first cell to disappear *(black arrow);* GC are small with scarce apoptotic bodies; the follicle is surrounded by a thick hypertrophied theca interna *(white arrow)* (scale bar = 65 μm). **B** to **E,** Subsequent stages of atresia in follicles larger than 1 mm (*B, C, D* scale bar = 220 μm; *E* scale bar = 180 μm; *b, c, d, e* scale bar = 55 μm). **B,** At Stage A up to 20% of GC are apoptotic. **b,** Higher magnification of the same follicle shows that theca interna and granulosa layers are not markedly altered despite the presence of numerous apoptotic bodies. **C,** At Stage B 10% to 50% of the granulosa wall has disappeared. **c,** Higher magnification of the same follicle shows that the theca layer is not altered and that the granulosa layer has disappeared, whereas many apoptotic GC *(black arrow)* float in follicular fluid. **D,** At Stage C, the follicle presented here is spherical, but many follicles at this stage of atresia are more or less shrunken. The cumulus oophorus persists despite the disappearance of GC. **d,** Higher magnification of the same follicle shows that the theca layer has changed into an interstitial gland and that basal lamina is thickened with a thin strip of fibroblasts at the junction with the antrum. **E,** At Stage D, the ultimate stage of degeneration, the follicule varies from a spheroid to a completely collapsed shape; the antrum is more (terminal stage) or less (early stage) invaded by fibroblasts, the cumulus oophorus have disappeared, and, when not degenerated, the oocyte is floating free in the antral cavity. **e,** Higher magnification of the same follicle shows that GC and theca-interstitial gland have diappeared although the basal lamina is thick.

and is inversely related to circulating FSH levels. The highest incidence of atresia is observed during the midluteal phase for 2 to 5 mm (class 5) and 6 to 10 mm (class 6) follicles, 73% and 100% respectively [84].

In the cyclic ovary, little is known as to which signal induces apoptosis; however, FSH is clearly involved in the prevention of apoptosis [8]. The course of follicular development from the initiation to the preovulatory stage is a long process, which implies that growing follicles are subjected to the continually changing hormone concentrations in the peripheral blood circulation and in the ovary itself. It could be hypothesized that from the continuum of growing follicles, only those reaching a critical stage of their development coincidentally with appropriate changes in serum gonadotropins, "being in the right state and place at the right time," [116] can continue their development until one is selected to undergo its preovulatory maturation.

Maturation of the Preovulatory Follicle

From the time it has been selected the follicle destined to ovulate greatly enlarges from 6.9 ± 0.5 mm (2 to 5 × 10^6 GC) during the early follicular phase to 18.8 ± 0.5 mm (50 to 100 × 10^6 GC) during the late follicular phase. During this final phase of growth, the granulosa layer is subjected to marked morphological transformations (Figure 2.8) resulting from a modulation of the actin cytoskeleton organization [47]. The volume of individual GC increases (see Table 2.3), approximately 30% of the entire plasma membrane is occupied by gap junction, smooth endoplasmic reticulum gradually extends, and mitochondria with tubular cristae and lipid droplets appear as steroidogenesis rises [47].

The expression "dominant follicle" is often used to denote the follicle destined to ovulate [117]. It represents a morphological situation: that of the arrest in follicular development from when the future ovulatory follicle commences its maturation. So, during the late follicular phase in humans [95] as in monkeys [97] most of the largest nonovulatory follicles become atretic. In humans it has been shown [99] that responsiveness of selectable follicles to an hMG injection decreases as the time of ovulation approaches, and in sheep [118] and cattle [119], steroid- and inhibin-depleted follicular fluid inhibit follicular development. Finally, follicle dominance appears to be controlled by a number of mechanisms acting in concert, including a drop in circulating FSH concentration [120] in response to estradiol and inhibin secreted by the dominant follicle, as well as the production of putative local ovarian factors [121], which can inhibit the development of subordinate follicles. However, the nature of this (these) putative inhibitory factor(s), which acts via systemic mechanisms, remains unknown.

Preovulatory Maturation before the Midcycle Gonadotropin Surge

From the time it has been selected the follicle destined to ovulate shows marked changes in its steroidogenic activity. In conjunction with an enhanced androgen production by theca cells (Figure 2.6, *C*), likely in response to increasing production of inhibin [122, 123], aromatase, which is detected only in GC from follicles larger or equal to 10 mm [88], is stimulated by an increasing production of IGF-II [124], leading to a maximal intrafollicular estradiol concentration at the time of the plasma estradiol peak. So, from the early to late follicular phase, estradiol in human follicular fluid increases from 658 to 2583 ng/ml (see Table 2.4) and there is an excellent positive correlation between GC aromatase, number of GC, and concentration of estradiol in follicular fluid [125]. As the follicle matures, the GC become able to bind LH [62, 63]. From this time, LH can replace FSH, the circulating levels of which are strongly decreased in response to estradiol and inhibin production by the preovulatory follicle. So, it has been recently demonstrated that LH optimizes late folliculogenesis when administered with recombinant hFSH by accelerating

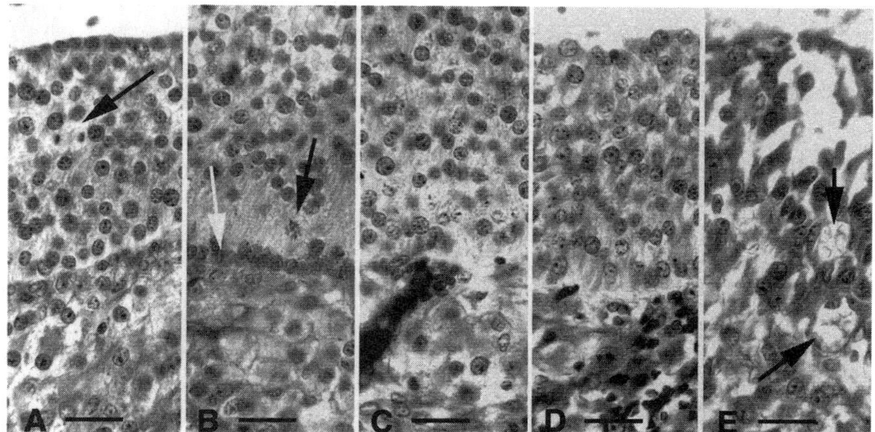

FIGURE 2.8 Follicular wall changes during the preovulatory follicle maturation. GC (*top*) are separated from theca interna cells (*bottom*) by the basal lamina (scale bar = 30 μm). **A,** During the midfollicular phase, GC proliferate (*black arrow*) at a high rate. **B,** During the plasma estradiol peak, the GC proliferate (*black arrow*) and those that border the basal lamina (*white arrow*) assume a columnar appearance with nuclei ranked along the basal lamina, whereas other GC are polyhedral in shape. **C,** During the preovulatory gonadotropin surge the columnar appearance of the basal layer of GC disappears and the basal lamina becomes blurred. **D,** Just after the midcycle gonadotropin surge, the basal lamina disappears, there are no more mitosis, and blood invades the theca interna layer. **E,** A few hours before ovulation, the GC dissociate from each other and become spindle-shaped. Capillaries (*black arrow*) from the theca interna invade the granulosa layer.

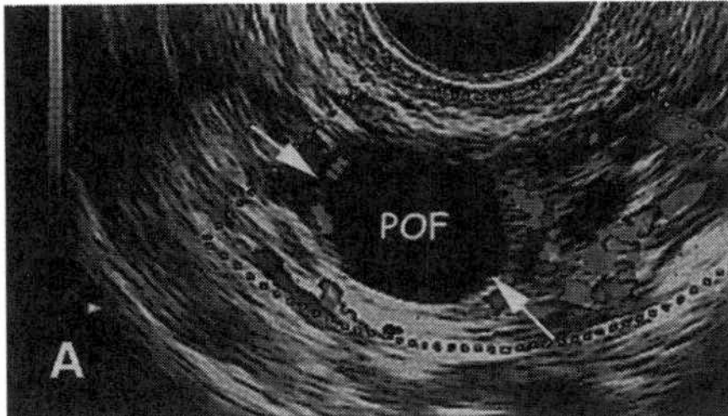

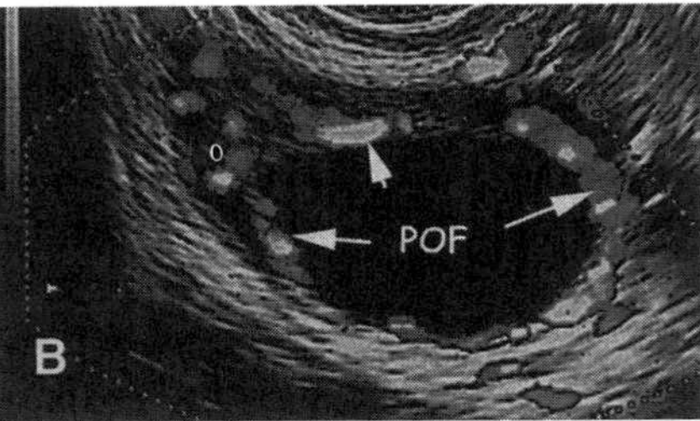

FIGURE 2.9 Color Doppler aspect of the human preovulatory follicle (POF). **A,** Before the preovulatory gonadotropin surge, the red spots are scarce. **B,** After the preovulatory gonadotropin surge, the POF is highly vascularized and diplays many red and yellow thick spots that reflect a high velocity of the blood flow. (Courtesy of Dr. Yves Ardaens.) (See color plate.)

follicle growth, reducing FSH dose requirements and small follicle development, thereby preventing patients from experiencing severe complications such as ovarian hyperstimulation syndrome [126]. This observation supports the possibility that when LH enters the follicle during the late follicular phase, it may be an important effector of GC function, perhaps even replacing FSH, as the principle regulator of GC differentiation. From the midfollicular phase the primate preovulatory follicle becomes a highly vascularized structure with the area of the theca occupied by blood vessels twice larger than in other follicles within the same or contralateral ovary [127]. The considerable increase in thecal blood vascularization occurs as a result of an active endothelial cell proliferation of thecal blood capillaries induced by angiogenic factors [128].

Preovulatory Maturation after the Midcycle Gonadotropin Surge

After the midcycle gonadotropin surge, the preovulatory follicle switches from an estradiol-producing to a progestin-producing structure, GC proliferation arrests, both mural and cumulus GC dissociate, and capillaries from the theca layers invade the granulosa. The production of steroids strongly increases, rising from a mean follicular fluid concentration of 4800 ng/ml before the surge to 11,000 ng/ml after (see Table 2.4). The rising production of progesterone results from two additive effects. Firstly, both 3βHSD [89, 129] and P450scc [88] appear in GC after the gonadotropin surge. Secondly, as a result of the breakdown of the basal lamina, the cholesterol substrate required by GC for progestin production, which is provided to cells in the form of lipoprotein-bound cholesterol, can now reach the follicle via the blood supply (for review, see [47]). In addition to the possibility that after the LH surge GC become incapable of proliferating after completing the final step of their maturation, a direct action of progesterone to block GC mitosis has been suggested [130].

Whereas FSH increases acquisition of gap junctions by GC, the gonadotropin surge causes a significant decline in gap junctions [47] leading to dissociation of mural GC and expansion of cumulus cells. In addition, GDF-9 stimulates the expression of hyaluronan synthase, cyclooxygenase 2, which are associated with cumulus expansion, and steroid acute regulatory protein (StAR) as well as progesterone production [131]. Some hours before ovulation and in response to angiogenic factors produced by GC [128], the granulosa wall, which was avascular before the midcycle gonadotropin surge, appears to be bloody after invasion of blood vessels originating from the theca (Figure 2.8, *E*). These changes in the follicular wall can be detected by color Doppler studies (Figure 2.9).

CONCLUSION

There is no doubt that our knowledge of how follicles develop in the human ovary has greatly increased during the last ten years. Whereas the role of FSH and LH as primary triggers of folliculogenesis remains indisputable, the role played by local factors has become increasingly apparent during the past decade. Both granulosa and theca cells, and more surprisingly, the oocyte, produce a variety of peptides that act broadly to influence gonadotropin action, either positively or negatively. In this respect, it is fascinating to note the large number of follicular functions that are controlled by a balance between activating and inhibiting factors. However, despite this better understanding of human folliculogenesis, many processes remain poorly understood. Among them, depletion of the ovarian reserve, either by apoptosis or by activation of nongrowing follicles, and acquisition by GC of their full responsiveness to FSH are of the greatest interest and constitute challenges for the new millenium to improve women's health and fertility.

References

1. Eppig, J. J., Wigglesworth, K., and Pendola, F. L. (2002). The mammalian oocyte orchestrates the rate of ovarian follicular development. *Proc. Natl. Acad. Sci. USA* 99, 2890–2894.
2. Baker, T. G. (1963). Quantitative and cytological study of germ cells in human ovaries. *Proc. R. Soc. Ser. B.* 158, 417–433.
3. Forabosco, A., Sforza, C., de Pol, A., Vizzotto, L., Marzona, L., and Ferrario, V. (1991). Morphometric study of the human neonatal ovary. *Anat. Rec.* 231, 201–208.
4. Gougeon, A., Ecochard, R., and Thalabard, J. C. (1994). Age-related changes of the population of human ovarian follicles: Increase in the disappearance rate of nongrowing

and early-growing follicles in aging women. *Biol. Reprod.* 50, 653–663.

5. Faddy, M. J., Gosden, R. G., Gougeon, A., Richardson, S. J., and Nelson, J. F. (1992). Accelerated disappearance of ovarian follicles in mid-life: Implications for forecasting menopause. *Hum. Reprod.* 7, 1342–1346.
6. Fauser, B. C. J. M. (2000). Follicle pool depletion: Factors involved and implications. *Fertil. Steril.* 74, 629–630.
7. Westhoff, C., Murphy, P., and Heller, D. (2000). Predictors of ovarian follicle number. *Fertil. Steril.* 74, 624–628.
8. Tilly, J. L. (2004). Apoptosis and follicular atresia. In *The Ovary,* 2d ed., eds. P. K. C. Leung and E. Y. Adashi. Boston: Elsevier.
9. Ratts, V. S., Flaws, J. A., Kolp, R., Sorenson, C. M., and Tilly, J. L. (1995). Ablation of bcl-2 gene expression decreases the numbers of oocytes and primordial follicles established in the postnatal female mouse gonad. *Endocrinology* 136, 3665–3668.
10. Hsu, S. Y., Lai, R. J. M., Finegold, M., and Hsueh, A. J. W. (1996). Targeted overexpression of bcl-2 in ovaries of transgenic mice leads to decreased follicle apoptosis, enhanced folliculogenesis, and increased germ cell tumorigenesis. *Endocrinology* 137, 4837–4843.
11. Perez, G. I., Robles, R., Knudson, C. M., Flaws, J. A., Korsmeyer, S. J., and Tilly, J. L. (1999). Prolongation of ovarian lifespan into advanced chronological age by *bax*-deficiency. *Nature Genetics* 21, 200–203.
12. Hirshfield, A. N. (1991). Development of follicles in the mammalian ovary. *Int. Rev. Cytol.* 124, 43–101.
13. Meredith, S., Dudenhoeffer, G., and Jackson, K. (2000). Classification of small type B/C follicles as primordial follicles in mature rats. *J. Reprod. Fertil.* 119, 43–48.
14. van Wezel, I. L., and Rodgers, R. J. (1996). Morphological characterization of bovine primordial follicles and their environment in vivo. *Biol. Reprod.* 55, 1003–1011.
15. Gougeon, A., and Chainy, G. B. N. (1987). Morphometric studies of small follicles in ovaries of women at different ages. *J. Reprod. Fertil.* 81, 433–442.
16. Oktay, K., Schenken, R. S., and Nelson, J. F. (1995). Proliferating cell nuclear antigen marks the initiation of follicular growth in the rat. *Biol. Reprod.* 53, 295–301.
17. Gaytan, F., Morales, C., Bellido, C., Aguilar, E., and Sanchez-Criado, J. E. (1996). Proliferative activity in the different ovarian compartments in cycling rats estimated by the 5-bromodeoxyuridine technique. *Biol. Reprod.* 54, 1356–1365.
18. Hirshfield, A. N., and DeSanti, A. M. (1995). Patterns of ovarian cell proliferation in rats during the embryonic period and the first three weeks postpartum. *Biol. Reprod.* 53, 1208–1221.
19. Packer, A. I., Hsu, Y. C., Besmer, P., and Bachvarova, R. F. (1994). The ligand of the *c-kit* receptor promotes oocyte growth. *Dev. Biol.* 161, 194–205.
20. Huang, E. J., Manova, K., Packer, A. I., Sanchez, S., Bachvarova, R. F. and Besmer, P. (1993). The murine steel panda mutation affects kit ligand expression and growth of early ovarian follicles. *Dev. Biol.* 157, 100–109.
21. Yoshida, H., Takakura, N., Kataoka, H., Kunisada, T., Okamura, H., and Nishikawa, S-I. (1997). Stepwise requirement of c-kit tyrosine kinase in mouse ovarian follicle development. *Dev. Biol.* 184, 122–137.
22. Parrott, J. A., and Skinner, M. K. (1999). Kit-ligand/stem cell factor induces primordial follicle development and initiates folliculogenesis. *Endocrinology* 140, 4262–4271.
23. Klinger, F. G., and De Felici, M. (2002). In vitro development of growing oocytes from fetal mouse oocytes: Stage-specific regulation by stem cell factor and granulosa cells. *Dev. Biol.* 244, 85–95.
24. Nilsson, E., Parrott, J. A., and Skinner, M. K. (2001). Basic fibroblast growth factor induces primordial follicle development and initiates folliculogenesis. *Mol. Cell. Endocrinol.* 175, 123–130.
25. Gougeon, A., and Busso, D. (2000). Morphologic and functional determinants of primordial and primary follicles in the monkey ovary. *Mol. Cell. Endocrinol.* 163, 33–41.
26. Horie, K., Fujita, J., Takakura, K., Kanzaki, H., Suginami, H., Iwai, M., Nakayama, H., and Mori, T. (1993). The expression of *c-kit* protein in human adult and fetal tissues. *Hum. Reprod.* 8, 1955–1962.
27. Yamamoto, S., Konishi, I., Nanbu, K., Komatsu, T., Mandai, M., Kuroda, H., Matsushita, K., and Mori, T. (1997). Immunohistochemical localization of basic fibroblast growth factor (bFGF) during folliculogenesis in the human ovary. *Gynecol. Endocrinol.* 11, 223–230.
28. Skinner, M. K., and Coffey, Jr., R. J. (1988). Regulation of ovarian cell growth through the local production of transforming growth factor-a by theca cells. *Endocrinology* 123, 2632–2638.
29. Durlinger, A. L., Gruijters, M. J., Kramer, P., Karels, B., Ingraham, H. A., Nachtigal, M. W., Uilenbroek, J. T., Grootegoed, J. A., and Themmen, A. P. (2002) Anti-Mullerian hormone inhibits initiation of primordial follicle growth in the mouse ovary. *Endocrinology* 143, 1076–1084.

29a. Gougeon (unpublished data).

30. Rajkumar, K., Kerr, D. E., Kirkwood, R. N., and Laarveld, B. (1992). Inhibitory action of somatostatin-14 on hormone-stimulated cAMP induction in porcine granulosa and luteal cells. *J. Endocrinol.* 134, 397–406.

30a. Lornage et al. (unpublished data).

31. Goddard, I., Bauer, S., Gougeon, A., Lopez, F., Giannetti, N., Susini, C., Benahmed, M., and Krantic, S. (2001). Somatostatin inhibits stem cell factor messenger RNA expression by sertoli cells and stem cell factor-induced DNA synthesis in isolated seminiferous tubules. *Biol. Reprod.* 65, 1732–1742.
32. Heinrich, M. C., Dooley, D. C., and Keeble, W. W. (1995). Transforming growth factor beta 1 inhibits expression of the gene products for steel factor and its receptor (c-kit). *Blood* 85, 1769–1280.
33. Puente, E., Saint-Laurent, N., Torrisani, J., Furet, C., Schally, A. V., Vaysse, N., Buscail, L., and Susini, C. (2001). Transcriptional activation of mouse sst2 somatostatin receptor promoter by transforming growth factor-beta: Involvement of Smad4. *J. Biol. Chem.* 276, 13461–13468.
34. Dissen, G. A., Paredes, A., Romero, C., Dees, W. L., and Ojeda, S. (2004). Neural and neurotrophic control of ovarian development. In *The Ovary,* 2d ed., eds. P. K. C. Leung and E. Y. Adashi, Boston: Elsevier.
35. Hirshfield, A. N. (1994). Relationship between the supply of primordial follicles and the onset of follicular growth in rats. *Biol. Reprod.* 50, 421–428.

36. Halpin, D. M. G., and Charlton, H. M. (1988). Effects of short-term injection of gonadotrophins on ovarian follicle development in hypogonadal *(hpg)* mice. *J. Reprod. Fertil.* 82, 393–400.
37. Meredith, S., Kirkpatrick-Keller, D., and Butcher, R. (1986). The effect of food restriction and hypophysectomy on numbers of primordial follicles and concentrations of hormones in rats. *Biol. Reprod.* 35, 68–73.
38. Flaws, J. A., Abbud, R., Mann, R. J., Nilson, J. H., and Hirshfield, A. N. (1997). Chronically elevated luteinizing hormone depletes primordial follicles in the mouse ovary. *Biol. Reprod.* 57, 1233–1237.
39. Meredith, S., Dudenhoeffer, G., Butcher, R. L., Sperner, S. P., and Walls, T. (1992). Unilateral ovariectomy increases loss of primordial follicles and is associated with increased metestrous S concentration of follicle-stimulating hormone. *Biol. Reprod.* 47, 162–168.
40. Lee, S. J., Lenton, E. A., Sexton, L., and Cooke, I. D. (1988). The effect of age on the cyclical patterns of plasma LH, FSH, oestradiol and progesterone in women with regular menstrual cycles. *Hum. Reprod.* 3, 851–855.
41. Oktay, K., Briggs, D., and Gosden, R. G. (1997). Ontogeny of follicle-stimulating hormone receptor gene expression in isolated human ovarian follicles. *J. Clin. Endocrinol. Metab.* 82, 3748–3751.
42. Wandji, S. A., Fortier, M. A., and Sirard, M. A. (1992). Differential response to gonadotropins and prostaglandins E_2 in ovarian tissue during prenatal and postnatal development in cattle. *Biol. Reprod.* 46, 1034–1041.
43. Oktay, K., Newton, H., Mullan, J., and Gosden, R. G. (1998). Development of human primordial follicles to antral stages in *SCID/hpg* mice stimulated with follicle stimulating hormone. *Hum. Reprod.* 13, 1133–1138.
44. Kumar, T. R., Wang, Y., Lu, N., and Matzuk, M. M. (1997). Follicle stimulating hormone is required for ovarian follicle maturation but not for male fertility. *Nature Genetics* 15, 201–204.
45. Dierich, A., Sairam, M. R., Monaco, L., Fimia, G. M., Gansmuller, A., LeMeur, M., and Sassone-Corsi, P. (1998). Impairing follicle-stimulating hormone (FSH) signaling in vivo: Targeted disruption of the FSH receptor leads to aberrant gametogenesis and hormonal imbalance. *Proc. Natl. Acad. Sci. USA.* 95, 13612–13617.
46. Barnes, R. B., Namnoum, A. B., Rosenfield, R. L., and Layman, L. C. (2002). The role of LH and FSH in ovarian androgen secretion and ovarian follicular development: Clinical studies in a patient with isolated FSH deficiency and multicystic ovaries. *Hum. Reprod.* 17, 88–91.
47. Amsterdam, A., and Rotmensch, S. (1987). Structure-function relationships during granulosa cell differentiation. *Endocr. Rev.* 8, 309–337.
48. Juneja, S. C., Barr, K. J., Enders, G. C., and Kidder, G. M. (1999). Defects in the germ line and gonads of mice lacking connexin-43. *Biol. Reprod.* 60, 1263–1270.
49. Wassarman, P. M., Liu, C., and Litscher, E. S. (1996). Constructing the mammalian egg zona pellucida: Some new pieces of an old puzzle. *J. Cell Sci.* 109, 2001–2004.
50. Irving-Rodgers, H. F., and Rodgers, R. J. (2000). Ultrastructure of the basal lamina of bovine ovarian follicles and its relationship to the membrana granulosa. *J. Reprod. Fertil.* 118, 221–228.
51. Gougeon, A. (1996). Regulation of ovarian follicular development in primates: Facts and hypotheses. *Endocr. Rev.* 17, 121–155.
52. Anderson, E., and Albertini, D. F. (1976). Gap junctions between the oocyte and companion follicle cells in the mammalian ovary. *J. Cell. Biol.* 71, 680–686.
53. Simon, A. M., Goodenough, D. A., Li, E., and Paul, D. L. (1997). Female infertility in mice lacking connexin-37. *Nature* 385, 525–528.
54. Koering, M. J. (1983). Preantral follicle development during the menstrual cycle in the Macaca mulatta ovary. *Am. J. Anat.* 166, 429–443.
55. Wassarman, P. M. (1988). The mammalian ovum. In *Physiology of Reproduction,* Vol. 1, eds. E. Knobil, J. D. Neill, L. L. Ewing, C. L. Markert, G. S. Greenwald, and D. W. Pfaff, 69–102. New York : Raven Press.
56. Dong, J., Albertini, D. F., Nishimori, K., Kumar, T. R., Lu, N., and Matzuk, M. M. (1996). Growth differentiation factor-9 is required during ovarian early folliculogenesis. *Nature* 383, 531–535.
57. Carabatsos, M. J., Elvin, J., Matzuk, M. M., and Albertini, D. F. (1998). Characterization of oocyte and follicle development in growth differentiation factor-9—deficient mice. *Dev. Biol.* 204, 373–384.
58. Parrott, J. A., and Skinner, M. K. (2000). Kit ligand actions on ovarian stromal cells: Effects on theca cell recruitment and steroid production. *Mol. Reprod. Dev.* 55, 55–64.
59. Erickson, G. F., and Case, E. (1983). Epidermal growth factor antagonizes ovarian theca-interstitial cytodifferentiation. *Mol. Cell. Endocrinol.* 31, 71–76.
60. Burns, K. H., Owens, G. E., Fernandez, J. M., Nilson, J. H., and Matzuk, M. M. (2002). Characterization of integrin expression in the mouse ovary. *Biol. Reprod.* 67, 743–751.
61. Erickson, G. F., Magoffin, D. A., Dyer, C. A., and Hofeditz, C. (1985). The ovarian androgen producing cells: A review of structure/function relationships. *Endocr. Rev.* 6, 371–399.
62. Shima, K., Kitayama, S., and Nakano, R. (1987). Gonadotropin binding sites in human ovarian follicles and corpora lutea during the menstrual cycle. *Obstet. Gynecol.* 69, 800–806.
63. Kobayashi, M., Nakano, R., and Ooshima, A. (1990). Immunocytochemical localization of pituitary gonadotrophins and gonadal steroids confirms the "two-cell, two gonadotrophins" hypothesis of steroidogenesis in the human ovary. *J. Endocrinol.* 126, 483–488.
64. Magoffin, D. A., and Weitsman, S. R. (1994). Insulin-like growth factor-l regulation of luteinizing hormone (LH) receptor messenger ribonucleic acid expression and LH-stimulated signal transduction in rat ovarian theca-interstitial cells. *Biol. Reprod.* 51, 766–775.
65. Richards, J. S. (2001). New signaling pathways for hormones and cyclic adenosine 3′,5′-monophosphate action in endocrine cells. *Mol. Endocrinol.* 15, 209–218.
66. Wang, X. N., and Greenwald, G. S. (1993). Hypophysectomy of the cyclic mouse. 1. Effects on folliculogenesis, oocyte growth, and FSH and HCG receptors. *Biol. Reprod.* 48, 585–594.

67. van Capellen, W. A., Meijs-Roelofs, H. M. A., Kramer, P., and van den Dungen, H. M. (1989). Ovarian follicle dynamics in immature rats treated with a luteinizing hormone-releasing hormone antagonist (Org. 30276). *Biol. Reprod.* 40, 1247–1256.
68. Eshkol, A., Lunenfeld, B., and Peters, H. (1970). Ovarian development in infant mice. Dependence on gonadotropic hormones. In *Gonadotrophins and Ovarian Development,* eds. W. R. Butt, A. C. Crooke, and M. Ryle, 249–258. Edinburgh: Churchill Livingstone.
69. Arendsen de Wolff Exalto, E. (1982). Influence of gonadotrophins on early follicle cell development and early oocyte growth in the immature rat. *J. Reprod. Fertil.* 66, 537–542.
70. Palter, S. F., Tavares, A. B., Hourvitz, A., Veldhuis, J. D., and Adashi, E. Y. (2001). Are estrogens of import to primate/human ovarian folliculogenesis? *Endocr. Rev.* 22, 389–424.
71. Beau, I., Touraine, P., Meduri, G., Gougeon, A., Desroches, A., Matuchansky, C., Milgrom, E., Kutten, F., and Misrahi, M. (1998). A novel phenotype related to partial loss of function mutations of the follicle-stimulating hormone receptor. *J. Clin. Invest.* 102, 1–8.
72. Touraine, P., Beau, I., Gougeon, A., Meduri, G., Desroches, A., Pichard, A., Detoeuf, M., Paniel, B., Prieur, M., Zorn, J.-R., Milgrom, E., Kuttenn, F., and Misrahi, M. (1999). New natural inactivating mutations of the FSH receptor: Correlations between receptor function and phenotype. *Mol. Endocrinol.* 13, 1844–1854.
73. Yokota, H., Yamada, K., Liu, X., Kobayashi, J., Abe, Y., Mizunuma, H., and Ibuki, Y. (1997). Paradoxical action of activin A on folliculogenesis in immature and adult mice. *Endocrinology* 138, 4572–4576.
74. Roy, S. K. (1993). Epidermal growth factor and transforming growth factor-β modulation of FSH-induced DNA synthesis in hamster preantral and early antral follicles. *Biol. Reprod.* 48, 552–557.
75. Liu, X., Andoh, K., Abe, Y., Kobayashi, J., Yamada, K., Mizunuma, H., and Ibuki, Y. (1999). A comparative study on transforming growth factor-beta and activin A for preantral follicles from adult, immature, and diethylstilbestrol-primed immature mice. *Endocrinology* 140, 2480–2845.
76. Parrott, J. A., Vigne, J. L., Chu, B. Z., and Skinner, M. K. (1994). Mesenchymal-epithelial interactions in the ovarian follicle involve keratinocyte and hepatocyte growth factor production by thecal cells and their action on granulosa cells. *Endocrinology* 135, 569–575.
77. Hayashi, M., McGee, E. A., Min, G., Klein, C., Rose, U. M., van Duin, M., and Hsueh, A. J. W. (1999). Recombinant growth differentiation factor-9 (GDF-9) enhances growth and differentiation of cultured early ovarian follicles. *Endocrinology* 140, 1236–1244.
78. Otsuka, F., Yao, Z., Lee, T., Yamamoto, S., Erickson, G. F., and Shimasaki, S. (2000). Bone morphogenetic protein-15. Identification of target cells and biological functions. *J. Biol. Chem.* 275, 39523–39528.
79. Vendola, K. A., Zhou, J., Adesanya, O. O., Weil, S. J., and Bondy, C. A. (1998). Androgens stimulate early stages of follicular growth in the primate ovary. *J. Clin. Invest.* 101, 2622–2629.
80. Hild-Petito, S., Brenner, R. M., and Stouffer, R. L. (1991). Localization of androgen receptor in the follicle and corpus luteum of the primate ovary during the menstrual cycle. *Biol. Reprod.* 44, 561–568.
81. Weil, S., Vendola, K., Zhou, J., and Bondy, C. A. (1999). Androgen and follicle-stimulating hormone interactions in primate ovarian follicle development. *J. Clin. Endocrinol. Metab.* 84, 2951–2956.
82. Hsueh, A. J. W., McGee, E. A., Hayashi, M., and Hsu, S. Y. (2000). Hormonal regulation of early follicle development in the rat ovary. *Mol. Cell. Endocrinol.* 163, 95–100.
83. Nakamura, M., Nakamura, K., Igarashi, S., Tano, M., Miyamoto, K., Ibuki, Y., and Minegishi, T. (1995). Interaction between activin A and cAMP in the induction of FSH receptor in cultured rat granulosa cells. *J. Endocrinol.* 147, 103–110.
84. Gougeon, A. (1984). Influence of cyclic variations in gonadotrophin and steroid hormones on follicular growth in the human ovary. In *Clinical Pathology of the Endocrine Ovary,* eds. J. de Brux and J. P. Gautray, 63–72. Lancaster, UK: MTP Press.
85. Mizunuma, H., Liu, X., Andoh, K., Abe, Y., Kobayashi, J., Yamada, K., Yokota, H., Ibuki, Y., and Hasegawa, Y. (1999). Activin from secondary follicles causes small preantral follicles to remain dormant at the resting stage. *Endocrinology* 140, 37–42.
86. Chun, S. Y., McGee, E. A., Hsu, S. Y., Minami, S., LaPolt, P. S., Yao, H. H., Bahr, J. M., Gougeon, A., Schomberg, D. W., and Hsueh, A. J. W. (1999). Restricted expression of wt1 messenger ribonucleic acid in immature ovarian follicles: Uniformity in mammalian and avian species and maintenance during reproductive senescence. *Biol. Reprod.* 60, 365–373.
87. Durlinger, A. L., Gruijters, M. J., Kramer, P., Karels, B., Kumar, T. R., Matzuk, M. M., Rose, U. M., de Jong, F. H., Uilenbroek, J. T., Grootegoed, J. A., and Themmen, A. P. (2001). Anti-Mullerian hormone attenuates the effects of FSH on follicle development in the mouse ovary. *Endocrinology* 142, 4891–4899.
88. Sasano, H., Okamoto, M., Mason, J. I., Simpson, E. R., Mendelson, C. R., Sasano, N., and Siverberg, S. G. (1989). Immunolocalization of aromatase, 17α-hydroxylase and side-chain cleavage cytochrome P-450 in the human ovary. *J. Reprod. Fertil.* 85, 163–169.
89. Sasano, H., Mori, T., Sasano, N., Nagura, H., and Mason, J. I. (1990). Immunolocalization of 3β-hydroxysteroid dehydrogenase in human ovary. *J. Reprod. Fertil.* 89, 743–751.
90. Tilly, J. L., LaPolt, P. S., and Hsueh, A. J. W. (1992). Hormonal regulation of follicle-stimulating hormone receptor messenger ribonucleic acid levels in cultured rat granulosa cells. *Endocrinology* 130, 1296–1302.
91. Qu, I., Nisolle, M., and Donnez, J. (2000). Expression of transforming growth factor-alpha, epidermal growth factor, and epidermal growth factor receptor in follicles of human ovarian tissue before and after cryopreservation. *Fertil. Steril.* 74, 113–121.
92. Parrott, J. A., and Skinner, M. K. (1997). Direct actions of kit-ligand on theca cell growth and differentiation during follicle development. *Endocrinology* 138, 3819–3827.

93. Otsuka, F., Yamamoto, S., Erickson, G. F., and Shimasaki, S. (2001). Bone morphogenetic protein-15 inhibits follicle-stimulating hormone (FSH) action by suppressing FSH receptor expression. *J. Biol. Chem.* 276, 11387–11392.
94. Monget, P., and Bondy, C. (2000). Importance of the IGF system in early folliculogenesis. *Mol. Cell. Endocrinol.* 163, 89–93.
95. Gougeon, A., and Lefèvre, B. (1983). Evolution of the diameters of the largest healthy and atretic follicles during the human menstrual cycle. *J. Reprod. Fertil.* 69, 497–502.
96. McNatty, K. P., Hillier, S. G., Van den Boogaard, A. M. J., Trimbos-Kemper, T. C. M., Reichert, L. E. , and Van Hall, E. V. (1983). Follicular development during the luteal phase of the human menstrual cycle. *J. Clin. Endocrinol. Metab.* 56, 1022–1031.
97. Koering, M. J. (1969). Cyclic changes in ovarian morphology during the menstrual cycle in Macaca mulatta. *Am. J. Anat.* 126, 73–101.
98. Pache, T. D., Wladimiroff, J. W., de Jong, F. H., Hop, W. C., and Fauser, B. C. J. M. (1990). Growth patterns of non-dominant ovarian follicles during the normal menstrual cycle. *Fertil. Steril.* 54, 638–642.
99. Gougeon, A., and Testart, J. (1990). Influence of human menopausal gonadotropin on the recruitment of human ovarian follicles. *Fertil. Steril.* 54, 848–852.
100. Mason, H. D., Carr, L., Leake, R., and Franks, S. (1995). Production of transforming growth factor-alpha by normal and polycystic ovaries. *J. Clin. Endocrinol. Metab.* 80, 2053–2056.
101. Westergaard, L. G. and Andersen, C. Y. (1989). Epidermal growth factor (EGF) in human preovulatory follicles. *Hum. Reprod.* 4, 257–260.
102. Mason, H. D., Margara, R., Winston, R. M. L., Beard, R. W., Reed, M. J., and Franks, S. (1990). Inhibition of oestradiol production by epidermal growth factor in human granulosa cells of normal and polycystic ovaries. *Clin. Endocrinol.* 33, 511–517.
103. Nahum, R., Thong, K. J., and Hillier, S. G. (1995). Metabolic regulation of androgen production by human thecal cells in vitro. *Hum. Reprod.* 10, 75–81.
104. Soules, M. R., Steiner, R. A., Clifton, D. K., Cohen, N. L., Aksel, S., and Bremner, W. J. (1984). Progesterone modulation of pulsatile luteinizing hormone secretion in normal women. *J. Clin. Endocrinol. Metab.* 58, 378–383.
105. Solovyeva, E. V., Hayashi, M., Margi, K., Barkats, C., Klein, C., Amsterdam, A., Hsueh, A. J., and Tsafriri, A. (2000). Growth differentiation factor-9 stimulates rat theca-interstitial cell androgen biosynthesis. *Biol. Reprod.* 63, 1214–1218.
106. Goodman, A. L. and Hodgen, G. S. (1983). The ovarian triad of the primate menstrual cycle. *Recent. Prog. Horm. Res.* 39, 1–73.
107. Macklon, N. S., and Fauser, B. C. M. J. (1998). Follicle development during the normal menstrual cycle. *Maturitas* 30, 181–188.
108. Gougeon, A. (1982). Rate of follicular growth in the human ovary. In *Follicular Maturation and Ovulation,* eds. R. Rolland, E. V. Van Hall, S. G. Hillier, K. P. McNatty, and J. Schoemaker, 155–163. Amsterdam: Excerpta Medica.
109. McNatty, K. P. (1982). Ovarian follicular development from the onset of luteal regression in humans and sheep. In *Follicular Maturation and Ovulation,* eds. R. Rolland, E. V. Van Hall, S. G. Hillier, K. P. McNatty, and J. Schoemaker, 1–18. Amsterdam: Excerpta Medica.
110. Yong, E. L., Baird, D. T., Yates, R., Reichert, Jr., L. E., and Hillier, S. G. (1992). Hormonal regulation of the growth and steroidogenic function of human granulosa cells. *J. Clin. Endocrinol. Metab.* 74, 842–849.
111. Poretsky, L., Cataldo, N. A., Rosenwaks, Z., and Giudice, L. C. (1999). The insulin-related ovarian regulatory system in health and disease. *Endocr. Rev.* 20, 535–582.
112. Mason, H. D., Cwyfan-Hughes, S., Holly, J. M., and Franks, S. (1998). Potent inhibition of human ovarian steroidogenesis by insulin-like growth factor binding protein-4 (IGFBP-4). *J. Clin. Endocrinol. Metab.* 83, 284–287.
113. Hourvitz, A., Widger, A. E., Filho, F. L., Chang, R. J., Adashi, E. Y., and Erickson, G. F. (2000). Pregnancy-associated plasma protein-A gene expression in human ovaries is restricted to healthy follicles and corpora lutea. *J. Clin. Endocrinol. Metab.* 85, 4916–4920.
114. Lawrence, J. B., Oxvig, C., Overgaard, M. T., Sottrup-Jensen, L., Gleich, G. J., Hays, L. G., Yates III, J. R., and Conover, C. A. (1999). The insulin-like growth factor (IGF)-dependent IGF binding protein-4 protease secreted by human fibroblasts is pregnancy-associated plasma protein-A. *Proc. Natl. Acad. Sci. USA* 96, 3149–3153.
115. Gougeon, A., and Testart, J. (1986). Germinal vesicle beakdown in oocytes of human atretic follicles during the menstrual cycle. *J. Reprod. Fertil.* 78, 389–401.
116. Ryan, K. J. (1981). Follicular atresia—some speculations of biochemical markers and mechanisms. In *Dynamics of Ovarian Function,* eds. N. B. Schwartz and M. Hunzicker-Dunn, 1–11. New York: Raven Press.
117. Hodgen, G. D. (1982). The dominant ovarian follicle. *Fert. Steril.* 38, 640–647.
118. Campbell, B. K., Picton, H. M., Mann, G. E., McNeilly, A. S., and Baird, D. T. (1991). Effect of steroid- and inhibin-free ovine follicular fluid on ovarian follicles and ovarian hormone secretion. *J. Reprod. Fertil.* 93, 81–96.
119. Law, A. S., Baxter, G., Logue, D. N., O'Shea, T., and Webb, R. (1992). Evidence for the action of bovine follicular fluid factor(s) other than inhibin in suppressing follicular development and delaying oestrus in heifers. *J. Reprod. Fertil.* 96, 603–616.
120. Zeleznik, A. J. (1981). Premature elevation of systemic estradiol reduces serum levels of follicle-stimulating hormone and lengthens the follicular phase of the menstrual cycle in rhesus monkeys. *Endocrinology* 109, 352–355.
121. DiZerega, G. S., Marrs, R. P., Campeau, J. D., and Kling, O. R. (1983). Human granulosa cell secretion of protein(s) which suppress follicular response to gonadotropins. *J. Clin. Endocrinol. Metab.* 56, 147–155.
122. Hillier, S. G., Yong, E. L., Illingworth, P. J., Baird, D. T., Schwall, R. H., and Mason, A. J. (1991). Effect of recombinant inhibin on androgen synthesis in cultured human thecal cells. *Mol. Cell. Endocrinol.* 75, R1–R6.
123. Roberts, V. J., Barth, S., El-Roeiy, A., and Yen, S. S. C. (1993). Expression of inhibin/activin subunits and follis-

tatin messenger ribonucleic acids and proteins in ovarian follicles and the corpus luteum during the human menstrual cycle. *J. Clin. Endocrinol. Metab.* 77, 1402–1410.

124. Hernandez, E. R., Hurwitz, A., Vera, A., Pellicer, A., Adashi, E. Y., LeRoith, D., and Roberts, Jr., C. T. (1992). Expression of the genes encoding the insulin-like growth factors and their receptors in the human ovary. *J. Clin. Endocrinol. Metab.* 74, 419–425.
125. Hillier, S. G. (1985). Sex steroid metabolism and follicular development in the ovary. *Oxford Rev. Reprod. Biol.* 7, 168–222.
126. Filicori, M., Cognigni, G. E., Taraborrelli, S., Spettoli, D., Ciampaglia, W., Tabarelli De Fatis, C., Pocognoli, P., Cantelli, B., and Boschi, S. (2001). Luteinzing hormone activity in menotropins optimizes folliculogenesis and treatment in controlled ovarian stimulation. *J. Clin. Endocrinol. Metab.* 86, 337–343.
127. Zeleznik, A. J., Schuler, H. M., and Reichert, Jr., L. E. (1981). Gonadotropin-binding sites in the rhesus monkey ovary: Role of the vasculature in the selective distribution of human chorionic gonadotropin to the preovulatory follicle. *Endocrinology* 109, 356–362.
128. Geva, E., and Jaffe, R. (2004). Ovarian angiogenesis. In *The Ovary*, 2d ed., eds P. K. C. Leung and E. Y. Adashi. Boston: Elsevier.
129. Gougeon, A. (1977). Steroid 3β-ol-dehydrogenase activity in the largest healthy and atretic follicles in the human ovary during the menstrual cycle. *Ann. Biol. Anim. Biochim. Biophys.* 17, 1087–1094.
130. Chaffkin, L. M., Luciano, A. A., and Peluso J. J. (1992). Progesterone as an autocrine/paracrine regulator of human granulosa cell proliferation. *J. Clin. Endocrinol. Metab.* 75, 1404–1408.
131. Elvin, J. A., Clark, A. T., Wang, P., Wolfman, N. M., and Matzuk, M. M. (1999). Paracrine actions of growth differentiation factor-9 in the mammalian ovary. *Mol. Endocrinol.* 13, 1035–1048.

CHAPTER 3

Dynamics of Primate Follicular Growth: A Physiological Perspective

ANTHONY J. ZELEZNIK

INTRODUCTION

During the follicular phase of the primate menstrual cycle a single follicle usually grows to the preovulatory stage and releases its oocyte for potential fertilization. Because many follicles can be stimulated to mature when exogenous gonadotropins are administered, the process of follicle maturation during the spontaneous menstrual cycle must represent the culmination of a stringent regulatory process by which one follicle gains and maintains advantage over all other maturing follicles that also would be capable of reaching preovulatory status if provided with exogenous gonadotropins. This chapter summarizes the current views on the process of follicle selection, with particular emphasis on identification of the control mechanisms that may operate in vivo to ensure the successful maturation of a single preovulatory follicle. Most of the concepts presented here are derived from studies with human and nonhuman primates; when appropriate data are unavailable from primates, extrapolations are made from data obtained from other species.

STAGES OF FOLLICULOGENESIS

As described by Gougeon [1] and summarized in Figure 3.1, follicular maturation to the preovulatory stage is the culmination of a lengthy process in which the maturation of dormant primordial follicles is initiated as the granulosa cells (GC) begin to proliferate and form preantral follicles. GC division continues and the number of GC layers increases as the preantral follicle grows. After the preantral follicle attains six or seven GC layers, the theca interna layer becomes pronounced and the formation of the antral cavity begins. In the absence of appropriate gonadotropic stimulation, follicles do not develop beyond the early antral stage and atresia occurs. The failure of follicles to develop beyond the early antral stages in the absence of appropriate gonadotropic stimulation appears to be typical of primate and nonprimate species [2–4]. One reason for the pronounced atresia seen in early antral follicles suggests that they have reached a critical surface to volume ratio such that the thickness of GC in these follicles may approach the limits for adequate diffusion of oxygen [5].

In primates, early antral follicles are present in ovaries throughout the follicular and the luteal phase and even before the onset of puberty. It is generally held that the stages of follicular development up to and including the early antral follicle are relatively independent of the pituitary gonadotropins, follicle-stimulating hormone (FSH), and luteinizing hormone (LH). In nonhuman primates, autoradiographical studies have shown that preantral follicles posses FSH receptors but not LH receptors, which is similar to that previously shown in rats [6, 7]. Because early antral follicles are FSH responsive and are present throughout the menstrual cycle as a product of the continual supply of preantral follicles from the primordial pool, it is generally concluded that the process of preantral folliculogenesis serves to provide a constantly available source of maturing follicles for final maturation to the preovulatory stage when provided with the appropriate hormonal support. Maturation to the preovulatory stage begins at the onset of puberty in primates.

INITIATION OF PREOVULATORY FOLLICULOGENESIS

During the luteal phase of the menstrual cycle, preantral folliculogenesis is ongoing as reflected by the uptake of ^{3}H-thymidine into nuclei of GC from all sizes of preantral follicles [8]. The failure of follicles to grow to the preovulatory stage during the luteal phase of the menstrual cycle is not because of a deficit in the supply of early antral follicles but rather is caused by the failure of these early antral follicles to enter into the final stages of preovulatory follicle growth. Because preovulatory follicle development can be rapidly initiated during the luteal phase by the administration of exogenous gonadotropins [9, 10], it is likely that the failure of follicles to develop beyond the early antral stage is caused by insufficient concentrations of FSH and LH. It is well established that the corpus luteum is the

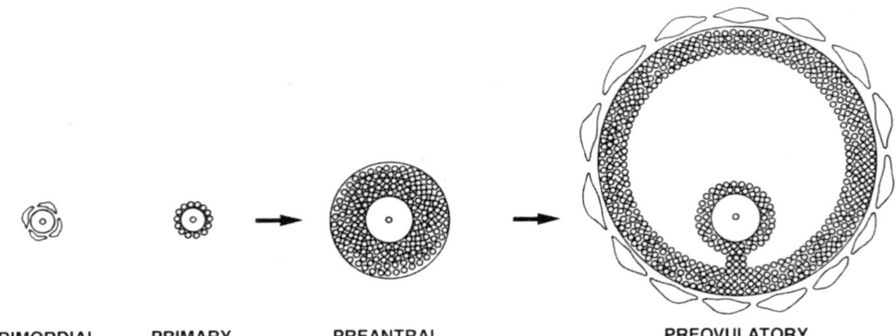

FIGURE 3.1 Stages of mammalian follicular development.

primary source of circulating estradiol, progesterone, and inhibin, all of which are present in the blood in high concentrations during the luteal phase of the menstrual cycle and all of which have been shown to exert negative feedback effects on gonadotropin secretion on the hypothalamic-pituitary axis [11–13]. Beginning 5 to 6 days before the onset of menstruation, there is a concordant reduction in plasma estradiol, progesterone, and inhibin concentrations caused by the gradual demise of the corpus luteum. Associated with these reductions is a reciprocal increase in plasma FSH concentrations [14]. Because FSH is the primary hormone involved in preovulatory follicular growth, it is reasonable to conclude that the initiation of preovulatory follicular growth following regression of the corpus luteum is caused by the removal of feedback inhibition of luteal secretions on FSH secretion. Because estradiol, progesterone, and inhibin concentrations decrease as the corpus luteum regresses, it is difficult to assign a primary role to any of these as being the principal mediator of the suppression of FSH secretion and causing the concomitant hiatus of preovulatory follicle growth during the luteal phase.

Because many follicles can develop to the preovulatory stage as a result of administration of exogenous gonadotropins, there must be a precise and highly efficient regulatory mechanism by which only one of the many follicles that have the potential to ovulate actually attains its ultimate maturational state. As gonadotropin secretion rises following luteal regression, early antral follicles enter into the pool of developing follicles from which the preovulatory follicle will emerge. Although this process is usually called *recruitment,* it should be reinforced that the actual recruitment of follicles, as defined by the development of early antral follicles from the pool of primordial follicles, is not restricted to any one stage of the menstrual cycle but rather continues unabated throughout life until the supply of primordial follicles is exhausted and menopause ensues. From this population of early antral follicles present in the ovaries at the end of the luteal phase, one will attain superiority over all others and mature to the preovulatory stage whereas others will undergo atresia. In simple terms, the process of follicle selection can be defined by explaining how one follicle gains dominance over other follicles and continues to mature in an environment that cannot support the growth of less mature follicles.

MECHANISM BY WHICH A DEVELOPING FOLLICLE GAINS DOMINANCE OVER OTHERS

As follicles develop beyond the early antral stage under the influence of FSH, GC undergo striking developmental changes that transform the follicle from being steroidogenically quiescent to being capable of producing large quantities of estrogen. As is well known, estrogen is responsible for the endometrial proliferation that prepares the uterus for implantation and for the coordination of the timing of the ovulatory discharge of LH such that the stimulus for the follicle to ovulate occurs only when preovulatory follicle development is completed [15]. As will now be discussed, not only does estrogen serve a coordinating role between follicle maturity and the timing of the onset of the LH surge but it also serves as the principal factor responsible for the establishment of dominance of a maturing follicle. Figure 3.2 summarizes the cellular control of follicular estrogen secretion.

The limiting step in follicular estrogen biosynthesis is the acquisition of aromatase by the GC that enables these cells to convert the thecally produced androgens into estrogen [16]. FSH mediates the induction of aromatase [17]. Thus an early manifestation of preovulatory follicular development is the acquisition of its ability to secrete estrogen. By collecting blood from the ovarian veins of monkeys and humans, it has been shown that asymmetrical production of estrogen (hence the presence of a selected follicle) is evident approximately 7 to 8 days before ovulation [18, 19]. When asymmetrical ovarian estrogen secretion becomes evident, systemic concentrations of estrogen in blood begin to rise indicating that the increasing estrogen concentrations during the mid- through late follicular phase are directly related to

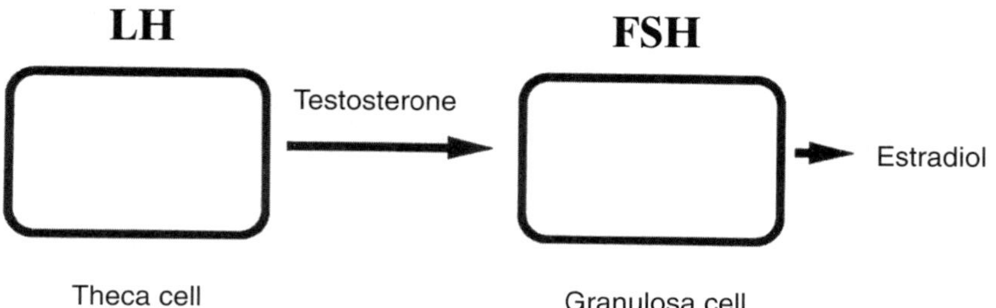

FIGURE 3.2 Two cell–two gonadotropin model for estrogen biosynthesis.

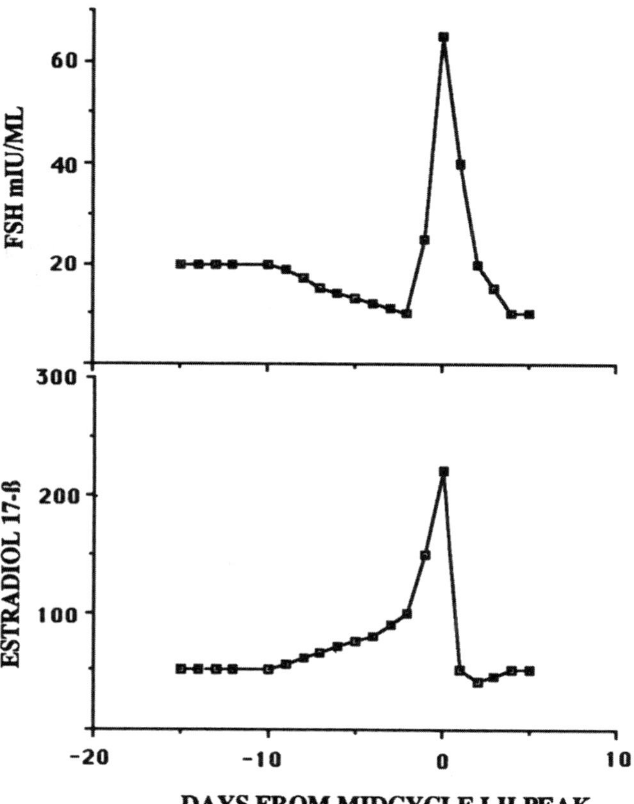

FIGURE 3.3 Concentrations of FSH and estrogen during the follicular phase of the menstrual cycle.

the presence and continued maturation of the selected follicle.

As discussed previously, estrogen is a highly efficient negative feedback modulator of gonadotropin secretion and it is this action of estrogen that is responsible for the acquisition of follicular dominance. Figure 3.3 illustrates a typical profile of plasma concentrations of FSH and estradiol during the follicular phase of the menstrual cycle.

It can be seen that as serum estrogen concentrations begin to rise approximately 6 to 7 days before midcycle, there is a corresponding decrease in plasma FSH concentrations such that immediately before the midcycle gonadotropin surge, FSH concentrations are about 50% of values seen during the early follicular phase, before the emergence of a maturing follicle. It may be hypothesized that this feedback system functions in the following manner. Since preantral folliculogenesis is inherently asynchronous because of the continuous exit of follicles from the primordial pool, there will always be a maturationally distinct distribution of early antral follicles within the ovaries that are available for continued maturation under the influence of FSH. As FSH concentrations rise after regression of the corpus luteum, follicles will be stimulated and when aromatase is induced sufficiently to cause peripheral estrogen concentrations to increase, FSH secretion will be inhibited thus depriving other follicles of their gonadotropic support. The preantral follicle that ultimately achieves dominance and ovulates is likely to be the one at the most advanced stage of maturation and/or the follicle with the greatest access to FSH at the time when FSH concentrations rise at the end of the previous menstrual cycle.

This model for follicle selection has been tested experimentally by manipulating the pattern of FSH secretion during the follicular phase of the menstrual cycle. If the model is correct, one would predict that administration of estrogen during the early follicular phase, before a leading follicle emerges, would cause a premature reduction in FSH concentrations that, in turn, would inhibit spontaneous follicular development. Studies in rhesus monkeys have shown that a premature elevation in systemic estrogen concentrations from 50 to 80 pg/ml on days 3 to 6 of the follicular phase resulted in a slight—but significant—decrease in plasma FSH concentrations and an interruption of spontaneous follicular development. Preovulatory follicular growth was arrested until the exogenous source estrogen was removed whereupon FSH concentrations once again became elevated, the follicular phase began anew, and ovulation occurred 12 to 14 days later [20]. Similarly, in humans, oral administration of ethinyl estradiol on days 1 to 8 of the follicular phase led to a suppression of plasma gonadotropin concentrations and a lengthening of the follicular phase [21].

This model for follicular selection would also predict that interfering with the gonadotropin suppressing effects of estrogen should prevent the decrease in FSH concentrations during the mid- through late follicular phase of the menstrual cycle and result in the maturation of more than one preovulatory follicle. When rhesus monkeys were passively immunized with ovine antiestradiol gamma globulins to neutralize endogenously produced estrogen, serum FSH concentrations did not fall during the midfollicular phase of the menstrual cycle and multiple preovulatory follicles were present within the ovaries at the expected time of ovulation [22]. In humans, it is well known that blockage of the biological actions of estrogen with the antiestrogen clomiphene citrate results in an augmentation of gonado-tropin levels and the maturation of more than a single preovulatory follicle [23].

Thus there is solid experimental evidence that supports the hypothesis that the maturing follicle establishes its dominance over other follicles by feedback inhibition of FSH secretion. Although the aforementioned studies are consistent with the notion that this feedback inhibition is mediated by estrogen, it must be noted that the maturing follicle also produces the glycoprotein inhibin, which has been shown to suppress FSH secretion in primate and subprimate model systems [12, 24, 25]. Since inhibin and estrogen are produced because of preovulatory follicular growth, it has been difficult to establish the relative contributions of estradiol and inhibin with respect to the suppression of FSH secretion [26]. However, it should be noted in the passive immunization studies described previously that neutralization of estrogen resulted in the maturation of more than a single follicle, presumably in the presence of elevated inhibin concentrations that would result from the ensuing ovarian hyperstimulation [22, 27]. In addition, the phenotype of a woman with an inactivating mutation of the aromatase gene is consistent with a primary role for estrogen in the regulation of FSH secretion in humans. This individual exhibited elevated FSH concentrations and the presence of multiple bilateral ovarian cysts (follicles), both of which were resolved by the administration of exogenous estradiol [28]. Although these aforementioned studies indicate that estrogen is the principal regulator of FSH secretion during the follicular phase of the menstrual cycle, until passive immunization studies are conducted in primates with anti-inhibin antibodies and/or a genetic mutation in the ability to produce inhibin is identified, a conclusion regarding the contributions of inhibin and estrogen in the feedback regulation of FSH secretion in primates cannot be ascertained. It should be reinforced that there may be significant interspecies differences regarding the roles of inhibin and estrogen in the feedback control of FSH secretion and that inhibin may have a more pronounced role in the control of FSH secretion in some species [11, 24, 25]. Regardless whether inhibin or estrogen is the primary controller of FSH secretion during the follicular phase, because the maturing follicle produces both, the important fact is that the maturing follicle establishes its dominance over other follicles by feedback inhibition of FSH secretion.

MECHANISM BY WHICH THE MATURING FOLLICLE MAINTAINS ITS DOMINANCE OVER OTHER FOLLICLES

Given (1) that FSH is required for follicles to proceed in development beyond the early antral stage by suppressing FSH secretion, and (2) that the maturing follicle inhibits the development of less mature follicles, how is it then that (3) the maturing follicle is spared from the inhibitory influences (suppression of FSH secretion) it imposes on all other follicles? The mechanism by which the maturing follicle escapes its own inhibition must be elucidated to completely explain the process of follicular selection.

Figure 3.3 shows that estrogen concentrations continue to increase while FSH concentrations decrease. The only explanation for this phenomenon is that as the follicle matures, it is less dependent on FSH such that the concentration of FSH necessary to *maintain* preovulatory follicular development is less than the concentration of FSH necessary to *initiate* preovulatory follicular development. This hypothesis was tested in cynomolgus monkeys by directly modulating serum FSH and LH concentrations [29]. Animals were equipped with indwelling intravenous catheters that were attached to remote sampling devices that permitted constant access to the circulation for infusion and blood sampling. The animals were treated with a potent gonadotropin-releasing hormone (Gn-RH) antagonist to interrupt spontaneous gonadotropin secretion; thereafter the monkeys received hourly pulses of highly purified human FSH and human LH. With this experimental system, absolute plasma concentrations of FSH and LH are controlled independently by adjusting the concentration of each hormone in the infusate. Figure 3.4 illustrates data from these animals.

As can be seen from the lower panel in Figure 3.4, there was no evidence of estrogen secretion in the control animals thus demonstrating that concentrations of FSH less than 10 mIU/ml cannot initiate preovulatory follicular development. However, as can be seen from the solid lines, when FSH concentrations are elevated to 15 to 20 mIU/ml, preovulatory follicular development is initiated as reflected by increasing concentrations of estrogen. Moreover, once FSH stimulated preovulatory follicular growth, reduction of plasma FSH concentrations to 8 to 10 mIU/ml over 5 days was associated with a continued rise in estrogen production. Thus data these demonstrate that the concentration of FSH necessary to *initiate* follicular growth is greater than the concentration required to *maintain* preovulatory follicular growth. Therefore this answers the question of how the selected follicle inhibits the development of less mature follicles but does not inhibit its own

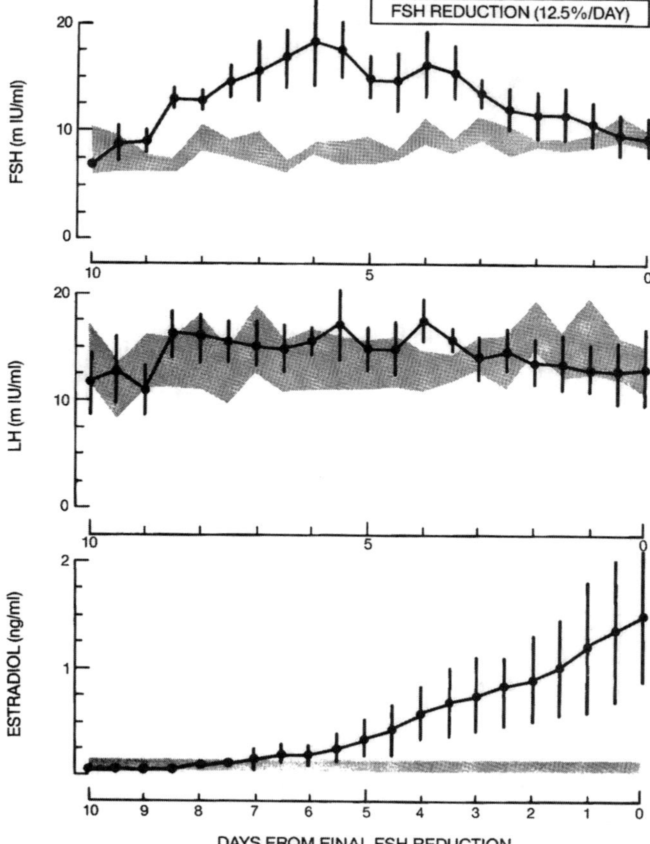

FIGURE 3.4 Titration of the ovarian response to exogenous FSH and LH. The shaded areas depict data from control cynomolgus monkeys in which plasma FSH and LH concentrations were maintained constant at 8 to 10 mIU/ml and 10–15 mIU/ml respectively for 14 days. The line graph represents data from animals in which FSH concentrations were gradually elevated until estrogen secretion became evident and then reduced to 8 to 10 mIU/ml for 5 days. Note that following reduction of FSH concentrations in the experimental group, estrogen secretion continued in the presence of FSH concentrations that were unable to initiate estrogen secretion in the control animals.

growth—it accomplishes this by becoming more sensitive to FSH. These results also demonstrate that there is a threshold concentration of FSH (15–20 mIU/ml) that must be reached to initiate preovulatory follicle development. Once this threshold concentration is reached, follicles readily enter the final stages of preovulatory follicle growth and the number of follicles that reach maturity is dependent on the duration that FSH concentrations are maintained above the threshold level rather than the absolute concentration of FSH [29]. Not surprisingly, this experimentally determined threshold concentration of FSH is close to the actual concentration of FSH measured during the early follicular phase of the human menstrual cycle when the initiation of preovulatory follicular development occurs [30]. The FSH threshold concept and the importance of the feedback control of FSH secretion pertain to humans as well [31].

MECHANISM(S) RESPONSIBLE FOR THE REDUCED REQUIREMENT FOR FOLLICLE-STIMULATING HORMONE BY THE MATURING FOLLICLE

As presented in the previous sections, follicular selection can be explained by the operation of an exquisitely sensitive negative feedback relationship between estrogen and FSH. As an early antral follicle progresses into the final stages of preovulatory growth under the stimulation of FSH, aromatase is induced, which allows for the conversion of thecally produced androgens into estrogen. As peripheral estradiol concentrations increase, FSH secretion decreases below the threshold value necessary to initiate preovulatory follicular development and maturation of other follicles ceases thereby establishing the dominance of the FSH-stimulated, estrogen-producing follicle. Implicit in this model is that the maintenance of follicular dominance must be caused by adaptations directly at the follicular level that enable the dominant follicle to survive in the presence of FSH concentrations that are too low to maintain the growth of other less mature follicles.

As follicles undergo stimulation by FSH and mature to the preovulatory stage, there are marked changes in the functional activity of the GC. Some of these changes contribute to the functioning of the follicle as an endocrine organ, such as the induction of enzymes necessary for the production of estrogen and progesterone, which are obligatory for endometrial development as well as the modulation of gonadotropin secretion by the hypothalamic-pituitary axis. In addition to these functional changes that affect nonovarian target organs, there are changes in cellular functions of the FSH-stimulated follicle that have local influences on the follicular apparatus and most likely contribute the diminished requirement of the maturing follicle to FSH that is necessary for the follicle to maintain its growth and dominance as plasma FSH concentrations fall. These development-dependent changes may act at different levels of follicular function and, most importantly, the contributions that each may provide to the follicle are not mutually exclusive but rather likely provide a variety of fail-safe factors that ensure that the maturing follicle is spared from the reduction in FSH concentrations.

Follicle-stimulating Hormone Mediated Induction of Luteinizing Hormone Receptors on Granulosa Cells

A hallmark effect of FSH on the GC is to induce cell surface receptors for LH [7]. When this phenomenon was

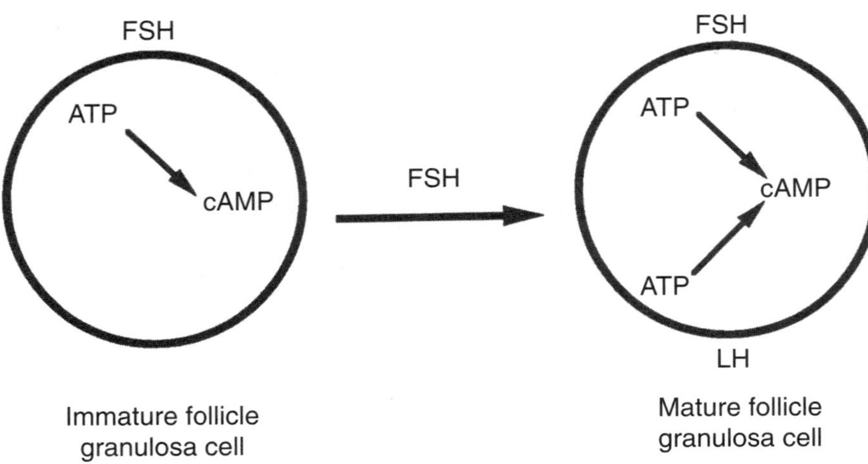

FIGURE 3.5 Gonadotropin responsiveness of GC from immature and mature follicles. Note that in mature follicles, both FSH and LH can stimulate cAMP production.

first described, it was generally—and correctly—assumed that the acquisition of LH receptors on GC during preovulatory follicular development was an important determinant in the ability of the follicle to luteinize in response to the midcycle LH surge [32]. However, the presence of LH receptors on GC of developing follicles could also serve to protect the follicle from the fall in plasma FSH concentrations as schematically illustrated in Figure 3.5.

GC from preantral and early antral follicles posses only FSH receptors that, acting through the cyclic adenosine monophosphate (cAMP) system, are responsible for stimulating GC differentiation. Because of FSH stimulation, the GC acquire LH receptors, which also act through the cAMP system to stimulate GC function. From studies conducted primarily in rats, it has been shown that GC with FSH and LH receptors respond identically to FSH and LH, as would be predicted if both hormones act through the cAMP system [33, 34]. Although preovulatory follicles are responsive to FSH and LH, preantral and early antral follicles are responsive to only FSH. A reduction in FSH concentrations therefore would remove the only source of support to early antral follicles, whereas preovulatory follicles would still have the LH-mediated cAMP system available for their support and thus be spared from the fall in FSH concentrations. It has been shown that GC from early antral follicles collected at the end of the luteal phase in humans are responsive to FSH but not human chorionic gonadotropin (hCG; used in place of LH) with respect to the stimulation of aromatase [35], whereas GC collected from preovulatory follicles are responsive to both FSH and LH [36]. Accordingly, these data are consistent with the hypothesis that the maturing follicle may be protected from the fall in FSH concentrations by becoming responsive to LH.

The availability of pure FSH and LH obtained by recombinant deoxyribonucleic acid (DNA) technology has allowed this hypothesis to be tested directly in vivo [37]. In 24 women, pituitary gonadotropin secretion was down regulated with a Gn-RH agonist and follicular growth was stimulated with recombinant human FSH (r-hFSH) until a 14-mm follicle was identified by ultrasound. The women were then randomly placed in one of the following four groups for 2 days: (1) continued r-hFSH treatment, (2) substitution of r-hFSH with saline, (3) substitution of r-hFSH with low-dose recombinant human LH (r-hLH; 150 IU twice a day [bid]), or (4) substitution of r-hFSH with high-dose r-hLH (375 IU bid). Serum estradiol concentrations in the women who received saline declined by the end of 2 days. In contrast, serum estradiol concentrations continued to rise in women who received either r-hFSH or r-hLH when compared with the saline treated group. These findings indicate that once FSH initiates follicular growth, either FSH or LH can sustain follicular estradiol production, which is consistent with the idea that the maturing follicle may be protected from the fall in FSH concentrations by the acquisition of LH receptors. Recent studies by Filicori et al. [38] have provided additional evidence to support the hypothesis that LH plays an important role in follicle selection in humans. These findings indicate that the FSH-mediated induction of aromatase concurrent with the induction of LH receptors are the principal mechanisms responsible for the process of follicle selection. The induction of aromatase results in the rise in peripheral levels of estrogen that, as noted earlier, suppress FSH secretion such that plasma concentrations of FSH fall below the threshold necessary to stimulate the maturation of other less mature follicles. The concurrent induction of LH receptors provides the maturing follicle with an additional source of growth support that enables it to continue to mature in the presence of FSH concentrations that are insufficient to support the development of other follicles.

The "LH hypothesis" may provide a novel approach for controlled ovarian stimulation in humans. If a specific "cut-off point" could be identified below which follicles are unresponsive to LH, it may be possible to develop a sequential FSH–LH stimulation regimen that effectively

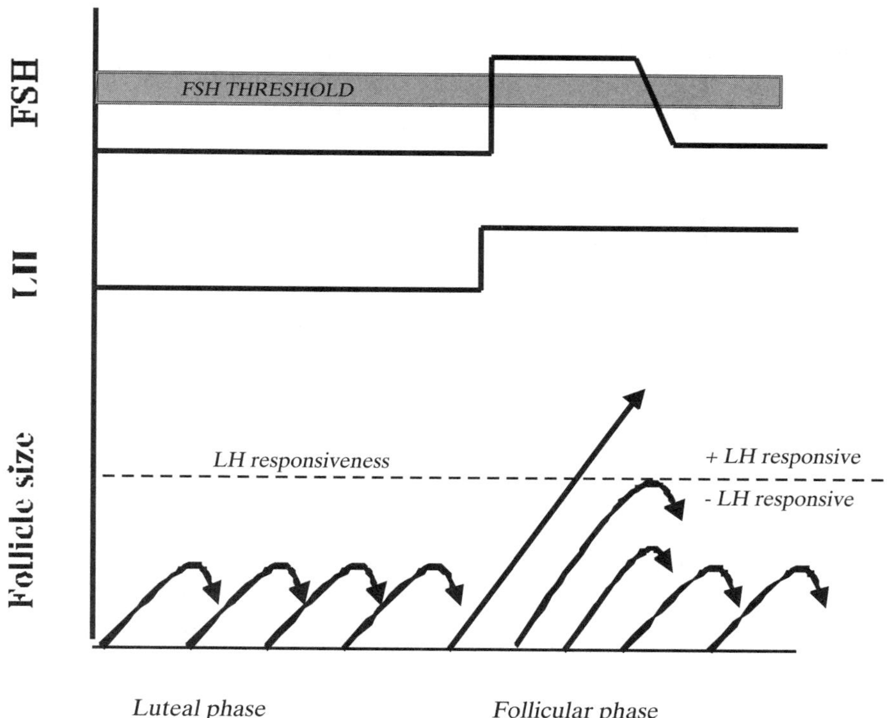

FIGURE 3.6 Schematic diagram of the "FSH threshold" theory for the selection of the preovulatory follicle in primates. During the luteal phase of the menstrual cycle, blood FSH concentrations are held below threshold by the secretions of the corpus luteum and developing follicles do not advance beyond the early antral stage. On the regression of the corpus luteum, the negative feedback restraint on FSH secretion is relieved and blood FSH concentrations rise above the FSH threshold. One (or sometimes more) of the maturing preantral or early antral follicles is stimulated in response to the elevated FSH concentrations and develops both the aromatase enzyme and LH receptors. The acquisition of aromatase results in a rise in systemic estradiol levels that results in the suppression of FSH secretion, which in turn prevents the maturation of other less mature follicles. The FSH-mediated induction of LH receptors on granulosa cells of the stimulated follicle allows it to continue to mature in the presence of FSH concentrations that are insufficient to stimulate the maturation of other less mature follicles.

limits follicular recruitment, which could reduce the risk of unplanned ovarian hyperstimulation. Additional studies are needed to determine at which stage of preovulatory follicular development the maturing follicle acquires sufficient LH responsiveness to allow it to escape the fall in serum FSH concentrations (Figure 3.6).

Ovarian Angiogenesis

The vascularity of the follicle increases as preovulatory follicular maturation progresses and an increase in vascularity results in preferential delivery of radiolabeled gonadotropin to the maturing follicle [5]. Because extracts of follicle cells or conditioned tissue culture media from GC stimulate endothelial cell proliferation, it has been suggested that the follicle may produce diffusible angiogenic factors that cause selective vascularization of the follicle [39]. An early candidate for an ovarian angiogenic factor was basic fibroblast growth factor (bFGF) because this protein is a potent angiogenic substance and is produced by the ovaries [40]. However, it now appears that bFGF is an intracellular protein rather than a secreted protein; hence it is questionable as to whether it would fulfill the requirements for a diffusible angiogenic factor [41]. Recently, a new member of the heparin-binding growth factor, vascular endothelial growth factor (VEGF), has been identified and cloned [42]. VEGF is a secretory protein that induces angiogenesis under in vivo conditions in the chick chorioallantoic membrane bioassay and stimulates proliferation of endothelial cells in tissue culture. Messenger RNA (mRNA) has been found for VEGF in the rat corpus luteum and recently has been shown to be present in the monkey preovulatory follicle as well as the corpus luteum [43, 44]. The localization of mRNA for VEGF in structures within the ovary in which angiogenesis is thought to play an important role in development and function is consistent with the possibility that VEGF may be involved in the neovascularization that accompanies preovulatory follicular growth. Indeed, recent studies with nonhuman primates have demonstrated that the administration of antagonists to VEGF blocks the development of a preovulatory follicle [45, 46]. This block in folliculogenesis was accompanied by an elevation of FSH as would be expected because estrogen secretion was also inhibited [45]. This indicates that a state of "FSH resistance" was produced by the inhibition of ovarian angiogenesis, presumably by interfering with the delivery of FSH from the vasculature to early antral follicles that are dependent on FSH for continued development. Because ovarian stromal blood flow appears to decline as a function of aging [47], it is possible that the "FSH resistance" (as indicated by elevated follicular phase blood FSH levels) that occurs during aging may not be the result of impaired responses of follicles to FSH but rather to insufficient delivery of FSH to follicles. If this is true, improvement in ovarian stromal blood flow might lead to better responses of ovaries to ovulation induction in aging women.

CONCLUSION

Substantial progress has been made in the understanding of the regulation of folliculogenesis. This information will likely contribute to the development of new approaches for ovulation induction. In addition, understanding the mechanisms that govern normal folliculogenesis is a prerequisite for exploring pathophysiological alterations in ovarian function. For example, over the past decade it has become increasingly apparent from in vitro studies that not only are ovarian cells regulated by the pituitary gonadotropins FSH and LH but also by locally produced factors that act either on the cell that produces them (autocrine) or on neighboring cells (paracrine) and that these factors can directly modulate the target cells' responsiveness to FSH and/or LH in either a stimulatory or an inhibitory manner. To date, however, virtually all information on the biological actions of nongonadotropic regulators of ovarian function are based on in vitro studies; therefore the extent to which results from these investigations can be extrapolated to the in vivo state remains uncertain. Further progress in our understanding of ovarian function depends on the development of in vivo paradigms to investigate the potential role of these factors in normal and abnormal ovarian function.

References

1. Gougeon, A. (1996). Regulation of ovarian follicular development in primates: Facts and hypotheses. *Endocr. Rev.* 17, 121–155.
2. Koering, M. J. (1987). Follicular maturation and atresia: Morphological correlates. In *The Primate Ovary*, ed. R. L. Stouffer, 3–23. New York: Plenum Press.
3. Zeleznik, A. J., Hutchison, J. S., and Schuler, H. M. (1987). Passive immunization with anti-oestradiol antibodies during the luteal phase of the primate menstrual cycle potentiates the perimenstrual rise in serum gonadotropin concentrations and stimulates follicular growth in the cynomolgus monkey. *J. Reprod. Fertil.* 80, 403–410.
4. Hirshfield, A. N. (1988). Size-frequency analysis of atresia in cycling rats. *Biol. Reprod.* 38, 1181–1188.
5. Hirshfield, A. N. (1991). Development of follicles in the mammalian ovary. *Int. Rev. Cytol.* 124, 43–101.
6. Zeleznik, A. J., Schuler, H. M., and Reichert, Jr., L. E. (1981). Gonadotropin binding sites in the rhesus monkey ovary: Role of the vasculature in the selective distribution of human chorionic gonadotropin to the maturing follicle. *Endocrinology* 109, 356–362.
7. Zeleznik, A. J., Midgley, Jr., A. R., and Reicherrt, Jr., L. E. (1974). Granulosa cell maturation in the rat: Increased binding of human chorionic gonadotropin following treatment with follicle stimulating hormone in vivo. *Endocrinology* 95, 818–825.
8. Zeleznik, A. J., Wildt, L., and Schuler, H. M. (1980). Characterization of folliculogenesis during the luteal phase of the menstrual cycle in rhesus monkeys using [^{3}-H] thymidine autoradiography. *Endocrinology* 107, 982–988.
9. Zeleznik, A. J., and Resko, J. A. (1980). Progesterone does not inhibit gonadotropin-induced follicular maturation in the female rhesus monkey. *Endocrinology* 106, 1820–1826.
10. diZerega, G. S., and Hodgen, G. D. (1980). Cessation of folliculogenesis during the primate luteal phase. *J. Clin. Endocrinol. Metab.* 51, 158–165.
11. Bassett, S. G., and Zeleznik, A. J. (1990). Acute suppression of FSH secretion by oestradiol in the ovariectomized rhesus monkey. *J. Reprod. Fertil.* 88, 441–446.
12. Channing, C. P., Anderson, L. D., Hoover, D. J., Gagliano, P., and Hodgen, G. D. (1981). Inhibitory effects of porcine follicular fluid on monkey serum FSH levels and follicular maturation. *Biol. Reprod.* 25, 885–903.
13. Karsch, F. J., Weick, J., Hotchkiss, J., Dierschke, D. J., Weiss, G., and Knobil, E. (1973). An analysis of the negative feedback control of gonadotropin secretion utilizing chronic implantation of ovarian steroids into ovariectomized rhesus monkeys. *Endocrinology* 93, 478–486.
14. Roseff, S. J., Bangah, M. L., Kettel, L. M., Vale, W., Rivier, J., Burger, H. G., and Yen, S. S. C. (1989). Dynamic changes in circulating inhibin levels during the luteal-follicular transition of the human menstrual cycle. *J. Clin. Endocrinol. Metab.* 69, 1033–1039.
15. Knobil, E. (1974). On the control of gonadotropin secretion in the rhesus monkey. *Rec. Prog. Hormone Res.* 30, 1–46.
16. Falck, B. (1959). Site of production of oestrogen in rat ovary as studied in microtransplants. *Acta Physiologica* 193 (Suppl), 1–101.
17. Steinkampf, M. P., Mendelson, C. R., and Simpson, E. R. (1987). Regulation by follicle stimulating hormone of the synthesis of aromatase cytochrome P-450 in human granulosa cells. *Mol. Endocrinol.* 1, 465–471.
18. Baird, D. T., and Fraser, I. S. (1975). Concentrations of oestrone and oestradiol in follicular fluid and ovarian venous blood of women. *Clin. Endocrinol.* 4, 259–266.
19. diZerega, G. S., and Hodgen, G. D. (1981). Initiation of asymmetrical ovarian estrogen secretion in the primate ovarian cycle after luteectomy. *Endocrinology* 108, 1233–1236.
20. Zeleznik, A. J. (1981). Premature elevation of systemic estradiol reduces serum levels of follicle stimulating hormone and

lengthens the follicular phase of the menstrual cycle in rhesus monkeys. *Endocrinology* 109, 352–357.
21. Vaitukaitis, J. L., Bermudez, J. A., Cargille, C. M., Lipsett, M. B., and Ross, G. T. (1971). New evidence for an anti-estrogenic of clomiphene citrate in women. *J. Clin. Endocrinol. Metab*. 32, 503–509.
22. Zeleznik, A. J., Hutchison, J. S., and Schuler, H. M. (1985). Interference with the gonadotropin suppressing actions of estradiol in macaques overrides the selection of a single preovulatory follicle. *Endocrinology* 117, 991–995.
23. Speroff, L., Glass, R. H., and Kase, N. G. (1983). *Clinical Gynecologic Endocrinology and Infertility*, 3d ed. Baltimore: Williams & Wilkins.
24. Schwartz, N. B., and Channing, C. P. (1971). Evidence for ovarian "inhibin": Suppression of the secondary rise in serum follicle-stimulating hormone levels in proestrus rats by injection of porcine follicular fluid. *Proc. Natl. Acad. Sci. USA* 74, 5721–5724.
25. Martin, G. B., Price, C. A., Thiery, J. C., and Webb, R. (1988). Interaction between inhibin, oestradiol, and progesterone in the control of gonadotropin secretion in the ewe. *J. Reprod. Fertil*. 82, 319–328.
26. Lenton, E. A., DeKretser, D. M., Woodward, A. J., and Robertson, D. M. (1991). Inhibin concentrations throughout the menstrual cycles of normal, infertile, and older women compared with those during spontaneous conception cycles. *J. Clin. Endocrinol. Metab*. 73, 1180–1190.
27. McLachlan, R. I., Robertson, D. M., Healy, D. L., Burger, H. G., and de Kretser, D. M. (1986). Plasma inhibin levels during gonadotropin induced ovarian hyperstimulation for IVF: A new index of follicular maturation? *Lancet* 1, 233–234.
28. Conte, F. A., Grumbach, M. M., Ito, Y., Fisher, C. R., and Simpson, E. R. (1994). A syndrome of female pseudohermaphrodism, hypergonadotropic hypogonadism, and multicystic ovaries associated with missense mutations in the gene encoding aromatase (P450arom). *J. Clin. Endocrinol. Metab*. 78, 1287–1292.
29. Zeleznik, A. J., and Kubik, C. J. (1986). Ovarian responses in macaques to pulsatile infusion of follicle stimulating hormone and luteinizing hormone: Increased sensitivity of the maturing follicle to FSH. *Endocrinology* 119, 2025–2032.
30. Ross, G. T., Cargille, C. M., Lipsett, M. B., Rayford, P. L., Marshall, J. R., Strott, C. A., and Rodbard, D. (1970). Pituitary and gonadal hormones during spontaneous and induced menstrual cycles. *Rec. Prog. Hormone. Res*. 26, 1–62.
31. Fauser, B., and Heusden, A. V. (1997). Manipulation of human ovarian function: Physiological concepts and clinical consequences. *Endocr. Rev*. 18, 71–106.
32. Zeleznik, A. J., Keyes, P. L., Menon, K. M. J., Midgley, Jr., A. R., and Reichert, Jr., L. E. (1977). Development-dependent responses of ovarian follicles to FSH and hCG. *Am. J. Physiol*. 233, E229–234.
33. Hillier, S. G., Zeleznik, A. J., and Ross, G. T. (1978). Independence of steroidogenic capacity and luteinizing hormone receptor induction in developing granulosa cells. *Endocrinology* 102, 937–946.
34. Richards, J. S., Jahnsen, T., Hedin, L., Lifka, J., Ratoosh, S. L., Durcia, J. M., and Goldring, N. B. (1987). Ovarian follicular development: From physiology to molecular biology. *Rec. Prog. Hormone Res*. 43, 321–270.
35. Hillier, S. G., Reichert, Jr., L. E., and Van Hall, E. V. (1981). Control of preovulatory estrogen biosynthesis in the human ovary. *J. Clin. Endocrinol. Metab*. 52, 847–856.
36. Zeleznik, A. J., and Hillier, S. G. (1984). The role of gonadotropins in the selection of the preovulatory follicle. *Clin. Obstet. Gynec*. 27, 927–940.
37. Sullivan, M. W., Stewart-Aikers, A., Krasnow, J. F., Berga, S. L., and Zeleznik, A. J. (1999). Ovarian responses in women to recombinant follicle stimulating hormone and luteinizing hormone: A role for LH in the final stages of follicular maturation. *J. Clin. Endocrinol. Metab*. 84, 228.
38. Filicori, M., Cognigni, G. E., Tabarelli, C., Pocognoli, P., Taraborrelli, S., Spettoli, D., and Ciampaglia, W. (2002). Stimulation and growth of antral ovarian follicles by selective LH activity administration in women. *J. Clin. Endocrinol. Metab*. 87, 1156.
39. Koos, R. D., and LeMaire, W. J. (1983). Factors that may regulate the growth and regression of blood vessels in the ovary. *Sem. Reprod. Endocrinol*. 1, 295–2307.
40. Neufeld, G., Ferrara, N., Schweigerer, L., Mitchell, R., and Gospordarowicz, D. (1987). Bovine granulosa cells produce basic fibroblast growth factor. *Endocrinology* 121, 597–603.
41. Abraham, J., Mergia, A., Whang, J. L., Tumulo, A., Friedman, J., Hjerrild, K., Gospodarowicz, D., and Fiddes, J. (1986). Nucleotide sequence of a bovine clone encoding the angiogenic protein, basic fibroblast growth factor. *Science* 233, 545–548.
42. Leung, D. W., Cachianes, G., Kuang, W-J., and Ferrara, N. (1989). Vascular endothelial growth factor is a secreted angiogenic mitogen. *Science* 246, 1306–1309.
43. Phillips, H. S., Hains, J., Leung, D. W., and Ferrara, N. (1990). Vascular endothelial growth factor is expressed in rat corpus luteum. *Endocrinology* 127, 965–967.
44. Ravindranath, N., Little-Ihrig, L., Phillips, H. S., Ferrara, N., and Zeleznik, A. J. (1992). Vascular endothelial growth factor expression in the primate ovary. *Endocrinology* 245–260.
45. Zimmermann, R. C., Xiao, E., Bohlen, P., and Ferin, M. (2002). Administration of antivascular endothelial growth factor receptor-2 antibody in the early follicular phase delays follicular selection and development in the rhesus monkey. *Endocrinology* 143, 2496–2502.
46. Wulff, C., Wilson, H., Wiegand, S. J., Rudge, J. S., and Fraser, H. M. (2002). Prevention of thecal angiogenesis, antral follicular growth, and ovulation in the primate by treatment with vascular endothelial growth factor Trap R1R2. *Endocrinology* 143, 2797–2807.
47. Pan, H. A., Cheng, Y. C., Li, C. H., Wu, M. H., and Chang, F. M. (2002). Ovarian stroma flow intensity decreases by age: A three-dimensional power Doppler ultrasonographic study. *Ultrasound Med. Biol*. 28, 425–430.

CHAPTER **4**

Functional Consequences of Mutations and Polymorphisms in Gonadotropin and Gonadotropin Receptor Genes

ILPO HUHTANIEMI

ABSTRACT

The two pituitary gonadotropins, luteinizing hormone (LH) and follicle-stimulating hormone (FSH), and the placental homologue of LH, human chorionic gonadotropin (hCG), play a pivotal role in the regulation of ovarian differentiation, growth, and endocrine and gametogenic functions. The gonadotropins are dimeric proteins, composed of a common α-subunit and a hormone-specific β-subunit, coupled by noncovalent interactions. Two receptor molecules, those for LH/hCG and FSH, belonging to the 7-transmembrane (TM) domain G-protein associated receptors, mediate gonadotropin effects on specific ovarian target cells. Gonadotropin action is transmitted to target cells through multiple signaling mechanisms, of which that mediated by cyclic AMP (cAMP) is best characterized. Several mutations and polymorphisms have been recently discovered in the genes of gonadotropins and their receptors. Although the mutations are rare, because of their deleterious effects on reproduction, they have been elucidating by unraveling several poorly known aspects of gonadotropin action. The purpose of this chapter is to review the current knowledge on structure-function relationships of gonadotropins and their receptors, based mainly on the known human mutations in their genes, and on experimental data on structures of the proteins encoded. This information improves our knowledge about the molecular pathogenesis of disturbances in gonadotropin function and helps in design of improved diagnostics and rational treatment strategies.

INTRODUCTION

The hypothalamic-pituitary-gonadal axis forms the backbone of the endocrine regulation of gonadal function. The key players in this regulation are the two pituitary gonadotropins, LH and FSH, and their cognate receptors (R), the LHR and FSHR, each expressed in specific gonadal target cells. Placental hCG, structurally and functionally close to pituitary LH, is the other hormone that can activate LHR function. Like all genes, those of the gonadotropins and their receptors are polymorphic, containing neutral and functional polymorphisms and genuine mutations. The mutations in these genes are relatively rare, evidently because of the deleterious effects on reproductive functions. Nevertheless, a number of such mutations, causing partly expected, partly unexpected phenotypes, are known today. The gonadotropin and gonadotropin receptor genes (i.e., encoded proteins and partly their tertiary structures) and the natural and genetically engineered mutations have taught us about gonadotropin action. This chapter reviews the current knowledge about the structure-function relationships of gonadotropins and their receptors during normal hormonal function, the functional impact of mutations and functional polymorphisms in these genes, and how the functional alterations can be explained by the mutated proteins. This information is important for our understanding of the molecular basis of certain pathologies of reproductive functions, and it provides us with the basic knowledge in attempts to develop novel molecules with gonadotropic or antigonadotropic action for the manipulation of pituitary-gonadal function in various clinical situations.

STRUCTURAL FEATURES OF GONADOTROPINS AND GONADOTROPIN RECEPTORS

Gonadotropins

The two gonadotropins, LH and FSH, along with placental hCG and thyroid-stimulating hormone (TSH) belong to the family of glycoprotein hormones. They consist of two subunits coupled by noncovalent interactions: the common α-subunit and the hormone-specific β-subunit. hCG is the dimer of common α-subunit and CGβ-subunit, which is structurally so close to LH that the two ligands share the same LH/hCG receptor. They are relatively large proteins (30–40 kDa), and in addition to the protein core, the gonadotropins are glycosylated through N-linked bonds (Figure 4.1). The carbohydrate content of LH is approximately 15%, that of FSH 20%, and that of hCG 30% [1, 2]. The circulatory half-lives of the gonadotropins are about 20 minutes for LH, about 2 hours for FSH, and 12 to 24 hours for hCG. The long half-life of hCG is mainly explained by the 24–amino acid C-terminal extension of its β-subunit, in comparison with LHβ, which is heavily glycosylated through O-linked glycosylation sites (see Figure 4.1). The high proportion of terminal sulfate groups in its carbohydrates contributes to the short half-life of LH; a specific hepatic receptor speeds up the elimination of this type of glycoprotein from the circulation [3].

We will first discuss briefly the specific features of the gonadotropin subunit genes and proteins and the tertiary structure of the hormone dimers, of which two, hCG and FSH, have been crystallized [4, 5].

GONADOTROPIN SUBUNIT GENES AND PROTEINS

The single *common α-subunit gene* is localized on chromosome 6q12.21 and it consists of four exons, of which the first one is noncoding [6]. The α-subunit propeptide has a 24–amino acid signal peptide in its N-terminal end, which is cleaved during the process of synthesis and secretion of the mature hormone dimers. The mature α-subunit is 92 amino acids long, and it contains 10 cysteines participating in intrasubunit disulfide linkages and two N-linked carbohydrate side chains attached to Asn52 and Asn78.

The seven-gene *CGβ/LHβ* cluster is localized on chromosome 19q13.32, and both the single LHβ and the six CGβ genes consist of three exons [6, 7]. Both propeptides have a 20–amino acid signal sequence, and the length of the mature LHβ protein is 121, that of CGβ 145 amino acids. Both proteins contain 12 cysteine residues that can form six intrasubunit disulfide bridges. LHβ contains one N-linked carbohydrate side chain attached to Asn30; CGβ has an additional N-linked glycosylation site at Asn13. The main difference of CGβ from LHβ is its 24–amino acid C-terminal peptide (CTP), which is heavily glycosylated through four

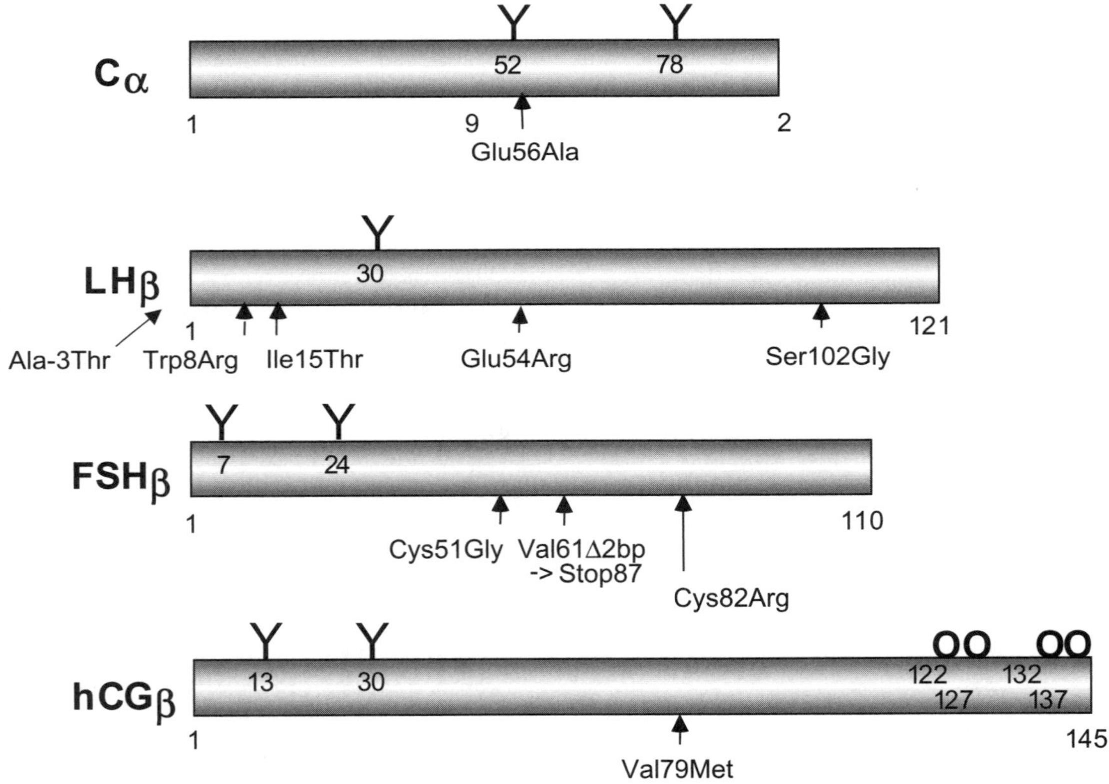

FIGURE 4.1 Schematic presentation of sizes, locations of the carbohydrate side chains, and currently known mutations and polymorphisms in the gonadotropin subunits (i.e., common α-subunit [Cα], LHβ, FSHβ, and hCGβ). The numbers below the right ends of the bars indicate the number of amino acids in the mature subunit proteins. Symbols "Y" and "O" indicate the locations of N-linked and O-linked carbohydrate side chains, respectively. The arrows below the bars indicate the locations of point mutations and polymorphisms. For references, see the text.

O-linked carbohydrate moieties (see Figure 4.1). Of the six CGβ genes and pseudogenes, number 5 is the one most actively transcribed and translated into protein [7].

The *FSHβ* gene also consists of three exons, the first of which is noncoding, and it is localized on chromosome 11p13 [6]. Its signal sequence and mature peptide are 18 and 111 amino acids in length, respectively. Like the other β-subunits, that of FSH contains 12 cysteines for disulfide formation, and its two N-linked carbohydrate side chains are located on Asn7 and Asn24.

The carbohydrate moieties of the gonadotropins show considerable differences among the different hormones and microheterogeneity among molecules of the same hormone [8, 9]. Besides prolonging the circulatory half-life, the carbohydrate composition apparently plays a role in heterodimer stability and in the intrinsic bioactivity of a molecule, which may vary according to the functional state of pituitary gonadotropin synthesis and secretion [9, 10]. The physiological significance of this phenomenon has not been thoroughly studied. Deglycosylation of gonadotropins does not affect receptor binding but abolishes signal transduction [11].

Three-Dimensional Structure of Human Chorionic Gonadotropin and Follicle-Stimulating Hormone

The crystal structures of deglycosylated hCG [4] and FSH [5] have been described, and as expected they are similar. Crystallization of hCG was achieved by removal of the bulk of carbohydrates by treatment with anhydrous hydrofluoric acid [4]. The remaining deglycosylated hormone was found to maintain its ability of receptor binding. The crystal structure revealed that the hormone belongs to the superfamily of cystine knot growth factors (Figure 4.2), which is characterized by a cluster of three cystine disulfide bonds in each subunit. This is similar to the folding found in some protein growth factors, such as nerve growth factor, transforming growth factor-β, and platelet-derived growth factor-β. Although the α- and β-subunits show no amino acid sequence similarity, they have remarkable three-dimensional structural similarity, including two β-hairpin loops (L1 and L3) on one side and a single loop (L2) on the opposite side of the cystine knot structure. The β-hairpins are stabilized by additional disulfide bridges. The two subunits are associated in a head-to-tail orientation, which forms an elongated slightly curved structure (see Figure 4.2). The dimeric molecule is stabilized by a "seat-belt" structure formed by the C-terminal amino acids of the β-subunit wrapped around the α-subunit and stabilized by one of the disulfide bonds. This extraordinary structure is essential for the association of the subunits through non-covalent interactions and for receptor binding.

Analysis of the sequence conservation between various species in structure of the α-subunit reveals strict conservation of 30 residues, of which 10 are disulfide-bonded cystines (i.e., all cysteines of the molecule are conserved). Of these, three participate in the formation of the cystine knot. Extensive studies on site-directed mutagenesis have unraveled the role of a number of amino acids in the tertiary structure of this subunit, including the structures necessary for glycosylation, proper folding, heterodimerization with the β-subunit, and receptor binding and signal transduction of the dimeric hormone (for reviews, see [10–13]).

When the primary sequences of the β-subunits of LH, FSH, hCG, and TSH are compared, a subset of conserved residues are revealed. Among the 27 conserved residues, 12 are cystines, and again three pairs form the cystine knot. One of the remaining cystine disulfide bonds participates in the formation of the seat belt around the long loop of α [4, 5].

The crystalline structure of hFSH, reported recently, is similar to that of hCG [5], but LH has not yet been crystallized. The crystallization of FSH confirms its similar overall structure with LH and hCG. Each FSH subunit contains the same three hairpin loops extending from the central cystine knot. When the crystalline structure of FSH is compared with that of hCG, their overall structures were found to be similar [4, 5]. However, several differences were observed that could be important with respect to hormonal specificity and signal transduction. These differences include conformational changes and/or differential distribution of polar or charged residues at the end of the β-hairpin loops (especially L3). No information about the functional significance of these loops is currently available. The other differences include the β-carboxy-terminal loop, the cystine noose (a short loop in the middle of the molecule, created by a disulfide bridge), and the hydrophobic patch area between loops αL1, αL3, and βL2 that have different surface characteristics. These structures are located on the concave side of the molecule, which results in a face different than FSH and hCG. Because the same area plays a role in receptor binding, these differences may be pivotal in determining the hormonal specificity of the two molecules. It was also found that glycosylation has no global effect on gonadotropin conformation [4, 5].

Gonadotropin Receptors

The gonadotropin receptors belong, together with that of the third glycoprotein hormone, TSH, to the large family of G protein-coupled receptors (GPCRs) [14–17]. LHR is expressed in the ovarian theca, late-stage granulosa, and luteal and interstitial cells. The only ovarian cell type that expresses FSHR is the granulose cell. In agreement with the orientation and overall topography of these receptors, gonadotropin receptors consist of three functional domains: (1) the N-terminal extracellular ligand-binding domain (or *exodomain*), (2) a seven-times plasma-membrane spanning TM domain (or *endodomain*) connected by three intracellular and three extracellular loops,

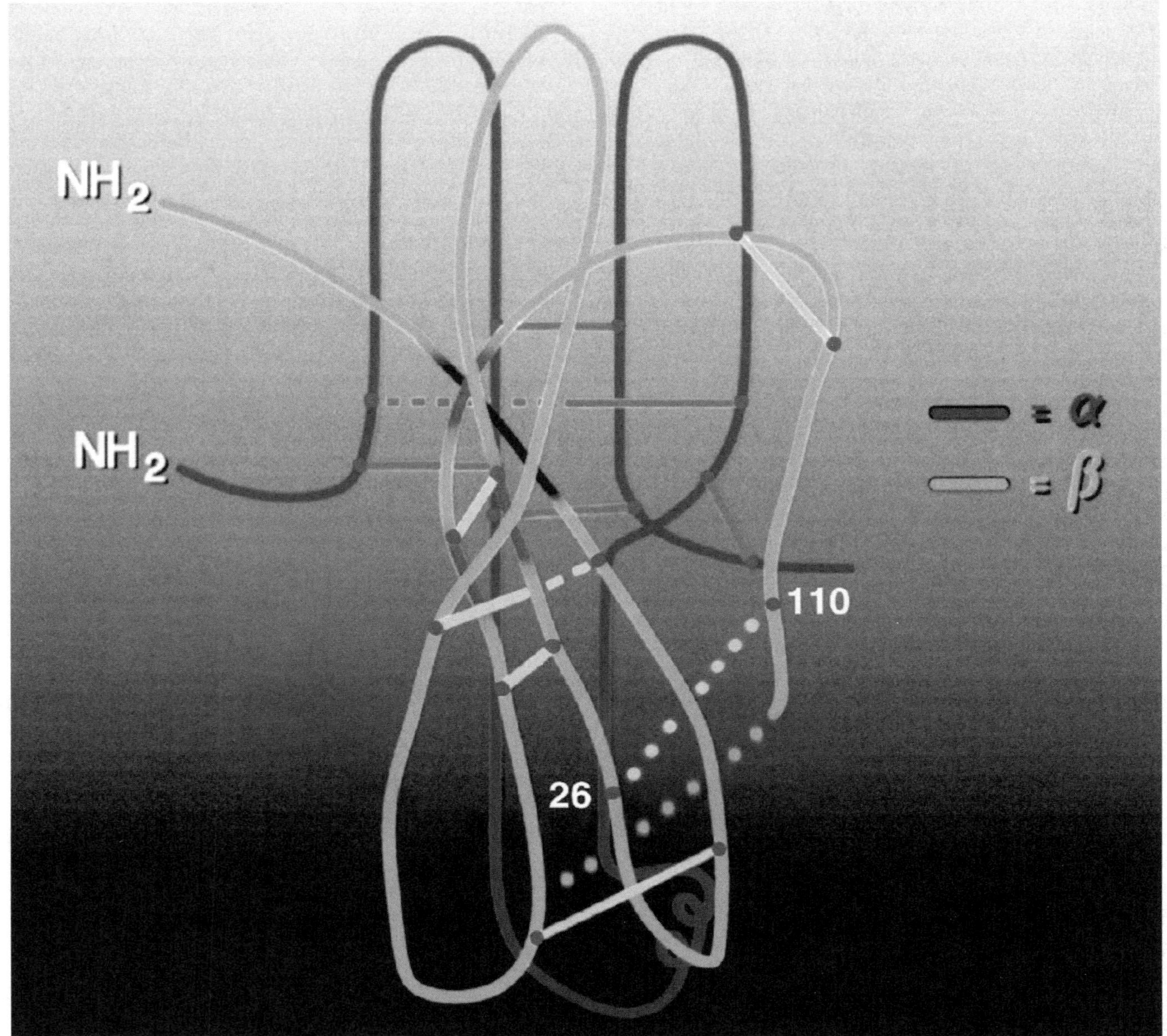

FIGURE 4.2 Diagram of the crystal structure of hCG. Intrasubunit disulfide bonds are shown in yellow and orange for the α (*purple*) and β (*blue*) subunits, respectively. Disulfide bond 26-110 of β-subunit belongs to the stabilizing "seat-belt" structure. (From Ref. [12], with permission.) (See color plate.)

and (3) a C-terminal intracellular tail. Unlike most other GPCRs, the oxodomain of the glycoprotein hormone receptors comprises about half the size of the molecule. In addition, the gonadotropin receptors are glycosylated, but the role of these structures has not yet been fully elucidated. The genes of gonadotropin receptors have been cloned from a number of animal species, including humans, some monkeys, several domestic animals, rodents, *Xenopus,* and catfish (for reviews, see [15, 16]). When possible the information reviewed below is based on the human gonadotropin receptors and in some cases on the rat and mouse, the main experimental models of reproduction research. The features of the LHR and FSHR are similar, but because LHR has been more widely studied [1, 14, 17], the general features of the receptors are described with it, and we refer to FSHR where it differs from LHR.

The Luteinizing Hormone Receptor

The Luteinizing Hormone Receptor Gene, Messenger Ribonucleic Acid, and Protein. A single gene located on chromosome 2p21 encodes the human LHR. This gene is about 50 kb and consists of 11 exons and 10 intervening introns. The long eleventh exon encodes the C-terminal end of the hinge region, the TM region, and the intracellular tail. Almost the entire extracellular domain is encoded by the first 10 exons. Although the coding sequences of the different mammalian LHRs have considerable homology, the human LHR 5′-flanking region with the putative promoter elements differs considerably from those of the rodents [18]. The latter lack TATA and CAAT consensus sequences, have multiple transcription start sites, are G/C rich, and have multiple Sp1 sites, as is typical of housekeeping genes. Findings on function of the human LHR promoter differ, because one study reported a single transcription start site [18], whereas another detected multiple transcription start sites [19]. Surprisingly little information exists today about function of the human LHR promoter.

The LHR gene is transcribed into a number of messenger ribonucleic acid (mRNA) splice variants with differing abundance of the variants between the ovary and testis and between different species [14, 15]. The major splice variants range from 1.8 kb to 7 kb, besides the 2.6 kb message encoding the full-length LHR protein. They apparently arise through the use of different transcription initiation sites, alternative splicing, and differences in polyadenylation. At least some of the splicing signals are embedded in the promoter region, because different lengths of the murine LHR promoter attached in front of the β-galactosidase reporter gene gave rise to differentially spliced β-galactosidase messages [20]. One prominent splice variant of 1.8 kb encodes the entire extracellular domain of the receptor, but findings whether it would be secreted to the extracellular space and thus modulate LH action are not conclusive. Interestingly, this mRNA species seems to be the first detectable message when gonadal LHR expression starts during the ontogeny [21, 22].

The hLHR propeptide has a 24–amino acid signal peptide, and the mature protein consists of 675 residues. The molecular mass of the native receptor protein expressed at target cell surface is 85 to 90 kDa, which is somewhat larger than the predicted size of about 75 kDa and is caused by glycosylation [14, 15]. LHR-expressing cells always contain both the mature cell surface protein, the lower molecular weight precursor present in the endoplasmic reticulum, and apparent aggregates with higher molecular size (150 to 200 kDa). The extracellular domain of the receptor has six consensus sites for glycosylation (Asn-X-Ser/Thr), and most of them, but probably not necessarily all, are glycosylated in the native functional receptor protein [23]. However, individual mutations in any of the glycosylation sites or removal of all carbohydrates from the receptor either during its synthesis or after insertion into the plasma membrane do not affect the folding during synthesis or function of the LHR [24]. Finally, the role of the carbohydrate side chains may be to facilitate the synthesis and functions at the plasma membrane of the LHR protein.

One of the most characteristic features of the extracellular receptor domain is the 8 to 9 imperfect leucine-rich repeats (LRR), with the total of about 25 amino acids (Figure 4.3) [15, 25, 26]. The extracellular domain of the receptor can be divided into three regions: the N-terminal cysteine-rich region (encoded by exon 1, about 200 bp), the 8 to 9 LRRs (encoded by exons 2 to 9, 70 to 80 bp each), and the C-terminal cysteine-rich or hinge region (encoded by exon 10, 81 bp). LRRs are found in many types of proteins with protein-protein interaction function, in the case of LHR in agreement with the contention that ligand recognition and high-affinity binding occur to this domain of the receptor [27]. The predicted structure of this domain of the receptor is based on homology modeling with ribonuclease inhibitor, a LRR protein of known structure [28]. The LRRs form repetitive hairpinlike units composed of a β-sheet and an α-helix segment (see Figure 4.3). These structures are lined in a horseshoelike super helix structure so that all α-helixes are lined on its outside and β-sheets on its inside. This model and the known three-dimensional structures of hCG and FSH allow further studies to understand the steric events in the interaction of gonadotropins and their receptors. It is expected that the extracellular domains of the gonadotropin receptors soon will be crystallized.

The TM serpentine domain of LHR has a canonical GPCR structure of seven TM α-helixes joined by three intra- and extracellular loops (Figure 4.4). It plays a crucial role in G-protein associated signal transduction of the receptor. Through the use of (1) the crystal structure of another receptor in the same GPCR subfamily, that of rhodopsin [29], as template; (2) comparisons with other GPCR sequences; and (3) extensive computer modeling, it has recently been possible to understand the molecular basis of the role of the TM region in LHR activation and the influence of various mutations on its function [30]. The TM helices of the LHR are arranged in the plasma membrane in a slightly diagonal circle, and the interaction with G proteins is thought to involve the intracellular loops (IL) and the iuxtacytoplasmic parts of the TM helices. In particular, the carboxyterminal part of IL3 is probably involved in G protein activation [31, 32]. Interactions among the TM regions stabilize the structure of the inactive LHR, and either ligand binding or activating receptor mutations (see below) induce structural modifications at the interfaces, especially of TM3 and TM6. Likewise, the cytosolic ends of TM5 and TM6 and IL3 are involved in the G protein activation. What is still unknown is how ligand binding to the extracellular domain results in the conformational changes that are needed for activation of signal transduction.

The three-dimensional structure of the intracellular tail has not been studied in detail. It apparently contains an

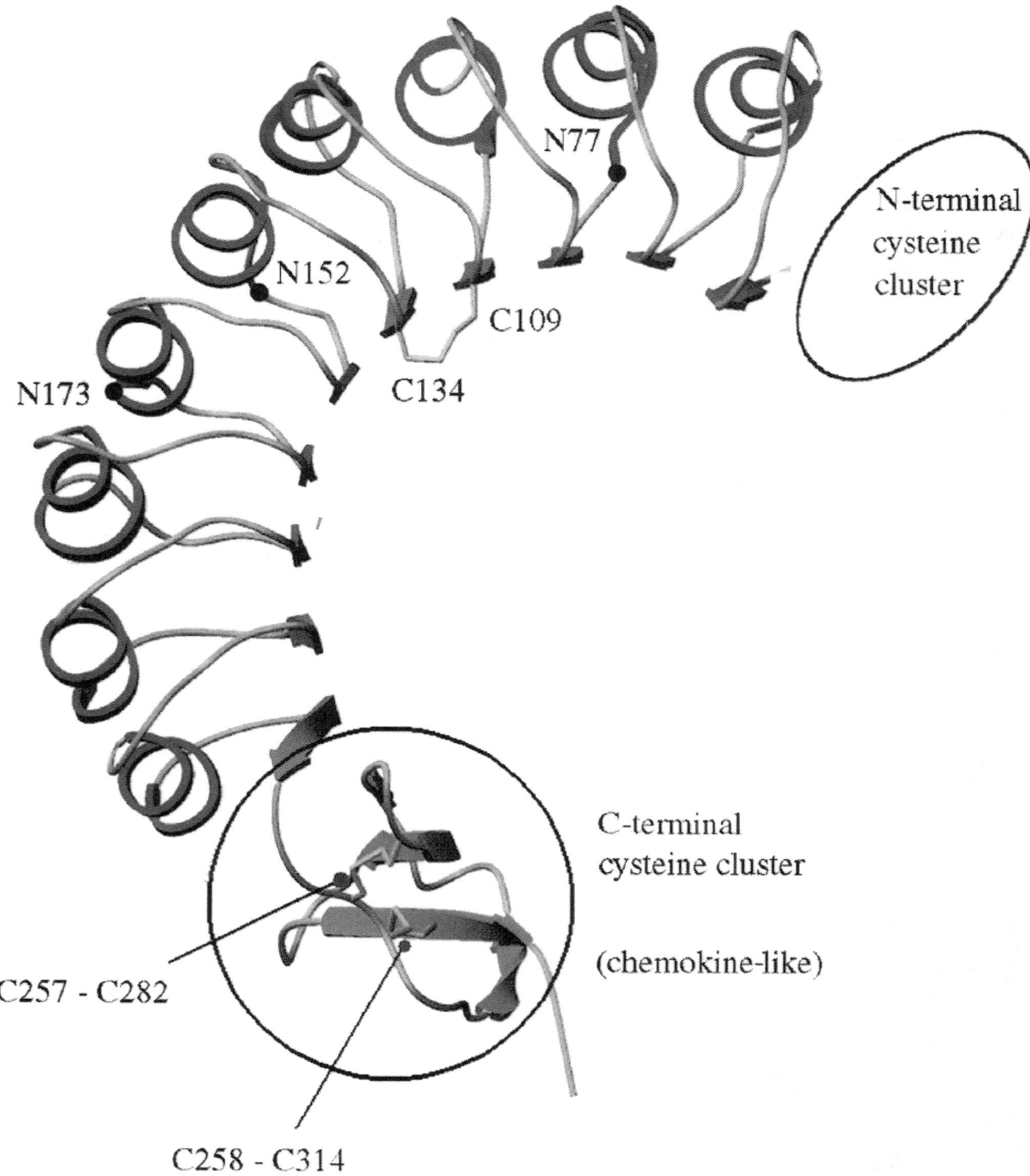

FIGURE 4.3 A ribbon diagram of the LRR structure of extracellular domain of LHR. Potential disulfides are illustrated and the potential N-linked glycosylation sites on the LRR segment of the structure. (From Ref. [25], with permission.) (See color plate.)

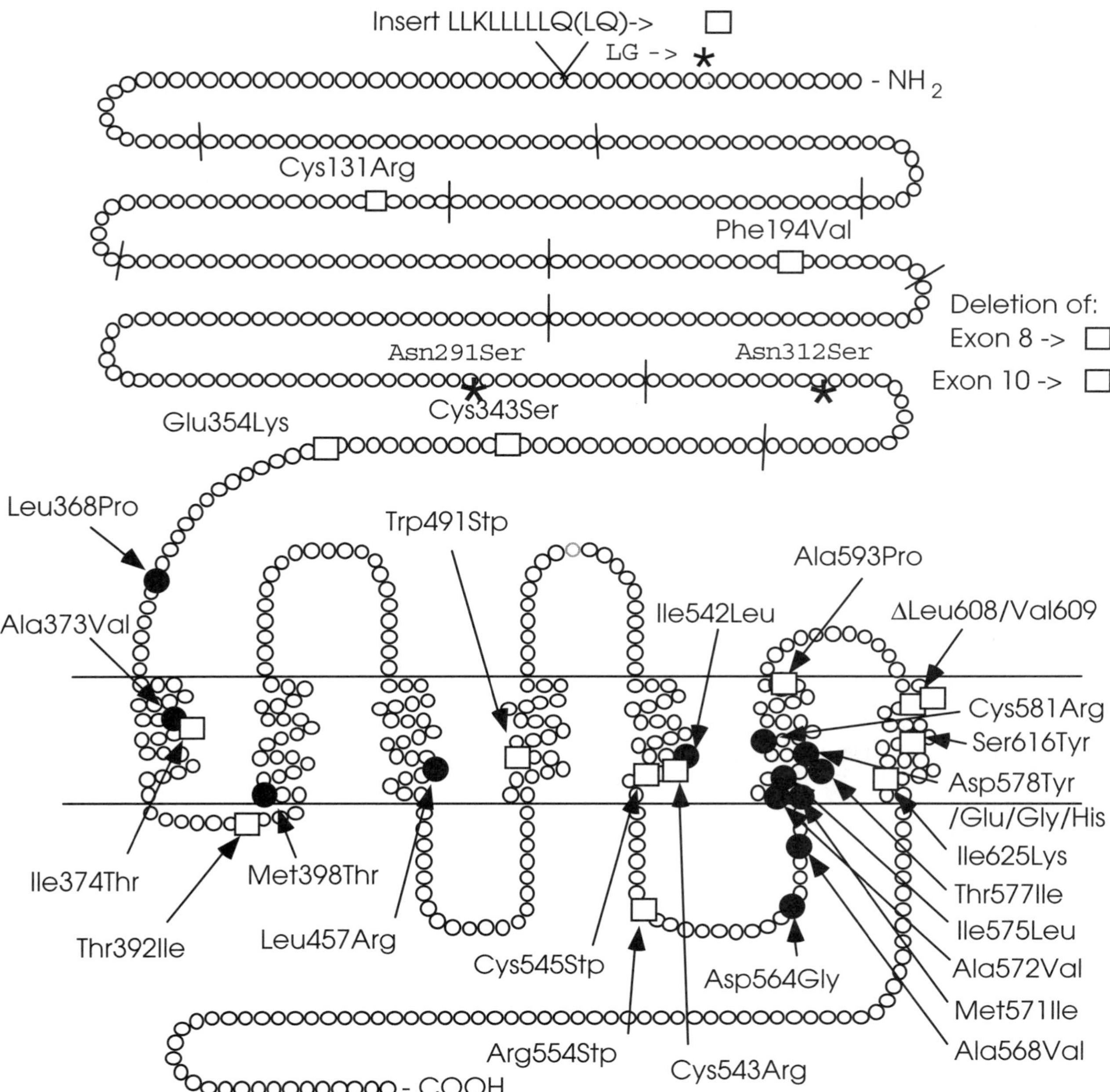

FIGURE 4.4 Orientation across the plasma membrane and locations of the currently known mutations of the human LHR. ●, Activating mutation; □, inactivating mutation; *, polymorphism. The short lines across the peptide chain depict the exon boundaries. For references, see the text.

eighth α-helical segment that is entirely cytoplasmic [15], and it is the site of two posttranslational modifications—palmitoylation and phosphorylation. Palmitoylation occurs at two conserved cysteines near the cytoplasmic end of the seventh TM helix and anchors the cytoplasmic region to the plasma membrane as a fourth intracellular loop. Palmitoylation does not affect the LHR ligand binding or signal transduction, but it apparently enhances its rate of internalization [33]. Several intracellular serine residues of the LHR can be phosphorylated, which occurs on stimulation of LHR expressing cells with LH/hCG, cAMP, or phorbol ester [34]. Phosphorylation apparently plays a role in the process of receptor uncoupling after activation by the ligand.

Activation and Signal Transduction of the Luteinizing Hormone Receptor. The main signaling cascade activated by binding of LH/hCG to the LHR is that involving the Gs/adenylyl/cyclase/cAMP/PKA pathway (for reviews, see [15, 17]). There is now evidence that at least the inositol trisphosphate (IP3) pathway is also activated by LHR stimulation. There is still uncertainty as to the G proteins that are activated by LHR stimulation. The activation of Gs is apparent, but findings on the others, whether Gq/11, G12, or G13, differ among the experimental models [15, 35–37]. Likewise, the type of Gi protein activated has not been widely addressed. Whereas Gs activation is detected in all cell types examined, the IP3 activation cannot always be demonstrated, and its ED50 to LH/hCG stimulation is higher than that of cAMP. It is unknown whether the two signaling pathways evoke the same or different responses in their target cells. The lower sensitivity of the IP3 response has been suggested to be functional at the time of high ligand stimulation (i.e., during the periovulatory phase and in pregnancy) [38]. The third signaling pathway that has been demonstrated to be activated by LHR is the MAPK cascade [39].

The Follicle-Stimulating Hormone Receptor

The Follicle-stimulating Hormone Receptor Gene, Messenger Ribonucleic Acid, and Protein. The FSHR gene is structurally similar to LHR, and it is encoded by a single gene located in the human on the same chromosome 2p21 [10, 16]. The FSHR gene is about 215 kb and consists of 10 exons and 9 intervening introns. As with LHR the last exon encodes the C-terminal end of the hinge region, the TM region, and the intracellular tail. The promoter region of FSHR is G/C rich, lacks the TATA and CAAT elements, and has multiple Sp1 sites. In addition, FSHR transcribes into a number of mRNA splice variants with differing abundance between the ovary and testis and different species. The major splice variants range, besides the 2.5 kb species encoding the full-length receptor protein, up to 7 kb [40].

The mature hFSHR polypeptide chain consists of 678 residues, and the primary sequence contains an additional 17–aminon acid leader peptide [10, 16]. The molecular mass of the native receptor protein expressed at target cell surface is 85 to 90 kDa, again larger than the predicted size because of glycosylation. The extracellular domain of the human receptor has four consensus sites for glycosylation signals, and when compared with the other glycoprotein receptors only two are conserved. Glycosylation is most likely concerned with stability of the protein and the process of folding of the nascent protein on its synthesis and transit to the cell membrane. Site-directed mutagenesis studies on abolition of some or all at the glycosylation sites indicate that carbohydrates are essential for receptor folding and transport to the cell surface but not for hormone binding [41].

The structural organization of the FSHR is similar to that of LHR (Figure 4.5): N- and C-terminal cysteine-rich regions of the extracellular domain, nine leucine-rich repeats between them, the TM serpentine domain with seven TM α-helixes joined by three intra- and extracellular loops, and the intracellular tail. On functional characterization of the different domains of FSHR, it has been found that the N-terminal cysteine cluster is important for proper trafficking of the receptor to the cell membrane [10]. The middle leucine-rich repeats participate in ligand binding and determine its specificity [42].

Activation and Signal Transduction of the Follicle-stimulating Hormone Receptor. As with LHR the best characterized, and probably main signaling pathway, is the cAMP-mediated activation of adenylyl cyclase and PKA [10, 16]. PKA phosphorylates structural proteins, enzymes, and transcription factors, which alters the functional state of target cells. FSH-dependent changes in phosphorylation of the cAMP responsive element (CRE) binding proteins (CREBs) and modulators (CREMs) belong to the latter category [43]. The CREM isoform ICER is involved in down-regulation of CREM expression [44]. FSHR activation is also linked to Gi protein activation, which may provide negative modulation of the PKA pathway. Depending on the cellular model, FSH stimulation either stimulates [45] or inhibits [46] the PKC/IP3 pathway. FSH stimulation increases intracellular calcium levels in granulose cells [47], and this probably involves the PKA-mediated entry of extracellular calcium.

EFFECTS OF MUTATIONS AND POLYMORPHISMS IN GONADOTROPIN AND GONADOTROPIN RECEPTOR GENES ON OVARIAN FUNCTION

In principle, mutations can be classified into three types: activating, inactivating, and neutral mutations or polymorphisms. Concerning hormonal ligands, the latter two types are known almost exclusively. In the special case of gonadotropins, the inactivating mutations are rare, probably because of their deleterious effect on reproductive fitness, for which reason they are rapidly eliminated from the genetic pool. The gonadotropin receptor mutations likewise are rare, and they have been found to exist in all three categories. We discuss next the phenotypic effects of the different types of mutations in women. Some mutations have only been found in men, in which case they are briefly described, and the putative female phenotype is suggested. The knockout mouse models for the gonadotropin ligands or receptors are also discussed because they have elucidated further the pathogenesis of inactivation of gonadotropin function. Finally, we summarize the molecular level structure-function alterations brought about by the mutations.

Gonadotropin Subunits

Common α-Subunit

There are several reports on neutral polymorphisms in the human glycoprotein hormone common α-subunit [17],

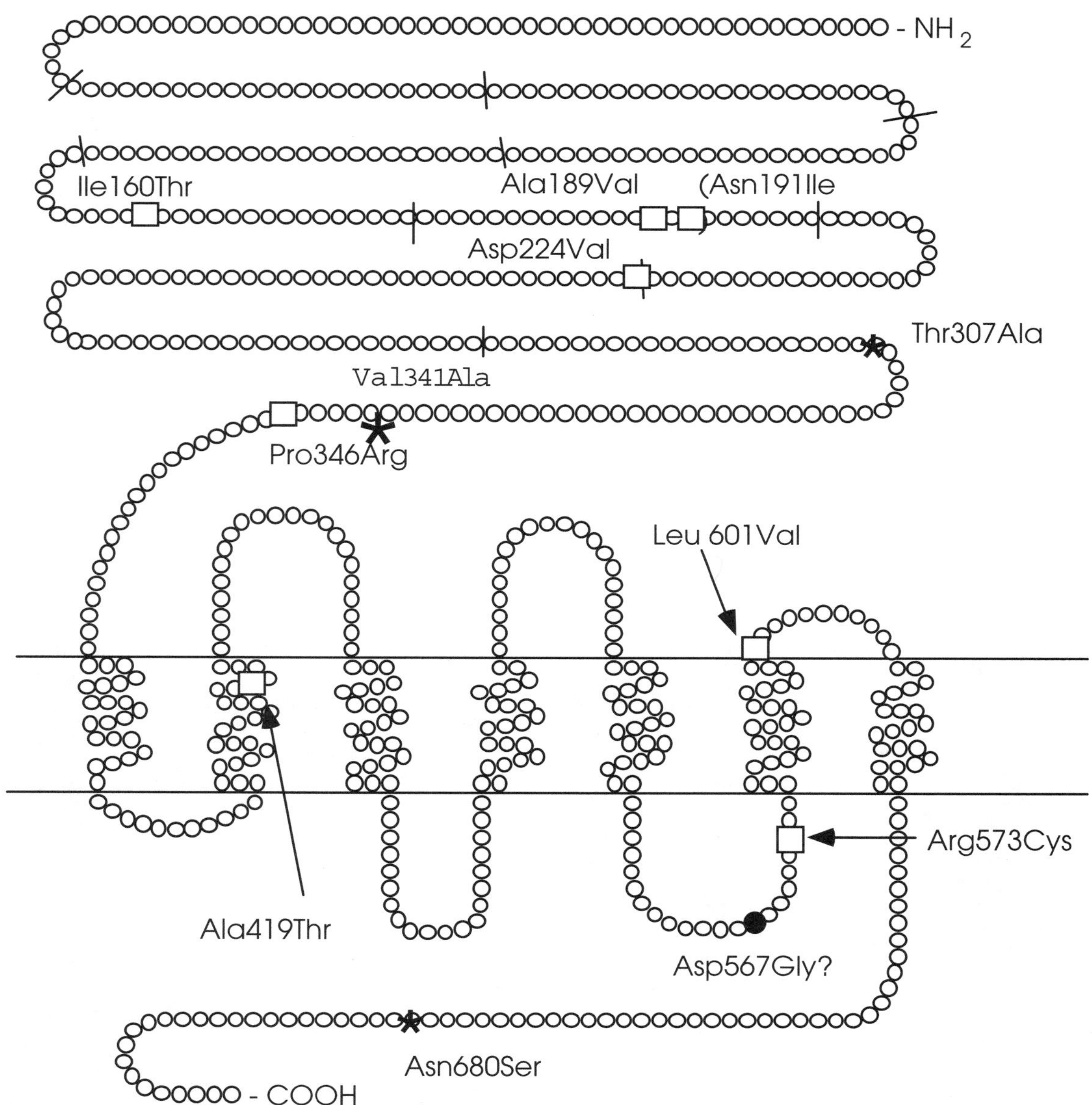

FIGURE 4.5 Orientation across the plasma membrane and locations of the currently known mutations of the human FSHR. ●, Activating mutation; □, inactivating mutation; *, polymorphism. The short lines across the peptide chain depict the exon boundaries. For references, see the text.

but no reports seem to alter the peptide sequence of the encoded protein. Some of these polymorphisms have been associated with neoplasms, but the mechanisms by which they could bring about this predisposition remain obscure, probably through linkage with genuine mutations in neighboring genes. A Glu56Ala mutation has been found in the α-subunit produced extopically by a human carcinoma (see Figure 4.1), but this appears to represent a sporadic somatic mutation [48]. Self-dimerization and failure to associate with the β-subunit were found to cause the suppressed biological activity of this mutant peptide. The lack of proven germline mutations in the α-subunit could mean that such mutations are lethal, because homozygous individuals would also lack hCG and TSH, which might be incompatible with a successful pregnancy. Surprisingly, mice with targeted disruption of the α-subunit are viable, although they are hypogonadal and hypothyroid [49]. However, because these mice do not produce chorionic gonadotropin, they may not be a proper model for humans in this regard. The question about the human phenotype of an inactivating α-subunit mutation therefore remains open. Such an individual, if viable, would undoubtedly be hypo-thyroid and hypogonadal, and if genetically male, a pseudohermaphrodite.

LHβ-Subunit

Mutations. Only one inactivating mutation of the LHβ-subunit gene has so far been described in the literature [50]. The subject described was a 17-year-old boy with delayed puberty who belonged to a previously described family with several infertile men; however, his mother and sister had normal reproductive histories. He had low testosterone, normal FSH, and a high serum concentration of immunoreactive LH. His testosterone responded normally to LH and hCG stimulation, but his serum LH remained undetectable when measured by in vitro bioassay [51]. These findings suggested, along with the family history of consanguinity and male infertility, an inherited defect in the structure of his LH. The subject responded to long-term hCG treatment with testicular enlargement, normal virilization, and onset of spermatogenesis, but he remained infertile. When studied at the age of 44 years, the subject's gonadotropins were greatly elevated (LH 64 IU/L, FSH 114 IU/L) [52]. The age-related increase in FSH suggested a failure in Sertoli cell function.

Sequencing of the LHβ-subunit of the subject revealed a homozygous A to G missense mutation in codon 54, predicting a Glu to Arg substitution (see Figure 4.1). The proband's mother, sister, and three uncles were heterozygous for the same mutation. A gene conversion with an exchange from one of the CGβ genes with the LHβ gene was excluded, indicating that the alteration in the LHβ structure was a spontaneous germline mutation. When the mutant LHβ was coexpressed with wild-type (WT) α-subunit in Chinese hamster ovary cells, the synthesized LH α/β heterodimer was immunoreactive yet unable to bind to LHR in radioreceptor assay. The mutated Glu54 is conserved in all glycoprotein hormone β-subunits, and it falls within a long loop of the protein that has been implicated in receptor binding (Figure 4.6), in line with the findings that the recombinant mutant hormone is synthesized and dimerized normally and maintains its immunoreactivity normally but is unable to bind to LHR.

This rare case complies with the current views about the developmental role of pituitary LH. The proband was nor-

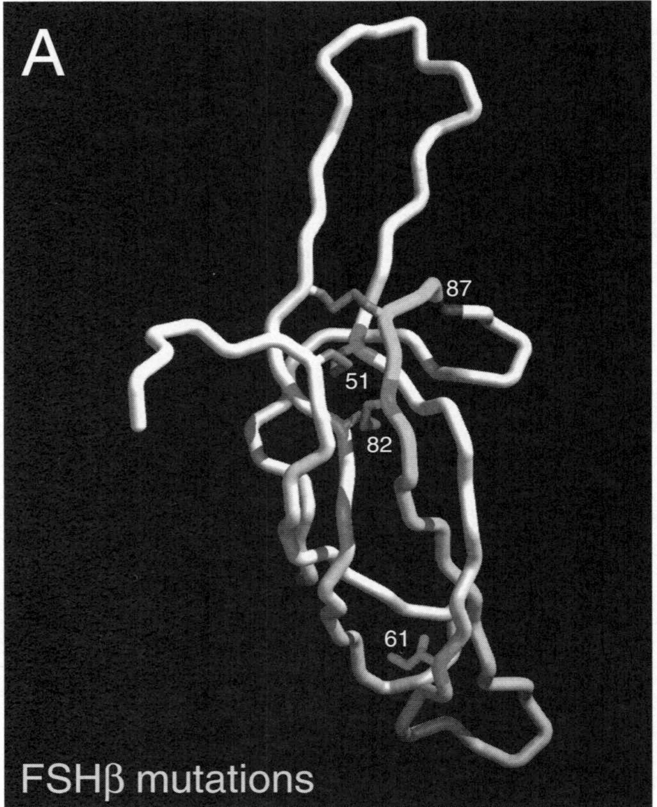

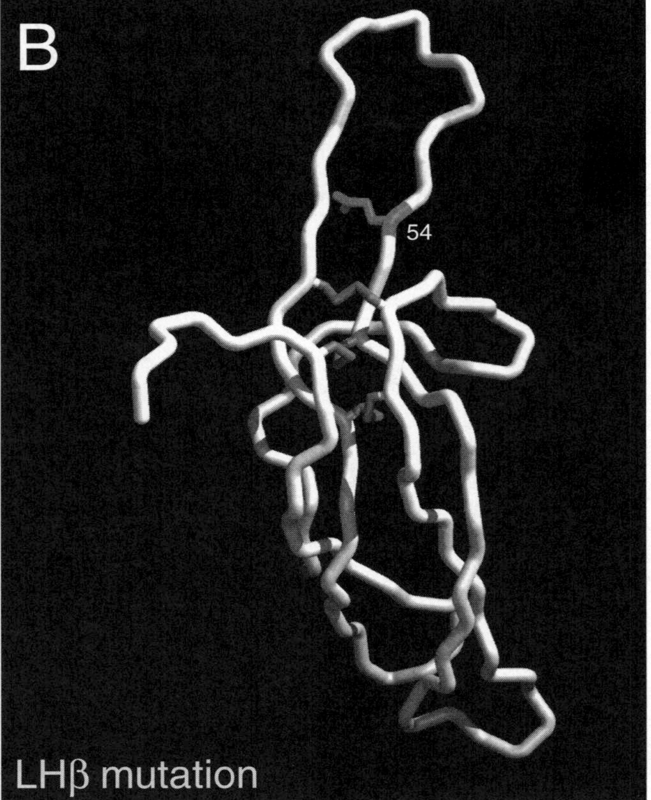

FIGURE 4.6 Locations of reported mutations in the FSHβ **(A)** and LHβ **(B)** subunits. Identified mutations in hFSH and hLH were mapped onto the crystal structure of hCG [4] relative to the positions of the cysteine residues, which are fully conserved among the three β-subunits. Mutated residues are shown in green. Residue numbers (*white*) refer to the position in the FSH and LH β-subunits rather than the number of the residue in the hCG structure. The three disulfide bridges involved in the cystine-knot motif are shown in blue. In **A,** a 2-base pair deletion at residue 61 changes the ensuing sequence (*yellow*) up to residue 86 and results in a stop codon at residue 87 (*red*). (From Ref. [52], with permission.) (See color plate.)

mally masculinized at birth, because hCG is the gonadotropin that stimulates fetal testicular steroidogenesis. Testicular function becomes postnatally dependent on pituitary LH, which explains why the subject never developed spontaneous puberty. It is curious that no females with inactivating LHβ mutation have been detected. It can be speculated that the phenotype of such women would be similar to those with inactivating LHR mutation [17, 53] with normal pubertal development but anovulatory infertility. The phenotype of the female mouse LHR knockout (see below), with normal sexual differentiation, delayed puberty, anovulatory infertility, and hypoestrogenism, is probably also close to the putative phenotype of LHβ inactivation in women. Another male subject with inactivating LHβ mutation and a similar phenotype to the first case [50] has been recently discovered but not yet reported [53a]. These cases are therefore apparently rare but will likely be discovered sporadically in the future, possibly also in women.

Polymorphisms of the LHβ-Subunit. There is a common genetic variant (V) of the LHβ with carrier frequency from 0% (the Kotas from Western India) to 53.5% (Aboriginal Australians) [54]. In Caucasian populations the carrier frequency varies between 10% and 30%. It was initially discovered as an immunologically anomalous form of LH in a healthy Finnish woman with two children [55]. Subsequently, the same LH variant was detected in Japan, and sequencing of the LHβ gene of the affected individuals revealed two amino acid–changing mutations: Trp8Arg (TGG → CGG) and Ile15Thr (ATC → ACC) [56–59]. Whereas the Finnish subjects who were homo- or heterozygous for the polymorphic LHβ allele were largely healthy, the reports from Japan associated the homozygotes with recurrent spontaneous abortions [57], menstrual irregularities with infertility [56], and polycystic ovarian syndrome (PCOS) [56, 60]. Subsequently, various disturbances in pituitary-ovarian function have also been found in V-LHβ heterozygotes [61, 62]. Clear findings of association of V-LHβ with pathologies of ovarian function have not been made in Caucasian populations [54], although in one study on a predominately Jewish population from New England, heterozygous women had significantly more frequent history of infertility treatments [63]. In Finland, no association of V-LH was found in women with history of recurrent miscarriages [64]. In subjects from the United Kingdom, V-LHβ was associated with higher serum oestradiol and probably secondary elevation of sex hormone binding globulin (SHBG) and testosterone, which suggests that the variant form of LH may be associated with subtle changes in the function of the hypothalamic-pituitary-gonadal axis [65]. The finding of higher testosterone production in carriers of the V-LHβ was confirmed in another sample of healthy Caucasian women [66]. In a multicenter study from Finland, the United Kingdom, the Netherlands, and the United States, with 1466 subjects, of whom 363 had polycystic ovarian syndrome (PCOS) and 79 had polycystic ovaries (PCO) without other symptoms of PCOS, it was found that the V-LHβ frequency was five- to sevenfold lower in obese women with PCOS compared with lean subjects with PCOS and lean and obese controls [67]. V-LHβ may thus protect obese women from developing symptomatic PCOS, which indicates that WT-LH is more likely to induce pathological ovarian responses. Considerable variation was in the findings among the different ethnic groups. Although the compiled samples showed the finding described above, this was not found in the U.K. population. This is in keeping with the multifactorial pathogenesis of PCOS and emphasizes the importance of genetic background on phenotypic effects of the mild alterations in protein function that are likely to be caused by polymorphisms. Considerable evidence showed that V-LHβ on specific genetic and/or environmental backgrounds may be a significant contributing factor to the individual variability that is observed in gonadotropin action.

Concerning the molecular alterations of V-LHβ, the Ile15Thr mutation creates an extra glycosylation signal (Asn-X-Thr) into the LHβ chain, which introduces an oligosaccharide side chain into Asn13 [68]. This mutation changes the structure of LH closer to hCG, which has glycosylated Asn13 in the same position. This extra glycosylation site probably rescues the LHβ subunit from disulfide-linked aggregation or homodimerization [69]. Experiments with recombinant human V-LH proteins with either of the two mutations showed that the altered immunoreactivity was mostly caused by the Trp8Arg mutation [68]. Findings on serum samples of variant homozygotes [70] and on the recombinant protein [68, 71] show that V-LH is more active than WT-LH in bioassays in vitro, but it has a shorter half-life in circulation. The effect of the shorter half-life of hormone can possibly be at least partly compensated by enhanced promoter activity of the gene. When promoter sequences of the WT- and V-LHβ subunit genes were compared, eight single nucleotide differences were found. Functional testing of the promoters in transfected cell cultures showed that the activity of the V-LHβ promoter was about 40% higher than that of the WT promoter [72]. Because the WT- and V-LH hormones are functionally different, with V-LH having short but highly potent action and that of WT-LH being more prolonged but less potent, it is expected that the phenotypic expression of the hormone types may be different. In addition, the combination of the two forms of LH (i.e., heterozygotes for WT- and V-LH) could differ from both of the homozygous phenotypes. Heterozygous individuals may have the most dramatic phenotypic changes because of combined action of the two different hormone types with differing functional features. Because of the rarity of V-LH homozygotes, no clear picture of the phenotypic effects of the homozygous variant has been formed.

Two other variants of the LH β-subunit have been found to be population-specific according to screenings of various ethnic groups. The first variant was found during single strand conformational polymorphism (SSCP) analysis in Singapore—a G-to-A transition in nucleotide 1502 that replaced Ser102 with Gly in exon 3 of the LH β-subunit gene [73]. This mutation was found in 4% of 176 Singaporean women with menstrual disorders [74]. Recently, the Ser102Gly mutation was screened in Finnish, Danish, Bengali, and Rwandan populations, but no positive sample for the mutation were found [75]. Therefore, it seems that the occurrence of this mutation is specific for some Asian populations. Likewise, it was found in the latter study that a recombinant form of the mutated LH did not differ in its in vitro bioactivity from WT-LH. The mechanism whereby this mutation is related to menstrual disorders in the Singapore population thus remains open and may represent linkage disequilibrium to an adjacent gene with the causative mutation.

While screening for the LHβ gene polymorphisms in various populations, a new variant was recently found [76]. Direct sequencing revealed a heterozygous G52A mutation in exon 2, resulting in Thr-3Ala amino acid substitution in the LHβ signal peptide. The variant was found in 3 out of 100 deoxyribonucleic acid (DNA) samples from Rwanda thus indicating African origin of the mutation and possibly its limited existence in populations of this continent. Protein sequencing of a recombinant form of the LH variant revealed that the mutation did not interfere with signal peptide cleavage. Neither were the secretory proportions of intact LH and free subunits significantly different among HEK293 cells expressing WT or variant LHβ chain, which indicates that the signal peptide mutation does not markedly influence the efficacy of heterodimerization. However, some alterations were found in the signal transduction of the variant LH; it was less potent in stimulating cAMP and more potent in stimulating IP3 response than WT-LH. The cause for this difference remains unclear, but the slightly altered signal peptide structure may influence the intracellular processing and tertiary structure of the hormone and thus its interaction with LHR.

Human Chorionic Gonadotropin β-Subunit

Several polymorphisms have been detected in the seven-gene hCGβ/LHβ gene complex by restriction fragment length polymorphism analysis [15], but whether they result in sequence alterations in LH or hCG has not been studied in detail. Layman et al. [77] were unable to detect large deletions or duplications of the hCGβ/LHβ gene complex by genomic Southern blotting in patients with suspected disorders of hCG production. A recent study, using PCR and single strand conformational polymorphism analysis, showed that of the six hCGβ genes present in the human genome, the one most highly expressed, number 5, is highly conserved. An A-to-G transition, predicting a Val79Met mutation in exon 3 of hCGβ 5 (see Figure 4.1) and linked to a silent C-to-T transition in codon 82, was found in 4.2% of the random population studied [78]. When the mutated gene was coexpressed with WT common α-subunit in CHO cells, the assembly of the two subunits was found to be ineffective, although the dimers that did form had normal bioactivity. It can be speculated that this polymorphism could play a role in female infertility by reducing the production of bioactive hCG needed for the maintenance of pregnancy. If found in other populations, its relationship, for instance, to habitual abortions would be worth exploring.

Follicle-stimulating Hormone β-Subunit

A total of seven subjects (four women and three men) with different inactivating mutations of the FSHβgene have so far been described in the literature (see Figure 4.1). The first mutation reported was a homozygous 2 bp deletion in the codon of Val61 in a woman suffering from delayed puberty, absent breast development, primary amenorrhea, and infertility [79]. The mutation gave rise to a completely altered amino acid sequence between codons 61 and 86 of the FSHβ chain, which was followed by a premature stop codon and lack of translation of amino acids 87 to 111. The translation product of the mutated FSHβ gene was unable to associate with the common α-subunit to form bioactive or immunoreactive α/β dimers. This is apparently because the C-terminal end of the FSHβ-subunit (which contributes to the dimer stabilizing "seat belt," one of the cysteines contributing to the cystine-knot structure) and the amino acids forming the cystine-noose structure [5] were missing in the mutated β-chain (see Figure 4.5). The affected woman had apparently had normal adrenarche but no menarche or telarche. Treatment of the patient with exogenous FSH induced follicular maturation, ovulation, and successful pregnancy. Her mother, heterozygous for the mutation, had suffered from menstrual irregularity and infertility, but these symptoms were likely unrelated to the mutation, because the heterozygous relatives of other similar patients have been reported to be free from symptoms.

The second woman with inactivating FSHβ mutation had a similar phenotype (i.e., primary amenorrhea and poorly developed secondary sex characteristics) [80]. Her serum FSH and estradiol were undetectable, LH was high, and the FSH response to the gonadotropin-releasing hormone (Gn RH) stimulation test was absent. DNA sequencing revealed that she was a compound heterozygote for two FSHβ mutations: one was the same as the mutation described by Matthews et al. [79]; the other was a missense T-to-G mutation, causing a Cys51 to Gly transition in the mature FSHβ protein. Cells transfected with FSHβ harboring this mutation failed to produce immunoreactive FSH, apparently because of the loss of a cysteine participating in formation of the cystine-knot structure essential for organizing the core of the protein and determining its folding (see Figure 4.5). No symptoms were found in the relatives heterozygous for either of the two FSHβ mutations of the proband, suggesting that one intact FSHβ gene is sufficient for functionally adequate FSH secretion.

The third female patient with isolated FSH deficiency was found to have the previously identified homozygous 2 bp deletion in codon 61 of FSHβ [81].

The fourth female with FSHβ mutation was homozygous for a Tyr76X nonsense mutation [82]. Unlike the other three cases, she had some evidence of puberty, including partial breast development (Tanner stage II–III), primary amenorrhea, and low estradiol. The phenotype appeared despite immeasurable FSH by immunoassay and in vitro bioassay, which suggests that other factors might preserve gonadal steroidogenesis in the absence of FSH or that the very low levels of FSH were not measurable by the assays used. The FSHβ peptide encoded by the gene with the Tyr76X mutation missed amino acids 76 to 111. Both interference with the cystine-knot, cystine-noose, and "seat-belt" formation (see Figure 4.5) can explain the lack of synthesis of functional FSH in the affected individuals. An additional inactivating FSHβ mutation, Cys82Arg, also affecting the cysteine-knot formation, has been described in a male subject with normal puberty but infertility caused by azoospermia [83].

Hence, it is common for all the currently known inactivating mutations of the FSHβ gene that they either alter single amino acids participating in the cystine-knot formation or truncate the C-terminal end such that the cysteine-knot, cysteine-noose, or "seat-belt" structures are altered or abolished. The female subjects with FSHβ inactivation are in good agreement and demonstrate that FSH is necessary for normal follicular development, ovulation, and fertility. Likewise, pubertal development is hampered in the absence of sufficient numbers of later stage follicles to harbor the granulosa cells needed for adequate estrogen production. As described below, this phenotype is practically identical to that caused by inactivating FSHR mutation.

The ovaries of the second woman [80, see p. 66] were studied recently by ultrasonography, and they were found to be multicystic, to contain antral follicles 3 to 5 mm in diameter, and to respond readily to FSH with an increase of estradiol and inhibin B [84]. It was concluded that follicular development is possible in the absence of FSH. The ovarian finding is different from that of women with inactivating FSHR mutation, where in the majority of cases, only primordial or primary follicles are found [85, 86]. The finding about more severe phenotype of the receptor mutation is in line with our recent comparison of phenotypes of FSHβ and FSHR knockout mice, where the ovarian phenotype was more severe in the receptor knockout [87]. This difference might be because the receptor without a ligand possesses some level of constitutive activity [88].

Recently, three men with FSHβ mutations have been described in the literature [82, 83, 89]. Surprisingly, all were azoospermic, which is in contrast to the mild to severe oligozoospermia found in men with inactivating FSHR mutation [90] and mice with FSHβ and FSHR knockout [91–93]. This conundrum has been discussed in detail elsewhere [17, 94].

Gonadotropin Receptors

Mutations have been identified in LHR and FSHR, but curiously the individual LHR mutations reported outnumber those of FSHR by 33 to 7 (see Figures 4.4 and 4.5). The receptor mutations can be activating and inactivating. The former are more common because heterozygosity is sufficient to cause a phenotype, whereas only homozygotes or compound heterozygotes have a phenotype in the case of inactivating mutations. Because the affected individuals with these mutations are infertile or subfertile, this eliminates the mutated alleles from the genetic pool and explains their rarity.

Activating or gain-of-function mutations can be classified into four categories according to the functional alteration they bring about: (1) constitutive receptor activation in the absence of ligand hormone, (2) increased sensitivity of the receptor toward its normal ligand, (3) relaxed specificity of the receptor to ligands, and (4) acquired novel functions of the mutated receptor. Most of the activating gonadotropin receptor mutations so far characterized belong to category 1. They are mainly inherited via germline, but some of those encountered in tumors may also be somatic.

Inactivating receptor mutations can be brought about by several means, which include the following:

1. Decreased synthesis of the receptor protein
2. Aberrant intracellular processing during transcription or translation
3. Impaired or missing ligand binding activity
4. Impairment or lack of signal transduction
5. Inability to anchor to the plasma membrane
6. Inability to dimerize, if needed for signal transduction
7. Increased degradation

Most of these mechanisms have been shown to be responsible for the inactivating mutations that are known today for LHR and FSHR.

Luteinizing Hormone Receptor

Both activating and inactivating LHR mutations have been discovered. Curiously, the former seems to cause phenotype only in men, whereas the inactivating mutations affect sexual differentiation and/or fertility in both sexes.

Activating Luteinizing Hormone Receptor Mutations. The first gonadotropin receptor mutations detected, apparently because of their striking phenotype, were those activating constitutively the LHR [17, 95, 96]. The syndrome caused by this mutation (i.e., familial male-limited precocious puberty [FMPP]) is a gonadotropin-independent form of precocious puberty, also called *testotoxicosis.* Boys with FMPP begin to develop puberty between 1 and 3 years of age. The phenotype is the consequence of premature constitutive activation of Leydig cell testosterone production before the pubertal onset of LH secretion.

These mutations are not of major importance to ovarian function because, curiously, no phenotype has been detected in affected women [17]. One explanation is that the initiation of LH action in the ovary requires FSH priming, and FSH dependent paracrine factors may be needed to induce the LHR expression in theca cells. Because FSH secretion starts in these women at the normal age of puberty, one cannot expect the constitutively activated LHR to be prematurely functional. The lack of LHR in prepubertal granulosa cells is evident because they only acquire this receptor during later stages of follicular maturation. Then it does not matter whether there is an activating mutation in the LHR if the gene is not expressed before the normal age of puberty. However, it is curious why no hyperandrogenism is detected in the affected women of adult age although their theca cells should be under constant LH stimulation.

Today, 15 activating mutations of the LHR gene are known (see Figure 4.4), and except for one mutation (Leu368Pro), they are all localized in the cytoplasmic halves of the TM region or in the ILs because of their crucial role in LH signal transduction [17]. TM6 and IL3 are the mutational hot spots of these alterations. The mutations apparently change the TM domain into activated conformation in the absence of ligand. The Asp578Gly mutation is the most common in the United States, and there is considerable geographic variability in the occurrence of these mutations [17]. The mutations apparently change the conformation of the TM region of the receptor in such a fashion that it assumes, at least partially, activated conformation in the absence of ligand (see below). In cell transfections, the mutated receptor protein usually displays nearly a 10-fold increase in basal cAMP production, whereas the maximal stimulation can be unaltered, suppressed, or increased, probably depending on efficacy of transport of the mutated receptor to the plasma membrane [17]. Reduced cell surface expression may explain why in some cases no phenotype is associated with a documented activating mutation. The maximum response to ligand activation has apparently no physiological importance, because at the circulating levels of LH the receptor occupancy remains relatively low. The other signaling systems operative on LHR activation have not been systematically studied, but in some cases, there is also activation of the IP3 pathway (see below).

A novel phenotype of activating LHR mutations associated with Leydig cell tumors was described recently in three boys with isosexual precocious puberty without family history of the condition [97]. Besides the symptoms and findings of FMPP, Leydig cell adenomas were found in all boys. When genomic DNA was extracted from the tumor tissues and peripheral blood leucocytes, it was found that the tumor tissues, but not leucocytes, contained a heterozygous somatic mutation encoding an Asp578His replacement in LHR. When the mutated receptor was transfected into COS-7 cells, it was found that, besides the clear constitutive activation of cAMP production in the absence of ligand, IP production was also constitutively activated, a finding that was not made with other activating LHR mutations. Besides the tumorous phenotype, these subjects differed from FMPP because their LHR mutations were somatic. This particular mutation has not been detected in the germline. Two other reports with similar phenotype and causative LHR mutation have appeared recently [98, 99]. It remains to be seen whether this particular mutation is the only one that causes Leydig cell tumorigenesis.

Another report concerned nodular Leydig cell hyperplasia of a boy with FMPP, which is not a normal finding in this syndrome [100]. The heterozygous germline mutation Asp564Gly detected in this boy did not cause great activation of cAMP production, and similar Leydig cell alterations were not found in other patients affected with the same mutation. Therefore, the mechanism of the nodular hyperplasia is apparently different from the three cases presented earlier. A third type of tumor that has been detected in one patient with FMPP, caused by a germline Asp578Gly mutation, is testicular seminoma detected at the age of 36 years [101]. Although no causative relationship was available for the LHR mutation and seminoma, the possibility remains that prolonged high intertesticular testosterone concentrations, caused by LHR stimulation, could be oncogenic.

The situation with activating LHR mutations is somewhat analogous to familial nonimmunogenic hyperthyroidism and sporadic thyroid adenomas caused by germline and somatic mutations of the TSHR gene, respectively [102, 103]. As in these cases, the somatic mutations seem to bring about greater constitutive activity of the receptor than the germline mutations. The severe forms would probably be eliminated from the genetic pool because of their strong deleterious effects. The mutation detected in the Leydig cell tumors occurred in a position where three other amino acid substituting mutations have been detected in Asp578 to Tyr/Glu/Gly [17, see Figure 4.4]. The other forms cause milder receptor activation, and at most patchy Leydig cell hyperplasia, but no tumors. Hence, the high basal stimulation of the receptor seems to be important for adenoma formation. Whether high cAMP production alone or additive or synergistic effect of the concomitantly stimulated phospholipase C pathway are involved in tumorigenesis remains to be seen. In fact, the analogous mutation in the TSHR, Asp633His, has been found in a patient with insular thyroid carcinoma with metastasis [104]. On the basis of these findings, it is possible that some ovarian stromal tumors could be induced by somatic mutations of LHR.

Two groups have addressed by theoretical modeling the activating LHR mutations, using three-dimensional model building and molecular dynamics simulations [105, 106]. The recently described crystal structure of another GPCR, that of rhodopsin [29], has been used as template in these modelings [30]. Several mutations that bring about constitutive LHR activation are close in interhelical positions in the inactive state, either in TM6 or in its vicinity (Figure 4.7). Movement of TM6 either through ligand binding to the extracellular ends of the TM regions, or through mutations altering the stabilizing interhelical H-bond network between the TMs, will then generate a docking site for G protein that includes regions at the cytoplasmic end of TMs 3, 5, and 6. The theoretical models are consistent with the view that a rearrangement in the relative position of helix 3 and 6 is a fundamental step in GPCR activation [107]. It provides insight into the structural sites of the LHR that are susceptible for spontaneous activating mutations and prediction of the functional features. Because of various degrees of activation of the different signaling cascades by specific mutations, it is apparent that there are multiple distinctly activated confirmations of LHR both on ligand binding and following activating mutations.

Inactivating Luteinizing Hormone Receptor Mutations. Currently, a total of 17 inactivating LHR mutations have been identified, ranging from partial to complete inactivation (see Figure 4.4). In the partially inactivating forms, some receptor activity remains and the LH-dependent target cell functions are not entirely absent. In the complete form, all LHR activity is lost. In men, depending on completeness of the inactivation, these mutations cause a wide spectrum of phenotypes, ranging from complete lack of masculinization (46,XY male pseudohermaphroditism) to mild undervirilization with only micropenis or perineoscrotal hypospadias [17]. Individuals with complete receptor inactivation have female external genitals, low testosterone and high LH levels, normal FSH levels, a total lack of responsiveness to LH/hCG challenge, and no development of secondary male or female sex characteristics. The expression of LHR begins already in utero, where they mediate the stimulatory effect of hCG on fetal Leydig cell testosterone and insulin-like factor (INSL) 3 production. In the male fetus, testosterone stabilizes the

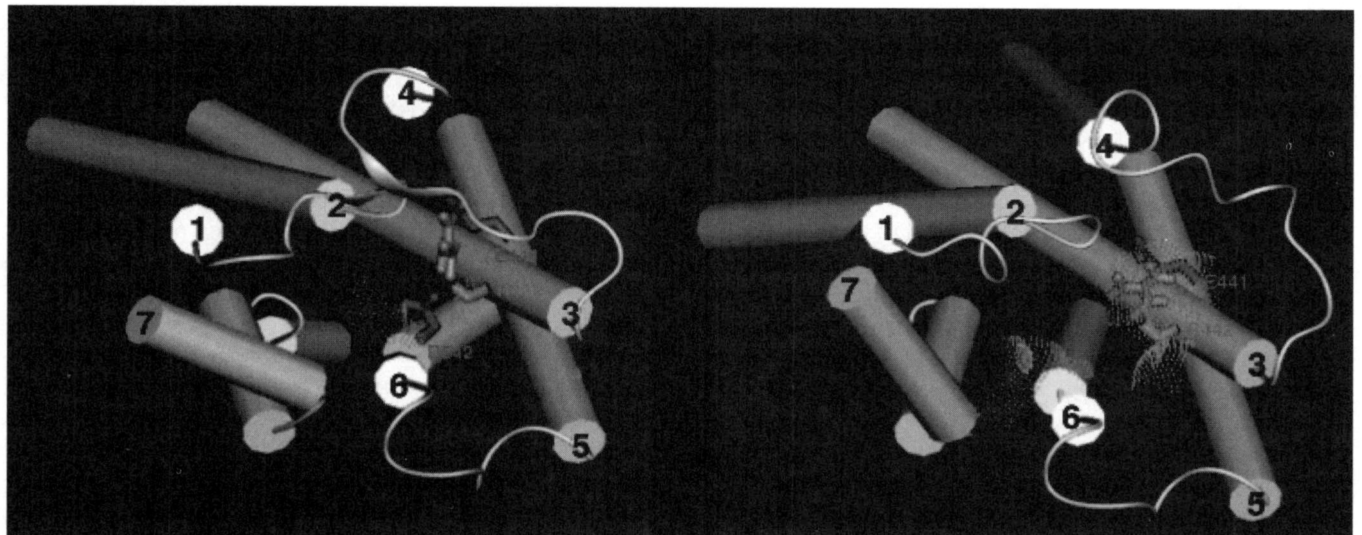

FIGURE 4.7 Average minimized structures of WT-LHR (*left*) and the D542G constitutively activating mutant (*right*). The cylinders represent the helix bundles, whereas thin ribbons represent the three intracellular loops. The extracellular domains are not shown in this figure. The structures are viewed from the intracellular side in a direction almost perpendicular to the membrane surface. The side chains of Glu-441, Arg-442, Asp-542, and Gly-542 are represented by sticks and are colored according to their polarity. The composite solvent-accessible surface computed over the amino acids Arg-442, Thr-445, Ile-446, and Lys-541 is also shown, represented by green dots. (From Ref. [30], with permission.) (See color plate.)

wolffian ducts and induces their differentiation into male accessory sex organs (prostate, seminal vesicles), and INSL3 regulates the transabdominal phase of testicular descent [108]. However, the uterus is missing because the fetal Sertoli cells still produce antimüllerian hormone. It is, however, noteworthy that the individuals have epididymides, as a sign of minimal autonomous testosterone production and paracrine action on stabilization of the wolffian ductal structures closest to the testes [109]. As expected on histological examination, the testes contain no mature Leydig cells and spermatogenesis is completely arrested [109, 110]. There is a notable lack of breast development at the age of puberty, which discriminates this syndrome from the complete form of androgen insensitivity syndrome (AIS, testicular feminization), because of inactivating androgen receptor mutations. As with the subjects with AIS, the XY individuals with complete LHR inactivation are reared as women.

Genetic women with LHR inactivation have a milder phenotype, with normal development of internal and external genitalia and normal pubertal maturation, but they have primary or secondary amenorrhea, hypoestrogenism, high LH, normal FSH, cystic ovaries, and osteopenia [111]. Histological examination of ovarian biopsies reveals all stages of follicular development up to antral follicles with a well-developed theca cell layer but conspicuously no preovulatory follicles or corpora lutea. Nonovulated follicles may give rise to cysts. On clinical examination, the patients all have a small uterus, a normal-sized vagina with hyposecretory function and thin walls, and decreased bone mass. These symptoms are indicative of low estrogen levels and strongly support the view that LH is essential for ovulation and sufficient estrogen production, whereas follicular development is initially autonomous and becomes, on FSH action at later stages, dependent. Normal feminization at puberty with inactivating LHR mutation indicates that this process in girls is mainly FSH dependent.

In vitro studies of function of the mutated receptors show clear correlation between the extent of receptor inactivation and severity of the symptoms [17]. The inactivating mutations are scattered throughout the LHR protein (see Figure 4.4), and most of them are total (i.e., neither ligand binding nor signal transduction can be demonstrated in cells transfected with cDNA for the mutant receptor). In all these cases the phenotype is complete (i.e. Leydig cell hypoplasia with male pseudohermaphroditism). The most likely reason for receptor inactivation in these cases is sequestration of the mutated protein inside the cell during its synthesis, as has been demonstrated with some of the mutations [111, 113]. In contrast, some mutations in TM helices 6 and 7 (e.g., Ala593Pro and Ile625Lys) display significant ligand binding but severely reduced signal transduction [17, 111, 114]. However, the signal transduction in these cases is apparently not totally lost, because their phenotypes are partial with a variable degree of undermasculinization (cryptorchidism, micropenis, hypospadias). An interesting case of LHR inactivation occurred where exon 10, comprising the hinge region of the receptor protein, was deleted [115]. The affected man had normal intrauterine masculinization but failed to develop normally in puberty. It was found that the mutated LHR could respond to hCG but not to pituitary LH, which explained this man's phenotype.

The phenotype of LHR knockout mice was recently reported [116, 117], and the women are a close phenocopy of the human cases with complete LHR inactivation. Homozygous female knockout mice were infertile, because of poor estrogen synthesis and lack of follicular maturation beyond the early antral stage. The lack of progression of follicular growth from the antral to preovulatory stage emphasizes the importance of LH action at the final stages of follicular maturation before ovulation. This finding may be of clinical significance because it provides experimental evidence for the timing of gonadotropin treatment schemes on in vitro fertilization, which demonstrates the dependence of the final preovulatory stages of follicular maturation on LH/hCG. The male knockout mice are indistinguishable from controls at birth, displaying full intrauterine masculinization. This is a clear difference from humans, where the individuals with fully inactivated LHR function are born with feminized external genitalia. It indicates that some nongonadotropic factors can maintain fetal Leydig cell androgen production. In this respect, the mouse differs from humans where normal LHR function is essential for prenatal masculinization. However, the LHR male knockout mice totally lacked postnatal sexual development, in agreement with inactivating LHR mutations in humans.

Polymorphisms. Several polymorphisms have been detected in the LHR gene [17], but most of them are silent and unlikely to have functional significance. The associations of the amino acid altering polymorphisms (LQ insertion between codons 8 and 9, Asn291Ser, and Asn312Ser) was studied recently with undermasculinization in boys [118]. The LQ polymorphism was associated with (1) long androgen receptor CAG repeats (≥ 26) in undermasculinization; (2) homozygosity was more frequent for Asn291 and less frequent for Asn312 in undermasculinization; and (3) in combination of the two polymorphisms, the association was still stronger. These findings demonstrate that although LHR polymorphisms alone may have only marginal effects on the phenotype, in combination with other polymorphisms their impact could be significant. Such effects on ovarian function have not yet been studied.

Follicle-stimulating Hormone Receptor

Activating Mutation. There is one uncertain finding about an activating mutation of the human FSHR gene [119]. This finding concerned a man who was hypophysectomized because of a pituitary tumor, and despite immeasurable gonadotropin levels, he displayed persistent spermatogenesis during testosterone treatment. Androgen treatment is normally not sufficient to maintain spermatogenesis in the absence of gonadotropins. A heterozygous Asp567Gly mutation was found in the third intracellular domain of exon 10 of his FSHR gene (see Figure 4.5), and it was shown in vitro to have marginal constitutive activity. Given that the WT-FSHR has a considerable constitutive activity without ligand in such cell-line transfection studies [87], the marginal elevation of cAMP production in the presence of the FSHR mutation must be interpreted with caution. The same authors recently published a transgenic mouse model, where human FSHR with the Asp567Gly mutation was expressed in mice at the gonadotropin-deficient hpg background [120]. Some FSH-like effects on testicular function were found, which were interpreted to demonstrate the constitutive activity of the transgenic FSHR. However, no controls with transgenic overexpression of WT-FSHR were included, and because the WT receptor possesses significant constitutive activity in the absence of ligand [87], it still remains open whether the Asp567Gly mutation represents a genuine activating FSHR mutation or a neutral polymorphism.

A fair conclusion at this point is that unequivocal information about the phenotype on an activating FSHR mutation in humans is not yet available. Such mutations are, however, possible, as has been shown with site-directed mutagenesis in vitro [121], but whether they cause a phenotype in vivo has not been resolved. The search for FSHR mutations in candidate diseases such as premature ovarian failure, ovarian tumors, megalotestes, precocious puberty, and twin pregnancies have yielded negative results [122–126]. It also remains a possibility that activating FSHR mutation has no phenotype or that it differs totally from our educated guesses. An animal model would be seminal in resolving this question.

Inactivating Mutations. Only a few inactivating mutations have been identified in the FSHR gene (see Figure 4.5). A selection mechanism may be operative against them based on their strong antifertility effect, precluding the inheritance of the faulty alleles. In the first successful search for loss-of-function FSHR mutations, advantage was taken of the enrichment of mutations for certain recessively inherited disorders in Finland [127]. On linkage analysis, a cohort of patients with hypergonadotropic ovarian dysgenesis, with primary and early-onset secondary amenorrhea and variable development of secondary sex characteristics, revealed a locus on chromosome 2p that was associated with recessive inheritance pattern of the syndrome. A missense Ala189Val mutation was found in the extracellular domain of the FSHR, and it segregated perfectly with the phenotype. Ligand binding activity and signal transduction of the mutated receptor were severely reduced, and the mutated receptor protein was sequestered almost entirely within the cells [128]. When the mutated receptor was overexpressed in COS-7 cells, low cAMP response could be measured, but the IP3 response was lost. When two women and one man homozygous for the same mutation were treated with massive doses of recombinant FSH (300 to 900 IU/day), no functional responses of the ovaries or testes were observed [86]. Therefore, this mutation must be considered from the physiological point of view as totally inactivating. It is curious that such a conserved mutation as Ala to Val causes such a dramatic alteration in behavior of the receptor protein. This indicates that the FSHR is sensitive to structural alterations that interfere easily with synthesis of the protein causing its intracellular sequestration. Similar observations have been made on site-directed mutagenesis studies of the FSHR.

All homozygous female carriers of the Ala189Val FSHR mutation showed follicles in their ovaries, usually in the primordial stage, but occasionally at more advanced stages of development [85]. In contrast, total absence of follicles was observed in the cases of hypergonadotropic hypogonadism where no FSHR mutation could be detected. Thus the FSHR mutation phenotype is distinct from the common form of ovarian dysgenesis (e.g., Turner syndrome) with streak ovaries and absence of growing follicles.

Recently, two pairs of compound heterozygous FSHR mutations were described in women with primary or secondary amenorrhea, normal pubertal development, and follicular development up to the antral stage [129, 130]. Two of the mutations, Ile160Thr and Asp224Val, present in the extracellular domain of the receptor (see Figure 4.5), caused near-complete loss of FSH binding. Confocal microscopy showed impaired targeting to the cell membrane with both mutants. Indeed, cells expressing these receptor mutants showed absent or marginal cAMP response to FSH stimulation. The other two mutations, Arg573Cys and Leu601Val, in the TM region, caused less complete receptor inactivation. Whereas the ligand binding was only marginally inhibited, the effect on signal transduction was inhibited more severely, although not totally.

A functionally tested inactivating Asn191Ile mutation has been found in a healthy German woman in heterozygous form, in close vicinity of the Ala189Val mutation [131]. Recently, another woman with normal secondary sex characteristics but primary hypergonadotropic amenorrhea was identified in Finland [132]. She was a compound heterozygote for the original Ala189Val mutation and a novel Ala419Thr mutation located in the second TM loop of the FSH. The mutated FSHR displayed slightly reduced ligand binding capacity with unaltered affinity, but the cAMP signal transduction was lost. The mutation entails substitution of a small nonpolar amino acid alanine with a larger uncharged polar amino acid threonine in the second hydrophobic helix of the TM domain. The mutation is located in a highly conserved region, which indicated its functional significance, apparently for signal transduction. The last mutation detected is Pro348Arg in the extracellular part of exon 10 in a hypergonadotropic woman with delayed puberty and primary amenorrhea [133]. This mutation totally abolished ligand binding, but it was not studied whether it was caused by sequestration of the receptor inside the cell or genuine lack of ligand binding to an otherwise normally exteriorized receptor protein.

Despite the rarity of the currently known FSHR mutations there is good correlation between the phenotype and the degree of receptor inactivation, and the site of mutation and its functional consequences, in the same fashion as with the larger number of LHR mutations [17]. All mutation in the extracellular region (1le160Thr, Ala189Val, Asp224Val, and Pro346Arg) cause a defect in targeting of the protein to the cell membrane. In contrast, the three mutations in the TM region (Ala419Thr, Arg573Cys, and Leu602Va) have minimal effect on ligand binding but impair the signal transduction to various extents but not totally. It also seems that the location, rather than the nature of amino acid alteration, determines the functional response. The mutations in the TM region, in addition, seem to be less total in the receptor inactivation. It is important to know that the ovaries of patients with the milder forms of mutations may respond to high-dose FSH stimulation [129, 130], whereas no response was found with the complete form of receptor inactivation [127, 128]. Hence, the molecular diagnosis of these rare patients may help in design of rational treatment for their infertility. All heterozygotes for the mutations so far studied have been free from phenotype, which indicated that one functional FSHR allele is sufficient to maintain normal reproductive function.

The first inactivating FSHR mutation, Ala189Val (C566T transition) [127, see above], is located in exon 7 in the middle of the ligand binding extracellular domain. This mutation is located within a five-amino acid stretch, Ala-Phe-Asn-Glu-Thr (AFNQT), that is highly conserved within the gonadotropin and TSHR sequences, indicating its functional significance. A homologous Phe194Val (T-to-G transversion) was recently described to cause LHR inactivation in a case of male pseudohermaphroditism [134]. The inactivating heterozygous Asn191Ile mutation in the FSHR [131, see above] is located in the same region, and site directed mutagenesis has demonstrated that mutations in the other amino acids of the 5–amino acid stretch are also candidates for total or partial LHR and FSHR mutations [134]. It is possible that mutations in this region cause receptor inactivation by the same mechanism. In the case of the FSHR, the conserved Ala198Val mutation was found to abolish receptor binding and signal transduction almost completely, but when the mutant receptor was over-expressed in transfected cells, the cAMP generation per expressed receptor was roughly the same as with WT receptor [127]. It was shown by immunofluorescence that the majority of the mutated receptor immunoreactivity was sequestered within the cells. Apparently, only a minute fraction of the mutated FSHR molecules can reach the plasma membrane, but when they reach this site they can still bind FSH with unaltered affinity and activate the cAMP and steroidogenic responses. Whether this occurs constitutively (i.e., in the absence of ligand, as is possible to some extent for the FSHR [87]) or after ligand binding is unknown. Nevertheless, the functional significance of the residual bioactivity of the mutated receptor is negligible, and in functional terms, this particular mutation can be considered to bring about total inactivation of FSH action. The AFNQT domain could thus play a role in the receptor folding during its synthesis, but its last three amino acids also form a glycosylation signal (NXS/T). Studies on rat FSHR have shown that inactivation of the glycosylation signal per se does not affect functions of the receptor, but the type of amino acid inserted in the mutant may affect the transit of the receptor to the plasma membrane [23].

Follicle-stimulating Hormone Receptor Polymorphisms. Several polymorphisms have been detected in FSHR (see Figure 4.5), but relatively little is known about their possible functional correlates. The polymorphisms Thr307/Asn680 and Ala307/Ser680 appear to be in linkage disequilibrium in some populations and the frequency of both alleles is almost equal, at least in Caucasian populations [135]. It was recently reported in Germany that in women undergoing ovulation induction, the basal FSH concentration of the Asn/Asn genotype (6.4 ± 0.4 IU/L) was significantly lower than that of the Ser/Ser genotype (8.3 ± 0.6 IU/L) and that the latter group needed about 50% more FSH ampoules for stimulation of follicular growth [135]. However, this finding was recently disputed by the same authors when a more extensive group of patients with combined German and Dutch heritage was studied, although the Ser/Ser patients still displayed higher basal FSH than the Asn/Asn or Asn/Ser variants [136]. Likewise, no correlation to spermatogenesis or reproductive endocrine parameters was found with the polymorphic FSHR genotype in men [137]. Hence, the role of this polymorphism in gonadal function, if any, remains open.

CONCLUSION

Concerning mutations in the gonadotropin subunit genes, the following conclusions can be drawn:

- No germline mutations of the common α-subunit are known, apparently because of the dramatic phenotypic effects they would have, with possible embryo lethality.
- Only one inactive LHβ mutation has been described in a man with normal prenatal sex differentiation but

arrested pubertal development. Additional cases, including women, are likely to be found.
- A common polymorphism exists in the LHβ subunit. It affects the bioactivity of the hormone and has multiple phenotypic effects, including borderline compromising effects on female fertility. Its effect of reproductive functions may be strongly dependent on the genetic background of an individual.
- FSHβ mutations in women cause disturbances in pubertal development and disturbances in follicular maturation.

The following conclusions can be made about gonadotropin receptor mutations and polymorphisms:

- Constitutively activating LHR mutations give rise to early-onset gonadotropin-independent precocious puberty in boys, but no female phenotype has been identified.
- No unequivocally activating FSHR mutations have been described, and studies on candidate syndromes (e.g., familial twinning) have yielded negative results.
- Inactivating LHR mutation cause a relatively mild phenotype in women: anovulatory infertility without apparent disturbance in pubertal development. The male phenotype ranges, depending on the completeness of the receptor inactivation, from XY pseudohermaphroditism to mild undermasculinization with hypospadias and micropenis.
- Inactivating FSHR mutations cause in women, depending on completeness of the inactivation, phenotypes ranging from FSH-responsive secondary amenorrhea to total arrest of follicular maturation, including arrested pubertal maturation.

Despite their rarity, the gonadotropin and gonadotropin receptor mutations have been informative, because they have clarified the molecular pathogenesis of conditions associated with disturbed gonadotropin secretion or action. They have also clarified some poorly known or controversial issues in the physiology of gonadotropin function. This new information will make it possible to design more rational treatment regimens for gonadotropin therapy in general, and more specifically, for the cases where a genuine mutation in the genes involved has been discovered. Some of the common polymorphisms discovered in the genes of gonadotropins and their receptors may prove to be important contributing factors, in conjunction with specific genetic backgrounds, in the pathogenesis of certain reproductive disturbances, or in the individual response to hormonal therapies. The structure-function relations of gonadotropin action at the three-dimensional level of molecule interaction will enable the design of small molecular form gonadotropin agonists and antagonists for future therapeutic applications.

References

1. Morgan, F. J., Kammerman, S., and Canfield, R. E. (1973). Chemistry of human chorionic gonadotropin. In *Handbook of Physiology, Vol. II, Female Reproductive System,* Part 2, eds. R. O. Greep and E. A. Astwood, 311–322. Washington, D.C.: American Physiological Society Edition.
2. Sairam, M. R., and Parkoff, H. (1973). Chemistry of pituitary gonadotropins. In *Handbook of Physiology, Vol. IV, The Pituitary Gland and Its Neuroendocrine Control,* Part 2, eds. R. O. Greep and E. A. Astwood, 111–131. Washington, D.C.: American Physiological Society Edition.
3. Fiete, D., Srivastava, V., Hindsgaul, O., and Baenziger, J. U. (1991). A hepatic reticuloendothelial cell receptor specific for SO4-4GalNAc beta 1,4GlcNAc beta 1,2Man alpha that mediates rapid clearance of lutropin. *Cell* 67, 1103–1110.
4. Lapthorn, A. J., Harris, D. C., Littlejohn, A., Lustbader, J. W., Canfield, R. E., Machin, K. J., Morgan, F. J., and Isaacs, N. W. (1994). Crystal structure of human chorionic gonadotropin. *Nature* 369, 455–461.
5. Fox, K. M., Dias, J. A., and Van Roey, P. (2001). Three-dimensional structure of human follicle-stimulating hormone. *Mol. Endocrinol.* 15, 378–389.
6. Bousfield, G. R., Perry, W. M., and Ward, D. N. (1994). Gonadotropins. Chemistry and biosynthesis. In *The Physiology of Reproduction,* 2d ed., eds. E. Knobil, and J. D. Neill, 1749–1792. New York: Raven Press.
7. Bo, M., and Boime, I. (1992). Identification of the transcriptionally active genes of the chorionic gonadotropin β gene cluster in vitro. *J. Biol. Chem.* 267, 3179–3184.
8. Dias, J. A. (2001). Is there any physiological role for gonadotropin oligosaccharide heterogeneity in humans? II. A biochemical point of view. *Hum. Reprod.* 16, 825–830.
9. Ulloa-Aguirre, A., Maldonado, A., Damian-Matsumura, P., and Timossi, C. (2001). Endocrine regulation of gonadotropin glycosylation. *Arch. Med. Res.* 32, 520–532.
10. Dias, J., and Van Roey, P. (2001). Structural biology of human follitropin and its receptor. *Arch. Med. Res.* 32, 510–519.
11. Chen, H. C., Shimohigashi, Y., Dufau, M. L., and Catt, K. J. (1982). Characterization and biological properties of chemically deglycosylated human chorionic gonadotropin. Role of carbohydrate moieties in adenylate cyclase activation. *J. Biol. Chem.* 257, 14446–14452.
12. Garcia-Campayo, V., and Boime, I. (2001). Novel recombinant gonadotropins. *Trends Endocrinol. Metab.* 12, 72–77.
13. Lustbader, J. W., Lobel, L., Wu, H., and Elliott, M. M. (1998). Structural and molecular studies of human chorionic gonadotropin and its receptor. *Rec. Prog. Hormone Res.* 53, 395–424.
14. Segaloff, D. L., and Ascoli, M. (1993). The lutropin/choriogonadotropin receptor . . . 4 years later. *Endocr. Rev.* 14, 324–347.
15. Ascoli, M., Fanelli, F., and Segaloff, D. L. (2002). The lutropin/choriogonadotropin receptor: A 2002 perspective. *Endocr. Rev.* 23, 141–174.
16. Simoni, M., Gromoll, J., and Nieschlag, E. (1997). The follicle-stimulating hormone receptor: Biochemistry, molecular biology, physiology, and pathophysiology. *Endocr. Rev.* 18, 739–773.

17. Themmen, A. P. N., and Huhtaniemi, I. T. (2000). Mutations of gonadotropins and gonadotropin receptors: Elucidating the physiology and pathophysiology of pituitary-gonadal function. *Endocr. Rev*. 21, 551–583.
18. Atger, M., Misrahi, M., Sar, S., Le Flem, L., Dessen, P., and Milgrom, E. (1995). Structure of the human luteinizing hormone-choriogonadotropin receptor gene: Unusual promoter and 5′ non-coding regions. *Mol. Cell. Endocrinol.* 111, 113–123.
19. Tsai-Morris, C. H., Geng, Y., Buczko, E., and Dufau, M. L. (1998). A novel human luteinizing hormone receptor gene. *J. Clin. Endocrinol. Metab*. 83, 288–291.
20. Hämäläinen, T., Poutanen, M., and Huhtaniemi, I. (2001). Promoter function of different lengths of the murine luteinizing hormone receptor gene 5′-flanking region in transfected gonadal cells and in transgenic mice. *Endocrinology* 142, 2427–2434.
21. Zhang, F.-P., Hämäläinen, T., Kaipia, A., Pakarinen, P., and Huhtaniemi, I. (1994). Ontogeny of luteinizing hormone receptor gene expression in the rat testis. *Endocrinology* 134, 2206–2213.
22. Sokka, T. A., Hämäläinen, T. M., Kaipia, A., Warren, D. W., and Huhtaniemi, I. T. (1996). Development of luteinizing hormone action in the perinatal rat ovary. *Biol. Reprod*. 55, 663–670.
23. Davis, D. P., Rozell, T. G., Liu, X., and Segaloff, D. L. (1997). The six N-linked carbohydrates of the lutropin/choriogonadotropin receptor are not absolutely required for correct folding, cell surface expression, hormone binding, or signal transduction. *Mol. Endocrinol.* 11, 550–562.
24. Tapanainen, J. S., Bo, M., Dunkel, L., Billig, H., Perlas, E., Boime, I., and Hsueh, A. J. W. (1993). Deglycosylation of the human luteinizing hormone receptor does not affect ligand binding and signal transduction. *Endocrine* 1, 219–225.
25. Bhowmick, N., Huang, J., Puett, D., Isaacs, N. W., and Lapthorn, A. J. (1996). Determination of residues important in hormone binding to the extracellular domain of the luteinizing hormone/chorionic gonadotropin receptor by site-directed mutagenesis and modeling. *Mol. Endocrinol.* 10, 1147–1159.
26. Song, Y. S., Ji, I., Beauchamp, J., Isaacs, N. W., and Ji, T. H. (2001). Hormone interactions to Leu-rich repeats in the gonadotropin receptors. I. Analysis of Leu-rich repeats of human luteinizing hormone/chorionic gonadotropin receptor and follicle-stimulating hormone receptor. *J. Biol. Chem.* 276, 3426–3435.
27. Kajava, A. V. (1998). Structural diversity of leucine-rich repeat proteins. *J. Mol. Biol.* 277, 519–527.
28. Kobe, B., and Deisenhofer, J. (1994). The leucine-rich repeat: A versatile binding motif. *Trends Biochem. Sci.* 19, 415–421.
29. Palczewski, K., Kumasaka, T., Hori, T., Behnke, C. A., Motoshima, H., Fox, B. A., Le Trong, I., Teller, D. C., Okada, T., Stenkamp, R. E., Yamamoto, M., and Miyano, M. (2000). Crystal structure of rhodopsin: A G protein–coupled receptor. *Science* 289, 739–745.
30. Angelova, K., Fanelli, F., and Puett, D. (2002). A model for constitutive lutropin receptor activation based on molecular simulation and engineered mutations in transmembrane helices 6 and 7. *J. Biol. Chem.* 277, 32202–32213.
31. Abell, A. N., and Segaloff, D. L. (1997). Evidence for the direct involvement of transmembrane region 6 of the lutropin/choriogonadotropin receptor in activating Gs. *J. Biol. Chem.* 272, 14586–14591.
32. Kudo, M., Osuga, Y., Kobilka, B. K., and Hsueh, A. J. (1996). Transmembrane regions V and VI of the human luteinizing hormone receptor are required for constitutive activation by a mutation in the third intracellular loop. *J. Biol. Chem.* 271, 22470–22478.
33. Kawate, N., Peegel, H., and Menon, K. M. (1997). Role of palmitoylation of conserved cysteine residues of luteinizing hormone/human choriogonadotropin receptors in receptor down-regulation. *Mol. Cell. Endocrinol.* 127, 211–219.
34. Hipkin, R. W., Sanchez-Yague, J., and Ascoli, M. (1993). Agonist-induced phosphorylation of the luteinizing hormone/chorionic gonadotropin receptor expressed in a stably transfected cell line. *Mol. Endocrinol*. 7, 823–832.
35. Gudermann, T., Schoneberg, T., and Schultz, G. (1997). Functional and structural complexity of signal transduction via G protein–coupled receptors. *Annu. Rev. Neurosci.* 20, 399–427.
36. Kuhn, B., and Gudermann, T. (1999). The luteinizing hormone receptor activates phospholipase C via preferential coupling to Gi2. *Biochemistry* 38, 12490–12498.
37. Rajagopalan-Gupta, R. M., Lamm, M. L., Mukherjee, S., Rasenick, M. M., and Hunzicker-Dunn, M. (1998). Luteinizing hormone/choriogonadotropin receptor-mediated activation of heterotrimeric guanine nucleotide binding proteins in ovarian follicular membranes. *Endocrinology* 139, 4547–4555.
38. Gudermann, T., Birnbaumer, M., and Birnbaumer, L. (1992). Evidence for dual coupling of the murine luteinizing hormone receptor to adenylyl cyclase and phosphoinositide breakdown and Ca2+ mobilization. Studies with the cloned murine luteinizing hormone receptor expressed in L cells. *J. Biol. Chem*. 267, 4479–4488.
39. Hirakawa, T., Galet, C., and Ascoli, M. (2002). MA-10 cells transfected with the human lutropin/choriogonadotropin receptor (hLHR): A novel experimental paradigm to study the functional properties of the hLHR. *Endocrinology* 143, 1026–1035.
40. Tilly, J. L., LaPolt, P. S., and Hsueh, A. J. (1992). Hormonal regulation of follicle-stimulating hormone receptor messenger ribonucleic acid levels in cultured rat granulosa cells. *Endocrinology* 130, 1296–1302.
41. Davis, D., Liu, X., and Segaloff, D. L. (1995). Identification of the sites of N-linked glycosylation on the follicle-stimulating hormone (FSH) receptor and assessment of their role in FSH receptor function. *Mol. Endocrinol*. 9, 159–170.
42. Braun, T., Schofield, P. R., and Sprengel, R. (1991). Amino-terminal leucine-rich repeats in gonadotropin receptors determine hormone selectivity. *EMBO J*. 10, 1885–1890.
43. Sassone-Corsi, P. (1998). CREM: A master-switch governing male germ cells differentiation and apoptosis. *Semin. Cell. Dev. Biol.* 9, 475–482.
44. Don, J., and Stelzer, G. (2002). The expanding family of CREB/CREM transcription factors that are involved with spermatogenesis. *Mol. Cell. Endocrinol.* 187, 115–124.
45. Quintana, J., Hipkin, R. W., Sanchez-Yague, J., and Ascoli, M. (1994). Follitropin (FSH) and a phorbol ester stimulate

the phosphorylation of the FSH receptor in intact cells. *J. Biol. Chem.* 269, 8772–8779.

46. Monaco, L., Adamo, S., and Conti, M. (1988). Follicle-stimulating hormone modulation of phosphoinositide turnover in the immature rat Sertoli cell in culture. *Endocrinology* 123, 2032–2039.
47. Grasso, P., and Reichert, Jr., L. E. (1993). Induction of calcium transport into cultured rat Sertoli cells and liposomes by follicle-stimulating hormone. *Rec. Prog. Hormone Res.* 48, 517–521.
48. Nishimura, R., Shin, J., Ji, I., Middaugh, C. R., Kruggel, W., Lewis, R. V., and Ji, T. H. (1986). A single amino acid substitution in an ectopic α-subunit of a human carcinoma choriogonadotropin. *J. Biol. Chem.* 261, 10475–10477.
49. Kendall, S. K., Samuelson, L. C., Saunders, T. L., Wood, R. I., and Camper, S. A. (1995). Targeted disruption of the pituitary glycoprotein hormone α-subunit produces hypogonadal and hypothyroid mice. *Genes Dev.* 9, 2007–2019.
50. Weiss, J., Axelrod, L., Whitcomb, R. W., Crowley, Jr., W. F., and Jameson, J. L. (1992). Hypogonadism caused by a single amino acid substitution in the beta-subunit of luteinizing hormone. *N. Engl. J. Med.* 326, 179–183.
51. Beitins, I. Z., Axelrod, L., Ostrea, T., Little, R., and Badger, T. M. (1981). Hypogonadism in a male with an immunologically active, biologically inactive luteinizing hormone: Characterization of the abnormal hormone. *J. Clin. Endocrinol. Metab.* 52, 1143–1149.
52. Achermann, J. C., Weiss, J., Lee, E. J., and Jameson, J. L. (2001). Inherited disorders of the gonadotropin hormones. *Mol. Cell. Endocrinol.* 179, 89–96.
53. Toledo, S. P., Brunner, H. G., Kraaij, R., Post, M., Dahia, P. L., Hayashida, C. Y., Kremer, H., and Themmen, A. P. (1996). An inactivating mutation of the luteinizing hormone receptor causes amenorrhea in a 46,XX female. *J. Clin. Endocrinol. Metab.* 81, 3850–3854.

53a. Gaillard, R., and Beckers, A., personal communication.

54. Lamminen, T., and Huhtaniemi, I. (2001). A common genetic variant of luteinizing hormone: Relation to normal and aberrant pituitary-gonadal function. *Eur. J. Pharmacol.* 414, 1–7.
55. Pettersson, K., Ding, Y. Q., and Huhtaniemi, I. (1992). An immunologically anomalous luteinizing hormone variant in a healthy woman. *J. Clin. Endocrinol. Metab.* 74, 164–171.
56. Furui, K., Suganuma, N., Tsukahara, S., Asada, Y., Kikkawa, F., Tanaka, M., Ozawa, T., and Tomoda, Y. (1994). Identification of two point mutations in the gene coding luteinizing hormone (LH) beta-subunit, associated with immunologically anomalous LH variants. *J. Clin. Endocrinol. Metab.* 78, 107–113.
57. Okuda, K., Yamada, T., Imoto, H., Komatsubara, H., and Sugimoto, O. (1994). Antigenic alteration of an anomalous human luteinizing hormone caused by two chorionic gonadotropin-type amino-acid substitutions. *Biochem. Biophys. Res. Commun.* 200, 584–590.
58. Pettersson, K., Mäkelä, M. M., Dahlén, P., Lamminen, T., Huoponen, K., and Huhtaniemi, I. (1994). Genetic polymorphism found in the LHβ gene of an immunologically anomalous variant of human luteinizing hormone. *Eur. J. Endocrinol.* 130 (Suppl 2), 65.
59. Nilsson, C., Jiang, M., Pettersson, K., Iitiä, A., Mäkelä, M., Simonsen, H., Easteal, S., Herrera, R. J., and Huhtaniemi, I. (1998). Determination of a common genetic variant of luteinizing hormone using DNA hybridization and immunoassays. *Clin. Endocrinol. (Oxf.)* 49, 369–376.
60. Suganuma, N., Furui, K., Furuhashi, M., Asada, Y., Kikkawa, F., and Tomoda, Y. (1995). Screening of the mutations in luteinizing hormone beta-subunit in patients with menstrual disorders. *Fertil. Steril.* 63, 989–995.
61. Takahashi, K., Kurioka, H., Ozaki, T., Kanasaki, H., Kohsaka, M., Miyazaki, K., and Karino, K. (1998). Increased prevalence of luteinizing hormone beta-subunit variant in Japanese infertility patients. *Hum. Reprod.* 13, 3338–3344.
62. Takahashi, K., Ozaki, T., Okada, M., Kurioka, H., Kanasaki, H., and Miyazaki, K. (1999). Increased prevalence of luteinizing hormone beta-subunit variant in patients with premature ovarian failure. *Fertil. Steril.* 71, 96–101.
63. Cramer, D. W., Petterson, K. S., Barbieri, R. L., and Huhtaniemi, I. T. (2000). Reproductive hormones, cancers, and conditions in relation to a common genetic variant of luteinizing hormone. *Hum. Reprod.* 15, 2103–2107.
64. Tulppala, M., Huhtaniemi, I., and Ylikorkala, O. (1998). Genetic variant of luteinizing hormone in women with a history of recurrent miscarriage. *Hum. Reprod.* 13, 2699–2702.
65. Rajkhowa, M., Talbot, J. A., Jones, P. W., Pettersson, K., Haavisto, A. M., Huhtaniemi, I., and Clayton, R. N. (1995). Prevalence of an immunological LH beta-subunit variant in a UK population of healthy women and women with polycystic ovary syndrome. *Clin. Endocrinol. (Oxf.)* 43, 297–303.
66. Hill, M., Huhtaniemi, I. T., Hampl, R., and Starka, L. (2001). Genetic variant of luteinizing hormone: Impact on gonadal steroid sex hormones in women. *Physiol. Res.* 50, 583–587.
67. Tapanainen, J. S., Koivunen, R., Fauser, B. C., Taylor, A. E., Clayton, R. N., Rajkhowa, M., White, D., Franks, S., Anttila, L., Pettersson, K. S., and Huhtaniemi, I. T. (1999). A new contributing factor to polycystic ovary syndrome: The genetic variant of luteinizing hormone. *J. Clin. Endocrinol. Metab.* 84, 1711–1715.
68. Suganuma, N., Furui, K., Kikkawa, F., Tomoda, Y., and Furuhashi, M. (1996). Effects of the mutations (Trp8 → Arg and Ile15 → Thr) in human luteinizing hormone (LH) beta-subunit on LH bioactivity in vitro and in vivo. *Endocrinology* 137, 831–838.
69. Suzuki, S., Furuhashi, M., and Suganuma, N. (2000). Additional N-glycosylation at Asn(13) rescues the human LHbeta-subunit from disulfide-linked aggregation. *Mol. Cell. Endocrinol.* 160, 157–163.
70. Haavisto, A.-M., Pettersson, K., Bergendahl, M., Virkamäki, A., and Huhtaniemi, I. (1995). Occurrence and biological properties of a common genetic variant of luteinizing hormone. *J. Clin. Endocrinol. Metab.* 80, 1257–1263.
71. Manna, P. R., Joshi, L., Reinhold, V. N., Aubert, M. L., Suganuma, N., Pettersson, K., and Huhtaniemi, I. T. (2002). Synthesis, purification and structural and functional characterization of recombinant form of a common genetic variant of human luteinizing hormone. *Hum. Mol. Genet.* 11, 301–315.

72. Jiang, M., Pakarinen, P., Zhang, F.-P., El-Hefnawy, T., Koskimies, P., Pettersson, K., and Huhtaniemi, I. (1999). A common polymorphic allele of the human luteinizing hormone beta-subunit gene: Additional mutations and differential function of the promoter sequence. *Hum. Mol. Genet.* 8, 2037–2046.
73. Roy, A. C., Liao, W. X., Chen, Y., Arulkumaran, S., and Ratnam, S. S. (1996). Identification of seven novel mutations in LH beta-subunit gene by SSCP. *Mol. Cell. Biochem.* 165, 151–153.
74. Ramanujam, L. N., Liao, W. X., Roy, A. C., Loganath, A., Goh, H. H., and Ng, S. C. (1999). Association of molecular variants of luteinizing hormone with menstrual disorders. *Clin. Endocrinol. (Oxf.)* 51, 243–246.
75. Lamminen, T., Jiang, M., Manna, P. R., Pakarinen, P., Simonsen, H., Herrera, R. J., and Huhtaniemi, I. (2002). Functional study of a recombinant form of human LHβ-subunit variant carrying the Glu^{102}Ser mutation in Asian populations. *Mol. Hum. Reprod.* 10, 887–892.
76. Jiang, M., Lamminen, T., Pakarinen, P., Hellman, J., Manna, P., Herrera, R. J., and Huhtaniemi, I. (2002). A novel Ala(-3)Thr mutation in the signal peptide of human luteinizing hormone beta-subunit: Potentiation of the inositol phosphate signaling pathway and attenuation of the adenylate cyclase pathway by recombinant variant hormone. *Mol. Hum. Reprod.* 8, 201–212.
77. Layman, L. C., Edwards, J. L., Osborne, W. E., Peak, D. B., Gallup, D. G., Tho, S. P., Reindollar, R. H., Roach, D. J., McDonough, P. G., and Lanclos, K. D. (1997). Human chorionic gonadotropin-beta gene sequences in women with disorders of HCG production. *Mol. Hum. Reprod.* 3, 315–320.
78. Miller-Lindholm, A. K., Bedows, E., Bartels, C. F., Ramey, J., Maclin, V., and Ruddon, R. W. (1999). A naturally occurring genetic variant in the human chorionic gonadotropin-beta gene 5 is assembly inefficient. *Endocrinology* 140, 3496–3506.
79. Matthews, C. H., Borgato, S., Beck-Peccoz, P., Adams, M., Tone, Y., Gambino, G., Casagrande, S., Tedeschini, G., Benedetti, A., and Chatterjee, V. K. (1993). Primary amenorrhoea and infertility caused by a mutation in the beta-subunit of follicle-stimulating hormone. *Nat. Genet.* 5, 83–86.
80. Layman, L. C., Lee, E. J., Peak, D. B., Namnoum, A. B., Vu, K. V., van Lingen, B. L., Gray, M. R., McDonough, P. G., Reindollar, R. H., and Jameson, J. L. (1997). Delayed puberty and hypogonadism caused by mutations in the follicle-stimulating hormone beta-subunit gene. *N. Engl. J. Med.* 337, 607–611.
81. Matthews, C., and Chatterjee, V. K. (1997). Isolated deficiency of follicle-stimulating hormone re-revisited. *N. Engl. J. Med.* 337, 642.
82. Layman, L. C., Porto, A. L. A., Xie, J., da Motta, L. A., da Motta, L. D., Weiser, W., and Sluss, P. M. (2002). FSHβ gene mutations in a female with a partial breast development and a male sibling with normal puberty and azoospermia. *J. Clin. Endocrinol. Metab.* 87, 3702–3707.
83. Lindstedt, G., Nyström, E., Matthews, C., Ernest, I., Janson, P. O., and Chatterjee, K. (1998). Follitropin (FSH) deficiency in an infertile male due to FSHbeta gene mutation. A syndrome of normal puberty and virilization but underdeveloped testicles with azoospermia, low FSH but high lutropin and normal serum testosterone concentrations. *Clin. Chem. Lab. Med.* 36, 663–665.
84. Barnes, R. B., Namnoum, A. B., Rosenfield, R. L., and Layman, L. C. (2002). The role of LH and FSH in ovarian androgen secretion and ovarian follicular development: Clinical studies in a patient with isolated FSH deficiency and multicystic ovaries. *Hum. Reprod.* 17, 88–91.
85. Aittomäki, K., Herva, R., Stenman, U.-H., Juntunen, K., Ylöstalo, P., Hovatta, O., and de la Chapelle, A. (1996). Clinical features of primary ovarian failure caused by a point mutation in the follicle-stimulating hormone receptor gene. *J. Clin. Endocrinol. Metab.* 81, 3722–3726.
86. Vaskivuo, T. E., Aittomäki, K., Anttonen, M., Ruokonen, A., Herva, R., Osawa, Y., Heikinheimo, M., Huhtaniemi, I., and Tapanainen, J. S. (2002). Effects of follicle-stimulating hormone (FSH) and human chorionic gonadotropin in individuals with inactivating mutation of the FSH receptor. *Fertil. Steril.* 78, 108–113.
87. Abel, M. H., Huhtaniemi, I., Pakarinen, P., Kumar, R., and Charlton, H. M. (2003). Age related uterine and ovarian hypertrophy in follicle stimulating hormone (FSH) receptor knockout and FSHβ subunit knockout mice. *Reproduction*, in press.
88. Baker, P. J., Pakarinen, P., Huhtaniemi, I. T., Abel, M. H., Charlton, H. M., Kumar, T. R., and O'Shaughnessy, P. J. (2003). Failure of normal Leydig cell development in FSH receptor-deficient mice, but not FSHβ deficient mice: Role for constitutive FSH receptor activity. *Endocrinology* 144, 138–145.
89. Phillip, M., Arbelle, J. E., Segev, Y., and Parvari, R. (1998). Male hypogonadism due to a mutation in the gene for the beta-subunit of follicle-stimulating hormone. *N. Engl. J. Med.* 338, 1729–1732.
90. Tapanainen, J. S., Aittomäki, K., Min, J., Vaskivuo, T., and Huhtaniemi, I. T. (1997). Men homozygous for an inactivating mutation of the follicle-stimulating hormone (FSH) receptor gene present variable suppression of spermatogenesis and fertility. *Nat. Genet.* 15, 205–206.
91. Kumar, T. R., Wang, Y., Lu, N., and Matzuk, M. M. (1997). Follicle stimulating hormone is required for ovarian follicle maturation but not male fertility. *Nat. Genet.* 15, 201–204.
92. Dierich, A., Sairam, M. R., Monaco, L., Fimia, G. M., Gansmuller, A., LeMeur, M., and Sassone-Corsi, P. (1998). Impairing follicle-stimulating hormone (FSH) signaling in vivo: Targeted disruption of the FSH receptor leads to aberrant gametogenesis and hormonal imbalance. *Proc. Natl. Acad. Sci. USA* 95, 13612–13617
93. Abel M. H., Wootton, A. N., Wilkins, V., Huhtaniemi, I., Knight, P. G., and Charlton, H. M. (2000). The effect of a null mutation in the follicle-stimulating hormone receptor gene on mouse reproduction. *Endocrinology* 141, 1795–1803.
94. Huhtaniemi, I. (2002). The role of mutations affecting gonadotropin secretion and action in disorders of pubertal development. *Best Pract. and Res.; Clin. Endocrinol. & Metab.* 16, 123–138.
95. Kremer, H., Mariman, E., Otten, B. J., Moll, Jr., G. W., Stoelinga, G. B., Wit, J. M., Jansen, M., Drop, S. L., Faas, B.,

Ropers, H. H., Themmen, A. P. N., and Brunner, H. G. (1993). Cosegregation of missense mutations of the luteinizing hormone receptor gene with familial male-limited precocious puberty. *Hum. Mol. Genet.* 2, 1779–1783.

96. Shenker, A., Laue, L., Kosugi, S., Merendino, Jr., J. J., Minegishi, T., and Cutler, Jr., G. B. (1993). A constitutively activating mutation of the luteinizing hormone receptor in familial male precocious puberty. *Nature* 365, 652–654.

97. Liu, G., Duranteau, L., Carel, J. C., Monroe, J., Doyle, D. A., and Shenker, A. (1999). Leydig-cell tumors caused by an activating mutation of the gene encoding the luteinizing hormone receptor. *N. Engl. J. Med.* 341, 1731–1736.

98. Canto, P., Söderlund, D., Ramón, G., Nishimura, E., and Méndez, J. P. (2002). Mutational analysis of the luteinizing hormone receptor gene in two individuals with Leydig cell tumors. *Am. J. Med. Genet.* 108, 148–152.

99. Richter-Unruh, A., Wessels, H. T., Menken, U., Bergmann, M., Schmittmann-Ohters, K., Schaper, J., Tappeser, S., and Hauffa, B. P. (2002). Male LH-independent sexual precocity in a 3.5-year-old boy caused by somatic activating mutation of the LH receptor in a Leydig cell tumor. *J. Clin. Endocrinol. Metab.* 87, 1052–1056.

100. Leschek, E. W., Chan, W. Y., Diamond, D. A., Kaefer, M., Jones, J., Barner, K. M., and Cutler, Jr., G. B. (2001). Nodular Leydig cell hyperplasia in a boy with male-limited precocious puberty. *J. Pediatr.* 138, 949–951.

101. Martin, M. M., Wu, S.-M., Martin, A. L. A., Rennert, O. M., and Chan, W.-Y. (1998). Testicular seminoma in a patient with a constitutively activating mutation of the luteinizing hormone/chorionic gonadotropin receptor. *Eur. J. Endocrinol.* 139, 101–106.

102. Paschke, R., and Ludgate, M. (1997). The thyrotropin receptor in thyroid diseases. *N. Engl. J. Med.* 337, 1675–1681.

103. Parma, J., Duprez, L., Van Sande, J., Hermans, J., Rocmans, P., Van Vliet, G., Costagliola, S., Rodien, P., Dumont, J. E., and Vassart, G. (1997). Diversity and prevalence of somatic mutations in the thyrotropin receptor and Gsa genes as a cause of toxic thyroid adenomas. *J. Clin. Endocrinol. Metab.* 82, 2695–2701.

104. Russo, D., Tumino, S., Arturi, F., Vigneri, P., Grasso, G., Pontecorvi, A., Filetti, S., and Belfiore, A. (1997). Detection of an activating mutation of the thyrotropin receptor in a case of an autonomously hyperfunctioning thyroid insular carcinoma. *J. Clin. Endocrinol. Metab.* 82, 735–738.

105. Fanelli, F. (2000). Theoretical study on mutation-induced activation of the luteinizing hormone receptor. *J. Mol. Biol.* 296, 1333–1351.

106. Shenker, A. (2002). Activating mutations of the lutropin choriogonadotropin receptor in precocious puberty. *Receptors Channels* 8, 3–18.

107. Gether, U. (2000). Uncovering molecular mechanisms involved in activation of G protein–coupled receptors. *Endocr. Rev.* 21, 90–113.

108. Nef, S., and Parada, L. F. (2000). Hormones in male sexual development. *Genes Dev.* 14, 3075–3086.

109. Kremer, H., Kraaij, R., Toledo, S. P., Post, M., Fridman, J. B., Hayashida, C. Y., van Reen, M., Milgrom, E., Ropers, H. H., Mariman, E., Themmen, A. P. N., and Brunner, H. G. (1995). Male pseudohermaphroditism due to a homozygous missense mutation of the luteinizing hormone receptor gene. *Nat. Genet.* 9, 160–164.

110. Latronico, A. C., Anasti, J., Arnhold, I. J., Rapaport, R., Mendonca, B. B., Bloise, W., Castro, M., Tsigos, C., and Chrousos, G. P. (1996). Testicular and ovarian resistance to luteinizing hormone caused by inactivating mutations of the luteinizing hormone receptors gene. *N. Engl. J. Med.* 331, 507–512.

111. Toledo, S. P., Brunner, H. G., Kraaij, R., Post, M., Dahia, P. L., Hayashida, C. Y., Kremer, H., and Themmen, A. P. (1996). An inactivating mutation of the luteinizing hormone receptor causes amenorrhea in a 46,XX female. *J. Clin. Endocrinol. Metab.* 81, 3850–3854.

112. Laue, L., Wu, S. M., Kudo, M., Hsueh, A. J., Cutler, Jr., G. B., Griffin, J. E., Wilson, J. D., Brain, C., Berry, A. C., Grant, D. B., and Chan, W. Y. (1995). A nonsense mutation of the human luteinizing hormone receptor gene in Leydig cell hypoplasia. *Hum. Mol. Genet.* 4, 1429–1433.

113. Martens, J. W. M., Lumbroso, S., Verhoef-Post, M., Georget, V., Richter-Unruh, A., Szarras-Czapnik, M., Romer, T. E., Brunner, H. G., Themmen, A. P. N., and Sultan, C. (2002). Mutant luteinizing hormone receptors in a compound heterozygous patient with complete Leydig cell hypoplasia: Abnormal processing causes signaling deficiency. *J. Clin. Endocrinol. Metab.* 87, 2506–2513.

114. Martens, J. W., Verhoef-Post, M., Abelin, N., Ezabella, M., Toledo, S. P., Brunner, H. G., and Themmen, A. P. (1998). A homozygous mutation in the luteinizing hormone receptor causes partial Leydig cell hypoplasia: Correlation between receptor activity and phenotype. *Mol. Endocrinol.* 12, 775–784.

115. Gromoll, J., Eiholzer, U., Nieschlag, E., and Simoni, M. (2000). Male hypogonadism caused by homozygous deletion of exon 10 of the luteinizing hormone (LH) receptor: Differential action of human chorionic gonadotropin and LH. *J. Clin. Endocrinol. Metab.* 85, 2281–2286.

116. Zhang, F.-P., Poutanen, M., Wilbertz, J., and Huhtaniemi, I. (2001). Normal prenatal but arrested postnatal sexual development of luteinizing hormone receptor knockout (LuRKO) mice. *Mol. Endocrinol.* 15, 172–183.

117. Lei, Z. M., Mishra, S., Zou, W., Xu, B., Foltz, M., Li, X., and Rao, C. V. (2001). Targeted disruption of luteinizing hormone/human chorionic gonadotropin receptor gene. *Mol. Endocrinol.* 15, 184–200.

118. Mongan, N. P., Hughes, I. A., and Lim, H. N. (2002). Evidence that luteinising hormone receptor polymorphisms may contribute to male undermasculinisation. *Eur. J. Endocrinol.* 147, 103–107.

119. Gromoll, J., Simoni, M., and Nieschlag, E. (1996). An activating mutation of the follicle-stimulating hormone receptor autonomously sustains spermatogenesis in a hypophysectomized man. *J. Clin. Endocrinol. Metab.* 81, 1367–1370.

120. Haywood, M., Tymchenko, N., Spaliviero, J., Koch, A., Jimenez, M., Gromoll, J., Simoni, M., Nordhoff, V., Handelsman, D.J., and Allan, C. M. (2002). An activated human follicle-stimulating hormone (FSH) receptor stimulates FSH-like activity in gonadotropin-deficient transgenic mice. *Mol. Endocrinol.* 16, 2582–2591.

121. Tao, Y. X., Abell, A. N., Liu, X., Nakamura, K., and Segaloff, D. L. (2000). Constitutive activation of G protein–coupled receptors as a result of selective substitution of a conserved leucine residue in transmembrane helix III. *Mol. Endocrinol.* 14, 1272–1282.
122. Gicalglia, L. R., da Fonte Kohek, M. B., Carvalho, F. M., Villares Fragaso, M. C. B., Mendonca, B. B., and Latronico, A. C. (2000). No evidence of somatic activating mutations on gonadotropin receptor genes in sex cord stromal tumors. *Fertil. Steril.* 64, 992–995.
123. Takakura, K., Takebayashi, K., Wang, H.-Q., Kimura, F., Kasahara, K., and Noda, Y. (2001). Follicle-stimulating hormone receptor gene mutations are rare in Japanese women with premature ovarian failure and polycystic ovary syndrome. *Fertil. Steril.* 75, 207–209.
124. Tong, Y., Liao, W. X., Roy, A. C., and Ng, S. C. (2001). Absence of mutations in the coding regions of follicle-stimulating hormone receptor gene in Singapore Chinese women with premature ovary failure and polycystic ovary syndrome. *Horm. Metab. Res.* 33, 221–226.
125. de la Chesnaye, E., Canto, P., Ulloa-Aguirre, A., and Mendez, J. P. (2001). No evidence of mutations in the follicle-stimulating hormone receptor gene in Mexican women with 46,XX pure gonadal dysgenesis. *Am. J. Med. Genet.* 98, 129–135.
126. Montgomery, G. W., Duffy, D. L., Hall, J., Kudo, M., Martin, N. G., and Hsueh, A. J. (2001). Mutations in the follicle-stimulating hormone receptor and familial dizygotic twinning. *Lancet* 357, 773–774.
127. Aittomäki, K., Dieguez Lucena, J. L., Pakarinen, P., Sistonen, P., Tapanainen, J., Gromoll, J., Kaskikari, R., Sankila, E.-M., Lehväslaiho, H., Reyes Engel, A., Nieschlag, E., Huhtaniemi, I., and de la Chapelle, A. (1995). Mutation in the follicle-stimulating hormone receptor gene causes hereditary hypergonadotropic ovarian failure. *Cell.* 82, 959–968.
128. Rannikko, A., Pakarinen, P., Manna, P. R., Beau, I., Misrahi, M., Aittomäki, K., and Huhtaniemi, I. (2002). Functional characterization of the human FSH receptor with an inactivating Ala189Val mutation. *Mol. Hum. Reprod.* 8, 311–317.
129. Beau, I., Touraine, P., Meduri, G., Gougeon, A., Desroches, A., Matuchansky, C., Milgrom, E., Kuttenn, F., and Misrahi, M. (1998). A novel phenotype related to partial loss of function mutations of the follicle stimulating hormone receptor. *J. Clin. Invest.* 102, 1352–1359.
130. Touraine, P., Beau, I., Gougeon, A., Meduri, G., Desroches, A., Pichard, C., Detoeuf, M., Paniel, B., Prieur, M., Zorn, J. R., Milgrom, E., Kuttenn, F., and Misrahi, M. (1999). New natural inactivating mutations of the follicle-stimulating hormone receptor: Correlations between receptor function and phenotype. *Mol. Endocrinol.* 13, 1844–1854.
131. Gromoll, J., Simoni, M., Nordhoff, V., Behre, H.M., De Geyter, C., and Nieschlag, E. (1996). Functional and clinical consequences of mutations in the FSH receptor. *Mol. Cell. Endocrinol.* 125, 177–182.
132. Doherty, E., Pakarinen, P., Tiitinen, A., Kiilavuori, A., Huhtaniemi, I., Forrest, S., and Aittomaki, K. (2002). A novel mutation in the FSH receptor inhibiting signal transduction and causing primary ovarian failure. *J. Clin. Endocrinol. Metab.* 87, 1151–1155.
133. Allen, L. A., Achermann, J. C., Pakarinen, P., Kotlar, T. J., Huhtaniemi, I. T., Jameson, L. J., Cheetham, T. D., and Ball, S. G. (2003). A novel loss of function mutation in exon 10 of the FSH receptor gene causing hypergonadotropic hypogonadism: Clinical and molecular characteristics. *Hum. Reprod.*, in press.
134. Gromoll, J., Schulz, A., Borta, H., Gudermann, T., Teerds, K. J., Greschniok, A., Nieschlag, E., and Seif, F. J. (2002). Homozygous mutation within the conserved Ala-Phe-Asn-Glu-Thr motif of exon 7 of the LH receptor causes male pseudohermaphroditism. *Eur. J. Endocrinol.* 147, 597–608.
135. Perez Mayorga, M., Gromoll, J., Behre, H. M., Gassner, C., Nieschlag, E., and Simoni, M. (2000). Ovarian response to follicle-stimulating hormone (FSH) stimulation depends on the FSH receptor genotype. *J. Clin. Endocrinol. Metab.* 85, 3365–3369.
136. Laven, J. S., Mulders, A. G., Simoni, M., Gromoll, J., and Fauser, B. C. (2002). Follicle-stimulating hormone (FSH) receptor genotype in normogonadotropic anovulatory infertile (WHO II) patients and normo-ovulatory controls. The Endocrine Society, Annual Meeting, June 2002, Abstract no. OR60-1.
137. Asantiani, K., Gromoll, J., Eckardstein, S. V., Zitzmann, M., Nieschlag, E., and Simoni, M. (2002). Distribution and function of FSH receptor genetic variants in normal men. *Andrologia* 34, 172–176.

CHAPTER 5

Regulation of Gonadotropin Receptor in the Ovary

TAKASHI MINEGISHI

INTRODUCTION

Just as how follicles can be stimulated to maturity when exogenous gonadotropins are administered, the process that enables a follicle to reach preovulatory status depends on the gonadotropins. During the follicular phase of the primate menstrual cycle, a single follicle usually grows to the preovulatory stage and releases its oocyte for fertilization. The process of follicle maturation during the spontaneous menstrual cycle represents the selection by which one follicle gains and maintains advantage over all other maturing follicles.

Gonadotropins regulate the ovarian functions under the circumstances in which various regulatory factors act through endocrine, paracrine, and autocrine modes and induce proper numbers of follicles to ovulate at the time of ovulation. On the other hand, administration of gonadotropins has been the standard treatment for certain types of anovulatory infertility. Although pregnancy rates improve with this treatment, it has not been possible to induce a therapeutic regimen that avoids the risks of multiple ovulation and births. The initial event in the action of gonadotropins is the binding to highly specific receptors located in the membrane of the target cells. Because the structures of gonadotropin receptors are known, it should be possible for patients to be treated by individual manipulations that provide a single ovulation. To achieve this clinical goal, it is important to know the mechanisms of regulation of gonadotropin receptors.

FOLLICLE-STIMULATING HORMONE AND LUTEINIZING HORMONE RECEPTOR STRUCTURE AND FUNCTION

The receptors of follicle-stimulating hormone (FSH) and luteinizing hormone (LH) are glycoproteins that belong to the superfamily of G protein–coupled receptors. These G protein–linked cell surface receptors mediate their intracellular actions through the activation of one or more guanine-nucleotide binding, signal-transducing proteins (G proteins). Receptors that belong to this superfamily consist of a single polypeptide chain of variable length that contains seven transmembrane (TM) segments connected by three extracellular loops and three intracellular loops. The glycoprotein hormone receptors for FSH, LH, and thyroid-stimulating hormone (TSH) represent a small subclass of the rhodopsin/β-adrenergic large subfamily that is characterized by the presence of a large N-terminal extracellular domain. The cloning to the rat LH and porcine complementary deoxyribonucleic acids (cDNAs) was quickly followed by the cloning of cDNA for the human LH receptor (hLHR) [1–3].

The hLHR is encoded by a single gene located in the short arm of chromosome 2 (2p21) [4], and the human FSH receptor (hFSHR) gene is localized on chromosome 2p21-p16, which suggests that these two genes encode closely related glycoproteins [4, 5]. The hLHR gene is about 80 kb and consists of 10 introns and 11 exons [6, 7]. The TM and C-terminal domains of the LHR are encoded in exon 11. This exon also codes for the C-terminal end of the hinge region of the extracellular domain. The N-terminal cysteine-rich region and the N-terminal end of the hinge region of the extracellular domain arise from the splicing of exons 1 to 10. Transcription of hLHR gene gives rise to multiple messenger ribonucleic acid (mRNA) species in gonadal tissues [8]. These different transcripts are thought to occur as a result of the use of different transcriptional start sites, alternate splicing of the gene, and/or differences in polyadenylation [1, 2]. The marmoset monkey provides an example of splice variant of the LHR that is translated into a stable protein. The LHR gene of the marmoset monkey consists of 11 exons, but exon 10 is spliced out of the mature mRNA [9]. Despite this deletion, the mature marmoset LHR can bind human chorionic gonadotropin (hCG) with a high affinity, comparable with that of the hLHR, and the binding of hCG can be translated into increases in cyclic adenosine monophosphate (cAMP) and inositol phosphate production [9].

Sequence homology of the hFSHR with the hLHR is about 50% (45% in the large extracellular domain; 70% in the TM domain; and 61% and 10% in the NH_2-terminus and the COOH-terminus of the intracellular domain, respectively). In the rat and the human, the FSHR gene consists of 10 exons separated by 9 introns; the 9 exons of the gene code for the large NH_2-terminal extracellular domain whereas the single large exon encodes the seven TM-spanning regions and the COOH-terminal tail of the protein. The organization of the FSHR gene is similar to that present in the TSH and LH receptor genes, again an indication of its common evolutionary origin.

The mutations explain certain pathologies in the thyroid gland and gonadal function. In the former, constitutive activation of the TSH receptor (TSHR) brings about toxic adenomas and hyperplasia, and inactivating mutations cause hypothyroidism. In gonads, the male-limited familial gonadotropin-independent form of precocious puberty (testotoxicosis) has been found to be caused by a number of constitutively activating point mutations of the LHR gene. Inactivating mutations of the LHR gene cause male pseudohermaphroditism with Leydig cell hypoplasia and in amenorrhea in women.

In contrast to the heterogeneous location of the naturally occurring loss-of-function mutations of the hLHR, all naturally occurring gain-of-function mutations reported to date are localized to exon 11 in the TM region of the hLHR [10–12]. These mutants display different degrees of constitutive activity. The recent data demonstrated that certain mutations of the hinge region of the hLHR can also induce constitutive activation [13]. In addition, naturally occurring activating mutations have been recently identified in the hinge region of the extracellular domain of the structurally related TSHR [14]. It is possible that further studies will reveal the presence of activating mutations of the hLHR elsewhere.

FUNCTIONAL CHARACTERISTICS OF THE EXTRACELLULAR AND THE TRANSMEMBRANE DOMAINS

In contrast to other members of the rhodopsin/β-adrenergic subfamily of G protein–coupled receptors, which exhibit relatively short extracellular domains, the glycoprotein receptors have large extracellular domains that display to 14 sequence repeats (encoded by exons 2 to 9) built on a motif similar to other leucine-rich glycoproteins [15, 16]. In the FSHR, these leucine-rich repeats (in particular, composite regions encompassed by repeats 1 to 11), which favor the formation of amphipathic peptide surfaces optimal for specific protein-protein interactions, are involved in high affinity binding and binding specificity. The particular structure of this region and the conformational changes that occur on recognition of the β-subunit of the hormone allow receptor stimulation after proper orientation and positioning of specific regions located in both subunits of the dimer into a receptor activation site defined by the exoloops and the TM domains of the receptor [15].

The extracellular domain, which is essential for specific binding to FSH and LH, contains three or four consensus sequences (Asn-Xaa-Ser/Thr) for N-linked glycosylation [17]; whereas glycosylation of the FSHR is not involved directly in hormone binding, the receptor strictly requires at least one N-linked glycosylated site for proper folding, membrane expression, and function [18].

An inactivating mutation of the FSHR gene was found in connection with hypergonadotropic ovarian failure (HOF) [19], a condition often called *resistant ovary syndrome*. The study was initiated by a population-based investigation [20] where 75 such patients were identified in Finland. A systematic search for linkage was completed in the many families, and a locus for the ovarian failure related to HOF was mapped to chromosome 2p, with a maximum lod score of 4.71 with chromosome 2p-specific markers. All affected individuals were homozygous for a C- to T-transition in position 566 of exon 7 of the FSHR gene, predicting a change of alanine 189 to valine. About 40% of the HOF cases in Finland are caused by the 566C T- point mutation of the FSHR gene [19].

It is of interest to compare the phenotypic effects of the inactivating FSHR mutation with those of the cases of selective FSH deficiency. The phenotype of the FSH-deficient women resembles HOF with primary amenorrhea and infertility, but these women can become pregnant with FSH treatment [21]. No means are available to stimulate follicular maturation in FSHR-deficient women despite the abundance of primordial follicles in their ovaries. In the affected families, there were also men homozygous for the 566C T mutation. The results showed that FSH is needed in men to stimulate pubertal proliferation of Sertoli's cells, which is an important determinant of final testicular size. FSH is also needed for maintenance of quantitatively normal spermatogenesis, but this process does not need FSH, which indicates that FSH is more critical for female than male fertility.

ROLE OF THE INTRACELLULAR DOMAINS IN G PROTEIN COUPLING AND ACTIVATION

G proteins are heterotrimers, individually termed *α-, β-,* and *γ-subunits,* that are encoded by distinct genes [22]. They are signal-transducing molecules regulated by guanine nucleotides that carry the information received by the receptor to downstream specific cellular effectors including enzymes and ion channels. The FSHR, LHR, and TSHR are preferentially coupled to the protein G_s, which activates the enzyme adenyl cyclase to enhance the synthesis of the second messenger cAMP, which in turns activates protein kinase A (PKA).

One form of desensitization, called *uncoupling*, is relatively fast and is caused by the prevention of the FSHR and LHR interacting with G proteins. The other form of desensitization, called *down-regulation*, is relatively slow and is caused by a reduction in the density of cell surface receptors. It now appears that the FSH- and LH-induced uncoupling and down-regulation of the FSHR and LHR are mediated by a family of G protein–coupled receptor (GPCR)-binding proteins called the *β-arrestins*.

The large number of studies conducted with the adrenergic receptors and other GPCRs have shown the formation of a GPCR/β-arrestin complex (for reviews, see [23, 24]). The GPCRs are phosphorylated in serine and/or threonine residues that are usually located in the C-terminal tail. This phosphorylation event, which is catalyzed by a family of serine/threonine kinases called GPCR kinase (GRK), enhances the affinity of the GPCRs for the β-arrestins. The GPCR/β-arrestin complex is a common molecular intermediate **that** uncouples the GPCRs from the G proteins by preventing G protein binding [25]. It may also activate other signaling components (e.g., Src and members of the MAPK cascade) and provide the GPCRs to clathrin-coated pits for subsequent internalization [24]. Two of these events, the β-arrestin-dependent uncoupling and internalization, seem to be involved in the posttranscriptional regulation of the FSHR and LHR.

REGULATION OF FOLLICLE-STIMULATING HORMONE RECEPTOR MESSENGER RIBONUCLEIC ACID

The expression of activin subunit mRNA in granulosa cells is limited in growing follicles, but there is no expression in atretic follicles [26]. These data indicate that activin may be an important factor in initiating the growth of primary follicles before the initial FSH surge. Incubation with 8-Br-cAMP produced a dose-related response in FSHR mRNA in the granulosa cells of diethylstilbestrol (DES)-primed immature rats. These results fully support the results of nuclear run-on experiments in which 8-Br-cAMP significantly stimulated the rate of transcription of the FSHR gene [27]. In addition, the effects of activin and cAMP on FSHR induction are additive and activin regulates FSHR gene expression through transcriptional and posttranscriptional mechanisms [28]. Activin supported granulosa cell survival and cell proliferation and maintained the functional FSHR in the absence of FSH throughout long-term culture [29]. In our cultured cells, the level of FSHR was maintained for several days without any stimulus. There appeared to be an increase in the basal level of activin as the cells were cultured for increasing lengths of time in the absence of stimulus [30].

Desensitization is used to describe the ability of target cells to turn off an agonist response in the face of continuous agonist exposure; it is an important regulation of hormone actions and can occur at multiple levels. FSH induced a dose-dependent and a rapid yet transient down-regulation effect on the FSHR mRNA in granulosa cells [31, 32]. Although the down- and up-regulation of the FSHR might occur simultaneously or sequentially, we might find the experimental conditions in which each factor for the regulation could be isolated and analyzed. FSH treatment decreased FSHR mRNA levels with a maximum of about 60% of that of the control at 6 hours, as consistent with a previous observation [31]. However, granulosa cells cultured for 6 hours in the presence of 30 ng/ml of FSH and in increasing concentrations of activin resulted in a dose-dependent recovery in FSHR mRNA and the presence of 100 ng/ml of activin reversed the loss of FSHR mRNA observed in FSH-treated cells [30]. Follicular selection is known to be affected by gonadotropins, and the development of larger follicles is stimulated by and dependent on FSH. In the growing follicle, it is important to keep responsive to FSH by maintaining its FSHR, because follicular atresia occurs at all stages of follicle growth and development [33]. From this point of view, the fact that activin reversed the loss of FSH-induced FSHR mRNA might be an important factor in keeping the granulosa cell responsive to FSH. These data suggest that activin and FSH interact to regulate follicular selection and atresia in vivo.

On the other hand, follistatin, the activin-binding protein, is produced from granulosa cells under the control of FSH. It has been shown that 8-Br-cAMP increases follistatin in mRNA accumulations and that the promoter of the rat follistatin gene contains functional cAMP-responsive *cis*-elements [34, 35]. Follistatin suppressed the effect of activin on FSHR mRNA levels in the presence of FSH. Therefore, those data confirmed previous data that the stimulating effect of activin on FSH binding levels by cultured rat granulosa cells was inhibited by follistatin, which alone had no influence on FSH binding. The previous in vivo studies have shown that the levels of activin (mRNA and protein) fall sharply in the granulosa cells after LH/FSH surge on proestrus, and cells in the corpora lutea manifest a nearly complete absence of these subunits. However, the signals for the follistatin mRNA and its proteins continue to be intense in the preovulatory follicles and corpora lutea after LH/FSH surge [26, 36].

Granulosa cells seem to undergo progressive differentiation as follicles increase in size and granulosa cell number. Although the DES-treated granulosa cells may not be relevant to small growing follicles, the data were interpreted to suggest that granulosa cell differentiation may be regulated, at least in part, by activin-follistatin interrelationship in an autocrine and/or paracrine manner. Because the levels of activin A were suppressed by the addition of 8-Br-cAMP in a dose-dependent manner, cAMP might antagonize the effect of activin by decreasing the activin level, depending on the duration of the exposure. Based on

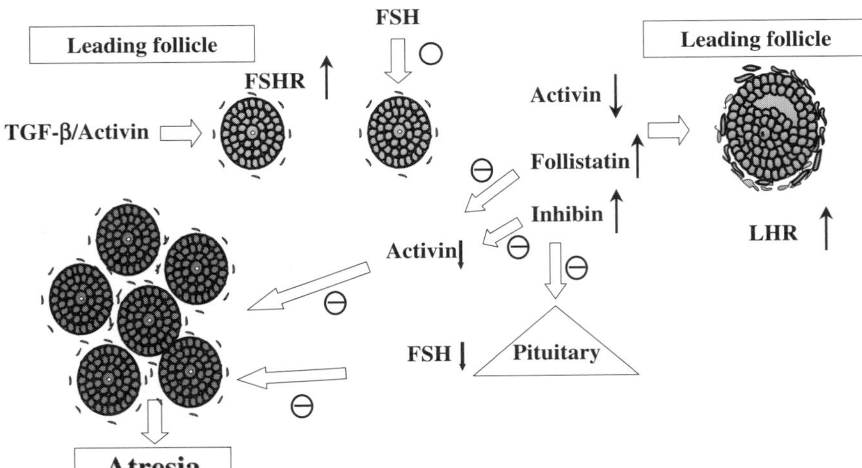

FIGURE 5.1 Activin/inhibin and selection of follicle. Activin stimulates the expression of FSHR, and the susceptibility to the circulating level of FSH is increased by the action of activin. FSH stimulates the production of steroid hormones, follistatin and inhibin, and reduces the production of activin in the granulosa cells. The increased inhibin production results in reduction of peripheral serum FSH concentration, and this decrease of FSH may produce an atretic effect on the other follicles. Therefore, the small difference of FSHR expression between the follicles might cause the big difference in the end of the process of follicular growth.

these observations, it is possible that cAMP has stimulatory and inhibitory effects on the expression of FSHR. The overall influence of cAMP on the expression of FSHR might be determined by the integration of effect direct on transcription of FSHR and effect mediated by the activin-follistatin production.

In addition, TGF-β, either alone or with FSH, stimulates the expression of FSHR mRNA in a dose- and time-dependent manner. Although the addition of TGF-β did not increase levels of FSH-induced intracellular cAMP, the response to cAMP analogs was enhanced in granulosa cells, which suggests that TGF-β potentiates the action of FSH at sites distal to cAMP generation in these rat cells [37]. Because TGF-β clearly prolonged FSHR mRNA stability according to the result of time-course and half-life experiments, TGF-β may relate to the production of certain proteins that stabilize the FSHR mRNA in granulosa cells.

Granulosa cells respond to FSH in part by elaborating peptide autocrine/paracrine factors, such as inhibin, activin, and TGF-β [38]. Activin and TGF-β stimulate the expression of follistatin mRNA in cultured granulosa cells. In addition, activin has a strong positive effect on the expression of FSHR mRNA as described before, and TGF-β also induces and prolongs the elevated level of FSHR mRNA compared with the time course of activin action. Because activin and TGF-β have a common signal transduction system, which consists of serine/threonine kinase receptor type I and type II and Smad proteins [39], one may expect an similar effect to these two reagents. However, the effect of TGF-β on the FSHR mRNA was not neutralized by the addition of follistatin, in the condition where the effect of activin was completely neutralized. Because the effect of TGF-β on FSHR mRNA lasted longer compared with that of activin, this result may be caused by lack of sensitivity of TGF-β against follistatin, which may be produced by the presence of activin and TGF-β (Figure 5.1).

FSH increases the production of follistatin and reduces the production of activin, which results in the suppression of activin bioactivity [27, 35, 40]. The effect of activin on the granulosa cell starts by increasing the sensitivity to FSH, which causes an increase of follistatin and suppression of the production of activin. TGF-β and activin stimulate the expression of FSHR either alone or in the presence of FSH, and both are important local factors that modulate folliculogenesis. However, TGF-β action is completely different from that of activin in terms of auto feedback regulation by production of follistatin. In addition, activins and inhibins [41], structurally related members of the TGF-β superfamily of growth and differentiation factors [39], are mutually antagonistic regulators of reproductive and other functions [38, 41]. Activins bind specific type II receptor serine kinases (ActR II or II B) [42, 43] to promote the recruitment and phosphorylation of the type I receptor serine kinase [44], which then regulates gene expression by activating Smad proteins [39]. Inhibins also bind type II activin receptors but do not recruit type I receptors, providing a competitive model for the antagonism of activin by inhibin [45]. Inhibins fail to antagonize activin in some tissues and cells, however, this suggests that additional components are required for inhibin action [46]. Betaglycan [47, 48] can function as an inhibin coreceptor with ActR II. Betaglycan binds inhibin with high affinity and enhances binding in cells that coexpress ActR II and betaglycan. Inhibin also forms cross-linked complexes with both recombinant and ectogenously expressed betaglycan and ActR II [49].

Taken together, local feedback terminates activin action after only a short period. FSH induces the production of

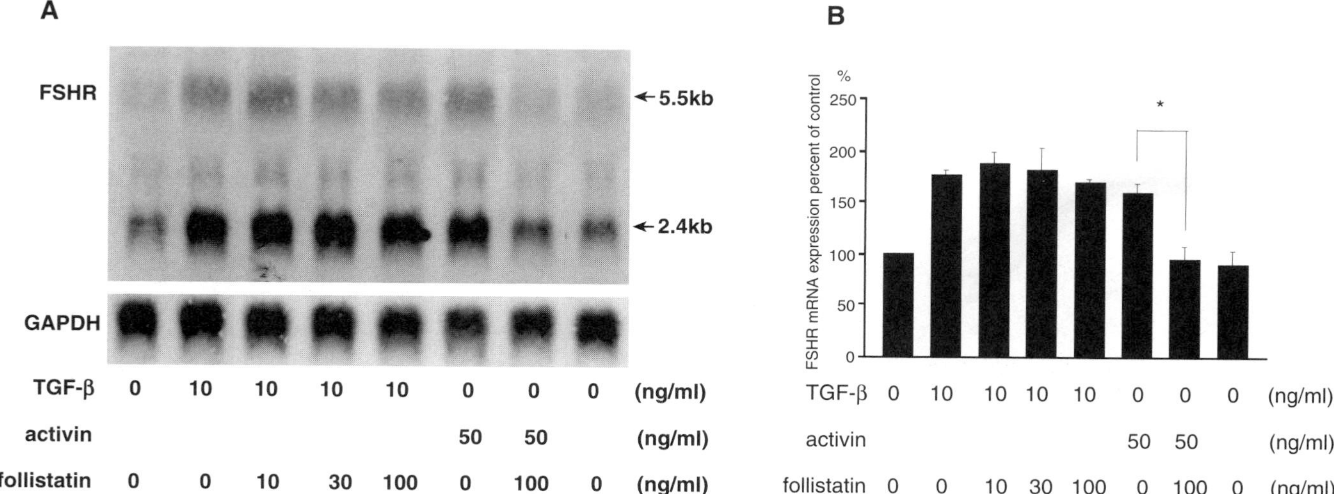

FIGURE 5.2 The effect of follistatin on activin and TGF-β induced FSH mRNA. **A,** Granulosa cells from DES-primed immature rats were cultured for 24 hours alone and then cultured in the presence and absence of TGF-β (10 ng/ml) and activin (50 ng/ml) with increasing concentrations of follistatin for 48 hours. FSHR mRNA levels were measured using Northern blot analysis. **B,** Luminescence detection of FSHR (2.4 kb) mRNA were quantified by densitometric scanning. The amount of FSHR mRNA without TGF-β activin was taken as 100%. Data were normalized for GAPDH mRNA levels in each sample and expressed as a value relative to the control. The absorbance values obtained from this experiment as well as those from the two other experiments were standardized in relation to the control values and are represented (mean ± SE; n = 3) in the bar graphs. The data shown are means ± SE of three independent experiments. *Difference from the control value at $P < 0.05$.

follistatin, betaglycan, and inhibin and reduces the production of activin; these effects of FSH antagonize to the action of activin at the local area and inhibin in particular reduces the production of FSH from the pituitary (Figure 5.2). These processes might be important for the selection by which one follicle gains and maintains advantage over all other maturing follicles. Moreover, we speculate that the suspended effect of activin might interfere with the physiological action of gonadotropin. For example, inhibin α knockout mice produce gonadal tumors, and there is a report of increased activin and FSH production in those mice [50]. The authors of the report suggested that the uncontrolled production of activin eventually caused the tumor growth in the mouse gonads.

Vitamin A is required for various fundamental physiological processes including vertebrate development, cellular differentiation, vision, and reproduction [51]. The biologically active form of vitamin A is retinoic acid (RA), which includes all-trans-retinoic acid and 9-cis-retinoic acid [52]. The biological response of retinoic acid is mediated through two families of nuclear receptors, the *retinoic acid receptors (RARs)* and the *retinoid X receptors,* each of which consists of three receptor subtypes, α, β, and γ [53]. The stage specificity of RAR isotypes expression during testicular development [54] and folliculogenesis in which the granulosa cells in the primary follicle express higher levels of RARs than in the developed and mature follicle [55] also suggest their potential role for modulating target gene expression.

Recent data show that granulosa cells from the ovaries of eCG-treated immature rats and luteal cells from the ovaries of eCG/hCG-treated immature rats synthesized markedly higher amounts of retinoic acid when cultured alone compared with granulosa cells cultured from the ovaries of the prepubertal rat treated with the control vehicle [56]. Moreover, the presence of RARs in ovary cells, including granulosa cells, germinal epithelial cells, and some luteal cells, indicate that these cells would also be targets for retinoic acid [57]. These data suggest that retinoic acid may regulate the ovarian function by autocrine and/or paracrine action. Our studies provide evidence for a dramatic down-modulation of the FSHR mRNA when retinoic acid (RA) is added to granulosa cells in the presence of FSH. The receptor depletion by RA was concentration dependent, and RA (10^{-8} M) abolished the effect of FSH on FSHR mRNA (Figure 5.3). The response of FSHR mRNA to cAMP analogs was inhibited by RA in granulosa cells in these experiments, which suggests that RA diminished the action of FSH at sites distal to cAMP generation in the granulosa cells.

RA did not change the FSHR mRNA stability in rat granulosa cells, and the results of the nuclear run-on experiments demonstrate that RA inhibits the rate of transcription of the FSHR gene (Figure 5.4). It seems probable that different members of the steroid/retinoid hormone receptor superfamily may act using similar mechanisms. For example, transcriptional repression may act either by receptor competition with positive transactivating factors

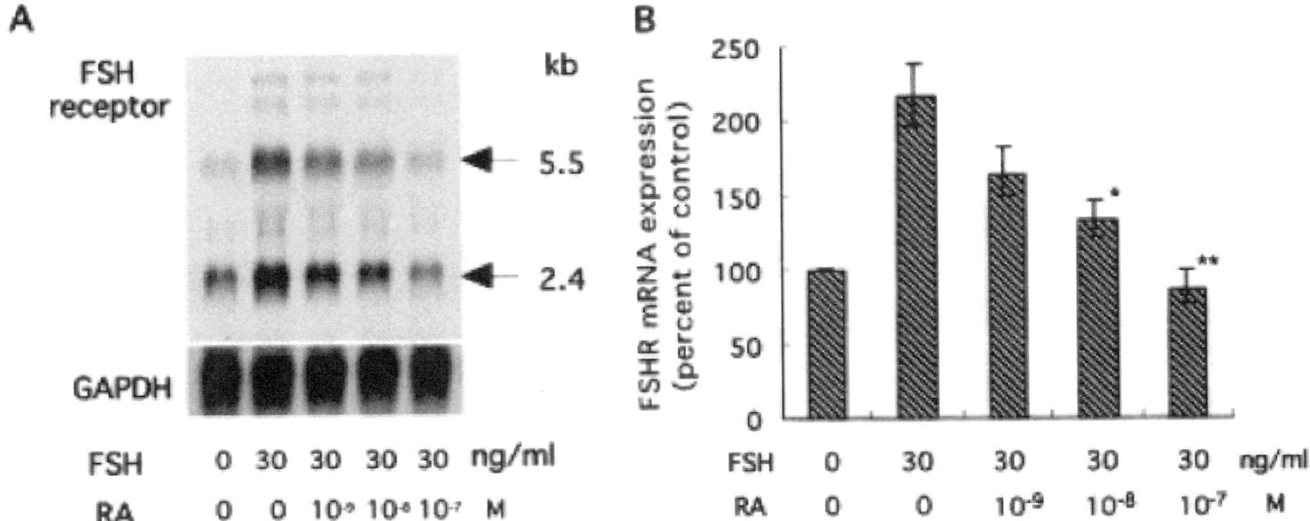

FIGURE 5.3 Dose-related effect of RA on FSH-induced FSHR mRNA. **A,** Granulosa cells from DES-primed immature rats were cultured alone for 24 hours. They were then cultured with 30 ng/ml FSH alone and FSH (30 ng/ml) plus increasing concentrations of RA for another 48 hours. FSHR mRNA levels were measured using the Northern blot analysis. **B,** Luminescence detection of FSHR mRNA (2.4 kb) were quantified by densitometric scanning. The amount of FSHR mRNA cultured with FSH alone was taken as 100%. Data were normalized for GAPDH mRNA levels in each sample and expressed relative to the control. The absorbency values obtained from this experiment as well as those from two other studies were standardized relative to the control and are represented (mean ± SE; n = 4) in the bar graphs. $*P < 0.05$. $**P < 0.01$.

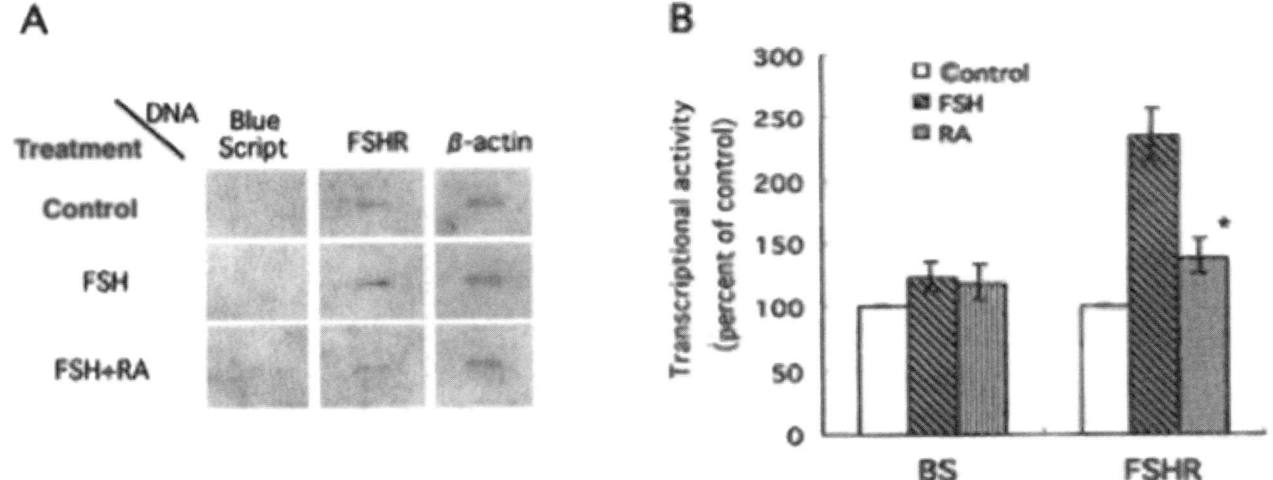

FIGURE 5.4 Stimulation of FSHR gene transcription by FSH and RA. **A,** Granulosa cells were cultured in 60-mm dishes containing 5×10^6 cells in a 5 ml serum-free medium. After 24 hours in the culture, granulosa cells were incubated in the presence or absence of RA (10^{-8} M) for another 24 hours and nuclear run-on assays were then performed as described in *B*. **B,** Data acquired from the nuclear run-on experiments shown in *A* were quantitated by a fluoro-image analyzer (BAS 2000). Data were normalized for β-actin levels in each sample and are expressed relative to the control value. Transcriptional activities after incubation with FSH and RA are expressed relative to the activity affected by FSH alone. The data shown are mean ± SE of the three independent experiments. $*P < 0.05$.

for deoxyribonucleic acid (DNA) binding to overlapping sequences or by interference with their transactivating action through direct protein–protein interaction. As described by Goetz et al. [58], an E box is required for full promoter function of the rat FSHR gene. The promoters of the rat, human, sheep, and mouse FSHR genes all contain an E box consensus sequence, CANNTG, which is known to bind members of the basic helix-loop-helix (bHLH) family of proteins that consist mostly of transcriptional regulators involved in the control of growth and differentiation [59].

Mutation studies revealed that the DNA binding sites for RAR and steroidogenic factor 1 (SF-1) shared at least one AGGTCA motif, because a mutation of a half retinoic acid response element (RARE) affected both RAR and SF-1 binding [60]. During growth of follicles, SF-1 binds to the half sites of RARE with a higher affinity and recruits coactivators such as steroid receptor coactivator (SRC) and cAMP response element binding protein (CBP) to activate transcription. In the presence of RARs and their ligand, RARs readily displace SF-1, bind to SF-1 sites, and recruit their corepressors such as nuclear receptor corepressor (N-CoR) and silencing mediator of retinoic acid (SMRT), and thyroid hormone receptor to repress transcription. The important role of SF-1 in endocrine regulation is evident from its involvement in the transcriptional control of a number of genes important for either the biosynthesis or regulation of steroid hormones [61]. For example, SF-1 has been shown to regulate the genes for the gonadotropin β-subunit, the Gn-RH receptor, and the α-subunit for the FSH-regulatory protein inhibin [62–67]. It has been shown that SF-1 acts at another level of the axis to modulate FSH response in the gonads through transcriptional regulation of the FSHR gene. Within this axis, SF-1 appears to regulate both FSH production and response. Thus, through its regulation of the α-subunit of the FSH-regulatory protein inhibin, SF-1 can directly influence FSH production in the pituitary, and through its regulation of FSHR, SF-1 can influence FSH response.

Granulosa cells differentiate and proliferate by the stimulation of pituitary glycoprotein hormone FSH [68]. FSH induces various granulosa cell genes by the cAMP dependent pathway, and we identified granulosa cell genes rapidly induced by FSH by means of subtraction cloning. Among granulosa cell genes, we focused our study on cAMP responsive element modulator (CREM) gene products, because CREM and its isoforms are expressed in a tissue and cell specific manner and are often highly expressed and regulated in neuroendocrine organs [69, 70]. Functionally distinct CREM proteins are produced by the use of alternative promoters and ribonucleic acid (RNA) processing [71]. The CREM isoforms act either as cAMP-regulated activators or repressors of target gene transcription. One of the well-characterized repressor isoforms is inducible cAMP early repressor (ICER) [71].

Northern blot analysis revealed that mRNA sizes (1.4 kb and 2 kb) rapidly induced by FSH corresponded to the sizes of ICER isoforms. The induction of only the ICER isoforms was demonstrated by the RT-PCR study. It was also demonstrated that ICER gene expression could be induced by a variety of treatments known to increase intracellular cAMP levels, whereas a reagent that stimulates protein kinase C system had no effect on the induction of ICER gene expression. This indicates that PKA-mediated signal transduction is the major pathway for ICER gene induction. It is also noteworthy that the induction of ICER is transient as demonstrated by RT-PCR. Molina et al. [72] have proposed that ICER is a key signal that is transiently induced to attenuate the cAMP-dependent signaling pathway. It has been previously shown that FSH itself down-regulates FSHR gene expression in cultured rat granulosa cells soon after the stimulation [73]. The down-regulation of FSHRs is thought to attenuate the cAMP-dependent signaling pathway. Our observations suggest that the induction of ICER may play an important role for the rapid down-regulation of FSHRs by FSH itself in the granulosa cells. Monaco et al. [74] have also reported that FSH induced ICER gene expression with a peak 4 hours after treatment in the primary culture of rat Sertoli's cells and that induction of the ICER accompanied early down-regulation of the FSHR transcript. Their observations in Sertoli's cells are consistent with our data in granulosa cells. ICER may also participate in the down-regulation of LHR in the luteinized granulosa cells. On the other hand, gene expression as well as protein levels of CREM-τ, one of the activator isoforms, were nearly constant regardless of FSH stimulation. Function of CREM-τ is mainly regulated by phosphorylation of a serine residue in a kinase inducible domain [75]. Phosphorylation and dephosphorylation of the serine residue in CREM-τ regulate the activator function of CREM-τ in the cAMP-dependent signal transduction process. In the current case, CREM-τ expression is not affected by FSH although its function may be affected by phosphorylation through the PKA pathway induced by FSH.

REGULATION OF LUTEINIZING HORMONE RECEPTOR MESSENGER RIBONUCLEIC ACID

IGF-I is capable of synergizing with FSH in the expression of LHR mRNA in a dose- and time-dependent manner (Figure 5.5). Our results confirm previous reports indicating that IGF-I stimulates LHR expression and cell differentiation [76]. Although the addition of IGF-I did not increase levels of FSH-induced intracellular cAMP, the response to cAMP analogs is enhanced in granulosa cell in this experiment, which suggests that IGF-I potentiates the action of FSH at sites distal to cAMP generation in these rat cells.

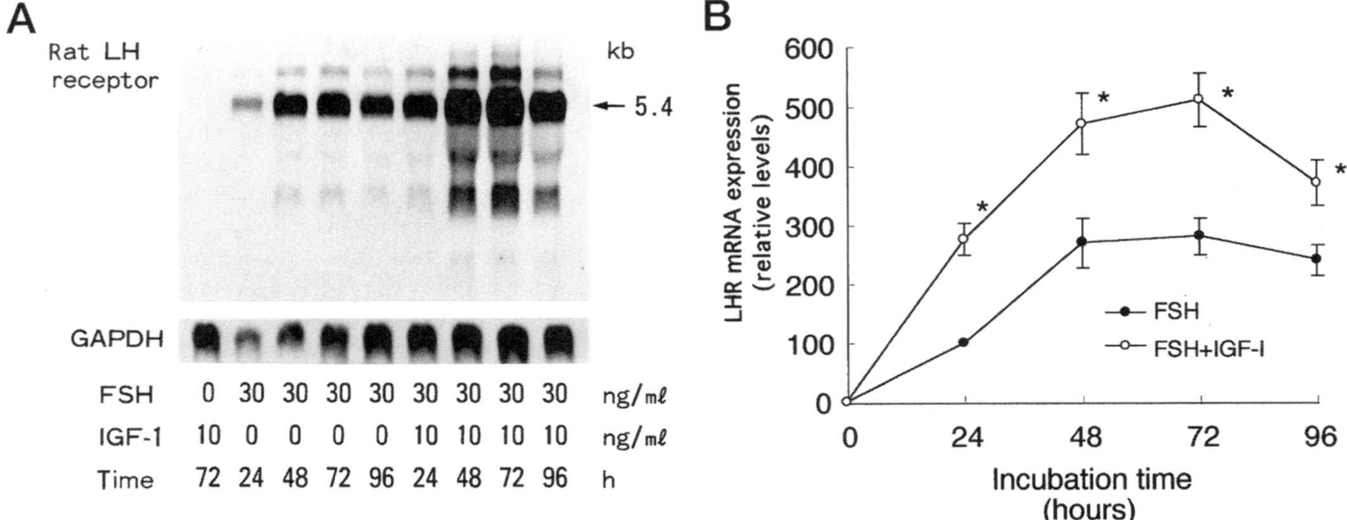

FIGURE 5.5 Time course of IGF-I's effect on the FSH-induced LHR mRNA. **A,** Granulosa cells from DES-primed immature rats were cultured for 24 hours (0; control = 0 h), then in 30 ng/ml FSH alone or with 10 ng/ml IGF-I. After various incubation times, total RNA was extracted, and LHR mRNA levels were measured using Northern blot analysis. **B,** Autoradiographs of LHR mRNA (5.4 kb) were quantified by densitometric scanning. The amount of LHR mRNA with FSH alone was taken as 100%. Data were normalized for GAPDH mRNA levels in each sample and expressed relative to the control value (FSH alone, 48 h). The absorbance values obtained from this study as well as from three other studies were standardized to the 48-hour control and are represented (mean ± SE; n = 3) in the graph. *Difference from the control (FSH alone) at each time, $P < 0.05$.

It has been shown that, when levels of LHR mRNA are altered, all transcripts (7.5, 5.4, 3.8, 2.3, and 1.2 kb) appear to be coordinately regulated, and the turnover of the receptor transcripts could be occurring via a common mechanism. The 5′-flanking region of the rat LHR gene is characteristic of that in the so-called "housekeeping" genes in that this region has no apparent TATA or CAAT boxes, is rich in G and C residues, and contains multiple potential transcriptional start sites [77]. Although FSH administration increased the transcription of the LHR gene, IGF-I did not have any effect on FSH-induced transcription.

To assess the degradation rates of LHR mRNA transcripts, granulosa cells were preincubated for 24 hours with FSH alone or with FSH and IGF-I. Cells were harvested at 0, 3, 6, 9, and 12 hours after addition of actinomycin D, and mRNA levels were quantitated by Northern blot analysis. As shown in Figure 5.6, the decay curves for the 5.4-kb LHR mRNA transcript in primary granulosa cells were significantly altered in the presence of IGF-I and increased the half-life of the LHR mRNA transcript (see Figure 5.6). The data suggest a possible role for changes in LHR mRNA stability in the IGF-I induced regulation of LHR in rat granulosa cells [78]. Previous observations have suggested that a labile destabilizing factor may constitutively degrade the LHR mRNA [79]. Our data suggest that IGF-I may act to increase LHR mRNA by preventing the synthesis or actions of an LHR mRNA–destabilizing factor in the presence of FSH. It has been also well established that the expression of specific, highly regulated mRNAs such as c-fos, c-myc, and β-adrenergic receptor are controlled, at least in part, at the level of mRNA degradation [80, 81]. In the majority of instances of posttranscriptional mRNA regulation, the changes in stability of a particular mRNA appear to result from changes in the binding of specific proteins to defined sequences and/or structures in the target mRNA. The RNA sequences recognized by regulatory proteins often are located within discrete regions of the mRNA. In terms of LHR mRNA, a LHR mRNA binding protein, which is a candidate for a transacting factor involved in the hormonal regulation of LHR mRNA stability in rat the ovary, has been reported [82]. In the rat ovary, differences in LHR number seen during follicular development, ovulation, and luteinization involve concomitant changes in receptor mRNA levels [83]. Because levels of LHR mRNA closely parallel receptor number, it is likely that posttranscriptional regulation plays a pivotal role in mediating physiological changes in receptor expression during the ovarian cycle.

IGF-I enhances the expression of LHR only in the presence of FSH whereas IGF-I alone does not induce LHR mRNA. Therefore, it is possible that IGF-I has a primary effect on FSHR expression that secondarily potentiates FSH action and results in augmentation of LHR mRNA. Previous studies showed that IGF-I is selectively expressed in a subset of relatively healthy-appearing follicles in the

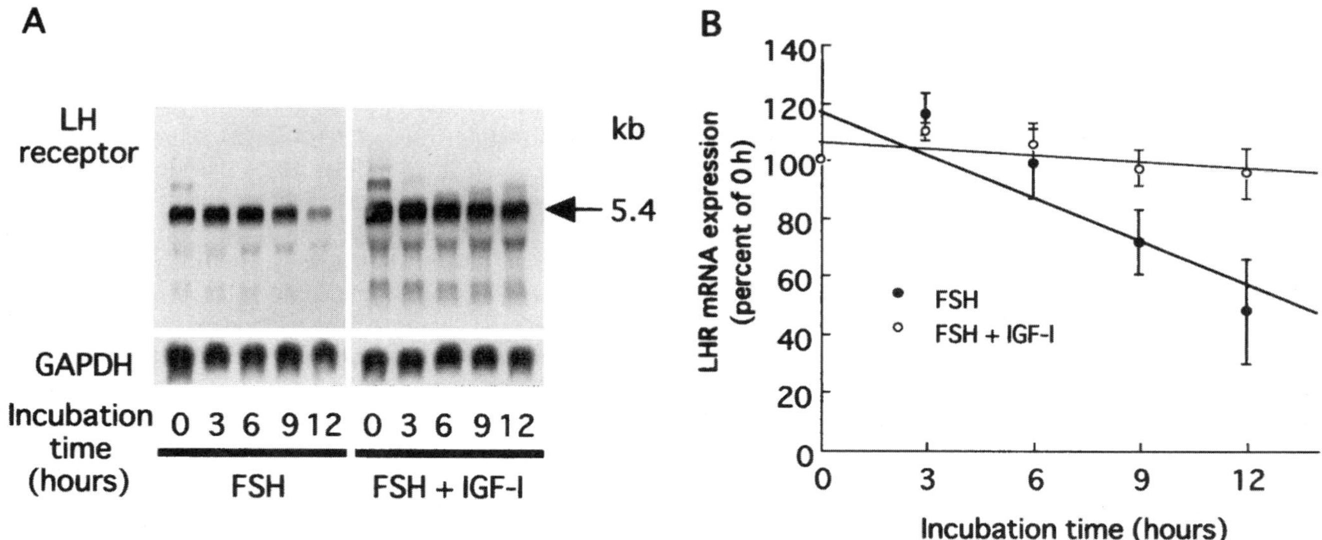

FIGURE 5.6 Effect of IGF-I on LHR mRNA transcripts. **A,** Granulosa cells were preincubated for 24 hours with FSH alone or with FSH and IGF-I. After preincubation, 5 μM actinomycin D was added to arrest new RNA synthesis. Cells were harvested at 0, 3, 6, 9, and 12 hours after addition of the transcription inhibitor, and LHR mRNA levels were quantified by Northern blot analysis. **B,** mRNA levels at time zero were assigned a relative value of 100%, and mRNA levels at all other times are expressed as percentages of the time zero value.

rat ovary [84], which suggests that IGF-I is a marker for follicular selection. IGF-I enhances the proliferation of many cell types, and because it has been previously shown that the FSH receptor is coexpressed with IGF-I in ovarian follicles [84], it seems likely that IGF-I may act in an autocrine/paracrine manner to stimulate granulosa cell proliferation. For example, IGF-I amplifies FSH-induced aromatase expression and LHR induction [85]. In addition, amplification by IGF-I of FSHR expression is positively reinforced by FSH-induced augmentation of IGF-I receptor expression, which has been demonstrated in vivo at the mRNA level [84] and in vitro at the IGF-I-binding level [86]. This local IGF-I expression creates an intrafollicular positive feedback loop in which IGF-I enhances FSH action and FSH enhances IGF-I action through mutual complementary receptor up-regulation [87]. In addition, the effect of IGF-I on the induction of FSHR enhances FSH action of cAMP production, which results secondarily in augmentation of the LHR gene. However, the cAMP dose does not completely compensate for the effect of FSH to maintain mRNA levels of LHR, and IGF-I has a direct effect on LHR mRNA half-life in granulosa cells. Therefore, it is also suspected that IGF-I has a primary effect on LHR production in the presence of FSH.

Our previous findings provide yet another example of the inhibitory nature of prolactin (PRL) as it acts in the stages of folliculogenesis [88]. Although treatment of cells with PRL alone had no effect, cotreatment of cells with FSH and PRL reduced FSH-induced LHR mRNA levels. Granulosa cells from preantral follicles have a negligible number of LH binding sites, whereas priming with FSH induced functional LH and PRL receptors [89, 90]. Once induced, LHR are maintained by FSH and LH [90]. The maintenance of rat LHR by FSH and LH is consistent with the luteotropic action of LH in rats and indicates the important role played by LHRs in corpora luteal development.

In contrast to the LHR mRNA, PRL in combination with FSH had no effect on FSHR mRNA levels, which are also maintained by cAMP. Therefore the result that PRL did not affect cAMP production is not in conflict with the data that FSHR mRNA did not decrease by PRL treatment. In addition, because PRL did not inhibit cAMP production, PRL can be considered to specifically affect the production of LHR mRNA. The current observations, such as those of Dorrington and Gore-Langton [91], further indicate that the ability of PRL to attenuate FSH hormonal action also involves post-cAMP site(s). Our results showed that the suppression of LH binding sites by PRL was correlated with the decreases in receptor mRNA levels. Additional trials were therefore required to further clarify the mechanisms of PRL action in LHR regulation. In these experiments, the promoter region of the LHR gene provided an interesting model for analyzing the mechanisms involved in the inhibitory actions of PRL. On the other hand, although FSH administration increased the transcription of the LHR gene in a dose-dependent manner, PRL did not have any effect on FSH-induced transcription.

Based on the observed expression of LHR mRNA, PRL might not affect the maximum level induced by FSH, but thereafter the maximum levels of LHR mRNA disappear faster than those of the control. These results suggest that there is normally a labile factor(s) that destabilizes the LHR mRNA and that inhibition of its synthesis results in an increased stability of LHR mRNA. It may be that PRL also acts to stimulate the labile LHR mRNA destabilizing factors. Although PRL did not result in an inhibition of FSH action as assessed by the generation of FSHR mRNA, PRL stimulate the decay of LHR mRNA that is induced by FSH.

In previous experiments, hCG-induced down-regulation of LHR mRNA levels was followed by down-regulation of membrane receptor levels in the pseudopregnant rat ovary [92–94], which indicates that the loss of LH binding seen during hCG-induced down-regulation was, at least in part, caused by the loss of receptor mRNA. Consistent with previous studies [79, 95], our data showed that FSH could induce LHR and LHR mRNA expression in granulosa cells from DES-primed immature rats from almost undetectable basal levels. There is a lag time of at least 24 hours after FSH addition before increases in either LHR or LHR mRNA levels [96]. Thus a second addition of FSH after the increase of LHR was performed to see the down-regulation of LHR in the cultured granulosa cells. FSH, hCG, or 8-Br-cAMP added to this granulosa cell culture transiently decreased LHR mRNA levels, which was followed by a subsequent increase in message levels. As cAMP is the established second messenger that mediates FSH-induced granulosa cell differentiation, it was of interest to evaluate the effect of cAMP on LHR mRNA. The time courses and magnitude of the effect of gonadotropins and 8-Br-cAMP on LHR mRNA were found to be comparable.

These data support the idea that the FSH- or hCG-induced loss of LHR mRNA in granulosa cells is mediated by cAMP. These observations suggest that a labile destabilizing factor, which is induced by cAMP, may degrade the LHR mRNA. The existence of such a destabilizing factor might explain the rapid decrease and increase after the transient decrease in mRNA levels. Because there was a long lag time before FSH- or 8-Br-cAMP-stimulated increases in LHR gene transcription, the LHR gene appears to be an unusually slow response gene probably requiring the synthesis of a new transactivation factor for expression. According to the time course of changes in LHR mRNA levels, FSH, LH, and cAMP may act to increase LHR mRNA levels and simultaneously might increase levels of the destabilizing factor.

The increase in LHR mRNA after 6 hours of incubation could be because cAMP sustains the increase in LHR gene transcription for longer than the increase in destabilizing factors. The changes in LHR gene transcription elicited by 8-Br-cAMP suggest that FSH and LH mediate this effect through the cAMP-dependent protein kinase pathway. The LH-induced loss of LHR mRNA occurs relatively quickly, and hormone-induced changes in the numbers of LHR in the rat ovary were associated with changes in the amounts of relative abundance of LHR mRNA transcripts.

We previously reported that incubation of granulosa cells with optimal concentrations of activin and FSH resulted in induction of LHR mRNA and protein. The addition of activin with FSH might therefore be expected to prevent FSH-induced LHR down-regulation. However, the presence of activin was more effective than FSH alone in inducing LHR mRNA down-regulation in rat granulosa cells. There was a rapid decrease in levels of LHR mRNA expression, declining to 50% of control values between 3 hours and 6 hours incubation. The dose-dependent effects of activin on LHR mRNA levels were examined in cells incubated for 6 hours with FSH and activin. The LHR mRNA levels decreased in a dose-dependent manner compared with the control in the presence of increasing concentrations (30–100 ng/ml) of activin with FSH. Because in our experiment activin sustained the decrease of LHR induced by gonadotropins, it was suggested that activin has a negative effect on LH action in cultured granulosa cells through the down-regulation of the LHR [97]. The data from the rat and bovine models support the hypothesis that activin regulates granulosa cells in an autocrine fashion and that the action of activin is related to the stage of follicular maturity.

CONCLUSION

The pituitary gonadotropins are the key hormones in the regulation of folliculogenesis. It is clear that the ability of gonadotropins to modulate ovarian function depends not only on the circulating levels of the gonadotropins but also on the expression of appropriate receptor proteins by potential target cells in the ovary. The early stages of follicles grow in a gonadotropin independent manner; thus the expression of FSHR is essential to response to FSH and is affected by the ovum and granulosa cells by the autocrine/paracrine manners. The expression of receptors for LH is one of the major markers of the FSH-induced differentiation of granulosa cells and this process is also modified by many growth factors.

The mechanisms by which these factors regulate the expression of FSHR mRNA and LHR mRNA are complex. The regulation might be dependent on gene transcription and/or receptor mRNA stability. The expression of FSHR is mainly controlled by the gene transcription, probably because the follicles must become responsive to FSH in a competitive manner, and is affected by the intraovarian growth factors. On the other hand, the LHR is essential for elevated levels of progesterone to maintain pregnancy during the first trimester; the maintenance of the expression of LHR is a key factor to control the duration of luteal function. Therefore, the expression of LHR might be regulated by the stability of the receptor mRNA. Identification of the regulatory molecules involved in these regulations for FSHR and LHR will remain as challenges for the near future in gonadal cell biology.

References

1. McFarland, K., Sprengel, R., Phillips, H. S., Kohler, M., Rosemblit, N., Nikolics, K., Segaloff, D. L., and Seeburg, P. H. (1989). Lutropin-choriogonadotropin receptor: an unusual member of the G protein-coupled receptor family. *Science* 245, 494–499.
2. Loosfelt, H., Misrahi, M., Atger, M., Salesse, R., Vu Hai-Luu, T., Vu Hai-Luu Thi, M. T., Jolivet, A., Guiochon-Mantel, A., Sar, S., Jallal, B., Garnier, J., and Milgrom, E. (1989). Cloning and sequencing of porcine LH-hCG receptor cDNA: variants lacking transmembrane domain. *Science* 245, 525–528.
3. Minegishi, T., Nakamura, K., Takakura, Y., Miyamoto, K., Hasegawa, Y., Ibuki, Y., and Igarashi, M. (1990). Cloning and sequencing of human LH/hCG receptor cDNA. *Biochem. Biophys. Res. Commun.* 172, 1049–1054.
4. Rousseau-Merck, M. F., Misrahi, M., Atger, M., Loosfelt, H., Milgrom, E., and Berger, R. (1990). Localization of the human luteinizing hormone/choriogonadotropin receptor gene (LHCGR) to chromosome 2p21. *Cytogenet. Cell Genet.* 54, 77–79.
5. Rousseau-Merck, M. F., Atger, M., Loosfelt, H., Milgrom, E., and Berger, R. (1993). The chromosomal localization of the human follicle-stimulating hormone receptor gene (FSHR) on 2p21-p16 is similar to that of the luteinizing hormone receptor gene. *Genomics* 15, 222–224.
6. Atger, M., Misrahi, M., Sar, S., Le Flem, L., Dessen, P., and Milgrom, E. (1995). Structure of the human luteinizing hormone-choriogonadotropin receptor gene: unusual promoter and 5′ non-coding regions. *Mol. Cell Endocrinol.* 111, 113–123.
7. Tsai-Morris, C. H., Buczko, E., Wang, W., Xie, X. Z., and Dufau, M. L. (1991). Structural organization of the rat luteinizing hormone (LH) receptor gene. *J. Biol. Chem.* 266, 11355–11359.
8. Minegishi, T., Tano, M., Abe, Y., Nakamura, K., Ibuki, Y., and Miyamoto, K. (1997). Expression of luteinizing hormone/human chorionic gonadotrophin (LH/HCG) receptor mRNA in the human ovary. *Mol. Hum. Reprod.* 3, 101–107.
9. Zhang, F. P., Rannikko, A. S., Manna, P. R., Fraser, H. M., and Huhtaniemi, I. T. (1997). Cloning and functional expression of the luteinizing hormone receptor complementary deoxyribonucleic acid from the marmoset monkey testis: absence of sequences encoding exon 10 in other species. *Endocrinology* 138, 2481–2490.
10. Shenker, A., Laue, L., Kosugi, S., Merendino, J. J. J., Minegishi, T., and Cutler, J. G. B. (1993). A constitutively activating mutation of the luteinizing hormone receptor in familial male precocious puberty. *Nature* 365, 652–654.
11. Kremer, H., Mariman, E., Otten, B. J., Moll, J. G. W., Stoelinga, G. B. A., Wit, J. M., Jansen, M., Drop, S. L., Faas, B., Ropers, H.-H., and Brunner, H. G. (1993). Cosegregation of missense mutations of the luteinizing hormone receptor gene with familial male-limited precocious puberty. *Hum. Mol. Genet.* 2, 1779–1783.
12. Liu, G., Duranteau, L., Carel, J. C., Monroe, J., Doyle, D. A., and Shenker, A. (1999). Leydig-cell tumors caused by an activating mutation of the gene encoding the luteinizing hormone receptor. *N. Engl. J. Med.* 341, 1731–1736.
13. Nakabayashi, K., Kudo, M., Kobilka, B., and Hsueh, A. J. W. (2000). Activation of the luteinizing hormone receptor following substitution of Ser-277 with selective hydrophobic residues in the ectodomain hinge region. *J. Biol. Chem.* 275, 30264–30271.
14. Kopp, P., Muirhead, S., Jourdain, N., Gu, W. X., Jameson, J. L., and Rodd, C. (1997). Congenital hyperthyroidism caused by a solitary toxic adenoma harboring a novel somatic mutation (serine281 → isoleucine) in the extracellular domain of the thyrotropin receptor. *J. Clin. Invest.* 100, 1634–1649.
15. Braun, T., Schofield, P. R., and Sprengel, R. (1991). Amino-terminal leucine-rich repeats in gonadotropin receptors determine hormone selectivity. *EMBO J.* 10, 1885–1890.
16. Thomas, D., Rozell, T. G., Liu, X., and Segaloff, D. L. (1996). Mutational analyses of the extracellular domain of the full-length lutropin/choriogonadotropin receptor suggest leucine-rich repeats 1–6 are involved in hormone binding. *Mol. Endocrinol.* 10, 760–768.
17. Minegishi, T., Nakamura, K., Takakura, Y., Ibuki, Y., and Igarashi, M. (1991). Cloning and sequencing of human FSH receptor cDNA. *Biochem. Biophys. Res. Commun.* 175, 1125–1130.
18. Davis, D., Liu, X., and Segaloff, D. L. (1995). Identification of the sites of N-linked glycosylation on the follicle-stimulating hormone (FSH) receptor and assessment of their role in FSH receptor function. *Mol. Endocrinol.* 9, 159–170.
19. Aittomaki, K., Lucena, J. L., Pakarinen, P., Sistonen, P., Tapanainen, J., Gromoll, J., Kaskikari, R., Sankila, E. M., Lehvaslaiho, H., and Engel, A. R. (1995). Mutation in the follicle-stimulating hormone receptor gene causes hereditary hypergonadotropic ovarian failure. *Cell* 82, 959–968.
20. Aittomaki, K. (1994). The genetics of XX gonadal dysgenesis. *Am. J. Hum. Genet.* 54, 844–851.
21. Matthews, C. H., Borgat, O. S., Beck-Peccoz, P., Adams, M., Tone, Y., Gambino, G., Casagrande, S., Tedeschini, G., Benedetti, A., and Chatterjee, V. K. (1993). Primary amenorrhoea and infertility due to a mutation in the beta-subunit of follicle-stimulating hormone. *Nat. Genet.* 5, 83–86.
22. Sprang, S. R. (1997). G protein mechanisms: insights from structural analysis. *Annu. Rev. Biochem.* 66, 639–678.
23. Pitcher, J. A., Freedman, N. J., and Lefkowitz, R. J. (1998). G protein-coupled receptor kinases. *Annu. Rev. Biochem.* 67, 653–692.
24. Ferguson, S. S. (2001). Evolving concepts in G protein-coupled receptor endocytosis: the role in receptor desensitization and signaling. *Pharmacol. Rev.* 53, 1–24.
25. Freedman, N. J., and Lefkowitz, R. J. (1996). Desensitization of G protein-coupled receptors. *Recent Prog. Horm. Res.* 51, 319–351; discussion 352–353.
26. Woodruff, T. K., D'Agostino, J., Schwartz, N. B., and Mayo, K. E. (1988). Dynamic changes in inhibin messenger RNAs

in rat ovarian follicles during the reproductive cycle. *Science* 239, 1296–1299.

27. Tano, M., Minegishi, T., Nakamura, K., Karino, S., Ibuki, Y., and Miyamoto, K. (1997). Transcriptional and post-transcriptional regulation of FSH receptor in rat granulosa cells by cyclic AMP and activin. *J. Endocrinol.* 153, 465–473.
28. Nakamura, M., Minegishi, T., Hasegawa, Y., Nakamura, K., Igarashi, S., Ito, I., Shinozaki, H., Miyamoto, K., Eto, Y., and Ibuki, Y. (1993). Effect of an activin A on follicle-stimulating hormone (FSH) receptor messenger ribonucleic acid levels and FSH receptor expressions in cultured rat granulosa cells. *Endocrinology* 133, 538–544.
29. Li, R., Phillips, D. M., Moore, A., and Mather, J. P. (1997). Follicle-stimulating hormone induces terminal differentiation in a predifferentiated rat granulosa cell line (ROG). *Endocrinology* 138, 2648–2657.
30. Minegishi, T., Kishi, H., Tano, M., Kameda, T., Hirakawa, T., and Miyamoto, K. (1999). Control of FSH receptor mRNA expression in rat granulosa cells by 3′,5′-cyclic adenosine monophosphate, activin, and follistatin. *Mol. Cell Endocrinol.* 149, 71–77.
31. Minegishi, T., Tano, M., Nakamura, K., Karino, S., Miyamoto, K., and Ibuki, Y. (1995). Regulation of follicle-stimulating hormone receptor messenger ribonucleic acid levels in cultured rat granulosa cells. *Mol. Cell Endocrinol.* 108, 67–73.
32. Minegishi, T., Tano, M., Kishi, H., Kameda, T., and Miyamoto, K. (1997). Follicle-stimulating hormone regulation on its receptor messenger ribonucleic acid levels in cultured rat granulosa cells. *Biochim. Biophys. Acta.* 1359, 165–173.
33. Byskov, A. G. (1974). Cell kinetic studies of follicular atresia in the mouse ovary. *J. Reprod. Fertil.* 37, 277–285.
34. Miyanaga, K., Erickson, G. F., DePaolo, L. V., Ling, N., and Shimasaki, S. (1993). Differential control of activin, inhibin and follistatin proteins in cultured rat granulosa cells. *Biochem. Biophys. Res. Commun.* 194, 253–258.
35. Tano, M., Minegishi, T., Nakamura, K., Nakamura, M., Karino, S., Miyamoto, K., and Ibuki, Y. (1995). Regulation of follistatin messenger ribonucleic acid in cultured rat granulosa cells. *Mol. Cell Endocrinol.* 109, 167–174.
36. Nakatani, A., Shimasaki, S., Depaolo, L. V., Erickson, G. F., and Ling, N. (1991). Cyclic changes in follistatin messenger ribonucleic acid and its protein in the rat ovary during the estrous cycle. *Endocrinology* 129, 603–611.
37. Inoue, K., Nakamura, K., Abe, K., Hirakawa, T., Tsuchiya, M., Matsuda, H., Miyamoto, K., and Minegishi, T. (2002). Effect of transforming growth factor Beta on the expression of luteinizing hormone receptor in cultured rat granulosa cells. *Biol. Reprod.* 67, 610–615.
38. Matzuk, M. M., Kumar, T. R., Shou, W., Coerver, K. A., Lau, A. L., Behringer, R. R., and Finegold, M. J. (1996). Transgenic models to study the roles of inhibins and activins in reproduction, oncogenesis, and development. *Recent Prog. Horm. Res.* 51, 123–154; discussion 155–157.
39. Massague, J. (1998). TGF-beta signal transduction. *Annu. Rev. Biochem.* 67, 753–791.
40. Kishi, H., Minegishi, T., Tano, M., Kameda, T., Ibuki, Y., and Miyamoto, K. (1998). The effect of activin and FSH on the differentiation of rat granulosa cells. *FEBS Lett.* 422, 274–278.
41. Vale, W., Rivier, C., Hsueh, A., Campen, C., Meunier, H., Bicsak, T., Vaughan, J., Corrigan, A., Bardin, W., and Sawchenko, P. (1988). Chemical and biological characterization of the inhibin family of protein hormones. *Recent Prog. Horm. Res.* 44, 1–34.
42. Mathews, L. S., and Vale, W. W. (1991). Expression cloning of an activin receptor, a predicted transmembrane serine kinase. *Cell* 65, 973–982.
43. Attisano, L., Wrana, J. L., Cheifetz, S., and Massague, J. (1992). Novel activin receptors: distinct genes and alternative mRNA splicing generate a repertoire of serine/threonine kinase receptors. *Cell* 68, 97–108.
44. Carcamo, J., Weis, F. M., Ventura, F., Wieser, R., Wrana, J. L., Attisano, L., and Massague, J. (1994). Type I receptors specify growth-inhibitory and transcriptional responses to transforming growth factor beta and activin. *Mol. Cell Biol.* 14, 3810–3821.
45. Xu, J., McKeehan, K., Matsuzaki, K., and McKeehan, W. L. (1995). Inhibin antagonizes inhibition of liver cell growth by activin by a dominant-negative mechanism. *J. Biol. Chem.* 270, 6308–6313.
46. Draper, L. B., Matzuk, M. M., Roberts, V. J., Cox, E., Weiss, J., Mather, J. P., and Woodruff, T. K. (1998). Identification of an inhibin receptor in gonadal tumors from inhibin alpha-subunit knockout mice. *J. Biol. Chem.* 273, 398–403.
47. Lopez-Casillas, F., Cheifetz, S., Doody, J., Andres, J. L., Lane, W. S., and Massague, J. (1991). Structure and expression of the membrane proteoglycan betaglycan, a component of the TGF-beta receptor system. *Cell* 67, 785–795.
48. Wang, X. F., Lin, H. Y., Ng-Eaton, E., Downward, J., Lodish, H. F., and Weinberg, R. A. (1991). Expression cloning and characterization of the TGF-beta type III receptor. *Cell* 67, 797–805.
49. Lewis, K. A., Gray, P. C., Blount, A. L., MacConell, L. A., Wiater, E., Bilezikjian, L. M., and Vale, W. (2000). Betaglycan binds inhibin and can mediate functional antagonism of activin signalling. *Nature* 404, 411–414.
50. Matzuk, M. M., Finegold, M. J., Su, J. G., Hsueh, A. J., and Bradley, A. (1992). Alpha-inhibin is a tumour-suppressor gene with gonadal specificity in mice. *Nature* 26, 313–319.
51. De Luca, L. M. (1991). Retinoids and their receptors in differentiation, embryogenesis, and neoplasia. *FASEB J.* 5, 2924–2933.
52. Napoli, J. L. (1996). Retinoic acid biosynthesis and metabolism. *FASEB J.* 10, 993–1001.
53. Chambon, P. (1996). A decade of molecular biology of retinoic acid receptors. *FASEB J.* 10, 940–954.
54. Mollard, R., Viville, S., Ward, S. J., Decimo, D., Chambon, P., and Dolle, P. (2000). Tissue-specific expression of retinoic acid receptor isoform transcripts in the mouse embryo. *Mech Dev.* 94, 223–232.
55. Kascheike, B., Ivell, R., and Walther, N. (1997). Alterations in the chromatin structure of the distal promoter region of the bovine oxytocin gene correlate with ovarian expression. *DNA Cell Biol.* 16, 1237–1248.
56. Zheng, W. L., Bucco, R. A., Sierra-Rievera, E., Osteen, K. G., Melner, M. H., and Ong, D. E. (1999). Synthesis of retinoic acid by rat ovarian cells that express cellular retinoic acid-binding protein-II. *Biol. Reprod.* 60, 110–114.
57. Zhuang, Y. H., Ylikomi, T., Lindfors, M., Piippo, S., and Tuohimaa, P. (1994). Immunolocalization of retinoic acid re-

ceptors in rat, mouse and human ovary and uterus. *J. Steroid Biochem. Mol. Biol.* 48, 61–68.

58. Goetz, T. L., Lloyd, T. L., and Griswold, M. D. (1996). Role of E box and initiator region in the expression of the rat follicle-stimulating hormone receptor. *J. Biol. Chem.* 271, 33317–33324.
59. Murre, C., McCaw, P. S., Vaessin, H., Caudy, M., Jan, L. Y., Jan, Y. N., Cabrera, C. V., Buskin, J. N., Hauschka, S. D., and Lassar, A. B., et al. (1989). Interactions between heterologous helix-loop-helix proteins generate complexes that bind specifically to a common DNA sequence. *Cell* 58, 537–544.
60. Xing, W., and Sairam, M. R. (2002). Retinoic acid mediates transcriptional repression of ovine follicle-stimulating hormone receptor gene via a pleiotropic nuclear receptor response element. *Biol. Reprod.* 67, 204–211.
61. Parker, K. L., and Schimmer, B. P. (1997). Steroidogenic factor 1: a key determinant of endocrine development and function. *Endocr. Rev.* 18, 361–377.
62. Duval, D. L., Nelson, S. E., and Clay, C. M. (1997). A binding site for steroidogenic factor-1 is part of a complex enhancer that mediates expression of the murine gonadotropin-releasing hormone receptor gene. *Biol. Reprod.* 56, 160–168.
63. Ito, M., Park, Y., Weck, J., Mayo, K. E., and Jameson, J. L. (2000). Synergistic activation of the inhibin alpha-promoter by steroidogenic factor-1 and cyclic adenosine 3′,5′-monophosphate. *Mol. Endocrinol.* 14, 66–81.
64. Wolfe, M. W., and Call, G. B. (1999). Early growth response protein 1 binds to the luteinizing hormone-beta promoter and mediates gonadotropin-releasing hormone-stimulated gene expression. *Mol. Endocrinol.* 13, 752–763.
65. Barnhart, K. M., and Mellon, P. L. (1994). The orphan nuclear receptor, steroidogenic factor-1, regulates the glycoprotein hormone alpha-subunit gene in pituitary gonadotropes. *Mol. Endocrinol.* 8, 878–885.
66. Ngan, E. S., Cheng, P. K., Leung, P. C., and Chow, B. K. (1999). Steroidogenic factor-1 interacts with a gonadotrope-specific element within the first exon of the human gonadotropin-releasing hormone receptor gene to mediate gonadotrope-specific expression. *Endocrinology* 140, 2452–2462.
67. Tremblay, J. J., and Drouin, J. (1999). Egr-1 is a downstream effector of GnRH and synergizes by direct interaction with Ptx1 and SF-1 to enhance luteinizing hormone beta gene transcription. *Mol. Cell Biol.* 19, 2567–2576.
68. Richards, J. S., Fitzpatrick, S. L., Clemens, J. W., Morris, J. K., Alliston, T., and Sirois, J. (1995). Ovarian cell differentiation: a cascade of multiple hormones, cellular signals, and regulated genes. *Recent Prog. Horm. Res.* 50, 223–254.
69. Foulkes, N. S., Mellstrom, B., Benusiglio, E., and Sassone-Corsi, P. (1992). Developmental switch of CREM function during spermatogenesis: from antagonist to activator. *Nature* 355, 80–84.
70. Waeber, G., Meyer, T. E., LeSieur, M., Hermann, H. L., Gerard, N., and Habener, J. F. (1991). Developmental stage-specific expression of cyclic adenosine 3′,5′-monophosphate response element-binding protein CREB during spermatogenesis involves alternative exon splicing. *Mol. Endocrinol.* 5, 1418–1430.
71. Delmas, V., Laoide, B. M., Masquilier, D., de Groot, R. P., Foulkes, N. S., and Sassone-Corsi, P. (1992). Alternative usage of initiation codons in mRNA encoding the cAMP-responsive-element modulator generates regulators with opposite functions. *Proc. Natl. Acad. Sci. U S A.* 89, 4226–4230.
72. Molina, C. A., Foulkes, N. S., Lalli, E., and Sassone-Corsi, P. (1993). Inducibility and negative autoregulation of CREM: an alternative promoter directs the expression of ICER, an early response repressor. *Cell* 75, 875–886.
73. Minegishi, T., Tano, M., Shinozaki, H., Nakamura, K., Abe, Y., Ibuki, Y., and Miyamoto, K. (1997). Dual coupling and down regulation of human FSH receptor in CHO cells. *Life Sci.* 60, 2043–2050.
74. Monaco, L., Foulkes, N. S., and Sassone-Corsi, P. (1995). Pituitary follicle-stimulating hormone (FSH) induces CREM gene expression in Sertoli cells: involvement in long-term desensitization of the FSH receptor. *Proc. Natl. Acad. Sci. U S A.* 92, 10673–10677.
75. Gonzalez, G. A., Yamamoto, K. K., Fischer, W. H., Karr, D., Menzel, P., Biggs, W. R., Vale, W. W., and Montminy, M. R. (1989). A cluster of phosphorylation sites on the cyclic AMP-regulated nuclear factor CREB predicted by its sequence. *Nature* 337, 749–752.
76. Adashi, E. Y., Resnick, C. E., Hernandez, E. R., May, J. V., Knecht, M., Svoboda, M. E., and Van, W. J. (1988). Insulin-like growth factor-I as an amplifier of follicle-stimulating hormone action: studies on mechanism(s) and site(s) of action in cultured rat granulosa cells. *Endocrinology* 122, 1583–1591.
77. Wang, H., Nelson, S., Ascoli, M., and Segaloff, D. L. (1992). The 5′-flanking region of the rat luteinizing hormone/chorionic gonadotropin receptor gene confers Leydig cell expression and negative regulation of gene transcription by 3′,5′-cyclic adenosine. *Mol. Endocrinol.* 6, 320–326.
78. Hirakawa, T., Minegishi, T., Abe, K., Kishi, H., Ibuki, Y., and Miyamoto, K. (1999). A role of insulin-like growth factor I in luteinizing hormone receptor expression in granulosa cells. *Endocrinology* 140, 4965–4971.
79. Shi, H., and Segaloff, D. L. (1995). A role for increased lutropin/choriogonadotropin receptor (LHR) gene transcription in the follitropin-stimulated induction of the LHR in granulosa cells. *Mol. Endocrinol.* 9, 734–744.
80. Sachs, A. B. (1993). Messenger RNA degradation in eukaryotes. *Cell* 74, 413–421.
81. Port, J. D., Huang, L. Y., and Malbon, C. C. (1992). Beta-adrenergic agonists that down-regulate receptor mRNA up-regulate a M(r) 35,000 protein(s) that selectively binds to beta-adrenergic receptor mRNAs. *J. Biol. Chem.* 267, 24103–24108.
82. Kash, J. C., and Menon, K. M. (1998). Identification of a hormonally regulated luteinizing hormone/human chorionic gonadotropin receptor mRNA binding protein. Increased mrna binding during receptor down-regulation. *J. Biol. Chem.* 273, 10658–10664.
83. Segaloff, D. L., and Ascoli, M. (1993). The lutropin/choriogonadotropin receptor . . . 4 years later. *Endocr. Rev.* 14, 324–347.
84. Zhou, J., Chin, E., and Bondy, C. (1991). Cellular pattern of insulin-like growth factor-I (IGF-I) and IGF-I receptor gene expression in the developing and mature ovarian follicle. *Endocrinology* 129, 3281–3288.
85. Adashi, E. Y., Resnick, C. E., Svoboda, M. E., and Van, W. J. (1985). Somatomedin-C enhances induction of luteinizing hormone receptors by follicle-stimulating hormone in

cultured rat granulosa cells. *Endocrinology* 116, 2369–2375.

86. Adashi, E. Y., Resnick, C. E., Hernandez, E. R., Svoboda, M. E., and Van, W. J. (1988). In vivo regulation of granulosa cell somatomedin-C/insulin-like growth factor I receptors. *Endocrinology* 122, 1383–1389.
87. Zhou, J., Kumar, T. R., Matzuk, M. M., and Bondy, C. (1997). Insulin-like growth factor I regulates gonadotropin responsiveness in the murine ovary. *Mol. Endocrinol.* 11, 1924–1933.
88. Kauppila, A., Kirkinen, P., Orava, M., and Vihko, R. (1984). Effects of metoclopramide-induced hyperprolactinemia during early follicular development on human ovarian function. *J. Clin. Endocrinol. Metab.* 59, 875–881.
89. Erickson, G. F., Wang, C., and Hsueh, A. J. (1979). FSH induction of functional LH receptors in granulosa cells cultured in a chemically defined medium. *Nature* 279, 336–338.
90. Jia, X. C., and Hsueh, A. J. (1984). Homologous regulation of hormone receptors: luteinizing hormone increases its own receptors in cultured rat granulosa cells. *Endocrinology* 115, 2433–2439.
91. Dorrington, J., and Gore-Langton, R. E. (1981). Prolactin inhibits oestrogen synthesis in the ovary. *Nature* 290, 600–602.
92. Nakamura, K., Minegishi, T., Takakura, Y., Miyamoto, K., Hasegawa, Y., Ibuki, Y., and Igarashi, M. (1991). Hormonal regulation of gonadotropin receptor mRNA in rat ovary during follicular growth and luteinization. *Mol. Cell Endocrinol.* 82, 259–263.
93. Hu, Z. Z., Tsai-Morris, C. H., Buczko, E., and Dufau, M. L. (1990). Hormonal regulation of LH receptor mRNA and expression in the rat ovary. *FEBS Lett.* 274, 181–184.
94. LaPolt, P. S., Oikawa, M., Jia, X. C., Dargan, C., and Hsueh, A. J. (1990). Gonadotropin-induced up- and down-regulation of rat ovarian LH receptor message levels during follicular growth, ovulation and luteinization. *Endocrinology* 126, 3277–3279.
95. Segaloff, D. L., and Limbird, L. E. (1983). Luteinizing hormone receptor appearance in cultured porcine granulosa cells requires continual presence of follicle-stimulating hormone. *Proc. Natl. Acad. Sci. U S A.* 80, 5631–5635.
96. Nakamura, K., Nakamura, M., Igarashi, S., Miyamoto, K., Eto, Y., Ibuki, Y., and Minegishi, T. (1994). Effect of activin on luteinizing hormone-human chorionic gonadotropin receptor messenger ribonucleic acid in granulosa cells. *Endocrinology* 134, 2329–2335.
97. Kishi, H., Minegishi, T., Tano, M., Abe, Y., Ibuki, Y., and Miyamoto, K. (1997). Down-regulation of LH/hCG receptor in rat cultured granulosa cells. *FEBS Lett.* 402, 198–202.

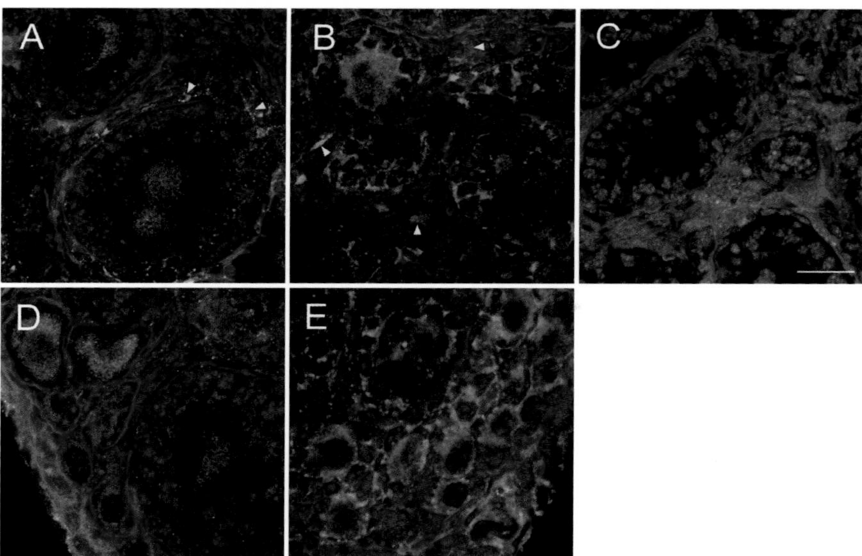

FIGURE 1.4 Detection of trkA *(green label)* and p75^{NTR} *(red label)* immunoreactive material in infantile (7-day-old) ovaries from wild-type and NGF –/– mice by immunohistofluorescence-confocal microscopy. Cell nuclei stained with the vital dye Hoechst are shown in blue. *A*, Detection of trkA positive cells in interstitial cells, prethecal cells of secondary follicles *(arrowheads)*, and in subsets of granulosa cells in the same follicles (ovary from a wild-type animal). p75^{NTR}-positive cells are mostly confined to the interstitial-prethecal compartments of the ovary. *B*, Abundant trkA immunoreactivity in granulosa cells of growing primary follicles and discrete localization in subsets of interstitial cells *(arrowheads)* (ovary from an NGF –/– mouse). *C*, Control section incubated without the trkA antibody but in the presence of the p75^{NTR} antibody (ovary from a wild-type mouse). *D*, Example of different levels of trkA immunoreactivity in oocytes in different phases of development and of a discrete content of trkA-like material in granulosa cells of a secondary follicle (ovary from a wild-type mouse). *E*, Example of a subset of primordial follicles containing oocytes strongly immunoreactive for trkA (ovary from an NGF –/– mouse). Bar = 25 μm. (From Ref. [118], with permission.)

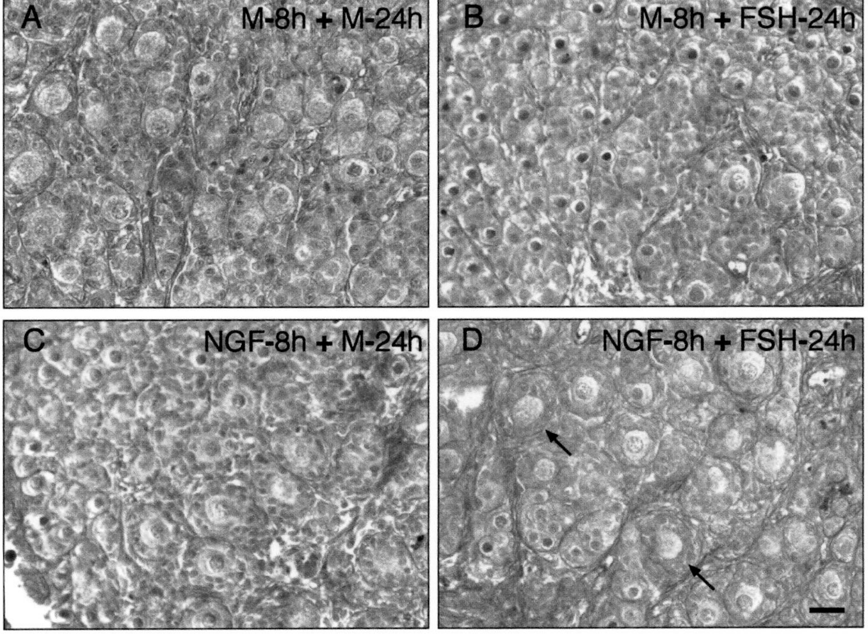

FIGURE 1.7 **A**, Histological aspect of 2-day-old rat ovaries cultured for 32 hours in medium alone. **B**, Cultured for 8 hours in medium alone followed by a 24-hour treatment with FSH (500 ng/ml). **C**, Cultured for 8 hours in medium containing NGF (100 ng/ml) followed by 24 hours in medium alone. **D**, Treated with NGF for 8 hours and then with FSH for 24 hours. Arrows = Growing follicles with three or more layers of granulosa cells; bar = 20 μm. (From Ref. [124], with permission).

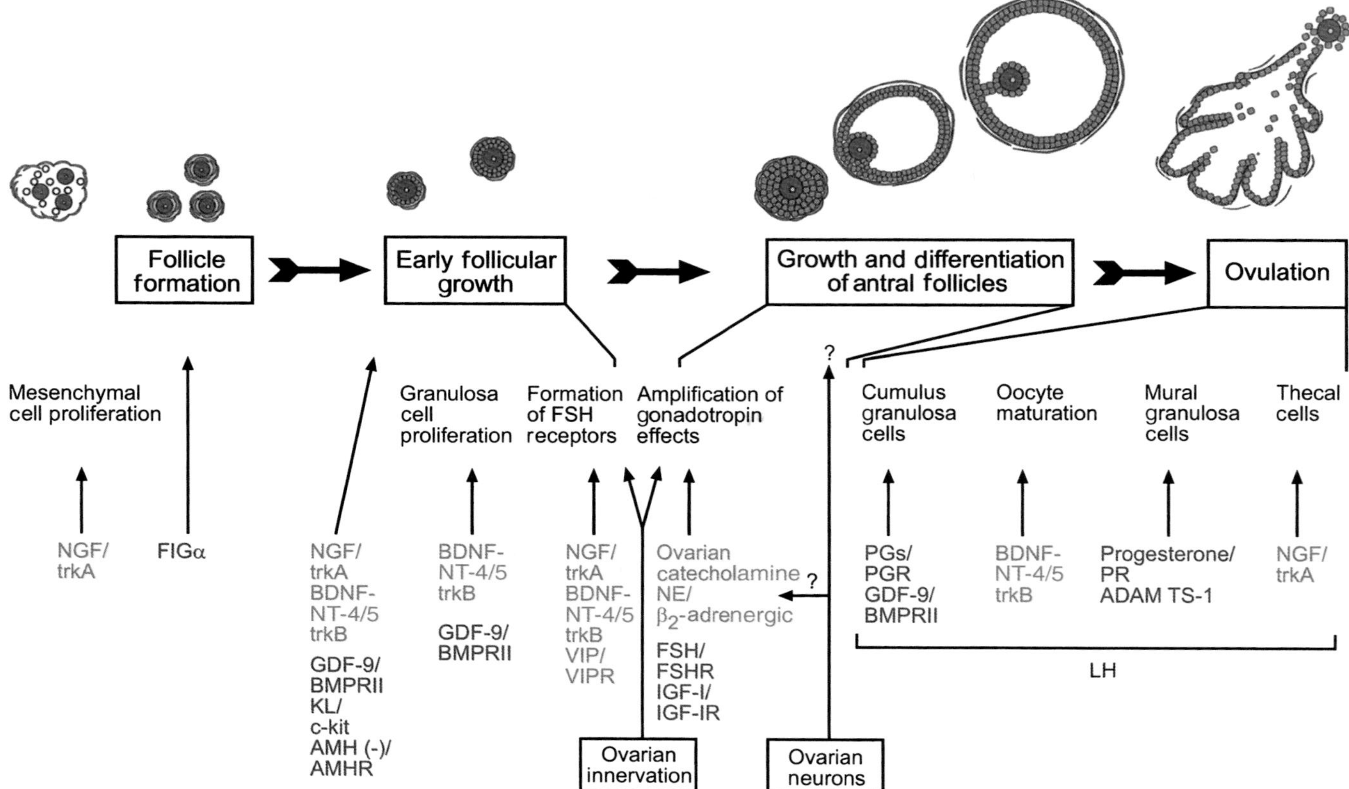

FIGURE 1.12 Postulated role of different components of the ovarian neuroendocrinotrophic complex (NTs, nerves and local sources of neurotransmitters) in follicular growth and ovulation. Components of the ovarian neuroendocrinotrophic complex are shown in red. Depicted in blue are select factors other than NTs shown to be involved in follicular development and ovulation. *ADAM TS1*, A disintegrin and matrix metalloproteinase with thrombospondin-like repeats; *AMHR*, antimüllerian hormone receptor; *FIGα*, factor in the germline α; *IGF-I*, insulin-like growth factor-I; *IGF-IR*, insulin-like growth factor-I receptor; *PGs*, prostaglandins; *PGR*, prostaglandin receptor; *PR*, progesterone receptor; *VIPR*, vasoactive intestinal peptide receptor. For a detailed account of all factors involved, see references [138, 139]. (Modified from Ref. [154], with permission.)

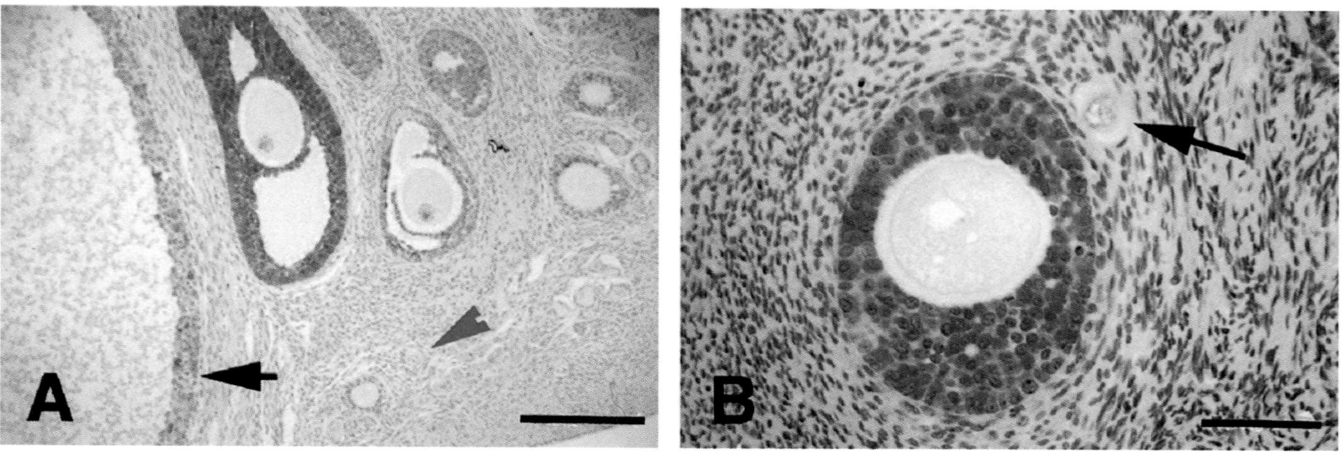

FIGURE 2.4 Immunodetection of AMH in the primate ovary. **A,** AMH immunostaining in the macaca ovary. Non-growing follicles (*red arrow*) are not immunostained. On contrary to small follicles that display a strong immunostaining in their GC, both early growing and large antral (*black arrow*) follicles display a low staining in the presence of the antibody for AMH (scale bar = 170 μm). **B,** AMH immunostaining in the human ovary. The GC of a preantral follicle stain positively for AMH, whereas those of a primordial follicle (*black arrow*) stain negatively (scale bar = 65 μm). (The AMH antibody was a gift from Dr. Nathalie Josso.)

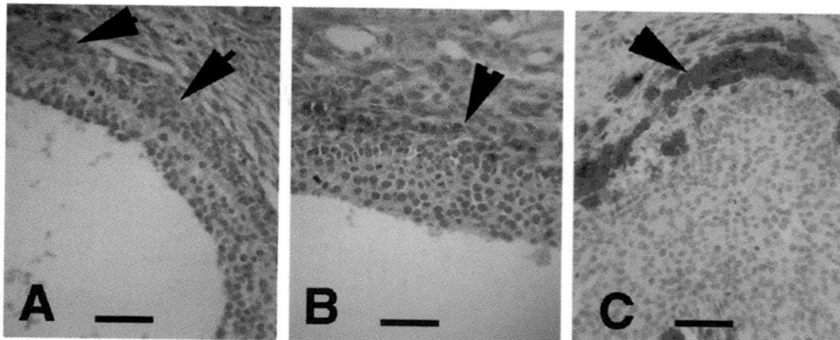

FIGURE 2.6 Thecal steroidogenesis, immunohistochemical detection of P450$_{c17\alpha/lyase}$ (*black arrows*), during human folliculogenesis (scale bar = 50 μm). **A,** Weak immunostaining in the theca interna of a class 3 follicle. **B,** Moderate immunostaining in the theca interna of a selectable follicle. **C,** Strong immunostaining in the theca interna of a preovulatory follicle. (The P450$_{c17\alpha/lyase}$ antibody was a gift from Dr. Shiro Kominami.)

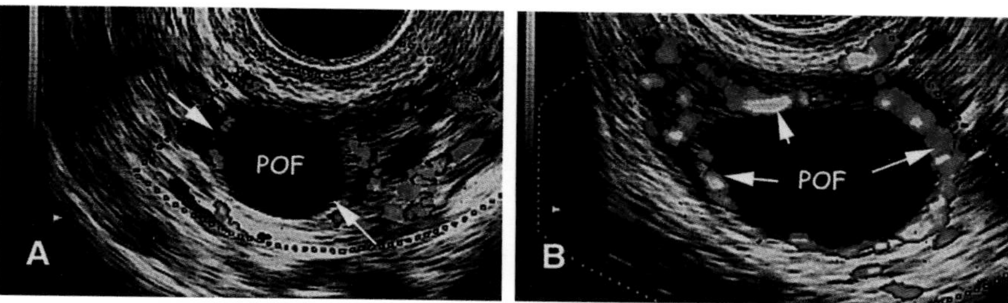

FIGURE 2.9 Color Doppler aspect of the human preovulatory follicle (POF). **A,** Before the preovulatory gonadotropin surge the red spots are scarce. **B,** After the preovulatory gonadotropin surge the POF is highly vascularized and diplays many red and yellow thick spots that reflect a high velocity of the blood flow. (Courtesy Dr. Yves Ardaens.)

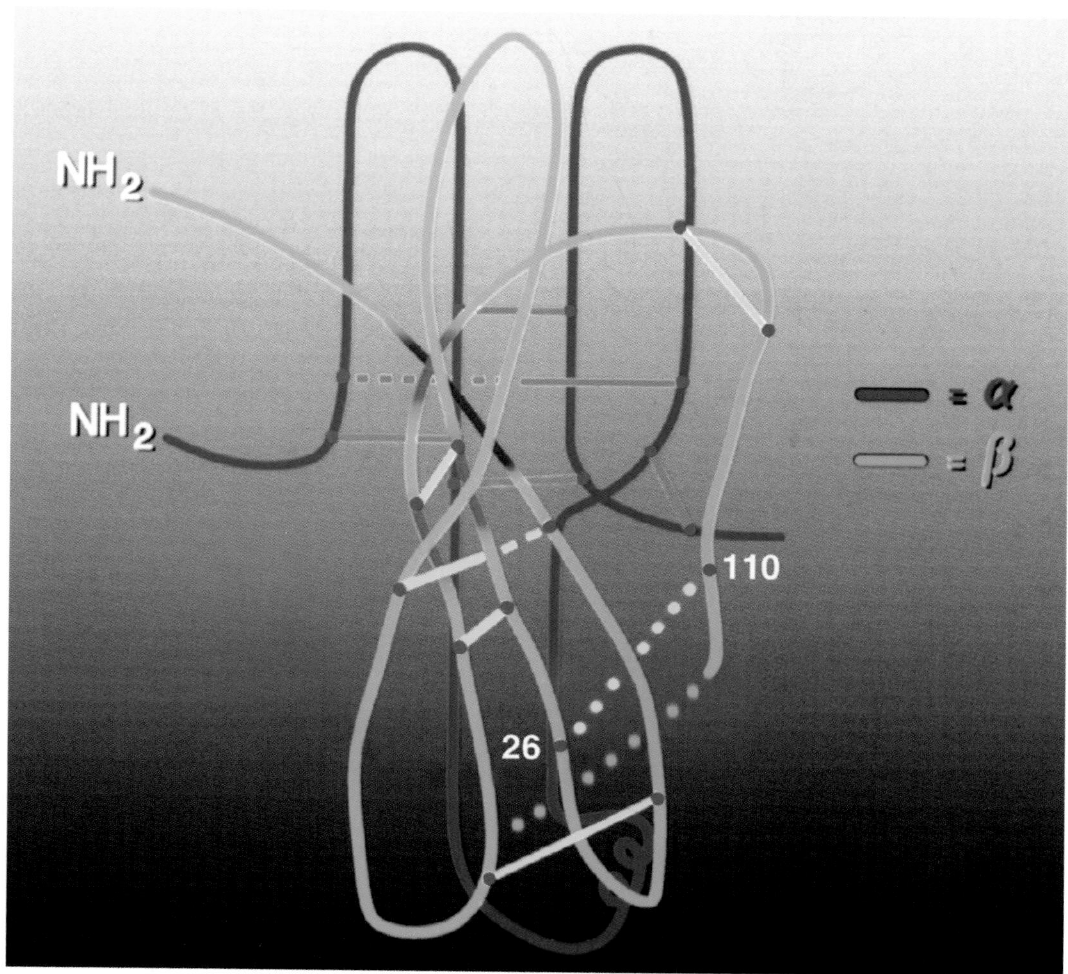

FIGURE 4.2 Diagram of the crystal structure of hCG. Intrasubunit disulfide bonds are shown in yellow and orange for the α (purple) and β (blue) subunits, respectively. Disulfide bond 26–110 of β-subunit belongs to the stabilizing "seat belt" structure. (From Ref. [12], with permission.)

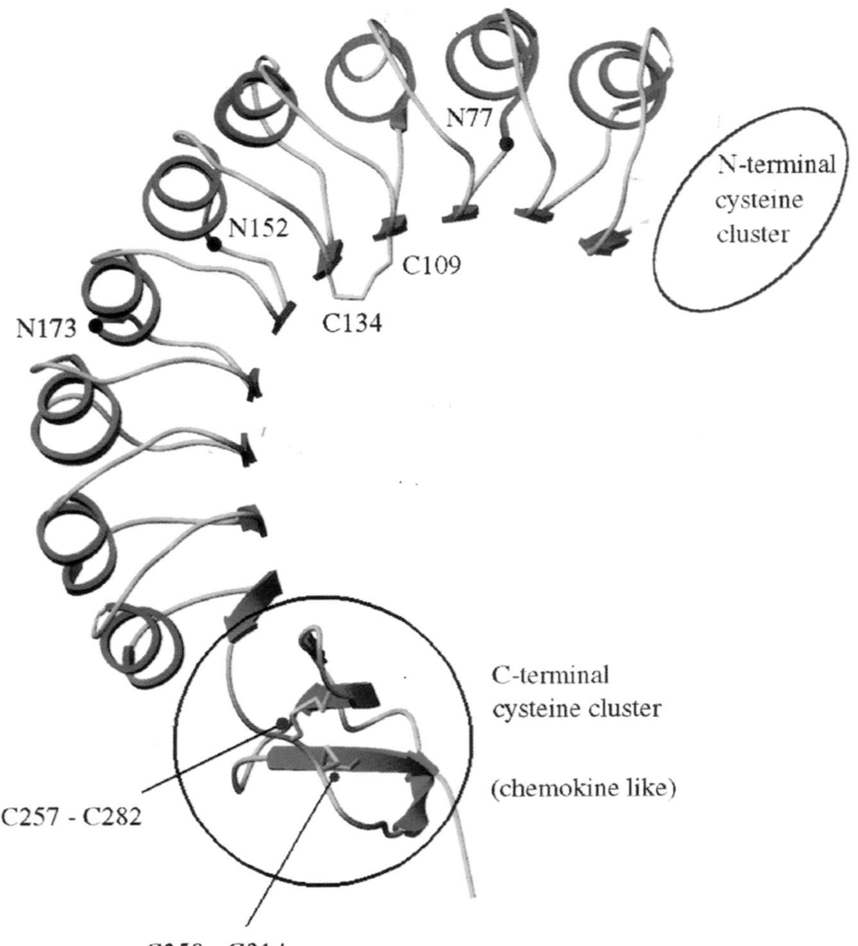

FIGURE 4.3 A ribbon diagram of the LRR structure of extracellular domain of LHR. Potential disulfides are illustrated and the potential N-linked glycosylation is sited on the LRR segment of the structure. [From Ref. [25], with permission.)

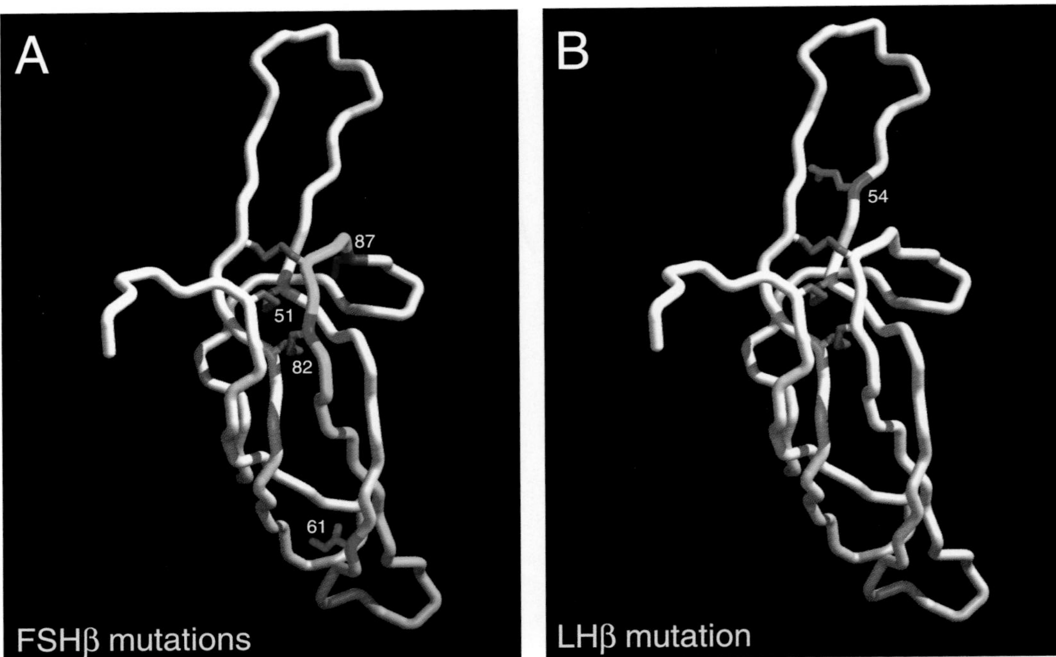

FIGURE 4.6 Locations of reported mutations in the FSHβ and LHβ subunits. Identified mutations in hFSH and hLH were mapped onto the crystal structure of hCG [4] relative to the positions of the cysteine residues, which are fully conserved among the three β-subunits. Mutated residues are shown in green. Residue numbers *(white)* refer to the position in the FSH and LH β-subunits rather than the number of the residue in the hCG structure. The three disulfide bridges involved in the "cysteine knot" motif are shown in blue. In *A*, a 2 bp deletion at residue 61 changes the ensuing sequence *(yellow)* up to residue 86 and results in a stop codon at residue 87 *(red)*. (From Ref. 52, with permission.)

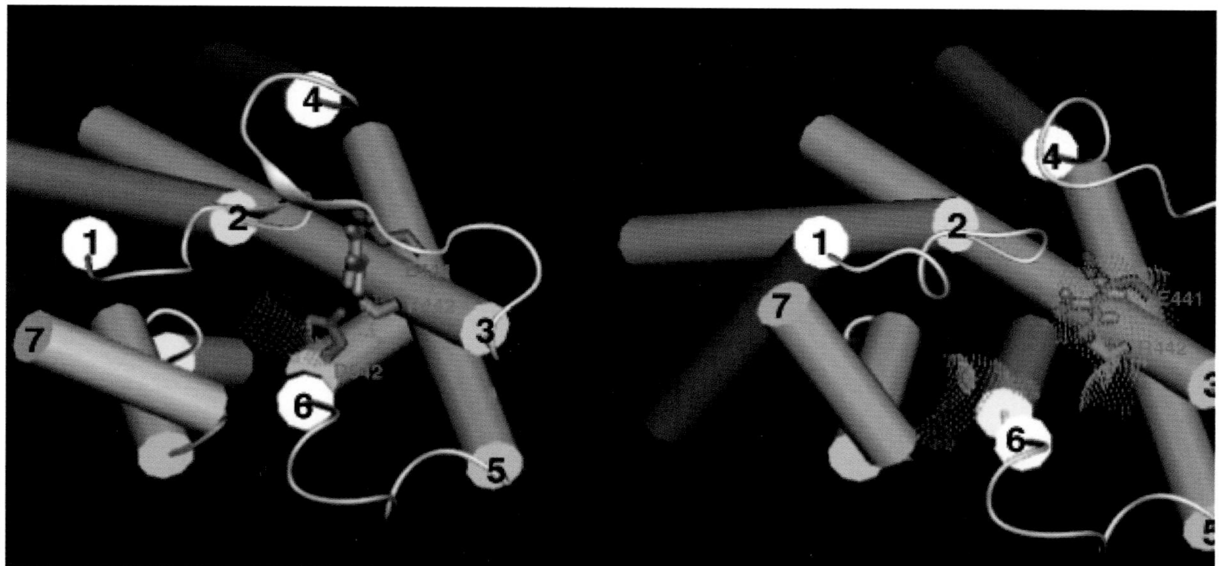

FIGURE 4.7 Average minimized structures of WT-LHR *(top and bottom left)* and the D542G constitutively activating mutant *(top and bottom right)*. In the top panel, cylinders represent the helix bundles, whereas thin ribbons represent the three intracellular loops. The extracellular domains are not shown in this figure. The structures are viewed from the intracellular side in a direction almost perpendicular to the membrane surface. The side chains of Glu-441, Arg-442, Asp-542, and Gly-542 are represented by sticks and are colored according to their polarity. The composite solvent-accessible surface computed over the amino acids Arg-442, Thr-445, Ile-446, and Lys-541 is also shown, represented by green dots. (From Ref. [30], with permission.)

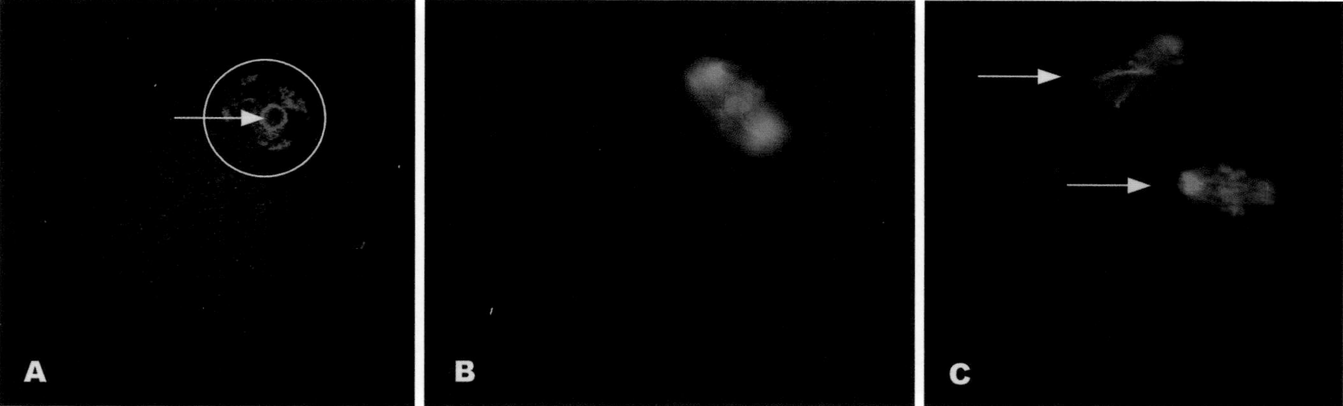

FIGURE 7.1 Nuclear maturation of mouse oocytes. Mouse oocytes were isolated from large antral follicles and allowed to undergo spontaneous maturation in culture. Deoxyribonucleic acid (DNA) is visualized by staining with propidium iodide *(red)* and anti_β-tubulin was used for the detection of the spindle microtubules *(green)*. **A**, Germinal vesicle (GV) stage oocyte. Contents of GV are circled in white. Note that the nucleolus *(arrow)* is surrounded by densely packed chromatin. **B**, Oocyte at MI. Homologous chromosomes *(red)* are aligned on the metaphase plate and attached to a barrel-shaped spindle *(green)*. **C**, Oocyte at MII. The yellow arrow delineates the haploid number of chromosomes on the MII spindle and the contents of the first polar body are also seen *(white arrow)*.

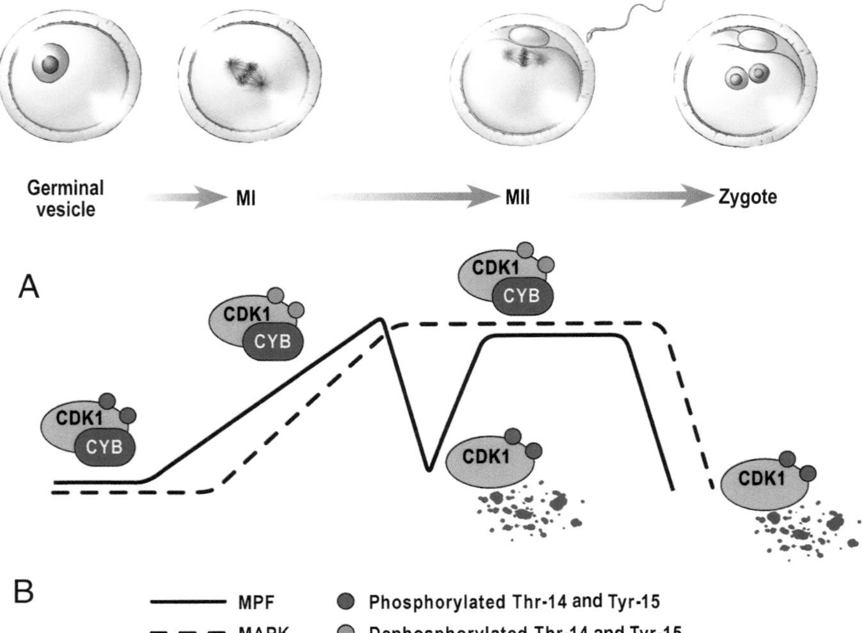

FIGURE 7.2 **A**, Diagram of the major steps in the progression of nuclear maturation. **B**, Diagram of the activity of maturation-promoting factor *(MPF = solid line)* and MAPK *(dashed line)* during nuclear maturation. MPF activity is defined by the activation of the CDK1 protein kinase component of MPF, whose activity is regulated by dephosphorylation at Thr-14 and Tyr-15 *(green)*. Loss of CDK1 activity is brought about at anaphase I or II by the rephosphorylation *(red)* of CDK1 and the proteolytic degradation of the cyclin B (CYB) regulatory component of MPF.

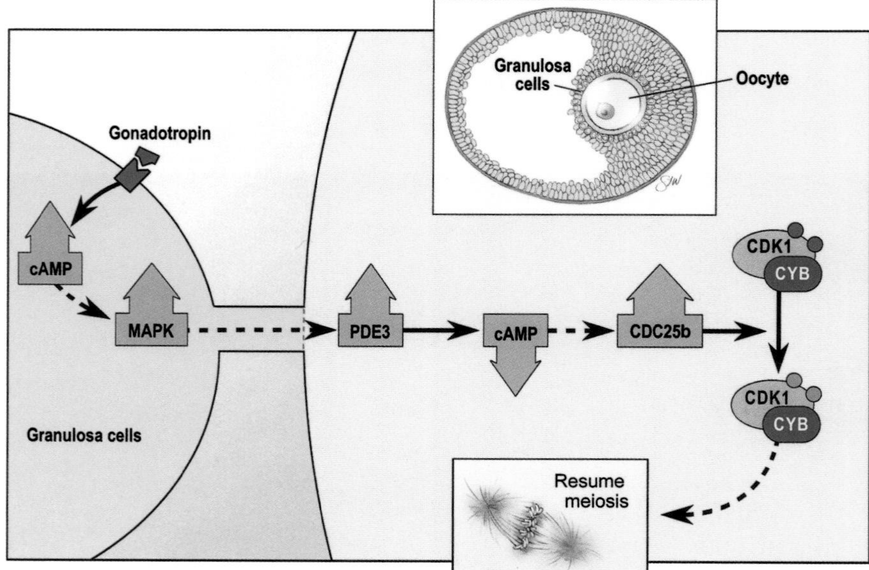

FIGURE 7.3 Hypothesis for the mechanism of gonadotropin-induced resumption of meiosis. Pink arrows indicate an increase or decrease in the activity or level of the indicated molecule. Dashed lines indicate that multiple steps might be involved in progression to the next event. Gonadotropin stimulation increases granulosa cell cAMP levels bringing about increased MAPK activity. This results in the generation of an unknown signal by the granulosa cells that traverses the gap junctions that couple the somatic cells with the oocyte. This signal increases the activity of PDE3, thus decreasing cAMP levels in the oocyte. It is also possible that the signal decreases adenylyl cyclase activity in the oocyte (not shown). It is also likely that, after transmission of the positive signal, the transfer of molecules promoting meiotic arrest terminates.

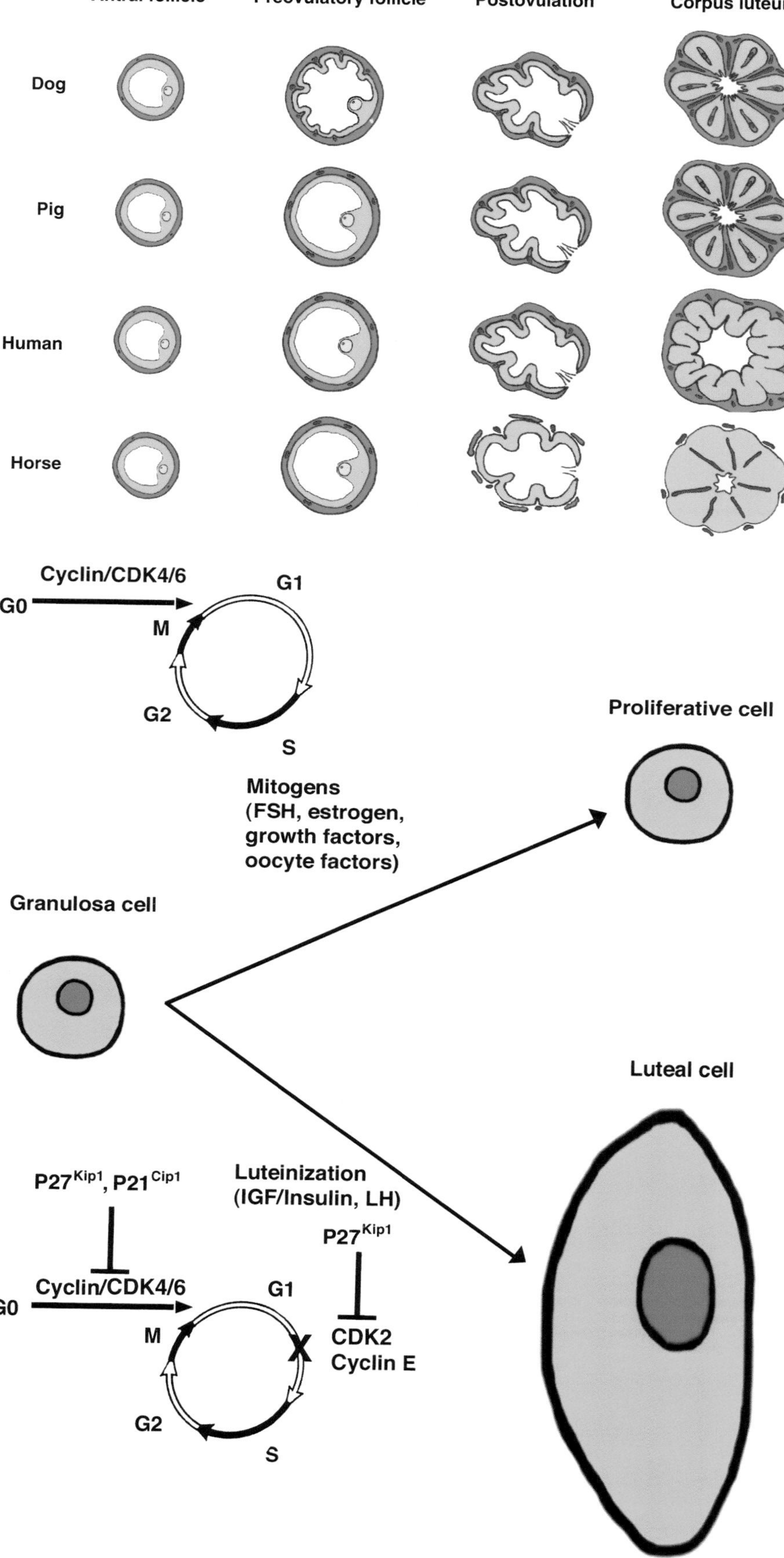

FIGURE 11.1 Variation in the process of luteinization among mammals. In the general model, represented by the pig, collapse of the follicle following ovulation allows the incursion of thecal blood vessels *(red)* and the theca layer *(blue)* to invade the granulosa *(yellow)* compartment of the follicle. The theca cells, borne by the invading vasculature, become dispersed throughout the luteal parenchyma. In the dog, the luteal invasion of the theca layer precedes ovulation, and there is substantial progesterone secretion by the follicle before ovulation. In humans, there is a similar neovascularization of the granulosa cell compartment, but the theca- and the granulosa-derived components of the CL remain discrete entities. In the horse, the theca cells degenerate during the periovulatory period and the consequent CL is derived from the granulosa cell component of the follicle.

FIGURE 11.2 The proliferation/luteinization decision in granulosa cells. Proliferation is associated with continuation of the cell cycle as described in the text. Luteinization has been associated with the expression of the cell cycle inhibitors $P27^{Kip1}$ and $P21^{Cip1}$, which inhibit multiple CDKs during the G1 phase of the cycle and prevent the hyperphosphorylation of retinoblastoma proteins. This results in cell cycle arrest and consequent terminal differentiation of granulosa cells.

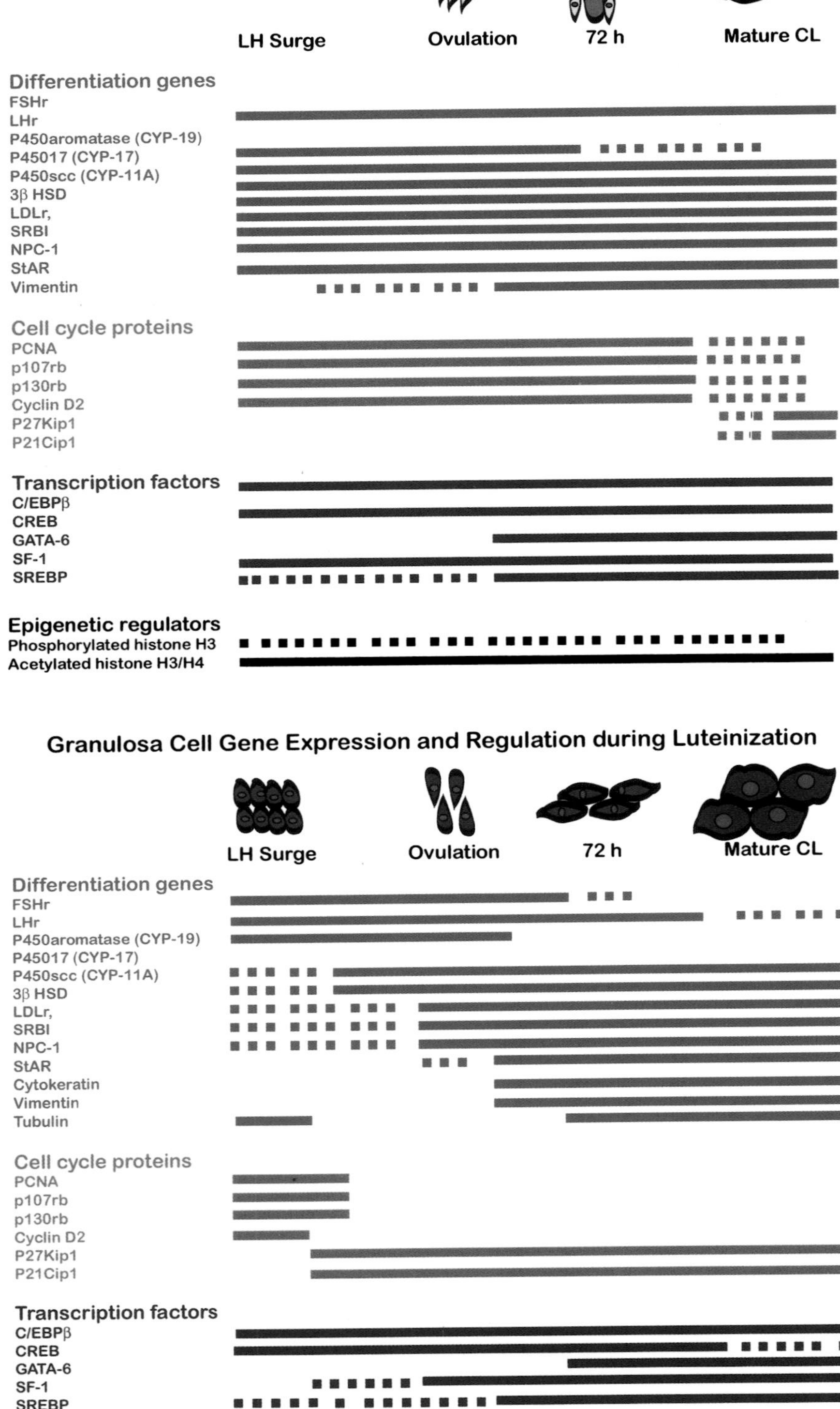

FIGURE 11.3 Generalized view of the gene expression and its regulation in the ovarian cells during the formation of the CL, based on observations in rodents, primates, and artiodactyls. The evolution of morphological changes for the theca **(A)** and granulosa **(B)** cells is depicted in the diagram at the top of the figure. Solid lines = strong and uninterrupted expression of the factor in question; dotted lines = low-level or intermittent expression.

CHAPTER 6

Intracellular Cholesterol Dynamics in Steroidogenic Cells

CLEMENT K. M. HO, LANE K. CHRISTENSON, AND JEROME F. STRAUSS III

INTRODUCTION

Steroid hormones including estrogens, androgens, progestins, glucocorticoids, and mineralocorticoids are derived from a common sterol precursor, cholesterol. The first committed step in the process of steroidogenesis in response to tropic hormone stimulation is catalyzed by the cholesterol side chain cleavage enzyme (CYP11A). The side chain cleavage enzyme complex, consisting of a flavoprotein, an iron-sulfur protein, and the side chain cleavage enzyme itself, removes the side chain of cholesterol between C20 and C22, producing the 21-carbon molecule, pregnenolone. This complex is situated on the matrix side of the inner mitochondrial membrane. For many years, cholesterol side chain cleavage was considered the rate-limiting step in steroidogenesis. However, when hydroxylated analogs of cholesterol, which can readily diffuse across the mitochondrial membranes, were provided to steroidogenic cells, high levels of steroids were formed in the absence of tropic stimulation [1–3]. These observations not only indicated that it was the availability of cholesterol that limited pregnenolone production in earlier studies but also highlighted the importance of cellular cholesterol trafficking to steroidogenesis. In this chapter, we review the current understanding of the various sources of cholesterol available to steroidogenic cells and the mechanisms by which cholesterol is transported from the cellular cholesterol pools to the inner mitochondrial membrane, where the side chain cleavage enzyme complex resides.

Cholesterol exists in two forms in cells and plasma lipoproteins, namely free cholesterol and cholesteryl ester. Free cholesterol is the precursor substrate for steroidogenesis. It is nonuniformly distributed among cell membranes, concentrated mainly in the plasma membrane and to a lesser extent in intracellular organelle membranes [4–6]. Cholesteryl esters, on the other hand, consist of cholesterol esterified through the 3β-hydroxyl group to polyunsaturated fatty acids or to sulfate. Present in cytoplasmic lipid droplets and lipoprotein particles, the fatty acid esters of cholesterol can neither replace free cholesterol as a structural ingredient of the plasma membrane nor serve as direct substrates for steroid production. Cholesteryl esters appear to function as depots of excess cellular cholesterol. To illustrate the mechanisms by which cholesterol and cholesteryl esters are transported into and within the steroidogenic cell, we first summarize the subcellular structural characteristics of a steroidogenic cell that are crucial to intracellular cholesterol dynamics.

STRUCTURAL CHARACTERISTICS OF THE STEROIDOGENIC CELL

Steroidogenic cells exhibit many unique structural characteristics that facilitate the acquisition of cholesterol and the process of converting cholesterol into steroid hormones. Active steroidogenic cells are characterized by numerous microvilli and clathrin-coated pits on the plasma membrane [7]. Clathrin-coated pits are invaginations of the plasma membrane stabilized on the cytoplasmic surface by interlocking heterodimers of clathrin heavy and light chains [8]. Compared with the rest of the plasma membrane, clathrin-coated pits contain little free cholesterol and are the sites from which many integral proteins of the plasma membrane, including membrane-spanning receptor proteins, are internalized. For example, receptors for low-density lipoproteins (LDLs), important for cholesterol uptake by steroidogenic cells, are located on microvilli and in coated pits [7, 9]. Receptors for high-density lipoproteins (HDLs) are also preferentially localized on the microvilli of steroidogenic cells and liver cells, where they provide means of cholesterol uptake destined for steroidogenesis and bile acid formation, respectively [10].

Smooth endoplasmic reticulum (ER) is in general abundant in steroidogenic cells [11]. Steroidogenic cells can have up to 10-fold more smooth ER than rough ER, whereas nonsteroidogenic cells typically contain little smooth ER but a more significant amount of rough ER. Smooth ER is the site where 3-hydroxy-3-methylglutaryl-coenzyme A (HMG-CoA) reductase, the rate-limiting enzyme in de novo cholesterol synthesis, as well as some other enzymes participating in cholesterol production reside [12]. Moreover, enzymes involved in steroid hormone synthesis, including 17α-hydroxylase, 17–20 lyase (CYP17), 3β-hydroxysteroid dehydrogenase, 21-hydroxylase (CYP21), and aromatase (CYP19), are also located in the smooth ER [13]. A remarkable observation is that in human granulosa cells, smooth ER content increases concurrently with the dramatic increases in cellular steroidogenic capacity during the luteinization process. Nonetheless, the factors driving the formation of the extensive amount of smooth ER during luteinization are not fully understood.

Another prominent feature of most steroidogenic cells is the presence of abundant cytoplasmic lipid droplets. These lipid droplets contain cholesterol esterified primarily to long chain polyunsaturated fatty acids, though triglycerides and some phospholipids are also present [14, 15]. As much as 80% of the total cellular cholesterol content can be found as cholesteryl esters in such lipid droplets. The subcellular components involved in the formation of cytoplasmic lipid droplets have not been fully elucidated. One possible mechanistic explanation lies in the unique ability of steroidogenic cells to continue LDL receptor production and LDL uptake even in the face of high intracellular cholesterol levels [16]. Lipid droplets are an important source of cholesterol substrate for steroidogenesis, as illustrated by the depletion of lipid droplets from highly active steroidogenic cells [11]. Conversely, treatment of rats with aminoglutethimide, a CYP11A inhibitor, promoted ovarian cholesteryl ester storage content and lipid droplet formation [17].

Given the localization of CYP11A to the inner mitochondrial membrane, it is not surprising that large numbers of mitochondria are also characteristic of steroidogenic cells. These mitochondria exhibit a unique morphology, being spherical in shape with tubulovesicular cristae instead of the usual elongated mitochondria with lamellar cristae [14, 15, 18]. The cholesterol side chain cleavage enzyme system, which consists of CYP11A and its associated flavoprotein and iron-sulfur electron transport system, and 11β-hydroxylase, the enzyme that converts 11-deoxycortisol to form cortisol, are located on the matrix side of the inner mitochondrial membrane [13]. Mitochondrial membranes have a relatively low cholesterol content, as indicated by the cholesterol/phospholipid ratios compared with other intracellular organelles: mitochondrial membrane = 0.03, endoplasmic reticulum = 0.08, lysosomal membrane = 0.49, and plasma membrane = 0.4 to 0.76 [6]. Therefore, intracellular pathways must exist to direct cholesterol to the mitochondria, where the first step in the process of steroidogenesis takes place.

ACQUISITION OF CHOLESTEROL BY THE STEROIDOGENIC CELL

De Novo Biosynthesis of Cholesterol

Most nucleated mammalian cells synthesize cholesterol in a multistep pathway. The synthesis of cholesterol starts with acetyl coenzyme A (CoA), which is generated in the mitochondria by catabolism of either pyruvate or fatty acid substrates [19]. Acety CoA then undergoes a series of enzymatic steps, including the formation of 3-hydroxy-3-methylglutaryl CoA (HMG-CoA) by the enzyme HMG-CoA synthase, and the rate-limiting conversion of HMG-CoA to mevalonate, catalyzed by the microsomal HMG-CoA reductase. The pivotal role of cholesterol biosynthesis in fetal development is emphasized by the recent elucidation of the etiology underlying the Smith-Lemli-Opitz (SLO) syndrome, an autosomal recessive disorder that occurs in approximately 1 in 20,000 births and is characterized by craniofacial dysmorphism, mental retardation, and multiple congenital anomalies including defects in male sexual differentiation as a result of reduced fetal testicular androgen production [20]. Biochemically, activity of 7-dehydrocholesterol reductase, which catalyzes the final step of the cholesterol synthetic pathway by reduction of the Δ7 double bond of 7-dehydrocholesterol to form cholesterol, is deficient in patients with the SLO syndrome. Their plasma and tissue levels of cholesterol are low, whereas levels of 7-dehydrocholesterol are abnormally high [21]. Molecular genetic analysis revealed that patients with the SLO syndrome were homozygotes or compound heterozygotes harboring various mutations in the 7-dehydrocholesterol reductase (DHCR7) gene, which led to deficient 7-dehydrocholesterol reductase activity [22].

De Novo Biosynthesis versus Receptor-Mediated Uptake

The previous example of SLO syndrome clearly illustrates the importance of cholesterol synthesis in fetal development. However, the role of de novo cholesterol synthesis in supporting steroidogenesis is less certain when there is an ample supply of lipoprotein cholesterol, although it is well established that steroidogenic cells are capable of de novo cholesterol synthesis. Human adults given HMG-CoA reductase inhibitors did not exhibit significant changes in adrenal or testicular steroid output [23, 24]). In vitro studies using fetal adrenal cells to examine the rate of de novo cholesterol synthesis simultaneously with the rate of lipoprotein uptake suggested that de novo synthesis contributed less than 30% of the cholesterol used for steroidogenesis [25]. In addition, although the ovary can produce cholesterol using the conventional biosynthetic pathway, inhibition of cholesterol formation in luteinized human granulosa cells grown in medium containing serum did not blunt their secretion of progestin in response to hormonal stimulation [26]. Taken together, these in vitro and in vivo studies clearly suggest that cholesterol derived from sources other than de novo synthesis plays the key role in supporting steroid hormone production.

Lipoprotein-Mediated Cholesterol Uptake

Neutral lipids, including cholesterol, cholesteryl ester, and triglyceride, have limited solubility in water and are thus transported in plasma as lipoproteins. Lipoproteins are macromolecular complexes, spherical in shape; the surface shell of the molecule consists primarily of a phospholipid monolayer and surrounds a core of water-insoluble neutral lipids [27, 28]. Cholesterol is present in free and/or esterified form in all of the normal lipoprotein classes including chylomicron, very low-density lipoprotein (VLDL), LDL, and HDL. Within the lipoprotein molecule, cholesterol is localized to the shell and the core, whereas cholesteryl ester distributes predominantly to the core [28] and constitutes the major nonpolar lipid fraction in LDL and HDL [27]. Receptors for LDL and HDL are responsible for specific, high-affinity binding of the corresponding lipoproteins and mediate the uptake of cholesterol and cholesteryl esters into steroidogenic cells.

Low-Density Lipoprotein Pathway

Expression of LDL receptors is generally high in steroidogenic organs including the adrenal gland and gonads. The mechanism of cholesterol uptake by LDL receptor mediated endocytosis is well established and has been extensively reviewed [27, 29]. In brief, the receptor/LDL complexes cluster in clathrin-coated pits on the plasma membrane surface and are internalized in coated endocytotic vesicles. The clathrin coat then disappears quickly before multiple endocytotic vesicles fuse with one another to form a larger endosome. Under the acidic environment within the endosome, LDL dissociates from its receptor. The receptor subsequently returns to the plasma membrane surface while the LDL-containing endosome fuses with a lysosome, where LDL is subject to further degradation.

Free cholesterol can also be internalized from LDL by selective transfer, without concomitant internalization of the LDL molecule. Cell-surface clathrin-coated pits, which contain little free cholesterol, mediated this selective uptake of free cholesterol via a high-capacity, low-affinity pathway whose magnitude was similar in normal and LDL receptor-deficient skin fibroblasts in culture [30, 31]. Nonetheless, acquisition of LDL-derived free cholesterol by selective uptake was estimated to be eightfold less efficient than by LDL receptor-mediated endocytosis [31]. Besides free cholesterol, cholesteryl esters derived from LDL were also demonstrated to be selectively taken up by murine ovarian granulosa cells [32].

LDL-derived cholesterol, be it in its free or esterified form acquired by either selective uptake or internalization of the LDL receptor, is crucial to steroidogenesis in humans. The importance of LDL-derived cholesterol is illustrated by the condition of familial hypobetalipoproteinemia, a condition characterized by the virtual absence of any circulating LDL and VLDL. Maximal steroid output in response to tropic hormone stimulation in patients with familial hypobetalipoproteinemia is far below that observed in control subjects [33]. Female patients also have markedly lower progesterone levels during the menstrual cycle and pregnancy [34, 35], indicating that LDL-derived cholesterol is an important source of substrate for steroid hormone production.

At the other end of the clinical spectrum lies another inborn error of lipid metabolism—familial hypercholesterolemia, a disease characterized by marked elevations in serum LDL levels and deposition of LDL-derived cholesterol in tendons, skin, and arteries [29]. In 95% of the patients, the condition results from an inherited defect in the LDL receptor. When the LDL receptor is deficient or defective, the rate of LDL removal from plasma declines and levels of LDL become abnormally high [29]. Hypercholesterolemia caused by LDL receptor defects is inherited as an autosomal dominant trait with a gene dosage effect, such that homozygotes are more severely affected than heterozygotes. Patients with homozygous familial hypercholesterolemia were shown to have modestly impaired adrenal corticosteroid biosynthesis; this impairment was more evident following adrenocorticotropic hormone (ACTH) stimulation [33]. However, these patients do not exhibit reproductive or adrenal dysfunction presumably because of enhanced compensatory de novo sterol biosynthesis and/or cellular uptake of cholesterol via other means such as the HDL pathway.

High-Density Lipoprotein Pathway

A breakthrough in the understanding of the process by which steroidogenic tissues and the liver acquire cholesteryl esters from HDL was the molecular identification of a functional HDL receptor [10]. The murine scavenger receptor class B, type 1 (SR-BI), was revealed to bind HDL with high affinity and mediate selective uptake of cholesteryl esters from HDL [10] and LDL [36]. SR-BI expression is highest in the liver, ovary, adrenal gland, and testis [10, 37]. In rats and mice, steroidogenic cells acquire cholesterol mainly via selective uptake of HDL-cholesteryl ester without the uptake or degradation of the HDL particle; SR-BI expression was shown to be tightly associated with the levels of HDL-cholesteryl ester uptake by the rat ovary [38] and Leydig cells [39]. At the electron microscopic level, SR-BI was most clearly associated with microvilli and microvillar channels (gaps between closely apposed surface microvilli) on the luteal cell surface [38]. Microvillar area and microvillar channel formation, together with SR-BI expression especially in the microvillar compartment, increased significantly after tropic hormone stimulation in rat adrenocortical cells, reflecting not only a close relationship between SR-BI expression and structural configuration of the surface of steroidogenic cells but also the responsiveness of the microvillar compartment to hormonal stimuli [40].

The human CD36 and LIMPII analogous-1 (CLA-1), a close structural homologue of SR-BI, was found to be strongly expressed in the adrenal gland, ovary, testis, and liver [41, 42]. Unlike SR-BI in rodents, however, CLA-1 is also highly expressed in the human placenta [42]. Apart from sharing high sequence identity with SR-BI, CLA-1 is functionally related to its rodent homologue too. Transfected cells expressing CLA-1 not only demonstrated HDL-binding affinity similar to that of SR-BI but also accumulated HDL-derived cholesteryl esters without internalization or degradation of apolipoprotein, suggesting that CLA-1, like SR-BI, could play a role in the metabolism of HDL [41]. When cholesterol-depleted and SR-BI–expressing COS-7 cells were incubated with HDL, there was net cholesterol influx into the cells; conversely, incubation of cholesterol-rich, SR-BI–expressing COS-7 cells with HDL resulted in net efflux of cell cholesterol [43]. Likewise, COS-7 cells expressing CLA-1 also displayed bidirectional cholesterol transport observed in cells expressing SR-BI [43].

Mutations of ABCA1, a member of the ATP-binding cassette (ABC) transporter gene family, were recently identified to be the cause of the rare autosomal recessive disorder, Tangier disease, and familial HDL deficiency (see [44] and references therein). Tangier disease homozygotes are characterized by very low levels of plasma HDL and apolipoprotein A-I, associated with low plasma LDL levels, hypertriglyceridemia, accumulation of cholesteryl esters in many organs, and atherosclerosis. Because of a potential role for ABCA1 in HDL metabolism, a mouse model with targeted disruption of the ABCA1 gene was developed [45]. Homozygous mutant mice demonstrated lipid deposition in their liver, thymus, and testes and minimal plasma HDL-cholesterol levels; cholesteryl esters and free cholesterol were, however, undetectable in the adrenal glands and ovaries. During pregnancy, mutants also exhibited placental malformation, leading to intrauterine growth retardation and fetal death, presumably because of significantly lower progesterone (53%) and estrogen (63%) levels than control mice [45]. This placental phenotype has not been described in Tangier disease, probably because mice have low LDL levels and a limited capacity to compensate for the loss of HDL, the main circulating lipoprotein in this species.

CHOLESTERYL ESTER

The steady state concentration of intracellular free cholesterol in steroidogenic tissues is maintained at a relatively low level, with any additional free cholesterol being esterified for storage in cytoplasmic droplets [46]. Cholesteryl esters derived from HDL and LDL can also accumulate in the pool of lipid droplets; nonhydrolysable tracers of HDL- and LDL-cholesteryl esters injected to rats were recovered in cytoplasmic lipid droplets in the adrenal glands 24 hours after injection [47]. Cholesteryl esters found in steroidogenic cells are rich in polyunsaturated fatty acids, including linolenic acid, arachidonic acid, docosahexaenoic acid, and docosapentenoic acid [48, 49]. Although little is known about the functions of these fatty acids in steroidogenic cells, the observation that the pattern of fatty acids esterified to cholesteryl esters changed with the functional status of steroidogenic cells [49] suggests possible roles for these lipids in the cells, perhaps as precursors of prostanoids and lipoxygenase products [11].

Cholesteryl Ester Formation

The formation of cholesteryl ester from the esterification of free cholesterol and fatty acyl CoA is catalyzed by the microsomal acyl coenzyme A:cholesterol acyltransferase (ACAT). Newly synthesized cholesteryl esters accumulate within the rough ER and bud off as cytoplasmic lipid droplets; the abundance of the latter is a key feature of steroidogenic cells [11]. The magnitude of this cholesteryl ester pool in steroidogenic cells varies from substantial in the adrenal cortex, to moderate in the ovary, to low in the testis and placenta [46].

Studies have provided evidence that two ACAT enzymes exist in mammals. ACAT-1 was identified by expression cloning from human macrophages [50]. ACAT-1 messenger ribonucleic acid (mRNA) was detected in many tissues, with the highest expression levels in the preputial gland, ovary, testis, adrenal gland, aorta, and macrophages, whereas expression levels in the liver and small intestine were low [51]. In accordance with biochemical studies that have identified ACAT activity in microsomes [52], immunochemical studies also localized the ACAT-1 protein to the ER in several cell types [53]. ACAT activity is regulated to a large extent at the post-translational level (e.g., through substrate availability and substrate-induced modulation of enzyme activity) [54].

In 1998, a second ACAT was identified in humans and mice [55, 56]. The mouse ACAT-2 protein has 44% amino acid sequence identity with the mouse ACAT-1 protein and high cholesterol esterification activity when expressed in a baculovirus system [57]. In sharp contrast with ACAT-1, ACAT-2 was expressed primarily in the mouse liver and small intestine, supporting the hypothesis that ACAT-2 contributes to cholesterol esterification in these tissues

[56, 57]. ACAT-2 expression was not detectable by Northern analysis in the ovary, testis, brain, heart, lung, spleen, or thymus. To date, the role of ACAT-2 in sterol metabolism remains to be determined.

Cholesteryl Ester Hydrolysis

To enter the steroidogenic pathway, cholesteryl ester needs to be hydrolyzed to free the cholesterol moiety. Cholesteryl esters derived from LDL receptor mediated uptake are hydrolyzed by lysosomal acid lipase. After uptake of the LDL receptor–clathrin-coated pit complex, the clathrin coat is removed and the LDL-containing endosomes fuse to form multivesicular bodies, which in turn fuse with primary lysosomal vesicles harboring acid hydrolytic enzymes [29]. Some of the free cholesterol produced by cholesteryl ester hydrolysis is redirected to the plasma membrane, whereas the majority enters the ER (Figure 6.1), where it affects the activity of ACAT and/or the transcriptional regulation of genes involved in cholesterol metabolism including LDL receptor and HMG-CoA reductase.

Two diseases are characterized by a deficiency in lysosomal acid lipase (LAL) activity: Wolman's disease and cholesteryl ester storage disease (CESD). Usually manifested in infancy, Wolman's disease is nearly always fatal before 1 year of age and in most cases results from a homozygous mutation that leads to an inactive or truncated protein missing the carboxy-terminus, which contains the catalytic domain of the enzyme [58, 59]. Because of the virtual absence of LAL, there is marked accumulation of cholesteryl esters and triglycerides within the lysosomes in the liver, adrenal gland, small intestine, and other organs [60]. The inability by affected cells to release free cholesterol causes the up-regulation of genes involved in cholesterol uptake and de novo cholesterol synthesis, leading to a vicious cycle of cholesterol overload in lysosomes. In comparison, a single genetic defect (a splice junction mutation in exon eight) accounts for the majority of CESD cases, leading to the loss of 24 amino acids from the mature LAL protein (see [58] and references therein). The mutation, however, allows about 3% of normal splicing to occur, ensuring some residual LAL activity, which frees enough cholesterol to down-regulate LDL receptor formation and prevents the vicious cycle observed in Wolman's disease. CESD is a milder and later-onset disease; some patients may survive beyond middle age [60]. A mouse model of Wolman's disease and CESD was produced by targeted disruption of the gene encoding LAL [61]. Resembling the histological profile observed in Wolman's disease, homozygous

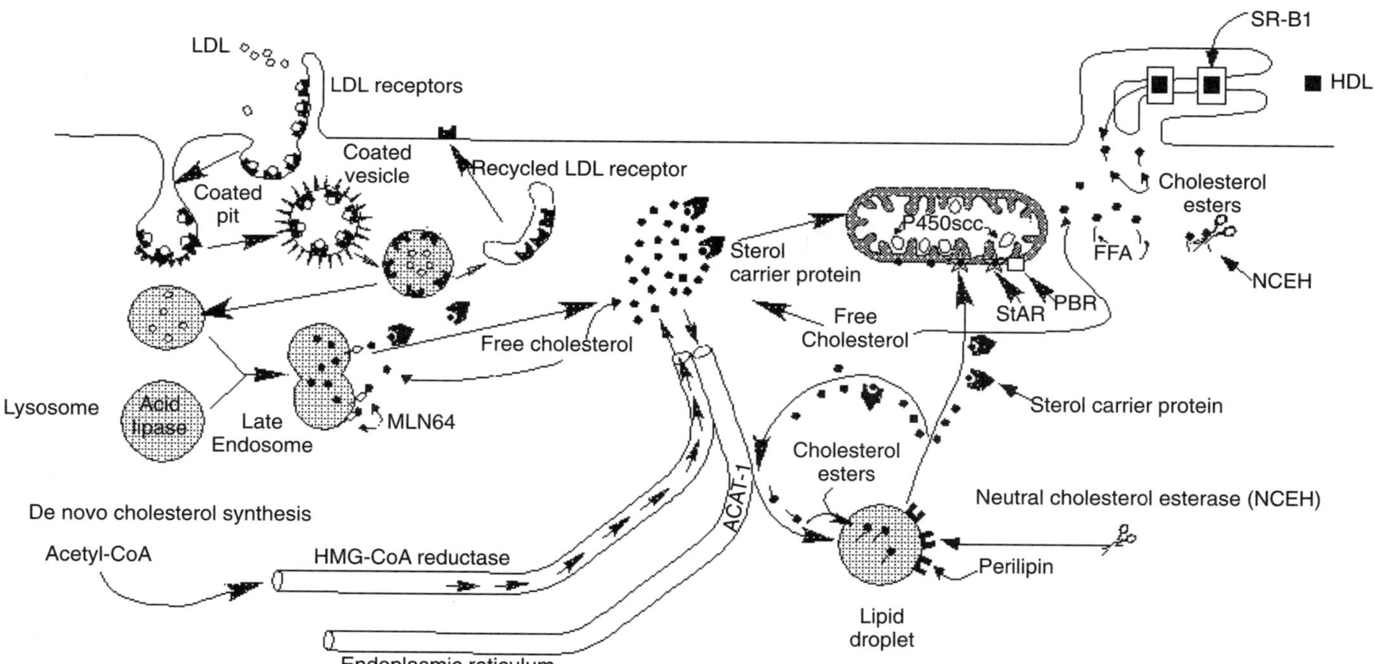

FIGURE 6.1 The acquisition, storage, and trafficking of cholesterol in steroidogenic cells. *FFA,* Free fatty acid; *HDL,* high-density lipoprotein; *HMG-CoA,* 3-hydroxy-3-methylglutaryl-coenzyme A; *LDL,* low-density lipoprotein; *P450scc,* cholesterol side chain cleavage enzyme; *PBR,* peripheral benzodiazepine receptor; *SR-BI,* scavenger receptor class B, type 1; *StAR,* steroidogenic acute regulatory protein.

null mutants demonstrated substantial accumulation of cholesteryl esters and triglycerides in various organs. However, similar to human CESD subjects, these knockout mice developed to reproductive age and were reproductively fertile [61]. The unaffected steroidogenesis and fertility in the mouse model can probably be attributed to the murine use of HDL-derived cholesterol, which bypasses the lysosomal pathway, as the major precursor for steroidogenesis. The above mouse model and CESD in humans highlight the importance of alternative pathways for cholesterol acquisition by cells to support steroidogenesis; these include de novo synthesis, HDL pathway, LDL pathway, and lysosomal and extralysosomal hydrolysis of cholesteryl esters.

Cholesteryl esters found in cytoplasmic lipid droplets are hydrolyzed by an extralysosomal enzyme, neutral cholesteryl ester hydrolase (NCEH), also called *hormone sensitive lipase* because its activity is tightly regulated within steroidogenic tissues by tropic hormones including follicle-stimulating hormone (FSH), luteinizing hormone (LH), and human chorionic gonadotropin (hCG) [62–64]. This enzyme is activated by cyclic adenosine monophosphate (cAMP)-dependent protein kinase phosphorylation of serine residues on the protein and has an optimal activity at neutral pH [11, 46]. Upon phosphorylation, NCEH is translocated from the cytoplasm to the surface of lipid droplets, where it exerts its catalytic function [65]. A line of gene-targeted mice with complete NCEH deficiency revealed marked accumulation of lipid droplets in the homozygous mutants' zona glomerulosa and zona fasciculata [66]. Basal levels of corticosterone in NCEH-deficient mice were not different from those in normal mice. However, after ACTH stimulation, mutant mice demonstrated significantly lower corticosterone levels than normal controls. Aldosterone levels were also similar in the two groups. This observation of normal basal corticosterone and aldosterone levels in NCEH-deficient mice indicates that cholesterol can be acquired for steroid production via a pathway independent of NCEH [66].

Perilipins, a group of related proteins, were shown to be associated with cholesteryl ester droplets in two steroidogenic cell lines: Y-1 adrenal cortical cells and MA-10 Leydig cells [67, 68]. They are localized to the periphery of lipid droplets of steroidogenic cells and adipocytes [68]. Cholesteryl ester hydrolysis is activated by protein kinase A, which also polyphosphorylates perilipins in response to lipolytic stimuli, suggesting a role for these proteins in lipid metabolism [67]. A single gene *Plin* gives rise to three perilipin protein isoforms by alternative mRNA splicing, named perilipin A, B, and C [69]. Targeted disruption of *Plin* resulted in healthy mice that have constitutively activated adipocyte NCEH [70]. Homozygous mutant mice showed elevated basal lipolysis and were resistant to diet-induced obesity, suggesting a role for perilipins in regulating lipolysis and basal NCEH activity [70].

INTRACELLULAR CHOLESTEROL TRANSPORT

To initiate steroidogenesis, cholesterol must leave the cholesterol pool and traverse the aqueous environment of the cell interior to reach the inner mitochondrial membrane, where the side chain cleavage enzyme complex is located. The precise routes via which unesterified cholesterol reaches the inner mitochondrial membrane are not yet completely defined. Possible mechanisms include diffusion within membranes, aqueous diffusion, vesicular transport, and carrier-mediated transfer. Owing to its hydrophobicity, cholesterol does not move freely within the cell interior by aqueous diffusion. Although cholesterol is poorly soluble in water, it can spontaneously desorb from one isolated organelle membrane and redistribute to another [71]. However, a number of observations indicated that neither diffusion nor spontaneous desorption can be the major mode of sterol transport among cellular organelles: (1) spontaneous intracellular sterol trafficking was vectorial; (2) the initial rate of sterol transfer between membranes was not necessarily proportional to the rate of sterol desorption from the donor membrane and was in fact more dependent on the type of acceptor than donor membrane; (3) sterol transfer between membranes did not obligatorily take place down the cholesterol concentration gradient [71]. Therefore, additional means must exist to actively guide intracellular cholesterol trafficking. Several key players in this directional transport of cholesterol have been identified; here we summarize the current understanding of some of these mechanisms.

Cytoskeleton

Three types of cytoskeletal filaments are important in the spatial organization of cellular structures. Microfilaments, also called *actin filaments,* and microtubules are polymers of the proteins actin and tubulin, respectively. Intermediate filaments consist of a heterogeneous group of intermediate filament proteins including vimentin. Mitochondria, lipid droplets, and ER in adrenocortical cells were shown by electron microscopy to be in direct contact with intermediate filaments (see [72] and references therein). Intermediate filaments were also demonstrated to spread radially from the nucleus, penetrate the actomyosin ring underneath the plasma membrane, form a mixed network with actin and myosin, and extend as far as the plasma membrane. Acrylamide, a known disruptor of intermediate filaments, stimulated steroid production in adrenal cells, suggesting that the collapse of intermediated filaments could bring lipid droplets, with its rich content of cholesteryl esters, and mitochondria closer together and thus enhance steroidogenesis [73]. Alternatively, intermediate filaments may serve as a network within which cholesterol and/or cholesterol-binding proteins can be transported from the ER, plasma membrane, or other cellular organelles to the outer mitochondrial membrane. Indeed, a role for vimentin in cholesterol transport was confirmed by studies in a human adrenal cell line deficient in vimentin [74]. The defect in transport of LDL-derived cholesterol from lysosomes to the site of esterification was corrected by expression of mouse vimentin in these cells. However, the exact role of intermediate filaments and the cytoskeleton in intracellular trafficking of cholesterol is still unclear.

Niemann-Pick Disease Type C

Niemann-Pick disease type C (NPC) provides a clue that cholesterol is transported by a protein from lysosomes to regulatory sites. Inherited in an autosomal recessive manner, NPC is a neurovisceral disorder characterized by an error in intracellular trafficking of LDL-derived cholesterol that is associated with accumulation of unesterified cholesterol in the lysosomes and Golgi complex [75]. Although endocytosed LDL is degraded normally in lysosomes by NPC cells, the subsequent induction of all cholesterol-mediated homeostatic responses is retarded, including delayed down-regulation of de novo cholesterol synthesis and LDL receptor levels, as well as repressed cholesterol esterification [76]. However, the transport of endogenously synthesized cholesterol and HDL-derived cholesterol is not affected in NPC cells [77, 78], whereas plasma membrane-derived 6-dansyl cholesterol, a fluorescent cholesterol analog, was recently shown to accumulate in enlarged lipid droplets in human NPC fibroblasts [79].

At least two separate gene loci are responsible for the NPC disease. The *NPC1* gene is mutated in the majority of documented cases (approximately 95%) [80]. NPC2 patients have clinical signs similar to NPC1 patients and their fibroblasts show an identical biochemical phenotype and pattern of disrupted intracellular cholesterol transport [81, 82], indicating that the sterol transport pathway or pathways may involve multiple proteins acting in tandem or in sequence.

The amino acid sequence of the NPC1 protein predicts a sterol-sensing domain, an ER signal peptide, a leucine zipper (suggesting a role in protein-protein interaction), transmembrane domains, and an endosome/lysosome targeting motif [83]. The NPC1 protein is synthesized in the ER and passes through the trans-Golgi network before entering the late endosomal compartment [84]. In human granulosa-lutein cells, NPC1 was localized to a subset of lysosomes and NPC1-containing vesicles were distributed in the cytoplasm in a random pattern distinctly different from those of free cholesterol and cytoplasmic neutral lipid droplets [84]. The NPC1 protein spans the surface membrane of the late endosomal compartment, and cellular uptake of LDL promotes the enrichment of NPC1 in late endosomes [85–87]. The mechanism by which NPC1 effects cholesterol unloading is not entirely clear. Its sequence similarity with the putative sterol-sensing domains of sterol regulatory element binding protein (SREBP), cleavage-activating protein (SCAP), and HMG-CoA reductase indicates that NPC1 may function in the targeting of cholesterol-containing vesicles [83, 88, 89]. Findings based on site-directed mutagenesis and protein trafficking analysis confirmed that the sterol-sensing domain of NPC1 was critical for cholesterol transfer [85–87]. As suggested by its homology with PATCHED, a membrane receptor that mediates the Hedgehog signal transduction pathway, NPC1 may act as a receptor for protein(s) involved in cholesterol transport [88]. Alternatively, based on its structural homology to prokaryotic resistance-nodulation-division (RND) proteins, NPC1 may function as a permease that promotes material transfer across the endosomal/lysosomal limiting membrane [90].

The role of another protein, the major secretory protein of human epididymis (HE1), in cholesterol unloading from lysosomes was confirmed when the HE1 gene was found to be mutated in the rare NPC2 disease; it is therefore the *NPC2* gene. NPC2 encodes a soluble cholesterol-binding protein, localized to lysosomes by subcellular fractionation [91, 92]. Treatment of NPC2 fibroblasts with exogenous recombinant NPC2 protein diminished the lysosomal accumulation of LDL-derived cholesterol [92]. The similar clinical and biochemical phenotypes of the two NPC subtypes suggest that the two proteins may interact or function sequentially within a common pathway.

Sterol Carrier Protein 2

Multiple lines of evidence suggest that sterol carrier protein 2 (SCP2), also called *nonspecific lipid transfer protein* because of its ability to facilitate the transfer of other lipids, plays a role in steroidogenesis. The *SCP2* gene, which has two transcriptional start sites, encodes a 58-kDa SCPx protein and a 15-kDa pro-SCP2 protein. A 20–amino acid N-terminal sequence in the 15-kDa pro-SCP2 is cleaved posttranslationally to yield the "mature" 13-kDa SCP2, whereas the 58-kDa SCPx represents a fusion protein between a thiolase domain and C-terminal SCP2 and is cleaved partially and posttranslationally to the 13-kDa SCP2 [93, 94]. Besides cholesterol, SCP2 transfers a variety of lipids including oxysterols, sitosterols, ergosterols, and major phospholipids and glycolipids [95]. The N-terminal sequence contains features similar to those of known mitochondrial targeting sequences in that it appears to form an alpha helix and consists mainly of basic and hydrophobic residues [93]. Another feature of the SCP2 amino acid sequence is the presence of a C-terminal peroxisome targeting tripeptide Ala-Lys-Leu [96, 97]. Peroxisomes are abundant in steroidogenic cells and known to participate in cholesterol synthesis and β-oxidation of fatty acids. Indeed, SCP2 has been localized to peroxisomes, ER, and mitochondria [98, 99].

Multiple studies have demonstrated a role for SCP2 in steroidogenesis. Firstly, purified SCP2 from rat liver stimulated pregnenolone synthesis from endogenous cholesterol by isolated adrenal mitochondria; such effects were neutralized by an anti-SCP2 antibody [100]. Secondly, coexpression of SCP2 with CYP11A and adrenodoxin in COS-7 cells enhanced synthesis of pregnenolone and progesterone when compared with expression of the steroidogenic enzyme system alone [97]. Thirdly, in the rat ovary, SCP2 mRNA levels were shown to be highest in the most steroidogenically active compartments and increased in response to gonadotropin or cAMP analogue stimulation [101]. The following possible mechanisms by which SCP2 stimulates steroidogenesis were summarized by Schroeder and colleagues [149]:

1. By binding to specific intracellular vesicles such as peroxisomes, SCP2 may mediate the trafficking of these vesicles within the cell.
2. SCP2 may enhance and/or target cholesterol transfer between membranes by interacting with cholesterol in either the donor or acceptor membrane or both.
3. SCP2 has been shown to bind several intermediate molecules of cholesterol synthesis (e.g., lanosterol). SCP2 may thus facilitate the transfer of these molecules into and out of peroxisomes, expediting the course of cholesterol synthesis.

However, SCP2 was shown not to be obligatory to steroidogenesis by the SCP2 knockout mouse model [95, 102]. Homozygous mutant mice reached fertility at the normal age and interbred to give rise to viable offspring; levels of testosterone, progesterone, and glucocorticoids were not different between mutant and control mice, although triglycerides were slightly higher and free fatty acid concentrations were moderately lower in SCP2-deficient mice. Nevertheless, SCP2 knockout mice demonstrated markedly increased hepatic peroxisome proliferation and induction of peroxisomal and mitochondrial enzymes for straight-chain fatty acid β-oxidation [95].

Steroidogenic Acute Regulatory Protein

To initiate steroid synthesis, cholesterol must traverse the aqueous space between the cholesterol-rich outer mitochondrial membrane and the cholesterol-poor inner membrane to reach CYP11A. Studies in the early 1960s established that the acute increase in adrenal steroid production in response to tropic hormone stimulation had an absolute requirement for the synthesis of new proteins [103, 104]. Further studies in the ensuing decades demonstrated no effect by the inhibition of protein synthesis on the delivery of cellular cholesterol to the outer mitochondrial membrane, but cholesterol transport from the outer to the inner mitochondrial membranes was completely inhibited by cycloheximide (for reviews, see [105]). This led to the notion that the acute regulation of steroidogenesis is characterized by its dependency on a hormone-stimulated, rapidly synthesized, cycloheximide-sensitive, and highly labile protein whose function is to mediate the transfer of cholesterol from the outer mitochondrial membrane to the inner mitochondrial membrane [105]. After years of intense research, purification of a 30 kDa protein from MA-10 cells and amino acid sequence analysis allowed cloning of cDNA and identification of a novel protein in mice and humans [106], designated as *steroidogenic acute regulatory protein (StAR)*.

As predicted from the importance of cholesterol transport to the inner mitochondrial membrane in steroidogenesis, mutations of the StAR gene have severe consequences. Congenital lipoid adrenal hyperplasia (lipoid CAH), a rare form of congenital adrenal hyperplasia (CAH) except in Japan and Korea where it accounts for 5% or more of all CAH cases [107], is the most severe form of CAH and is characterized by marked reduction in biosynthesis of all adrenal and gonadal steroid hormones. Known to be inherited in an autosomal recessive pattern, lipoid CAH was initially thought to be caused by mutations in the CYP11A gene. However, mitochondria isolated from adrenal tissues affected by lipoid CAH were able to convert 20α-hydroxycholesterol into pregnenolone, whereas cholesterol was not efficiently metabolized into pregnenolone, indicating the presence of a functional CYP11A enzyme [108]. Subsequent studies showed that the CYP11A gene was normal in patients with lipoid CAH and that CYP11A protein was present in their testicular homogenates [109–111]. Molecular analyses of more than 60 unrelated patients with lipoid CAH confirmed the presence of mutations in the StAR gene in the majority of cases [107, 112–116], which included frame shifts caused by deletions or insertions, splicing errors, and nonsense and missense mutations. All such mutations resulted in the absence of StAR protein or the production of functionally inactive proteins.

Steroidogenic cells of the enlarged adrenal cortices in these patients are engorged with lipid droplets containing cholesteryl esters, giving rise to the inherited condition's name. Profound adrenocortical insufficiency occurs shortly after birth, leading to salt wasting, hyponatremia, hyperkalemia, hypovolemia, and acidosis [113]. Increased production of pro-opiomelanocortin results in hyperpigmentation, whereas deficient testicular androgen production leads to the typical phenotype of male pseudohermaphroditism [117]. The metabolic defect in lipoid CAH appears to be progressive. Adrenal and gonadal steroidogenesis becomes increasingly affected with time after birth. A model explaining the pathophysiology of lipoid CAH has been proposed by Bose et al. [113]. This model indicates that some StAR-independent steroidogenesis exists before the severe cellular damage resulting from cholesterol accumulation that culminates in a nonfunctional steroidogenic cell. Comparison of the clinical course of 46,XX female patients with that of 46,XY ones supported the pathophysiological mechanism implicated by the model [112, 118]. 46,XX females underwent spontaneous puberty and secondary sexual development, whereas 46,XY patients had insufficient testicular androgen production in utero for masculinization of their external genitalia and were unable to undergo spontaneous puberty. The sparing of some ovarian function despite mutations inactivating the StAR protein suggests the presence of sufficient StAR-independent steroidogenic activity in ovarian follicles to support estradiol synthesis. Because the ovary is essentially quiescent during fetal life and follicles only produce steroids when they are recruited to mature, most follicles at birth are spared from the adverse effects of cholesterol accumulation, leaving a source of viable cells capable of steroidogenesis at the time of puberty.

Targeted disruption of the StAR gene in mice has confirmed an important role for the protein in steroidogenesis [119]. Regardless of genotype, all knockout mice had female external genitalia, as seen in the human condition of lipoid CAH. Growth in these animals was impaired and death occurred within a short period, presumably because of adrenocortical insufficiency, which was confirmed by low levels of serum corticosterone and aldosterone. Immunohistochemistry demonstrated lipid deposits in the adrenal cortex of the StAR knockout mice. Even though the male StAR knockout mice were all phenotypically sex reversed, their testes appeared normal on gross inspection. However, specific staining again indicated the presence of elevated levels of lipids in the testes. In contrast, the ovaries of knockout mice were essentially indistinguishable from those of wild type animals, a situation similar to that observed in human subjects with mutations in the StAR gene.

Although StAR is demonstrated to be crucial to steroidogenesis by both the mouse knockout model and natural mutations of the gene in human subjects, the precise mechanism by which StAR facilitates the transfer of cholesterol to the inner mitochondrial membrane is currently unclear. An initial model put forward by Stocco and Clark [120] proposed that as the 37 kDa precursor protein is imported into the mitochondrial compartment, contact sites between the inner and outer membranes are formed. With the formation of contact sites, the water barrier to cholesterol translocation is thus removed, allowing cholesterol to flow down a chemical gradient to reach CYP11A. After processing of StAR, the membranes separate again and further cholesterol transport is prevented without additional synthesis of StAR precursor proteins (for reviews, see [105]). Unexpectedly, mutant proteins with deletion of up to 62 residues from the N-terminus (N-62), which contain the mitochondrial targeting sequence, did not significantly affect steroidogenesis-enhancing activity, whereas removal of the 28 C-terminal amino acids (C-28) inactivated the StAR protein [121], indicating that mitochondrial targeting is not absolutely indispensable for StAR protein activity. The cytoplasmic distribution of the N-62 mutant StAR protein contrasted remarkably with the almost exclusive intramitochondrial distribution of the wild-type StAR. Electron microscopy and import assays verified that the N-62 mutant protein was not imported into mitochondria [121, 122]. These data indicate that StAR entry into mitochondria is not essential for steroidogenesis stimulation because removal of the mitochondrial import N-terminal sequence does not affect StAR's function. All in all, from the above studies it can be concluded that the N-terminal mitochondrial targeting sequence determines the subcellular specificity of StAR protein's action, whereas the C-terminal region confers steroidogenesis-enhancing activity.

More recently, a cholesterol desorption model of StAR action (figure 6.2) proposed that StAR, targeted to mitochondria by its N-terminal mitochondrial targeting sequence, ejects cholesterol from the sterol-rich outer mitochondrial membrane, causing it to move to the sterol-poor inner mitochondrial membrane, probably via proteineous bridges between the mitochondrial membranes [123, 124] (Figure 6.2). The 37 kDa StAR is then imported into the mitochondria and processed by a metalloendopeptidase to yield the mature 30 kDa protein. Importation of StAR removes the protein from its site of action, thereby terminating StAR-activated cholesterol translocation to the inner mitochondrial membrane, which is in keeping with the rapid action and functional life of StAR and the requirement for continuous StAR synthesis to sustain steroidogenesis. Studies examining the role of StAR as a sterol transfer protein have lent support to this model [125, 126]. The recombinant N-62 StAR protein stimulated the transfer of cholesterol and β-sitosterol from liposomes to heat-treated mitochondria isolated from various animal sources, to mitochondria that were trypsin treated, and to microsomes, demonstrating that StAR has sterol transfer activity. A possible mechanism is the enhancement of cholesterol desorption from sterol-rich donor membranes to acceptor organelles [125]. Indeed, the N-62 mutant StAR protein was shown to facilitate cholesterol transfer from synthetic donor vesicles to acceptor vesicles containing the side chain cleavage enzyme system without inducing fusion between vesicles; these data also demonstrate the sterol-transferring ability of N-62 in the absence of mitochondria [126]. To determine the site of StAR's action, Bose et al. [127] fused StAR mutants with the mitochondrial proteins Tom (translocase, outer mitochondrial membrane) or Tim (translocase, inner mitochondrial membrane). Expression of N-62 StAR fused with the carboxy terminus of Tom in COS-1 cells affixed StAR to the cytoplasmic side of the outer mitochondrial membrane and resulted in more cholesterol conversion to pregnenolone than expression in the same cells of the full-length StAR, N-62 StAR, or protein constructs affixing StAR to the matrix side of the inner mitochondrial membrane or intermembranous space of the mitochondrion [127]. These researchers contended that StAR's activity is determined by its mitochondrial location rather than by its size.

An alternative model of StAR action emerged from the crystal structure modeling of a domain of the MLN64 protein homologous to StAR, designated as the StAR-related lipid-transfer (START) domain [128]. The START domain of StAR (StAR-START) is prone to aggregation at high protein concentration and therefore unsuitable for crystallization studies; in comparison, the START domain of MLN64 (MLN64-START) is relatively soluble and does not aggregate under conditions required for crystallization. The crystal structure of MLN64-START was determined to form a predominantly hydrophobic tunnel just large enough to accommodate one molecule of cholesterol. The tunnel contained a buried charged pair of residues Asp 332 and Arg 351, potentially capable of interacting with the 3-hydroxyl group of cholesterol [128]. Because of the high sequence homology between the START domains of StAR and MLN64, Tsujishita and Hurley [128] inferred that their overall structures are highly similar to each other and that StAR binds one cholesterol molecule at a time and shuttles it across the intermembranous space of the mitochondrion (figure 6.2). This model is supported by the observation of saturable binding of cholesterol by StAR-START and MLN64-START at a stoichiometry of 0.9:1 and 0.8:1, respectively [128]. The predicted three-dimensional structure of the START domain is, however, inconsistent with physico-chemical studies on recombinant StAR protein suggesting that it is a molten globule and has a dynamic protein structure at pH 3.5 to 4.0, a pH that may be generated at the vicinity of the mitochondria [129]. Moreover, the shuttle model cannot explain how low concentrations of StAR usually found in steroidogenic cells can transfer substantial amounts of cholesterol between membranes [125]. More recently, Mathieu et al. [130] revealed by homology modeling the structures of the human and hamster StAR proteins to be similar to the crystalline structure of human MLN64-START, except that the cholesterol binding site of StAR was an oval cavity instead of tunnel-shaped. Similar to MLN64, the StAR molecule was also found to contain two charged amino acid residues (Glu 169 and Arg 188, human StAR numbering) forming a salt bridge situated at the bottom of the cavity. Expression of mutant hamster StAR protein harboring mutation of either of the two charged amino acids to a hydrophobic residue led to significantly reduced production of pregnenolone in COS-1 cells, suggesting an important role for the salt bridge in promoting a correct orientation of the cholesterol molecule within the binding cavity and/or maintaining proper folding of the StAR molecule itself [130].

Two phosphorylation models of StAR action have also been proposed to explain the posttranslational regulation of StAR activity by phosphorylation (summarized in [123]). Cyclic AMP-mediated phosphorylation of serine 195 in the START domain may reduce the inhibitory effects of the N-terminal targeting sequence, allowing more efficient interaction between the protein and the outer mitochondrial membrane. Alternatively, this phosphorylation step might alleviate the inhibitory action of the N-terminal targeting sequence on the START domain's sterol transport activity. At the time of writing, no single model of StAR action can fully explain all the experimental findings. The exact mechanism of StAR-facilitated transfer of cholesterol across the intermembranous space of the mitochondrion remains to be investigated.

MLN64

StAR mRNA transcripts are not detected in the human placenta, a steroidogenic organ secreting large amounts of steroid hormones during pregnancy [106]. This StAR-independent steroidogenesis in placental tissues raised the possibility that another protein may have similar functions as StAR. MLN64, first identified as a gene highly expressed in certain breast carcinoma cells [131], was also found in many other human tissues including the placenta, brain, and theca and granulosa cells [132]. The human MLN64 is a 445–amino acid protein that contains two distinct domains. The N-terminal domain consists of four transmembrane regions and the C-terminal domain from 218 to 445 is 37% identical to StAR [133]. Other StAR homologues in addition to MLN64 have also been identified by protein sequence comparison algorithms, including various animal and plant proteins. This led to the notion that these proteins all contain a similar lipid-binding START domain [134].

Functionally, wild-type MLN64 increased pregnenolone secretion in COS-1 cells cotransfected with plasmids expressing the human cholesterol side-chain cleavage enzyme system by more than twofold when compared with controls [132]. The steroidogenic activity of MLN64 was revealed to reside in the C-terminus of the protein, because mutant proteins from which the C-terminal START domain was deleted had no steroidogenic activity [132], whereas recombinant MLN64 START domain stimulated progestin synthesis by isolated human placental mitochondria [135]. The crystal structure of the MLN64 START domain shows that it contains a hydrophobic barrel capable of accommodating a cholesterol molecule [128]. Of note, removal of N-terminal sequences increased MLN64's steroidogenesis-enhancing activity in transfected COS-1 cells [132], possibly because the full-length MLN64 is bound to membranes by its transmembrane domains and cannot diffuse freely through an aqueous environment.

The study of GFP-tagged MLN64 in living CHO cells showed that MLN64 is synthesized in the ER and travels first to the plasma membrane before being targeted to late

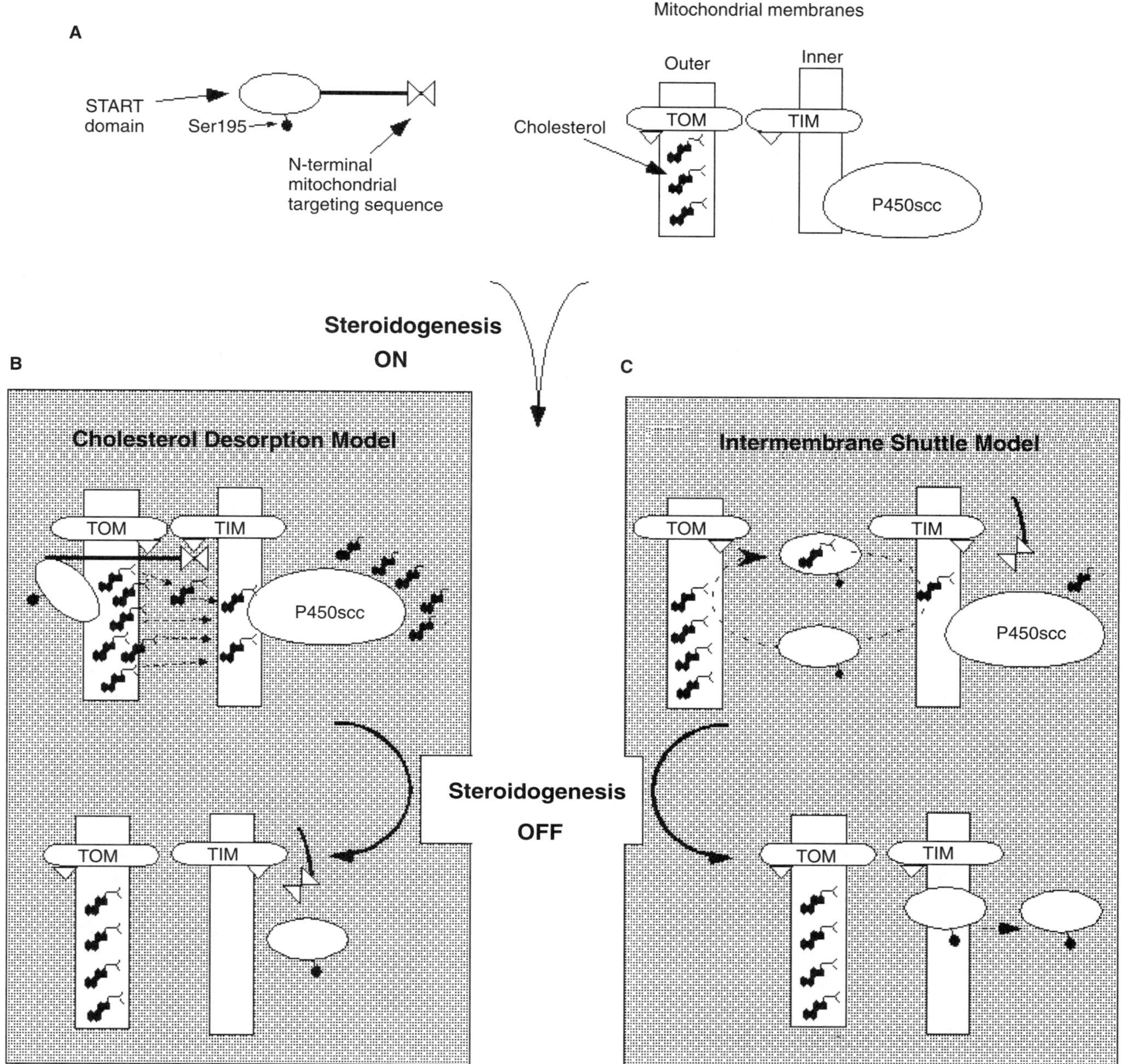

FIGURE 6.2 Two models of StAR action. **A**, The N-terminal mitochondrial targeting sequence of StAR targets the 37 kDa protein to one or more of the mitochondrial transporter molecules, Tom (translocase, outer mitochondrial membrane) and Tim (translocase, inner mitochondrial membrane). StAR facilitates the transfer of cholesterol from the cholesterol-rich outer mitochondrial membrane to the inner mitochondrial membrane, where cholesterol side chain cleavage enzyme (P450scc) resides. **B**, The StAR-related lipid-transfer (START) domain stimulates desorption of cholesterol from the outer mitochondrial membrane. Importation of StAR removes the protein from its site of action and StAR is processed to the mature 30 kDa form during or after importation. **C**, StAR is imported into the intermembranous space, where its N-terminus is cleaved, leaving the START domain to oscillate between the outer and inner membranes and cholesterol one molecule at a time.

endosomes [135]. Expression of a truncated form of MLN64 containing the N-terminal transmembrane domains but not the START domain (MLN64-ΔSTART) led to the accumulation of free cholesterol in lysosomes, a phenotype reminiscent of the cholesterol trafficking defects in NPC1 and NPC2 cells. The MLN64-ΔSTART followed a biosynthetic trafficking pathway similar to that of wild-type MLN64, first to the plasma membrane and then to the cholesterol-laden lysosomes, indicating that MLN64-ΔSTART contained the essential signals for plasma membrane localization and lysosomal targeting. In contrast, mutant MLN64 protein lacking the N-terminal domain was present only in a cytoplasmic and nuclear pattern, further substantiating the role of the N-terminal domain in intracellular localization of MLN64 [135]. The topology of MLN64 in late endosomal membranes predicts that the START domain projects into the cytoplasm and the N-terminal leader sequence in the vesicle core, suggesting that it is positioned to effect cholesterol transfer to opposing membranes [89, 136]. The colocalization of MLN64 in the same late endosomal compartment as NPC1 raises the possibility that MLN64 functions in concert with NPC1 [89, 135]. In CHO and COS-7 cells, the dominant negative action of the mutant MLN64-ΔSTART caused extensive cholesterol accumulation associated with inhibition of late endosomal tubular trafficking, similar to the NPC phenotype that is caused by the loss of function of NPC1 or NPC2 [135]. Whether MLN64, NPC1, and NPC2 serve the same function in cholesterol and/or vesicular transport awaits further investigation.

Peripheral Benzodiazepine Receptor

Originally discovered as another class of binding sites for benzodiazepines distinct from the central gamma aminobutyric acid $(GABA)_A$/benzodiazepine neurotransmitter receptors, peripheral benzodiazepine receptor (PBR) was primarily localized to the outer mitochondrial membrane of steroidogenic cells [137]. PBR ligands were shown to stimulate, in a dose-dependent manner, pregnenolone production by isolated mitochondria when supplied with exogenous cholesterol; this effect was not observed with mitochondria devoid of their outer membranes [138]. Similarly, agonists of PBR stimulated progesterone production in primary cultures of differentiated granulosa cells and transformed granulosa cell lines [139]. A role for PBR in steroidogenesis was further confirmed by targeted disruption of the PBR gene in the R2C rat Leydig cell line [140]. Compared with control R2C cells, PBR-negative R2C cells exhibited minimal progesterone production, whereas addition of the water-soluble 22R-hydroxycholesterol or transfection with PBR cDNA rescued progesterone production in these cells [140]. Diazepam binding inhibitor (DBI), an endogenous PBR ligand, was also found to be highly expressed in steroidogenic cells [137].

Abundantly expressed in steroidogenic cells, the 18kDa human PBR protein consists of 169 amino acids, with high-sequence homology across species [137]. Three-dimensional molecular modeling of the known amino acid sequence of PBR predicted five membrane-spanning domains, with the N-terminus within the mitochondrial intermembranous space and the C-terminus in the cytoplasm [141]. PBR was isolated as a complex with the 34 kDa voltage-dependent anion channel (VDAC) and the inner mitochondrial membrane adenine nucleotide carrier, suggesting that it is part of a multimeric protein complex [142]. More recently, PBR was shown to bind cholesterol with high affinity [143, 144], whereas a theoretical three-dimensional model suggested that the five transmembrane domains of PBR form a five-helix bundle, through which a cholesterol molecule can cross from one side of the membrane to another [145].

Based on their findings that despite high levels of StAR, reduction of PBR levels decreased steroid production in vitro and in vivo, Papadopoulos et al. [146] proposed that the site of action of StAR is at a step before or at PBR. To address the question whether StAR and PBR interact with each other, West et al. [147] fused fluorescent proteins to StAR and PBR and determined the fluorescent energy transfer between the 37kDa StAR and PBR expressed in COS-7 cells to be fivefold above background levels. Assuming that energy transfer occurs to a measurable extent only when donor and acceptor molecules are separated by less than 100 angstroms, they concluded that such high values of energy transfer were indicative of a close association between the two molecules in mitochondrial membranes and that these molecules might interact with each other in facilitating cholesterol transport.

Expression of PBR in bacteria, which do not have PBR or cholesterol, resulted in uptake of radiolabeled cholesterol; subsequent treatment of cholesterol-loaded bacterial membranes with a PBR ligand released cholesterol from the membranes [148]. These observations suggest that cholesterol captured by PBR is released on ligand binding of the receptor. Studies using mutant PBR proteins demonstrated that the C-terminus of PBR, which lies on the cytoplasmic side of the membrane, is essential for cholesterol uptake [148]. It was proposed that cholesterol coming from the cytoplasm, probably bound to a protein such as SCP2 or StAR, may bind to the C-terminus of PBR, followed by entry into its transmembrane channel, whose open/release state is controlled by PBR ligand binding [137].

CONCLUSION

Much has been learned from inherited human diseases, mouse models, and in vitro studies about cholesterol acquisition by and transport in steroidogenic cells. The genes of many candidate proteins in intracellular cholesterol dynamics have now been cloned. Yet many pieces in the puzzle remain to be discovered. Although it appears that the acute regulator of steroid biosynthesis, StAR, has been identified after decades of intense research in this field, the precise mechanism by which cholesterol is transported to the inner mitochondrial membrane still remains uncertain. With the molecular identification of NPC1, NPC2, and MLN64, the complicated picture of cholesterol trafficking is only beginning to unravel. Outstanding questions include the elucidation of the proteins and mechanisms by which cholesterol is transported to mitochondria from the plasma membrane and other intracellular organelles.

References

1. Tuckey, R. C., and Stevenson, P. M. (1984). Properties of ferredoxin reductase and ferredoxin from the bovine corpus luteum. *Int. J. Biochem.* 16, 489–495.
2. Tuckey, R. C., and Atkinson, H. C. (1989). Pregnenolone synthesis from cholesterol and hydroxycholesterols by mitochondria from ovaries following the stimulation of immature rats with pregnant mare's serum gonadotropin and human choriogonadotropin. *Eur. J. Biochem.* 186, 255–259.
3. Tuckey, R. C. (1992). Cholesterol side-chain cleavage by mitochondria from the human placenta. Studies using hydroxycholesterols as substrates. *J. Steroid. Biochem. Mol. Biol.* 42, 883–890.
4. Schroeder, F., and Nemecz, G. (1990). Transmembrane cholesterol distribution. In *Advances in Cholesterol Research*, eds. M. Esfahnani, and J. B. Swaney, 47–87. Caldwell, N.J.: Telford Press.
5. Liscum, L., and Underwood, K. W. (1995). Intracellular cholesterol transport and compartmentation. *J. Biol. Chem.* 270, 15443–15446.
6. Schroeder, F., Frolov, A. A., Murphy, E. J., Atshaves, B. P., Jefferson, J. R., Pu, L., Wood, W. G., Foxworth, W. B., and Kier, A. B. (1996). Recent advances in membrane cholesterol domain dynamics and intracellular cholesterol trafficking. *Proc. Soc. Exp. Biol. Med.* 213, 150–177.
7. Paavola, L. G., Strauss, III, J. F., Boyd, C. O., and Nestler, J. E. (1985). Uptake of gold- and [3H]cholesteryl linoleate-labeled human low-density lipoprotein by cultured rat granulosa cells: Cellular mechanisms involved in lipoprotein metabolism and their importance to steroidogenesis. *J. Cell. Biol.* 100, 1235–1247.
8. Fielding, C. J., and Fielding, P. E. (1997). Intracellular cholesterol transport. *J. Lipid Res.* 38, 1503–1521.
9. Malassine, A., Besse, C., Roche, A., Alsat, E., Rebourcet, R., Mondon, F., and Cedard, L. (1987). Ultrastructural visualization of the internalization of low-density lipoprotein by human placental cells. *Histochemistry* 87, 457–464.
10. Acton, S., Rigotti, A., Landschulz, K. T., Xu, S., Hobbs, H. H., and Krieger, M. (1996). Identification of scavenger receptor SR-BI as a high-density lipoprotein receptor. *Science* 271, 518–520.
11. Nestler, J., Takagi, K., and Strauss III, Jerome F. (1990). Lipoprotein and cholesterol metabolism in cells that synthesize steroid hormones. In *Advances in Cholesterol Research*, eds. Esfahani, M., and Swaney, J. B., 133–169. Caldwell, N.J.: Telford Press.
12. Reinhart, M. P., Billheimer, J. T., Faust, J. R., and Gaylor, J. L. (1987). Subcellular localization of the enzymes of cholesterol biosynthesis and metabolism in rat liver. *J. Biol. Chem.* 262, 9649–9655.
13. Hall, P. F. (1986). Cytochromes P-450 and the regulation of steroid synthesis. *Steroids* 48, 131–196.
14. Nussdorfer, G. G. (1986). Cytophysiology of the adrenal cortex. *Int. Rev. Cytol.* 98, 1–405.
15. Belloni, A. S., Mazzocchi, G., Mantero, F., and Nussdorfer, G. G. (1987). The human adrenal cortex: Ultrastructure and baseline morphometric data. *J. Submicrosc. Cytol.* 19, 657–668.
16. Golos, T. G., and Strauss, III, J. F. (1988). 8-bromoadenosine cyclic 3′,5′-phosphate rapidly increases 3-hydroxy-3-methylglutaryl coenzyme A reductase mRNA in human granulosa cells: Role of cellular sterol balance in controlling the response to tropic stimulation. *Biochemistry* 27, 3503–3506.
17. Tavani, D. M., Tanaka, T., Strauss, III, J. F., and Billheimer, J. T. (1982). Regulation of acyl coenzyme Acholesterol acyltransferase in the luteinized rat ovary: Observations with an improved enzymatic assay. *Endocrinology* 111, 794–800.
18. Enders, A. C. (1973). Cytology of the corpus luteum. *Biol. Reprod.* 8, 158–182.
19. Faust, J. R. Cholesterol synthesis. (1988). In *Biology of Cholesterol*, ed. P. Yeagle, 19–38. Boca Raton, Fla.: CRC Press.
20. Opitz, J. M. (1994). RSH/SLO ("Smith-Lemli-Opitz") syndrome: Historical, genetic, and developmental considerations. *Am. J. Med. Genet.* 50, 344–346.
21. Tint, G. S., Irons, M., Elias, E. R., Batta, A. K., Frieden, R., Chen, T. S., and Salen, G. (1994). Defective cholesterol biosynthesis associated with the Smith-Lemli-Opitz syndrome. *N. Engl. J. Med.* 330, 107–113.
22. Waterham, H. R., Wijburg, F. A., Hennekam, R. C., Vreken, P., Poll-The, B. T., Dorland, L., Duran, M., Jira, P. E., Smeitink, J. A., Wevers, R. A., and Wanders, R. J. (1998). Smith-Lemli-Opitz syndrome is caused by mutations in the 7-dehydrocholesterol reductase gene. *Am. J. Hum. Genet.* 63, 329–338.
23. Jay, R. H., Sturley, R. H., Stirling, C., McGarrigle, H. H., Katz, M., Reckless, J. P., and Betteridge, D. J. (1991). Effects of pravastatin and cholestyramine on gonadal and adrenal steroid production in familial hypercholesterolaemia. *Br. J. Clin. Pharmacol.* 32, 417–422.
24. Laue, L., Hoeg, J. M., Barnes, K., Loriaux, D. L., and Chrousos, G. P. (1987). The effect of mevinolin on steroidogenesis in patients with defects in the low-density lipoprotein receptor pathway. *J. Clin. Endocrinol. Metab.* 64, 531–535.
25. Carr, B. R., and Simpson, E. R. (1981). Lipoprotein utilization and cholesterol synthesis by the human fetal adrenal gland. *Endocr. Rev.* 2, 306–326.
26. Tureck, R. W., and Strauss, III, J. F. (1982). Progesterone synthesis by luteinized human granulosa cells in culture: The role of de novo sterol synthesis and lipoprotein-carried sterol. *J. Clin. Endocrinol. Metab.* 54, 367–373.
27. Bradley, W. A., and Gianturco, S. H. (1988). Lipoprotein receptors in cholesterol metabolism. In *Biology of Cholesterol*, ed. P. Yeagle, 95–120. Boca Raton, Fla.: CRC Press.
28. Mims, M. P., and Morrisett, J. D. (1988). Lipolysis of phospholipids in model cholesteryl ester rich lipoproteins and related systems: Effect of core and surface lipid phase state. *Biochemistry* 27, 5290–5295.
29. Goldstein, J. L., Hobbs, H. H., and Brown, M. S. (2000). Familial hypercholesterolemia. In *The Metabolic and Molecular Basis of Inherited Diseases*, 8th ed., eds. C. R. S. W. Scriver, B. Childs, A. L. Beaudet, D. Valle, K. W. Kinzler, and B. Vogelstein, 2863–2914. New York: McGraw-Hill.

30. Fielding, P. E., and Fielding, C. J. (1996). Intracellular transport of low-density lipoprotein derived free cholesterol begins at clathrin-coated pits and terminates at cell surface caveolae. *Biochemistry* 35, 14932–14938.
31. Fielding, C. J., and Fielding, P. E. (1995). Role of an N-ethylmaleimide-sensitive factor in the selective cellular uptake of low-density lipoprotein free cholesterol. *Biochemistry* 34, 14237–14244.
32. Azhar, S., Luo, Y., Medicherla, S., and Reaven, E. (1999). Upregulation of selective cholesteryl ester uptake pathway in mice with deletion of low-density lipoprotein receptor function. *J. Cell. Physiol.* 180, 190–202.
33. Illingworth, D. R., Kenny, T. A., and Orwoll, E. S. (1982). Adrenal function in heterozygous and homozygous hypobetalipoproteinemia. *J. Clin. Endocrinol. Metab.* 54, 27–33.
34. Illingworth, D. R., Corbin, D. K., Kemp, E. D., and Keenan, E. J. (1982). Hormone changes during the menstrual cycle in abetalipoproteinemia: Reduced luteal phase progesterone in a patient with homozygous hypobetalipoproteinemia. *Proc. Natl. Acad. Sci. USA* 79, 6685–6689.
35. Parker, Jr., C. R., Illingworth, D. R., Bissonnette, J., and Carr, B. R. (1986). Endocrine changes during pregnancy in a patient with homozygous familial hypobetalipoproteinemia. *N. Engl. J. Med.* 314, 557–560.
36. Stangl, H., Hyatt, M., and Hobbs, H. H. (1999). Transport of lipids from high- and low-density lipoproteins via scavenger receptor-BI. *J. Biol. Chem.* 274, 32692–32698.
37. Landschulz, K. T., Pathak, R. K., Rigotti, A., Krieger, M., and Hobbs, H. H. (1996). Regulation of scavenger receptor, class B, type I, a high-density lipoprotein receptor, in liver and steroidogenic tissues of the rat. *J. Clin. Invest.* 98, 984–995.
38. Reaven, E., Nomoto, A., Leers-Sucheta, S., Temel, R., Williams, D. L., and Azhar, S. (1998). Expression and microvillar localization of scavenger receptor, class B, type I (a high-density lipoprotein receptor) in luteinized and hormone-desensitized rat ovarian models. *Endocrinology* 139, 2847–2856.
39. Reaven, E., Zhan, L., Nomoto, A., Leers-Sucheta, S., and Azhar, S. (2000). Expression and microvillar localization of scavenger receptor class B, type I (SR-BI) and selective cholesteryl ester uptake in Leydig cells from rat testis. *J. Lipid Res.* 41, 343–356.
40. Azhar, S., Nomoto, A., and Reaven, E. (2002). Hormonal regulation of adrenal microvillar channel formation. *J. Lipid Res.* 43, 861–871.
41. Murao, K., Terpstra, V., Green, S. R., Kondratenko, N., Steinberg, D., and Quehenberger, O. (1997). Characterization of CLA-1, a human homologue of rodent scavenger receptor BI, as a receptor for high-density lipoprotein and apoptotic thymocytes. *J. Biol. Chem.* 272, 17551–17557.
42. Cao, G., Garcia, C. K., Wyne, K. L., Schultz, R. A., Parker, K. L., and Hobbs, H. H. (1997). Structure and localization of the human gene encoding SR-BI/CLA-1. Evidence for transcriptional control by steroidogenic factor 1. *J. Biol. Chem.* 272, 33068–33076.
43. de La Llera-Moya, M., Connelly, M. A., Drazul, D., Klein, S. M., Favari, E., Yancey, P. G., Williams, D. L., and Rothblat, G. H. (2001). Scavenger receptor class B type I affects cholesterol homeostasis by magnifying cholesterol flux between cells and HDL. *J. Lipid Res.* 42, 1969–1978.
44. Oram, J. F. (2000). Tangier disease and ABCA1. *Biochim. Biophys. Acta.* 1529, 321–330.
45. Christiansen-Weber, T. A., Voland, J. R., Wu, Y., Ngo, K., Roland, B. L., Nguyen, S., Peterson, P. A., and Fung-Leung, W. P. (2000). Functional loss of ABCA1 in mice causes severe placental malformation, aberrant lipid distribution, and kidney glomerulonephritis as well as high-density lipoprotein cholesterol deficiency. *Am. J. Pathol.* 157, 1017–1029.
46. Pedersen, R. C. (1988). Cholesterol biosynthesis, storage, and mobilization in steroidogenic organs. In *Biology of Cholesterol*, ed. P. Yeagle, 36–69. Boca Raton, Fla.: CRC Press.
47. Sparrow, C. P., and Pittman, R. C. (1990). Cholesterol esters selectively taken up from high-density lipoproteins are hydrolyzed extralysosomally. *Biochim. Biophys. Acta.* 1043, 203–210.
48. Strauss, III, J. F., Seifter, E., Lien, E. L., Goodman, D. B., and Stambaugh, R. L. (1977). Lipid metabolism in regressing rat corpora lutea of pregnancy. *J. Lipid Res.* 18, 246–258.
49. Tuckey, R. C., and Stevenson, P. M. (1979). Free and esterified cholesterol concentration and cholesteryl ester composition in the ovaries of maturing and superovulated immature rats. *Biochim. Biophys. Acta.* 575, 46–56.
50. Chang, C. C., Huh, H. Y., Cadigan, K. M., and Chang, T. Y. (1993). Molecular cloning and functional expression of human acyl-coenzyme A:cholesterol acyltransferase cDNA in mutant Chinese hamster ovary cells. *J. Biol. Chem.* 268, 20747–20755.
51. Uelmen, P. J., Oka, K., Sullivan, M., Chang, C. C., Chang, T. Y., and Chan, L. (1995). Tissue-specific expression and cholesterol regulation of acylcoenzyme A:cholesterol acyltransferase (ACAT) in mice. Molecular cloning of mouse ACAT cDNA, chromosomal localization, and regulation of ACAT in vivo and in vitro. *J. Biol. Chem.* 270, 26192–26201.
52. Goodman, D. S., Deykin, D., and Shiratoe, T. (1964). The formation of cholesterol esters with rat liver enzymes. *J. Biol. Chem.* 239, 1335–1345.
53. Chang, C. C., Chen, J., Thomas, M. A., Cheng, D., Del Priore, V. A., Newton, R. S., Pape, M. E., and Chang, T. Y. (1995). Regulation and immunolocalization of acyl-coenzyme A:cholesterol acyltransferase in mammalian cells as studied with specific antibodies. *J. Biol. Chem.* 270, 29532–29540.
54. Chang, T. Y., Chang, C. C., and Cheng, D. (1997). Acyl-coenzyme A:cholesterol acyltransferase. *Annu. Rev. Biochem.* 66, 613–638.
55. Oelkers, P., Behari, A., Cromley, D., Billheimer, J. T., and Sturley, S. L. (1998). Characterization of two human genes encoding acyl coenzyme A:cholesterol acyltransferase-related enzymes. *J. Biol. Chem.* 273, 26765–26771.
56. Cases, S., Novak, S., Zheng, Y. W., Myers, H. M., Lear, S. R., Sande, E., Welch, C. B., Lusis, A. J., Spencer, T. A., Krause, B. R., Erickson, S. K., and Farese, Jr., R. V. (1998). ACAT-2, a second mammalian acyl-Co A:cholesterol acyltransferase. Its cloning, expression, and characterization. *J. Biol. Chem.* 273, 26755–26764.
57. Farese, R. V., Cases, S., and Novak, S. (1998). Intracellular sterol esterification: Two acyl-Co A:cholesterol acyltransferases in mammals. In *Intracellular Cholesterol Trafficking*, ed. T. Y. Chang and D. A. Freeman, 29–42. Boston: Kluwer Academic.

58. Lohse, P., Maas, S., Sewell, A. C., van Diggelen, O. P., and Seidel, D. (1999). Molecular defects underlying Wolman disease appear to be more heterogeneous than those resulting in cholesteryl ester storage disease. *J. Lipid Res.* 40, 221–228.
59. Pagani, F., Pariyarath, R., Garcia, R., Stuani, C., Burlina, A. B., Ruotolo, G., Rabusin, M., and Baralle, F. E. (1998). New lysosomal acid lipase gene mutants explain the phenotype of Wolman disease and cholesteryl ester storage disease. *J. Lipid Res.* 39, 1382–1388.
60. Assman, G., and Seedorf, U. (2000). Acid lipase deficiency: Wolman disease and cholesteryl ester storage disease. In *The Metabolic and Molecular Basis of Inherited Diseases*, 8th ed., eds. C. R. S. W. Scriver, B. Childs, A. L. Beaudet, D. Valle, K. W. Kinzler, and B. Vogelstein, 3551–3572. New York: McGraw-Hill.
61. Du, H., Duanmu, M., Witte, D., and Grabowski, G. A. (1998). Targeted disruption of the mouse lysosomal acid lipase gene: Long-term survival with massive cholesteryl ester and triglyceride storage. *Hum. Mol. Genet.* 7, 1347–1354.
62. Aten, R. F., Kolodecik, T. R., Macdonald, G. J., and Behrman, H. R. (1995). Modulation of cholesteryl ester hydrolase messenger ribonucleic acid levels, protein levels, and activity in the rat corpus luteum. *Biol. Reprod.* 53, 1110–1117.
63. Kraemer, F. B., Patel, S., Saedi, M. S., and Sztalryd, C. (1993). Detection of hormone-sensitive lipase in various tissues. I. Expression of an HSL/bacterial fusion protein and generation of anti-HSL antibodies. *J. Lipid Res.* 34, 663–671.
64. Trzeciak, W. H., Sonnenborn, U., Balkow, C., and Kunau, W. H. (1984). Regulation of steroidogenesis in rat adrenal gland: Identification of the bifunctional, hormone-sensitive cholesterol esterase—triacylglycerol lipase enzyme protein and its discrimination from hormone-insensitive lipases. *Mol. Cell. Endocrinol.* 35, 131–141.
65. Holm, C., Osterlund, T., Laurell, H., and Contreras, J. A. (2000). Molecular mechanisms regulating hormone-sensitive lipase and lipolysis. *Annu. Rev. Nutr.* 20, 365–393.
66. Li, H., Brochu, M., Wang, S. P., Rochdi, L., Cote, M., Mitchell, G., and Gallo-Payet, N. (2002). Hormone-sensitive lipase deficiency in mice causes lipid storage in the adrenal cortex and impaired corticosterone response to corticotropin stimulation. *Endocrinology* 143, 3333–3340.
67. Servetnick, D. A., Brasaemle, D. L., Gruia-Gray, J., Kimmel, A. R., Wolff, J., and Londos, C. (1995). Perilipins are associated with cholesteryl ester droplets in steroidogenic adrenal cortical and Leydig cells. *J. Biol. Chem.* 270, 16970–16973.
68. Londos, C., Brasaemle, D. L., Gruia-Gray, J., Servetnick, D. A., Schultz, C. J., Levin, D. M., and Kimmel, A. R. (1995). Perilipin: Unique proteins associated with intracellular neutral lipid droplets in adipocytes and steroidogenic cells. *Biochem. Soc. Trans.* 23, 611–615.
69. Zweytick, D., Athenstaedt, K., and Daum, G. (2000). Intracellular lipid particles of eukaryotic cells. *Biochim. Biophys. Acta.* 1469, 101–120.
70. Martinez-Botas, J., Anderson, J. B., Tessier, D., Lapillonne, A., Chang, B. H., Quast, M. J., Gorenstein, D., Chen, K. H., and Chan, L. (2000). Absence of perilipin results in leanness and reverses obesity in Lepr(db/db) mice. *Nat. Genet.* 26, 474–479.
71. Nagy, L., and Freeman, D. A. (1990). Effect of cholesterol transport inhibitors on steroidogenesis and plasma membrane cholesterol transport in cultured MA-10 Leydig tumor cells. *Endocrinology* 126, 2267–2276.
72. Hall, P. F., and Almahbobi G. (1997). Roles of microfilaments and intermediate filaments in adrenal steroidogenesis. *Microsc. Res. Tech.* 36, 463–479.
73. Shiver, T. M., Sackett, D. L., Knipling, L., and Wolff, J. (1992). Intermediate filaments and steroidogenesis in adrenal Y-1 cells: Acrylamide stimulation of steroid production. *Endocrinology* 131, 201–207.
74. Sarria, A. J., Panini, S. R., and Evans, R. M. (1992). A functional role for vimentin intermediate filaments in the metabolism of lipoprotein-derived cholesterol in human SW-13 cells. *J. Biol. Chem.* 267, 19455–19463.
75. Patterson, M. C., Vanier, M. T., Suzuki, K., Morris, J. A., Carstea, E., Neufeld, E. B., Blanchette-Mackie, J. E., and Pentchev, P. (2000). Niemann-Pick disease type C: A lipid trafficking disorder. In *The Metabolic and Molecular Basis of Inherited Diseases*, 8th ed., eds. C. R. S. W. Scriver, B. Childs, A. L. Beaudet, D. Valle, K. W. Kinzler, and B. Vogelstein, 3611–3634. New York: McGraw-Hill.
76. Pentchev, P. G., Brady, R. O., Blanchette-Mackie, E. J., Vanier, M. T., Carstea, E. D., Parker, C. C., Goldin, E., and Roff, C. F. (1994). The Niemann-Pick C lesion and its relationship to the intracellular distribution and utilization of LDL cholesterol. *Biochim. Biophys. Acta.* 1225, 235–243.
77. Liscum, L., Ruggiero, R. M., and Faust, J. R. (1989). The intracellular transport of low-density lipoprotein-derived cholesterol is defective in Niemann-Pick type C fibroblasts. *J. Cell. Biol.* 108, 1625–1636.
78. Shamburek, R. D., Pentchev, P. G., Zech, L. A., Blanchette-Mackie, J., Carstea, E. D., VandenBroek, J. M., Cooper, P. S., Neufeld, E. B., Phair, R. D., Brewer, Jr., H. B., Brady, R. O., and Schwartz, C. C. (1997). Intracellular trafficking of the free cholesterol derived from LDL cholesteryl ester is defective in vivo in Niemann-Pick C disease: Insights on normal metabolism of HDL and LDL gained from the NP-C mutation. *J. Lipid Res.* 38, 2422–2435.
79. Wiegand, V., Chang, T. Y., Strauss, I. J., Fahrenholz, F., and Gimpl. G. (2003). Transport of plasma membrane-derived cholesterol in dependence on the function of Niemann-Pick C1 protein. *FASEB* **17**: 782–4.
80. Morris, J. A., Zhang, D., Coleman, K. G., Nagle, J., Pentchev. P. G., and Carstea, E. D. (1999). The genomic organization and polymorphism analysis of the human Niemann-Pick C1 gene. *Biochem. Biophys. Res. Commun.* 261, 493–498.
81. Steinberg, S. J., Ward, C. P., and Fensom, A. H. (1994). Complementation studies in Niemann-Pick disease type C indicate the existence of a second group. *J. Med Genet.* 31, 317–320.
82. Vanier, M. T., Duthel, S., Rodriguez-Lafrasse, C., Pentchev, P., and Carstea, E. D. (1996). Genetic heterogeneity in Niemann-Pick C disease: A study using somatic cell hybridization and linkage analysis. *Am. J. Hum. Genet.* 58, 118–125.
83. Liscum, L., and Munn, N. J. (1999). Intracellular cholesterol transport. *Biochim. Biophys. Acta.* 1438, 19–37.
84. Watari, H., Blanchette-Mackie, E. J., Dwyer, N. K., Sun, G., Glick, J. M., Patel, S., Neufeld, E. B., Pentchev, P. G., and

Strauss, III, J. F. (2000). NPC1-containing compartment of human granulosa-lutein cells: A role in the intracellular trafficking of cholesterol supporting steroidogenesis. *Exp. Cell. Res.* 255, 56–66.

85. Watari, H., Blanchette-Mackie, E. J., Dwyer, N. K., Watari, M., Neufeld, E. B., Patel, S., Pentchev, P. G., and Strauss, III, J. F. (1999). Mutations in the leucine zipper motif and sterol-sensing domain inactivate the Niemann-Pick C1 glycoprotein. *J. Biol. Chem.* 274, 21861–21866.
86. Zhang, M., Dwyer, N. K., Love, D. C., Cooney, A., Comly, M., Neufeld, E., Pentchev, P. G., Blanchette-Mackie, E. J., and Hanover, J. A. (2001). Cessation of rapid late endosomal tubulovesicular trafficking in Niemann-Pick type C1 disease. *Proc. Natl. Acad. Sci. USA* 98, 4466–4471.
87. Zhang, M., Dwyer, N. K., Neufeld, E. B., Love, D. C., Cooney, A., Comly, M., Patel, S., Watari, H., Strauss, III, J. F., Pentchev, P. G., Hanover, J. A., and Blanchette-Mackie, E. J. (2001). Sterol-modulated glycolipid sorting occurs in Niemann-Pick C1 late endosomes. *J. Biol. Chem.* 276, 3417–3425.
88. Carstea, E. D., Morris, J. A., Coleman, K. G., Loftus, S. K., Zhang, D., Cummings, C., Gu, J., Rosenfeld, M. A., Pavan, W. J., Krizman, D. B., Nagle, J., Polymeropoulos, M. H., Sturley, S. L., Ioannou, Y. A., Higgins, M. E., Comly, M., Cooney, A., Brown, A., Kaneski, C. R., Blanchette-Mackie, E. J., Dwyer, N. K., Neufeld, E. B., Chang, T. Y., Liscum, L., Tagle, D. A., et al. (1997). Niemann-Pick C1 disease gene: Homology to mediators of cholesterol homeostasis. *Science* 277, 228–231.
89. Strauss, J. F., Liu, P., Christenson, L. K., and Watari, H. (2002). Sterols and intracellular vesicular trafficking: Lessons from the study of NPC1. *Steroids.* 67, 947–951.
90. Davies, J. P., and Ioannou, Y. A. (2000). Topological analysis of Niemann-Pick C1 protein reveals that the membrane orientation of the putative sterol-sensing domain is identical to those of 3-hydroxy-3-methylglutaryl-CoA reductase and sterol regulatory element binding protein cleavage-activating protein. *J. Biol. Chem.* 275, 24367–24374.
91. Okamura, N., Kiuchi, S., Tamba, M., Kashima, T., Hiramoto, S., Baba, T., Dacheux, F., Dacheux, J. L., Sugita, Y., and Jin, Y. Z. (1999). A porcine homolog of the major secretory protein of human epididymis, HE1, specifically binds cholesterol. *Biochim. Biophys. Acta.* 1438, 377–387.
92. Naureckiene, S., Sleat, D. E., Lackland, H., Fensom, A., Vanier, M. T., Wattiaux, R., Jadot, M., and Lobel, P. (2000). Identification of HE1 as the second gene of Niemann-Pick C1 disease. *Science* 290, 2298–2301.
93. Pfeifer, S. M., Furth, E. E., Ohba, T., Chang, Y. J., Rennert, H., Sakuragi, N., Billheimer, J. T., and Strauss, III, J. F. (1993). Sterol carrier protein 2: A role in steroid hormone synthesis? *J. Steroid. Biochem. Mol. Biol.* 47, 167–172.
94. Chanderbhan, R. F., Karroubi, A., Pastuszyn, A., Gallo, L. L., and Sacllen, T. (1998). Direct evidence for sterol carrier protein-2 participation in ACTH stimulated steroidogenesis in isolated adrenal cells. In *Intracellular Cholesterol Trafficking*, ed. T. Y. Chang and D. A. Freeman, 197–212. Boston: Kluwer Academic.
95. Seedorf, U. (1998). Functional analysis of sterol carrier protein-2 (SCP2) in the SCP2 knockout mouse. In *Intracellular Cholesterol Trafficking*, ed. T. Y. Chang and D. A. Freeman, 235–249. Boston: Kluwer Academic.
96. Billheimer, J. T., Strehl, L. L., Davis, G. L., Strauss, III, J. F., and Davis, L. G. (1990). Characterization of a cDNA encoding rat sterol carrier protein 2. *DNA Cell. Biol.* 9, 159–165.
97. Yamamoto, R., Kallen, C. B., Babalola, G. O., Rennert, H., Billheimer, J. T., and Strauss, III, J. F. (1991). Cloning and expression of a cDNA encoding human sterol carrier protein 2. *Proc. Natl. Acad. Sci. USA* 88, 463–467.
98. Mendis-Handagama, S. M., Watkins, P. A., Gelber, S. J., and Scallen, T. J. (1992). Leydig cell peroxisomes and sterol carrier protein-2 in luteinizing hormone-deprived rats. *Endocrinology* 131, 2839–2845.
99. Starodub, O., Jolly, C. A., Atshaves, B. P., Roths, J. B., Murphy, E. J., Kier, A. B., and Schroeder, F. (2000). Sterol carrier protein-2 localization in endoplasmic reticulum and role in phospholipid formation. *Am. J. Physiol. Cell. Physiol.* 279, C1259–1269.
100. Chanderbhan, R., Tanaka, T., Strauss, J. F., Irwin, D., Noland, B. J., Scallen, T. J., and Vahouny, G. V. (1983). Evidence for sterol carrier protein 2-like activity in hepatic, adrenal, and ovarian cytosol. *Biochem. Biophys. Res. Commun.* 117, 702–709.
101. Rennert, H., Amsterdam, A., Billheimer, J. T., and Strauss, III, J. F. (1991). Regulated expression of sterol carrier protein 2 in the ovary: A key role for cyclic AMP. *Biochemistry* 30, 11280–11285.
102. Seedorf, U., Raabe, M., Ellinghaus, P., Kannenberg, F., Fobker, M., Engel, T., Denis, S., Wouters, F., Wirtz, K. W., Wanders, R. J., Maeda, N., and Assmann, G. (1998). Defective peroxisomal catabolism of branched fatty acyl coenzyme A in mice lacking the sterol carrier protein-2/sterol carrier protein-x gene function. *Genes Dev.* 12, 1189–1201.
103. Ferguson, J. J. (1962). Puromycin and adrenal responsiveness to adrencorticotropic hormone. *Biochim. Biophys. Acta.* 57, 616–617.
104. Ferguson, J. J. (1963). Protein synthesis and adrenocorticotropin responsiveness. *J. Biol. Chem.* 238, 2754–2759.
105. Stocco, D. M., and Strauss, I. J. (1998). Intramitochondrial cholesterol transfer in steroidogenic cells. In *Intracellular Cholesterol Trafficking*, ed. T. Y. Chang and D. A. Freeman, 169–182. Boston: Kluwer Academic.
106. Sugawara, T., Holt, J. A., Driscoll, D., Strauss, III, J. F., Lin, D., Miller, W. L., Patterson, D., Clancy, K. P., Hart, I. M., Clark, B. J., et al. (1995). Human steroidogenic acute regulatory protein: Functional activity in COS-1 cells, tissue-specific expression, and mapping of the structural gene to 8p11.2 and a pseudogene to chromosome 13. *Proc. Natl. Acad. Sci. USA* 92, 4778–4782.
107. Nakae, J., Tajima, T., Sugawara, T., Arakane, F., Hanaki, K., Hotsubo, T., Igarashi, N., Igarashi, Y., Ishii, T., Koda, N., Kondo, T., Kohno, H., Nakagawa, Y., Tachibana, K., Takeshima, Y., Tsubouchi, K., Strauss, III, J. F., and Fujieda, K. (1997). Analysis of the steroidogenic acute regulatory protein (StAR) gene in Japanese patients with congenital lipoid adrenal hyperplasia. *Hum. Mol. Genet.* 6, 571–576.
108. Degenhart, H. J., Visser, H. K., Boon, H., and O'Doherty, N. J. (1972). Evidence for deficient 20a-cholesterol-hydroxylase activity in adrenal tissue of a patient with lipoid adrenal hyperplasia. *Acta. Endocrinol. (Copenh.)* 71, 512–518.
109. Lin, D., Gitelman, S. E., Saenger, P., and Miller, W. L. (1991). Normal genes for the cholesterol side chain cleavage

enzyme, P450scc, in congenital lipoid adrenal hyperplasia. *J. Clin. Invest.* 88, 1955–1962.

110. Saenger, P., Lin, D., Gitelman, S. E., and Miller, W. L. (1993). Congenital lipoid adrenal hyperplasia—genes for P450scc, side chain cleavage enzyme, are normal. *J. Steroid. Biochem. Mol. Biol.* 45, 87–97.
111. Sakai, Y., Yanase, T., Okabe, Y., Hara, T., Waterman, M. R., Takayanagi, R., Haji, M., and Nawata, H. (1994). No mutation in cytochrome P450 side chain cleavage in a patient with congenital lipoid adrenal hyperplasia. *J. Clin. Endocrinol. Metab.* 79, 1198–1201.
112. Fujieda, K., Tajima, T., Nakae, J., Sageshima, S., Tachibana, K., Suwa, S., Sugawara, T., and Strauss, III, J. F. (1997). Spontaneous puberty in 46,XX subjects with congenital lipoid adrenal hyperplasia. Ovarian steroidogenesis is spared to some extent despite inactivating mutations in the steroidogenic acute regulatory protein (StAR) gene. *J. Clin. Invest.* 99, 1265–1271.
113. Bose, H. S., Sugawara, T., Strauss, III, J. F., and Miller, W. L. (1996). The pathophysiology and genetics of congenital lipoid adrenal hyperplasia. International Congenital Lipoid Adrenal Hyperplasia Consortium. *N. Engl. J. Med.* 335, 1870–1878.
114. Lin, D., Sugawara, T., Strauss, III, J. F., Clark, B. J., Stocco, D. M., Saenger, P., Rogol, A., and Miller, W. L. (1995). Role of steroidogenic acute regulatory protein in adrenal and gonadal steroidogenesis. *Science* 267, 1828–1831.
115. Okuyama, E., Nishi, N., Onishi, S., Itoh, S., Ishii, Y., Miyanaka, H., Fujita, K., and Ichikawa, Y. (1997). A novel splicing junction mutation in the gene for the steroidogenic acute regulatory protein causes congenital lipoid adrenal hyperplasia. *J. Clin. Endocrinol. Metab.* 82, 2337–2342.
116. Tee, M. K., Lin, D., Sugawara, T., Holt, J. A., Guiguen, Y., Buckingham, B., Strauss, III, J. F., and Miller, W. L. (1995). T→A transversion 11 bp from a splice acceptor site in the human gene for steroidogenic acute regulatory protein causes congenital lipoid adrenal hyperplasia. *Hum. Mol. Genet.* 4, 2299–2305.
117. Miller, W. L., and Strauss, III, J. F. (1999). Molecular pathology and mechanism of action of the steroidogenic acute regulatory protein, StAR. *J. Steroid. Biochem. Mol. Biol.* 69, 131–141.
118. Bose, H. S., Pescovitz, O. H., and Miller, W. L. (1997). Spontaneous feminization in a 46,XX female patient with congenital lipoid adrenal hyperplasia due to a homozygous frameshift mutation in the steroidogenic acute regulatory protein. *J. Clin. Endocrinol. Metab.* 82, 1511–1515.
119. Caron, K. M., Soo, S. C., Wetsel, W. C., Stocco, D. M., Clark, B. J., and Parker, K. L. (1997). Targeted disruption of the mouse gene encoding steroidogenic acute regulatory protein provides insights into congenital lipoid adrenal hyperplasia. *Proc. Natl. Acad. Sci. USA* 94, 11540–11545.
120. Stocco, D. M., and Clark, B. J. (1996). Regulation of the acute production of steroids in steroidogenic cells. *Endocr. Rev.* 17, 221–244.
121. Arakane, F., Sugawara, T., Nishino, H., Liu, Z., Holt, J. A., Pain, D., Stocco, D. M., Miller, W. L., and Strauss, III, J. F. (1996). Steroidogenic acute regulatory protein (StAR) retains activity in the absence of its mitochondrial import sequence: Implications for the mechanism of StAR action. *Proc. Natl. Acad. Sci. USA* 93, 13731–13736.
122. Arakane, F., Kallen, C. B., Watari, H., Foster, J. A., Sepuri, N. B., Pain, D., Stayrook, S. E., Lewis, M., Gerton, G. L., and Strauss, III, J. F. (1998). The mechanism of action of steroidogenic acute regulatory protein (StAR). StAR acts on the outside of mitochondria to stimulate steroidogenesis. *J. Biol. Chem.* 273, 16339–16345.
123. Christenson, L. K., and Strauss, III, J. F. (2000). Steroidogenic acute regulatory protein (StAR) and the intramitochondrial translocation of cholesterol. *Biochim. Biophys. Acta.* 1529, 175–187.
124. Christenson, L. K., and Strauss, III, J. F. (2002). Cholesterol metabolism in steroidogenic tissues. In *Genetics of Steroid Biosynthesis and Function*, ed., J. I. Mason pp. 115–144. London: Taylor & Francis.
125. Kallen, C. B., Billheimer, J. T., Summers, S. A., Stayrook, S. E., Lewis, M., and Strauss, III, J. F. (1998). Steroidogenic acute regulatory protein (StAR) is a sterol transfer protein. *J. Biol. Chem.* 273, 26285–26288.
126. Tuckey, R. C., Headlam, M. J., Bose, H. S., and Miller, W. L. (2002). Transfer of cholesterol between phospholipid vesicles mediated by the steroidogenic acute regulatory protein (StAR). *J. Biol. Chem.* 277, 47123–47128.
127. Bose, H., Lingappa, V. R., and Miller, W. L. (2002). Rapid regulation of steroidogenesis by mitochondrial protein import. *Nature.* 417, 87–91.
128. Tsujishita, Y., and Hurley, J. H. (2000). Structure and lipid transport mechanism of a StAR-related domain. *Nat. Struct. Biol.* 7, 408–414.
129. Bose, H. S., Whittal, R. M., Baldwin, M. A., and Miller, W. L. (1999). The active form of the steroidogenic acute regulatory protein, StAR, appears to be a molten globule. *Proc. Natl. Acad. Sci. USA* 96, 7250–7255.
130. Mathieu, A. P., Lavigne, P., and LeHoux, J. G. (2002). Molecular modeling and structure-based thermodynamic analysis of the StAR protein. *Endocr. Res.* 28, 419–423.
131. Moog-Lutz, C., Tomasetto, C., Regnier, C. H., Wendling, C., Lutz, Y., Muller, D., Chenard, M. P., Basset, P., and Rio, M. C. (1997). MLN64 exhibits homology with the steroidogenic acute regulatory protein (StAR) and is over-expressed in human breast carcinomas. *Int. J. Cancer* 71, 183–191.
132. Watari, H., Arakane, F., Moog-Lutz, C., Kallen, C. B., Tomasetto, C., Gerton, G. L., Rio, M. C., Baker, M. E., and Strauss, III, J. F. (1997). MLN64 contains a domain with homology to the steroidogenic acute regulatory protein (StAR) that stimulates steroidogenesis. *Proc. Natl. Acad. Sci. USA* 94, 8462–8467.
133. Bose, H. S., Baldwin, M. A., and Miller, W. L. (2000). Evidence that StAR and MLN64 act on the outer mitochondrial membrane as molten globules. *Endocr. Res.* 26, 629–637.
134. Ponting, C. P., and Aravind, L. (1999). START: A lipid-binding domain in StAR, HD-ZIP, and signalling proteins. *Trends Biochem. Sci.* 24, 130–132.
135. Zhang, M., Liu, P., Dwyer, N. K., Christenson, L. K., Fujimoto, T., Martinez, F., Comly, M., Hanover, J. A., Blanchette-Mackie, E. J., and Strauss, III, J. F. (2002). MLN64 mediates mobilization of lysosomal cholesterol to steroidogenic mitochondria. *J. Biol. Chem.* 277, 33300–33310.

136. Alpy, F., Stoeckel, M. E., Dierich, A., Escola, J. M., Wendling, C., Chenard, M. P., Vanier, M. T., Gruenberg, J., Tomasetto, C., and Rio, M. C. (2001). The steroidogenic acute regulatory protein homolog MLN64, a late endosomal cholesterol-binding protein. *J. Biol. Chem.* 276, 4261–4269.
137. Culty, M., Li, H., Boujrad, N., Amri, H., Vidic, B., Bernassau, J. M., Reversat, J. L., and Papadopoulos, V. (1999). In vitro studies on the role of the peripheral-type benzodiazepine receptor in steroidogenesis. *J. Steroid. Biochem. Mol. Biol.* 69, 123–130.
138. Papadopoulos, V., Mukhin, A. G., Costa, E., and Krueger, K. E. (1990). The peripheral-type benzodiazepine receptor is functionally linked to Leydig cell steroidogenesis. *J. Biol. Chem.* 265, 3772–3779.
139. Amsterdam, A., and Suh, B. S. (1991). An inducible functional peripheral benzodiazepine receptor in mitochondria of steroidogenic granulosa cells. *Endocrinology* 129, 503–510.
140. Papadopoulos, V., Amri, H., Li, H., Boujrad, N., Vidic, B., and Garnier, M. (1997). Targeted disruption of the peripheral-type benzodiazepine receptor gene inhibits steroidogenesis in the R2C Leydig tumor cell line. *J. Biol. Chem.* 272, 32129–32135.
141. Joseph-Liauzun, E., Delmas, P., Shire, D., and Ferrara, P. (1998). Topological analysis of the peripheral benzodiazepine receptor in yeast mitochondrial membranes supports a five-transmembrane structure. *J. Biol. Chem.* 273, 2146–2152.
142. McEnery, M. W., Snowman, A. M., Trifiletti, R. R., and Snyder, S. H. (1992). Isolation of the mitochondrial benzodiazepine receptor: Association with the voltage-dependent anion channel and the adenine nucleotide carrier. *Proc. Natl. Acad. Sci. USA* 89, 3170–3174.
143. Li, H., Yao, Z., Degenhardt, B., Teper, G., and Papadopoulos, V. (2001). Cholesterol binding at the cholesterol recognition/interaction amino acid consensus (CRAC) of the peripheral-type benzodiazepine receptor and inhibition of steroidogenesis by an HIV TAT-CRAC peptide. *Proc. Natl. Acad. Sci. USA* 98, 1267–1272.
144. Lacapere, J. J., Delavoie, F., Li, H., Peranzi, G., Maccario, J., Papadopoulos, V., and Vidic, B. (2001). Structural and functional study of reconstituted peripheral benzodiazepine receptor. *Biochem. Biophys. Res. Commun.* 284, 536–541.
145. Bernassau, J. M., Reversat, J. L., Ferrara, P., Caput, D., and Lefur, G. (1993). A 3D model of the peripheral benzodiazepine receptor and its implication in intramitochondrial cholesterol transport. *J. Mol. Graph.* 11, 236–244, 235.
146. Papadopoulos, V., Amri, H., Boujrad, N., Cascio, C., Culty, M., Garnier, M., Hardwick, M., Li, H., Vidic, B., Brown, A. S., Reversa, J. L., Bernassau, J. M., and Drieu, K. (1997). Peripheral benzodiazepine receptor in cholesterol transport and steroidogenesis. *Steroids* 62, 21–28.
147. West, L. A., Horvat, R. D., Roess, D. A., Barisas, B. G., Juengel, J. L., and Niswender, G. D. (2001). Steroidogenic acute regulatory protein and peripheral-type benzodiazepine receptor associate at the mitochondrial membrane. *Endocrinology* 142, 502–505.
148. Li, H., and Papadopoulos, V. (1998). Peripheral-type benzodiazepine receptor function in cholesterol transport. Identification of a putative cholesterol recognition/interaction amino acid sequence and consensus pattern. *Endocrinology* 139, 4991–4997.
149. Schroeder, F., Frolov, A., Schoer, J. K., Gallegos, A. M., Atshaves, B. P., Stolowich, N. J., Scott, A. I., Kier, A. B. (1998). Intracellular Sterol binding proteins: Cholesterol transport and membrane domains. In: Intracellular Cholesterol Trafficking eds. T. Y. Chang and D. A. Freeman, 213–234. Boston: Kluwer Academic.

PART II

Oocyte Maturation and Ovulation

CHAPTER 7

Regulation of Mammalian Oocyte Maturation

JOHN J. EPPIG, MARIA M. VIVEIROS, CARRIE MARIN BIVENS, AND RABINDRANATH DE LA FUENTE

ABSTRACT

Oocyte maturation stands uniquely at the foundation and culmination of developmental and reproductive biology. The processes comprising maturation are essential for the transition from a gamete to an embryo which, upon fertilization is competent to give rise to a healthy new individual. This chapter describes three oocyte maturational processes: (1) nuclear maturation, (2) epigenetic maturation, and (3) cytoplasmic maturation. Nuclear maturation refers to the resumption of meiosis and its progression to metaphase II. Epigenetic maturation occurs during oocyte growth and refers to genomic modifications that regulate gene expression during oocyte development and postfertilization. Cytoplasmic maturation includes processes, exclusive of meiosis, that prepare the oocyte for fertilization and embryogenesis and occur throughout oocyte growth and concurrently with nuclear maturation.

INTRODUCTION

Oocyte maturation encompasses three developmental programs that are essential for the production of an egg competent to undergo fertilization and embryogenesis: (1) nuclear maturation, which includes the reinitiation and completion of the first meiotic division and the maintenance of a stable metaphase II arrest, (2) epigenetic maturation, which occurs during oocyte growth and results in genomic modifications regulating gene expression, and (3) cytoplasmic maturation, commonly defined as the processes occurring in the cytoplasm of developing oocytes that are essential for fertilization and early embryonic development.

NUCLEAR MATURATION

Meiosis is a unique cell division that occurs exclusively in gametes to reduce the number of chromosomes from a diploid (2N) to haploid number (N). In female mammals this process is initiated early in fetal development. Primordial germ cells (PGC), first discernible in the extraembryonic mesoderm of the mouse embryo at day 7.2 (E7.2) [1], migrate through the hindgut and dorsal mesentery to colonize the genital ridge. Throughout their migration, PGC undergo mitotic divisions; however, around E13 mitosis ceases and the entire population enters prophase of the first meiotic division (meiosis I) [2]. This change from mitotic proliferation into the first meiotic division defines the transition from oogonia to oocytes. Fetal oocytes progress through zygotene pachytene and early diplotene stages, but subsequently all arrest at the dictyate stage of prophase I. Completion of the first meiotic division occurs only after the oocyte and the ovarian follicle that encompasses it have undergone extensive growth.

In the perinatal ovary, following meiotic arrest, oocytes become surrounded by a single (squamous) layer of the precursors to the follicular somatic cells and form primordial follicles. Thus at birth the ovaries contain a female's full complement of gametes, all in the large population of nongrowing primordial follicles [3]. Only a small fraction of oocytes, however, will ultimately be ovulated and thus have a chance to be fertilized. The remainder of the oocytes will accompany follicular somatic cells into atretic degeneration. Follicles that escape atresia and are recruited from the primordial pool become primary follicles as the oocyte begins an extensive growth phase while the surrounding somatic cells (now called *granulosa cells*) become cuboidal and proliferative. Complex interactions between the oocyte and granulosa cells are essential for the development and function of both cell types. As follicles progress to the secondary stage, they are characterized by oocytes at midgrowth, surrounded by multiple layers of granulosa cells. Follicles then develop to the antral stage containing fully grown oocytes. The transition from preantral to antral stage is a significant juncture during which the oocyte acquires the capacity to resume meiosis [4].

Fully grown oocytes resume meiosis in response to the preovulatory surge of luteinizing hormone (LH). Oocytes arrested at prophase I are characterized by an intact nuclear membrane and the nucleus is called a *germinal vesicle (GV)*. The most obvious manifestation of the resumption of meiosis is the disappearance or breakdown of the GV (GVB), chromosome condensation, and the assembly of a bipolar metaphase I (MI) spindle (Figure 7.1). During the first meiotic division, homologous chromosomes segregate and one set is extruded into the first

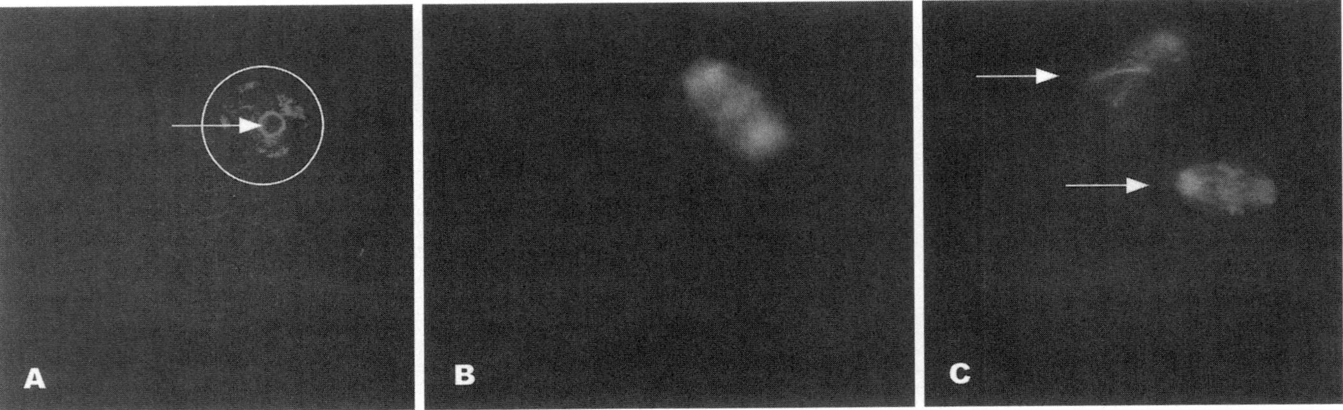

FIGURE 7.1 Nuclear maturation of mouse oocytes. Mouse oocytes were isolated from large antral follicles and allowed to undergo spontaneous maturation in culture. Deoxyribonucleic acid (DNA) is visualized by staining with propidium iodide (*red*) and anti-tabulin was used for the detection of the spindle microtubules (*green*). **A**, Germinal vesicle (GV) stage oocyte. Contents of GV are circled in white. Note that the nucleolus (*arrow*) is surrounded by densely packed chromatin. **B**, Oocyte at MI. Homologous chromosomes (*red*) are aligned on the metaphase plate and attached to a barrel-shaped spindle (*green*). **C**, Oocyte at MII. The yellow arrow delineates the haploid number of chromosomes on the MII spindle and the contents of the first polar body are also seen (*white arrow.*) (See color plate.)

polar body, resulting in a haploid genome. A second meiotic spindle is then assembled and oocytes enter metaphase II (MII), where they normally remain arrested until activation by a spermatozoon.

In most mammals, meiotic maturation to the MII stage is completed by the time of ovulation, but the correlation between maturation and ovulation can be experimentally dissociated [5]. LH-independent (spontaneous) maturation occurs upon removal of the oocyte-cumulus cell complex from antral follicles and culture in an appropriate medium [6, 7]. Thus hormonal induction of ovulation is not necessary for the initiation of the nuclear maturation program. Conversely, precocious induction of ovulation by injection of gonadotropins early in the estrous cycle of pigs resulted in the ovulation of primary (diploid) oocytes [5]. Oocytes are also ovulated at MI in specific mouse strains that exhibit defects in the progression of meiosis [8]. These studies demonstrate that ovulation does not depend on completion of oocyte maturation. Moreover, there is a naturally occurring, but atypical, relationship between oocyte maturation and ovulation in the *Canidae*. In contrast to other mammals, oocytes of dogs and foxes are ovulated at GV-stage [9–11]. Nevertheless, the centrally positioned GV migrates peripherally in fox oocytes before ovulation [11], suggesting that some aspects of maturation may be initiated before ovulation even in the *Canidae*.

Key Cell Cycle Molecules Driving Nuclear Maturation

As indicated, meiosis occurs solely in germ cells to reduce the number of chromosomes to a haploid complement. This process entails two successive divisions, with homologous chromosomes segregating during anaphase I, to produce the haploid condition, and sister chromatids at anaphase II, with no intervening deoxyribonucleic acid (DNA) replication (S phase). Similar to the mitotic cycle in somatic cells, meiosis is regulated by oscillations in the activity of $p34^{cdc2}$ kinase (CDK1), a protein kinase regulated by cyclin B (CYB) (Figure 7.2). These are components of a functional activity generally called *maturation-* (or *M-phase*) *promoting factor (MPF)* [12, 13], which was first described in frog oocytes [14]. In oocytes, CDK1 is activated (see Figure 7.2) shortly before the resumption of meiosis and is necessary for GVB; its activity rises and reaches a plateau at MI. During the transition between MI and MII, when the first polar body is extruded, CDK1 activity decreases significantly. However, it is reestablished and maintained at a high level during MII arrest [14–18].

The activation status of CDK1 is regulated by the modulation of CYB levels and the phosphorylation of the CDK1 kinase domain at specific amino acid residues [16–22]. CYB synthesis increases during meiotic maturation and is highest at the end of the first meiotic M-phase [17, 22]; however, with the onset of anaphase I it is rapidly degraded by an ubiquitin-dependent pathway [23]. In turn, newly synthesized CYB is essential to reestablish CDK1 activity at MII. Inhibition of protein synthesis, including CYB, at the end of MI prevents the restoration of CDK1 activity and leads to the failure of MII arrest [24, 25]. The amount of CYB present in oocytes is key to progression through meiosis. The rate of progression from the GV stage to MI is dependent on the balance of the rate of CYB synthesis and its degradation [18, 22]. Thus entry into metaphase is driven by CYB synthesis and activation of

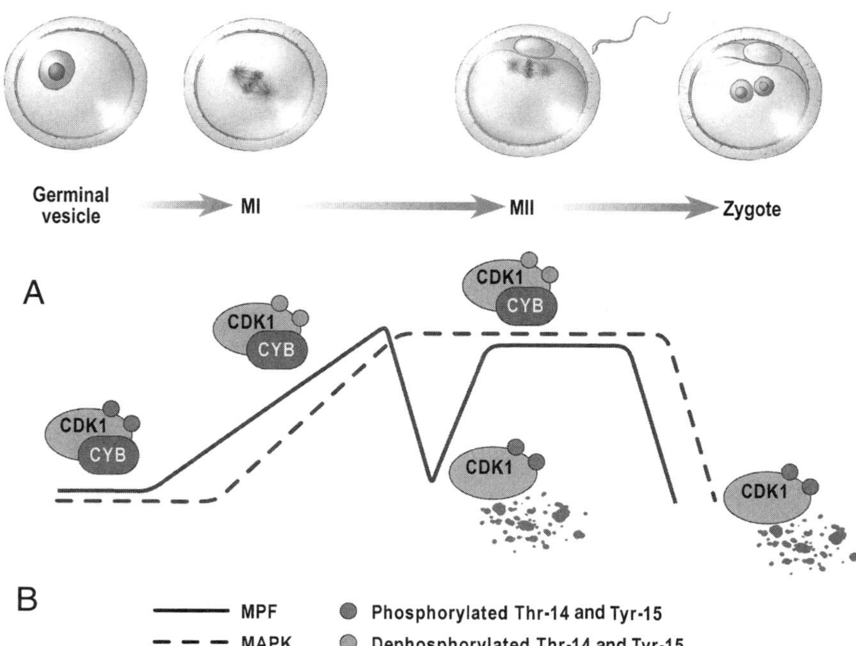

FIGURE 7.2 **A**, Diagram of the major steps in the progression of nuclear maturation. **B**, Diagram of the activity of MPF (*solid line*) and mitogen-activated protein kinase (MAPK; *dashed line*) during nuclear maturation. MPF activity is defined by the activation of the CDK1 protein kinase component of MPF, whose activity is regulated by dephosphorylation at Thr-14 and Tyr-15 (*green*). Loss of CDK1 activity is brought about at anaphase I or II by the rephosphorylation (*red*) of CDK1 and the proteolytic degradation of the CYB regulatory component of MPF. (See color plate.)

CDK1, whereas entry into anaphase is correlated with ubiquitin-mediated CYB degradation, and consequent decrease in CDK1 activity, as well as proteolysis of proteins involved in the adhesion of homologous chromosomes (anaphase I) or sister chromatids (anaphase II) [26, 27].

In addition to association with CYB, the activity of CDK1 is regulated by the phosphorylation and dephosphorylation of critical amino acid residues. CDK1 is maintained in an inactive state during prophase I arrest by phosphorylation on Thr-14 and Tyr-15 by the inhibitory kinases MYT1 and WEE1 [28]. Before the onset of GVB, these sites on CDK1 are dephosphorylated by the dual-specificity phosphatase, CDC25, and CDK1 becomes active [21]. Recent studies revealed that mice with a null mutation for CDC25b are ovulated at the GV stage; these oocytes cannot undergo GVB or enter MI [29]. Hence, CDC25b is the key phosphatase isoform essential for CDK1 activation at the G2/M transition in mouse oocytes.

On completion of the first meiotic division, appropriate control mechanisms function to maintain mature eggs arrested at MII until fertilization. In a seminal experiment, Masui and Markert demonstrated that injection of cytoplasm from a mature MII egg into one blastomere of a two-cell embryo prevented cleavage division and maintained a metaphase configuration in the injected blastomere [14]. This cell cycle arresting activity was termed *cytostatic factor (CSF)* and was postulated to be responsible for sustaining meiotic MII arrest in unfertilized vertebrate eggs; CSF activity was detected at MII and disappeared soon after fertilization [15, 16, 30]. Subsequent studies have since demonstrated that the product of the *Mos* proto-oncogene (MOS protein), its target, mitogen-activated protein kinase kinase (MAPKK/MEK1), and the MEK1 substrate MAPK are essential components of CSF [31–34]. MAPK becomes active only after CDK1 activation and following the resumption of meiosis; its activity increases during meiotic maturation and is sustained during the progression from MI to MII (see Figure 7.2). Various studies have confirmed that MAPK is necessary to sustain MII arrest [31–35]. Mice with a homozygous deletion in the *Mos* gene provided direct genetic evidence that the MOS/MAPK pathway is vital for CSF activity. Oocytes from *Mos*-null females express no detectable MAPK activity; these oocytes progress through the first meiotic division but fail to arrest at MII and undergo spontaneous parthenogenetic activation [31, 32]. It has been proposed that the function of MOS is to prevent the meiotic to mitotic conversion until after fertilization [36]. Correlated with the loss of CSF activity *Mos* messenger ribonucleic acid (mRNA) and protein are rapidly degraded after fertilization and egg activation. On entry into interphase, MAPK activity is slowly inactivated subsequent to the decrease in CDK1 activity [16, 37].

Significant strides have been made in understanding the regulatory control mechanisms that govern the process of meiotic maturation since MPF and CSF activities were first described in oocytes. However, it has also become evident that these processes involve an extensive and complex signaling network that operates during both mitosis and meiosis—understanding the defining differences is the current challenge. Though MAPK is undoubtedly essential for CSF activity, the precise mechanisms by which CSF maintains MII arrest are not yet fully understood. The protein kinase p90(RSK) has been identified as an important molecular target of MAPK in both *Xenopus* and mouse oocytes [38–40]. It has been suggested that RSK may play a role in repressing S-phase entry between MI and MII, possibly through the reactivation of CDK1 activity. RSK was shown to participate in meiosis I entry [41] by inhibiting MYT1 to activate CDK1 [42]. Moreover, a compelling connection between RSK and CSF activity has been established. For example, depletion of RSK from *Xenopus* egg extracts eliminates CSF activity [39]. Additionally, injection of a constitutively active form of RSK, which does not require MAPK for its activation, into one blastomere of a two-cell embryo was shown to prevent cleavage [40]. Metaphase arrest occurred without activating the endogenous MAPK/RSK pathway and thus indicated that RSK was necessary and sufficient to promote CSF arrest in *Xenopus*. Nevertheless, recent studies with mouse oocytes have attributed the regulation of MII spindle integrity to a novel MAPK substrate, MAPK-interacting and spindle-stabilizing protein (MISS) [43]. Hence, although common molecules may mediate MAPK-dependent CSF arrest in oocytes, species-specific pathways are also likely to exist.

A recent and intriguing association has also been established between the MAPK/RSK pathway and the spindle checkpoint [44–46]. In somatic cells, this checkpoint links the initiation of anaphase to spindle assembly and the completion of chromosome-microtubule attachment. Anaphase onset is effectively prevented by inhibition of the anaphase-promoting complex (APC) until all the chromosomes are correctly attached to the spindle apparatus [47]. In *Xenopus*, BUB1, an upstream component of the kinetochore attachment checkpoint, is dependent on MAPK for activation during meiosis. Moreover, RSK can activate BUB1 in vitro and in vivo [44]. These data support the concept that the mechanism of CSF arrest might involve the regulation of APC and the spindle assembly checkpoint [46].

Meiotic Competence

The ability (competence) to resume and complete meiotic maturation is gradually acquired during oocyte growth. Although fully grown oocytes can spontaneously resume meiosis in culture, oocytes from preantral follicles cultured under the same conditions fail to mature. Acquisition of competence to undergo GVB is correlated with the stage of follicle development and oocyte size. Oocytes initially acquire the ability to undergo GVB when partially grown, but interestingly they are not competent to complete maturation at this stage and therefore arrest at or about metaphase I. It is only with further development that oocytes can progress through metaphase I to metaphase II to become mature eggs [4, 48, 49].

Resumption and completion of meiosis necessitates that key proteins essential for nuclear maturation are available and functional. These proteins activate when oocytes are removed from the suppressive influence of follicular somatic components. That growing oocytes from preantral follicles are not able to undergo spontaneous maturation when isolated from their follicles and grown in culture suggests that either they do not contain sufficient quantities of the proteins essential to drive nuclear maturation or that subcellular distribution or associations are not appropriate for activation. The number of molecules per oocyte of CDK1 and CYB increases dramatically as oocytes acquire competence to undergo GVB [50, 51]. The number of transcripts encoding these proteins does not change, thus indicating that protein concentration is under translational control [50]. Moreover, CDK1 and CYB are apparently translocated to the GV as oocytes become competent to undergo GVB [52]. Oocytes lacking CDC25b cannot undergo GVB even when fully grown, but injection of CDC25b mRNA promotes GVB [29]. It appears, therefore, that GVB incompetence is caused by deficiencies in sufficient levels of key regulatory molecules and their maintenance in an appropriate state and/or subcellular distribution. The signal(s) instigating the transition from GVB incompetence to competence are not known, but companion granulosa cells appear to play a key role. Studies demonstrate that although oocytes can accumulate CDK1 without granulosa cells, they cannot become fully competent to undergo GVB [53].

As indicated, when developing oocytes are first able to undergo GVB, they cannot complete nuclear maturation and arrest at metaphase I; these oocytes are considered only partially competent. The molecular basis of this deficiency is not clear. However, recent studies in mice indicate that inhibition of protein kinase C (PKC) in partially competent oocytes promotes progression to metaphase II. Moreover, stimulation of PKC activity in fully competent oocytes arrests the progression of nuclear maturation at the GV stage or at metaphase I in oocytes that have undergone GVB [54–57]. Therefore, acquiring the ability to suppress PKC activity might be an important component of the developmental program required to complete the first meiotic division. The role of PKC activity during earlier oocyte development is, however, unknown.

Evidence that the capacity to complete nuclear maturation involves a cytoplasmic component derives from experiments in which the GV of primordial mouse oocytes was microsurgically transferred to enucleated fully grown oocytes. These oocytes were able to mature to metaphase II [58]. However, despite the completion of meiotic maturation, neither a female nor male pronucleus formed after insemination. Competence for pronuclear formation became established only when the GV-donor oocyte was obtained from more advanced secondary preantral follicles (8-day-old mice) [59]. It has been suggested that a nucleoplasmic component is required to mix with ooplasm to complete nuclear maturation and promote the formation of female and male pronuclei on fertilization [59].

Maintenance of Prophase Arrest in Oocytes of Antral Follicles

Incompetent oocytes from preantral follicles are arrested at the GV stage because they lack the cytoplasmic factors necessary to drive nuclear maturation. However, competent oocytes that are fully grown contain these key molecules yet they still remain in the GV stage until the LH surge. What are the mechanisms that restrain these oocytes at prophase I? The spontaneous maturation observed in oocytes on release from the follicular environment [6, 7] led to the hypothesis that somatic cells of antral follicles maintain oocytes in meiotic arrest. Thus atretic degeneration of the follicle would cause a disruption of its meiosis-arresting system and result in oocyte maturation. The identification of specific molecules that participate in the maintenance of meiotic arrest is the subject of extensive experimentation. Many potential factors have been put forward; however, the discussion here is limited to those where evidence of participation in the maintenance of meiotic arrest is most convincing.

It was long believed that factors present in follicular fluid are essential for sustaining oocytes at prophase [60]. Although these early studies suggested that one of these factors may be a peptide [60], it was later found that the purine hypoxanthine, which is present in millimolar concentrations in porcine and mouse fluids, can maintain oocytes in meiotic arrest [61–63]. However, it is more likely that meiotic arrest is sustained by granulosa cell-derived signals whose communication to the oocyte is mediated by cell contact [64], perhaps by the gap junctions that metabolically couple oocytes and granulosa cells. Mural granulosa cells appear associated in a functional syncytium by gap junctions, and cumulus cells, including those located several ranks of cells away from the oocyte, communicate with the oocyte via gap junctions [65, 66]. Thus molecules maintaining the oocyte at the GV stage could originate throughout the granulosa cell compartment of the follicle and be transmitted to the oocyte via gap junctions without passage through follicular fluid. This does not, however, exclude a possible role for follicular fluid-borne factors in augmenting or supplementing the action of contact-mediated arrest.

There is compelling evidence that oocyte cyclic adenosine monophosphate (cAMP) levels regulate the resumption of meiosis. It is well documented that membrane permeable analogs of cAMP maintain meiotic arrest in vitro [67, 68], although oocytes of laboratory rodents are more sensitive to these compounds than bovine [69, 70] or primate oocytes [71]. Moreover, treatment of cumulus cell denuded oocytes with forskolin, a direct agonist of adenylyl cyclase (AC), delays the onset of GVB [72, 73], and micro-injection of mouse oocytes with the catalytic subunit of protein kinase A (PKA) inhibits spontaneous maturation [74]. General cAMP phosphodiesterase (PDE) inhibitors also prevent GVB. Intriguingly, it was recently demonstrated that oocytes express a unique PDE, PDE3, and that PDE3-specific inhibitors prevent GVB in vitro [75]. In a key experiment, it was found that injection of rats with a PDE3-specific inhibitor results in the ovulation of oocytes arrested at prophase I [76, 77]. This is persuasive evidence that PDE3 in oocytes is a necessary physiological regulator of nuclear maturation and that the concentration of cAMP in oocytes is crucial for the maintenance of meiotic arrest. This mechanism probably functions only in fully grown competent oocytes. cAMP is unlikely to play a role in meiotic arrest in incompetent oocytes from preantral follicles because microinjection of PKA inhibitors cannot induce GVB in these oocytes [78]. The substrates for PKA in competent oocytes are not clear. However, PKA directly phosphorylates CDC25 in frog oocyte lysates and CDC25 is dephosphorylated in intact oocytes just before CDK1 dephosphorylation [79]. Thus PKA potentially maintains CDC25 in the inactive phosphorylated state thereby preventing the dephosphorylation-dependent activation of CDK1 [79].

The steady-state level of oocyte cAMP is the net of synthesis and degradation, and it is important to assess how sufficient GVB-inhibiting levels of cAMP are sustained in oocytes. It is possible that additions to the oocyte pool of cAMP can originate from intrinsic and extrinsic sources. Cyclic AMP produced in cumulus cells could translocate to the oocyte by heterologous gap junctional complexes that couple the two cell types [80, 81]. Treatment of isolated oocyte-cumulus cell complexes with follicle-stimulating hormone (FSH) elevates cAMP levels in cumulus cells and oocytes [81], and because oocytes do not express FSH-receptors, the initial assumption might be that cAMP moves from the cumulus cells to the oocyte, presumably via gap junctions. Although some evidence indicates that cAMP can traverse gap junctions [82], it is not conclusive [83]. Adenylyl cyclase (AC) is present in the oocyte plasma membrane [84] because stimulation of cumulus cell denuded oocytes with forskolin, a direct activator of AC, delays the onset of GVB [72, 73]. Therefore, it is possible to explain the increase in oocyte cAMP observed after hormone stimulation of cumulus cells as the result of the generation of a gonadotropin-dependent signal by the cumulus cells to promote the generation of oocyte cAMP; this possibility is discussed later.

PDE3 is expressed in ovarian follicles, exclusively by the oocyte. It is not clear, however, how PDE3 activity is regulated. Ovarian follicular fluid contains high concentrations of the purine hypoxanthine, which has PDE inhibitory activity [85–87]. High concentrations of hypoxanthine can maintain cumulus cell-enclosed mouse oocytes in meiotic arrest and the cumulus cells, which might transport the hypoxanthine (or active metabolites) to the oocyte, mediate most of the inhibitory action of the purine. Inhibitors of inosine monophosphate (IMP) dehydrogenase abrogate hypoxanthine-mediated meiotic arrest in vitro [88]. Moreover, injection of these inhibitors into mice induces the maturation of almost all GVB-competent oocytes within the ovary [89]. This is compelling evidence that purines participate in the maintenance of meiotic arrest in vivo. IMP dehydrogenase catalyzes the conversion of IMP to xanthosine monophosphate, which is then converted to guanosine monophosphate (GMP). Therefore, the production of GMP is essential for the maintenance of meiotic arrest.

The most likely potential fate of GMP is conversion to guanosine triphosphate (GTP) and subsequent binding to G proteins. These proteins, which are important in the transduction of chemical signals to produce specific cellular responses, are present on the oolemma and plasma membranes of cumulus cells [90]. Microinjection of cumulus cell-free mouse oocytes with a nonhydrolyzable GTP analog, GTPγS, suppresses GVB [91]. Cholera toxin, which catalyzes the adenosine diphosphate (ADP)-ribosylation of the γ subunit of G proteins, augments the meiosis-arresting action of cAMP-elevating agents in mouse oocytes [91, 92]. These actions of cholera toxin are consistent with activation of G_s and the elevation of cAMP in oocytes. Considering these results together, IMP dehydrogenase inhibitors might suppress cAMP production in either granulosa cells or oocytes, or both, and thereby allow oocyte PDE3 to reduce cAMP concentration below the threshold required for meiotic arrest.

Consistent with this idea, microinjection of oocytes with a neutralizing antibody to G_s protein promotes GVB within intact antral follicles [93] indicating that oocyte AC requires the function of a G_s-type G protein. This observation implies the existence of a ligand/receptor-mediated mechanism to stimulate an oocyte intrinsic AC and thereby produce cAMP, which is necessary to maintain meiotic arrest. Although cumulus cell-derived cAMP may be transferred to oocytes, and although this cAMP may be essential for maintaining meiotic arrest, it is not sufficient. The ligand activating the oocyte AC is not known, nor is its origin. However, it is reasonable to infer that the ligand originates in a follicular somatic cell. If the source is the granulosa/cumulus cells, these cells might elevate oocyte cAMP levels by transfer of cAMP to the oocyte and by activation of oocyte AC.

The Induction of Nuclear Maturation

Pituitary-derived gonadotropins induce fully grown oocyte GVB in antral follicles or isolated cumulus cell-enclosed oocytes grown in vitro and in vivo; however, they fail to induce GVB in oocytes lacking somatic cells [94–97]. Thus gonadotropins induce the resumption of meiosis in oocytes via an indirect mechanism mediated by follicular somatic cells. The precise mechanisms underlying the induction of nuclear maturation are not clearly resolved. A positive stimulus generated by the follicular somatic cells and/or deprivation of meiosis-arresting factors could be involved.

Gonadotropins might initiate nuclear maturation by releasing the oocyte from meiotic arrest because fully grown oocytes removed from Graafian follicles spontaneously resume meiosis when maintained in culture [6, 7]. Therefore, LH stimulation could simply disrupt the transfer of inhibitory signal(s) originating within the somatic cells and allow nuclear maturation. According to one version of this model, the LH surge disrupts the physical communication between the oocyte and somatic cells via the gap junctions and decreases transport cAMP [80]. In support of this hypothesis, functional changes in the levels and the phosphorylation status of the gap junction protein connexin-43 expressed by granulosa cells appear coordinated with GVB [80, 98–101]. In fact, phosphorylation of granulosa cell connexin-43 can occur within 10 minutes of LH treatment [102]. However, it is not clear whether these changes terminate the movement of key meiosis-inhibitory factors to the oocytes before they become committed to resume meiosis [103, 104].

Evidence using in vitro systems involving the reversal of meiosis-arresting factors, such as hypoxanthine, cAMP analogs, or PDE inhibitors, indicate that a meiosis-inducing signal is generated by granulosa cells in response to gonadotropin stimulation [97]. Moreover, the communication of this signal to the oocyte requires functional gap junctions [105, 106].

Although the identity of the meiosis-inducing signal remains elusive, both cAMP and MAPK pathways in the granulosa cells seem to participate in the induction of GVB. It has been known for some time that LH induces a rise in cAMP levels in the follicular somatic cells [75]. Moreover, treatment of isolated oocyte-cumulus cell complexes, in which the progression of meiosis was arrested with hypoxanthine, with 8-Bromo-cAMP or forskolin stimulated the resumption of meiosis. Thus elevation of granulosa cell cAMP levels induces GVB. LH in vivo, or FSH or 8-Bromo-cAMP in vitro, stimulates activation of MAPK in cumulus cells. In addition, treatment of the complexes with inhibitors of MAPK blocked the induction of GVB by gonadotropin or 8-Bromo-cAMP. Because MAPK activity in oocytes is not required for GVB [31, 32], it has been postulated that it is the MAPK activity in granulosa cells that is necessary for hormone induced GVB [107, 108].

The collective evidence suggests the following putative mechanism for hormone-induced GVB (Figure 7.3). Gonadotropins stimulate elevation of cAMP and active MAPK levels in granulosa cells. This results in the generation of a meiosis-inducing signal by the granulosa cells

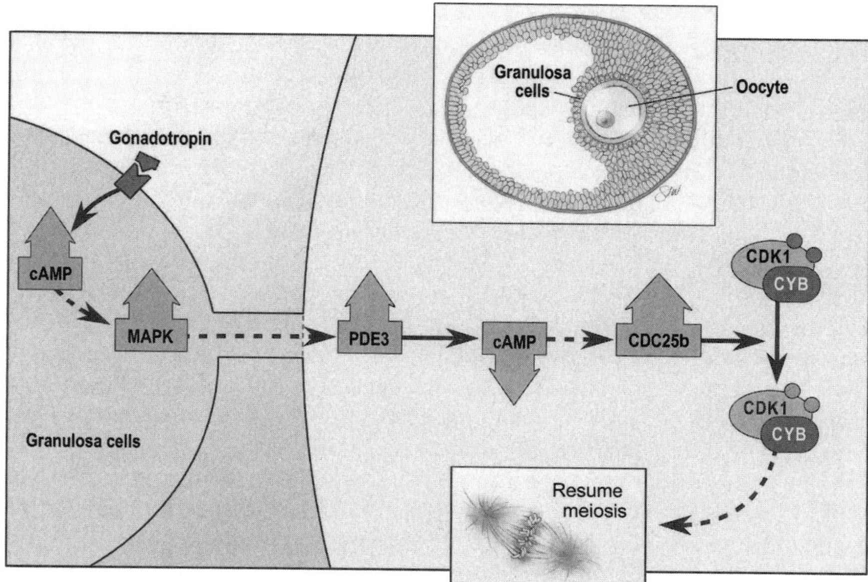

FIGURE 7.3 Hypothesis for the mechanism of gonadotropin-induced resumption of meiosis. Pink arrows indicate an increase or decrease in the activity or level of the indicated molecule. Dashed lines indicate that multiple steps might be involved in progression to the next event. Gonadotropin stimulation increases granulosa cell cAMP levels bringing about increased MAPK activity. This results in the generation of an unknown signal by the granulosa cells that traverses the gap junctions that couple the somatic cells with the oocyte. This signal increases the activity of PDE3, thus decreasing cAMP levels in the oocyte. It is also possible that the signal decreases adenylyl cyclase activity in the oocyte (not shown) and that following transmission of the positive signal, the transfer of molecules promoting meiotic arrest terminates. (See color plate.)

that is communicated to the oocyte via gap junctions. This signal activates PDE3 in the oocytes, resulting in decreased cAMP levels (specifically in oocytes) and, after a currently unknown number of downstream steps, activates CDC25b and thus MPF. Subsequently, and perhaps as a backup to the GVB-inducing signal, gap junctional communication between granulosa cells and the oocyte is dismantled hence terminating transmission of meiosis-arresting factors to the oocyte.

Metabolism of Maturation

The energy sources utilized for oocyte maturation are different for oocytes and their companion somatic cells. Mouse oocytes denuded of cumulus cells undergo nuclear maturation when cultured in medium supplemented with pyruvate or oxaloacetate, but not with glucose [109], and this unusual demand for substrates persists through early embryonic cleavage stages [110–112]. The poor use of glucose as an energy source by oocytes, a condition prevalent throughout oocyte growth [113], appears to be caused by a low hexokinase activity [114–116]. However, cumulus cell–enclosed oocytes undergo GVB in medium containing only glucose as an energy source [109], which suggests some metabolic cooperation between oocytes and cumulus cells. Stimulation of oocyte–cumulus cell complexes with FSH increased glucose use and the production of pyruvate [117]. Moreover, maturing oocytes appear to have a greater requirement for pyruvate than either GV- or MII-stage oocytes [117]. It is likely that cumulus cells metabolize glucose to pyruvate or ATP, which can be used by the oocyte, and transfer them to the oocyte either by gap junctions or secretion [106, 118–120].

The ability of hypoxanthine or cAMP analogs to maintain cumulus cell-enclosed oocytes in meiotic arrest in vitro requires the presence of glucose [105, 120]. The reversal of this inhibition by various ligands, however, also depends on available glucose [105, 120]. Because the oocytes cannot effectively use glucose, use of this hexose by cumulus cells probably mediates arresting and inducing mechanisms.

EPIGENETIC MATURATION

Epigenetic phenomena are stable and heritable chromatin modifications that influence gene expression without changing the DNA sequence. In oogenesis, epigenetic modifications to chromatin serve not only to set gamete-specific imprints on the genome but also to regulate gene expression during the maturation process. This section focuses on recent evidence describing the ontogeny of epigenetic modifications that regulate imprinting and global- and single-copy gene transcription, with a focus on model systems for in vitro gametogenesis that have significant potential to contribute to the molecular dissection of the mechanisms establishing epigenetic modifications during oogenesis.

Establishment of Epigenetic Modifications during Oogenesis

During their passage through oogenesis or spermatogenesis, germ cells undergo a series of reversible epigenetic modifications that ultimately confer the genome with a sex-specific mark or genomic imprint. Reciprocal imprinting during gametogenesis establishes functional differences between maternal and paternal alleles. Paternal and maternal genomes are thus complementary and essential for successful embryonic development in mammals [121, 122]. The possible mechanisms involved in the maintenance and reprogramming of parental imprinting during critical developmental transitions have been the subject of intense investigation [123, 124]. However, despite the importance of genomic imprinting as a mechanism for the control of gene expression, the nature of the primary signal responsible for the establishment of gamete-specific epigenetic modifications remains elusive.

Changes in DNA methylation, as well as acetylation and methylation of different lysine residues in histone proteins, cooperate to establish and maintain epigenetic marks in the mammalian genome [125]. One of the most widely studied types of epigenetic modifications is the differential pattern of cytosine methylation observed in regulatory sequences of imprinted genes. Approximately 45 genes have been identified as imprinted in mice and humans (Medical Research Council, Mammalian Genetics Unit, Harwell, United Kingdom; www.mgu.har.mrc.ac.uk), and the accumulating evidence seems to indicate that the majority of methylation changes at specific imprinting control regions, termed *differentially methylated regions (DMRs)*, take place postnatally during the passage of germ cells through oogenesis [123, 126].

Genome-wide epigenetic reprogramming takes place in mouse PGC on days 10.5 and 12.5 of fetal development [127, 128], a time at which PGC initially colonize the genital ridge and immediately before the initiation of meiosis in female germ cells. With each generation, erasure of DNA methylation patterns in imprinted and nonimprinted genes takes place over 24 hours and results in the acquisition of an equivalent epigenetic state in the germ cells of male and female embryos [127]. The mechanisms of epigenetic reprogramming in the germline are not fully understood; however, a strong transmodification activity present in PGC [129] has been demonstrated to induce epigenetic reprogramming (including global demethylation, erasure of allele-specific parental imprints, and the reactivation of the inactive X chromosome) after fusion with somatic cells [129]. Global demethylation in PGC is independent of DNA replication, suggesting the existence of an active demethylation event. However, the presence of a demethylase enzyme in PGC has yet to be demonstrated [127, 130].

Sex-specific genomic modifications in the germline are then reestablished at different times in different imprinted loci during the course of gametogenesis [131–133]. Importantly, epigenetic modifications during oocyte growth are known to be required for complete embryonic development. This was recently shown by elegant nuclear transfer studies indicating that the acquisition of the primary epigenetic imprint begins in dictyate oocytes around day 16 of postnatal development [58, 134, 135].

The mechanisms responsible for the developmental regulation of epigenetic modifications during oogenesis are not known. However, it has been suggested that they may be similar to the mechanisms operating during X chromosome inactivation in which a noncoding RNA, the X inactive-specific transcript (Xist), induces the repression of an entire X chromosome. The establishment of gametic imprints may be based on the assembly in cis orientation of a putative "imprint initiation complex." This may nucleate from those regulatory sequences on imprinted genes that induce changes in chromatin structure and facilitate the binding of maintenance methylases [136]. Consistent with this hypothesis, the maternal X chromosome acquires a gamete-specific imprint during oogenesis that precludes its inactivation in the extraembryonic tissues of the future embryo, resulting in the preferential inactivation of the paternal X chromosome in the trophectoderm cell line of the female conceptus [137]. Furthermore, recent evidence indicates that oocytes obtained from mice deficient for the DNA methyl transferase–like protein (DNMT3L) show abnormal DNA methylation patterns for several imprinted genes [138, 139]. DNMT3L shares a similar plant homeo domain (PHD) with other methyltransferases, but lacks enzymatic activity and may thus require the interaction with other methyltransferases (DNMT3a and DNMT3b) to establish oocyte-specific imprints [139]. The oocyte-specific methyltransferase (DNMT1o) is essential for the maintenance, but not the establishment, of maternal imprints during embryogenesis [140]. The recent identification of molecules with chromatin boundary or insulator activity such as CTCF [141, 142] and the DNA binding protein Brother of the Regulator of Imprinted Sites (BORIS) in mouse testis [143] suggests that methylation-sensitive chromatin insulators may be an essential component for the establishment and or maintenance [144] of sex-specific epigenetic modifications in the germline. Interestingly, different mechanisms seem to be set in place to control the epigenetic reprogramming of repetitive DNA elements such as Line 1 and intracisternal A particles [127, 138], which might play an essential role in the formation of a repressive chromatin environment to prevent the expression of retrotransposons or alternative intragenomic parasites during gametogenesis [145, 146].

In summary, both the mechanisms and timing for the epigenetic processes of imprint establishment and maintenance during oogenesis are emerging, though much remains to be learned. At least some of these processes seem tied to the developmental events of oocyte maturation, and their successful completion is essential for the competence of the oocyte to support normal embryonic development.

Control of Global and Specific Gene Expression during Oocyte Growth

Different organisms have evolved unique strategies for transcriptional regulation in the germline [147]. Complex mechanisms ensure the temporal regulation of gene expression during the course of mammalian oogenesis to meet the metabolic demands imposed by a requirement to sustain continuous oocyte growth as well as for the accumulation and storage of molecules essential for embryogenesis. To establish this stored maternal contribution, transcriptional activation in growing diplotene-stage oocytes is followed by selective translational repression and storage of dormant maternal RNAs, a process controlled by cycles of cytoplasmic polyadenylation and deadenylation of regulatory sequences [148, 149].

To sustain the completion of meiosis, fertilization, and preimplantation development, it is essential to maintain high rates of transcription to ensure that maternal messages, ribosomes, and other cytoplasmic organelles accumulate in growing oocytes. Total RNA content increases 300-fold during oocyte growth and the majority of this corresponds to ribosomal RNA [150, 151]. Mouse oocytes seem to rely on basonuclin, an rDNA-specific transcription factor to support this high demand for rRNA transcription [152]. Modulation of chromatin structure in specific regulatory sequences provides a local mechanism for the control of transcription on a locus-by-locus basis. For example, transcription of the *Xenopus* oocyte-specific 5S rRNA is controlled by a local interaction with the DNA binding protein histone H1A [153]. Failure to maintain transcription during oocyte growth and complete the maternal program for embryogenesis may have severe consequences on meiotic and developmental competence (see discussion under "Cytoplasmic Maturation").

Importantly, the oocyte genome is subject to additional levels of regulation, and functional differentiation of chromatin structure provides an important epigenetic mechanism for the developmental control of gene expression [154]. Changes in large-scale chromatin structure (at the chromosomal level) provide an important mechanism to repress global transcription before the resumption of meiosis. This cessation of transcription is most dramatically reflected in the morphology of the chromatin. The chromatin in the GV changes from a diffuse configuration (nonsurrounded nucleolus [NSN]), found predominantly in growing oocytes, toward a progressive condensation around the nucleolus (surrounded nucleolus [SN]; see Figure 7.1, *A*) in fully-grown oocytes [155–157]. Acquisition of an SN configuration is associated with global repression of transcriptional activity in vivo [158, 159]. Moreover, prolongation of the interval between global transcriptional silencing and the resumption of meiosis result in decreased developmental competence of the preimplantation embryo [159]. Thus the timing of transcriptional silencing, the resumption of meiosis, and ovulation must be strictly regulated.

The mechanisms involved in modulating higher order chromatin structure during mouse oocyte growth are not known. Nevertheless, established models for in vitro gametogenesis [160, 161] are of great value to address this question. Experimental manipulation of cultured oocyte-somatic cell complexes revealed that oocyte-associated granulosa cells play an essential role in the developmental regulation of global transcriptional silencing in preovulatory oocytes [159]. This suggests that companion granulosa cells provide the oocyte with as yet unidentified signals controlling oocyte gene expression perhaps in response to ovarian endocrine and paracrine interactions. Modification of oocyte histones is likely to play an important role in global transcriptional regulation. The presence of a mouse oocyte-specific histone has recently been described [162], although its function has not yet been defined. Interestingly, the ability to transfer histones to chromatin is acquired in oocytes, by a calcium-dependent process, about the time they become competent to resume meiosis; however, these two developmental steps appear to be independent [163].

The control of chromatin conformation during oocyte growth and maturation is likely part of a complex physiological pathway. Multiple signaling pathways converge to induce posttranslational modifications at specific amino acid residues of several histone proteins [164–166]. Moreover, many chromatin-remodeling enzymes use metabolic intermediates such as adenosine triphosphatase (ATPases) and NAD proteins suggesting that histone modifications may also play a role in regulating gene expression in response to environmental stimuli [167, 168].

In summary, local and global changes in large-scale chromatin structure during gametogenesis cooperate to regulate gene expression and to establish a sexually dimorphic epigenetic status between parental genomes. Further studies using established systems for in vitro gametogenesis are needed to understand the cellular and molecular processes associated with the developmental regulation of genomic modifications during oogenesis.

CYTOPLASMIC MATURATION

Cytoplasmic maturation is commonly defined as the processes occurring in developing oocytes that are essential for fertilization and early embryonic development. Although generally thought to occur in parallel with nuclear maturation, key steps also occur during oocyte growth, before the resumption of meiosis.

Maternal Effect Genes

Oocytes accumulate dormant maternal RNA and proteins, called *maternal-effect factors*, that are essential for the egg-to-embryo transition and for early embryogenesis. These factors are encoded by maternal effect genes and can be synthesized during oocyte growth, maturation, or after fertilization. Importantly, maternal RNA synthesized during oocyte growth is stored in a dormant form and selectively translated at the appropriate time after undergoing polyadenylation in the cytoplasm. The timing and activation of polyadenylation is determined by sequences in the 3′-UTR [169]. Translation is dependent on a UA-rich cytoplasmic polyadenylation element (CPE) in the 3′-UTR [149]. This CPE element is present in transcripts controlling a large number of genes involved in the egg-to-embryo transition [170] and requires the action of a CPE binding protein (CPEB) for its function [171]. Targeted deletion of the gene encoding CPEB (*Cpeb*), results in defects in the translation of key synaptonemal complex proteins, failure of chromosomal synapsis and arrest of meiosis at the pachytene stage [172]. Thus translational control mechanisms requiring the participation of CPEB are crucial even before the resumption of meiosis at the diplotene stage.

Although the existence of maternal effect genes expressed in mammalian oocytes has been inferred from studies on lower vertebrates and invertebrates, few such genes have been identified in mammalian oocytes. Oocytes from DDK mice fertilized with DDK sperm produce normal embryos, but embryonic development fails when DDK oocytes are inseminated with sperm from other strains. It has been determined that a maternal factor in DDK oocytes fails to interact appropriately with the paternal genome delivered by sperm from other strains [173]. Nevertheless, the identity of this maternal factor remains unknown. "Maternal antigen that embryos require" (*Mater*, for short) is a maternal effect gene expressed only in oocytes, with no mRNA detected in early embryos. Targeted deletion of *Mater* in mice produces embryos unable to develop beyond the two-cell stage [174] and a human homologue of *Mater* (*MATER*) has been described [175]. Although the precise function of MATER protein is unknown, specific domains indicate that it might function in protein-protein interactions [174]. A maternal effect gene that appears to function even earlier than *Mater* is zygotic arrest-1 (*Zar1*). Oocytes from *Zar1* null mice, expressing no ZAR1 protein, fail to progress beyond male and female pronucleus stage after insemination. Thus the final stages of fertilization fail to occur [176]. The identification and characterization of maternal effect genes expressed only in oocytes are key to increasing our understanding of the processes of cytoplasmic maturation.

Competence to Undergo Egg Activation

Eggs undergo a series of activation events after insemination including the release of cortical granules, pronuclear formation, and initiation of the first mitotic cell cycle. These processes occur as a consequence of sperm-initiated oscillations in free calcium ions. Insemination of GV-stage oocytes does not induce the calcium oscillations similar to those induced in MII oocyte or other events of egg activation. Therefore, the processes of cytoplasmic maturation endow the oocyte with competence to undergo activation. Calcium release is mediated by a 1, 4, 5-inositol trisphosphate (IP_3)-dependent mechanism [177]. Development of IP3 sensitivity is acquired gradually during oocyte meiotic maturation [178] and corresponds with the reorganization of the smooth endoplasmic reticulum [179, 180] and increase in the number and location of IP3-receptors [181]. Without these cytoplasmic maturation changes in parallel with nuclear maturation, normal fertilization and egg activation are not possible [182–184]. Moreover, the pattern of calcium oscillations initiating egg activation is directly related to normal embryonic and fetal development [185, 186].

Decondensation of the sperm nucleus is an early step in the formation of the male pronucleus. This is probably essential for subsequent programming of the male genome for participation in embryogenesis. Glutathione has been implicated in remodeling of sperm chromatin and the concentration of this thiol increases during oocyte maturation [187]. Blocking glutathione production during oocyte maturation in vitro prevents the acquisition of sperm nucleus decondensing activity [188, 189]. Cumulus cells increase the rate of accumulation of glutathione in oocytes during maturation in vitro [190, 191]. Moreover, there are undoubtedly other oocyte factors that promote sperm pronuclear formation and programming. The presence of oocyte cytoplasmic factors involved in remodeling the sperm nucleus are also central to nuclear reprogramming after transfer of somatic nuclei for animal cloning or the production of early embryos needed to generate embryonic stem cells.

Stepwise Acquisition of Cytoplasmic Maturational Competence

The developmental competence of oocytes from small antral follicles is restricted compared with oocytes from large antral follicles [192–196]. For example, although oocytes isolated from small and large antral follicles of mouse ovaries cleave to the two-cell stage at approximately the same frequency after maturation and insemination in vitro, those from small antral follicles complete the transition to the blastocyst stage at a much lower frequency [192]. Many of these oocytes in small antral follicles are, therefore, "embryogenesis restricted." This restriction is not because of the size of the oocyte but reflects a qualitative difference in the oocytes, the basis of which is currently not known. There could be global deficiencies in the production of maternal effect factors or a possible failure to degrade mRNA transcripts during oocyte maturation that are detrimental to embryonic development. Alternatively, there could be deficiencies in the expression of specific maternal effect genes, such as *Mater*, known to be essential for successful embryogenesis. Nevertheless, it is clear that important changes occur in the differentiation of GV-stage oocytes during late folliculogenesis. It is likely that the interactions between cumulus granulosa cells and the oocyte play a crucial role in this stage of oocyte development.

Coordination of Nuclear and Cytoplasmic Maturation

Oocytes become competent to complete nuclear and cytoplasmic maturation only during the final stages of antral follicle development, before the preovulatory surge of gonadotropins. However, this temporal association is not necessarily indicative of a functional linkage. Despite their isolation from large antral follicles, some mouse oocytes become arrested at metaphase I. Nonetheless, on insemination some of these oocytes were competent to develop to the blastocyst stage. As expected, such embryos usually contained a triploid complement of chromosomes and could not therefore develop to term. Similarly, despite their isolation from small antral follicles, some mouse oocytes were competent to complete nuclear maturation, but these were rarely able to develop to the blastocyst stage [197]. These results demonstrate that nuclear and cytoplasmic maturation are experimentally separable and not strictly linked functionally. Yet, certain aspects of cytoplasmic maturation may be dependent on nuclear maturation. For example, the formation of the male pronucleus, generally considered a consequence of cytoplasmic maturation, requires mixing of the contents of the GV with the cytoplasm and thus probably requires GVB [198]. Thus this key aspect of cytoplasmic maturation is linked with the initial steps of nuclear maturation, but processes downstream of release of GV contents are not sufficient for promoting full cytoplasmic maturation. Moreover, maturational changes in the patterns of protein synthesis in maturing rat oocytes occur in the absence of the GV and are thus under cytoplasmic control [199].

CONCLUSION

Oocyte maturation stands uniquely at the foundation and culmination of developmental and reproductive biology. The processes comprising oocyte maturation are essential for the transition from a gamete to an embryo competent to give rise to a healthy new individual. Concurrently these same processes also represent the final stage in the generation of a highly differentiated cell, the egg. Although this chapter's descriptions of the processes of oocyte maturation may seem complete to the novice, those working this field will recognize that the story is incomplete—a work in progress—with many key questions remaining to be resolved. What are the mechanisms of homologous chromosome pairing and recombination? Although several key molecules governing the starts and stops of meiosis in oocytes are known, major questions regarding their origin and function remain. What are their molecular partners and substrates? How does their distribution and organization in cells affect function? In addition, the identities of putative granulosa cell-derived ligands promoting cAMP generation in oocytes or signaling the resumption of nuclear maturation are still unknown. Vital maternal effect genes remain to be discovered. Answers to these, and many other related questions are essential for understanding the fundamental mechanisms of reproduction and thus critical for devising novel approaches to fertility control and reducing the incidence of birth defects, as well as facilitating production and use of totipotent stem cells, efficient domestic animal production, and propagation of endangered species.

ACKNOWLEDGMENTS

The authors thank Drs. Mary Ann Handel and Laurinda Jaffee, for their many helpful suggestions and insights in the preparation of this chapter, and Sarah Williamson, for preparation of the artwork.

References

1. Ginsburg, M., Snow, M. H. L., and McLaren, A. (1990). Primordial germ cells in the mouse embryo during gastrulation. *Development* 110, 521–528.
2. McLaren, A., and Southee, D. (1997). Entry of mouse embryonic germ cells into meiosis. *Dev. Biol.* 187, 107–113.
3. Peters, H. (1969). The development of the mouse ovary from birth to maturity. *Acta. Endocrinol.* 62, 98–116.
4. Sorensen, R. A., and Wassarman, P. M. (1976). Relationship between growth and meiotic maturation of the mouse oocyte. *Dev. Biol.* 50, 531–536.
5. Hunter, R. H. F., Cook, B., and Baker, T. G. (1976). Dissociation of response to injected gonadotropin between the Graafian follicle and oocyte in pigs. *Nature* (London) 260, 156–157.
6. Pincus, G., and Enzmann, E. V. (1935). The comparative behavior of mammalian eggs in vivo and in vitro. I. The activation of ovarian eggs. *J. Exp. Med.* 62, 655–675.
7. Edwards, R. G. (1965). Maturation in vitro of mouse, sheep, cow, pig, rhesus monkey, and human ovarian oocytes. *Nature* 208, 349–351.
8. Eppig, J. J., Kozak, L. P., Eicher, E. M., and Stevens, L. C. (1977). Ovarian teratomas in mice are derived from oocytes that have completed the first meiotic division. *Nature* 269, 517–518.
9. Van der Stricht, O. (1923). Etude comparee des ovules des mammiferes aux differentes periodes de l'ovogenese, d'apres les travaux du Laboratoire d'Histologie et d'Embryologie de l'Universite de Grand. *Arch. Biol.* (Paris) 33, 229–300.
10. Pearson, O. P., and Enders, R. K. (1943). Ovulation, maturation, and fertilization in the fox. *Anat. Rec.* 85, 69–81.

11. Hyttel, P., Farstad, W., Mondain-Monval, M., Lajord, K. B., and Smith, A. J. (1990). Structural aspects of oocyte maturation in the blue fox (Alopex lagopus). *Anat. Embryol.* 181, 325–331.
12. Norbury, C., and Nurse, P. (1992). Animal cell cycles and their control. *Ann. Rev. Biochem.* 61, 441–470.
13. Murray, A. (1995). Cyclin ubiquitination: the destructive end of mitosis. *Cell* 81, 149–152.
14. Masui, Y., and Markert, C. L. (1971). Cytoplasmic control of nuclear behavior during meiotic maturation of frog oocytes. *J. Exp. Zool.* 177, 129–146.
15. Kubiak, J. Z., Weber, M., Géraud, G., and Maro, B. (1992). Cell cycle modification during the transitions between meiotic M-Phases in mouse oocytes. *J. Cell Sci.* 102, 457–467.
16. Verlhac, M.-H., Kubiak, J. Z., Clarke, H. J., and Maro, B. (1994). Microtubule and chromatin behavior follow MAP kinase activity but not MPF activity during meiosis in mouse oocytes. *Development* 120, 1017–1025.
17. Hampl, A., and Eppig, J. J. (1995). Analysis of the mechanism(s) of metaphase I arrest in maturing mouse oocytes. *Development* 121, 925–933.
18. Polanski, Z., Ledan, E., Brunet, S., Louvet, S., Verlhac, M. H., Kubiak, J. Z., and Maro, B. (1998). Cyclin synthesis controls the progression of meiotic maturation in mouse oocytes. *Development* 125, 4989–4997.
19. Murray, A. W., Solomon, M. J., and Kirschner, M. W. (1989). The role of cyclin synthesis and degradation in the control of maturation promoting factor activity. *Nature* 339, 280–286.
20. Choi, T., Aoki, F., Mori, M., Yamashita, M., Nagahama, Y., and Kohmoto, K. (1991). Activation of p34cdc2 protein kinase activity in meiotic and mitotic cell cycles in mouse oocytes and embryos. *Development* 113, 789–795.
21. Coleman, T. R., and Dunphy, W. G. (1994). Cdc2 regulatory factors. *Curr. Opin. Cell Biol.* 6, 877–882.
22. Ledan, E., Polanski, Z., Terret, M. E., and Maro, B. (2001). Meiotic maturation of the mouse oocyte requires an equilibrium between cyclin B synthesis and degradation. *Dev. Biol.* 232, 400–413.
23. Glotzer, M., Murray, A. W., and Kirschner, M. W. (1991). Cyclin is degraded by the ubiquitin pathway. *Nature* 349, 132–138.
24. Clarke, H. J., and Masui, Y. (1983). The induction of reversible and irreversible chromosome decondensation by protein synthesis inhibition during meiotic maturation of mouse oocytes. *Dev. Biol.* 97, 291–301.
25. Hashimoto, H., and Kishimoto, T. (1988). Regulation of meiotic metaphase by a cytoplasmic maturation-promoting factor during mouse oocyte maturation. *Dev. Biol.* 126, 242–252.
26. Bickel, S. E., and Orr-Weaver, T. L. (1996). Holding chromatids together to ensure they go their separate ways. *Bioessays* 18, 293–300.
27. Peters, J. M. (2002). The anaphase-promoting complex: Proteolysis in mitosis and beyond. *Mol. Cell.* 9, 931–43.
28. Parker, L. L., and Piwnica-Worms, H. (1992). Inactivation of the $p34^{cdc2}$-cyclin B complex by the human WEE1 tyrosine kinase. *Science* 257, 1955–1957.
29. Lincoln, A. J., Wickramasinghe, D., Stein, P., Schultz, R. M., Palko, M. E., De Miguel, M. P., Tessarollo, L., and Donovan, P. J. (2002). Cdc25b phosphatase is required for resumption of meiosis during oocyte maturation. *Nat. Genet.* 30, 446–449.
30. Masui, Y. (1991). The role of "cytostatic factor (CSF)" in the control of oocyte cell cycles: A summary of 20 years of study. *Dev. Growth Differ.* 33, 543–551.
31. Colledge, W. H., Carlton, M. B. L., Udy, G. B., and Evans, M. J. (1994). Disruption of c-mos causes parthenogenetic development of unfertilized mouse eggs. *Nature* 370, 65–68.
32. Hashimoto, N., Watanabe, N., Furuta, Y., Tamemoto, H., Sagata, N., Yokoyama, M., Okazaki, K., Nagayoshi, M., Takeda, N., Ikawa, Y., et al. (1994). Parthenogenetic activation of oocytes in c-mos-deficient mice. *Nature* 370, 68–71.
33. Verlhac, M. H., Kubiak, J. Z., Weber, M., Geraud, G., Colledge, W. H., Evans, M. J., and Maro, B. (1996). Mos is required for MAP kinase activation and is involved in microtubule organization during meiotic maturation in the mouse. *Development* 122, 815–822.
34. Sagata, N. (1997). What does Mos do in oocytes and somatic cells? *BioEssays* 19, 13–21.
35. Phillips, K. P., Petrunewich, M. A., Collins, J. L., Booth, R. A., Liu, X. J., and Baltz, J. M. (2002). Inhibition of MEK or cdc2 kinase parthenogenetically activates mouse eggs and yields the same phenotypes as Mos (–/–) parthenogenotes. *Dev. Biol.* 247, 210–23.
36. Tachibana, K., Tanaka, D., Isobe, T., and Kishimoto, T. (2000). c-Mos forces the mitotic cell cycle to undergo meiosis II to produce haploid gametes. *Proc. Natl. Acad. Sci. USA* 97, 14301–14306.
37. Moos, J., Xu, Z., Schultz, R. M., and Kopf, G. S. (1996). Regulation of nuclear envelope assembly disassembly by MAP kinase. *Dev. Biol.* 175, 358–361.
38. Kalab, P., Kubiak, J. Z., Verlhac, M.-H., Colledge, W. H., and Maro, B. (1996). Activation of $p90^{rsk}$ during meiotic maturation and first mitosis in mouse oocytes and eggs: MAP kinase–independent and –dependent activation. *Development* 122, 1957–1964.
39. Bhatt, R. R., and Ferrell, Jr., J. E. (1999). The protein kinase p90 rsk as an essential mediator of cytostatic factor activity. *Science* 286, 1362–1365.
40. Gross, S. D., Schwab, M. S., Lewellyn, A. L., and Maller, J. L. (1999). Induction of metaphase arrest in cleaving Xenopus embryos by the protein kinase p90Rsk. *Science* 286, 1365–1367.
41. Gross, S. D., Lewellyn, A. L., and Maller, J. L. (2001). A constitutively active form of the protein kinase p90(Rsk1) is sufficient to trigger the G(2)/M transition in Xenopus oocytes. *J. Biol. Chem.* 276, 46099–46103.
42. Palmer, A., Gavin, A. C., and Nebreda, A. R. (1998). A link between MAP kinase and p34(cdc2)/cyclin B during oocyte maturation: p90(rsk) phosphorylates and inactivates the p34(cdc2) inhibitory kinase Myt1. *EMBO J.* 17, 5037–5047.
43. Lefebvre, C., Terret, M. E., Djiane, A., Rassinier, P., Maro, B., and Verlhac, M. H. (2002). Meiotic spindle stability depends on MAPK-interacting and spindle-stabilizing protein (MISS), a new MAPK substrate. *J. Cell. Biol.* 157, 603–613.
44. Schwab, M. S., Roberts, B. T., Gross, S. D., Tunquist, B. J., Taieb, F. E., Lewellyn, A. L., and J. L., Maller, M. (2001). Bub1 is activated by the protein kinase p90(Rsk) during Xenopus oocyte maturation. *Curr. Biol.* 11, 141–150.

45. Tunquist, B. J., Schwab, M. S., Chen, L. G., and Maller, J. L. (2002). The spindle checkpoint kinase bub1 and cyclin e/cdk2 both contribute to the establishment of meiotic metaphase arrest by cytostatic factor. *Curr. Biol.* 12, 1027–1033.
46. Maller, J. L., Schwab, M. S., Gross, S. D., Taieb, F. E., Roberts, B. T., and Tunquist, B. J. (2002). The mechanism of CSF arrest in vertebrate oocytes. *Mol. Cell. Endocrinol.* 187, 173–178.
47. Morgan, D. O. (1999). Regulation of the APC and the exit from mitosis. *Nat. Cell. Biol.* 1, E47–53.
48. Iwamatsu, T., and Yanagimachi, R. (1975). Maturation in vitro of ovarian oocytes of prepubertal and adult hamsters. *J. Reprod. Fert.* 45, 83–90.
49. Szybek, K. (1972). In vitro maturation of oocytes from sexually immature mice. *J. Endocrinol.* 54, 527–528.
50. Kanatsu-Shinohara, M., Schultz, R. M., and Kopf, G. S. (2000). Acquisition of meiotic competence in mouse oocytes: Absolute amounts of p34(cdc2), cyclin b1, cdc25C, and wee1 in meiotically incompetent and competent oocytes. *Biol. Reprod.* 63, 1610–1616.
51. de Vantery, C., Stutz, A., Vassalli, J. D., and Schorderet-Slatkine, S. (1997). Acquisition of meiotic competence in growing mouse oocytes is controlled at both translational and posttranslational levels. *Dev. Biol.* 187, 43–54.
52. Mitra, J., and Schultz, R. M. (1996). Regulation of the acquisition of meiotic competence in the mouse: Changes in the subcellular localization of cdc2, cyclin b1, cdc25C and wee1, and in the concentration of these proteins and their transcripts. *J. Cell. Sci.* 109, 2407–2415.
53. Chesnel, F., Wigglesworth, K., and Eppig, J. J. (1994). Acquisition of meiotic competence by denuded mouse oocytes: Participation of somatic-cell products and cAMP. *Dev. Biol.* 161, 285–295.
54. Urner, F., and Schorderet-Slatkine, S. (1984). Inhibition of denuded mouse oocyte meiotic maturation by tumor-promoting phorbol esters and its reversal by retinoids. *Exp. Cell Res.* 154, 600–605.
55. Bornslaeger, E. A., Poueymirou, W. T., Mattei, P., and Schultz, R. M. (1986). Effects of protein kinase C activators on germinal vesicle breakdown and polar body emission of mouse oocytes. *Exp. Cell Res.* 165, 507–517.
56. Lefèvre, B., Pesty, A., Koziak, K., and Testart, J. (1992). Protein kinase C modulators influence meiosis kinetics but not fertilizability of mouse oocytes. *J. Exp. Zool.,* 264, 206–213.
57. Downs, S. M., Cottom, J., and Hunzicker-Dunn, M. (2001). Protein kinase C and meiotic regulation in isolated mouse oocytes. *Mol. Reprod. Dev.* 58, 101–15.
58. Kono, T., Obata, Y., Yoshimzu, T., Nakahara, T., and Carroll, J. (1996). Epigenetic modifications during oocyte growth correlates with extended parthenogenetic development in the mouse. *Nat. Genet.* 13, 91–94.
59. Bao, S., Obata, Y., Ono, Y., Futatsumata, N., Niimura, S., and Kono, T. (2002). Nuclear competence for maturation and pronuclear formation in mouse oocytes. *Hum. Reprod.* 17, 1311–1316.
60. Tsafriri, A., Channing, C. P., Pomerantz, S. H., and Lindner, H. R. (1977). Inhibition of maturation of isolated rat oocytes by porcine follicular fluid. *J. Endocrinol.* 75, 285–291.
61. Downs, S. M., Coleman, D. L., Ward-Bailey, P. F., and Eppig, J. J. (1985). Hypoxanthine is the principal inhibitor of murine oocyte maturation in a low molecular weight fraction of porcine follicular fluid. *Proc. Nat. Acad. Sci. USA* 82, 454–458.
62. Eppig, J. J., Ward-Bailey, P. F., and Coleman, D. L. (1985). Hypoxanthine and adenosine in murine ovarian follicular fluid: Concentrations and activity in maintaining oocyte meiotic arrest. *Biol. Reprod.* 33, 1041–1049.
63. Miyano, T., Ebihara, M., Goto, Y., Hirao, W., Nagai, T., and Kato, S. (1995). Inhibitory action of hypoxanthine on meiotic resumption of denuded pig follicular oocytes in vitro. *J. Exp. Zool.* 273, 70–75.
64. Eppig, J. J. (1991). Maintenance of meiotic arrest and the induction of oocyte maturation in mouse oocyte-granulosa cell complexes developed in vitro from preantral follicles. *Biol. Reprod.* 45, 824–830.
65. Albertini, D. F., and Anderson, E. (1974). The appearance and structure of the intercellular connections during the ontogeny of the rabbit ovarian follicle with special reference to gap junctions. *J. Cell Biol.* 63, 234–250.
66. Anderson, E., Wilkinson, R. F., Lee, G., and Meller, S. (1978). A correlative microscopical analysis of differentiating ovarian follicles of mammals. *J. Morph.* 156, 339–366.
67. Cho, W. K., Stern, S., and Biggers, J. D. (1974). Inhibitory effect of dibutyryl cAMP on mouse oocyte maturation in vitro. *J. Exp. Zool.* 187, 383–386.
68. Dekel, N., and Beers, W. H. (1978). Rat oocyte maturation in vitro: Relief of cAMP inhibition with gonadotropins. *Proc. Nat. Acad. Sci. USA* 75, 4369–4373.
69. Homa, S. T. (1988). Effect of cyclic AMP on the spontaneous meiotic maturation of cumulus-free bovine oocytes cultured in chemically defined medium. *J. Exp. Zool.* 248, 222–231.
70. Sirard, M. A., and First, N. L. (1988). In vitro inhibition of oocyte nuclear maturation in the bovine. *Biol. Reprod.* 39, 229–234.
71. Warikoo, P. K., and Bavister, B. D. (1989). Hypoxanthine and cyclic adenosine 5′-monophosphate maintain meiotic arrest of rhesus monkey oocytes in vitro. *Fert. Steril.* 51, 886–889.
72. Bornslaeger, E. A., and Schultz, R. M. (1985). Adenylate cyclase activity in zona-free mouse oocytes. *Exp. Cell Res.* 156, 277–281.
73. Dekel, N., Aberdam, E., and Sherizly, I. (1984). Spontaneous maturation in vitro of cumulus-enclosed rat oocytes is inhibited by forskolin. *Biol. Reprod.* 31, 244–250.
74. Bornslaeger, E. A., Mattei, P. M., and Schultz, R. M. (1986). Involvement of cAMP-dependent protein kinase and protein phosphorylation in regulation of mouse oocyte maturation. *Dev. Biol.* 114, 453–462.
75. Tsafriri, A., Chun, S. Y., Zhang, R., Hsueh, A. J. W., and Conti, M. (1996). Oocyte maturation involves compartmentalization and opposing changes of cAMP levels in follicular somatic and germ cells: Studies using selective phosphodiesterase inhibitors. *Dev. Biol.* 178, 393–402.
76. Wiersma, A., Hirsch, B., Tsafriri, A., Hanssen, R. G. J. M., VandeKant, M., Kloosterboer, H. J., Conti, M., and Hsueh, A. J. W. (1998). Phosphodiesterase 3 inhibitors suppress oocyte maturation and consequent pregnancy without affecting ovulation and cyclicity in rodents. *J. Clin. Invest.* 102, 532–537.

77. Conti, M., Andersen, C. B., Richard, F., Mehats, C., Chun, S. Y., Horner, K., Jin, C., and Tsafriri, A. (2002). Role of cyclic nucleotide signaling in oocyte maturation. *Mol. Cell. Endocrinol.* 187, 153–159.
78. Bornslaeger, E. A., Mattei, P. M., and Schultz, R. M. (1988). Protein phosphorylation in meiotically competent and incompetent mouse oocytes. *Mol. Reprod. Dev.* 1, 19–25.
79. Duckworth, B. C., Weaver, J. S., and Ruderman, J. V. (2002). G2 arrest in Xenopus oocytes depends on phosphorylation of cdc25 by protein kinase A. *Proc. Natl. Acad. Sci. USA* 99, 16794–16799.
80. Dekel, N. (1988). Spatial relationship of follicular cells in the control of meiosis. In *Progress in Clinical and Biological Research. Meiotic Inhibition: Molecular Control of Meiosis,* eds., F. P. Haseltine, and N. L. First, 87–101. New York: Alan R. Liss, Inc.
81. Webb, R. J., Marshall, F., Swann, K., and Carroll, J. (2002). Follicle-stimulating hormone induces a gap junction-dependent dynamic change in [cAMP] and protein kinase A in mammalian oocytes. *Dev. Biol.* 246, 441–454.
82. Lawrence, T. S., Beers, W. H., and Gilula, N. B. (1978). Transmission of hormonal stimulation by cell-to-cell communication. *Nature* 272, 501–506.
83. Qu, Y., and Dahl, G. (2002). Function of the voltage gate of gap junction channels: Selective exclusion of molecules. *Proc. Natl. Acad. Sci. USA* 99, 697–702.
84. Kuyt, J. R. M., Kruip, T. A. M., and DeJong-Brink, M. (1988). Cytochemical localization of adenylate cyclase in bovine cumulus-oocyte complexes. *Exp. Cell Res.* 174, 139–145.
85. Downs, S. M., Coleman, D. L., and Eppig, J. J. (1986). Maintenance of murine meiotic arrest: Uptake and metabolism of hypoxanthine and adenosine by cumulus cell-enclosed and denuded oocytes. *Dev. Biol.* 117, 174–183.
86. Downs, S. M., Daniel, S. A. J., Bornslaeger, E. A., Hoppe, P. C., and Eppig, J. J. (1989). Maintenance of meiotic arrest in mouse oocytes by purines: Modulation of cAMP levels and cAMP phosphodiesterase activity. *Gamete Res.* 23, 323–334.
87. Downs, S. M. (1993). Purine control of mouse oocyte maturation: Evidence that nonmetabolized hypoxanthine maintains meiotic arrest. *Mol. Reprod. Dev.* 35, 82–94.
88. Downs, S. M. (1994). Induction of meiotic maturation in vivo in the mouse by IMP dehydrogenase inhibitors: Effects on the developmental capacity of ova. *Mol. Reprod. Dev.* 38, 293–302.
89. Downs, S. M., and Eppig, J. J. (1987). Induction of mouse oocyte maturation in vivo by perturbants of purine metabolism. *Biol. Reprod.* 36, 431–437.
90. Garty, N. B., Galiani, D., Aharonheim, A., Ho, Y.-K., Phillips, D. M., and Salomon, Y. (1988). G-proteins in mammalian gametes: An immunocytochemical study. *J. Cell Sci.* 91, 21–31.
91. Downs, S. M., Buccione, R., and Eppig, J. J. (1992). Modulation of meiotic arrest in mouse oocytes by guanyl nucleotides and modifiers of G-proteins. *J. Exp. Zool.* 262, 391–404.
92. Vivarelli, E., Conti, M., DeFelici, M., and Siracusa, G. (1983). Meiotic resumption and intracellular cAMP levels in mouse oocytes with compounds which act on cAMP metabolism. *Cell Diff.* 12, 1170–1172.
93. Mehlmann, L. M., Jones, T. L., and Jaffe, L. A. (2002). Meiotic arrest in the mouse follicle maintained by a G_s protein in the oocyte. *Science* 297, 1343–1345.
94. Tsafriri, A., Lindner, H. R., Zor, U., and Lamprecht, S. A. (1972). In vitro induction of meiotic division in follicle-enclosed rat oocytes by LH, cAMP, and prostaglandin E. *J. Reprod. Fert.* 31, 39–50.
95. Baker, T. G., and Neal, P. (1973). Initiation and control of meiosis and follicular growth in ovaries of the mouse. *Ann. Biol. Anim. Biochim. Biophys.* 13, 137–144.
96. Lindner, H. R., Tsafriri, A., Lieberman, M. E., Zor, U., Koch, Y., Bauminger, S., and Barnea, A. (1974). Gonadotropin action on cultured Graafian follicles: Induction of maturation division of the mammalian oocyte and differentiation of the luteal cell. *Rec. Prog. Hormone Res.* 30, 79–138.
97. Downs, S. M., Daniel, S. A. J., and Eppig, J. J. (1988). Induction of maturation in cumulus cell–enclosed mouse oocytes by follicle-stimulating hormone and epidermal growth factor: Evidence for a positive stimulus of somatic cell origin. *J. Exp. Zool.* 245, 86–96.
98. Larsen, W. J., Wert, S. E., and Brunner, G. D. (1987). Differential modulation of rat follicle cell gap junction populations at ovulation. *Dev. Biol.* 122, 61–71.
99. Wert, S. E., and Larsen, W. J. (1989). Meiotic resumption and gap junction modulation in the cultured rat cumulus-oocyte complex. *Gamete Res.* 22, 143–162.
100. Racowsky, C., and Baldwin, K. V. (1989). In vitro and in vivo studies reveal that hamster oocyte meiotic arrest is maintained only transiently by follicular fluid, but persistently by membrana/cumulus granulosa cell contact. *Dev. Biol.* 134, 297–306.
101. Granot, I., and Dekel, N. (2002). The ovarian gap junction protein connexin-43: Regulation by gonadotropins. *Trends Endocrinol. Metab.* 13, 310–313.
102. Granot, I., and Dekel, N. (1994). Phosphorylation and expression of connexin-43 ovarian gap junction protein are regulated by luteinizing hormone. *J. Biol. Chem.* 269, 30502–30509.
103. Eppig, J. J., and Ward-Bailey, P. F. (1982). The mechanism of cumulus cell-oocyte uncoupling: Evidence for the participation of both cumulus cells and the oocyte. *Gamete Res.* 6, 145–154.
104. Eppig, J. J., and Downs, S. M. (1988). Gonadotropin-induced murine oocyte maturation in vivo is not associated with decreased cyclic adenosine monophosphate in the oocyte-cumulus cell complex. *Gamete Res.* 20, 125–131.
105. Fagbohun, C. F., and Downs, S. M. (1991). Metabolic coupling and ligand-stimulated meiotic maturation in the mouse oocyte-cumulus cell complex. *Biol. Reprod.* 45, 851–859.
106. Downs, S. M. (1995). The influence of glucose, cumulus cells, and metabolic coupling on ATP levels and meiotic control in the isolated mouse oocyte. *Dev. Biol.* 167, 502–512.
107. Su, Y. Q., Rubinstein, S., Luria, A., Lax, Y., and Breitbart, H. (2001). Involvement of mek-mitogen-activated protein kinase pathway in follicle-stimulating hormone-induced but not spontaneous meiotic resumption of mouse oocytes. *Biol. Reprod.* 65, 358–365.
108. Su, Y. Q., Wigglesworth, K., Pendola, F. L., O'Brien, M. J., and Eppig, J. J. (2002). Mitogen-activated protein kinase (MAPK) activity in cumulus cells is essential for

gonadotropin-induced oocyte meiotic resumption and cumulus expansion in the mouse. *Endocrinology* 143, 2221–2232.

109. Biggers, J. D., Whittingham, D. G., and Donahue, R. P. (1967). The pattern of energy metabolism in the mouse oocyte and zygote. *Proc. Nat. Acad. Sci. USA* 58, 560–567.
110. Brinster, R. L. (1969). Radioactive carbon dioxide production from pyruvate and lactate by the preimplantation rabbit embryo. *Exp. Cell Res.* 54, 205–209.
111. Leese, H. J. (1990). *The Energy Metabolism of the Preimplantation Embryo*. New York: Alan R. Liss, Inc.
112. Lane, M., and Gardner, D. K. (2000). Lactate regulates pyruvate uptake and metabolism in the preimplantation mouse embryo. *Biol. Reprod.* 62, 16–22.
113. Eppig, J. J. (1976). Analysis of mouse oogenesis in vitro. Oocyte isolation and the utilization of exogenous energy sources by growing oocytes. *J. Exp. Zool.* 198, 375–386.
114. Brinster, R. L. (1968). Hexokinase activity in the preimplantation mouse embryo. *Enzymologia* 34, 304–308.
115. Chi, M. M., Manchester, J. K., Yang, V. C., Curato, A. D., Strickler, R. C., and Lowry, O. H. (1988). Contrast in levels of metabolic enzymes in human and mouse ova. *Biol. Reprod.* 39, 295–307.
116. Tsutsumi, O., Yano, T., Satoh, K., Mizuno, M., and Kato, T. (1990). Studies of hexokinase activity in human and mouse oocyte. *Am. J. Obstet. Gynecol.* 162, 1301–1304.
117. Downs, S. M., Humpherson, P. G., and Leese, H. J. (2002). Pyruvate utilization by mouse oocytes is influenced by meiotic status and the cumulus oophorus. *Mol. Reprod. Dev.* 62, 113–123.
118. Donahue, R. P., and Stern, S. (1968). Follicular cell support of oocyte maturation: Production of pyruvate in vitro. *J. Reprod. Fertil.* 17, 395–398.
119. Leese, H. J., and Barton, A. M. (1984). Pyruvate and glucose uptake by mouse ova and preimplantation embryos. *J. Reprod. Fertil.* 72, 9–13.
120. Downs, S. M., and Mastropolo, A. M. (1994). The participation of energy substrates in the control of meiotic maturation in murine oocytes. *Dev. Biol.* 162, 154–168.
121. Surani, M., Barton S. C., and Norris M. L. (1984). Development of reconstituted mouse eggs suggests imprinting of the genome during gametogenesis. *Nature* 308, 548–550.
122. McGrath, J., and Solter, D. (1984). Completion of mouse embryogenesis requires both the maternal and paternal genomes. *Cell* 37, 179–183.
123. Reik, W., Dean, W., and Walter, J. (2001). Epigenetic reprogramming in mammalian development. *Science* 293, 1089–1093.
124. Surani, M. (2001). Reprogramming of genome function through epigenetic inheritance. *Nature* 414, 122–128.
125. Richards, E. J., and Elgin, S. C. (2002). Epigenetic codes for heterochromatin formation and silencing: Rounding up the usual suspects. *Cell* 108, 489–500.
126. Ferguson-Smith, A. C., and Surani, M. A. (2001). Imprinting and the epigenetic asymmetry between parental genomes. *Science* 293, 1086–1089.
127. Hajkova, P., Erhardt, S., Lane, N., Haaf, T., El-Maarri, O., Reik, W., Walter, J., and Surani, M. A. (2002). Epigenetic reprogramming in mouse primordial germ cells. *Mech. Dev.* 117, 15–23.
128. Lee, J., Inoue K., Ono, R., Ogonuki, N., Kohda, T., Kaneko-Ishino, T., Ogura, A., and Ishino, F. (2002). Erasing genomic imprinting memory in mouse clone embryos produced from day 11.5 primordial germ cells. *Development* 129, 1807–1817.
129. Tada, T., Tada, M., Hilton, K., Barton, S. C., Sado, T., Takagi, N., and Surani, M. A. (1998). Epigenotype switching of imprintable loci in embryonic germ cells. *Dev. Genes Evo.* 207, 551–561.
130. Kafri, T., Gao, X., and Razin, A. (1993). Mechanistic aspects of genome-wide demethylation in the preimplantation mouse embryo. *Proc. Natl. Acad. Sci. USA* 90, 10558–10562.
131. Brandeis, M., Kafri, T., Ariel, M., Chaillet, J. R., McCarrey, J., Razin, A., and Cedar, H. (1993). The ontogeny of allele-specific methylation associated with imprinted genes in the mouse. *EMBO J.* 12, 3669–3667.
132. Shemer, R., Birger, Y., Riggs, A. D., and Razin, A. (1997). Structure of the imprinted mouse Snrpn gene and establishment of its parental-specific methylation pattern. *Proc. Natl. Acad. Sci. USA* 94, 10267–10272.
133. Lucifero, D., Mertineit, C., Clarke, H. J., Bestor, T. H., and Trasler, J. M. (2002). Methylation dynamics of imprinted genes in mouse germ cells. *Genomics* 79, 530–538.
134. Obata, Y., Kaneko-Ishino, T., Koide, T., Takai, Y., Ueda, T., Domeki, I., Shiroshi, T., Ishino, F., and Kono, T. (1998). Disruption of primary imprinting during oocyte growth leads to the modified expression of imprinted genes during embryogenesis. *Development* 125, 1553–1560.
135. Bao, S., Obata, Y., Carroll, J., Domeki, I., and Kono, T. (2000). Epigenetic modifications necessary for normal development are established during oocyte growth in mice. *Biol. Reprod.* 62, 616–621.
136. Surani, M. A. (1998). Imprinting and the initiation of gene silencing in the germ line. *Cell* 93, 309–312.
137. Tada, T., Obata, Y., Tada, M., Goto, Y., Nakatsuji, N., Tan, S. S., Kono, T., and Takagi, N. (2000). Imprint switching for non-random X-chromosome inactivation during mouse oocyte growth. *Development* 127, 3101–3105.
138. Bourc'his, D., Xu, G. L., Lin, C. S., Bollman, B., and Bestor, T. H. (2001). Dnmt3L and the establishment of maternal genomic imprints. *Science* 294, 2536–2539.
139. Hata, K., Okano, M., Lei, H., and Li, E. (2002). Dnmt3L cooperates with the Dnmt3 family of de novo DNA methyltransferases to establish maternal imprints in mice. *Development* 129, 1983–1993.
140. Howell, C. Y., Bestor, T. H., Ding, F., Latham, K. E., Mertineit, C., Trasler, J. M., and Chaillet, J. R. (2001). Genomic imprinting disrupted by a maternal effect mutation in the Dnmt1 gene. *Cell* 104, 829–838.
141. Bell, A. C., and Felsenfeld, G. (2000). Methylation of a CTCF-dependent boundary controls imprinted expression of the Igf2 gene. *Nature* 405, 482–485.
142. Hark, A. T., Schoenherr, C. J., Katz, D. J., Ingram, R. S., Levorse, J. M., and Tilghman, S. M. (2000). CTCF mediates methylation-sensitive enhancer-blocking activity at the H19/Igf2 locus. *Nature* 405, 486–489.
143. Loukinov, D. I., Pugacheva, E., Vatolin, S., Pack, S. D., Moon, H., Chernukhin, I., Mannan, P., Larsson, E., Kanduri, C., Vostrov, A. A., Cui, H., Niemitz, E. L., Rasko, J. E., Docquier, F. M., Kistler, M., Breen, J. J., Zhuang, Z., Quitschke, W. W., Renkawitz, R., Klenova, E. M., Feinberg, A. P., Ohlsson, R.,

Morse, H. C., and Lobanenkov, V. V. (2002). BORIS, a novel male germline-specific protein associated with epigenetic reprogramming events, shares the same 11-zinc-finger domain with CTCF, the insulator protein involved in reading imprinting marks in the soma. *Proc. Natl. Acad. Sci. USA* 99, 6806–6811.

144. Schoenherr, C., Levorse J. M., and Tilghman, S. M. (2003). CTCF maintains differential methylation at the Igf2/H19 locus. *Nat. Genet.* 33, 66–69.
145. Yoder, J. A., Walsh, C. P., and Bestor, T. H. (1997). Cytosine methylation and the ecology of intragenomic parasites. *Trends Genet.* 13, 335–340.
146. Walsh, C. P., Chaillet, J. R., and Bestor, T. H. (1998). Transcription of IAP endogenous retroviruses is constrained by cytosine methylation. *Nat. Genet.* 20, 116–117.
147. Seydoux, G., and Strome, S. (1999). Launching the germline in Caenorhabditis elegans: Regulation of gene expression in early germ cells. *Development* 126, 3275–3283.
148. Bachvarova, R. F. (1992). A maternal tail of poly(A): The long and the short of it. *Cell* 69, 895–897.
149. Richter, J. D. (1996). Dynamics of poly(A) addition and removal during development. In *Translational Control,* ed. J. W. B. Hershey, M. B. Mathews, N. Sonenberg, 481–503. Cold Spring Harbor Laboratory Press, Cold Spring Harbor, N.Y.
150. Wassarman, P. M., and Kinloch, R. A. (1992). Gene expression during oogenesis in mice. *Mutat. Res.* 296, 3–15.
151. Bachvarova, R. (1985). Gene expression during oogenesis and oocyte development in mammals. In *Developmental Biology: A Comprehensive Synthesis,* ed. L. W. Browder, 453–524. New York: Plenum Press.
152. Tian, Q., Kopf, G. S., Brown, R. S., and Tseng, H. (2001). Function of basonuclin in increasing transcription of the ribosomal RNA genes during mouse oogenesis. *Development* 128, 407–416.
153. Kandolf, H. (1994). The H1A histone variant is an in vivo repressor of oocyte-type 5S gene transcription in Xenopus laevis embryos. *Proc. Natl. Acad. Sci. USA* 91, 7257–7261.
154. Patterton, D., and Wolffe, A. P. (1996). Developmental roles for chromatin and chromosomal structure. *Dev. Biol.* 173, 2–13.
155. Debey, P., Szöllösi, M. S., Szöllösi, D., Vautier, D., Girousse, A., and Besombes, D. (1993). Competent mouse oocytes isolated from antral follicles exhibit different chromatin organization and follow different maturation dynamics. *Mol. Reprod. Dev.* 36, 59–74.
156. Mattson, B. A., and Albertini, D. F. (1990). Oogenesis: Chromatin and microtubule dynamics during meiotic prophase. *Mol. Reprod. Dev.* 25, 374–383.
157. Wickramasinghe, D., Ebert, K. M., and Albertini, D. F. (1991). Meiotic competence acquisition is associated with the appearance of M-phase characteristics in growing mouse oocytes. *Dev. Biol.* 143, 162–172.
158. BouniolBaly, C., Hamraoui, L., Guibert, J., Beaujean, N., Szollosi, M. S., and Debey, P. (1999). Differential transcriptional activity associated with chromatin configuration in fully grown mouse germinal vesicle oocytes. *Biol. Reprod.* 60, 580–587.
159. De La Fuente, R., and Eppig, J. J. (2001). Transcriptional activity of the mouse oocyte genome: Companion granulosa cells modulate transcription and chromatin remodeling. *Dev. Biol.* 229, 224–236.
160. Eppig, J. J., and O'Brien, M. J. (1996). Development in vitro of mouse oocytes from primordial follicles. *Biol. Reprod.* 54, 197–207.
161. Obata, Y., Kono, T., and Hatada, I. (2002). Maturation of mouse fetal germ cells in vitro. *Nature* 418, 497.
162. Tanaka, M., Hennebold, J. D., Macfarlane, J., and Adashi, E. Y. (2001). A mammalian oocyte-specific linker histone gene H1oo: Homology with the genes for the oocyte-specific cleavage stage histone (cs-H1) of sea urchin and the B4/H1M histone of the frog. *Development* 128, 655–664.
163. McLay, D. W., Carroll, J., and Clarke, H. J. (2002). The ability to develop an activity that transfers histones onto sperm chromatin is acquired with meiotic competence during oocyte growth. *Dev. Biol.* 241, 195–206.
164. Cheung, P., Allis, C. D., and Sassone-Corsi, P. (2000). Signaling to chromatin through histone modifications. *Cell* 103, 263–271.
165. Grunstein, M. (1997). Histone acetylation in chromatin structure and transcription. *Nature* 389, 349–352.
166. Wolffe, A. P., and Pruss, D. (1996). Targeting chromatin disruption: Transcription regulators that acetylate histones. *Cell* 84, 817–819.
167. Imai, S.-I., Armstrong, C. M., Kaeberlein, M., and Guarente, L. (2000). Transcriptional silencing and longevity protein Sir2 is an NAD-dependent histone deacetylase. *Nature* 403, 795–800.
168. Jenuwein, T., and Allis, C. D. (2001). Translating the histone code. *Science* 293, 1074–1080.
169. Oh, B., Hwang, S. Y., McLaughlin, J., Solter, D., and Knowles, B. B. (2000). Timely translation during the mouse oocyte-to-embryo transition. *Development* 127, 3795–3803.
170. Hwang, S. Y., Oh, B., Knowles, B. B., Solter, D., and Lee, J. S. (2001). Expression of genes involved in mammalian meiosis during the transition from egg to embryo. *Mol. Reprod. Dev.* 59, 144–158.
171. Gebauer, F., and Richter, J. D. (1996). Mouse cytoplasmic polyadenylylation element binding protein: An evolutionarily conserved protein that interacts with the cytoplasmic polyadenylylation elements of c-mos mRNA. *Proc. Natl. Acad. Sci. USA* 93, 14602–14607.
172. Tay, J., and Richter, J. D. (2001). Germ cell differentiation and synaptonemal complex formation are disrupted in CPEB knockout mice. *Dev. Cell.* 1, 201–213.
173. Renard, J. P., Baldacci, P., Richoux-Duranthon, V., Pournin, S., and Babinet, C. (1994). A maternal factor affecting mouse blastocyst formation. *Development* 120, 797–802.
174. Tong, Z. B., Gold, L., Pfeifer, K. E., Dorward, H., Lee, E., Bondy, C. A., Dean, J., and Nelson, L. M. (2000). *Mater*, a maternal effect gene required for early embryonic development in mice. *Nat. Genet.* 26, 267–268.
175. Tong, Z. B., Bondy, C. A., Zhou, J., and Nelson, L. M. (2002). A human homologue of mouse *Mater*, a maternal effect gene essential for early embryonic development. *Hum. Reprod.* 17, 903–911.
176. Wu, X., Viveiros, M. M., Eppig, J. J., Bai, Y., Fitzpatrick, S. L., and Matzuk, M. M. (2003). Zygotic arrest-1 (*Zar1*) is a novel maternal-effect gene critical for the oocyte-to-embryo transition. *Nat. Genet.* (in press).
177. Miyazaki, S., and Shirakawa, H. (1993). Ca2+-induced Ca2+ release mediated by the IP3 receptor is responsible for Ca2+

waves and Ca2+ oscillations at fertilization of mammalian eggs. *Biomed. Res.* 14, 35–38.
178. Mehlmann, L. M., and Kline, D. (1994). Regulation of intracellular calcium in the mouse egg: Calcium release in response to sperm or inositol trisphosphate is enhanced after meiotic maturation. *Biol. Reprod.* 51, 1088–1098.
179. Mehlmann, L. M., Terasaki, M., Jaffe, L. A., and Kline, D. (1995). Reorganization of the endoplasmic reticulum during meiotic maturation of the mouse oocyte. *Dev. Biol.* 170, 607–615.
180. Fissore, R. A., Longo, F. J., Anderson, E., Parys, J. B., and Ducibella, T. (1999). Differential distribution of inositol trisphosphate receptor isoforms in mouse oocytes. *Biol. Reprod.* 60, 49–57.
181. Mehlmann, L. M., Mikoshiba, K., and Kline, D. (1996). Redistribution and increase in cortical inositol 1,4,5-trisphosphate receptors after meiotic maturation of the mouse oocyte. *Dev. Biol.* 180, 489–498.
182. Ducibella, T. (1996). The cortical reaction and development of activation competence in mammalian oocytes. *Hum. Reprod.* 2, 29–42.
183. Abbott, A. L., Fissore, R. A., and Ducibella, T. (2001). Identification of a translocation deficiency in cortical granule secretion in preovulatory mouse oocytes. *Biol. Reprod.* 65, 1640–1647.
184. Ducibella, T., Huneau, D., Angelichio, E., Xu, Z., Schultz, R. M., Kopf, G. S., Fissore, R., Madoux, S., and Ozil, J. P. (2002). Egg-to-embryo transition is driven by differential responses to Ca2+ oscillation number. *Dev. Biol.* 250, 280–291.
185. Bos-Mikich, A., Whittingham, D. G., and Jones, K. T. (1997). Meiotic and mitotic Ca^{2+} oscillations affect cell composition in resulting blastocysts. *Dev. Biol.* 182, 172–179.
186. Ozil, J. P., and Huneau, D. (2001). Activation of rabbit oocytes: The impact of the Ca2+ signal regime on development. *Development* 128, 917–928.
187. Perreault, S. D., Wolff, R. A., and Zirkin, B. R. (1984). The role of disulfide bond reduction during mammalian sperm nuclear decondensation in vivo. *Dev. Biol.* 101, 160–167.
188. Perreault, S. D., Barbee, R. R., and Slott, V. L. (1988). Importance of glutathione in the acquisition and maintenance of sperm nuclear decondensation activity in maturing hamster oocytes. *Dev. Biol.* 125, 181–186.
189. Sutovsky, P., and Schatten, G. (1997). Depletion of glutathione during bovine oocyte maturation reversibly blocks the decondensation of the male pronucleus and pronuclear apposition during fertilization. *Biol. Reprod.* 56, 1503–1512.
190. deMatos, D. G., Furnus, C. C., and Moses, D. F. (1997). Glutathione synthesis during in vitro maturation of bovine oocytes: Role of cumulus cells. *Biol. Reprod.* 57, 1420–1425.
191. Tatemoto, H., Sakurai, N., and Muto, N. (2000). Protection of porcine oocytes against apoptotic cell death caused by oxidative stress during in vitro maturation: Role of cumulus cells. *Biol. Reprod.,* 63, 805–810.
192. Eppig, J. J., Schroeder, A. C., and O'Brien, M. J. (1992). Developmental capacity of mouse oocytes matured in vitro: Effects of gonadotropic stimulation, follicular origin, and oocyte size. *J. Reprod. Fert.* 95, 119–127.
193. Pavlok, A., Lucas-Hahn, A., and Niemann, H. (1992). Fertilization and developmental competence of bovine oocytes derived from different categories of antral follicles. *Mol. Reprod. Dev.* 31, 63–67.
194. Lonergan, P., Monaghan, P., Rizos, D., Boland, M. P., and Gordon, I. (1994). Effect of follicle size on bovine oocyte quality and developmental competence following maturation, fertilization, and culture in vitro. *Mol. Reprod. Dev.* 37, 48–53.
195. Cognie, Y., Benoit, F., Poulin, N., Khatir, H., and Driancourt, M. A. (1998). Effect of follicle size and of the Fec(B) Booroola gene on oocyte function in sheep. *J. Reprod. Fertil.* 112, 379–386.
196. Crozet, N., Ahmed-Ali, M., and Dubos, M. P. (1995). Developmental competence of goat oocytes from follicles of different size categories following maturation, fertilization, and culture in vitro. *J. Reprod. Fertil.* 103, 293–298.
197. Eppig, J. J., Schultz, R. M., O'Brien, M., and Chesnel, F. (1994). Relationship between the developmental programs controlling nuclear and cytoplasmic maturation of mouse oocytes. *Dev. Biol.* 164, 1–9.
198. Borsuk, E. (1991). Anucleate fragments of parthenogenetic eggs and of maturing oocytes contain complementary factors required for development of a male pronucleus. *Mol. Reprod. Dev.* 29, 150–156.
199. Meng, L., Rutledge, J., Zhu, Y., Kidder, G. M., Khamsi, F., and Armstrong, D. T. (1996). Role of germinal vesicle on protein synthesis in rat oocyte during in vitro maturation. *Mol. Reprod. Dev.* 43, 228–235.

CHAPTER **8**

Oocyte-Granulosa Cell Interactions

ANTONIETTA SALUSTRI, CSABA FULOP, ANTONELLA CAMAIONI, AND VINCENT C. HASCALL

ABSTRACT

Intimate association between oocyte and follicle cells is established before or shortly after birth when the oocyte arrests in the prophase of the first meiotic division and becomes surrounded by a single layer of somatic cells to form primordial follicles. During the following steps of folliculogenesis, growth and maturation of the oocyte and proliferation and differentiation of follicle cells are highly coordinated to produce an oocyte competent to undergo fertilization and to form a corpus luteum required for successful implantation of the embryo. Gonadotropins produced by the pituitary gland have a critical role in the regulation of these processes. In vitro culture of oocytes and follicular cells, either isolated or in association, have provided evidence that the execution of such a program is also strictly dependent on a complex bidirectional communication between germ cells and somatic cells accomplished by either cell contact and/or paracrine factors. These findings, together with the identification of growth factors specifically expressed by the oocyte and the study of natural and experimental mutation of related genes, highlight the pivotal role of the oocyte in mammalian folliculogenesis. In this chapter, we summarize how granulosa cells influence the oocyte during follicular development and discuss in more detail how the oocyte regulates granulosa cell differentiation and function.

DEVELOPMENT OF THE OVARIAN FOLLICLE

In mammals, female germ cells enter meiosis during fetal life and arrest in the prophase of the first meiotic division. Consequently, postnatal ovaries contain a finite number of quiescent oocytes that progressively decreases during life from their recruitment with time to develop further. As soon as the oocytes enter the diplotene stage, they become surrounded by a monolayer of flattened somatic cells and by a basement membrane to form primordial follicles. Subsequent follicle development can be divided in two principal stages: *preantral* and *antral phases*.

In the preantral phase, follicle cells become cuboidal and proliferate to form a stratified epithelium. The oocyte grows in size and forms a glycoprotein coat, the zona pellucida. An extensive network of gap junctions is formed among follicle cells and between follicle cells and oocyte, which provides a mechanism for coordinating their function [1–3]. Additionally, somatic cells in the adjacent interstitial tissue differentiate into thecal cells and form the external cellular envelope of the follicle. At this stage, the follicle cells appear to be a homogeneous population by morphological and immunological criteria, and they acquire high-affinity receptors for follicle-stimulating hormone (FSH) and estrogen [4, 5]. At the end of the preantral stage, the oocyte has almost completed its growth, but it is unable to resume meiosis [6]. Follicle development from primordial to early antral stage is controlled mainly by intraovarian and intrafollicular mechanisms, because it takes place also in the absence of gonadotropins [7, 8]. Conversely, the growth of the antral follicles and their acquisition of the ability to respond to an ovulatory stimulus absolutely requires the action of FSH secreted by the anterior pituitary gland [9].

In the antral phase, fluid accumulates between follicle cells and a central cavity, the follicular antrum, is formed, with most of the follicle cells (approximately 50,000/follicle in a mouse [10]), now called *mural granulosa cells,* located at the periphery. The oocyte remains surrounded by closely associated granulosa cells (approximately 1000/oocyte in a mouse [11]), called *cumulus cells,* forming the cumulus cell–oocyte complex (COC). During antral follicle growth, granulosa cells located in different regions of the follicle acquire different morphological and functional properties [12–20]. Those located most peripherally and adjacent to the basement membrane elongate, stop proliferating, synthesize enzymes involved in estrogen production, and acquire luteinizing hormone (LH) receptors. In contrast, the innermost layers of mural granulosa cells lining the antrum and the cumulus cells remain polyhedral, continue to proliferate, show limited steroidogenic activity, and acquire fewer LH receptors. In addition, these two cell populations differ in growth factor expression. For example, periantral granulosa cells and cumulus cells have higher messenger ribonucleic acid (mRNA) levels of insulin-like growth factor [21], vascular endothelial growth factor [22], inhibin beta A [23], and Mullerian inhibiting substance [24], whereas peripheral granulosa cells have higher kit ligand (KL) mRNA levels [25, 26]. Critical developmental changes also take place in the oocytes, they acquire competence to resume meiosis and to undergo fertilization and preimplantation development [27, 28].

The systemic surge of LH and FSH induces the large antral follicles to enter into the final stage of development. The oocytes resume meiosis and they reach the metaphase of the second meiotic division. The cumulus cells and the periantral granulosa cells start to synthesize and deposit a mucoelastic extracellular matrix promoting a 20- to 40-fold increase in volume of the cumulus mass, a process called *cumulus expansion* or *mucification* [11]. Because of the formation of this matrix, the COC detaches from the follicle wall. Conversely, the mural granulosa cells start to synthesize progesterone that, acting in an autocrine way, induces the expression of proteolytic enzymes, leading to the degradation of the perifollicular matrix [29]. About the time the oocyte reaches metaphase of the second meiotic division and the cumulus cells are uniformly dispersed in the matrix, the follicle wall breaks and the expanded COC is extruded from the ovary. The cumulus cells and their surrounding matrix provide the proper environment in the oviduct for successful fertilization [30, 31]. The peripheral granulosa cells together with the theca cells form the corpus luteum, which produces the high levels of progesterone required for successful implantation of the embryo and maintenance of the pregnancy.

For many years it was generally thought that such high coordination between oocyte development and granulosa cell differentiation was under the exclusive control of the somatic cells. In this scenario progressive differentiation of follicle cells would promote the generation of signals able to regulate the growth and maturation of the oocyte. The hypothesis that the oocyte could take part in the control of the follicle cell functions was first advanced in 1970 when it was reported that surgical removal of oocytes from antral follicles in vivo resulted in an increase in circulating progesterone levels [32, 33]. The authors concluded that the oocyte produces a luteostatic factor that prevents premature granulosa cell luteinization, but these findings were disputed in later works [34, 35]. Further persuasive evidence of oocyte influence on follicle somatic cell behavior was only provided 20 years later. It was shown that in vitro induction of COC expansion by FSH treatment was prevented by mechanically removing the enclosed oocyte and that addition back of the oocyte or oocyte-conditioned medium to the culture restored the normal response of cumulus cells to the hormone [36, 37]. Among several tested known growth factors, only TGFβ-1 could mimic oocyte action, but neutralizing antibodies against TGFβ-1 failed to inhibit the oocyte factor activity [38]. Thus it was proposed that the oocyte factor could be a member of the TGFβ family, different from TGFβ-1, but triggering similar intracellular signals. A new member of the TGFβ family, called *growth differentiation factor 9 (GDF-9)*, was identified in 1993 [39] and was shown to be specifically expressed in the ovary by oocytes from the beginning of follicle growth through ovulation [40]. This observation prompted the authors to state as follows: "Such relatively long window of GDF-9 expression during oocyte development suggests that perhaps GDF-9 may play multiple regulatory roles." GDF-9-null mice were generated in 1996 and proved to be infertile because of a block in folliculogenesis at the primary one-layer follicle stage, providing the first evidence that oocyte-secreted factors play a critical role in modulating follicular cell function in vivo [41]. Currently, two other members of the TGFβ superfamily, namely bone morphogenetic protein-15 (BMP-15), also called *GDF-9B*, and BMP-6, are known to be expressed by oocytes with a temporal pattern similar to that of GDF-9 [42–44]. In vitro and in vivo studies have demonstrated that these factors deeply affect several follicle functions throughout folliculogenesis (Figure 8.1).

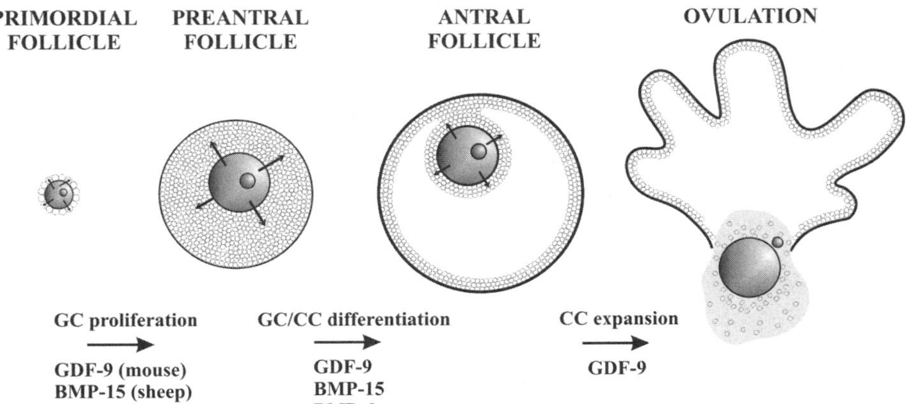

FIGURE 8.1 Schematic drawing of follicle development showing the stage-dependent regulation of granulosa cell (GC) and cumulus cell (CC) functions by oocyte factors (GDF-9, BMP-15, and BMP-6).

INTERACTIONS BETWEEN OOCYTE AND GRANULOSA CELLS DURING FOLLICLE DEVELOPMENT

From Primordial to Early Antral Follicle

The formation of the primordial follicle can be considered the first functional interaction between the germ cell and somatic cells in the ovary because it fails to organize in pathological or experimental conditions in which germ cells are induced to degenerate. In addition, in mutant mice lacking factor in the germline, alpha (FIGα), an oocyte-specific transcription factor, somatic cells do not surround the oocytes at birth, and the oocytes degenerate within 7 days [45], in contrast to the follicle-enclosed oocytes in wild type mice, which can be preserved for years. The downstream targets of FIGα in the oocyte required for establishing an intimate association with follicle cells remain to be determined. In any event, this observation clearly indicates that follicle cells are essential for oocyte survival and that the oocyte plays an active role in their recruitment.

Primordial follicles in the postnatal ovary do not initiate growth at the same time. Therefore, a complex interaction between stimulatory and inhibitory signals generated locally by different intragonadal components such as ovarian epithelium, stromal cells, and neighboring follicles are likely to be involved in this control. Follicle development involves tight oocyte-granulosa cell interactions necessary to achieve the high coordination between proliferation and differentiation of follicle cells and oocyte growth. Studies performed on the first wave of follicle recruitment suggest that follicle cell production of KL and the activation of the KL receptor, c-kit, in the oocyte play a key role in activating the resting oocyte. In fact, KL treatment in vitro is sufficient to initiate growth of oocytes isolated from prenatal ovaries and cultured without somatic cells [46]. Moreover, an antibody blocking c-kit prevents the growth of oocytes when either injected into newborn mice or added to the culture of early postnatal ovarian fragments [47, 48]. Of note, follicle cells encircling these oocytes change from flattened to cuboidal shape, indicative of a functional differentiation, but they do not proliferate. These observations suggest that secretion of KL by follicle cells induces the oocytes to grow and, at the same time, to generate a positive signal that stimulates follicle cells to proliferate. Such oocyte control on follicle cell function is mainly accomplished by the production of soluble growth factors.

GDF-9 and BMP-15 are specifically expressed by oocytes of all examined mammalian species from the first stages of follicle development to ovulation [40, 42, 49–52]. In mice, GDF-9 expression begins in the early primary follicles [40]. Accordingly, homozygous disruption of the GDF-9 gene by homologous recombination does not prevent the transition of primordial follicle to primary follicle. However, GDF-9-null mice are sterile because of the arrest of folliculogenesis at the primary one-layer follicle stage [41]. BMP-15-null female mice do not show gross defects in ovarian morphology, suggesting that this growth factor is less crucial than GDF-9 in mouse follicle growth [53]. However, female mice with homozygous disruption of the BMP-15 gene show reduced fertility as a result of defects occurring at the preovulatory follicle stage (see "From Preovulatory Follicle to Ovulation"), implying that some molecular mechanisms involved in normal development of the follicle are altered in the absence of BMP-15.

Naturally occurring homozygous mutations in the BMP-15 gene in *Inverdale* ($FecX^I$) and *Hanna* ($FecX^H$) sheep cause a block at the primary follicle stage, similar to what is observed in GDF-9-null mice [54]. It has been speculated that the difference in the phenotype of BMP-15-null mice and the mutant sheep could be explained by different roles played by GDF-9 and BMP-15 in the folliculogenesis of mono-ovulatory vs polyovulatory animals. An alternative hypothesis is that natural mutations in the BMP-15 gene lead to the synthesis of altered BMP-15 protein that produces effects different from those caused by the lack of the protein. The latter hypothesis finds support in a recent study in which either the normal or the mutant *Inverdale* form of BMP-15 was coexpressed with GDF-9 in a stably transfected cell line [55]. These experiments demonstrated that GDF-9 and BMP-15 can form homodimers and heterodimers. However, when *Inverdale* mutant BMP-15 was coexpressed with GDF-9, secretion of mutant BMP-15 was abolished and that of GDF-9 was severely impaired probably because of altered post-transcriptional processing of the mature proteins. These findings led the authors to hypothesize that insufficient secretion of GDF-9 could cause the folliculogenesis arrest in homozygous *Inverdale* ewes. Although this hypothesis is intriguing, mice carrying the *Inverdale* or *Hanna* mutation in the BMP-15 gene need to be generated to verify this.

Paradoxically, inactivation of one copy of BMP-15 ($FecX^I/FecX^+$ and $FecX^H/Fec^+$) in sheep increases the ovulation rate and litter size [56], suggesting that lower levels of this growth factor allow the formation of a larger number of follicles responsive to the LH ovulatory stimulus. The mechanism underlying this phenotype in BMP-15 heterozygotes is not clear. However, it seems that ovarian follicles in these animals undergo precocious maturation and ovulate at a smaller size [57]. Indeed, follicle cells in relatively small antral follicles show an increased LH responsiveness [58]. In agreement with this observation, BMP-15 has been reported to stimulate in vitro the proliferation of preantral granulosa cells and antagonize FSH-dependent differentiation in these cells by downregulating the expression of FSH receptor [59]. These observations suggest that levels of BMP-15 are critical for regulating timing and extent of follicle cell maturation.

Although the receptor for BMP-15 has not been identified, a natural homozygous mutation in the Bmpr-IB gene was found to be associated with the hyperprolific pheno-type of the Booroola strain of Australian Mérino sheep *(FecB^B/FecB^B)*, resembling that of heterozygous BMP-15 sheep [60, 61]. Structural modeling of the protein suggests that the mutation would produce partial inhibition of the receptor activity, thereby mimicking a condition in which availability of the ligand is reduced. In addition, female Bmpr-IB-null mice show an ovarian phenotype similar to that of BMP-15-null mice [62]. These results are consistent with the hypothesis that Bmpr-IB may be involved with BMP-15 signaling. This is also supported by recent studies on the intracellular signaling pathway elicited by BMP-15 in primary cultures of rat granulosa cells [63]. However, many other members of the TGFβ superfamily are present in the follicle, and among them, BMP-4 and BMP-7 are expressed by theca cells and are known to signal through Bmpr-IB in vitro [64, 65]. In addition, expression of Bmpr-IB mRNA has been observed in oocytes and granulosa cells [63–66]. Whether this receptor mediates the action of BMP-15 and/or other ligands involved in the complex regulation of follicle development remains to be elucidated.

Although BMP-6 is expressed by the oocytes and attenuates the FSH-induced cytodifferentiation in granulosa cell cultures [67], BMP-6-null female mice have normal fertility, which suggests that BMP-6 plays a redundant role in follicle development [68].

Bidirectional communication between the oocyte and the surrounding granulosa cells is also critical for oocyte development. Physical contact and intercellular communication between granulosa cells and oocytes are apparently necessary throughout the preantral follicle stage for sustaining normal growth and development of oocytes. For example, oocytes isolated at midgrowth stages cannot grow significantly in vitro without physical association with granulosa cells [46, 69]. In addition, oocytes lacking connexin type-Cx37 do not show detectable gap junction-type intercellular communications with follicle cells and do not complete their growth [2]. Mammalian oocytes are apparently deficient in the transport systems necessary for the uptake of some metabolic precursors such as amino acids and nucleotides, and gap junctions efficiently mediate the transfer of these molecules from follicle cells to the oocyte [69]. Therefore, such heterologous metabolic coupling may be essential for sustaining high levels of synthetic activity in growing oocytes. Besides the nutritional role, follicle cells appear to exert a specific stimulatory activity on oocyte growth through the secretion of paracrine factors, because oocytes that establish in vitro heterologous gap junctions with somatic cells other than follicle cells do not grow unless a follicle cell conditioned medium is added to the culture [70]. Several observations suggest that KL can be one of the factors involved in this control. Follicle cells produce KL in preantral follicles, and addition of KL to oocyte–granulosa cell cocultures enhances and/or accelerates the growth of small oocytes [46, 48]. Furthermore, growing oocytes increases the steady state levels of KL mRNA in preantral follicle cells cultured in vitro [48], suggesting that a positive interaction loop may occur between germ cells and somatic cells. Interestingly, in the antral follicles, once the oocyte reaches full size, cumulus cells cease to synthesize KL, whereas the mural granulosa cells increase KL expression [25, 26]. In vitro studies suggest that this is mainly caused by the suppressive action of fully grown oocytes on cumulus cells, because removal of oocytes from isolated COCs results in increased KL mRNA [71]. In addition, fully grown oocytes inhibit KL expression by preantral granulosa cells [72], and they also suppress the ability of preantral granulosa cells to induce growth of midsize oocytes in coculture systems [73]. These findings suggest that the oocyte produces qualitatively or quantitatively different factors during its development that may determine the temporal pattern of KL expression by the surrounding granulosa cells, thereby controlling its own growth. Interestingly, KL expression is upregulated in GDF-9-null mice [74], and the oocytes grow at an accelerated rate even though proliferation of follicle cells is impaired and the follicle does not develop beyond the primary stage [75]. In addition, GDF-9 and BMP-15 show opposite effects on KL production by preantral granulosa cells in vitro, being suppressive and stimulatory, respectively [71, 72, 76]. Therefore, a balance of these two growth factors might be involved in modulating granulosa cell function to achieve high coordination between oocyte growth and granulosa cell differentiation.

Evidence that the oocyte plays a dominant role in follicle development has been elegantly provided by Eppig and collaborators [77]. They showed that midgrowth 12-day-old oocytes reaggregated in vitro with primordial follicle cells from newborn mice form primordial follicles that subsequently develop to the antral follicle stage in 9 days instead of the normal 21 days, following implantation beneath the renal capsule. This implies that the oocyte regulates the proliferation and differentiation rate of the follicle cells according to its own developmental stage.

From Early Antral to Preovulatory Follicle

During development of antral follicles, the oocyte acquires full competence to complete meiotic maturation and preimplantation embryo development. Somatic cells appear to influence these processes positively although molecular mechanisms regulating such interaction are still unclear [69, 78]. In addition, premature meiotic resumption is likely to be prevented by the follicular environment, because oocytes spontaneously resume meiosis when they are isolated from antral follicles and cultured in vitro [79, 80]. This is also supported by the observation that meiosis does not resume when the cumulus-enclosed oocytes are cultured in contact with mural granulosa cells [81–83]. Several studies have attempted to identify the inhibitor, but results have been inconclusive, although cyclic adenosine monophosphate (cAMP) and hypoxanthine appear to be potential candidates [84–86].

The acquisition of LH receptors by granulosa cells takes place during this phase in response to FSH stimulation and constitutes an essential differentiative step to progress further to the final phase of ovulation and luteinization. However, expression of LH receptor is not homogenous in the antral follicle, showing a decreasing gradient from the outermost layers of mural granulosa cells to cumulus cells [13, 17]. The most extreme situation occurs in mice where functional LH receptors are undetectable in cumulus cells [87]. In vitro studies suggest that the oocyte has a critical role in establishing such different functional patterns in follicle subpopulations. Removal of the oocyte from isolated mouse COCs produces an elevation of the steady-state levels of LH receptor mRNA in cumulus cells [88]. This increased expression is prevented when cumulus cells are cultured in the presence of oocyte-conditioned medium, indicating that the oocyte exerts its suppressive action by the secretion of soluble factors. Mural granulosa cells are also sensitive to the inhibitory action of oocytes, because the LH receptor mRNA levels are drastically reduced in these cells when cultured in vitro with oocytes. This observation suggests that molecular mechanisms are activated in vivo to limit the sphere of oocyte action to cumulus cells and therefore to allow mural granulosa cells to appropriately respond to FSH stimulus and to proceed in their differentiation. GDF-9 suppresses basal and FSH-induced expression of LH receptor by in vitro cultured mural granulosa cells, suggesting that the action of the oocyte is mediated by this growth factor [89]. The purpose for establishing this different distribution of LH receptors in the preovulatory follicle is not known. It can be hypothesized that a lower increase of cAMP levels needs to be generated in cumulus cells than in mural granulosa cells after LH surge to favor the suppressive action of the oocyte on the expression of cAMP-dependent genes that could hinder the formation of the cumulus matrix, such as on the expression of the proteolytic enzymes. Indeed, an increase of cAMP levels stimulates the expression of the serine protease urokinase plasminogen activator (uPA) in cumulus cells and in mural granulosa cells, whereas oocyte soluble factors inhibit the expression of this enzyme in cumulus cells [90] (see "From Preovulatory Follicle to Ovulation").

As mentioned earlier, many other genes are expressed in a different pattern in mural and cumulus granulosa cells. Most likely, opposite gradients of soluble factors generated by theca cells and by oocytes are mainly responsible for the generation of such different cell phenotypes in response to FSH stimulus. This is supported by studies on the regulation of KL expression. In vitro experiments show that FSH-induced KL expression is suppressed in cumulus cells by the oocyte and GDF-9 [71, 72], whereas it is increased in mural granulosa cells by testosterone and keratinocyte growth factor produced by theca cells [71, 91].

A potential role of the oocyte in inhibiting precocious luteinization of mural granulosa cells before the LH surge was first advanced many years ago [32, 33]. Indeed, the oocyte exerts a clear inhibitory effect on progesterone synthesis by the cumulus cells both before and after the LH surge [92]. However, factors produced by theca cells might be mainly involved in such control in mural granulosa cells because BMP-4 and BMP-7, which are highly expressed in the adult ovary, especially in theca cells of large antral follicles, increase estradiol production and inhibit progesterone synthesis by mural granulosa cells stimulated with FSH [66].

From Preovulatory Follicle to Ovulation

Because mouse oocytes and cumulus cells have no detectable LH receptors, it is likely that LH induction of oocyte meiotic resumption and cumulus expansion is mediated by mural granulosa cells. That brief treatment with derivatives of cAMP or with inhibitors of phosphodiesterase, both increasing cAMP levels, can mimic the effects of LH in follicles cultured in vitro and provides evidence for a primary role of cAMP in mediating the action of granulosa cells [93–95]. How to reconcile the increases of cAMP in ovarian follicles with oocyte meiotic resumption is still a problem, because it is generally accepted that high levels of cAMP block meiotic resumption and that transfer of cAMP from somatic cells to the oocyte via gap junctions might constitute one of the mechanisms to maintain meiotic arrest. One hypothesis is that an LH-induced increase in cAMP may disrupt the gap junction network, leading to a decrease in oocyte cAMP [96–98]. However, attempts to define the precise timing of gap junction disruption between mural granulosa cells and cumulus cells and between cumulus cells and the oocyte have given inconsistent results [99–101]. An alternative hypothesis is that LH can promote meiotic resumption by generating a positive signal in somatic cells, which promotes cAMP degradation in oocytes (i.e., activation of phosphodiesterase activity) or that overrides cAMP-mediated meiotic arrest directly [102–104].

Before discussing the regulatory control of cumulus expansion, it is important to consider briefly some structural aspects of the cumulus matrix. The major component of the cumulus viscoelastic matrix is hyaluronan (HA) [87, 105, 106], a very large, polyanionic glycosaminoglycan consisting of repeating disaccharide units:

$$(\text{-}\beta 1,4\text{-glucuronic acid-}\beta 1,3\text{-N-acetylglucosamine-})_n$$

where n can be 50,000 or more (molecular weights of 10 million or more). Because of their large size and polyanionic nature, HA molecules have extended hydrodynamic domains that occupy large solvent volumes thereby

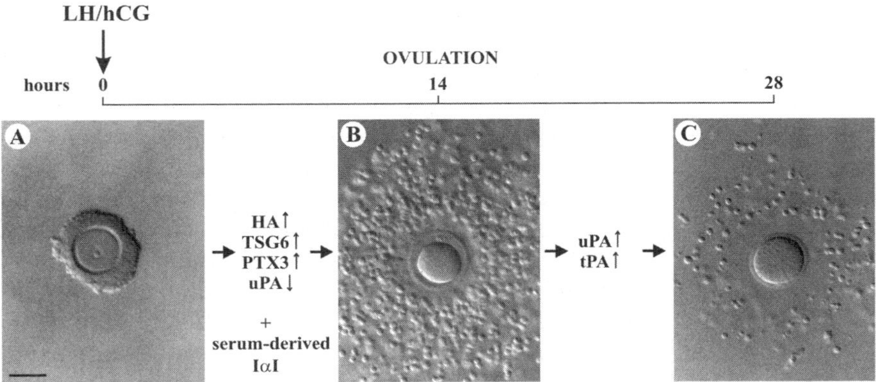

FIGURE 8.2 Stage-dependent expression of specific genes by COCs following LH/human chorionic gonadotropin (hCG) stimulation. **A**, Compact; **B**, expanded; and, **C**, dissociated COC isolated from the ovarian follicles (**A**) or the oviducts (**B** and **C**) at different times from an ovulatory dose of LH or hCG. IαI is not locally produced but diffuses from the blood into the follicle after LH surge and participates in the formation of the cumulus expanded matrix. (Scale bar = 50 μm.)

causing the increase in cumulus size. This glycosaminoglycan is synthesized by hyaluronan synthase 2 (Has2), whose expression is rapidly upregulated after the LH surge [107]. Synthesis of HA is necessary but not sufficient for the process of cumulus expansion. Synthesized HA must be organized into an extracellular matrix that fills the space between cumulus cells. One of the proteins responsible for retaining HA in the matrix is inter alpha trypsin inhibitor (IαI) [108], a serum protein that diffuses into the follicle when the ovulatory stimulus of LH makes the follicle permeable to high-molecular-weight serum proteins [109]. IαI is a complex serum molecule composed of a small protein, called *bikunin* or *light chain,* with a chondroitin sulfate moiety that contains two additional proteins, called *heavy chains*. A pivotal step of the HA assembly in the matrix is the covalent transfer of the heavy chains from the chondroitin sulfate to HA through a transesterification process [110]. It has been suggested that these transferred heavy chains could crosslink HA strands through covalent and ionic bonds and thereby stabilize the mucified COC matrix [111]. Tumor necrosis factor-induced protein-6 (TNFIP6 or TSG6), a protein with HA-binding ability, is synthesized by cumulus cells after the midcycle LH surge [112, 113] and plays a key role in the cumulus matrix formation by facilitating the covalent transfer of heavy chains to HA [113a]. Knockout studies have demonstrated that IαI and TSG6 are critical for cumulus matrix assembly [113a, 114]. Only a few cumulus-free oocytes are ovulated by these mutated mice and, because of the essential role of the expanded cumulus in oocyte fertilization in vivo [30–31], they are not fertilized. Recently, high expression of the long pentraxin Ptx3 gene has been found in cumulus cells after the LH surge. Targeted mutation of this gene causes instability of the cumulus matrix [115] and female sterility [115, 116], resembling the phenotype of IαI- and TSG6-mutated mice. This protein seems to exert its stabilizing effect through a mechanism independent from IαI, because covalent transfer of IαI heavy chains to HA occurs normally in these mice [116a]. In addition, cumulus cells express lower levels of the proteolytic enzyme uPA [90, 117] and higher levels of a proteinase inhibitor nexin-1 [117] than mural granulosa cells, most likely for preventing precocious degradation of the cumulus matrix (Figure 8.2, *A* and *B*).

LH or hCG fail to induce expansion of mouse COC in vitro [87], a result consistent with the undetectable levels of LH receptors in the mouse cumulus cells in the preovulatory follicles. However, HA synthesis and COC expansion can be induced in vitro by FSH [87, 105]. FSH stimulates cAMP production by the cumulus cells, and dibutyryl cAMP, a cAMP analogue, shows a potency and temporal course of HA induction similar to that observed with FSH [118]. Interestingly, a level of 14 fmol of cAMP/COC is sufficient for stimulating maximum HA synthesis by COCs cultured in the presence of FSH, and a similar cAMP level is achieved by COCs in vivo 2 to 4 hours after hCG injection into mice [119, 120], a time at which HA synthesis is initiated. Because, mouse cumulus cells do not appear to have LH receptors, the LH-dependent cAMP elevation observed in cumulus cells in vivo is likely mediated by mural granulosa cells either by transfer of cAMP via gap junctions or by the synthesis or activation of a molecule that can stimulate adenylate cyclase (AC) in the cumulus cells. Based on these findings, it is reasonable to hypothesize a primary role for cAMP in regulating HA synthesis and in promoting cumulus expansion in vivo. However, epidermal growth factor, signaling through a tyrosine kinase transduction pathway, is equally able to induce in vitro HA synthesis and cumulus expansion [38, 118, 121], suggesting that this process might not be exclusively elicited by cAMP in vivo. Recent findings suggest that these two membrane transduction signals may converge on a common pathway at the step of mitogen-activated protein kinase (MAPK) activation [122]. Prostaglandin E_2 is rapidly synthesized by mural granulosa cells and cumulus cells after hCG stimulation [123] and can induce expansion in vitro [124]. Involvement of prostaglandin E_2 in the regulation of cumulus expansion is indicated from the altered formation of the cumulus matrix and the sterility of cyclooxygenase-2 and EP2 prostaglandin E_2-receptor-null female mice [125–127].

However, the synthesis of HA is not prevented and that of TSG6 is only reduced in these mutated mice [128]. This suggests that prostaglandin E_2 may serve in vivo to support final stabilization of the cumulus matrix rather than to serve as its primary inducer. In contrast to mouse COCs, detectable expansion can be induced in COCs obtained from other species by treatment with high doses of LH, suggesting that they might not require mural granulosa cell mediation to be activated in vivo by the LH surge [129–132].

The oocyte plays a key role in mouse cumulus expansion. When the oocyte is mechanically removed from the COC, isolated cumulus cells synthesize low levels of HA in the presence of FSH, and they do not form an expanded matrix [36, 37]. Furthermore, in the absence of oocytes, FSH-stimulated cumulus cells secrete much higher levels of the serine protease uPA than intact COCs [90]. Both a high level of HA synthesis and a low level of uPA activity are restored in FSH-stimulated cumulus cells by adding either oocytes or oocyte-conditioned medium to the cultures. Therefore, soluble factors released by the oocyte appear to be important paracrine regulators of endocrine stimulus on the cumulus cells, facilitating matrix formation and inhibiting its degradation. Oocytes acquire this ability at the end of their growth [133]. Although oocyte meiotic maturation and cumulus expansion are temporally related in physiological conditions, cumulus expansion is also achieved, both in vitro and in vivo, when oocyte meiotic resumption is prevented [36, 37, 134, 135], suggesting that the factor promoting cumulus expansion is constitutively produced by fully grown oocytes. It is likely that continuous production of oocyte factors is required to maintain and modulate the response of cumulus cells to the gonadotropin stimulus. Indeed, isolated mouse cumulus cells, precultured in basal medium, rapidly lose their ability to synthesize HA and expand when they are stimulated at a later time with FSH or dbcAMP in the presence of oocytes. However, they retain such ability when precultured in the presence of oocyte or oocyte-conditioned medium [136]. In addition, whereas FSH or dbcAMP need be present only for the first 2 hours for stimulating maximal HA synthesis, the oocyte must be continuously present to achieve maximum synthesis of HA and full expansion [118]. Therefore, it can be hypothesized that the oocyte exerts a continuous control at the transcriptional level in cumulus cells that serves to modulate the signals elicited by cAMP in these cells.

GDF-9, but not BMP-15 or BMP-6, induces in vitro mouse cumulus expansion and upregulates the expression of all genes known to be involved in cumulus matrix formation and stability (i.e., Has2, TSG6, cyclooxygenase-2, EP2 prostaglandin E_2 receptor, and PTX3), while it suppresses that of the possibly destabilizing enzyme uPA by mural granulosa cells in vitro [89]. These findings strongly suggest that GDF-9 is the oocyte factor that regulates cumulus expansion (see Figure 8.2). The obligatory role of GDF-9 at the early stages of folliculogenesis hinders verifying its role in vivo at the preovulatory follicle stage. As reported earlier, recombinant BMP-15 does not have the ability to induce in vitro cumulus expansion. However, homozygous disruption of BMP-15 produces instability of the cumulus matrix in vivo, and this effect is more pronounced in double mutant female mice homozygous for BMP-15 and heterozygous for GDF-9 [53], suggesting a cooperation between BMP-15 and GDF-9 in vivo in the control of cumulus expansion. However, it cannot be excluded that the lack of BMP-15 during the follicle development can prevent proper differentiation of cumulus cells so that they cannot fully respond to GDF-9 and/or to cAMP at later stages. Indeed, several abnormalities were observed in ovaries from these mice, including reduction in the number of follicles and formation of cysts. Similar consideration could be made for mice deficient in Bmpr-IB that exhibit an abnormal cumulus expansion together with irregular estrous cycles and impaired pseudopregnancy response [62]. Although the receptor for GDF-9 has not been identified, it has been recently shown that this growth factor induces the phosphorylation of SMAD2 [137, 138], a signal transduction pathway generally used by TGFβ members of the TGFβ superfamily but not by BMPs [139]. This is in agreement with the ability of TGFβ1 to stimulate cumulus expansion [38], and it suggests that GDF-9 might bind to a similar receptor. Nuclear convergence of cAMP and TGFβ signaling pathways at the level of transcriptional complex formation has been reported in other cell types [140]. Therefore, it is likely that cAMP elevation in cumulus cells following the LH surge promotes the phosphorylation and activation of cAMP-dependent transcription factors that interact with SMAD2, the GDF-9 signal-transducing molecule. This leads to the activation of Has2 (as well as of other genes that are required for production and organization of the extracellular matrix) and suppression of uPA (and possibly of other unknown proteolytic enzyme genes), depending on the structure of promoter regions of target genes.

Mural granulosa cells isolated from preovulatory follicles and cultured in vitro with oocytes assume a cumulus cell phenotype. However, mural granulosa cells apparently do not require other stimuli than the oocyte or GDF-9 for increasing the expression of Has2, TSG6, cyclooxygenase-2, EP2 prostaglandin E_2 receptor, and PTX3 and for decreasing that of uPA [38, 89, 90, 141]. This is at least in part because mural granulosa cells spontaneously produce prostaglandin E_2 that can act in an autocrine way to interplay with GDF-9 [38, 142]. These results indicate that, although mural granulosa cells show functional specificity, they still can be modulated in their function by the oocyte. Because media conditioned by cumulus cell–enclosed oocytes show significantly lower effect on mural granulosa cells than media conditioned by isolated oocytes [11], it is reasonable to hypothesize that cumulus cells bind or inactivate the oocyte factor, a process that could create a decreasing concentration gradient of active factor with increasing distance from the oocyte. In agreement with this hypothesis, the innermost layers of mural granulosa cells lining the antrum show an intermediate phenotype between cumulus and mural granulosa cells. This mechanism might have a major role in limiting the range of the oocyte's influence in vivo.

Cumulus cells from pigs, cows, and rats, in contrast to those from mice, can be stimulated to expand in vitro in the absence of oocytes [143–146]. Oocytes from these species, however, do produce the factor because they can induce mouse cumulus cell expansion. Moreover, rat cumulus cells, similar to mouse cumulus cells, rapidly lose their ability to expand in response to FSH unless cocultured with oocytes, whereas pig cumulus cells can retain their responsiveness to the gonadotropin without oocytes [145]. These species differences among cumulus cells may be related to the stability of the cumulus cell response. Alternatively, in these species, the oocyte might induce functional changes in the cumulus cells before LH surge, making them partially independent of the oocyte thereafter. This hypothesis is supported by the observation that pig cumulus cells seem to secrete a factor functionally similar to that synthesized by the oocytes (able to induce mouse cumulus expansion), that could act in an autocrine way [147], but, at the same time, they appear to require the presence of the oocyte to achieve maximal HA synthesis [148, 149].

Within a few hours after ovulation, cumulus cells begin to synthesize high levels of uPA despite the fact that the enclosed mature oocyte still expresses GDF-9 and has the ability to suppress the expression of uPA by preovulatory cumuli [150]. These findings suggest that cumulus cells become insensitive to oocyte influence after ovulation. The enclosed mature oocyte also begins to secrete proteases (i.e., tissue type plasminogen activator) [150]. Shortly after, degradation of the matrix occurs, leading to cumulus dispersion and oocyte denudation (see Figure 8.2, *B* and *C*). Therefore the oocyte determines matrix stability before ovulation and facilitates matrix degradation thereafter. It is likely that such cumulus cell–oocyte interplay is designed to promote fertilization of newly ovulated oocytes and to prevent that of aged oocytes. In fact, ovulated oocytes rapidly undergo changes that affect their ability to develop in a normal embryo [151, 152].

CONCLUSION

In recent years, a body of evidence has been provided that the oocyte exerts an array of paracrine controls on granulosa cell function. The identification of growth factors specifically expressed by the oocyte has allowed significant progress of the knowledge in this field. Although mRNAs for these growth factors have been detected in the oocyte from the beginning of the growth to fertilization, nothing is known about the temporal pattern of synthesis and/or activation of the transcripts. In addition, the characterization of the specific receptors and intracellular signaling pathways used by these factors are still incomplete. This information will be essential for understanding how the oocyte can modulate the variety of stimuli involved in the complex process of granulosa cell differentiation during follicle development.

ACKNOWLEDGMENTS

This work was supported by a Ministero dell' Istruzione, dell' Università e della Ricerca (MIUR) grant for National Project "Molecular mechanisms of germ cell development and differentiation in in vivo experimental models."

References

1. Grazul-Bilska, A. T., Reynolds, L. P., and Redmer, D. A. (1997). Gap junctions in the ovaries. *Biol. Reprod.* 57, 947–957.
2. Simon, A., Goodenough, D. A., Li, E., and Paul, D. L. (1997). Female infertility in mice lacking connexin-37. *Nature* 385, 525–529.
3. Ackert, C. L., Gittens, J. E., O'Brien, M. J., Eppig, J. J., and Kidder, G. M. (2001). Intercellular communication via connexin-43 gap junctions is required for ovarian folliculogenesis in the mouse. *Dev. Biol.* 233, 258–270.
4. Richards, J. S. (1975). Estradiol receptor content in rat granulosa cells during follicular development: Modification by estradiol and gonadotropins. *Endocrinology* 97, 1174–1184.
5. Richards, J. S., Ireland, J. J., Rao, M. C., Bernath, G. A., Midgley, Jr., A. R., and Reichert, Jr., L. E. (1976). Ovarian follicular development in the rat: Hormone receptor regulation by estradiol, follicle stimulating hormone, and luteinizing hormone. *Endocrinology* 99, 1562–1570.
6. Sorensen, R. A., and Wasserman, P. M. (1976). Relationship between growth and meiotic maturation of the mouse oocyte. *Dev. Biol.* 50, 531–536.
7. Cattanach, B. M., Iddon, C. A., Charlton, H. M., Chiappa, S. A., and Fink, G. (1977). Gonadotrophin-releasing hormone deficiency in a mutant mouse with hypogonadism. *Nature* 269, 338–340.
8. Halpin, D. M., Charlton, H. M., and Faddy, M. J. (1986). Effects of gonadotrophin deficiency on follicular development in hypogonadal (hpg) mice. *J. Reprod. Fertil.* 78, 119–125.
9. Kumar, T. R., Wang, Y., Lu, N., and Matzuk, M. M. (1997). Follicle-stimulating hormone is required for ovarian follicle maturation but not male fertility. *Nat. Genet.* 15, 201–204.
10. Pedersen, T. (1970). Follicle kinetic in the ovary of the cyclic mouse. *Acta. Endocrinol.* 64, 304–323.
11. Salustri, A., Yanagishita, M., Underhill, C. B., Laurent, T. C., and Hascall, V. C. (1992). Localization of hyaluronic acid in

the cumulus cells and mural granulosa cells of the preovulatory follicle. *Dev. Biol.* 151, 541–551.
12. Rodgers, R. J., Rodgers, H. F., Hall, P. F., Waterman, M. R., and Simpson, E. R. (1975). Immunolocalization of cholesterol side-chain-cleavage cytochrome P-450 and 17-alpha-hydroxylase cytochrome P-450 in bovine ovarian follicles. *J. Reprod. Fertil.* 78, 627–638.
13. Amsterdam, A., Koch, Y., Lieberman, M. E., and Lindner, H. R. (1975). Distribution of binding sites for human chorionic gonadotropin in the preovulatory follicle of the rat. *J. Cell. Biol.* 67, 894–900.
14. Zoller, L. C., and Weisz, J. (1979). A quantitative cytochemical study of glucose-6-phosphate dehydrogenase and follicle. *Histochemistry* 62, 125–135.
15. Lawrence, T. S., Dekel, N., and Beers, W. H. (1980). Binding of human chorionic gonadotropin by rat cumuli oophori and granulosa cells: A comparative study. *Endocrinology* 106, 1114–1118.
16. Channing, C. P., Bae, I. H., Stone, S. L., Anderson, L. D., Edelson, S., and Fowler, S. C. (1981). Porcine granulosa and cumulus cell properties. LH/hCG receptors, ability to secrete progesterone, and ability to respond to LH. *Mol. Cell. Endocrinol.* 22, 359–370.
17. Oxberry, B. A., and Greenwald, G. S. (1982). An autoradiographic study of the binding of 125 I-labeled follicle-stimulating hormone, human chorionic gonadotropin, and prolactin to the hamster ovary throughout the estrous cycle. *Biol. Reprod.* 27, 505–516.
18. Zoller, L. C. (1984). A quantitative electron microscopic analysis of the membrane granulosa of rat preovulatory follicle. *Acta. Anat.* 118, 218–223.
19. Zlotkin, T., Farkash, Y., and Orly, J. (1986). Cell-specific expression of immunoreactive cholesterol side-chain cleavage cytochrome P-450 during follicular development in the rat ovary. *Endocrinology* 119, 2809–2820.
20. Hirshfield, A. N. (1986). Patterns of [3H] thymidine incorporation differ in immature rats and mature, cycling rats. *Biol. Reprod.* 34, 229–235.
21. Oliver, J. E., Aitman, T. J., Powell, J. F., Wilson, C. A., and Clayton, R. N. (1989). Insulin-like growth factor I gene expression in the rat ovary is confined to the granulosa cells of the developing follicles. *Endocrinology* 124, 2671–2679.
22. Dissen, G. A., Lara, H. E., Fahrenbach, W. H., Costa, M. E., and Ojeda, S. R. (1994). Immature rat ovaries become revascularized rapidly after autotransplantation and show a gonadotropin-dependent increase in angiogenic factor gene expression. *Endocrinology* 134, 1146–1154.
23. Braw-Tal, R. (1994). Expression of mRNA for follistatin and inhibin/activin subunits during follicular growth and atresia. *J. Mol. Endocrinol.* 13, 253–264.
24. Ueno, S., Takahashi, M., Manganaro, T. F., Ragin, R. C., and Donahoe, P. K. (1989). Cellular localization of mullerian inhibiting substance in the developing rat ovary. *Endocrinology* 124, 1000–1006.
25. Manova, K., Huang, E. J., Angeles, M., De Leon, V., Sanchez, S., Pronovost, S. M., Besmer, P., and Bachvarova, R. F. (1993). The expression pattern of the c-kit ligand in gonads of mice supports a role for the c-kit receptor in oocyte growth and in proliferation of spermatogonia. *Dev. Biol.* 157, 85–99.
26. Motro, B., and Bernstein, A. (1993). Dynamic changes in ovarian c-kit and steel expression during the estrous reproductive cycle. *Dev. Dynam.* 197, 69–79.
27. Sorensen, R. A., and Wasserman, P. M. (1976). Relationship between growth and meiotic maturation of the mouse oocyte. *Dev. Biol.* 50, 531–536.
28. Eppig, J. J., Schultz, R. M., O'Brien, M., and Chesnel, F. (1994). Relationship between the developmental programs controlling nuclear and cytoplasmic maturation of mouse oocytes. *Dev. Biol.* 164, 1–9.
29. Richards, J. S., Russell, D. L., Ochsner, S., and Espey, L. L. (2002). Ovulation: New dimensions and new regulators of the inflammatory-like response. *Annu. Rev. Physiol.* 64, 69–92.
30. Hizaki, H., Segi, E., Sugimoto, Y., Hirose, M., Saji, T., Ushikubi, F., Matsuoka, T., Noda, Y., Tanaka, T., Yoshida, N., Narumiya, S., and Ichikawa, A. (1999). Abortive expansion of the cumulus and impaired fertility in mice lacking the prostaglandin E receptor subtype EP(2). *Proc. Natl. Acad. Sci. USA* 96, 10501–10506.
31. Tilley, S. L., Audoly, L. P., Hicks, E. H., Kim, H. S., Flannery, P. J., Coffman, T. M., and Koller, B. H. (1999). Reproductive failure and reduced blood pressure in mice lacking the EP2 prostaglandin E2 receptor. *J. Clin. Invest.* 103, 1539–1545.
32. El-Fouly, M. A., Cook, B., Nekola, M., and Nalbandov, A. V. (1970). Role of the ovum in follicular luteinization. *Endocrinology* 87, 288–293.
33. Nekola, M. V., and Nalbandov, A. V. (1971). Morphological changes of rat follicular cells as influenced by oocytes. *Biol. Reprod.* 4, 154–160.
34. Lindner, H. R., Tsafriri, A., Liebfrman, M. E., Zor, U., Koch, Y., Bauminger, S., and Barnea, A. (1974). Gonadotropin action on cultured Graafian follicles: Induction of maturation division of the mammalian oocyte and differentiation of the luteal cell. *Rec. Prog. Hormone Res.* 30, 79–138.
35. Channing, C., and Tsafriri, A. (1977). Lack of an inhibitory influence of oocytes upon luteinization of porcine granulosa cells in culture. *J. Reprod. Fertil.* 50, 103–105.
36. Buccione, R., Vanderhyden, B. C., Caron, P. J., and Eppig, J. J. (1990). FSH-induced expansion of the mouse cumulus oophorus in vitro is dependent upon a specific factor(s) secreted by the oocyte. *Dev. Biol.* 138, 16–25.
37. Salustri, A., Yanagishita, M., and Hascall, V. C. (1990). Mouse oocytes regulate hyaluronic acid synthesis and mucification by FSH-stimulated cumulus cells. *Dev. Biol.* 138, 26.
38. Salustri, A., Ulisse, S., Yanagishita, M., and Hascall, V. C. (1990). Hyaluronic acid synthesis by mural granulosa cells and cumulus cells in vitro is selectively stimulated by a factor produced by oocytes and by transforming growth factor-β. *J. Biol. Chem.* 265, 19517–19523.
39. McGrath, S. A., Esquela, A. F., and Lee, S. J. (1993). GDF-3 and GDF-9: Two new members of the transforming growth factor-beta superfamily containing a novel pattern of cysteines. *J. Biol. Chem.* 268, 3444.
40. McGrath, S. A., Esquela, A. F., and Lee, S. J. (1995). Oocyte-specific expression of growth/differentiation factor-9. *Mol. Endocrinol.* 9, 131–136.
41. Dong, J., Albertini, D. F., Nishimori, K., Kumar, T. R., Lu, N., and Matzuk, M. M. (1996). Growth differentiation

factor-9 is required during early ovarian folliculogenesis. *Nature* 383, 531–535.

42. Dube, J. L., Wang, P., Elvin, J., Lyons, K. M., Celeste, A. J., and Matzuk, M. M. (1998). The bone morphogenetic protein 15 gene is X-linked and expressed in oocytes. *Mol. Endocrinol.* 12, 1809–1817.
43. Laitinen, M., Vuojolainen, K., Jaatinen, R., Ketola, I., Aaltonen, J., Lehtonen, E., Heikinheimo, M., and Ritvos, O. (1998). A novel growth differentiation factor-9 (GDF-9) related factor is co-expressed with GDF-9 in mouse oocytes during folliculogenesis. *Mech. Dev.* 78, 135–140.
44. Lyons, K. M., Pelton, R. W., and Hogan, B. L. (1989). Patterns of expression of murine Vgr-1 and BMP-2a RNA suggest that transforming growth factor-beta–like genes coordinately regulate aspects of embryonic development. *Genes Dev.* 3, 1657–1668.
45. Soyal, S. M., Amleh, A., and Dean, J. (2000). FIGalpha, a germ cell–specific transcription factor required for ovarian follicle formation. *Development* 127, 4645–4654.
46. Klinger, F. G., and De Felici, M. (2002). In vitro development of growing oocytes from fetal mouse oocytes: Stage-specific regulation by stem cell factor and granulosa cells. *Dev. Biol.* 244, 85–95.
47. Yoshida, H., Takakura, N., Kataoka, H., Kunisada, T., Okamura, H., and Nishikawa, S. I. (1997). Stepwise requirement of c-kit tyrosine kinase in mouse ovarian follicle development. *Dev. Biol.* 184, 122–137.
48. Packer, A. I., Chang Hsu, Y., Besmer, P., and Bachvarova, R. F. (1994). The ligand of c-kit receptor promotes oocyte growth. *Dev. Biol.* 161, 194–205.
49. Aaltonen, J., Laitinen, M. P., Vuojolainen, K., Jaatinen, R., Horelli-Kuitunen, N., Seppa, L., Louhio, H., Tuuri, T., Sjoberg, J., Butzow, R., Hovata, O., Dale, L., and Ritvos, O. (1999). Human growth differentiation factor 9 (GDF-9) and its novel homolog GDF-9B are expressed in oocytes during early folliculogenesis. *J. Clin. Endocrinol. Metab.* 84, 2744–2750.
50. Bodensteiner, K. J., Clay, C. M., Moeller, C. L., and Sawyer, H. R. (1999). Molecular cloning of the ovine growth/differentiation factor-9 gene and expression of growth/differentiation factor-9 in ovine and bovine ovaries. *Biol. Reprod.* 60, 381–386.
51. Jaatinen, R., Laitinen, M. P., Vuojolainen, K., Aaltonen, J., Louhio, H., Heikinheimo, K., Lehtonen, E., and Ritvos, O. (1999). Localization of growth differentiation factor-9 (GDF-9) mRNA and protein in rat ovaries and cDNA cloning of rat GDF-9 and its novel homolog GDF-9B. *Mol. Cell. Endocrinol.* 25, 156.
52. Eckery, D. C., Whale, L. J., Lawrence, S. B., Wylde, K. A., McNatty, K. P., and Juengel, J. L. (2002). Expression of mRNA encoding growth differentiation factor 9 and bone morphogenetic protein 15 during follicular formation and growth in a marsupial, the brushtail possum (Trichosurus vulpecula). *Mol. Cell. Endocrinol.* 192, 115–126.
53. Yan, C., Wang, P., DeMayo, J., DeMayo, F. J., Elvin, J. A., Carino, C., Prasad, S. V., Skinner, S. S., Dunbar, B. S., Dube, J. L., Celeste, A. J., and Matzuk, M. M. (2001). Synergistic roles of bone morphogenetic protein 15 and growth differentiation factor 9 in ovarian function. *Mol. Endocrinol.* 15, 854–866.
54. Galloway, S. M., McNatty, K. P., Cambridge, L. M., Laitinen, M. P., Juengel, J. L., Jokiranta, T. S., McLaren, R. J., Luiro, K., Dodds, K. G., Montgomery, G. W., Beattie, A. E., Davis, G. H., and Ritvos, O. (2000). Mutations in an oocyte-derived growth factor gene (BMP-15) cause increased ovulation rate and infertility in a dosage-sensitive manner. *Nat. Genet.* 25, 279–283.
55. Liao, W. X., Moore, R. K., Otsuka, F., and Shimasaki, S. (2003). Effect of intracellular interactions on the processing and secretion of bone morphogenetic protein-15 (BMP-15) and growth and differentiation factor-9. Implication of the aberrant ovarian phenotype of BMP-15 mutant sheep. *J. Biol. Chem.* 278, 3713–3719.
56. Davis, G. H., McEwan, J. C., Fennessy, P. F., Dodds, K. G, and Farquhar, P. A. (1991). Evidence for the presence of a major gene influencing ovulation rate on the X chromosome of sheep. *Biol. Reprod.* 44, 620–624.
57. Davis, G. H., McEwan, J. C., Fennessy, P. F., Dodds, K. G., McNatty, K. P., and O, W. S. (1992). Infertility due to bilateral ovarian hypoplasia in sheep homozygous (FecXI FecXI) for the Inverdale prolificacy gene located on the X chromosome. *Biol. Reprod.* 46, 636–640.
58. Shackell, G. H., Hudson, N. L., Heath, D. A., Lun, S., Shaw, L., Condell, L., Blay, L. R., and McNatty, K. P. (1993). Plasma gonadotropin concentrations and ovarian characteristics in Inverdale ewes that are heterozygous for a major gene (FecX1) on the X chromosome that influences ovulation rate. *Biol. Reprod.* 48, 1150–1156.
59. Otsuka, F., Yamamoto, S., Erickson, G. F., and Shimasaki, S. (2001). Bone morphogenetic protein-15 inhibits follicle-stimulating hormone (FSH) action by suppressing FSH receptor expression. *J. Biol. Chem.* 276, 11387–11392.
60. Mulsant, P., Lecerf, F., Fabre, S., Schibler, L., Monget, P., Lanneluc, I., Pisselet, C., Riquet, J., Monniaux, D., Callebaut, I., Cribiu, E., Thimonier, J., Teyssier, J., Bodin, L., Cognie, Y., Chitour, N., and Elsen, J. M. (2001). Mutation in bone morphogenetic protein receptor-IB is associated with increased ovulation rate in Booroola Merino ewes. *Proc. Natl. Acad. Sci. USA* 98, 5104–5109.
61. Wilson, T., Wu, X. Y., Juengel, J. L., Ross, I. K., Lumsden, J. M., Lord, E. A., Dodds, K. G., Walling, G. A., McEwan, J. C., O'Connell, A. R., McNatty, K. P., and Montgomery, G. W. (2001). Highly prolific Booroola sheep have a mutation in the intracellular kinase domain of bone morphogenetic protein IB receptor (ALK-6) that is expressed in both oocytes and granulosa cells. *Biol. Reprod.* 64, 1225–1235.
62. Yi, S. E., LaPolt, P. S., Yoon, B. S., Chen, J. Y., Lu, J. K., and Lyons, K. M. (2001). The type I BMP receptor BmprIB is essential for female reproductive function. *Proc. Natl. Acad. Sci. USA* 98, 7994–7999.
63. Moore, R. K., Otsuka, F., and Shimasaki, S. (2003). Molecular basis of bone morphogenetic protein-15 signaling in granulosa cells. *J. Biol. Chem.* 278, 304–310.
64. ten Dijke, P., Yamashita, H., Sampath, T. K., Reddi, A. H., Estevez, M., Riddle, D. L., Ichijo, H., Heldin, C. H., and Miyazono, K. (1994). Identification of type I receptors for osteogenic protein-1 and bone morphogenetic protein-4. *J. Biol. Chem.* 269, 16985–16988.
65. Liu, F., Ventura, F., Doody, J., and Massague, J. (1995). Human type II receptor for bone morphogenic proteins

(BMPs): Extension of the two-kinase receptor model to the BMPs. *Mol. Cell. Biol.* 15, 3479–3486.
66. Shimasaki, S., Zachow, R. J., Li, D., Kim, H., Iemura, S., Ueno, N., Sampath, K., Chang, R. J., and Erickson, G. F. (1999). A functional bone morphogenetic protein system in the ovary. *Proc. Natl. Acad. Sci. USA* 96, 7282–7287.
67. Otsuka, F., Moore, R. K., and Shimasaki, S. (2001). Biological function and cellular mechanism of bone morphogenetic protein-6 in the ovary. *J. Biol. Chem.* 276, 32889–32895.
68. Solloway, M. J., Dudley, A. T., Bikoff, E. K., Lyons, K. M., Hogan, B. L., and Robertson, E. J. (1998). Mice lacking BMP-6 function. *Dev. Genet.* 22, 321–339.
69. Eppig, J. J., O'Brien, M., and Wigglesworth, K. (1996). Mammalian oocyte growth and development in vitro. *Mol. Reprod. Dev.* 44, 260–273.
70. Buccione, P., Cecconi, S., Tatone, C., Mangia, F., and Colonna, R. (1987). Follicle cell regulation of mammalian oocyte growth. *J. Exp. Zool.* 242, 351–354.
71. Joyce, I. M., Pendola, F. L., Wigglesworth, K., and Eppig, J. J. (1999). Oocyte regulation of kit ligand expression in mouse ovarian follicles. *Dev. Biol.* 214, 342–353.
72. Joyce, I. M., Clark, A. T., Pendola, F. L., and Eppig, J. J. (2000). Comparison of recombinant growth differentiation factor-9 and oocyte regulation of kit ligand messenger ribonucleic acid expression in mouse ovarian follicles. *Biol. Reprod.* 63, 1669–1675.
73. Cecconi, S., and Rossi, G. (2001). Mouse antral oocytes regulate preantral granulosa cell ability to stimulate oocyte growth in vitro. *Dev. Biol.* 233, 186–191.
74. Elvin, J. A., Yan, C., Wang, P., Nishimori, K., and Matzuk, M. M. (1999). Molecular characterization of the follicle defects in the growth differentiation factor 9-deficient ovary. *Mol. Endocrinol.* 13, 1018–1034.
75. Carabatsos, M. J., Elvin, J., Matzuk, M. M., and Alberini, D. F. (1998). Characterization of oocyte and follicle development in growth differentiation factor-9-deficient mice. *Dev. Biol.* 204, 373–384.
76. Otsuka, F., and Shimasaki, S. (2002). A negative feedback system between oocyte bone morphogenetic protein 15 and granulosa cell kit ligand: Its role in regulating granulosa cell mitosis. *Proc. Natl. Acad. Sci. USA* 99, 8060–8065.
77. Eppig, J. J., Wigglesworth, K., and Pendola, F. L. (2002). The mammalian oocyte orchestrates the rate of ovarian follicular development. *Proc. Natl. Acad. Sci. USA* 99, 2890–2894.
78. De La Fuente, R., and Eppig, J. J. (2001). Transcriptional activity of the mouse oocyte genome: Companion granulosa cells modulate transcription and chromatin remodelling. *Dev. Biol.* 229, 224–236.
79. Pincus, G., and Enzmann, E. V. (1935). The comparative behavior of mammalian eggs in vivo and in vitro I. The activation of ovarian eggs. *J. Exp. Med.* 62, 655–675.
80. Edwards, R. G. (1965). Maturation in vitro of mouse, sheep, cow, pig, rhesus monkey, and human ovarian oocytes. *Nature* 208, 349–351.
81. Tsafriri, A., and Channing, C. P. (1975). An inhibitory influence of granulosa cells and follicular fluid upon oocyte meiosis in vitro. *Endocrinology* 96, 922–927.
82. Leibfried, L., and First, N. L. (1980). Effect of bovine and porcine follicular fluid and granulosa cells on maturation of oocytes in vitro. *Biol. Reprod.* 23, 699–704.
83. Racowsky, C., and Baldwin, K. V. (1989). In vitro and in vivo studies reveal that hamster oocyte meiotic arrest is maintained only transiently by follicular fluid, but persistently by membrana/cumulus granulosa cell contact. *Dev. Biol.* 134, 297–306.
84. Cho, W. K., Stern, S., and Biggers, J. D. (1974). Inhibitory effect of dibutyryl cAMP on mouse oocyte maturation in vitro. *J. Exp. Zool.* 187, 383–386.
85. Downs, S. M., Coleman, D. L., Ward-Bailey, P. F., and Eppig, J. J. (1985). Hypoxanthine is the principal inhibitor of murine oocyte in a low molecular weight fraction of porcine follicular fluid. *Proc. Nat. Acad. Sci. USA* 82, 454–458.
86. Salustri, A., Petrungaro, S., De Felici, M., Conti, M., and Siracusa G. (1985). Effect of follicle-stimulating hormone on cyclic adenosine monophosphate level and on meiotic maturation in mouse cumulus cell-enclosed oocytes cultured in vitro. *Biol. Reprod.* 33, 797–802.
87. Eppig, J. J. (1979). FSH stimulates hyaluronic acid synthesis by oocyte–cumulus cell complexes from mouse preovulatory follicles. *Nature* 281, 483–484.
88. Eppig, J. J., Wigglesworth, K., Pendola, F. L., and Hirao, J. (1997). Murine oocytes suppress expression of luteinizing hormone receptor messenger ribonucleic acid by granulosa cells. *Biol. Reprod.* 56, 976–984.
89. Elvin, J. A., Clark, A. T., Wang, P., Wolfman, N. M., and Matzuk, M. M. (1999). Paracrine actions of growth differentiation factor-9 in the mammalian ovary. *Mol. Endocrinol.* 13, 1035–1048.
90. Canipari, R., Epifano, O., Siracusa, G., and Salustri, A. (1995). Mouse oocytes inhibit plasminogen activator production by ovarian cumulus and granulosa cells. *Dev. Biol.* 167, 371–378.
91. Parrott, J. A., and Skinner, M. K. (1998). Thecal cell-granulosa cell interactions involve a positive feedback loop among keratinocyte growth factor, hepatocyte growth factor, and kit ligand during ovarian follicular development. *Endocrinology* 139, 2240–2245.
92. Vanderhyden, B. C., and Macdonald, E. A. (1998). Mouse oocytes regulate granulosa cell steroidogenesis throughout follicular development. *Biol. Reprod.* 59, 1296–1301.
93. Dekel, N., Galiani, D., and Sherizly, I. (1988). Dissociation between inhibitory and stimulatory action of cAMP on maturation of rat oocytes. *Mol. Cell. Encodrinol.* 56, 115–121.
94. Dekel, N., Galiani, D., and Beers, W. H. (1988). Induction of maturation in follicle-enclosed oocytes: The response to gonadotropins at different stages of follicular development. *Biol. Reprod.* 38, 517–521.
95. Phillips, D. M., and Dekel, N. (1982). Effect of gonadotropins and prostaglandin on cumulus mucification in cultures of intact follicles. *J. Exp. Zool.* 221, 275–282.
96. Larsen, W. J., Wert, S. E., and Brunner, G. D. (1987). Differential modulation of rat follicle cell gap junction populations at ovulation. *Dev. Biol.* 122, 61–71.
97. Dekel, N. (1987). Interaction between the oocyte and the granulosa cells in the preovulatory follicle. In *Endocrinology and Physiology of Reproduction*, eds. D. T. Armstrong, et al., 197–209. New York: Plenum Press.
98. Granot, I., and Dekel, N. (2002). The ovarian gap junction protein connexin-43: Regulation by gonadotropins. *Trends Endocrinol. Metab.* 13, 310–313.

99. Moor, R. M., Smith, M. W., and Dawson, R. M. (1980). Measurement of intercellular coupling between oocytes and cumulus cells using intracellular markers. *Exp. Cell. Res.* 126, 15–29.
100. Eppig, J. J. (1982). The relationship between cumulus cell-oocyte coupling, oocyte meiotic maturation, and cumulus expansion. *Dev. Biol.* 89, 268–272.
101. Salustri, A., and Siracusa, G. (1983). Metabolic coupling, cumulus expansion and meiotic resumption in mouse cumuli oophori cultured in vitro in the presence of FSH or dbcAMP or stimulated in vivo by hCG. *J. Reprod. Fertil.* 68, 335–341.
102. Richard, F. J., Tsafriri, A., and Conti, M. (2001). Role of phosphodiesterase type 3A in rat oocyte maturation. *Biol. Reprod.* 65, 1444–1451.
103. Downs, S. M., Daniel, S. A., and Eppig, J. J. (1988). Induction of maturation in cumulus cell-enclosed mouse oocytes by follicle-stimulating hormone and epidermal growth factor: Evidence for a positive stimulus of somatic cell origin. *J. Exp. Zool.* 245, 86–96.
104. Fagbohun, C. F., and Downs, S. M. (1991). Metabolic coupling and ligand-stimulated meiotic maturation in the mouse oocyte-cumulus cell complex. *Biol. Reprod.* 45, 851–859.
105. Salustri, A., Yanagishita, M., and Hascall, V. C. (1989). Synthesis and accumulation of hyaluronic acid and proteoglycans in the mouse cumulus cell–oocyte complex during follicle-stimulating hormone-induced mucification. *J. Biol. Chem.* 264, 13840–13847.
106. Chen, L., Russell, P. T., and Larsen, W. J. (1993). Functional significance of cumulus expansion in the mouse: Roles for the preovulatory synthesis of hyaluronic acid within the cumulus mass. *Mol. Reprod. Dev.* 34, 87–93.
107. Fulop, C., Salustri, A., and Hascall, V. C. (1997). Coding sequence of a hyaluronan synthase homologue expressed during expansion of the mouse cumulus-oocyte complex. *Arch. Biochem. Biophys.* 337, 261–266.
108. Chen, L., Mao, S. J., and Larsen, W. J. (1992). Identification of a factor in fetal bovine serum that stabilizes the cumulus extracellular matrix. A role for a member of the inter-alpha-trypsin inhibitor family. *J. Biol. Chem.* 267, 12380–12386.
109. Powers, R. W., Chen, L., Russell, P. T., and Larsen, W. J. (1995). Gonadotropin-stimulated regulation of blood-follicle barrier is mediated by nitric oxide. *Am. J. Physiol.* 269, 290–298.
110. Chen, L., Mao, S. J., McLean, L. R., Powers, R. W., and Larsen, W. J. (1994). Proteins of the inter-alpha-trypsin inhibitor family stabilize the cumulus extracellular matrix through their direct binding with hyaluronic acid. *J. Biol. Chem.* 269, 28282–28287.
111. Chen, L., Zhang, H., Powers, R. W., Russell, P. T., and Larsen, W. J. (1996). Covalent linkage between proteins of the inter-alpha-inhibitor family and hyaluronic acid is mediated by a factor produced by granulosa cells. *J. Biol. Chem.* 271, 19409–19414.
112. Fulop, C., Kamath, R. V., Li, Y., Otto, J. M., Salustri, A., Olsen, B. R., Glant, T. T., and Hascall, V. C. (1997). Coding sequence, exon-intron structure and chromosomal localization of murine TNF-stimulated gene 6 that is specifically expressed by expanding cumulus cell-oocyte complexes. *Gene* 202, 95–102.
113. Yoshioka, S., Ochsner, S., Russell, D. L., Ujioka, T., Fujii, S., Richards, J. S., and Espey, L. L. (2000). Expression of tumor necrosis factor-stimulated gene-6 in the rat ovary in response to an ovulatory dose of gonadotropin. *Endocrinology* 141, 4114–4119.
113a. Fülöp, C., Szántó, S., Mukhopadhyay, D., Bárdos, T., Kamath, R.V., Rugg, M.S., Day, A. J., Salustri, A., Hascall, V. C., Glant, T. T., and Mikecz, K. (2003). Impaired cumulus mucification and female sterility in tumor necrosis factor-induced protein-6 deficient mice. *Development*, 130, 2253–2261.
114. Zhuo, L., Yoneda, M., Zhao, M., Yingsung, W., Yoshida, N., Kitagawa, Y., Kawamura, K., Suzuki, T., and Kimata, K. (2001). Defect in SHAP-hyaluronan complex causes severe female infertility. A study by inactivation of the bikunin gene in mice. *J. Biol. Chem.* 276, 7693–7696.
115. Varani, S., Elvin, J. A., Yan, C., DeMayo, J., DeMayo, F. J., Horton, H. F., Byrne, M. C., and Matzuk, M. M. (2002). Knockout of pentraxin 3, a downstream target of growth differentiation factor-9, causes female subfertility. *Mol. Endocrinol.* 16, 1154–1167.
116. Garlanda, C., Hirsch, E., Bozza, S., Salustri, A., De Acetis, M., Nota, R., Maccagno, A., Riva, F., Bottazzi, B., Peri, G., Doni, A., Vago, L., Botto, M., De Santis, R., Carminati, P., Siracusa, G., Altruda, F., Vecchi, A., Romani, L., and Mantovani, A. (2002). Non-redundant role of the long pentraxin PTX3 in anti-fungal innate immune response. *Nature* 420, 182–186.
116a. Salustri, et al., in press.
117. Hagglund, A. C., Ny, A., Liu, K., and Ny, T. (1996). Coordinated and cell-specific induction of both physiological plasminogen activators creates functionally redundant mechanisms for plasmin formation during ovulation. *Endocrinology* 137, 5671–5677.
118. Tirone, E., D'Alessandris, C., Hascall, V. C., Siracusa, G., and Salustri, A. (1997). Hyaluronan synthesis by mouse cumulus cells is regulated by interactions between follicle-stimulating hormone (or epidermal growth factor) and a soluble oocyte factor (or transforming growth factor beta 1). *J. Biol. Chem.* 272, 4787–4794.
119. Schultz, R. M., Montgomery, R. R., and Belanoff, J. R. (1983). Regulation of mouse oocyte meiotic maturation: Implication of a decrease in oocyte cAMP and protein dephosphorylation in commitment to resume meiosis. *Dev. Biol.* 97, 264–273.
120. Eppig, J. J., and Downs, S. M. (1988). Gonadotropin-induced murine oocyte maturation in vivo is not associated with decreased cyclic adenosine monophosphate in the oocyte–cumulus cell complex. *Gamete Res.* 20, 125–131.
121. Downs, S. M. (1989). Specificity of epidermal growth factor action on maturation of the murine oocyte and cumulus oophorus in vitro. *Biol. Reprod.* 41, 371–379.
122. Su, Y. Q., Wigglesworth, K., Pendola, F. L., O'Brien, M. J., and Eppig, J. J. (2002). Mitogen-activated protein kinase activity in cumulus cells is essential for gonadotropin-induced oocyte meiotic resumption and cumulus expansion in the mouse. *Endocrinology* 143, 2221–2232.
123. Joyce, I. M., Pendola, F. L., O'Brien, M., and Eppig, J. J. (2001). Regulation of prostaglandin-endoperoxide synthase 2 messenger ribonucleic acid expression in mouse granulosa cells during ovulation. *Endocrinology* 142, 3187–3197.

124. Eppig, J. J. (1981). Prostaglandin E2 stimulates cumulus expansion and hyaluronic acid synthesis by cumuli oophori isolated from mice. *Biol. Reprod.* 25, 191–195.
125. Lim, H., Paria, B. C., Das, S. K., Dinchuk, J. E., Langenbach, R., Trzaskos, J. M., and Dey, S. K. (1997). Multiple female reproductive failures in cyclooxygenase 2-deficient mice. *Cell* 91, 197–208.
126. Tilley, S. L., Audoly, L. P., Hicks, E. H., Kim, H. S., Flannery, P. J., Coffman, T. M., and Koller, B. H. (1999). Reproductive failure and reduced blood pressure in mice lacking the EP_2 prostaglandin E2 receptor. *J. Clin. Invest.* 103, 1539–1545.
127. Kennedy, C. R., Zhang, Y., Brandon, S., Guan, Y., Coffee, K., Funk, C. D., Magnuson, M. A., Oates, J. A., Breyer, M. D., and Breyer, R. M. (1999). Salt-sensitive hypertension and reduced fertility in mice lacking the prostaglandin EP_2 receptor. *Nat. Med.* 5, 217–220.
128. Ochsner, S. A., Russell, D. L., Day, A. J., Breyer, R. M., and Richards, J. S. (2003). Decreased expression of tumor necrosis factor-alpha-stimulated gene 6 in cumulus cells of the cyclooxygenase-2 and EP_2-null mice. *Endocrinology* 144, 1008–1019.
129. Dekel, N., and Kraicer, P. F. (1978). Induction in vitro of mucification of rat cumulus oophorus by gonadotrophins and adenosine 3′,5′-monophosphate. *Endocrinology* 102, 1797–1802.
130. Hillensjo, T., and Channing, C. P. (1980). Gonadotropin stimulation of steroidogenesis and cellular dispersion in cultured porcine cumuli oophori. *Gamete Res.* 3, 223–240.
131. Singh, B., Barbe, G. J., and Armstrong, D. T. (1993). Factors influencing resumption of meiotic maturation and cumulus expansion of porcine oocyte–cumulus cell complexes in vitro. *Mol. Reprod. Dev.* 36, 113–119.
132. Choi, Y. H., Carnevale, E. M., Seidel, Jr., G. E., and Squire, E. L. (2001). Effects of gonadotropins on bovine oocytes matured in TCM-199. *Theriogenology* 56, 661–670.
133. Vanderhyden, B. C., Caron, P. J., Buccione, R., and Eppig, J. J. (1990). Developmental pattern of the secretion of cumulus expansion-enabling factor by mouse oocytes and the role of oocytes in promoting granulosa cell differentiation. *Dev. Biol.* 140, 307–317.
134. Tsafriri, A., Chun, S. Y., Zhang, R., Hsueh, A. J., and Conti, M. (1996). Oocyte maturation involves compartmentalization and opposing changes of cAMP levels in follicular somatic and germ cells: Studies using selective phosphodiesterase inhibitors. *Dev. Biol.* 178, 393–402.
135. Wiersma, A., Hirsch, B., Tsafriri, A., Hanssen, R. G., Van de Kant, M., Kloosterboer, H. J., Conti, M., and Hsueh, A. J. (1998). Phosphodiesterase 3 inhibitors suppress oocyte maturation and consequent pregnancy without affecting ovulation and cyclicity in rodents. *J. Clin. Invest.* 102, 532–537.
136. Tirone, E., Siracusa, G., Hascall, V. C., Frajese, G., and Salustri, A. (1993). Oocytes preserve the ability of mouse cumulus cells in culture to synthesize hyaluronic acid and dermatan sulfate. *Dev. Biol.* 160, 405–412.
137. Roh, J. S., Bondestam, J., Mazerbourg, S., Kaivo-Oja, N., Groome, N., Ritvos, O., and Hsueh, A. J. (2003). Growth differentiation factor-9 stimulates inhibin production and activates Smad2 in cultured rat granulosa cells. *Endocrinology* 144, 172–178.
138. Kaivo-Oja, N., Bondestam, J., Kamarainen, M., Koskimies, J., Vitt, U., Cranfield, M., Vuojolainen, K., Kallio, J. P., Olkkonen, V. M., Hayashi, M., Moustakas, A., Groome, N. P., ten Dijke, P., Hsueh, A. J., and Ritvos, O. (2003). Growth differentiation factor-9 induces Smad2 activation and inhibin B production in cultured human granulosa-luteal cells. *J. Clin. Endocrinol. Metab.* 88, 755–762.
139. Massague, J., and Chen, Y. G. (2000). Controlling TGF-beta signaling. *Genes Dev.* 14, 627–644.
140. Warner, D. R., Pisano, M. M., and Greene, R. M. (2003). Nuclear convergence of the TGFbeta and cAMP signal transduction pathways in murine embryonic palate mesenchymal cells. *Cell Signal* 15, 235–242.
141. Elvin, J. A., Yan, C., and Matzuk, M. M. (2000). Growth differentiation factor-9 stimulates progesterone synthesis in granulosa cells via a prostaglandin E2/EP2 receptor pathway. *Proc. Natl. Acad. Sci. USA* 97, 10288–10293.
142. Salustri, A., Petrungaro, S., and Siracusa, G. (1985). Granulosa cells stimulate in vitro the expansion of isolated mouse cumuli oophori: Involvement of prostaglandin E2. *Biol. Reprod.* 33, 229–234.
143. Prochazka, R., Nagyova, E., Rimkevicova, Z., Nagai, T., Kikuchi, K., and Motlik, J. (1991). Lack of effect of oocytectomy on expansion of the porcine cumulus. *J. Reprod. Fertil.* 93, 569–576.
144. Singh, B., Zhang, X., and Armstrong, D. T. (1993). Porcine oocytes release cumulus expansion-enabling activity even though porcine cumulus expansion in vitro is independent of the oocyte. *Endocrinology* 132, 1860–1862.
145. Vanderhyden, B. C. (1993). Species differences in the regulation of cumulus expansion by an oocyte-secreted factor(s). *J. Reprod. Fertil.* 98, 219–227.
146. Ralph, J. H., Telfer, E. E., and Wilmut, I. (1995). Bovine cumulus cell expansion does not depend on the presence of an oocyte secreted factor. *Mol. Reprod. Dev.* 42, 248–253.
147. Prochazka, R., Nagyova, E., Brem, G., Schellander, K., and Motlik, J. (1998). Secretion of cumulus expansion-enabling factor (CEEF) in porcine follicles. *Mol. Reprod. Dev.* 49, 141–149.
148. Nakayama, T., Inoue, M., and Sato, E. (1996). Effect of oocytectomy on glycosaminoglycan composition during cumulus expansion of porcine cumulus-oocyte complexes cultured in vitro. *Biol. Reprod.* 55, 1299–1304.
149. Kimura, N., Konno, Y., Miyoshi, K., Matsumoto, H., and Sato, E. (2002). Expression of hyaluronan synthases and CD44 messenger RNAs in porcine cumulus-oocyte complexes during in vitro maturation. *Biol. Reprod.* 66, 707–717.
150. D'Alessandris, C., Canipari, R., Di Giacomo, M., Epifano, O., Camaioni, A., Siracusa, G., and Salustri, A. (2001). Control of mouse cumulus cell–oocyte complex integrity before and after ovulation: Plasminogen activator synthesis and matrix degradation. *Endocrinology* 142, 3033–3040.
151. Xu, Z., Abbott, A., Kopf, G. S., Schultz, R. M., and Ducibella, T. (1997). Spontaneous activation of ovulated mouse eggs: Time-dependent effects on M-phase exit, cortical granule exocytosis, maternal messenger ribonucleic acid recruitment, and inositol 1,4,5-trisphosphate sensitivity. *Biol. Reprod.* 57, 743–750.
152. Igarashi, H., Takahashi, E., Hiroi, M., and Doi, K. (1997). Aging-related changes in calcium oscillations in fertilized mouse oocytes. *Mol. Reprod. Dev.* 48, 383–390.

CHAPTER 9

Ovulation: An Inflammatory Cascade of Gene Expression

LAWRENCE L. ESPEY, ADAM S. BELLINGER, AND JANE A. HEALY

ABSTRACT

New methods in molecular biology have produced a significant increase in our current knowledge of ovarian gene expression and the biochemical events of ovulation. This chapter provides an overview of the scope and diversity of approximately 60 genes that contribute to the ovulatory process. Most of the genes have been directly or indirectly associated with acute inflammatory reactions, and the references are specifically selected in an effort to characterize the role of each gene in inflammation. The various genes are discussed in terms of their contributions to (1) an immediate early gene response that initiates an inflammatory reaction, (2) proinflammatory events that lead to proteolytic degradation of ovulatory follicles, (3) endogenous anti-inflammatory activity that promotes healing and repair of the traumatized ovary, and (4) protection of the tissue from oxidative stress that is generated locally during the ovulatory process. In addition, this chapter considers ovarian steroidogenesis and angiogenesis that occur during the transition of an ovulatory follicle into a metabolically active corpus luteum. Collectively, this overview of ovarian gene expression makes it clear that the molecular and biochemical events of ovulation are far more complicated than was imagined only a decade ago. It also appears that only a fraction of the entire complement of ovulation-related genes has been discovered thus far. Nevertheless, based on current information about the cascade of ovarian gene expression at the time of ovulation, the data support the idea that a surge in gonadotropin induces an acute inflammatory reaction in the granulosa layer of ovulatory follicles.

INTRODUCTION

In mammals the ovulatory process begins at the moment an endogenous surge in luteinizing hormone (LH) stimulates G protein–coupled LH/human chorionic gonadotropin (hCG) receptors that are abundantly distributed on the surface of granulosa and theca cells of a mature ovarian follicle. The process ends some hours later at the instant a follicle ruptures and releases a fertile egg. Superimposed on this ovulatory process is the luteinization process, which also begins at the moment of the LH surge but does not end until a number of days after ovulation. Thus ovulation (i.e., follicular rupture) is a distinct morphological phenomenon that occurs during the transformation of an ovarian follicle into a corpus luteum [1].

The changes that take place in the tissue at the site of rupture are pathophysiological in nature in that they require acute disruption of the dense layers of collagenous tissues consisting of the theca externa around individual follicles and the tunica albuginea that encapsulates the entire ovary [2]. The local damage includes hemorrhage in the vicinity of the lesion on the surface of the ovary. However, the structural changes are not limited solely to the area that ruptures at the follicular surface. The ovulatory process affects the entire stratum granulosum and the adjacent theca interna [2]. That is to say, virtually every portion of the two innermost layers of the follicle wall transform into active luteal tissue. This should not be surprising, because the LH/hCG receptors that respond to the ovulatory stimulus are distributed throughout the stratum granulosum and the adjacent theca interna. Therefore, it is predictable that gonadotropin-induced gene expression in ovarian follicles should be generally distributed throughout the granulosa and/or thecal layers of the ovarian follicles.

The duration of the ovulatory process varies from mammal to mammal. It is as short as 9.5 to 10 hours in the rabbit and as much as 32 to 36 hours in the human [1]. Therefore, any effort to integrate the scientific literature on ovarian gene expression during ovulation is complicated by the species-specific variation in the duration of the ovulatory process. Fortunately, most of the data on the temporal pattern of expression of ovulation-related genes have been obtained from the immature rat model. In this experimental animal, ovarian follicles begin rupturing at 12 hours after injecting LH (or its homologue hCG) into the rat, and most of the mature follicles have ruptured by 16 hours after induction of the process. Accordingly, this chapter concentrates on ovarian gene expression in the rat (and other rodents), but it also summarizes certain information about gene expression in the ovaries of several other mammals.

Until recently, it was assumed that ovulation was a relatively simple phenomenon, involving a small number of regulatory factors activated by a surge in the secretion of gonadotropin [3–5]. It was thought that minimal metabolic changes were needed to activate proteolytic enzymes that could degrade the apical-most area of the largest ovarian follicles. However, during the past decade, our image of ovulation has changed drastically. Modern methods in molecular biology and recombinant deoxyribonucleic acid (DNA) technologies that allow the detection of differentially expressed genes have led investigators to a number of novel agents that factor into the mechanism of ovulation. It is now clear that the ovulatory process is dependent on expression of numerous genes. To date, approximately 65 to 70 such ovulation-related genes have been discovered, and there probably are hundreds more to be found. The objective of this chapter is to summarize the omnium-gatherum of knowledge that currently exists about ovulation-related gene expression. However, this account is abridged, in part because of the allotted space, but mainly because of the unfathomable magnitude of the current literature.

Most of the genes that have been identified as components of the ovulatory process are, according to the literature search for this chapter, associated with acute inflammatory reactions. Therefore, the focus of this chapter is on the cascade of gene expression that mediates inflammation. It is also evident that a subset of genes is expressed to moderate the inflammatory reaction, and these genes will be considered as a separate group of endogenous anti-inflammatory agents. Concomitant with the inflammatory cascade, there is a cluster of genes that yield protein products to counteract the oxidative stress that is generated in inflamed tissues, and these "protective" genes will be depicted as a separate, but integral, faction of the ovarian inflammatory reaction. Similarly, the immediate-early gene response, steroidogenesis, and angiogenesis will be covered as interdependent events that are discernible components of the ovulatory process.

THE IMMEDIATE-EARLY GENE RESPONSE

When hormones such as gonadotropins stimulate target tissues such as mature ovarian follicles, the ligand-receptor coupling induces specific gene expression in the stimulate cells. The genomic response usually includes the induction of so-called *immediate-early genes* that transcribe and translate into cytoplasmic proteins that translocate into the nucleus and regulate the expression of numerous other genes. The first segment of this review describes several such genes that are transcribed during the early stages of the ovulatory process.

1. *Early Growth Response Protein-1.* Early growth response protein-1 (Egr-1) is a zinc-finger transcription factor that promotes the expression of an estimated 80 to 100 other genes [6–8]. Among the downstream target genes are interleukin-1β (IL-1β) [9] and tumor necrosis factor-α (TNF-α) [10], two principal mediators of inflammatory reactions that have been implicated in the ovulatory process [11, 12]. Egr-1 messenger ribonucleic acid (mRNA) begins to increase in the granulosa layer of rat follicles within 30 minutes after the ovulatory process has been initiated by hCG [13]. Expression of this gene reaches a peak during the first 4 hours of the ovulatory process and then declines to 0-h control levels by 10 to 12 hours after the follicles have ruptured.
2. *Interleukins.* The interleukins (ILs), especially IL-1β and IL-6, are firmly established as early-response cytokines [14]. They also are well characterized as principal mediators of inflammatory reactions. Therefore, they are further described in the later part of this chapter that deals more specifically with proinflammatory genes. For the moment, it is important to note that the genes for both IL-1β and IL-6 [15–17] have been implicated in the ovulatory process.
3. *Tumor Necrosis Factor-α.* TNF-α is another proinflammatory cytokine that has been characterized as a mediator of the immediate-early response [14]. Although this cytokine has not been studied in ovulation as extensively as the ILs, and although a significant increase in ovarian TNF-α mRNA during ovulation is not as evident as transcription of many of the other genes that are covered in this chapter [12], it is nevertheless included as a probable component of the immediate-early gene response to an ovulatory stimulus.
4. *Cyclooxygenase-2.* Cyclooxygenase-2 (COX-2) is an immediate-early gene that is rapidly induced by a variety of stimuli, including tumor promoters, growth factors, and inflammation mediators [18, 19]. The expression of COX-2 is stimulated by the proinflammatory cytokines IL-1β and TNF-α [19], and the enzyme is well known for its induction of prostaglandin synthesis [20]. COX-2 itself reportedly increases the expression of vascular endothelial growth factor (VEGF) [18]. During ovulation, COX-2 increases sharply in the granulosa layer of mature follicles at 4 hours after hCG treatment of rats, and then it rapidly declines before the follicles actually begin rupturing [3]. Targeted disruption of this gene causes ovulation failure and infertility in mice [21].

MEDLINE during the past decade alone. (This list of publications was narrowed to approximately 2000 by using the term *inflammatory gene*.) Therefore, it would be a gargantuan task to analyze and condense the current knowledge about inflammatory reactions. Even so, the accumulating data make it evident that inflammatory stimuli induce cascades of gene expression, and the principal components of these cascades are being delineated, step by step. For example, it is now established that acute inflammatory responses usually involve the activation of several major transcription factors, including NF-kB, AP-1, and CREB [32, 41, 61]. It is also clear that inflammatory reactions can be subdivided into proinflammatory elements that cause tissue damage as part of a natural defense mechanism and anti-inflammatory elements that are responsible for sequential repair and healing of the damaged tissue. The primary objective of this review is to summarize the characteristics of at least some of the ovulation-specific genes that are known to be associated with inflammation. The proinflammatory genes are listed first, followed by the anti-inflammatory genes. A distinct part of the anti-inflammatory response is a group of anti-inflammatory genes that serves to minimize the oxidative stress created by an acute inflammatory reaction. These genes are discussed later as a separate group in the section "Oxidative Stress."

Predominantly Proinflammatory Genes

1. *Interleukins*. IL gene expression in the ovary at the time ovulation has been studied extensively during the past decade [3, 11, 15, 16, 17, 62–64]. IL-1β and IL-6 are of particular relevance because they are commonly recognized as early-response cytokines that have a central role in the regulation of inflammatory reactions [14, 39]. Transcripts of IL-1β (along with its receptors) and IL-6 increase in the granulosa and surrounding theca interna within 4 hours after hCG stimulation of the ovulatory process in rats [17, 63, 64]. It has been proposed that IL-1β induces a host of ovulation-related genes, including the genes for VEGF [64] and COX-2 [16, 62].
2. *Tumor Necrosis Factor-α*. TNF-α and IL-1β are perhaps best known for their role in inflammatory reactions [14]. In addition, it is now clear that one of the common downstream products of TNF-α signaling is the proinflammatory transcription factor NF-κB [61]. Although TNF-α has been strongly implicated as a major component of ovulation, the temporal and spatial patterns of mRNA expression of this cytokine during ovulation have not been clearly delineated [12, 65].
3. *CCAAT/Enhancer-Binding Protein Gene*. CCAAT/enhancer-binding proteins (C/EBPs) are a family of leucine zipper transcription factors that function to regulate various aspects of inflammatory reactions [66]. It is interesting that members of the NF-κB family of transcription factors interact with C/EBP as well as with the inflammation mediators IL-1β and IL-6. A C/EBP mRNA and protein are induced rapidly in rat granulosa cells following an ovulatory dose of hCG, and the protein appears to play a key role in regulating induction of the COX-2 gene before ovulation [67]. In addition, it has been reported that interference with the expression of the C/EBP proteins in the ovary causes a decrease in the ovulation rate [68, 69].
4. *Cytokine-Induced Neutrophil Chemoattractant*. Cytokine-induced neutrophil chemoattractants (CINCs, also called *growth-regulated oncogenes*, or *GROs*) comprise a family of chemokines that are expressed at sites of inflammation and play an important role in neutrophil infiltration [70–72]. CINC mRNA and the CINC protein increase rapidly to a peak at 6 hours after hCG injection into the gonadotropin-primed immature rat [73]. In the rat, this chemokine is expressed in the thecal tissue of antral follicles but not in the granulosa layer. However, in large human follicles, CINC has been identified in the thecal layer and in the granulosa cells [74, 75]. The expression of ovarian CINC reportedly is stimulated by IL-1β and TNF-α [73, 75, 76].
5. *Early Growth Response Protein-1*. Egr-1, which was described previously as a component of the immediate-early gene response, is a transcription factor that serves as a master switch to promote the expression of numerous genes important in inflammation, vascular hyperpermeability, coagulation, and other events associated with tissue damage [10, 77]. Downstream target genes include IL-1β and TNF-α [9, 10]. Egr-1 mRNA expression in the granulosa layer of rat follicles begins as early as 30 minutes after stimulating the ovulatory process with hCG, and this transcription factor reaches peak expression at 4 hours after hCG [13].
6. *Nerve Growth Factor* and *NGF Receptor*. Nerve growth factor (NGF) is an autocrine hormone that has a role in inflammatory responses and tissue repair. Cells such as fibroblasts [78] and macrophages [79] not only produce NGF but also express the NGF tyrosine kinase receptor (trkA). In the immature rat model, ovarian mRNAs for NGF and trkA are significantly but transiently expressed in the thecal and stromal tissues during the ovulatory process [80]. In addition, there is detectable expression of trkA mRNA in granulosa cells [81]. The ovarian expression of NGF and trkA mRNA are enhanced by IL-1β [80].
7. *Vascular Endothelial Growth Factor*. VEGF is a mitogen that promotes angiogenesis in inflamed

tissues by stimulating the proliferation of endothelial cells of preexisting capillaries [82–84]. Ovarian VEGF transcripts were first detected in cultured bovine granulosa cells [85] and in granulosa and thecal cells of immature rat ovaries within only several hours after hCG treatment [86]. There is evidence that IL-1β might regulate the expression of rat ovarian VEGF mRNA [64].

8. *Corticotropin-Releasing Factor* and *CRF Receptor*. Corticotropin-releasing factor (CRF) is usually thought of as a hypothalamic neuropeptide that regulates the secretion of adrenocorticotropic hormone (ACTH) from the anterior pituitary. However, in the past decade it has become evident that CRF is also produced peripherally at sites of inflammation, where it acts in a paracrine manner as a proinflammatory cytokine that binds to CRF receptors [87–89]. CRF and CRF1 receptor mRNAs have been detected in adult rats on the afternoon of proestrus in the ovarian stroma and thecal tissue of ovulatory follicles [87–90]. Thus it appears that CRF may have a functional role in the ovulatory process.
9. *Cyclooxygenase-2*. COX-2 is rapidly induced and dramatically upregulated at sites of inflammation [19, 91]. COX-2 is well known for its central role in the conversion of arachidonic acid to prostaglandins that mediate inflammatory reactions. COX-2 mRNA expression in the granulosa layer of rat follicles reaches a sharp but transient peak at 4 hours after hCG [3], and mice with the targeted disruption of the COX-2 gene fail to ovulate [21]. Therefore, it appears that the proinflammatory effects of COX-2 gene expression are important for ovulation.
10. *Epiregulin*. Epiregulin is a relatively new member of the epidermal growth factor (EGF) family [92]. Although its functions are not yet clear, it is relevant that epiregulin has been associated with Egr-1 mRNA expression [93], and it has recently been identified as an NF-κB-dependent gene (along with C/EBP) during an inflammatory reaction [94]. In the ovary of the immature rat model the temporal and spatial patterns of expression of epiregulin are essentially identical to COX-2—with a sharp peak in expression occurring at 4 hours after hCG [3]. Thus epiregulin might be important in the expression of COX-2 mRNA and protein [95].
11. *Myeloid Cell Leukemia-1*. In acute inflammatory reactions, a cascade of gene expression to promote apoptosis occurs parallel to the cascade of proinflammatory gene expression [96–98]. In a physiologically-induced inflammatory process such as ovulation, it may be vital to suppress the apoptotic events while permitting the proinflammatory signaling pathways to operate. Therefore, because Mcl-1 is an antiapoptotic protein under the transcriptional regulation of CREB [99], the expression of this message in granulosa and thecal cells of ovulatory follicles [23] may function to delay apoptosis during ovulation and postovulatory luteinization of ruptured follicles.
12. *Phosphodiesterases*. Phosphodiesterases (PDEs) regulate intracellular cyclic nucleotide concentration by hydrolysis of cyclic adenosine and guanosine monophosphates that are generated by activation of G protein–coupled receptors [100, 101]. Some PDEs such as PDE4 reportedly influence the release of proinflammatory agents such as NF-κB and TNF-α [102–104], and PDE4 inhibitors are currently being considered as anti-inflammatory drugs [101]. Therefore, it is significant that PDE4 has been detected in rat ovarian thecal and stromal tissue [100], and mice deficient in PDE4 exhibit diminished ovulation and fertility [105]. In the immature rat model, ovarian PDE4 mRNA expression is significantly elevated during the 2 to 12 hours after an hCG injection (i.e., for the duration of the ovulatory process) [3].
13. *Nuclear Receptor-Interacting Protein*. Nuclear receptor-interacting protein (Nrip, or RIP) is a family of Ser/Thr kinases that have an indispensable role in interacting with the TNF-R1 receptor to induce NF-κB activation during inflammatory reactions [98, 61, 106]. Ovarian expression of Nrip1 is reportedly essential for ovulation, even though mice that are null for this protein can nevertheless develop follicles that undergo luteinization without ever having ruptured [107, 108].
14. *Nitric Oxide Synthases*. Nitric oxide synthases (NOSs) are a family of enzymes that oxidize arginine to produce nitric oxide [109]. The two principal groups of NOSs include the constitutively expressed endothelial cell NOS (eNOS) and the inducible (iNOS) form that has an important role in physiological processes such as inflammation [109–111]. In inflamed tissues, the short-lived nitric oxide promotes vasodilation, edema, and other features of a local inflammatory reaction [109, 111]. Unfortunately, the information on these potentially important NOSs in ovulation is confusing and contradictory. One recent report concludes that iNOS mRNA, which was greater in granulosa cells than in thecal cells, decreased during the ovulatory process in rats [112]. In contrast, the same study found that eNOS, which was expressed mainly in the thecal tissue, increased significantly during ovulation. Thus it appears that iNOS was not induced, whereas the constitutive form was induced. A study of iNOS mRNA and iNOS protein in the ovaries of adult rats, which are difficult to stage in relation to the LH surge, does not help to clarify the temporal and spatial patterns of expres-

sion of these nitric oxide (NO)-generating elements [113]. In one immunohistochemical study, iNOS levels increased in thecal tissue during the ovulatory process, whereas iNOS was detected in thecal cells and stroma, and increased mainly after ovulation [114]. In another immunohistochemical study, eNOS also reportedly increases in the immature rat ovary following an hCG injection, whereas iNOS decreased at the time of ovulation. Thus it would be useful to have a clearer delineation of the spatial and temporal patterns of eNOS and iNOS mRNA expression during the ovulatory process in a common experimental animal such as the rat.

15. *A Disintegrin and Metalloproteinase with Thrombospondin Motifs-1.* A disintegrin and metalloproteinase with thrombospondin motifs-1 (ADAMTS-1) is the first known member of a novel family of extracellular proteases that has rapidly grown to at least 18 members [115–117]. The ADAMTS family of enzymes is involved in inflammation and angiogenesis [115, 118]. The expression of mRNA for this enzyme increases steadily during the ovulatory process—reaching a peak in the granulosa layer of ovarian follicles at 12 hours after hCG (i.e., at the time follicles begin to rupture) [57]. This ovulatory expression of ADAMTS-1 mRNA is dependent on increases in both progesterone [57] and PR [54], two ovarian factors that are known to be essential for ovulation. Ovarian ADAMTS-1 enzyme activity is reportedly inhibited by tissue inhibitor of metalloproteinase TIMP-2 and TIMP-3 [119].
16. *Cathepsin L.* Cathepsin L is an elastinolytic cysteine protease that is active during inflammatory responses [120, 121]. The mRNA for this protease is maximally expressed in the ovary at 12 to 16 hours after induction of the ovulatory process by gonadotropin, and as with ovarian ADAMTS-1, this expression is dependent on progesterone and PR [54, 122]. Thus it appears that cathepsin L also has a role in degrading the tensile strength of the follicle wall at the time of ovulation.
17. *Matrix Metalloproteinases.* Matrix metalloproteinases (MMPs) are a family of zinc- and calcium-requiring enzymes that degrade the extracellular matrix found in collagenous connective tissues such as exists in the thecal layers and the stromal tissue of the mammalian ovary. The four classes of MMPs that have been associated with acutely inflamed tissues are the collagenases, gelatinases, membrane-type metalloproteinases, and stromelysins [123, 124]. These proteolytic enzymes have been studied in ovarian tissues for more than a decade [125], and much of the work related to ovulation has been reviewed recently [126]. Transcription and translation of MMP genes in the thecal and stromal tissues of the gonadotropin-primed ovary includes collagenase-3 [127], MMP-2 [128, 129], MMP-9 [126, 128, 129], and MMP-19 [130]. Increases in the granulosa layer of ovulatory follicles include mRNAs for MMP-2 [128, 129] and MMP-19 [130]. Based on data from the monkey, the ovarian expression of mRNA for interstitial collagenase and MMP-9 might be dependent on a local increase in progesterone levels [27].
18. *Plasminogen Activators and Plasmin.* The production of plasmin from ubiquitous plasminogen by urokinase (uPA) and tissue-type plasminogen activator (tPA) is the central step in activation of the four classes of inflammatory MMPs mentioned in the preceding paragraph [123]. The potential role of PAs in ovulation has been studied for more than two decades [131, 132], but the importance of this class of serine proteases in ovulation has not been firmly established. In immature rats, ovarian mRNA for tPA increases within several hours after hCG and remains elevated in the granulosa cells and the surrounding connective tissues at the time of ovulation [133]. However, mice lacking plasminogen activator gene function have little or no impairment of ovulation efficiency [134, 135], and plasmin does not appear to be required for follicular rupture in mice [136].
19. *CD63.* Cell surface antigen CD63 is a member of the tetraspanin superfamily that has been associated with the activation of membrane proteins on mast cells [137], on polymorphonuclear leukocytes [138, 139], and on the surface of endothelial cells in areas of vascular injury and inflammation [140] during systemic inflammatory responses. Quite different from other genes that are expressed in the rat ovary during ovulation, CD63 is expressed constitutively in the thecal and stromal tissue of the ovary but not in the granulosa layer of the ovarian follicles [3]. However, from 4 to 8 hours after hCG treatment of the animals, CD63 increases significantly but transiently in the granulosa cells. This surface protein might be related in some way to the vascular changes that take place during transformation of ovulatory follicles into corpora lutea.
20. *Glucocorticoid-Induced Receptor.* There is another ovulation-related gene in the thecal and stromal tissue whose expression is strongly induced by hCG injections into rats [3]. Although the gene was first sequenced and initially characterized as a glucocorticoid-induced receptor (GIR) more than a decade ago [141], its function has not been defined and it is frequently called an "orphan" G protein–coupled receptor [142–145]. A human form of the GIR gene, known as GPR54, has been identified in the placenta, pituitary, pancreas, and spinal cord [142]. Various

other homologues of this gene reportedly are related to a peptide receptor subfamily [143]; rat galanin receptors [146]; human P2Y receptor, or GPR86 [144]; and tachykinin receptors that are called *GPR72*, or JP05 [145]. The sequence of its transmembrane regions suggest it might be related to the rat galanin receptor. In the rat ovary the temporal and spatial pattern of expression of GIP mRNA is similar to carbonyl reductase (CBR) (see the discussion of carbonyl reductase under "Oxidative Stress") [3]. GIP gene transcription is strongly upregulated in the thecal connective tissue around follicles by 4 hours after hCG. Expression reaches a peak by 8 hours after hCG, and then declines to preovulatory control levels by 24 hours after hCG (i.e., when ovulation is complete). Although the function of GIP has not been determined, its location on the surface of thecal cells outside the transcriptionally active granulosa layer is of special interest. It is likely that the granulosa cells are the principal target of hCG action that initiates an inflammatory cascade [1]. Eventually the events that start in this innermost layer of the follicle spill out into the surrounding connective tissue, and the thecal fibroblasts become aroused from their quiescent state [1]. This activation of the fibroblasts could result in induction of MMP gene expression that contributes to softening of the collagenous layers of tissue that serve as the principal barrier between the cumulus mass and the oviduct. Thus GIP could serve as an important receptor in the theca externa and stromal tissue that is responsive to the inflammatory signals from the granulosa layer of ovulatory follicles.

21. *Pancreatitis-Associated Protein-III.* Pancreatitis-associated protein-III (PAP-III) is a member of the C-type lectin supergene family, but its physiological function has not been clearly established [147, 148]. Some evidence suggests that PAP proteins might act as endogenous protective agents during inflammation [149]. Therefore, it is possible that ovarian PAP-III might be expressed in conjunction with a protective response to the hyperemia and inflammation that occurs during the pathophysiological events of ovulation [3]. In any case, the expression of this gene in the ovary is different from all of the other ovulation-related genes that have been discovered to date. PAP-III mRNA is expressed mainly at 8 hours after hCG in the immature rat, and it is located primarily in the hilar region of the ovarian stroma, with most of the signal emanating from endothelial cells that line the inner walls of blood vessels [150].
22. *Macrophage Migration Inhibiting Factor.* Macrophage migration inhibiting factor (MIF) is a proinflammatory cytokine that reportedly is an essential component of inflammatory responses [151]. Although this cytokine has not been studied in rodents, it is worthwhile to note that it has been analyzed in relation to human granulosa cells. MIF increases significantly in the culture media of granulosa cells that have been stimulated with hCG [152]. Therefore, it is possible that the MIF gene is expressed as a part of the ovulatory cascade.
23. *Cutaneous Fatty Acid-Binding Protein.* Cutaneous fatty acid-binding protein (C-FABP) is a relatively new discovery, and its function has not been well defined. There are reports that it may be important in the transport and synthesis of fatty acids [153], but it has also been described as a metastasis-inducing agent in prostate and breast carcinomas [154]. Although it is not yet clear whether this protein should be categorized as a proinflammatory factor, it is tentatively included under this heading because of evidence that expression of the VEGF gene is increased significantly in C-FABP-transfected cells [155]. In the gonadotropin-primed ovary of the rat, an increase in C-FABP mRNA has been detected by microarray [156]. The message for C-FABP is elevated in the thecal cells of ovulatory follicles at 6 hours after administration of hCG.
24. *Prepronociceptin.* Prepronociceptin (PPN) is another recently discovered protein whose gene transcribes the neuropeptide nociceptin during carrageenan-induced acute inflammation [157–159]. The gene apparently binds SP1 transcription factor [159], and it has several cAMP-responsive elements within 250 bp (basepairs) of the start of transcription [160, 161]. It should be noted that the processing of PPN transcripts also yields a biologically active peptide that has been named *nocistatin,* which reportedly exerts antihyperalgesic effects at sites of inflammation [157, 162]. Nevertheless, it is listed here tentatively as a proinflammatory factor because its expression is down-regulated by anti-inflammatory steroids [161]. Like C-FABP mRNA, PPN mRNA has been detected by microarray in the thecal cells of ovulatory follicles at 6 hours after administration of hCG [156].
25. *Additional Remarks.* It is obvious that the inflammatory cascade of gene expression in ovulatory follicles is highly complex. It is also likely that there are a 100 or more genes still to be identified and characterized as part of this proinflammatory cascade in the ovary, because the literature on acute inflammatory reactions is now known to consist of a substantial number of gene components [96, 97]. As more knowledge is gained, it is also possible that some of the genes (e.g., CD63, PAP-III, C-FABP) that have been tentatively listed here as part of the proinflammatory phase of the reaction might be more appropriately categorized as part of the anti-inflammatory reaction that is now recognized as an integral part of the events in an acute inflammatory reaction [96, 97].

Predominantly Anti-inflammatory Genes

1. *Regulator of G Protein Signaling Protein-2*. Regulator of G protein signaling protein-2 (RGS2) is characterized as a GTPase-activating protein (GAP) that attenuates ligand-induced signaling by hydrolyzing GTP to guanidine diphosphate (GDP) on the α-subunit of an activated G-protein [163, 164]. Thus GAPs such as RGS2 are important in regulating the duration and intensity of signal transduction processes that are initiated when a ligand such as hCG couples with the LH/hCG receptors on the membranes of granulosa cells and theca interna cells of mature ovarian follicles. In the ovary of the immature rat model, RGS2 mRNA expression is upregulated substantially at 4 to 8 hours after the ovaries are stimulated by hCG [165]. The spatial pattern of expression of this transcript in the granulosa layer is atypical in that RGS2 mRNA appears to be especially dense along the antral border of the mural granulosa of large follicles as well as within the cumulus mass of cells surrounding the oocyte. The function of RGS2 presumably is to attenuate the initial proinflammatory signaling that is induced by LH/hCG at the beginning of the ovulatory process.
2. *Pituitary Adenylate Cyclase Activating Polypeptide*. Pituitary adenylate cyclase activating polypeptide (PACAP), which is structurally and functionally related to vasoactive intestinal peptide (VIP), suppresses inflammatory reactions by inhibiting the production of proinflammatory cytokines and nitric oxide while stimulating the production of the anti-inflammatory cytokine IL-10 [165–167]. In the rat ovary, PACAP mRNA is intensely but transiently expressed in the granulosa layer from 3 to 9 hours after induction of the ovulatory process by hCG [3, 168–170]. There is substantial evidence that ovarian expression of the mRNA for this anti-inflammatory factor is dependent on the ovulatory elevation in progesterone and PR expression [3, 168, 170]. However, there is also a contradictory report that PACAP stimulates the production of progesterone, rather than vice versa [169]. There is also a report that, by operating through the different subtypes of PACAP receptors, PACAP treatment of cultured granulosa cells induces an increase in tPA activity while simultaneously causing a decrease in uPA activity [171].
3. *Tissue Inhibitors of Metalloproteinases*. In the remodeling of an inflamed extracellular matrix, the intensity of tissue degradation at any given phase of an inflammatory reaction depends on the imbalance between the expression of proinflammatory MMP enzyme activity vs the expression of tissue inhibitors of metalloproteinases (TIMPs) [172, 173]. Furthermore, it appears inevitable that TIMPs are produced at virtually any site where MMPs are active. Depending on the tissue and the type of MMP(s) in a given area of inflammation, one or more of four TIMPs are coexpressed in the vicinity of the metalloproteinase(s). Therefore, it is not surprising that several mRNAs for TIMPs are expressed in ovarian follicles concomitant with the expression of MMPs. In particular, the constitutive levels of TIMP-1 and TIMP-3 mRNAs are significantly upregulated in the ovarian stromal and thecal tissue (and to a lesser extent, the granulosa) of ovulatory follicles in rats [3, 129, 174, 175]. In contrast, TIMP-2 and TIMP-4 mRNAs remain at background levels at the time of ovulation [129, 176]. At least TIMP-1 mRNA expression peaks simultaneously with ADAMTS-1 mRNA at 12 hours after stimulating the immature rat with hCG [177], and the expression of this MMP inhibitor returns to the preovulatory constitutive level within 2 to 3 days after ovulation [177, 178].
4. *α2-Macroglobulin*. In addition to being inhibited by TIMPs, the inflammatory MMPs are also affected by less-specific inhibitors such as α2-macroglobulin (α2-M) [173]. In rat ovarian follicles, α2-M mRNA increases in ovulatory follicles by 12 hours after hCG, and this transcript continues to be upregulated in corpora lutea for at least 4 days into the lutein phase [179].
5. *TNF-α-Stimulated Gene-6*. The cytokines IL-1β and TNF-α activate a number of inflammation-related genes, including TNF-α-stimulated gene-6 (TSG-6) [180]. The protein product of TSG-6 serves a critical negative feedback function in inflammation by forming a complex with inter alpha trypsin inhibitor to block serine protease activity that is needed for activation of the MMPs [173, 180, 181]. In ovulatory follicles of the immature rat model, TSG-6 mRNA is expressed mainly at 4 to 8 hours after hCG [182]. Although this transcript increases significantly throughout the granulosa layer during the ovulatory process, there is a perceptibly greater amount in the cumulus mass and the antral granulosa cells of the largest follicles [182], and this observation is consistent with the immunolocalization of TSG-6 protein mainly in the cumulus mass [183].
6. *Heparan Sulfate-Antithrombin System*. The heparan sulfate-antithrombin system consists of heparan sulfate proteoglycans (HSPGs) that bind to and activate several serine protease inhibitors including antithrombin III, protease nexin-1 (PN-1), and plasminogen activator inhibitor-1 (PAI-1), which function to suppress inflammation and local coagulation [184–187]. Expression of ovarian mRNA for each of these factors has not been clearly defined, but in the mouse, PN-1 is reportedly high during the entire

periovulatory period, whereas PAI-1 is relatively low [188]. In contrast, another report claims that PAI-1 mRNA is expressed in the theca externa and ovarian stroma of the rat at 4 hours after hCG treatment [133]. For comparison, there is a recent study in rats of the protein products of these genes that found that during folliculogenesis the granulosa cells contain PN-1, during the periovulatory period they contain antithrombin III, and after ovulation the lutein tissue contains PAI-1 [187]. Thus it appears the ovulatory role(s) of these serine protease inhibitors warrant further evaluation, especially in view of evidence that the proinflammatory cytokines IL-1β and TNF-α stimulate their secretion [184, 189].

7. *Apolipoprotein E.* Apolipoprotein E (apoE) is an endogenous anti-inflammatory agent produced by the liver, by macrophages, and by other peripheral tissues, including those engaged in steroidogenesis [190–192]. ApoE has a prominent role in cholesterol transport, and this property might be a determinant in its ability to attenuate the inflammatory response [193, 194]. The limited data on expression of apoE in the rat ovary is inconsistent. One report claims that apoE mRNA is localized in the theca externa and ovarian stroma throughout the periovulatory period and is absent from granulosa cells [190]. In contrast, another report states that, whereas apoE mRNA is localized predominantly in the thecal tissue, it increases in granulosa cells as the time of ovulation approaches [195].
8. *Tumor Suppressor p53.* The precise function of the tumor suppressing protein p53 is not clear [196, 197]. Nonetheless, because tumor suppressors usually exhibit anti-inflammatory properties, this factor is included in this particular section. p53 mRNA expression occurs at peak level in the mouse ovary around 6 to 12 hours after hCG administration [198]. The proposed role of ovarian p53 is the differentiation of granulosa cells into luteal cells.
9. *Interleukin-4 Receptor-α.* Although the IL cytokines that have been discussed earlier are distinctly of the proinflammatory type, IL-4 is different in that it suppresses inflammation when it interacts with interleukin-4 receptor-α (IL-4Rα) [199–201]. IL-4Rα has been detected on a variety of cells, and it is reportedly present on all fibroblasts [202]. This distribution of IL-4Rα includes the thecal fibroblasts of follicles during the ovulatory process [156]. With regard to the potential role of this anti-inflammatory factor in ovulation, it may be relevant that the interaction of IL-4 with IL-4Rα reportedly suppresses production of the proinflammatory cytokines IL-1β and TNF-α by monocytes [199].
10. *Metallothionein-1.* Metallothionein-1 (MT-1) is one of several small, ubiquitous, cysteine-rich proteins induced by mediators of inflammation [203]. MT-1 is a zinc-binding protein that can chelate and release several heavy metals during the enzymatic regulation of cellular homeostasis [204]. After almost 50 years of investigation, its precise biological role has not been established, but it is clear this thiol agent has potent metal-binding and redox capabilities. During ovulation, expression of the MT-1 gene is not upregulated in the rat ovary until several hours after the follicles have ruptured [3, 177]. Therefore, ovarian MT-1 exhibits latent expression following an ovulatory dose of hCG, and it may contribute in some as of yet undefined way to the suppression of the ovarian inflammatory reaction during ovulation.
11. *Additional Remarks.* It is important to emphasize that an integral part of inflammatory responses is the capacity of tissues to resolve inflammation by active, endogenous processes [97]. This programmed anti-inflammatory action that assists in repair and healing of locally inflamed areas is based on timely gene expression that overlaps the proinflammatory events [96]. The earlier segment of this review covers some of the ovulation-related genes that encode stop signals and other moderating components of the inflammatory reaction. There are, undoubtedly, other anti-inflammatory genes that remain to be discovered as integral components of the ovulatory process.

OXIDATIVE STRESS

Inflammatory responses are associated with local development of oxidative stress in the affected tissue [94, 205]. As a component of mammalian inflammatory responses, reactive oxygen species (ROS), along with reactive nitrogen species (RNS), are generated especially in the vicinity of hypoxic or reoxygenated mitochondria [206–209]. The superoxides, including O_2^-, OH^-, and H_2O_2, contribute to local cell injury through release of proteases and eicosanoids [207], secretion of proinflammatory cytokines and chemokines [210], and recruitment of leucocytes into the affected tissue [211]. To prevent excessive necrosis and apoptosis in the area (and especially in the highly sensitive endothelial cells), the inflammatory cascade includes activation of genes to minimize the deleterious consequences of oxidative stress. This section identifies several such genes that have been described in relation to ovulation. In addition, it considers several other genes that encode enzymes that possess redox properties.

1. *γ-Glutamylcysteine Synthetase.* γ-Glutamylcysteine synthetase (γ-GCS) is a zinc metalloprotein that serves as the rate-limiting enzyme for synthesis of glutathione [212–214]. Glutathione is a ubiquitous tripeptide that protects cells against oxidative stress and nitrosating species during inflammatory reactions and other con-

ditions that cause cellular injury [215–217]. There is limited evidence that glutathione is synthesized in the ovary near the time of ovulation [218, 219]. More recent data shows that expression of the principal gene for glutathione synthesis, namely γ-GCS, is upregulated in ovarian thecal and granulosa cells during ovulation in the rat [3]. Measurable γ-GCS mRNA increases transiently between 2 to 8 hours after hCG, with the peak occurring at 4 hours. Assuming that synthesis of the glutathione peptide follows the same temporal pattern in the ovary, the data suggest that ovulatory follicles experience maximum oxidative stress before actual rupture of the follicles.

2. *Glutathione S-Transferase.* Glutathione S-transferase (GST) is a member of a large family of soluble enzymes that catalyze the conjugation of glutathione to electrophilic compounds such as unsaturated carbonyls to protect against oxidative stress [220–222]. In addition to protection from the products of ROS-mediated reactions, GST also modulates eicosanoid synthesis [223]. In view of these properties of GST, it would seem likely that the gene for GST would be expressed in a pattern concomitant with γ-GCS. However, on the contrary, GST mRNA (of the T-1 variety) is transcribed in significant amounts only in postovulatory lutein tissue of immature rats that have been stimulated with gonadotropins [3]. Therefore, it appears that ovarian GST has a function that is independent of ovarian γ-GCS.
3. *Superoxide Dismutase.* Another endogenous defense mechanism against damage from oxidative stress are the superoxide dismutases (SODs) that scavenge superoxide anions [224–226]. The Cu,Zn-SOD form is localized in the cytoplasm, whereas the Mn-SOD type reportedly is localized in the mitochondrial matrix [224]. The latter variety, which is induced by factors such as IL-6 and TNF-α, is important for protection against severe mitochondrial dysfunction during local conditions that cause an elevation in ROS [224, 225]. More than a decade ago, SOD activity was described in granulosa cells of growing, ovulatory, and postovulatory follicles of the rat ovary [227]. However, subsequent studies have made it uncertain whether Mn-SOD mRNA is upregulated in the granulosa cells [228], the theca interna cells [229], or in both types of cells [230]. In consideration of the potential significance of ovarian SOD activity during ovulation, this natural antioxidant warrants further assessment in future studies on ovulation.
4. *3α-Hydroxysteroid Dehydrogenase.* 3α-Hydroxysteroid dehydrogenase (3α-HSD) acts with nicotinamide adenine dinucleotide diphosphate (NADPH) to catalyze the oxidoreduction of steroids and other compounds that possess aldehyde and ketone functional groups [231, 232]. In the ovary of the gonadotropin-primed immature rat, there is a slight but detectable amount of 3α-HSD mRNA in the steroidogenically active theca interna of mature follicles even before the ovaries are stimulated by hCG [233]. During ovulation, 3α-HSD mRNA began to increase in the granulosa layer at 2 hours after hCG, and it reached a peak at 8 hours after hCG. A proposed function of the oxidoreductase enzyme that is translated from the 3α-HSD mRNA might be to reduce the toxic aldehyde and ketone components of the steroids and eicosanoids that accumulate in the mammalian ovary at the time of ovulation [233].
5. *Carbonyl Reductase.* Similar to 3α-HSD, carbonyl reductase (CBR) is an NADPH-dependent aldo-keto reductase with broad specificity for converting carbonyl compounds into alcohols [234]. In addition, in the immature rat ovary the temporal pattern of expression of CBR mRNA is parallel to the ovulatory transcription of 3α-HSD mRNA—reaching a peak at 8 hours after hCG treatment of the animals [235]. However, the spatial pattern of ovarian CBR mRNA expression is different from 3α-HSD mRNA. It is limited to the ovarian thecal and stromal areas, with negligible expression in the granulosa layer. The translated CBR enzyme possibly functions to protect the ovarian connective tissue around follicles from excessive exposure to the aldo-keto functional groups that exist on the steroids and eicosanoids that increase so markedly in ovulatory follicles [235].
6. *Additional Remarks.* It is evident that the detrimental components of an acute inflammatory reaction such as the ovulatory process include oxidative stress generated by upregulated metabolic events that elevate local ROS and RNS in ovulatory follicles and in the surrounding ovarian stromal tissue. In addition to the gene transcripts identified earlier, other ovarian factors that probably are involved in antioxidant and redox activity during ovulation include AhR [236], p53 tumor suppressor protein [237, 238], and the CCAAT transcription factor that is important for the transactivation of the CYP1A1 gene promoter [238, 239]. Collectively, these agents serve to minimize the cytotoxic effects of oxidants, aldehydes, and ketones that are generated during the dynamic changes in ovarian follicles as they undergo metabolic transformation into functional corpora lutea.

ANGIOGENESIS

When a follicle ruptures and begins to transform into lutein tissue, angiogenesis is essential for establishing and maintaining a metabolically viable corpus luteum. Many of the gene transcripts that have been described earlier have a direct or indirect influence on the ovarian neovascularization that begins during the ovulatory process. Therefore, before concluding this chapter, it is appropriate to provide a brief overview of angiogenesis and some of the ovulation-related genes that may regulate this process in the ovary.

Angiogenesis is a sequence of events that occurs in normal physiological processes and in a variety of pathological conditions [240]. Angiogenesis commonly begins with vasodilation and an increase in vascular permeability in the affected tissue [241]. In addition, early stages of the process require proteolytic degradation of the extracellular matrix that surrounds the existing capillaries. Once the matrix is more pliable and has been infiltrated by plasma proteins, the local conditions are favorable for proliferation and migration of the endothelial cells that make up the walls of the capillaries already in the area [241, 242]. Eventually, as the new vessels begin to take shape, they are stabilized by recruitment of pericytes and smooth muscle cells around them.

As stated earlier, inflammation is mediated by TNF-α, IL-1β, and numerous other factors [83, 243]. These proinflammatory agents induce production of VEGF, a potent endothelial cell agonist that is secreted by virtually all mammalian cells [244]. In an inflamed area, the local overexpression of VEGF and other vasoactive agents such as the prostanoids causes the capillaries to become dilated and hyperpermeable [82]. The prostanoids are products of COX-2 activity, which promotes angiogenesis [245]. Therefore, predictably, nonsteroidal anti-inflammatory agents and celecoxib that inhibit COX-2 suppress angiogenesis [245–248]. In view of this information, because the ovulatory process is considered to be an inflammatory process, it is likely that ovarian TNF-α, IL-1β, COX-2, and VEGF all influence ovarian angiogenesis during ovulation and luteinization.

There are a variety of other ovulation-related factors that are known to influence angiogenesis. MMPs dissolve the extracellular matrix and promote angiogenesis, whereas TIMPs markedly inhibit such neovascular activity [249–253]. Likewise, antiproteases such as antithrombin-III and PAI-1 inhibit angiogenesis [253, 254]. Other factors such as p53 tumor suppressor [255, 256], HSPGs [257], and MIF [151, 258] might also influence ovarian angiogenesis at the time of ovulation. Thus many of the genes that regulate the ovarian inflammatory reaction during ovulation appear to affect ovarian angiogenesis as well.

CONCLUSION

The most obvious conclusion that can be drawn from this overview of ovarian gene expression is that the molecular and biochemical events of ovulation are far more complicated than was imagined only a few years ago. This chapter has covered approximately 60 different genes that have already been firmly established, or strongly implicated, as ovulation-related genes. With additional efforts to apply differential display, microarray, and other molecular methods that allow the discovery of differential gene expression, many more genes will probably be identified as components of the ovulatory process. This prediction is based on the assumption that an increase in the knowledge of transcription factors such as Egr-1, NF-κB, and AP-1 will reveal that there are massive cascades of gene expression during tissue responses during ovulation, as well as in a variety of other experimental models.

Although it is likely that only a fraction of the ovulation-related genes have been discovered to date, it is already difficult to integrate the extant information into a meaningful picture of the relationships among these genes and the significance of their specific roles in ovulation. In part, the difficulty is because only a portion of the "ovulation puzzle" has been placed on the assembly table. That is to say, there are too many gaps in the current data to link the existing compilation into a unified whole. The task is compounded further because different investigators use diverse methodologies, different experimental animals, and dissimilar experimental designs. Although there is certain value to the individuality and diversity of investigators and investigations that study specific phenomena in the biomedical sciences, the single most confounding obstacle to a more comprehensive integration of the information covered in this review was the inconsistency in the methods and the models that were used by different investigators. It was relatively easy to integrate the data that was obtained from rodents in studies that extracted RNA at four to six fixed intervals during the periovulatory period. Data from a group of animals in which the duration of the ovulatory process is relatively constant allows for a more reliable assessment of the chronology of gene expression. As more ovulation-related genes are discovered, the challenge of integrating the omnium-gatherum of genes into one meaningful picture of the molecular events of ovulation will be influenced by the consistency in the experimental designs of studies to detect differential gene expression in the ovary.

In this survey of ovarian gene expression, several inferences can be drawn with regard to what does *not* occur in ovulatory follicles. Firstly, over the past century there have been numerous reports that have stressed that the mechanism of ovulation is based on gonadotropin-induced contraction of smooth muscle tissue in and around the mature follicles [2, 259]. However, the current assessment of ovarian gene expression has uncovered virtually no information to suggest that the protein products of ovulation-related genes function to initiate local contractility. The preponderance of the literature corroborates the idea that ovulation is an inflammatory reaction that includes a complement of proteases to degrade the connective tissue elements at the apex of the follicle wall. Secondly, old and new studies have hypothesized that the single layer of surface epithelial cells that surround the ovary have a central role in the mechanism of ovulation [260–262]. However, based on the literature survey for this chapter, there are no definitive reports of novel gene expression in the thin surface epithelium in response to an ovulatory surge in gonadotropin. In contrast, the data collectively and consistently show that the granulosa layer and the thecal tissues are the principal sites of ovulation-related molecular events.

Based on the information to date, it is reasonable to conclude that the ovulatory process is initiated in the dormant stratum granulosum and perhaps the steroidogenically active theca interna of mature follicles. The inflammatory cascade of gene expression in these inner layers of the follicle generate transcripts that "spill out" to the fibroblast-rich collagenous connective tissue that comprises most of the theca externa and much of the ovarian stromal tissue. The granulosa is the principal source of inflammatory cytokines and vasoactive agents such as the prostanoids and VEGF. The granulosa is also the source of the novel metalloproteinase ADAMTS-1. However, it remains to be determined whether the role of this enzyme is limited to the dislodging of the cumulus mass in preparation for release of the oocyte from ovulatory follicles, or whether ADAMTS-1 also contributes to digestion of the collagenous connective tissue that serves as the principal barrier to follicular rupture. In any case, it is clear that the fibroblasts, which dominate the theca externa and the tunica albuginea at the apex of a follicle, undergo striking morphological changes from their preovulatory quiescent state to become elongated motile cells [1]. As these cells begin to actively move within the collagenous extracellular matrix of the follicle, it is difficult to imagine they do not produce proteases such as the MMPs that contribute in a significant way to the breakdown of the follicle wall. Finally, in the coming decade, with more precise information about the temporal and spatial pattern of expression of the genes covered in this review and of genes yet to be discovered, the overall picture of the molecular events of ovulation should become more clear.

ACKNOWLEDGMENTS

This review is an outgrowth of an undergraduate conference course at Trinity University, San Antonio, Texas, on the topic of cell signaling processes. The study was supported in part by National Science Foundation (NSF) Grants 9870793 and 0234358.

References

1. Espey, L. L. (1999) Ovulation. In *Encyclopedia of Reproduction*, Vol. 3, eds. E. Knobil and J. D. Neill, 605–614. San Diego: Academic Press.
2. Espey, L. L., and Lipner, H. (1994). Ovulation. In *The Physiology of Reproduction*, eds. E. Knobil and J. D. Neill, 725–780. New York: Raven Press.
3. Espey, L. L., and Richards, J. S. (2002). Temporal and spatial patterns of ovarian gene transcription following an ovulatory dose of gonadotropin in the rat. *Biol. Reprod.* 67, 1662–1670.
4. Richards, J. S., Russell, D. L., Ochsner, S., and Espey, L. L. (2002). Ovulation: New dimensions and new regulators of the inflammatory-like response. *Annu. Rev. Physiol.* 64, 69–92.
5. Richards, J. S., Russell, D. L., Ochsner, S., Hsieh, M., Doyle, K. H., Falender, A. E., Lo, Y. K., and Sharma, S. C. (2002). Novel signaling pathways that control ovarian follicular development, ovulation, and luteinization. *Rec. Prog. Hormone Res.* 57, 195–220.
6. Gashler, A., and Sukhatme, V. P. (1995). Early growth response protein 1 (Egr-1): Prototype of a zinc-finger family of transcription factors. *Prog. Nucleic Acids Res. Mol. Biol.* 50, 191–224.
7. Kachigian, L. M., and Collins, T. (1998). Early growth response factor 1: A pleiotropic mediator of inducible gene expression. *J. Mol. Med.* 76, 613–616.
8. Beckmann, A. M., and Wilce, P. A. (1997). Egr transcription factors in the nervous system. *Neurochem. Int.* 31, 477–510.
9. Okada, M., Fujita, T., Olson, K. E., Collins, T., Stern, D. M., Yan, S. F., and Pinsky, D. J. (2001). Extinguishing Egr-1-dependent inflammatory and thrombotic cascades after lung transplantation. *FASEB J.* 15, 2757–2759.
10. Silverman, E. S., DeSanctis, G. T., Boyce, J., Maclean, J. A., Jiao, A., Green, F. H., Grasemann, H., Faunce, D., Fitzmaurice, G., Shi, G. P., Stein-Streilein, J., Milbrandt, J., Collins, T., and Drazen, J. M. (2001). The transcription factor early growth-response factor 1 modulates tumor necrosis factor-α, immunoglobulin E, and airway responsiveness in mice. *Am. J. Respir. Crit. Care Med.* 163, 778–785.
11. Adashi, E. Y. (1990). The potential relevance of cytokines to ovarian physiology: The emerging role of resident ovarian cells of the white blood cell series. *Endocr. Rev.* 11, 454–464.
12. Terranova, P. F., and Rice, V. M. (1997). Review: Cytokine involvement in ovarian processes. *Am. J. Reprod. Immunol.* 37, 50–63.
13. Espey, L. L., Ujioka, T., Russell, D., Skelsey, M., Vladu, B., Robker, R. L., Okamura, H., and Richards, J. S. (2000). Induction of early growth response protein 1 gene expression in the rat ovary in response to an ovulatory dose of human chorionic gonadotropin. *Endocrinology* 141, 2385–2391.
14. Saliba, E., and Henrot, A. (2001). Inflammatory mediators and neonatal brain damage. *Biol. Neonate* 79, 224–227.
15. Adashi, E. Y. (1998). The potential role of interleukin-1 in the ovulatory process: An evolving hypothesis. *Mol. Cell. Endocrinol.* 140, 77–81.
16. Kol, S., Kehat, I., and Adashi, E. Y. (2001). Ovarian interleukin-1-induced gene expression: Privileged genes threshold theory. *Med. Hypotheses* 58, 6–8.
17. Chung, K. W., Ando, M., and Adashi, E. Y. (2000). Periovulatory and interleukin (IL)-1-dependent regulation of IL-6 in the immature rat ovary: A specific IL-1 receptor-mediated eicosanoid-dependent effect. *J. Soc. Gynecol. Investig.* 7, 301–308.

18. Gately, S. (2000). The contributions of cyclooxygenase-2 to tumor angiogenesis. *Cancer Metastasis Rev.* 19, 19–27.
19. Crofford, L. J. (1997). COX-1 and COX-2 tissue expression: Implications and predictions. *J. Rheumatol.* 49 (Suppl), 15–19.
20. Wadleigh, D. J., Reddy, S. T., Kopp, E., Ghosh, S., and Herschman, H. R. (2000). Transcriptional activation of the cyclooxygenase-2 gene in endotoxin-treated RAW 264.7 macrophages. *J. Biol. Chem.* 275, 6259–6266.
21. Lim, H., Paria, B. C., Das, S. K., Dinchuk, J. E., Langenbach, R., Trzaskos, J. M., and Dey, S. K. (1997). Multiple female reproductive failures in cyclooxygenase 2–deficient mice. *Cell* 91, 197–208.
22. Wang, J. M., Chao, J. R., Chen, W., Kuo, M. L., Yen, J. J., and Yang-Yen, H. F. (1999). The antiapoptotic gene mcl-1 is up-regulated by the phosphatidylinositol 3 kinase/Akt signaling pathway through a transcription factor complex containing CREB. *Mol. Cell. Biol.* 19, 6195–6206.
23. Leo, C. P., Hsu, S. Y., Chun, S. Y., Bae, H. W., and Hsueh, A. J. (1999). Characterization of the antiapoptotic Bcl-2 family member myeloid cell leukemia-1 (Mcl-1) and the stimulation of its message by gonadotropins in the rat ovary. *Endocrinology* 140, 5465–5468.
24. Wilson, C. L., and Safe, S. (1998). Mechanisms of ligand-induced aryl hydrocarbon receptor-mediated biochemical and toxic responses. *Toxicol. Pathol.* 26, 672–673.
25. Harper, P. A., Wong, J. Y., Lam, M. S., and Okey, A. B. (2002). Polymorphisms in the human AH receptor. *Chem. Biol. Interact.* 141, 161–187.
26. Durocher, F., Morissette, J., and Simard, J. (1998). Genetic linkage mapping of the CYP11A1 gene encoding the cholesterol side-chain cleavage P450scc close to the CYP1A1 gene and D15S204 in the chromosome 15q22.33-q23 region. *Pharmacogenetics* 8, 49–53.
27. Chaffin, C. L., Stouffer, R. L., and Duffy, D. M. (1999). Gonadotropin and steroid regulation of steroid receptor and aryl hydrocarbon receptor messenger ribonucleic acid in macaque granulosa cells during the periovulatory interval. *Endocrinology* 140, 4753–4760.
28. Mizuyachi, K., Son, D. S., Rozman, K. K., and Terranova, P. F. (2002). Alteration in ovarian gene expression in response to 2,3,7,8-tetrachlorodibenzo-p-dioxin: Reduction of cyclooxygenase-2 in the blockage of ovulation. *Reprod. Toxicol.* 16, 299–307.
29. Oh-hama, T. (1997). Evolutionary consideration on 5-aminolevulinate synthase in nature. *Origins Life Evol. Biosph.* 27, 405–412.
30. Thunell, S. (2000). Porphyrins, porphyrin metabolism, and porphyrias. I. Update. *Scand. J. Clin. Lab. Invest.* 60, 509–540.
31. Suffredini, A. F., Fantuzzi, G., Badolato, R., Oppenheim, J. J., and O'Grady, N. P. (1999). New insights into the biology of the acute phase response. *J. Clin. Immunol.* 19, 203–214.
32. Rosenberg, D., Groussin, L., Jullian, E., Perlemoine, K., Bertagna, X., and Bertherat, J. (2002). Role of the PKA-regulated transcription factor CRB in development and tumorigenesis of endocrine tissues. *Ann. N. Y. Acad. Sci.* 968, 65–74.
33. Quinn, P. G. (2002). Mechanisms of basal and kinase-inducible transcription activation by CREB. *Prog. Nucleic Acid Res. Mol. Biol.* 72, 269–305.
34. Don, J., and Stelzer, G. (2002). The expanding family of CREB/CREM transcription factors that are involved with spermatogenesis. *Mol. Cell. Endocrinol.* 187, 115–124.
35. Servillo, G., Della Fazia, M. A., and Sassone-Corsi, P. (2002). Coupling cAMP signaling to transcription in the liver: Pivotal role of CREB and CREM. *Exp. Cell. Res.* 275, 143–154.
36. Benyo, D. F., and Zeleznik, A. J. (1997). Cyclic adenosine monophosphate signaling in the primate corpus luteum: Maintenance of protein kinase A activity throughout the luteal phase of the menstrual cycle. *Endocrinology* 138, 3452–3458.
37. Somers, J. P., DeLoia, J. A., and Zeleznik, A. J. (1999). Adenovirus-directed expression of a nonphosphorylatable mutant of CREB (cAMP response element-binding protein) adversely affects the survival, but not the differentiation, of rat granulosa cells. *Mol. Endocrinol.* 13, 1364–1372.
38. Mukherjee A., Urban, J., Sassone-Corsi, P., and Mayo, K. E. (1998). Gonadotropins regulate inducible cyclic adenosine 3′5′-monophosphate early repressor in the rat ovary: Implications for inhibit-α subunit gene expression *Mol. Endocrinol.* 12, 785–800.
39. Stylianou, E., and Saklatvala, J. (1998). Interleukin-1. *Int. J. Biochem. Cell. Biol.* 30, 1075–1079.
40. Baud, V., and Karin, M. (2001). Signal transduction by tumor necrosis factor and its relatives. *Trends Cell Biol.* 11, 372–377.
41. Matt, T. (2002). Transcriptional control of the inflammatory response: A role for the CREB-binding protein (CBP). *Acta Med. Austriaca* 29, 77–79.
42. Niswender, G. D. (2002). Molecular control of luteal secretion of progesterone. *Reproduction* 123, 333–339.
43. Herrmann, M., Scholmerich, J., and Straub, R. H. (2002). Influence of cytokines and growth factors on distinct steroidogenic enzymes in vitro: A short tabular data collection. *Ann. N. Y. Acad. Sci.* 996, 166–168.
44. Hum, D. W., and Miller, W. L. (1993). Transcriptional regulation of human genes for steroidogenic enzymes. *Clin. Chem.* 39, 333–340.
45. Kaynard, A. H., Periman, L. M., Simard, J., and Melner, M. H. (1992). Ovarian 3β-hydroxysteroid dehydrogenase and sulfated glycoprotein-2 gene expression are differentially regulated by the induction of ovulation, pseudopregnancy, and luteolysis in the immature rat. *Endocrinology* 130, 2192–2200.
46. Boerboom, D., and Sirois, J. (2001). Equine P450 cholesterol side-chain cleavage and 3β-hydroxysteroid dehydrogenase/Δ(5)-Δ(4) isomerase molecular cloning and regulation of their messenger ribonucleic acids in equine follicles during the ovulatory process. *Biol. Reprod.* 64, 206–215.
47. Chaffin, C. L., Dissen, G. A., and Stouffer, R. L. (2000). Hormonal regulation of steroidogenic enzyme expression granulosa cells during the periovulatory interval in monkeys. *Mol. Hum. Reprod.* 6, 11–18.
48. Stocco, D. M. (2001). StAR protein and the regulation of steroid hormone biosynthesis. *Annu. Rev. Physiol.* 63, 193–213.
49. Ronen-Fuhrmann, T., Timberg, R., King, S. R., Hales, K. H., Hales, D. B., Stocco, D. M., and Orly, J. (1998). Spatiotemporal expression patterns of steroidogenic acute regula-

tory protein (StAR) during follicular development in the rat ovary. *Endocrinology* 139, 303–315.

50. Kerban, A., Boerboom, D., and Sirois, J. (1999). Human chorionic gonadotropin induces an inverse regulation of steroidogenic acute regulatory protein messenger ribonucleic acid in theca interna and granulosa cells of equine preovulatory follicles. *Endocrinology* 140, 667–674.
51. Grinberg, A. V., Hannemann, F., Schiffler, B., Muller, J., Heinemann, U., and Bernharddt, R. (2000). Adrenodoxin: Structure, stability, and electron transfer properties. *Proteins* 40, 590–612.
52. Selvaraj, N., Dantes, A., and Amsterdam, A. (2000). Establishment and characterization of steroidogenic granulosa cells expressing β_2-adrenergic receptor: Regulation of adrenodoxin and steroidogenic acute regulatory protein by adrenergic agents. *Mol. Cell. Endocrinol.* 168, 53–63.
53. Natraj, U., and Richards, J. S. (1993). Hormonal regulation, localization, and functional activity of the progesterone receptor in granulosa cells of rat preovulatory follicles. *Endocrinology* 133, 761–769.
54. Robker, R. L., Russell, D. L., Espey, L. L., Lydon, J. P., O'Malley, B. W., and Richards, J. S. (2000). Progesterone-regulated genes in the ovulation process: ADAMTS-1 and cathepsin L proteases. *Proc. Natl. Acad. Sci. USA* 97, 4689–4694.
55. Snyder, B. W., Beecham, G. D., and Schane, H. P. (1984). Inhibition of ovulation in rats with epostane, an inhibitor of 3β-hydroxysteroid dehydrogenase. *Proc. Soc. Exp. Biol. Med.* 176, 238–242.
56. Espey, L. L., Adams, R. F., Tanaka, N., and Okamura, H. (1990). Effects of epostane on ovarian levels of progesterone, 17β-estradiol, prostaglandin E_2, and prostaglandin $F_{2\alpha}$ during ovulation in the gonadotropin-primed immature rat. *Endocrinology* 127, 259–263.
57. Espey, L. L., Yoshioka, S., Russell, D. L., Robker, R. L., Fujii, S., and Richards, J. S. (2000). Ovarian expression of a disintegrin and metalloproteinase with thrombospondin motifs during ovulation in the gonadotropin-primed immature rat. *Biol. Reprod.* 62, 1090–1095.
58. Espey, L. L., Tanaka, N., Adams, R. F., and Okamura, H. (1991). Ovarian hydroxyeicosatetraenoic acids compared to prostanoids and steroids during ovulation in the rat. *Am. J. Physiol.* 260, E163–E169.
59. Espey, L. L. (1980). Ovulation as an inflammatory reaction—A hypothesis. *Biol. Reprod.* 22, 73–106.
60. Espey, L. L. (1994). Current status of the hypothesis that mammalian ovulation is comparable to an inflammatory reaction. *Biol. Reprod.* 50, 233–238.
61. Chen, G., and Goeddel, D. V. (2002). TNF-R1 signaling: A beautiful pathway. *Science* 296, 1634–1635.
62. Ando, M., Kol, S., Kokia, E., Ruutiainen-Altman, K., Sirois, J., Rohan, R. M., Payne, D. W., and Adashi, E. Y. (1998). Rat ovarian prostaglandin endoperoxide synthase-1 and -2: Periovulatory expression of granulosa cell-based interleukin-1-dependent enzymes. *Endocrinology* 139, 2501–2508.
63. Kol, S., Ruutiainen-Altman, K., Scherzer, W. J., Ben-Shlomo, I., Ando, M., Rohan, R. M., and Adashi, E. Y. (1999). The rat intraovarian interleukin (IL)-1 system: Cellular localization, cyclic variation, and hormonal regulation of IL-1β and of the type I and type II IL-1 receptors. *Mol. Cell. Endocrinol.* 149, 115–128.
64. Levitas, E., Chamoun, D., Udoff, L. C., Ando, M., Resnick, C. E., and Adashi, E. Y. (2000). Periovulatory and interleukin-1β-dependent up-regulation of intraovarian vascular endothelial growth factor (VEGF) in the rat: Potential role for VEGF in the promotion of periovulatory angiogenesis and vascular permeability. *J. Soc. Gynecol. Investig.* 7, 51–60.
65. Chen, Y. J., Feng, Q., and Liu, Y. X. (1999). Expression of the steroidogenic acute regulatory protein and luteinizing hormone receptor and their regulation by tumor necrosis factor alpha in rat corpora lutea. *Biol. Reprod.* 60, 419–427.
66. Poli, V. (1998). The role of C/EBP isoforms in the control of inflammatory and native immunity functions. *J. Biol. Chem.* 273, 29279–29282.
67. Sirois, J., and Richards, J. S. (1993). Transcriptional regulation of the rat prostaglandin endoperoxide synthase 2 gene in granulosa cells. Evidence for the role of a cis-acting C/EBPβ promoter element. *J. Biol. Chem.* 268, 21931–21938.
68. Piontkewitz, Y., Enerback, S., and Hedin, L. (1996). Expression of CCAAT enhancer binding protein-α (C/EBPα) in the rat ovary: Implications for follicular development and ovulation. *Dev. Biol.* 179, 288–296.
69. Pall, M., Hellberg, P., Brännström, M., Mikuni, M., Peterson, C. M., Sundfeldt, K., Norden, B., Hedin, L., and Enerback, S. (1997). The transcription factor C/EBP-β and its role in ovarian function: Evidence for direct involvement in the ovulatory process. *EMBO J.* 16, 5273–5279.
70. Sahnoun Z., Jamoussi, K., Zeghal, K. M. (1998). Free radicals and antioxidants: Physiology, human pathology, and therapeutic aspects (part II). *Therapie* 53, 315–339.
71. Suzuki, H., Mori, M., Seto, K., Shibata, F., Nagahashi, S., Kawaguchi, C., Suzuki, M., Matsui, H., Watanabe, K., Miura, S., and Ishii, H. (2000). Rat CXC chemokine GRO/CINC-1 paradoxically stimulate the growth of gastric epithelial cells. *Aliment. Pharmacol. Ther.* 14 (Suppl 1), 94–100.
72. Shibata, F. (2002). The role of rat cytokine-induced neutrophil chemoattractants (CINCs) in inflammation. *Yakugaku Zasshi* 122, 263–268.
73. Ushigoee, K., Irahara, M., Fukumochi, M., Kamada, M., and Aono, T. (2000). Production and regulation of cytokine-induced neutrophil chemoattractant in rat ovulation. *Biol. Reprod.* 63, 121–126.
74. Oral, E., Seli, E., Bahtiyar, M. O., Jones, E. E., and Arici, A. Growth-regulated-α expression in human preovulatory follicles and ovarian cells. *Am. J. Reprod. Immunol.* 38, 19–25.
75. Karstrom-Encrantz, L., Runesson, E., Bostrom, E. K., and Brännström, M. (1998). Selective presence of the chemokine growth-regulated oncogene-α (GRO-α) in the human follicle and secretion from cultured granulosa-lutein cells at ovulation. *Mol. Hum. Reprod.* 4, 1077–1083.
76. Irahara, M., Yasui, T., Tezuka, M., Ushigoe, K., Yamano, S., Kamada, M., and Aono, T. (2000). Evidence that Toki-Shakuyaku-san and its ingredients enhance the secretion of a cytokine-induced neutrophil chemoattractant (CINC/gro) in the ovulatory process. *Methods Find. Exp. Clin. Pharmacol.* 22, 725–730.
77. Yan, S. F., Fujita, T., Lu, J., Okada, K., Shan Zou, Y., Mackman, N., Pinsky, D. J., and Stern, D. M. (2000). Egr-1, a

master switch coordinating upregulation of divergent gene families underlying ischemic stress. *Nat. Med.* 6, 1355–1361.

78. Micera, A., Vigneti, E., Pickholtz, D., Reich, R., Pappo, O., Bonini, S., Maquart, F. X., Aloe, L., and Levi-Schaffer, F. (2001). Nerve growth factor displays stimulatory effects on human skin and lung fibroblasts, demonstrating a direct role for this factor in tissue repair. *Proc. Natl. Acad. Sci. USA* 98, 6162–6167.
79. Barouch, R., Kazimirsky, G., Appel, E., and Brodie, C. (2001). Nerve growth factor regulates TNF-α production in mouse macrophages via MAP kinase activation. *J. Leukoc. Biol.* 69, 1019–1026.
80. Dissen, G. A., Hill, D. F., Costa, M. E., Les Dees, C. W., Lara, H. E., and Ojeda, S. R. (1996). *Endocrinology* 137, 198–209.
81. Dissen, G. A., Parrott, J. A., Skinner, M. K., Hill, D. F., Costa, M. E., and Ojeda, S. R. (2000). Direct effects of nerve growth factor on thecal cells from antral ovarian follicles. *Endocrinology* 141, 4736–4750.
82. Dvorak, H. F., Nagy, J. A., Feng, D., Brown, L. F., and Dvorak, A. M. (1999). Vascular permeability factor/vascular endothelial growth factor and the significance of microvascular hyperpermeability in angiogenesis. *Curr. Top. Microbiol. Immunol.* 237, 97–132.
83. van Hinsbergh, V. W., Collen, A., and Koolwijk, P. (2001). Role of fibrin matrix in angiogenesis. *Ann. N. Y. Acad. Sci.* 936, 426–437.
84. Thurston, G. (2002). Complementary actions of VEGF and angiopoietin-1 on blood vessel growth and leakage. *J. Anat.* 200, 575–580.
85. Garrido, C., Saule, S., and Gospodarowicz, D. (1993). Transcriptional regulation of vascular endothelial growth factor gene expression in ovarian bovine granulosa cells. *Growth Factors* 8, 109–117.
86. Koos, R. D. (1995). Increased expression of vascular endothelial growth/permeability factor in the rat ovary following an ovulatory gonadotropin stimulus: Potential roles in follicular rupture. *Biol. Reprod.* 52, 1426–1435.
87. Mastorakos, G., Webster, E. L., Friedman, T. C., and Chrousos, G. P. (1993). Immunoreactive corticotropin-releasing hormone and its binding sites in the rat ovary. *J. Clin. Invest.* 92, 961–968.
88. Schafer, M., Mousa, S. A., and Stein, C. (1997). Corticotropin-releasing factor in antinociception and inflammation. *Eur. J. Pharmacol.* 323, 1–10.
89. Baigent, S. M. (2001). Peripheral corticotropin-releasing hormone and urocortin in the control of the immune response. *Peptides* 22, 809–820.
90. Nappi, R. E., and Rivest, S. (1995). Stress-induced genetic expression of a selective corticotropin-releasing factor-receptor subtype within the rat ovaries, an effect dependent on the ovulatory cycle. *Biol. Reprod.* 53, 1417–1428.
91. Turini, M. E., and DuBois, R. N. (2002). Cyclooxygenase-2: A therapeutic target. *Annu. Rev. Med.* 53, 35–57.
92. Shirakata, Y., Komurasaki, T., Toyoda, H., Hanakawa, Y., Yamasaki, K., Tokumaru, S., Sayama, K., and Hashimoto, K. (2000). Epiregulin, a novel member of the epidermal growth factor family, is an autocrine growth factor in normal human keratinocytes. *J. Biol. Chem.* 275, 5748–5753.
93. Robert, C., Gagne, D., Bousquet, D., Barnes, F. L., and Sirard, M. A. (2001). Differential display and suppressive subtractive hybridization used to identify granulosa cell messenger RNA associated with bovine oocyte developmental competence. *Biol. Reprod.* 64, 1812–1820.
94. Li, X., Massa, P. E., Hanidu, A., Peet, G. W., Aro, P., Savitt, A., Mische, S., Li, J., and Marcu, K. B. (2002). IKKα, IKKβ, and NEMO/IKKγ are each required for the NF-κB-mediated inflammatory response program. *J. Biol. Chem.* 227, 45129–45140.
95. Sasaki, E., Pai, R., Halter, F., Komurasaki, T., Arakawa, T., Kobayashi, K., Kuroki, T., and Tarnawski, A. S. (1998). Induction of cyclooxygenase-2 in a rat gastric epithelial cell line by epiregulin and basic fibroblast growth factor. *J. Clin. Gastroenterol.* 27 (Suppl 1), S21–S27.
96. Nathan, C. (2002). Points of control in inflammation. *Nature* 420, 846–852.
97. Lawrence, T., Willoughby, D. A., and Gilroy, D. W. (2002). Anti-inflammatory lipid mediator and insights into the resolution of inflammation. *Nat. Rev. Immunol.* 2, 787–795.
98. Jung, Y., Isaacs, J. S., Lee, S., Trepel, J., Liu, Z. G., and Neckers, L. (2003). Hypoxia-inducible factor induction by tumor necrosis factor in normoxic cells requires receptor-interacting protein-dependent nuclear factor kappa beta activation. *Biochem. J.* 370, 1011–1017, 2003.
99. Kupfner, J. G., Arcaroli, J. J., Yum, H. K., Nadler, S. G., Yang, K. Y., and Abraham, E. (2001). Role of NF-κB in endotoxemia-induced alterations of lung neutrophil apoptosis. *J. Immunol.* 167, 7044–7051.
100. Taylor, C. C., Limback, D., and Terranova, P. F. (1997). Src tyrosine kinase activity in rat thecal-interstitial cells and mouse TM3 Leydig cells is positively associated with cAMP-specific phosphodiesterase activity. *Mol. Cell. Endocrinol.* 126, 91–100.
101. Burnouf, C., and Pruniaux, M. P. (2002). Recent advances in PDE4 inhibitors as immunoregulators and anti-inflammatory drugs. *Curr. Pharm. Des.* 8, 1255–1296.
102. Combes, P., and Dickenson, J. M. (2001). Inhibition of NF-κB-mediated gene transcription by human A2B adenosine receptor in Chinese hamster ovary cells. *J. Pharm. Pharmacol.* 53, 1153–1156.
103. Kasyapa, C. S., Stentz, C. L., Davey, M. P., and Carr, D. W. (1999). Regulation of IL-15-stimulated TNF-α production by rolipram. *J. Immunol.* 163, 2836–2843.
104. Jin, S. L., and Conti, M. (2002). Induction of the cyclic nucleotide phosphodiesterase PDE4B is essential for LPS-activated TNF-α responses. *Proc. Natl. Acad. Sci. USA* 99, 7628–7633.
105. Jin, S. L., Richard, F. J., Kuo, W. P., D'Ercole, A. J., and Conti, M. (1999). Impaired growth and fertility of cAMP-specific phosphodiesterase PDE4D-deficient mice. *Proc. Natl. Acad. Sci. USA* 96, 11998–12003.
106. Fiorentino, L., Stehlik, C., Oliveira, V., Ariza, M. E., Godzik, A., and Reed, J. C. (2002). A novel PAAD-containing protein that modulates NF-κB induction by cytokines tumor necrosis factor-α and interleukin-1β. *J. Biol. Chem.* 277, 35333–35340.
107. White, R., Leonardsson, G., Rosewell, I., Ann Jacobs, M., Milligan, S., and Parker, M. (2000). The nuclear receptor co-repressor nrip1 (RIP140) is essential for female fertility. *Nat. Med.* 6, 1368–1374.

108. Leonardsson, G., Jacobs, M. A., White, R., Jeffery, R., Poulsom, R., Milligan, S., and Parker, M. (2002). Embryo transfer experiments and ovarian transplantation identify the ovary as the only site in which nuclear receptor interacting protein 1/RIP140 action is crucial for female fertility. *Endocrinology* 143, 700–707.
109. Abramson, S. B., Amin, A. R., Clancy, R. M., and Attur, M. (2001). The role of nitric oxide in tissue destruction. *Best Pract. Res. Clin. Rheumatol.* 15, 831–845.
110. Coleman, J. W. (2002). Nitric oxide: A regulator of mast cell activation and mast cell mediated inflammation. *Clin. Exp. Immunol.* 129, 4–10.
111. Blantz, R. C., and Munger, K. (2002). Role of nitric oxide in inflammatory conditions. *Nephron* 90, 373–378.
112. Yamagata, Y., Nakamura, Y., Sugino, N., Harada, A., Takayama, H., Kashida, S., and Kato, H. (2002). Alterations in nitrate/nitrite and nitric oxide synthase in preovulatory follicles in gonadotropin-primed immature rats. *Endocr. J.* 49, 219–226.
113. Srivastava, V., Jones, B. J., Dookwah, H., Hiney, J. K., and Dees, W. L. (1997). Ovarian nitric oxide synthase (NOS) gene expression during peripubertal development. *Life Sci.* 61, 1507–1516.
114. Jablonka-Shariff, A., and Olson, L. M. (1997). Hormonal regulation of nitric oxide synthases and their cell-specific expression during follicular development in the rat ovary. *Endocrinology* 138, 460–468.
114a. Nakamura, Y., Kashida, S., Nakata, M., Takiguchi, S., Yamagata, Y., Takayama, H., Sugino, N., and Kato, H. (1999). Changes in nitric oxide synthase activity in the ovary of gonadotropin treated rats: the role of nitric oxide during ovulation. Endocr. J. 46, 529–538.
115. Kuno, K., Kanada, N., Nakashima, E., Fujiki, F., Ichimura, F., and Matsushima, K. (1997). Molecular cloning of a gene encoding a new type of metalloproteinase-disintegrin family protein with thrombospondin motifs as an inflammation associated gene. *J. Biol. Chem.* 272, 556–562.
116. Tang, B. L. (2001). ADAMTS: a novel family of extracellular matrix proteases. *Int. J. Biochem. Cell Biol.* 33, 33–44.
117. Thai, S. N., and Iruela-Arispe, M. L. (2002). Expression of ADAMTS1 during murine development. *Mech. Dev.* 115, 181–185.
118. Sugiura, T. (2003). Baculoviral expression of correctly processed ADAMTS proteins fused with the human IgG-Fc region. *J. Biotechnol.* 100, 193–201.
119. Rodriguez-Manzaneque, J. C., Westling, J., Thai, S. N., Luque, A., Knauper, V., Murphy, G., Sandy, J. D., and Iruela-Arispe, M. L. (2002). ADAMTS1 cleaves aggrecan at multiple sites and is differentially inhibited by metalloproteinase inhibitors. *Biochem. Biophys. Res. Commun.* 293, 501–508.
120. Dong, Z., Katar, M., Linebaugh, B. E., Sloane, B. F., and Berk, R. S. (2001). Expression of cathepsins B, D, and L in mouse corneas infected with Pseudomonas aeruginosa. *Eur. J. Biochem.* 268, 6408–6416.
121. Fiebiger, E., Maehhr, R., Villadangos, J., Weber, E., Erickson, A., Bikoff, E., Ploegh, H. L., and Lennon-Dumenil, A. M. (2002). Invariant chain controls the activity of extracellular cathepsin L. *J. Exp. Med.* 196, 1263–1269.
122. Robker, R. L., Russell, D. L., Yoshioka, S., Sharma, C., Lydon, J. P., O'Malley, B. W., Espey, L. L., and Richards, J. S. (2000). Ovulation: A multigene, multistep process. *Steroids* 65, 559–570.
123. Cuzner, M. L., and Opdenakker, G. (1999). Plasminogen activators and matrix metalloproteases, mediators of extracellular proteolysis in inflammatory demyelination of the central nervous system. *J. Neuroimmunol.* 94, 1–14.
124. Ohbayashi, H. (2002). Matrix metalloproteinases in lung diseases. *Curr. Protein Pept. Sci.* 3, 409–421.
125. Curry, Jr., T. E., Mann, J. S., Huang, M. H., and Keeble, S. C. (1992). Gelatinase and proteoglycanase activity during the periovulatory period in the rat. *Biol. Reprod.* 46, 256–264.
126. Curry, Jr., T. E., and Osteen, K. G. (2001). Cyclic changes in the matrix metalloproteinase system in the ovary and uterus. *Biol. Reprod.* 64, 1285–1296.
127. Balbin, M., Fueyo, A., Lopez, J. M., Diez-Itza, I., Velasco, G., and Lopez-Otin, C. (1996). Expression of collagenase-3 in the rat ovary during the ovulatory process. *J. Endocrinol.* 149, 405–415.
128. Bagavandoss, P. (1998). Differential distribution of gelatinases and tissue inhibitor of metalloproteinase-1 in the rat ovary. *J. Endocrinol.* 158, 221–228.
129. Curry, Jr., T. E., Song, L., and Wheeler, S. E. (2001). Cellular localization of gelatinases and tissue inhibitors of metalloproteinases during follicular growth, ovulation, and early luteal formation in the rat. *Biol. Reprod.* 65, 855–865.
130. Hagglund, A. C., Ny, A., Leonardsson, G., and Ny, T. (1999). Regulation and localization of matrix metalloproteinases and tissue inhibitors of metalloproteinases in the mouse ovary during gonadotropin-induced ovulation. *Endocrinology* 140, 4351–4358.
131. Beers, W. H. (1975). Follicular plasminogen and plasminogen activator and the effect of plasmin on ovarian follicle wall. *Cell* 6, 379–386.
132. Shimada, H., Mori, T., Takada, A., Takada, Y., Noda, Y., Takai, I., Kohda, H., and Nishimura, T. (1981). Use of chromogenic substrate S-2251 for determination of plasminogen activator in rat ovaries. *Thromb. Haemost.* 46, 507–510.
133. Shen, X., Minoura, H., Yoshida, T., and Toyoda, N. (1997). Changes in ovarian expression of tissue-type plasminogen activator and plasminogen activator inhibitor type-1 messenger ribonucleic acids during ovulation in rat. *Endocr. J.* 44, 341–348.
134. Leonardsson, G., Peng, X. R., Liu, K., Nordstrom, L., Carmeliet, P., Mulligan, R., Collen, D., and Ny, T. (1995). Ovulation efficiency is reduced in mice that lack plasminogen activator gene function: Functional redundancy among physiological plasminogen activator. *Proc. Natl. Acad. Sci. USA* 92, 12446–12450.
135. Ny, A., Nordstrom, L., Carmeliet, P., and Ny, T. (1997). Studies of mice lacking plasminogen activator gene function suggest that plasmin production prior to ovulation exceeds the amount needed for optimal ovulation efficiency. *Eur. J. Biochem.* 244, 487–493.
136. Ny, A., Leonardsson, G., Hagglund, A. C., Hagglof, P., Ploplis, V. A., Carmeliet, P., and Ny, T. (1999). Ovulation in plasminogen-deficient mice. *Endocrinology* 140, 5030–5035.
137. Valent, P., Schernthaner, G. H., Sperr, W. R., Fritsch, G., Agis, H., Willheim, M., Buhring, H. J., Orfao, A., and Escribano, L. (2001). Variable expression of activation-linked surface anti-

gens on human mast cells in health and disease. *Immunol. Rev.* 179, 74–81.

138. Zhang, H., Downey, G. P., Suter, P. M., Slutsky, A. S., and Ranieri, V. M. (2002). Conventional mechanical ventilation is associated with bronchoalveolar lavage-induced activation of polymorphonuclear leukocytes: A possible mechanism to explain the systemic consequences of ventilator-induced lung injury in patients with ARDS. *Anesthesiology* 97, 1426–1433.
139. Dijkstra, G., Zandvoort, A. J., Kobold, A. C., de Jager-Krikken, A., Heeringa, P., van Goor, H., van Dullemen, H. M., Tervaert, J. W., van de Loosdrecht, A., Moshage, H., and Jansen, P. L. (2002). Increased expression of inducible nitric oxide synthase in circulating monocytes from patients with active inflammatory bowel disease. *Scand. J. Gastroenterol.* 37, 546–554.
140. Vischer, U. M., and Wagner, D. D. (1993). CD63 is a component of Weibel-Palade bodies of human endothelial cells. *Blood* 82, 1184–1191.
141. Harrigan, M. T., Campbell, N. F., and Bourgeois, S. (1991). Identification of a gene induced by glucocorticoids in murine T-cells: A potential G protein-coupled receptor. *Mol. Endocrinol.* 5, 1331–1338.
142. Kotani, M., Detheux, M., Vandenbogaerde, A., Communi, D., Vanderwinden, J. M., Le Poul, E., Brezillon, S., Tyldesley, R., Suarez-Huerta, N., Vandeput, F., Blanpain, C., Schiffmann, S. N., Vassart, G., and Parmentier, M. (2001). The metastasis suppressor gene KiSS-1 encodes kisspeptins, the natural ligands of the orphan G protein-coupled receptor GPR54. *J. Biol. Chem.* 276, 34631–34636.
143. Wang, D., Herman, J. P., Pritchard, L. M., Spitzer, R. H., Ahlbrand, R. L., Kramer, G. L., Petty, F., Sallee, F. R., and Richtand, N. M. (2001). Cloning, expression, and regulation of a glucocorticoid-induced receptor in rat brain: Effect of repetitive amphetamine. *J. Neurosci.* 21, 9027–9035.
144. Communi, D., Gonzalez, N. S., Detheux, M., Brezillon, S., Lannoy, V., Parmentier, M., and Boeynaems, J. M. (2001). Identification of a novel human ADP receptor coupled to G(i). *J. Biol. Chem.* 276, 41479–41485.
145. Brezillon, S., Detheux, M., Parmentier, M., Hokfelt, T., and Hurd, Y. L. (2001). Distribution of an orphan G-protein coupled receptor (JP05) mRNA in the human brain. *Brain Res.* 921, 21–30.
146. Lee, D. K., Nguyen, T., O'Neill, G. P., Cheng, R., Liu, Y., Howard, A. D., Coulombe, N., Tan, C. P., Tang-Nguyen, A. T., George, S. R., and O'Dowd, B. F. (1999). Discovery of a receptor related to the galanin receptors. *FEBS Lett.* 446, 103–107.
147. Katsumata, N., Chakraborty, C., Myal, Y., Schroedter, I. C., Murphy, L. J., Shiu, R. P., and Friesen, H. G. (1995). Molecular cloning and expression of peptide 23, a growth hormone releasing hormone-inducible pituitary protein. *Endocrinology* 136, 1332–1339.
148. Chakraborty, C., Katsumata, N., Myal, Y., Schroedter, I. C., Brazeau, P., Murphy, L. J., Shiu, R. P., and Friesen, H. G. (1995). Age-related changes in peptide-23/pancreatitis-associated protein and pancreatic stone protein/reg gene expression in the rat and regulation by growth hormone-releasing hormone. *Endocrinology* 136, 1843–1849.
149. Heller, A., Fiedler, F., Schmeck, J., Luck, V., Iovanna, J., and Koch, T. (1999). Pancreatitis-associated protein protects the lung from leukocyte-induced injury. *Anesthesiology* 91, 1408–1414.
150. Yoshioka, S., Fujii, S., Richards, J. S., and Espey, L. L. (2002). Gonadotropin-induced expression of pancreatitis-associated protein-III mRNA in the rat ovary at the time of ovulation. *J. Endocrinol.* 174, 485–492.
151. Mitchell, R. A., and Bucala, R. (2000). Tumor growth-promoting properties of macrophage migration inhibitory factor (MIF). *Semin. Cancer Biol.* 10, 359–366.
152. Wada, S., Kudo, T., Kudo, M., Sakuragi, N., Hareyama, H., Nishihira, J., and Fujimoto, S. (1999). Induction of macrophage migration inhibitory factor in human ovary by human chorionic gonadotrophin. *Hum. Reprod.* 14, 395–399.
153. Watanabe, R., Fujii, H., Yamamoto, A., Yamaguchi, H., Takenouchi, T., Kameda, K., Ito, M., and Ono, T. (1996). Expression of cutaneous fatty acid-binding protein and its mRNA in rat skin. *Arch. Dermatol. Res.* 289, 184.
154. Jing, C., Beesley, C., Foster, C. S., Rudland, P. S., Fujii, H., Ono, T., Chen, H., Smith, P. H., and Ke, Y. (2000). Identification of the messenger RNA for human cutaneous fatty acid-binding protein as a metastasis inducer. *Cancer Res.* 60, 2390–2398.
155. Jing, C., Beesley, C., Foster, C. S., Chen, H., Rudland, P. S., West, D. C., Fujii, H., Smith, P. H., and Ke, Y. (2001). Human cutaneous fatty acid-binding protein induces metastasis by up-regulating the expression of vascular endothelial growth factor gene in rat Rama 37 model cells. *Cancer Res.* 61, 4357–4364.
156. Leo, C. P., Pisarska, M. D., and Hsueh, A. J. (2001). DNA array analysis of changes in preovulatory gene expression in the rat ovary. *Biol. Reprod.* 65, 269–276.
157. Nakagawa, T., Kaneko, M., Inamura, S., and Satoh, M. (1999). Intracerebroventricular administration of nocistatin reduces inflammatory hyperalgesia in rats. *Neurosci. Lett.* 265, 64–66.
158. Itoh, M., Takasaki, I., Andoh, T., Nojima, H., Tominaga, M., and Kuraishi, Y. (2001). Induction by carrageenan inflammation of prepronociceptin mRNA in VR1-immunoreactive neurons in rat dorsal root ganglia. *Neurosci. Res.* 40, 227–233.
159. Zaveri, N. T., Green, C. J., Polgar, W. E., Huynh, N., and Toll, L. (2002). Regulation of transcription of the human prepronociceptin gene by Sp1. *Gene* 290, 45–52.
160. Zaveri, N. T., Green, C. J., and Toll, L. (2000). Transcriptional regulation of the human prepronociceptin gene. *Biochem. Biophys. Res. Commun.* 276, 710–717.
161. Xie, G. X., Ito, E., Maruyama, K., Suzuki, Y., Sugano. S., Sharma, M., Pietruck, C., and Palmer, P. P. (1999). The promoter region of human prepro-nociceptin gene and its regulation by cyclic AMP and steroid hormones. *Gene* 238, 427–436.
162. Okuda-Ashitaka E., and Ito, S. (2000). Nocistatin: A novel neuropeptide encoded by the gene for the nociceptin/orphanin FQ precursor. *Peptides* 21, 1101–1109.
163. Berman, D. M., and Gilman, A. G. Mammalian RGS proteins: Barbarians at the gate. *J. Biol. Chem.* 273, 1269–1272.
164. Hepler, J. R. (1999). Emerging roles for RGS proteins in cell signaling. *Trends Pharmacol. Sci.* 20, 376–382.
165. Ujioka, T., Russell, D. L., Okamura, H., Richards, J. S., and

Espey, L. L. (2000). Expression of regulatory of G-protein signaling protein-2 gene in the rat ovary at the time of ovulation. *Biol. Reprod.* 63, 1513–1517.

166. Ganea, D., and Delgado, M. (2002). Vasoactive intestinal peptide (VIP) and pituitary adenylate cyclase-activating polypeptide (PACAP) as modulators of both innate and adaptive immunity. *Crit. Rev. Oral Biol. Med.* 13, 229–237.
167. Martinez, C., Abad, C., Delgado, M., Arranz, A., Juarranz, M. G., Rodriguez-Hench, N., Brabet, P., Leceta, J., and Gomariz, R. P. (2002). Anti-inflammatory role in septic shock of pituitary adenylate cyclase-activating polypeptide receptor. *Proc. Natl. Acad. Sci. USA* 99, 1053–1058.
168. Ko, C., In, Y. H., Park-Sarge, O. K. (1999). Role of progesterone receptor activation in pituitary adenylate cyclase-activating polypeptide gene expression in rat ovary. *Endocrinology* 140, 5185–5194.
169. Koh, P. O., Kwak, S. D., Kang, S. S., Cho, G. J., Chun, S. Y., Kwon, H. B., and Choi, W. S. (2000). Expression of pituitary adenylate cyclase activating polypeptide (PACAP) and PACAP type I A receptor mRNAs in granulosa cells of preovulatory follicles of the rat ovary. *Mol. Reprod. Dev.* 55, 379–386.
170. Park, J. I., Kim, W. J., Wang, L., Park, H. J., Lee, J., Park, J. H., Kwon, H. B., Tsafriri, A., and Chun, S. Y. (2000). Involvement of progesterone in gonadotrophin-induced pituitary adenylate cyclase-activating polypeptide gene expression in pre-ovulatory follicles of rat ovary. *Mol. Hum. Reprod.* 6, 238–245.
171. Apa, R., Lanzone, A., Miceli, F., Vaccari, S., Macchione, E., Stefanini, M., and Canipari, R. (2002). Pituitary adenylate cyclase-activating polypeptide modulates plasminogen activator expression in rat granulosa cell. *Biol. Reprod.* 66, 830–835.
172. Reynolds, J. J. (1996). Collagenases and tissue inhibitors of metalloproteinases: A functional balance in tissue degradation. *Oral Dis.* 2, 70–76.
173. Opdenakker, G., Van den Steen, P. E., Dubois, B., Nelissen, I., Van Coillie, E., Masure, S., Proost, P., and Van Damme, J. (2001). Gelatinase B functions as regulator and effector in leukocyte biology. *J. Leukoc. Biol.* 69, 851–859.
174. Simpson, K. S., Byers, M. J., and Curry, Jr., T. E. (2001). Spatiotemporal messenger ribonucleic acid expression of ovarian tissue inhibitors of metalloproteinases throughout the rat estrous cycle. *Endocrinology* 142, 2058–2069.
175. Komar, C. M., Matousek, M., Mitsube, K., Mikuni, M., Brännström, M., and Curry, Jr., T. E. (2001). Effects of genistein on the periovulatory expression of messenger ribonucleic acid for matrix metalloproteinases and tissue inhibitors of metalloproteinases in the rat ovary. *Reproduction* 121, 259–265.
176. Simpson, K. S., Komar, C. M., and Curry, Jr., T. E. (2003). Localization and expression of tissue inhibitor of metalloproteinase-4 in the immature gonadotropin-stimulated and adult rat ovary. *Biol. Reprod.* 68, 214–221.
177. Espey, L. L., Ujioka, T., Okamura, H., and Richards, J .S. (2003). Metallothionein-1 messenger RNA transcription in steroid-secreting cells of the rat ovary during the periovulatory period *Biol. Reprod.* 68, 1895–1902.
178. Curry, Jr., T. E., and Wheeler, S. E. (2002). Cellular localization of tissue inhibitors of metalloproteinase in the rat ovary throughout pseudopregnancy. *Biol. Reprod.* 67, 1943–1951.
179. Gaddy-Kurten, D., Hickey, G. J., Fey, G. H., Gauldie, J., and Richards, J. S. (1989). Hormonal regulation and tissue-specific localization of α2-macroglobulin in rat ovarian follicles and corpora lutea. *Endocrinoloogy* 125, 2985–2995.
180. Bardos, T., Kamath, R. V., Mikecz, K., and Glant, T. T. (2001). Anti-inflammatory and chondroprotective effect of TSG-6 (tumor necrosis factor-α-stimulated gene-6) in murine models of experimental arthritis. *Am. J. Pathol.* 159, 1711–1721.
181. Glant, T. T., Kamath, R. V., Bardos, T., Gal, I., Szanto, S., Murad, Y. M., Sandy, J. D., Mort, J. S., Roughley, P. J., and Mikecz, K. (2002). Cartilage-specific constitutive expression of TSG-6 protein (product of tumor necrosis factor α-stimulated gene 6) provides a chondroprotective, but not anti-inflammatory, effect in antigen-induced arthritis. *Arthritis Rheum.* 46, 2207–2218.
182. Yoshioka, S., Ochsner, S., Russell, D. L., Ujioka, T., Fujii, S., Richards, J. S., and Espey, L. L. (2000). Expression of tumor necrosis factor-stimulated gene-6 in the rat ovary in response to an ovulatory dose of gonadotropin. *Endocrinology* 141, 4114–4119.
183. Carrette, O., Nemade, R. V., Day, A. J., Brickner, A., and Larsen, W. J. (2001). TSG-6 is concentrated in the extracellular matrix of mouse cumulus oocyte complexes through hyaluronan and inter-α-inhibitor binding. *Biol. Reprod.* 65, 301–308.
184. Mbebi, C., Hantai, D., Jandrot-Perrus, M., Doyennette, M. A., Verdiere-Sahuque, M. (1999). Protease nexin I expression is up-regulated in human skeletal muscle by injury-related factors. *J. Cell Physiol.* 179, 305–314.
185. Wiedermann, C. J., and Roemisch, J. (2002). The anti-inflammatory actions of antithrombin-a review. *Acta Med. Austriaca* 29, 89–92.
186. Opal, S. M., Kessler, C. M., Roemisch, J., and Knaub, S. (2002). Antithrombin, heparin, and heparan sulfate. *Crit. Care Med.* 30 (Suppl 5), S325–S331.
187. Hasan, S., Hosseini, G., Princivalle, M., Dong, J. C., Birsan, D., Cagide, C., and de Agostini, A. I. (2002). Coordinate expression of anticoagulant heparan sulfate proteoglycans and serine protease inhibitors in the rat ovary: A potent system of proteolysis control. *Biol. Reprod.* 66, 144–158.
188. Hagglund, A. C., Ny, A., Liu, K., and Ny, T. (1996). Coordinated and cell-specific induction of both physiological plasminogen activators creates functionally redundant mechanisms for plasmin formation during ovulation. *Endocrinology* 137, 5671–5677.
189. Kasza, A., Kowanetz, M., Poslednik, K., Witek, B., Kordula, T., and Koj, A. (2001). Epidermal growth factor and pro-inflammatory cytokines regulate the expression of components of plasminogen activation system in U373-MG astrocytoma cells. *Cytokine* 16, 187–190.
190. Nicosia, M., Moger, W. H., Dyer, C. A., Prack, M. M., and Williams, D. L. (1992). Apolipoprotein-E messenger RNA in rat ovary is expressed in theca and interstitial cells and presumptive macrophage, but not in granulosa cells. *Mol. Endocrinol.* 6, 978–988.
191. Larkin, L., Khachigian, L. M., and Jessup, W. (2000). Regulation of apolipoprotein E production in macrophages (review). *Int. J. Mol. Med.* 6, 253–258.

192. LaDu, M. J., Shah, J. A., Reardon, C. A., Getz, G. S., Bu, G., Hu, J., Guo, L., Van Eldik, L. J. (2001). Apolipoprotein E and apolipoprotein E receptors modulate A β-induced glial neuroinflammatory responses. *Neurochem. Int.* 39, 427–434.
193. Curtiss, L. K., and Boisvert, W. A. (2000). Apolipoprotein E and atherosclerosis. *Curr. Opin. Lipidol.* 11, 243–251.
194. Riddell, D. R., and Owen, J. S. (1999). Nitric oxide and platelet aggregation. *Vitam. Horm.* 57, 25–48.
195. Polacek, D., Beckmann, M. W., and Schreiber, J. R. (1992). Rat ovarian apolipoprotein E: Localization and gonadotropic control of messenger RNA. *Biol. Reprod.* 46, 65–72.
196. Yodoi, J., Nakamura, H., and Masutani, H. (2002). Redox regulation of stress signals: Possible roles of dendritic stellate TRX producer cells (DST cell types). *Biol. Chem.* 383, 585–590.
197. Fitzpatrick, F. A. (2001). Inflammation, carcinogenesis, and cancer. *Int. Immunopharmacol.* 1, 1651–1667.
198. Yaron, Y., Schwartz, D., Evans, M. I., Aloni, R., Kapon, A., and Rotter, V. (1999). P53 tumor suppressor gene expression in the mouse ovary during an artificially induced ovulatory cycle. *J. Reprod. Med.* 44, 107–114.
199. Bonder, C. S., Dickensheets, H. L., Finlay-Jones, J. J., Donnelly, R. P., and Hart, P. H. (1998). Involvement of the IL-2 receptor γ-chain (γc) in the control by IL-4 of human monocyte and macrophage proinflammatory mediator production. *J. Immunol.* 160, 4048–4056.
200. Mozo, L., Gayo, A., Suarez, A., Rivas, D., Zamorano, J., and Gutierrez, C. (1998). Glucocorticoids inhibit IL-4 and mitogen-induced IL-4Rα chain expression by different posttranscriptional mechanisms. *J. Allergy Clin. Immunol.* 102, 968–976.
201. Hart, P. H., Bonder, C. S., Balogh, J., Dickensheet, H. L., Donnelly, R. P., and Finlay-Jones, J. J. (1999). Differential responses of human monocytes and macrophages to IL-4 and IL-13. *J. Leukoc. Biol.* 66, 575–578.
202. Doucet, C., Brouty-Boye, D., Pottin-Clemenceau, C., Canonica, G. W., Jasmin, C., and Azzarone, B. (1998). Interleukin (IL)-4 and IL-13 act on human lung fibroblasts. Implication in asthma. *J. Clin. Invest.* 101, 2129–2139.
203. Coyle, P., Philcox, J. C., Carey, L. C., Rofe, A. M. (2002). Metallothionein: The multipurpose protein. *Cell. Mol. Life Sci.* 59, 627–647.
204. Miles, A. T., Hawksworth, G. M., Beattie, J. H., and Rodilla, V. (2000). Induction, regulation, degradation, and biological significance of mammalian metallothioneins. *Crit. Rev. Biochem. Mol. Biol.* 35, 35–70.
205. Holmes-McNary, M. (2002). Nuclear factor κB signaling in catabolic disorders. *Curr. Opin. Clin. Nutr. Metab. Care* 5, 255–263.
206. Davies, K. J. (1995). Oxidative stress: The paradox of aerobic life. *Biochem. Soc. Symp.* 61, 1–31.
207. Mills, P. C., and Higgins, A. J. (1997). Oxidant injury, nitric oxide, and pulmonary vascular function: Implications for the exercising horse. *Vet. J.* 153, 125–148.
208. Li, C., and Jackson, R. M. (2002). Reactive species mechanisms of cellular hypoxia-reoxygenation injury. *Am. J. Physiol. Cell. Physiol.* 282, C227-C241.
209. Melov, S. (2002). Animal models of oxidative stress, aging, and therapeutic antioxidant interventions. *Int. J. Biochem. Cell. Biol.* 34, 1395–1400.
210. Bautista, A. P. (2001). Free radicals, chemokines, and cell injury in HIV-1 and SIV infections and alcoholic hepatitis. *Free Radic. Biol. Med.* 31, 1527–1532.
211. Laroux, F. S., Pavlick, K. P., Hines, I. N., Kawachi, S., Harada, H., Bharwani, S., Hoffman, J. M., and Grisham, M. B. (2001). Role of nitric oxide in inflammation. *Acta Physiol. Scand.* 173, 113–118.
212. Rahman, I. (1999). Inflammation and the regulation of glutathione level in lung epithelial cells. *Antioxid. Redox Signal* 1, 425–447.
213. Soltaninassab, S. R., Sekhar, K. R., Meredity, M. J., and Freeman, M. L. (2000). Multifaceted regulation of γ-glutamylcysteine synthetase. *J. Cell Physiol.* 182, 163–170.
214. Wild, A. C., and Mulcahy, R. T. (2000). Regulation of γ-glutamylcysteine synthetase subunit gene expression: Insights into transcriptional control of antioxidant defenses. *Free Radic. Res.* 31, 281–301.
215. Anderson, M. E. (1998). Glutathione: An overview of biosynthesis and modulation. *Chem. Biol. Interact.* 111–112, 1–14.
216. Rahman, I., and MacNee, W. (2000). Oxidative stress and regulation of glutathione in lung inflammation. *Eur. Respir. J.* 16, 534–554.
217. Griffith, O. W. (1999). Biologic and pharmacologic regulation of mammalian glutathione synthesis. *Free Radic. Biol. Med.* 27, 922–935.
218. Clague, N., Sevcik, M., Stuart, G., Brännström, M., Janson, P. O., and Jarrell, J. F. (1992). The effect of estrous cycle and buthionine sulfoximine on glutathione release from the in vitro perfused rat ovary. *Reprod. Toxicol.* 6, 533–539.
219. Jarrell, J. F., Sevcik, M., and Stuart, G. (1992). Regulation of total ovarian glutathione content in the rat. *Reprod. Toxicol.* 6, 133–135.
220. Hayes, J. D., and Strange, R. C. (2000). Glutathione S-transferase polymorphisms and their biological consequences. *Pharmacology* 61, 154–166.
221. Rahman, Q., Abidi, P., Afaq, F., Schiffmann, D., Mossman, B. T., Kamp, D. W., and Athar, M. (1999). Glutathione redox system in oxidative lung injury. *Crit. Rev. Toxicol.* 29, 543–568.
222. Adler, V., Yin, Z., Tew, K. D., and Ronai, Z. (1999). Role of redox potential and reactive oxygen species in stress signaling. *Oncogene* 18, 6104–6111.
223. Spiteri, M. A., Biancoo, A., Strange, R. C., and Fryer, A. A. (2000). Polymorphisms at the glutathione S-transferase, GSTP1 locus: A novel mechanism for susceptibility and development of atopic airway inflammation. *Allergy* 55 (Suppl 66), 15–20.
224. Fujii, J., Suzuki, K., and Taniguchi, N. (1995). Physiological significance of superoxide dismutase isozymes. *Nippon Rinsho.* 53, 1227–1231.
225. Macmillan-Crow, L. A., and Cruthirds, D. L. (2001). Invited review: Manganese superoxide dismutase in disease. *Free Radic. Res.* 34, 325–336.
226. Maier, C. M., and Chan, P. H. (2002). Role of superoxide dismutases in oxidative damage and neurodegenerative disorders. *Neuroscientist* 8, 323–334.
227. Laloraya, M., Kumar, G. P., and Laloraya, M. M. (1989). Histochemical study of superoxide dismutase in the ovary

of the rat during the oestrous cycle. *J. Reprod. Fertil.* 86, 583–587.

228. Sato, E. F., Kobuchi, H., Edashige, K., Takahashi, M., Yoshioka, T., Utsumi, K., and Inoue, M. (1992). Dynamic aspects of ovarian superoxide dismutase isozymes during the ovulatory process in the rat. *FEBS Lett.* 303, 121–125.
229. Sasaki, J., Sato, E. F., Nomura, T., Mori, H., Watanabe, S., Kanda, S., Watanabe, H., Utsumi, K., and Inoue, M. (1994). Detection of manganese superoxide dismutase mRNA in the theca interna cells of rat ovary during the ovulatory process by in situ hybridization. *Histochemistry* 102, 173–176.
230. Nomura, T., Sasaki, J., Mori, H., Sato, E. F., Watanabe, S., Kanda, S., Matsuura, J., Watanabe, H., and Inoue, M. (1996). Expression of manganese superoxide dismutase mRNA in reproductive organs during the ovulatory process and the estrous cycle of the rat. *Histochem. Cell Biol.* 105, 1–6.
231. Penning, T. M., Pawlowski, J. E., Schlegel, B. P., Jez, J. M., Lin, H. K., Hoog, S. S., Bennett, M. J., and Lewis, M. (1996). Mammalian 3α-hydroxysteroid dehydrogenases. *Steroids* 61, 508–523.
232. Ma, H., and Penning, T. M. (1999). Conversion of mammalian 3α-hydroxysteroid dehydrogenase to 20α-hydroxysteroid dehydrogenase using loop chimeras: Changing specificity from androgens to progestins. *Proc. Natl. Acad. Sci. USA* 96, 11161–11166.
233. Espey, L. L., Yoshioka, S., Ujioka, T., Fujii, S., and Richards, J. S. (2001). 3α-Hydroxysteroid dehydrogenase messenger RNA transcription in the immature rat ovary in response to an ovulatory dose of gonadotropin. *Biol. Reprod.* 65, 72–78.
234. Forrest, G. L., and Gonzalez, B. (2000). Carbonyl reductase. *Chem. Biol. Interact.* 129, 21–40.
235. Espey, L. L., Yoshioka, S., Russell, D., Ujioka, T., Vladu, B., Skelsey, M., Fujii, S., Okamura, H., and Richards, J. S. (2000). Characterization of ovarian carbonyl reductase gene expression during ovulation in the gonadotropin-primed immature rat. *Biol. Reprod.* 62, 390–397.
236. Dalton, T. P., Puga, A., and Shertzer, H. G. (2002). Induction of cellular oxidative stress by aryl hydrocarbon receptor activation. *Chem. Biol. Interact.* 141, 77–95.
237. Balint, E. E., and Vousden, K. H. (2001). Activation and activities of the p53 tumour suppressor protein. *Br. J. Cancer* 85, 1813–1823.
238. Matuoka, K., and Chen, K. Y. (2002). Transcriptional regulation of cellular ageing by the CCAAT box-binding factor CBF/NF-Y. *Ageing Res. Rev.* 1, 639–651.
239. Barouki, R., and Morel, Y. (2001). Repression of cytochrome P450 1A1 gene expression by oxidative stress: Mechanisms and biological implications. *Biochem. Pharmacol.* 61, 511–516.
240. Bouma-ter Steege, J. C., Mayo, K. H., and Griffioen, A. W. (2001). Angiostatic proteins and peptides. *Crit. Rev. Eukaryot. Gene Expr.* 11, 319–334.
241. Distler, O., Neidhart, M., Gay, R. E., and Gay, S. (2002). The molecular control of angiogenesis. *Int. Rev. Immunol.* 21, 33–49.
242. Nguyen, M., Arkell, J., and Jackson, C. J. (2001). Human endothelial gelatinases and angiogenesis. *Int. J. Biochem. Cell. Biol.* 33, 960–970.
243. Martin, J. (2000). Learning from vascular remodelling. *Clin. Exp. Allergy* 30 (Suppl 1), 33–36.
244. Pages, G., Milanini, J., Richard, D. E., Berra, E., Gothie, E., Vinals, F., and Pouyssegur, J. (2000). Signaling angiogenesis viap42/p44 MAP kinase cascade. *Ann. N. Y. Acad. Sci.* 902, 187–200.
245. Masferrer, J. (2001). Approach to angiogenesis inhibition based on cyclooxygenase-2. *Cancer J.* 7 (Suppl 3), S144–S150.
246. Dermond, O., and Ruegg, C. (2001). Inhibition of tumor angiogenesis by nonsteroidal anti-inflammatory drugs: Emerging mechanisms and therapeutic perspectives. *Drug Resist. Updat.* 4, 314–321.
247. Lema, M. J. (2002). Emerging options with coxib therapy. *Cleve. Clin. J. Med.* 69 (Suppl 1), S176–184.
248. Wilson, K. T. (2002). Angiogenic markers, neovascularization, and malignant deformation of Barrett's esophagus. *Dis. Esophagus* 15, 16–21.
249. Sang, Q. X. (1998). Complex role of matrix metalloproteinases in angiogenesis. *Cell Res.* 8, 171–177.
250. Jackson, C., Nguyen, M., Arkell, J., and Sambrook, P. (2001). Selective matrix metalloproteinase (MMP) inhibition in rheumatoid arthritis—targetting gelatinase A activation. *Inflamm. Res.* 50, 183–186.
251. Collen, A., Hanemaaijer, R., Lupu, F., Quax, P. H., Van Lent, N., Grimbergen, J., Peters, E., Koolwijk, P., and Van Hinsbergh, V. W. (2003). Membrane-type matrix metalloproteinase mediated angiogenesis in a fibrin-collagen matrix. *Blood* 101, 1810–1817.
252. Mannello, F., and Gazzanelli, G. (2001). Tissue inhibitors of metalloproteinases and programmed cell death: Conundrums, controversies, and potential implications, *Apoptosis* 6, 479–482.
253. Pepper, M. S. (2001). Role of the matrix metalloproteinase and plasminogen activator-plasmin systems in angiogenesis. *Arterioscler. Thromb. Vasc. Biol.* 21, 1104–1117.
254. Wojtukiewicz, M. Z., Sierko, E., Klement, P., and Rak, J. (2001). The hemostatic system and angiogenesis in malignancy. *Neoplasia* 3, 371–384.
255. Klafter, R., and Arbiser, J. L. (2000). Regulation of angiogenesis and tumorigenesis by signal transduction cascades: Lessons from benign and malignant endothelial tumors. *J. Investig. Dermatol. Symp. Proc.* 5, 79–82.
256. Xu, H., and Raafat el-Gewely, M. (2001). P53-responsive genes and the potential for cancer diagnostics and therapeutics development. *Biotechnol. Annu. Rev.* 7, 131–164.
257. Iozzo, R. V., and San Antonio, J. D. (2001). Heparan sulfate proteoglycans: Heavy hitters in the angiogenesis arena. *J. Clin. Invest.* 108, 349–355.
258. Nishihira, J. (2000). Macrophage migration inhibitory factor (MIF): Its essential role in the immune system and cell growth. *J. Interferon Cytokine Res.* 20, 751–762.
259. Espey, L. L. (1978). Ovarian contractility and its relationship to ovulation: A review. *Biol. Reprod.* 19, 540–555.
260. Bjersing, L., and Cajander, S. (1974). Ovulation and the mechanism of follicle rupture. III. Transmission electron microscopy of rabbit germinal epithelium prior to induced ovulation. *Cell Tissue Res.* 149, 313–327.
261. Murdoch, W. J. (2000). Proteolytic and cellular death mechanisms in ovulatory ovarian rupture. *Biol. Signals Recept.* 9, 102–114.
262. Murdoch, W. J., and McDonnel, A. C. (2002). Roles of the ovarian surface epithelium in ovulation and carcinogenesis. *Reproduction* 123, 743–750.

PART III

The Corpus Luteum

CHAPTER **10**

The Functions and Regulation of Cell Populations Comprising the Corpus Luteum during the Ovarian Cycle

RICHARD L. STOUFFER

ABSTRACT

Using molecular and cellular techniques and cell-sorting methods, investigators are elucidating the dynamics, functions, and regulation of cell populations within the corpus luteum during the ovarian cycle. Significant advances are increasing our understanding of cell-cell interactions and the role of local factors in mediating or modulating the actions of luteotropic and luteolytic hormones in the corpus luteum. For example, it is now clear that recently discovered endothelial-specific growth factors (e.g., vascular endothelial growth factors [VEGFs] and angiopoietins [Angs]) are produced by luteinizing cells in response to the luteinizing hormone (LH) surge and play a vital role in the neovascularization and development of the functional corpus luteum. Conversely, it appears that the endothelin (ET-1) system, involving endothelial synthesis of ET-1 precursor, luteal cell activation, and ET-1 receptor signaling, plays a role in prostaglandin (PG) $F_{2\alpha}$-induced luteal regression. In addition, resident or migrating immune cells may play a vital role in the tissue reorganization that occurs during development and dissolution of the corpus luteum; again, chemokines (e.g., monocyte chemotactic protein-1 [MCP-1]) produced by luteal and nonluteal cells appear to promote these processes. Nevertheless, significant differences between species likely exist in cell-cell interactions and roles of local and hormonal factors. As our perceptions of luteal structure-function become increasingly complex, the challenge remains to discern the primary vs supportive pathways that control the development, function, and regression of the corpus luteum.

INTRODUCTION

The compartmentalization of somatic cells in the developing follicle facilitates the isolation and study of follicular cell types, notably granulosa and theca cells, and the understanding of processes regulating follicle growth and differentiation. Although this tissue compartmentalization is lost as the corpus luteum develops from the ovulatory follicle, early anatomists recognized that luteal tissue of several species contained morphologically distinct subpopulations of luteal cells, plus nonluteal cells from the vascular and immune systems. The recent combination of cellular and molecular techniques, along with cell-sorting procedures, is elucidating the dynamics of cell populations that differ in function and regulation during the life span of the corpus luteum in the ovarian cycle. Investigators are also unraveling cell-cell interactions and the role of local paracrine or autocrine factors in mediating or modulating the actions of luteotropic and luteolytic hormones in the corpus luteum. By no means encompassing, this chapter emphasizes some of the general concepts or hypotheses arising from studies since the first edition of this text [1] that increase our understanding of cell types within the corpus luteum. Comparisons are included to demonstrate potential differences and similarities among rodent, domestic animal, and primate species. It is hoped that this discussion complements other reviews and stimulates further investigations of fundamental, unanswered questions regarding the development, function, and regression of the corpus luteum.

THE VASCULATURE OF THE CORPUS LUTEUM

Dynamics of the Luteal Vasculature during the Ovarian Cycle

The changes in vascularity associated with the development of the corpus luteum are remarkable (for review, see [2]). Before ovulation, the antral follicle consists of a fluid-filled antrum surrounded by an avascular layer of granulosa cells and a basement membrane, with all blood vessels limited to the theca interna and externa cell layers. In the ovulatory, luteinizing follicle, the capillary network expands by "sprouting" into the avascular granulosa layer to form a dense network of capillaries in the developing corpus luteum. The interval of the angiogenic process varies between species, but in primates the capillaries reach the central cavity by day 4 and venules appear along the cavity border that lead back through the luteal tissue to large veins outside the corpus luteum by day 6 of the luteal phase. The extensive angiogenesis is illustrated by reports that the vascular space within the bovine and human corpus luteum increases from the early to midluteal phase, with the number of nonsteroidogenic cells (i.e., primarily cells associated with the microvasculature) continuing to increase to the late luteal phase [3]. Although there is evidence for early migration of microvascular cells into the luteinizing granulosa layer, much of the capillary expansion appears caused by cellular hyperplasia. The level of cellular proliferation in the corpus luteum is highest during luteal development; using dual-label immunocytochemical techniques, Christenson and Stouffer determined that 85% to 95% of the proliferating (Ki-67 positive) cells in the monkey corpus luteum were vascular endothelial (PECAM-1 positive) cells [4]. The extensive vascularity of the functional corpus luteum is reflected by the fact that cells associated with the microvasculature comprise about 50% of the total cell population and are adjacent to virtually every steroidogenic cell.

There are also important changes in the vasculature of the corpus luteum during luteolysis near the end of the ovarian cycle. The volume density of blood vessels declines during luteolysis in several species, including humans [3]. The cellular processes responsible for this decline are unknown, but it appears that endothelial cell proliferation declines and cells are lost perhaps by apoptosis, sloughing into the blood, and/or white cell scavenging [5, 6]. Nevertheless, there is evidence that the luteal vasculature remains relatively intact, without major changes in blood flow, during the early events in functional luteolysis [7]. Collectively, reports suggest that although portions of the luteal capillary beds degenerate during structural luteolysis, the larger microvessels remain intact, perhaps to assist in resorption of the luteal mass.

Regulation and Role of Luteal Angiogenesis

The ovary, and notably the corpus luteum, is one of the unique sites in the healthy adult where the growth, maturation, and degeneration of blood vessels occurs in a physiologic state. Since the discovery that follicular fluid and ovarian extracts contained "angiogenic activity" [8, 9], investigators have strived to identify factors that control vascular events in the follicle and corpus luteum. Major advances occurred when researchers determined that newly discovered endothelial-specific growth factors associated with pathologic angiogenesis (e.g., during tumor growth) were also present in the ovary. Recent studies support the hypothesis that such factors also play key roles in physiologic angiogenesis in the ovary.

1. Vascular endothelial growth factor (VEGF), also called *vascular permeability factor (VPF)*, specifically acts on microvascular endothelial cells to promote proliferation and migration and to enhance vascular permeability [10]. Five molecular forms of VEGF (121, 145, 165, 189, and 206 amino acids), which are produced by alternative splicing, differ in solubility and heparin binding ability. Recent evidence for tissue-specific and dynamic regulation of VEGF expression [11] indicates that the isoforms may promote different physiologic functions [12]. The family of VEGF proteins has now grown to include structurally related proteins that share homology with VEGF (now called *VEGF-A*)—VEGF-B, -C, -D, and -E. In addition, considerable progress occurred in identifying high-affinity receptors (VEGFR-1, -2, and -3) and coreceptors (neuropilin-1 and -2) on target cells that mediate and facilitate, respectively, VEGF actions [13].

   Recent evidence indicates that VEGF-A is dynamically expressed in the maturing follicle and corpus luteum in several species (for review, see [2]). VEGF messenger ribonucleic acid (mRNA) and protein appear nondetectable in primordial and primary follicles but become evident in the theca of developing antral follicles and in granulosa cells, particularly around the oocyte, in the Graafian follicle. After the gonadotropin surge, luteinizing granulosa cells express high levels of VEGF as ovulation approaches and VEGF expression appears highest in the developing corpus luteum. Although VEGF remains detectable in the developed corpus luteum during the luteal phase, there is little expression by luteal regression late in the cycle in primates or domestic animals. Current studies relying primarily on immunocytochemical and in situ hybridization techniques to localize VEGF protein and mRNA indicate that luteal steroidogenic (theca and granulosa-derived cells [14, 15]) and perhaps endothelial support cells (e.g., pericytes [16]) produce VEGF-A. However, there are few studies to date on specific cell types that directly evaluate the production and regulation of VEGF isoforms or types in the corpus luteum [17].

   Limited studies suggest that regulation of VEGF expression in the ovary may be different from that in many tissues. It is generally believed that a decline in local oxygen concentrations (hypoxia) is a primary stimulator of VEGF production and angiogenesis in normal and pathologic conditions [2]. However, Martinez-Chequer and colleagues [18] recently observed that hypoxic conditions did not increase VEGF-A production by nonluteinized granulosa cells from the preovulatory follicle or luteinizing granulosa cells from the ovulatory follicle in rhesus monkeys. Rather, evidence from several species [17–20] indicates that gonadotropin, and particularly the midcycle gonadotropin surge, promotes VEGF production in the luteinizing granulosa layer and developing corpus luteum. In addition, local factors such as insulin-like growth factors (IGF-1 and -2) may modulate or synergize with gonadotropin to control VEGF expression [18]. However, the control of VEGF expression in luteal cells of the corpus luteum has not been examined in detail. Preliminary results suggest that following the LH induction process in luteinizing tissue, gonadotropins may be less or not important and local regulators including hypoxia may predominate in differentiated luteal cells [21].

Recent investigations established a critical role for VEGF-A in ovarian angiogenesis and corpus luteum development or function. The ability of an anti-VEGF antibody to neutralize 30% of the mitogenic activity and 65% of migratory activity (as measured in endothelial cell assays) led Doraiswamy and colleagues [22] to conclude that potent VEGF activity was present in the developing corpus luteum in domestic animals. To eliminate antecedent effects during follicular development, administration of VEGF-A antagonists to mice or monkeys either at the time of ovulation (i.e., during luteal development [23, 24]) or at the midluteal phase (i.e., after luteal development [25]) markedly suppressed subsequent luteal structure-function. The suppression in luteal endothelial proliferation, concomitant decrease in endothelial cell area, and marked drop in circulating progesterone levels demonstrated that luteal vascular development and steroidogenic activity was compromised by anti-VEGF treatment. Collectively, these data, plus recent evidence that the direct injection of VEGF antagonist into the periovulatory follicle of monkeys can block follicle rupture and suppress luteal development and function [26], suggest that (1) VEGF is important for ovulation of the mature follicle, development of the corpus luteum, and maintenance of the functional corpus luteum, and (2) VEGF acts primarily through local effects in the follicle and corpus luteum; actions in other tissues to indirectly control ovarian function (e.g., in the hypothalamus or pituitary to control follicle-stimulating hormone [FSH] and LH secretion) appear minimal in adults during the reproductive cycle [27]. Nevertheless, there have been few studies on the mechanisms of action or specific effects of VEGF on ovarian cells, except one report that VEGF stimulates proliferation of endothelial cells isolated from the monkey corpus luteum [28].

2. The Angs are a new family of angiogenic factors discovered in the last 5 years that, unlike VEGF, are not mitogens but nevertheless are essential for normal vascular development [29]. Currently, four different Angs have been identified in the mouse or human and are designated Ang-1, -2, -3 (mouse), and -4 (human). They all bind to the same Tie-2 receptor as either an agonist (Ang-1 and -4) or natural antagonist (Ang-2 and -3). An intriguing model by Hanahan [30] proposes that the interaction between Ang agonists/antagonists and VEGF is critical for the development and maturation of vessels during embryogenesis. Whereas VEGF stimulates proliferation and migration of endothelial cells followed by capillary tube formation, Ang-1 and -2 play critical roles for capillary growth, maintenance, or degeneration. Ang-2 may loosen the extracellular matrix allowing VEGF to stimulate endothelial cell events leading to capillary growth, whereas Ang-1 may recruit periendothelial cells (i.e., pericytes) to stabilize and mature growing vessels. In the absence of VEGF or other angiogenic factors, Ang-2 may destabilize vessels and cause capillary degeneration, especially those that are not supported by periendothelial cells.

   It is tempting to consider that a similar balance between angiogenic (VEGF) and stabilizing (Ang-1) vs destabilizing (Ang-2) factors could be important in the vascular events that occur during the development, maintenance, and regression of the corpus luteum (for review, see [2]). Both Ang-1 and Ang-2 plus Tie-2 receptor mRNA and/or protein have been detected in luteal and endothelial cells, respectively, in the corpus luteum of several species. Limited reports on (1) the different temporal expression patterns for Ang-1/-2 and VEGF during the luteal life span [15, 31] and (2) the preponderance of immature vessels (not supported by periendothelial cells) in the corpus luteum [32] are consistent with such a model. However, considerable research is needed to define the spatial and cellular patterns of Ang-Tie expression in the corpus luteum and the specific actions of Ang-1 to -4 in luteal development, function, and regression. Likewise, little is known about the regulation of Ang expression, except gonadotropin exposure may also stimulate Ang-1 (if not Ang-2) expression in luteinizing granulosa cells of the ovulatory follicle [33], as well as Ang-1 and -2 expression in the corpus luteum [31]. However, given the delayed (36 hours) response in the ovulatory follicle [33], it is not clear whether this is a direct effect of gonadotropin or mediated by local factors.
3. Endocrine-gland derived endothelial growth factor (EG-VEGF) was discovered in 2001 [34] and established for the first time that there were angiogenic factors that are specific for vascular beds of certain tissues. EG-VEGF stimulates the proliferation and migration of microvascular endothelial cells from

steroidogenic tissues but not from other organs. Although it exhibits VEGF-like bioactivities, it is structurally distinct from VEGF and identical to prokineticin 1, which acts to control gastrointestinal motility [35]. Initial screening of human tissues indicated that the highest expression of EG-VEGF/prokineticin 1 was in the ovary. In situ hybridization data led LeCouter and colleagues [34] to suggest that there is a compartmentalization of angiogenic factors in the primate ovary, with EG-VEGF highly expressed in the ovarian stroma and in developing follicles and VEGF expressed at the highest level in the corpus luteum. Although inferred that EG-VEGF is not expressed in the corpus luteum, Borman and colleagues [36] recently detected significant EG-VEGF mRNA levels in macaque luteal tissue. Further studies are needed to clarify the regulation and actions of tissue-specific angiogenic factors (e.g., EG-VEGF/prokineticin 1) in the corpus luteum.

Cell-Cell Interactions in Luteal Angiogenesis

Advances described in the previous section have added cellular and molecular details to the concept (Figure 10.1) that luteinization of the ovulatory follicle includes critical events whereby the luteinizing cells, notably those in the avascular granulosa layer, produce angiogenic factors that promote neovascularization of the developing corpus luteum. Although the granulosa luteal cell would appear to be a major source of these factors, this does not rule out a role for theca luteal cells or advancing pericytes, at least in some species such as the sheep [16]. To date, VEGF-A has received the most attention, but future research must resolve the possible roles of other factors including promiscuous growth factors (e.g., bFGF [8]) or tissue-specific endothelial growth factors (i.e., EG-VEGF) that may synergize with or complement VEGF actions. Whereas VEGF action in promoting angiogenesis seems assured, its roles in maintaining newly formed vessels in the functional corpus luteum or causing their degeneration in the regressing corpus luteum remain unclear. Likewise, the proposed roles of the Ang agonists and antagonists (e.g., Ang-1 and Ang-2) in promoting vessel stability, maturation, or degeneration await investigation. Detailed studies are warranted to elucidate the regulation of VEGF and Ang production by luteal cell types, plus the actions of VEGF and Ang on microvascular cells from the corpus luteum at specific stages of the luteal life span during the ovarian cycle. There have been relatively few studies to date on the microvascular endothelial cells [37, 38] or their supporting pericytes [16, 32] in the ovulatory follicle or corpus luteum. However, such studies are essential following mounting evidence for functional and regulatory differences between vascular beds of various tissues, as well as heterogeneity within the vasculature of individual tissues, including the corpus luteum [39, 40]. Therefore, definitive experiments advancing our understanding of such interactions as proposed in Figure 10.1 will require steroidogenic cells, endothelial cells, and pericytes from the corpus luteum.

HORMONE-PRODUCING CELLS OF THE CORPUS LUTEUM

Origins and Dynamics of Luteal Cell Subpopulations

It has been more than 80 years since investigators first proposed that the mammalian corpus luteum consisted of at least two subpopulations of luteal cells, based on differences in size, morphology, and staining properties [41]. In domestic animals the large luteal cells contain more smooth and rough endoplasmic reticulum, mitochondria, extensive Golgi apparati, and secretory granules than small luteal cells—features that are consistent with greater endocrine (either steroid or peptide/protein hormone) activity in the large cells [42] (for review, see [1]). The often-stated opinion is that large luteal cells are derived from the granulosa layer, whereas small luteal cells originate from the theca layer of the ovulatory follicle. Although this concept has never been definitively tested, Meidan and colleagues [43] reported that in vitro luteinization of granulosa and theca cell preparations from preovulatory follicles of domestic animals by pharmacologic methods resulted in cells with many of the characteristics of large and small luteal cells, respectively. However, limited evidence suggests that this concept is an oversimplification. Using monoclonal antibodies (Abs) to granulosa and theca cell surface antigens, Alila and Hansel [44] determined that small luteal cells bound the theca-specific Ab, whereas large luteal cells in the bovine corpus luteum bound either granulosa-specific or theca-specific Abs. In addition, the percentage of large luteal cells that bound the granulosa-specific Ab declined as the corpus luteum aged, whereas those that bound the theca-specific Ab increased. The evidence implies that small cells become large cells as the life span of the corpus luteum progresses. But whether this scenario (1) implies further cell differentiation and hypertrophy, or (2) is conceptually relevant to other species, has not been examined.

Although theca- and granulosa-derived luteal cells integrate in the luteal tissue of some species, such as the sheep and cow, cell segregation is evident in the fully developed corpus luteum of other species, notably primates. Paraluteal cells located along the periphery and in invaginations of primate luteal tissue are morphologically distinct from "true" luteal cells in the central parenchyma. Immunocytochemical evidence supports compartmentalization of P450 17α-hydroxylase to the theca interna of preovulatory follicles and the paraluteal regions of the

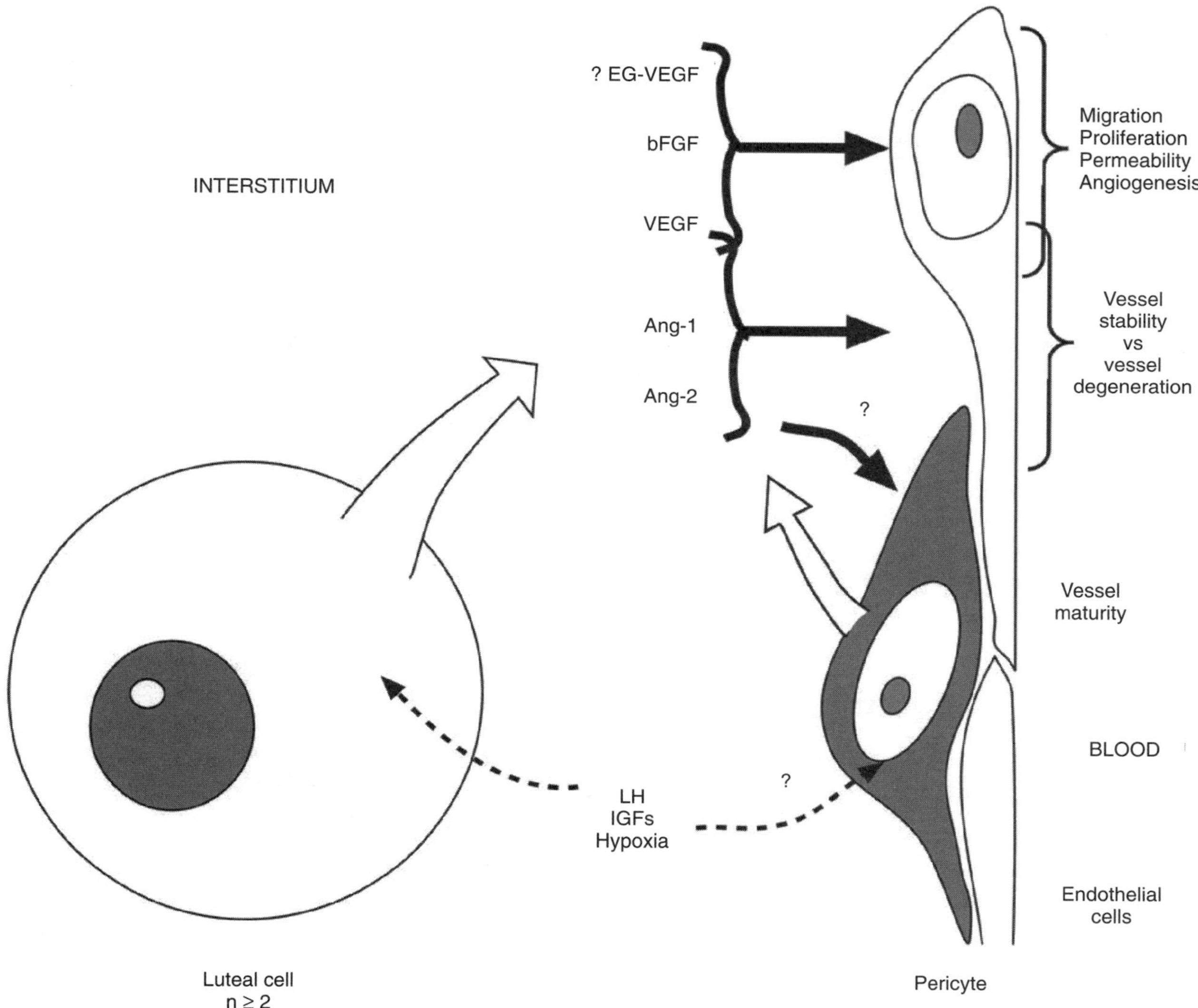

FIGURE 10.1 Conceptual diagram of the interactions between luteal cells, capillary endothelial cells, and periendothelial support cells (pericytes) for the production of angiogenic factors that promote the development, maintenance, and regression of the microvasculature of the corpus luteum during the reproductive cycle. Dotted arrows = regulators of VEGF/Ang expression; white arrows = VEGF/Ang synthesis; black arrows = VEGF/Ang actions; question marks = possible events. See text for details.

corpus luteum in monkeys [45] and women [46], whereas P450 aromatase is localized to the follicular granulosum and central luteal tissue. The data suggest that (1) the paraluteal and luteal cells are of theca and granulosa origin, respectively, and (2) the primate corpus luteum retains some compartmental analogy to the follicle that facilitates provision of substrate (androgen) for estrogen production. Such compartmentalization may also occur in the equine corpus luteum [47].

Studies in several species indicate that the number and size of luteal cells in the subpopulations change during the life span of the corpus luteum (for review, see [1]). In general, the numbers and sizes of steroidogenic luteal cells increase as the corpus luteum develops (e.g., during the early-to-mid-luteal phase in domestic animals and primates) whereas the number and size of cells decline during luteal regression near the end of the cycle. It is likely that increases in luteal cell number and size and vascular development (increased endothelial cells) influence corpus luteum activity after ovulation because these events parallel the rise in circulating progesterone levels. Moreover, removal of granulosa cells from preovulatory follicles to reduce the source of luteal cells markedly decreased luteal mass and serum progesterone levels (but not luteal life span) in primates [48] and domestic animals [49]. These studies also established the critical importance of granulosa-derived luteal cells as the predominant source of progesterone in the corpus luteum during the ovarian cycle. However, it is likely that marked changes in function occur in luteal cells before changes in cell number and size at luteal regression. Moreover, morphometric evaluation of cellular constituents in a limited number of species indicates that cellular destruction during luteolysis does not occur simultaneously in all cell types. For example, studies indicated that small luteal cells and endothelial cells were the first cell types to decrease in the ovine corpus luteum, followed by a loss of large luteal cells [50]. However, because luteolysis involves a decline in cell size as a result of cell shrinkage in apoptosis (rather than cell swelling in necrosis) or loss of lipid droplets, it is difficult to establish whether large cells are lost as opposed to no longer meeting the size criterion. In primates, notably the human, luteolysis appears to occur first in the granulosa-derived luteal tissue; Sasano and Suzuki [51] noted that the number of steroidogenically active granulosa-luteal cells decreased by the late luteal phase, whereas the paraluteal region of presumed theca-luteal cells remained prominent and steroidogenically active.

Function and Regulation of Luteal Cell Subpopulations

Further characterization of luteal cell types followed the success in isolating enriched preparations of cell subpopulations based on differences in cell size and density [1]. Considerable progress was made by investigators such as Juengel, Hoyer, Diaz, Meidan, and colleagues [50, 52–54] who took advantage of the relative ease and greater numbers of small and large luteal cells that could be obtained from the corpus luteum of domestic animals. Their studies and others continue to elaborate the functional differences between luteal cell types, their divergence in regulation by hormonal and local factors, and the molecular pathways that are active in these cells, particularly as related to the primary activity of the corpus luteum–progesterone production.

Consistent with fine structural analyses of cell organelles, the large luteal cells ($\geq 20\,\mu m$; $30\,\mu m$ diameter in sheep and cows) isolated from various nonprimate species secrete 10- to 30-fold more progesterone than small luteal cells ($< 20\,\mu m$; $17\,\mu m$ in sheep and cows) [53]. This difference is apparent during acute incubation in control media or in the presence of the immediate precursor, pregnenolone; however, longer-term culture requires the presence of lipoprotein precursor (high-density lipoproteins [HDL] in ruminants) to sustain the cell difference [53]. In the ovine corpus luteum the high progesterone synthetic activity in large luteal cells is associated with greater expression of P450 side-chain cleavage (P450scc) and 3β-hydroxysteroid dehydrogenase (3β-HSD), and inner mitochondrial transport appears elevated (because of steroid acute regulatory protein [StAR] expression), but the mechanisms responsible for maintaining this high level of steroidogenic activity are not well defined [53]. Other reports indicate that the large luteal cells in domestic animals and primates are the primary, although not necessarily exclusive [55], producer of the peptide hormone called *relaxin* [56, 57]. This research suggests that large luteal cells can produce more than one hormone (e.g., dual secretor of steroid and peptide/protein hormones) but also emphasizes that arbitrary designation of two luteal cell types based on size, rather than function, is an oversimplification. Taylor and colleagues [58] identified four subtypes of large luteal cells in the pig by combining histochemical and hemolytic plaque assays to detect steroid and relaxin production. Other investigators also suggested that large and small cells can be divided into subclasses based on lipoprotein uptake [59] or oxytocin release [60, 61].

Small and large luteal cell preparations that differ in steroidogenic activity have also been prepared from the primate corpus luteum. In monkeys the 30- to 40-fold greater level of basal progesterone production by large cells than small cells is comparable with that observed in other species [62, 63], whereas smaller three- to fourfold differences are generally observed between luteal cell types in the human [64, 65]. A critical unanswered question is how these different-sized cell types in primates compare with the paraluteal and true luteal cells observed in situ. In some species, including rhesus monkeys and humans, the corpus luteum secretes significant quantities of estrogen; immunocytochemical analyses suggest the primate [45, 46] and equine [47] corpus luteum retains a two-cell model for estrogen synthesis similar to that in the follicle. Thus the $P450_{c17}$ confined to the paraluteal region is the source of androgen for P450 aromatase in the central luteal tissue that catalyzes its conversion to estrogen [66]. If the small luteal cells, which are thought to be of thecal origin in other species, correspond to the paraluteal cells, they would be expected to synthesize androgens. Conversely, the large luteal cells, presumably of granulosa origin, might be the site of aromatase activity. Evidence indicates that basal estrogen production by small and large luteal cells is low, with only the large cells having the capacity to convert exogenous androgen to estrogen [62, 64]. However, androgen synthetic activity was also 10-fold greater in large cells vs small cells from the macaque corpus luteum [67]; reports on human luteal cells are conflicting [64, 68]. These data suggest that size alone does not necessarily distinguish between paraluteal and luteal cells in the primate corpus luteum. Rather, the large cell population may be comprised of highly steroidogenic (both progestogenic and either androgenic or estrogenic) cells from granulosa and theca origin, as suggested by the original work of Alila and Hansel [44]. Whether the small luteal cells are of granulosa and theca origin in the primate corpus luteum is unknown.

There are also marked differences between small and large luteal cells in their responsiveness/receptor levels for luteotropic and luteolytic factors. For example, ovine large cells are minimally responsive to a gonadotropin (LH), cyclic adenosine monophosphate (cAMP), or other activators of the protein kinase A (PKA) pathway, whereas small cells respond markedly with a 10-fold increase in progesterone production [53]. Related evidence and calculations led to the proposal that in ruminants the chronic elevated steroidogenic activity of large luteal cells is "constitutive" (i.e., minimally stimulated by further hormone exposure) and responsible for 80% or more of the circulating progesterone. Although LH exposure or pulses can increase progesterone levels somewhat through acute or chronic actions on small luteal cells, a reduction in progesterone synthetic activity may occur initially through the action of luteolytic factors, notably $PGF_{2\alpha}$, on large luteal cells [50]. In ruminants such as the sheep and cow, large luteal cells express much greater levels of $PGF_{2\alpha}$ receptor (FP receptor) than small luteal cells [50, 53]. It appears that $PGF_{2\alpha}$ action involves activation of the phosphatidyl inositol (PI) pathway, because an increase in PI turnover in response to $PGF_{2\alpha}$ was observed in a variety of species, including primates [69]. There is evidence that both branches of PI signaling are involved in $PGF_{2\alpha}$ regulation of luteal cells, with elevated intracellular Ca^{+2} levels and protein kinase C (PKC) activation occurring primarily in large cells of ruminants. Hoyer [52] summarizes evidence suggesting that $PGF_{2\alpha}$ activation of the PKC branch mediates the loss of steroidogenic function, whereas the Ca^{+2} (IP_3) branch could promote the loss (via apoptosis) of large cells during luteolysis.

Recently, Diaz and colleagues [53] noted that treatment of large luteal cells with $PGF_{2\alpha}$ or activation of the PI pathway markedly increased cellular production of $PGF_{2\alpha}$. $PGF_{2\alpha}$ production appears to be stimulated by the translocation and activation of cytosolic phospholipase A_2 (thereby hydrolyzing arachidonic acid from membrane phospholipids) and the expression of cyclooxygenase-2 (COX-2, which catalyzes the conversion of arachidonate to PGH_2). These and other data led to the intriguing concept that there is an amplification loop in the corpus luteum whereby the luteolysin $PGF_{2\alpha}$ stimulates the further production of $PGF_{2\alpha}$ by luteal cells. In ruminants, this process would allow minute amounts of $PGF_{2\alpha}$ (luteolytic signal) from the uterus to be amplified to a large increase in $PGF_{2\alpha}$ (luteolytic action) in the corpus luteum. In many primates including women, the signal for luteolysis at the end of the menstrual cycle is not known, but it clearly does not originate from the uterus [70]. It is possible that the so-called *self-destruct mechanism* for luteolysis in the primate ovary involves the development of an autoamplification loop for luteolysin (e.g., $PGF_{2\alpha}$) production or action in luteal cells.

Although the sheep and cow are excellent large animal models for such studies, important species differences are likely in the regulation and response of luteal cell types. For example, although small luteal cells from primate species respond to LH-like hormones [64, 68, 71], there are reports that large luteal cells also respond (e.g., women [72]) or are more responsive (e.g., rhesus monkeys [63, 73]) than small luteal cells. This controversy remains unresolved. Some differences may be technique related [74]; for example, the human corpus luteum is difficult to dissociate and the prevalent use of harsh proteases may alter cell responsiveness or cause damage particularly to the friable large cells. This may explain why reports on steroid production by large vs small cells from women often are much less than that observed in other species. However, Brannian and colleagues [75] noted that the use of similar techniques (i.e., collagenase digestion and flow cytometry to separate small and large cells from the sheep and monkey corpus luteum) supported species differences. As expected, small cells from the ovine corpus luteum at the midluteal phase of the cycle were much more responsive to LH than large luteal cells; however, the opposite was true for the macaque corpus luteum—the large cells were more responsive to LH. These findings would suggest that the large and small luteal cells can respond to LH/chorionic gonadotropin (CG) in the primate corpus luteum during the menstrual cycle.

This difference, if confirmed and extended (e.g., detailed studies on LH receptors or LH receptor–activated pathways in primate luteal cell types are limited [68]), may relate to the apparent difference in the luteotropic role(s) of LH/CG in primates vs ruminants. In their review, Diaz and colleagues [53] note that studies using a gonadotropin-releasing hormone (Gn-RH) antagonist to eliminate pulsatile LH secretion report only a modest (50%) or no effect on circulating progesterone levels in cows or sheep depending on the stage of the luteal phase. In contrast, Gn-RH antagonist causes a rapid and complete suppression of progesterone levels in primates (monkeys and women [76, 77]) and early regression of the corpus luteum at all stages of luteal phase. Likewise, the entrainment of LH pulses to progesterone secretion by mid-to-late luteal phase in primates, with steroid levels at baseline in the lengthening intervals between LH pulses [78], demonstrates (1) the absolute requirement of primate luteal cells for LH exposure to maintain and stimulate progesterone secretion, and hence (2) the absence of any luteal cell type that constitutively produces progesterone. Whether the purported role of constitutive vs luteotropic hormone stimulation of progesterone production by luteal cell types varies between species, or during the life span of the corpus luteum, warrants further evaluation.

The effects of other luteotropic or luteolytic hormones on luteal cell populations have received little attention. Estradiol is the major luteotropin in the rabbit, and Arioua and colleagues [79] propose that LH participates indirectly by stimulating estradiol production from small cells, which then acts on small and large cells to promote progesterone production. Notably, large luteal cells in sheep also have greater numbers of estradiol and growth hormone (GH) receptors than small cells (see [50, 53]), whereas Di Simone and colleagues [65] reported that small, not large, luteal cells from women responded to GH with enhanced progesterone production. Prolactin (PRL) is the major luteotropic hormone in some species, particularly rodents, and there are limited reports of different steroidogenic responses of small and large luteal cells to PRL [80].

In addition to cell separation procedures, the use of immunohistochemical and in situ hybridization techniques to localize proteins and gene expression has greatly enhanced our understanding of cellular processes in the corpus luteum during its life span in the ovarian cycle. For example, localization of LH receptor protein or gene expression suggests that LH action is predominantly in the periphery of the corpus luteum of such diverse species as the pig [81] and human [82]. The data would suggest that any luteotropic actions of LH in the central luteal tissue are indirect, perhaps via steroids or growth factors synthesized by the peripheral luteal cells. The insulin-like growth factor (IGF) system is believed to play an important role in controlling follicle development vs atresia [83], and there are suggestions that the dynamic, cell-specific expression of components of the IGF system influences the corpus luteum as well. For example, the expression of specific carrier or binder proteins (BPs) varies between cell types, with evidence that IGFBP-1 is associated with the granulosa luteal cells, rather than the theca paraluteal cells of the primate corpus luteum [84]. In contrast, IGFBP-3 is primarily expressed by endothelial cells in the capillaries and microvessels of the corpus luteum [85]. The effects of BPs may be either stimulatory (to sequester IGF in a local site) or inhibitory (depriving cells of free, bioactive IGF). Because IGFBP-1 expression correlated with progesterone profiles, the former was proposed to occur especially during luteal development. In contrast, IGFBP-3 expression may be related to endothelial cell loss during luteolysis, although this process appears to differ between rodents and primates [85]. Clearly, whereas such approaches can identify heretofore unknown differences in regulation or cell activity (e.g., protease expression [86, 87]) between cell types and luteal compartments, further studies are needed to evaluate the physiologic relevance of these phenomena.

Cell-Cell Interactions in Luteal Function/Life Span

There is mounting evidence, both circumstantial and direct, suggesting that luteal cells transfer molecules that are important in cell signaling or as hormone precursors [88]. The immunocytochemical localization of $P450_{c17}$ and $P450_{arom}$ in different cell types (i.e., luteal and paraluteal cells, respectively) infers a critical role for two cells in estrogen production by the primate corpus luteum. In addition, morphometric evaluation of cellular constituents in the ovine corpus luteum suggests that cell-cell interactions are important in luteal regression. Although there is evidence that the large luteal cell is the predominant target for $PGF_{2\alpha}$, leading to speculation that this cell type is the ultimate director of luteolysis, there are reports that the numbers of small luteal cells and endothelial cells decrease before any reduction in large luteal cells [50, 52, 53]. Biochemical evidence for apoptosis in small cells before large cells [52] supports this concept and suggests that paracrine signals are important for procession of luteolytic events leading to cell destruction and loss of luteal structure-function.

Cell-cell interactions may involve any of a number of cytokines that either promote and/or inhibit luteal function and structure, at least in vitro. For example, recent work, particularly by Meidan, Levy, and Milvae [54, 89], suggests that ET-1 is an important factor controlling luteolysis in ruminants. ET-1, which is a member of the peptide family containing ET-2, -3, and sarafotoxins, was originally defined by its cardiovascular actions, notably vasoconstriction [90]. However, ET-1 has also emerged as a local modulator in the reproductive system, including the ovary [91]. Several key discoveries regarding the corpus luteum [54, 89] included evidence that the endothelial cells are the primary site of ET-1 gene expression. However, ET-1 is transcribed as prepro ET-1 and the active peptide is ultimately formed from the intermediate big ET-1, by the action of endothelin-converting enzyme (ECE-1), in endothelial cells and luteal cells. Thus the microvasculature can secrete precursor big ET-1 and mature ET-1, whereas steroidogenic cells may cleave endogenous big ET-1 to the active ET-1. In addition, at least one of the endothelin receptors, type A (ETA receptor), is expressed not only on endothelial cells but also on both types of luteal cells. The presence of the ET-1 system in the corpus luteum supports reports [92] that ET-1 inhibits basal and LH-stimulated progesterone production by mixed cell populations dispersed from the corpus luteum. However, in purified cell preparations, ET-1 inhibited progesterone secretion from large luteal cells, but not small luteal cells, although the latter contains ET-1 binding sites. Notably, preincubation of cells with an ETA receptor antagonist not only prevented the inhibitory effect of added ET-1 but also prevented the antisteroidogenic effect of $PGF_{2\alpha}$ in luteal slices. These data led to the novel concept that ET-1 may play a local inhibitory role in the corpus luteum including mediating, at least in part, $PGF_{2\alpha}$ actions in luteal regression [54, 89]. The latter is supported by evidence that intraluteal injection of an ETA receptor antagonist delayed somewhat the luteolytic effect of exogenous $PGF_{2\alpha}$ [93], plus the report that combined treatment of ET-1 plus a subluteolytic dose of $PGF_{2\alpha}$ produced complete luteolysis [92]. Finally, recent data on the dynamic expression and regulation of components of the ET-1 system led Meidan and Levy [54] to propose that such changes could explain the refractoriness of the corpus luteum to luteolytic $PGF_{2\alpha}$ in the first half of the luteal phase.

Collectively, evidence suggests that the ET-1 system is active, regulated by luteotropic and luteolytic hormones, and plays a key role in mediating or amplifying $PGF_{2\alpha}$-induced luteal regression in domestic animals. However, key experiments remain to be performed, including proof that modulating endogenous ET-1 synthesis or action alters the function or life span of the corpus luteum in the natural cycle. Although limited evidence suggests that the ET system is present in the corpus luteum of other species, including primates [94–96], further studies are needed to establish its importance, if any, in controlling the corpus luteum in these species. In addition, clarification is needed on the importance of direct $PGF_{2\alpha}$ action on the steroidogenic luteal cell vs endothelial cell [50] and the local amplification of $PGF_{2\alpha}$ [53] vs ET-1 [54] in the cascade of events leading to loss of luteal function and structure during luteolysis. Figure 10.2 offers a conceptual view of $PGF_{2\alpha}$ and ET-1 synthesis and action in the corpus luteum in response to the uterine $PGF_{2\alpha}$ luteolytic signal.

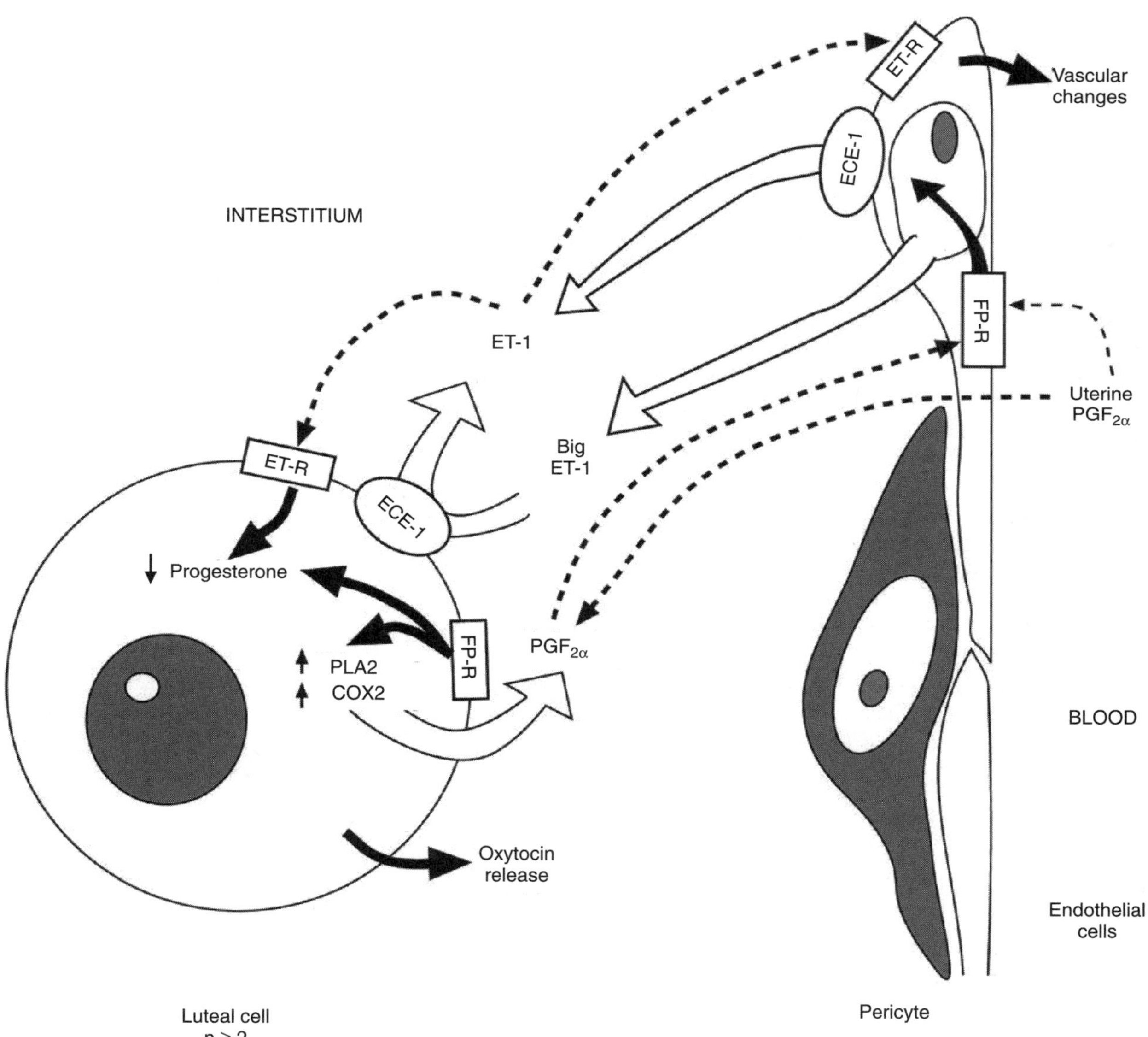

FIGURE 10.2 Diagram of proposed interactions between luteal cells and microvascular cells for the production and actions of local endothelin (ET-1) and prostaglandin ($PGF_{2\alpha}$) in response to the uterine luteolysin, $PGF_{2\alpha}$. It is hypothesized that the initial $PGF_{2\alpha}$ signal is amplified or mediated by positive feedback loops to increase intraluteal concentrations of $PGF_{2\alpha}$ and active ET-1, which then inhibit cell function and cause tissue regression. Dotted lines = $PGF_{2\alpha}$ and ET-1 action on cell types; white arrows = $PGF_{2\alpha}$ and ET-1 synthesis; black arrows = possible effects. See text and Refs. [53, 54] for further details.

IMMUNE CELLS IN THE CORPUS LUTEUM

Dynamics of the Immune System in Luteal Tissue

In the past few years, increasing attention has been directed at the cells of the immune system that, either residing throughout or attracted at specific stages, comprise a significant portion of the luteal tissue (for reviews, see [97, 98]). All types of leukocytes, including neutrophilic and eosinophilic granulocytes, macrophages, and lymphocytes, appear present with their relative numbers changing during the life span of the corpus luteum, sometimes in a species-specific manner. For example, neutrophils are at their highest density early in luteal development in the rat (i.e., early in pregnancy or pseudopregnancy), although considerable presence was also observed at luteal regression [99]. In contrast, few neutrophils were detected in the porcine corpus luteum [100], and although large numbers were demonstrated in the human corpus luteum, no difference in density was noted at luteal regression [101]. Eosinophils, on the other hand, are relatively sparse in the rat corpus luteum [99], yet infiltrate the ovine corpus luteum in large numbers after ovulation and are implied to have an important role in the luteolytic process in sheep [97]. Likewise, the numbers of lymphocyte subtypes such as cytotoxic T cells, helper T (T-h) cells, and natural killer (NK) cells in the corpus luteum vary markedly among species. In the human corpus luteum, B lymphocytes and NK cells were sparse to nondetectable [101, 102], although T-h cells were present especially at luteal regression in several species [99, 103]. Nevertheless, macrophages were typically identified in the corpus luteum and may comprise more than 10% of all cells in human luteal tissue [102]. Moreover, an increase in macrophage density was detected in a number of species during luteal regression, suggesting an active role in luteolysis [97].

In general, the changes in leukocyte cell density during the early and late luteal phase correlate with the initial and final tissue reorganization that occurs during development and dissolution of the corpus luteum, respectively. Investigators [104–107] have related these events to an acute inflammatory response/tissue repair (ovulation and luteinization) and an immune reaction/tissue elimination (luteolysis). It is well established that various leukocytes express a cell-specific array of cytokines, degrading enzymes, and reactive oxygen species that can elicit destruction of extracellular matrix or cells for tissue reorganization or destruction [97, 98]. Alternatively, cytokines may act to acutely stimulate or inhibit steroid synthesis, at least as demonstrated in numerous in vitro experiments [108, 109]. Finally, macrophages reportedly serve to eliminate dying cells or cell fragments (apoptotic bodies) by phagocytosis [6]. Brännström and Friden [97] provide a useful schematic of potential luteotropic vs luteolytic actions of leukocytes on cell types in the corpus luteum.

Despite the progress on categorizing leukocyte subpopulations in the corpus luteum and demonstrating cytokine actions on luteal cells in vitro, only limited evidence to date supports its physiologic relevance to controlling luteal function or life span during the ovarian cycle. In part, this is because of the difficulty in specifically modulating leukocyte cell numbers or action in the corpus luteum in vivo. One early approach, to suppress macrophages and T-lymphocytes with glucocorticoid administration, yielded mixed results. Seiner and colleagues [110] reported that methylprednisolone treatment essentially eliminated T lymphocytes and major histocompatability complex (MHC) class II antigen expression plus reduced macrophage numbers by 70%, yet the circulating progesterone levels and luteal life span was not altered during pseudopregnancy in rabbits. In contrast, Wang and colleagues [111] noted that dexamethasone treatment blocked luteal regression, as defined by sustained circulating progesterone levels, in uterine-intact or hysterectomized rats during pseudopregnancy; however, leukocyte numbers or function were not evaluated. Moreover, such approaches do not eliminate the possible direct actions of glucocorticoids in luteal tissue, via receptor-specific pathways [112]. In an opposite approach using mouse models, Bagavant and colleagues [113] reported that an inflammatory response and elevated cytokine levels in the ovaries, mediated by T-h1 cells, were compatible with normal ovarian cyclicity, ovulation, and fertility. Further studies are needed to establish the importance and roles of the various leukocyte subpopulations throughout the functional life span of the corpus luteum.

Cell-Cell Interactions in the Corpus Luteum

Recent research increased our understanding of the cell-cell interactions that may lead to leukocyte migration or accumulation and activation in the corpus luteum. This work followed the discovery of chemokines, defined as a family of small cytokines with selective chemoattractant and activating properties on leukocytes. As reviewed by Bukulmez and Arici [98], these factors have either two cysteine residues adjacent to each other (C-C family) or one intervening amino acid (C-X-C family). Although chemokine biology is an emerging area of research, initial reports suggest that members of both families may be present (interleukin [IL]-8 and monocyte chemotactic protein [MCP]-1) or absent (RANTES) from the ovary of certain species. Based on a 16-fold increase in IL-8 in follicular fluid following the midcycle gonadotropin surge, Arici and colleagues [114] proposed that this chemokine promotes the accumulation and activation of neutrophils that play a role in ovulation and early development (neovascularization) of the corpus luteum. Evidence that IL-8 antiserum inhibits gonadotropin-induced ovulation and neutrophil elastase activity in rabbits [115] supports this hypothesis. The chemokine that has received the greatest attention to date is MCP-1, which attracts and activates monocytes/macrophages and also attracts T-lymphocyte subtypes. Increased MCP-1 mRNA expression was observed in the corpus luteum of rodents, domestic animals, and primates during luteolysis [116–118], and luteolytic agents, including $PGF_{2\alpha}$, increase expression in luteal tissue either directly or indirectly via production of other cytokines [119]. The cellular source(s) of MCP-1 are unclear; various cell types including endothelial cells, T-lymphocytes, and fibroblasts can secrete MCP-1, and there are conflicting reports regarding the ability of luteal cells to express MCP-1 [120, 121]. Nevertheless, the data are consistent with a role for MCP-1 in the influx of macrophages that occurs in the aging corpus luteum and that these cells play a role in structural, if not functional, luteolysis. As proposed by Penny [119], chemokines such as MCP-1 may well prove to be another paracrine link between hormonal and cellular events within the corpus luteum involving steroidogenic, endothelial, and immune cell types (Figure 10.3).

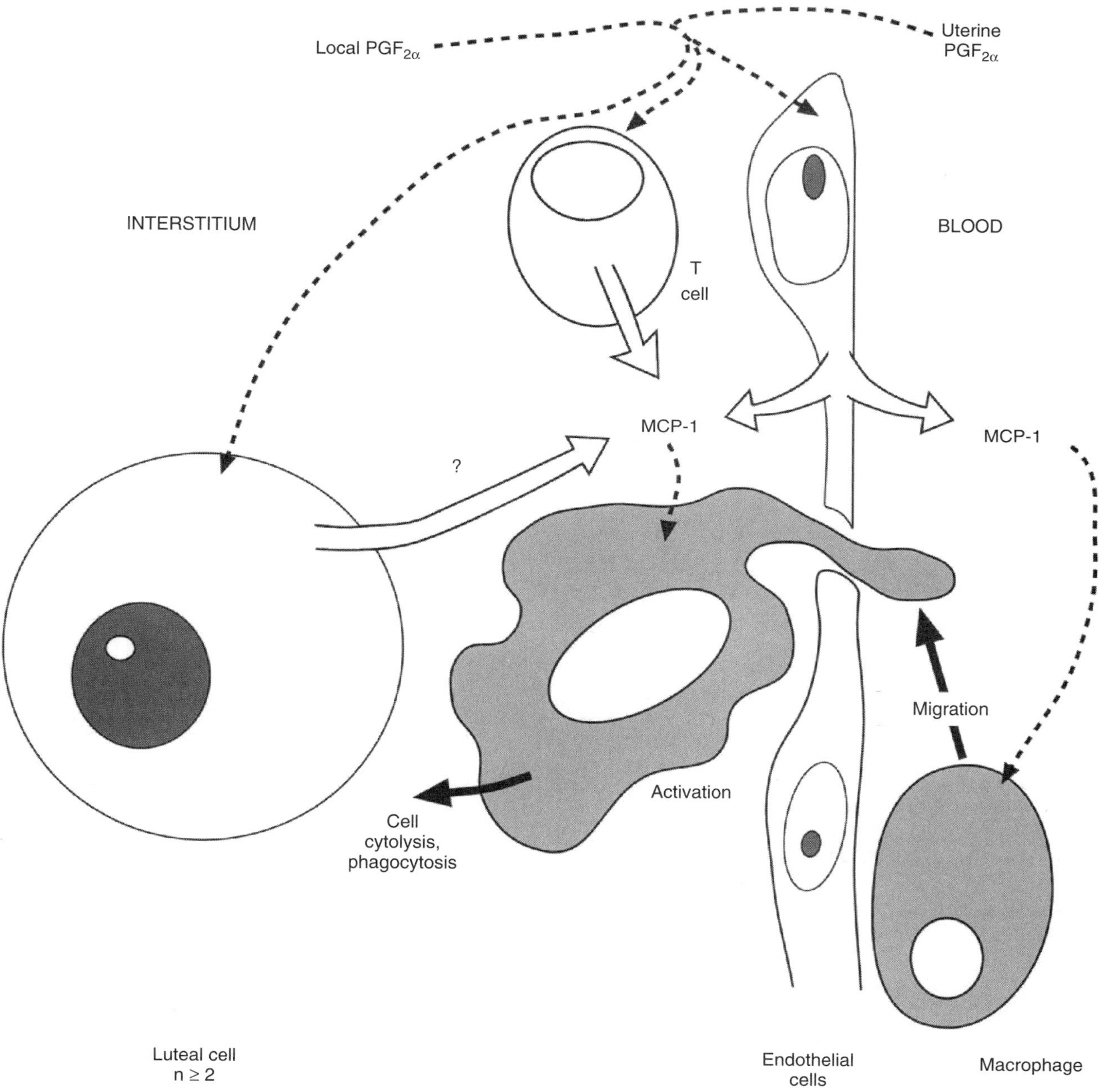

FIGURE 10.3 Conceptual diagram of proposed interactions between luteal cells, microvascular cells, and immune cells for the production and actions of MCP-1 during $PGF_{2\alpha}$-induced luteolysis. It is hypothesized that uterine and/or local $PGF_{2\alpha}$ acts on one or more cell types to stimulate MCP-1 production, which then acts to attract and activate macrophages involved in tissue regression. Dotted lines = $PGF_{2\alpha}$ and MCP-1 action; white arrows = MCP-1 synthesis; black arrows = MCP-1 effects; question mark = possible event. See text and Ref. [119] for further details.

CONCLUSION

The past decade witnessed important advances in our understanding of the activities and regulation of steroidogenic and nonsteroidogenic cell types comprising the corpus luteum. Moreover, novel cellular (e.g., laser capture microscopy) and molecular (e.g., genomics and proteomics) approaches offer great promise for incremental increases in our insight in the biology of the corpus luteum. Undoubtedly, new regulatory factors and generally ignored (e.g., lymphatics [122]) or undefined (e.g., large luteal cell subpopulations) cell types may emerge as vital components. However, the most promising avenues will continue to unravel the interactions that occur between cell types that control luteal structure-function. Promising examples provided in this review (see Figures 10.1 to 10.3) illustrate the need to consider physical and chemical links, as well as feedback control loops between steroidogenic, microvascular, immune, and other cells in the corpus luteum—similar to how earlier reproductive biologists studied hypothalamic-pituitary-ovarian interactions. Although the complexity increases with the discovery of more local factors (including angiogenic factors and cytokines/chemokines), creative efforts should assist in understanding the events that control the formation, function, and regression of the corpus luteum in rodents, domestic animals, and primates.

ACKNOWLEDGMENTS

The author acknowledges the input provided by Drs. Rina Meidan and Milo Wiltbank, as well as the assistance of Carol Gibbins in preparing this manuscript. The author's work described in this chapter was supported by NIH/NICHD through cooperative agreement U54 HD18185 as part of the Specialized Cooperative Centers Program in Reproduction Research, R01 HD22408, and NIH/NCRR RR00163.

References

1. Stouffer, R. L., and Brannian, J. D. (1993). The function and regulation of cell populations composing the corpus luteum of the ovarian cycle. In *The Ovary,* 1st ed., eds. E. Y. Adashi and P. C. K. Leung, 245–259. New York: Raven Press.
2. Hazzard, T. M., and Stouffer, R. L. (2000). Angiogenesis in ovarian follicular and luteal development. In *Clinical Obstetrics and Gynaecology: Angiogenesis in the Female Reproductive Tract,* ed. S. Arulkumaran, 883–900. London: Bailliere Tindall.
3. Lei, Z. M., Chegini, N., and Rao, C. V. (1991). Quantitative cell composition of human and bovine corpora lutea from various reproductive states. *Biol. Reprod.* 44, 1148–1156.
4. Christenson, L. K., and Stouffer, R. L. (1996). Proliferation of microvascular endothelial cells in the primate corpus luteum during the menstrual cycle and simulated early pregnancy. *Endocrinology* 137, 367–374.
5. Knickerbocker, J. J., Wiltbank, M. C., and Niswender, G. D. (1988). Mechanisms of luteolysis in domestic livestock. *Domest. Anim. Endocrinol.* 5, 91–107.
6. Paavola, L. G. (1979). The corpus luteum of the guinea pig. IV. Fine structure of macrophages during pregnancy and postpartum luteolysis and the phagocytosis of luteal cells. *Am. J. Anat.* 154, 337–364.
7. Gaytan, F., Morales, C., Garcia-Pardo, L., Reymundo, C., Bellido, C., and Sanchez-Criado, J. E. (1999). A quantitative study of changes in the human corpus luteum microvasculature during the menstrual cycle. *Biol. Reprod.* 60, 914–919.
8. Reynolds, L. P., and Redmer, D. A. (1998). Expression of the angiogenic factors, basic fibroblast growth factor and vascular endothelial growth factor, in the ovary. *J. Anim. Sci.* 76, 1671–1681.
9. Koos, R. D. (1993). Ovarian angiogenesis. In *The Ovary,* 1st ed., eds. E. Y. Adashi and P. C. K. Leung, 433–453. New York: Raven Press.
10. Stacker, S. A., and Achen, M. G. (1999). The vascular endothelial growth factor family: Signalling for vascular development. *Growth Factors* 17, 1–11.
11. Ancelin, M., Buteau-Lozano, H., Meduri, G., Osborne-Pellegrin, M., Sordello, S., Plouet, J., and Perrot-Applanat, M. (2002). A dynamic shift of VEGF isoforms with a transient and selective progesterone-induced expression of VEGF189 regulates angiogenesis and vascular permeability in human uterus. *Proc. Natl. Acad. Sci. USA* 99, 6023–6028.
12. Stalmans, I., Ng, Y.-S., Rohan, R., Fruttiger, M., Bouche, A., Yuce, A., Fujisawa, H., Hermans, B., Shani, M., Jansen, S., Hicklin, D., Anderson, D. J., Gardiner, T., Hammes, H.-P., Moons, L., Dewerchin, M., Collen, D., Carmeliet, P., and D'Amore, P. A. (2001). Arteriolar and venular patterning in retinas of mice selectively expressing VEGF isoforms. *J. Clin. Invest.* 109, 327–336.
13. Robinson, C. J., and Stringer, S. E. (2001). The splice variants of vascular endothelial growth factor (VEGF) and their receptors. *J. Cell Sci.* 114, 853–865.
14. Ravindranath, N., Little-Ihrig, L., Phillips, H. S., Ferrara, N., and Zeleznik, A. J. (1992). Vascular endothelial growth factor messenger ribonucleic acid expression in the primate ovary. *Endocrinology* 131, 254–260.
15. Hazzard, T. M., Christenson, L. K., and Stouffer, R. L. (2000). Changes in expression of vascular endothelial growth factor and angiopoietin-1 and -2 in the macaque corpus luteum during the menstrual cycle. *Mol. Hum. Reprod.* 6, 993–998.
16. Redmer, D. A., Doraiswamy, V., Bortnem, B. J., Fisher, K., Jablonka-Shariff, A., Grazul-Bilska, A. T., and Reynolds, L. P. (2001). Evidence for a role of capillary pericytes in vascular growth of the developing ovine corpus luteum. *Biol. Reprod.* 65, 879–889.
17. Laitinen, M., Ristimaki, A., Honkasalo, M., Narko, K., Paavonen, K., and Ritvos, O. (1997). Differential hormonal regulation of vascular endothelial growth factors VEGF, VEGF-B, and VEGF-C messenger ribonucleic acid levels in cultured human granulosa-luteal cells. *Endocrinology* 138, 4748–4756.
18. Martinez-Chequer, J. C., Stouffer, R. L., Hazzard, T. M., Patton, P. E., and Molskness, T. A. (2003). Insulin-like growth

factor (IGF)-1 and -2, but not hypoxia, synergize with gonadotropin hormone to promote vascular endothelial growth factor (VEGF)-A secretion by monkey granulosa cells from preovulatory follicles. *Biol. Reprod.* 68:1112–1118.

19. Koos, R. D. (1995). Increased expression of vascular endothelial growth/permeability factor in the rat ovary following an ovulatory gonadotropin stimulus: Potential roles in follicle rupture. *Biol. Reprod.* 52, 1426–1435.
20. Christenson, L. K., and Stouffer, R. L. (1997). Follicle-stimulating hormone and luteinizing hormone/chorionic gonadotropin stimulation of vascular endothelial growth factor production by macaque granulosa cells from pre- and periovulatory follicles. *J. Clin. Endocrinol. Metab.* 82, 2135–2142.
21. Molskness, T. A., and Stouffer, R. L. (2002). Hypoxia, but not gonadotropin, stimulates vascular endothelial growth factor production by primate luteal cells in vitro. *Biol. Reprod.* 66 (Suppl 1), 283–284 (abstract 457).
22. Doraiswamy, V., Grazul-Bilska, A. T., Ricke, W. A., Redmer, D. A., and Reynolds, L. P. (1995). Immunoneutralization of angiogenic activity from ovine corpora lutea (CL) with antibodies against fibroblast growth factor (FGF)-2 and vascular endothelial growth factor (VEGF). *Biol. Reprod.* 52 (Suppl 1) 112 (abstract 223).
23. Zimmermann, R. C., Hartman, T., Bohlen, P., Sauer, M. V., and Kitajewski, J. (2001). Preovulatory treatment of mice with anti-VEGF receptor 2 antibody inhibits angiogenesis in corpora lutea. *Microvasc. Res.* 62, 15–25.
24. Fraser, H. M., Dickson, S. E., Lunn, S. F., Wulff, C., Morris, K. D., Carroll, V. A., and Bicknell, R. (2000). Suppression of luteal angiogenesis in the primate after neutralization of vascular endothelial growth factor. *Endocrinology* 141, 995–1000.
25. Dickson, S. E., Bicknell, R., and Fraser, H. M. (2001). Mid-luteal angiogenesis and function in the primate is dependent on vascular endothelial growth factor. *J. Endocrinol.* 168, 409–416.
26. Hazzard, T. M., Xu, F., and Stouffer, R. L. (2002). Injection of soluble vascular endothelial growth factor receptor 1 into the preovulatory follicle disrupts ovulation and subsequent luteal function in rhesus monkeys. *Biol. Reprod.* 67, 1305–1312.
27. Zimmermann, R. C., Xiao, E., Bohlen, P., and Ferin, M. (2002). Administration of antivascular endothelial growth factor receptor 2 antibody in the early follicular phase delays follicular selection and development in the rhesus monkey. *Endocrinology* 143, 2496–2502.
28. Christenson, L. K., and Stouffer, R. L. (1996). Isolation and culture of microvascular endothelial cells from the primate corpus luteum. *Biol. Reprod.* 55, 1397–1404.
29. Ward, N. L., and Dumont, D. J. (2002). The angiopoietins and Tie2/Tek: Adding to the complexity of cardiovascular development. *Cell Dev. Biol.* 13, 19–27.
30. Hanahan, D. (1997). Signaling vascular morphogenesis and maintenance. *Science* 277, 48–50.
31. Wulff, C., Wilson, H., Largue, P., Duncan, W. C., Armstrong, D. G., and Fraser, H. M. (2000). Angiogenesis in the human corpus luteum: Localization and changes in angiopoietins, Tie-2, and vascular endothelial growth factor messenger ribonucleic acid. *J. Clin. Endocrinol. Metab.* 85, 4302–4309.
32. Goede, V., Schmidt, T., Kimmina, S., Kozian, D., and Augustin, H. G. (1998). Analysis of blood vessel maturation processes during cyclic ovarian angiogenesis. *Lab. Invest.* 78, 1385–1394.
33. Hazzard, T. M., Molskness, T. A., Chaffin, C. L., and Stouffer, R. L. (1999). Vascular endothelial growth factor (VEGF) and angiopoietin regulation by gonadotrophin and steroids in macaque granulosa cells during the periovulatory interval. *Mol. Hum. Reprod.* 5, 1115–1121.
34. LeCouter, J., Kowalski, J., Foster, J., Hass, P., Zhang, Z., Dillard-Telm, L., Frantz, G., Rangell, L., DeGuzman, L., Keller, G. A., Peale, F., Gurney, A., Hillan, K. J., and Ferrara, N. (2001). Identification of an angiogenic mitogen selective for endocrine gland endothelium. *Nature* 412, 877–884.
35. Masuda, Y., Takatsu, Y., Terao, Y., Kumano, S., Ishibashi, Y., Suenaga, M., Abe, M., Fukusumi, S., Watanabe, T., Shintani, Y., Yamada, T., Hinuma, S., Inatomi, N., Ohtaki, T., Onda, H., and Fujino, M. (2002). Isolation and identification of EG-VEGF/prokineticins as cognate ligands for two orphan G-protein-coupled receptors. *Biochem. Biophys. Res. Commun.* 293, 396–402.
36. Borman, S. M., Hennebold, J. D., and Stouffer, R. L. (2002). Endocrine gland-vascular endothelial growth factor (EG-VEGF) expression in the nonhuman primate corpus luteum during the natural menstrual cycle. Abstract from *Proceedings of the XIVth Ovarian Workshop,* Baltimore, MD.
37. Suzuki, T., Sasano, H., Takaya, R., Fukaya, T., Yajima, A., and Nagura, H. (1998). Cyclic changes of vasculature and vascular phenotypes in normal human ovaries. *Hum. Reprod.* 13, 953–959.
38. Ratcliffe, K. E., Anthony, F. W., Richardson, M. C., and Stones, R. W. (2000). Morphology and functional characteristics of human ovarian microvascular endothelium. *Hum. Reprod.* 14, 1549–1554.
39. Fenyves, A. M., Saxer, M., and Spanel-Borowski, K. (1994). Bovine microvascular endothelial cells of separate morphology differ in growth and response to the action of interferon-gamma. *Experientia* 50, 99–104.
40. Hixenbaugh, E. A., Strauss, III, J. F., and Paavola, L. G. (1993). Establishment of heterogeneity among blood vessels: Hormone-influenced appearance of hepatic lipase in specific subsets of the ovarian microvasculature. *Anat. Rec.* 235, 487–500.
41. Corner, G. W. (1919). On the origin of the corpus luteum of the sow from both granulosa and theca interna. *Am. J. Anat.* 26, 117–183.
42. Fields, P. A. (1991). Relaxin and other luteal secretory peptides: Cell localization and function in the ovary. In *Ultrastructure of the Ovary,* eds. G. Familiari, S. Makabe, and P. M. Motta, 177–198. Norwell, Mass.: Kluwer Academic Publishers.
43. Meidan, R., Girsh, E., Blum, O., and Aberdam, E. (1990). In vitro differentiation of bovine theca and granulosa cells into small and large luteal-like cells: Morphological and functional characteristics. *Biol. Reprod.* 43, 913–921.
44. Alila, H. W., and Hansel, W. (1984). Origin of different cell types in the bovine corpus luteum as characterized by specific monoclonal antibodies. *Biol. Reprod.* 31, 1015–1025.
45. Sanders, S. L., and Stouffer, R. L. (1996). Localization of steroidogenic enzymes in macaque luteal tissue during the

menstrual cycle and simulated early pregnancy: Immunohistochemical evidence supporting the two-cell model for estrogen production in the primate corpus luteum. *Biol. Reprod.* 56, 1077–1087.

46. Sasano, H., Okamoto, M., Mason, J. I., Simpson, E. R., Mendelson, C. R., Sasano, N., and Silverberg, S. G. (1989). Immunolocalization of aromatase, 17α-hydroxylase and side-chain-cleavage cytochromes P450 in the human ovary. *J. Reprod. Fertil.* 85, 163–165.
47. Watson, E. D. (2000). Compartmentalization of steroidogenesis by the equine corpus luteum. *Theriogenology* 53, 1459–1466.
48. Marut, E. L., Huang, S.-C., and Hodgen, G. D. (1983). Distinguishing the steroidogenic roles of granulosa and theca cells of the dominant ovarian follicle and corpus luteum. *J. Clin. Endocrinol. Metab.* 57, 925–930.
49. Milvae, R. A., Alila, H. W., Bushmich, S. L., and Hansel, W. (1991). Bovine corpus luteum function after removal of granulosa cells from the preovulatory follicle. *Domest. Anim. Endocrinol.* 8, 439–443.
50. Juengel, J. L., and Niswender, G. D. (1999). Molecular regulation of luteal progesterone synthesis in domestic ruminants. *J. Reprod. Fertil.* (Suppl.) 54, 193–205.
51. Sasano, H., and Suzuki, T. (1997). Localization of steroidogenesis and steroid receptors in human corpus luteum. *Semin. Reprod. Endocrinol.* 15, 345–351.
52. Hoyer, P. B. (1998). Regulation of luteal regression: The ewe as a model. *J. Soc. Gynecol. Invest.* 5, 49–57.
53. Diaz, F. J., Anderson, L. E., Wu, Y. L., Rabot, A., Tsai, S. J., and Wiltbank, M. C. (2002). Regulation of progesterone and prostaglandin F2α production in the CL. *Mol. Cell. Endocrinol.* 191, 65–80.
54. Meidan, R., and Levy, N. (2002). Endothelin-1 receptors and biosynthesis in the corpus luteum: Molecular and physiological implications. *Domest. Anim. Endocrinol.* 5340, 1–12.
55. Denning-Kendall, P. A., Guldenaar, S. E. F., and Wathes, D. C. (1989). Evidence for a switch in the site of relaxin production from small theca-derived cells to large luteal cells during early pregnancy in the pig. *J. Reprod. Fert.* 85, 261–271.
56. Brannian, J. D., and Stouffer, R. L. (1991). Cellular approaches to understanding the function and regulation of the primate corpus luteum. *Semin. Reprod. Endocrinol.* 9, 341–351.
57. Stoelk, E., Chegini, N., Lei, Z. M., Rao, C. V., Bryant-Greenwood, G., and Sanfilippo, J. (1991). Immunocytochemical localization of relaxin in human corpora lutea: Cellular and subcellular distribution and dependence on reproductive state. *Biol. Reprod.* 44, 1140–1147.
58. Taylor, M. J., Clark, C. L., and Frawley, L. S. (1987). Evidence for the existence of a luteal cell type that is steroidogenic and releases relaxin. *Proc. Soc. Exp. Biol. Med.* 185, 469–473.
59. Brannian, J. D., Shiigi, S. M., and Stouffer, R. L. (1991). Differential uptake of fluorescent-tagged low-density lipoprotein by cells from the primate corpus luteum: Isolation and characterization of subtypes of small and large luteal cells. *Endocrinology* 129, 3247–3253.
60. Fehr, S., Ivell, R., Koll, R., Schams, D., Fields, M., and Richter, D. (1987). Expression of the oxytocin gene in the large cells of the bovine corpus luteum. *FEBS Lett.* 210, 45–50.
61. Jarry, H., Hornschuh, R., Pitzel, L., and Wuttke, W. (1992). Demonstration of oxytocin release by bovine luteal cells utilizing the reverse hemolytic plaque assay. *Biol. Reprod.* 46, 408–413.
62. Hild-Petito, S. A., Shiigi, S. M., and Stouffer, R. L. (1989). Isolation and characterization of cell subpopulations from the monkey corpus luteum of the menstrual cycle. *Biol. Reprod.* 40, 1075–1085.
63. Brannian, J. D., and Stouffer, R. L. (1991). Progesterone production by monkey luteal cell subpopulations at different stages of the menstrual cycle: Changes in agonist responsiveness. *Biol. Reprod.* 44, 141–149.
64. Ohara, A., Mori, T., Taii, S., Ban, C., and Narimoto, K. (1987). Functional differentiation in steroidogenesis of two types of luteal cells isolated from mature human corpora lutea of menstrual cycle. *J. Clin. Endocrinol. Metab.* 65, 1192–1200.
65. Di Simone, N., Castellani, R., Lanzone, A., Caruso, A., and Mancuso, S. (1993). Human growth hormone enhances progesterone production by human luteal cells in vitro. II. Evidence of a distinct effect on two luteal cell types. *Fertil. Steril.* 60, 47–52.
66. Mori, T., Nihnobu, K., Takeuchi, S., Ohno, Y., and Tojo, S. (1983). Interrelation between luteal cell types in steroidogenesis in vitro of human corpus luteum. *J. Steroid. Biochem.* 19, 811–815.
67. Sanders, S. L., Stouffer, R. L., and Brannian, J. D. (1996). Androgen production by monkey luteal cell subpopulations at different stages of the menstrual cycle. *J. Clin. Endocrinol. Metab.* 81, 591–596.
68. Retamales, I., Carrasco, I., Troncoso, J. L., Las Heras, J., Devoto, L., and Vega, M. (1994). Morpho-functional study of human luteal cell subpopulations. *Hum. Reprod.* 9, 591–596.
69. Houmard, B. S., Guan, Z., Stokes, B. T., and Ottobre, J. S. (1992). Activation of the phosphatidylinositol pathway in the primate corpus luteum by prostaglandin $F_{2\alpha}$. *Endocrinology* 131, 743–748.
70. Metcalf, M. G., Braiden, V., and Livesey, J. H. (1992). Retention of normal ovarian function after hysterectomy. *J. Endocrinol.* 135, 597–602.
71. Carrasco, I., Troncoso, J. L., Devoto, L., and Vega, M. (1996). Differential steroidogenic response of human luteal cell subpopulations. *Hum. Reprod.* 11, 1609–1614.
72. Friden, B. E., Hagstrom, H.-G., Lindblom, B., Sjoblom, P., Wallin, A., Brännström, M., and Hahlin, M. (1999). Cell characteristics and functions of two enriched fractions of human luteal cells during prolonged culture. *Mol. Hum. Reprod.* 5, 714–719.
73. Sanders, S. L., and Stouffer, R. L. (1995). Gonadotropin- and lipoprotein-supported progesterone production by primate luteal cell types in culture. *Endocrine* 3, 169–175.
74. Broadley, C., Menzies, G. S., Bramley, T. A., and Watson, E. D. (1994). Isolation of cell populations from the mare corpus luteum: Comparison of mechanical and collagenase dissociation. *J. Reprod. Fertil.* 102, 7–15.
75. Brannian, J. D., Stouffer, R. L., Shiigi, S. M., and Hoyer, P. B. (1993). Isolation of ovine luteal cell subpopulations by flow cytometry. *Biol. Reprod.* 48, 495–502.
76. Duffy, D. M., Stewart, D. R., and Stouffer, R. L. (1999). Titrating luteinizing hormone replacement to sustain the structure and function of the corpus luteum after

gonadotropin-releasing hormone antagonist treatment in rhesus monkeys. *J. Clin. Endocrinol. Metab.* 84, 342–349.

77. Mais, V., Kazer, R. R., Cetel, N. S., Rivier, J., Vale, W., and Yen, S. S. C. (1986). The dependency of folliculogenesis and corpus luteum function on pulsatile gonadotropin secretion in cycling women using a gonadotropin-releasing hormone antagonist as a probe. *J. Clin. Endocrinol. Metab.* 62, 1250–1255.
78. Ellinwood, W. E., Norman, R. L., and Spies, H. G. (1984). Changing frequency of pulsatile luteinizing hormone and progesterone secretion during the luteal phase of the menstrual cycle of rhesus monkeys. *Biol. Reprod.* 31, 714–722.
79. Arioua, R. K., Benhaim, A., Feral, C., and Leymarie, P. (1997). Luteotrophic factors in hyperstimulated pseudopregnant rabbit: II—High sensitivity to hCG of luteal tissue and small luteal cells. *J. Endocrinol.* 154, 259–265.
80. Gregoraszczuk, E. L. (1990). Different response of porcine large and small luteal cells to PRL in terms of progesterone and estradiol secretion in vitro. *Exp. Clin. Endocrinol.* 96, 234–237.
81. Meduri, G., Vuhai-Luuthi, M. T., Jolivet, A., and Milgrom, E. (1992). New functional zonation in the ovary as shown by immunohistochemistry of luteinizing hormone receptor. *Endocinology* 131, 366–373.
82. Ottander, U., Nakata, M., Backstrom, T., Liu, K., Ny, T., and Olofsson, J. I. (1997). Compartmentalization of human chorionic gonadotrophin sensitivity and luteinizing hormone receptor mRNA in different subtypes of the human corpus luteum. *Hum. Reprod.* 12, 1037–1042.
83. Giudice, L. C. (2001). Insulin-like growth factor family in Graafian follicle development and function. *J. Soc. Gynecol. Invest.* 8, S26-S29.
84. Hartshorne, G. M., Bell, S. C., and Waites, G. T. (1990). Binding proteins for insulin-like growth factors in the human ovary: Identification, follicular fluid levels, and immunohistological localization of the 29–32 Kd type 1 binding protein, IGF-BP1. *Hum. Reprod.* 5, 649–660.
85. Fraser, H. M., Lunn, S. F., Kim, H., and Erickson, G. F. (1998). Insulin-like growth factor binding protein-3 mRNA expression in endothelial cells of the primate corpus luteum. *Hum. Reprod.* 13, 2180–2185.
86. Young, K. A., Hennebold, J. D., and Stouffer, R. L. (2002). Dynamic expression of mRNAs and proteins for matrix metalloproteinases and their tissue inhibitors in the primate corpus luteum during the menstrual cycle. *Mol. Hum. Reprod.* 8, 833–840.
87. Itskovitz-Eldor, J., Bruneval, P., Soubrier, F., Thaler, I., Corvol, P., and Sealey, J. E. (1992). Localization of renin gene expression to monkey ovarian theca cells by in situ hybridization. *J. Clin. Endocrinol. Metab.* 75, 1374–1380.
88. Grazul-Bilska, A. T., Redmer, D. A., and Reynolds, L. P. (1997). Cellular interactions in the corpus luteum. *Semin. Reprod. Endocrinol.* 15, 383–393.
89. Milvae, R. A. (2000). Inter-relationships between endothelin and prostaglandin $F_{2\alpha}$ in corpus luteum function. *Rev. Reprod.* 5, 1–5.
90. Nussdorfer, G. G., Rossi, G. P., Malendowicz, L. K., and Mazzocchi, G. (1999). Autocrine-paracrine endothelin system in the physiology and pathology of steroid-secreting tissues. *Pharmacol. Rev.* 51, 406–437.
91. Kennedy, R. L., Haynes, W. G., and Webb, D. J. (1993). Endothelins as regulators of growth and function in endocrine tissues. *Clin. Endocrinol.* 39, 259–265.
92. Girsh, E., Milvae, R. A., Wang, W., and Meidan, R. (1996). Effect of endothelin-1 on bovine luteal cell function: Role in PGF2α-induced anti-steroidogenic action. *Endocrinology* 137, 1306–1312.
93. Hinckley, S. T., and Milvae, R. A. (2001). Endothelin-1 mediates prostaglandin $F_{2\alpha}$-induced luteal regression in the ewe. *Biol. Reprod.* 64, 1619–1623.
94. Mancina, R., Barni, T., Calogero, A. E., Filippi, S., Amerini, S., Peri, A., Susini, T., Vannelli, G. B., Burrello, N., Forti, G., and Maggi, M. (1997). Identification, characterization, and biological activity of endothelin receptors in human ovary. *J. Clin. Endocrinol. Metab.* 82, 4122–4129.
95. Apa, R., Miceli, F., de Feo D., Mastrandrea, M. L., Mancuso, S., Napolitano, M., and Lanzone, A. (1998). Endothelin-1 inhibits basal and human chorionic gonadotrophin-stimulated progesterone production. *Hum. Reprod.* 13, 2425–2429.
96. Yoshioka, S., Fujiwara, H., Yamada, S., Tatsumi, K., Nakayama, T., Higuchi, T., Inoue, T., Maeda, M., and Fujii, S. (1998). Endothelin-converting enzyme-1 is expressed on human ovarian follicles and corpora lutea of menstrual cycle and early pregnancy. *J. Clin. Endocrinol. Metab.* 83, 3943–3950.
97. Brännström, M., and Friden, B. (1997). Immune regulation of corpus luteum function. *Semin. Reprod. Endocrinol.* 15, 363–370.
98. Bukulmez, O., and Arici, A. (2000). Leukocytes in ovarian function. *Hum. Reprod. Update* 6, 1–15.
99. Brännström, M., Giesecke, L., van den Heuvel, C. J., Moore, I. C., and Robertson, S. A. (1994). Leukocyte subpopulations in the rat corpus luteum during pregnancy and pseudopregnancy. *Biol. Reprod.* 50, 1161–1167.
100. Standaert, F. S., Zamor, C. S., and Chew, B. P. (1991). Quantitative and qualitative changes in blood leukocytes in the porcine ovary. *Am. J. Reprod. Immunol.* 215, 163–168.
101. Brännström, M., Pascoe, V., Norman, R. J., and McClure, N. (1994). Localization of leukocyte subsets in the follicle wall and in the corpus luteum throughout the human menstrual cycle. *Fertil. Steril.* 61, 488–495.
102. Wang, L. J., Pascoe, V., Petrucco, O. M., and Norman, R. J. (1992). Distribution of leukocyte subpopulations in the human corpus luteum. *Hum. Reprod.* 7, 197–202.
103. Bagavandoss, P., Wiggins, R. C., Kunkel, S. L., Remick, D. G., and Keyes, P. L. (1990). Tumor necrosis factor production and accumulation of inflammatory cells in the corpus luteum of pseudopregnancy and pregnancy in rabbits. *Biol. Reprod.* 42, 367–376.
104. Murdoch, W. J., Steadman, L. E., and Belden, E. L. (1988). Immunoregulation of luteolysis. *Med. Hypotheses* 27, 197–199.
105. Mori, T. (1990). Immuno-endocrinology of cyclic ovarian function. *Am. J. Reprod. Immunol.* 23, 80–89.
106. Bukovsky, A., Caudle, M. R., Keenan, J. A., Wimalasena, J., Upadhyaya, N. B., and Van Meter, S. E. (1995). Is corpus luteum regression an immune-mediated event? Localization of immune system components and luteinizing hormone receptor in human corpora lutea. *Biol. Reprod.* 53, 1373–1384.

107. Pate, J. L., and Keyes, P. L. (2001). Immune cells in the corpus luteum: Friends or foes. *Reproduction* 122, 665–676.
108. Castro, A., Castro, O., Troncoso, J. L., Kohen, P., Simon, C., Vega, M., and Devoto, L. (1998). Luteal leukocytes are modulators of the steroidogenic process of human mid-luteal cells. *Hum. Reprod.* 13, 1584–1589.
109. Hashii, K., Fujiwara, H., Yoshioka, S., Kataoka, N., Yamada, S., Hirano, T., Mori, T., Fujii, S., and Maeda, M. (1998). Peripheral blood mononuclear cells stimulate progesterone production by luteal cells derived from pregnant and non-pregnant women: Possible involvement of interleukin-4 and interleukin-10 in corpus luteum function and differentiation. *Hum. Reprod.* 13, 2738–2744.
110. Seiner, S. J., Schramm, W., and Keyes, P. L. (1992). Effect of treatment with methylprednisolone on duration of pseudopregnancy and on macrophages and T lymphocytes in rabbit corpora lutea. *J. Reprod. Fertil.* 96, 347–353.
111. Wang, F., Riley, J. C. M., and Behrman, H. R. (1993). Immunosuppressive levels of glucocorticoid block extrauterine luteolysins in the rat. *Biol. Reprod.* 49, 66–73.
112. Gaytan, F., Morales, C., Bellido, C., and Sanchez-Criado, J. E. (2002). Selective apoptosis of luteal endothelial cells in dexamethasone-treated rats leads to ischemic necrosis of luteal tissue. *Biol. Reprod.* 66, 232–240.
113. Bagavant, H., Adams, S., Terranova, P., Chang, A., Kraemer, F. W., Lou, Y., Kasai, K., Luo, A. M., and Tung, K. S. K. (1999). Autoimmune ovarian inflammation triggered by proinflammatory (Th1) T cells is compatible with normal ovarian function in mice. *Biol. Reprod.* 61, 635–642.
114. Arici, A., Oral, E., Bukulmez, O., Buradagunta, S., Engin, O., and Olive, D. L. (1996). Interleukin-8 expression and modulation in human preovulatory follicles and ovarian cells. *Endocrinology* 137, 3762–3769.
115. Ujioka, T., Matsukawa, A., Tanaka, N., Matsuura, K., Yoshinaga, M., and Okamura, H. (1998). Interleukin-8 as an essential factor in the human chorionic gonadotropin-induced rabbit ovulatory process: Interleukin-8 induces neutrophil accumulation and activation in ovulation. *Biol. Reprod.* 58, 526–530.
116. Townson, D. H., Warren, J. S., Flory, C. M., and Keyes, P. L. (1996). Expression of monocyte chemoattractant protein-1 in the corpus luteum in the rat. *Biol. Reprod.* 54, 513–520.
117. Penny, L. A., Armstrong, D. G., Baxter, G., Hogg, C., Kindahl, H., Bramley, T., Watson, E. D., and Webb, R. (1998). Expression of monocyte chemoattractant protein-1 in the bovine corpus luteum around the time of natural luteolysis. *Biol. Reprod.* 59, 1464–1469.
118. Senturk, L. M., Seli, E., and Gutierrez, L. S. (1999). Monocyte chemotactic protein-1 expression in human corpus luteum. *Mol. Hum. Reprod.* 5, 697–702.
119. Penny, L. A. (2000). Monocyte chemoattractant protein 1 in luteolysis. *Rev. Reprod.* 5, 63–66.
120. Haworth, J. D., Rollyson, M. K., Silva, P., McIntush, E. W., and Niswender, G. D. (1998). Messenger ribonucleic acid encoding monocyte chemoattractant protein 1 is expressed by the ovine corpus luteum in response to prostaglandin $F_{2\alpha}$. *Biol. Reprod.* 58, 169–174.
121. Hosang, K., Knoke, I., Klaudiny, J., Wempe, F., Wuttke, W., and Scheit, K. H. (1994). Porcine luteal cells express monocyte chemoattractant protein 1 (MCP-1): Analysis by polymerase chain reaction and cDNA cloning. *Biochem. Biophys. Res. Commun.* 199, 962–968.
122. Ichikawa, S., Uchino, S., and Hirata, Y. (1987). Lymphatic and blood vasculature of the forming corpus luteum. *Lymphology* 20, 73–83.

CHAPTER **11**

Luteinization

BRUCE D. MURPHY

ABSTRACT

A morphological and biochemical remodeling process known as *luteinization* ensues following rupture of the preovulatory ovarian follicle, resulting in the formation of a transient but essential ovarian organ called the *corpus luteum (CL)*. In most species studied, the two endocrine cells of the follicle, the theca cells and the granulosa cells, contribute to the CL. The process of luteinization includes modification of expression of steroidogenic enzymes and the steroidogenic acute regulatory protein to bring about large-scale synthesis of progesterone by the CL. There are concomitant changes in expression of proteins that provide cholesterol, the parent molecule for steroidogenesis to the luteal cells, including the low- and high-density lipoprotein receptors and the intracellular cholesterol delivery protein, known as the *Niemann-Pick C-1 protein* (NPC-1). Luteinization is a process of terminal differentiation of the component steroidogenic cells and thus consists of the exit from the cell cycle, occurring first in the granulosa cell component and then more gradually in the theca cells of the CL. Removal of the oocyte from a follicle provokes luteinization, which suggests inhibitory control. Nonetheless, the usual in vivo stimulus for luteinization is the preovulatory luteinizing hormone (LH) surge, and LH can induce luteinization of follicles that contain an oocyte, which indicates multiple levels of control. The most important intracellular pathway regulating formation of the CL is the cyclic adenosine monophosphate (cAMP)-protein kinase A cascade. Recent investigation has shed light on the molecular mechanisms of luteinization. Transactivation by several transcription factors induces the expression of the genes that mark the luteinization process. Luteinization is associated with a covalent modification of the deoxyribonucleic acid (DNA) packaging proteins, histone H3 and H4. In conclusion, luteinization is a coordinated program of gene expression that brings about an extensive change in two cell types of the ovarian follicle, resulting in a focus on the synthesis of progesterone.

INTRODUCTION

The CL forms in the ovary following rupture and collapse of the ovulating follicle. Luteal formation, also called *luteinization,* is an event of cell and tissue remodeling that engenders extensive change in the morphology, intracellular regulation, and gene expression in the follicular elements. Luteal formation is a mammalian hallmark, essential for early embryo survival, embryo implantation, and, ultimately, viviparity. Nonetheless, functional, progesterone-synthesizing CL can be found in species of nonmammalian vertebrates, including cartilaginous and bony fish, amphibians, and reptiles [1]. Luteinization is the terminal phase of differentiation of somatic cells of the ovary. By definition, it engenders an escape of the granulosa cells from the influences of the oocyte and has been described as the definitive exit from the cell cycle by the ovarian follicular cells. The rate of angiogenesis associated with conversion of the avascular follicular compartment to the highly vascularized CL is without parallel, even by comparison to the rapid vascular development during placentogenesis and tumor formation [2]. Whereas the process of formation of the CL and the cellular provenance of luteal components varies significantly among mammals, the CL appears to be present in and necessary for regulation of early gestation in all mammalian species.

This chapter comprises discussion of the process of luteinization and includes information on the morphological, intracellular, and regulatory events of CL formation in mammals. Although much of the information available is derived from rodent models, observations of nonrodent species have been included and a comparative approach has been taken where possible. Aspects of luteal function have been addressed elsewhere by the contributors to this volume, including luteal cell populations (Chapter 10), luteal regulation during pregnancy (Chapter 12), and angiogenesis (Chapter 18). These topics will not be discussed herein.

MORPHOLOGICAL EVENTS IN THE FORMATION OF THE CORPUS LUTEUM

In Vivo Luteinization

Mammalian evolution has provided variation on the theme of the luteinization process among orders of mammals. A common course of action involves the rupture and collapse of the follicle at ovulation and the invasion of extrafollicular elements, including the theca and blood vessels and reticuloendothelial components. In contrast, in the canid follicle, invasion is initiated days in advance of ovulation, with consequent differentiation of theca and granulosa components to secrete progesterone [3] (Figure 11.1). In the pig and other artiodactyloid species, the collapse of the follicle at ovulation results in rapid invasion by blood vessels originating in the theca layer of the follicle. This vascular invasion transports the theca cells toward the antrum of the collapsing follicle. They are then dispersed throughout the parenchyma of the CL [4] (see Figure 11.1). Similar dispersion of thecal cells throughout the granulosa compartment in the incipient CL characterizes rodent luteinization. In the human CL, the theca layer breaches the follicular basement membrane at ovulation, but the granulosa and theca compartments remain discrete throughout the luteal phase [5] (see Figure 11.1). The consequent theca-lutein cells represent a smaller proportion of the total population of luteal cells relative to their granulosa-derived counterparts. In at least two species, the marmoset and the horse, the theca does not persist as a functional element of the CL. In the mare, theca proliferation and hypertrophy precedes ovulation, followed by degeneration of these cells by 24 hours after ovulation [6] (see Figure 11.1). In the marmoset, the CL consists of steroidogenic cells of uniform size, suggesting similar persistence of granulosa-derived cells and loss of the thecal component [7].

Follicular cells undergo extensive modification accompanying the large-scale tissue remodeling that character-

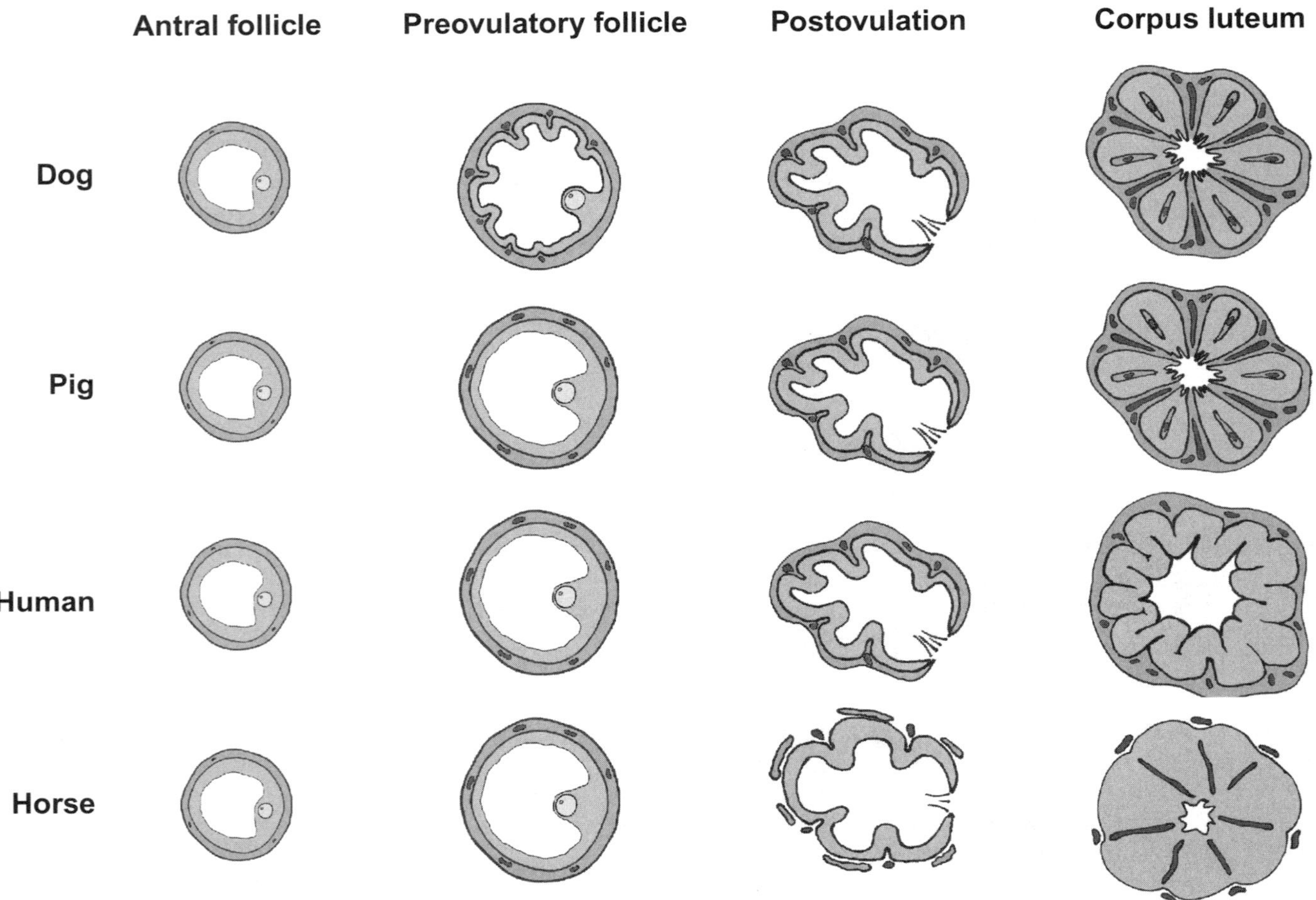

FIGURE 11.1 Variation in the process of luteinization among mammals. In the general model, represented by the pig, collapse of the follicle following ovulation allows the incursion of thecal blood vessels (*red*) and the theca layer (*blue*) to invade the granulosa (*yellow*) compartment of the follicle. The theca cells, borne by the invading vasculature, become dispersed throughout the luteal parenchyma. In the dog, the luteal invasion of the theca layer precedes ovulation, and there is substantial progesterone secretion by the follicle before ovulation. In the human, there is a similar neovascularization of the granulosa cell compartment, but the theca- and the granulosa-derived components of the CL remain discrete entities. In the horse, the theca cells degenerate during the periovulatory period and the consequent CL is derived from the granulosa cell component of the follicle. (See color plate.)

izes luteinization. Granulosa cells of the developing follicle function as a syncytium because of the presence of intracellular gap junctions [8]. Expression of connexin-43 in the theca cells of large rat follicles indicates similar interconnections [9]. The ovulatory process appears to completely disrupt intracellular bridges between the populations of granulosa [4, 10] and theca [11] cells. During luteinization, cellular connections are reestablished, as indicated by gap junction proteins localized to intracellular bridges [12], suggesting extensive intracellular communication in the luteal parenchyma.

There is a large increase in the volume of granulosa cells during luteinization, as much as 10-fold [13], and this major hypertrophy contributes to the growth of the CL. In most species, small luteal cells have been identified throughout the life span of CL. These are generally believed to be theca cells or theca cell descendents. It has been suggested that the small luteal cells of early luteinization differentiate into their larger counterpart in the mature CL, based on the numbers of large and small cells in the estrous cycle of sheep [14].

The cytoskeleton plays an important role in steroidogenesis [15], and there is some information to indicate that cytoskeleton is remodeled in theca and granulosa cells associated with formation of the CL. Immunohistochemical studies demonstrate that granulosa-derived luteal cells acquire the expression of smooth muscle actin, as well as cytokeratin, vimentin, and desmin, during the process of luteinization, whereas theca-lutein cells express only vimentin in quantity [16]. Ovine granulosa cells rapidly lose expression of tubulin after the ovulatory stimulus, tubulin synthesis is recovered during early luteinization, and tubulin is strongly expressed in large luteal cells [17]. Remodeling of extracellular surface glycoproteins, including the integrins, during luteinization has also been reported [18]. Integrin β3 messenger ribonucleic acid (mRNA) is expressed in theca cells and is upregulated in the mouse CL [19]. Of particular interest is the loss of integrin α6β1, which, in combination with its ligand, appears to suppress steroidogenesis in the follicle [18]. Removal of this integrin-mediated inhibition following ovulation may be an important element of functional luteinization. Thus, the extensive architectural remodeling of the follicular cells, particularly the granulosa cells, is an important element of the luteinization process.

In Vitro Luteinization

Granulosa and theca cells spontaneously luteinize in vitro, as demonstrated by the shift in the principal secretory product to progesterone from other steroids in culture [20]. Both cell types have altered morphology in their in vitro luteinized state, relative to their structure at isolation from the follicle. There is a two- to three-fold increase in cell volume associated with in vitro luteinization in theca and granulosa cells [20]. The overall form of the granulosa cell changes as it converts from a fibroblastic to epithelial phenotype. This engenders cytoskeletal modifications, particularly the enlargement of the actin network [21]. Luteinization in vitro is associated with intracellular accumulation of lipid droplets in granulosa [22] and theca [20] cells, indicating increased storage of cholesterol for steroidogenesis.

FUNCTIONAL CHANGES DURING LUTEINIZATION

The pattern of steroid synthesis and much of the information about its regulation in the developing follicle were determined some years ago. In most species studied, the two-cell hypothesis of Armstrong and Dorrington [23] has been confirmed. In this model, the early steps of steroidogenesis take place only in the theca, such that cholesterol is converted into progesterone and consequently to androgens, principally testosterone and androstenedione. These androgens pass by diffusion into the avascular granulosa cell compartment of the ovarian follicle, where, under the influence of follicle-stimulating hormone (FSH), they are converted into estrogens by the cytochrome p450 aromatase (CYP-19) enzyme of the granulosa cells [24]. Luteinization causes an important change in the principal product of the follicular structure, as estrogens synthesized by the follicle are replaced by progesterone produced by the incipient CL. This shift in steroid product takes place by differentiation-dependent modification of the steroidogenic pathway, part of the process of biochemical remodeling of the granulosa cells. The important changes include modification of the rate-limiting element of steroid synthesis, the steroidogenic acute regulatory protein (StAR). This protein transfers cholesterol from the cytoplasm to the inner mitochondrial membrane [25] where it is converted to pregnenolone by the cytochrome P450 side-chain cleavage enzyme (CYP-11A). StAR and CYP-11A are present in the theca before and after luteinization in all species in which they have been studied. In some species, including the pig [26] and the cow [27], StAR is not expressed in the granulosa cells of the follicle but is acquired during the first 48 hours following ovulation [27]. StAR appears to be present in low abundance in granulosa cells of large follicles in other species, particularly primates [28, 29]. The expression of StAR is strongly upregulated in theca and granulosa compartments during the process of luteinization. In rat granulosa cells, StAR mRNA becomes abundant in a biphasic manner, with an early peak and decline after the ovulatory stimulus, followed by gradual increase to an elevated steady state level a few days after ovulation [30]. Similar patterns have been observed in other species including the cow [27] and the macaque [28]. Development of CYP-11A expression likewise characterizes the differentiation of the follicular granulosa cell to its luteal counterpart, because the enzyme is not present or present only in low abundance in granulosa cells of the preovulatory follicle [28]. To convert pregnenolone to progesterone, the enzyme 3β-hydroxysteroid dehydrogenase (3β-HSD) is required, and its expression is upregulated in theca and granulosa cells during luteinization [31]. The enzymes associated with androgen synthesis, cytochrome P450 17-hydroxylase-lyase (CYP-17) [32], and estrogen synthesis, CYP-19 [21], in the follicle are greatly reduced or disappear as the CL develops. They appear to persist in the CL of primates [33] and in the mare [33]. It would appear that the theca-derived luteal cells of the human CL retain their capability to produce androgens, whereas the granulosa-derived component continues to produce estrogens [34]. These observations notwithstanding, the major steroid output of the two cellular subtypes during their life span as components of the CL is progesterone.

In addition to the shift in the principal steroidogenic product from estrogens in the follicle to progesterone in the CL during luteinization, there is a large-scale increase in total steroid synthesis. Among mammalian species, the CL displays steroid production that is two to three orders of magnitude or more greater than the steroid output of the follicle. It has been estimated that the human CL secretes as much as 40 mg of progesterone per day during the midluteal phase of the menstrual cycle [35]. To achieve this amplification in synthesis, a major increase in the amounts of the parent molecule, cholesterol, is required. The process of intracellular de novo synthesis of cholesterol from two carbon precursors has been extensively studied. It is well known that the enzyme 3-hydroxy-3-methylglutaryl coenzyme A reductase (HMG-CoA) limits an early step in the de novo synthesis of cholesterol. Expression of HMG-CoA [36] does not vary during the luteal phase, and pharmacological blockade of its activity does not alter progesterone secretion [37]. This indicates that cholesterol derived from de novo synthesis is not an important source of substrate for progesterone. It is, in fact, the extracellular sources, the high- and low-density lipoproteins (HDL and LDL) that deliver the cholesterol that provides the majority of the precursor for luteal progesterone synthesis [38]. Most species can use either HDL- or LDL-derived cholesterol for steroid synthesis, but there are clear species preferences. HDL cholesterol is the principal substrate in rodents, whereas LDL-derived cholesterol is more important in other species [38]. Predictably, there are major increases in the expression of proteins that make up the HDL and LDL cholesterol importation pathways in the CL during the luteinization process. These include the receptors for LDL [36] and HDL [39, 40], both of which display several-fold increases in abundance associated with formation of the CL. Other elements of the pathways are less well characterized. The NPC-1 protein, a bulk cholesterol transfer protein that regulates movement of LDL-derived cholesterol from the late endosome to the Golgi apparatus, is likewise upregulated several-fold during the luteinization process [41]. MLN-64, a StAR-like protein found in the endosomes, participates in steroidogenesis [42] and may play a role in delivery of cholesterol in the CL.

In addition to the enzymes that regulate steroidogenesis and elements of cholesterol importation pathways, there are numerous other genes displaying a pattern of variation associated with the biochemical remodeling during luteinization [30]. These include metallothionein-1 [30], metalloproteinases and their inhibitors [43], and the peptides relaxin [44] and relaxin-like factor [45]. Investigation of differential gene expression in the rat CL by microarray analysis revealed upregulation of β2-microglobulin, tissue inhibitors of metalloproteinase 2 (TIMP2), cytochrome C oxidase IV, cathepsin H and L, copper-zinc superoxide dismutase, elongation factor SIII, heat shock protein-60, and mitochondrial ATP synthase-D [46]. The role of the proteins coded by these genes in luteinization is not currently known, and unraveling of the complex pattern of biochemical evolution of the granulosa and theca cells and their luteal counterparts will require significant investigational effort.

LUTEINIZATION AS TERMINAL DIFFERENTIATION OF FOLLICULAR CELLS

The long developmental journey of theca and granulosa cells, from their initial differentiation in the embryo, terminates with their conversion into luteal cells. It has been hypothesized that luteinization ends follicular cell proliferation. The case for this tenet is stronger for the granulosa cell. In a model of rat luteinization in which granulosa cells were harvested at various times after the ovulatory stimulus, mitotic activity ceased within 7 hours after gonadotropin treatment [47]. In the macaque, there is reduction in the number of proliferating granulosa cells as early as 12 hours after the ovulatory stimulus, but attenuation of cell cycle activity was not complete at the last time examined in the study—36 hours after gonadotropin treatment [48]. Proliferation in pig granulosa cells persists through ovulation [4]. Generalized mitotic activity can be found throughout the life span of the CL in this species, although the frequency of dividing cells declines dramatically with the age of the CL [49]. Definitive evidence for luteal cell mitosis can be found in the colocalization of mitotic markers and steroidogenic enzymes, which occurs with varying frequency among species studied [49, 50]. Much is unknown about theca cell luteinization, largely because of the absence of reliable markers to identify theca cells after their dispersal in the luteal parenchyma. Estimates made in the human CL, where the two compartments remain separate, indicate that there is proliferation of theca cells well into the midluteal phase [51]. Proliferation of bovine theca and granulosa cells luteinized in vitro has been recorded over 14 days in culture [20], indicating that luteinization per se does not result in the loss of mitotic potential. A summary of available evidence suggests mitosis continues into the luteal phase in vivo in the theca and the granulosa components of the CL, with progressive restriction in proliferative capacity as the CL matures.

The decision to divide, differentiate, or terminally differentiate in cells is the result of an intricate balance among cell cycle proteins, oncogenes, and tumor suppressor genes. The mechanisms of luteal cell differentiation and mitotic arrest are far from understood, although considerable progress has been made in other cell models [52]. The mitotic decision in eukaryotic cells is made at the G1 phase of the cell cycle, when mitogens initiate the division process. This is accomplished by bringing about the association of cyclin D and the closely related cyclin dependent kinases (CDK) 4 and 6, thereby inducing kinase activity. CDK4 and 6 initiates hyperphosphorylation of the retinoblastoma tumor suppressor proteins, and the actions of cyclin E/CDK2 complete the hyperphosphorylation [52]. Hyperphosphorylation permits liberation of the transcription factors of the E2F family that upregulate expression of the cyclins, kinases, and other proteins necessary for continuation through the S and G2 phases of the cell cycle [53]. Proteins of the cell cycle are essential to luteal formation, as can be seen in the CDK4 knockout mouse, which displays normal follicular development but impaired luteinization [54].

Progress has also been made in understanding this process relative to cell cycle arrest in luteal cells [55, 56]. There is dephosphorylation of the mitotic initiators, the retinoblastoma proteins p107 and p130 during luteinization, which attenuates the activity of the cell cycle promoters (i.e., cyclins D1, D2, and E). A second level of cell cycle control is exerted by the CDK inhibitors that bind to these kinases and inhibit their activity [53]. The cell cycle inhibitors $p27^{Kip1}$ and $p21^{Cip1}$ appear to be the most important of these CDK inhibitors in granulosa cells, attenuating the actions of the cyclin E partner, CDK2 [57]. The expression of $p21^{Cip1}$ occurs as a transient event following the ovulatory stimulus in the primate ovary, whereas the second CDK inhibitor, $p27^{Kip1}$, appears later and endures in the CL [48]. Mice bearing a mutation inactivating the $p27^{Kip1}$ gene display granulosa cells that become luteinized but that have a persistent S phase [58]. The $p27^{Kip1}$ inhibitor has become a marker for exit from the cell cycle in ovarian cells, as it is strongly expressed in the primate [48] and mouse CL [54]. Figure 11.2 summarizes current views on the regulation of luteal cell cycle arrest following luteinization. It is important to note that differentiation and mitosis are not mutually exclusive in the early stages of CL formation, particularly in the theca cells. Further studies are essential if we are to understand the mechanisms by which luteal cells come to express their terminally differentiated phenotype.

ENDOCRINE, PARACRINE, AND AUTOCRINE REGULATION OF LUTEINIZATION

Early experimentation demonstrated that removal of the oocyte from the follicle resulted in in situ luteinization [59], suggesting an inhibitory influence from the oocyte that prevents the differentiation of the follicle to a CL before ovulation. More recent investigations have shown that the oocyte directs steroidogenesis and plays an important role in maintaining the follicular phenotype of granulosa cells [60, 61]. Two direct effects have been reported: (1) oocytes increase estrogen synthesis while suppressing the production of progesterone, thereby maintaining the follicular phenotype [62]; and (2) oocytes suppress LH receptor expression in granulosa cells [63, 64]. Indeed, there is further evidence for the autonomy of luteinization from endocrine control. It is clear that a process approximately recapitulating luteinization in vivo occurs in theca and granulosa cells in culture. Thus it would seem that luteinization is provoked by removal of the inhibitory influence of the oocytes. The nature of oocytic control and the factor(s) that prevent spontaneous luteinization remain unknown [65]. Candidate molecules include the bone morphogenetic proteins (BMPs) that inhibit gonadotropin and steroid stimulation of granulosa cell function [66]. Other potential factors include endothelin, which is present in follicular fluid and suppresses luteinization in vitro [67, 68].

This notwithstanding, it is known that luteinization can occur without ovulation, with the oocyte remaining trapped within the follicle. This occurs spontaneously in some species [69] and as a pathological condition in primates [70, 71]. In mice, the null mutation of either the progesterone receptor [72] or the nuclear corepressor RIP40 results in corpora lutea with entrapped oocytes [73]. Together these findings suggest that other stimuli, in addition to oocyte removal, can induce luteinization and that absence of the oocyte is not the prerequisite for luteinization. It is evident that the normal functional stimulus for luteinization is the LH surge that induces ovulation. This stimulus has multiple effects on the periovulatory follicle, including induction of prostanoid synthesis and consequent hyperemia of the follicle [10, 74]. Microarray analysis has revealed that a number of genes are expressed by granulosa cells in the rat following the LH surge that provokes ovulation. These include proteases, presumably necessary for breaching the follicular wall to allow the escape of the oocyte, and several others of unknown function in ovulation [30]. In most species studied, there is little doubt

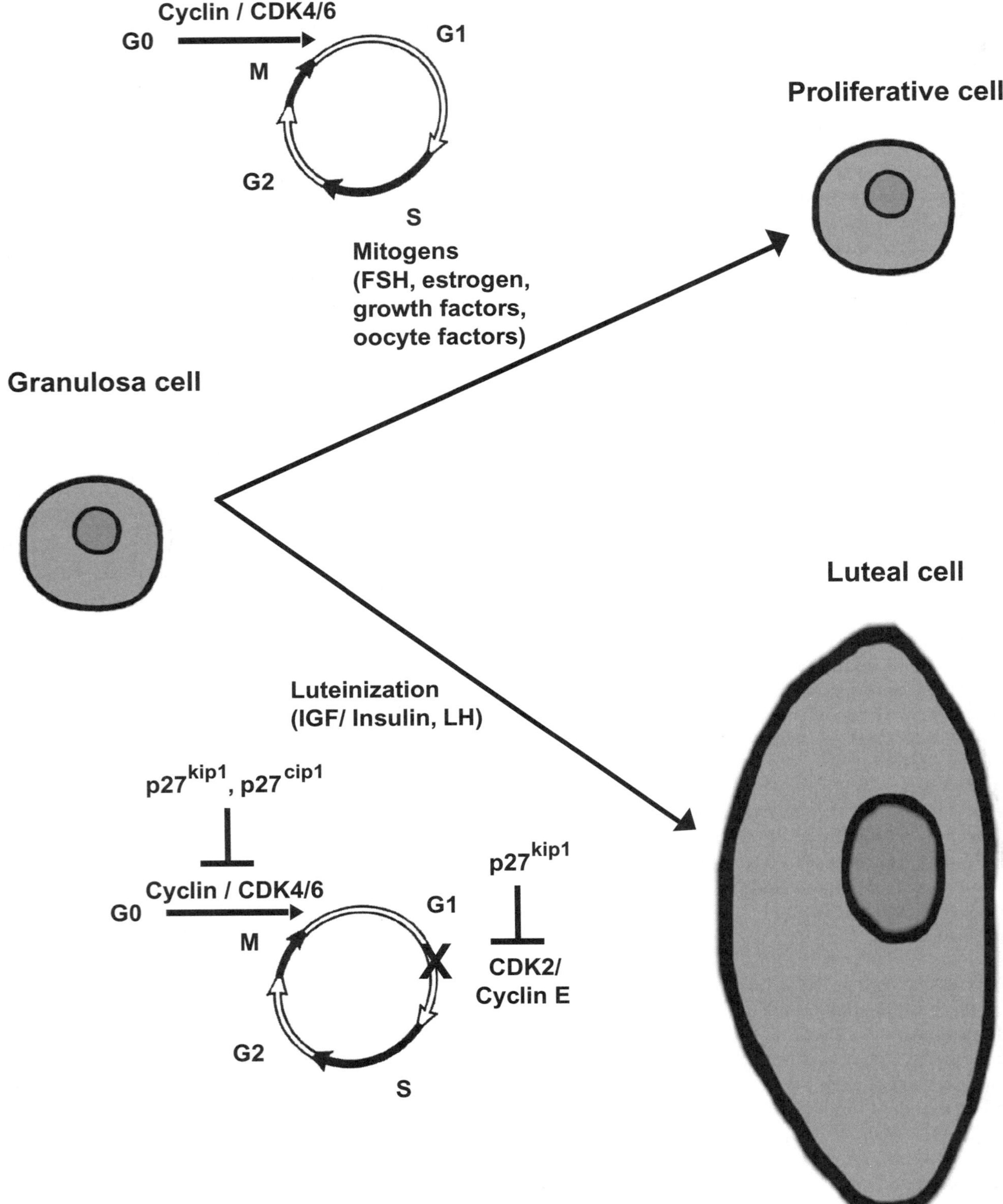

FIGURE 11.2 The proliferation/luteinization decision in granulosa cells. Proliferation is associated with continuation of the cell cycle as described in the text. Luteinization has been associated with the expression of the cell cycle inhibitors $P27^{Kip1}$ and $P21^{Cip1}$, which inhibit multiple CDKs during the G1 phase of the cycle and prevent the hyperphosphorylation of retinoblastoma proteins. This results in cell cycle arrest and consequent terminal differentiation of granulosa cells. (See color plate.)

that LH is necessary for maintenance of the CL [14]. Whether it is necessary for induction of luteinization is less clear. StAR mRNA abundance in the bovine [27] and human [34] CL during the early stages of formation is consistent with the view that LH induces this important change in steroidogenic protein expression. Intriguing evidence comes from a new study in which granulosa cell tumors in the ovaries of mice were converted to luteomas by the action of the LH-like hormone, human chorionic gonadotropin (hCG) [75]. These effects occurred in the absence of an ovulatory process and suggest that LH, in itself, plays a role in initiating or regulating the conversion of granulosa cells to luteal cells.

There is a view that progesterone, acting in a paracrine or intracrine mode, induces luteinization or maintains the CL, thereby providing positive feedback and constitutive steroidogenesis. Indeed, the null mutation of the progesterone receptor prevents ovulation [76]. Nonetheless, morphological and functional luteinization follows gonadotropin stimulation in progesterone receptor knockout mice [72]. Furthermore, there is recent evidence to indicate that the newly formed rat CL does not express the progesterone receptor. This notwithstanding, it would appear that progesterone provides luteal support even in the absence of the classic nuclear progesterone receptor [77]. This may indicate that the effects of progesterone on luteinization and luteal maintenance result from stimulation of an intermediate effector cell that then expresses a paracrine support factor.

Among the experimental approaches useful to understanding luteinization has been the development of cell culture methods that preserve the follicular phenotype. The absence of serum in the culture medium appears to be the most important factor in maintaining theca [78, 79] and granulosa [80, 81] cell cultures that do not luteinize in vitro. Follicular fluid is a serum filtrate, and in many ways contains the same factors including gonadotropins. It is reasonable to suggest that, following removal of the oocyte and its inhibitory influence, the granulosa cells undergo luteinization in response to components of the follicular fluid. The serum factors that induce luteinization have not been determined, and this may be a difficult task, because serum used to supplement culture media is undefined and variable. The growth factors that promote progesterone synthesis and luteinization are good candidates. Insulin-like growth factor-1 (IGF-1) functions as a gonadotropin in induction of progesterone synthesis by luteinized granulosa cells [82] and accelerates the sequence of expression of luteinization specific genes [21]. Adhesion proteins, including collagen, fibronectin, and laminin are present in serum, and these factors may influence cell-cell interactions and luteinization [83]. Indeed, bovine granulosa cells do not acquire luteal morphology when cultured in anchorage-independent conditions [84], which indicates that cellular attachment is important for luteinization.

Establishment of the CL is the first phase of the continuum of events in its evolution and eventual dissolution by the process known as *luteolysis*. Clues about luteal formation and early steps in CL regulation can be derived from studies of gene knockouts with a phenotype of luteal disruption. Generalization to species other than the mouse may be less appropriate, given the considerable variation in the endocrine maintenance of the early CL among mammals. In rodents, prolactin is an important luteotropin for rescue of the CL of the cycle and its transformation into the CL of pregnancy [85]. Mice bearing a null mutation in the prolactin receptor have insufficient luteal function, and their infertility can be reversed by progesterone treatment to induce embryo implantation [86]. In general, knockout of cytokine genes reduces the number of CL but appears not to interfere with luteinization (e.g., colony-stimulating factor-1 [87]). Spontaneous mutation in the leptin gene results in infertility, and this state can be corrected by leptin [88]. Leptin has direct effects on granulosa cells in vitro, compatible with the induction of luteinization, including inhibition of CYP-19 expression [89] and, in some studies, stimulation of progesterone synthesis [90].

CELLULAR AND MOLECULAR MECHANISMS OF LUTEINIZATION

Intracellular Signaling Pathways and Luteinization

As noted earlier, the widespread remodeling of the follicle to produce the CL involves important changes to the theca cells and the granulosa cells, along with extensive redeployment of blood supply to service the highly active luteal tissue. The changes in each of the cell types that contribute to the CL are subject to controls at several levels—endocrine, paracrine, and autocrine. Thus, a generalized view of cellular mechanisms of luteinization does not readily emerge from the ensemble of observations. Nonetheless, some generalizations can be made about intracellular pathways that bring about luteinization and maintain the young CL. Furthermore, genes that become upregulated during the luteinization are known, and the information available about the molecular regulation of their expression can provide some insight into the mechanisms that direct CL formation. The linear pathway of gonadotropin-cAMP-protein kinase A (PKA) phosphorylation has been implicated in the formation and early maintenance of the CL. One view of luteinization in vivo based on observations in the rat indicates that cAMP is the initial signal for luteinization of granulosa cells [91] followed by a period in which they become refractory to cAMP stimulation [92, 93]. In support of this view are the observations of the principal transcriptional effector of the cAMP pathway, cAMP response element binding protein

(CREB). This protein undergoes transient phosphorylation early during the luteinization of rat granulosa cells but then becomes refractory to further cAMP stimulation of the cells [94]. Expression of a CREB isoform disappears during luteinization in the primate CL [95]. In the longer term, there is sustained phosphorylation of CREB in the rat CL, perhaps via interactions between the cAMP and mitogen activated protein kinase pathways [96]. It is clear that granulosa cells of virtually every species studied respond to cAMP stimulation in vitro by progesterone synthesis. In addition, blockade of PKA action attenuates steroidogenesis in granulosa cells in vitro [97]. Theca-derived luteal cells remain responsive to cAMP throughout the luteal phase [14]. In overview, it would appear that in the model of gonadotropin stimulation of luteinization, the cAMP cascade is essential. Understanding its role in the model of oocyte-removed induction of luteinization requires further investigation.

Molecular Regulation of Luteinization

The cellular remodeling that characterizes luteinization is the result of differential expression of genes and the consequences of their expression. As noted earlier, several classes of gene products display differential expression during the formation of the CL, including the genes for steroidogenic proteins; those for the importation and processing of the steroid parent molecule, cholesterol; cytoskeletal and adhesion proteins; cell membrane receptors; and the intracellular signaling pathways. Regulation of expression of this multitude is the result of transcriptional and epigenetic mechanisms. Transcriptional regulation is a dynamic process that has for the most part been studied in a static context. The transcription factors that regulate a particular gene in isolation are known, although the sequence of events and the interactions of transcription factors in the expression or suppression of a particular gene remain unknown.

Among the transcriptional regulators of luteinization is the constitutively expressed transcription factor, CREB [98]. The genes known to be transcriptionally upregulated by CREB include StAR [99], the Niemann-Pick C-1 protein in the LDL pathway [100] and CYP-11A [101, 102]. Another transcriptional activator of the steroid-thyroid superfamily, steroidogenic factor-1 (SF-1), has proven to be an essential regulator of numerous genes associated with luteinization, including StAR, CYP-11A [103], and 3β-HSD [104]. Knockout of SF-1 confers gonadal agenesis [105], whereas CREB knockout results in perinatal lethality [106]. It has therefore not been possible to explore their roles in luteinization, beyond cataloging the genes that they regulate. One transcription factor that is clearly implicated in the luteinization process is the CCAAT/enhancer binding protein β (C/EBPβ). It is induced rapidly in rat granulosa cells in response to the ovulatory stimulus [107]. Mice bearing an inactivating mutation of the C/EBPβ gene do not develop CL, either spontaneously or in response to an ovulatory dose of LH [108]. Other potential molecular regulators of CL formation are the transcription factors bearing the T/AGATAG/A motif known as the GATA family. The most significant of these to luteinization is GATA-6, which is strongly expressed in developing mature mouse CL [109]. In addition to its role in regulating the expression of steroidogenic proteins [110, 111], GATA-6 has also been implicated in promoting the $P21^{cip1}$ induction of cell cycle arrest and cell differentiation [112]. The latter effect is reminiscent of the process of terminal differentiation of the granulosa cell component of the CL.

A transcriptional process regulates cholesterol transport genes, including the LDL receptor (NPC-1), savenger receptor B-1 (SRBI), and StAR proteins that provide the substrate for progesterone synthesis and deliver it to the mitochondria. This transcriptional regulation involves the sterol regulatory element binding proteins (SREBPs). They exist in three isoforms as integral proteins of the endoplasmic reticulum and nuclear membranes of cells [113]. Cholesterol depletion causes the cleavage of the transcriptionally active component of SREBP that then migrates to the nucleus where it interacts with cognate promoter sequences called sterol regulatory elements (SREs). The result is transactivation of genes that import and distribute cholesterol. It is of interest that StAR, the acknowledged trigger for steroidogenesis in the ovary, is also regulated in part by SREBP [114]. This suggests that steroid synthesis involves an intracellular negative feedback mechanism where depletion of cholesterol upregulates cholesterol supply and cholesterol metabolism to pregnenolone.

Epigenetic regulation refers to the regulatory mechanisms independent of the DNA code of a gene. It can include posttranscriptional mechanisms such as alteration of mRNA persistence (half-life) and differential glycosylation. The best known are effected by epigenetic mechanisms modification of histones, particularly histones H3 and H4. Transcriptional changes in cell cycle proteins resulting in cell proliferation have been associated with the covalent phosphorylation of histone H3. Acetylation, another covalent modification of histones, correlates with transcriptional activation and differentiation, whereas histone methylation has been related to the induction of transcription and to gene silencing. Studies have begun on epigenetic modification of luteinization by histones. It has recently been reported that histone H3 phosphorylation is induced by FSH [115] and LH [116] in rat granulosa cells. Immunoprecipitation studies have shown that acetylated histone H3 associates with the cAMP-sensitive promoter regions of the StAR [117] and NPC-1 [100] genes. Furthermore, global histone hyperacetylation, effected by inhibition of histone deacetylases, increases transcription of StAR [117] and NPC-1 [100]. The most compelling evidence for a role of histone acetylation in luteinization can be found in the acetylation patterns of the StAR promoter in human granulosa cells. There is a several-fold increase in the acetylated H3 associated with the promoter in luteinized cells relative to their nonluteinized counterparts [117], suggesting that this covalent modification of chromatin is an essential element of granulosa cell differentiation. A lesser-known level of epigenetic regulation involves chromatin modification complexes of the switch/sucrose nonfermenting (SWI/SNF) family, driven by adenosine triphosphate (ATP) breakdown. At least one of these, Snf2l, is preferentially expressed during early luteinization in rodent ovaries [118], but its role in CL formation is obscure at this time. There is much to learn about the epigenetic mechanisms that regulate the formation of the mammalian CL.

CONCLUSION

The mammalian CL forms from the elements of the ovarian follicle after ovulation. There appear to be two redundant stimuli for induction of luteinization. In the normal biological context, the LH surge that provokes ovulation has direct effects on the theca and granulosa components of the follicle to bring about their differentiation into luteal cells. Removal of the oocyte of large antral follicles likewise induces luteinization of the granulosa component of the follicle, independent of the preovulatory peak of LH. The latter induction of granulosa cell differentiation occurs in vitro but requires serum in the culture medium, suggesting an important role for growth factors in the process.

There are numerous similarities in the process of luteal formation among mammals, and a generalized portrait of the process can be drawn. The caveat is that, despite the similarities, there are important differences, particularly in the steroidogenic products and pathways among species. This notwithstanding, Figure 11.3 presents an overview of the process of luteinization in the theca and granulosa cells. Morphological changes in theca cells (see Figure 11.3, *A*) include their disaggregation and consequent rupture of intercellular bridges. They then migrate with the angiogenic incursion of the collapsing follicle following ovulation. In the mature CL, theca cells are often found in association with vascular elements. These cells continue to express the genes associated with differentiation of the CL, including the LH receptor, StAR, NPC-1, CYP-11A, and the lipoprotein receptors (LDLr and SRBI). In addition, there is a large increase in expression of the cytoskeletal protein, vimentin. The enzyme responsible for androgen synthesis, CYP-17, continues to be expressed, probably at a much lower level than the other steroidogenic elements. Little is known about the cell cycle during theca cell luteinization, but it is believed that much of the continued mitosis of steroidogenic cells in the CL represents theca cell mitosis. The molecular mechanisms that regulate luteinization in the theca cells are likewise not well known, but, based on the genes that are expressed, including the steroidogenic and cholesterol trafficking proteins, there is transcriptional regulation by C/EBPβ, SF-1, and SREBP. The elevated expression of GATA-6 indicates it likewise plays a role in theca luteinization and acquisition of the capacity for progesterone synthesis on a luteal scale.

More information is available on luteinization in granulosa cells, perhaps because they are a more tractable model for in vitro study. An important change occurs in their morphology, which includes cellular hypertrophy and attendant expression of the cytoskeletal proteins, cytokeratin and vimentin. It has been shown that granulosa cells lose expression of the FSH receptor associated with luteinization, whereas the LH receptor appears to persist well into the luteal phase. Its expression is eventually lost by the large luteal cell, best studied in ruminant species. The qualitative shift from estrogen production in the follicle to progesterone synthesis by the luteal cell of granulosa descent is accompanied by a large increase in total steroid output. There is corresponding downregulation of CYP-19 and upregulation of StAR, CYP-11A, and the cholesterol supply proteins, LDLr and SRBI. The definitive formation of the CL probably marks the end of granulosa cell division, with associated loss in the phosphorylation of the retinoblastoma proteins, reduction in cyclin and CDK expression, and upregulation of the cell cycle inhibitors of the P21 and P27 families. There is good evidence that transactivation of the genes for cholesterol import and trafficking by SREBP plays an important role in the differentiation from the granulosa cell of the follicle to its luteal counterpart. Furthermore, CREB, C/EBPβ, GATA-6, and SF-1 regulate important luteal genes, including StAR and CYP-11A. Epigenetic inputs associated with differentiation include a shift from mitotic and mitogenic covalent modification of histones by phosphorylation to their pattern of acetylation. Current evidence indicates that this may be an important component in the cascade of events that regulate StAR expression in the CL.

ACKNOWLEDGMENTS

Thanks are owed to Joëlle Desmarais for the artwork in Figures 11.1 and 11.2. Studies of luteinization in the author's laboratory have been supported by grants from the Canadian Institutes of Health Research and the Natural Sciences and Engineering Research Council of Canada.

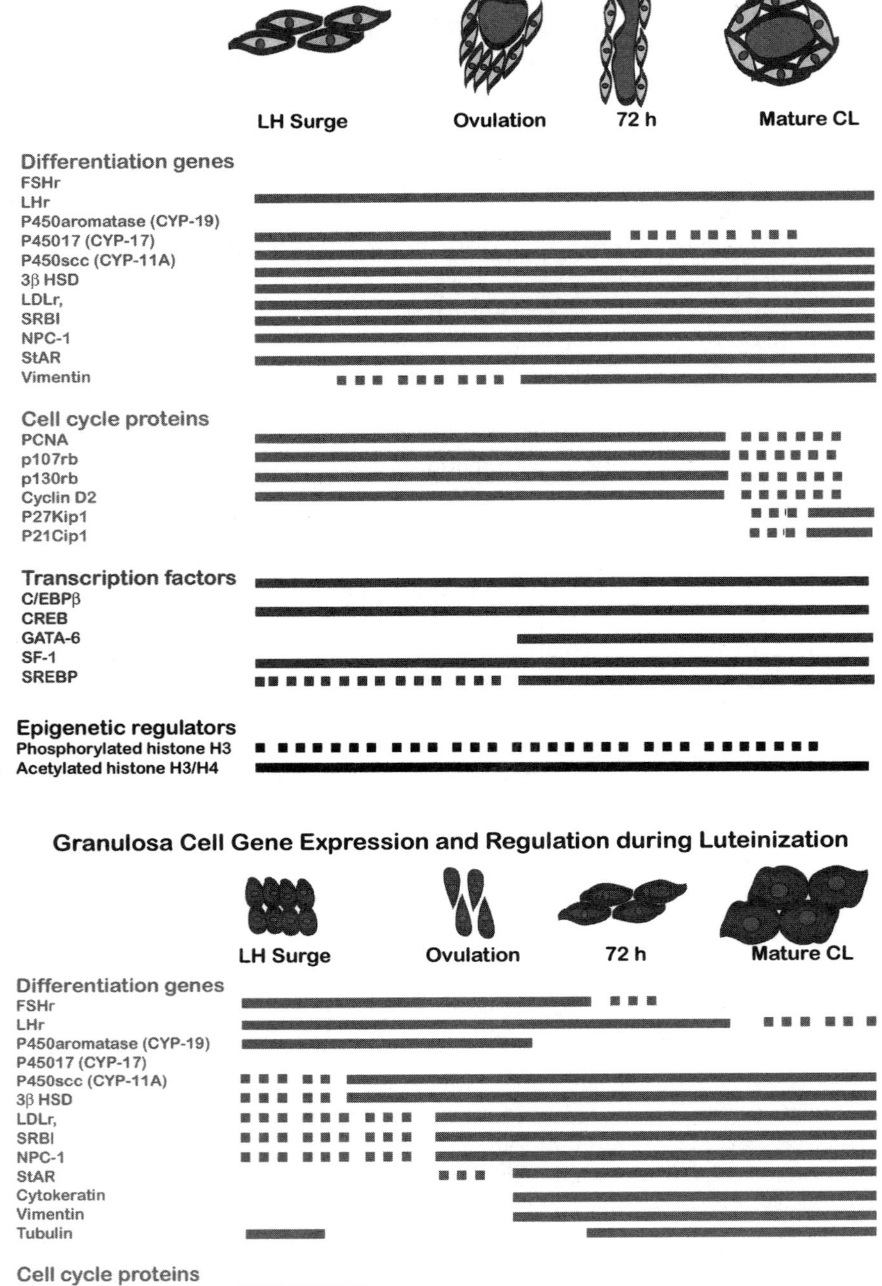

FIGURE 11.3 Generalized view of the gene expression and its regulation in the ovarian cells during the formation of the CL, based on observations in rodents, primates, and artiodactyls. The evolution of morphological changes for the theca **(A)** and granulosa **(B)** cells is depicted in the diagram at the top of the figure. Solid lines = strong and uninterrupted expression of the factor in question; dotted lines = low-level or intermittent expression. (See color plate.)

References

1. Gemmell, R. T. (1995). A comparative study of the corpus luteum. *Reprod. Fert. Dev.* 7, 303–312.
2. Fraser, H. M., and Lunn, S. F. (2001). Regulation and manipulation of angiogenesis in the primate corpus luteum. *Reproduction* 121, 355–362.
3. Concannon, P., Hansel, W., and McEntee, K. (1977). Changes in LH, progesterone and sexual behavior associated with preovulatory luteinization in the bitch. *Biol. Reprod.* 17, 604–613.
4. Murphy, B. D., Gevry, N., Ruiz-Cortes, T., Cote, F., Downey, B. R., and Sirois, J. (2001). Formation and early development of the corpus luteum in pigs. *Reproduction* 58 (Suppl), 47–63.
5. Corner, Jr., G. (1956). The histological dating of the human corpus luteum of menstruation. *Am. J. Anat.* 98, 377–392.
6. Van Niekerk, C. H., Morgenthal, J. C., and Gerneke, W. H. (1975). Relationship between morphology of and progesterone production by the corpus luteum of the mare. *J. Reprod. Fertil.* 23 (Suppl), 171–175.
7. Webley, G. E., Richardson, M. C., Smith, C. A., Masson, G. M., and Hearn, J. P. (1990). Size distribution of luteal cells from pregnant and non-pregnant marmoset monkeys and a comparison of the morphology of marmoset luteal cells with those from the human corpus luteum. *J. Reprod. Fertil.* 90, 427–437.
8. Kidder, G. M., and Mhawi, A. A. (2002). Gap junctions and ovarian folliculogenesis. *Reproduction* 123, 613–620.
9. Mayerhofer, A., and Garfield, R. E. (1995). Immunocytochemical analysis of the expression of gap junction protein connexin 43 in the rat ovary. *Mol. Reprod. Dev.* 41, 331–338.
10. Kerban, A., Dore, M., and Sirois, J. (1999). Characterization of cellular and vascular changes in equine follicles during hCG-induced ovulation. *J. Reprod. Fertil.* 117, 115–123.
11. Mayerhofer, A., Dissen, G. A., Parrott, J. A., Hill, D. F., Mayerhofer, D., Garfield, R. E., Costa, M. E., Skinner, M. K., and Ojeda, S. R. (1996). Involvement of nerve growth factor in the ovulatory cascade: trkA receptor activation inhibits gap junctional communication between thecal cells. *Endocrinology* 137, 5662–5670.
12. Reynolds, L. P., and Redmer, D. A. (1999). Growth and development of the corpus luteum. *J. Reprod. Fertil.* 54 (Suppl), 181–191.
13. Smith, M. F., McIntush, E. W., and Smith, G. W. (1994). Mechanisms associated with corpus luteum development. *J. Animal Sci.* 72, 1857–1872.
14. Niswender, G. D. (2002). Molecular control of luteal secretion of progesterone. *Reproduction* 123, 333–339.
15. Hall, P. F., and Almahbobi, G. (1997). Roles of microfilaments and intermediate filaments in adrenal steroidogenesis. *Microsc. Res. Tech.* 36, 463–479.
16. Khan-Dawood, F. S., Yusoff Dawood, M., and Tabibzadeh, S. (1996). Immunohistochemical analysis of the microanatomy of primate ovary. *Biol. Reprod.* 54, 734–742.
17. Murdoch, W. J. (1996). Microtubular dynamics in granulosa cells of periovulatory follicles and granulosa-derived (large) lutein cells of sheep: Relationships to the steroidogenic folliculo-luteal shift and functional luteolysis. *Biol. Reprod.* 54, 1135–1140.
18. Fujiwara, H., Kataoka, N., Honda, T., Ueda, M., Yamada, S., Nakamura, K., Suginami, H., Mori, T., and Maeda, M. (1998). Physiological roles of integrin alpha 6 beta 1 in ovarian functions. *Horm. Res.* 50 (Suppl 2), 25–29.
19. Burns, K. H., Owens, G. E., Fernandez, J. M., Nilson, J. H., and Matzuk, M. M. (2002). Characterization of integrin expression in the mouse ovary. *Biol. Reprod.* 67, 743–751.
20. Meidan, R., Girsh, E., Blum, O., and Aberdam, E. (1990). In vitro differentiation of bovine theca and granulosa cells into small and large luteal-like cells: Morphological and functional characteristics. *Biol. Reprod.* 43, 913–921.
21. Pescador, N., Stocco, D. M., and Murphy, B. D. (1999). Growth factor modulation of steroidogenic acute regulatory protein and luteinization in the pig ovary. *Biol. Reprod.* 60, 1453–1461.
22. Richards, J. S., Hedin, L., and Caston, L. (1986). Differentiation of rat ovarian thecal cells: Evidence for functional luteinization. *Endocrinology* 118, 1660–1668.
23. Armstrong, D. T., and Dorrington, J. H. (1977). Estrogen biosynthesis in the ovaries and testes. *Adv. Sex Horm. Res.* 3, 217–258.
24. Richards, J. S. (1980). Maturation of ovarian follicles: Actions and interactions of pituitary and ovarian hormones on follicular cell differentiation. *Physiol. Rev.* 60, 51–89.
25. Stocco, D. M. (2001). StAR protein and the regulation of steroid hormone biosynthesis. *Ann. Rev. Physiol.* 63, 193–213.
26. Pescador, N., Houde, A., Stocco, D. M., and Murphy, B. D. (1997). Follicle-stimulating hormone and intracellular second messengers regulate steroidogenic acute regulatory protein (StAR) mRNA in luteinized granulosa cells. *Biol. Reprod.* 57, 660–668.
27. Pescador, N., Soumano, K., Stocco, D. M, Price, C. A., and Murphy, B. D. (1996). Steroidogenic acute regulatory protein in bovine corpora lutea. *Biol. Reprod.* 55, 485–491.
28. Chaffin, C. L., Dissen, G. A., and Stouffer, R. L. (2000). Hormonal regulation of steroidogenic enzyme expression in granulosa cells during the periovulatory interval in monkeys. *Mol. Hum. Reprod.* 6, 11–18.
29. Jakimiuk, A. J., Weitsman, S. R., Navab, A., and Magoffin, D. A. (2001). Luteinizing hormone receptor, steroidogenesis acute regulatory protein, and steroidogenic enzyme messenger ribonucleic acids are overexpressed in thecal and granulosa cells from polycystic ovaries. *J. Clin. Endocrinol. Metab.* 86, 1318–1323.
30. Espey, L. L., and Richards, J. S. (2002). Temporal and spatial patterns of ovarian gene transcription following an ovulatory dose of gonadotropin in the rat. *Biol. Reprod.* 67, 1662–1670.
31. Chedrese, P. J., Zhang, D., Luu The V, Labrie, F., Juorio, A. V., and Murphy, B. D. (1990). Regulation of mRNA expression of 3 beta-hydroxy-5-ene steroid dehydrogenase in porcine granulosa cells in culture: A role for the protein kinase-C pathway. *Mol. Endocrinol.* 4, 1532–1538.
32. Conley, A. J., Kaminski, M. A., Dubowsky, S. A., Jablonka-Shariff, A., Redmer, D. A., and Reynolds, L. P. (1995). Immunohistochemical localization of 3 beta-hydroxysteroid dehydrogenase and P450 17 alpha-hydroxylase during follicular and luteal development in pigs, sheep, and cows. *Biol. Reprod.* 52, 1081–1094.

33. Albrecht, B. A., MacLeod, J. N., and Daels, P. F. (2001). Expression of 3 beta-hydroxysteroid dehydrogenase, cytochrome p450 17 alpha-hydroxylase/17,20-lyase, and cytochrome p450 aromatase enzymes in corpora lutea of diestrous and early pregnant mares. *Theriogenology* 55, 551–561.
34. Devoto, L., Kohen, P., Vega, M., Castro, O., Gonzalez, R. R., Retamales, I., Carvallo, P., Christenson, L. K., and Strauss, J. F. (2002). Control of human luteal steroidogenesis. *Mol. Cell. Endocrinol.* 186, 137–141.
35. Lipsett, M. B. Steroid hormones. (1978). In *Reproductive Endocrinology*, ed., Yen, S. C., and Jaffe, R. B. Philadelphia: W.B. Saunders.
36. LaVoie, H. A., Benoit, A. M., Garmey, J. C., Dailey, R. A., Wright, D. J., and Veldhuis, J. D. (1997). Coordinate developmental expression of genes regulating sterol economy and cholesterol side-chain cleavage in the porcine ovary. *Biol. Reprod.* 57, 402–407.
37. Plotkin, D., Miller, S., Nakajima, S., Peskin, E., Burkman, R., Richardson, D., Mitchel, Y., Waldstreicher, J., Liu, M., Shapiro, D., and Santoro, N. (2002). Lowering low-density lipoprotein cholesterol with simvastatin, a hydroxy-3-methylglutaryl-coenzyme α reductase inhibitor, does not affect luteal function in premenopausal women. *J. Clin. Endocrinol. Metab.* 87, 3155–3161.
38. Murphy, B. D., and Silavin, S. L. (1989). Luteotropic agents and steroid substrate utilization. *Oxford Rev. Reprod. Biol.* 11, 180–223.
39. Li, X., Peegel, H., and Menon, K. M. (1998). In situ hybridization of high-density lipoprotein (scavenger, type 1) receptor messenger ribonucleic acid (mRNA) during folliculogenesis and luteinization: Evidence for mRNA expression and induction by human chorionic gonadotropin specifically in cell types that use cholesterol for steroidogenesis. *Endocrinology* 139, 3043–3049.
40. Rajapaksha, W. R., McBride, M., Robertson, L., and O'Shaughnessy, P. J. (1997). Sequence of the bovine HDL-receptor (SR-BI) cDNA and changes in receptor mRNA expression during granulosa cell luteinization in vivo and in vitro. *Mol. Cell. Endocrinol.* 134, 59–67.
41. Gevry, N., Lacroix, D., Song, J. H., Pescador, N., Dobias, M., and Murphy, B. D. (2002). Porcine Niemann Pick-C1 protein is expressed in steroidogenic tissues and modulated by cAMP. *Endocrinology* 143, 708–716.
42. Zhang, M., Liu, P., Dwyer, N. K., Christenson, L. K., Fujimoto, T., Martinez, F., Comly, M., Hanover, J. A., Blanchette-Mackie, E. J., and Strauss, III, J. F. (2002). MLN64 mediates mobilization of lysosomal cholesterol to steroidogenic mitochondria. *J. Biol. Chem.* 277, 33300–33310.
43. Curry, Jr., T. E., Song, L., and Wheeler, S. E. (2001). Cellular localization of gelatinases and tissue inhibitors of metalloproteinases during follicular growth, ovulation, and early luteal formation in the rat. *Biol. Reprod.* 65, 855–865.
44. Bagnell, C. A., Zhang, Q., Ohleth, K., Connor, M. L., Downey, B. R., Tsang, B. K., and Ainsworth, L. (1993). Developmental expression of the relaxin gene in the porcine corpus luteum. *J. Mol. Endocrinol.* 10, 87–97.
45. Ivell, R., and Bathgate, R. A. (2002). Reproductive biology of the relaxin-like factor (RLF/INSL3). *Biol. Reprod.* 67, 699–705.
46. Stocco, C., Callegari, E., and Gibori, G. (2001). Opposite effect of prolactin and prostaglandin F(2 alpha) on the expression of luteal genes as revealed by rat cDNA expression array. *Endocrinology* 142, 4158–4161.
47. Richards, J. S., Russell, D. L., Robker, R. L., Dajee, M., and Alliston, T. N. (1998). Molecular mechanisms of ovulation and luteinization. *Mol. Cell. Endocrinol.* 145, 47–54.
48. Chaffin, C. L., Schwinof, K. M., and Stouffer, R. L. (2001). Gonadotropin and steroid control of granulosa cell proliferation during the periovulatory interval in rhesus monkeys. *Biol. Reprod.* 65, 755–762.
49. Ricke, W. A., Redmer, D. A., and Reynolds, L. P. (1999). Growth and cellular proliferation of pig corpora lutea throughout the estrous cycle. *J. Reprod. Fertil.* 117, 369–377.
50. Christenson, L. K., and Stouffer, R. L. (1996). Proliferation of microvascular endothelial cells in the primate corpus luteum during the menstrual cycle and simulated early pregnancy. *Endocrinology* 137, 367–374.
51. Gaytan, F., Morales, C., Garcia-Pardo, L., Reymundo, C., Bellido, C., and Sanchez-Criado, J. E. (1998). Macrophages, cell proliferation, and cell death in the human menstrual corpus luteum. *Biol. Reprod.* 59, 417–425.
52. Lundberg, A. S., and Weinberg, R. A. (1999). Control of the cell cycle and apoptosis. *Eur. J. Cancer* 35, 531–539.
53. Zhu, L., and Skoultchi, A. I. (2001). Coordinating cell proliferation and differentiation. *Curr. Opin. Genetics Dev.* 10, 91–97.
54. Moons, D. S., Jirawatnotai, S., Tsutsui, T., Franks, R., Parlow, A. F., Hales, D. B., Gibori, G., Fazleabas, A. T., and Kiyokawa, H. (2002). Intact follicular maturation and defective luteal function in mice deficient for cyclin-dependent kinase-4. *Endocrinology* 143, 647–654.
55. Hampl, A. O., Pachernik, J., and Dvorak, P. (2000). Levels and interactions of p27, cyclin D3 and CDK4 during the formation and maintenance of the corpus luteum in mice. *Biol. Reprod.* 62, 1393–1401.
56. Green, C., Chatterjee, R., McGarrigle, H. H. G., Ahmed, F., and Thomas, N. S. B. (2000). p107 is active in the nucleolus of nondividing human granulosa lutein cells. *J. Mol. Endocrinol.* 25, 275–286.
57. Robker, R. L., and Richards, J. S. (1998). Hormone-induced proliferation and differentiation of granulosa cells: A coordinated balance between cell cycle regulators D2 and $p27^{Kip1}$. *Mol. Endocrinol.* 12, 924–940.
58. Tong, W., Kiyokawa, H., Soos, T. J., Park, M. S., Soares, V. C., Manova, K., Pollard, J. W., and Koff, A. (1998). The absence of $P27^{Kip1}$, an inhibitor of G1 cyclin-dependent kinases, uncouples differentiation and growth arrest during the granulosa-luteal transition. *Cell Growth Differ.* 9, 787–794.
59. el-Fouly, M. A., Cook, B., Nekola, M., and Nalbandov, A. V. (1970). Role of the ovum in follicular luteinization. *Endocrinology* 87, 286–293.
60. Coskun, S., Uzumcu, M., Lin, Y. C., Friedman, C. I., and Alak, B. M. (1995). Regulation of cumulus cell steroidogenesis by the porcine oocyte and preliminary characterization of oocyte-produced factor(s). *Biol. Reprod.* 53, 670–675.
61. Vanderhyden. B. C., and Macdonald, E. A. (1998). Mouse oocytes regulate granulosa cell steroidogenesis throughout follicular development. *Biol. Reprod.* 59, 1296–1301.

62. Vanderhyden, B. C., and Tonary, A. M. (1995). Differential regulation of progesterone and estradiol production by mouse cumulus and mural granulosa cells by A factor(s) secreted by the oocyte. *Biol. Reprod.* 53, 1243–1250.
63. Eppig, J. J., Chesnel, F., Hirao, Y., O'Brien, M. J., Pendola, F. L., Watanabe, S., and Wigglesworth, K. (1997). Oocyte control of granulosa cell development: How and why. *Hum. Reprod.* 12, 127–132.
64. Eppig, J. J., Wigglesworth, K., Pendola, F., and Hirao, Y. (1997). Murine oocytes suppress expression of luteinizing hormone receptor messenger ribonucleic acid by granulosa cells. *Biol. Reprod.* 56, 976–984.
65. Vanderhyden, B. (2002). Molecular basis of ovarian development and function. *Front. Biosci.* 7, d2006–2022.
66. Monget, P., Fabre, S., Mulsant, P., Lecerf, F., Elsen, J. M., Mazerbourg, S., Pisselet, C, and Monniaux, D. (2002). Regulation of ovarian folliculogenesis by IGF and BMP system in domestic animals. *Domest. Anim. Endocrinol.* 23, 139–154.
67. Tedeschi, C., Hazum, E., Kokia, E., Ricciarelli, E., Adashi, E. Y., and Payne, D. W. (1992). Endothelin-1 as a luteinization inhibitor: Inhibition of rat granulosa cell progesterone accumulation via selective modulation of key steroidogenic steps affecting both progesterone formation and degradation. *Endocrinology* 131, 2476–2478.
68. Iwai, M., Hasegawa, M., Taii, S., Sagawa, N., Nakao, K., Imura, H., Nakanishi, S., and Mori, T. (1991). Endothelins inhibit luteinization of cultured porcine granulosa cells. *Endocrinology* 129, 1909–1914.
69. Douglas, D. A., Pierson, R. A., and Murphy, B. D. (1994). Ovarian follicular development in mink (Mustela vison). *J. Reprod. Fertil.* 100, 583–590.
70. Zaidi, J., Jurkovic, D., Campbell, S., Collins, W., McGregor, A., and Tan, S. L. (1995). Luteinized unruptured follicle: Morphology, endocrine function and blood flow changes during the menstrual cycle. *Hum. Reprod.* 10, 44–49.
71. D'Hooghe, T. M., Bambra, C. S., Raeymaekers, B. M., and Koninckx, P. R. (1996). Increased incidence and recurrence of recent corpus luteum without ovulation stigma (luteinized unruptured follicle syndrome?) in baboons with endometriosis. *J. Soc. Gynecol. Investig.* 3, 140–144.
72. Robker, R. L., Russell, D. L., Espey, L. L., Lydon, J. P., O'Malley, B. W., and Richards, J. S. (2000). Progesterone-regulated genes in the ovulation process: ADAMTS-1 and cathepsin L proteases. *Proc. Natl. Acad. Sci. USA* 97, 4689–4694.
73. White, R., Leonardsson, G., Rosewell, I., Jacobs, M. A., Milligan, S., and Parker, M. (2000). The nuclear receptor co-repressor nrip1 (RIP140) is essential for female fertility. *Nat. Med.* 6, 1368–1374.
74. Coté, F., Sirois, J., Doré, M., and Downey, B. R. (2001). Induction of prostaglandin G/H synthase-2 in preovulatory follicles of equine chorionic gonadotropin/human chorionic gonadotropin treated prepubertal gilts. *Biol. Reprod.* 63 (Suppl 1), 161.
75. Owens, G. E., Keri, R. A., and Nilson, J. H. (2002). Ovulatory surges of human CG prevent hormone-induced granulosa cell tumor formation leading to the identification of tumor-associated changes in the transcriptome. *Mol. Endocrinol.* 16, 1230–1242.
76. Conneely, O. M., Mulac-Jericevic, B., DeMayo, F., Lydon, J. P., and O'Malley, B. W. (2002). Reproductive functions of progesterone receptors. *Rec. Prog. Hormone Res.* 57, 339–355.
77. Goyeneche, A. A., Deis, R. P., Gibori, G., and Telleria, C. M. (2003). Progesterone promotes survival of the rat corpus luteum in the absence of cognate receptors. *Biol. Reprod.* 68, 151–158.
78. Demeter-Arlotto, M., Rainey, W. E., and Simpson, E. R. (1993). Maintenance and regulation of 17 alpha-hydroxylase expression by bovine thecal cells in primary culture. *Endocrinology* 132, 1353–1358.
79. Campbell, B. K., Baird, D. T., and Webb, R. (1998). Effects of dose of LH on androgen production and luteinization of ovine theca cells cultured in a serum-free system. *J. Reprod. Fertil.* 112, 69–77.
80. Gutierrez, C. G., Campbell, B. K., and Webb, R. (1997). Development of a long-term bovine granulosa cell culture system: Induction and maintenance of estradiol production, response to follicle-stimulating hormone, and morphological characteristics. *Biol. Reprod.* 56, 608–616.
81. Picton, H. M., Campbell, B. K., and Hunter, M. G. (1999). Maintenance of oestradiol production and expression of cytochrome P450 aromatase enzyme mRNA in long-term serum-free cultures of pig granulosa cells. *J. Reprod. Fertil.* 115, 67–77.
82. Sekar, N., Lavoie, H. A., and Veldhuis, J. D. (2000). Concerted regulation of steroidogenic acute regulatory gene expression by luteinizing hormone and insulin (or insulin-like growth factor I) in primary cultures of porcine granulosa-luteal cells. *Endocrinology* 141, 3983–3992.
83. Sites, C. K., Kessel, B., and LaBarbera, A. R. (1996). Adhesion proteins increase cellular attachment, follicle-stimulating hormone receptors, and progesterone production in cultured porcine granulosa cells. *Proc. Soc. Exp. Biol. Med.* 212, 78–83.
84. Lavranos, T. C., Rodgers, H. F., Bertoncello, I., and Rodgers, R. J. (1994). Anchorage-independent culture of bovine granulosa cells: The effects of basic fibroblast growth factor and dibutyryl cAMP on cell division and differentiation. *Exp. Cell. Res.* 211, 245–251.
85. Harris, K. H., and Murphy, B. D. (1981). Prolactin in maintenance of the corpus luteum of early pseudopregnancy in the golden hamster. *J. Endocrinol.* 90, 145–150.
86. Reese, J., Binart, N., Brown, N., Ma, W. G., Paria, B. C., Das, S. K., Kelly, P. A., and Dey, S. K. (2000). Implantation and decidualization defects in prolactin receptor (PRLR)-deficient mice are mediated by ovarian but not uterine PRLR. *Endocrinology* 141, 1872–1881.
87. Cohen, P. E., Zhu, L., and Pollard, J. W. (1997). Absence of colony stimulating factor-1 in osteopetrotic (csfmop/csfmop) mice disrupts estrous cycles and ovulation. *Biol. Reprod.* 56, 110–118.
88. Ruiz-Cortes, T., Ledoux, S., and Murphy, B. D. (2003). The adipose-reproduction axis. *Reproduction* (in press).
89. Zachow, R. J., and Magoffin, D. A. (1997). Direct intraovarian effects of leptin: Impairment of the synergistic action of insulin-like growth factor-I on follicle-stimulating hormone-dependent estradiol-17 beta production by rat ovarian granulosa cells. *Endocrinology* 138, 847–850.
90. Ruiz-Cortes, Z. T., Kennes, Y. M., Gévry, N. Y., Palin, M. F., Downey, B. R., Lacroix, D. A., and Murphy, B. D. (2003).

Biphasic effects of leptin in porcine granulosa cells. *Biol. Reprod.* 68: 789–796.

91. Richards, J. S., Fitzpatrick, S. L., Clemens, J. W., Morris, J. K., Alliston, T., and Sirois, J. (1995). Ovarian cell differentiation: A cascade of multiple hormones, cellular signals, and regulated genes. *Rec. Prog. Hormone Res.* 50, 223–254.
92. Oonk, R. B., Parker, K. L., Gibson, J. L., and Richards, J. S. (1990). Rat cholesterol side-chain cleavage cytochrome P-450 (P450scc) gene. Structure and regulation by cAMP in vitro. *J. Biol. Chem.* 265, 22392–22401.
93. Oonk, R. B., Krasnow, J. S., Beattie, W. G., and Richards, J. S. (1989). CAMP-dependent and -independent regulation of cholesterol side chain cleavage cytochrome P450 (P450scc) in rat ovarian granulosa cells and corpora lutea. cDNA and deduced amino acid sequence of rat P450scc. *J. Biol. Chem.* 264, 21934–21942.
94. Gonzalez-Robayna, I. J., Alliston, T. N., Buse, P., Firestone, G. L., and Richards, J. S. (1999). Functional and subcellular changes in the A-kinase-signaling pathway: Relation to aromatase and Sgk expression during the transition of granulosa cells to luteal cells. *Mol. Endocrinol.* 13, 1318–1337.
95. Somers, J. P., Benyo, D. F., Little-Ihrig, L. L., and Zeleznik, A. J. (1995). Luteinization in primates is accompanied by a loss of a 43-kilodalton adenosine 3′5′-monophosphate response element binding protein isoform. *Endocrinology* 136, 4262–4268.
96. Maizels, E. T., Mukherjee, A., Sithanandam, G., Peters, C. A., Cottom, J., Mayo, K. E., and Hunzicker-Dunn, M. (2001). Developmental regulation of mitogen-activated protein kinase-activated kinases-2 and -3 (MAPKAPK-2/-3) in vivo during corpus luteum formation in the rat. *Mol. Endocrinol.* 15, 716–733.
97. Haynes-Johnson, D., Lai, M. T., Campen, C., and Palmer, S. (1999). Diverse effects of tyrosine kinase inhibitors on follicle-stimulating hormone-stimulated estradiol and progesterone production from rat granulosa cells in serum-containing medium and serum-free medium containing epidermal growth factor. *Biol. Reprod.* 61, 147–153.
98. Richards, J. S. (2001). New signaling pathways for hormones and cyclic adenosin 3′5′-monophosphate action in endocrine cells. *J. Mol. Endocrinol.* 15, 209–218.
99. Manna, P. R., Dyson, M. T., Eubank, D. W., Clark, B. J., Lalli, E., Sassone-Corsi, P., Zeleznik, A. J., and Stocco, D. M. (2002). Regulation of steroidogenesis and the steroidogenic acute regulatory protein by a member of the cAMP response-element binding protein family. *Mol. Endocrinol.* 16, 184–199.
100. Gevry, N., Lalli, E., Sassone-Corsi, P., and Murphy, B. D. (2003). Regulation of Niemann-Pick C1 gene expression by the 3′5′ cyclic adenosine monophosphate pathway in steroidogenic cells. *Mol. Endocrinol.* 17, 704–715.
101. Liu, Z, and Simpson, E. R. (1999). Molecular mechanism for cooperation between Sp1 and steroidogenic factor-1 (SF-1) to regulate bovine CYP11A gene expression. *Mol. Cell. Endocrinol.* 153, 183–196.
102. Liu, Z, and Simpson, E. R. (1997). Steroidogenic factor 1 (SF-1) and SP1 are required for regulation of bovine CYP-11A gene expression in bovine luteal cells and adrenal Y1 cells. *Mol. Endocrinol.* 11, 127–137.
103. Hanley, N. A., Ikeda, Y., Luo, X., and Parker, K. L. (2000). Steroidogenic factor 1 (SF-1) is essential for ovarian development and function. *Cell. Mol. Endocrinol.* 163, 27–32.
104. Leers-Sucheta, S., Morohashi, K., Mason, J. I., and Melner, M. H. (1997). Synergistic activation of the human type II 3beta-hydroxysteroid dehydrogenase/delta5-delta4 isomerase promoter by the transcription factor steroidogenic factor-1/adrenal 4-binding protein and phorbol ester. *J. Biol. Chem.* 272, 7960–7967.
105. Majdic, G., Young, M., Gomez-Sanchez, E., Anderson, P., Szczepaniak, L. S., Dobbins, R. L., McGarry, J. D., and Parker, K. L. (2002). Knockout mice lacking steroidogenic factor 1 are a novel genetic model of hypothalamic obesity. *Endocrinology* 143, 607–614.
106. Bleckmann, S. C., Blendy, J. A., Rudolph, D., Monaghan, A. P., Schmid, W., and Schutz, G. (2002). Activating transcription factor 1 and CREB are important for cell survival during early mouse development. *Mol. Cell. Biol.* 22, 1919–1925.
107. Sirois, J., and Richards, J. S. (1993). Transcriptional regulation of the rat prostaglandin endoperoxidase synthase 2 gene in granulosa cells. *J. Biol. Chem.* 268, 21931–21938.
108. Sterneck, E., Tessarollo, L., and Johnson, P. F. (1997). An essential role for C/EBPβ in female reproduction. *Genes Dev.* 11, 2153–2162.
109. Heikinheimo, M., Ermolaeva, M., Bielinska, M., Rahman, N. A., Narita, N., Huhtaniemi, I. T., Tapanainen, J. S., and Wilson, D. B. (1997). Expression and hormonal regulation of transcription factors GATA-4 and GATA-6 in the mouse ovary. *Endocrinology* 138, 3505–3514.
110. Tremblay, J. J., Hamel, F., and Viger, R. S. (2002). Protein kinase A-dependent cooperation between GATA and CCAAT/enhancer-binding protein transcription factors regulates steroidogenic acute regulatory protein promoter activity. *Endocrinology* 143, 3935–3945.
111. Tremblay, J. J., and Viger, R. S. (2001). GATA factors differentially activate multiple gonadal promoters through conserved GATA regulatory elements. *Endocrinology* 142, 977–986.
112. Perlman, H., Suzuki, E., Simonson, M., Smith, R. C., and Walsh, K. (1998). GATA-6 induces p21(Cip1) expression and G1 cell cycle arrest. *J. Biol. Chem.* 273, 13713–13718.
113. Brown, M. S., and Goldstein, J. L. (1999). A proteolytic pathway that controls the cholesterol content of membranes, cells, and blood. *Proc. Natl. Acad. Sci. USA* 96, 11041–11048.
114. Shea-Eaton, W. K., Trinidad, M. J., Lopez, D., Nackley, A., and McLean, M. P. (2001). Sterol regulatory element binding protein-1a regulation of the steroidogenic acute regulatory protein gene. *Endocrinology* 142, 1525–1533.
115. Salvador, L. M., Park, Y., Cottom, J., Maizels, E. T., Jones, J. C., Schillace, R. V., Carr, D. W., Cheung, P., Allis, C. D., Jameson, J. L., and Hunzicker-Dunn, M. (2001). Follicle-stimulating hormone stimulates protein kinase A-mediated histone H3 phosphorylation and acetylation leading to select gene activation in ovarian granulosa cells. *J. Biol. Chem.* 276, 40146–40155.
116. Salvador, L. M., Maizels, E., Hales, D. B., Miyamoto, E., Yamamoto, H., and Hunzicker-Dunn, M. (2002). Acute signaling by the LH receptor is independent of protein kinase C activation. *Endocrinology* 143, 2986–2994.

117. Christenson, L. K., Stouffer, R. L., and Strauss, III, J. F. (2001). Quantitative analysis of the hormone-induced hyperacetylation of histone H3 associated with the steroidogenic acute regulatory protein gene promoter. *J. Biol. Chem.* 276, 27392–27399.

118. Lazzaro, M. A., and Picketts, D. J. (2001). Cloning and characterization of the murine Imitation Switch (ISWI) genes: Differential expression patterns suggest distinct developmental roles for Snf2h and Snf2l. *J. Neurochem.* 77, 1145–1156.

CHAPTER **12**

The Corpus Luteum of Pregnancy

JENNIFER M. BOWEN-SHAUVER AND GEULA GIBORI

ABSTRACT

In the last 10 years many exciting discoveries have been made regarding the development, function, and regression of the corpus luteum (CL) of pregnancy. Techniques such as microarray analysis have enhanced the speed with which new genes of interest are identified, and transgenic technology has revealed the frequently surprising functions of known and novel factors. The field of angiogenesis has blossomed, and the remarkably intense and rapid angiogenesis that occurs in the CL has made it an organ of choice for studies of this process. The cloning of steroid ogenic acute regulatory protein (StAR) has changed the way we think about steroidogenesis in the CL. Although StAR is no longer a novelty, the mechanism of its action continues to be a controversial topic and an exciting field of research. Similarly, the cloning of 17β-hydroxysteroid dehydrogenase type 7 has filled in one of the missing pieces of the steroidogenic puzzle in the CL of the rodent; however, more questions remain unanswered. A luteotropic role for progesterone, proposed long ago, has now been supported by numerous studies, and our knowledge of the mechanisms by which this and other hormones act on the CL continues to expand. In this chapter, we summarize the current body of knowledge, in particular the new information of the last 10 years of research, to present a complete picture of the CL of pregnancy. This fascinating organ, with its rapid formation and destruction and its complex regulation, continues to be a fertile field for research.

INTRODUCTION

The CL is an endocrine gland that is unique because of its ephemeral nature. It is a hormone-regulated structure that is rapidly formed from the remains of the ovarian follicle following ovulation, that is essential for the establishment of pregnancy and that, in the absence of pregnancy or at the end of pregnancy, undergoes a process of regression resulting in physical destruction and removal from the ovary. The existence of the CL as an ovarian structure was described by Falloppio in 1561 [1], by de Graaf in 1672 [2], and by Malpighi in 1685 [3]. Malpighi gave this structure the Latin name *corpus luteum*—literally, "yellow body." This terminology is however misleading, because in most species, the highly vascular state of the CL gives it a red or purple appearance.

The association of CL with pregnancy and the number of subsequent offspring was observed by de Graaf (quoted from [4]), but the importance of the CL to the establishment of pregnancy was not discovered until much later. In 1898 Prenant described the CL as a gland and the source of an internal secretion [5]. The search for the critical factor produced by the CL began when two independent investigators, Fraenkel and Magnus, ablated the CL of rabbits and determined from the resulting abortions that the CL permitted the process of implantation and establishment of pregnancy [6–8]. In 1929 Allen and Corner maintained pregnancy in ovariectomized rabbits by treatment with a luteal extract and concluded that the CL contained a hormone that acted on the uterine endometrium to prepare it for implantation [9]. This hormone was simultaneously isolated in the early 1930s by four groups, working independently [10–13], and was named *progesterone* for its progestational actions.

Although production of progesterone to establish and support pregnancy is a universal characteristic, the nature of the CL varies by species, and even within species several types of CL can be formed. Animals that undergo spontaneous ovulation normally form a CL after each ovulation. These CL develop and persist for a distinct and regular period, called a *luteal phase,* which is sufficient to allow embryonic implantation. If no embryo is present, the CL will regress at the end of the luteal phase. The presence of an implanted embryo, however, will result in the "rescue" of the CL, which will then develop into a CL of pregnancy. Induced ovulators, which ovulate in response to the stimulus of mating, similarly form a CL after ovulation. If a fertile mating occurs, this CL develops into a CL of pregnancy. If the mating is sterile, however, the CL will regress after a fixed period. This is similar to the luteal phase of a spontaneous ovulator and is called *pseudopregnancy.*

ACKNOWLEDGMENT: Writing of this chapter was supported by NIH grants HD 11119, HD 12356 and U54 HD 4009 (G.G.) and T32 HL 07692 (J.B-S).

The rat, mouse, and some other rodent species have a wider range of possible luteal phenotypes. In these species, ovulation is spontaneous, but mating is required to stimulate the development of the CL into a structure that can secrete sufficient progesterone to allow decidualization and implantion to occur. Therefore the following three types of CL are possible:

1. If ovulation occurs in the absence of mating, the follicle reorganizes into the CL of the cycle. This is a small, minimally developed structure that secretes little progesterone and that begins to regress after only 3 days.
2. In contrast, when the animal mates at the time of ovulation, the physical stimulus of mating induces secretion of prolactin (PRL) from the pituitary, and this hormone stimulates development of the CL into a structure that is capable of secreting large amounts of progesterone.
3. If implantation takes place, this CL will develop into the CL of pregnancy. Alternatively, in the event of a sterile mating, a pseudopregnancy will occur in which the CL regresses after a period three or four times the length of the normal cycle.

In rodents, CL of the cycle and of pseudopregnancy can be considered largely laboratory artifacts, because in the wild these animals will normally be in contact with fertile males and will become pregnant at each mating.

In this chapter, we focus on the CL of pregnancy, a physiologically meaningful structure in all species and one that is critical for the development of pregnancy. The immense amount of variation among species precludes us from detailing each species individually. Therefore, in this chapter, we focus primarily on rodents, while including some information on humans and primates.

FORMATION OF THE CORPUS LUTEUM

Differentiation

Formation of the CL begins concomitant with ovulation and is stimulated by the same surge of luteinizing hormone (LH). The LH surge induces expression of a number of genes essential for ovulation and luteinization (for reviews, see [14, 15]). Several transiently induced genes such as progesterone receptor, CCAAT enhancer binding protein β, and cyclooxygenase-2 (COX-2) appear to be essential for the ovulation process itself (for review, see [15]), whereas others may be important for early luteinization.

The process of luteinization involves rapid and radical changes in the follicular cells. Luteinizing theca and granulosa cells cease to divide and undergo hypertrophy consisting of an increase in cytoplasmic volume of the cells and in the number of intracellular organelles and lipid droplets. These changes in cellular growth patterns are reflected by changes in cell cycle regulatory genes. As follicular cells luteinize, they cease to express the cell cycle activators cyclin D2, cyclin D1, and cyclin E and begin to express the cell cycle inhibitors $p21^{Cip}$ and $p27^{Kip}$ [16–19]. In mice lacking $p27^{KIP1}$, partial differentiation of follicular cells occurs, but the new luteal cells continue to proliferate for at least 3 days after ovulation and demonstrate abnormalities in estradiol production [20]. Cyclin D3 also increases with luteinization, and a trimeric complex of cyclin D3/p27/cyclin dependent kinase 4 (CDK4) that may have a kinase activity separate from control of cell cycle progression is found in luteal cells [19].

New luteal cells must rapidly begin to generate large amounts of progesterone, and several genes involved in steroidogenesis become expressed at high levels in luteal cells as compared with the originating follicular cells. These include 3β-hydroxysteroid dehydrogenase (3β-HSD) [21–23], CYP-11A1, the gene encoding P450 cholesterol side-chain cleavage (P450scc) [22–24], and StAR [25, 26]. Two other steroidogenic enzymes, P450 17α hydroxylase ($P450_{17\alpha}$) and P450 aromatase ($P450_{AROM}$), are essential to synthesis of androgen and estradiol by the follicle. Transcription of CYP-17, the gene for $P450_{17\alpha}$, is decreased by the LH surge and the onset of luteinization [22, 27]. $P450_{17\alpha}$ and $P450_{AROM}$ are present and active, however, in CL of rats and humans, which produce estradiol [22, 27]. In other species such as the cow and rabbit the CL does not produce estrogens, and the activity of these enzymes disappears following luteinization (for review, see [28]).

Changes in hormone receptors and signaling factors also occur as follicular cells luteinize. Two key ovarian receptors (follicle-stimulating hormone receptors [FSHR] and prolactin receptors [PRLR]) are affected oppositely by luteinization. Whereas, for a reason yet unknown, the receptor for FSH disappears totally [29], PRLR is upregulated and levels remain high until the end of pregnancy in rats and mice [30–32]. Expression of Stat 5, a transcription factor involved in mediating the luteotropic actions of PRL, is also induced at this time [30, 33]. Expression of several other receptors and transcription factors for which specific functions are currently unknown is also regulated by luteinization. Expression of Frizzled-1, a G-protein coupled receptor, drops during luteinization of granulosa cells, whereas expression of the related receptor Frizzled-4 rises. Interestingly, the levels of Wnt-4, a ligand for Frizzled-4, also rise with luteinization. This led Hsich and collaborators to suggest a role for the Wnt/Frizzled signaling system in regulation of the CL [34]. Luteinization also leads to increased expression of Sgk kinase and a forkhead transcription factor, AFX/Foxo4 [35, 36], while causing a reduction in levels of another forkhead transcription factor, FKHR/Foxo1 [35]. In addition, expression of the transcription factors of the mitogen-activated protein (MAP) kinase pathway, Fra2 and JunD [37], becomes substantial following luteinization. The significance of the changes in the level of expression of these transcription factors and the exact role of the Sgk/forkhead and MAP kinase pathways in luteinization and luteal cell function remains unclear.

Finally, the LH surge induces expression of several matrix metalloproteinases (MMPs) and their tissue inhibitors (TIMPs) [38] (for review, see [39]). The pattern of this induction is consistent with a role for these factors in remodeling and vascularization of the new CL. LH or chorionic gonadotrophin (CG) may also be important for the production of other factors involved in the angiogenesis of early luteal formation. Treatment of marmosets with a gonadotrophin-releasing hormone (Gn-RH) antagonist immediately after ovulation resulted in a dramatic and near-total reduction in endothelial cell proliferation [40], and there is additional temporal and experimental evidence linking LH/CG with vascular endothelial growth factor (VEGF) expression, angiopoietin expression, and endothelial cell proliferation in humans and primates [41–43] (for review, see [44]).

Vascularization

Among the rapidly induced events of the luteinization process is angiogenesis and neovascularization of the CL. Angiogenesis is the development of new blood vessels from existing vasculature through a process of endothelial cell proliferation and outgrowth (sprouting). In the adult animal this process is normally restricted to wound healing and pathological situations such as tumor growth. The reproductive tissues of the female, however, are exceptions to that rule, and cyclic alterations in vascularization occur regularly in the ovaries and uterus. The CL undergoes particularly intense and rapid angiogenesis during which the proliferation of endothelial cells is on a par with that observed in the most aggressive of tumors. In primates, which have a long luteal phase, the midluteal phase CL has a fully developed vascular network, and no additional angiogenesis is induced following maternal recognition of pregnancy [45–47]. A recent study, however, indicated that the human CL of early pregnancy does undergo additional intense angiogenesis, along with pericyte proliferation and vessel stabilization [42]. In the pregnant rat the process of establishing a vascular network is complete by 4 days after ovulation [48]; however, an additional and dramatic burst of endothelial cell proliferation and angiogenesis occurs at midpregnancy [49].

The process of angiogenesis in the CL includes breakdown of the basement membrane separating the granulosa and theca layers of the preovulatory follicle, followed by expansion of the capillaries of the thecal layer into the previously avascular granulosa [50–52]. This expansion forms a dense capillary network that supplies nutrients efficiently to the luteal cells and provides a mechanism for speedy and efficient output of progesterone from the CL. As the CL matures during pregnancy or during a long luteal phase, the vessels also stabilize and undergo some maturation. Pericytes from the thecal capillaries migrate into the granulosa area of the follicle during the initial expansion stage, and these proliferate so that a large percentage of vessels in the mature CL contain pericytes [53, 54]. A venous system, beginning with venules in the center of the structure, develops within the CL; however, there is little arteriolization, and the blood flow of the CL is largely controlled by systemic pressure [55].

Regulation of angiogenesis in the CL is complex and involves a large number of identified factors (for review, see [56]). Several of the most important factors are described here. Figure 12.1 provides a theoretical overview of the angiogenic process in the CL.

Proteases and Protease Inhibitors

Angiogenesis cannot occur without remodeling of the extracellular matrix (ECM) to permit the migration of endothelial cells. The ECM is a complex system that has structural roles in the support and division of tissue compartments and that influences many basic cellular processes. Remodeling of the ECM during processes such as angiogenesis is tightly regulated by interactions between proteases and their inhibitors.

Members of both the plasminogen activator family and the MMP family of proteases, along with their inhibitors, are expressed during luteal remodeling (for reviews, see [39, 57, 58]). Expression of MMPs is elevated during luteal formation in a number of species, including the rat [38, 59–62]. TIMPs are believed to be important in regulating the activity of MMPs in reproductive tissues, and expression of some of these inhibitors is increased during early luteal formation [38, 61] (for review, see [39]). Although there are some disparities in results for individual factors, it is generally agreed that the expression of proteases and protease inhibitors is absent or reduced during the majority of the luteal phase or pregnant state, when the CL is fully developed and functional, and that these factors do not again become elevated until tissue regression is under way (for reviews, see [39, 57, 58]). One protease inhibitor that has a different pattern of expression is α2-macroglobulin (α2-MG), a broad-spectrum protease inhibitor produced in the rat CL. This protease inhibitor is produced by luteal cells in response to prolactin or placental lactogens and is not highly expressed during luteal formation. Expression increases between days 11 to 21 of pregnancy, with peak expression beginning on day 15 [63], just as a dramatic burst of endothelial cell proliferation and angiogenesis occurs in the CL [49].

Although both proteases and their inhibitors are upregulated during luteal remodeling, regional distribution of these products within the CL varies [58, 38, 62, 64]. For example, messenger ribonucleic acid (mRNA) for tissue-type plasminogen activator appears to be highly expressed throughout newly formed CL in the rat, but the inhibitor,

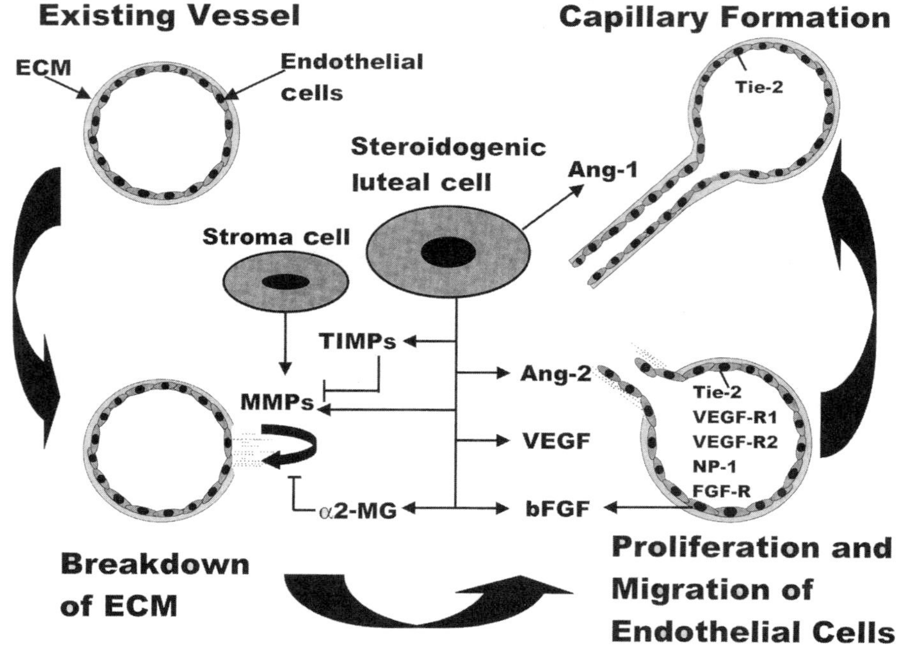

FIGURE 12.1 A theoretical overview of angiogenesis in the CL, depicted as a counterclockwise progression. An existing vessel, with a layer of endothelial cells surrounded and embedded in extracellular matrix (ECM) proteins is at the top left. At the onset of angiogenesis, the ECM is degraded by MMPs secreted from nonsteroidogenic (stromal) cells in the CL and from steroidogenic luteal cells and endothelial cells themselves. This proteolytic degradation is controlled by inhibitors, TIMPs and α2-macroglobulin (α2-MG), secreted by the steroidogenic luteal cells. Once the ECM has been degraded, endothelial cells proliferate and migrate into the CL to form new capillaries. This process appears to be stimulated by Ang-2 and VEGF secreted by the steroidogenic luteal cells and by basic fibroblast growth factor (bFGF) secreted by the steroidogenic cells and endothelial cells. These factors act through receptors (Tie-2, VEGF-R1, VEGF-R2, NP-1, and FGF-R) present on the endothelial cells. Finally, after the new capillary has formed, stabilization of the vessel is promoted by Ang-1 from the steroidogenic cells, which acts through the Tie-2 receptor on the endothelial cells.

plasminogen activator inhibitor type 1, is expressed mainly in the central part of the developing CL [64]. Similarly, in the human CL, MMPs are expressed largely in the connective tissue, vasculature, and theca layer, whereas granulosa-lutein cells express large amounts of the inhibitor TIMP-1 [62]. The localized production of proteases and their inhibitors is almost certainly critical to the effectiveness of the remodeling process. Some inhibitors may also function as activators for other proteases; thus their concomitant expression is not detrimental to protease action. For example, TIMP-2 can facilitate the activation of MMP-2 [65].

Overall, the presence of proteases and their inhibitors during early luteal development is indicative of the large amount of ECM remodeling that must occur during this time as part of breakdown of the follicular basement membrane and invasion of newly sprouting capillaries into the avascular granulosum. There is likely to be considerable overlap in function between these factors; however, the importance of one protease inhibitor, TIMP-1, has been determined using genetic manipulation. Mice lacking a functional TIMP-1 gene have severe reproductive defects, including disrupted estrous cycle length [66]. In contrast, deletion of the α2-MG gene had no deleterious effect on reproduction [67].

Vascular Endothelial Growth Factor

One critical angiogenic factor involved in CL vascularization is vascular endothelial growth factor (VEGF), also known as *vascular permeability factor (VPF)*. VEGF is a basic, heparin-binding homodimeric glycoprotein that was originally characterized based on its ability to promote vascular endothelial proliferation and increase vascular permeability [68]. Five different isoforms of VEGF, produced by alternative splicing of a single gene transcript, have been identified in mammals. The size and binding characteristics of these isoforms varies; the two largest isoforms are bound in the ECM, whereas the three smaller isoforms are secreted [69]. There are two well-described VEGF receptors, the tyrosine kinases VEGF-R1 (Flt-1) and

VEGF-R2 (KDR/Flk-1), as well as a third, closely related receptor VEGF-R3/Flt-4 (for review, see [68]). VEGF-R2 is more strongly phosphorylated than VEGF-R1 in response to VEGF binding and induces a broader range of responses than does VEGF-R1 [70]. Thus this receptor is likely to be critical to VEGF function. In addition to these receptors, certain isoforms of VEGF have recently been shown to bind to two neuropilins, the type 1 transmembrane receptors NP-1 and NP-2 [71, 72].

Studies of transgenic mice have clearly indicated the importance of VEGF in angiogenesis. Elimination of the VEGF gene at even one allele in mice results in disrupted fetal angiogenesis and embryonic lethality, indicating not only the critical role of VEGF in angiogenesis but the importance of the amount of VEGF expression in the correct functioning of this factor [73, 74]. Deletions of the VEGF-R1 and VEGF-R2 genes also result in embryonic lethality [75, 76], although the phenotypes generated by the two mutations are different (for review, see [44]). Five additional VEGF proteins (VEGFs B-F) have been identified by sequence homology to VEGF (now also known as *VEGF-A*). These VEGF proteins appear to have more circumscribed and tissue-specific roles, and mice null for VEGF-B retain normal fertility, which suggests that this isoform at least is not essential for luteal angiogenesis [77].

Expression of VEGF mRNA and protein across species is greatest during early luteal development, continues throughout the luteal phase, and is greatly reduced at the time of luteal regression (for reviews, see [44, 52, 53]). In the primate, all isoforms of VEGF-A have been detected in the ovary as have VEGF-R1, VEGF-R2 and NP-1 (for reviews, see [44, 52]). VEGF has been localized to steroidogenic luteal cells within the CL of rodents and primates [45, 78, 79], identified largely as luteal cells of granulosa origin in human studies [41, 80–84]. VEGF-R has been localized on vascular endothelial cells in rodents [78, 85], and a study in rats has reported immunohistochemical localization of VEGF-R1 and VEGF-R2 to steroidogenic luteal cells [85]. Receptors for VEGF have been found in steroidogenic luteal cells and endothelial cells in the human [80, 83, 85a] but were localized exclusively in the endothelium in marmoset [86, 45]. It has been reported that factors in the VEGF system are more intensely expressed in the CL of pregnancy than in those of the cycle in humans and rodents, which may reflect greater angiogenic development in CL of pregnancy [83, 85, 85a]. This is not the case in the marmoset, where increased angiogenesis does not seem to occur during establishment of pregnancy [45].

Studies using antibodies and other blockers of VEGF activity have clearly indicated the importance of VEGF in luteal angiogenesis and function. In the sheep the majority of endothelial chemotactic activity produced by the CL shortly after ovulation can be neutralized by anti-VEGF, indicating that it is a major player in the rapid onset of angiogenesis at this time [53]. Treatment of pregnant rats with anti-VEGF antibody interfered with estradiol-induced increases in vascular density in the CL [87], and anti-VEGF-R2 antibody was found to inhibit luteal angiogenesis in mice [88]. Treatment with soluble, truncated VEGF receptors reduced luteal formation in the rat, which frequently resulting in central ischaemic necrosis [89] and impaired luteal development and function in rhesus monkeys [90]. In marmosets, treatment with soluble, truncated VEGF receptors either immediately after ovulation or during the midluteal phase also had dramatic effects on luteal development, including reductions in endothelial cell proliferation, failure of capillary formation, and significant declines in progesterone production [86, 91, 92] (for review, see [93]). However, when immunoneutralization of VEGF was carried out during luteal development in marmosets housed with fertile males, normal pregnancies occurred in half of the treated animals despite a considerable reduction in circulating progesterone concentrations [45]. This suggests that normal progesterone production in this species is in excess of that required for the establishment of pregnancy.

Angiopoietins

Angiopoietins are an endothelial-specific family of growth factors that are not endothelial cell mitogens but appear to be critical for angiogenesis and vessel integrity. Four angiopoietins have been identified to date, of which angiopoietin-1 (Ang-1) and angiopoietin-2 (Ang-2) are the best characterized [94]. Ang-1 signals through a tyrosine kinase receptor, Tie-2, located on endothelial cells. Ang-2 also binds to Tie-2 but functions as a natural antagonist of signal transduction through this receptor [95]. Deletion of Tie-2 in mice results in embryonic death, and the phenotype suggests that Tie-2 activity is essential for maintenance of vessel integrity [96]. A closely related receptor, Tie-1, has also been identified, but the role of this receptor is currently unknown [94].

Ang-1 is widely expressed in adult tissues; however, Ang-2 is primarily expressed in tissues that undergo cyclic angiogenesis (e.g., ovary, uterus) and in the placenta [95]. During formation of the mouse CL, Ang-2 was detected in the theca layer and in new, invading blood vessels, whereas Ang-1 was present in the theca layer of the preovulatory follicle and then within the CL during vessel invasion [95]. In the marmoset, Ang-1 was uniformly found in luteal and endothelial cells with the greatest expression occurring early in the luteal phase, whereas Ang-2 was expressed in a subpopulation of luteal and endothelial cells [86]. Tie-2, as expected, was expressed only in endothelial cells. Expression of Ang-2 and Tie-2 appeared to increase following luteal rescue of the human CL by CG [41], a treatment associated with enhanced angiogenesis [42].

The angiopoietins have been shown to interact with VEGF in the control of angiogenesis. Ang-1 can prevent vessel leakiness caused by VEGF-A without interfering with induction of angiogenesis [97, 98] and enhances the stability of endothelial cell vascular networks [99]. Meanwhile, Ang-2, which blocks the function of Ang-1 in vitro [95], is expressed with VEGF-A at sites of new vessel formation [100, 101]. This has led to the proposal that Ang-1 is involved in vessel stabilization, whereas Ang-2 blocks the effects of Ang-1 and thus makes mature vessels unstable and sensitive to VEGF-A. The interactions among Ang-1, Ang-2, and VEGF-A have been elegantly tested by Visconti and colleagues using mice in which genes for single or multiple angiogenic factors were deleted [102]. These authors found that Ang-2 synergized with VEGF-A in the induction of capillary angiogenesis and that Ang-1 acted as a negative regulator of VEGF-induced angiogenesis. Although Ang-2 synergizes with VEGF-A when expression of that factor is elevated, it has been suggested that Ang-2 may act to induce vascular regression via competitive inhibition of Ang-1 when VEGF-A levels are reduced. In situ hybridization data from rat tumors supports this theory [103], and it has been proposed that this mechanism may contribute to the degeneration of luteal vasculature during luteal regression [104].

Basic Fibroblast Growth Factor

Basic fibroblast growth factor (bFGF; FGF-2) is a heparin-binding protein and member of the fibroblast growth factor family that was among the first angiogenic factors identified in the ovary [53, 105]. bFGF is produced by steroidogenic and endothelial cells of rat [106], human [107], and ruminant CL (for review, see 53]). The overall expression of bFGF mRNA and protein in the CL does not vary significantly across the luteal phase [53], although a decrease in granulosa-lutein expression of this factor has been reported in the late luteal stage of the human [107]. Receptors for bFGF have been identified in steroidogenic and endothelial cells of the ovine CL [108] and are most abundantly expressed late in the luteal phase, well after the majority of luteal angiogenesis has been completed. Nonetheless, bFGFs have been found to stimulate proliferation and motility of luteal endothelial cells, particularly those from the early CL [53, 109, 110], and treatment with antibodies to bFGF will suppress approximately 80% of endothelial cell proliferative activity in extracts of CL from cows, sheep, and pigs (for review, see [53]). Similar approaches carried out in vivo, however, blocked only 25% of endothelial chemotactic activity produced by ovine CL [53]. Therefore although bFGF may play a subsidiary role in angiogenesis in the CL, it does not appear to be a crucial angiogenic factor. This is further suggested by deletion of the bFGF gene in mice, which results in no developmental disruption or loss of fertility [111].

LUTEAL STEROIDOGENESIS AND ITS REGULATION

The ability of the CL to synthesize steroids depends in large part on the capacity to acquire the substrate for steroidogenesis, cholesterol, and to transport it to the site of steroid synthesis. Cholesterol for steroidogenesis is preferentially obtained from circulating high- and low-density lipoproteins (HDL, LDL), with the relative contribution of these two types of lipoproteins varying by species or tissue [112–115]. In rodents, steroidogenic cells obtain the majority of their cholesterol from HDL. This cholesterol is taken up through transfer to the plasma membrane without endocytosis or degradation of the HDL particle [116–119]. Uptake of HDL-derived cholesterol ester is mediated by the scavenger receptor, class B, type 1 (SR-B1) [120–122]. The uptake process also requires apolipoprotein A-I (apoA-I), which binds SR-B1 and facilitates the transfer of HDL-derived cholesterol ester [123, 124]. The findings that mice lacking either SR-B1 or apoA-I have reduced cholesterol reserve in the ovaries [125, 126] suggest that HDL-derived cholesterol ester is not only the substrate for steroidogenesis but also a major source of intracellular cholesterol esters. Indeed, an increase in luteal high-affinity HDL-binding sites accompanies the rise in cholesterol storage and steroidogenesis by rat luteal cells between days 12 and 18 of pregnancy [127]. This may be caused by increased SR-B1 gene expression stimulated by estradiol [128] and PRL [129].

Because the solubility of cholesterol ester in the plasma membrane is limited, the transfer of HDL-derived cholesterol ester into the cytosol of steroidogenic cells requires an active transfer process. This transfer system remains unknown. Another mechanism by which luteal cells can increase the availability of substrate for steroidogenesis is by hydrolysis of intracellular stores of cholesterol ester by the enzyme hormone sensitive lipase, also called *cholesterol esterase,* which is stimulated by LH [130–133] and PRL [134–136]. Cholesterol must then be transported to the mitochondria and, within the mitochondria, from the outer to the inner mitochondrial membrane, the location of $P450_{scc}$. Transport of cholesterol to the outer mitochondrial membrane appears to require an intact cytoskeleton and can be prevented by inhibition of either microtubule or microfilament formation [137]. Sterol binding proteins have also been implicated in binding cholesterol and directing its movement toward the mitochondria (for review, see [138]). Sterol carrier protein 2 (SCP2) is expressed in the rat CL [129, 139–141], and greater amounts of this protein are found in the highly steroidogenic large luteal cells than in the less steroidogenic small luteal cells [139]. SCP2 is a phosphoprotein that is a specific substrate for protein kinase C (PKC) [142], and, interestingly, PKC reduces progesterone biosynthesis by luteal cells at the level of cholesterol transport [143–145].

Although the mechanism of the transport of cholesterol to the outer mitochondrial membrane is not yet known, the mechanism of transport from the outer to the inner mitochondrial membrane has attracted intense investigation (for reviews, see [146–148]). It was early discovered that this transport step was the site of acute regulation of steroidogenesis by second messenger systems and was dependent on the synthesis of a short-lived protein. However, it took several decades for this protein to be identified, cloned, and named *steroidogenic acute regulatory protein (StAR)* [149] (for review, see [150]). StAR is synthesized as a 37 kDa precursor protein that is transported from the cytoplasm to the mitochondria, where it undergoes cleavage to acidic or basic 30 kDa forms. The presence of StAR transcripts in steroidogenic cells is directly correlated with steroidogenesis, and transcription of StAR is rapidly stimulated by LH activation of cyclic adenosine monophosphate (cAMP) (for reviews, see [147, 151, 152]). Mutations in the StAR gene in humans cause congenital lipoid adrenal hyperphasia, a disease characterized by an inability to synthesize adequate amounts of steroids, and this phenotype is replicated when the StAR gene is rendered nonfunctional in mice [153].

Whereas the critical role of StAR in cholesterol transport is certain, the mechanism by which StAR facilitates this process is still under investigation. It was originally thought that StAR might act as an intermitochondrial shuttle. However, restriction of StAR to the cytoplasm does not inhibit its activity (for reviews, see [147, 154]), although importation of StAR into mitochondria eliminates its activity [154], implying that StAR acts on the outer surface of the mitochondria. It has also been suggested that StAR interacts with proteins on the mitochondrial outer membrane. The peripheral benzodiazepine receptor (PBR), which is closely associated with StAR on the outer mitochondrial membrane [155], has been implicated in transport of cholesterol across the mitochondrial membranes [156] and seems to be a promising partner for StAR. However, although StAR is targeted to the mitochondrial membrane by specific sequences [157], it does not appear to require a mitochondrial receptor protein to carry out efficient sterol transfer once it reaches the membrane [158, 159]. One possible nonprotein mechanism for StAR interaction with the outer mitochondrial membrane is through insertion into the membrane in a molten globule state, a semidisorganized state achieved by StAR at low pH [160]. Recent studies have shed some light on how StAR carries cholesterol. A StAR-related lipid transfer (START) domain exists at the carboxy terminus of StAR [161]. Recently, the crystal structure of the START domain in a related protein was determined and found to indicate the formation of a hydrophobic tunnel within the protein capable of containing cholesterol [162]. Furthermore, cholesterol associates with the predicted region in the StAR protein [163]. A scenario that combines this finding with the molten globule theory has been put forward [148].

Once cholesterol reaches the intramitochondrial membrane, its transformation into steroid hormones begins. An overview of steroidogenic pathways in the rat CL is provided in Figure 12.2. The capacity to transform cholesterol to progesterone is a universal characteristic of the CL, and the enzymes necessary for such transformation, P450ssc and 3β-HSD, are expressed in the CL of all species. Although these enzymes are considered to be constitutively expressed [21–24, 164], several researchers have shown that they are regulated by PRL in the rat CL [129, 165–167]. Additional steroidogenic enzymes involved in the production of androgens and estrogen, such as $P450_{17\alpha}$, $P450_{AROM}$, and 17β-hydroxysteroid dehydrogenase (17β-HSD), are found in the CL of a few species including the rat, mouse, and human [168–172]. $P450_{17\alpha}$, the enzyme responsible for the conversion of progesterone to androstenedione, is hormonally and developmentally regulated in the rat. It is stimulated by LH [173–175], and its expression declines at midpregnancy in the rat [23], when LH drops to a nadir [176]. At this stage in pregnancy the placenta becomes the primary source of androgen for estradiol biosynthesis by the ovaries (for review, see [177]). The major androgen produced by the placenta is androstenedione (for review, see [177]), which is converted by $P450_{AROM}$ to estrone. In contrast to $P450_{17\alpha}$, the expression and activity of $P450_{AROM}$ increases from midpregnancy, reaching a peak around day 15 [27, 178, 179]. This enhanced expression of $P450_{AROM}$ in rat CL appears to be caused by PRL and placental lactogen [167, 180]. As the rat CL secretes primarily estradiol [181], an additional enzyme capable of converting estrone to estradiol, and/or androstenedione to testosterone, must be present in the gland. Such an enzyme, 17β-hydroxysteroid dehydrogenase type 1 (17β-HSD 1), is present in follicular granulosa cells and human CL [180, 181, 172] but has not been located in the rodent CL [182, 168]. Recently, however, a novel 17β-HSD isoform, 17β-HSD 7, was discovered in the rodent CL [169, 170, 183]. This enzyme is a major luteal protein from midpregnancy on [184, 185]; is upregulated by the luteotropic factors PRL, estradiol, and LH [186–188]; and is mostly located in the highly steroidogenic large luteal cells [187]. Interestingly, rat 17β-HSD 7 associates specifically with the short form of the PRL receptor (leading to the initial name of *PRL receptor associated protein [PRAP]*) [189]. It is possible that PRL plays a role in regulating 17β-HSD 7 stability through this association, as PRL treatment increased 17β-HSD 7 protein without affecting mRNA levels [188]. 17β-HSD 7 has a site for Jak2 phosphorylation [189]. That the direct association of 17β-HSD 7 with the short form of the PRL-R and Jak2 and its phosphorylation on tyrosine may directly affect its stability or activity is an intriguing possibility. We have shown 17β-HSD 7 to be a potent converter of estrone to estradiol [170]. It does not, however, act to interconvert androgen substrates, and an additional, undiscovered enzyme may carry out this process in the CL.

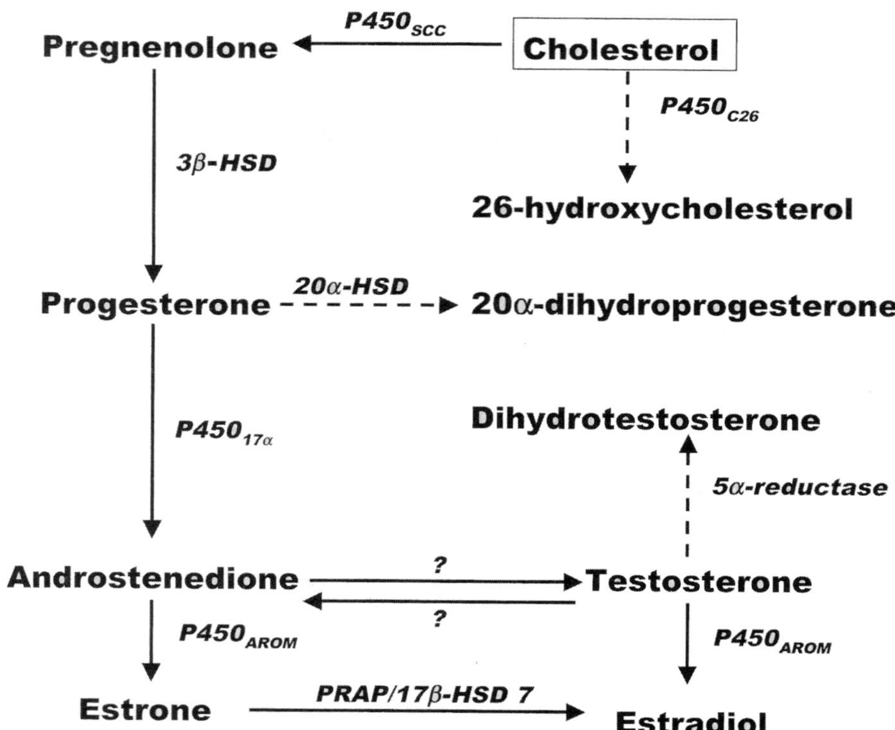

FIGURE 12.2 Steroidogenic pathways in the CL of pregnancy in the rat. Steroid synthesis begins with conversion of cholesterol to pregnenolone by $P450_{scc}$ on the inner membrane of the mitochondria. Pregnenolone is transported to the endoplasmic reticulum and converted by 3β-HSD to progesterone. Progesterone is then converted to androgens, androstenedione and testosterone, in either the CL or the placenta. Androstenedione is the major substrate for aromatase ($P450_{AROM}$) in the CL and is converted first to estrone by this enzyme and then from estrone to estradiol by 17β-HSD type 7 (also called *PRAP*). Estradiol can also be produced by aromatase conversion of testosterone. It is likely that interconversion of androstenedione and testosterone occurs in the rat CL; however, an enzyme capable of this conversion has not yet been found. Pathways indicated with dashed lines are those active during functional regression of the CL and act to reduce steroid production by reducing substrate or by metabolizing progesterone and testosterone to inactive or antigestational forms.

A decline in luteal progesterone production occurs at the end of pregnancy, before parturition. The major factor in this decline is 20α-hydroxysteroid dehydrogenase (20α-HSD), which metabolizes progesterone into gestationally inactive 20α-dihydroprogesterone (20α-DHP). Expression and activity of this enzyme are downregulated during pregnancy by PRL and placental lactogens [190–193]. Immediately before parturition, expression of 20α-HSD mRNA increases [190, 191], accompanied by a sharp increase in 20α-DHP and a concomitant fall in progesterone [194]. Expression of $P450_{C26}$, which catalyzes the conversion of cholesterol to 26-hydroxycholesterol, also rises at the end of pregnancy and could reduce progesterone secretion by limiting substrate [195]. Conversion of testosterone to dihydrotestosterone (DHT) by luteal 5α-reductase has also been implicated in the functional demise of the CL, because rat CL secrete DHT at the end of pregnancy and exogenous DHT can decrease progesterone biosynthesis [196, 197]. However, although deletion of the 5α-reductase type I gene did result in parturition defects, it did not prevent the fall in progesterone at the end of pregnancy [198].

CELLULAR INTERACTIONS

The CL is a highly heterogenous tissue containing a variety of cell types besides the steroidogenic luteal cells. These include vascular cells, such as endothelial cells and pericytes, cells of immune origin, and the fibroblasts that make up the connective tissue of the organ. Interactions between these various cell types are likely to be essential in maintaining the health and function of the CL. Indeed, it has been demonstrated that culture of luteal steroidogenic cells in isolation from nonluteal cellular components greatly reduced the secretion of progesterone by the steroidogenic cells [199, 200].

As previously mentioned, the intense angiogenesis necessary to provide a blood supply to luteal steroidogenic cells results in a large, nonluteal cell population of endothelial cells and pericytes in the mature CL. The endothelial cells divide and spread into the new CL, as do pericytes derived from the thecal capillaries. During the early luteal phase, 85% of the dividing cells in the primate CL are endothelial cells [201], which is necessary to provide rapid development of a capillary system that will support luteal steroidogenesis and transport progesterone to the uterus and other target tissues. The immense number of endothelial cells present in the CL reflects the vascularization of the tissue. Indeed, blood flow in the fully developed CL is greater than that of any other tissue [55], and each steroidogenic luteal cell has physical contact with the capillary system [202–204].

Immune cells are also present in the CL and may have functional roles within the tissue. The presence of macrophages and/or lymphocytes in CL throughout the luteal phase of the cycle and pregnancy has been described for numerous species, including the rodent and human

[205–209]. In general, greater numbers of these cells, particularly macrophages, are seen during development and regression of the CL. Leukocytes are often associated with tissue remodeling events such as those that occur during development and regression of the CL [210]. Inhibition of leukocyte infiltration in sheep resulted in luteal deficiency [211], which suggests that these immune cells may play a critical role in luteal development, possibly through communication with vascular cells [212]. Considerable attention has been given to the potential roles of luteal immune cells in terminating luteal function and assisting in involution of the CL. Their role during pregnancy, however, is unknown, although in vitro studies using coculture of macrophages and luteal cells have suggested a possible role for immune cells in maintenance of steroidogenesis (for review, see [213]). In the human, it has been reported that fewer lymphocytes are present in the CL of pregnancy compared with those of the cycle, although the macrophage population appears similar to that of the midluteal phase [206]. Reduced numbers of immune cells in pregnancy, compared with the luteal phase, have also been reported for cows [214].

The steroidogenic luteal cells are themselves nonhomogenous. Granulosa and theca cells from the follicle differentiate into steroidogenic luteal cells after ovulation. The differentiated luteal cells can be separated into two populations based on size. It is widely believed that the origin of the large luteal cells is the follicular granulosa cells, whereas the follicular theca cells differentiate into small luteal cells; however, though this hypothesis is well supported in the human, there is little evidence to indicate these cellular origins in the rat [199]. There is considerable mixing of large and small cell types during reorganization of the follicle into the CL such that, in most species, the two cell types are in contact with each other. Primates are an exception, with the two cell populations remaining relatively separate, and in primates the two populations of luteal cells are generally called *granulosa lutein* and *theca lutein* [215]. These two cell populations can be distinguished in tissue sections by their location. Theca lutein cells form an irregular, often interrupted layer around the circumference of the CL and are found accompanying areas of vascular invasion or infolding. Granulosa lutein cells are large, polygonal cells with abundant cytoplasm and a centrally located nucleus. Theca lutein cells are smaller and have less cytoplasm than granulosa lutein, but cell types contain many lipid droplets in the cytoplasm [204]. The theca lutein cells of the human CL are small and do not hypertrophy during the luteal phase. In contrast, the granulosa lutein cells undergo considerable hypertrophy, which contributes significantly to the growth of the CL [42]. In the rat, small and large luteal cells are intermingled within the CL. In culture, each group has a distinct phenotype. The small luteal cells (12 to 20 μm) have a large, oval nucleus; contain little lipid; and flatten into an epithelioid morphology in culture. In contrast, the large luteal cells (30 μm) have a small spherical nucleus and plentiful lipid droplets and do not completely flatten in culture [199].

Although both populations of luteal cells produce progesterone, there are distinct functional differences between large and small luteal cells. In general, the basal secretion of progesterone by large cells is significantly greater than for small cells, and thus the large luteal cells are responsible for the majority of progesterone production. The large luteal cells of the rat also contain more lipid than do the small cells and secrete more androgen, estradiol, and progesterone [199, 139]. Consistent with their greater steroidogenic role, these large cells contain a greater amount of steroidogenic enzymes, including cytochrome $P450_{scc}$, $P450_{AROM}$, and $P450_{17\alpha}$ [199, 139]. The large cells of the rat also bind the major luteotropic hormones, LH and PRL, more effectively than do small luteal cells [199]. Despite this, large and small luteal cells respond to LH stimulation with a similar increase in steroid production [216]. This contrasts with the situation in domestic ruminants (for reviews, see [146, 215, 217]) and humans [218, 219], in which only the small luteal cells produce more progesterone in response to LH stimulation. In addition, in contrast to the rat, the small (theca) steroidogenic cells of the human CL bind more LH than do the large cells [219], although both cell types contain LH receptors.

In the rhesus macaque, immunostaining for P450ssc and 3β-HSD, the enzymes necessary for progesterone production, was homogenous throughout the CL, but immunostaining for $P450_{17\alpha}$ was localized to cells in the periphery and along vascular tracts [220]. This suggests that only luteal cells of theca origin produce androgens in the primate. The distribution of $P450_{AROM}$, in contrast, was heterogenous among cells but not localized to a specific area, indicating that androgens produced by peripheral cells are aromatized to estrogen in a different luteal cell population [220]. Other studies in primates and humans support the idea that theca lutein cells produce the majority of androgens, whereas granulosa lutein cells are responsible for converting that androgen to estrogen [218, 221]. In sharp contrast, both luteal cell types in the rat express $P450_{AROM}$ and $P450_{17\alpha}$ and produce both steroids [139]. In addition, the protein profile of both cell types is largely similar, with the only major difference being the abundant expression of PRAP/17β-HSD in the large luteal cells and its essential absence from the small luteal cells [187].

Interactions between the multiple cell types in the CL can certainly be mediated through paracrine-secreted factors, such as cytokines (for review, see [213]) and steroids. Additionally, cell types within the CL may interact directly through gap junctions, which have been described in the CL of several species and which appear to be regulated by luteotropic and luteolytic factors (for review, see [222]).

MAINTENANCE AND REGULATION OF THE CORPUS LUTEUM

The essential and defining function of the CL is the secretion of progesterone, a steroid hormone that is essential for the initiation and maintenance of pregnancy. The sum total of progesterone's effects is to induce uterine quiescence and to prepare a nourishing and protective uterine environment for the embryo by causing differentiation of endometrial stromal cells, stimulating glandular secretions by the endometrium, and causing thickening of the cervical mucus (for reviews, see [215, 223]).

The ability of the CL to produce progesterone is regulated, in general, by factors derived from the pituitary, ovaries, and placenta. However, the relative importance of the signals produced by each of these glands varies among species and developmentally within a species. In the rabbit, all three of these organs are necessary for the normal secretion of progesterone throughout pregnancy. In contrast, the rat does not require the presence of the pituitary from midpregnancy on, and in the human the ovary (including the CL) is dispensable from an early stage of pregnancy. Both the rat and the human rely on placental products for the continued maintenance of pregnancy. In the human and nonhuman primate, the placenta rapidly gains the ability to secrete progesterone in sufficient quantities to sustain fetal survival. In the rat, the CL remains essential throughout pregnancy; however, from midpregnancy the placenta is the major source of tropic factors and substrates necessary for luteal maintenance and steroidogenesis.

Hormonal Regulation of the Rat Corpus Luteum at Different Stages of Pregnancy

Maintenance of the CL of pregnancy in the rat involves interactions between several important tropic factors. The most significant factors are PRL (or PRL-related proteins) and androgens, the substrate for intraluteal estradiol. The source of PRL/lactogenic stimulation changes from the pituitary to the decidua and the trophoblast as pregnancy progresses. Similarly, the source of androgens changes over time. Originally, the androgen substrate for estradiol biosynthesis originates in the ovaries. However, in the second half of pregnancy, androgens are derived from the trophoblast. Conversion to estradiol still occurs in the CL, using secreted, circulating placental androgens as substrate.

Days 1 to 6

During the first week of pregnancy, the CL is dependent on pituitary PRL for its maintenance and development. In the rodent, stimulation of the cervix during mating results in the generation of a neural signal that ascends to specific areas of the brain through the spinal cord (for review, see [224]) and results in secretion of PRL from the pituitary in two daily surges, a diurnal surge and a nocturnal surge, for 10 to 12 days [225, 226]. This PRL stimulation results in rescue and continued development of the CL of the cycle and thus in development of the pseudopregnant or pregnant state. During the first week of pregnancy or pseudopregnancy, PRL alone is capable of sustaining basal levels of progesterone secretion, and inhibition of PRL secretion curtails progesterone production [227]. PRL also induces luteal responsiveness to estradiol by stimulating transcription of estrogen receptor α and β in luteal cells [228, 229], and luteal estradiol then acts to enhance PRL-induced progesterone production [230]. The essential role of PRL in development of the CL has been further substantiated by the deletion of either the PRL or PRL-receptor genes, or by deletion of the genes for significant signal transduction molecules in the PRL signaling pathway. Mice with these deletions are infertile [231–233]. Ovulation and luteinization take place; however, CL regress rapidly and progesterone production is defective [234, 235]. Therefore it is clear that PRL is the most significant factor regulating early luteal function in the rodent.

Days 7 to 11

Interestingly, despite the fact that pituitary PRL continues to be secreted until approximately day 10 of pregnancy, it is no longer essential after day 6 [236]. This is the result of expression of PRL-like luteotropic factors by the maturing decidua and placenta. One such PRL-like factor is expressed in a discrete population of decidual cells during this period of pregnancy [237, 238] and was originally named *decidual luteotropin* [239]. This hormone is capable of sustaining pseudopregnancy for a short period after the termination of pituitary PRL secretion [239] and was found to bind to the PRL receptor [240–242]. In 1999, Prigent-Tessier and colleagues cloned rat decidual luteotropin and determined that it was in fact PRL that was produced in the decidua but identical in sequence to pituitary-derived PRL [243]. This was consistent with the long-established production of PRL in the human decidua that is identical to pituitary PRL in sequence, immunoreactivity, and bioactivity (for review, see 244]). Although decidual PRL can act as a luteotropic factor, the physiologic role of this hormone in pregnancy is most likely to be at the local level within the decidua, which expresses PRL receptors [241, 245].

Experiments in which rats were hypophysectomized between days 6 and 11 of pregnancy indicated that PRL acted in concert with LH to sustain progesterone secretion at this time [246]. Administration of either estradiol or aromatizable androgen could compensate for LH when administered to hypophysectomized pregnant rats [246, 247] or rats treated with LH antiserum [230, 248–250]. Therefore it appears that stimulation of the CL by LH results from LH-stimulated production of luteal androgen and aromatization of that androgen to estradiol [230] (for review, see [177]). The absolute requirement for estradiol at this stage in pregnancy is a new development compared with the first week, where estradiol was dispensible. PRL is still essential and required for the actions of LH [251] and estradiol [230] on progesterone secretion. This is probably because of PRL regulation of luteal expression of LH [252–254] and estrogen receptors [228, 229, 255, 256].

Days 12 to 21

Dramatic changes in regulation of the CL occur at midpregnancy. At this stage in gestation the pituitary PRL surges abruptly terminate, circulating LH falls to low levels [176], and removal of the pituitary has no effect on the maintenance of pregnancy [257]. In addition, production of decidual PRL [237, 238, 243] declines. Despite the fall in these stimulatory factors, the CL increases in weight, vascularization, and steroidogenic capacity from midpregnancy as a result of secretion of tropic factors by the placenta. A critical PRL-like luteotropin produced at this stage in pregnancy is rat placental lactogen I (PL-I), which is produced by trophoblast giant cells. Expression of mRNA for PL-I has been detected shortly after implantation [258]; however, the protein is detectable in serum around midpregnancy only [259]. PL-I is secreted as a glycosylated protein complex of 36–40 kDa [258, 260], with an extremely long half-life in the circulation [261, 262]. This luteotropin acts by binding to the PRL receptor [263] and has been experimentally demonstrated to have identical actions to PRL in the CL and decidua [191, 228, 264–267]. The mouse also produces a PL-I that binds to the PRL receptor [268] and is a potent luteotropin [269, 270].

Lactogenic stimulation of the CL continues throughout late pregnancy, mediated by another PRL-related placental protein. This protein, placental lactogen II (PL-II), is a 25 kDa nonglycosylated protein [258, 260] with a short half-life [261]. Like PL-I, PL-II is produced by the trophoblast giant cells. Production increases with time of gestation, and onset of expression of PL-II by these cells precedes the decline in expression of PL-I [258]. PL-II concentrations in serum rise from midgestation until parturition in the rat and mouse [259]. Although it was recognized early that PL-II could bind to the PRL receptor, it was at first believed not to have luteotropic activity [263]. It has since been found that PL-II has identical actions to PRL and PL-I in the CL and the decidua [191, 228, 264, 267] and that this hormone is responsible for maintenance of the CL of late pregnancy. Mouse PL-II, which like rat PL-II is a short-lived protein, [271], has also been demonstrated to be a luteotropic hormone [269, 270].

Although the rodent placenta produces PRL-like hormones, it does not express an LH-like hormone such as the CG of primates. However, the fall in LH is compensated for by secretion of new products from the placenta. As discussed previously, the essential role of LH in the CL is to stimulate androgen production, as a substrate for conversion to estradiol (for review, see [177]). From midpregnancy, circulating levels of LH are inadequate to stimulate follicular [174] or luteal [173] androgen secretion. However, androgen levels in the maternal blood rise dramatically [272] because of placental androgen production (for review, see 177]). Androgen biosynthesis takes place in trophoblast cells, which rapidly acquire $P450_{17\alpha}$ at this point in pregnancy [273, 274]. The placenta abundantly secretes androstenedione and some testosterone [177, 274], which are converted by the ovaries to estradiol [275]. The acquisition of P450–17α by the placenta appears to depend on a drop in circulating LH. When the decline in LH activity at midpregnancy was prevented by administration of gonadotropin, a marked increase in ovarian androgen secretion and concomitant decline in placental androgen secretion and P450–17α mRNA content were observed [273, 276].

At this stage in pregnancy, the CL also begins to express relaxin [277], a protein hormone that appears to be essential for birth and survival of pups through actions on the cervix, myometrium, and mammary gland [278–280]. Expression of this hormone is regulated by placental lactogens and estrogen [266].

Role of Tropic Hormones

There are a wide variety of luteotropic factors, which vary in importance among species. The single most universally significant luteotropin is LH, whether acting directly or through stimulation of estradiol secretion. In the rodent, PRL or PRL-like hormones are also critical to luteal function. Additional factors that have been described as luteotropic in various species include growth hormone (GH), insulin-like growth factor-1 (IGF-1), oxytocin, prostaglandins E2 and I2, estrogen, and progesterone. Actions of one luteotropic factor can be mediated or modulated by another. Tropic actions can include effects on growth and differentiation and vascularization of the CL, in addition to direct actions on steroidogenesis.

Prolactin and Placental Lactogens

PRL is an essential luteotropic hormone in the rodent; its actions on the CL in this species have been recently reviewed [281]. The critical role of PRL in sustaining the CL of the rodent has been illustrated by the generation of mice lacking either PRL or the PRL receptor [231, 232]. Female mice with these mutations cannot become either pseudopregnant or pregnant, resulting in sterility, but the observed defects in embryonic development, implantation, and decidualization can be rescued by administration of progesterone [234, 235]. This indicates that the major and essential action of PRL in early pregnancy is to sustain progesterone production from the CL. Progesterone replacement in PRL and PRL receptor null mice cannot, however, prevent fetal death at midpregnancy, suggesting that there are additional, critical local actions of PRL within the decidua. Indeed, PRL has been shown to regulate the expression of several decidual genes that could have negative or positive effects on the establishment of pregnancy [266, 267, 281–283]. After the early stages of pregnancy in the rodent, the actions of PRL on the CL are taken over by the trophoblast-derived placental lactogens, which bind to the prolactin receptor [263, 264] and which have been demonstrated to have identical actions to PRL in the CL [191, 228, 264, 265, 269, 270].

PRL acts through a specific PRL receptor. There are two PRL receptor isoforms in the rat, called *long* and *short forms,* both of which are expressed in the CL throughout pregnancy [31]. Expression of both PRL receptor isoforms is induced by luteinization [30, 31], as is expression of the transcription factor Stat5 [30, 33]. PRL also appears to stimulate the expression of its own receptor [31]. PRL has been shown to activate a number of signal transduction pathways through its receptors. However, the majority of investigations into the luteotropic actions of PRL have concentrated on the Jak2/Stat5 signal transduction pathway activated by the long form of the receptor (for review, see [281]). The importance of this signal transduction pathway to PRL's luteotropic actions has been demonstrated by elimination of both isoforms of Stat5 in mice. This mutation results in female infertility caused by inadequate luteal development [233]. Deletion of either the Stat5a or the Stat5b gene alone is insufficient to render the animals infertile [284, 285], indicating that the two isoforms have interchangeable actions in the CL. Whereas the Jak2/Stat5 pathway appears to be the major mediator of PRL's luteotropic actions, several kinase pathways are activated by PRL in other tissues, including PI3 kinase/AKT, MAP kinase, and c-src (for review, see [281]). Activation of an additional kinase, protein kinase C delta (PKCδ), by PRL has recently been observed in the rat CL [286]. This activation has been shown to be essential for PRL stimulation of relaxin expression in the CL [266].

PRL has been shown to directly stimulate progesterone production in vitro by luteal cells from a wide variety of species, including rodents and humans (for review, see 281]). There are several potential mechanisms for these actions of PRL (Figure 12.3). The first, and probably a lesser mechanism, is upregulation of cholesterol availability from extracellular and intracellular sources. PRL was identified early as a factor that could elevate luteal stores of cholesterol [251, 287, 288]. Thereafter, PRL was shown to increase the number of lipoprotein binding sites on luteal cells [289] and to enhance cholesterol uptake [290]. As previously mentioned, PRL also activates hormone sensitive lipase (HSL), thus increasing the availability of free cholesterol for steroidogenesis [134–136]. Microarray analysis has recently revealed that many of these PRL effects are mediated at the transcriptional level, including increases in gene expression of the HDL receptor SR-B1, HSL, and SCP-2 [129]. The second mechanism by which PRL affects steroidogenesis is by regulating steroidogenic enzymes. PRL has been shown to upregulate expression of P450ssc and 3β-HSD [165–167] (for review, see [281]), but these enzymes are generally expressed in excess and are not rate limiting in the production of progesterone. Total inhibition of 20α-HSD gene expression appears in contrast to be a critically important action of PRL. This action of PRL prevents catabolism of progesterone within the CL [190–192]. An additional steroigodenic enzyme that may be regulated by PRL is 17β-hydroxysteroid dehydrogenase 7 (17β-HSD 7), which is involved in estradiol synthesis. This enzyme has been identified in the rodent CL from midpregnancy [169, 170, 185] and, in the rat, was formerly named *prolactin receptor associated protein (PRAP)* because of its association with the short form of the PRL receptor [188, 189]. Treatment with PRL appears to stabilize this protein through an unknown mechanism [188].

In addition to its effect on progesterone synthesis, PRL may have a protective role in the CL through stimulation of the expression of superoxide dismutases, enzymes that scavenge free radicals [265, 129]. Prolactin also affects hypertrophy of luteal cells through direct and indirect mechanisms. Directly, hypertrophy may be enhanced by PRL-induced activation of elongation factor 2 (EF2), a protein that acts to catalyze protein translation events [291]. Indirectly, PRL has been shown to stimulate expression of IGF-1 in a rat luteal cell line [292]. IGF-1 has been shown to regulate protein synthesis and growth in many tissues (for review, see [293]). Receptors for this growth factor are present in the rat CL [292, 294–296]. IGF-1 receptors are preferentially localized to the large cells of the CL, and only the large cells respond to IGF stimulation [295], which suggests a role for IGF-1 in cellular hypertrophy.

PRL has also been implicated in vascularization of the CL. It has been suggested that both full-length and proteolytically cleaved PRL have direct angiogenic effects in some tissues (for review, see [297]). However, in the CL, the actions of PRL on vascular development are likely to be indirectly mediated through estradiol. PRL plays a key role in the production and action of estradiol, a factor known to be involved in angiogenesis in the CL [49, 177], by enhancing luteal content of $P450_{AROM}$ and 17β-HSD [167, 178, 180, 188] and by stimulating the expression of both forms of estradiol receptor [228, 229, 255, 256]. PRL also increases expression of receptors for LH [252–254], which has been implicated as an enhancer of luteal angiogenesis. Finally, as previously mentioned, PRL stimulates production of the broad-spectrum protease inhibitor α2-MG in the rat CL [63]. The role of α2-MG is unknown, but it may play a role in regulating angiogenesis by inactivating proteases or by binding to the angiogenic factor bFGF [298]. α2-MG can also bind to the growth factor IGF-1

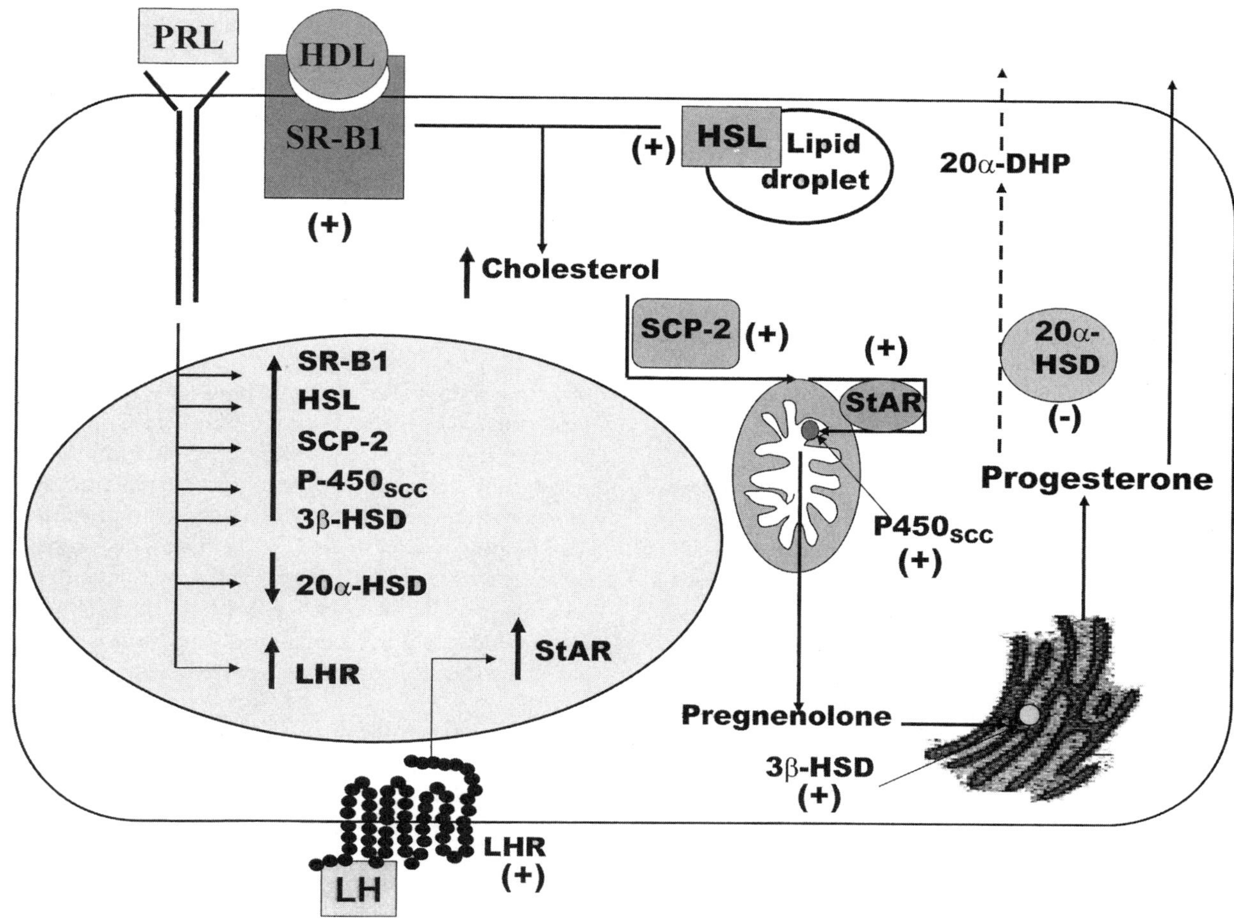

FIGURE 12.3 Effects of PRL/lactogens on progesterone production by the rat CL. PRL acts directly and indirectly to enhance progesterone production. Directly, PRL increases cholesterol availability and transport by inducing transcription of SR-B1, HSL, and SCP-2. Transport of cholesterol to the mitochondrial inner membrane is indirectly regulated. PRL stimulates production of luteinizing hormone receptors (LHR). LH then increases transcription of StAR and thus cholesterol transport to the site of P450scc. PRL induces transcription of P450scc and 3β-HSD, the enzymes responsible for progesterone production. Simultaneously, PRL decreases transcription of 20α-HSD and thus prevents the metabolism of progesterone to a gestationally inactive metabolite, 20α-dihydroprogesterone.

[299]. Whether this binding inhibits or enhances the actions of these factors is not known.

Luteinizing Hormone/Chorionic Gonadotrophin

LH is the most universally important luteotropic hormone across species. It is well known for its role in regulation of steroidogenesis and has also been implicated in luteal development, intraluteal communication, and vascularization. LH acts through the LH/CG receptor, a member of the superfamily of G-protein coupled receptors. Signaling through this receptor generally involves activation of adenylate cyclase and production of cAMP (for review, see [300]). In the rodent, LH has acute and sustained effects on steroidogenesis. The acute effect is mediated via LH stimulation of StAR [301], whereas the sustained effect of LH is mediated by estradiol [249]. In rodents, whereas LH can have an acute, direct action on progesterone secretion [216], it acts primarily to support estrogen production through stimulation of luteal $P450_{17\alpha}$ expression [173, 174]. Interestingly, the tropic action of LH is limited to only a few days during pregnancy [236]. Furthermore, LH is dispensible from midpregnancy, when the placenta becomes the major source of androgens (for review, see [177]).

In primate and ruminant species, LH/CG is the primary stimulator of luteal progesterone synthesis. The ruminant requires pituitary LH secretion throughout pregnancy to sustain luteal progesterone production [215]. In contrast, in primates, luteal progesterone and estradiol production are stimulated by LH only during the menstrual cycle. Early in pregnancy, the CL of the cycle is rescued by a placental luteotropin, CG (for review, see [302]). This protein hormone is secreted into the maternal bloodstream from the time of implantation, acts through the LH/CG receptor, and is essential to maintain luteal progesterone production and early pregnancy in the primate. Interestingly, the CL becomes refractory to CG stimulation while levels of this hormone are still high and luteal progesterone production declines. By the eighth week of pregnancy in humans, and at equivalent times in nonhuman primates, the placenta is the major source of progesterone and has the dominant role in the maintenance of pregnancy (for review, see [302]).

LH/CG stimulates the expression of steroidogenic enzymes in CL of ruminants and primates [215, 302, 303]. However, it is believed the primary mechanism by which these hormones regulate steroidogenesis is via stimulation of cholesterol transport. The process of luteinization is associated with a dramatic upregulation of StAR [25, 26]. In the human, this protein is abundant in the early and midluteal phase, but expression declines or becomes variable in the late luteal phase, as progesterone production declines [304, 305]. However, expression of StAR and of steroidogenic enzymes, which also begin to decline at this stage [22, 304, 305], can be sustained by "rescue" of the CL with CG [304]. The molecular mechanism by which LH/CG stimulates StAR transcriptional activity has been the subject of extensive investigation [306–311]. Although regulation of StAR is probably the most critical role of LH/CG, these hormones have also been shown to increase LDL receptors and LDL uptake [312–315] and to enhance breakdown of cholesterol esters to free cholesterol [130–133].

In addition to its roles in steroidogenesis, LH/CG has been linked to development and vascularization of the CL. LH has been shown to enhance gap junctional communication between luteal cells, which may be important in development (for review, see [222]). Withdrawal of gonadotropic support shortly after ovulation in the marmoset causes a disruption in the structure of the CL, suggesting changes in cell-to-cell communication [93]. Other studies have linked LH/CG with VEGF expression, angiopoietin expression, and endothelial cell proliferation in humans and primate species [41–43] (for review, see [44]).

Growth Hormone/Insulin-Like Growth Factor 1

Direct ovarian effects of GH have been reported (for review, see [316]); however, the majority of the effects of this hormone on the CL are likely to be mediated through GH-induced elevations in circulating IGF-1. There are indications that GH/IGF-1 may be important in luteal development. For example, although replacement of LH in hypophysectomized ewes supports normal progesterone secretion in the early CL both LH and GH are required for normal luteal weight and development [215]. IGF-1 has been shown to stimulate progesterone secretion from luteal cells of several species [295, 296, 317–322], and the stimulatory action of LH on StAR gene expression in the human is augmented by IGFs [321, 322]. In the rat, prolactin causes upregulation of IGF-1 production in luteal cells and IGF-1 treatment has in turn been shown to increase expression of ERβ in those cells [292].

Progesterone

Rothchild [323] first proposed in 1981 that progesterone itself stimulates progesterone production by the CL. This theory has since been supported by several studies in rats and nonhuman primates using progesterone receptor (PR) antagonists or inhibitors of progesterone synthesis [324–327]. Two studies have suggested that progesterone may mediate some of the actions of CG on the CL. In one study, treatment of human luteal cells in culture with a progesterone receptor antagonist did not result in an inhibition of basal progesterone secretion; however, a dose-related inhibition of CG-stimulated progesterone production was observed [328]. Another study in nonhuman primates suggested that progesterone mediated actions of hCG on luteal growth and integrity [329]. This is consistent with a recent report that, in the rat, blockade of progesterone action causes apoptosis of luteal cells [327].

The nuclear PRs A and B have been identified in the CL of humans [328, 330–333] and nonhuman primates [334–336], and it appears that progesterone is able to stimulate the expression of its own receptor in these species [328, 337]. Gonadotropins can also stimulate expression of luteal PR in the primate [337]. In contrast, the rat CL does not contain a cognate PR [338–340]. Despite this lack, progesterone has been shown to inhibit the expression of 20α-HSD and thus prevent its own catabolism in a rat luteal cell line [341]. It is likely that progesterone acts in this case through the ubiquitously expressed glucocorticoid receptor [341]. It is also possible that a previously unidentified PR is present in the rat CL, similar perhaps to the membrane-bound PR that has been identified in the bovine CL [342].

Estrogen

Estrogen is an essential luteotropic hormone during midpregnancy in the rat. Both estrogen receptor α and β (ERα and ERβ) are expressed in the rat CL during pregnancy [228], although ERα is expressed at much higher levels [229]. Generation of mice lacking one or the other of these receptors has indicated that whereas estrogen is critical for CL formation and maintenance, it can act through either receptor to carry out these actions [343]. Estrogen has many actions, some of which complement prolactin's effects on the CL. For example, estrogen induces a significant increase in luteal cell protein content [344], at least in part by increasing expression of EF2 in luteal cells [345], which is then activated by PRL [291]. Estrogen also increases the expression of 17β-HSD [186, 188], which is stabilized by PRL [188], and enhances PRL-induced stimulation of relaxin expression [266], possibly by increasing PKCδ.

Estrogen has direct steroidogenic actions in the CL, enhancing luteal cell uptake and cholesterol mobilization. Originally, estradiol was shown to stimulate lipoprotein binding and use [346, 347] and to enhance the transport capacity of SCP-2 [140]. Recent investigations have revealed that these estradiol effects are caused, at least in part, by transcriptional stimulation of the HDL receptor SR-B1 gene [128, 129]. In rabbits, estradiol has also been linked with elevated production of StAR in luteal cells [348] and with greater cholesterol accumulation in mitochondria [349].

A critical action of estrogen in the CL is stimulation of vascularization, particularly at midpregnancy [49]. The effects of estrogen on angiogenesis are not confined to the CL and have been recently reviewed [350]. Estrogen receptors are present on endothelial cells [350], and angiogenesis is impaired in mice lacking ERα [351]. Angiogenesis can also be inhibited by treatment with antiestrogens [352]. The mechanism by which estradiol stimulates angiogenesis in the CL is unclear. However, estradiol has been shown to induce proliferation of endothelial cells during vascularization of the CL [49], and this action has been linked to upregulation of bFGF [353]. Estradiol has also been shown to stimulate VEGF expression in the uterus and in granulosa cells of various species [354–356] and to restore VEGF expression in the CL of hypophysectomized and hysterectomized pregnant rats [88]. This hormone has recently been shown to regulate Ang-1, Ang-2, and Tie-2 expression in nonreproductive tissues [357], although reproductive tissues were not examined in this study.

REGRESSION OF THE CORPUS LUTEUM

The process of luteal regression consists of the cessation of progesterone production (functional regression) and physical involution of the CL (structural regression). Regression of the CL has been the subject of a number of reviews; an excellent and comprehensive recent review is that of Davis and Rueda [358].

In the human, the CL of pregnancy is rendered unnecessary for continued pregnancy at an early stage, and luteal progesterone production declines at this time [302]. In rodents, functional regression of the CL occurs shortly before parturition. The fall in progesterone secretion at the end of pregnancy occurs through the abrupt expression of the enzyme 20α-HSD, which converts progesterone to a gestationally inactive metabolite. This enzyme is suppressed throughout pregnancy by PRL and placental lactogens, acting through the PRL receptor [190, 193]. At the end of pregnancy in the rat, luteal expression of both PRL receptor isoforms decreases dramatically [31], thus effectively terminating the luteotropic effects of placental lactogens. Although the loss of PRL/placental lactogen stimulation may be essential for the rapid expression of 20α-HSD, a key role for prostaglandin $F_{2\alpha}$ ($PGF_{2\alpha}$) in regulating transcription of this enzyme has recently been reported [129, 359]. $PGF_{2\alpha}$, which stimulates luteal 20α-HSD activity [339, 360–364] and can induce abortion in rats [360, 364], appears to be a physiologically relevant signal for the termination of luteal progesterone secretion in the rodent. Administration of a prostaglandin inhibitor to pregnant rats delays the drop in progesterone and parturition, and this effect can be reversed by $PGF_{2\alpha}$ [365]. Mice lacking the receptor for $PGF_{2\alpha}$ also do not undergo the normal preparturition drop in progestone and fail to undergo parturition, but ovariectomy of these animals initiates parturition within 24 hours [366, 367]. Similarly, mice lacking critical genes in the pathway for prostaglandin synthesis, phospholipase A2 [368, 369] and prostaglandin synthase 1 [370], also have abnormal parturition and continued high levels of progesterone. Parturition can be restored in these two mutant strains by administration of an antiprogestin [368, 371], indicating that the failure to undergo functional regression is the critical defect. The luteal defect has been examined in mice lacking the receptor for $PGF_{2\alpha}$ and it has been determined that in these animals 20α-HSD is not upregulated at the end of pregnancy [359] (Figures 12.4 and 12.5), supporting the concept that expression of this enzyme is the major factor in the termination of luteal progesterone secretion.

Signaling via the $PGF_{2\alpha}$ receptor has been reviewed by Davis and Rueda [358], as well as others [215, 372]. A recent study determined that $PGF_{2\alpha}$ acts on the 20α-HSD promoter through the transcription factor NUR77 to induce increased expression of this enzyme [359]. There is additional recent evidence that $PGF_{2\alpha}$ may act to inhibit lactogenic suppression of 20α-HSD expression by increasing expression of a member of the suppressors of cytokine signaling family, SOCS-3 [373], which has been demonstrated to interfere with signaling through the Jak2/Stat5 pathway [374]. $PGF_{2\alpha}$ may also act to inhibit steroidogenesis independently of effects on 20α-HSD by decreasing StAR protein in the rat CL [375].

In ruminant species, $PGF_{2\alpha}$ is accepted to be the major luteolytic signal (for review, see [215]). In these species, $PGF_{2\alpha}$ is produced by the uterus, and hysterectomy prolongs the luteal phase. In the rodent, hysterectomy of pseudopregnant animals will prolong luteal life span [376–378], suggesting a role for the nonpregnant uterus in inducing luteal regression. However, it has also been noted that $PGF_{2\alpha}$ stimulates expression of prostaglandin synthase-2 in the CL, thus enabling intraluteal production of $PGF_{2\alpha}$ [379] in a potential feed-forward mechanism. Therefore an intraluteal mechanism for the termination of luteal progesterone production is also feasible.

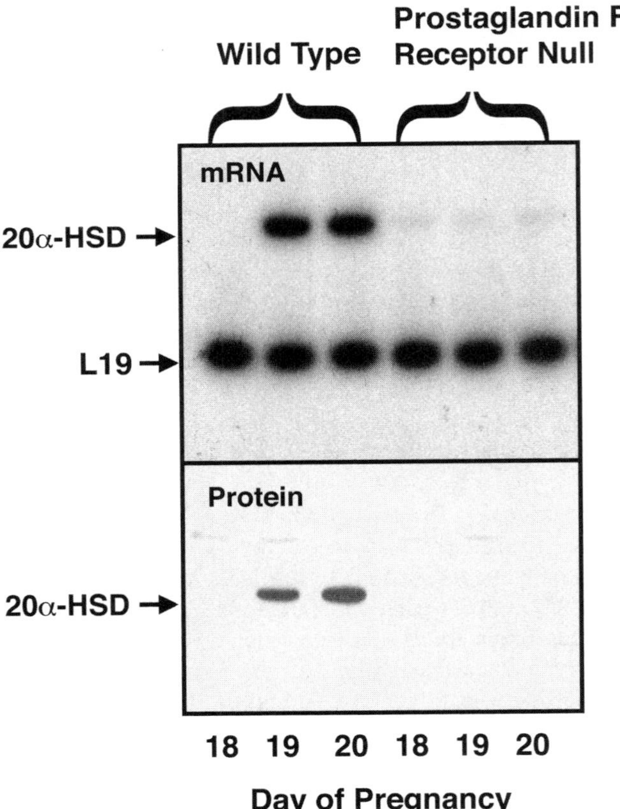

FIGURE 12.4 Detection of mRNA for 20α-HSD by semiquantitative RT-PCR and of 20α-HSD protein by Western blotting in CL of prostaglandin F receptor null mice and wild-type littermates on days 18 to 20 of pregnancy. Levels of mRNA for 20α-HSD were normalized to expression of mRNA for the ribosomal protein L19. (Adapted from [359].)

Although the CL of pregnancy in the rat ceases to produce significant progesterone before parturition, involution of luteal tissue occurs only after parturition. Cell death in the CL occurs by a process of apoptosis. A low level of apoptosis is observed throughout pregnancy [340], but dramatic apoptosis only occurs after parturition, when it results in a rapid reduction in luteal weight [340, 380]. Apoptosis-associated genes have been observed to increase before parturition [380], perhaps prompted by the fall in progesterone, which has been implicated as a luteal survival factor [327, 339, 340]. Expression of Fas and Fas ligand were detected in CL of the rat throughout pregnancy, and expression rose at the time of parturition, suggesting a possible involvement of this system in apoptosis of the postpartum CL [381]. The rapid postpartum destruction of the CL is associated with an infiltration of immune cells, primarily macrophages, although this infiltration is less intense than that seen during luteal maturation [209]. An influx of immune cells is also seen during regression of the CL of the cycle in many species (for review, see [213]). It is unknown whether these immune cells actively stimulate cell death in the CL or whether they are merely present to remove cellular debris. The arguments regarding the role of these cells during luteal regression have been recently reviewed [213]. The presence of immune cells in the regressing CL appears to be mediated via chemoattractive cues, of which the most widely demonstrated is the chemokine MCP-1 (for review, see [382]). Unlike the CL of the rat estrous cycle, in which PRL has been implicated as a stimulus for structural regression (for review, see [281]), the postpartum CL of pregnancy appears to be stimulated by PRL. These CL regain the PRLR following parturition, and apoptosis in these CL is

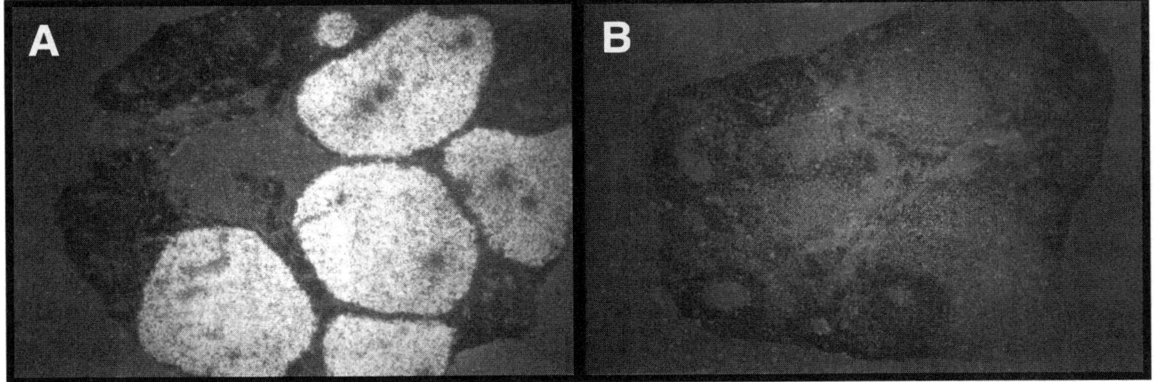

FIGURE 12.5 mRNA for 20α-HSD detected by in situ hybridization in ovaries of wild-type and prostaglandin F receptor null mice on day 20 of pregnancy.

delayed by the high PRL levels of suckled compared with unsuckled animals [383].

The rapid breakdown of the CL associated with mass apoptosis of luteal cells also involves destruction of ECM and involution of vasculature. Increases in proteases and their inhibitors are observed during the late luteal phase and at the end of pseudopregnancy in the rat (for reviews, see [39, 57, 58]). One study of the postpartum rat CL indicated a rise in TIMP-2 postpartum [61]. Overall, it is expected that these factors will be elevated during the extreme tissue disintegration that occurs postpartum.

CONCLUSION

Over the past decade, state-of-the art technology has dramatically advanced our understanding of the CL. The use of transgenic and knockout mice and of genomics and proteonomics has opened the doors to many discoveries. Exciting new information has been published on differentiation, angiogenesis, steroidogenesis, and regression of the CL. Almost 450 years after it was first described, this unique and fascinating organ continues to hold mysteries for researchers. We anticipate that research in the CL will continue to flourish in the decade to come.

References

1. Falloppio, G. (1561). *Observationes Anatomicae,* translator L. G. Wilson. Venice.
2. de Graaf, R. (1672). De Mulerium Organis Generationi Inservientibus Tractatus Novus. Leydon, The Netherlands: Hackiana.
3. Malpighi, M. (1685). Praeclarissimo et Eruditissimo Viro D. Jacobo Sponio Medicinae Doctori et Lugdeunensi Anatomico Accuratissimo. *Phil. Trans. R. Soc. (Lond.)* 14, 630.
4. Short, R. V. (1977). The discovery of the ovaries. In *The Ovary*, 2d ed., eds. P. L. Zuckerman and B. J. Weir, 1–40. New York: Academic Press.
5. Prenant, A. (1898). La valeur morphologique du corps jaune. Son action physiologique et therapeutique possible. *Rev. Gen. Scie. Pure. Appl.* 9, 646–650.
6. Fraenkel, L. (1903). Die function des corpus luteum. *Arch. Gynaekol.* 68, 438–545.
7. Fraenkel, L., and Cohn, F. (1901). Experimentalle untersuchungen uber den einfluss des corpus luteum auf de insertion des eies. *Anat. Anz.* 20, 294–300.
8. Magnus, V. (1901). Ovariets betydning for svangerskabet med saerligt hensyn til corpus luteum. *Nor. Mag. Laegevidensk.* 62, 1138–1145.
9. Allen, W. M., and Corner, G. W. (1929). Physiology of the corpus luteum. VII. Maintenance of pregnancy in the rabbit after very early castration by corpus luteum extract. *Proc. Soc. Exp. Biol. Med.* 27, 403–405.
10. Allen, W. M., and Wintersteiner, O. (1934). Crystalline progestin. *Science* 80, 190–191.
11. Butenandt, A., Westphal, U., and Cobler, H. (1934). Uber einen abbau des stigma-sterins zu corpus-luteum-worksamen stoffen; ein beltrag zur konstitution des corpus-luteum-hormons (vorlauf mitteil). *Ber. Dtsch. Chem. Ges.* 67, 1611–1616.
12. Hartmann, M., and Wettstein, A. (1934). Zur kenntis der corpus-luteum hormone (2. Mitteilung). *Helv. Chem. Acta.* 17, 1365–1370.
13. Slotta, K. H., Rushig, H., and Fells, W. (1934). Reindarstellung der hormone aus dem corpus luteum. *Ber. Dtsch. Chem. Ges.* 67, 1270.
14. Richards, J. S., Russell, D. L., Ochsner, S., and Espey, L. L. (2002). Ovulation: New dimensions and new regulators of the inflammatory-like response. *Annu. Rev. Physiol.* 64, 69–92.
15. Richards, J. S. (2001). Perspective: The ovarian follicle—a perspective in 2001. *Endocrinology* 142, 2184–2193.
16. Robker, R. L., and Richards, J. S. (1998). Hormone-induced proliferation and differentiation of granulosa cells: A coordinated balance of the cell cycle regulators cyclin D2 and $p27^{Kip1}$. *Mol. Endocrinol.* 12, 924–940.
17. Robker, R. L., and Richards, J. S. (1998). Hormonal control of the cell cycle in ovarian cells: Proliferation versus differentiation. *Biol. Reprod.* 59, 476–482.
18. Kiyokawa, H., Kineman, R. D., Manova-Todorova, K. O., Soares, V. C., Hoffman, E. S., Ono, M., Khanam, D., Hayday, A. C., Frohman, L. A., and Koff, A. (1996). Enhanced growth of mice lacking the cyclin-dependent kinase inhibitor function of $p27^{Kip1}$. *Cell* 85, 721–732.
19. Hampl, A., Pacherník, J., and Dvorák, P. (2000). Levels and interactions of p27, cyclin D3, and CDK4 during the formation and maintenance of the corpus luteum in mice. *Biol. Reprod.* 62, 1393–1401.
20. Tong, W., Kiyokawa, H., Soos, T. J., Park, M. S., Soares, V. C., Manova, K., Pollard, J. W., and Koff, A. (1998). The absence of $p27^{Kip1}$, an inhibitor of G1 cyclin-dependent kinases, uncouples differentiation and growth arrest during the granulosa-luteal transition. *Cell Growth Differ.* 9, 787–794.
21. Kaynard, A. H., Periman, L. M., Simard, K., and Melner, M. H. (1992). Ovarian 3β-hydroxysteroid dehydrogenase and sulfated glycoprotein-2 gene expression are differentially regulated by the induction of ovulation, pseudopregnancy, and luteolysis in the immature rat. *Endocrinology* 130, 2192–2200.
22. Doody, K. J., Lorence, M. C., Mason, J. I., and Simpson, E. R. (1990). Expression of messenger ribonucleic acid species encoding steroidogenic enzymes in human follicles and corpora lutea throughout the menstrual cycle. *J. Clin. Endocrinol. Metab.* 70, 1041–1045.
23. Doody, K. J., Lephard, E. D., Stirling, D., Lorence, M. C., Magness, R. R., McPhaul, M. J., and Simpson, E. R. (1991). Expression of mRNA species encoding steroidogenic enzymes in the rat ovary. *J. Mol. Endocrinol.* 6, 153–162.
24. Goldring, N. B., Durica, J. M., Lifka, J., Hedin, L., Ratoosh, S. L., Miller, W. L., Orly, J., and Richards, J. S. (1987). Cholesterol side-chain cleavage P450 (P450scc) mRNA: Evidence for hormonal regulation in rat ovarian follicles and constitutive expression in corpora lutea. *Endocrinology* 120, 1942–1950.

25. Kiriakidou, M., McAllister, J. M., Sugawara, T., and Strauss, III, J. F. (1996). Expression of steroidogenic acute regulatory protein (StAR) in the human ovary. *J. Clin. Endocrinol. Metab.* 81, 4122–4128.
26. Sandhoff, T. W., and McLean, M. P. (1996). Hormonal regulation of steroidogenic acute regulatory (StAR) protein messenger ribonucleic acid expression in the rat ovary. *Endocrine* 4, 259–267.
27. Hickey, G. J., Chen, S. A., Besman, M. J., Shively, J. E., Hall, P. F., Gaddy-Kurten, D., and Richards, J. S. (1988). Hormonal regulation, tissue distribution, and content of aromatase cytochrome P450 messenger ribonucleic acid and enzyme in rat ovarian follicles and corpora lutea: Relationship to estradiol biosynthesis. *Endocrinology* 122, 1426–1436.
28. Keyes, P. L., and Wiltbank, M. C. (1988). Endocrine regulation of the corpus luteum. *Annu. Rev. Physiol.* 50, 465–482.
29. Camp, T. A., Rahal, J. O., and Mayo, K. E. (1991). Cellular localization and hormonal regulation of follicle-stimulating hormone and luteinizing hormone receptor messenger RNAs in the rat ovary. *Mol. Endocrinol.* 5, 1405–1417.
30. Russell, D. L., and Richards, J. S. (1999). Differentiation-dependent PRL responsiveness and stat (signal transducers and activators of transcription) signaling in rat ovarian cells. *Mol. Endocrinol.* 13, 2049–2064.
31. Telleria, C. M., Parmer, T. G., Zhong, L., Clarke, D. L., Albarracin, C. T., Duan, W. R., Linzer, D. I., and Gibori, G. (1997). The different forms of the PRL receptor in the rat corpus luteum: Developmental expression and hormonal regulation in pregnancy. *Endocrinology* 138, 4812–4820.
32. Clarke, D. L., and Linzer, D. I. H. (1993). Changes in prolactin receptor expression during pregnancy in the mouse ovary. *Endocrinology* 133, 224–232.
33. Ruff, S. J., Leers-Sucheta, S., Melner, M. H., and Cohen, S. (1996). Induction and activation of Stat 5 in the ovaries of pseudopregnant rats. *Endocrinology* 137, 4095–4099.
34. Hsieh, M., Johnson, M. A., Greenberg, N. M., and Richards, J. S. (2002). Regulated expression of Wnts and Frizzleds at specific stages of follicular development in the rodent ovary. *Endocrinology* 143, 898–908.
35. Richards, J. S., Sharma, S. C., Falender, A. E., and Lo, Y. H. (2002). Expression of FKHR, FKHRL1, and AFX genes in the rodent ovary: Evidence for regulation by IGF-1, estrogen, and the gonadotropins. *Mol. Endocrinol.* 16, 580–599.
36. Alliston, T. N., Gonzalez-Robayna, I. J., Buse, P., Fireston, G. L., and Richards, J. S. (2000). Expression and localization of serum/glucocorticoid-induced kinase in the rat ovary: Relation to follicular growth and differentiation. *Endocrinology* 141, 385–395.
37. Sharma, S. C., and Richards, J. S. (2000). Regulation of AP1 (Jun/Fos) factor expression and activation in ovarian granulosa cells: Relation of JunD and Fra2 to terminal differentiation. *J. Biol. Chem.* 275, 33718–33728.
38. Curry, Jr., T. E., Song, L., and Wheeler, S. E. (2001). Cellular localization of gelatinases and tissue inhibitors of metalloproteinases during follicular growth, ovulation, and early luteal formation in the rat. *Biol. Reprod.* 65, 855–865.
39. Curry, Jr., T. E., and Osteen, K. G. (2001). Cyclic changes in the matrix metalloproteinase system in the ovary and uterus. *Biol. Reprod.* 64, 1285–1296.
40. Dickson, S. E., and Fraser, H. M. (2000). Inhibition of early luteal angiogenesis by gonadotropin-releasing hormone antagonist treatment in the primate. *J. Clin. Endocrinol. Metab.* 85, 2339–2344.
41. Wulff, C., Wilson, H., Largue, P., Duncan, W. C., Armstrong, D. G., and Fraser, H. M. (2000). Angiogenesis in the human corpus luteum: Localization and changes in angiopoietins, Tie-2 and vascular endothelial growth factor messenger ribonucleic acid. *J. Clin. Endocrinol. Metab.* 85, 4302–4309.
42. Wulff, C., Dickson, S. E., Duncan, W. C., and Fraser, H. M. (2001). Angiogenesis in the human corpus luteum: Simulated early pregnancy by hCG treatment is associated with both angiogenesis and vessel stabilization. *Hum. Reprod.* 16, 2515–2524.
43. Lee, A., Christenson, L. K., Patton, P. E., Burry, K. A., and Stouffer, R. L. (1997). Vascular endothelial growth factor production by human luteinized granulosa cells in vitro. *Hum. Reprod.* 12, 2756–2761.
44. Geva, E., and Jaffe, R. B. (2000). Role of vascular endothelial growth factor in ovarian physiology and pathology. *Fertil. Steril.* 74, 429–438.
45. Rowe, A. J., Morris, K. D., Bicknell, R., and Fraser, H. M. (2002). Angiogenesis in the corpus luteum of early pregnancy in the marmoset and the effects of vascular endothelial growth factor immunoneutralization on establishment of pregnancy. *Biol. Reprod.* 67, 1180–1188.
46. Christenson, L. K., and Stouffer, R. L. (1996). Proliferation of microvascular endothelial cells in the primate corpus luteum during the menstrual cycle and simulated early pregnancy. *Endocrinology* 137, 367–374.
47. Rodger, F. E., Young, F. M., Fraser, H. M., and Illingworth, P. J. (1997). Endothelial cell proliferation follows the mid-cycle luteinizing hormone surge, but not human chorionic gonadotrophin rescue, in the human corpus luteum. *Hum. Reprod.* 12, 1723–1729.
48. Meyer, G. T., and Bruce, N. W. (1980). Quantitative cell changes and vascularization in the early corpus luteum of the pregnant rat. *Anat. Rec.* 197, 369–374.
49. Tamura, H., and Greenwald, G. (1987). Angiogenesis and its hormonal control in the corpus luteum of the pregnant rat. *Biol. Reprod.* 36,1149–1154.
50. Meyer, G. T., and McGeachie, J. K. (1988). Angiogenesis in the developing corpus luteum of pregnant rats: A stereologic and autoradiographic study. *Anat. Rec.* 222, 18–25.
51. Reynolds, L. P., Grazul-Bilska, A. T., and Redmer, D. A. (2000). Angiogenesis in the corpus luteum. *Endocrine* 12, 1–9.
52. Stouffer, R. L., Martinez-Chequer, J. C., Molskness, T. A., Xu, F., and Hazzard, T. M. (2001). Regulation and action of angiogenic factors in the primate ovary. *Arch. Med. Res.* 32, 567–575.
53. Reynolds, L. P., and Redmer, D. A. (1999). Growth and development of the corpus luteum. *J. Reprod. Fertil. Suppl.* 54, 181–191.
54. Goede, V., Schmidt, T., Kimmina, S., Kozian, D., and Augustin, H. G. (1998). Analysis of blood vessel maturation

processes during cyclic ovarian angiogenesis. *Lab. Invest.* 78, 1385–1394.

55. Wiltbank, M. C., Dysko, R. C., Gallagher, K. P., and Keyes, P. L. (1988). Relationship between blood flow and steroidogenesis in the rabbit corpus luteum. *J. Reprod. Fertil.* 84, 513–520.
56. Talks, K. L., and Harris, A. L. (2000). Current status of antiangiogenic factors. *Br. J. Haematol.* 109, 477–489.
57. Ny, T., Wahlberg, P., and Brandstrom, I. J. M. (2002). Matrix remodeling in the ovary: Regulation and functional role of the plasminogen activator and matrix metalloproteinase systems. *Mol. Cell. Endocrinol.* 187, 29–38.
58. Duncan, W. C. (2000). The human corpus luteum: Remodelling during luteolysis and maternal recognition of pregnancy. *Rev. Reprod.* 5, 12–17.
59. Nothnick, W. B., Keeble, S. C., and Curry, Jr., T. E. (1996). Collagenase, gelatinase, and proteoglycanase mRNA expression and activity during luteal development, maintenance, and regression in the pseudopregnant rat ovary. *Biol. Reprod.* 54, 616–624.
60. Liu, K., Olofsson, J. I., Wahlberg, P., and Ny, T. (1999). Distinct expression of gelatinase A (matrix metalloproteinase [MMP-2]), collagenase-3 (MMP-13), membrane type MMP 1 (MMP-14), and tissue inhibitor of MMPs type 1 mediated by physiological signals during formation and regression of the rat corpus luteum. *Endocrinology* 140, 5330–5338.
61. Li, Q. L., Wang, H. M., Lin, H. Y., Liu, D. L., Zhang, X., Liu, G. Y., Qian, D., and Zhu, C. (2000). Expression of gelatinases and their tissue inhibitors in rat corpus luteum during pregnancy and postpartum. *Mol. Reprod. Dev.* 63, 273–281.
62. Duncan, W. C., McNeilly, A. S., and Illingworth, P. J. (1998). The effect of luteal "rescue" on the expression and localization of matrix metalloproteinases and their tissue inhibitors in the human corpus luteum. *J. Clin. Endocrinol. Metab.* 83, 2470–2478.
63. Gaddy-Kurten, D., Hicky, G. J., Fey, G. H., Gauldie, J., and Richards, J. S. (1989). Hormonal regulation and tissue-specific localization of alpha 2-macroglobulin in rat ovarian follicles and corpora lutea. *Endocrinology* 125, 2985–2995.
64. Liu, K., Brandstrom, A., Liu, Y.-X., Ny, T., and Selstam, G. (1996). Coordinated expression of tissue-type plasminogen activator and plasminogen activator inhibitor type 1 during corpus luteum formation and luteolysis in the adult pseudopregnant rat. *Endocrinology* 137, 2126–2132.
65. Wang, Z., Juttermann, R., and Soloway, P. D. (2000). TIMP-2 is required for efficient activation of proMMP-2 in vivo. *J. Biol. Chem.* 275, 26411–26415.
66. Nothnick, W. B. (2000). Disruption of the tissue inhibitor of metalloproteinase-1 gene results in altered reproductive cyclicity and uterine morphology in reproductive-age female mice. *Biol. Reprod.* 63, 905–912.
67. Umans, L., Serneels, L., Overbergh, L., Lorent, K., Van Leuven, F., and Van den Berghe, H. (1995). Targeted inactivation of the mouse alpha 2-macroglobulin gene. *J. Biol. Chem.* 270, 19778–19785.
68. Ferrarra, N., and Davis-Smyth, T. (1997). The biology of vascular endothelial growth factor. *Endocr. Rev.* 18, 4–25.
69. Park, J. E., Keller, G. A., and Ferrara, N. (1993). The vascular endothelial growth factor (VEGF) isoforms: Differential deposition into the subepithelial extra-cellular matrix and bioactivity of extracellular matrix-bound VEGF. *Mol. Biol. Cell.* 4, 1317–1326.
70. Waltenberger, J., Claesson-Welsh, L., Siegbahn, A., Shibuya, M., and Heldin, C. H. (1994). Different signal transduction properties of KDR and Flt1, two receptors for vascular endothelial growth factor. *J. Biol. Chem.* 269, 26988–26995.
71. Soker, S., Takashima, S., Miao, H. Q., Neufeld, G., and Klagsbrun, M. (1998). Neuropilin-1 is expressed by endothelial and tumor cells as an isoform-specific receptor for vascular endothelial growth factor. *Cell* 92, 735–745.
72. Gluzman-Poltorak, Z., Cohen, T., Herzog, Y., and Neufeld, G. (2000). Neuropilin-2 is a receptor for the vascular endothelial growth factor (VEGF) forms VEGF-145 and VEGF-165. *J. Biol. Chem.* 275, 18040–18045.
73. Carmeliet, P., Ferreira, V., Breier, G., Pollefeyt, S., Kieckens, L., Gertsenstein, M., Fahrig, M., Vandenhoeck, A., Harpal, K., Eberhardt, C., Declercq, C., Pawling, J., Moons, L., Collen, D., Risau, W., and Nagy, A. (1996). Abnormal blood vessel development and lethality in embryos lacking a single VEGF allele. *Nature* 380, 435–439.
74. Ferrara, N., Carver-Moore, K., Chen, H., Dowd, M., Lu, L., O'Shea, K. S., Powell-Braxton, L., Hillan, K. J., and Moore, M. W. (1996). Heterozygous embryonic lethality induced by targeted inactivation of the VEGF gene. *Nature* 380, 439–442.
75. Shalaby, F., Rossant, J., Yamaguchi, T. P., Gertsenstein, M., Wu, X. F., Breitman, M. L., and Schuh, A. (1995). Failure of blood-island formation and vasculogenesis in Flk-1-deficient mice. *Nature* 376, 62–66.
76. Fong, G. H., Rossant, J., Gertsenstein, M., and Breitman, M. L. (1995). Role of the Flt-1 receptor tyrosine kinase in regulating the assembly of vascular endothelium. *Nature* 376, 66–70.
77. Bellomo, D., Headrick, J. P., Silins, G. U., Paterson, C. A., Thomas, P. S., Gartside, M., Mould, A., Cahill, M. M., Tonks, I. D., Grimmond, S. M., Townson, S., Wells, C., Little, M., Cummings, M. C., and Kay, G. F. (2000). Mice lacking the vascular endothelial growth factor-B gene (Vegfb) have smaller hearts, dysfunctional coronary vasculature, and impaired recovery from cardiac ischemia. *Circ. Res.* 86, E29–35.
78. Shweiki, D., Itin, A., Neufeld, G., Gitay-Goren, H., and Keshet, E. (1993). Patterns of expression of vascular endothelial growth factor (VEGF) and VEGF receptors in mice suggest a role in hormonally regulated angiogenesis. *J. Clin. Invest.* 91, 2235–2243.
79. Hazzard, T. M., Christenson, L. K., and Stouffer, R. L. (2000). Changes in expression of vascular endothelial growth factor and angiopoietin-1 and -2 in the macaque corpus luteum during the menstrual cycle. *Mol. Hum. Reprod.* 6, 993–998.
80. Endo, T., Kitajima, Y., Nishikawa, A., Manase, K., Shibuya, M., and Kudo, R. (2001). Cyclic changes in expression of mRNA of vascular endothelial growth factor, its receptors Flt-1 and KDR/Flk-1, and Ets-1 in human corpora lutea. *Fertil. Steril.* 76, 762–768.
81. Kamat, B. R., Brown, L. F., Manseau, E. J., Senger, D. R., and Dvorak, H. F. (1995). Expression of vascular perme-

ability factor/vascular endothelial growth factor by human granulosa and theca lutein cells. Role in corpus luteum development. *Am. J. Pathol.* 146, 157–165.

82. Gordon, J. D., Mesiano, S., Zaloudek, C. J., and Jaffe, R. B. (1996). Vascular endothelial growth factor localization in human ovary and fallopian tubes: Possible role in reproductive function and ovarian cyst formation. *J. Clin. Endocrinol. Metab.* 81, 353–359.
83. Otani, N., Minami, S., Yamoto, M., Shikone, T., Otani, H., Nishiyama, R., Otani, T., and Nakano, R. (1999). The vascular endothelial growth factor/fms-like tyrosine kinase system in human ovary during the menstrual cycle and early pregnancy. *J. Clin. Endocrinol. Metab.* 84, 3845–3851.
84. Yamamoto, S., Konishi, I., Tsuruta, Y., Nanbu, K., Mandai, M., Kuroda, H., Matsushita, K., Hamid, A. A., Yura, Y., and Mori, T. (1997). Expression of vascular endothelial growth factor (VEGF) during folliculogenesis and corpus luteum formation in the human ovary. *Gynecol. Endocrinol.* 11, 371–381.
85. Sugino, N., Kashida, S., Takiguchi, S., Karube-Harada, A., and Kato, H. (2001). Expression of vascular endothelial growth factor (VEGF) receptors in rat corpus luteum: Regulation by oestradiol during mid-pregnancy. *Reproduction* 122, 875–881.
85a. Sugino, N., Kashida, S., Takiguchi, S., Karube, A., and Kato, H. (2000). Expression of vascular endothelial growth factor and its receptors in the human corpus luteum during the menstrual cycle and in early pregnancy. *J. Clin. Endocrinol. Metab.* 85, 3919–3924.
86. Wulff, C., Wilson, H., Rudge, J. S., Wiegand, S. J., Lunn, S. F., and Fraser, H. M. (2001). Luteal angiogenesis: Prevention and intervention by treatment with vascular endothelial growth factor $trap_{A40}$. *J. Clin. Endocrinol. Metab.* 86, 3377–3386.
87. Kashida, S., Sugino, N., Takiguchi, S., Karube, A., Takayama, H., Yamagata, Y., Nakamura, Y., and Kato, H. (2001). Regulation and role of vascular endothelial growth factor in the corpus luteum during mid-pregnancy in rats. *Biol. Reprod.* 64, 317–323.
88. Zimmerman, R. C., Hartman, T., Bohlen, P., Sauer, M. V., and Kitajewski, J. (2001). Preovulatory treatment of mice with anti-VEGF receptor 2 antibody inhibits angiogenesis in corpora lutea. *Microvasc. Res.* 62, 15–25.
89. Ferrara, N., Chen, H., Davis-Smyth, T., Gerber, H. P., Nguyen, T. N., Peers, D., Chisholm, V., Hillan, K. J., and Schwall, R. H. (1998). Vascular endothelial growth factor is essential for corpus luteum angiogenesis. *Nat. Med.* 4, 336–340.
90. Hazzard, T. M., Xu, F., and Stouffer, R. L. (2002). Injection of soluble vascular endothelial growth factor receptor 1 into the preovulatory follicle disrupts ovulation and subsequent luteal function in rhesus monkeys. *Biol. Reprod.* 67, 1305–1312.
91. Dickson, S. E., Bicknell, R., and Fraser, H. M. (2001). Mid-luteal angiogenesis and function in the primate is dependent upon vascular endothelial growth factor. *J. Endocrinol.* 168, 409–416.
92. Fraser, H. M., Dickson, S. E., Lunn, S. F., Wulff, C., Morris, K. D., Carroll, V., and Bicknell, R. (2000). Suppression of luteal angiogenesis in the primate after neutralization of vascular endothelial growth factor. *Endocrinology* 141, 995–1000.
93. Fraser, H. M., and Wulff, C. (2001). Angiogenesis in the primate ovary. *Reprod. Fertil. Dev.* 13, 557–566.
94. Gale, N. W., and Yancopoulos, G. D. (1999). Growth factors acting via endothelial cell specific receptor tyrosine kinases: VEGFs, angiopoietins, and ephrins in vascular development. *Genes Dev.* 13, 1055–1066.
95. Maisonpierre, P. C., Suri, C., Jones, P. F., Bartunkova, S., Wiegand, S. J., Radziejewski, C., Compton, D., McClain, J., Aldrich, T. H., Papadopoulos, N., Daly, T. J., Davis, S., Sato, T. N., and Yancopoulos, G. D. (1997). Angiopoietin-2, a natural antagonist for Tie2 that disrupts in vivo angiogenesis. *Science* 277, 55–60.
96. Dumont, D. J., Gradwohl, G., Fong, G. H., Puri, M. C., Gertsenstein, M., Auerbach, A., and Breitman, M. L. (1994). Dominant-negative and targeted null mutations in the endothelial receptor tyrosine kinase, tek, reveal a critical role in vasculogenesis of the embryo. *Genes Dev.* 8, 1897–1909.
97. Thurston, G., Suri, C., Smith, K., McClain, J., Sato, T. N., Yancopoulos, G. D., and McDonald, D. M. (1999). Leakage-resistant blood vessels in mice transgenically overexpressing angiopoietin-1. *Science* 286, 2511–2514.
98. Thurston, G., Rudge, J. S., Ioffe, E., Zhou, H., Ross, L., Croll, S. D., Glazer, N., Holash, J., McDonald, D. M., and Yancopoulos, G. D. (2000). Angiopoietin-1 protects the adult vasculature against plasma leakage. *Nat. Med.* 6, 460–463.
99. Papapetropoulos, A., Garcia-Cardena, G., Dengler, T. J., Maisonpierre, P. C., Yancopoulos, G. D., and Sessa, W. C. (1999). Direct actions of angiopoietin-1 on human endothelium: Evidence for network stabilization, cell survival, and interaction with other angiogenic growth factors. *Lab. Invest.* 79, 213–223.
100. Holash, J., Maisonpierre, P. C., Compton, D., Boland, P., Alexander, C. R., Zagzag, D., Yancopoulos, G. D., and Wiegand, S. J. (1999). Vessel cooption, regression, and growth in tumors mediated by angiopoietins and VEGF. *Science* 284, 1994–1998.
101. Stratmann, A., Risau, W., and Plate, K. H. (1998). Cell type-specific expression of angiopoietin-1 and angiopoietin-2 suggests a role in glioblastoma angiogenesis. *Am. J. Pathol.* 153,1459–1466.
102. Visconti, R. P., Richardson, C. D., and Sato, T. N. (2002). Orchestration of angiogenesis and arteriovenous contribution by angiopoietins and vascular endothelial growth factor (VEGF). *Proc. Natl. Acad. Sci. USA* 99, 8219–8224.
103. Holash, J., Maisonpierre, P. C., Compton, D., Boland, P., Alexander, C. R., Zagzag, D., Yancopoulos, G. D., and Wiegand, S. J. (1999). Vessel cooption, regression, and growth in tumors mediated by angiopoietins and VEGF. *Science* 284, 1994–1998.
104. Wiegand, S. J., Boland, P., and Yancopoulos, G. D. (2000). Cooperative roles of the angiopoietins and vascular endothelial growth factor in ovarian angiogenesis. In *Ovulation: Evolving Scientific and Clinical Concepts*, ed. E. Y. Adashi, 175–186. New York: Springer-Verlag.
105. Gospodarowicz, D., Cheng, J., Lui, G. M., Baird, A., Esch, F., and Bohlen, P. (1985). Corpus luteum angiogenic factor

is related to fibroblast growth factor. *Endocrinology* 117, 2383–2391.

106. Guthridge, M., Bertolini, J., Cowling, J., and Hearn, M. T. (1992). Localization of bFGF mRNA in cyclic rat ovary, diethylstilbesterol primed rat ovary, and cultured rat granulosa cells. *Growth Factors* 7, 15–25.
107. Yamamoto, S., Konishi, I., Nanbu, K., Komatsu, T., Mandai, M., Kuroda, H., Matsushita, K., and Mori, T. (1997). Immunohistochemical localization of basic fibroblast growth factor (bFGF) during folliculogenesis in the human ovary. *Gynecol. Endocrinol.* 11, 223–230.
108. Doraiswamy, V., Knutson, D. L., Grazul-Bilska, A. T., Redmer, D. A., and Reynolds, L. P. (1998). Fibroblast growth factor receptor (FGFR)-1 and -2 in the ovine corpus luteum throughout the estrous cycle. *Growth Factors* 16, 125–135.
109. Gospodarowicz, D., Massoglia, S., Cheng, J., and Fujii, D. K. (1986). Effect of fibroblast growth factor and lipoproteins on the proliferation of endothelial cells derived from bovine adrenal cortex, brain cortex, and corpus luteum capillaries. *J. Cell. Physiol.* 127, 121–136.
110. Grazul-Bilska, A. T., Redmer, D. A., Jablonka-Shariff, A., Biondini, M. E., and Reynolds, L. P. (1995). Proliferation and progesterone production of ovine luteal cells from several stages of the estrous cycle: Effects of fibroblast growth factors and luteinizing hormone. *Can. J. Physiol. Pharmacol.* 73, 491–500.
111. Ortega, S., Ittmann, M., Tsang, S. H., Ehrlich, M., and Basilico, C. (1998). Neuronal defects and delayed wound healing in mice lacking fibroblast growth factor 2. *Proc. Natl. Acad. Sci. USA* 95, 5672–5677.
112. Carr, B. R., Sadler, R. K., Rochelle, D. B., Stalmach, M. A., MacDonald, P. C., and Simpson, E. R. (1981). Plasma lipoprotein regulation of progesterone biosynthesis by human corpus luteum tissue in organ culture. *J. Clin. Endocrinol. Metab.* 52, 875–881.
113. Gwynne, J. T., and Strauss, III, J. F. (1982). The role of lipoproteins in steroidogenesis and cholesterol metabolism in steroidogenic glands. *Endocr. Rev.* 3, 299–329.
114. Ishii, T., Hasegawa, T., Pai, C-I, Yvgi-Ohana, N., Timberg, R., Zhao, L., Majdic, G., Chung, B-C, Orly, J., and Parker, K. L. (2002). The roles of circulating high-density lipoproteins and trophic hormones in the phenotype of knockout mice lacking the steroidogenic acute regulatory protein. *Mol. Endocrinol.* 16, 2297–2309.
115. Rainey, W. E., Rodgers, R. J., and Mason, J. I. (1992). The role of bovine lipoproteins in the regulation of steroidogenesis and HMG-CoA reductase in bovine adrenocortical cells. *Steroids* 57, 167–173.
116. Balasubramaniam, S., Goldstein, J. L., Faust, J. R., Brunschede, G. Y., and Brown, M. S. (1977). Lipoprotein-mediated regulation of 3-hydroxy-3-methylglutaryl coenzyme A reductase activity and cholesteryl ester metabolism in the adrenal gland of the rat. *J. Biol. Chem.* 252, 1771–1779.
117. Andersen, J. M., and Dietschy, J. M. (1978). Relative importance of high and low density lipoproteins in the regulation of cholesterol synthesis in the adrenal gland, ovary and tests of the rat. *J. Biol. Chem.* 253, 9024–9032.
118. Kovanen, P. T., Schneider, W. J., Hillman, G. M., Goldstein, J. L, and Brown, M. S. (1979). Separate mechanisms for the uptake of high and low density lipoproteins by mouse adrenal gland in vivo. *J. Biol. Chem.* 254, 5498–5505.
119. Gwynne, J. T., and Hess, B. (1980). The role of high density lipoproteins in rat adrenal cholesterol metabolism and steroidogenesis. *J. Biol. Chem.* 255, 10875–10883.
120. Acton, S., Rigotti, A., Landschulz, K. T., Xu, S., Hobbs, H. H., and Krieger, M. (1996). Identification of scavenger receptor SR-B1 as a high density lipoprotein receptor. *Science* 271, 518–520.
121. Cao, G., Zhao, L., Stangl, H., Hasegawa, T., Richardson, J. A., Parker, K. L, and Hobbs, H. H. (1999). Developmental and hormonal regulation of murine scavenger receptor, class B, type 1. *Mol. Endocrinol.* 13, 1460–1473.
122. Trigatti, B., Rigotti, A., and Krieger, M. (2000). The role of the high-density lipoprotein receptor SR-B1 in cholesterol metabolism. *Curr. Opin. Lipidol.* 11, 123–131.
123. Glass, C., Pittman, R. C., Civen, M., and Steinberg, D. (1985). Uptake of high-density lipoprotein-associated apoprotein A-I and cholesterol esters by 16 tissues of the rat in vivo and by adrenal cells and hepatocytes in vitro. *J. Biol. Chem.* 260, 744–750.
124. Glass, C., Pittman, R. C., Weinstein, D. B., and Steinberg, D. (1983). Dissociation of tissue uptake of cholesterol ester from that of apoprotein A-I of rat plasma high density lipoprotein: Selective delivery of cholesterol ester to liver, adrenal, and gonad. *Proc. Natl. Acad. Sci. USA* 80, 5435–5439.
125. Rigotti, A., Trigatti, B. L., Penman, M., Rayburn, H., Herz, J., and Krieger, M. (1997). A targeted mutation in the murine gene encoding the high density lipoprotein (HDL) receptor scavenger receptor class B type I reveals its key role in HDL metabolism. *Proc. Natl. Acad. Sci. USA* 94, 12610–12615.
126. Plump, A. S., Erickson, S. K., Weng, W., Partin, J. S., Breslow, J. L., and Williams, D. L. (1996). Apolipoprotein A-I is required for cholesteryl ester accumulation in steroidogenic cells and for normal adrenal steroid production. *J. Clin. Invest.* 97, 2660–2671.
127. Azhar, S., Khan, I., Puryear, T., Chen, Y. D., and Gibori, G. (1988). Luteal cell 3-hydroxy-3-methylglutaryl coenzyme A reductase activity and cholesterol metabolism throughout pregnancy in the rat. *Endocrinology* 123,1495–1503.
128. Lopez, D., Sanchez, M. D., Shea-Eaton, W., and McLean, M. P. (2002). Estrogen activates the high-density lipoprotein receptor gene via binding to estrogen response elements and interaction with sterol regulatory element binding protein-1A. *Endocrinology* 143, 2155–2168.
129. Stocco, C., Callegari, E., and Gibori, G. (2001). Opposite effect of PRL and prostaglandin $F_{2\alpha}$ on the expression of luteal genes as revealed by rat cDNA expression array. *Endocrinology* 149, 4158–4161.
130. Behrman, H. R., and Armstrong, D. T. (1969). Cholesterol esterase stimulation by luteinizing hormone in luteinized rat ovaries. *Endocrinology* 85, 474–480.
131. Leaver, H. A., and Boyd, G. S. (1981). Action of gonadotrophic hormones on cholesterol side chain cleavage and cholesterol ester hydrolase in the ovary of the immature rat. *J. Reprod. Fertil.* 63, 101–108.
132. Trzeciak, W. H., and Boyd, G. S. (1974). Activation of cholesteryl esterase in bovine adrenal cortex. *Eur. J. Biochem.* 46, 201–207.

133. Caffrey, J. L., Fletcher, P. W., Diekman, M. A., O'Callaghan, P. L., and Niswender, G. D. (1979). The activity of ovine luteal cholesterol esterase during several experimental conditions. *Biol. Reprod.* 21, 601–608.
134. Behrman, H. R., Orczyk, G. P., Macdonald, G. J., and Greep, R. O. (1970). Prolactin induction of enzymes controlling luteal cholesterol ester turnover. *Endocrinology* 87, 1251–1256.
135. Klemcke, H. G., and Brinkley, H. J. (1980). Effects of bromocriptine and PRL on luteal and adrenal cholesterol ester hydrolase and serum progesterone concentrations in mature pseudopregnant rats. *Biol. Reprod.* 22, 1029–1039.
136. Aten, R. F., Kolodecik, T. R., Macdonald, G. J., and Behrman, H. R. (1995). Modulation of cholesteryl esterase hydrolase messenger ribonucleic acid levels, protein levels, and activity in the rat corpus luteum. *Biol. Reprod.* 53, 1110–1117.
137. Crivello, J. F., and Jefcoate, C. R. (1978). Mechanisms of corticotropin action in rat adrenal cells. I. The effects of inhibitors of protein synthesis and of microfilament formation on corticosterone synthesis. *Biochim. Biophys. Acta.* 542, 315–329.
138. Scallen, T. J., Pastuszyn, A., Nolan, B. J., Chanderbhan, R., Kharroubi, A., and Vahouny, G. V. (1985). Sterol carrier and lipid transfer proteins. *Chem. Phys. Lipids* 38, 239–261.
139. McLean, M. P., Nelson, S. E., Billheimer, J. T., and Gibori, G. (1992). Differential capacity for cholesterol transport and processing in large and small rat luteal cells. *Endocrinology* 131, 2203–2212.
140. McLean, M. P., Puryear, T. K., Khan, I., Azhar, S., Beillheimer, J. T., Orly, J., and Gibori, G. (1989). Estradiol regulation of sterol carrier protein 2 independent of cytochrome P450 side-chain cleavage expression in the rat corpus luteum. *Endocrinology* 125, 1337–1344.
141. Tanaka, T., Billheimer, J. T., Strauss, III, J. F. (1984). Luteinized rat ovaries contain a sterol carrier protein. *Endocrinology* 114, 533–540.
142. Steinschneider, A., McLean, M. P., Billheimer, J. T., Azhar, S., and Gibori, G. (1989). Protein kinase C catalyzed phosphorylation of sterol carrier protein 2. *Endocrinology* 125, 569–571.
143. Leung, P. C. K., Minegishi, T., and Wang, J. (1988). Inhibition of FSH and cyclic adenosine-3′,5′-monophosphate induced progesterone production by calcium and protein kinase C in the rat ovary. *Am. J. Obstet. Gynecol.* 158, 350–356.
144. Baum, M. S., and Rosberg, S. (1987). A phorbol ester, phorbol 12-myristate 13-acetate, and a calcium ionophore, A23187, can mimic the luteolytic effect of prostaglandin $F_{2\alpha}$ in isolated rat luteal cells. *Endocrinology* 120, 1019–1026.
145. Wiltbank, M. C., Knickerbocker, J. J., and Niswender, G. D. (1989). Regulation of the corpus luteum by protein kinase C. I. Phosphorylation activity and steroidogenic action in large and small ovine luteal cells. *Biol. Reprod.* 40, 1194–1200.
146. Niswender, G. D. (2002). Molecular control of luteal secretion of progesterone. *Reproduction* 123, 333–339.
147. Christenson, L. K., and Strauss, III, J. F. (2001). Steroidogenic acute regulatory protein: An update on its regulation and mechanism of action. *Arch. Med. Res.* 32, 576–586.
148. Clark, B. J., Wells, J., King, S. R., and Stocco, D. M. (1994). The purification, cloning, and expression of a novel luteinizing hormone-induced mitochondrial protein in MA-10 mouse Leydig tumor cells. Characterization of the steroidogenic acute regulatory protein (StAR). *J. Biol. Chem.* 269, 28314–28322.
149. Stocco, D. M. (1999). Steroidogenic acute regulatory protein. *Vitam. Horm.* 55, 399–441.
150. Stocco, D. M., and Clark, B. J. (1996). Regulation of the acute production of steroids in steroidogenic cells. *Endocr. Rev.* 17, 221–244.
151. Clark, B. J., Soo, S. C., Caron, K. M., Ikeda, Y., Parker, K. L., and Stocco, D. M. (1995). Hormonal and developmental regulation of the sterodogenic acute regulatory protein. *Mol. Endocrinol.* 9, 1346–1355.
152. Caron, K. M., Soo, S. C., Wetsel, W. C., Stocco, D. M., Clark, B. J., and Parker, K. L. (1997). Targeted disruption of the mouse gene encoding steroidogenic acute regulatory protein provides insights into congenital lipoid adrenal hyperplasia. *Proc. Natl. Acad. Sci. USA* 94, 11540–11545.
153. Bose, H. S., Lingappa, V. R., and Miller, W. L. (2002). Rapid regulation of steroidogenesis by mitochondrial protein import. *Nature* 417, 87–91.
154. West, A., Horvat, R. D., Roess, D. A., Barisas, B. G., Juengel, J. L., and Niswender, G. D. (2001). Steroidogenic acute regulatory protein and peripheral-type benzodiazepine receptor associate at the mitochondrial membrane. *Endocrinology* 142, 502–505.
155. Papadopoulos, V. (1993). Peripheral-type benzodiazepine/diazepam binding inhibitor receptor: Biological role in steroidogenic cell function. *Endocr. Rev.* 14, 222–240.
156. Arakane, F., Kallen, C. B., Watari, H., Stayrook, S. E., Lewis, M., and Strauss, III, J. F. (1998). Steroidogenic acute regulatory protein (StAR) acts on the outside of mitochondria to stimulate steroidogenesis. *Endocr. Rev.* 24, 463–468.
157. Kallen, C. B., Billheimer, J. T., Summers, S. A., Stayrook, S. E., Lewis, M., and Strauss, III, J. F. (1998). Steroidogenic acute regulatory protein (StAR) is a sterol transfer protein. *J. Biol. Chem.* 273, 26285–26288.
158. Christinsen, K., Bose, H. S., Harris, F. M., Miller, W. L., and Bell, J. D. (2001). Binding of steroidogenic acute regulatory protein to synthetic membranes suggests an active molten globule. *J. Biol. Chem.* 276, 17044–17051.
159. Bose, H. S., Baldwin, M. A., and Miller, W. L. (2000). Evidence that StAR and MLN64 act on the outer mitochondrial membrane as molten globules. *Endocr. Res.* 26, 629–637.
160. Ponting, C. P., and Aravind, L. (1999). START: A lipid-binding domain in StAR, HD-ZIP and signaling proteins. *Trends Biochem. Sci.* 24, 130–132.
161. Tsujishita, Y., and Hurley, J. H. (2000). Structure and lipid transport mechanism of a StAR-related domain. *Nat. Struct. Biol.* 7, 408–414.
162. Petrescu, A. D., Gallegos, A. M., Okamura, Y., and Strauss, III, J. F., and Shroeder, F. (2001). Steroidogenic acute regulatory protein binds cholesterol and modulates mitochondrial membrane sterol domain dynamics. *J. Biol. Chem.* 276, 36970–36982.
163. Stocco, D. M. (2001). Tracking the role of a StAR in the sky of the new millennium. *Mol. Endocrinol.* 15, 1245–1254.

164. Oonk, R. B., Krasnow, J. S., Beattie, W. G., and Richards, J. S. (1989). Cyclic AMP-dependent and -independent regulation of cholesterol side chain cleavage cytochrome P450 in rat ovarian granulosa cells and corpora lutea. *J. Biol. Chem.* 264, 21934–21942.
165. Martel, C., Gagne, D., Couet, J., Labrie, Y., Simard, J., and Labrie, F. (1994). Rapid modulation of ovarian 3-β-hydroxysteroid dehydrogenase/Δ5-Δ4 isomerase gene expression by prolactin and human chorionic gonadotropin in the hypophysectomized rat. *Mol. Cell. Endocrinol.* 99, 63–71.
166. Jone, P. B., Valk, C. A., and Hsueh, A. J. (1983). Regulation of progestin biosynthetic enzymes in cultured rat granulosa cells: Effects of prolactin, beta 2-adrenergic agonist, human chorionic gonadotropin and gonadotropin releasing hormone. *Biol. Reprod.* 29, 572–585.
167. Hickey, G. J., Oonk, R. B., Hall, P. F., and Richards, J. S. (1989). Aromatase cytochrome P450 and cholesterol side-chain cleavage cytochrome P450 in corpora lutea of pregnant rats: Diverse regulation by peptide and steroid hormones. *Endocrinology* 125, 1673–1682.
168. Akinola, L. A., Poutanen, M., Vihko, R., and Vihko, P. (1997). Expression of 17β-hydroxysteroid dehydrogenase type 1 and type 2, P450 aromatase, and 20α-hydroxysteroid dehydrogenase enzymes in immature, mature, and pregnant rats. *Endocrinology* 138, 2886–2892.
169. Nokelainen, P., Peltoketo, H., Vihko, R., and Vihko, P. (1998). Expression cloning of a novel estrogenic mouse 17β-hydroxysteroid dehydrogenase/17-ketosteroid reductase (m17HSD7), previously described as a prolactin receptor-associated protein (PRAP) in rat. *Mol. Endocrinol.* 12, 1048–1059.
170. Risk, M., Duan, W. R., Nelson, S., Azhar, S., and Gibori, G. (1999). Characterization of PRAP as a novel 17β-hydroxysteroid dehydrogenase (17βHSD) enzyme. *Biol. Reprod. Suppl* 60 (1), 162 Abstract #221.
171. Pelletier, G., Luu-The, V., Tetu, B., and Labrie, F. (1999). Immunocytochemical localization of type 5 17β-hydroxysteroid dehydrogenase in human reproductive tissues. *J. Histochem. Cytochem.* 47, 731–738.
172. Zhang, Y., Word, R. A., Fesmire, S., Carr, B. R., and Rainey, W. E. (1996). Human ovarian expression of 17β-hydroxysteroid dehydrogenase types 1, 2, and 3. *J. Clin. Endocrinol. Metab.* 81, 3594–3598.
173. Khan, I., Sridaran, R., Johnson, D. C., and Gibori, G. (1987). Selective stimulation of luteal androgen biosynthesis by luteinizing hormone: Comparison of hormonal regulation of $P450_{17\alpha}$ activity in corpora lutea and follicles. *Endocrinology* 121, 1312–1319.
174. Bogovich, K., Richards, J. S., and Reichert, Jr., L. E. (1981). Obligatory role of luteinizing hormone (LH) in the initiation of preovulatory follicular growth in the pregnant rat: Specific effects of human chorionic gonadotropin and follicle-stimulating hormone on LH receptors and steroidogenesis in theca, granulosa, and luteal cells. *Endocrinology* 109, 860–867.
175. Bogovich, K., and Richards, J. S. (1982). Androgen biosynthesis in developing ovarian follicles: Evidence that luteinizing hormone regulates thecal 17α-hydroxylase and $C_{17\text{-}20}$ lyase activities. *Endocrinology* 111,1201–1208.
176. Morishige, W. K., Pepe, G. J., and Rothchild, I. (1973). Serum luteinizing hormone, PRL, and progesterone levels during pregnancy in the rat. *Endocrinology* 92, 1527–1530.
177. Gibori, G., Khan, I., Warshaw, M. L., McLean, M. P., Puryear, T. K., Nelson, S., Durkee, T. J., Azhar, S., Steinschneider, A., and Rao, M. C. (1988). Placental derived regulators and the complex control of luteal cell function. *Rec. Prog. Hormone Res.* 44, 377–429.
178. Gibori, G., Sridaran, R., and Basuray, R. (1982). Control of aromatase activity in luteal and ovarian nonluteal tissue of pregnant rats. *Endocrinology* 111, 781–788.
179. Lephart, E. D., Simpson, E. R., and McPhaul, M. J. (1992). Ovarian aromatase cytochrome P450 mRNA levels correlate with enzyme activity and serum estradiol levels in anestrous, pregnant and lactating rats. *Mol. Cell. Endocrinol.* 85, 205–214.
180. Krasnow, J. S., Hickey, G. J., and Richards, J. S. (1990). Regulation of aromatase mRNA and estradiol biosynthesis in rat ovarian granulosa and luteal cells by PRL. *Mol. Endocrinol.* 4, 13–21.
181. Shaikh, A. A. (1971). Estrone and estradiol levels in the ovarian venous blood from rats during the estrous cycle and pregnancy. *Biol. Reprod.* 5, 297–307.
182. Ghersevich, S. A., Poutanen, M. H., Rajaniemi, H. J., and Vihko, R. K. (1994). Expression of 17β-hydroxysteroid dehydrogenase in the rat ovary during follicular development and luteinization induced with pregnant mare serum gonadotrophin and human chorionic gonadotrophin. *J. Endocrinol.* 140, 409–417.
183. Nokelainen, P., Puranen, T., Peltoketo, H., Orava, M., Vihko, P., and Vihko, R. (1996). Molecular cloning of mouse 17β-hydroxysteroid dehydrogenase type 1 and characterization of enzyme activity. *Eur. J. Biochem.* 236, 482–490.
184. Parmer, T. G., McLean, M. P., Duan, W. R., Nelson, S. E., Albarracin, C. T., Khan, I., and Gibori, G. (1992). Hormonal and immunological characterization of the 32 kilodalton ovarian-specific protein. *Endocrinology* 131, 2213–2221.
185. Nokelainen, P., Peltoketo, H., Mustonen, M., and Vihko, P. (2000). Expression of mouse 17β-hydroxysteroid dehydrogenase/17-ketosteroid reductase type 7 in the ovary, uterus, and placenta: Localization from implantation to late pregnancy. *Endocrinology* 141, 772–778.
186. Gibori G., Stocco C., Risk, M., Smith, C., Duan, W. R., and Rohan, R. (1999). Opposite effect of estradiol on $P450_{17\alpha}$ and PRAP/17β-HSD expression in the rat corpus luteum leads to differential expression of these genes throughout pregnancy. *Biol. Reprod. Suppl.* 60 (1), 154 Abstract #195.
187. McLean, M. P., Nelson, S., Parmer, T., Khan, I., Steinschneider, A., Puryear, T., and Gibori, G. (1990). Identification and characterization of an abundant phosphoprotein specific to the large luteal cell. *Endocrinology* 126, 1796–1805.
188. Duan, W. R., Parmer, T. G., Albarracin, C. T., Zhong, L., and Gibori, G. (1997). PRAP, a prolactin receptor associated protein: Its gene expression and regulation in the corpus luteum. *Endocrinology* 138, 3216–3221.
189. Duan, W. R., Linzer, D. I. H., and Gibori, G. (1996). Cloning and characterization of an ovarian-specific protein that associates with the short form of the prolactin receptor. *J. Biol. Chem.* 271, 15602–15607.

190. Albarracin, C. T., Parmer, T. G., Duan, W. R., Nelson, S. E., and Gibori, G. (1994). Identification of a major PRL-regulated protein as 20α-hydroxysteroid dehydrogenase: Coordinate regulation of its activity, protein content, and messenger ribonucleic acid expression. *Endocrinology* 134, 2453–2460.
191. Zhong, L., Parmer, T. G., Robertson, M. C., and Gibori, G. (1997). PRL-mediated inhibition of 20α-hydroxysteroid dehydrogenase gene expression and the tyrosine kinase system. *Biochem. Biophys. Res. Commun.* 235, 587–592.
192. Albarracin, C. T., and Gibori, G. (1991). PRL action on luteal protein expression in the corpus luteum. *Endocrinology* 129, 1821–1830.
193. Lamprecht, S. A., Lindner, H. R., and Strauss III, J. F. (1969). Induction of 20 alpha hydroxysteroid dehydrogenase in rat corpora lutea by pharmacological blockade of pituitary PRL secretion. *Biochim. Biophys. Acta.* 187, 133–143.
194. Wiest, W. G., Kidwell, W. R., and Bologh, Jr., K. (1968). Progesterone catabolism in the rat ovary: A regulatory mechanism for progestational potency during pregnancy. *Endocrinology* 82, 844–852.
195. Yoshida, S., Kubota, K., Sasaki, H., Hasegawa, T., Nishihara, M., Terada, M., and Takahashi, M. (1999). 26-cholesterol hydroxylase in rat corpora lutea: A negative regulator of progesterone secretion. *Biol. Reprod.* 61, 557–562.
196. Sridaran, R., and Gibori, G. (1989). Dihydrotestosterone secretion in pregnant and pseudopregnant rats. *Proc. Soc. Biol. Med.* 192, 281–284.
197. Sridaran, R., and Gibori, G. (1981). Induction of luteolysis by dihydrotestosterone in the pregnant rat. *Am. J. Physiol.* 241, E444–448.
198. Mahendroo, M. S., Porter, A., Russell, D. W., and Word, R. A. (1999). The parturition defect in steroid 5α-reductase type 1 knockout mice is due to impaired cervical ripening. *Mol. Endocrinol.* 13, 981–992.
199. Nelson, S. E., McLean, M. P., Jayatilak, P. G., and Gibori, G. (1992). Isolation, characterization and culture of cell subpopulations forming the pregnant rat corpus luteum. *Endocrinology* 130, 954–966.
200. Girsh, E., Greber, Y., and Meidan, R. (1995). Luteotropic and luteolytic interactions between bovine small and large luteal-like cells and endothelial cells. *Biol. Reprod.* 52, 954–962.
201. Christenson, L. K., and Stouffer, R. L. (1996). Proliferation of microvascular endothelial cells in the primate corpus luteum during the menstrual cycle and simulated early pregnancy. *Endocrinology* 137, 367–374.
202. Suzuki, T., Sasano, H., Takaya, R., Fukaya, T., Yajima, A., and Nagura, H. (1998). Cyclic changes of vasculature and vascular phenotypes in normal human ovaries. *Hum. Reprod.* 13, 953–959.
203. Gaytan, F., Morales, C., Garcia-Pardo, L., Reymundo, C., Bellido, C., Sanchez-Criado, J. E. (1999). A quantitative study of changes in the human corpus luteum microvasculature during the menstrual cycle. *Biol. Reprod.* 60, 914–919.
204. Gillim, S. W., Christensen, A. K., and McLennan, C. F. (1969). Fine structure of the human menstrual corpus luteum at its stage of maximum secretory activity. *Am. J. Anat.* 126, 409–415.
205. Petrovska, M., Dimitrov, D. G., and Michael, S. D. (1996). Quantitative changes in macrophage distribution in normal mouse ovary over the course of the estrous cycle examined with an image analysis system. *Am. J. Reprod. Immunol.* 36, 175–183.
206. Bukovsky, A., Caudle, M. R., Keenan, J. A., Wimalasena, J., Upadhyaya, N. B., and Van Meter, S. E. (1995). Is corpus luteum regression an immune-mediated event? Localization of immune system components and luteinizing hormone receptor in human corpora lutea. *Biol. Reprod.* 53, 1373–1384.
207. Brannstrom, M., Mayrhofer, G., and Robertson, S. A. (1993). Localization of leukocyte subsets in the rat ovary during the periovulatory period. *Biol. Reprod.* 48, 277–286.
208. Brannstrom, M., Pascoe, V., Norman, R. J., and McClure, N. (1994). Localization of leukocyte subsets in the follicle wall and in the corpus luteum throughout the human menstrual cycle. *Fertil. Steril.* 61, 488–495.
209. Brannstrom, M., Giesecke, L., Moore, I. C., van den Heuvel, C. J., and Robertson, S. A. (1994). Leukocyte subpopulations in the rat corpus luteum during pregnancy and pseudopregnancy. *Biol. Reprod.* 50, 1161–1167.
210. Smith, M. F., McIntush, E. W., and Smith, G. W. (1994). Mechanisms associated with corpus luteum development. *J. An. Sci.* 72, 1857–1872.
211. Murdoch, W. J., and McCormick, R. J. (1993). Mechanisms and physiological implications of leucocyte chemoattraction into periovulatory ovine follicles. *J. Reprod. Fertil.* 97, 375–380.
212. Presl, J., and Bukovsky, A. (1986). Role of Thy-1+ and Ia+ cells in ovarian function. *Biol. Reprod.* 34, 159–169.
213. Pate, J. L., and Keyes, P. L. (2001). Immune cells in the corpus luteum: Friends or foes? *Reproduction* 122, 665–676.
214. Lobel, B. L., and Levy, E. (1968). Enzymatic correlates of development, secretory function and regression of follicles and corpora lutea in the bovine ovary. II. Formation, development and involution of corpora lutea. *Acta. Endocrinol. (Copenh.) Suppl.* 132, 5–63.
215. Niswender, G. D., Juengel, J. L., Silva, P. J., Rollyson, M. K., and McIntush, E. W. (2000). Mechanisms controlling the function and life span of the corpus luteum. *Physiol. Rev.* 80, 1–29.
216. Nelson, S. E., Gibori, G., and Hunzicker-Dunn, M. (1992). The cap-dependent signaling cascade in the two luteal cell types of the pregnant rat corpus luteum. *Mol. Cell. Endocrinol.* 85, 195–203.
217. Niswender, G. D., Juengel, J. L., McGuire, W. J., Belfiore, C. J., and Wiltbank, M. C. (1994). Luteal function: The estrous cycle and early pregnancy. *Biol. Reprod.* 50, 239–247.
218. Ohara, A., Mori, T., Taii, S., Ban, C., and Narimoto, K. (1987). Functional differentiation in steroidogenesis of two types of luteal cells isolated from mature human corpora lutea of menstrual cycle. *J. Clin. Endocrinol. Metab.* 65, 1192–1200.
219. Retamales, I., Carrasco, I., Troncoso, J. L., Las Heras, J., Devoto, L., Vega, M. (1994). Morpho-functional study of human luteal cell subpopulations. *Hum. Reprod.* 9, 591–596.
220. Sanders, S. L., and Stouffer, R. L. (1997). Localization of steroidogenic enzymes in macaque luteal tissue during the menstrual cycle and simulated early pregnancy: Immuno-

histochemical evidence supporting the two-cell model for estrogen production in the primate corpus luteum. *Biol. Reprod.* 56, 1077–1087.

221. Sanders, S. L., Stouffer, R. L., and Brannian, J. D. (1996). Androgen production by monkey luteal cell subpopulations at different stages of the menstrual cycle. *J. Clin. Endocrinol. Metab.* 81, 591–596.
222. Grazul-Bilska, A. T., Redmer, D. A., Reynolds, L. P. (1997). Cellular interactions in the corpus luteum. *Sem. Reprod. Endocrinol.* 15, 383–393.
223. Porter, D. J., and Finn, C. A. (1997). The biology of the uterus. In *Frontiers in Reproduction and Fertility Control,* eds. R. O. Greep and M. A. Koblinsky, 132–145. Cambridge, Mass.: MIT Press.
224. Freeman, M. E. (1994). The neuroendocrine control of the ovarian cycle in the rat. In *The Physiology of Reproduction,* 2d ed., Vol. 2, eds. E. Knobil and J. D. Neill, 613–658. New York: Raven Press.
225. Butcher, R. L., Fugo, N. W., and Collins, W. C. (1972). Semicircadian rhythm in plasma levels of PRL during early gestation in the rat. *Endocrinology* 90, 1125–1127.
226. Freeman, M. E., and Neill, J. D. (1972). The pattern of PRL secretion during pseudopregnancy in the rat: A daily nocturnal surge. *Endocrinology* 90, 1292–1298.
227. Kraicer, P. F., and Shelesnyak, M. C. (1964). Studies on the mechanism of nidation. IX. Analysis of the response to ergocornine, an inhibitor of nidation. *J. Reprod. Fertil.* 8, 225–233.
228. Telleria, C. M., Zhong, L., Deb, S., Srivastava, R. K., Park, K. S., Sugino, N., Park-Sarge, O. K., and Gibori, G. (1998). Differential expression of the estrogen receptors α and β in the rat corpus luteum of pregnancy: Regulation by PRL and placental lactogens. *Endocrinology* 139, 2432–2442.
229. Frasor, J., Park, K., Byers, M., Telleria, C., Kitamura, T., Yu-Lee, L. Y., Djiane, J., Park-Sarge, O. K., and Gibori, G. (2001). Differential roles for signal transducers and activators of transcription 5a and 5b in PRL stimulation of ERα and ERβ transcription. *Mol. Endocrinol.* 15, 2172–2181.
230. Gibori, G., and Keyes, P. L. (1980). Luteotropic role of estrogen in early pregnancy in the rat. *Endocrinology* 106, 1584–1588.
231. Horseman, N. D., Zhao, W., Montecino-Rodriguez, E., Tanaka, M., Nakashima, K., Engle, S. J., Smith, F., Markoff, E., and Dorshkind, K. (1997). Defective mammopoiesis, but normal hematopoiesis, in mice with a targeted disruption of the PRL gene. *EMBO J.* 16, 6926–6935.
232. Ormandy, C. J., Camus, A., Barra, J., Damotte, D., Lucas, B., Buteau, H., Edery, M., Brousse, N., Babinet, C., Binart, N., and Kelly, P. A. (1997). Null mutation of the PRL receptor gene produces multiple reproductive defects in the mouse. *Genes Dev.* 11, 167–168.
233. Teglund, S., McKay, C., Schuetz, E., van Deursen, J. M., Stravopodis, D., Wang, D., Brown, M., Bodner, S., Grosveld, G., Ihle, J. N. (1998). Stat5a and Stat5b proteins have essential and nonessential, or redundant, roles in cytokine responses. *Cell* 93, 841–850.
234. Binart, N., Helloco, C., Ormandy, C. J., Barra, J., Clement-Lacroix, P., Baran, N., and Kelly, P. A. (2000). Rescue of preimplantatory egg development and embryo implantation in PRL receptor-deficient mice after progesterone administration. *Endocrinology* 141, 2691–2697.
235. Reese, J., Binart, N., Brown, N., Ma, W. G., Paria, B. C., Das, S. K., Kelly, P. A., and Dey, S. K. (2000). Implantation and decidualization defects in PRL receptor (PRLR)-deficient mice are mediated by ovarian but not uterine PRLR. *Endocrinology* 141, 1872–1881.
236. Morishige, W. K., and Rothchild, I. (1974). Temporal aspects of the regulation of corpus luteum function by luteinizing hormone, PRL and placental luteotrophin during the first half of pregnancy in the rat. *Endocrinology* 95, 260–274.
237. Jayatilak, P. G., Puryear, T. K., Herz, Z., Fazleabas, A., and Gibori, G. (1989). Protein secretion by mesometrial and antimesometrial decidual tissue: Evidence for differential gene expression. *Endocrinology* 125, 659–666.
238. Jayatilak, P. G., Glaser, L. A., Basuray, R., Kelly, P. A., and Gibori, G. (1985). Identification and partial characterization of a PRL-like hormone produced by the rat decidual tissue. *Proc. Natl. Acad. Sci. USA* 82, 217–221.
239. Gibori, G., Rothchild, I., Pepe, G. J., Morishige, W. K., and Lam, P. (1974). Luteotropic action of decidual tissue in the rat. *Endocrinology* 95, 1113–1118.
240. Basuray, R., and Gibori, G. (1980). Luteotropic action of decidual tissue in the pregnant rat. *Biol. Reprod.* 23, 507–512.
241. Jayatilak, P. G., and Gibori, G. (1986). Ontogeny of PRL receptors in rat decidual tissue: Binding by a locally produced PRL-like hormone. *J. Endocrinol.* 110, 115–121.
242. Herz, Z., Khan, I., Jayatilak, P. G., and Gibori, G. (1986). Evidence for the synthesis and secretion of decidual luteotropin: A PRL-like hormone produced by rat decidual cells. *Endocrinology* 118, 2203–2209.
243. Prigent-Tessier, A., Tessier, C., Hirosawa-Takamori, M., Boyer, C., Ferguson-Gottschall, S., and Gibori, G. (1999). Rat decidual PRL: Identification, molecular cloning, and characterization. *J. Biol. Chem.* 274, 37982–37989.
244. Jabbour, H. N., and Critchley, H. O. D. (2001). Potential roles of decidual prolactin in early pregnancy. *Reproduction* 121, 197–205.
245. Gu, Y., Srivastava, R. K., Clarke, D. L., Linzer, D. I. H., and Gibori, G. (1996). The decidual PRL receptor and its regulation by decidua-derived factors. *Endocrinology* 137, 4878–4885.
246. Jayatilak, P. G., Glaser, L. A., Warshaw, M. L., Herz, Z., Gruber, J. R., and Gibori, G. (1984). Relationship between LH and decidual luteotropin in the maintenance of luteal steroidogenesis. *Biol. Reprod.* 31, 556–564.
247. Gibori, G., Basuray, R., and McReynolds, B. (1981). Luteotropic role of the decidual tissue in the rat: Dependency on intraluteal estradiol. *Endocrinology* 108, 2060–2066.
248. Gibori, G., Rodway, R., and Rothchild, I. (1977). The luteotropic effect of estradiol in the rat: Prevention by estradiol of the luteolytic effect of an antiserum of LH in the pregnant rat. *Endocrinology* 101, 1683–1689.
249. Gibori, G., Keyes, P. L., and Richards, J. S. (1978). A role for intraluteal estrogen in the mediation of LH action on the rat corpus luteum during pregnancy. *Endocrinology* 103, 162–169.

250. Keyes, P. L., Gibori, G., Possley, R. R., and Brown, J. M. (1980). Early changes in luteal function associated with the luteotropic effect of testosterone in the pregnant rat. *Biol. Reprod.* 22, 1142–1148.
251. Armstrong, D. T., Miller, L. V., and Knudsen, K. A. (1969). Regulation of lipid metabolism and progesterone production in rat corpora lutea and ovarian interstitial elements by PRL and luteinizing hormone. *Endocrinology* 85, 393–401.
252. Segaloff, D., Wang, H. Y., and Richards, J. S. (1990). Hormonal regulation of luteinizing hormone/chorionic gonadotropin receptor mRNA in rat ovarian cells during follicular development and luteinization. *Mol. Endocrinol.* 4, 1856–1865.
253. Gafvels, M., Bjurulf, E., and Selstam, G. (1992). PRL stimulates the expression of luteinizing hormone/chorionic gonadotropin receptor messenger ribonucleic acid in the rat corpus luteum and rescues early pregnancy from bromocriptine-induced abortion. *Biol. Reprod.* 47, 534–540.
254. Bjurulf, E., Selstam, G., and Olofsson, J. I. (1994). Increased LH receptor mRNA and extended corpus luteum function induced by PRL and indomethacin treatment in vivo in hysterectomized pseudopregnant rats. *J. Reprod. Fertil.* 102, 139–145.
255. Gibori, G., Richards, J. S., and Keyes, P. L. (1979). Synergistic effects of PRL and estradiol in the luteotropic process in the pregnant rat: Regulation of estradiol receptor by PRL. *Biol. Reprod.* 21, 419–423.
256. Frasor, J., Barkai, U., Zhong, L., Fazleabas, A. T., and Gibori, G. (2001). PRL-induced ERα gene expression is mediated by janus kinase (Jak 2) while signal transducer and activator of transcription 5b (Stat5b) phosphorylation involves jak2 and a second tyrosine kinase. *Mol. Endocrinol.* 15, 1941–1952.
257. Pencharz, R. I., and Long, J. A. (1931). The effect of hypophysectomy on gestation in the rat. *Science* 74, 206.
258. Faria, T. N., Deb, S., Kwok, S. C. M., Talamantes, F., and Soares, M. J. (1990). Ontogeny of placental lactogen-I and placental lactogen-II expression in the developing rat placenta. *Dev. Biol.* 141, 279–291.
259. Ogren, L., and Talamantes, F. (1988). Prolactins of pregnancy and their cellular source. *Intl. Rev. Cytol.* 112, 1–65.
260. Soares, M. J., Faria, T. N., Roby, K. F., and Deb, S. (1991). Pregnancy and the PRL family of hormones: Coordination of anterior pituitary, uterine, and placental expression. *Endocr. Rev.* 12, 402–423.
261. Glaser, L. A., Khan, I., Pepe, G. J., Kelly, P. A., and Gibori, G. (1985). Further studies on rat placental lactogens. In *Prolactin: Basic and Clinical Correlates,* Vol. I, Section VII, eds. R. M. MacLeod, M. O. Thorner, and U. Scapagnini, Fidia Research Series, 495–499. Padova: Livania Press.
262. Kelly, P. A., Shiu, R. P. C., Robertson, M. C., and Friesen, H. G. (1975). Characterization of rat chorionic mammotropin. *Endocrinology* 96, 1187–1195.
263. Glaser, L. A., Kelly, P. A., and Gibori, G. (1984). Differential action and secretion of rat placental lactogens. *Endocrinology* 115, 969–976.
264. Sugino, N., Hirosawa-Takamori, M., Zhong, L., Telleria, C. M., Shiota, K., and Gibori, G. (1998). Hormonal regulation of copper-zinc superoxide dismutase and manganese superoxide dismutase in the rat corpus luteum: Induction by PRL and placental lactogens. *Biol. Reprod.* 59, 599–605.
265. Peters, C. A., Maizels, E. T., Robertson, M. C., Shiu, R. P. C., Soloff, M. S., and Hunzicker-Dunn, M. (2000). Induction of relaxin messenger RNA expression in response to prolactin receptor activation requires protein kinase C δ signaling. *Mol. Endocrinol.* 14, 576–590.
266. Tessier, C., Deb, S., Prigent-Tessier, A., Ferguson-Gottschall, S., Gibori, G.B., Shiu, R. P. C., and Gibori, G. (2000). Estrogen receptors α and β in rat decidua cells: Cell-specific expression and differential regulation by steroid hormones and prolactin. *Endocrinology* 141, 3842–3851.
267. Tessier, C., Prigent-Tessier, A., Ferguson-Gottschall, S., Gu, Y., and Gibori, G. (2001). PRL antiapoptotic effect in the rat decidua involves the PI3K/protein kinase B-mediated inhibition of caspase-3 activity. *Endocrinology* 142, 4086–4094.
268. MacLeod, K. R., Smith, W. C., Ogren, L., and Talamantes, F. (1989). Recombinant mouse placental lactogen-I binds to lactogen receptors in mouse liver and ovary: Partial characerization of the ovarian receptor. *Endocrinology* 125, 2258–2266.
269. Galosy, S. S., and Talamantes, F. (1995). Luteotropic actions of placental lactogens at midpregnancy in the mouse. *Endocrinology* 136, 3993–4003.
270. Thordarson, G., Galosy, S., Gudmundsson, G. O., Newcomer, B., Sridaran, R., and Talamantes, F. (1997). Interaction of mouse placental lactogens and androgens in regulating progesterone release in cultured mouse luteal cells. *Endocrinology* 138, 3236–3241.
271. Pinon, I., Kishi, K., and Talamantes, F. (1988). The kinetics of disappearance of endogenous mouse placental lactogen-II in intact and hypophysectomized pregnant mice. *Mol. Cell. Endocrinol.* 55, 45–51.
272. Gibori, G., Chatterton, Jr., R. T., and Chien, J. L. (1979). Ovarian and serum concentrations of androgen throughout pregnancy in the rat. *Biol. Reprod.* 21, 53–56.
273. Durkee, T. J., McLean, M. P., Hales, D. B., Payne, A. H., Waterman, M. R., Khan, I., and Gibori, G. (1992). $P450_{17\alpha}$ and $P450_{scc}$ gene expression and regulation in the rat trophoblast. *Endocrinology* 130, 1309–1317.
274. Warshaw, M. L., Johnson, D. C., Khan, I., Eckstein, B., and Gibori, G. (1986). Placental secretion of androgens in the rat. *Endocrinology* 119, 2642–2648.
275. Jackson, J. A., and Albrecht, E. D. (1985). The development of placental androstenedione and testosterone production and their utilization by the ovary for aromatization to estrogen during rat pregnancy. *Biol. Reprod.* 33, 451–457.
276. Warshaw, M. L., Johnson, D. C., Azhar, S., and Gibori, G. (1987). Opposite effect of human chorionic gonadotropin in placental and ovarian synthesis of androstenedione. *Endocrinology* 120, 2003–2010.
277. Gunnersen, J. M., Crawford, R. J., and Tregear, G. W. (1995). Expression of the relaxin gene in rat tissues. *Mol. Cell. Endocrinol.* 110, 55–64.
278. Lao Guico-Lamm, M., and Sherwood, O. D. (1988). Monoclonal antibodies specific for rat relaxin. II. Passive immunization with monoclonal antibodies throughout the second half of pregnancy disrupts birth in intact rats. *Endocrinology* 123, 2479–2485.
279. Hwang, J. J., and Sherwood, O. D. (1988). Monoclonal antibodies specific for rat relaxin. III. Passive immunization

with monoclonal antibodies throughout the second half of pregnancy reduces cervical growth and extensibility in intact rats. *Endocrinology* 123, 2486–2490.

280. Zhao, L., Roche, P. J., Gunnersen, J. M., Hammond, V. E., Tregear, G. W., Wintour, E. M., and Beck, F. (1999). Mice without a functional relaxin gene are unable to deliver milk to their pups. *Endocrinology* 140, 445–453.
281. Risk, M., and Gibori, G. (2001). Mechanisms of luteal cell regulation by prolactin. In *Prolactin,* ed. N. D. Horseman, 265–295. Boston: Kluwer Academic Publishers.
282. Prigent-Tessier, A., Barkai, U., Tessier, C., Cohen, H., and Gibori, G. (2001). Characterization of a rat uterine cell line, UIII cells: Prolactin (PRL) expression and endogenous regulation of PRL-dependent genes; Estrogen receptor β, α2-macroglobulin, and decidual PRL involving the Jak2 and Stat5 pathway. *Endocrinology* 142, 1242–1250.
283. Deb, S., Tessier, C., Prigent-Tessier, A., Barkai, U., Ferguson-Gottschall, S., Srivastava, R. K., Faliszek, J., and Gibori, G. (1999). The expression of interleukin-6 (IL-6), IL-6 receptor, and gp130-kilodalton glycoprotein in the rat decidua and a decidual cell line: Regulation by 17β-estradiol and prolactin. *Endocrinology* 140, 4442–4450.
284. Liu, X., Robinson, G. W., Wagner, K. U., Garrett, L., Wynshaw-Boris, A., Hennighausen, L. (1997). Stat5a is mandatory for adult mammary gland development and lactatogenesis. *Genes Dev.* 11, 179–186.
285. Udy, G. B., Towers, R. P., Snell, R. G., Wilkins, R. J., Park, S. H., Ram, P. A., Waxman, D. J., and Davey, H. W. (1997). Requirement of Stat5b for sexual dimorphism of body growth rates and liver gene expression. *Proc. Natl. Acad. Sci. USA* 94, 7239–7244.
286. Peters, C. A., Maizels, E. T., and Hunzicker-Dunn, M. (1999). Activation of PKC δ in the rat corpus luteum during pregnancy: Potential role of prolactin signaling. *J. Biol. Chem.* 274, 37499–37505.
287. Zarrow, M. X., and Clark, J. H. (1969). Gonadotropin regulation of ovarian cholesterol levels in the rat. *Endocrinology* 84, 340–346.
288. Armstrong, D. T., Knudsen, K. A., and Miller, L. S. (1970). Effects of prolactin upon cholesterol metabolism and progesterone biosynthesis in corpora lutea of rats hypophysectomized during pseudopregnancy. *Endocrinology* 86, 634–641.
289. Rajkumar, K., Couture, R. L., and Murphy, B. D. (1985). Binding of high-density lipoproteins to luteal membranes: The role of prolactin, luteinizing hormone, and circulating lipoproteins. *Biol. Reprod.* 32, 546–555.
290. Menon, M., Peegel, H., and Menon, K. M. (1985). Lipoprotein augmentation of human chorionic gonadotropin and prolactin stimulated progesterone synthesis by rat luteal cells. *J. Steroid. Biochem.* 22, 79–84.
291. Albarracin, C. T., Palfrey, H. C., Duan, W. R., Rao, M. C., and Gibori, G. (1994). PRL regulation of the calmodulin-dependent protein kinase III elongation factor-2 system in the rat corpus luteum. *J. Biol. Chem.* 269, 7772–7776.
292. Sugino, N., Telleria, C. M., Tessier, C., and Gibori, G. (1999). Regulation and role of the insulin-like growth factor I system in rat luteal cells. *J. Reprod. Fertil.* 115, 349–355.
293. LeRoith, D., Werner, H., Beitner-Johnson, D., and Roberts, Jr., C. T. (1995). Molecular and cellular aspects of the insulin-like growth factor I receptor. *Endocr. Rev.* 16, 143–163.
294. Zhou, J., Chin, E., and Bondy, C. (1991). Cellular pattern of insulin-like growth factor-I (IGF-1) and IGF-1 receptor gene expression in the developing and mature ovarian follicle. *Endocrinology* 129, 3281–3288.
295. Parmer, T. G., Roberts, Jr., C. T., LeRoith, D., Adashi, E. Y., Khan, I., Solan, N., Nelson, S., Zilberstein, M., and Gibori, G. (1991). Expression, action, and steroidal regulation of insulin-like growth factor-I (IGF-1) and IGF-1 receptor in the rat corpus luteum: Their differential role in the two cell populations forming the corpus luteum. *Endocrinology* 129, 2924–2932.
296. Talavera, F., and Menon, K. M. J. (1991). Studies on rat luteal cell response to insulin-like growth factor-1 (IGF-1): Identification of a specific cell membrane receptor for IGF-1 in the luteinized rat ovary. *Endocrinology* 129, 1340–1346.
297. Corbacho, A. M., Martinez de la Escalera, G., and Clapp, C. (2002). Roles of PRL and related members of the PRL/growth hormone/placental lactogen family in angiogenesis. *J. Endocrinol.* 173, 219–238.
298. Dennis, P. A., Sarsela, O., Harpel, P., and Rifkin, D. B. (1989). Alpha 2-macroglobulin is a binding protein for basic fibroblast growth factor. *J. Biol. Chem.* 264, 7210–7216.
299. da Silva, G. C., Teixeira, N. J., and Bell, S. C. (1996). Major secretory product of the mesometrial decidua in the rat, a variant of alpha-2-macroglobulin, binds insulin-like growth factor I via a protease-dependent mechanism. *Mol. Reprod. Dev.* 44, 103–110.
300. Ji, T. H., Ryu, K. S., Gilchrist, R., and Ji, I. (1997). Interaction, signal generation, signal divergence, and signal transduction of LH/CG and the receptor. *Rec. Prog. Hormone Res.* 52, 431–453.
301. Chen, Z., and Menon, K. M. J. (1994). Expression of high density lipoprotein-binding protein messenger ribonucleic acid in the rat ovary and its regulation by gonadotropin. *Endocrinology* 134, 2360–2366.
302. Zeleznik, A. J., and Benyo, D. F. (1994). Control of follicular development, corpus luteum function, and the recognition of pregnancy in higher primates. In The Physiology of Reproduction, 2d ed., Vol. 2, eds. E. Knobil, and J. D. Neill, 751–782. New York: Raven Press.
303. Ravindranath, N., Little-Ihrig, L. L., Benyo, D. F., and Zeleznik, A. J. (1992). Role of luteinizing hormone in the expression of cholesterol side-chain cleavage cytochrome P450 and 3β-hydroxysteroid dehydrogenase, delta 4–5 isomerase messenger ribonucleic acids in the primate corpus luteum. *Endocrinology* 131, 2065–2070.
304. Duncan, W. C., Cowen, G. M., and Illingworth, P. J. (1999). Steroidogenic enzyme expression in human corpora lutea in the presence and absence of exogenous human chorionic gonadotrophin (HCG). *Mol. Hum. Reprod.* 5, 291–298.
305. Devoto, L., Kohen, P., Vega, M., Castro, O., Gonzalez, R. R., Retamales, I., Carvallo, P., Christenson, L. K., Strauss, III, J. F. (2002). Control of human luteal steroidogenesis. *Mol. Cell. Endocrinol.* 186, 137–141.
306. Reinhart, A. J., Williams, S. C., and Stocco, D. M. (1999). Transcriptional regulation of the StAR gene. *Mol. Cell. Endocrinol.* 151, 161–169.
307. Shea-Eaton, W., Sandhoff, T. W., Lopez, D., Hales, D. B., and McLean, M. P. (2002). Transcriptional repression of the rat steroidogenic acute regulatory (StAR) protein gene by

the AP-1 family member c-Fos. *Mol. Cell. Endocrinol.* 188, 161–170.

308. Nackley, A. C., Shea-Eaton, W., Lopez, D., and McLean, M. P. (2002). Repression of the steroidogenic acute regulatory gene by the multifunctional transcription factor Yin Yang 1. *Endocrinology* 143, 1085–1096.
309. Sandhoff, T. W., Hales, D. B., Hales, K. H., and McLean, M. P. (1998). Transcriptional regulation of the rat steroidogenic acute regulatory protein gene by steroidogenic factor I. *Endocrinology* 139, 4820–4831.
310. Granot, Z., Silverman, E., Friedlander, R., Melamed-Book, N., Eimerl, S., Timberg, R., Hales K. H., Hales, D. B., Stocco, D. M., and Orly, J. (2002). The life cycle of the steroidogenic acute regulatory (StAR) protein: From transcription through proteolysis. *Endocr. Res.* 28, 375–386.
311. Sandhoff, T. W., and McLean, M. P. (1999). Repression of the rat steroidogenic acute regulatory (StAR) protein gene by $PGF_{2\alpha}$ is modulated by the negative transcription factor DAX-1. *Endocrine* 10, 83–91.
312. Ghosh, D. K., and Menon, K. M. (1987). Induction of high-density lipoprotein receptors in rat corpus luteum by human choriogonadotropin. Evidence of protein synthesis de novo. *Biochem. J.* 244, 471–479.
313. Li, X., Peegel, H, and Menon, K. M. (1998). In situ hybridization of high density lipoprotein (scavenger, type 1) receptor messenger ribonucleic acid (mRNA) during folliculogenesis and luteinization: Evidence for mRNA expression and induction by human chorionic gonadotropin specifically in cell types that use cholesterol for steroidogenesis. *Endocrinology* 139, 3043–3049.
314. Golos, T. G., Soto, E. A., Tureck, R. W., and Strauss, III, J. F. (1985). Human chorionic gonadotropin and 8-bromo-adenosine 3',5'–monophosphate stimulate [^{125}I] low density lipoprotein uptake and metabolism by luteinized human granulosa cells in culture. *J. Clin. Endocrinol. Metab.* 61, 633–638.
315. Murphy, B. D., Rajkumar, K., McKibbin, P. E., Macdonald, G. J., Buhr, M. M. and Grinwich, D. L. (1985). The effects of hypophysectomy and administration of pituitary hormones on luteal function and uptake of high density lipoproteins by luteinized ovaries and adrenals of the rat. *Endocrinology* 116, 1587–1597.
316. Hull, K. L., and Harvey, S. (2001). Growth hormone: Roles in female reproduction. *J. Endocrinol.* 168, 1–23.
317. Schams, D., Koll, R., and Li, C. H. (1988). Insulin-like growth factor-1 stimulates oxytocin and progesterone production by bovine granulosa cells in culture. *J. Endocrinol.* 116, 97–100.
318. Constantino, C. X., Keyes, P. L., and Kostyo, J. L. (1991). Insulin-like growth factor-1 stimulates steroidogenesis in rabbit luteal cells. *Endocrinology* 128, 1702–1708.
319. McArdle, C. A., and Holtorf, A.-P. (1989). Oxytocin and progesterone release from bovine corpus luteal cells in culture: Effects of insulin-like growth factor I, insulin and prostaglandins. *Endocrinology* 124, 1278–1286.
320. Khan-Dawood, F. S., Gargiulo, A. R., and Dawood, M. Y. (1994). In vitro microdialysis of the ovine corpus luteum of pregnancy: Effects of insulin-like growth factor on progesterone secretion. *Biol. Reprod.* 51, 1299–1306.
321. Devoto, L., Christenson, L. K., McAllister, J. M., Makrigiannakis, A., Strauss, III, J. F. (1999). Insulin and insulin-like growth factor-I and II modulate human granulosa-lutein cell steroidogenesis: Enhancement of steroidogenic acute regulatory protein (StAR) expression. *Mol. Hum. Reprod.* 5, 1003–1010.
322. Devoto, L., Kohen, P., Castro, O., Vega, M., Troncoso, J. L., and Charreau, E. (1995). Multihormonal regulation of progesterone synthesis in cultured human midluteal cells. *J. Clin. Endocrinol. Metab.* 80, 1566–1570.
323. Rothchild, I. (1981). Regulation of the mammalian corpus luteum. *Rec. Prog. Hormone Res.* 37, 183–298.
324. Duffy, D. M., Hess, D. L., and Stouffer, R. L. (1994). Acute administration of a 3β-hydroxysteroid dehydrogenase inhibitor to rhesus monkeys at the midluteal phase of the menstrual cycle: Evidence for possible autocrine regulation of the primate corpus luteum by progesterone. *J. Clin. Endocrinol. Metab.* 79, 1587–1594.
325. Telleria, C. M., and Deis, R. P. (1994). Effect of RU486 on ovarian progesterone production at pro-oestrus and during pregnancy: A possible dual regulation of the biosynthesis of progesterone. *J. Reprod. Fertil.* 102, 379–384.
326. Singh, G., Singh, M. M., Maitra, S. C., Elger, W., Kalra, V., Upadhyay, S. N., Chowdhury, S. R., and Kamboj, V.P. (1988). Luteolytic actions of two antiprogestational agents (RU-38486 and ZK-98734) in the rat. *J. Reprod. Fertil.* 83, 73–83.
327. Telleria, C. M., Goyeneche, A. A., Cavicchia, J. C., Stati, A. O., and Deis, R. P. (2001). Apoptosis induced by antigestagen RU486 in rat corpus luteum of pregnancy. *Endocrine* 15, 147–155.
328. Ottander, U., Hosokawa, K., Liu, K., Bergh, A., Ny, T., and Olofsson, J. I. (2000). A putative stimulatory role of progesterone acting via progesterone receptors in the steroidogenic cells of the human corpus luteum. *Biol. Reprod.* 62, 655–663.
329. Duffy, D. M., and Stouffer, R. L. (1997). Gonadotropin versus steroid regulation of the corpus luteum of the rhesus monkey during simulated early pregnancy. *Biol. Reprod.* 57, 1451–1460.
330. Iwai, T., Nanbu, Y., Iwai, H., Taii, S., Fujii, S., and Mori, T. (1990). Immunohistochemical localization of oestrogen receptors and progesterone receptors in the human ovary throughout the menstrual cycle. *Virchows Arch. Pathol. Anat. Histopathol.* 417, 369–375.
331. Suzuki, T., Sasano, H., Kimura, N., Tamura, M., Fukaya, T., Yajima, A., and Nagura, H. (1994). Immunohistochemical distribution of progesterone, androgen and oestrogen receptors in the human ovary during the menstrual cycle: Relationship to expression of steroidogenic enzymes. *Hum. Reprod.* 9, 1589–1595.
332. Revelli, A., Pacchioni, D., Cassoni, P., Bussolati, G., and Massobrio, M. (1996). In situ hybridization study of messenger RNA for estrogen receptor and immunohistochemical detection of estrogen and progesterone receptors in the human ovary. *Gynaecol. Endocrinol.* 10, 177–186.
333. Misao, R., Nakanishi, Y., Iwagaki, S., Fujimoto, J., and Tamaya, T. (1998). Expression of progesterone receptor isoforms in corpora lutea of human subjects: Correlation with serum oestrogen and progesterone concentration. *Mol. Hum. Reprod.* 4, 1045–1052.

334. Duffy, D. M., Wells, T. R., Haluska, G. J., and Stouffer, R. L. (1997). The ratio of progesterone receptor isoforms changes in the monkey corpus luteum during the luteal phase of the menstrual cycle. *Biol. Reprod.* 57, 693–699.
335. Hild-Petito, S., Stouffer, R. L., and Brenner, R. M. (1988). Immunocytochemical localization of estrogen and progesterone receptors in the monkey ovary throughout the menstrual cycle. *Endocrinology* 123, 2896–2905.
336. Hild-Petito, S., and Fazleabas, A. T. (1997). Expression of steroid receptors and steroidogenic enzymes in the baboon (Papio anubis) corpus luteum during the menstrual cycle and early pregnancy. *J. Clin. Endocrinol. Metab.* 82, 995–962.
337. Duffy, D. M., Molskness, T. A., and Stouffer, R. L. (1996). Progesterone receptor messenger ribonucleic acid and protein in luteinized granulosa cells of rhesus monkeys are regulated in vitro by gonadotropins and steroids. *Biol. Reprod.* 54, 888–895.
338. Park-Sarge, O. K., Parmer, T. G., Gu, Y., and Gibori G. (1995). Does the rat corpus luteum express the progesterone receptor gene? *Endocrinology* 136, 1537–1543.
339. Telleria, C. M., Stocco, C. O., Stati, A. O., and Deis, R. P. (1999). Progesterone receptor is not required for progesterone action in the rat corpus luteum of pregnancy. *Steroids* 64, 760–766.
340. Goyeneche A. A., Deis, R. P., Gibori, G., and Telleria, C. M. (2003). Progesterone promotes survival of the rat corpus luteum in the absence of cognate receptors. *Biol. Reprod.* 68, 151–158.
341. Sugino, N., Telleria, C. M., and Gibori, G. (1997). Progesterone inhibits 20α-hydroxysteroid dehydrogenase expression in the rat corpus luteum through the glucocorticoid receptor. *Endocrinology* 138, 4497–4500.
342. Rae, M. T., Menzies, G. S., and Bramley, T. A. (1998). Bovine ovarian, non-genomic progesterone binding sites: Presence in follicular and luteal cell membranes. *J. Endocrinol.* 159, 413–427.
343. Rosenfeld, C. S., Wagner, J. S., Roberts, R. M., and Lubahn, D. B. (2001). Intraovarian actions of oestrogen. *Reproduction* 122, 215–226.
344. McLean, M. P., Khan, I., Puryear, T. K., and Gibori, G. (1990). Induction and repression of specific estradiol sensitive proteins in the rat corpus luteum. *Chin. J. Physiology.* 33, 353–366.
345. Rao, M. C., Palfrey, H. C., Nash, N. T., Greisman, A., Jayatilak, P. G., and Gibori, G. (1987). Effects of estradiol on calcium-specific protein phosphorylation in the rat corpus luteum. *Endocrinology* 120, 1010–1018.
346. Gibori, G., Chen, Y.-D.I., Khan, I., Azhar, S., and Reaven, G. M. (1984). Regulation of luteal cell lipoprotein receptors, sterol content and steroidogenesis by estradiol in the pregnant rat. *Endocrinology* 114, 609–617.
347. Khan, I., Belanger, A., Chen, Y.-D. I., and Gibori, G. (1985). Influence of high-density lipoprotein on estradiol stimulation of luteal steroidogenesis. *Biol. Reprod.* 32, 96–104.
348. Townson, D. H., Wang, X. J., Keyes, P. L., Kostyo, J. L., and Stocco, D. M. (1996). Expression of the steroidogenic acute regulatory protein in the corpus luteum of the rabbit: Dependence upon the luteotropic hormone, estradiol-17β. *Biol. Reprod.* 55, 868–874.
349. Cok, S. J., Hay, R. V., and Holt, J. A. (1997). Estrogen-mediated mitochondrial cholesterol transport and metabolism to pregnenolone in the rabbit luteinized ovary. *Biol. Reprod.* 57, 360–366.
350. Losordo, D. W., and Isner, J. M. (2001). Estrogen and angiogenesis: A review. *Arterioscler. Throm. Vasc. Biol.* 21, 6–12.
351. Johns, A., Freay, A. W., Fraser, D., Korach, K. S., and Rubanyi, G. M. (1996). Disruption of estrogen receptor gene prevents 17 beta estradiol-induced angiogenesis in transgenic mice. *Endocrinology* 137, 4511–4513.
352. Gagliardi, A., and Collins, D. C. (1993). Inhibition of angiogenesis by antiestrogens. *Cancer Res.* 53, 533–535.
353. Guthridge, M., Bertolini, J., Cowling, J., and Hearn, M. T. (1992). Localization of bFGF mRNA in cyclic rat ovary, diethylstilbesterol primed rat ovary, and cultured rat granulosa cells. *Growth Factors* 7, 15–25.
354. Garrido, C., Saule, S., and Gospodarowicz, D. (1993). Transcriptional regulation of vascular endothelial growth factor gene expression in ovarian bovine granulosa cells. *Growth Factors* 8, 109–117.
355. Cullinan-Bove, K., and Koos, R. D. (1993). Vascular endothelial growth factor/vascular permeability factor expression in the rat uterus: Rapid stimulation by estrogen correlates with estrogen-induced increases in uterine capillary permeability and growth. *Endocrinology* 133, 829–837.
356. Shifren, J. L., Tseng, J. F., Zaloudek, C. J., Ryan, I. P., Meng, Y. G., Ferrara, N., Jaffe, R. B., and Taylor, R. N. (1996). Ovarian steroid regulation of vascular endothelial growth factor in the human endometrium: Implications for angiogenesis during the menstrual cycle and in the pathogenesis of endometriosis. *J. Clin. Endocrinol. Metab.* 81, 3112–3118.
357. Ye, F., Florian, M., Magder, S. A., and Hussain, S. N. A. (2002). Regulation of angiopoietin and Tie–2 receptor expression in non-reproductive tissues by estrogen. *Steroids* 67, 305–310.
358. Davis, J. S., and Rueda, B. R. (2002). The corpus luteum: An ovarian structure with maternal instincts and suicidal tendencies. *Front Biosci.* 7, 1949–1978.
359. Stocco, C. O., Zhong, L., Sugimoto, Y., Ichikawa, A., Lau, L. F., and Gibori, G. (2000). Prostaglandin $F_{2\alpha}$-induced expression of 20α-hydroxysteroid dehydrogenase involves the transcription factor NUR77. *J. Biol. Chem.* 275, 37202–37211.
360. Deis, R. P. (1971). Induction of lactogenesis and abortion by prostaglandin F2-alpha in pregnant rats. *Nature* 229, 568.
361. Fuchs, A. R., and Mok, E. (1974). Histochemical study of the effects of prostaglandins $F_{2\alpha}$ and E_2 on the corpora lutea of pregnant rats. *Biol. Reprod.* 10, 24–38.
362. Bussmann, L. E., and Deis, R. P. (1979). Studies concerning the hormonal induction of lactogenesis by prostaglandin $F_{2\alpha}$ in pregnant rats. *J. Steroid. Biochem.* 11, 1485–1489.
363. Pharriss, B. B., and Wyngarden, L. J. (1969). The effect of prostaglandin $F_{2\alpha}$ on the progestagen content of ovaries from pseudopregnant rats. *Proc. Soc. Exp. Biol. Med.* 130, 92–94.
364. Strauss, III, J. F., and Stambaugh, R. L. (1974). Induction of 20α-hydroxysteroid dehydrogenase in rat corpora lutea of pregnancy by prostaglandin $F_{2\alpha}$. *Prostaglandins* 5, 73–85.
365. Fuchs, A. R., Smitasiri, Y., and Chantharaksri, U. (1976). The effect of indomethacin on uterine contractility and

luteal regression in pregnant rats at term. *J. Reprod. Fertil.* 48, 331–340.

366. Sugimoto, Y., Yamasaki, A., Segi, E., Tsuboi, K., Aze, Y., Nishimura, T., Oida, H., Yhosida, N., Tanaka, T., Katsuyama, M., Hasumoto, K., Murata, T., Hirata, M., Ushikubi, F., Negishi, M., Ichikawa, A., Narumiya, S. (1997). Failure of parturition in mice lacking the prostaglandin F receptor. *Science* 277, 681–683.
367. Sugimoto, Y., Segi, E., Tsuboi, K., Ichikawa, A., and Narumiya, S. (1998). Female reproduction in mice lacking the prostaglandin F receptor. Roles of prostaglandin and oxytocin receptors in parturition. *Adv. Exp. Med. Biol.* 449, 317–321.
368. Uozumi, N., Kume, K., Nagase, T., Nakatani, N., Ishii, S., Tashiro, F., Komagata, Y., Maki, K., Ikuta, K., Ouchi, Y., Miyazaki, J., and Shimizu, T. (1997). Role of cytosolic phospholipase A2 in allergic response and parturition. *Nature* 390, 618–622.
369. Bonventre, J. V., Huang, Z., Taheri, M. R., O'Leary, E., Li, E., Moskowitz, M. A., and Sapirstein, A. (1997). Reduced fertility and postischaemic brain injury in mice deficient in cytosolic phospholipase A2. *Nature* 390, 622–625.
370. Langenbach, R., Morham, S. G., Tiano, H. F., Loftin, C. D., Ghanayem, B. I., Chulada, P. C., Mahler, J. F., Lee, C. A., Goulding, E. H., Kluckman, K. D. et al. (1995). Prostaglandin synthase 1 gene disruption in mice reduces arachidonic acid-induced inflammation and indomethacin-induced gastric ulceration. *Cell* 83, 483–492.
371. Gross, G. A., Imamura, T., Luedke, C., Vogt, S. K., Olson, L. M., Nelson, D. M., Sadovsky, Y., and Muglia, L.J. (1998). Opposing actions of prostaglandins and oxytocin determine the onset of murine labor. *Proc. Natl. Acad. Sci. USA* 95, 11875–11879.
372. Narumiya, S., Sugimoto, Y., and Ushikubi, F. (1999). Prostanoid receptors: Structures, properties, and functions. *Physiol. Rev.* 79, 1193–1226.
373. Curlewis, J. D., Tam, S. P., Lau, P., Kusters, D. H., Barclay, J. L., Anderson, S. T, and Waters, M. J. (2002). A prostaglandin F2α analog induces suppressors of cytokine signaling-3 expression in the corpus luteum of the pregnant rat: A potential new mechanism in luteolysis. *Endocrinology* 143, 3984–3993.
374. Tam, S. P., Lau, P., Djiane, J., Hilton, D. J., and Waters, M. J. (2001). Tissue-specific induction of SOCS gene expression by PRL. *Endocrinology* 142, 5015–5026.
375. Fiedler, E. P., Plouffe, Jr., L., Hales, D. B., Hales, K. H., and Khan, I. (1999). Prostaglandin $F_{2\alpha}$ induces a rapid decline in progesterone production and steroidogenic acute regulatory protein expression in isolated rat corpus luteum without altering messenger ribonucleic acid expression. *Biol. Reprod.* 61, 643–650.
376. Pepe, G. J., and Rothchild, I. (1974). A comparative study of serum progesterone levels in pregnancy and in various types of pseudopregnancy in the rat. *Endocrinology* 95, 275–279.
377. Critser, E. S., Rutledge, J. J., and French, L. R. (1980). Role of the uterus and the conceptus in regulating luteal lifespan in the mouse. *Biol. Reprod.* 23, 558–563.
378. Duby, R. T., McDaniel, J. W., Spilman, C. H., and Black D. L. (1969). Utero-ovarian relationships in the golden hamster. I. Ovarian periodicity following hysterectomy. *Acta. Endocrinol. (Copenh.)* 60, 595–602.
379. Narayansingh, R. M., Senchyna, M., and Carlson, J. C. (2002). Treatment with prostaglandin $F_{2\alpha}$ increases expression of prostaglandin synthase-2 in the rat corpus luteum. *Prostaglandins Other Lipid Mediat.* 70, 145–160.
380. Guo, K., Wolf, V., Dharmarajan, A. M., Feng, Z., Bielke, W., Saurer, S., and Friis, R. (1998). Apoptosis-associated gene expression in the corpus luteum of the rat. *Biol. Reprod.* 58, 739–746.
381. Roughton, S. A., Lareu, R. R., Bittles, A. H., and Dharmarajan, A. M. (1999). Fas and Fas ligand messenger ribonucleic acid and protein expression in the rat corpus luteum during apoptosis-mediated luteolysis. *Biol. Reprod.* 60, 797–804.
382. Penny, L. A. (2000). Monocyte chemoattractant protein 1 in luteolysis. *Rev. Reprod.* 5, 63–66.
383. Goyeneche, A. A., Martinez, I. L., Deis, R. P., Gibori, G., and Telleria, C. M. (2003). In vivo hormonal environment leads to differential susceptibility of the corpus luteum to apoptosis in vitro. *Biol. Reprod.*

PART IV

Intraovarian Regulators

CHAPTER 13

Prostaglandin Biosynthesis and Action in the Ovary

JEAN SIROIS, DEREK BOERBOOM, AND KHAMPOUNE SAYASITH

ABSTRACT

The prostaglandins are a family of bioactive lipid molecules believed to be synthesized by every cell type in the body. The last three decades of biomedical research have shown them to function as mediators of a wide range of physiological and pathological processes, from renal hemodynamics and gastrointestinal cytoprotection to inflammation and tumorigenesis. In addition, some of the most important advances in the field of reproductive biology have resulted from the elucidation of the roles played by prostaglandins in the female reproductive tract. Notably, strong lines of pharmacological, biochemical, and genetic evidence now indicate that prostaglandins are crucial for proper ovulation, luteolysis, implantation, decidualization, and parturition. This chapter reviews fundamental aspects of prostaglandin synthesis and action and summarizes our current understanding of prostaglandin function in the ovary.

PROSTAGLANDINS AND THEIR RECEPTORS

Prostaglandins: Structure and Nomenclature

Prostaglandins are members of the eicosanoid biomolecule family, which also includes prostacyclin, thromboxane, leukotrienes, and lipoxins [1, 2]. They are derived from open-chain, 20-carbon polyunsaturated fatty acids, typically arachidonic acid. Whereas leukotrienes and lipoxins are formed directly from their parent fatty acid, prostaglandins, prostacyclin, and thromboxanes are derived from a cyclic endoperoxide intermediate, prostaglandin H_2 (PGH_2) (Figure 13.1). Various classes of prostaglandins can be synthesized from this precursor, and these are categorized into subfamilies according to specific structural criteria. Whereas all prostaglandins consist of a cyclopentane ring to which two side chains are attached at positions 8 and 12, it is the nature of the additional substituents on the ring that categorizes them into a particular series, which are named as the letters A through J. For instance, prostaglandin F (PGF) compounds have hydroxyls at the C-9 and C-11 positions, and prostaglandin E (PGE) compounds are characterized by a hydroxyl and a ketone group. Additional information in subscripts indicates the number of double bonds in the molecule, and the letter α denotes that the C-9 substituent is located behind the plane of the ring, as in $PGF_{2\alpha}$ (see Figure 13.1) [2].

Biosynthetic Enzymes

PHOSPHOLIPASES

Arachidonic acid, the principal substrate for prostaglandin biosynthesis, is mainly stored in an esterified state at the *sn*2 position of cell membrane phospholipids [3]. The first regulated step involved in prostaglandin formation in all tissues involves the hydrolytic release of arachidonate (see Figure 13.1). This is believed to be principally mediated by members of the phospholipase A_2 (PLA_2) enzyme family. Originally isolated from pancreatic juices and snake venom, the PLA_2 family now includes several structurally and functionally diverse enzymes that are involved in different biological processes [3, 4]. Among the PLA_2 enzymes involved in prostaglandin biosynthesis is the group IV or cytosolic PLA_2 ($cPLA_2$). This enzyme rapidly translocates to the membrane fraction and binds phospholipids in response to receptor activation-induced rises in intracellular Ca^{2+} levels. Once in the membrane fraction, $cPLA_2$ acts to release the arachidonate needed for the acute/early phase of prostaglandin synthesis [3, 4]. Whereas $cPLA_2$ continues to function in late-phase prostaglandin formation and its expression can be induced by cytokines and mitogens, the type IIA enzyme (called *soluble* PLA_2 or $sPLA_2$) has been shown to be critical in situations where a priming or activation period is required [3, 4]. A current model proposes that in conditions where receptor activation is prolonged, $sPLA_2$ is induced along with the downstream biosynthetic machinery (see later discussion), thereby permitting sustained prostaglandin synthesis [4]. Because $sPLA_2$ is a secreted enzyme, its induction also creates a paracrine amplification loop

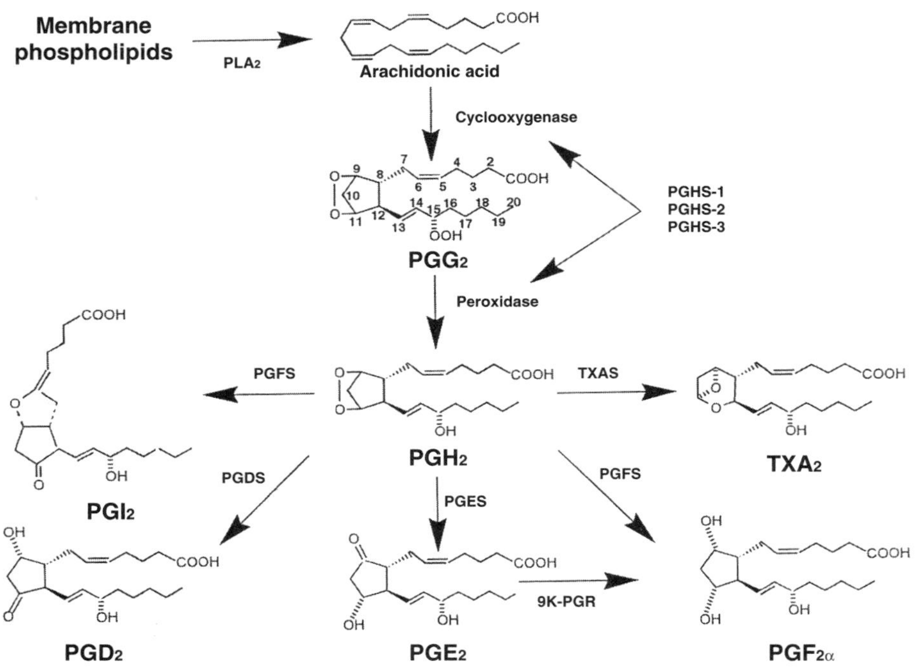

FIGURE 13.1 The prostaglandin biosynthetic pathway. (Modified from Ref. [1], with permission from the American Physiological Society.)

because its action on the surface of neighboring cells elicits additional prostaglandin synthesis [4].

Prostaglandin G/H Synthases

PGHS-1, PGHS-2, and PGHS-3. Following its release, arachidonate is converted to PGH_2 by the action of prostaglandin G/H synthase (PGHS) (see Figure 13.1), which is situated on the luminal surface of the endoplasmic reticulum and the outer envelope of the nuclear membrane [5]. Numerous studies have demonstrated the existence of two distinct genes encoding isoforms of PGHS, named *PGHS-1* and *PGHS-2*. Both enzymes possess a PGG_2-synthetic cyclooxygenase activity that has resulted in their being colloquially referred to as *cyclooxygenase-1* and *-2* (or *COX-1* and *-2*), but they are also responsible for the rapid conversion of PGG_2 to PGH_2 via a peroxidase activity [6]. Despite catalytic and structural similarities, PGHS-1 and -2 differ in most other respects, including gene structure and regulation, tissue distribution, and messenger ribonucleic acid (mRNA) stability [6, 7]. In almost all cases, PGHS-1 is considered to play a housekeeping role, because it is constitutively expressed at low levels in most tissues [7]. It is associated with the homeostatic levels of prostaglandin production required for the maintenance of blood perfusion in the kidney and gastric mucosa and for thromboxane synthesis in platelets [7]. PGHS-2 however is normally absent from most tissues but is readily inducible by hormones, cyclic adenosine monophosphate (cAMP), inflammatory factors, growth factors, tumor promoters, and cytokines in a variety of cell systems [6, 7]. Notable examples of PGHS-2 function in physiological and pathological processes include kidney development; tumorigenesis; embryonic implantation; and mediation of inflammation, fever, and pain [7]. Recently, a third PGHS isoform (called *PGHS-3* or *COX-3*) has been identified and shown to consist of an alternate splicing variant of the PGHS-1 gene in which intron 1 has been retained. This isoform is constitutively expressed at relatively high levels in the cerebral cortex and heart, is highly sensitive to acetaminophen, and is thought to be involved in sensing pain [8].

Nonsteroidal Antiinflammatory Drugs and Selective Cyclooxygenase Inhibitors. Although nonsteroidal antiinflammatory drugs (NSAIDs) have been widely used as pharmacological treatments for a variety of ailments for more than 100 years, it only become clear in the 1970s that they suppress inflammation by inhibiting PGHS activity [9, 10]. This discovery was followed by the elucidation of aspirin's mechanism of action, which was found to irreversibly inactivate the cyclooxygenase active sites of PGHS-1 and -2 by acetylating them at a single serine residue [10, 11]. In large part because of this lack of PGHS isoform selectivity, the use of aspirin and other traditional NSAIDs often results in renal, gastrointestinal, and other deleterious side effects [10, 11]. The pharmaceutical industry was therefore prompted to develop a new class of COX-2 specific inhibitors (COXIBs), which aimed to improve the therapeutic profile of NSAIDS by targeting the pathological effects of PGHS-2 without disrupting the homeostatic functions of PGHS-1. Two COXIB drugs (celecoxib and rofecoxib) are now available on the U.S. market, with a second and third generation of COXIBs now in development [11]. Although widespread use of COXIBs has only just begun, early reports indicate significant reductions in NSAID-associated side effects [12], and new therapeutic applications are under evaluation for conditions such as cancer and Alzheimer's disease [9, 11].

Terminal Enzymes

Subsequent to PGH_2 formation by PGHS, specific prostaglandins are synthesized in given cell types according to the particular enzymatic machinery that they express (see Figure 13.1) [7]. Among the more extensively characterized prostaglandin-synthetic enzymes is PGD synthase (PGDS), of which two isoforms have been identified, the lipocalin-type PGDS (also known as *beta-trace*) and the hematopoietic PGDS [13]. Much like the PGHS enzymes, a constitutive and an induced isoform of PGE synthase have been identified. Microsomal PGE synthase (mPGES, also known as *mGST-L1*) is a glutathione-dependent enzyme of the MAPEG (*m*embrane-*a*ssociated *p*roteins involved in *e*icosanoid and *g*lutathione metabolism) enzyme family [2]. Whereas mPGES can be readily induced by interleukin-1β (IL-1β) and other cytokines, cytosolic PGE synthase (cPGES) expression generally remains basal in the presence of proinflammatory stimuli [2]. Interestingly, evidence is now accumulating that indicates a functional coupling of $cPLA_2$ and PGHS-1 to cPGES as well as $cPLA_2$ and PGHS-2 to mPGES [4]. This coupling could coordinate the activities of these enzymes and thereby provide a novel, subtle level of regulation of prostaglandin biosynthesis [4]. PGF synthase (PGFS) has been characterized most extensively in the bovine species, where "lung-type" and "liver-type" isoforms have been isolated. Both enzymes are members of the aldo-keto reductase superfamily and can catalyze a variety of biochemical reactions, although they differ in tissue distribution and kinetic properties [14, 15]. The enzyme 9-keto-PGE_2 reductase (9K-PGR), which converts PGE_2 into $PGF_{2\alpha}$, offers an alternative pathway for the biosynthesis of $PGF_{2\alpha}$ [14]. Only one prostacyclin (PGI_2) synthase (PGIS) gene has been characterized. A member of the cytochrome P450 family, PGIS localizes to the endoplasmic reticulum membrane where it presumably coordinates with PGHS to ensure efficient PGI_2 synthesis [16, 17].

Prostaglandin Transporters

Following their synthesis, prostaglandins are believed to diffuse freely toward the extracellular compartment to act in a paracrine and/or endocrine manner [18]. To permit their metabolic clearance after their interaction with cell surface receptors, prostaglandins must then perform a second passage through a plasma membrane so as to be inactivated (oxidized) by intracellular prostaglandin dehydrogenase. Unlike the initial efflux, this reuptake of prostaglandins is energy-dependent and requires a specific carrier mechanism. The first protein found to possess such an activity, the aptly named *prostaglandin transporter (PGT),* is expressed in a range of tissues and has been shown to coordinately regulate with PGHS-2 [18]. Consisting of 12 transmembrane spans, PGT is believed to mediate the reuptake of prostaglandins into various cell types by functioning as a lactate/prostaglandin exchanger [18]. More recently, additional mediators of prostaglandin transport have been identified that are phylogenetically related to PGT (including LST-1, moat1, and OAT-K2) and together form the organic anion transporting polypeptide (OATP) family. Furthermore, a separate family dubbed the *organic anion transporters (OATs)* also appears capable of catalyzing prostaglandin uptake [18]. Beyond its role in the clearance of prostaglandins, transport is now thought to play additional, subtle roles in prostaglandin signaling, such as modulating their interaction with cognate receptors by regulating their pericellular concentrations [18].

Prostaglandin Receptors

Prostaglandins target specific cells by binding cognate cell surface receptors. To date, four receptor subtypes that bind PGE_2 (EP_1-EP_4) have been characterized, two for PGD_2 (DP_1 and DP_2) and one each for $PGF_{2\alpha}$ and PGI_2 (FP and IP, respectively) [19, 20]. In addition, multiple splice variants of EP_1, EP_3, and FP have been identified, creating additional levels of modulation of intracellular signaling [20]. With the exception of DP_2, which is a chemoattractant receptor, all prostaglandin receptors are rhodopsin-type G-protein coupled receptors with seven transmembrane domains [19, 20]. On the basis of homology, physiological properties, and signal transduction mechanisms, these receptors have been subdivided into three groups [19, 21]. Group 1 receptors (IP, DP_1, EP_2, EP_4), known as the *relaxant receptors* for their effects on smooth muscle, are linked to heterotrimeric G-proteins whose $G_{s\alpha}$ subunit stimulates adenylate cyclase to increase intracellular cAMP concentrations. The group 2 *contractile receptors,* which include EP_1, FP, and the thromboxane A_2 receptor, signal through $G_{\alpha q}$ and the phospholipase C pathway to increase intracellular Ca^{2+} levels. The EP_3 subtype is the only member of the third group and is called an *inhibitory receptor* because it couples to the $G_{i\alpha}$ family to decrease cAMP formation. The physiological functions of these receptors have recently been studied in a series of gene knockout experiments that have contributed to our understanding of prostaglandin receptor function [21, 22]. In addition to the classic, membrane-bound receptors, recent evidence now indicates that the peroxisomal proliferator-activated receptor (PPAR) family of ligand-activated transcription factors can also function as eicosanoid receptors [19, 23]. Notably, PGI_2-mediated activation of PPARδ could be involved in such wide-ranging processes as embryo implantation, colorectal cancer, and apoptosis [23].

However, rigorous proof of eicosanoids functioning as genuine PPAR ligands in vivo has yet to be obtained [19].

PROSTAGLANDINS AND THE OVARIAN FOLLICLE

Prostaglandins in Preovulatory Follicles: 30 Years and Counting . . .

The potential role of prostaglandins in ovarian follicular function was initially proposed in 1972 when indomethacin and aspirin were shown to block ovulation in rats and rabbits [24, 25]. These pioneering studies were followed by numerous investigations that confirmed the inhibitory effect of NSAIDs on ovulation in various species (for reviews, see [26–28]). Concerns were raised initially regarding whether indomethacin blocked ovulation directly at the ovarian level or indirectly via inhibition of gonadotropin secretion at the hypothalamo-pituitary level. However, the matter was resolved by several lines of investigation that showed, for example, that indomethacin does not block the preovulatory luteinizing hormone (LH) surge and that ovulation could be blocked by NSAIDs in an in vitro model using perfused ovaries [26–28].

Another line of evidence supporting the role of prostaglandins during the ovulatory process emerged when it became clear that the preovulatory LH surge causes a marked increase in concentrations of PGE_2 and $PGF_{2\alpha}$ in ovarian follicles just before ovulation [26–28]. This gonadotropin-dependent induction of prostaglandin synthesis in preovulatory follicles was documented in rodents, rabbits, pigs, sheep, primates, cows, and mares, with the granulosa cell layer generally recognized as the primary site of synthesis. However, the theca interna is also thought to be an important site of prostaglandin production in some species. The ability of indomethacin to block this preovulatory rise in follicular prostaglandins was seen as further evidence of the role of prostaglandins in ovulation. This concept was strengthened by studies in which systemic or intrafollicular administration of antisera to prostaglandins was shown to be antiovulatory in rabbits and mice [26, 28].

Although PGE_2 is produced in larger amounts than $PGF_{2\alpha}$ in several species, the relative importance of each prostaglandin during ovulation became the subject of controversy. The debate was fueled by conflicting results on their respective ability to restore ovulation in indomethacin-treated animals and the ability of PGE_2 vs $PGF_{2\alpha}$ antibodies to inhibit follicular rupture [27, 31]. A more fundamental dispute emerged when even the role of prostaglandins during ovulation was questioned because, for example, prostaglandins were unable to reverse the antiovulatory effect of indomethacin in some studies [27–30]. Although the precise basis for these contradictory findings remains unclear, results from genetic studies in mice now provide convincing evidence for an obligatory role of prostaglandins during ovulation, with PGE_2 serving as the principal actor in this species [31].

The preovulatory LH surge is the most potent physiological stimulator of ovarian prostaglandin synthesis and acts primarily via stimulation of an adenylate cyclase coupled membrane receptor. However, several other agonists acting at various stages of follicular development have been identified in ovarian cells. Gonadotropin-releasing hormone (Gn-RH) is a strong agonist of prostaglandin production in rodents and acts via specific phospholipase C-coupled receptors present on granulosa cells [32, 33]. Other stimulators include several growth factors, such as growth differentiation factor-9 (GDF-9), transforming growth factor-α (TGF-α), basic fibroblast growth factor (bFGF), nerve growth factor (NGF), insulin-like growth factor 1 (IGF-1), as well as IGF binding protein-3 [34–38]. IL-1β, oxytocin, estradiol, and tumor necrosis factor-α (TNF-α) are also thought to be produced locally within the ovary and to stimulate prostaglandin synthesis [38–41]. In contrast, few negative regulators of follicular prostaglandin production have been identified. They include TGF-β [35] and progesterone that, by virtue of decreasing gonadotropin-stimulated PGE_2 synthesis in rat preovulatory follicles, could act as an antiinflammatory steroid to limit the inflammatory reaction associated with the ovulatory process [42].

Numerous roles have been ascribed to prostaglandins during ovulation. They were proposed to be involved in inducing a local inflammatory reaction, acting as vasoactive agents and contributing to hyperemia, causing contraction of smooth muscle fibers in theca layers, affecting progesterone synthesis by granulosa cells, and regulating hyaluronan synthesis by cumulus cells [27, 29, 43]. More recently, they were also shown to mediate, at least in part, the gonadotropin-regulated and protein kinase C-dependent production of reactive oxygen species in preovulatory follicles [44]. The effect of prostaglandins on the enzymatic breakdown of the follicular wall, and more precisely on the regulation of plasminogen activator and follicular collagenases, has been extensively studied [29, 45]. Results from investigations in the early 1990s suggest that they would be important in mediating the gonadotropin-dependent induction of interstitial collagenolytic activity, responsible for the degradation of interstitial collagen present in the theca and tunica albuginea layers at the time of follicular rupture [45]. Indomethacin was shown to suppress the hCG-induced rise in interstitial collagenase but not that of collagenase IV responsible for the disintegration of the basement membrane, which provided a potential molecular basis for intraovarian ovulation observed in indomethacin-treated animals. Further evidence for such uncontrolled follicular collagenolytic activities in NSAID-treated animals was recently provided in meticulous histological studies in which follicular rupture was found to be abnormal but not inhibited [46]. Such a finding suggests that counting oocytes in the oviducts is not an accurate predictor of follicular rupture in indomethacin-treated animals [46].

Regulation of Follicular Phospholipases A_2

The mobilization of arachidonic acid from cell membrane phospholipids by PLA_2 is the initial step in prostaglandin biosynthesis, and $cPLA_2$ and $sPLA_2$ have been detected in ovarian follicles. In hen granulosa cells, $cPLA_2$ is expressed at various stages of follicular development, with TGF-α stimulating and TGF-β inhibiting expression of the enzyme. Such reciprocal regulation of $cPLA_2$ was proposed to modulate the prostaglandin synthetic capacity and mitogenic response of granulosa cells to growth factors during follicular development [47]. Studies in rats suggest that the expression $cPLA_2$ and $sPLA_2$ increases with advancing stages of follicular development, with both enzymes present in large mature follicles. Despite the marked increase in prostaglandin synthesis before ovulation, the expression of $cPLA_2$ and $sPLA_2$ was shown to remain relatively constant during the periovulatory period in vivo [48, 49]. However, studies in vitro using isolated granulosa cells or dispersed whole rat ovaries identified various agonists (IL-1β, human chorionic gonadotropin [hCG], follicle-stimulating hormone (FSH), and TGF-α) and antagonists (TGF-β and dexamethasone) of $cPLA_2$ and $sPLA_2$ expression [47, 50, 51]. The ability of a specific $cPLA_2$ inhibitor to reduce ovarian PGE_2 content and ovulation rate in rats suggests that the enzyme is involved in this process [48]. However, the modest reduction in ovulation rate observed in $cPLA_2$-deficient mice indicates that the role of the enzyme, in contrast to COX-2, is limited [52].

Hormonal Regulation of Prostaglandin G/H Synthase Expression

Expression of PGHS-2

Induction of PGHS-2 in Rat Preovulatory Follicles. The regulation of PGHS enzymes in preovulatory follicles was first reported more than 15 years ago (for review, see [28]). Initial studies performed in rats showed that the induction of PGHS protein in vivo was tissue specific and gonadotropin dependent. Induced expression of PGHS was detected in follicles of preovulatory size but not in smaller antral and preantral follicles and was limited to the granulosa cell layer. The induction required an ovulatory dose of hCG and was transient in nature. Subsequent studies in vitro further established the ability of gonadotropins to induce PGHS enzyme in rat follicular cells. Unknowingly, the success of these early investigations depended on the ability of the anti-PGHS antisera to cross-react with a second PGHS isoform that would soon be discovered.

The identification of two molecular weight variants of PGHS enzymes in the rat ovary was documented in the early 1990s [53]. They were shown to vary only slightly in size (69,000 vs 72,000 molecular weight), with only the larger isoform being induced by gonadotropins in rat granulosa cells during ovulation. Purification of this isoform by anionic exchange chromatography and size fractionation and sequencing of its N-terminus revealed that it represented a novel isoform of PGHS enzyme that was, at the time, called the *inducible PGHS* [54]. The characterization of this distinct PGHS protein coincided with the cloning of a new PGHS-related complementary deoxyribonucleic acid (cDNA), which collectively contributed to establish the identity of a novel PGHS isoform now called *PGHS-2*. Subsequent Northern blot analyses using a PGHS-2 specific cDNA probe showed that the gonadotropin-dependent induction of PGHS-2 protein in rat preovulatory follicles was preceded by a transient induction of PGHS-2 transcript [55].

Regulation of Follicular PGHS-2 Expression in Other Species. A series of studies in different species showed that the molecular process of induction of PGHS-2 in granulosa cells before ovulation was highly conserved [28]. However, the time-course of PGHS-2 induction varied greatly among species and appeared directly related to length of the ovulatory process. In rats, a species with a short ovulatory process (12 to 14 hours post-hCG), the induction of PGHS-2 was rapid and occurred 2 to 4 hours post-hCG. In cattle, a species with a relatively long process (28 to 30 hours post-hCG), the induction of PGHS-2 was delayed and occurred only 18 hours post-hCG. In mares, a species with an even longer ovulatory process (39 to 42 hours post-hCG), the induction of PGHS-2 was further delayed to 30 hours post-hCG. Interestingly, the interval of time from PGHS-2 induction to follicular rupture appeared highly conserved (10 hours post-hCG in rats, cows, and mares), which suggests that the molecular control of PGHS-2 induction could act as a determinant of the species-specific length of the ovulatory process [56] (Figure 13.2).

The induction of PGHS-2 during ovulation has been studied in mice, and results showed that the enzyme is induced not only in mural granulosa cells but also in cumulus cells surrounding the oocyte and that factor(s) produced by the oocyte could promote PGHS-2 expression [31, 57, 58]. Moreover, reports in mice and cattle suggest that the expression of PGHS-2 in cumulus cells may influence proper expansion of the cumulus cell-oocyte complexes (COC) and oocyte maturation [31, 58, 59]. A gonadotropin-dependent induction of PGHS-2 before ovulation has also been documented in monkeys [60]. In humans, although ethical reasons preclude the isolation of ovarian tissues at various time points, current reports demonstrate that PGHS-2 is present in granulosa cells obtained from follicular aspirates of women enrolled in in

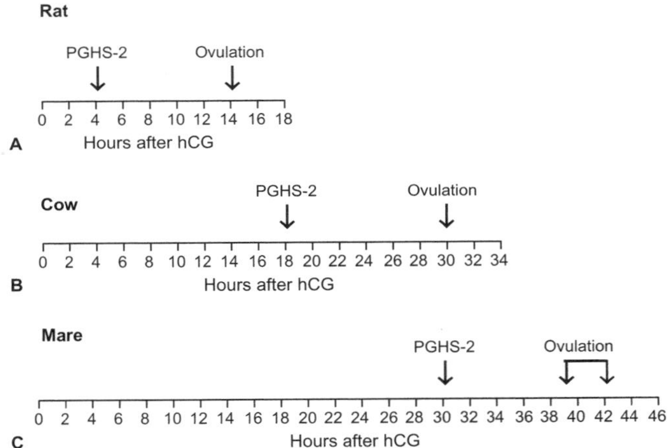

FIGURE 13.2 Relationship among PGHS-2 induction, time of ovulation, and length of the ovulatory process in rats **(A)**, cows **(B)**, and mares **(C)**. (From Ref. [56], with permission from the Endocrine Society.)

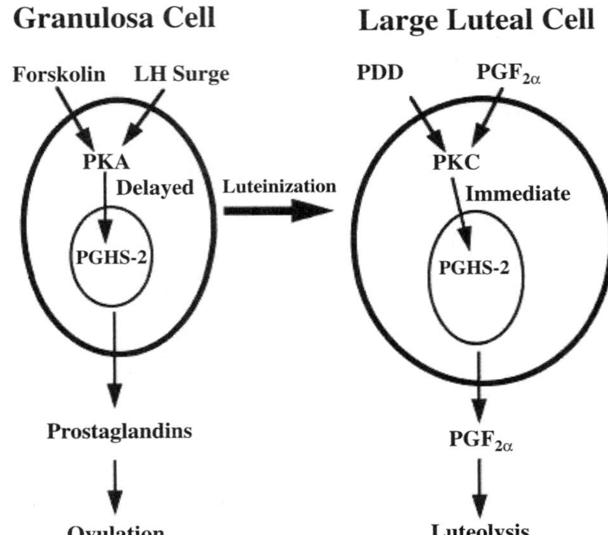

FIGURE 13.3 Proposed model for the regulation of PGHS-2 in granulosa cells and large luteal cells. *PDD*, Phorbol didecanoate. (Modified from Ref. [67], with permission from Elsevier, Inc.)

vitro fertilization programs [61]. The expression of PGHS-2 following ovarian hyperstimulation has also been studied in cattle [62]. Results showed that, whereas the majority of follicles larger than 8 mm were PGHS-2 positive, an important proportion of follicles (24%) did not express PGHS-2. Interestingly, the proportion of PGHS-2 negative follicles was similar to the reported incidence of anovulatory follicles following ovarian hyperstimulation [62].

Molecular Control of PGHS-2 Gene Expression. The preovulatory LH surge is considered the primary regulator of PGHS-2 expression in preovulatory follicles, but other gonadotropins (FSH and hCG) and activators of the cAMP-dependent protein kinase (PKA) pathway have been shown to be equally effective [28]. Moreover, numerous additional agonists working through various signaling pathways have been implicated in the regulation of PGHS-2 in ovarian cells, including GnRH, $PGF_{2\alpha}$, IL-1β, GDF-9, and reactive oxygen species [34, 35, 55, 63–65]. Recent elegant studies have revealed that the regulation of PGHS-2 expression switches from a predominant PKA-dependent pathway in preovulatory follicles to a predominant PKC-dependent pathway in the corpus luteum (Figure 13.3) [66, 67].

Early investigations established that the preovulatory induction of PGHS-2 in granulosa cells was dependent on transcriptional events [68], which prompted an interest in characterizing the regulation of the PGHS-2 promoter. Initial studies showed that the proximal 200 base pairs (bp) of the rat PGHS-2 promoter were sufficient to confer basal and forskolin/gonadotropin inducible activities [69]. Several consensus *cis*-acting elements were identified in this region, including a C/EBP, an ATF/CRE, and an E-box element. Site-directed mutagenesis studies and electrophoretic mobility shift assays revealed that the E-box element plays a crucial role in the regulation of the PGHS-2 promoter in rat granulosa cells, and that upstream stimulatory factor (USF) transcription factors could bind to this element [70]. The subsequent characterization of the bovine PGHS-2 promoter identified similar elements and confirmed the central role played by the E-box in bovine granulosa cells [66, 71]. Interestingly, differences in the kinetics and nature of transcription factors binding to the rat and bovine PGHS-2 promoters were tentatively implicated in the rapid vs delayed induction of PGHS-2 [71]. Part of the molecular basis for the switch from PKA- to PKC-dependence during bovine granulosa cell luteinization in vitro has also been elucidated at the promoter level [66]. Likewise, the induction of the ovine PGHS-2 promoter in large luteal cells was shown to be PKC-dependent and to involve primarily, but not exclusively, the E-box element [72].

Expression of PGHS-1

In contrast to PGHS-2, the expression of PGHS-1 in the ovary has not received much attention, most likely because of the absence of regulation of this isoform in ovarian follicles [53, 60, 64]. PGHS-1 is either undetectable or constitutively expressed at low levels in follicles of different developmental stages, with theca interna serving as the predominant site of expression. Investigations in several species show that the dramatic increase in prostaglandin synthesis just before ovulation is PGHS-2-dependent and not associated with any regulation of PGHS-1.

Chemical and Genetic Inactivation of PGHS

In recent years the development of selective PGHS-2 inhibitors led to investigations that used these drugs to demonstrate the role of the enzyme in the ovulatory process. NS-398 significantly reduced LH/hCG-stimulated production of PGE_2 and the number of ovulations in vivo and in vitro in rats [73], whereas the highly PGHS-2 selective NSAID meloxicam was shown to inhibit ovulation in rabbits [74]. Likewise, the selective PGHS-2 inhibitor rofecoxib proved to delay follicular rupture in women but to have no effect on peripheral steroid profiles, signs reminiscent of the luteinized unruptured-follicle (LUF) syndrome [75]. Thus the use of these selective inhibitors and other NSAIDs is not recommended for women attempting to become pregnant because of their potential association with anovulatory and infertile cycles [76].

Gene-targeting studies have clearly demonstrated the obligatory role of PGHS-2, but not of PGHS-1, in the ovulatory process. PGHS-2-deficient female mice proved infertile because of failures in various reproductive processes, including a marked inhibition in ovulation [77]. Interestingly, the administration of PGE_2 but not of $PGF_{2\alpha}$ was able to restore ovulation in PGHS-2-deficient mice thus establishing the predominant role of PGE_2 in mice [31].

Regulation of Terminal Prostaglandin Synthases

Subsequent to the induction of PGHS-2, the expression of terminal enzymes is required for the synthesis of prostaglandins with biological functions. PGES catalyzes the conversion of PGH_2 into PGE_2 and, of the two PGES isoforms recently identified, only mPGES expression has thus far been described in the ovary [78–80]. In the bovine preovulatory follicle, there is a marked induction of mPGES transcript and protein just before ovulation in vivo, with the induction occurring predominantly in granulosa cells (Figure 13.4) [78]. Thus the dramatic increase in PGE_2 synthesis in bovine follicles just before ovulation results from a concomitant induction of PGHS-2 and mPGES. Similar studies during the ovulatory process have not been performed in other species, but expression of mPGES has been detected in mouse follicular cells and oocytes [79, 80].

Ovulation is also accompanied by a marked increase in $PGF_{2\alpha}$ synthesis [26–29], and yet the regulation of PGFS or 9K-PGR mRNAs and proteins has not been investigated in ovarian follicles. However, a significant increase in 9K-PGR activity has been observed in ovine follicles just before ovulation [81].

Studies on the expression of PGIS showed that the enzyme is constitutively expressed in rat follicles with no significant changes during ovulation [82, 83]. Although the thecal layer is the predominant site of expression of the enzyme, low levels of PGIS are also detected in granulosa cells. Thus the reported rise in concentrations of PGI_2 in preovulatory follicles of several species likely results from conversion of increased PGH_2 precursors (following PGHS-2 induction) but not from PGIS regulation.

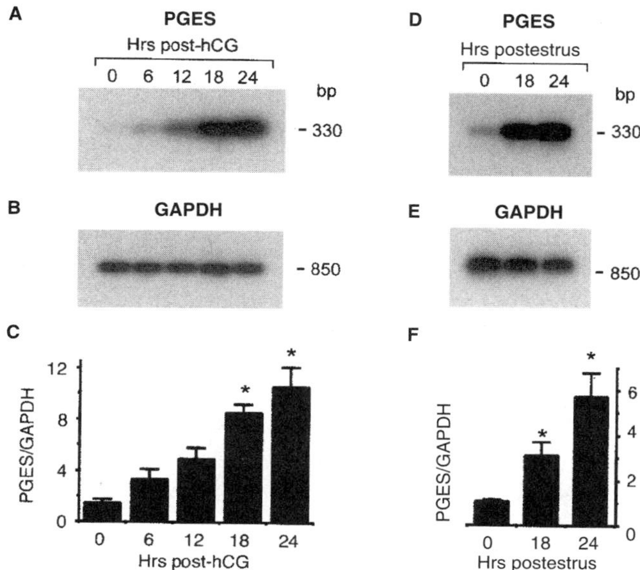

FIGURE 13.4 Regulation of PGES mRNA in bovine preovulatory follicles during hCG-induced ovulation or after onset of natural estrus. Semiquantitative RT-PCR/Southern blot analysis of total ribonucleic acid (RNA) extracted from bovine preovulatory follicles isolated 0, 6, 12, 18, and 24 hours post-hCG (**A**, **B**, **C**), or 0, 18, and 24 hours after onset of natural estrus (**D**, **E**, **F**). Samples were analyzed for PGES (**A** and **D**) and GAPDH (**B** and **E**; control gene) content. Graphs in **C** and **F** show relative changes in PGES transcripts ($n = 2$ to 4 follicles per time point). Bars with asterisk are significantly different from the 0h time point ($p < 0.05$) (Modified from Ref. [78], with permission from the American Society for Biochemistry and Molecular Biology.)

Lastly, there has been no report on the regulation of TXA synthase (TXAS) and PGD synthase (PGDS) in ovarian follicles, although both enzymes have been localized in the human corpus luteum [84]. However, a significant increase in TXA_2 or its stable metabolite (TXB_2) has been described in ovarian follicles before ovulation [85, 86], but platelet aggregates adhering to the follicular endothelial cells were considered as the predicted source of thromboxanes [85].

Prostaglandin Receptors

Of all the prostaglandin receptors inactivated by gene-targeting studies, only EP_2-deficient mice were shown to exhibit a change in ovarian follicular phenotype. Female mice deficient in EP_2 were shown to have a reduced litter size, but some controversy exists as to the precise nature of the defect. Whereas some reports identified impaired cumulus expansion and fertilization as the primary defects [87, 88], another study revealed that the reduced fertility was caused by severely impaired ovulation [89]. This apparent discrepancy among studies was attributed to the use of different genetic backgrounds and/or ages of mice (e.g., impaired ovulation was observed in adult but not in immature EP_2-deficient mice) [89]. Studies in wild-type female mice show that the EP_2 mRNA is expressed at low levels in thecal cells of preovulatory follicles before hCG treatment and is induced in cumulus cells 4 to 12 hours post-hCG in vivo [87]. The transcript has also been detected in cumulus and granulosa cells of other species [90, 91].

Studies on FP receptors in ovarian follicles indicate low or undetectable expression in granulosa cells before ovulation, but a marked induction of the transcript is observed after ovulation in luteal cells where it is thought to mediate $PGF_{2\alpha}$-induced luteolysis later in the cycle [92, 93]. Likewise, stimulation of bovine preovulatory granulosa cells or human granulosa-luteal cells with hCG, forskolin, and other PKA activators causes a marked increase in FP receptor expression in vitro. The fact that FP-deficient female mice are fertile supports the apparent limited role of this receptor in follicular development [94]. However, the central role of FP in parturition was demonstrated in these mice that were unable to deliver fetuses at term [95].

There has been no report on the expression of IP and TP receptors in ovarian follicles, and only a limited number of studies have investigated the presence and regulation of EP_1, EP_3, and EP_4. EP_1 mRNA has been detected in human granulosa-luteal cells obtained from follicular aspirates [95], but the transcript could not be detected in bovine COCs [91]. In contrast, although EP_3 is present at low levels and is not regulated in granulosa and thecal cells of bovine follicles before ovulation [92], its transcript increases during maturation of COCs in vitro and is more highly expressed in COCs of better quality [91]. EP_4 has been detected in freshly isolated human granulosa-luteal cells [89]. However, it should be noted that female mice deficient in IP, EP_1, EP_3, EP_4, or TP are fertile, which suggests nonessential roles of these receptors in female reproduction [96].

PROSTAGLANDINS AND THE CORPUS LUTEUM

Luteolysis

Regulation of Ovarian $PGF_{2\alpha}$ Synthesis and Action

Luteolysis, defined as a loss of function of the corpus luteum and/or its involution, is a key event in the normal ovarian cycle and in parturition in many species [97, 98]. Although the subject of controversy for many years, $PGF_{2\alpha}$ is now widely accepted as the principal physiological luteolysin in many mammalian species and, according to species, can originate mainly from the uterus or the corpus luteum itself [98]. The regulated synthesis of luteolytic $PGF_{2\alpha}$ by the uterus has been extensively studied (for reviews, see [98–101]). The exact manner in which $PGF_{2\alpha}$ synthesis by the corpus luteum is regulated remains somewhat more speculative, and various agents including progesterone, IL-1β, TNF-α, interferon γ, and endothelin-1 (ET-1) have been proposed as potential modulators of $PGF_{2\alpha}$ production [101]. In ruminants, $PGF_{2\alpha}$ has been shown to upregulate the expression of PGHS-2 in luteal cells [63, 98, 101]. This has been proposed to create an autocrine-signaling loop that would amplify the effects of uterine $PGF_{2\alpha}$ by stimulating high-level synthesis of $PGF_{2\alpha}$ locally within the corpus luteum [97]. Whether or not this is required for luteolysis to take place has yet to be demonstrated. In humans, whereas it has been established that $PGF_{2\alpha}$ levels in ovarian venous blood increase in the late luteal phase, underlying regulatory mechanisms have not been reported thus far [98].

Whether of ovarian or uterine origin, $PGF_{2\alpha}$ acts on the corpus luteum by binding FP, which is expressed to varying degrees in subsets of luteal cells in a species-specific manner [97]. Predictably, FP expression increases during the late luteal phase in most species [97, 98]. Another mechanism by which $PGF_{2\alpha}$ action may be modulated at the level of the receptor is via the expression of FP isoforms that differ in their intracellular signaling mechanisms and desensitization properties, which could result in the activation of additional signaling pathways or serve to regulate each other's activity [97].

Roles and Mechanisms of $PGF_{2\alpha}$ Action in the Corpus Luteum

Amplification of the Luteolytic Signal. Binding of $PGF_{2\alpha}$ to FP at the luteal cell surface rapidly leads to the activation of phospholipase C, the release of intracellular Ca^{2+} from the endoplasmic reticulum, and ultimately to the activation of PKC isoforms [97]. In ruminants, this signaling pathway effectively amplifies the luteolytic uterine $PGF_{2\alpha}$ signal by inducing PGHS-2 expression (as described earlier) but also by provoking the exocytosis of oxytocin granules [97, 98]. According to a current model based largely on experiments performed in sheep, oxytocin release by the corpus luteum occurs in response to low-level $PGF_{2\alpha}$ release by the uterus, which itself is provoked by oxytocin secreted from the pituitary gland (Figure 13.5). This $PGF_{2\square}$ binds FP in a putative high sensitivity state (HFPR) (see Figure 13.5), resulting in the release of luteal oxytocin that effectively supplements the oxytocin of pituitary origin, thereby amplifying the release of $PGF_{2\alpha}$ by the uterus [98]. The functioning of these feedback loops presumably results in the eventual accumulation of levels of $PGF_{2\alpha}$ high enough to activate FP in its low sensitivity state (LFPR) (see Figure 13.5) and thereby triggers luteolysis. In this manner the uterus can be viewed as a transducer of the luteolytic signal, converting central oxytocin secretion

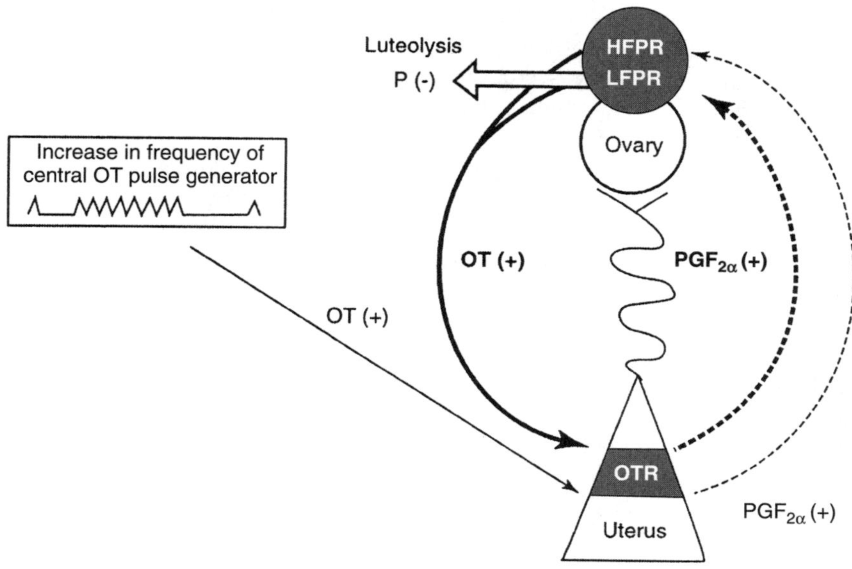

FIGURE 13.5 Proposed model for the regulation of $PGF_{2\alpha}$ during luteolysis in sheep. *HFPR*, High sensitivity state of the $PGF_{2\alpha}$ receptor; *LFPR*, low sensitivity state of the $PGF_{2\alpha}$ receptor; *OT*, oxytocin; *OTR*, oxytocin receptor; *P*, progesterone. (Modified from Ref. [98], with permission from the American Physiological Society.)

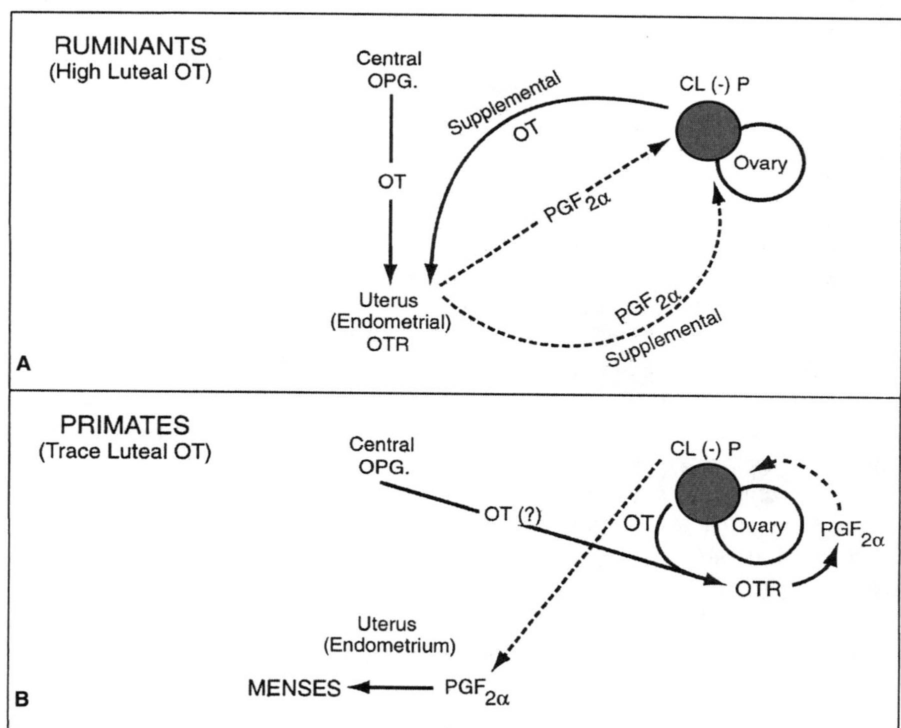

FIGURE 13.6 Comparative models for the control of luteolysis in, **A**, ruminants and, **B**, primates. *CL*, Corpus luteum; *OPG*, oxytocin pulse generator; *OT*, oxytocin; *OTR*, oxytocin receptor; *P*, progesterone. (Modified from Ref. [98], with permission from the American Physiological Society.)

into the production of $PGF_{2\alpha}$, and the corpus luteum serves as an amplifier of the uterine signal that brings about its own demise [98].

In primates there is evidence suggesting that a similar process may occur but without use of the uterus as an intermediate. Indeed, components of the luteolytic signaling such as oxytocin, oxytocin receptor, $PGF_{2\alpha}$, and FP are present in the primate corpus luteum. Thus a central oxytocin signal could trigger a self-contained, ovarian autocrine/paracrine loop, with oxytocin triggering $PGF_{2\alpha}$ release, resulting in local oxytocin secretion, and so on until luteolysis is initiated (Figure 13.6) [98]. Unlike ruminants, luteolysis in primates can therefore be regarded as an ovary-mediated event [98].

Functional Luteolysis. An initial event in luteolysis is a reduction in progesterone secretion by the corpus luteum. Although this precedes the actual involution of the tissue, the reduction of circulating progesterone levels mediates most of the physiological consequences of luteolysis and is thus referred to as *functional luteolysis.* Evidence now suggests that $PGF_{2\alpha}$ can induce functional luteolysis by inhibiting the import of cholesterol via a decrease in the activity and mRNA levels of sterol carrier protein-2 [102], as well as by decreasing the expression of steroidogenic acute regulatory protein (StAR) [103, 104]. A similar $PGF_{2\alpha}$-induced reduction in luteal mRNA levels also occurs with 3β-hydroxysteroid dehydrogenase (3β-HSD) [105]. Whereas these antisteroidogenic effects lie downstream of protein kinase C signaling, there is also evidence that other signaling pathways contribute to $PGF_{2\alpha}$-induced functional luteolysis. $PGF_{2\alpha}$-mediated rises in intracellular Ca^{2+} levels lead to the induction of the transcription factor nur77, which results in the induction of 20α-hydroxysteroid dehydrogenase [106, 107]. This enzyme then presumably interferes with progesterone action by converting it into an inactive metabolite. An intermediate step in this Ca^{2+}-dependent $PGF_{2\alpha}$ signaling pathway involves the activation of extracellular signal-regulated kinase (Erk), a mitogen-activated protein (MAP) kinase [106]. Interestingly, other recent reports have shown that Erk signaling can interfere with the ability of gonadotropins to upregulate StAR expression and progesterone secretion in ovarian cells [97]. Further studies are required to evaluate the importance of MAP kinase pathways in mediating the luteolytic effects of $PGF_{2\alpha}$, as well as to better define how they are activated by $PGF_{2\alpha}$ in luteal cells.

Recent studies have also shown that the endothelial cell-derived peptide endothelin-1 (ET-1) could be an important mediator of $PGF_{2\alpha}$-induced antisteroidogenic effects. ET-1 expression is induced by $PGF_{2\alpha}$ and oxytocin, and it was shown to inhibit progesterone secretion by luteal cells in vitro [98]. Furthermore, ET-1 expression in the corpus luteum is elevated at the time of its spontaneous regression and can be rapidly induced by the administration of exogenous $PGF_{2\alpha}$ [97, 98]. Although apparently insufficient by itself to induce luteolysis, ET-1 has been shown to cause premature regression of the corpus luteum when administered with a subluteolytic dose of $PGF_{2\alpha}$ [108]. ET-1 is therefore generally believed to enhance or potentiate the antisteroidogenic effects of $PGF_{2\alpha}$ in luteal cells.

Structural Luteolysis. Structural luteolysis, defined as the involution of the corpus luteum, is a complex process involving a number of mediators and signaling pathways [97]. Whereas the role of $PGF_{2\alpha}$ as a mammalian luteolysin is no longer contested, it remains somewhat unclear if it is directly involved in the death of luteal cells. For instance, in the ewe, the subset of luteal cells that express FP is not the first to die during $PGF_{2\alpha}$-induced luteolysis [97]. In addition, $PGF_{2\alpha}$ appears unable to induce the death of steroidogenic luteal cells in vitro, and the administration of subluteolytic doses of $PGF_{2\alpha}$ in ewes can reduce progesterone secretion without causing an appreciable loss of luteal cells. It has been proposed that the principal role of $PGF_{2\alpha}$ may be to mediate functional luteolysis, whereas its perceived role in the involution of the corpus luteum could in fact be a predominantly indirect effect, at least in certain species [97, 98].

Nonetheless, $PGF_{2\alpha}$ has been shown to modulate several cellular and gene regulation events that could be involved in structural luteolysis [97, 98]. It was originally hypothesized that $PGF_{2\alpha}$ could contribute to luteolysis via its vasoconstrictive properties by reducing ovarian blood flow. Although some initial experimental data seemed to support this, it is now accepted that functional luteolysis induced by $PGF_{2\alpha}$ precedes any measurable changes in luteal blood flow. Furthermore, whether changes in blood flow are causal or consequential events in structural luteolysis, if they are mediated by $PGF_{2\alpha}$ or even if they are required for involution to occur, remains unclear.

More recently $PGF_{2\alpha}$ was shown to induce the luteal expression of monocyte chemoattractant protein-1 (MCP-1). This presumably results in increased monocyte/macrophage migration into the corpus luteum, where these cells could serve to phagocytose luteal cells and to produce other cytokines [98, 109]. In addition, $PGF_{2\alpha}$ reduces the luteal expression of tissue inhibitor of metalloproteinase-1 (TIMP-1), possibly leading to increased metalloproteinase activity associated with structural regression [110]. Another level at which $PGF_{2\alpha}$ could participate in structural luteolysis is by regulating components of apoptotic signaling cascades, because apoptosis is now believed to be a central process in the involution of the corpus luteum [97]. Notably, caspase-3 has been shown to be required for proper luteal regression to occur, and caspase-3 activity is believed to be induced by $PGF_{2\alpha}$ [111]. The exact roles and relative importance of $PGF_{2\alpha}$ in mediating structural luteolysis therefore remain poorly defined but should become more clear as the underlying cellular and molecular processes mediating luteal involution are elucidated.

Luteotropic and Luteoprotective Prostaglandins

Although much attention has been focused on the luteolytic properties of $PGF_{2\alpha}$, it has long been known that other prostaglandins, most notably PGE_2 and prostacyclin, exert opposite effects. For instance, both stimulate the secretion of progesterone from luteal cells in vitro, and PGE_2 can protect the corpus luteum from the luteolytic effects of $PGF_{2\alpha}$ when they are administered simultaneously [98, 112]. The most intensely investigated effect of PGE_2, however, is its luteoprotective action during pregnancy. Uterine PGE_2 production increases during early pregnancy in species such as ruminants and pigs, and intrauterine infusions of PGE_2 in these species can protect the corpus luteum against the luteolytic effects of endogenous or exogenous $PGF_{2\alpha}$ [98]. Although uterine $PGF_{2□}$ production is not completely blocked during early pregnancy, the PGE_2:$PGF_{2\alpha}$ ratio increases markedly when compared with the nongravid uterus at the end of the luteal phase, and it is this ratio rather than the absolute amount of PGE_2 secretion that is most closely associated with the luteoprotective effects of PGE_2 [98, 113]. Because of its luteotropic and luteoprotective properties, $PGE_{2\alpha}$ is often regarded as a likely mediator of the maternal recognition of pregnancy in certain species. Consistent with this notion, compounds originating from the conceptus such as estrogen (in pigs) and interferon tau (in cows) appear able to increase the PGE_2:$PGF_{2\alpha}$ production ratio by the endometrium [113, 114]. Despite these advances, however, basic principles such as the mechanism by which PGE_2 exerts its luteoprotective effects have yet to be elucidated.

ACKNOWLEDGMENTS

Studies from the authors' laboratories were funded in part by the Canadian Institutes of Health Research (CIHR) Grant MT-13190 and Fonds pour la Formation de Chercheurs et l'Aide à la Recherche Grant 99-ER-3016. Jean Sirois is supported by a CIHR Investigator Award. Derek Boerboom is supported by a CIHR postdoctoral research fellowship.

References

1. Narumiya, S., Sugimoto, Y., and Ushikubi, F. (1999). Prostanoid receptors: Structures, properties, and functions. *Physiol. Rev.* 79, 1193–1226.
2. Norman, A. W., and Litwack, G. (1997). Prostaglandins. In *Hormones*, eds. A. W. Norman and G. Litwack, 445–470. San Diego: Academic Press.
3. Crofford, L. J. (2001). Prostaglandin biology. *Gastroenterol. Clin. North Am.* 30, 863–876.
4. Fitzpatrick, F. A., and Soberman, R. (2001). Regulated formation of eicosanoids. *J. Clin. Invest.* 107, 1347–1351.
5. Spencer, A. G., Woods, J. W., Arakawa, T., Singer, I. I., and Smith, W. L. (1998). Subcellular localization of prostaglandin endoperoxide H synthases-1 and -2 by immunoelectron microscopy. *J. Biol. Chem.* 273, 9886–9893.
6. Smith, W. L., DeWitt, D. L., and Garavito, R. M. (2000). Cyclooxygenases: Structural, cellular, and molecular biology. *Annu. Rev. Biochem.* 69, 145–182.
7. Dubois, R. N., Abramson, S. B., Crofford, L., Gupta, R. A., Simon, L. S., Van De Putte, L. B., and Lipsky, P. E. (1998). Cyclooxygenase in biology and disease. *FASEB J.* 12, 1063–1073.
8. Chandrasekharan, N. V., Dai, H., Roos, K. L., Evanson, N. K., Tomsik, J., Elton, T. S., and Simmons, D. L. (2002). COX-3, a cyclooxygenase-1 variant inhibited by acetaminophen and other analgesic/antipyretic drugs: Cloning, structure, and expression. *Proc. Natl. Acad. Sci. USA* 99, 13926–13931.
9. Turini, M. E., and DuBois, R. N. (2002). Cyclooxygenase-2: A therapeutic target. *Annu. Rev. Med.* 53, 35–57.
10. FitzGerald, G. A., and Patrono, C. (2001). The coxibs, selective inhibitors of cyclooxygenase-2. *N. Engl. J. Med.* 345, 433–442.
11. Everts, B., Wahrborg, P., and Hedner, T. (2000). COX-2-specific inhibitors—the emergence of a new class of analgesic and anti-inflammatory drugs. *Clin. Rheumatol.* 19, 331–343.
12. Patrono, C., Patrignani, P., and Garcia Rodriguez, L. A. (2001). Cyclooxygenase-selective inhibition of prostanoid formation: Transducing biochemical selectivity into clinical read-outs. *J. Clin. Invest.* 108, 7–13.
13. Urade, Y., and Hayaishi, O. (2000). Prostaglandin D synthase: Structure and function. *Vitam. Horm.* 58, 89–120.
14. Watanabe, K. (2002). Prostaglandin F synthase. *Prostaglandins Other Lipid Mediat.* 68–69, 401–407.
15. Suzuki, T., Fujii, Y., Miyano, M., Chen, L. Y., Takahashi, T., and Watanabe, K. (1999). cDNA cloning, expression, and mutagenesis study of liver-type prostaglandin F synthase. *J. Biol. Chem.* 274, 241–248.
16. Tanabe, T., and Ullrich, V. (1995). Prostacyclin and thromboxane synthases. *J. Lipid Mediat. Cell. Signal.* 12, 243–255.
17. Deng, H., Huang, A., So, S. P., Lin, Y. Z., and Ruan, K. H. (2002). Substrate access channel topology in membrane-bound prostacyclin synthase. *Biochem. J.* 362 (Pt 3), 545–551.
18. Schuster, V. L. (2002). Prostaglandin transport. *Prostaglandins Other Lipid Mediat.* 68–69, 633–647.
19. Funk, C. D. (2001). Prostaglandins and leukotrienes: Advances in eicosanoid biology. *Science* 294, 1871–1875.
20. Breyer, R. M., Bagdassarian, C. K., Myers, S. A., and Breyer, M. D. (2001). Prostanoid receptors: Subtypes and signaling. *Annu. Rev. Pharmacol. Toxicol.* 41, 661–690.
21. Wright, D. H., Abran, D., Bhattacharya, M., Hou, X., Bernier, S. G., Bouayad, A., Fouron, J. C., Vazquez-Tello, A., Beauchamp, M. H., Clyman, R. I., Peri, K., Varma, D. R., and Chemtob, S. (2001). Prostanoid receptors: Ontogeny and implications in vascular physiology. *Am. J. Physiol. Regul. Integr. Comp. Physiol.* 281, R1343–R1360.
22. Narumiya, S., and FitzGerald, G. A. (2001). Genetic and pharmacological analysis of prostanoid receptor function. *J. Clin. Invest.* 108, 25–30.
23. Lim, H., and Dey, S. K. (2002). A novel pathway of prostacyclin signaling—hanging out with nuclear receptors. *Endocrinology* 143, 3207–3210.
24. Orczyk, G. P., and Behrman, H. R. (1972). Ovulation blockade by aspirin or indomethacin—in vivo evidence for a role of prostaglandin in gonadotrophin secretion. *Prostaglandins* 1, 3–20.
25. Armstrong, D. T., and Grinwich, D. L. (1972). Blockade of spontaneous and LH-induced ovulation in rats by indomethacin, an inhibitor of prostaglandin biosynthesis. *Prostaglandins* 1, 21–28.
26. Armstrong, D. T. (1981). Prostaglandins and follicular functions. *J. Reprod. Fertil.* 62, 283–291.
27. Murdoch, W. J., Hansen, T. R., and McPherson, L. A. (1993). A review—role of eicosanoids in vertebrate ovulation. *Prostaglandins* 46, 85–115.

28. Sirois, J., Liu, J., Boerboom, D., and Antaya, M. (2000). Prostaglandins and ovulation: From indomethacin to PGHS-2 knockout. In *Ovulation: Evolving Scientific and Clinical Concepts,* ed. E. Y. Adashi, 208–220. New York: Springer.
29. Espey, L. L., and Lipner, H. (1994). Ovulation. In *Physiology of Reproduction,* Vol. 1, eds. E. Knobil, and J. D. Neill, 725–781. New York: Raven Press.
30. Murdoch, W. J. (1996). Differential effects of indomethacin on the sheep ovary: Prostaglandin biosynthesis, intracellular calcium, apoptosis, and ovulation. *Prostaglandins* 52, 497–506.
31. Davis, B. J., Lennard, D. E., Lee, C. A., Tiano, H. F., Morham, S. G., Wetsel, W. C., and Langenbach, R. (1999). Anovulation in cyclooxygenase-2-deficient mice is restored by prostaglandin E2 and interleukin-1β. *Endocrinology* 140, 2685–2695.
32. Naor, Z., Zilberstein, M., Zakut, H., and Dekel, N. (1984). Gonadotropin releasing hormone: Regulation of phospholipid turnover and prostaglandin production in ovarian granulosa cells. *Life Sci.* 35, 389–398.
33. Wang, J., Lee, V., and Leung, P. C. (1989). Differential role of protein kinase C in the action of luteinizing hormone-releasing hormone on hormone production in rat ovarian cells. *Am. J. Obstet. Gynecol.* 160, 984–989.
34. Elvin, J. A., Clark, A. T., Wang, P., Wolfman, N. M., and Matzuk, M. M. (1999). Paracrine actions of growth differentiation factor-9 in the mammalian ovary. *Mol. Endocrinol.* 13, 1035–1048.
35. Li, J., Simmons, D. L., and Tsang, B. K. (1996). Regulation of hen granulosa cell prostaglandin production by transforming growth factors during follicular development: Involvement of cyclooxygenase II. *Endocrinology* 137, 2522–2529.
36. LaPolt, P. S., Yamoto, M., Veljkovic, M., Sincich, C., Ny, T., Tsafriri, A., and Hsueh, A. J. (1990). Basic fibroblast growth factor induction of granulosa cell tissue-type plasminogen activator expression and oocyte maturation: Potential role as a paracrine ovarian hormone. *Endocrinology* 127, 2357–2363.
37. Dissen, G. A., Parrott, J. A., Skinner, M. K., Hill, D. F., Costa, M. E., and Ojeda, S. R. (2000). Direct effects of nerve growth factor on thecal cells from antral ovarian follicles. *Endocrinology* 141, 4736–4750.
38. Sirotkin, A. V., Makarevich, A. V., Corkins, M. R., Kotwica, J., Kwon, H. B., Bulla, J., and Hetenyi, L. (2001). Secretory activity of bovine ovarian granulosa cells transfected with sense and antisense insulin-like growth factor (IGF) binding protein-3 and the response to IGF-I, GH, LH, oxytocin and oestradiol. *J. Mol. Endocrinol.* 27, 329–338.
39. Kokia, E., Hurwitz, A., Ricciarelli, E., Tedeschi, C., Resnick, C. E., Mitchell, M. D., and Adashi, E. Y. (1992). Interleukin-1 stimulates ovarian prostaglandin biosynthesis: Evidence for heterologous contact-independent cell-cell interaction. *Endocrinology* 130, 3095–3097.
40. Sirotkin, A. V., Schaeffer, H. J., Mlyncek, M., Missik, J., and Bulla, J. (1996). Oxytocin affects the release of steroids, insulin-like growth factor-I, prostaglandin F2α and cyclic nucleotides by human granulosa cells in vitro. *Hum. Reprod.* 11, 152–155.
41. Wang, L. J., Brannstrom, M., Robertson, S. A., and Norman, R. J. (1992). Tumor necrosis factor alpha in the human ovary: Presence in follicular fluid and effects on cell proliferation and prostaglandin production. *Fertil. Steril.* 58, 934–940.
42. Hedin, L., and Eriksson, A. (1997). Prostaglandin synthesis is suppressed by progesterone in rat preovulatory follicles in vitro. *Prostaglandins* 53, 91–106.
43. Priddy, A. R., and Killick, S. R. (1993). Eicosanoids and ovulation. *Prostaglandins Leukot. Essent. Fatty Acids* 49, 827–831.
44. Kodaman, P. H., and Behrman, H. R. (2001). Endocrine-regulated and protein kinase C-dependent generation of superoxide by rat preovulatory follicles. *Endocrinology* 142, 687–693.
45. Tsafriri, A., Chun, S. Y., and Reich, R. (1993). Follicular rupture and ovulation. In *Ovulation*, eds. E. Y. Adashi and P. C. K. Leung, 227–244. New York: Raven Press.
46. Gaytan, F., Tarradas, E., Morales, C., Bellido, C., and Sanchez-Criado, J. E. (2002). Morphological evidence for uncontrolled proteolytic activity during the ovulatory process in indomethacin-treated rats. *Reproduction* 123, 639–469.
47. Li, J., Li, M., and Tsang, B. K. (1997). Regulation of cytosolic phospholipase A2 in hen granulosa cells by transforming growth factors at different stages of follicular development. *Biol. Reprod.* 57, 929–935.
48. Kurusu, S., Iwao, M., Kawaminami, M., and Hashimoto, I. (1998). Involvement of cytosolic phospholipase A2 in the ovulatory process in gonadotropin-primed immature rats. *Prostaglandins Leukot. Essent. Fatty. Acids* 58, 405–411.
49. Kol, S., Ruutiainen-Altman, K., Ben-Shlomo, I., Payne, D. W., Ando, M., and Adashi, E. Y. (1997). The rat ovarian phospholipase A2 system: Gene expression, cellular localization, activity characterization, and interleukin-1 dependence. *Endocrinology* 138, 322–331.
50. Ben-Shlomo, I., Kol, S., Ando, M., Altman, K. R., Putowski, L. T., Rohan, R. M., and Adashi, E. Y. (1997). Ovarian expression, cellular localization, and hormonal regulation of rat secretory phospholipase A2: Increased expression by interleukin-1 and by gonadotropins. *Biol. Reprod.* 57, 217–225.
51. Kol, S., Ben-Shlomo, I., Payne, D. W., Ando, M., Rohan, R. M., and Adashi, E. Y. (1998). Glucocorticoids suppress basal (but not interleukin-1-supported) ovarian phospholipase A2 activity: Evidence for glucocorticoid receptor-mediated regulation. *Mol. Cell. Endocrinol.* 137, 117–125.
52. Song, H., Lim, H., Paria, B. C., Matsumoto, H., Swift, L. L., Morrow, J., Bonventre, J. V., and Dey, S. K. (2002). Cytosolic phospholipase A2alpha is crucial for "on-time" embryo implantation that directs subsequent development. *Development* 129, 2879–2889.
53. Wong, W. Y., and Richards, J. S. (1991). Evidence for two antigenically distinct molecular weight variants of prostaglandin H synthase in the rat ovary. *Mol. Endocrinol.* 5, 1269–1279.
54. Sirois, J., and Richards, J. S. (1992). Purification and characterization of a novel, distinct isoform of prostaglandin endoperoxide synthase induced by human chorionic gonadotropin in granulosa cells of rat preovulatory follicles. *J. Biol. Chem.* 267, 6382–6388.
55. Sirois, J., Simmons, D. L., and Richards, J. S. (1992). Hormonal regulation of messenger ribonucleic acid encoding a

novel isoform of prostaglandin endoperoxide H synthase in rat preovulatory follicles. Induction in vivo and in vitro. *J. Biol. Chem.* 267, 11586–11592.

56. Sirois, J., and Dore, M. (1997). The late induction of prostaglandin G/H synthase-2 in equine preovulatory follicles supports its role as a determinant of the ovulatory process. *Endocrinology* 138, 4427–4434.
57. Rose, U. M., Hanssen, R. G., and Kloosterboer, H. J. (1999). Development and characterization of an in vitro ovulation model using mouse ovarian follicles. *Biol. Reprod.* 61, 503–511.
58. Joyce, I. M., Pendola, F. L., O'Brien, M., and Eppig, J. J. (2001). Regulation of prostaglandin-endoperoxide synthase 2 messenger ribonucleic acid expression in mouse granulosa cells during ovulation. *Endocrinology* 142, 3187–3197.
59. Nuttinck, F., Reinaud, P., Tricoire, H., Vigneron, C., Peynot, N., Mialot, J. P., Mermillod, P., and Charpigny, G. (2002). Cyclooxygenase-2 is expressed by cumulus cells during oocyte maturation in cattle. *Mol. Reprod. Dev.* 61, 93–101.
60. Duffy, D. M., and Stouffer, R. L. (2001). The ovulatory gonadotrophin surge stimulates cyclooxygenase expression and prostaglandin production by the monkey follicle. *Mol. Hum. Reprod.* 7, 731–739.
61. Narko, K., Ritvos, O., and Ristimaki, A. (1997). Induction of cyclooxygenase-2 and prostaglandin F2α receptor expression by interleukin-1β in cultured human granulosa-luteal cells. *Endocrinology* 138, 3638–3644.
62. Liu, J., and Sirois, J. (1998). Follicle size-dependent induction of prostaglandin G/H synthase-2 during superovulation in cattle. *Biol. Reprod.* 58, 1527–1532.
63. Tsai, S. J., and Wiltbank, M. C. (2001). Differential effects of prostaglandin F2α on in vitro luteinized bovine granulosa cells. *Reproduction* 122, 245–253.
64. Ando, M., Kol, S., Kokia, E., Ruutiainen-Altman, K., Sirois, J., Rohan, R. M., Payne, D. W., and Adashi, E. Y. (1998). Rat ovarian prostaglandin endoperoxide synthase-1 and -2: Periovulatory expression of granulosa cell-based interleukin-1-dependent enzymes. *Endocrinology* 139, 2501–2508.
65. Nakamura, T., and Sakamoto, K. (2001). Reactive oxygen species up-regulates cyclooxygenase-2, p53, and Bax mRNA expression in bovine luteal cells. *Biochem. Biophys. Res. Commun.* 284, 203–210.
66. Wu, Y. L., and Wiltbank, M. C. (2002). Transcriptional regulation of the cyclooxygenase-2 gene changes from protein kinase (PK) A- to PKC-dependence after luteinization of granulosa cells. *Biol. Reprod.* 66, 1505–1514.
67. Wu, Y. L., and Wiltbank, M. C. (2001). Differential regulation of prostaglandin endoperoxide synthase-2 transcription in ovine granulosa and large luteal cells. *Prostaglandins Other Lipid Mediat.* 65, 103–116.
68. Wong, W. Y., DeWitt, D. L., Smith, W. L., and Richards, J. S. (1989). Rapid induction of prostaglandin endoperoxide synthase in rat preovulatory follicles by luteinizing hormone and cAMP is blocked by inhibitors of transcription and translation. *Mol. Endocrinol.* 3, 1714–1723.
69. Sirois, J., Levy, L. O., Simmons, D. L., and Richards, J. S. (1993). Characterization and hormonal regulation of the promoter of the rat prostaglandin endoperoxide synthase 2 gene in granulosa cells. Identification of functional and protein-binding regions. *J. Biol. Chem.* 268, 12199–12206.
70. Morris, J. K., and Richards, J. S. (1996). An E-box region within the prostaglandin endoperoxide synthase-2 (PGS-2) promoter is required for transcription in rat ovarian granulosa cells. *J. Biol. Chem.* 271, 16633–16643.
71. Liu, J., Antaya, M., Boerboom, D., Lussier, J. G., Silversides, D. W., and Sirois, J. (1999). The delayed activation of the prostaglandin G/H synthase-2 promoter in bovine granulosa cells is associated with down-regulation of truncated upstream stimulatory factor-2. *J. Biol. Chem.* 274, 35037–35045.
72. Wu, Y. L., and Wiltbank, M. C. (2001). Transcriptional regulation of cyclooxygenase-2 gene in ovine large luteal cells. *Biol. Reprod.* 65, 1565–1572.
73. Mikuni, M., Pall, M., Peterson, C. M., Peterson, C. A., Hellberg, P., Brannstrom, M., Richards, J. S., and Hedin, L. (1998). The selective prostaglandin endoperoxide synthase-2 inhibitor, NS-398, reduces prostaglandin production and ovulation in vivo and in vitro in the rat. *Biol. Reprod.* 59, 1077–1083.
74. Salhab, A. S., Gharaibeh, M. N., Shomaf, M. S., and Amro, B. I. (2001). Meloxicam inhibits rabbit ovulation. *Contraception* 63, 329–333.
75. Pall, M., Friden, B. E., and Brannstrom, M. (2001). Induction of delayed follicular rupture in the human by the selective COX-2 inhibitor rofecoxib: A randomized double-blind study. *Hum. Reprod.* 16, 1323–1328.
76. Norman, R. J. (2001). Reproductive consequences of COX-2 inhibition. *Lancet* 358, 1287–1288.
77. Lim, H., Paria, B. C., Das, S. K., Dinchuk, J. E., Langenbach, R., Trzaskos, J. M., and Dey, S. K. (1997). Multiple female reproductive failures in cyclooxygenase 2-deficient mice. *Cell* 91, 197–208.
78. Filion, F., Bouchard, N., Goff, A. K., Lussier, J. G., and Sirois, J. (2001). Molecular cloning and induction of bovine prostaglandin E synthase by gonadotropins in ovarian follicles prior to ovulation in vivo. *J. Biol. Chem.* 276, 34323–34330.
79. Guan, Y., Zhang, Y., Schneider, A., Riendeau, D., Mancini, J. A., Davis, L., Komhoff, M., Breyer, R. M., and Breyer, M. D. (2001). Urogenital distribution of a mouse membrane-associated prostaglandin E(2) synthase. *Am. J. Physiol. Renal Physiol.* 281, F1173–1177.
80. Ni, H., Sun, T., Ding, N. Z., Ma, X. H., and Yang, Z. M. (2002). Differential expression of microsomal prostaglandin E synthase at implantation sites and in decidual cells of mouse uterus. *Biol. Reprod.* 67, 351–358.
81. Murdoch, W. J., and Farris, M. L. (1988). Prostaglandin E2-9-ketoreductase activity of preovulatory ovine follicles. *J. Anim. Sci.* 66, 2924–2929.
82. Hedin, L., Gaddy-Kurten, D., Kurten, R., DeWitt, D. L., Smith, W. L., and Richards, J. S. (1987). Prostaglandin endoperoxide synthase in rat ovarian follicles: Content, cellular distribution, and evidence for hormonal induction preceding ovulation. *Endocrinology* 121, 722–731.
83. Hellberg, P., Larson, L., Olofsson, J., Hedin, L., and Brannstrom, M. (1991). Stimulatory effects of bradykinin on the ovulatory process in the in vitro-perfused rat ovary. *Biol. Reprod.* 44, 269–274.
84. Mitchell, D. E., Lei, Z. M., and Rao, C. V. (1991). The enzymes in cyclooxygenase and lipoxygenase pathways of

arachidonic acid metabolism in human corpora lutea: Dependence on luteal phase, cellular and subcellular distribution. *Prostaglandins Leukot. Essent. Fatty Acids.* 43, 1–12.
85. Murdoch, W. J. (1986). Accumulation of thromboxane B2 within periovulatory ovine follicles: Relationship to adhesion of platelets to endothelium. *Prostaglandins* 32, 597–604.
86. Watson, E. D., and Sertich, P. L. (1991). Concentrations of arachidonate metabolites, steroids, and histamine in preovulatory horse follicles after administration of human chorionic gonadotrophin and the effect of intrafollicular injection of indomethacin. *J. Endocrinol.* 129, 131–139.
87. Hizaki, H., Segi, E., Sugimoto, Y., Hirose, M., Saji, T., Ushikubi, F., Matsuoka, T., Noda, Y., Tanaka, T., Yoshida, N., Narumiya, S., and Ichikawa, A. (1999). Abortive expansion of the cumulus and impaired fertility in mice lacking the prostaglandin E receptor subtype EP(2). *Proc. Natl. Acad. Sci. USA* 96, 10501–10506.
88. Tilley, S. L., Audoly, L. P., Hicks, E. H., Kim, H. S., Flannery, P. J., Coffman, T. M., and Koller, B. H. (1999). Reproductive failure and reduced blood pressure in mice lacking the EP2 prostaglandin E2 receptor. *J. Clin. Invest.* 103, 1539–1545.
89. Matsumoto, H., Ma, W., Smalley, W., Trzaskos, J., Breyer, R. M., and Dey, S. K. (2001). Diversification of cyclooxygenase-2-derived prostaglandins in ovulation and implantation. *Biol. Reprod.* 64, 1557–1565.
90. Narko, K., Saukkonen, K., Ketola, I., Butzow, R., Heikinheimo, M., and Ristimaki, A. (2001). Regulated expression of prostaglandin E(2) receptors EP2 and EP4 in human ovarian granulosa-luteal cells. *J. Clin. Endocrinol. Metab.* 86, 1765–1768.
91. Calder, M. D., Caveney, A. N., Westhusin, M. E., and Watson, A. J. (2001). Cyclooxygenase-2 and prostaglandin E(2) (PGE[2]) receptor messenger RNAs are affected by bovine oocyte maturation time and cumulus-oocyte complex quality, and PGE(2) induces moderate expansion of the bovine cumulus in vitro. *Biol. Reprod.* 65, 135–140.
92. Tsai, S. J., Wiltbank, M. C., and Bodensteiner, K. J. (1996). Distinct mechanisms regulate induction of messenger ribonucleic acid for prostaglandin (PG) G/H synthase-2, PGE (EP3) receptor, and PGF2α receptor in bovine preovulatory follicles. *Endocrinology* 137, 3348–3355.
93. Narko, K., Ritvos, O., and Ristimaki, A. (1997). Induction of cyclooxygenase-2 and prostaglandin F2α receptor expression by interleukin-1β in cultured human granulosa-luteal cells. *Endocrinology* 138, 3638–3644.
94. Sugimoto, Y., Yamasaki, A., Segi, E., Tsuboi, K., Aze, Y., Nishimura, T., Oida, H., Yoshida, N., Tanaka, T., Katsuyama, M., Hasumoto, K., Murata, T., Hirata, M., Ushikubi, F., Negishi, M., Ichikawa, A., and Narumiya, S. (1997). Failure of parturition in mice lacking the prostaglandin F receptor. *Science* 277, 681–683.
95. Harris, T. E., Squires, P. E., Michael, A. E., Bernal, A. L., and Abayasekara, D. R. (2001). Human granulosa-lutein cells express functional EP1 and EP2 prostaglandin receptors. *Biochem. Biophys. Res. Commun.* 285, 1089–1094.
96. Ushikubi, F., Sugimoto, Y., Ichikawa, A., and Narumiya, S. (2002). Roles of prostanoids revealed from studies using mice lacking specific prostanoid receptors. *Jpn. J. Pharmacol.* 83, 279–285.
97. Davis, J. S., and Rueda, B. R. (2002). The corpus luteum: An ovarian structure with maternal instincts and suicidal tendencies. *Front. Biosci.* 7, d1949–d1978.
98. McCracken, J. A., Custer, E. E., and Lamsa, J. C. (1999). Luteolysis: A neuroendocrine-mediated event. *Physiol. Rev.* 79, 263–323.
99. Niswender, G. D., Juengel, J. L., Silva, P. J., Rollyson, M. K., and McIntush, E. W. (2000). Mechanisms controlling the function and life span of the corpus luteum. *Physiol. Rev.* 80, 1–29.
100. Pate, J. L., and Landis Keyes, P. (2001). Immune cells in the corpus luteum: Friends or foes? *Reproduction* 122, 665–676.
101. Diaz, F. J., Anderson, L. E., Wu, Y. L., Rabot, A., Tsai, S. J., and Wiltbank, M. C. (2002). Regulation of progesterone and prostaglandin F2α production in the CL. *Mol. Cell. Endocrinol.* 191, 65–80.
102. McLean, M. P., Billheimer, J. T., Warden, K. J., and Irby, R. B. (1995). Prostaglandin F2α mediates ovarian sterol carrier protein-2 expression during luteolysis. *Endocrinology* 136, 4963–4972.
103. Juengel, J. L., Meberg, B. M., Turzillo, A. M., Nett, T. M., and Niswender, G. D. (1995). Hormonal regulation of messenger ribonucleic acid encoding steroidogenic acute regulatory protein in ovine corpora lutea. *Endocrinology* 136, 5423–5429.
104. Fiedler, E. P., Plouffe, Jr., L., Hales, D. B., Hales, K. H., and Khan, I. (1999). Prostaglandin F2α induces a rapid decline in progesterone production and steroidogenic acute regulatory protein expression in isolated rat corpus luteum without altering messenger ribonucleic acid expression. *Biol. Reprod.* 61, 643–650.
105. McGuire, W. J., Juengel, J. L., and Niswender, G. D. (1994). Protein kinase C second messenger system mediates the antisteroidogenic effects of prostaglandin F2α in the ovine corpus luteum in vivo. *Biol. Reprod.* 51, 800–806.
106. Stocco, C. O., Lau, L. F., and Gibori, G. (2002). A calcium/calmodulin-dependent activation of ERK1/2 mediates JunD phosphorylation and induction of nur77 and 20α-hsd genes by prostaglandin F2α in ovarian cells. *J. Biol. Chem.* 277, 3293–3302.
107. Stocco, C. O., Zhong, L., Sugimoto, Y., Ichikawa, A., Lau, L. F., and Gibori, G. (2000). Prostaglandin F2alpha-induced expression of 20α-hydroxysteroid dehydrogenase involves the transcription factor NUR77. *J. Biol. Chem.* 275, 37202–37211.
108. Hinckley, S. T., and Milvae, R. A. (2001). Endothelin-1 mediates prostaglandin F2α-induced luteal regression in the ewe. *Biol. Reprod.* 64, 1619–1623.
109. Townson, D. H., O'Connor, C. L., and Pru, J. K. (2002). Expression of monocyte chemoattractant protein-1 and distribution of immune cell populations in the bovine corpus luteum throughout the estrous cycle. *Biol. Reprod.* 66, 361–366.
110. Duncan, W. C., Illingworth, P. J., and Fraser, H. M. (1996). Expression of tissue inhibitor of metalloproteinases-1 in the primate ovary during induced luteal regression. *J. Endocrinol.* 151, 203–213.

111. Rueda, B. R., Hendry, I. R., Tilly, J. L., and Hamernik, D. L. (1999). Accumulation of caspase-3 messenger ribonucleic acid and induction of caspase activity in the ovine corpus luteum following prostaglandin F2α treatment in vivo. *Biol. Reprod.* 60, 1087–1092.

112. Silvia, W. J. (1999). Eicosanoids. In *Encyclopedia of Reproduction*, Vol. I, eds. E. Knobil and J. D. Neill, 991–1001. San Diego: Academic Press.

113. Ziecik, A. J. (2002). Old, new and the newest concepts of inhibition of luteolysis during early pregnancy in pig. *Domest. Anim. Endocrinol.* 23, 265–275.

114. Asselin, E., Bazer, F. W., and Fortier, M. A. (1997). Recombinant ovine and bovine interferons tau regulate prostaglandin production and oxytocin response in cultured bovine endometrial cells. *Biol. Reprod.* 56, 402–408.

CHAPTER **14**

Actions of Insulin and Insulin-Like Growth Factor-1 on Sterol-Metabolizing Gene Expression in Ovarian Cells

SEKAR NATESAMPILLAI AND JOHANNES D. VELDHUIS

ABSTRACT

The mammalian female reproductive cycle is an intricately regulated process. In normal physiology, insulin-like peptides and gonadotropic hormones such as follicle-stimulating hormone (FSH) and luteinizing hormone (LH) initiate signaling cascades that are critical for follicular growth, ovulation, luteinization, steroidogenesis, fertilization, and successful implantation. The pituitary gonadotropins, FSH and LH, play primary roles in directing steroid-hormone biosynthesis and cognate gene expression. In addition, insulin, insulin-like growth factors 1 and 2 (IGF-1 and IGF-2), members of the transforming growth factor-beta (TGF-β) family (e.g., inhibin, activin, follistatin), bone morphogenetic protein (BMG), and growth differentiation factor (GDF) contribute to cytodifferentiative control. This chapter highlights the physiological importance of insulin and IGF-1 in steroidogenic gene regulation where relevant transgenic (murine) models are illustrated.

INTRODUCTION

The pleiotropic effects of IGF-1 and insulin on cellular metabolism, mitogenesis, apoptosis, and survival and cytodifferentiation are mediated by a complex network of intracellular signaling pathways [1]. Signaling is initiated by ligand-specific activation of cell surface receptors with intrinsic tyrosine kinase activity. Proximate kinase substrates include the receptor itself and several insulin-receptor substrates (IRS) such as IRS-1, IRS-2, IRS-3, and IRS-4. Phosphorylated IRS interacts with *src* homology 2 domain (SH_2)-containing proteins including phosphatidylinositol 3-kinase (PI3-K), adapter molecule (Grb_2), and phosphotyrosine phosphatase (SHP_2), among others. PI3-K activation stimulates a pivotal main downstream effector, protein kinase B (Akt/PKB). The latter drives selected biological responses (e.g., glucose transport, cell proliferation, and escape from apoptosis). Association of IRS and Grb_2 leads to recruitment of son of sevenless (SOS) and Ras and results in activation of the mitogen-activated protein kinase (MAPK) pathway, which provides crucial signals to gene transcription and repression.

Insulin regulates more than 100 genes, primarily at the transcriptional level, in diverse organs that include the ovary [2]. The biological impact of insulinomimetic peptides on ovarian steroidogenesis was suggested by clinical observations. One example is that type 1 diabetes, a disorder characterized by systemic insulinopenia, is associated with increased risk of primary amenorrhea, delayed menarche, anovulation, subfertility, and early menopause [3]. In the experimental studies, streptozotocin or alloxan-induced diabetes mellitus reduces the number and size of follicles, delays oocyte maturation, increases follicular atresia, and limits fertility. Early insulin repletion in the diabetic animal restores reproductive function [4, 5]. Peripheral insulin-resistance syndromes in the human are often accompanied by clinical manifestations of ovarian theca-cell hyperstimulation such as hyperandrogenism [2, 6].

Steroidogenesis requires effectual delivery, uptake, and use of sterol by an array of specific steroidogenic enzymes. In some measure, virtually all steps in the biosynthetic cascade require the actions of FSH, LH, and growth factors [7–11]. *Do novo* steroidogenesis is limited by the inner-mitochondrial availability of free cholesterol imported by steroidogenic acute regulatory protein (StAR) [12]. Additional rate-determining and steroid-defining steps involve specific cytochrome P450 enzymes [13]. Cellular cholesterol is acquired principally from blood-borne lipoproteins, which associate with specific cell-membrane receptors (high- or low-density lipoprotein receptor [HDL-R or LDL-R]). Receptor-directed pathways facilitate sterol uptake, use, and/or storage [14, 15]. Subsequent access of cholesterol to the inner mitochondrial membrane requires StAR [16, 17]. The first irreversible enzymatic action entails cleavage of the cholesterol side-chain at the C20–26 bond by the cytochrome P450 side-chain cleavage

(CYP11A) oxidoreductive complex [18]. The proximate product, pregnenolone, is metabolized outside mitochondria to 17-hydroxypregnenolone and dehydroepiandrosterone by 17α-hydroxylase/17,20-lyase (CYP-17) and further via 3β-hydroxysteroid dehydrogenase and 17β-hydroxysteroid dehydrogenase to androgens, such as androstenedione and testosterone, and reduced metabolites [18]. The aromatase complex catalyzes the conversion of testosterone and androstenedione to estradiol-17β and estrone, respectively [19].

INSULIN AND IGF-1: ROLES IN STEROIDOGENESIS

Trophic actions of the gonadotropins and cyclic adenosine monophosphate/protein kinase A (cAMP/PKA) effectors are augmented markedly by the intrafollicular peptide, IGF-1, and systemic insulin [20–23]. In contrast, in extragonadal tissues (i.e., liver, muscle, fat), insulin receptor-mediated tyrosine kinase typically triggers opposing responses to the cAMP/PKA signaling system. In the mouse the IGF-1 gene and homologous receptor are expressed principally by granulosa cells in healthy follicles [24–26]. The IGF-1 receptor is especially abundant in the oocyte of murine and human follicles [25, 27]. FSH stimulates granulosa-cell IGF-1 production in several mammalian species [28, 29]. Transgenically targeted silencing of the Igf1 gene causes infertility in mice because of follicular arrest at the late preantral stage [30]. This mode of ovarian failure resembles that resulting from of deletion of the FSHβ subunit or cognate receptor genes [28, 29]. On the other hand, mice lacking Ir are born at term with only slight growth retardation but die shortly thereafter because of severe diabetes ketoacidosis [31]. Neuron-specific Ir disruption induces diet-responsive diabetes mellitus and impairs follicle maturation because of hypothalamic dysregulation of LH secretion [32]. In ovarian organ culture, insulin facilitates the transition of primordial to primary follicles at low concentration [33, 34], whereas IGF-1 is ineffectual [34]. The molecular basis for the latter distinction is not defined.

In the pig and human, insulinomimetic peptides stimulate granulosa-cell steroidogenesis in vitro [35–38]. In the rodent, pig, and human, insulin and IGF-1 act additively or synergistically with FSH and/or LH [20, 36, 37, 39–42]. In rodent models, these growth factors are relatively inactive in promoting progesterone or estrogen biosynthesis in granulosa cells when gonadotropins are not present [42–45]. In the rat, IGF-1 is produced by granulosa cells of mature follicles [46] and IGF-1 synergizes with FSH in driving progesterone production in vitro [46]. In theca cells, IGF-1 synergizes with LH in increasing androgen biosynthesis [47–50]. In organ culture of large preantral follicles, insulin or FSH/LH will trigger growth and estradiol secretion, and combined agonists initiate antrum formation and estradiol production more effectively than insulin alone [51].

Insulinomimetic effects on ovarian cells are mediated via the type-I IGF-1 or insulin receptor [2], with apparent potentiation by inositol-glycan signaling pathways [52]. Receptor autophosphorylation [53, 54] and competitive binding analyses indicate that insulin and IGF-1 receptors are expressed in granulosa cells [55]. Insulin receptor messenger ribonucleic acid (mRNA) and immunoreactive protein are detected in situ in granulosa, theca, and stroma cells [56]. Depending on the species, low concentrations of insulin may act through autologous rather than IGF-1 receptors [43]. On the other hand, insulin and IGF-1 can upregulate the heterologous receptor [57]. In view of species, concentration, cell density, receptor, and postreceptor distinctions in insulin action, any of the homologous insulin receptors, type-I IGF-1 receptor, and putatively hybrid insulin-IGF-1 receptors may transduce a given cellular effect.

GENES RESPONSIBLE FOR STEROIDOGENESIS: REGULATION BY INSULIN OR IGF-1

High- and Low-Density Lipoprotein-Receptor Regulation in the Ovary

Cholesterol used in steroid biosynthesis by ovarian cells is derived from *de novo* synthesis from two-carbon fragments and by cellular uptake of lipoprotein cholesterol. The majority of cholesterol is transported in the blood by LDL or HDL with relative predominance depending on the species [58] (e.g., the principal carrier protein is HDL in the rat and LDL in the cow, pig, monkey, and human). Cholesterol derived from HDL and LDL is delivered to steroidogenic cells via specific scavenger receptors (HDL) and apolipoprotein B receptor-mediated endocytosis and lysosomal release of free sterol (LDL) to the sterol transport protein (SCP-2) and StAR [59, 60]. The LDL and LDL-receptor pathways are governed by insulin or FSH/LH or cAMP-mediated pathways [61–66]. An example is that gonadotropins and insulinomimetic peptides stimulate LDL receptor gene expression synergistically in immature swine granulosa cells [64].

FSH and LH alone each stimulate LDL receptor transcript accumulation [64, 66, 67]. Insulin and IGF-1 further enhance the latter effect additively or synergistically (Figure 14.1) depending on model context [42, 61, 64]. Recent cloning of a 5′-untranslated region of the porcine LDL receptor gene (–1076 bp) has identified a critical hormone-responsive *cis*-acting deoxyribonucleic acid (DNA) region containing a sterolregulatory element (SRE) and three Sp1/Sp3 binding sites (–255 to –136 bp

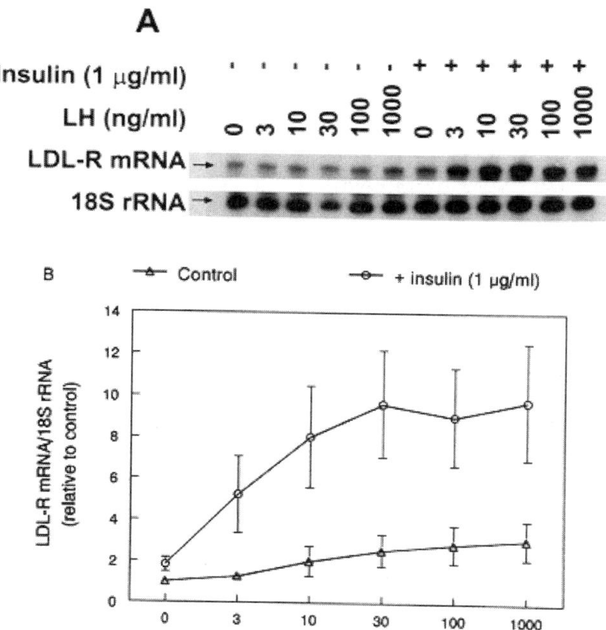

FIGURE 14.1 **A,** Representative autoradiogram illustrates the effects of varying concentrations of LH and/or insulin on specific porcine granulosa-cell LDL-receptor mRNA expression. Granulosa cells were exposed to the indicated concentrations of LH and/or insulin for 48 hours in serum-free media after an initial attachment period. Ten-microgram aliquots of total RNA were subjected to RNase protection assay. **B,** Summary quantitation of LDL-receptor mRNA following incubation with LH and/or insulin. Data are the mean ± SEM optical density units of LDL-receptor mRNA normalized to 18S rRNA and expressed as fold-increases relative to the control value.

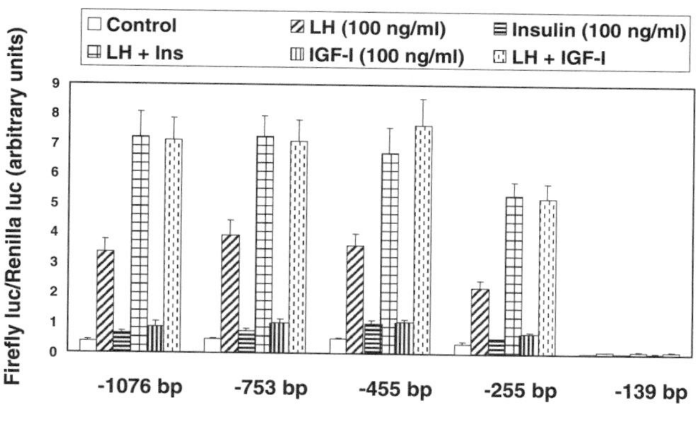

FIGURE 14.2 Effects of LH and/or insulin (or IGF-1) on expression of full-length (−1076 to +11 bp) and selected 5′-deletion fragments of the 5′-upstream putative promoter of the porcine LDL receptor gene driving a cDNA encoding a cytoplasmically localizing luciferase in cultured swine granulosa-luteal cells. After in vitro attachment and lutein-like maturation, cells were transfected for 6 hours with equimolar amounts of full-length or progressive 5′-deletion LDL-receptor promoter fragments. Thereafter, granulosa-luteal cells were exposed to LH and/or insulin or IGF-1 for 4 hours. Data represent the mean ± SEM of three separate experiments (each performed in duplicate) using TK-driven *Renilla* (sea pansy) luciferase to normalize transfectional efficiency.

upstream) [64, 68]. Insulin and IGF-1 amplify transcriptional activity via SREBP-1 action on the SRE site [68, 69]. Whereas the human LDL receptor shows variable responsiveness to cAMP in human granulosa-luteal cells [70, 71], the porcine LDL receptor promoter is strongly induced by FSH [64] and LH [68]. Although not fully explicated mechanistically, synergy between LH and insulin/IGF-1 (Figure 14.2) in the swine model entails joint activation of PKA, PI3-K, and MAPK signaling pathways [68].

Steroidogenic Acute Regulatory Protein

Trophic hormones stimulate adrenal and gonadal steroid biosynthesis over an initial period of minutes, followed by sustained upregulation over hours. Induction of the StAR protein mediates rapid transfer of sterol substrate into mitochondria in proximity to catalytic cytochrome P450 CYP11A [12]. The StAR protein has two key functional domains. The C-terminal domain sequences promote sterol desorption from the sterol-rich outer mitochondrial membrane, which drives substrate to the relatively sterol-poor inner membrane. The N-terminal domain confers mitochondrial targeting from the site of endoplasmic reticular synthesis but is not required for sterol transport [72]. StAR protein is expressed ubiquitously in steroid-producing cells, except the trophoblast of the human placenta. In diverse genetic contexts, relative StAR availability predicts capacity for steroidogenesis. Gonadotropins and cAMP agonists induce StAR mRNA accumulation in granulosa and granulosa-luteal cells [37, 42, 45]. StAR activity is also controlled posttranscriptionally and posttranslationally by PKA-dependent serine phosphorylation mediated by PKA, a process that is essential for maximizing StAR activity [73, 74].

StAR gene mutations establish the indispensable role of the cognate protein. Congenital lipoid adrenal hyperplasia (lipoid CAH) is a rare and potentially lethal autosomal recessive syndrome attributable to loss-of-function mutation(s) of StAR with attendant impoverishment of all steroidogenic activity. In the transgenic counterpart. StAR gene deletion abrogated prenatal masculinization, blunted in vitro growth, and caused neonatal death [75, 76]. The ovaries of StAR knockout mice appear normal at birth but then undergo progressive histopathological disruption. Pubertal females exhibit limited follicular development and prominent interstitial lipid deposits with stromal luteinization, which culminates in primary ovarian failure [75]. In an in vivo animal model of equine chorionic gonadotropin (eCG)/human chorionic gonadotropin (hCG)-primedprepubertal gilts, StAR mRNA increases in parallel with luteal-phase progesterone production [77].

In primary culture of human granulosa-lutein cells, IGF-1, IGF-2, and insulin stimulate the accumulation of StAR mRNA and protein, but 8Br-cAMP does not amplify the action of IGF-1 [44]. In granulosa cells isolated from the estradiol-primed rat and plated in serum-coated wells, FSH alone induces the StAR gene transcript and IGF-1 enhances the latter effect modestly [78]. In a porcine system, insulin and IGF-1 do not stimulate StAR mRNA or promoter expression in granulosa [37, 79] or granulosa-luteal [42, 45] cells. However, insulin or IGF-1 combined with FSH/LH in granulosa or theca cells are synergistic at the level of StAR mRNA (Figure 14.3) [37, 42, 45, 49, 79] and StAR hnRNA [49]. In analysis of the mechanisms of hormonal control of StAR gene transcription, truncated regions of the −1423 to +30 bp 5′-upstream sequence of the porcine gene responded to LH alone and showed synergistic upregulation by LH and insulin/IGF-1 [45, 79].

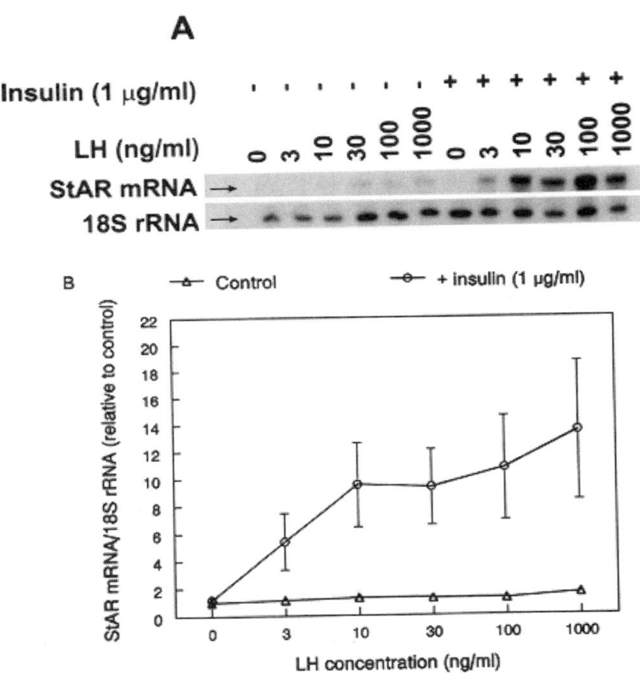

FIGURE 14.3 **A,** Autoradiogram of protected bands for StAR mRNA and constitutively expressed 18S rRNA monitored in response to varying concentrations of LH with or without insulin in cultured porcine granulosa cells. Ten-microgram aliquots of total RNA were subjected to RNase production assay. **B,** StAR mRNA expression as quantitated by RNase protection assay. Data are the mean ± SEM optical density units of StAR mRNA normalized to 18S rRNA and expressed as fold-increases relative to the control value.

Accordingly, maximal stimulation of the StAR promoter may require cAMP/PKA-dependent and -independent mechanisms [37, 42, 44]. Indeed, other pathways impinge on StAR regulation, such as protein kinase C [80, 81], calcium calmodulin [82], and growth factors [44, 83]. In this regard, the proximal StAR promoter region (−110 to −64 bp) responds to diverse transcription factors like SF-1 [84–87], Sp1 [84], C/EBP [88–90], GATA4 [86, 88, 89], SREBP [91, 92], and c-Fos [93]. A plausible formulation is that insulinomimetic peptides and LH confer maximal responsiveness to the porcine StAR gene via SREBP, SP1, and SF-1-like transcriptional factors, which are activated by signaling intermediates, including PI3-K and MAPK [68, 94, 95].

Cytochrome P450 Cholesterol Side-Chain Cleavage Enzyme (CYP11A)

The mitochondrial enzyme, CYP11A, catalyzes the conversion of cholesterol to pregnenolone as the enzymatically rate-limiting step in the biosynthesis of steroid hormone in the adrenal gland, ovary, testis, and placenta [18]. Whereas CYP11A content is nonuniform among steroidogenic tissues and species, it is highly correlated with maximal steroid synthesis under trophic-factor drive. In the cyclic pig, CYP11A expression rises just before and on the day that proestrus estradiol secretion increases by preovulatory follicles; CYP11A expression then declines and surges in corpora lutea [77]. Preovulatory follicles express abundant CYP11A mRNA and protein in granulosa and theca cells [9]. In the cow, CYP11A mRNA decreases transiently in follicles after the LH surge and then increases markedly as the corpus luteum develops, before declining with steroidogenic regression [96]. In the rat, CYP11A mRNA levels remain relatively constant during the brief window of luteinization [97].

The 5′-flanking sequence of CYP11A genes in different species exhibit several putative *cis*-acting DNA elements required for cAMP-dependent or independent transcription, including Sp1, SF-1, AP2, cAMP responsive element (CRE), and IGF-responsive elements (IGFRE) [98–105]. SF-1 is a ubiquitous factor associated with steroidogenic lineage, which will upregulate human CYP11A promoter sequences in adrenal cell lines [101]. A novel transcriptional-regulating protein (TreP-132) may form a complex with SF-1 and CBP/p300 that regulates CYP11A transcription [106]. A large CYP11A promoter (2.32 kb) fragment transfected in porcine granulosa cells is inducible by FSH or a PKA minigene encoding the constitutively active β catalytic subunit and is repressed by a rabbit heart-muscle PKA inhibitor (PKI) [107]. The interaction between SF-1 and Sp1 may also require cAMP PKA [100], with or without facilitation by an adapter protein, CREB binding protein (CBP). The latter serves as a common coactivator with SF-1/Sp1 complexes [101].

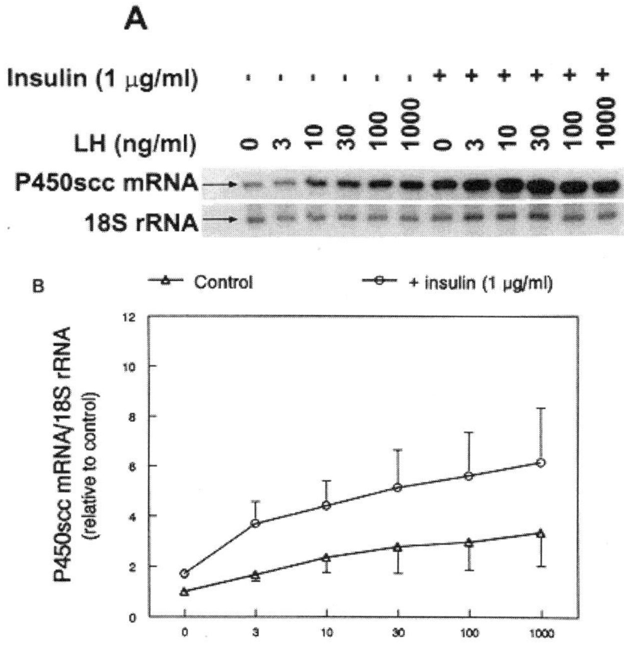

FIGURE 14.4 **A,** Autoradiogram identifying protected bands for the P450scc enzyme mRNA and constitutively expressed 18S rRNA, determined in granulosa cells exposed to varying concentrations of LH with or without insulin. Ten-microgram aliquots of total RNA were subjected to RNase production assay. **B,** Summary of P450scc enzyme mRNA expression estimated by RNase protection assay. Data are the mean ± SEM optical-density units of P450scc enzyme mRNA normalized to 18S rRNA and expressed as fold-increases relative to the control value.

In porcine granulosa-luteal cells, LH stimulates CYP11A mRNA expression by 3.3-fold and insulin augments this effect to 6.4-fold (Figure 14.4) [42]. Insulin alone increases CYP11A mRNA concentrations by 1.7-fold [42]. In rodent studies, IGF-1 alone has no effect, whereas addition of FSH induces CYP11A in estradiol-primed granulosa cells [78]. In the adult cow and pig, IGF-1 is active alone on this endpoint [108].

Urban et al. used a swine model to dissect some of the actions of IGF-1 on CYP11A. Studies were performed in the presence and absence of estradiol, LDL (to increase cholesterol delivery to granulosa cells), or aminoglutethimide (a CYP11A enzyme inhibitor). Estradiol and aminoglutethimide did not alter basal or IGF-1-stimulated CYP11A mRNA expression, but LDL enhanced the IGF-1 effect synergistically [38]. IGF-1 and FSH are active alone with FSH acting rapidly within 6 hours and IGF-1 more slowly after 24 to 48 hours to induce a proximal fragment (−130 to −100 bp) of the porcine CYP11A promoter [99]. An inferentially IGFRE in this gene binds Sp1 and a repressor protein, polypyrimidine tract-binding protein (PTB)-associated splicing factor (PSF), thereby allowing bidirectional control [105]. The NH_2-terminal region of PSF contains amino acid residues that bind to porcine CYP11A IGFRE sequences and repress transcriptional activity [109]. The interspecies generality of this novel regulatory mechanism is not yet known.

Cytochrome P450 17α-Hydroxylase/17,20-Lyase (CYP-17) Expression

CYP-17 is a single enzyme that mediates 17α-hydroxylase and 17,20-lyase activity by catalyzing both 17α-hydroxylation of pregnenolone and progesterone and 17,20-lysis of 17α-hydroxy pregnenolone and 17α-hydroxyprogesterone [110]. In rat theca-interstitial cells, IGF-1 is not active alone but synergizes with LH or hCG in stimulating CYP-17 mRNA [111]. The latter interaction is important in mature cells, because early differentiation of theca-interstitial cells in growing follicles is gonadotropin independent but does require IGF-1. In in vivo pig theca cell CYP-17 expression increases with follicular diameter from day 10 (midluteal phase) through day 19 (preovulatory phase) [112]. In in vitro porcine theca cells, LH and insulin (or IGF-1) individually promote androstenedione biosynthesis and interact synergistically [49]. The swine model illustrates that insulin and LH coamplify the accumulation of CYP-17 mRNA and hnRNA [49]. The molecular bases for synergy between a growth factor and a gonadotropin in this setting are not yet known.

Aromatase (CYP19) Expression

Aromatase (estrogen synthetase) is a cytochrome P450 containing enzyme that catalyzes the formation of aromatic C18 estrogens from C19 androgen precursors. CYP19 is localized to granulosa cells where it is under the control of FSH [113]. IGF-1 also drives CYP19 activity in the immature rat follicle, and cholera toxin augments this effect as well as that of pregnant mare serum gonadotropins (PMSG) [114]. Tyrosine kinase inhibitors (tyrphostins) block upregulating actions of FSH and IGF-1 on the gene without inhibiting cAMP accumulation in human granulosa cells [115]. CYP19 activity and estradiol synthesis in bovine granulosa cells are stimulated by FSH and/or IGF-1 and insulin [108, 116]. In human granulosa cells, insulin alone is effectual in this regard [117]. IGF-1 knockout mice fail to generate the midcycle rise in estradiol necessary to trigger an LH surge, possibly reflecting inadequate follicular aromatase expression and/or impaired theca-cell development [118]. Targeted disruption of exon 9 of the CYP19 gene (aromatase knockout [ArKO]) causes an anovulatory phenotype marked by failure of folliculogenesis despite secondarily elevated gonadotropins [119]. ArKO animals subsequently develop obesity, sarcopenia, hypercholesterolemia, hepatic steatosis, and insulin resistance [120].

Other Steroidogenic Ovarian Enzymes Regulated by Insulin

The enzyme 3β-hydroxysteroid dehydrogenase/Δ^5-Δ^4-isomerase (3β-HSD) catalyzes the transformation of pregnenolone to progesterone, 17α-hydroxypregnenolone to 17α-hydroxyprogesterone, dehydroepiandrosterone to 4-androstenedione, and 5-androstene-3β, 17β-diol to testosterone. Insulin alone induces the activity of this essential albeit non–rate-limiting enzyme, and FSH enhances this effect [117].

Regulation of Gonadotropin Receptors by Insulin-Like Peptides

Ovarian follicular growth begins and proceeds to the preantral stage independently of gonadotropin availability [121]. Further development depends on FSH acting via the cognate receptor expressed by granulosa cells. IGF-1 is also expressed in a subset of healthy-appearing follicles in the rat ovary [24, 25]. Based on receptor-knockout models, current interpretations are that IGF-1 and FSH receptors are selectively coexpressed in healthy follicles, and FSH does not affect IGF-1 receptor expression, but IGF-1 augments granulosa-cell FSH receptor expression responsiveness to FSH [118]. The pattern of expression of the FSH receptor changes with follicular growth. In situ hybridization data show that porcine FSH receptor mRNA increases in small antral follicles and disappears as maturation progresses [112]. Minegishi et al. observed that FSH, but not IGF-1, upregulates the FSH receptor gene in granulosa cells [122]. FSH-dependent autoregulation was conferred by the FSH-receptor promoter 5′-flanking region (−1862 to +1 bp), which was not responsive to IGF-1. These data may be harmonized by possible actions of IGF-1 on FSH-receptor mRNA stability in rat granulosa cells [122].

During growth and maturation, ovarian follicles acquire sensitivity to LH concomitantly with increased density of LH receptors on granulosa cells [123]. LH-receptor knockout mice are phenotypically normal at birth. Ovaries of null mice are small because of follicle development to the antral but not preovulatory stage, resulting in anovulation and infertility [124, 125]. In porcine ovaries, LH-receptor mRNA is detected in the theca interna of small antral follicles and increases in granulosa cells with increasing follicular diameter [112]. Porcine granulosa-luteal cells cultured with insulin or IGF-1 acquire LH-receptor mRNA [45]. In theca cells, IGF-1 alone does not stimulate StAR or CYP-17 mRNA but induces LH-receptor and CYP11A mRNA expression [126]. However, combined exposure to LH and insulin will reduce LH-receptor mRNA compared with treatment with insulin or IGF-1 alone [45]. In granulosa cells, FSH and IGF-1 together induce LH-receptor mRNA maximally [127]. Mechanistically, IGF-1 increases the stability of LH receptor transcripts in rat granulosa-luteal [127] and murine Leydig tumor cells [128].

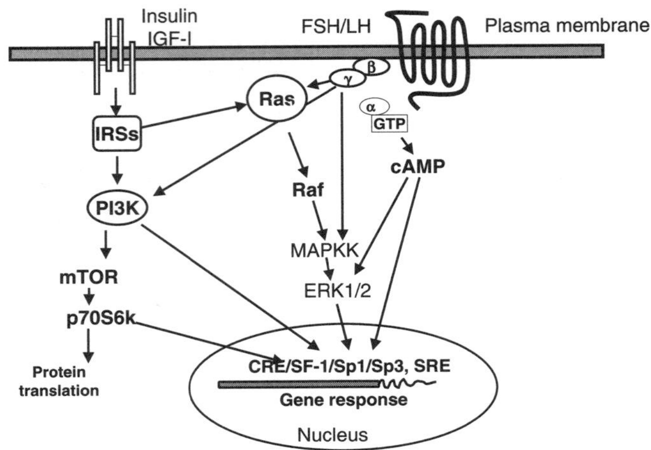

FIGURE 14.5 Schematic representation of interlinked signaling between insulin/IGF-1 and FSH/LH-driven pathways envisioned in ovarian cells.

CONCLUSION

This chapter summarizes the mechanisms by which FSH/LH and insulin/IGF-1 act in concert to stimulate steroidogenesis and LDL-receptor, StAR, and CYP11A gene expression in ovarian granulosa and theca cells. Our proposed models (Figure 14.5) and other literature support important signaling-pathway interactions driven by gonadotropin and insulin, which include at least PKA, PKC, PI3-K, MAPK, and unknown intermediates. Further analyses of the possible roles of phospholipases, Src, SH_2 proteins, Ras, cAMP-dependent guanine nucleotide exchange factor (GEF), relevant phosphatases, and other effector molecules should further clarify unique properties of bihormonal signal control in the ovary.

References

1. Virkamaki, A., Ueki, K., and Kahn, C. R. (1999). Protein–protein interaction in insulin signaling and the molecular mechanisms of insulin resistance. *J. Clin. Invest.* 103, 931–943.
2. Poretsky, L., Cataldo, N. A., Rosenwaks, Z., and Giudice, L. C. (1999). The insulin-related ovarian regulatory system in health and disease. *Endocr. Rev.* 20, 535–582.
3. Poretsky, L., and Kalin, M. F. (1987). The gonadotropic function of insulin. *Endocr. Rev.* 8, 132–141.
4. Diamond, M. P., Moley, K. H., Pellicer, A., Vaughn, W. K., and DeCherney, A. H. (1989). Effects of streptozotocin- and alloxan-induced diabetes mellitus on mouse follicular and early embryo development. *J. Reprod. Fertil.* 86, 1–10.
5. Edwards, J. L., Hughey, T. C., Moore, A. B., and Cox, N. M. (1996). Depletion of insulin in streptozocin-induced-diabetic

pigs alters estradiol, insulin-like growth factor (IGF)-I and IGF binding proteins in cultured ovarian follicles. *Biol. Reprod.* 55, 775–781.

6. Nestler, J. E. (1997). Insulin regulation of human ovarian androgens. *Hum. Reprod.* 12 (Suppl 1), 53–62.
7. Richards, J. S., Russell, D. L., Ochsner, S., Hsieh, M., Doyle, K. H., Falender, A. E., Lo, Y. K., and Sharma, S. C. (2002). Novel signaling pathways that control ovarian follicular development, ovulation, and luteinization. *Rec. Prog. Hormone Res.* 57, 195–220.
8. Richards, J. S. (1994). Hormonal control of gene expression in the ovary. Endocr. Rev. 15, 725–751.
9. Conley, A. J., Howard, H. J., Slanger, W. D., and Ford, J. J. (1994). Steroidogenesis in the preovulatory porcine follicle. *Biol. Reprod.* 51, 655–661.
10. Tian, X. C., Berndtson, A. K., and Fortune, J. E. (1995). Differentiation of bovine preovulatory follicles during the follicular phase is associated with increases in messenger ribonucleic acid for cytochrome P450 side-chain cleavage, 3 beta-hydroxysteroid dehydrogenase, and P450 17 alpha-hydroxylase, but not P450 aromatase. *Endocrinology* 136, 5102–5110.
11. Parker, K. L., and Schimmer, B. P. (1995). Transcriptional regulation of the genes encoding the cytochrome P-450 steroid hydroxylases. *Vitam. Horm.* 51, 339–370.
12. Stocco, D. M. (2001). Tracking the role of a star in the sky of the new millennium. *Mol. Endocrinol.* 15, 1245–1254.
13. Peter, M., and Dubuis, J. M. (2000). Transcription factors as regulators of steroidogenic P-450 enzymes. *Eur. J. Clin. Invest.* 30 (Suppl 3), 14–20.
14. Carroll, D. J., Grummer, R. R., and Mao, F. C. (1992). Progesterone production by cultured luteal cells in the presence of bovine low- and high-density lipoproteins purified by heparin affinity chromatography. *J. Anim. Sci.* 70, 2516–2526.
15. Ikonen, E. (1997). Molecular mechanisms of intracellular cholesterol transport. *Curr. Opin. Lipidol.* 8, 60–64.
16. Clark, B. J., Wells, J., King, S. R., and Stocco, D. M. (1994). The purification, cloning, and expression of a novel luteinizing hormone-induced mitochondrial protein in MA-10 mouse Leydig tumor cells. Characterization of the steroidogenic acute regulatory protein (StAR). *J. Biol. Chem.* 269, 28314–28322.
17. Arakane, F., Sugawara, T., Nishino, H., Liu, Z., Holt, J. A., Pain, D., Stocco, D. M., Miller, W. L., and Strauss, III, J. F. (1996). Steroidogenic acute regulatory protein (StAR) retains activity in the absence of its mitochondrial import sequence: Implications for the mechanism of StAR action. *Proc. Natl. Acad. Sci. USA* 93, 13731–13736.
18. Miller, W. L. (1988). Molecular biology of steroid hormone synthesis. *Endocr. Rev.* 9, 295–318.
19. Simpson, E. R., Mahendroo, M. S., Means, G. D., Kilgore, M. W., Hinshelwood, M. M., Graham-Lorence, S., Amarneh, B., Ito, Y., Fisher, C. R., Michael, M. D., et al. (1994). Aromatase cytochrome P450, the enzyme responsible for estrogen biosynthesis. *Endocr. Rev.* 15, 342–355.
20. Veldhuis, J. D., and Rodgers, R. J. (1987). Mechanisms subserving the steroidogenic synergism between follicle-stimulating hormone and insulin-like growth factor I (somatomedin C). Alterations in cellular sterol metabolism in swine granulosa cells. *J. Biol. Chem.* 262, 7658–7664.
21. Adashi, E. Y., Resnick, C. E., Hernandez, E. R., Svoboda, M. E., and Van Wyk, J. J. (1988). In vivo regulation of granulosa cell somatomedin-C/insulin-like growth factor I receptors. *Endocrinology* 122, 1383–1389.
22. McArdle, C. A., Kohl, C., Rieger, K., Groner, I., and Wehrenberg, U. (1991). Effects of gonadotropins, insulin and insulin-like growth factor I on ovarian oxytocin and progesterone production. *Mol. Cell. Endocrinol.* 78, 211–20.
23. Poretsky, L., Chandrasekher, Y. A., Bai, C., Liu, H. C., Rosenwaks, Z., and Giudice, L. (1996). Insulin receptor mediates inhibitory effect of insulin, but not of insulin-like growth factor (IGF)-I, on IGF binding protein 1 (IGFBP-1) production in human granulosa cells. *J. Clin. Endocrinol. Metab.* 81, 493–496.
24. Oliver, J. E., Aitman, T. J., Powell, J. F., Wilson, C. A., and Clayton, R. N. (1989). Insulin-like growth factor I gene expression in the rat ovary is confined to the granulosa cells of developing follicles. *Endocrinology* 124, 2671–2679.
25. Zhou, J., Chin, E., and Bondy, C. (1991). Cellular pattern of insulin-like growth factor-I (IGF-I) and IGF-I receptor gene expression in the developing and mature ovarian follicle. *Endocrinology* 129, 3281–3288.
26. Zhou, J., Refuerzo, J., and Bondy, C. (1995). Granulosa cell DNA synthesis is strictly correlated with the presence of insulin-like growth factor I and absence of c-fos/c-jun expression. *Mol. Endocrinol.* 9, 924–931.
27. Zhou, J., and Bondy, C. (1993). Anatomy of the human ovarian insulin-like growth factor system. *Biol. Reprod.* 48, 467–482.
28. Hammond, J. M., Mondschein, J. S., Samaras, S. E., and Canning, S. F. (1991). The ovarian insulin-like growth factors: A local amplification mechanism for steroidogenesis and hormone action. *J. Steroid Biochem. Mol. Biol.* 40, 411–46.
29. Samaras, S. E., Canning, S. F., Barber, J. A., Simmen, F. A., and Hammond, J. M. (1996). Regulation of insulin-like growth factor I biosynthesis in porcine granulosa cells. *Endocrinology* 137, 4657–4664.
30. Baker, J., Hardy, M. P., Zhou, J., Bondy, C., Lupu, F., Bellve, A. R., and Efstratiadis, A. (1996). Effects of an Igf1 gene null mutation on mouse reproduction. *Mol. Endocrinol.* 10, 903–918.
31. Accili, D., Drago, J., Lee, E. J., Johnson, M. D., Cool, M. H., Salvatore, P., Asico, L. D., Jose, P. A., Taylor, S. I., and Westphal, H. (1996). Early neonatal death in mice homozygous for a null allele of the insulin receptor gene. *Nat. Genet.* 12, 106–109.
32. Bruning, J. C., Gautam, D., Burks, D. J., Gillette, J., Schubert, M., Orban, P. C., Klein, R., Krone, W., Muller-Wieland, D., and Kahn, C. R. (2000). Role of brain insulin receptor in control of body weight and reproduction. *Science* 289, 2122–2125.
33. Yu, N., and Roy, S. K. (1999). Development of primordial and prenatal follicles from undifferentiated somatic cells and oocytes in the hamster prenatal ovary in vitro: Effect of insulin. *Biol. Reprod.* 61, 1558–1567.
34. Kezele, P. R., Nilsson, E. E., and Skinner, M. K. (2002). Insulin but not insulin-like growth factor-1 promotes the primordial to primary follicle transition. *Mol. Cell. Endocrinol.* 192, 37–43.

35. Veldhuis, J. D., Tamura, S., Kolp, L., Furlanetto, R. W., and Larner, J. (1984). Mechanisms subserving insulin action in the gonad: Evidence that insulin induces specific phosphorylation of its immunoprecipitable receptor on ovarian cells. *Biochem. Biophys. Res. Commun.* 120, 144–149.
36. Veldhuis, J. D., Kolp, L. A., Toaff, M. E., Strauss, III, J. F., and Demers, L. M. (1983). Mechanisms subserving the trophic actions of insulin on ovarian cells. In vitro studies using swine granulosa cells. *J. Clin. Invest.* 72, 1046–1057.
37. Balasubramanian, K., Lavoie, H. A., Garmey, J. C., Stocco, D. M., and Veldhuis, J. D. (1997). Regulation of porcine granulosa cell steroidogenic acute regulatory protein (StAR) by insulin-like growth factor I: Synergism with follicle-stimulating hormone or protein kinase A agonist. *Endocrinology* 138, 433–439.
38. Urban, R. J., Garmey, J. C., Shupnik, M. A., and Veldhuis, J. D. (1990). Insulin-like growth factor type I increases concentrations of messenger ribonucleic acid encoding cytochrome P450 cholesterol side-chain cleavage enzyme in primary cultures of porcine granulosa cells. *Endocrinology* 127, 2481–2488.
39. Davoren, J. B., and Hsueh, A. J. (1984). Insulin enhances FSH-stimulated steroidogenesis by cultured rat granulosa cells. *Mol. Cell. Endocrinol.* 35, 97–105.
40. Erickson, G. F., Garzo, V. G., and Magoffin, D. A. (1991). Progesterone production by human granulosa cells cultured in serum free medium: Effects of gonadotrophins and insulin-like growth factor I (IGF-I). *Hum. Reprod.* 6, 1074–1081.
41. Maitra, A., LaVoie, H. A., Day, R. N., Garmey, J. C., and Veldhuis, J. D. (1995). Regulation of porcine granulosa cell 3-hydroxy-3-methylglutaryl coenzyme A reductase by insulin and insulin-like growth factor I: Synergism with follicle-stimulating hormone or protein kinase A agonist. *Endocrinology* 136, 5111–5117.
42. Sekar, N., Garmey, J. C., and Veldhuis, J. D. (2000). Mechanisms underlying the steroidogenic synergy of insulin and luteinizing hormone in porcine granulosa cells: Joint amplification of pivotal sterol-regulatory genes encoding the low-density lipoprotein (LDL) receptor, steroidogenic acute regulatory (StAR) protein and cytochrome P450 side-chain cleavage (P450scc) enzyme. *Mol. Cell. Endocrinol.* 159, 25–35.
43. Gooneratne, A. D., Thacker, P. A., Laarveld, B., Murphy, B. D., and Rajkumar, K. (1990). Comparative effects of insulin and insulin-like growth factor-1 on follicle-stimulating hormone-induced responses in porcine granulosa cells. *Steroids* 55, 105–108.
44. Devoto, L., Christenson, L. K., McAllister, J. M., Makrigiannakis, A., and Strauss, III, J. F. (1999). Insulin and insulin-like growth factor-I and -II modulate human granulosa-lutein cell steroidogenesis: Enhancement of steroidogenic acute regulatory protein (StAR) expression. *Mol. Hum. Reprod.* 5, 1003–1010.
45. Sekar, N., LaVoie, H. A., and Veldhuis, J. D. (2000). Concerted regulation of steroidogenic acute regulatory gene expression by luteinizing hormone and insulin (or insulin-like growth factor I) in primary cultures of porcine granulosa-luteal cells. *Endocrinology* 141, 3983–3992.
46. Yoshimura, Y. (1998). Insulin-like growth factors and ovarian physiology. *J. Obstet. Gynaecol. Res.* 24, 305–323.
47. McGee, E. A., Sawetawan, C., Bird, I., Rainey, W. E., and Carr, B. R. (1996). The effect of insulin and insulin-like growth factors on the expression of steroidogenic enzymes in a human ovarian thecal-like tumor cell model. *Fertil. Steril.* 65, 87–93.
48. Willis, D., Mason, H., Gilling-Smith, C., and Franks, S. (1996). Modulation by insulin of follicle-stimulating hormone and luteinizing hormone actions in human granulosa cells of normal and polycystic ovaries. *J. Clin. Endocrinol. Metab.* 81, 302–309.
49. Zhang, G., Garmey, J. C., and Veldhuis, J. D. (2000). Interactive stimulation by luteinizing hormone and insulin of the steroidogenic acute regulatory (StAR) protein and 17alpha-hydroxylase/17,20-lyase (CYP17) genes in porcine theca cells. *Endocrinology* 141, 2735–2742.
50. Schoppee, P. D., Garmey, J. C., and Veldhuis, J. D. (2002). Putative activation of the peroxisome proliferator-activated receptor γ impairs androgen and enhances progesterone biosynthesis in primary cultures of porcine theca cells. *Biol. Reprod.* 66, 190–198.
51. Itoh, T., Kacchi, M., Abe, H., Sendai, Y., and Hoshi, H. (2002). Growth, antrum formation, and estradiol production of bovine preantral follicles cultured in a serum-free medium. *Biol. Reprod.* 67, 1099–1105.
52. Romero, G., Garmey, J. C., and Veldhuis, J. D. (1993). The involvement of inositol phosphoglycan mediators in the modulation of steroidogenesis by insulin and insulin-like growth factor-I. *Endocrinology* 132, 1561–1568.
53. Veldhuis, J. D., and Furlanetto, R. W. (1985). Trophic actions of human somatomedin C/insulin-like growth factor I on ovarian cells: In vitro studies with swine granulosa cells. *Endocrinology* 116, 1235–1242.
54. Chakravorty, A., Joslyn, M. I., and Davis, J. S. (1993). Characterization of insulin and insulin-like growth factor-I actions in the bovine luteal cell: Regulation of receptor tyrosine kinase activity, phosphatidylinositol-3-kinase, and deoxyribonucleic acid synthesis. *Endocrinology* 133, 1331–1340.
55. Quesnel, H. (1999). Localization of binding sites for IGF-I, insulin and GH in the sow ovary. *J. Endocrinol.* 163, 363–372.
56. el-Roeiy, A., Chen, X., Roberts, V. J., Shimasakai, S., Ling, N., LeRoith, D., Roberts, Jr., C. T., and Yen, S. S. (1994). Expression of the genes encoding the insulin-like growth factors (IGF-I and II), the IGF and insulin receptors, and IGF-binding proteins-1-6 and the localization of their gene products in normal and polycystic ovary syndrome ovaries. *J. Clin. Endocrinol. Metab.* 78, 1488–1496.
57. Jones, J. I., and Clemmons, D. R. (1995). Insulin-like growth factors and their binding proteins: Biological actions. *Endocr. Rev.* 16, 3–34.
58. Grummer, R. R., and Carroll, D. J. (1988). A review of lipoprotein cholesterol metabolism: Importance to ovarian function. *J. Anim. Sci.* 66, 3160–3173.
59. Hussain, M. M., Strickland, D. K., and Bakillah, A. (1999). The mammalian low-density lipoprotein receptor family. *Annu. Rev. Nutr.* 19, 141–172.
60. Temel, R. E., Trigatti, B., DeMattos, R. B., Azhar, S., Krieger, M., and Williams, D. L. (1997). Scavenger receptor class B, type I (SR-BI) is the major route for the delivery of high density lipoprotein cholesterol to the steroidogenic pathway

in cultured mouse adrenocortical cells. *Proc. Natl. Acad. Sci. USA* 94, 13600–13605.
61. Garmey, J. C., Day, R. N., Day, K. H., and Veldhuis, J. D. (1993). Mechanisms of regulation of ovarian sterol metabolism by insulin-like growth factor type II: In vitro studies with swine granulosa cells. *Endocrinology* 133, 800–808.
62. Reaven, E., Tsai, L., Spicher, M., Shilo, L., Philip, M., Cooper, A. D., and Azhar, S. (1994). Enhanced expression of granulosa cell low density lipoprotein receptor activity in response to in vitro culture conditions. *J. Cell. Physiol.* 161, 449–462.
63. Medicherla, S., Azhar, S., Cooper, A., and Reaven, E. (1996). Regulation of cholesterol responsive genes in ovary cells: Impact of cholesterol delivery systems. *Biochemistry* 35, 6243–6250.
64. LaVoie, H. A., Garmey, J. C., Day, R. N., and Veldhuis, J. D. (1999). Concerted regulation of low density lipoprotein receptor gene expression by follicle-stimulating hormone and insulin-like growth factor I in porcine granulosa cells: Promoter activation, messenger ribonucleic acid stability, and sterol feedback. *Endocrinology* 140, 178–186.
65. Rajkumar, K., Ly, H., Schott, P. W., and Murphy, B. D. (1989). Use of low-density and high-density lipoproteins in undifferentiated porcine granulosa cells. *Biol. Reprod.* 41, 855–861.
66. Veldhuis, J. D. (1988). Follicle-stimulating hormone regulates low density lipoprotein metabolism by swine granulosa cells. *Endocrinology* 123, 1660–1667.
67. Golos, T. G., Strauss, III, J. F., and Miller, W. L. (1987). Regulation of low density lipoprotein receptor and cytochrome P-450scc mRNA levels in human granulosa cells. *J. Steroid. Biochem.* 27, 767–773.
68. Sekar, N., and Veldhuis, J. D. (2001). Concerted transcriptional activation of the low density lipoprotein receptor gene by insulin and luteinizing hormone in cultured porcine granulosa-luteal cells: Possible convergence of protein kinase A, phosphatidylinositol 3-kinase, and mitogen-activated protein kinase signaling pathways. *Endocrinology* 142, 2921–2928.
69. Streicher, R., Kotzka, J., Muller-Wieland, D., Siemeister, G., Munck, M., Avci, H., and Krone, W. (1996). SREBP-1 mediates activation of the low density lipoprotein receptor promoter by insulin and insulin-like growth factor-I. *J. Biol. Chem.* 271, 7128–7133.
70. Takagi, K., Hoffman, E. K., and Strauss, III, J. F. (1988). The upstream promoter of the human LDL receptor gene does not contain a cyclic AMP response element. *Biochem. Biophys. Res. Commun.* 152, 143–148.
71. Golos, T. G., and Strauss, Jr., J. F. (1987). Regulation of low density lipoprotein receptor gene expression in cultured human granulosa cells: Roles of human chorionic gonadotropin, 8-bromo-3′,5′-cyclic adenosine monophosphate, and protein synthesis. *Mol. Endocrinol.* 1, 321–326.
72. Strauss, III, J. F., Kallen, C. B., Christenson, L. K., Watari, H., Devoto, L., Arakane, F., Kiriakidou, M., and Sugawara, T. (1999). The steroidogenic acute regulatory protein (StAR): A window into the complexities of intracellular cholesterol trafficking. *Rec. Prog. Hormone Res.* 54, 369–394; discussion 394–395.
73. Arakane, F., King, S. R., Du, Y., Kallen, C. B., Walsh, L. P., Watari, H., Stocco, D. M., and Strauss, III, J. F. (1997). Phosphorylation of steroidogenic acute regulatory protein (StAR) modulates its steroidogenic activity. *J. Biol. Chem.* 272, 32656–32662.
74. Miller, W. L., and Strauss, III, J. F. (1999). Molecular pathology and mechanism of action of the steroidogenic acute regulatory protein, StAR. *J. Steroid Biochem. Mol. Biol.* 69, 131–141.
75. Hasegawa, T., Zhao, L., Caron, K. M., Majdic, G., Suzuki, T., Shizawa, S., Sasano, H., and Parker, K. L. (2000). Developmental roles of the steroidogenic acute regulatory protein (StAR) as revealed by StAR knockout mice. *Mol. Endocrinol.* 14, 1462–1471.
76. Caron, K. M., Soo, S. C., Wetsel, W. C., Stocco, D. M., Clark, B. J., and Parker, K. L. (1997). Targeted disruption of the mouse gene encoding steroidogenic acute regulatory protein provides insights into congenital lipoid adrenal hyperplasia. *Proc. Natl. Acad. Sci. USA* 94, 11540–11545.
77. LaVoie, H. A., Benoit, A. M., Garmey, J. C., Dailey, R. A., Wright, D. J., and Veldhuis, J. D. (1997). Coordinate developmental expression of genes regulating sterol economy and cholesterol side-chain cleavage in the porcine ovary. *Biol. Reprod.* 57, 402–407.
78. Eimerl, S., and Orly, J. (2002). Regulation of steroidogenic genes by insulin-like growth factor-1 and follicle-stimulating hormone: Differential responses of cytochrome p450 side-chain cleavage, steroidogenic acute regulatory protein, and 3beta-hydroxysteroid dehydrogenase/isomerase in rat granulosa cells. *Biol. Reprod.* 67, 900–910.
79. LaVoie, H. A., Garmey, J. C., and Veldhuis, J. D. (1999). Mechanisms of insulin-like growth factor I augmentation of follicle-stimulating hormone-induced porcine steroidogenic acute regulatory protein gene promoter activity in granulosa cells. *Endocrinology* 140, 146–153.
80. Pescador, N., Houde, A., Stocco, D. M., and Murphy, B. D. (1997). Follicle-stimulating hormone and intracellular second messengers regulate steroidogenic acute regulatory protein messenger ribonucleic acid in luteinized porcine granulosa cells. *Biol. Reprod.* 57, 660–668.
81. Nishikawa, T., Sasano, H., Omura, M., and Suematsu, S. (1996). Regulation of expression of the steroidogenic acute regulatory (StAR) protein by ACTH in bovine adrenal fasciculata cells. *Biochem. Biophys. Res. Commun.* 225, 12–18.
82. Manna, P. R., Pakarinen, P., El-Hefnawy, T., and Huhtaniemi, I. T. (1999). Functional assessment of the calcium messenger system in cultured mouse Leydig tumor cells: Regulation of human chorionic gonadotropin-induced expression of the steroidogenic acute regulatory protein. *Endocrinology* 140, 1739–1751.
83. Pescador, N., Stocco, D. M., and Murphy, B. D. (1999). Growth factor modulation of steroidogenic acute regulatory protein and luteinization in the pig ovary. *Biol. Reprod.* 60, 1453–1461.
84. Sugawara, T., Saito, M., and Fujimoto, S. (2000). Sp1 and SF-1 interact and cooperate in the regulation of human steroidogenic acute regulatory protein gene expression. *Endocrinology* 141, 2895–2903.
85. Sugawara, T., Kiriakidou, M., McAllister, J. M., Kallen, C. B., and Strauss, III, J. F. (1997). Multiple steroidogenic factor 1 binding elements in the human steroidogenic acute regulatory protein gene 5′-flanking region are required for

maximal promoter activity and cyclic AMP responsiveness. *Biochemistry* 36, 7249–7255.

86. Wooton-Kee, C. R., and Clark, B. J. (2000). Steroidogenic factor-1 influences protein-deoxyribonucleic acid interactions within the cyclic adenosine 3,5-monophosphate-responsive regions of the murine steroidogenic acute regulatory protein gene. *Endocrinology* 141, 1345–1355.
87. Reinhart, A. J., Williams, S. C., Clark, B. J., and Stocco, D. M. (1999). SF-1 (steroidogenic factor-1) and C/EBP beta (CCAAT/enhancer binding protein-beta) cooperate to regulate the murine StAR (steroidogenic acute regulatory) promoter. *Mol. Endocrinol.* 13, 729–741.
88. Silverman, E., Eimerl, S., and Orly, J. (1999). CCAAT enhancer-binding protein beta and GATA-4 binding regions within the promoter of the steroidogenic acute regulatory protein (StAR) gene are required for transcription in rat ovarian cells. *J. Biol. Chem.* 274, 17987–17996.
89. Tremblay, J. J., Hamel, F., and Viger, R. S. (2002). Protein kinase A-dependent cooperation between GATA and CCAAT/enhancer-binding protein transcription factors regulates steroidogenic acute regulatory protein promoter activity. *Endocrinology* 143, 3935–3945.
90. Christenson, L. K., Johnson, P. F., McAllister, J. M., and Strauss, III, J. F. (1999). CCAAT/enhancer-binding proteins regulate expression of the human steroidogenic acute regulatory protein (StAR) gene. *J. Biol. Chem.* 274, 26591–26598.
91. Christenson, L. K., Osborne, T. F., McAllister, J. M., and Strauss, III, J. F. (2001). Conditional response of the human steroidogenic acute regulatory protein gene promoter to sterol regulatory element binding protein-1a. *Endocrinology* 142, 28–36.
92. Shea-Eaton, W. K., Trinidad, M. J., Lopez, D., Nackley, A., and McLean, M. P. (2001). Sterol regulatory element binding protein-1a regulation of the steroidogenic acute regulatory protein gene. *Endocrinology* 142, 1525–1533.
93. Shea-Eaton, W., Sandhoff, T. W., Lopez, D., Hales, D. B., and McLean, M. P. (2002). Transcriptional repression of the rat steroidogenic acute regulatory (StAR) protein gene by the AP-1 family member c-Fos. *Mol. Cell. Endocrinol.* 188, 161–170.
94. Gonzalez-Robayna, I. J., Falender, A. E., Ochsner, S., Firestone, G. L., and Richards, J. S. (2000). Follicle-stimulating hormone (FSH) stimulates phosphorylation and activation of protein kinase B (PKB/Akt) and serum and glucocorticoid-induced kinase (Sgk): Evidence for A kinase-independent signaling by FSH in granulosa cells. *Mol. Endocrinol.* 14, 1283–1300.
95. Makarevich, A., Sirotkin, A., Chrenek, P., Bulla, J., and Hetenyi, L. (2000) .The role of IGF-I, cAMP/protein kinase A and MAP-kinase in the control of steroid secretion, cyclic nucleotide production, granulosa cell proliferation and preimplantation embryo development in rabbits. *J. Steroid Biochem. Mol. Biol.* 73, 123–133.
96. Pescador, N., Stocco, D. M., and Murphy, B. D. (1999). Growth factor modulation of steroidogenic acute regulatory protein and luteinization in the pig ovary. *Biol. Reprod.* 60, 1453–1461.
97. Puryear, T. K., McLean, M. P., Khan, I., and Gibori, G. (1990). Mechanism for control of hydroxymethylglutaryl-coenzyme A reductase and cytochrome P-450 side chain cleavage message and enzyme in the corpus luteum. *Endocrinology* 126, 2910–2918.
98. Ahlgren, R., Simpson, E. R., Waterman, M. R., and Lund, J. (1990). Characterization of the promoter/regulatory region of the bovine CYP11A (P-450scc) gene. Basal and cAMP-dependent expression. *J. Biol. Chem.* 265, 3313–3319.
99. Urban, R. J., Shupnik, M. A., and Bodenburg, Y. H. (1994). Insulin-like growth factor-I increases expression of the porcine P-450 cholesterol side chain cleavage gene through a GC-rich domain. *J. Biol. Chem.* 269, 25761–25769.
100. Liu, Z., and Simpson, E. R. (1997). Steroidogenic factor 1 (SF-1) and Sp1 are required for regulation of bovine CYP11A gene expression in bovine luteal cells and adrenal Y1 cells. *Mol. Endocrinol.* 11, 127–137.
101. Monte, D., DeWitte, F., and Hum, D. W. (1998). Regulation of the human P450scc gene by steroidogenic factor 1 is mediated by CBP/p300. *J. Biol. Chem.* 273, 4585–4591.
102. Ahlgren, R., Suske, G., Waterman, M. R., and Lund, J. (1999). Role of Sp1 in cAMP-dependent transcriptional regulation of the bovine CYP11A gene. *J. Biol. Chem.* 274, 19422–19428.
103. Doi, J., Takemori, H., Lin, X. Z., Horike, N., Katoh, Y., and Okamoto, M. (2002). Salt-inducible kinase represses cAMP-dependent protein kinase-mediated activation of human cholesterol side chain cleavage cytochrome P450 promoter through the CREB basic leucine zipper domain. *J. Biol. Chem.* 277, 15629–15637.
104. Ben-Zimra, M., Koler, M., and Orly, J. (2002). Transcription of cholesterol side-chain cleavage cytochrome p450 in the placenta: Activating protein-2 assumes the role of steroidogenic factor-1 by binding to an overlapping promoter element. *Mol. Endocrinol.* 16, 1864–1880.
105. Urban, R. J., Bodenburg, Y., Kurosky, A., Wood, T. G., and Gasic, S. (2000). Polypyrimidine tract-binding protein-associated splicing factor is a negative regulator of transcriptional activity of the porcine p450scc insulin-like growth factor response element. *Mol. Endocrinol.* 14, 774–782.
106. Gizard, F., Lavallee, B., DeWitte, F., Teissier, E., Staels, B., and Hum, D. W. (2002). The transcriptional regulating protein of 132 kDa (TReP-132) enhances P450scc gene transcription through interaction with steroidogenic factor-1 in human adrenal cells. *J. Biol. Chem.* 277, 39144–39155.
107. Jayes, F. C. L., Day, R. N., Garmey, J. C., Urban, R. J., Zhang, G., and Veldhuis, J. D. (2000). Calcium ions positively modulate follicle-stimulating hormone- and exogenous cyclic 3′,5′-adenosine monophosphate-driven transcription of the P450scc gene in porcine granulosa cells. *Endocrinology* 141, 2377–2384.
108. Silva, J. M., and Price, C. A. (2002). Insulin and IGF-I are necessary for FSH-induced cytochrome P450 aromatase but not cytochrome P450 side-chain cleavage gene expression in oestrogenic bovine granulosa cells in vitro. *J. Endocrinol.* 174, 499–507.
109. Urban, R. J., Bodenburg, Y. H., and Wood, T. G. (2002). NH2 terminus of PTB-associated splicing factor binds to the porcine P450scc IGF-I response element. *Am. J. Physiol. Endocrinol. Metab.* 283, E423–E427.
110. Voutilainen, R., Tapanainen, J., Chung, B. C., Matteson, K. J., and Miller, W. L. (1986). Hormonal regulation of P450scc (20,22-desmolase) and P450c17 (17 alpha-hydroxy-

lase/17,20-lyase) in cultured human granulosa cells. *J. Clin. Endocrinol. Metab.* 63, 202–207.
111. Simone, D. A., Chorich, L. P., and Mahesh, V. B. (1993). Mechanisms of action for an androgen-mediated autoregulatory process in rat thecal-interstitial cells. *Biol. Reprod.* 49, 1190–1201.
112. Yuan, W., Lucy, M. C., and Smith, M. F. (1996). Messenger ribonucleic acid for insulin-like growth factors-I and -II, insulin-like growth factor-binding protein-2, gonadotropin receptors, and steroidogenic enzymes in porcine follicles. *Biol. Reprod.* 55, 1045–1054.
113. Adashi, E. Y. (1994). Endocrinology of the ovary. *Hum. Reprod.* 9, 815–827.
114. He, H., Herington, A. C., and Roupas, P. (1994). Involvement of G proteins in the effect of insulin-like growth factor I on gonadotropin-induced rat granulosa cell differentiation. *Growth Regul.* 4, 20–28.
115. Costrici, N., Lunenfeld, B., Pariente, C., Dor, J., Rabinovici, J., Kanety, H., and Karasik, A. (1994). Induction of aromatase in human granulosa cells by both follicle stimulating hormone and insulin-like growth factor-I involves tyrosine phosphorylation. *Gynecol. Endocrinol.* 8, 183–189.
116. Spicer, L. J., Chamberlain, C. S., and Maciel, S. M. (2002). Influence of gonadotropins on insulin- and insulin-like growth factor-I (IGF-I)-induced steroid production by bovine granulosa cells. *Dom. Anim. Endocrinology* 22, 237–254.
117. McGee, E., Sawetawan, C., Bird, I., Rainey, W. E., and Carr, B. R. (1995). The effects of insulin on 3 beta-hydroxysteroid dehydrogenase expression in human luteinized granulosa cells. *J. Soc. Gynecol. Investig.* 2, 535–541.
118. Zhou, J., Kumar, T. R., Matzuk, M. M., and Bondy, C. (1997). Insulin-like growth factor I regulates gonadotropin responsiveness in the murine ovary. *Mol. Endocrinol.* 11, 1924–1933.
119. Britt, K. L., Drummond, A. E., Dyson, M., Wreford, N. G., Jones, M. E. E., Simpson, E. R., and Findlay, J. K. (2001). The ovarian phenotype of the aromatase knockout (ArKO) mouse. *J. Steroid Biochem. Mol. Biol.* 79, 181–185.
120. Murata, Y., Robertson, K. M., Jones, M. E. E., and Simpson, E. R. (2002). Effect of estrogen deficiency in the male: The ArKO mouse model. *Mol. Cell. Endocrinology* 193, 7–12.
121. Kumar, T. R., Wang, Y., Lu, N., and Matzuk, M. M. (1997). Follicle stimulating hormone is required for ovarian follicle maturation but not male fertility. *Nat. Genet.* 15, 201–204.
122. Minegishi, T., Hirakawa, T., Kishi, H., Abe, K., Abe, Y., Mizutani, T., and Miyamoto, K. (2000). A role of insulin-like growth factor I for follicle-stimulating hormone receptor expression in rat granulosa cells. *Biol. Reprod.* 62, 325–333.
123. Richards, J. S. (1980). Maturation of ovarian follicles: Actions and interactions of pituitary and ovarian hormones on follicular cell differentiation. *Physiol. Rev.* 60, 51–89.
124. Zhang, F.-P., Poutanen, M., Wilbertz, J., and Huhtaniemi, I. (2001). Normal prenatal but arrested postnatal sexual development of luteinizing hormone receptor knockout (LuRKO) mice. *Mol. Endocrinol.* 15, 172–183.
125. Lei, Z. M., Mishra, S., Zou, W., Xu, B., Foltz, M., Li, X., and Rao, C. V. (2001). Targeted disruption of luteinizing hormone/human chorionic gonadotropin receptor gene. *Mol. Endocrinol.* 15, 184–200.
126. Huang, C. T., Weitsman, S. R., Dykes, B. N., and Magoffin, D. A. (2001). Stem cell factor and insulin-like growth factor-I stimulate luteinizing hormone-independent differentiation of rat ovarian theca cells. *Biol. Reprod.* 64, 451–456.
127. Hirakawa, T., Minegishi, T., Abe, K., Kishi, H., Ibuki, Y., and Miyamoto, K. (1999). A role of insulin-like growth factor I in luteinizing hormone receptor expression in granulosa cells. *Endocrinology* 140, 4965–4971.
128. Zhang, F.-P., El-Hafnawy, T., and Huhtaniemi, I. (1998). Regulation of luteinizing hormone receptor gene expression by insulin-like growth factor-I in an immortalized murine Leydig tumor cell line (BLT-1). *Biol. Reprod.* 59, 1116–11123.

CHAPTER **15**

Potential Role of Cytokines in Ovarian Physiology: The Case for Interleukin-1

MATS BRÄNNSTRÖM

INTRODUCTION

During the last decade it has become evident that cytokines are important intraovarian regulators in the mammalian ovary. The emerging concept is that the cytokines are instrumental in the regulation of folliculogenesis, ovulation, and corpus luteum function. The cytokines in the ovary are secreted both from immune cells that have been recruited from the blood circulation to the extravascular space in the ovarian stroma and the theca layer of the follicle and also from the somatic cells of the ovary, including the granulosa and theca cells. A number of cytokines such as interferon γ [1], granulocyte-macrophage colony–stimulating factor [2], interleukin-6 [3], and tumor necrosis factor-α [4] have been linked to some of these cyclic ovarian events. However, interleukin-1 (IL-1) stands out as a cytokine, which has major effects on functional and structural alterations within the ovary at all stages of the ovarian cycle.

The *polypeptide cytokine IL-1* is the term for two polypeptides, interleukin-1α (IL-1α) and interleukin-1β (IL-1β). They are initially synthesized as 31 kD precursors (pro-IL-1), which are further cleaved to generate mature IL-1. The two forms of IL-1 are different gene products but recognize the same cell surface receptors and will thereby share many biological activities. The effects by IL-1 are manifested in nearly every tissue, and IL-1 has a broad spectrum of inflammatory, metabolic, hematopoietic, and immunological functions.

This chapter discusses in detail the various roles that IL-1 plays in folliculogenesis, ovulation, and regulation of corpus luteum function.

FOLLICULOGENESIS

Folliculogenesis is the process whereby the primordial follicle is recruited for further development. The majority of the developing follicles will undergo atresia, but some will mature into preovulatory follicles. The primordial follicle is made up of an oocyte that is lined by flattened granulosa cells. Possibly by initiation from the oocyte, these cells start to grow and differentiate into cuboidal granulosa cells to form a primary follicle. By gonadotropin-independent mechanisms, the primary follicles grow into secondary follicles by enlargement of the oocyte and by mitotic activity among the granulosa cells. A preantral follicle is formed when a theca layer is generated from the surrounding connective tissue. From the preantral follicular stage, leukocytes such as macrophages, neutrophilic granulocytes, and T-lymphocytes are present in the tissue immediately around the follicle and occasionally in the theca layer [5, 6]. All these leukocyte subtypes secrete large quantities of IL-1 on activation. The follicle will later form a fluid-filled antrum, and from this stage until the preovulatory stage, the gonadotropin follicle-stimulating hormone (FSH) is the primary stimulus for growth and differentiation. The time span for the development of a primordial follicle into a preovulatory follicle that will be stimulated by the surge of luteinizing hormone (LH) to ovulate is about 6 months in the human [7] but shorter in the mouse, rat, and pig, the experimental animals that have mostly been used in studies of IL-1 action in folliculogenesis. Participation of cytokines, including IL-1, in several of the critical steps of folliculogenesis, has been suggested. The localization of the IL-1 system in the follicle and its actions on follicular growth and differentiation (Figure 15.1) are described in more detail later.

Localization of the Interleukin-1 System in Developing Follicles

There is compartmentalization of the different components of the IL-1 system in and around the follicle during folliculogenesis (see Figure 15.1), and there also seems to exist certain differences in this regard among species.

In the rat, the messenger ribonucleic acid (mRNA) for IL-1β was detected in the immature ovary, and a modest increase of the mRNA levels, following gonadotropic stimulation to induce follicular growth, was seen up to the preovulatory follicular stage [8].

With in situ hybridization technique, the transcript for IL-1β was localized to the mural granulosa cells, the inner-

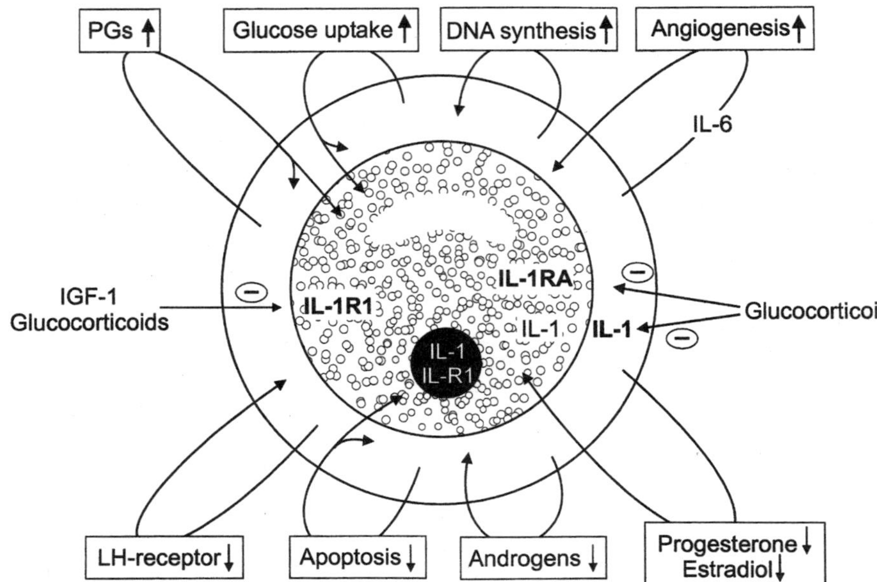

FIGURE 15.1 Distribution of the IL-1 system in developing follicles and its role and regulation during folliculogenesis. The distribution within the follicular compartments of the components of the IL-1 system (bold letters indicate the sites of their highest expression) and their regulation are shown. Curved arrows indicate effects by IL-1, with the origin of a curved arrow indicating the source of IL-1 and the arrowhead indicating the target for IL-1 for each specific effect. *IGF*, Insulin-like growth factor; *PG*, prostaglandin.

most layers of the theca, and the oocyte in preantral and early antral follicles [9]. The major receptor subtype in the rat ovary during folliculogenesis is the type 1 receptor (IL-1R1), which in the follicle is expressed at high but fairly constant levels, in contrast to very low IL-1R2 expression [10]. Detailed in situ hybridization studies showed that IL-1R1 was not expressed in primordial or primary follicles of the rat ovary but appeared in preantral follicles, where the strongest expression was seen in the granulosa cells [11]. More precisely, IL-1R1 was localized to mural, antral, and cumulus granulosa cells with a very modest staining also in the oocytes [12]. An important component of the intraovarian Il-1 system is the naturally occurring IL-1 receptor antagonist (IL-1RA), which acts as an attenuator of IL-1 action. The IL-1RA is expressed in granulosa cells of preantral follicles but not in follicles of earlier stages [11].

In the mouse ovary, the distribution of the proteins of the IL-system was characterized by immunohistochemistry. In contrast to the localization within the rat ovary, IL-1α, IL-1β, and IL-1R1 are present exclusively in the theca layer of growing follicles, with the exception that IL-1 R1 is also present in the cytoplasm of oocytes [13].

In the human ovary, both IL-1α and IL-1β are expressed in the granulosa cells with more pronounced IL-1β expression [14]. The actions of IL-1 in the human follicle during folliculogenesis are presumable both on the granulosa and theca cells because IL-1R1 is expressed in these two follicular compartments [14].

Effects of Interleukin-1 on Growth of Developing Follicles

During folliculogenesis, the oocyte enlarges and there is a tremendous mitotic activity among the follicular cells. The overall pattern is that IL-1 controls the transition of the follicular cells from a proliferative to a differentiated stage by facilitating proliferation and preventing premature differentiation (see Figure 15.1).

In the rat ovary, it was demonstrated that IL-1 promotes granulosa cell proliferation by attenuating the suppressive influence of FSH on deoxyribonucleic acid (DNA) synthesis in these cells [15]. A direct proliferative effect of IL-1 was also demonstrated in undifferentiated porcine granulosa cells [16]. Another way that IL-1 positively modulates follicular growth is by influencing apoptosis, the main component of follicular atresia. Thus it was shown that IL-1β suppresses apoptosis of rat ovarian follicles in culture, an effect that seemed to be nitric oxide (NO)-mediated [17]. Intraovarian IL-1 interacts with transforming growth factor-β1 (TGF-β1), which is expressed in granulosa and theca interstitial cells, during follicular development to inhibit cell proliferation and to facilitate differentiation [18]. In the immature rat ovary that contained follicles from the primordial stage up to the early antral stage, TGF-β1 inhibits IL-1-induced NO production [19], which would counteract the antiapoptotic role of IL-1β-induced NO [19a]. The multifunctional cytokine IL-6 has been linked to angiogenesis in developing follicles of the mouse ovary [20]. IL-1 induces an 11-fold induction of the IL-6 transcript in cultures of ovarian cellular dispersates from immature rats [21], which would further point toward a growth stimulatory role of IL-1β during folliculogenesis to facilitate angiogenesis and thereby blood flow and nourishment to the follicle.

Because of the high proliferative activity of the follicle, there exists increased metabolic demands, especially during the final growth of the follicle. The enhanced ovarian glucose uptake, which is seen during follicular development, would be essential in this regard. In a study in the rat, it was shown that the glucose transporters (Gluts), Glut-1 and Glut-3, are expressed in the immature ovary and that they are upregulated by IL-1β [22]. A corresponding IL-1β-induced increase in glucose consumption of the ovarian cells of the immature ovary was also seen. Taken together, the IL-1 system would thus directly stimulate granulosa cell proliferation and glucose uptake, inhibit apoptosis via NO, and facilitate angiogenesis via IL-6.

Effects of Interleukin-1 on Steroidogenesis and Differentiation of Developing Follicles

The developing follicle progressively differentiates by acquisition of gonadotropin receptors and steroidogenic enzymes to enable provision of androgens from the theca cells for aromatisation to estrogens in the granulosa cells. IL-1β [23] and IL-1α [24] dose-dependently inhibit FSH-induced estradiol synthesis from immature rat granulosa cells, and this effect is partly caused by IL-1β inhibition of aromatase activity [25] in the granulosa cells of these developing follicles. In an in vivo approach to characterize the effect of IL-1 on the ovary, it was demonstrated that IL-1α significantly decreased estradiol levels in the blood in hypophysectomized immature female rats that had been primed with gonadotropin [26]. In porcine granulosa cells obtained from medium-sized follicles, IL-1α [27] dose-dependently decreases both gonadotropin-stimulated and basal progesterone production. Likewise in the rat, IL-1β negatively regulates progesterone production from FSH-stimulated granulosa cells [28]. The IL-1β induced inhibition of progesterone accumulation in immature granulosa cells of the rat is caused by stimulation of progesterone degradation by induction of 20α-hydroxysteroid dehydrogenase [25].

IL-1 also affects androgen synthesis in the theca cells during follicular development. Both IL-1α and IL-1β inhibit gonadotropin-stimulated androstenedione production in highly purified theca interstitial cells from immature rat ovaries [29]. In this study, IL-1β was more potent than IL-1α, and the effect was IL-1-specific because a number of other ILs (e.g., 2 through 6) were without effect. In summary, IL-1 suppresses steroidogenesis during folliculogenesis by inhibiting progesterone, estrogen, and androgen synthesis during basal- and gonadotropin-stimulated conditions.

In this context it should also be noted that gonadotropins may modulate IL-1 secretion from immune cells outside the ovary during follicular development. It was shown that FSH, but not LH, stimulated the release of IL-1β from human peripheral blood monocytes, an effect that was seen during the follicular phase but not during the luteal phase [30].

The insulin growth factor-1 (IGF-1) system plays a role in the ovary during folliculogenesis to amplify the effects of FSH. In whole ovarian dispersates from immature rats, IGF-1 treatment decreased the IL-1R1 mRNA levels but was without effect on the IL-1β transcript [31]. Glucocorticoid receptors are present in the follicle during folliculogenesis [32], and glucocorticoids modulate FSH-induced steroidogenesis [33] and differentiation [34]. Glucocorticoids may modulate IL-1 action during folliculogenesis because dexamethasone inhibits IL-1-supported expression of cyclooxygenase-2 (COX-2) and the IL-1 mediated upregulation of IL-1β, IL-1RA, and IL-R1 in immature cells of the ovary [35]. It can be speculated that IGF-1 and glucocorticoids downregulate ovarian IL-1 action and thereby protect the follicles from premature initiation of ovulation-associated events.

IL-1 also effects the expression of gonadotropin receptors during the growth and development of follicles. Thus IL-1 inhibits FSH-induced LH receptor formation in immature granulosa cells of the rat [36]. The cultured granulosa cells had to be exposed to IL-1 for a minimum of 12 hours, which suggests the involvement of active protein synthesis [36].

PGs are produced in the follicle during folliculogenesis and are important intrafollicular regulators that control proliferation and differentiation [37, 38]. A mixture of cells of immature ovaries of rats produce PGs in large amounts, and IL-1 treatment increases the PG accumulation, which is larger for prostaglandin E (PGE) than for prostaglandin $F_{2\alpha}$ ($PGF_{2\alpha}$) [39]. In these studies, IL-1 treatment of whole ovarian dispersates in culture gave rise to greater accumulation of PGE as compared with cultured granulosa or theca cells of the same cell density, thereby suggesting that heterologous cell-cell interactions are required for optimal synthesis. The enzyme phospholipase A_2 (PLA_2), a key enzyme for production of all eicosanoids, is present in immature rat ovarian cells, and the mRNA levels are upregulated about twofold by IL-1β during long term cultures [40]. In the same study, it was demonstrated that PLA_2 is also upregulated by FSH, and this gonadotropin induction is blocked by the presence of IL-1RA, which suggests that FSH acts via IL-1 to regulate follicular PG levels.

OVULATION

The ovulatory process includes the local alternations in and around the follicle during the time from the start of the gonadotropin surge until follicular rupture when the fertilizable oocyte is released. During the relatively short ovulatory period, which is about 12 to 15 hours in rodents [41] and 36 to 38 hours in humans [42], prominent functional and structural changes occur.

In this process, LH sets in motion several intraovarian regulatory systems (Figure 15.2) that cooperatively and redundantly act to either degrade the extracellular matrix

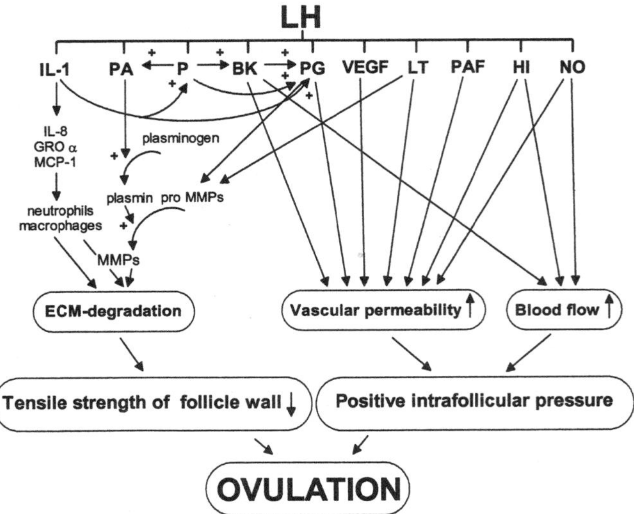

FIGURE 15.2 Overview of LH-induced pathways in the ovulatory cascade. LH induces synthesis of mediators that promote either degradation of the extracellular matrix (ECM) and/or vascular changes (permeability increase, blood flow increase). These changes lead to a decreased tensile strength and a positive intrafollicular pressure, and ovulation will occur when the tensile strength of the follicular wall can no longer withhold the outward force of the positive intrafollicular pressure. *BK*, Bradykinin; *GRO*, growth regulating oncogene; *HI*, histamine; *IL*, interleukin; *LT*, leukotriene; *MCP*, monocyte chemotactic protein; *MMP*, matrix metalloproteinase; *NO*, nitric oxide; *P*, progesterone; *PA*, plasminogen activator; *PAF*, platelet activating factor; *PG*, prostaglandin; *VEGF*, vascular endothelial growth factor.

(ECM) on the apex of the follicle or to induce vascular changes. The ECM degradation leads to a continuous decrease in tensile strength of the follicle. The vascular changes act to stabilize or increase the liquid pressure within the follicle [43] to avoid a collapse of the follicle during the late ovulatory stage when the follicle is leaking follicular fluid and to finally cause the rupture of the follicle. A major cellular event in ovulation, with relevance to action of IL-1 in this process, is that leukocytes are attracted to the follicle by chemokines [44, 45]. In particular, there is massive influx of neutrophils and macrophages to the theca layer of the ovulating follicle [5, 6], two subsets of leukocytes with great capacity for IL-1 secretion on activation.

Localization of the IL-1 System in the Preovulatory Follicle

The initial studies on possible influences of the IL-1 system in ovulation analyzed IL-1 levels in follicular fluids of in vitro fertilization (IVF) patients and compared these to levels in peripheral blood. Immunoreactive IL-1β was found in human follicular fluids of IVF patients, and a positive correlation was demonstrated between the levels in follicular fluid and blood plasma [46]. The IL-1β levels in the follicular fluids were about half of the plasma levels. In a more recent study [47], a correlation was found between IL-1α levels and the levels of leukotriene B4, a mediator in the ovulatory cascade [48]. The cytokine IL-1β is also present in follicular fluids of preovulatory follicles from natural unstimulated cycles [49], but the IL-1β levels in the follicular fluids of these preovulatory follicles of the menstrual cycle were markedly lower than in follicular fluid of IVF-cycles. From these early studies of IL-1 levels in follicular fluid, it is clear that IL-1β is present in the human follicle in concentrations that can have physiological implications in the regulation of ovulation. In the follicular tissue of the human ovary, mainly IL-1β is expressed and its expression increases at the preovulatory stage [14].

In the rat ovary, IL-1β mRNA levels increase after preovulatory gonadotropin administration, and maximal levels are reached 6 to 12 hours later [9, 50]. Maximal induction of IL-1β mRNA was seen when human chorionic gonadotropin (hCG) was given 48 hours after gonadotropin priming of immature ovaries as opposed to longer or shorter intervals between gonadotropin and hCG injection [50]. The mRNA levels do not necessarily reflect the actual protein levels, and an important contribution to our understanding of the IL-1 system in ovulation is the evaluation of the tissue levels of IL-1β protein during the periovulatory period. It was shown that the levels of IL-1β protein rapidly increased after hCG injection to a peak at 4 hours and returned to basal levels at 6 hours after hCG injection [51].

The theca layer is also the follicular compartment for IL-1β expression during ovulation, and an approximately fivefold increase in IL-1β levels in this compartment is seen from the preovulatory stage to the ovulatory phase in the rat [8], with the IL-1β message being induced by LH/hCG or by IL-1 itself. In addition, the IL-1 receptors are hormonally regulated during induced ovulation in the rat ovary with the expression of the IL-1R1 increasing sevenfold 6 hours after hCG administration [10]. The IL-1R1 mRNA is localized mainly in the granulosa cells (Figure 15.3) of the preovulatory follicle, and the level of IL-1R2 mRNA is only about 1% of that of IL-1R1 [10].

The levels of the IL-1β and IL-1RA proteins were measured in perfused rabbit ovaries. It was shown that administration of hCG increased the production of both these proteins, and maximal levels were reached 6 hours after hCG administration [52]. Calculations of the molar ratio demonstrated that several concentrations of IL-1RA were 100-fold higher compared with IL-1β. In the preovulatory follicle of the mouse ovary, both IL-1α and IL-1β proteins are present in the theca layer, and IL-1R1 is localized to the granulosa cells [13].

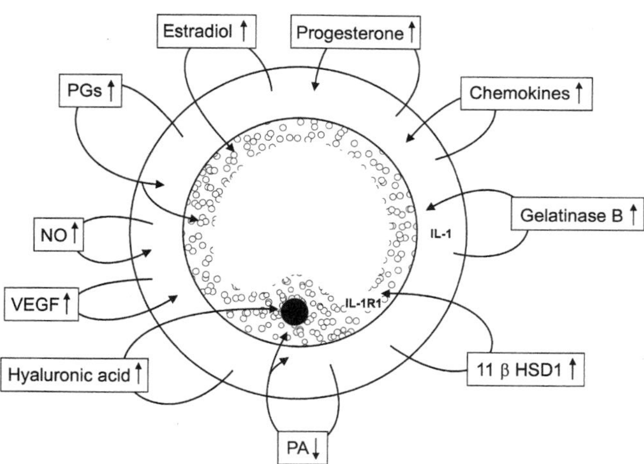

FIGURE 15.3 Distribution of the IL-1 system and its effect on the preovulatory follicle. Curved arrows indicate effects by IL-1, with the origin of a curved arrow indicating the source of IL-1 and the arrowhead indicating the target for IL-1 for each specific effect. *11β-HSD-1*, 11β-hydroxysteroid dehydrogenase-1; *NO*, nitric oxide; *PA*, plasminogen activator; *PG*, prostaglandin; *VEGF*, vascular endothelial growth factor.

Effects of Interleukin-1 on Ovulation

A clear role for IL-1 in ovulation was first demonstrated by the ability of IL-1β to independently induce ovulations and also to potentiate the LH-induced ovulatory effect in the in vitro perfused rat ovary [53]. In an almost identical in vitro perfusion system of the rat ovary, it was demonstrated that IL-1RA suppressed the number of LH-stimulated ovulations [54]. Moreover, in the perfused rabbit, ovary ovulation was inhibited by administration of antiserum toward IL-1β, and recombinant IL-1β induced ovulations on its own [52].

A role for the IL-1 system in ovulation was also demonstrated in vivo, where administration of IL-1RA into the ovarian bursal sac of preovulatory rat ovaries decreased the ovulatory response when IL-1RA was administered before hCG [50] or 5 hours after hCG [55a]. Furthermore, the ovulation rate in vivo in the rabbit ovary was decreased by around 40% when anti IL-1β was given 30 minutes before the ovulatory gonadotropin treatment [56].

Interleukin-1 and Ovulatory Mediators

Several studies have been performed to elucidate whether IL-1 affects (see Figure 15.3) any of the LH-induced mediator systems, which act to cause the changes necessary for follicular rupture (see Figure 15.2).

Steroids

The gonadotropin surge changes the steroid output from the follicle from secretion mainly of estradiol to secretion of progesterone. Progesterone seems to be obligatory for ovulation to occur as shown in experiments with progesterone synthesis blockers during in vitro perfusion [57] and in mice with deletions in the progesterone receptor gene [58]. The obligatory role of progesterone in ovulation seems to be connected to its function to upregulate several steps in ECM degradation at the follicle apex [58a]. In an in vitro study with isolated preovulatory follicles from the hamster, it was shown that IL-1α increases hCG-stimulated progesterone production, but IL-1α is without effect by itself [59]. In the same study, it was demonstrated that the follicular source of increased progesterone production was the theca layer. In experiments on isolated preovulatory follicles and enriched theca cells of the rat, IL-1β by itself stimulated progesterone production [60]. However, in perfused preovulatory rat ovaries with preserved tissue architecture and cell-cell contacts, IL-1β increased progesterone secretion only in the presence of LH [53]. In the bovine ovary, IL-1β stimulates estradiol release but inhibits androgen release from the preovulatory follicle [61]. The steroids may also feed back and affect the production of IL-1 from immune cells. Thus it has been shown that larger quantities of IL-1 are secreted from monocytes in peripheral blood isolated during the luteal phase as opposed to the follicular phase [62].

The enzyme 11β-hydroxysteroid dehydrogenase (11β-HSD) is expressed in granulosa cells in either of two isoforms, 11β-HSD-1 and 11β-HSD-2. There is an increase in 11β-HSD-1 expression at the time of ovulation, and it has been proposed that this is one important mechanism to create a local enhancement of the activity of antiinflammatory glucocorticoids by shifting from glucocorticoid inactivation to activation. The expression of 11β-HSD-1 is positively regulated in rat granulosa cells both by LH and IL-1β, with the interaction between them being additive [63].

Extracellular Matrix Remodelling

Prominent changes occur in the ECM during the ovulatory process to allow for site-specific rupture of the follicular wall, extrusion of the oocyte, and simultaneous protection from degradation at inappropriate sites. Degradation of four distinct collagenous layers on the apex of the follicle takes place during ovulation, and this is carried out by coordinated action of a series of proteolytic enzyme systems including the matrix metalloproteinases (MMPs) and plasminogen activators (PAs). The MMPs are zinc-dependent proteinases that are secreted as latent enzymes and are activated in the extracellular space. Plasmin, produced by PA cleavage of plasminogen, is a serine protease that activates latent MMP into active MMP. The four major subclasses of MMPs include collagenases, gelatinases, stromelysins, and membrane-bound MMPs. Gelatinases are important for the breakdown of the ECM in the follicle wall during ovulation because gelatinases are active on both interstitial collagen (in the tunica albuginea and the theca externa) and type IV collagen (in the lamina propria and under the ovarian surface epithelium). The two major gelatinases, a 72 kDa gelatinase (gelatinase A, MMP-2) and a 92 kDa gelatinase (gelatinase B, MMP-9), are present in the ovary at ovulation. In a study on the rat ovary, it was demonstrated that IL-1β produced a selective dose- and cell density-dependent increase in the accumulation of gelatinase B in cultures of whole ovarian dispersates [64]. The gelatinase B activity was more pronounced in theca—interstitial-enriched cultures than in isolated granulosa cell preparations, which further indicates that the expression is in proximity to the presumed action on the type IV collagen of basal membranes and on other ECM proteins.

Follicular production of proteoglycans is an important component of the periovulatory events, both for the final growth of the follicular antrum but also for the mucification of the cumulus granulosa cells. The cumulus mucification, which leads to expansion of the oocyte-cumulus complex, seems to be important for the protrusion of the oocyte through the rupture site because inhibition of hyaluronic acid synthesis at ovulation in mice reduced the ovulation rate by more than 90%, although normal rupture sites appeared [65]. Proteoglycan synthesis in the rat ovary is partly controlled by cytokines, and IL-1 may positively regulate proteoglycan synthesis to promote ovulation. In cultures of whole ovarian dispersates, IL-1β produced substantial increments in the accumulation of hyaluronic acid, heparan sulphate, and dermatan sulphate [66]. The largest IL-1β-induced increase of extracellular and cell-associated proteoglycan accumulation was seen for hyaluronic acid; this increase was effectively blocked by presence of IL-1RA.

The interstitial collagen of the theca externa and tunica albuginea is effectively degraded by MMP-1. Several proteases activate latent MMP-1 into active MMP-1, but a major follicular factor in this context is the PA/plasmin system.

In experiments on incubated preovulatory follicles of the rat [66a], it was shown that LH induced a time-dependent increase in PA activity, which was dose-dependently inhibited by IL-1β. Another study has shown that the PA activity in rat granulosa cells increases after hCG, and that this effect is attenuated by coadministration of IL-1 [67]. In theca-interstitial cells of the rat, a similar reduction in PA activity was seen in the presence of IL-1 [68]. The mechanism for IL-1-suppressed PA activity is at least partly mediated by an increase in PA inhibitor type-1 production [67]. It can be speculated that one role for IL-1 in ovulation would be to maintain control of PA and thereby MMP activation by a regulatory loop that ensures that the proteolysis is limited in extent and distribution so that the apical but not basal part of the follicular wall is degraded.

PROSTAGLANDINS

The prostaglandins are established key mediators in the ovulatory cascade [69, 70]. The ovulatory effect of the PGs is attributable to their effects on the follicular microvasculature to increase permeability and to stimulate MMP synthesis (see Figure 15.2). Studies have shown that follicular rupture is inhibited by pharmacological blockage of PG synthesis. Therefore the nonselective cyclooxygenase (COX)-inhibitor indomethacin [71] and a selective COX-2-inhibitor [72] inhibit or delay ovulation. The antiovulatory effect of these COX-inhibitors may be caused in part by blockade of a late PG-dependent component of ovarian IL-1 action, because indomethacin inhibits COX-2 expression in vitro in culture for 48 hours but not in short-term cultures [73].

The ability of the preovulatory ovary to release PGs in response to IL-1β was first shown in the in vitro perfused rat ovary where IL-1β increased the levels of PGE_2 in the perfusate [54]. The ovarian PG production in response to IL-1β is mainly from the preovulatory follicles, because IL-1β induced a dramatic elevation in production of PGE, $PGF_{2\alpha}$, and prostacyclin in incubated follicles [60]. The effect of IL-1β on PG release was also tested in bovine preovulatory follicles with implanted microdialysis tubing to evaluate tissue secretion [61]. In that study, IL-1β also clearly stimulated PGE release from these explanted bovine preovulatory follicles. A connection between the IL-1 and PG system in the human was first suggested by the existence of a positive correlation between follicular fluid levels of IL-1β and PGs in IVF-patients [74].

The IL-1 system seems to regulate PG production in the follicle by controlling the expression of the two key enzymes PLA_2 and COX-2. Thus the gonadotropin-induced upregulation of the PLA_2 transcript in ovarian cells is blocked by IL-1RA [40]. Furthermore, it was shown that the mRNA levels for PLA_2 were upregulated also by IL-1 with the effect being most pronounced in granulosa cells of periovulatory follicles. Expression of COX-1 and COX-2 are induced by IL-1β in ovarian cells of the rat, with expression of COX-2 being most profound [75]. In the latter study, the capacity for IL-1 to induce COX-2 was low in isolated granulosa or theca cells but markedly higher when they were cocultured, which suggests requirement of heterologous cell-to-cell contacts.

The crucial role for COX-2 in ovulation and its connection with IL-1β was demonstrated in a study with mice carrying null mutation for COX-2 [76]. In this study, mice deficient in COX-2 exhibited few ovulations and abnormal cumulus oophorum expansion was seen. Concurrent treatment with IL-1β or PGE_2 reversed the ovulation numbers, suggesting that IL-1 is downstream of COX-2 in the ovulatory cascade or that COX-2 or IL-1β pathways are partially redundant during ovulation.

Nitric Oxide

NO is a central mediator in the ovulatory process as demonstrated by the ability of NO synthase inhibitors to suppress ovulation in vitro [77] and in vivo [78]. The ovulatory effects of NO are related to its ability to increase (1) vascular permeability [79], (2) leukocyte transmigration to the follicle [78], and (3) ovarian blood flow [80]. A major inducer of NO production in the ovary during the periovulatory period is IL-1β, which in long-term cultures of rat ovarian cells induces expression of inducible NO synthase (iNOS), and thereby increased formation of nitrite [81]. In another study with a similar design, it was demonstrated that IL-1 produces a threefold increase in NO generation and that the effect is abolished by the IL-1RA [68]. The theca layer is the source of NO in the preovulatory follicle because endothelial cell NOS (eNOS) and iNOS are expressed in this compartment [82].

Supportive data shows that IL-1β also acts to generate NO in the human preovulatory follicle. Thus there is a positive correlation between follicular fluid levels of nitrite/nitrate and IL-1β levels, and a dose-dependent amplification of nitrate generation was seen by IL-1β in cultures of human follicular cells from IVF patients [83].

Vascular Changes

There are prominent alterations in the follicular microcirculation during ovulation with the preovulatory LH surge inducing increased blood flow to the follicle [84], redistribution of blood flow to the base of the follicle [85], and increased permeability [86]. The most prominent angiogenic mediator and permeability-inducing factor known today is vascular endothelial growth factor (VEGF). During ovulation in the rat there is a periovulatory increase in VEGF gene expression in theca interstitial cells, and this upregulation is partly dependent on IL-1β [87].

A major event in ovulation is the change in the expression of adhesion molecules in the follicular microcirculation [88], resulting in adherence and transmigration of leukocytes [5, 6]. Leukocytes, in turn, facilitate the ovulatory process [89, 90] possibly by secretion of ECM-degrading enzymes, cytokines, and vascular mediators. Chemokines are instrumental in attracting and activating these leukocytes to the theca layer of the human follicle at ovulation. The chemokines that act on neutrophils [45, 91] and monocytes [92] are abundantly expressed in the preovulatory follicle during ovulation. In the rat, it was shown that the neutrophil chemoattractant (CINC-gro), which belongs to the IL-8 family, is expressed during ovulation and that the CINC-gro protein levels in ovarian dispersates increase 60-fold in response to IL-1β [51].

Mast cells are present mostly in the ovarian medulla and hilus region of the ovary [93], and its preovulatory release of histamine [94] is one of the factors in the ovulatory cascade. IL-1 induces histamine release in the preovulatory rat ovary with a modest effect by itself but with a marked effect [95] in the presence of granulocyte-macrophage colony–stimulating factor (GM-CSF).

CORPUS LUTEUM FUNCTION

The ovulatory follicle is rapidly transformed into a corpus luteum, a tissue with progesterone production as its primary goal. At the transition into a corpus luteum, called *luteinization*, the steroidogenic machinery in the granulosa-lutein and theca-lutein cells are directed toward production of progesterone.

Localization of the Interleukin-1 System in the Corpus Luteum

IL-1β is present and active in the luteinized ovary as shown by its expression in human granulosa lutein cells (Figure 15.4) and in follicular fluid macrophages [96] that are natural components of the corpus luteum tissue. Moreover, bioactivity for IL-1 and IL-1RA is present in conditioned medium of cultured human granulosa lutein cells [97].

In the corpus luteum of the mouse, the luteal cells showed strong immunostaining for IL-1α, IL-1β, and IL-1R1 [13]. The staining intensity for three components of the IL-1 system increased during maturation of the corpus luteum. An upregulation of the IL-1 system during luteinization is also indicated by findings in studies of the rat ovary, where the IL-1R1 and IL-1RA expression was more pronounced in fully active corpus luteum compared with regressing ones [11].

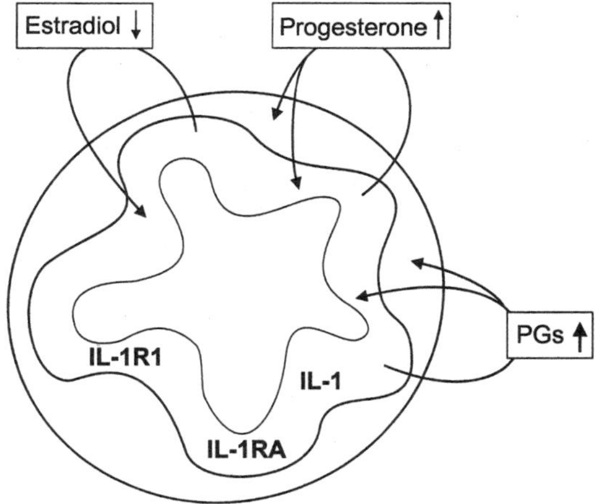

FIGURE 15.4 Distribution of the IL-1 system and its effects on the corpus luteum. Curved arrows indicate effects by IL-1, with the origin of a curved arrow indicating the source of IL-1 and the arrowhead indicating the target for IL-1 for each specific effect. *PGs*, Prostaglandins.

Effects of Interleukin-1 on Corpus Luteum Function

In cultures of human granulosa lutein cells, presence of IL-1RA inhibited hCG-stimulated progesterone release [97a], and another study demonstrated that IL-1α by itself and in combination with LH increased progesterone release [98]. However, IL-1 inhibited estradiol release from human granulosa-lutein cells [97b]. This suggests that IL-1 via an autocrine or paracrine regulatory loop acts to promote progesterone release at the expense of estradiol release.

The IL-1 system is also regulating the production of PGs within the corpus luteum cells. The PGs may have both stimulatory and inhibitory influences on steroid production within the corpus luteum depending on the stage of corpus luteum life. In long-term cultures of bovine luteal cells, presence of IL-1β dose-dependently increased production of the three major PGs [99]. In human granulosa lutein cells, IL-1 increased PGE production by 50% [100]. The effect by IL-1 on luteal PG production seems to be via regulation of COX-2. Therefore IL-1β elevated COX-2 mRNA levels in a concentration-dependent manner in cultured human granulosa-lutein cells, with part of the effect being an IL-1β-mediated inhibition of the degradation of COX-2 mRNA [101]. In the same study it was shown that IL-1β induces expression of mRNA for the $PGF_{2\alpha}$ receptor mRNA.

CONCLUSION

Immune cells and cytokines have been shown to be instrumental in the regulation of folliculogenesis, ovulation, and corpus luteum function. The multifunctional cytokine IL-1 is unique because it has major effects on both functional and structural alteration at all stages of the ovarian cycle. During folliculogenesis, IL-1 promotes proliferation and suppresses differentiation. In the ovulatory process, IL-1 increases the local production of the ecosanoids, steroids, MMPs, and vasoactive substances to promote ovulation. During corpus luteum life, IL-1 acts luteotropic to promote progesterone release.

References

1. Wang, H. Z., et al. (1992). Inhibitory effect of interferon and tumor necrosis factor on human luteal function in vitro. *Fertil. Steril.* 58 (5), 941–945.
2. Jasper, M. J., et al. (1996). Granulocyte-macrophage colony–stimulating factor: Presence in human follicular fluid, protein secretion and mRNA expression by ovarian cells. *Mol. Hum. Reprod.* 2 (8), 555–562.
3. Van der Hoek, K. H., et al. (1998). Effects of interleukin (IL)-6 on luteinizing hormone- and IL-1beta-induced ovulation and steroidogenesis in the rat ovary. *Biol. Reprod.* 58 (5), 1266–1271.
4. Brännström, M., et al. (1995). Effects of tumour necrosis factor alpha (TNF alpha) on ovulation in the rat ovary. *Reprod. Fertil. Dev.* 7 (1), 67–73.
5. Brännström, M., Mayrhofer, G., and Robertson, S. A. (1993). Localization of leukocyte subsets in the rat ovary during the periovulatory period. *Biol. Reprod.* 48 (2), 277–286.
6. Brännström, M., et al. (1994). Localization of leukocyte subsets in the follicle wall and in the corpus luteum throughout the human menstrual cycle. *Fertil. Steril.* 61 (3), 488–495.
7. Gougeon, A. (1996). Regulation of ovarian follicular development in primates: Facts and hypotheses. *Endocr. Rev.* 17 (2), 121–155.
8. Hurwitz, A., et al. (1991). Endocrine- and autocrine-mediated regulation of rat ovarian (theca-interstitial) interleukin-1 beta gene expression: Gonadotropin-dependent preovulatory acquisition. *Endocrinology* 129 (6), 3427–3429.
9. Kol, S., et al. (1999). The rat intraovarian interleukin (IL)-1 system: Cellular localization, cyclic variation and hormonal regulation of IL-1beta and of the type I and type II IL-1 receptors. *Mol. Cell. Endocrinol.* 149 (1–2), 115–128.
10. Scherzer, W. J., et al. (1996). Detection and in vivo hormonal regulation of rat ovarian type I and type II interleukin-I receptor mRNAs: Increased expression during the periovulatory period. *J. Soc. Gynecol. Investig.* 3 (3), 131–139.
11. Wang, L. J., et al. (1997). Localisation of mRNA for interleukin-1 receptor and interleukin-1 receptor antagonist in the rat ovary. J. Endocrinol. 152 (1), 11–17.
12. Kol, S., et al. (1999). Ovarian interleukin-1 receptor antagonist in rats: Gene expression, cellular localization, cyclic variation, and hormonal regulation of a potential determinant of interleukin-1 action. *Biol. Reprod.* 61 (1), 274–282.
13. Simon, C., et al. (1994). Immunohistochemical localization of the interleukin-1 system in the mouse ovary during follicular growth, ovulation, and luteinization. *Biol. Reprod.* 50 (2), 449–457.
14. Hurwitz, A., et al. (1992). Human intraovarian interleukin-1 (IL-1) system: Highly compartmentalized and hormonally dependent regulation of the genes encoding IL-1, its receptor, and its receptor antagonist. *J. Clin. Invest.* 89 (6), 1746–1754.
15. Karakji, E. G., and Tsang, B. K. (1995). Regulation of rat granulosa cell plasminogen activator system: Influence of interleukin-1 beta and ovarian follicular development. *Biol. Reprod.* 53 (6), 1302–1310.
16. Fukuoka, M., et al. (1989). Interleukin-1 stimulates growth and inhibits progesterone secretion in cultures of porcine granulosa cells. *Endocrinology* 124 (2), 884–890.
17. Chun, S. Y., et al. (1995). Interleukin-1 beta suppresses apoptosis in rat ovarian follicles by increasing nitric oxide production. *Endocrinology* 136 (7), 3120–3127.
18. Adashi, E. Y., and Reshick, C. E. (1986). Antagonistic interactions of transforming growth factors in the regulation of granulosa cell differentiation. *Endocrinology* 119 (4), 1879–1881.
19. Derman, S. G., et al. (1999). Transforming growth factor-beta1 is a potent inhibitor of interleukin-1beta action in whole ovarian dispersates. *J. Endocrinol.* 160 (3), 415–423.

20. Motro, B., et al. (1990). Pattern of interleukin 6 gene expression in vivo suggests a role for this cytokine in angiogenesis. *Proc. Natl. Acad. Sci. USA*87 (8), 3092–3096.
21. Chung, K. W., Ando, M., and Adashi, E. Y. (2000). Periovulatory and interleukin (IL)-1-dependent regulation of IL-6 in the immature rat ovary: A specific IL-1 receptor-mediated eicosanoid-dependent effect. *J. Soc. Gynecol. Investig.* 7 (5), 301–308.
22. Kol, S., et al. (1997). The midcycle increase in ovarian glucose uptake is associated with enhanced expression of glucose transporter 3. Possible role for interleukin-1, a putative intermediary in the ovulatory process. *J. Clin. Invest.* 99 (9), 2274–2283.
23. Gottschall, P. E., Katsuura, G., and Arimura, A. (1989). Interleukin-1 beta is more potent than interleukin-1 alpha in suppressing follicle-stimulating hormone-induced differentiation of ovarian granulosa cells. *Biochem. Biophys. Res. Commun.* 163 (2), 764–770.
24. Kasson, B. G., and Gorospe, W. C. (1989). Effects of interleukins 1, 2 and 3 on follicle-stimulating hormone-induced differentiation of rat granulosa cells. *Mol. Cell. Endocrinol.* 62 (1), 103–111.
25. Donesky, B. W., et al. (1998). Interleukin-1beta inhibits steroidogenic bioactivity in cultured rat ovarian granulosa cells by stimulation of progesterone degradation and inhibition of estrogen formation. *Biol. Reprod.* 58 (5), 1108–1116.
26. Rivier, C., and Vale, W. (1989). In the rat, interleukin-1 alpha acts at the level of the brain and the gonads to interfere with gonadotropin and sex steroid secretion. *Endocrinology* 124 (5), 2105–2109.
27. Fukuoka, M., et al. (1988). Interleukin-1 inhibits luteinization of porcine granulosa cells in culture. *Endocrinology* 122 (1), 367–369.
28. Gottschall, P. E., et al. (1987). Interleukin-1 inhibits follicle stimulating hormone-induced differentiation in rat granulosa cells in vitro. *Biochem. Biophys. Res. Commun.* 149 (2), 502–509.
29. Hurwitz, A., et al. (1991). Cytokine-mediated regulation of ovarian function: Interleukin-1 inhibits gonadotropin-induced androgen biosynthesis. *Endocrinology* 129 (3), 1250–1256.
30. Corwin, E. J., and Cannon, J. G. (1999). Gonadotropin modulation of interleukin-1 secretion. *J. Gend. Specif. Med.* 2 (6), 30–34.
31. Kol, S., et al. (1997). Insulin-like growth factor I affects the intraovarian interleukin-1 system: Evidence for suppression of type I interleukin-1 receptor expression and enhancement of secretory phospholipase A2 expression and activity. *Mol. Hum. Reprod.* 3 (12), 1095–1099.
32. Schreiber, J. R., Nakamura, K., and Erickson, G. F. (1982). Rat ovary glucocorticoid receptor: Identification and characterization. *Steroids* 39 (5), 569–584.
33. Hsueh, A. J., and Erickson, G. F. (1978). Glucocorticoid inhibition of FSH-induced estrogen production in cultured rat granulosa cells. *Steroids* 32 (5), 639–648.
34. Schoonmaker, J. N., and Erickson, G. F. (1983). Glucocorticoid modulation of follicle-stimulating hormone-mediated granulosa cell differentiation. *Endocrinology* 113 (4), 1356–1363.
35. Irahara, M., et al. (1999). Glucocorticoid receptor-mediated post-ceramide inhibition of the interleukin-1beta-dependent induction of ovarian prostaglandin endoperoxide synthase-2 in rats. *Biol. Reprod.* 60 (4), 946–953.
36. Gottschall, P. E., et al. (1988). Interleukin 1: An inhibitor of luteinizing hormone receptor formation in cultured rat granulosa cells. *FASEB J.* 2 (9), 2492–2496.
37. Li, J., and Tsang, B. K. (1995). Prostaglandins mediate the stimulation of deoxyribonucleic acid synthesis by transforming growth factor alpha in hen granulosa cells during ovarian follicular development. *Biol. Reprod.* 52 (5), 1050–1058.
38. Johnson, S. K., et al. (1992). Role of prostaglandin F2 alpha in follicular development and subsequent luteal life span in early postpartum beef cows. *Domest. Anim. Endocrinol.* 9 (1), 49–56.
39. Kokia, E., et al. (1992). Interleukin-1 stimulates ovarian prostaglandin biosynthesis: Evidence for heterologous contact-independent cell-cell interaction. *Endocrinology* 130 (5), 3095–3057.
40. Ben-Shlomo, I., et al. (1997). Ovarian expression, cellular localization, and hormonal regulation of rat secretory phospholipase A2: Increased expression by interleukin-1 and by gonadotropins. *Biol. Reprod.* 57 (2), 217–225.
41. Espey, L. L., Tanaka, N., and Okamura, H. (1989). Increase in ovarian leukotrienes during hormonally induced ovulation in the rat. *Am. J. Physiol.* 256 (6 Pt 1), E753–E759.
42. Andersen, A. G., et al. (1995). Time interval from human chorionic gonadotrophin (HCG) injection to follicular rupture. *Hum. Reprod.* 10 (12), 3202–3205.
43. Matousek, M., et al. (2001). Inhibition of ovulation in the rat by a leukotriene B(4) receptor antagonist. *Mol. Hum. Reprod.* 7 (1), 35–42.
44. Runesson, E., et al. (1996). The human preovulatory follicle is a source of the chemotactic cytokine interleukin-8. *Mol. Hum. Reprod.* 2 (4), 245–250.
45. Karstrom-Encrantz, L., et al. (1998). Selective presence of the chemokine growth-regulated oncogene alpha (GROalpha) in the human follicle and secretion from cultured granulosa-lutein cells at ovulation. *Mol. Hum. Reprod.* 4 (11), 1077–1083.
46. Wang, L. J., and Norman, R. J. (1992). Concentrations of immunoreactive interleukin-1 and interleukin-2 in human preovulatory follicular fluid. *Hum. Reprod.* 7 (2), 147–150.
47. Bili, H., et al. (1998). Cytokines in the human ovary: Presence in follicular fluid and correlation with leukotriene B4. *J. Assist. Reprod. Genet.* 15 (2), 93–98.
48. Matousek, M., et al. (2001). Novel method for intrafollicular pressure measurements in the rat ovary: Increased intrafollicular pressure after hCG stimulation. *Reproduction* 121 (2), 307–314.
49. Loret de Mola, J. R., et al. (1998). Gonadotropins induce the release of interleukin-1 beta, interleukin-6 and tumor necrosis factor-alpha from the human preovulatory follicle. *Am. J. Reprod. Immunol.* 39 (6), 387–390.
50. Ono, M., et al. (1997). Role of interleukin-1beta in superovulation in rats. *Endocr. J.* 44 (6), 797–804.
51. Ushigoe, K., et al. (2000). Production and regulation of cytokine-induced neutrophil chemoattractant in rat ovulation. *Biol. Reprod.* 63 (1), 121–126.

52. Takehara, Y., et al. (1994). Effect of interleukin-1 beta on ovulation in the in vitro perfused rabbit ovary. *Endocrinology* 134 (4), 1788–1793.
53. Brännström, M., Wang, L., and Norman, R. J. (1993). Ovulatory effect of interleukin-1 beta on the perfused rat ovary. *Endocrinology* 132 (1), 399–404.
54. Peterson, C. M., et al. (1993). Interleukin-1 beta (IL-1 beta) modulates prostaglandin production and the natural IL-1 receptor antagonist inhibits ovulation in the optimally stimulated rat ovarian perfusion model. *Endocrinology* 133 (5), 2301–2306.
55. Simon, C., et al. (1994). Interleukin-1 receptor antagonist suppresses human chorionic gonadotropin-induced ovulation in the rat. *Biol. Reprod.* 51 (4), 662–667.
56. Ujioka, T., et al. (1998). Analysis of the cytokine interaction among interleukin-1beta, interleukin-8, and interleukin-1 receptor antagonist in the rabbit ovulatory process. *Fertil. Steril.* 70 (4), 759–765.
57. Brännström, M., and Janson, P. O. (1989). Progesterone is a mediator in the ovulatory process of the in vitro-perfused rat ovary. *Biol. Reprod.* 40 (6), 1170–1178.
58. Lydon, J. P., et al. (1995). Mice lacking progesterone receptor exhibit pleiotropic reproductive abnormalities. *Genes Dev.* 9 (18), 2266–2278.
58a. Brännström, M., Mikuni, M., Peterson, C. M. (1996). Ovulation-associated intraovarian events. In *The Ovary, Regulation, Dysfunction, and Treatment* (eds. Filcori, M., Flamigni, C.) Amsterdam: Elsevier Science, pp. 113–123.
59. Nakamura, Y., Kato, H., and Terranova, P. F. (1990). Interleukin-1 alpha increases thecal progesterone production of preovulatory follicles in cyclic hamsters. *Biol. Reprod.* 43 (2), 169–173.
60. Brännström, M., Wang, L., and Norman, R. J. (1993). Effects of cytokines on prostaglandin production and steroidogenesis of incubated preovulatory follicles of the rat. *Biol. Reprod.* 48 (1), 165–171.
61. Acosta, T. J., et al. (1998). Local release of steroid hormones, prostaglandin E2, and endothelin-1 from bovine mature follicles in vitro: Effects of luteinizing hormone, endothelin-1, and cytokines. *Biol. Reprod.* 59 (2), 437–443.
62. Polan, M. L., et al. (1990). Cultured human luteal peripheral monocytes secrete increased levels of interleukin-1. *J. Clin. Endocrinol. Metab.* 70 (2), 480–484.
63. Tetsuka, M., et al. (1999). Regulation of 11beta-hydroxysteroid dehydrogenase type 1 gene expression by LH and interleukin-1beta in cultured rat granulosa cells. *J. Endocrinol.* 163 (3), 417–423.
64. Hurwitz, A., et al. (1993). Cytokine-mediated regulation of rat ovarian function: Interleukin-1 stimulates the accumulation of a 92-kilodalton gelatinase. *Endocrinology* 132 (6), 2709–2714.
65. Chen, L., Russell, P. T., and Larsen, W. J. (1993). Functional significance of cumulus expansion in the mouse: Roles for the preovulatory synthesis of hyaluronic acid within the cumulus mass. *Mol. Reprod. Dev.* 34 (1), 87–93.
66. Kokia, E., et al. (1993). Receptor-mediated stimulatory effect of IL-1 beta on hyaluronic acid and proteoglycan biosynthesis by cultured rat ovarian cells: Role for heterologous cell-cell interactions. *Endocrinology* 133 (5), 2391–2394.
66a. Bonello, N. P., Norman, R. J., Brännström, M. (1995). Interleukin-1β inhibits luteinizing bormone-induced plasminogen activator activity in rat preovulatory follicles in vitro. *Endocrine*. 3, 49–54.
67. Hurwitz, A., et al. (1995). Interleukin-1-mediated regulation of plasminogen activation in pregnant mare serum gonadotropin-primed rat granulosa cells is independent of prostaglandin production. *J. Soc. Gynecol. Investig.* 2 (5), 691–699.
68. Hurwitz, A., et al. (1997). In vitro modulation of plasminogen activator activity, prostaglandin E and nitric oxide production by interleukin-1 in pregnant mare serum gonadotrophin-primed theca-interstitial cells. *Hum. Reprod.* 12 (4), 774–779.
69. Brännström, M., et al. (1989). Regulation of prostaglandin endoperoxide synthase by cyclic adenosine 3′,5′-monophosphate in the in vitro-perfused rat ovary. *Biol. Reprod.* 41 (3), 513–521.
70. Hellberg, P., and Brännström, M. (1990). A prostacyclin analogue, iloprost, augments the ovulatory response of the LH-stimulated in vitro perfused rat ovary. *Prostaglandins* 40 (4), 361–371.
71. Murdoch, W. J. (1996). Differential effects of indomethacin on the sheep ovary: Prostaglandin biosynthesis, intracellular calcium, apoptosis, and ovulation. *Prostaglandins* 52 (6), 497–506.
72. Pall, M., Friden, B. E., and Brännström, M. (2001). Induction of delayed follicular rupture in the human by the selective COX-2 inhibitor rofecoxib: A randomized double-blind study. *Hum. Reprod.* 16 (7), 1323–1328.
73. Ando, M., et al. Non-steroidal anti-inflammatory drugs (NSAIDs) block the late, prostanoid-dependent/ceramide-independent component of ovarian IL-1 action: Implications for the ovulatory process. *Mol. Cell. Endocrinol.* (1999). 157 (1–2), 21–30.
74. Watanabe, H., et al. (1994). Concentration of interleukin-1 beta correlates with prostaglandin E2 and F2 alpha in human pre-ovulatory follicular fluid. *Hum. Reprod.* 9 (1), 9–12.
75. Ando, M., et al. (1998). Rat ovarian prostaglandin endoperoxide synthase-1 and -2: Periovulatory expression of granulosa cell-based interleukin-1-dependent enzymes. *Endocrinology* 139 (5), 2501–2508.
76. Davis, B. J., et al. (1999). Anovulation in cyclooxygenase-2-deficient mice is restored by prostaglandin E2 and interleukin-1beta. *Endocrinology* 140 (6), 2685–2695.
77. Mitsube, K., et al. (1999). Effects of a nitric oxide donor and nitric oxide synthase inhibitors on luteinizing hormone-induced ovulation in the ex-vivo perfused rat ovary. *Hum. Reprod.* 14 (10), 2537–2543.
78. Bonello, N., et al. (1996). Inhibition of nitric oxide: Effects on interleukin-1 beta-enhanced ovulation rate, steroid hormones, and ovarian leukocyte distribution at ovulation in the rat. *Biol. Reprod.* 54 (2), 436–445.
79. Hess, K. A., Chen, L., and Larsen, W. J. (1998). The ovarian blood follicle barrier is both charge- and size-selective in mice. *Biol. Reprod.* 58 (3), 705–711.
80. Mitsube, K., Zackrisson, U., and Brännström, M. (2002). Nitric oxide regulates ovarian blood flow in the rat during the periovulatory period. *Hum. Reprod.* 17 (10), 2509–2516.

81. Ellman, C., et al. (1993). Nitric oxide mediates interleukin-1-induced cellular cytotoxicity in the rat ovary. A potential role for nitric oxide in the ovulatory process. *J. Clin. Invest.* 92 (6), 3053–3056.
82. Zackrisson, U., et al. (1996). Cell-specific localization of nitric oxide synthases (NOS) in the rat ovary during follicular development, ovulation and luteal formation. *Hum. Reprod.* 11 (12), 2667–2673.
83. Tao, M., et al. (1997). Possible contribution of follicular interleukin-1beta to nitric oxide generation in human preovulatory follicles. *Hum. Reprod.* 12 (10), 2220–2225.
84. Janson, P. O. (1975). Effects of the luteinizing hormone on blood flow in the follicular rabbit ovary, as measured by radioactive microspheres. *Acta. Endocrinol. (Copenh)* 79 (1), 122–133.
85. Brännström, M., et al. (1998). Preovulatory changes of blood flow in different regions of the human follicle. *Fertil. Steril.* 69 (3), 435–442.
86. Abisogun, A. O., et al. (1988). Modulatory role of eicosanoids in vascular changes during the preovulatory period in the rat. *Biol. Reprod.* 38 (4), 756–762.
87. Levitas, E., et al. (2000). Periovulatory and interleukin-1 beta-dependent up-regulation of intraovarian vascular endothelial growth factor (VEGF) in the rat: Potential role for VEGF in the promotion of periovulatory angiogenesis and vascular permeability. *J. Soc. Gynecol. Investig.* 7 (1), 51–60.
88. Vigano, P., et al. (1998). Soluble intercellular adhesion molecule-1 in ovarian follicles: Production by granulosa luteal cells and levels in follicular fluid. *Fertil. Steril.* 69 (4), 774–779.
89. Hellberg, P., et al. (1991). Leukocyte supplementation increases the luteinizing hormone-induced ovulation rate in the in vitro-perfused rat ovary. *Biol. Reprod.* 44 (5), 791–797.
90. Brännström, M., et al. (1995). Reduction of ovulation rate in the rat by administration of a neutrophil-depleting monoclonal antibody. *J. Reprod. Immunol.* 29 (3), 265–270.
91. Runesson, E., et al. (2000). Gonadotropin- and cytokine-regulated expression of the chemokine interleukin 8 in the human preovulatory follicle of the menstrual cycle. *J. Clin. Endocrinol. Metab.* 85 (11), 4387–4395.
92. Arici, A., et al. (1997). Monocyte chemotactic protein-1 expression in human preovulatory follicles and ovarian cells. *J. Reprod. Immunol.* 32 (3), 201–219.
93. Jones, R. E., Duvall, D., and Guillette, Jr., L. J. (1980). Rat ovarian mast cells: Distribution and cyclic changes. *Anat. Rec.* 197 (4), 489–493.
94. Schmidt, G., Owman, C., and Sjoberg, N. O. (1988). Cellular localization of ovarian histamine, its cyclic variations, and histaminergic effects on ovulation in the rat ovary perfused in vitro. *J. Reprod. Fertil.* 82 (2), 409–417.
95. Tamura, K., and Kogo, H. (1999). Granulocyte-macrophage colony–stimulating factor enhances interleukin-1beta stimulated histamine release in the preovulatory rat ovary. *Eur. J. Pharmacol.* 373 (2–3), 207–213.
96. Machelon, V., et al. (1995). Macrophage and granulosa interleukin-1 beta mRNA in human ovulatory follicles. *Hum. Reprod.* 10 (8), 2198–2203.
97. Barak, V., et al. (1992). Interleukin-1: Local production and modulation of human granulosa luteal cells steroidogenesis. *Fertil. Steril.* 58 (4), 719–725.
97a. Barak, W., et al. (1992). Interleukin-1: local production and modulation of human granulosa luteal cells steroido genesis. *Fertil. Steril.* 58 (4), 884–890.
98. Sjogren, A., Holmes, P. V., and Hillensjo, T. (1991). Interleukin-1 alpha modulates luteinizing hormone stimulated cyclic AMP and progesterone release from human granulosa cells in vitro. *Hum. Reprod.* 6 (7), 910–913.
99. Nothnick, W. B., and Pate, J. L. (1990). Interleukin-1 beta is a potent stimulator of prostaglandin synthesis in bovine luteal cells. *Biol. Reprod.* 43 (5), 898–903.
100. Hurwitz, A., et al. (1995). Interleukin-1-mediated stimulation of prostaglandin E production is without effect on plasminogen activator activity in human granulosa lutein cell cultures. *J. Clin. Endocrinol. Metab.* 80 (10), 3018–3024.
101. Narko, K., Ritvos, O., and Ristimaki, A. (1997). Induction of cyclooxygenase-2 and prostaglandin F2alpha receptor expression by interleukin-1beta in cultured human granulosa-luteal cells. *Endocrinology* 138 (9), 3638–3644.

CHAPTER **16**

Activin, Inhibin, and Follistatin in Ovarian Physiology

STACEY C. CHAPMAN, HILARY A. KENNY, AND TERESA K. WOODRUFF

INTRODUCTION

Activin and inhibin are members of the transforming growth factor-β (TGF-β) superfamily of ligands, which also includes the bone morphogenic proteins (BMPs), müllerian inhibiting substance (MIS; antimüllerian hormone [AMH]), and growth differentiation factor 9 (GDF-9) [1]. Members of this family are assembled from large precursor proteins that are processed and assembled into mature dimers containing a common cysteine-knot motif [2]. The activins are dimers of two β-subunits, βA or βB, assembled into three possible activin dimers: activin A (βAβA), activin B (βBβB), or activin AB (βAβB). The inhibins are heterodimers of one activin β-subunit complexed to a unique α-subunit to produce two isoforms of inhibin: inhibin A (αβA) and inhibin B (αβB). Within the normal female reproductive axis, the inhibins act at two main sites: the pituitary gonadotrope and the ovary [3]. The inhibin α-subunit and mature inhibin dimers are exclusively produced by the granulosa cells of the ovary, whereas the β-subunits and activins are produced by and have actions on a large variety of tissues, including the ovary, the pituitary, the placenta, nervous tissue, and mammary tissue [4]. Activins and inhibins were first identified as opposing nonsteroidal gonadal hormones that regulate follicle-stimulating hormone (FSH) synthesis and secretion from the gonadotrope [5, 6]. Since their initial discovery, the activins and inhibins have also been characterized as paracrine acting factors within the ovary, where they modulate follicle growth and steroidogenesis [7–9]. The actions of activin are regulated in part by the activin-binding protein, follistatin, which sequesters activin and initiates its degradation [10–13]. Follistatin is produced in many of the same tissues as activin and regulates local paracrine and autocrine actions of activin in these tissues. In addition, the majority of circulating activin is bound by follistatin, suggesting that many, if not all, of activin's actions are paracrine or autocrine in nature [14–16]. This is in contrast to inhibin, which acts as a traditional endocrine hormone between the ovary and the pituitary, in addition to having local effects within the ovary.

GONADAL REGULATION OF ACTIVIN, INHIBIN, AND FOLLISTATIN

FSH regulates the expression of inhibin and activin subunits in the ovary. Accordingly, inhibin serum levels initially rise at and throughout puberty, when gonadotropin levels initially increase [17]. Inhibin A concentrations within the follicular fluid and the bloodstream fluctuate in parallel with estrogen throughout the estrous and menstrual cycles [18–24]. In the rat, the secondary FSH surge stimulates inhibin A expression, and the highest concentration of inhibin in the ovary and serum is detected when follicles are fully mature. Tissue and serum inhibin A then rapidly decline following the primary FSH surge, reaching a nadir that is inversely correlated to FSH [24–27]. Inhibin B is also made in response to FSH but reaches peak levels in the early follicular phase. Inhibin A and inhibin B follow similar trends following the midcycle FSH rise and during the late follicular phase of the menstrual cycle. Inhibins drop concurrent with the primary gonadotropin surge [23]. Additionally, the human corpus luteum (CL) produces inhibin A, but the regulation of this ligand in this ovarian compartment is not fully understood.

It is important to note that the inhibin α-subunit is consistently detected at higher levels than the β-subunits in the granulosa cells of healthy growing follicles, and although this suggests the preferential formation of inhibin αβ dimers, activin ββ dimers may also be assembled. In rats, inhibin α-, βA-, and βB-subunit messenger ribonucleic acid (mRNA) and protein are expressed in the granulosa cells of recruited follicles, and expression increases with follicle growth [28, 29]. In humans, α-subunit and protein is detected in the granulosa cells of growing follicles and in luteinized granulosa cells during the human menstrual cycle [30, 31]. Whereas α-subunit mRNA is expressed in the thecal cell layer of both small antral and dominant follicles, α-subunit protein is undetectable. Both βA- and βB-subunit mRNA and protein are expressed in the granulosa cells of small antral follicles; however, dominant follicles express primarily the βA-subunit.

The inhibin and activin subunits are differentially regulated by FSH and luteinizing hormone (LH) at the transcriptional level within the ovary. The gonadotropins, FSH and LH, bind to specific G-coupled protein receptors on follicular granulosa and thecal cells and stimulate adenyl cyclase activity and cyclic adenosine monophosphate (cAMP) production. In addition, LH receptor (LHR) can stimulate the phospholipase C (PLC) pathway [32]. Examination of the 5′ promoter region of the rat inhibin α-subunit reveals a cAMP-responsive element (CRE), and transient transfection of the α-subunit promoter connected to a luciferase reporter gene into rat granulosa cells confirmed its responsiveness to cAMP [33, 34]. Paradoxically, inhibin subunit and protein expression drops sharply at the gonadotropin surge, when supraphysiological levels of intracellular cAMP are stimulated in the follicle by the combined FSH and LH surges [26]. It was found that high levels of cAMP induce the expression of a transcriptional repressor, inducible cAMP early repressor (ICER), which inhibits α-subunit expression [35]. During the secondary FSH surge, when cAMP levels are lower, ICER is not expressed and inhibin subunit expression rebounds. Thus the relative levels of intracellular cAMP determine the degree of α-subunit expression and inhibin protein production.

Human and rat βA-subunit transcription is also upregulated by cAMP, in addition to phorbol esters and AP-1, indicating that the protein kinase C (PKC) signaling pathway is also involved in the regulation of this subunit [36–38]. It has been proposed that LH signaling through the PLC/PKC pathway may be responsible for βA-subunit expression. In contrast, the βB-subunit promoter does not contain a canonical CRE, and reporter constructs of the rat βB-subunit promoter are not responsive to cAMP when transfected into a granulosa cell line [39]. Both activin and TGF-β have been shown to upregulate βB-subunit expression [40–42], and more recently, BMP-2 was shown to selectively increase βB-subunit expression and inhibin B dimer secretion in cultured granulosa cells [43, 44]. In addition, members of the GATA family of transcription factors are selectively involved in βB-subunit transcription [45, 46].

Although expression of all inhibin subunits and secretion of inhibin A and B increase following the secondary FSH surge, the circulating levels of each inhibin isoform quickly diverge during metestrus and diestrus such that inhibin B exceeds inhibin A until the morning of proestrus [24]. Similarly, serum inhibin B is elevated compared with that of inhibin A following the intercycle FSH rise in humans [23, 47]. Inhibin A slowly increases throughout the early follicular phase and peaks with inhibin B just before the gonadotropin surge, at which time the levels of both isoforms fall rapidly to basal levels. It is believed that the differences in inhibin isoform expression are a reflection of follicle size: inhibin B is expressed mainly by newly recruited, small antral follicles and therefore is elevated during the early follicular phase, whereas inhibin A is produced by large, dominant follicles later in the follicular phase. This switch from inhibin B to inhibin A secretion correlates to the simultaneous increase in βA-subunit and decrease in βB-subunit expression observed in dominant follicles in the human ovary [31]. It has also been suggested that the switch from βB- to βA-subunit expression may occur in response to rising LH, which is capable of activating either the protein kinase A (PKA) or PLC pathways. PLC activates inositol triphosphate (IP3) and diacylglycerol (DAG), the latter of which goes on to activate PKC. Thus LHR-activated PKC may be responsible for stimulating inhibin A in large follicles [32]. It has been more difficult to determine differences in the expression patterns of βA- and βB-subunits in the rodent. All three subunits are expressed in identical follicle types, which suggests that biosynthesis, assembly, or secretion of inhibin A and inhibin B are also differentially regulated. The functional differences between the two inhibin isoforms have been difficult to ascertain.

The differential expression of the β-subunits and secretion of inhibin protein by the ovary during the follicular phase suggests that inhibin A and inhibin B play distinct roles in the hypothalamic-pituitary-gonadal (HPG) axis. Inhibin B is negatively correlated with FSH through the follicular phase of the estrus and menstrual cycles, whereas inhibin A correlates positively with estradiol [23, 24]. The relative effects of the inhibin A and inhibin B isoforms on FSH regulation in vivo is currently unknown. Interestingly, the only detectable isoform of circulating inhibin in male rats and primates is inhibin B [24, 48], and it displays a tight negative correlation with circulating FSH levels [49].

MOLECULAR MECHANISMS AND REGULATION OF ACTIVIN AND INHIBIN SIGNAL TRANSDUCTION

Activin, like most members of the TGF-β superfamily, signals through a heteromeric serine-threonine receptor complex comprised of a type II ligand binding receptor and a type I signal transducing receptor [1]. Activin directly binds to one of two type II receptors, ActRIIA or ActRIIB, which triggers the transphosphorylation of the activin type I receptor, activin-like kinase IB (ActRIB or ALK4). Transphosphorylation of ALK4 occurs within a glycine- and serine-rich domain (GS domain) that lies close to the inner surface of the cell membrane. The phosphorylated, activated activin type I receptor propagates the activin signal by phosphorylating the intracellular transducers, called Smads [1]. The Smad proteins are classified into three functional groups: (1) the receptor-regulated Smads (R-Smads), (2) the common mediator Smad (co-Smad), and (3) the inhibitory Smads (I-Smads). Some degree of signaling specificity by members of the TGF-β superfamily, including activin, is achieved at the level of the type I receptor and the R-Smads [1]. Ligand-specific R-Smads are directly phosphorylated on a C-terminal serine-rich domain by individual activated type I receptors. Activin signals are transduced inside the cell on phosphorylation of Smad2 or Smad3 by activated ALK4. TGF-β also stimulates the phosphorylation of Smad2 and Smad3 by its type I receptor, ALK5. How a cell distinguishes between TGF-β/ALK5 and activin/ALK4-stimulated Smad2 and Smad3 is not fully understood. Once phosphorylated, R-Smads associate with the co-Smad, Smad4, and the complex translocates to the nucleus where it acts as a transcriptional cofactor [1]. Smad action is modulated by the interaction with a variety of transcription factors at target deoxyribonucleic acid (DNA) promoters [50]. Interference with normal phosphorylation and translocation of the R-Smads is mediated by the I-Smads, Smad6 and Smad7. Transcription of the I-Smads is stimulated by both activin and TGF-β, which provides a mechanism for self-regulation of TGF-β superfamily signal transduction [51].

Activin-stimulated FSH synthesis and secretion in the pituitary is opposed by gonadal inhibin and locally produced follistatin. Both secreted or membrane-bound forms of follistatin bind and sequester activin such that it can not bind to its receptors or initiate signaling [52]. The mechanism by which inhibin antagonizes activin action is not fully understood, and at least four mechanisms have been proposed to date. First, inhibin shares a common β-subunit with activin. Thus, in cases where the inhibin α-subunit is produced in excess of the β-subunit, the assembly of inhibin dimers is favored over activin dimers, thereby attenuating activin signal transduction. Because the majority of inhibin α-subunit is produced in the granulosa cells of the ovary, this mechanism of antagonism would most likely regulate the paracrine effects of activin within this tissue. Second, inhibin is able to bind to the activin type II receptors, albeit at a much lower affinity than activin [53–55]. Excess inhibin from the ovary could compete with activin for binding to its own receptor and functionally antagonize endocrine and paracrine activin signaling.

However, in some cases, extremely high levels of inhibin are unable to antagonize activin signaling; for example, inhibin is unable to antagonize activin-stimulated apoptosis in hepatocytes or activin-suppressed adrenocorticotropin hormone from the AtT20 corticotrope cell line [56, 57]. This has lead to the suggestion that an inhibin binding coreceptor or accessory protein is necessary to increase inhibin affinity for the activin receptor or to disrupt activin receptor complex formation, thereby abrogating activin signaling. In contrast to other members of the TGF-β superfamily, no inhibin-specific receptor has been identified to date, though several high-affinity, high-specificity inhibin binding sites have been identified in the ovary, the testis, and the pituitary [58–63]. Recently, the TGF-β type III receptor, betaglycan, has been shown to bind inhibin A and inhibin B and increase their affinities for both activin type II receptor isoforms [64–66]. In addition, inhibin A forms a complex with betaglycan and the activin type IIA receptor that cannot be competed with activin, thus providing a mechanism for antagonism of activin signaling by inhibin.

Finally, inhibin action is not always in opposition to that of activin. For example, inhibin and activin both stimulate primate oocyte maturation in vitro and the expression of the steroidogenic enzyme cytochrome p450c$_{17\alpha}$ and the LH receptor in Leydig's cells [67, 68]. These data argue for the existence of an inhibin receptor that is capable of transducing a signal and cellular response independently of activin. It has been hypothesized that intracellular signaling proteins stimulated by an inhibin receptor would be able to antagonize activin signals downstream of the activin receptor complex. For instance, an inhibin signal may activate inhibitory Smad6 and Smad7, which would, in turn, interfere with activin-stimulated Smad2 and Smad3 activation. Alternatively, Smad proteins are targets of the mitogen-activated protein kinases (MAPKs), which negatively regulate R-Smad activity [69]. Activation of the MAPK cascade or other, as yet unidentified, signal transduction cascade by inhibin may lead to either antagonism of activin action or may mediate a direct inhibin-regulated cellular response.

INHIBIN AND ACTIVIN EXPRESSION AND ACTION IN THE PITUITARY

Early studies of FSH secretion by the pituitary suggested the existence of a nonsteroidal, gonadally-derived hormone that inhibits FSH [70]. With time, it was demonstrated that porcine follicular fluid selectively inhibits FSH, but not LH, secretion in rats in vivo [71, 72] and that ovariectomized rats exhibit elevated FSH levels but normal LH levels [20, 73]. This lead to the characterization of a gonadally-derived peptide, inhibin, that specifically inhibits pituitary FSH secretion [74, 75]. Injection of rats with recombinant human inhibin results in a selective decrease in plasma FSH levels [76–79], whereas passive immunoneutralization of inhibin leads to a rise in FSHβ-subunit expression [73, 80]. Inhibin treatment of cultured rat pituitary cells also results in the reduction of FSHβ-subunit expression and FSH secretion and is the basis of current inhibin bioassays [5].

Within the reproductive axis, inhibin works in concert with gonadotropin-releasing hormone (GnRH) and estrogen to tightly regulate FSH secretion [11]. After the secondary FSH surge (or the intercycle FSH rise), serum inhibin slowly rises through the early follicular phase of the cycle and maintains basal FSH levels [24, 26]. The continual inhibition of FSH release by inhibin during metestrus and diestrus prevents an otherwise slow, unchecked rise in serum FSH throughout the early part of the cycle. At the point when estrogen concentrations and GnRH pulse frequency peak, the negative feedback of inhibin on the pituitary is overwhelmed and permits a sharp, dramatic rise in FSH and LH.

Stimulation of FSH release is influenced by a protein closely related to inhibin, aptly named activin [81, 82]. In vitro, activin stimulates FSHβ-subunit expression and stability and upregulates FSH release from perifused rat pituitary tissues [5, 6, 83]. Injection of rats and primates with recombinant human activin results in a GnRH-independent rise in FSH levels [15, 84]. Activin is produced in a variety of tissues [25, 85], including the ovary and the pituitary; however, the majority of circulating activin is bound to the carrier protein follistatin and is inactive [16]. Accordingly, it is widely believed that activin produced within the anterior pituitary is responsible for autocrine stimulation of FSH in conjunction with hypothalamic GnRH [14, 15, 86, 87]. Activin action in the pituitary is opposed by locally produced follistatin in addition to gonadal inhibin. In vivo, follistatin levels negatively correlate with free activin, FSHβ subunit mRNA expression, and serum FSH concentrations [11], and overexpression of follistatin interferes with activin-stimulated FSH secretion in cultured rat anterior pituitary cells [13].

In the rat, α-subunit protein has been localized to the gonadotropes of the anterior pituitary, whereas the βB-subunit is ubiquitously expressed throughout the anterior, intermediate, and posterior pituitary [86]. Cultured pituitary cells synthesize primarily βB-subunit and secrete activin B [88]. Follistatin is also produced by the pituitary and fluctuates throughout the estrus cycle in rats [89]. In addition, it was recently demonstrated that inhibitory Smad7 is upregulated by activin and negatively modulates activin-stimulated gene expression in pituitary cell lines [90]. Together, these data further support the hypothesis that locally produced activin, specifically activin B, and follistatin contribute to FSH regulation during the reproductive cycle.

INHIBIN AND ACTIVIN EXPRESSION AND ACTION IN THE OVARY

Although inhibin and activin were initially characterized as modulators of FSH synthesis and secretion by anterior pituitary gonadotropes, they are now considered to be "multicrine" hormones that have additional paracrine and autocrine functions in the ovary [7–9]. In general, the majority of studies investigating inhibin and activin action in the ovary are descriptive of subunit expression and protein localization as indicators of ovarian health. Far fewer studies have elucidated the mechanism or significance of these effects in the ovary.

At Puberty

In human female neonates, inhibin levels increase in concert with the postnatal rise in gonadotropins, then subside until late prepuberty [91]. Inhibin A levels decrease to undetectable levels within 2 months after birth, whereas inhibin B levels decrease to detectable but low prepubertal levels by 6 months of life. It is not until several years before puberty that inhibin B levels rise again, indicating the resumption of ovarian cell activity. It is unclear whether this prepubertal increase in inhibin is gonadotropin dependent, because inhibin B levels begin to rise throughout early puberty, even before the first gonadotropin-stimulated ovulation. Inhibin B peaks at midpuberty and then plateaus, possibly reflecting the increasing number of growing ovarian follicles during this time. In contrast, inhibin A secretion begins only after the development and maintenance of full, ovulatory menstrual cycles, concomitant with the onset of the first proper LH surge and the first luteal phase [91]. This secretion pattern is consistent with the observation that βB-subunit (and inhibin B) is primarily produced by small antral follicles and βA-subunit (and inhibin A) by more developed, large antral follicles. [92, 93].

The effects of activin during puberty are less clear. Because the ovary produces far greater levels of the α-subunit, and thus inhibin dimers, the ovarian expression levels of the βA- or βB-subunits are not indicative of activin levels. Serum follistatin levels are at their highest during midpuberty, and then decrease in later puberty; all follistatin detected at these times is bound to activin [94]. Although these observations argue that activin signal transduction during puberty is most likely inhibited by either inhibin, follistatin, or both, the possibility that autocrine or paracrine signaling by any "free" activin in the follicle is occurring can not be ruled out. In vitro, preantral follicles from immature mice respond to activin, but not FSH, with a significant increase in follicle size, whereas growth of preantral follicles from adult mice is stimulated by FSH but not activin [95, 96]. These data suggest a mechanism of activin-stimulated early follicle development during the first stages of puberty, before gonadotropin influence. However, it is clear that additional studies are necessary to determine which dimeric ligand is produced in each size class of ovarian follicles before clearly delineated functions can be assigned to the inhibins and activins during puberty.

Normal Menstrual and Estrous Cycles

In addition to their role as regulators of pituitary FSH, activin and inhibin act as paracrine and autocrine modulators of ovarian follicle growth and maturation. Activin augments FSH-induced granulosa cell growth and follicle maturation in culture [97, 98]. Furthermore, activin treatment of small primary preantral follicles in culture results in follicle dormancy, whereas treatment of slightly larger preantral follicles initiates growth. Conversely, recombinant human inhibin A injected into the intrabursal space of immature rats causes follicle accumulation [99]. When superimposed on the expression patterns of inhibin and activin in the ovary during the estrous cycle, these data support a model in which the ovary makes a switch from activin-stimulated early follicle growth to inhibin-stimulated late follicle growth.

Activin and inhibin also regulate steroidogenesis in the ovary. In a developing follicle, the theca cells express LH receptors, whereas the granulosa cells express FSH receptors (FSHR) [100, 101]. In response to LH, the thecal cell layer produces androgens that are transported across the cell membrane and into the neighboring granulosa cell layer [102]. Granulosa cells exclusively express the aromatase enzyme, which converts thecal androgens to estrogens. Activin enhances FSH-stimulated aromatase activity and steroid secretion in cultured monkey and rat granulosa cells [103, 104] and steroid production in vivo during early follicle development [79, 105]. Inhibin augments LH-stimulated androgen production by thecal cell cultures and by their male equivalent, the Leydig cells [106–108]. On a transcriptional level, activin and inhibin have been shown to regulate the expression of several steroidogenic enzymes, including cholesterol side chain cleavage cytochrome p450c17α-hydroxylase 17, 20-lyase (cytP450c17) 3β-hydroxysteroid dehydro-genase (3β-HSD), and cytochrome P450 17α̃hydroxylase/17,20 lyase (cytP450c17) [68, 109, 110].

Finally, activin has been shown to upregulate FSHR expression, which may account for its ability to augment FSH-stimulated steroidogenesis in granulosa cells. Activin A treatment upregulates FSHR mRNA levels within 48 hours [111] and results in an increase in the number of FSHRs on the surface of cultured rat granulosa cells [112, 113]. The stimulatory effect of activin on FSHR mRNA and cell surface expression is maximal in the presence of cAMP and is partly caused by the stabilization of FSHR transcripts [114, 115].

Pregnancy and Labor

Although the major source of inhibins and activins during human pregnancy is the feto-placental unit, inhibin A is also secreted by the CL [116]. In the golden hamster, ovariectomy at day 12 of pregnancy results in a loss of inhibin A and B, which suggests that the ovary remains the main inhibin producing tissue, at least in early pregnancy in rodents. It is assumed that this inhibin is produced by follicles that continue to develop during pregnancy [117]. In primates, the function of the inhibins and activins during pregnancy is a continuing source of controversy, yet one possible action for ovarian activin in early pregnancy is in the initial recognition of the pregnant state. During the normal menstrual cycle, activin levels rise in the luteal phase, and in vitro data suggests that this activin inhibits human chorionic gonadotropin (hCG)-stimulated progesterone production by the CL [118, 119]. During the initial stages of pregnancy, high levels of hCG overwhelm the negative effect of activin on progesterone production. Thus the loss of activin activity by the CL may be a physiological signal that the pregnant state has been established and may also be crucial to the maintenance of the pregnant state [119]. Finally, activin A rises at the end of pregnancy and positively correlates with the onset of labor [120]. However, the role of this ligand in controlling maternal or fetal function is not known.

In Vitro Fertilization and Ovarian Follicle Reserve

In the fetal ovary, an oocyte population is first detected at 16 weeks of gestation and grows to its maximum number (approximately 7 million) by 5 months of gestation [121]. This population slowly declines throughout the remainder of gestation and postnatal life. At birth, massive follicular atresia, or programmed cell death of the oocyte and its surrounding cells, leaves approximately 1 million primordial follicles in the ovary. In the adult human, far more follicles enter into atresia than are ovulated. Under the influence of the secondary FSH surge (intercycle FSH rise), primordial follicles continually enter the growing follicle pool from the first menstrual cycle in puberty until the menopause. However, only a single dominant follicle reaches full maturity and releases its oocyte per menstrual cycle, thus only approximately 400 total oocytes undergo ovulation over a lifetime [121, 122].

As mentioned previously, inhibin B is secreted by the granulosa cells of small, FSH-selected antral follicles, and inhibin B serum levels are high during the early follicular phase of the menstrual cycle [22, 23, 31]. Thus, the circulating concentration of inhibin B in the follicular phase is considered reflective of the number and health of follicles recruited from the primordial pool. With age and many rounds of follicle selection, atresia, and ovulation, the population of primordial follicles declines, and less inhibin B is produced [119, 123, 124]. Therefore inhibin B levels are indicative of ovarian follicle reserve, or the number of follicles that are competent to enter into the maturation process and to reach ovulation [124]. The success of in vitro fertilization (IVF) and other assisted reproductive technologies (ART) is critically dependent on the health and responsiveness of the ovarian follicle reserve to exogenous hormone treatment. At one time, follicle health was suggested by the presence of normal cycling FSH levels, because a decline in the growing follicle population, and its associated loss of estrogen and inhibin feedback to the pituitary, leads to an upregulation of FSH levels. However, as the decrease in serum inhibin B levels precedes the perimenopausal increase in basal FSH [125], the measurement of serum inhibin B has become a useful clinical predictor of ovarian follicle reserve and the potential success of IVF treatments.

Ovarian Aging and the Menopause

Perimenopause, or the menopause transition, refers to the time in reproductive life when particular physiological changes, both histological and hormonal, are manifested. The most obvious of these is dysmenorrhea, an indicator of the disruption in normal endocrine signaling within the reproductive axis occurring at this time. Also during perimenopause, and continuing into postmenopause, both ovary size and total follicle number decrease [126–128]. By postmenopause, the ovaries primarily contain stromal cells, although intact follicles have been found in women more than 70 years of age [129, 130]. Several studies have found that FSH levels rise during the later stages of perimenopause and are significantly elevated in postmenopausal women [131–134]. Because increased FSH is not always correlated with changes in ovarian estrogen, the rise in FSH is at least partially attributed to lower levels of inhibin (specifically inhibin B) produced by the aging ovary [134–138]. In particular, women in early perimenopause exhibit significantly lower levels of inhibin B, which correlates with a small rise in FSH [133]. It is believed that the drop in inhibin B concentration at this time may be reflective of fewer selected early antral follicles in the ovaries of older women [135]. In addition, high serum activin A levels are detected throughout the menstrual cycle, and follistatin and activin concentrations in the follicular fluid are elevated in perimenopausal women [136, 139]. Thus, elevated activin A during the menopause transition, together with the loss of inhibin negative feedback, contribute to the maintenance of high FSH concentrations in these women [136]. Within several months of the final menstrual period and the beginning of the menopause, serum inhibin A and inhibin B levels drop to low or undetectable levels that are maintained postmenopausally [131, 140–142]. The finding that perimenopausal changes in inhibin B precede those of inhibin A has led some to consider inhibin B as the most important causal factor in the initial rise of FSH at this time and as a diagnostic marker for the onset of the menopause [133, 137]. However, further studies are needed to elucidate the changing actions of inhibin A, inhibin B, follistatin, and activin A throughout the menopause before these hormones can be used to reliably determine the reproductive status of individual women.

Animal Models of Human Ovarian Disease

The creation of mice null for the α-subunit gene led to an inhibin-deficient animal model. Both male and female α-subunit knockout mice develop sex-cord stromal tumors soon after birth and eventually die of a cachexia-like wasting syndrome [143]. Based on this observed phenotype, inhibins are described as tumor-suppressors specific to the reproductive organs. These α-subunit null mice also have elevated ovarian activin, which prompted the suggestion that increased activin, and not decreased inhibin, was responsible for the development of the tumors. However, in a series of experiments in which ovaries were cross-transplanted between wild type and inhibin null mice, it was demonstrated that the inhibin produced by the remaining wild type ovary was sufficient to prevent tumor formation [144, 145].

At least two mouse models of α-subunit overexpression have been created to date. In one line, a transgene encodes the α-subunit driven by the metallothionine promoter (α-MT) and is overexpressed in several tissues [146]. In female α-MT mice, inhibin α-subunit protein is overexpressed in the serum, pituitary, and ovary, and, predictably, FSH levels, ovulation rate, and fertility are decreased. In addition, the ovaries of female α-MT mice exhibit multiple ovarian cysts, often containing more than one ovum and fewer antral follicles or CL. Ovulation rate and fertility can be restored by exogenous pregnant mare serum gonadotropin (PMSG, an FSH analog) and hCG, suggesting that the reproductive deficiencies expressed by these mice are caused by decreased gonadotropin activity [147]. A second mouse model of inhibin overexpression uses a mifepristone-activated promoter system to upregulate α-subunit expression in the liver of either wild type or α-subunit null mice [148]. Female mice in which the inhibin α-subunit is inducibly overexpressed display an arrest in follicle development at the early antral stage and no CL, signifying a lack of successful ovulations.

Many knockout mice have been created to elucidate the role of activins in development and reproduction [144, 145]. Mice null for the βA-subunit are neonatal lethal and exhibit craniofacial defects, whereas mice lacking βB-subunit are viable but have eyelid closure defects, nursing defects, and delayed parturition [143, 149]. Mice deficient in both the βA- and βB-subunits display the combined abnormalities observed in the single knockouts but no additional defects, indicating distinct nonoverlapping roles in these subunits during development. Insertion of βB-subunit sequence into the βA-subunit locus in βA-subunit knockout mice results in partial rescue of the null phenotype but is consistent with distinct functions for each inhibin (or activin) isoform during development [150]. Unfortunately, although these data support a role for the activins in development, they have shed little light on the function of the activins in the adult animal.

In contrast, mice null for the type IIA activin receptor exhibit suppressed FSH levels, consistent with the established role of the activins in pituitary function. In addition, female ActRIIA knockout mice are infertile, have ovaries of reduced size, and develop fewer corpora lutea than their wild-type counterparts [143]. ActRIIB null mice die shortly after birth and therefore any effects on gonadotropin production have not been assessed. Thus the relative importance of each of these type II receptors in the mediation of activin-stimulated FSH synthesis and secretion is not yet known. Together, these mouse models demonstrate that although the activins are indispensable in normal development, activin signal transduction is also necessary for normal pituitary FSH production and ovarian function in the adult.

INHIBIN AND ACTIVIN IN OVARIAN PATHOLOGY

Ovarian Cancer

Ovarian cancer strikes 1 in every 100 women and is fatal in 55% of cases [151]. Ovarian carcinomas progress through four stages, and each stage is associated with decreased survival. The high mortality rate associated with ovarian cancer is primarily because of the inability to detect or diagnose the cancer while it is still in an early and treatable stage. Most ovarian cancers are detected at stage III, at which point the postsurgical survival rate has decreased to only 37% [152]. Approximately 90% of ovarian malignant neoplasias are derived from ovarian surface epithelium (OSE), compared with 5% to 10% arising from granulosa cells (granulosa cell tumors [GCTs]) and 1% developing from germ cells [153].

All ovarian tumors have been shown to express increased levels of activin and inhibin subunits [153, 154]. In addition, GCTs also express follistatin, activin type I and type II receptors, and betaglycan [155–163]. Serous cystadenomas are the most common of surface epithelial ovarian cancers (EOCs), and high concentrations of inhibin A and inhibin B have been found in the cystic fluid of these tumors [164]. Likewise, inhibin is elevated in the serum of patients with mucinous EOC, a population that represents 15% of ovarian cancer patients [165, 166]. Inhibin serum concentration declines following surgical ablation, and analysis of inhibin production using specific dimeric assays for inhibin A and inhibin B show that inhibin B is more frequently elevated than inhibin A in these tumors [167, 168]. Likewise, GCTs are associated with elevated circulating inhibin levels that are decreased following surgical resection [165–167, 169–172]. Specific dimeric inhibin enzyme-linked immunosorbent assays (ELISAs) have shown that the majority of GCTs studied secrete elevated levels of inhibin A, whereas only some of these tumors also hypersecrete inhibin B [168].

The observation that inhibin α–subunit knockout mice develop sex-cord stromal tumors, some of which are granulosa cell-derived, suggested a role for inhibins as tumor suppressors. Because all GCTs express the α-, βA-, and βB-subunits, it was hypothesized that deficiency in these subunits or dimeric inhibins could serve as markers for GCT progression. Paradoxically, serum inhibin levels are elevated in women with GCTs, indicating that other factors are involved in the development of this tumor type [160, 162]. Nevertheless, this finding led to several clinical studies that have upheld dimeric inhibin or the free α-subunit as markers of ovarian tumor progression [167, 168, 172–175]. A negative correlation between preoperative serum inhibin A levels in postmenopausal women with EOC and survival 5 years postsurgery supported the use of inhibin as a marker for the detection of EOC [153, 176]. Currently, dimeric inhibin assays are applied to the diagnosis of GCTs [172, 177]. Recently, one group described the preferential secretion of pro-α-C, a precursor form of the inhibin α-subunit, rather than the mature form of the α-subunit or dimeric inhibin A by EOCs [161], and a recent study demonstrated that the increased survival of women with primary EOCs is associated with preoperative elevated pro-α-C levels [175, 178]. Further development of a pro-α-C assay for use as a prognostic marker for ovarian cancer is underway.

Activin A has also been shown to be elevated in postmenopausal women with EOC [158]. As in GCTs, activin, ActRIA, ActRIIA, and ActRIIB are present in human OSE carcinomas [179, 180]. Through the use of the immortalized OSE cell line IOSE-29, it was observed that activin modulated growth inhibition and induced apoptosis in the early stages of ovarian cancer [181]. In addition, activin treatment of another OSE cancer line, OVCAR-3, resulted in the upregulation of inhibin α- and βA-, but not βB-, subunits, as well as cell proliferation. Significantly, these changes in subunit expression and cell growth were not observed in activin-treated nontumor OSE cells, suggesting that activin produced in OSE tumors may act as an autocrine regulator of tumor progression [181]. Similarly, activin stimulates proliferation in human ovarian cancer cell lines [182] but does not consistently affect primary cultures of epithelial ovarian cells [183]. The roles of activin and its receptors in tumorigenesis have yet to be defined, and the use of activin as a tumor marker in the diagnosis and screening of ovarian cancers warrants further evaluation.

Taken together, it is clear that the inhibin subunits and dimers are upregulated in certain human ovarian tumors, particularly GCTs. Inhibin dimers or the inhibin α-subunit are potentially useful markers for GCT progression. In OSE tumors, inhibin secretion is also elevated, but the source of inhibin is not thoroughly understood. In these cases the most useful tumor marker is still the CA125 antigen [172]. In addition, the combination of the pro-α-C and CA125 assays is being evaluated as a way to increase the power of diagnosis for all ovarian cancer groups [175, 178]. An understanding of the cellular mechanisms behind inhibin and activin action in cancer progression or suppression has been overshadowed by research investigating their use as diagnostic markers. The roles of the activins, inhibins, and their receptors in the progression of ovarian cancer are still under investigation [153].

Polycystic Ovarian Syndrome

Polycystic ovarian syndrome (PCOS) is a disorder associated with irregular periods, infertility, hirsutism, and increased risk of developing diabetes. It affects 4% to 12% of reproductive age women [184–186]. The earliest indicator of PCOS is chronic anovulation accompanied by high serum androgen levels. With progression of the disorder, a characteristic arrested growth of antral follicles at an early stage (less than 10mm in diameter) is observed. It is unclear how PCOS initially develops, but the disorder can be effectively treated by both antiestrogens and by exogenous FSH, suggesting that a primary disregulation of FSH production in the pituitary is involved. The suppression of FSH may be caused by the upregulation of feedback by estrogen or inhibin or by changes in local follistatin action in the pituitary. In a study of candidate genes implicated in PCOS in 39 affected sister pairs, the follistatin gene demonstrated the strongest linkage [187]. However, more recent studies have failed to identify any mutation in the follistatin gene linked to PCOS [188, 189].

Whether abnormal inhibin and activin action is involved in the development of PCOS is not completely clear. According to some studies, the serum concentrations of inhibin α-subunit, pro-alpha C, inhibin A, and inhibin B are elevated in PCOS patients [190–194]. Additionally, both ovarian expression and circulating concentrations of follistatin are higher and activin is lower in PCOS patients [195], suggesting that an imbalance in inhibin and activin secretion and action in the pituitary may contribute to the abnormal LH-to-FSH ratio characteristic of PCOS patients [196]. However, several reports describe little difference in the levels of inhibin B, activin A, and follistatin in the follicular fluid of normal and PCOS follicles, although inhibin A concentrations are lower in PCOS follicles than in normal follicles [197–200]. In addition, one study reported that α-subunit and βA-subunit mRNA levels are lower in PCOS follicles when compared with size-matched follicles from normal ovaries, whereas βB-subunit and follistatin mRNA levels are not significantly different in PCOS and normal follicles [201]. The significance of these data is not completely clear; however, a role for inhibins, activins, and follistatin in the abnormal suppression of FSH manifested in PCOS patients cannot be discounted as yet. A characterization of the ligand forms that are produced by PCOS follicles, as well as potential changes in circulating ligand half-life, are required before the ambiguities surrounding the regulation and role of the inhibins and activins in PCOS are resolved.

Inhibin α-Subunit Polymorphism

Premature ovarian failure (POF) results in hypergonadotropic amenorrhea occurring before the age of 40 years, and affects 1% to 3% of women [202]. The POF condition is inherited through either an autosomal dominant sex-limited transmission or is cross-linked with incomplete penetrance [203, 204]. Although the pathogenesis of POF is still unknown, several mechanisms have been suggested, including a reduction in the primordial follicle pool, accelerated follicular atresia, or alteration of follicular recruitment and maturation, all of which would lead to a loss of ovarian control (by estrogen or inhibin negative feedback) over gonadotropin release by the pituitary [205]. Although estrogen and progesterone replacement therapy restores normal LH levels in women with POF, plasma FSH levels remain elevated, which strongly indicates that another ovarian factor, perhaps inhibin, is necessary for normal FSH regulation [206]. This led to the evaluation of the loss of inhibin and inhibin-mediated downregulation of FSH as causal factors in the development of POF. In one study, a missense mutation (G796A transition) in exon 2 of the inhibin α-subunit gene that results in the substitution of a highly conserved alanine to a threonine was found to be significantly associated with patients with POF [207]. Another group assessed that the POF phenotype was not always associated with the G796A transition; however a single nucleotide polymorphism (129C-T) located in the 5′-UTR of the inhibin α-subunit gene was observed to occur with higher frequency in one cohort of patients with POF [208]. Certainly the body of evidence is growing that supports the inhibin α-subunit gene as a candidate for disruption in POF.

CONCLUSIONS AND FUTURE DIRECTIONS

The roles of inhibin and activin in the regulation of FSH have been established and are recognized as necessary for normal reproductive function. Less clear, however, are the signal transduction pathways regulated by these ligands that permit cell-specific responses. Moreover, the structural relationship between activin and its receptors, as well as the physical basis for the antagonism of activin action by inhibin, are not fully understood. Recent work on the three-dimensional structure of activins and inhibins bound to ActRIIB should begin to reveal the relationship between homomeric and heteromeric ligand-receptor interactions and activin and inhibin molecular function(s). Naturally occurring mutations in the inhibin and activin subunits identified in the human and associated with reproductive dysfunction are expected to map to biologically relevant interfaces between these ligands and their receptors. Finally, the regulation of inhibin and activin biosynthesis in normal ovarian follicles as well as in ovarian disease states remains to be resolved. Little is known regarding the differential processing and assembly of inhibin and activin dimers or the mechanism and significance of the observed independent secretion patterns of inhibin A and inhibin B during the cycle. These vitally important questions are currently being addressed in several laboratories. The answers to these questions are essential to a more comprehensive understanding of normal follicle function and how it influences communication between the ovary and pituitary. The pursuit of these and other aspects of inhibin and activin biology are the basis for the continued study of these ligands in reproductive function.

ACKNOWLEDGMENTS

Studies from the authors' laboratory were funded by the National Institutes for Health (NIH) grants HD037096 and HD041857. Stacey C. Chapman is supported by a fellowship from the Northwestern University Robert H. Lurie Comprehensive Cancer Carcinogenesis Training Grant CA009560. Hilary A. Kenny is supported by a fellowship from the Training Program in Reproductive Biology HD007068.

References

1. Piek, E., Heldin, C. H., and Ten Dijke, P. (1999). Specificity, diversity, and regulation in TGF-beta superfamily signaling. *FASEB J.* 13, 2105–2124.
2. Pangas, S. A., and Woodruff, T. K. (2000). Activin signal transduction pathways. *Trends. Endocrinol. Metab.* 11, 309–314.
3. Woodruff, T. K., and Mather, J. P. (1995). Inhibin, activin and the female reproductive axis. *Annu. Rev. Physiol.* 57, 219–244.
4. Luisi, S., Florio, P., Reis, F. M., and Petraglia, F. (2001). Expression and secretion of activin A: Possible physiological and clinical implications. *Eur. J. Endocrinol.* 145, 225–236.
5. Carroll, R. S., Corrigan, A. Z., Gharib, S. D., Vale, W., and Chin, W. W. (1989). Inhibin, activin, and follistatin: Regulation of follicle-stimulating hormone messenger ribonucleic acid levels. *Mol. Endocrinol.* 3, 1969–1976.
6. Weiss, J., Crowley, Jr., W. F., Halvorson, L. M., and Jameson, J. L. (1993). Perifusion of rat pituitary cells with gonadotropin-releasing hormone, activin, and inhibin reveals distinct effects on gonadotropin gene expression and secretion. *Endocrinology* 132, 2307–2311.
7. Ethier, J. F., and Findlay, J. K. (2001). Roles of activin and its signal transduction mechanisms in reproductive tissues. *Reproduction* 121, 667–675.
8. Findlay, J. K., Drummond, A. E., Dyson, M., Baillie, A. J., Robertson, D. M., and Ethier, J. (2001). Production and actions of inhibin and activin during folliculogenesis in the rat. *Mol. Cell. Endocrinol.* 180, 139–144.
9. Findlay, J. K., Drummond, A. E., Dyson, M. L., Baillie, A. J., Robertson, D. M., and Ethier, J. F. (2002). Recruitment and development of the follicle: The roles of the transforming growth factor-beta superfamily. *Mol. Cell. Endocrinol.* 191, 35–43.
10. de Winter, J. P., ten Dijke, P., de Vries, C. J., et al. (1996). Follistatins neutralize activin bioactivity by inhibition of activin binding to its type II receptors. *Mol. Cell. Endocrinol.* 116, 105–114.
11. Besecke, L. M., Guendner, M. J., Sluss, P. A., et al. (1997). Pituitary follistatin regulates activin-mediated production of follicle-stimulating hormone during the rat estrous cycle. *Endocrinology* 138, 2841–2848.
12. Hashimoto, O., Nakamura, T., Shoji, H., Shimasaki, S., Hayashi, Y., and Sugino, H. (1997). A novel role of follistatin, an activin-binding protein, in the inhibition of activin action in rat pituitary cells. Endocytotic degradation of activin and its acceleration by follistatin associated with cell-surface heparan sulfate. *J. Biol. Chem.* 272, 13835–13842.
13. Leal, A. M., Takabe, K., Wang, L., et al. (2002). Effect of adenovirus-mediated overexpression of follistatin and extracellular domain of activin receptor type II on gonadotropin secretion in vitro and in vivo. *Endocrinology* 143, 964–969.
14. Corrigan, A. Z., Bilezikjian, L. M., Carroll, R. S., et al. (1991). Evidence for an autocrine role of activin B within rat anterior pituitary cultures. *Endocrinology* 128, 1682–1684.
15. Besecke, L. M., Guendner, M. J., Schneyer, A. L., Bauer-Dantoin, A. C., Jameson, J. L., and Weiss, J. (1996). Gonadotropin-releasing hormone regulates follicle-stimulating hormone-beta gene expression through an activin/follistatin autocrine or paracrine loop. *Endocrinology* 137, 3667–3673.
16. McConnell, D. S., Wang, Q., Sluss, P. M., et al. (1998). A two-site chemiluminescent assay for activin-free follistatin reveals that most follistatin circulating in men and normal cycling women is in an activin-bound state. *J. Clin. Endocrinol. Metab.* 83, 851–858.
17. Burger, H. G., McLachlan, R. I., Bangah, M., et al. (1988). Serum inhibin concentrations rise throughout normal male and female puberty. *J. Clin. Endocrinol. Metab.* 67, 689–694.
18. McLachlan, R. I., Robertson, D. M., Healy, D. L., Burger, H. G., and de Kretser, D. M. (1987). Circulating immunoreactive inhibin levels during the normal human menstrual cycle. *J. Clin. Endocrinol. Metab.* 65, 954–961.
19. Hasegawa, Y., Miyamoto, K., and Igarashi, M. (1989). Changes in serum concentrations of immunoreactive inhibin during the oestrous cycle of the rat. *J. Endocrinol.* 121, 91–100.
20. Ackland, J. F., D'Agostino, J., Ringstrom, S. J., Hostetler, J. P., Mann, B. G., and Schwartz, N. B. (1990). Circulating radioimmunoassayable inhibin during periods of transient follicle-stimulating hormone rise: Secondary surge and unilateral ovariectomy. *Biol. Reprod.* 43, 347–352.
21. Reddi, K., Wickings, E. J., McNeilly, A. S., Baird, D. T., and Hillier, S. G. (1990). Circulating bioactive follicle-stimulating hormone and immunoreactive inhibin levels during the normal human menstrual cycle. *Clin. Endocrinol. (Oxf.)* 33, 547–557.
22. Groome, N. P., Illingworth, P. J., O'Brien, M., et al. (1994). Detection of dimeric inhibin throughout the human menstrual cycle by two-site enzyme immunoassay. *Clin. Endocrinol. (Oxf.)* 40, 717–723.

23. Groome, N. P., Illingworth, P. J., O'Brien, M., et al. (1996). Measurement of dimeric inhibin B throughout the human menstrual cycle. *J. Clin. Endocrinol. Metab.* 81, 1401–1405.
24. Woodruff, T. K., Besecke, L. M., Groome, N., Draper, L. B., Schwartz, N. B., and Weiss, J. (1996). Inhibin A and inhibin B are inversely correlated to follicle-stimulating hormone, yet are discordant during the follicular phase of the rat estrous cycle, and inhibin A is expressed in a sexually dimorphic manner. *Endocrinology* 137, 5463–5467.
25. Meunier, H., Rivier, C., Evans, R. M., and Vale, W. (1988). Gonadal and extragonadal expression of inhibin alpha, beta A, and beta B subunits in various tissues predicts diverse functions. *Proc. Natl. Acad. Sci. USA* 85, 247–251.
26. Woodruff, T. K., D'Agostino, J., Schwartz, N. B., and Mayo, K. E. (1989). Decreased inhibin gene expression in preovulatory follicles requires primary gonadotropin surges. *Endocrinology* 124, 2193–2199.
27. Schwall, R. H., Mason, A. J., Wilcox, J. N., Bassett, S. G., and Zeleznik, A. J. (1990). Localization of inhibin/activin subunit mRNAs within the primate ovary. *Mol. Endocrinol.* 4, 75–79.
28. Meunier, H., Cajander, S. B., Roberts, V. J., et al. (1988). Rapid changes in the expression of inhibin alpha-, beta A-, and beta B-subunits in ovarian cell types during the rat estrous cycle. *Mol. Endocrinol.* 2, 1352–1363.
29. Woodruff, T. K., D'Agostino, J., Schwartz, N. B., and Mayo, K. E. (1988). Dynamic changes in inhibin messenger RNAs in rat ovarian follicles during the reproductive cycle. *Science* 239, 1296–1299.
30. Smith, K. B., Millar, M. R., McNeilly, A. S., Illingworth, P. J., Fraser, H. M., and Baird, D. T. (1991). Immunocytochemical localization of inhibin alpha-subunit in the human corpus luteum. *J. Endocrinol.* 129, 155–160.
31. Roberts, V. J., Barth, S., el-Roeiy, A., and Yen, S. S. (1993). Expression of inhibin/activin subunits and follistatin messenger ribonucleic acids and proteins in ovarian follicles and the corpus luteum during the human menstrual cycle. *J. Clin. Endocrinol. Metab.* 77, 1402–1410.
32. Davis, J. S. (1994). Mechanisms of hormone action: Luteinizing hormone receptors and second-messenger pathways. *Curr. Opin. Obstet. Gynecol.* 6, 254–261.
33. Feng, Z. M., Li, Y. P., and Chen, C. L. (1989). Analysis of the 5'-flanking regions of rat inhibin alpha- and beta-B-subunit genes suggests two different regulatory mechanisms. *Mol. Endocrinol.* 3, 1914–1925.
34. Pei, L., Dodson, R., Schoderbek, W. E., Maurer, R. A., and Mayo, K. E. (1991). Regulation of the alpha inhibin gene by cyclic adenosine 3',5'-monophosphate after transfection into rat granulosa cells. *Mol. Endocrinol.* 5, 521–534.
35. Mukherjee, A., Urban, J., Sassone-Corsi, P., and Mayo, K. E. (1998). Gonadotropins regulate inducible cyclic adenosine 3',5'-monophosphate early repressor in the rat ovary: Implications for inhibin alpha subunit gene expression. *Mol. Endocrinol.* 12, 785–800.
36. Tanimoto, K., Yoshida, E., Mita, S., Nibu, Y., Murakami, K., and Fukamizu, A. (1996). Human activin betaA gene. Identification of novel 5' exon, functional promoter, and enhancers. *J. Biol. Chem.* 271, 32760–32769.
37. Tuuri, T., Eramaa, M., Van Schaik, R. H., and Ritvos, O. (1996). Differential regulation of inhibin/activin alpha- and beta A-subunit and follistatin mRNAs by cyclic AMP and phorbol ester in cultured human granulosa-luteal cells. *Mol. Cell. Endocrinol.* 121, 1–10.
38. Ardekani, A. M., Romanelli, J. C., and Mayo, K. E. (1998). Structure of the rat inhibin and activin betaA-subunit gene and regulation in an ovarian granulosa cell line. *Endocrinology* 139, 3271–3279.
39. Dykema, J. C., and Mayo, K. E. (1994). Two messenger ribonucleic acids encoding the common beta B-chain of inhibin and activin have distinct 5'-initiation sites and are differentially regulated in rat granulosa cells. *Endocrinology* 135, 702–711.
40. Eramaa, M., Tuuri, T., Hilden, K., and Ritvos, O. (1994). Regulation of inhibin alpha- and beta A-subunit messenger ribonucleic acid levels by chorionic gonadotropin and recombinant follicle-stimulating hormone in cultured human granulosa-luteal cells. *J. Clin. Endocrinol. Metab.* 79, 1670–1677.
41. Eramaa, M., and Ritvos, O. (1996). Transforming growth factor-beta 1 and -beta 2 induce inhibin and activin beta B-subunit messenger ribonucleic acid levels in cultured human granulosa-luteal cells. *Fertil. Steril.* 65, 954–960.
42. Liu, J., Hyden-Granskog, C., and Voutilainen, R. (2001). Gonadotrophins inhibit and activin induces expression of inhibin/activin beta(B) subunit mRNA in cultured human granulosa-luteal cells. *Mol. Hum. Reprod.* 7, 319–323.
43. Bondestam, J., Kaivo-oja, N., Kallio, J., et al. (2002). Engagement of activin and bone morphogenetic protein signaling pathway Smad proteins in the induction of inhibin B production in ovarian granulosa cells. *Mol. Cell. Endocrinol.* 195, 79.
44. Jaatinen, R., Bondestam, J., Raivio, T., et al. (2002). Activation of the bone morphogenetic protein signaling pathway induces inhibin beta(B)-subunit mRNA and secreted inhibin B levels in cultured human granulosa-luteal cells. *J. Clin. Endocrinol. Metab.* 87, 1254–1261.
45. Feng, Z. M., Wu, A. Z., and Chen, C. L. (1998). Testicular GATA-1 factor up-regulates the promoter activity of rat inhibin alpha-subunit gene in MA-10 Leydig tumor cells. *Mol. Endocrinol.* 12, 378–390.
46. Feng, Z. M., Wu, A. Z., Zhang, Z., and Chen, C. L. (2000). GATA-1 and GATA-4 transactivate inhibin/activin beta-B-subunit gene transcription in testicular cells. *Mol. Endocrinol.* 14, 1820–1835.
47. Robertson, D. M., Cahir, N., Findlay, J. K., Burger, H. G., and Groome, N. (1997). The biological and immunological characterization of inhibin A and B forms in human follicular fluid and plasma. *J. Clin. Endocrinol. Metab.* 82, 889–896.
48. Plant, T. M., Padmanabhan, V., Ramaswamy, S., et al. (1997). Circulating concentrations of dimeric inhibin A and B in the male rhesus monkey (Macaca mulatta). *J. Clin. Endocrinol. Metab.* 82, 2617–2621.
49. Illingworth, P. J., Groome, N. P., Byrd, W., et al. (1996). Inhibin-B: A likely candidate for the physiologically important form of inhibin in men. *J. Clin. Endocrinol. Metab.* 81, 1321–1325.
50. Attisano, L., and Wrana, J. L. (2000). Smads as transcriptional co-modulators. *Curr. Opin. Cell. Biol.* 12, 235–243.
51. Afrakhte, M., Moren, A., Jossan, S., et al. (1998). Induction of inhibitory Smad6 and Smad7 mRNA by TGF-beta family members. *Biochem. Biophys. Res. Commun.* 249, 505–511.

52. Phillips, D. J., and de Kretser, D. M. (1998). Follistatin: A multifunctional regulatory protein. *Front. Neuroendocrinol.* 19, 287–322.
53. Mathews, L. S., and Vale, W. W. (1991). Expression cloning of an activin receptor: A predicted transmembrane serine kinase. *Cell* 65, 973–982.
54. Xu, J., McKeehan, K., Matsuzaki, K., and McKeehan, W. L. (1995). Inhibin antagonizes inhibition of liver cell growth by activin by a dominant-negative mechanism. *J. Biol. Chem.* 270, 6308–6313.
55. Martens, J. W., de Winter, J. P., Timmerman, M. A., et al. (1997). Inhibin interferes with activin signaling at the level of the activin receptor complex in Chinese hamster ovary cells. *Endocrinology* 138, 2928–2936.
56. Bilezikjian, L. M., Blount, A. L., Campen, C. A., Gonzalez-Manchon, C., and Vale, W. (1991). Activin-A inhibits pro-opiomelanocortin messenger RNA accumulation and adrenocorticotropin secretion of AtT20 cells. *Mol. Endocrinol.* 5, 1389–1395.
57. Schwall, R. H., Robbins, K., Jardieu, P., Chang, L., Lai, C., and Terrell, T. G. (1993). Activin induces cell death in hepatocytes in vivo and in vitro. *Hepatology* 18, 347–356.
58. Lebrun, J. J., and Vale, W. W. (1997). Activin and inhibin have antagonistic effects on ligand-dependent heteromerization of the type I and type II activin receptors and human erythroid differentiation. *Mol. Cell. Biol.* 17, 1682–1691.
59. Draper, L. B., Matzuk, M. M., Roberts, V. J., et al. (1998). Identification of an inhibin receptor in gonadal tumors from inhibin alpha-subunit knockout mice. *J. Biol. Chem.* 273, 398–403.
60. Hertan, R., Farnworth, P. G., Fitzsimmons, K. L., and Robertson, D. M. (1999). Identification of high affinity binding sites for inhibin on ovine pituitary cells in culture. *Endocrinology* 140, 6–12.
61. Chong, H., Pangas, S. A., Bernard, D. J., et al. (2000). Structure and expression of a membrane component of the inhibin receptor system. *Endocrinology* 141, 2600–2607.
62. Farnworth, P. G., Harrison, C. A., Leembruggen, P., et al. (2001). Inhibin binding sites and proteins in pituitary, gonadal, adrenal, and bone cells. *Mol. Cell. Endocrinol.* 180, 63–71.
63. Harrison, C. A., Farnworth, P. G., Chan, K. L., et al. (2001). Identification of specific inhibin A-binding proteins on mouse Leydig (TM3) and sertoli (TM4) cell lines. *Endocrinology* 142, 1393–1402.
64. Lewis, K. A., Gray, P. C., Blount, A. L., et al. (2000). Betaglycan binds inhibin and can mediate functional antagonism of activin signalling. *Nature* 404, 411–414.
65. Esparza-Lopez, J., Montiel, J. L., Vilchis-Landeros, M. M., Okadome, T., Miyazono, K., and Lopez-Casillas, F. (2001). Ligand binding and functional properties of betaglycan, a co-receptor of the transforming growth factor-beta superfamily. Specialized binding regions for transforming growth factor-beta and inhibin A. *J. Biol. Chem.* 276, 14588–14596.
66. Chapman, S. C., Bernard, D. J., Jelen, J., and Woodruff, T. K. (2002). Properties of inhibin binding to betaglycan, InhBP/p120, and the activin type II receptors. *Mol. Cell. Endocrinol.* 196, 79.
67. Alak, B. M., Smith, G. D., Woodruff, T. K., Stouffer, R. L., and Wolf, D. P. (1996). Enhancement of primate oocyte maturation and fertilization in vitro by inhibin A and activin A. *Fertil. Steril.* 66, 646–653.
68. Lejeune, H., Chuzel, F., Sanchez, P., Durand, P., Mather, J. P., and Saez, J. M. (1997). Stimulating effect of both human recombinant inhibin A and activin A on immature porcine Leydig cell functions in vitro. *Endocrinology* 138, 4783–4791.
69. Kretzschmar, M., Doody, J., Timokhina, I., and Massague, J. (1999). A mechanism of repression of TGFbeta/Smad signaling by oncogenic Ras. *Genes Dev.* 13, 804–816.
70. McCullaugh, E. (1932). Dual endocrine activity of the testes. *Science* 76, 19–20.
71. Schwartz, N. B., and Channing, C. P. (1977). Evidence for ovarian "inhibin": suppression of the secondary rise in serum follicle stimulating hormone levels in proestrous rats by injection of porcine follicular fluid. *Proc. Natl. Acad. Sci. USA* 74, 5721–5724.
72. Lumpkin, M. D., DePaolo, L. V., and Negro-Vilar, A. (1984). Pulsatile release of follicle-stimulating hormone in ovariectomized rats is inhibited by porcine follicular fluid (inhibin). *Endocrinology* 114, 201–206.
73. Rivier, C., Rivier, J., and Vale, W. (1986). Inhibin-mediated feedback control of follicle-stimulating hormone secretion in the female rat. *Science* 234, 205–208.
74. DePaolo, L. V. (1991). Hypersecretion of follicle-stimulating hormone (FSH) after ovariectomy of hypophysectomized, pituitary-grafted rats: Implications for local regulatory control of FSH. *Endocrinology* 128, 1731–1740.
75. Robertson, D. M., Prisk, M., McMaster, J. W., Irby, D. C., Findlay, J. K., and de Kretser, D. M. (1991). Serum FSH-suppressing activity of human recombinant inhibin A in male and female rats. *J. Reprod. Fertil.* 91, 321–328.
76. Carroll, R. S., Kowash, P. M., Lofgren, J. A., Schwall, R. H., and Chin, W. W. (1991). In vivo regulation of FSH synthesis by inhibin and activin. *Endocrinology* 129, 3299–3304.
77. Rivier, C., Schwall, R., Mason, A., Burton, L., and Vale, W. (1991). Effect of recombinant inhibin on gonadotropin secretion during proestrus and estrus in the rat. *Endocrinology* 128, 2223–2228.
78. Rivier, C., Schwall, R., Mason, A., Burton, L., Vaughan, J., and Vale, W. (1991). Effect of recombinant inhibin on luteinizing hormone and follicle-stimulating hormone secretion in the rat. *Endocrinology* 128, 1548–1554.
79. Woodruff, T. K., Krummen, L. A., Lyon, R. J., Stocks, D. L., and Mather, J. P. (1993). Recombinant human inhibin A and recombinant human activin A regulate pituitary and ovarian function in the adult female rat. *Endocrinology* 132, 2332–2341.
80. Rivier, C., and Vale, W. (1989). Immunoneutralization of endogenous inhibin modifies hormone secretion and ovulation rate in the rat. *Endocrinology* 125, 152–157.
81. Ling, N., Ying, S. Y., Ueno, N., et al. (1986). Pituitary FSH is released by a heterodimer of the beta-subunits from the two forms of inhibin. *Nature* 321, 779–782.
82. Vale, W., Rivier, J., Vaughan, J., et al. (1986). Purification and characterization of an FSH releasing protein from porcine ovarian follicular fluid. *Nature* 321, 776–779.
83. Carroll, R. S., Corrigan, A. Z., Vale, W., and Chin, W. W. (1991). Activin stabilizes follicle-stimulating hormone-beta messenger ribonucleic acid levels. *Endocrinology* 129, 1721–1726.

84. Rivier, C., and Vale, W. (1991). Effect of recombinant activin-A on gonadotropin secretion in the female rat. *Endocrinology* 129, 2463–2465.
85. DePaolo, L. V., Bicsak, T. A., Erickson, G. F., Shimasaki, S., and Ling, N. (1991). Follistatin and activin: A potential intrinsic regulatory system within diverse tissues. *Proc. Soc. Exp. Biol. Med.* 198, 500–512.
86. Roberts, V., Meunier, H., Vaughan, J., et al. (1989). Production and regulation of inhibin subunits in pituitary gonadotropes. *Endocrinology* 124, 552–554.
87. DePaolo, L. V., Bald, L. N., and Fendly, B. M. (1992). Passive immunoneutralization with a monoclonal antibody reveals a role for endogenous activin-B in mediating FSH hypersecretion during estrus and following ovariectomy of hypophysectomized, pituitary-grafted rats. *Endocrinology* 130, 1741–1743.
88. Bilezikjian, L. M., Vaughan, J. M., and Vale, W. W. (1993). Characterization and the regulation of inhibin/activin subunit proteins of cultured rat anterior pituitary cells. *Endocrinology* 133, 2545–2553.
89. Halvorson, L. M., Weiss, J., Bauer-Dantoin, A. C., and Jameson, J. L. (1994). Dynamic regulation of pituitary follistatin messenger ribonucleic acids during the rat estrous cycle. *Endocrinology* 134, 1247–1253.
90. Bilezikjian, L. M., Corrigan, A. Z., Blount, A. L., Chen, Y., and Vale, W. W. (2001). Regulation and actions of Smad7 in the modulation of activin, inhibin, and transforming growth factor-beta signaling in anterior pituitary cells. *Endocrinology* 142, 1065–1072.
91. Sehested, A., Juul, A. A., Andersson, A. M., et al. (2000). Serum inhibin A and inhibin B in healthy prepubertal, pubertal, and adolescent girls and adult women: Relation to age, stage of puberty, menstrual cycle, follicle-stimulating hormone, luteinizing hormone, and estradiol levels. *J. Clin. Endocrinol. Metab.* 85, 1634–1640.
92. Bergada, I., Bergada, C., and Campo, S. (2001). Role of inhibins in childhood and puberty. *J. Pediatr. Endocrinol. Metab.* 14, 343–353.
93. Raivio, T., and Dunkel, L. (2002). Inhibins in childhood and puberty. *Best Pract. Res. Clin. Endocrinol. Metab.* 16, 43–52.
94. Foster, C. M., Phillips, D. J., Wyman, T., Evans, L. W., Groome, N. P., and Padmanabhan, V. (2000). Changes in serum inhibin, activin, and follistatin concentrations during puberty in girls. *Hum. Reprod.* 15, 1052–1057.
95. Yokota, H., Yamada, K., Liu, X., et al. (1997). Paradoxical action of activin A on folliculogenesis in immature and adult mice. *Endocrinology* 138, 4572–4576.
96. Liu, X., Andoh, K., Abe, Y., et al. (1999). A comparative study on transforming growth factor-beta and activin A for preantral follicles from adult, immature, and diethylstilbestrol-primed immature mice. *Endocrinology* 140, 2480–2485.
97. Miro, F., and Hillier, S. G. (1996). Modulation of granulosa cell deoxyribonucleic acid synthesis and differentiation by activin. *Endocrinology* 137, 464–468.
98. Zhao, J., Taverne, M. A., van der Weijden, G. C., Bevers, M. M., and van den Hurk, R. (2001). Effect of activin A on in vitro development of rat preantral follicles and localization of activin A and activin receptor II. *Biol. Reprod.* 65, 967–977.
99. Woodruff, T. K., Lyon, R. J., Hansen, S. E., Rice, G. C., and Mather, J. P. (1990). Inhibin and activin locally regulate rat ovarian folliculogenesis. *Endocrinology* 127, 3196–3205.
100. Uilenbroek, J. T., and Richards, J. S. (1979). Ovarian follicular development during the rat estrous cycle: Gonadotropin receptors and follicular responsiveness. *Biol. Reprod.* 20, 1159–1165.
101. Camp, T. A., Rahal, J. O., and Mayo, K. E. (1991). Cellular localization and hormonal regulation of follicle-stimulating hormone and luteinizing hormone receptor messenger RNAs in the rat ovary. *Mol. Endocrinol.* 5, 1405–1417.
102. Erickson G. (2001). Folliculogenesis, ovulation, and luteogenesis. In *Endocrinology*, 4th ed., eds. L. DeGroot and J. L. Jameson, 2061–2071. Philadelphia: W. B. Saunders Co.
103. Miro F, and Hillier SG. (1992). Relative effects of activin and inhibin on steroid hormone synthesis in primate granulosa cells. *J. Clin. Endocrinol. Metab.* 75, 1556–1561.
104. Miro, F., Smyth, C. D., and Hillier, S. G. (1991). Development-related effects of recombinant activin on steroid synthesis in rat granulosa cells. *Endocrinology* 129, 3388–3394.
105. Stouffer, R. L., Woodruff, T. K., Dahl, K. D., Hess, D. L., Mather, J. P., and Molskness, T. A. (1993). Human recombinant activin-A alters pituitary luteinizing hormone and follicle-stimulating hormone secretion, follicular development, and steroidogenesis during the menstrual cycle in rhesus monkeys. *J. Clin. Endocrinol. Metab.* 77, 241–248.
106. Hillier, S. G., Yong, E. L., Illingworth, P. J., Baird, D. T., Schwall, R. H., and Mason, A. J. (1991). Effect of recombinant inhibin on androgen synthesis in cultured human thecal cells. *Mol. Cell. Endocrinol.* 75, R1–R6.
107. Hillier, S. G., Yong, E. L., Illingworth, P. J., Baird, D. T., Schwall, R. H., and Mason, A. J. (1991). Effect of recombinant activin on androgen synthesis in cultured human thecal cells. *J. Clin. Endocrinol. Metab.* 72, 1206–1211.
108. Hsueh, A. J., Dahl, K. D., Vaughan, J., et al. (1987). Heterodimers and homodimers of inhibin subunits have different paracrine action in the modulation of luteinizing hormone-stimulated androgen biosynthesis. *Proc. Natl. Acad. Sci. USA* 84, 5082–5086.
109. Miro, F., Smyth, C. D., Whitelaw, P. F., Milne, M., and Hillier, S. G. (1995). Regulation of 3 beta-hydroxysteroid dehydrogenase delta 5/delta 4-isomerase and cholesterol side-chain cleavage cytochrome P450 by activin in rat granulosa cells. *Endocrinology* 136, 3247–3252.
110. Sawetawan, C., Carr, B. R., McGee, E., Bird, I. M., Hong, T. L., and Rainey, W. E. (1996). Inhibin and activin differentially regulate androgen production and 17 alpha-hydroxylase expression in human ovarian thecal-like tumor cells. *J. Endocrinol.* 148, 213–221.
111. Nakamura, M., Minegishi, T., Hasegawa, Y., et al. (1993). Effect of an activin A on follicle-stimulating hormone (FSH) receptor messenger ribonucleic acid levels and FSH receptor expressions in cultured rat granulosa cells. *Endocrinology* 133, 538–544.
112. Hasegawa, Y., Miyamoto, K., Abe, Y., et al. (1988). Induction of follicle stimulating hormone receptor by erythroid differentiation factor on rat granulosa cell. *Biochem. Biophys. Res. Commun.* 156, 668–674.
113. Xiao, S., Robertson, D. M., and Findlay, J. K. (1992). Effects of activin and follicle-stimulating hormone (FSH)-

suppressing protein/follistatin on FSH receptors and differentiation of cultured rat granulosa cells. *Endocrinology* 131, 1009–1016.

114. Nakamura, M., Nakamura, K., Igarashi, S., et al. (1995). Interaction between activin A and cAMP in the induction of FSH receptor in cultured rat granulosa cells. *J. Endocrinol.* 147, 103–110.
115. Tano, M., Minegishi, T., Nakamura, K., Karino, S., Ibuki, Y., and Miyamoto, K. (1997). Transcriptional and post-transcriptional regulation of FSH receptor in rat granulosa cells by cyclic AMP and activin. *J. Endocrinol.* 153, 465–473.
116. Lockwood, G. M., Ledger, W. L., Barlow, D. H., Groome, N. P., and Muttukrishna, S. (1998). Identification of the source of inhibins at the time of conception provides a diagnostic role for them in very early pregnancy. *Am. J. Reprod. Immunol.* 40, 303–308.
117. Ohshima, K., Arai, K. Y., Kishi, H., et al. (2002). Potential role of activin A in follicular development during the second half of pregnancy in the golden hamster: Utero-placental source of activin A. *J. Endocrinol.* 172, 247–253.
118. Brannian, J. D., Woodruff, T. K., Mather, J. P., and Stouffer, R. L. (1992). Activin-A inhibits progesterone production by macaque luteal cells in culture. *J. Clin. Endocrinol. Metab.* 75, 756–761.
119. Lockwood, G. M., Muttukrishna, S., and Ledger, W. L. (1998). Inhibins and activins in human ovulation, conception and pregnancy. *Hum. Reprod. Update* 4, 284–295.
120. Woodruff, T. K., Sluss, P., Wang, E., Janssen, I., and Mersol-Barg, M. S. (1997). Activin A and follistatin are dynamically regulated during human pregnancy. *J. Endocrinol.* 152, 167–174.
121. Baker, T. (1963). A quantitative and cytological study of germ cells in human ovaries. *Proc. R. Soc. Biol.* 158, 417.
122. Block, E. (1951). Quantitative morphological investigations of the follicular system in women. *Acta. Endocrinol.* 8, 33.
123. Richardson, S. J., Senikas, V., and Nelson, J. F. (1987). Follicular depletion during the menopausal transition: Evidence for accelerated loss and ultimate exhaustion. *J. Clin. Endocrinol. Metab.* 65, 1231–1237.
124. Seifer, D. B., Lambert-Messerlian, G., Hogan, J. W., Gardiner, A. C., Blazar, A. S., and Berk, C. A. (1997). Day 3 serum inhibin-B is predictive of assisted reproductive technologies outcome. *Fertil. Steril.* 67, 110–114.
125. Seifer, D. B., Scott, Jr., R. T., Bergh, P. A., et al. (1999). Women with declining ovarian reserve may demonstrate a decrease in day 3 serum inhibin B before a rise in day 3 follicle-stimulating hormone. *Fertil. Steril.* 72, 63–65.
126. Richardson, S. J., and Nelson, J. F. (1990). Follicular depletion during the menopausal transition. *Ann. N. Y. Acad. Sci.* 592, 13–20; discussion 44–51.
127. Tepper, R., Zalel, Y., Markov, S., Cohen, I., and Beyth, Y. (1995). Ovarian volume in postmenopausal women—suggestions to an ovarian size nomogram for menopausal age. *Acta. Obstet. Gynecol. Scand.* 74, 208–211.
128. Faddy, M. J., and Gosden, R. G. (1996). A model conforming the decline in follicle numbers to the age of menopause in women. *Hum. Reprod.* 11, 1484–1486.
129. Costoff, A., and Mahesh, V. B. (1975). Primordial follicles with normal oocytes in the ovaries of postmenopausal women. *J. Am. Geriatr. Soc.* 23, 193–196.
130. Klein, N. A., Battaglia, D. E., Miller, P. B., Branigan, E. F., Giudice, L. C., and Soules, M. R. (1996). Ovarian follicular development and the follicular fluid hormones and growth factors in normal women of advanced reproductive age. *J. Clin. Endocrinol. Metab.* 81, 1946–1951.
131. Hee, J., MacNaughton, J., Bangah, M., and Burger, H. G. (1993). Perimenopausal patterns of gonadotrophins, immunoreactive inhibin, oestradiol, and progesterone. *Maturitas* 18, 9–20.
132. Ala-Fossi, S. L., Maenpaa, J., Blauer, M., Aine, R., Tuohimaa, P., and Punnonen, R. (1998). Inhibin A and B in peri- and postmenopause. *Maturitas* 30, 273–281.
133. Burger, H. G., Cahir, N., Robertson, D. M., et al. (1998). Serum inhibins A and B fall differentially as FSH rises in perimenopausal women. *Clin. Endocrinol. (Oxf.)* 48, 809–813.
134. Soules, M. R., Battaglia, D. E., and Klein, N. A. (1998). Inhibin and reproductive aging in women. *Maturitas* 30, 193–204.
135. Klein, N. A., Illingworth, P. J., Groome, N. P., McNeilly, A. S., Battaglia, D. E., and Soules MR (1996). Decreased inhibin B secretion is associated with the monotropic FSH rise in older, ovulatory women: A study of serum and follicular fluid levels of dimeric inhibin A and B in spontaneous menstrual cycles. *J. Clin. Endocrinol. Metab.* 81, 2742–2745.
136. Santoro, N., Adel, T., and Skurnick, J. H. (1999). Decreased inhibin tone and increased activin A secretion characterize reproductive aging in women. *Fertil. Steril.* 71, 658–662.
137. Welt, C. K., McNicholl, D. J., Taylor, A. E., and Hall, J. E. (1999). Female reproductive aging is marked by decreased secretion of dimeric inhibin. *J. Clin. Endocrinol. Metab.* 84, 105–111.
138. Robertson, D. M., and Burger, H. G. (2002). Reproductive hormones: Ageing and the perimenopause. *Acta. Obstet. Gynecol. Scand.* 81, 612–616.
139. Klein, N. A., Battaglia, D. E., Woodruff, T. K., et al. (2000). Ovarian follicular concentrations of activin, follistatin, inhibin, insulin-like growth factor I (IGF-I), IGF-II, IGF-binding protein-2 (IGFBP-2), IGFBP-3, and vascular endothelial growth factor in spontaneous menstrual cycles of normal women of advanced reproductive age. *J. Clin. Endocrinol. Metab.* 85, 4520–4525.
140. MacNaughton, J., Banah, M., McCloud, P., Hee, J., and Burger, H. (1992). Age-related changes in follicle-stimulating hormone, luteinizing hormone, oestradiol, and immunoreactive inhibin in women of reproductive age. *Clin. Endocrinol. (Oxf.)* 36, 339–345.
141. Burger, H. G., Dudley, E. C., Hopper, J. L., et al. (1999). Prospectively measured levels of serum follicle-stimulating hormone, estradiol, and the dimeric inhibins during the menopausal transition in a population-based cohort of women. *J. Clin. Endocrinol. Metab.* 84, 4025–4030.
142. Longcope, C. (2001). Endocrine function of the postmenopausal ovary. *J. Soc. Gynecol. Investig.* 8, S67-S68.
143. Matzuk, M. M., Kumar, T. R., and Bradley, A. (1995). Different phenotypes for mice deficient in either activins or activin receptor type II. *Nature* 374, 356–360.
144. Matzuk, M. M., Kumar, T. R., Shou, W., et al. (1996). Transgenic models to study the roles of inhibins and activins in

reproduction, oncogenesis, and development. *Rec. Prog. Hormone Res.* 51, 123–154; discussion 155–157.

145. Chang, H., Lau, A. L., and Matzuk, M. M. (2001). Studying TGF-beta superfamily signaling by knockouts and knockins. *Mol. Cell. Endocrinol.* 180, 39–46.
146. Cho, B. N., McMullen, M. L., Pei, L., Yates, C. J., and Mayo, K. E. (2001). Reproductive deficiencies in transgenic mice expressing the rat inhibin alpha-subunit gene. *Endocrinology* 142, 4994–5004.
147. McMullen, M. L., Cho, B. N., Yates, C. J., and Mayo, K. E. (2001). Gonadal pathologies in transgenic mice expressing the rat inhibin alpha-subunit. *Endocrinology* 142, 5005–5014.
148. Pierson, T. M., Wang, Y., DeMayo, F. J., Matzuk, M. M., Tsai, S. Y., and Omalley, B. W. (2000). Regulable expression of inhibin A in wild-type and inhibin alpha null mice. *Mol. Endocrinol.* 14, 1075–1085.
149. Vassalli, A., Matzuk, M. M., Gardner, H. A., Lee, K. F., and Jaenisch, R. (1994). Activin/inhibin beta B subunit gene disruption leads to defects in eyelid development and female reproduction. *Genes Dev.* 8, 414–427.
150. Brown, C. W., Houston-Hawkins, D. E., Woodruff, T. K., and Matzuk, M. M. (2000). Insertion of Inhbb into the Inhba locus rescues the Inhba-null phenotype and reveals new activin functions. *Nat. Genet.* 25, 453–457.
151. Westhoff, C. (1996). Ovarian cancer. *Annu. Rev. Public Health* 17, 85–96.
152. Holschneider, C. H., and Berek, J. S. (2000). Ovarian cancer: Epidemiology, biology, and prognostic factors. *Semin. Surg. Oncol.* 19, 3–10.
153. Risbridger, G. P., Schmitt, J. F., and Robertson, D. M. (2001). Activins and inhibins in endocrine and other tumors. *Endocr. Rev.* 22, 836–858.
154. Zheng, W., Luo, M. P., Welt, C., et al. (1998). Imbalanced expression of inhibin and activin subunits in primary epithelial ovarian cancer. *Gynecol. Oncol.* 69, 23–31.
155. Flemming, P., Wellmann, A., Maschek, H., Lang, H., and Georgii, A. (1995). Monoclonal antibodies against inhibin represent key markers of adult granulosa cell tumors of the ovary even in their metastases. A report of three cases with late metastasis, being previously misinterpreted as hemangiopericytoma. *Am. J. Surg. Pathol.* 19, 927–933.
156. Gurusinghe, C. J., Healy, D. L., Jobling, T., Mamers, P., and Burger, H. G. (1995). Inhibin and activin are demonstrable by immunohistochemistry in ovarian tumor tissue. *Gynecol. Oncol.* 57, 27–32.
157. Flemming, P., Grothe, W., Maschek, H., Petry, K. U., Wellmann, A., and Georgii, A. (1996). The site of inhibin production in ovarian neoplasms. *Histopathology* 29, 465–468.
158. Arora, D. S., Cooke, I. E., Ganesan, T. S., et al. (1997). Immunohistochemical expression of inhibin/activin subunits in epithelial and granulosa cell tumours of the ovary. *J. Pathol.* 181, 413–8.
159. Fuller, P. J., Chu, S., Jobling, T., Mamers, P., Healy, D. L., and Burger, H. G. (1999). Inhibin subunit gene expression in ovarian cancer. *Gynecol. Oncol.* 73, 273–279.
160. Ala-Fossi, S. L., Aine, R., Punnonen, R., and Maenpaa, J. (2000). Is potential to produce inhibins related to prognosis in ovarian granulosa cell tumors? *Eur. J. Gynaecol. Oncol.* 21, 187–189.
161. Ala-Fossi, S. L., Maenpaa, J., Blauer, M., Tuohimaa, P., and Punnonen, R. (2000). Inhibin A, B, and pro-alphaC in serum and peritoneal fluid in postmenopausal patients with ovarian tumors. *J. Endocrinol. Eur. J. Endocrinol.* 142, 334–339.
162. Gebhart, J. B., Roche, P. C., Keeney, G. L., Lesnick, T. G., and Podratz, K. C. (2000). Assessment of inhibin and p53 in granulosa cell tumors of the ovary. *Gynecol. Oncol.* 77, 232–236.
163. Fuller, P. J., Zumpe, E. T., Chu, S., Mamers, P., and Burger, H. G. (2002). Inhibin-activin receptor subunit gene expression in ovarian tumors. *J. Clin. Endocrinol. Metab.* 87, 1395–1401.
164. Reis, F. M., Faletti, A., Luisi, S., et al. (2000). High concentrations of inhibin A and inhibin B in ovarian serous cystadenoma: Relationship with oestradiol and nitric oxide metabolites. *Mol. Hum. Reprod.* 6, 1079–1083.
165. Healy, D. L., Burger, H. G., Mamers, P., et al. (1993). Elevated serum inhibin concentrations in postmenopausal women with ovarian tumors. *N. Engl. J. Med.* 329, 1539–1542.
166. Burger, H. G., Baillie, A., Drummond, A. E., et al. (1998). Inhibin and ovarian cancer. *J. Reprod. Immunol.* 39, 77–87.
167. Burger, H. G., Robertson, D. M., Cahir, N., et al. (1996). Characterization of inhibin immunoreactivity in postmenopausal women with ovarian tumours. *Clin. Endocrinol. (Oxf.)* 44, 413–418.
168. Robertson, D. M., Cahir, N., Burger, H. G., Mamers, P., and Groome, N. (1999). Inhibin forms in serum from postmenopausal women with ovarian cancers. *Clin. Endocrinol. (Oxf.)* 50, 381–386.
169. Lappohn, R. E., Burger, H. G., Bouma, J., Bangah, M., Krans, M., and de Bruijn, H. W. (1989). Inhibin as a marker for granulosa-cell tumors. *N. Engl. J. Med.* 321, 790–793.
170. Healy, D. L., Mamers, P., Bangah, M., and Burger, H. G. (1993). Clinical and pathophysiological aspects of inhibin. *Hum. Reprod.* 8 (Suppl 2), 138–140.
171. Cooke, I., O'Brien, M., Charnock, F. M., Groome, N., and Ganesan, T. S. (1995). Inhibin as a marker for ovarian cancer. *Br. J. Cancer* 71, 1046–1050.
172. Burger, H. G., Fuller, P. J., Chu, S., et al. (2001). The inhibins and ovarian cancer. *Mol. Cell. Endocrinol.* 180, 145–148.
173. Petraglia, F., Luisi, S., Pautier, P., et al. (1998). Inhibin B is the major form of inhibin/activin family secreted by granulosa cell tumors. *J. Clin. Endocrinol. Metab.* 83, 1029–1032.
174. Lambert-Messerlian, G. M., Steinhoff, M., Zheng, W., et al. (1997). Multiple immunoreactive inhibin proteins in serum from postmenopausal women with epithelial ovarian cancer. *Gynecol. Oncol.* 65, 512–516.
175. Robertson, D. M., Stephenson, T., Pruysers, E., et al. (2002). Inhibins/activins as diagnostic markers for ovarian cancer. *Mol. Cell. Endocrinol.* 191, 97–103.
176. Frias, Jr., A. E., Li, H., Keeney, G. L., Podratz, K. C., and Woodruff, T. K. (1999). Preoperative serum level of inhibin A is an independent prognostic factor for the survival of postmenopausal women with epithelial ovarian carcinoma. *Cancer* 85, 465–471.
177. McCluggage, W. G. (2002). Recent advances in immunohistochemistry in gynaecological pathology. *Histopathology* 40, 309–326.
178. Robertson, D. M., Stephenson, T., Pruysers, E., et al. (2002). Characterization of inhibin forms and their measurement by an inhibin alpha-subunit ELISA in serum from post-

menopausal women with ovarian cancer. *J. Clin. Endocrinol. Metab.* 87, 816–824.

179. Minegishi, T., Kameda, T., Hirakawa, T., Abe, K., Tano, M., and Ibuki, Y. (2000). Expression of gonadotropin and activin receptor messenger ribonucleic acid in human ovarian epithelial neoplasms. *Clin. Cancer Res.* 6, 2764–2770.
180. Ito, I., Minegishi, T., Fukuda, J., Shinozaki, H., Auersperg, N., and Leung, P. C. (2000). Presence of activin signal transduction in normal ovarian cells and epithelial ovarian carcinoma. *Br. J. Cancer* 82, 1415–1420.
181. Choi, K. C., Kang, S. K., Nathwani, P. S., Cheng, K. W., Auersperg, N., and Leung, P. C. (2001). Differential expression of activin/inhibin subunit and activin receptor mRNAs in normal and neoplastic ovarian surface epithelium (OSE). *Mol. Cell. Endocrinol.* 174, 99–110.
182. Di Simone, N., Crowley, Jr., W. F., Wang, Q. F., Sluss, P. M., and Schneyer, A. L. (1996). Characterization of inhibin/activin subunit, follistatin, and activin type II receptors in human ovarian cancer cell lines: A potential role in autocrine growth regulation. *Endocrinology* 137, 486–494.
183. Welt, C. K., Lambert-Messerlian, G., Zheng, W., Crowley, Jr., W. F., and Schneyer, A. L. (1997). Presence of activin, inhibin, and follistatin in epithelial ovarian carcinoma. *J. Clin. Endocrinol. Metab.* 82, 3720–3727.
184. Knochenhauer, E. S., Key, T. J., Kahsar-Miller, M., Waggoner, W., Boots, L. R., and Azziz, R. (1998). Prevalence of the polycystic ovary syndrome in unselected black and white women of the southeastern United States: A prospective study. *J. Clin. Endocrinol. Metab.* 83, 3078–3082.
185. Dewailly, D. (2000). Definition of polycystic ovary syndrome. *Hum. Fertil. (Camb.)* 3, 73–76.
186. Dunaif, A., and Thomas, A. (2001). Current concepts in the polycystic ovary syndrome. *Annu. Rev. Med.* 52, 401–419.
187. Urbanek, M., Legro, R. S., Driscoll, D. A., et al. (1999). Thirty-seven candidate genes for polycystic ovary syndrome: Strongest evidence for linkage is with follistatin. *Proc. Natl. Acad. Sci. USA* 96, 8573–8578.
188. Liao, W. X., Roy, A. C., and Ng, S. C. (2000). Preliminary investigation of follistatin gene mutations in women with polycystic ovary syndrome. *Mol. Hum. Reprod.* 6, 587–590.
189. Urbanek, M., Wu, X., Vickery, K. R., et al. (2000). Allelic variants of the follistatin gene in polycystic ovary syndrome. *J. Clin. Endocrinol. Metab.* 85, 4455–4461.
190. Pigny, P., Cortet-Rudelli, C., Decanter, C., et al. (2000). Serum levels of inhibins are differentially altered in patients with polycystic ovary syndrome: Effects of being overweight and relevance to hyperandrogenism. *Fertil. Steril.* 73, 972–977.
191. Mizunuma, H., Andoh, K., Obara, M., et al. (1994). Serum immunoreactive inhibin levels in polycystic ovarian disease (PCOD) and hypogonadotropic amenorrhea. *Endocr. J.* 41, 409–414.
192. Pigny, P., Desailloud, R., Cortet-Rudelli, C., et al. (1997). Serum alpha-inhibin levels in polycystic ovary syndrome: Relationship to the serum androstenedione level. *J. Clin. Endocrinol. Metab.* 82, 1939–1943.
193. Anderson, R. A., Groome, N. P., and Baird, D. T. (1998). Inhibin A and inhibin B in women with polycystic ovarian syndrome during treatment with FSH to induce mono-ovulation. *Clin. Endocrinol. (Oxf.)* 48, 577–584.
194. Lockwood, G. M., Muttukrishna, S., Groome, N. P., Matthews, D. R., and Ledger, W. L. (1998). Mid-follicular phase pulses of inhibin B are absent in polycystic ovarian syndrome and are initiated by successful laparoscopic ovarian diathermy: A possible mechanism regulating emergence of the dominant follicle. *J. Clin. Endocrinol. Metab.* 83, 1730–1735.
195. Norman, R. J., Milner, C. R., Groome, N. P., and Robertson, D. M. (2001). Circulating follistatin concentrations are higher and activin concentrations are lower in polycystic ovarian syndrome. *Hum. Reprod.* 16, 668–672.
196. Lockwood, G. M. (2000). The role of inhibin in polycystic ovary syndrome. *Hum. Fertil. (Camb.)* 3, 86–92.
197. Lambert-Messerlian, G. M., Hall, J. E., Sluss, P. M., et al. (1994). Relatively low levels of dimeric inhibin circulate in men and women with polycystic ovarian syndrome using a specific two-site enzyme-linked immunosorbent assay. *J. Clin. Endocrinol. Metab.* 79, 45–50.
198. Erickson, G. F., Chung, D. G., Sit, A., DePaolo, L. V., Shimasaki, S., and Ling, N. (1995). Follistatin concentrations in follicular fluid of normal and polycystic ovaries. *Hum. Reprod.* 10, 2120–2124.
199. Magoffin, D. A., and Jakimiuk, A. J. (1998). Inhibin A, inhibin B, and activin A concentrations in follicular fluid from women with polycystic ovary syndrome. *Hum. Reprod.* 13, 2693–2698.
200. Laven, J. S., Imani, B., Eijkemans, M. J., de Jong, F. H., and Fauser, B. C. (2001). Absent biologically relevant associations between serum inhibin B concentrations and characteristics of polycystic ovary syndrome in normogonadotrophic anovulatory infertility. *Hum. Reprod.* 16, 1359–1364.
201. Fujiwara, T., Sidis, Y., Welt, C., et al. (2001). Dynamics of inhibin subunit and follistatin mRNA during development of normal and polycystic ovary syndrome follicles. *J. Clin. Endocrinol. Metab.* 86, 4206–4215.
202. Coulam, C. B., Adamson, S. C., and Annegers, J. F. (1986). Incidence of premature ovarian failure. *Obstet. Gynecol.* 67, 604–606.
203. Vegetti, W., Grazia, Tibiletti, M., Testa, G., et al. (1998). Inheritance in idiopathic premature ovarian failure: Analysis of 71 cases. *Hum. Reprod.* 13, 1796–1800.
204. van Kasteren, Y. M., Hundscheid, R. D., Smits, A. P., Cremers, F. P., van Zonneveld, P., and Braat, D. D. (1999). Familial idiopathic premature ovarian failure: An overrated and underestimated genetic disease? *Hum. Reprod.* 14, 2455–2459.
205. Christin-Maitre, S., Vasseur, C., Portnoi, M. F., and Bouchard, P. (1998). Genes and premature ovarian failure. *Mol. Cell. Endocrinol.* 145, 75–80.
206. Lutjen, P. J., Findlay, J. K., Trounson, A. O., Leeton, J. F., and Chan, L. K. (1986). Effect on plasma gonadotropins of cyclic steroid replacement in women with premature ovarian failure. *J. Clin. Endocrinol. Metab.* 62, 419–423.
207. Shelling, A. N., Burton, K. A., Chand, A. L., et al. (2000). Inhibin: A candidate gene for premature ovarian failure. *Hum. Reprod.* 15, 2644–2649.
208. Marozzi, A., Porta, C., Vegetti, W., et al. (2002). Mutation analysis of the inhibin alpha gene in a cohort of Italian women affected by ovarian failure. *Hum. Reprod.* 17, 1741–1745.

CHAPTER **17**

Gn-RH as an Autocrine Regulator in the Human Ovary

PETER C. K. LEUNG AND C. K. CHENG

ABSTRACT

Gonadotropin-releasing hormone (Gn-RH) is a decapeptide that plays a pivotal endocrine role in regulating mammalian reproductive processes. However, two forms of Gn-RHs, namely Gn-RH-I and Gn-RH-II, are also expressed locally in various human ovarian compartments, and their expressions in the ovary are differentially regulated by their own ligands, gonadal steroids and gonadotropins. Concomitantly, receptors specific for the Gn-RH-I (mammalian Gn-RH-I receptor) have also been detected in different ovarian cell types, and their nucleotide sequences are identical to those present in the gonadotropes. Functionally, these hormones regulate ovarian steroidogenesis, cell proliferation, and apoptosis via receptor-mediated mechanisms, supporting a notion that these peptides act as autocrine and/or paracrine regulators in the ovary. Unlike the classical signaling cascade in the gonadotropes, there is solid evidence that the mammalian Gn-RH-I receptor is coupled to the PTX-sensitive $G\alpha_i$ protein in ovarian tumors and mediates its antiproliferative effect via modulation of the extracellular signal-regulated kinase activity. Recent cloning of a second form of Gn-RH receptor (Gn-RH-II receptor) in monkeys reveals that it is structurally and functionally distinct from the mammalian Gn-RH-I receptor. In humans, this second receptor subtype has been shown to be expressed in the brain, anterior pituitary gland, and also certain ovarian cancer cell lines where treatment with Gn-RH-II exerts significantly stronger antiproliferative effect than equimolar doses of Gn-RH-I. Nevertheless, direct evidence to demonstrate the existence of a full-length and functional Gn-RH-II receptor transcript in human tissues is lacking, and whether this transcript could be identified under certain physiological conditions remains to be determined.

BACKGROUND

Gonadotropin-Releasing Hormone-I

Hypothalamic Gn-RH-I is a decapeptide (pGlu-His-Trp-Ser-Tyr-Gly-Leu-Arg-Pro-Gly-NH_2) that plays a pivotal role in the reproductive endocrine system in mammals. It is produced by hypothalamic neurosecretory cells and released in a pulsatile manner into the hypothalamo-hypophyseal portal circulation via which the hormone is transported to the anterior pituitary gland. After binding to its high-affinity receptors on the gonadotropes, the hormone stimulates the biosynthesis and secretion of luteinizing hormone (LH) and follicle-stimulating hormone (FSH), which in turn regulate the steroidogenic and gametogenic functions of gonads in both sexes [1]. Since its discovery some 30 years ago, thousands of Gn-RH-I analogs have been developed and studied extensively [2]. Clinically, some of these synthetic analogs have been used as an effective treatment for a variety of reproductive endocrinopathies such as prostate cancer [3], whereas others have been adopted as a component of the regimen for ovulation induction in women undergoing in vitro fertilization [4].

Cloning and characterization of the complementary deoxyribonucleic acid (cDNA) for the human Gn-RH-I gene reveal that it codes for a 92 amino acid-precursor protein in which the decapeptide is preceded by a signal peptide and followed by a Gly-Lys-Arg (G-K-R) sequence and a Gn-RH-associated peptide [5]. The G-K-R sequence signals amidation of the carboxyl terminus and enzymatic cleavage of the decapeptide from the precursor. In addition, the human gene has been mapped as a single copy to the short arm of chromosome 8 by chromosomal in situ hybridization [6] and was shown to contain four exons interrupted by three introns [7].

Gonadotropin-Releasing Hormone-II

Until recently, Gn-RH-I was believed to be the sole hypothalamic regulator that controls reproductive processes in

	1	2	3	4	5	6	7	8	9	10
Mammalian GnRH-I:	pGlu-	His-	Trp-	Ser-	**Tyr**-	Gly-	**Leu**-	**Arg**-	Pro-	Gly-NH_2
Chicken GnRH-II:	pGlu-	His-	Trp-	Ser-	**His**-	Gly-	**Trp**-	**Tyr**-	Pro-	Gly-NH_2

FIGURE 17.1 Comparison of the primary structures of mammalian Gn-RH-I and chicken Gn-RH-II. The primary sequences of these peptides are identical except at positions 5, 7, and 8 *(bold)*.

mammals. However, the identification of a second form of Gn-RH in chicken hypothalamus (termed *Gn-RH-II*) reveals that it is the most widely expressed form of Gn-RHs and that its structure is conserved among vertebrates from the primitive fish to human [8–17]. This second Gn-RH form defers from the mammalian Gn-RH-I by three amino acid residues at positions 5, 7, and 8 (His^5, Trp^7, Tyr^8) (Figure 17.1). Although the physiological significance of Gn-RH-II remains largely unknown to date, the wide distribution and conservation of this Gn-RH form over all vertebrate classes implies that this hormone may have vital biological functions.

The gene encoding Gn-RH-II has been cloned from monkey and human brains [18, 19], and the human gene has been mapped to chromosome 20p13 [19]. Nucleotide sequencing reveals that the human Gn-RH-II genomic and messenger ribonucleic acid (mRNA) structures parallel those of the Gn-RH-I, except the Gn-RH-II gene (2.1 kb) is remarkably shorter when compared with Gn-RH-I (5.1 kb). In addition, in contrast to Gn-RH-I, Gn-RH-II is expressed at significantly higher levels outside the brain, particularly in kidney, bone marrow, and prostate [19], suggesting that it may possess multiple functions other than neuroendocrine regulation.

Gonadotropin-Releasing Hormone-I Receptor

Gn-RH-I receptor is a member of the rhodopsin-like G protein-coupled receptors (GPCRs), which contain a characteristic seven-transmembrane domain and transmit their signals primarily through heterotrimeric G proteins. However, the mammalian Gn-RH-I receptor is unique among GPCRs in that it lacks the entire cytoplasmic carboxyl-terminal domain that is known to be responsible for receptor internalization and desensitization on ligand stimulation [20]. The nature of intracellular signaling elicited by the Gn-RH-I receptor is dependent on cellular contexts, and in the well-studied gonadotrope-derived αT3-1 cells, the receptor is coupled to the $G\alpha_{q/11}$ protein that activates phospholipase C_β, leading to the production of diacylglycerol and inositol 1,4,5-triphosphate. The latter messenger stimulates Ca^{2+} release from intracellular stores, which is known to be an important trigger for gonadotropin secretion [21–25]. In addition, the production of these intermediate messengers also leads to the activation of different protein kinase C subspecies, which act in a coordinated manner to induce various downstream signal transduction cascades including the extracellular signal-regulated kinase (Erk) and Jun N-terminal kinase (JNK) signaling pathways [26].

Our laboratory has previously mapped the human Gn-RH-I receptor gene to chromosome band 4q21.2 by fluorescence in situ hybridization [27]. In contrast to the genes of many other GPCRs, which do not have any introns and are believed to have arisen by retroposition [28], the entire coding region of the human Gn-RH-I receptor is distributed over three exons [29]. Further analysis of the 5′- and 3′-flanking regions of the human gene reveal that it contains multiple consensus TATA sequences, transcription start sites, and polyadenylation signals [30], indicating that its expression is under the control of complex transcriptional machinery.

Recently, receptors specific for Gn-RH-II have been cloned in a number of fish, amphibians, and monkeys [31–37]. Characterization of the primate Gn-RH-II receptors shows that this second receptor subtype contains an intracellular carboxyl-terminal tail and possesses distinct ligand selectivity. Additionally, this receptor subtype can elicit signal transduction pathways that are different from those triggered by the mammalian Gn-RH-I receptor [36, 37]. However, the biological roles of this second Gn-RH receptor subtype remain obscure; its significance in humans will be discussed in more detail in later sections.

EXPRESSION OF GN-RH-I, GN-RH-II, AND GN-RH-I RECEPTOR GENE IN THE HUMAN OVARY

In addition to their expressions in the brain area, human Gn-RH-I and Gn-RH-II mRNA transcripts have been shown to be expressed in various ovarian compartments including granulosa-luteal (GL) cells, ovarian surface epithelial (OSE) cells, and ovarian carcinomas by reverse transcription-polymerase chain reaction (RT-PCR) and Southern blot analysis. Nucleotide sequencing reveals that they are identical to their counterparts in the brain [38–42]. In addition, Ohno et al. demonstrated the expression and bioactivity of Gn-RH-I protein in human ovarian epithelial carcinomas [38].

High affinity binding sites specific for Gn-RH-I have been detected in human corpus lutea, luteinized granulosa cells, epithelial ovarian carcinomas, and a number of ovarian cancer cell lines [43–47]. However, the presence of Gn-RH-I binding sites in preovulatory follicles is controversial [47, 48]. In corpus luteum, binding of Gn-RH-I is closely associated with the levels of low-density lipoprotein receptors and is found to be highest during the midluteal phase and early pregnancy [43]. Expression of Gn-RH-I receptor mRNA has also been demonstrated in various ovarian cell types [39–41, 49, 50], although quantitative measurements show that the mRNA level is much lower in the ovary than in the pituitary [50, 51]. Nucleotide sequencing of the ovarian Gn-RH-I receptors from both normal and neoplastic tissues reveals that their sequences are identical to those found in the gonadotropes [41, 52].

REGULATION OF Gn-RH-I, Gn-RH-II, AND Gn-RH-I RECEPTOR GENE EXPRESSION IN THE HUMAN OVARY

In the ovary the expressions of the two forms of Gn-RHs are differentially controlled by their own ligands, gonadal steroids and gonadotropins, and a number of studies indicate that these regulators modulate the expressions of these hormones at the transcriptional level. In addition, these regulators also govern the ovarian Gn-RH-I receptor gene expression (Table 17.1). Interestingly, our recent study from the transcriptional regulation of the Gn-RH-I receptor gene in the human ovary has lead us to identify a novel ovarian-specific Gn-RH-I receptor promoter that is primarily used by GL cells, suggesting that tissue-specific expression of the human Gn-RH-I receptor gene is mediated at least in part by differential promoter usage in various cell types.

Homologous Regulation by Gn-RH-I and Gn-RH-II

In human OSE and GL cells, treatment with Gn-RH-I produces a biphasic response in its own mRNA level such that high concentrations (10^{-7} and 10^{-8} M) decrease the Gn-RH-I mRNA level, whereas low concentrations (10^{-10} and 10^{-11} M) increase Gn-RH-I gene expression [41, 53]. In contrast, treatment of GL cells with Gn-RH-II results in a homologous downregulation of its mRNA level at all concentrations (10^{-11} to 10^{-7} M) [53]. The expression of Gn-RH-I receptor mRNA is also differentially regulated by Gn-RH-I and Gn-RH-II in the GL cells. A biphasic change in the steady-state mRNA level of the Gn-RH-I receptor, similar to that of the Gn-RH-I, is observed following treatment with Gn-RH-I. However, treatment with Gn-RH-II results in suppression of Gn-RH-I receptor gene expression irrespective of the treated doses [53]. In fact, the Gn-RH-I-mediated repression of the human Gn-RH-I receptor gene expression has been studied at the transcriptional level in gonadotrope-derived αT3-1 cells [54]. It is demonstrated that the downregulatory effect of Gn-RH-I is mediated via the protein kinase C (PKC) signaling cascade and a putative activating protein-1 (AP-1) binding site within the human Gn-RH-I receptor 5′-flanking region and may possibly involve a change of c-fos gene expression in the Gn-RH-I-treated cells.

TABLE 17.1 Summary of the Regulation of Steady-State mRNA Expression Levels of Gn-RH-I, Gn-RH-II, and Gn-RH-I Receptor in Granulosa-Luteal (GL) Cells, Ovarian Surface Epithelial (OSE) Cells, and Ovarian Carcinoma (OVCAR-3) Cells

Cell Type	Treatment	Steady-State mRNA Level
GL	Gn-RH-I (low doses)	↑ Gn-RH-I and Gn-RH-I receptor
	Gn-RH-I (high doses)	↓ Gn-RH-I and Gn-RH-I receptor
	Gn-RH-II	↓ Gn-RH-II and Gn-RH-I receptor
	E_2	↓ Gn-RH-I and Gn-RH-I receptor
	FSH/hCG	↓ Gn-RH-I; ↑ Gn-RH-II
	hCG	↓ Gn-RH-I receptor
	Melatonin	↓ Gn-RH-I and Gn-RH-I receptor
OSE	Gn-RH-I (low doses)	↑ Gn-RH-I
	Gn-RH-I (high doses)	↓ Gn-RH-I
	E_2	↓ Gn-RH-I receptor
	E_2	↓ Gn-RH-I and Gn-RH-I receptor
	OVCAR-3	

hCG, Human chorionic gonadotropin.

Regulation by Gonadal Steroids

Both Gn-RH-I and Gn-RH-I receptor mRNA levels have been shown to be downregulated by 17β-estradiol (E_2) in human GL cells and ovarian epithelial carcinoma OVCAR-3 cells [55, 56], and this effect can be abolished by cotreatment with an estrogen antagonist, indicating that this E_2-induced downregulation of gene expression is mediated via the estrogen receptor (ER). Using an ER-negative CHO-K1 cell line as a model, Chen et al. demonstrated that E_2 could repress the human Gn-RH-I promoter activity when ERα was overexpressed and identified the estrogen responsive element to a region between 169 and 548 bp 5′ of the upstream transcription start site of the human Gn-RH-I gene [57]. This data strongly indicate that E_2 suppresses Gn-RH-I gene expression at the promoter level. In contrast, in normal OSE cells, the expression of human Gn-RH-I receptor but not Gn-RH-I mRNA is downregulated by E_2 although ERα and ERβ mRNA transcripts and proteins are expressed in these cells [56]. It is worth noting that in primary human GL cells, the expressions of ERα and ERβ genes are inhibited by treatment with a Gn-RH-I agonist. This effect can be mimicked by phorbol ester and abolished by cotreatment with a PKC inhibitor, indicating its mediation via a PKC-dependent pathway [58]. More importantly, these results demonstrate the existence of a negative feedback loop in controlling gene expressions between the E_2/ER and Gn-RH-I/Gn-RH-I receptor systems in the GL cells.

Although the regulation of human Gn-RH-II gene expression by estrogen has not been addressed in the ovary, our preliminary study indicated that E_2 increased Gn-RH-II mRNA level in human GL cells [59]. Likewise, a recent finding from Chen et al. provided evidence that the expressions of the human Gn-RH-I and Gn-RH-II genes were differentially regulated by E_2 in a neuronal cell line, TE-671 [60]. By RT-PCR and Southern blot analysis, the steroid was shown to upregulate the mRNA level of Gn-RH-II but downregulate that of Gn-RH-I in a time-dependent manner. Consistent with the findings from CHO-K1 cells, the authors also demonstrated that the inhibitory effect of E_2 on Gn-RH-I gene expression was mediated at the transcriptional level in the neuronal cells when ERα was overexpressed [60].

Regulation by Gonadotropins

Further evidence that the expressions of the two forms of Gn-RHs are differentially regulated in the ovary comes from their regulation by gonadotropins, which regulate ovarian functions by stimulating the production of intracellular cyclic 3′, 5′-adenosine monophosphate (cAMP) and activating the protein kinase A (PKA) signal transduction pathway. In human GL cells the expressions of Gn-RH-I and Gn-RH-II mRNAs have been shown to be regulated differentially by FSH and human chorionic gonadotropin (hCG) such that the gonadotropins increase the mRNA level of Gn-RH-II but decrease that of Gn-RH-I in a dose-dependent manner [53]. By RT-PCR and immunocytochemical analysis, upregulation of Gn-RH-II mRNA and protein levels by cAMP has also been demonstrated in the neuronal TE-671 cells [61]. This cAMP-stimulated Gn-RH-II gene expression was shown to be promoter mediated, and mutation of a putative cAMP-responsive element (CRE) within the human Gn-RH-II promoter drastically reduces the basal and cAMP-stimulated promoter activities [61], suggesting that the cAMP/PKA signal transduction pathway also plays a role in controlling the basal transcription of the human Gn-RH-II gene.

Several reports demonstrated that the regulation of Gn-RH-I receptor gene expression by gonadotropins is tissue specific. In human GL cells, treatment with hCG for 24 hours induces a dose-dependent inhibition of Gn-RH-I receptor mRNA level [39], a phenomenon that has also been demonstrated in rat granulosa cells and neuronal GT1-7 cells [62, 63]. However, opposing results are obtained from placental JEG-3 cells such that the hCG-activated cAMP pathway increases the expression level of the Gn-RH-I receptor mRNA [64], and this stimulatory effect was shown to be mediated in part by two putative CREs within the proximal human Gn-RH-I receptor promoter region [65].

Regulation by Melatonin

Melatonin is a pineal hormone that controls dynamic physiological adaptations in response to changes in day length in seasonally breeding mammals. Although its role in reproduction in humans remains obscure, there is increasing evidence that melatonin acts at the level of the ovary to modify ovarian functions via a receptor-mediated process [66–69]. In human GL cells, mRNA transcripts encoding two forms of melatonin receptor genes, MT_1-R and MT_2-R, have been detected, and sequence analysis reveals that the ovarian melatonin receptors are identical to their brain counterparts [69]. Treatment with melatonin significantly decreases the steady-state mRNA levels of Gn-RH-I and Gn-RH-I receptor but increases that of LH receptor in a dose-dependent manner in the GL cells [69]. Because Gn-RH-I has been implicated as a luteolytic factor that can induce apoptosis in the granulosa cells [55, 70, 71], this melatonin-mediated repression of Gn-RH-I and its receptor gene expressions may play a role in interfering with corpus luteum regression during the midluteal to late luteal phase.

Regulation by Differential Promoter Usage

Recently, we have identified and characterized a novel upstream Gn-RH-I receptor promoter in the ovary, in addition to the known placenta- and downstream gonadotrope-specific promoters [72–74]. Mutational analysis demonstrates the critical importance of three closely spaced CCAAT/enhancer binding protein and GATA motifs, which function cooperatively in regulating Gn-RH-I receptor gene transcription in GL cells. However, the use of this promoter appears to be restricted to the GL cells because this promoter exhibits relatively lower activities in immortalized OSE cells and OVCAR-3 cells [72]. These findings indicate that there are differential regulatory mechanisms controlling the basal transcription of the Gn-RH-I receptor gene among various ovarian compartments. Although the transcriptional regulation of the human Gn-RH-I gene in the ovary remains obscure, the identification of a major upstream transcription start site and an upstream Gn-RH-I promoter that are primarily used by reproductive tissues such as the ovary and placenta suggests a notion that tissue-specific expressions of the Gn-RH-I and Gn-RH-I receptor genes are mediated by differential promoter usage in various cell types [75, 76].

FUNCTIONAL ROLES OF GN-RH-I AND GN-RH-II IN THE HUMAN OVARY

In addition to its pivotal role in stimulating gonadotropin secretion, it is well established that Gn-RH-I functions as a local autocrine and/or paracrine factor in the human ovary by regulating steroidogenesis, cell proliferation, and apoptosis. Studies on the signal transduction mechanisms of the Gn-RH-I receptor reveal that the receptor is

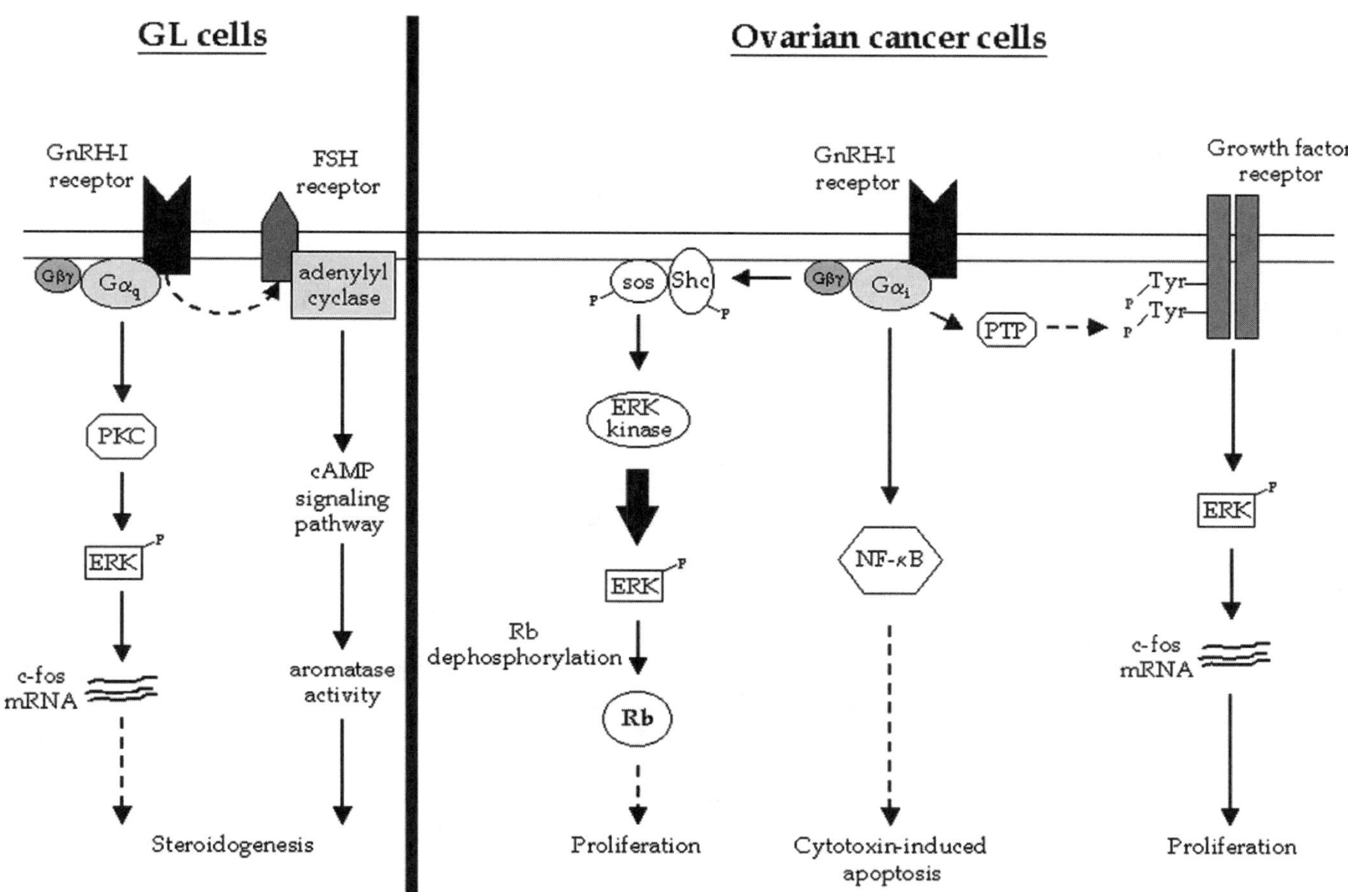

FIGURE 17.2 A diagrammatic representation of signal transduction mechanisms of the human Gn-RH-I receptor in the ovary. In human GL cells, the receptor mediates its antisteroidogenic effect through coupling to $G\alpha_q$ protein, which activates the Erk via a PKC-dependent pathway. In addition, the receptor specifically interferes with the FSH-mediated cAMP-dependent pathway to suppress aromatase activity and steroidogenesis in the GL cells. In contrast, the Gn-RH-I receptor is coupled to the pertussis toxin-sensitive $G\alpha_i$ protein in ovarian cancer cells and mediates its antiproliferative effect via dephosphorylation of the retinoblastoma protein (Rb), a process involving phosphorylation of Shc and son of sevenless (SOS) and prolonged stimulation of the Erk. Additionally, in certain ovarian cancer cell lines, the receptor antagonizes the growth factor-induced mitogenic signaling by stimulating phosphotyrosine phosphatase (PTP) activity, thereby inhibiting cell proliferation. Recently, the $G\alpha_i$-coupled Gn-RH-I receptor has also been shown to suppress cytotoxin-induced apoptosis via activation of the nuclear factor-κB (NF-κB) signaling cascade in ovarian cancer EFO-21 and EFO-27 cells. Solid and dotted arrows = positive and negative regulation, respectively. Thick solid arrow = sustained stimulation of Erk.

coupled to different Gα proteins in various ovarian cell types (Figure 17.2). In ovarian tumors, there is convincing evidence that the receptor is coupled to the $G\alpha_i$ protein and mediates its effects via pathways that are distinct from the classical Gn-RH-I receptor signaling cascade in the gonadotropes. Recent discovery of Gn-RH-II and its cognate receptor and the demonstration of their antigonadotropic and antiproliferative effects in the human ovary suggest the existence of an additional Gn-RH/Gn-RH receptor system in regulating local ovarian functions.

Roles of Gn-RH-I and Gn-RH-II in Ovarian Steroidogenesis

It is well documented that Gn-RH-I possesses antigonadotropic effect in the rat ovary by downregulating the expressions of FSH and LH receptors [77, 78], inhibiting gonadotropin-stimulated cAMP production [79, 80], and suppressing steroidogenic enzymes [81, 82]. In human GL cells, treatment with Gn-RH-I or its agonistic analogs at high doses suppress basal and FSH-stimulated steroidogenesis [83–86], possibly by downregulation of aromatase cytochrome P450 concentration and inhibition of the aromatase activity [85]. Consistent with these observations,

Furger et al. showed that Gn-RH-I could also inhibit cAMP-dependent morphological changes in the steroidogenic cells following FSH treatment [87]. However, the effects of Gn-RH-I on LH/hCG-regulated steroidogenesis appear to be controversial [53, 83, 84, 88, 89], and it has been demonstrated that treatment with Gn-RH-I has no influence on hCG- and forskolin-mediated responses [87]. These findings implicate that Gn-RH-I may specifically interact with the FSH-induced cAMP-dependent signaling pathway, at a level upstream that of cAMP generation in the GL cells. However, it should be mentioned in this context that at relatively lower concentrations of Gn-RH-I, the hormone stimulates aromatase activity and steroidogenesis in the GL cells via a PKC and Ca^{2+}-dependent pathway [85, 89], suggesting that Gn-RH-I may possess dual functional roles in regulating basal steroidogenesis in the human ovary. On the other hand, Gn-RH-I has been shown to functionally interact with prostaglandin $F_{2\alpha}$ ($PGF_{2\alpha}$) to significantly stimulate progesterone and estradiol production in GL cells [90]. This finding indicates that in addition to its antigonadotropic effect, Gn-RH-I may function as a permissive factor for the process of luteolysis by potentiating the luteolytic actions of $PGF_{2\alpha}$. Although the Gn-RH-I antagonist cetrorelix (Cetrotide) has been demonstrated to regulate the proliferation of some ovarian cancer cells (discussed in the next section), several reports have indicated that the analog exerts no effect on the basal and gonadotropin-regulated steroidogenesis in human GL cells in vitro [91–93].

Recently, our laboratory demonstrates that treatment of human GL cells with the Gn-RH-I agonist [D-Ala^6]LH-RH rapidly stimulates the phosphorylation and activity of Erk and causes a drastic increase in the c-fos mRNA level [94]. This Gn-RH-I-stimulated Erk activity was shown to be mediated via the $G\alpha_q$ protein and involves PKC activation because the effect can be mimicked by phorbol ester but abolished by a PKC inhibitor [94]. Pretreatment with the Erk kinase 1 inhibitor, PD98059, completely reverses Gn-RH-I-inhibited progesterone production in the GL cells [86]. Thus it is apparent that the antisteroidogenic action of Gn-RH-I in the human ovary is mediated via a PKC- and Erk-dependent signal transduction mechanism.

The role of Gn-RH-II in regulating ovarian steroidogenesis has recently been addressed. In human GL cells, treatment with Gn-RH-II or its agonist results in downregulation of basal and hCG-stimulated progesterone production [53]. This inhibitory effect of Gn-RH-II can be abolished by the Gn-RH-I antagonist antide. Similar to the effects produced by Gn-RH-I [94], Gn-RH-II does not interfere with the hCG-stimulated cAMP production in the GL cells. Rather, these hormones downregulate the steady-state mRNA expressions of FSH and LH receptors [53]. These findings suggest that Gn-RH-I and Gn-RH-II exert their antigonadotropic effects at the receptor level but not at the cAMP level. However, because antide can abolish the inhibitory effect of Gn-RH-II on ovarian steroidogenesis, it is not clear whether the antigonadotropic action of Gn-RH-II is the consequence of cross-interaction with the Gn-RH-I receptor in the GL cells.

Roles of Gn-RH-I and Gn-RH-II in Ovarian Cell Proliferation

The role of Gn-RH-I as a negative autocrine regulator of proliferation in OSE and ovarian cancer cells has been well documented [41, 46, 56, 95–97]. Because the growth of these cells can be significantly inhibited at nanomolar concentrations of Gn-RH-I agonists, it is believed that the antiproliferative action of the hormone is mediated via high-affinity Gn-RH-I receptors. This notion is further supported by the fact that the nucleotide sequences of the Gn-RH-I receptors in normal and neoplastic ovarian tissues are identical to those present in the gonadotropes [52]. On the other hand, some studies indicate that the Gn-RH-I antagonist cetrorelix (Cetrotide) can also suppress the growth of certain ovarian cancer cell lines in a dose-dependent manner [46, 96, 98], and interestingly, the antiproliferative effect of cetrorelix (Cetrotide) was demonstrated to be stronger than that produced by the agonist triptorelin in OV-1063 human epithelial ovarian cancer cells [96]. In addition, Yano et al. even demonstrated that the proliferation of OV-1063 xenografts in nude mice could only be suppressed by cetrorelix (Cetrotide) but not by the agonist [99]. A possible explanation for these observations is that Gn-RH-I agonists and antagonists may elicit their antiproliferative effects via different signaling transduction mechanisms from the Gn-RH-I receptor. Another possibility is that there may be a high-affinity Gn-RH-I antagonist binding site that is not recognizable by Gn-RH-I agonists, as previously reported in human breast cancer MCF-7 cells [100]. In fact, the latter hypothesis is supported by an earlier finding from Eidne et al., which showed that the proliferation of some human breast cancer cell lines could only be inhibited by antagonistic analogs of Gn-RH-I [101].

Several reports have demonstrated that Gn-RH-I agonists mediate their growth-inhibitory effects in ovarian cancer cells via regulation of the Erk signal transduction cascade. For instance, Kimura et al. showed that the antiproliferative effect of leuprolide on ovarian adenocarcinoma Caov-3 cells could be abolished by treatment with PD98059 [102]. Detailed characterization of the signaling pathway shows that the agonist causes a sustained activation of Erk, and this change is associated with concomitant stimulation of Erk kinase and phosphorylation of SOS and Shc. However, the agonist has no apparent effect on the activation of JNK. Activation of Erk by leuprolide was demonstrated to be independent on PKC and Ca^{2+}, which is known to be an important second messenger to mediate Gn-RH-I responses in gonadotropes. In addition, this Gn-RH-I-stimulated Erk activity in Caov-3 cells can be

TABLE 17.2 Comparison of the Gn-RH-I Receptor Signal Transduction Pathways Leading to Erk Activation in Gonadotropes and Ovarian Cancer Cells

	Gonadotropes	Ovarian Cancer Cells
Coupled G protein	$G\alpha_{q/11}$	$G\alpha_i$
PTX sensitivity	Insensitive	Sensitive
Ca^{2+}	Dependent	Independent
PKC	Dependent	Independent
Gβγ	Independent	Dependent
β-ARK	Independent	Dependent
Erk activation	Rapid and transient	Sustained

blocked by pertussis toxin (PTX) or by overexpressing the carboxyl terminus of the β-adrenergic receptor kinase (β-ARK), suggesting that the response is mediated via a PTX-sensitive Gα protein and involves the Gβγ subunit. Therefore it is obvious that the classical Gn-RH-I receptor signal transduction mechanisms in gonadotropes are not involved in mediating the antiproliferative effect of Gn-RH-I in ovarian cancer cells (Table 17.2). Further analysis of the downstream signaling cascade reveals that the prolonged stimulation of Erk by leuprolide induces dephosphorylation of the retinoblastoma protein [102], an event that is known to prevent cell cycle progression from G_1 to S phase. Similar observations have also been reported in other ovarian cancer cells such that treatment with Gn-RH-I agonists results in blockage of cell cycle transition to the S phase, which is associated with decreased DNA synthesis [103, 104]. Of particular interest, Gunthert et al. showed that the antiproliferative effect of Gn-RH-I might be partly attributed to its ability to increase the DNA binding activity of JunD, which has been suggested to be a negative regulator of cell proliferation [105].

The role of Erk signaling cascade in mediating the growth-suppressive effect of Gn-RH-I is further supported by the finding that the hormone is capable of antagonizing growth factor-induced mitogenic signaling in ovarian cancer cells [106]. However, unlike in the prostate cancer cell lines LNCaP and DU 145 [107], treatment of ovarian cancer EFO-21 and EFO-27 cells with triptorelin has no effect on their expressions of epidermal growth factor (EGF) receptors, suggesting that a mechanism downstream of growth factor binding to its receptor is responsible for the antiproliferative effect of Gn-RH-I in these ovarian cancer cell lines [106]. In primary ovarian carcinomas, Imai et al. provide evidence that the mammalian Gn-RH-I receptor is coupled to PTP because treatment with the Gn-RH-I agonist buserelin stimulates the PTP activity in a dose-dependent manner and results in a remarkable loss of phosphotyrosine residues from a 35 kDa protein from the membranes. Additionally, coincubation of the membranes with guanosine thiotriphosphate (GTP-γ-S) potentiates the stimulatory action of buserelin on PTP activity, whereas GDP-γ-S reverses the action of the agonist. These observations indicate that activation of PTP by Gn-RH-I is mediated via GTP-binding protein [108]. Subsequent experimentations demonstrate that the Gn-RH-I receptor is coupled to the PTX-sensitive $G\alpha_i$ protein of 41 kDa in the ovarian carcinomas [109]. In fact, similar results have recently been reported in the ovarian cancer cell lines EFO-21 and EFO-27 [110]. In this study, treatment with triptorelin results in a drastic stimulation of PTP activity, and this effect can be abolished by PTX, supporting the notion of mediation through the $G\alpha_i$ protein. In addition, this Gn-RH-I-stimulated PTP activity was shown to be associated with significant reduction of EGF-induced tyrosine autophosphorylation of the EGF receptor and could be attenuated by a PTP inhibitor. The fact that Gn-RH-I can antagonize growth factor-induced tyrosine phosphorylation implicates that the hormone may interfere with the downstream growth factor signal transduction mechanisms. Indeed, this idea is confirmed by an earlier finding which showed that treatment of ovarian cancer cells with triptorelin could almost completely nullify EGF-induced activation of Erk [106], which is generally considered to be the last event in the mitogenic signal transduction system in the cytoplasm [111]. Therefore, in contrast to the findings from Caov-3 cells [102], Gn-RH-I can negatively regulate Erk signaling cascade in certain ovarian cancer cells. More recently, Grundker et al. demonstrated that triptorelin treatment could dose-dependently suppress growth factor-induced expression of the early response gene c-fos [112], a component of the transcription factor AP-1, which is known to regulate the expressions of a wide variety of genes implicated in cell proliferation [113]. Taken together, these findings indicate that Gn-RH-I antagonizes growth factor-induced mitogenic signaling via coupling to the PTX-sensitive $G\alpha_i$ protein in ovarian cancers and that this coupling may account for the signal transduction mechanisms distinct from the classical pathways in the gonadotropes.

In addition to the modulation of PTP and Erk activities, other cellular mechanisms have been suggested to mediate the antiproliferative effect of Gn-RH-I in ovarian cancer cells. For instance, Gn-RH-I has been shown to inhibit the activity of phosphatidylinositol kinase in plasma membranes isolated from Gn-RH-I receptor positive-ovarian carcinomas in a dose-dependent manner [114]. On the other hand, Olson et al. demonstrated that in ovarian cancer cell lines MA 138 and OVCAR 433, triptorelin could downregulate the mRNA expression of vascular permeability factor/vascular endothelial growth factor (VPF/VEGF) and resulted in a concomitant decrease in the endothelium-specific mitogenic activity of the conditioned media [115]. This antiangiogenic activity of triptorelin may serve as an additional antiproliferative mechanism to suppress the growth of ovarian tumors. More recently, Imai et al. showed that the antiproliferative effect of the hormone might be caused by its ability to increase the hydrolysis of lysophosphatidic acid [116], which has been shown to stimulate the proliferation of ovarian cancer cells [117].

As previously mentioned, the proliferation of OV-1063 xenografts in nude mice can be inhibited by cetrorelix (Cetrotide). However, unlike the agonists, chronic treatment with cetrorelix (Cetrotide) results in drastic reduction of receptors for EGF and insulin-like growth factor-1 (IGF-1) in the tumor cell membranes [99, 118], thereby inhibiting growth factor-induced mitogenic signaling. The antagonist has also been demonstrated to directly suppress the proliferation of HTOA human epithelial ovarian cancer cells and arrest the cells at the G_1 phase of the cell cycle. This antiproliferative effect of cetrorelix (Cetrotide) involves upregulation of p21 (a cyclin-dependent kinase [CDK] inhibitor) and p53 protein levels, leading to subsequent downregulation of cyclin A-CDK2 complex formation [119], which is known to be required for transition from G_1 to S phase. Therefore these findings clearly indicate that distinct signal transduction pathways are triggered by Gn-RH-I agonists and cetrorelix (Cetrotide) in mediating their antiproliferative effects in ovarian cancer cells.

The role of Gn-RH-II as a negative autocrine growth factor in the human ovary has been demonstrated. Choi et al. showed that treatment with Gn-RH-II could dose-dependently inhibit the proliferation of nontumorigenic and tumorigenic immortalized OSE cells [42] (Figure 17.3). Consistent with previous identification of an additional Gn-RH binding site, which is of low affinity and high capacity, in human reproductive tract tumor cells [46, 120], Grundker et al. demonstrated the mRNA expression of the second form of Gn-RH receptor (Gn-RH-II receptor) in several endometrial and ovarian cancer cell lines. Proliferation of these cells was dose- and time-dependently suppressed by Gn-RH-II, and this antiproliferative effect was found to be significantly stronger than that produced by equimolar concentrations of triptorelin [121]. It should be mentioned in this context that in Gn-RH-II receptor-positive but Gn-RH-I receptor-negative SK-OV-3 cells, treatment with Gn-RH-I agonist has no apparent effect on cell proliferation [122]. This result indicates that the antiproliferative effect of Gn-RH-II on ovarian cancer cells is unlikely because of cross-binding to the Gn-RH-I receptor, and therefore the Gn-RH-II/Gn-RH-II receptor system represents an additional autocrine growth regulatory mechanism in ovarian cancers.

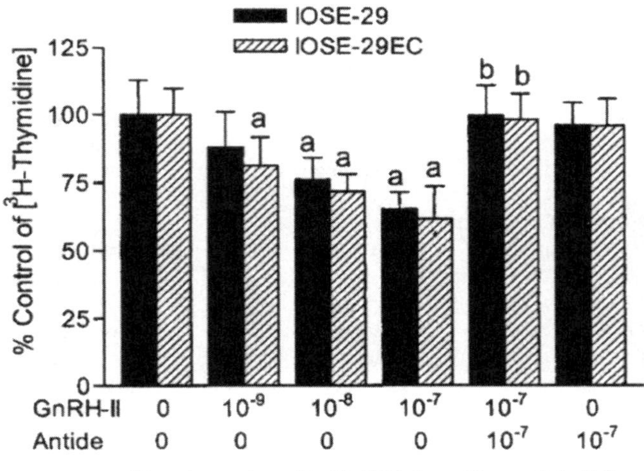

FIGURE 17.3 Effects of Gn-RH-II on the proliferation of nontumorigenic (IOSE-29) and tumorigenic (IOSE-29EC) immortalized OSE cells. A dose-dependent inhibition of [^{3}H-thymidine] incorporation is observed after treatment with Gn-RH-II, and this antiproliferative effect of the hormone can be abolished by the Gn-RH-I antagonist antide. Data are shown as the means of three individual experiments with triplicate and are represented as the mean ± SD. *a*, $P < 0.05$ vs untreated control; *b*, $P < 0.05$ vs Gn-RH-II (10^{-7}M) treatment. (From Ref. [42], with permission from The Endocrine Society.)

Roles of Gn-RH-I in Ovarian Cell Apoptosis

To date, the role of Gn-RH-I in regulating apoptosis in human ovarian cancer cells remains controversial. Imai et al. demonstrated that treatment with buserelin resulted in a dose-dependent stimulation of the expression of Fas ligand mRNA and protein in SK-OV-3, Caov-3 cells, and in cells isolated from Gn-RH-I receptor-bearing ovarian tumors. This hormonal activation of Fas ligand expression is receptor mediated because it can be abolished by treatment with antide [123]. Because Fas ligand is known to be an intrinsic inducer of apoptosis via binding to its cell surface receptor Fas, which is frequently expressed in Gn-RH-I receptor-positive tumors [124], it is speculated that Gn-RH-I may function as an autocrine factor to stimulate apoptotic cell death in Fas-positive tumors. This proapoptotic activity of Gn-RH-I may partly account for its antiproliferative effect in ovarian cancer cells. However, a recent study from Grundker et al. showed that treatment with triptorelin did not produce any morphological signs of programmed cell death in ovarian cancer EFO-21 and EFO-27 cells. In contrast, the agonist reduced cytotoxin-induced apoptosis in these cells via activation of nuclear factor-kappa B (NF-κB) signal transduction cascade [125]. NF-κB is a collective term referring to dimeric transcription factors that belong to the Rel family. The activity of NF-κB is strictly regulated by an inhibitor, IκB, which forms a complex with NF-κB and sequesters it in the cytoplasm [126]. When cells receive signals that activate NF-κB, IκB will be phosphorylated and degraded via ubiquitination and proteasome-mediated mechanism. The degradation of IκB triggers the translocation of NF-κB

(region 8p 11.2----p21). *Somat. Cell Mol. Genet.* 12, 95–100.

7. Adelman, J. P., Mason, A. J., Hayflick, J. S., and Seeburg, P. H. (1986). Isolation of the gene and hypothalamic cDNA for the common precursor of gonadotropin-releasing hormone and prolactin release-inhibiting factor in human and rat. *Proc. Natl. Acad. Sci. USA* 83, 179–183.
8. Miyamoto, K., Hasegawa, Y., Nomura, M., Igarashi, M., Kanagawa, K., and Matsuo, H. (1984). Identification of a second gonadotropin-releasing hormone in chicken hypothalamus: Evidence that gonadotropin secretion is probably controlled by two distinct gonadotropin-releasing hormones in avian species. *Proc. Natl. Acad. Sci. USA* 81, 3874–3878.
9. Powell, R. C., Millar, R. P., and King, J. A. (1986). Diverse molecular forms of gonadotropin-releasing hormone in an elasmobranch and teleost fish. *Gen. Comp. Endocrinol.* 63, 77–85.
10. Lovejoy, D. A., Fischer, W. H., Ngamvongchon, S., Craig, A. G., Nahorniak, C. S., Peter, R. E., Rivier, J. E., and Sherwood, N. M. (1992). Distinct sequence of gonadotropin-releasing hormone (Gn-RH) in goldfish brain provides insight into Gn-RH evolution. *Proc. Natl. Acad. Sci. USA* 89, 6373–6377.
11. King, J. A., and Millar, R. P. (1986). Identification of His^5, Trp^7, Tyr^8-Gn-RH (chicken Gn-RH II) in amphibian brain. *Peptides* 7, 827–834.
12. Sherwood, N. M., and Whittier, J. M. (1988). Gonadotropin-releasing hormone from brains of reptiles: Turtles (*Pseudemys Scripta*) and snakes (*Thamnophis sirtalis parietalis*). *Gen. Comp. Endocrinol.* 69, 319–327.
13. King, J. A., Steneveld, A. A., Curlewis, J. D., Rissman, E. F., and Millar, R. P. (1994). Identification of chicken Gn-RH-II in brains of metatherian and early evolved eutherian species of mammals. *Regul. Pept.* 54, 467–477.
14. Rissman, E. F., Alones, V. E., Craig-Veit, C. B., and Millam, J. R. (1995). Distribution of chicken gonadotropin-releasing hormone-II in mammalian brain. *J. Comp. Neurol.* 357, 524–531.
15. Kasten, T. L., White, S. A., Norton, T. T., Bond, C. T., Adelman, K. P., and Fernald, R. D. (1996). Characterization of two new preproGn-RH mRNAs in the tree shrew: First direct evidence for mesencephalic Gn-RH gene expression in a placental mammal. *Gen. Comp. Endocrinol.* 104, 7–19.
16. Lescheid, D. W., Teresawa, E., Abler, L. A., Urbanski, H. F., Warby, C. M., Millar, R. P., and Sherwood, N. M. (1997). A second form of gonadotropin-releasing hormone (Gn-RH) with characteristics of chicken Gn-RH-II is present in the primate brain. *Endocrinology* 138, 5618–5629.
17. Chen, A., Yahalom, D., Ben-Aroya, N., Kaganovsky, E., Okon, E., and Koch, Y. (1998). A second isoform of gonadotropin-releasing hormone is present in the brain of human and rodents. *FEBS Lett.* 435, 199–203.
18. Urbanski, H. F., White, R. B., Ferland, R. D., Kohama, S. G., Garyfallou, V. T., and Densmore, V. S. (1999). Regional expression of mRNA encoding a second form of gonadotropin-releasing hormone in the macaque brain. *Endocrinology* 140, 1945–1948.
19. White, R. B., Eisen, J. A., Kasten, T. L., and Fernald, R. D. (1998). Second form of gonadotropin-releasing hormone in humans. *Proc. Natl. Acad. Sci. USA* 95, 305–309.
20. Reinhart, J., Mertz, L. M., and Catt, K. J. (1992). Molecular cloning and expression of cDNA encoding the murine gonadotropin-releasing hormone receptor. *J. Biol. Chem.* 267, 21281–21284.
21. Stojilkovic, S. S., Reinhart, J., and Catt, K. J. (1994). Gonadotropin-releasing hormone receptors: Structural and signal transduction pathways. *Endocr. Rev.* 15, 462–499.
22. Shacham, S., Cheifetz, M. N., Lewy, H., Ashkenazi, I. E., Becker, O. M., Seger, R., and Naor, Z. (1999). Mechanism of Gn-RH receptor signaling: From the membrane to the nucleus. (Review). *Ann. Endocrinol. (Paris)* 60, 79–88.
23. Stojilkovic, S. S., Tomic, M., Kukuljan, M., and Catt, K. J. (1994). Control of calcium spiking frequency in pituitary gonadotrophs by a single-pool cytoplasmic oscillator. *Mol. Pharmacol.* 45, 1013–1021.
24. Stojilkovic, S. S., and Catt, K. J. (1995). Novel aspects of Gn-RH-induced intracellular signaling and secretion in pituitary gonadotrophs. (Review). *J. Neuroendocrinol.* 7, 739–757.
25. Tse, F. W., Tse, A., Hille, B., Jorstmann, H., and Almers, W. (1997). Local Ca2+ release from internal stores controls exocytosis in pituitary gonadotrophs. *Neuron* 18, 121–132.
26. Kraus, S., Naor, Z., and Seger, R. (2001). Intracellular signaling pathways mediated by the gonadotropin-releasing hormone (Gn-RH) receptor. *Arch. Med. Res.* 32, 499–509.
27. Leung, P. C., Squire, J., Peng, C., Fan, N., Hayden, M. R., and Olofsson, J. I. (1995). Mapping of the gonadotropin-releasing hormone (Gn-RH) receptor gene to human chromosome 4q21.2 by fluorescence in situ hybridization. *Mamm. Genome* 6, 309–310.
28. Brosius, J. (1991). Retroposons—seed of evolution. (Review). *Science* 251, 753.
29. Fan, N. C., Jeung, E. B., Peng, C., Olofsson, J. I., Krisinger, J., and Leung, P. C. (1994). The human gonadotropin-releasing hormone (Gn-RH) receptor gene: Cloning, genomic organization and chromosome assignment. *Mol. Cell. Endocrinol.* 103, R1–R6.
30. Fan, N. C., Peng, C., Krisinger, J., and Leung, P. C. (1995). The human gonadotropin-releasing hormone receptor gene: Complete structure including multiple promoters, transcription initiation sites, and polyadenylation signals. *Mol. Cell. Endocrinol.* 107, R1–R8.
31. Tensen, C., Okuzawa, K., Blomenrohr, M., Rebers, F., Keurs, R., Bogerd, J., Schultz, R., and Goos, H. (1997). Distinct efficacies for two endogenous ligands on a single cognate gonadoliberin receptor. *Eur. J. Biochem.* 243, 134–140.
32. Illing, N., Troskie, B. E., Nahorniak, C. S., Hapgood, J. P., Peter, R. E., and Millar, R. P. (1999). Two gonadotropin-releasing hormone receptor subtypes with distinct ligand selectivity and differential distribution in brain and pituitary in the goldfish (Varassius auratus). *Proc. Natl. Acad. Sci. USA* 96, 2526–2531.
33. Troskie, B. E., Hapgood, J. P., Millar, R. P., and Illing, N. (2000). Complementary deoxyribonucleic acid cloning, gene expression, and ligand selectivity of a novel gonadotropin-releasing hormone receptor expressed in the pituitary and midbrain of Xenopus laevis. *Endocrinology* 141, 1764–1771.
34. Wang, L., Bogerd, J., Choi, H. S., Seong, J. Y., Soh, J. M., Chun, S. Y., Blomenrohr, M., Troskie, B. E., Millar, R. P., Yu, M. H., McCann, S. M., and Kwon, H. B. (2001). Three distinct types

of Gn-RH receptor characterized in the bullfrog. *Proc. Natl. Acad. Sci. USA* 95, 361–366.

35. Okubo, K., Nagata, S., Ko, R., Kataoka, H., Yoshiura, Y., Mitani, H., Kondo, M., Naruse, K., Shima, A., and Aida, K. (2001). Identification and characterization of two distinct Gn-RH receptor subtypes in a teleost, the medaka Oryzias latipes. *Endocrinology* 142, 4729–4739.
36. Neill, J. D., Duck, L. W., Sellers, J. C., and Musgrove, L. C. (2001). A gonadotropin-releasing hormone (Gn-RH) receptor specific for Gn-RH II in primates. *Biochem. Biophys. Res. Commun.* 282, 1012–1018.
37. Millar, R., Lowe, S., Conklin, D., Pawson, A., Maudsley, S., Troskie, B., Ott, T., Millar, M., Lincoln, G., Sellar, R., Faurholm, B., Graeme, S., Kuestner, R., Teresawa, E., and Katz, A. (2001). A novel mammalian receptor for the evolutionarily conserved type II Gn-RH. *Proc. Natl. Acad. Sci. USA* 98, 9636–9641.
38. Ohno, T., Imai, A., Furui, T., Takahashi, K., and Tamaya, T. (1993). Presence of gonadotropin-releasing hormone and its messenger ribonucleic acid in human ovarian epithelial carcinoma. *Am. J. Obstet. Gynecol.* 169, 605–610.
39. Peng, C., Fan, N. C., Ligier, M., Vaananen, J., and Leung, P. C. (1994). Expression and regulation of gonadotropin-releasing hormone (Gn-RH) and Gn-RH receptor messenger ribonucleic acids in human granulosa-luteal cells. *Endocrinology* 135, 1740–1746.
40. Irmer, G., Burger, C., Muller, R., Ortmann, O., Peter, U., Kakar, S. S., Neill, J. D., Schulz, K. D., and Emons, G. (1995). Expression of the messenger RNAs for luteinizing hormone-releasing hormone (LHRH) and its receptor in human ovarian epithelial carcinoma. *Cancer Res.* 55, 817–822.
41. Kang, S. K., Choi, K. C., Cheng, K. W., Nathwani, P. S., Auersperg, N., and Leung, P. C. K. (2000). Role of gonadotropin-releasing hormone as an autocrine growth factor in human ovarian surface epithelium. *Endocrinology* 141, 72–80.
42. Choi, K. C., Auersperg, N., and Leung, P. C. K. (2001). Expression and anti-proliferative effect of a second form of gonadotropin-releasing hormone in normal and neoplastic ovarian surface epithelial cells. *J. Clin. Endocrinol. Metab.* 86, 5075–5078.
43. Bramley, T. A., Stirling, D., Swanston, I. A., Menzies, G. S., McNeilly, A. S., and Baird, D. T. (1987). Specific binding sites for gonadotropin-releasing hormone, LH/chorionic gonadotropin, low-density lipoprotein, prolactin and FSH in homogenates of human corpus luteum. II: Concentrations through the luteal phase of the menstrual cycle and early pregnancy. *J. Endocrinol.* 113, 317–327.
44. Pahwa, G. S., Vollmer, G., Knuppen, R., and Emons, G. (1989). Photoaffinity labelling of gonadotropin releasing hormone binding sites in human epithelial ovarian carcinomata. *Biochem. Biophys. Res. Commun.* 161, 1086–1092.
45. Emons, G., Pahwa, G. S., Brack, C., Sturm, R., Oberheuser, F., and Knuppen, R. (1989). Gonadotropin-releasing hormone binding sites in human epithelial ovarian carcinomata. *Eur. J. Cancer Oncol.* 25, 215–221.
46. Emons, G., Ortmann, O., Becker, M., Irmer, G., Springer, B., Laun, R., Holzel, F., Schulz, K. D., and Schally, A. V. (1993). High affinity binding and antiproliferative effects of LHRH analogues in human ovarian cancer cell lines. *Cancer Res.* 54, 5439–5446.
47. Brus, L., Lambalk, C. B., de Kniing, J., Helder, M. N., Janssens, R. M., and Schoemaker, J. (1997). Specific gonadotropin-releasing hormone analogue binding predominantly in human luteinized follicular aspirates and not in human pre-ovulatory follicles. *Hum. Reprod.* 12, 769–773.
48. Latouche, J., Crumeyrolle-Arias, M., Jordan, D., Kopp, N., Augendre-Ferrante, B., Cedard, L., and Haour, F. (1989). Gn-RH receptors in human granulosa cells: Anatomical localization and characterization by autoradiographic study. *Endocrinology* 125, 1739–1741.
49. Kakar, S. S., and Jennes, L. (1995). Expression of gonadotropin-releasing hormone and gonadotropin-releasing hormone receptor mRNAs in various non-reproductive human tissues. *Cancer Lett.* 98, 57–62.
50. Minaretzis, D., Jakubowski, M., Mortola, J. F., and Paylou, S. N. (1995). Gonadotropin-releasing hormone receptor gene expression in human ovary and granulosa-lutein cells. *J. Clin. Endocrinol. Metab.* 80, 430–434.
51. Fraser, H. M., Sellar, R. E., Illingworth, P. J., and Eidne, K. A. (1996). Gn-RH receptor mRNA expression by in situ hybridization in the primate pituitary and ovary. *Mol. Hum. Reprod.* 2, 117–121.
52. Kakar, S. S., Grizzle, W. E., and Neill, J. D. (1994). The nucleotide sequences of human Gn-RH receptors in breast and ovarian tumors are identical with that found in pituitary. *Mol. Cell. Endocrinol.* 106, 145–149.
53. Kang, S. K., Tai, C. J., Nathwani, P. S., and Leung, P. C. (2001). Differential regulation of two forms of gonadotropin-releasing hormone messenger ribonucleic acid in human granulosa-luteal cells. *Endocrinology* 142, 182–192.
54. Cheng, K. W., Ngan, E. S., Kang, S. K., Chow, B. K., and Leung, P. C. (2000). Transcriptional down-regulation of human gonadotropin-releasing hormone (Gn-RH) receptor gene by Gn-RH: Role of protein kinase C and activating protein 1. *Endocrinology* 141, 3611–3622.
55. Nathwani, P. S., Kang, S. K., Cheng, K. W., Choi, K. C., and Leung, P. C. K. (2000). Regulation of gonadotropin-releasing hormone and its receptor gene expression by 17β-estradiol in cultured human granulosa-luteal cells. *Endocrinology* 141, 1754–1763.
56. Kang, S. K., Choi, K. C., Tai, C. J., Auersperg, N., and Leung, P. C. K. (2001). Estradiol regulates gonadotropin-releasing hormone (Gn-RH) and its receptor gene expression and antagonizes the growth inhibitory effects of Gn-RH in human ovarian surface epithelium and ovarian cancer cells. *Endocrinology* 142, 580–588.
57. Chen, Z. G., Yu, K. L., Zheng, H. M., and Dong, K. W. (1999). Estrogen receptor-mediated repression of gonadotropin-releasing hormone (Gn-RH) promoter activity in transfected CHO-K1 cells. *Mol. Cell. Endocrinol.* 158, 131–142.
58. Chiang, C. H., Cheng, K. W., Igarashi, S., Nathwani, P. S., and Leung, P. C. K. (2000). Hormonal regulation of estrogen receptor α and β gene expression in human granulosa-luteal cells in vitro. *J. Clin. Endocrinol. Metab.* 85, 3828–3839.
59. Khosravi, S., and Leung, P. C. K. (2003). Differential regulation of Gn-RH-I and Gn-RH-II mRNA by gonadal steroids in human granulosa-luteal cells. *J. Clin. Endocrinol. Metab.* 88, 663–672.

60. Chen, A., Ziv, K., Laskar-Levy, O., and Koch, Y. (2002). The transcription of the hGn-RH-I and hGn-RH-II genes in human neuronal cells is differentially regulated by estrogen. *J. Mol. Neurosci.* 18, 67–76.
61. Chen, A., Laskar-Levy, O., Ben-Aroya, N., and Koch, Y. (2001). Transcriptional regulation of the human Gn-RH II gene is mediated by a putative cAMP response element. *Endocrinology* 142, 3483–3492.
62. Olofsson, J. I., Conti, C. C., and Leung, P. C. (1995). Homologous and heterologous regulation of gonadotropin-releasing hormone receptor gene expression in preovulatory rat granulosa cells. *Endocrinology* 136, 974–980.
63. Li, X., Lei, Z. M., and Rao, C. V. (1996). Human chorionic gonadotropin down-regulates the expression of gonadotropin-releasing hormone receptor gene in GT1–7 neurons. *Endocrinology* 137, 899–904.
64. Cheng, K. W., Nathwani, P. S., and Leung, P. C. (2000). Regulation of human gonadotropin-releasing hormone receptor gene expression in placental cells. *Endocrinology* 141, 2340–2349.
65. Cheng, K. W., and Leung, P. C. (2002). Human chorionic gonadotropin-activated cAMP pathway regulates human placental Gn-RH receptor gene transcription in choriocarcinoma JEG-3 cells. *J. Clin. Endocrinol. Metab.* 87, 3291–3299.
66. Brzezinski, A., Seibel, M. M., Lynch H. J., Deng, M-H., and Wurtman, R. J. (1987). Melatonin in human preovulatory follicular fluid. *J. Clin. Endocrinol. Metab.* 64, 865–867.
67. Ronnberg, L., Kauppila, A., Leppaluoto, J., Martikainen, H., and Vakkuri, O. (1990). Circadian and seasonal variation in human preovulatory follicular fluid melatonin concentration. *J. Clin. Endocrinol. Metab.* 80, 493–496.
68. Ayre, E. A., and Pang, S. F. (1994). 2-[125I]Iodomelatonin binding sites in the testis and ovary: Putative melatonin receptors in the gonads. *Biol. Signals* 3, 71–84.
69. Woo, M. M. M., Tai, C. J., Kang, S. K., Nathwani, P. S., Pang, S. F., and Leung, P. C. K. (2001). Direct action of melatonin in human granulosa-luteal cells. *J. Clin. Endocrinol. Metab.* 86, 4789–4797.
70. Billig, H., Furuta, I., and Hseuh, A. J. (1994). Gonadotropin-releasing hormone directly induces apoptotic cell death in the rat ovary: Biochemical and in situ detection of deoxyribonucleic acid fragmentation in granulosa cells. *Endocrinology* 134, 245–252.
71. Zhao, S., Saito, H., Wang, X., Saito, T., Kaneko, T., and Hiroi, M. (2000). Effects of gonadotropin-releasing hormone agonist on the incidence of apoptosis in porcine and human granulosa cells. *Gynecol. Obstet. Invest.* 49, 52–56.
72. Cheng, C. K., Yeung, C. M., Chow, B. K. C., and Leung, P. C. K. (2002). Characterization of a new upstream Gn-RH receptor promoter in human ovarian granulosa-luteal cells. *Mol. Endocrinol.* 16, 1552–1564.
73. Cheng, K. W., Chow, B. K. C., and Leung, P. C. K. (2001). Functional mapping of a placenta-specific upstream promoter for human gonadotropin-releasing hormone receptor gene. *Endocrinology* 14, 1506–1516.
74. Ngan, E. S. W., Cheng, P. K. W., Leung, P. C. K., and Chow, B. K. C. (1999). Steroidogenic factor-1 interacts with a gonadotrope-specific element within the first exon of the human gonadotropin-releasing hormone receptor to mediate gonadotrope-specific expression. *Endocrinology* 140, 2452–2462.
75. Dong, K. W., Yu, K. L., and Roberts, J. L. (1993). Identification of a major up-stream transcription start site for the human progonadotropin-releasing hormone gene used in reproductive tissues and cell lines. *Mol. Endocrinol.* 7, 1654–1666.
76. Dong, K. W., Yu, K. L., Chen, Z. G., Chen, Y. D., and Roberts, J. L. (1997). Characterization of multiple promoters directing tissue-specific expression of the human gonadotropin-releasing hormone gene. *Endocrinology* 138, 2752–2762.
77. Tilly, J. L., Lapolt, P. S., and Hseuh, A. J. W. (1992). Hormonal regulation of follicle-stimulating hormone receptor messenger ribonucleic acid levels in cultured rat granulosa cells. *Endocrinology* 130, 1296–1302.
78. Piquette, G. N., Lapolt, P. S., Oikawa, M., and Hseuh, A. J. W. (1991). Regulation of luteinizing hormone receptor messenger ribonucleic acid levels by gonadotropins, growth factors, and gonadotropin-releasing hormone in cultured rat granulosa cells. *Endocrinology* 128, 2449–2456.
79. Richards, J. S. (1994). Hormonal control of gene expression in the ovary. *Endocr. Rev.* 15, 725–751.
80. Knecht, M., Ranta, T., Feng, P., Shinohara, O., and Catt, K. J. (1985). Gonadotropin-releasing hormone as a modulator of ovarian functions. *J. Steroid. Biochem. Mol. Biol.* 23, 771–778.
81. Hsueh, A. J. W., and Schaffer, J. M. (1985). Gonadotropin-releasing hormone as a paracrine hormone and neurotransmitter in extra-pituitary sites. *J. Steroid. Biochem. Mol. Biol.* 23, 757–764.
82. Sridaran, R., Lee, M. A., Haynes, L., Srivastava, R. K., Ghose, M., Sridaran, G., and Smith, C. J. (1999). Gn-RH action on luteal steroidogenesis during pregnancy. *Steroids* 64, 618–623.
83. Parinaud, J., Beaur, A., Bourreau, E., Vieitez, G., and Pontonnier, G. (1988). Effect of a luteinizing hormone-releasing hormone agonist (Buserelin) on steroidogenesis of cultured human preovulatory granulosa cells. *Fertil. Steril.* 50, 597–602.
84. Kimura, A. (1992). Effect of gonadotropin releasing hormone agonist (Gn-RHa) on steroidogenesis in human and rat ovaries. *Nippon Sanka Fujunka Gakki Zasshi* 44, 1261–1268.
85. Maeda, K., Kitawaki, J., Yokota, K., Noguchi, T., Urabe, M., Yamamoto, T., and Honjo, H. (1996). Effects of gonadotropin-releasing hormone and its analogue (buserelin) on aromatase in cultured human granulosa cells. *Nippon Sanka Fujunka Gakki Zasshi* 48, 89–95.
86. Kang, S. K., Tai, C. J., Cheng, K. W., and Leung, P. C. K. (2000). Gonadotropin-releasing hormone activates mitogen-activated protein kinase in human ovarian and placental cells. *Mol. Cell. Endocrinol.* 170, 143–151.
87. Furger, C., Bourrie, N., Cedard, L., Ferre, F., and Zorn, J. R. (1996). Gonadotropin-releasing hormone and triptorelin inhibit the follicle stimulating hormone-induced response in human primary cultured granulosa-lutein cells. *Mol. Hum. Reprod.* 2, 259–264.
88. Olsson, J. H., Akesson, I., and Hillensjo, T. (1990). Effects of a gonadotropin-releasing hormone agonist on progesterone formation in cultured human granulosa cells. *Acta. Endocrinol.* 122, 427–431.

89. Hori, H., Uemura, T., and Minaguchi, H. (1998). Effects of Gn-RH on protein kinase C activity, Ca2+ mobilization and steroidogenesis of human granulosa cells. *Endocr. J.* 45, 175–182.
90. Vaananen, J. E., Tong, B. L., Vaananen, C. M., Chan, I. H., Yuen, B. H., and Leung, P. C. (1997). Interaction of prostaglandin F2alpha and gonadotropin-releasing hormone on progesterone and estradiol production in human granulosa-luteal cells. *Biol. Reprod.* 57, 1346–1353.
91. Weiss, J. M., Oltmanns, K., Gurke, E. M., Polack, S., Eick, F., Felberbaum, R., Diedrich, K., and Ortmann, O. (2001). Actions of gonadotropin-releasing hormone antagonists on steroidogenesis in human granulosa lutein cells. *Eur. J. Endocrinol.* 144, 677–685.
92. Mitwally, M. F., and Casper, R. F. (2002). Effect of in vivo Gn-RH agonist and Gn-RH antagonist on hCG and insulin-stimulated progesterone production by human granulosa-lutein cells in vitro. *J. Assist. Reprod. Genet.* 19, 384–389.
93. Demirel, L. C., Weiss, J. M., Polack, S., Unlu, C., Diedrich, K., and Ortmann, O. (2000). Effect of the gonadotropin-releasing hormone antagonist ganirelix on cyclic adenosine monophosphate accumulation of human granulosa-lutein cells. *Fertil. Steril.* 74, 1001–1007.
94. Kang, S. K., Tai, C. J., Nathwani, P. S., Choi, K. C., and Leung, P. C. K. (2001). Stimulation of mitogen-activated protein kinase by gonadotropin-releasing hormone in human granulosa-luteal cells. *Endocrinology* 142, 671–679.
95. Thompson, M. A., Adelson, M. D., and Kaufman, L. M. (1991). Lupron retards proliferation of ovarian tumor cells cultured in serum-free medium. *J. Clin. Endocrinol. Metab.* 72, 1036–1041.
96. Yano, T., Pinski, J., Radulovic, S., and Schally, A. V. (1994). Inhibition of human epithelial ovarian cancer cell growth in vitro by agonistic and antagonistic analogues of luteinizing hormone-releasing hormone. *Proc. Natl. Acad. Sci. USA* 91, 1701–1704.
97. Emons, G., Weiss, S., Ortmann, O., Grundker, C., and Schulz, K. D. (2000). Luteinizing hormone-releasing hormone (LHRH) might act as a negative autocrine regulator of proliferation of human ovarian cancer. *Eur. J. Endocrinol.* 142, 665–670.
98. Manetta, A., Gamboa-Vujicic, L., Paredes, P., Emma, D., Liao, S., Leong, L., Asch, B., and Schally, A. (1995). Inhibition of growth of human ovarian cancer in nude mice by luteinizing hormone-releasing hormone antagonist Cetrorelix (SB-75). *Fertil. Steril.* 63, 282–287.
99. Yano, T., Pinski, J., Halmos, G., Szepeshazi, K., and Schally, A. V. (1994). Inhibition of growth of OV-1063 human epithelial ovarian cancer xenografts in nude mice by treatment with luteinizing hormone-releasing hormone antagonist SB-75. *Proc. Natl. Acad. Sci. USA* 91, 7090–7094.
100. Segal-Abramson, T., Kitroser, H., Levy, J., Schally, A. V., and Sharoni, Y. (1992). Direct effects of luteinizing hormone-releasing hormone agonists and antagonists on MCF-7 mammary cancer cells. *Proc. Natl. Acad. Sci. USA* 89, 2336–2339.
101. Eidne, K. A., Flanagan, C. A., Harris, N. S., and Millar, R. P. (1987). Gonadotropin-releasing hormone (Gn-RH)-binding sites in human breast cancer cell lines and inhibitory effects of Gn-RH antagonists. *J. Clin. Endocrinol. Metab.* 64, 425–432.
102. Kimura, A., Ohmichi, M., Kurachi, H., Ikegami, H., Hayakawa, J., Tasaka, K., Kanda, Y., Nishio, Y., Jikihara, H., Matsuura, N., and Murata, Y. (1999). Role of mitogen-activated protein kinase/extracellular signal-regulated kinase cascade in gonadotropin-releasing hormone-induced growth inhibition of a human ovarian cancer cell line. *Cancer Res.* 59, 5133–5142.
103. Kim, J. H., Park, D. C., Kim, J. W., Choi, Y. K., Lew, Y. O., Kim, D. H., Jung, J. K., Lim, Y. A., and Namkoong, S. E. (1999). Antitumor effect of Gn-RH agonist in epithelial ovarian cancer. *Gynecol. Oncol.* 74, 170–180.
104. Gunthert, A. R., Grundker, C., Hollmann, K., and Emons, G. (2002). Luteinizing hormone-releasing hormone induces JunD-DNA binding and extends cell cycle in human ovarian cancer cells. *Biochem. Biophys. Res. Comm.* 294, 11–15.
105. Pfarr, C. M., Mechta, G., Spyrou, D., Lallemand, S., Carillo, M., and Yaniv, M. (1994). Mouse JunD negatively regulates fibroblast growth and antagonizes transformation by ras. *Cell* 76, 747–760.
106. Emons, G., Muller, V., Ortmann, O., Grossmann, G., Trautner, U. von Stuckrad, B., et al. (1996). Luteinizing hormone-releasing hormone agonist triptorelin antagonizes signal transduction and mitogenic activity of epidermal growth factor in human ovarian and endometrial cancer cell lines. *Int. J. Oncol.* 9, 1129–1137.
107. Motta, M., Dondi, D., Moretti, R. M., Montagnani Marelli, M., Pimpinelli, F., Magi, R., and Limonta, P. (1996). Role of growth factors, steroid and peptide hormones in the regulation of human prostatic tumor growth. (Review). *J. Steroid. Biochem. Mol. Biol.* 56, 107–111.
108. Imai, A., Takagi, H., Furui, T., Horibe, S., Fuseya, T., and Tamaya, T. (1996). Evidence for coupling of phosphotyrosine phosphatase to gonadotropin-releasing hormone receptor in ovarian carcinoma membrane. *Cancer* 77, 132–137.
109. Imai, A., Takagi, H., Horibe, S., Fuseya, T., and Tamaya, T. (1996). Coupling of gonadotropin-releasing hormone receptor to G_i protein in human reproductive tract tumors. *J. Clin. Endocrinol. Metab.* 81, 3249–3253.
110. Grundker, C., Volker, P., Gunthert, A. R., and Emons, G. (2001). Antiproliferative signaling of LHRH in human endometrial and ovarian cancer cells through G-protein αI-mediated activation of phosphotyrosine phosphatase. *Endocrinology* 142, 2369–2380.
111. Marshall, C. J. (1995). Specificity of receptor tyrosine kinase signaling: Transient versus sustained extracellular signal regulated kinase activation. *Cell* 80, 179–185.
112. Grundker, C., Volker, P., Schulz, K. D., and Emons, G. (2000). Luteinizing hormone-releasing hormone (LHRH) agonist triptorelin and antagonist cetrorelix inhibit EGF-induced *c-fos* expression in human gynecological cancers. *Gynecol. Oncol.* 78, 194–202.
113. Shaulian, E., and Karin, M. (2002). AP-1 as a regulator of cell life and death. (Review). *Nat. Cell Biol.* 4, E131–E136.
114. Takagi, H., Imai, A., Furui, T., Horibe, S., Fuseya, T., and Tamaya, T. (1995). Evidence for tight coupling of gonadotropin-releasing hormone receptors to phosphati-

dylinositol kinase in plasma membrane from ovarian carcinomas. *Gynecol. Oncol.* 58, 110–115.

115. Olson, T. A., Mohanraj, D., and Ramakrisknan, S. (1995). The selective inhibition of vascular permeability factor (VPF) expression in ovarian carcinoma cell lines by a gonadotropin-releasing hormone (Gn-RH) agonist. *Int. J. Oncol.* 6, 905–910.
116. Imai, A., Furui, T., Tamaya, T., and Mills, G. B. (2000). A gonadotropin-releasing hormone-responsive phosphatase hydrolyses lysophosphatidic acid within the plasma membrane of ovarian cancer cells. *J. Clin. Endocrinol. Metab.* 85, 3370–3375.
117. Xu, Y., Fang, X. J., Casey, G., and Mills, G. B. (1995). Lysophospholipids activate ovarian and breast cancer cells. *Biochem. J.* 309, 933–940.
118. Shirahige, Y., Cook, C., Pinski, J., Halmos, G., Nair, R., and Schally, A. V. (1994). Treatment with luteinizing hormone-releasing hormone antagonist SB-75 decreases levels of epidermal growth factor receptor and its mRNA in OV-1063 human epithelial ovarian cancer xenografts in nude mice. *Int. J. Oncol.* 5, 1031–1035.
119. Tang, X., Yano, T., Osuga, Y., Matsumi, H., Yano, N., Xu, J., Wada, O., Koga, K., Kugu, K., Tsutsumi, O., Schally, A. V., and Taketani, Y. (2002). Cellular mechanisms of growth inhibition of human epithelial ovarian cancer cell line by LH-releasing hormone antagonist Cetrorelix. *J. Clin. Endocrinol. Metab.* 87, 3721–3727.
120. Emons, G., Schroder, B., Ortmann, O., Westphalen, S., Schulz, K. D., and Schally, A. V. (1993). High affinity binding and direct antiproliferative effects of LHRH analogs in human endometrial cancer cell lines. *J. Clin. Endocrinol. Metab.* 77, 1458–1464.
121. Grundker, C., Gunthert, A. R., Millar, R. P., and Emons, G. (2002). Expression of gonadotropin-releasing hormone II (Gn-RH-II) receptor in human endometrial and ovarian cells and effects of Gn-RH-II on tumor cell proliferation. *J. Clin. Enodcrinol. Metab.* 87, 1427–1430.
122. Volker, P., Grundker, C., Schmidt, O., Schulz, K. D., and Emons, G. (2002). Expression of receptors for luteinizing hormone-releasing hormone in human ovarian and endometrial cancers: Frequency, autoregulation and correlation with direct antiproliferative activity of LHRH analogues. *Am. J. Obstet. Gynecol.* 186, 171–179.
123. Imai, A., Takagi, A., Horibe, S., Takagi, H., and Tamaya, T. (1998). Evidence for tight coupling of gonadotropin-releasing hormone receptor to stimulated Fas ligand expression in reproductive tract tumors: Possible mechanism for hormonal control of apoptotic cell death. *J. Clin. Endocrinol. Metab.* 83, 427–431.
124. Imai, A., Horibe, S., Takagi, A., Ohno, T., and Tamaya, T. (1997). Frequent expression of Fas in gonadotropin-releasing hormone receptor-bearing tumors. *Eur. J. Obstet. Gynecol. Reprod. Biol.* 74, 73–78.
125. Grundker, C., Schulz, K., Gunthert, A. R., and Emons, G. (2000). Luteinizing hormone-releasing hormone induces nuclear factor κB-activation and inhibits apoptosis in ovarian cancer cells. *J. Clin. Endocrinol. Metab.* 85, 3815–3820.
126. Ghosh, S., May, M. J., and Kopp, E. B. (1998). NF-kappa B and Rel proteins: Evolutionarily conserved mediators of immune responses. *Annu. Rev. Immunol.* 16, 225–260.
127. Chu, Z. L., McKinsey, T. A., Liu, L., Gentry, J. J., Malim, M. H., and Ballard, D. W. (1997). Suppression of tumor necrosis factor-induced cell death by inhibitor of apoptosis c-IAP2 is under NF-kappaB control. *Proc. Natl. Acad. Sci. USA* 94, 10057–10062.
128. You, M., Ku, P. T., Hrdlickova, R., and Bose, Jr., H. R. (1997). ch-IAP1, a member of the inhibitor-of-apoptosis protein family, is a mediator of the antiapoptotic activity of the v-Rel oncoprotein. *Mol. Cell. Biol.* 17, 7328–7341.
129. Zong, W. X., Edelstein, L. C., Chen, C., Bash, J., and Gelinas, C. (1999). The prosurvival Bcl-2 homolog Bfl-1/A1 is a direct transcriptional target of NF-kappaB that blocks TNFalpha-induced apoptosis. *Genes Dev.* 13, 382–387.
130. Wang, C. Y., Mayo, M. W., Korneluk, R. G., Goeddel, D. V., and Baldwin, Jr., A. S. (1998). NF-kappaB antiapoptosis: Induction of TRAF1 and TRAF2 and c-IAP1 and c-IAP2 to suppress caspase-8 activation. *Science* 281, 1680–1683.
131. Kreuz, S., Siegmund, D., Scheurich, P., and Wajant, H. (2001). NF-kappaB inducers upregulates cFLIP, a cycloheximide-sensitive inhibitor of death receptor signaling. *Mol. Cell. Biol.* 21, 3964–3973.
132. Yano, T., Yano, N., Matsumi, H., Morita, Y., Tsutsumi, O, Schally, A. V., and Taketani, Y. (1997). Effect of luteinizing hormone-releasing hormone analogs on the rat ovarian follicle development. *Horm. Res.* 48 (Suppl), 35–41.
133. Papadopoulos, V., Dharmarajan, A. M., Li, H., Culty, M., Lemay, M., and Sridaran, R. (1999). Mitochondrial peripheral-type benzodiazepine receptor expression. Correlation with gonadotropin-releasing hormone (Gn-RH) agonist-induced apoptosis in the corpus luteum. *Biochem. Pharmacol.* 58, 1389–1393.
134. Millar, R., Conklin, D., Lofton-Day, C., Hutchinson, E., Toskie, B., Illing, N., Sealfon, S. C., and Hapgood, J. (1999). A novel human Gn-RH receptor homolog gene: Abundant and wide tissue distribution of the antisense transcript. *J. Endocrinol.* 162, 117–126.
135. Conklin, D. C., Rixon, M. W., Kuestner, R. E., Maurer, M. F., Whitmore, T. E., and Millar, R. P. (2000). Cloning and gene expression of a novel human ribonucleoprotein. *Biochem. Biophys. Acta.* 1492, 465–469.
136. Neill, J. D. (2002). Minireview: Gn-RH and Gn-RH receptor genes in the human genome. *Endocrinology* 143, 737–743.
137. Lumpkin, M. D., Moltz, J. H., Yu, W. H., Samson, W. K., and McCann, S. M. (1987). Purification of FSH-releasing factor: Its dissimilarity from LHRH of mammalian, avian, and piscian origin. *Brain Res. Bull.* 18, 175–178.
138. Padmanabhan, V., and McNeilly, A. S. (2001). Is there an FSH-releasing factor? (Review). *Reproduction* 121, 21–30.
139. Yu, W. H., Karanth, S., Walczewska, A., Sower, S. A., and McCann, S. M. (1997). A hypothalamic follicle-stimulating hormone-releasing decapeptide in the rat. *Proc. Natl. Acad. Sci. USA* 94, 9499–9503.
140. Yu, W. H., Karanth, S., Sower, S. A., Parlow, A. F., and McCann, S. M. (2000). The similarity of FSH-releasing factor to lamprey gonadotropin-releasing hormone III (l-Gn-RH-III). *Proc. Soc. Exp. Biol. Med.* 224, 89–92.
141. Millar, R. P., Milton, R. C., Follet, B. K., and King, J. A. (1986). Receptor binding and gonadotropin-releasing

hormone ([His5, Trp7, Tyr8]Gn-RH) and a D-Arg6 analog. *Endocrinology* 119, 224–231.

142. Blomenrohr, M., Heding, A., Sellar, R., Leurs, R., Bogerd, J., Eidne, K. A., and Willars, G. B. (1999). Pivotal role for the cytoplasmic carboxyl-terminal tail of a nonmammalian gonadotropin-releasing hormone receptor in cell surface expression, ligand binding, and receptor phosphorylation and internalization. *Mol. Pharmacol.* 56, 1229–1237.

143. Ling, K., Wang, P., Zhao, J., Wu, Y-L., Cheng, Z-J., Ubi, G. X., Hu, W., Ma, L., and Pei, G. (1999). Five-transmembrane domains appear sufficient for a G protein-coupled receptor: Functional five-transmembrane domain chemokine receptors. *Proc. Natl. Acad. Sci. USA* 96, 7922–7927.

CHAPTER **18**

Ovarian Angiogenesis

ELI GEVA AND ROBERT B. JAFFE

ABSTRACT

Elucidating the genetic and molecular mechanisms that control the development and remodeling of capillary blood vessels is critical to an understanding of ovarian biology. Neovascularization, the formation of new blood vessels, can be considered as two distinct biologic processes: vasculogenesis and angiogenesis. Vasculogenesis refers to the de novo formation of blood vessels, observed primarily during embryogenesis, whereas angiogenesis refers to the process by which new capillaries develop from preexisting vessels. Angiogenesis occurs in physiologic and pathologic conditions, and this dichotomy is particularly evident in the human ovary. The vasculogenesis/angiogenesis process requires tight orchestration of vascular endothelial cell-specific growth factors, controlled by endocrine, paracrine, and autocrine regulation, as well as by a variety of other growth factors, cytokines, and a number of environmental influences such as hypoxia. Therefore the lack of appropriate integration of one or more of these factors may adversely affect ovarian physiology. In the normal ovary, angiogenesis likely plays an important role in folliculogenesis, ovulation, and corpus luteum function. Pathologic conditions involving the ovary also involve angiogenesis, including ovarian hyperstimulation syndrome, corpus luteum insufficiency, and benign and malignant neoplasms. This chapter focuses on physiological and pathological mechanisms of ovarian angiogenesis.

INTRODUCTION

Components of the female reproductive system undergo a number of programmed angiogenic processes that are coupled with cyclic evolution and decline of ovarian, endometrial, placental, and mammary gland structures. The development of a new vascular network requires exquisite coordination between different cell types undergoing complex changes. This implies that the expression of at least some of the inciting angiogenic factors are hormone dependent. Cycling in the ovary is initiated by cyclic and pulsatile secretion of gonadotropins. This pattern of gonadotropin secretion leads to cyclic steroidogenesis and ovulation within the ovary. Ovarian steroids also regulate endometrial cycles. Therefore it is likely that the waves of angiogenesis within the reproductive system are coordinated by gonadotropins and/or by ovarian steroids. This implies that the expression of the initiating angiogenic factors in the ovary is hormone dependent.

Vascular endothelial growth factor (VEGF), also known as *vascular permeability factor (VPF)*, is a potent angiogenic factor that is a mitogen and survival factor for the vascular endothelium [1]. Several studies have indicated that VEGF may be involved in the physiologic regulation of ovarian angiogenesis. VEGF is expressed and secreted in the human ovary in a manner that suggests a role for this growth factor in cyclic angiogenesis and regulation of vascular permeability, both of which are critical for ovarian folliculogenesis and normal reproductive function.

More recently, a second family of vascular endothelial growth factors was identified, the angiopoietins (Angs). Angs are vascular endothelial cell-specific growth factors that play important roles principally during later stages of angiogenesis and after induction of new capillaries by VEGF. They serve to trim and stabilize these newly formed vessels. The two Angs that have been studied most extensively to date are Ang-1 and Ang-2, both of which bind to the same tyrosine kinase receptor, Tie2. Ang-1 is ubiquitously expressed throughout the body, whereas Ang-2 is expressed primarily in the female reproductive tract (ovary, uterus, placenta) [2].

In this chapter, the process of angiogenesis, the molecules involved, and the regulation of angiogenesis in the normal human ovary during the menstrual cycle will be described. This will be followed by a discussion of the processes of angiogenesis and vascular permeability in ovarian pathology. Finally, insights into therapeutic strategies to treat these conditions will be discussed briefly.

ANGIOGENESIS

Vascular development occurs in two stages: an early stage, *vasculogenesis,* and a later stage termed *angiogenesis*. Vasculogenesis is the mechanism by which the primary capillary network is formed from mesoderm-derived precursors (hemangioblasts), through a process of differentiation, proliferation, and coalescence to form the primitive vascular network [3, 4]. Angiogenesis refers to the formation of new capillaries from preexisting vessels by remodeling of the primary plexus. The angiogenic process begins with endothelial cell proliferation and migration into the primary vascular network and leads to vascularization of previously avascular tissues and organs and to growth and remodeling of the initially homogeneous capillary plexus to form a new microcirculation.

This process consists of fragmentation of the basal lamina of the existing vessel, migration of endothelial cells from the existing vessel toward the angiogenic stimulus following proteolysis of the extracellular matrix, endothelial cell proliferation, and formation of the capillary lumina and is completed by differentiation into arterioles and venules (Figure 18.1) [3, 4].

The regulation of neovascularization is a dynamic process and represents a balance between stimulation and inhibition of angiogenesis. Thus factors that inhibit angiogenesis may be necessary to maintain normal physiologic blood vessel growth and thus prevent excessive and/or abnormal vascularization.

OVARIAN ANGIOGENESIS

During the fetal period and soon after birth, the ovary contains a reservoir of primordial follicles, composed of an oocyte surrounded by a single layer of granulosa cells. At puberty, during folliculogenesis the primordial follicles grow and continually recruit new follicles to develop from the nongrowing cohort. The majority of the growing follicles, however, never become ovulatory but rather undergo atresia.

In the ovary the vascular supply is formed on a cyclic basis. The smaller, primordial follicles do not possess an

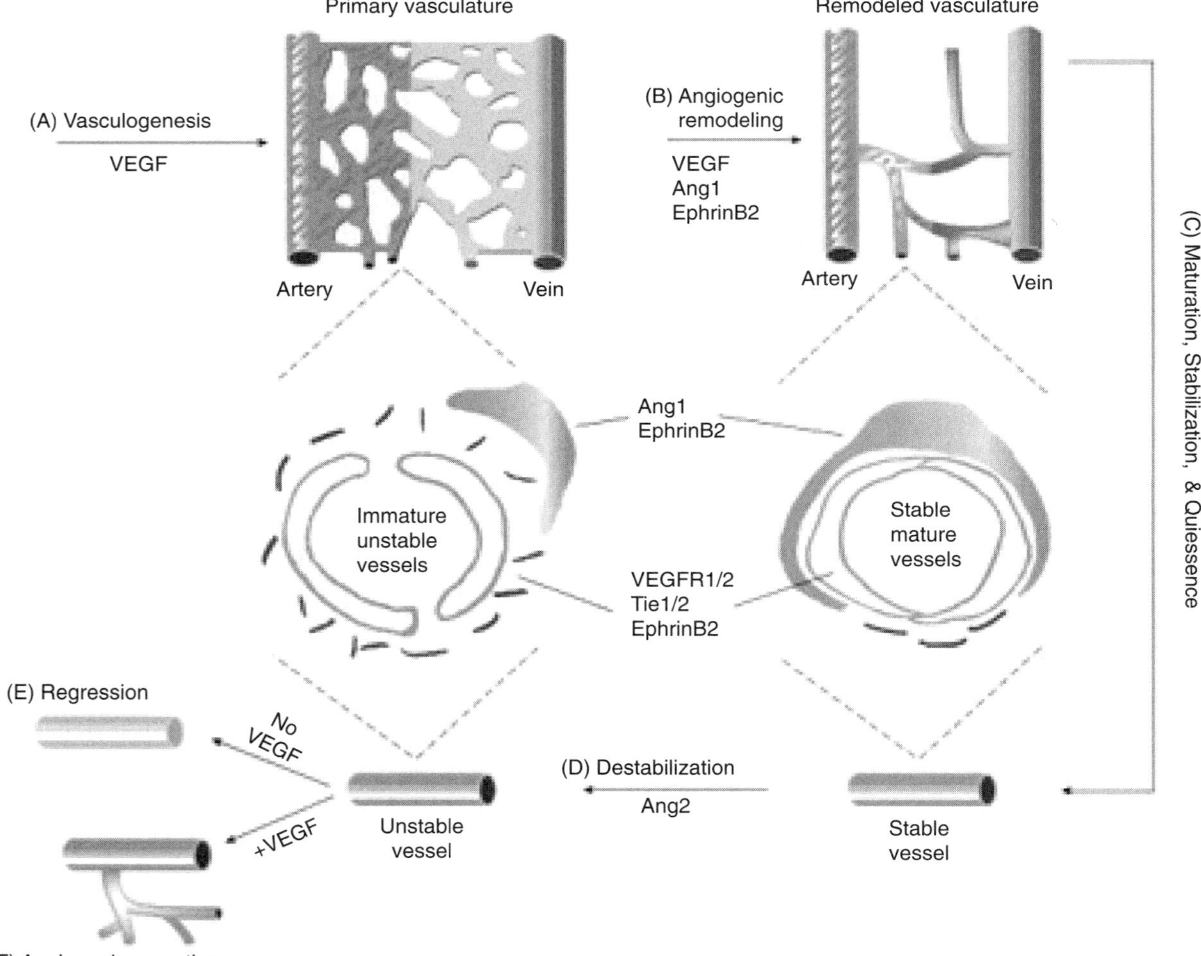

FIGURE 18.1 Stages of angiogenesis and roles of VEGF, angiopoietin (Ang) -1 and -2, and their receptors in the angiogenic process. Ephrin and its receptor are not discussed in the text. (From Ref. [2].) (See color plate.)

independent capillary network and are dependent on their proximity to the stromal vessels. The primary follicles develop an initial vascular supply consisting of one or two arterioles terminating in an increasingly complex wreath-like network as the follicle continues to grow. Soon after the antrum appears, the follicle acquires a vascular wreath in the thecal layer that, when fully established, consists of two concentric networks of vessels in the theca interna and externa, respectively. The arterioles and venules of the outer complex send tiny branches into the inner capillary plexus, which consists of a single layer of endothelial cells, which lies in the theca interna, immediately outside of the basement membrane. The capillaries do not penetrate the basement membrane nor enter the granulosa layer. The venous capillaries draining the inner capillary plexus collect into a few small vessels, which become continuous with the medullary veins [5–10].

The establishment of the vascular wreath, particularly the expansion of the inner capillary plexus of the theca interna, coincides with a period of rapid growth and differentiation of the follicle. The selection of the dominant follicle may be dependent on the differential formation of this rich vascular supply and on increased vascular permeability.

Shortly before ovulation, the basement membrane separating the highly vascular theca from the relatively avascular granulosa cell layer breaks down. The capillaries develop fenestrations, rapidly sprout, and invade the inner granulosa cell layer, whereas reduced follicular vascularity in parallel with reduced deoxyribonucleic acid (DNA) synthesis are found in the follicles undergoing atresia [11].

At the time of ovulation, the follicular wall ruptures and the follicle collapses to form folds that interdigitate with the luteinizing granulosa cells. Arterioles, venules, and lymphatic vessels form a complex capillary network, bringing each granulosa-lutein cell into close proximity to the vascular bed. Therefore the establishment and development of the complex capillary network requires exquisite timing, likely critical for appropriate steroid production. The process is completed in the early luteal phase (third day following ovulation) [5–10].

The very early corpus luteum is characterized by hemorrhage into the ovulatory cavity, which is accompanied by intense vascular sprouting. These sprouting vessels in the early corpus luteum have not yet developed a lumen. Individual sprouting vessels can be identified within 1 to 2 days following ovulation.

The developing corpus luteum continues to grow, acquiring a dense vascular network of immature, possibly leaky, microvessels [9]. Approximately 50% of the cells of the mature corpus luteum are endothelial cells arising from the thecal vascular plexus by proliferation, and the majority of the granulosa-lutein cells are adjacent to one or more capillaries [12], allowing optimal progesterone supply to support the developing pregnancy [13]. Therefore inadequate luteal function may be associated with decreased luteal vascularization [14].

The dissolution of the blood vessels of the regressing corpus luteum is associated with gradual rounding and condensation of the endothelial cells of the small vessels. All lutein cells disappear, leaving arteriole-like remnants of blood vessels with an onionskin arrangement of surrounding myo-fibroblastic cells and heavily condensed endothelial cells with dense connective tissue in the residual corpus luteum. Later, the corpus luteum completely disappears, leaving a small hyaline scar, the corpus albicans [9].

Blood vessel regression in the ovary does not appear to involve endothelial cell apoptosis. High power light microscopic analysis of the corpus luteum indicates that rounded endothelial cells detach from their basement membrane, leaving areas devoid of a covering endothelial cell monolayer, which is particularly prominent in the residual corpus luteum [9].

VASCULAR ENDOTHELIAL-SPECIFIC GROWTH FACTORS

Vascular Endothelial Growth Factor/Vascular Permeability Factor

(Note: See Figure 18.2 for an illustration of VEGF and its receptors and the angiopoietins and their receptor. See

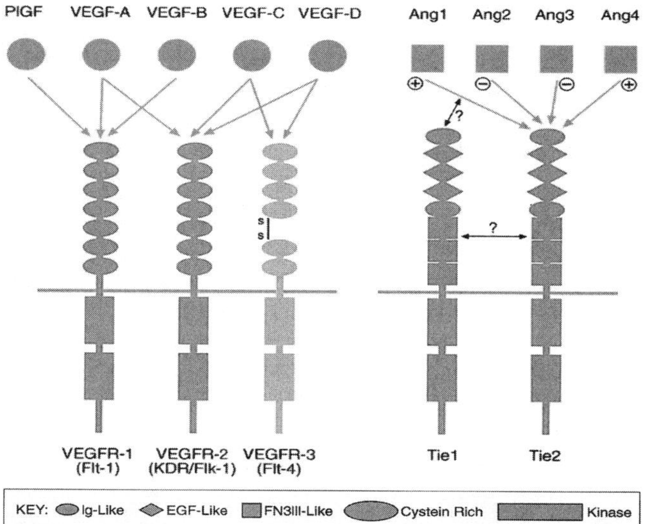

FIGURE 18.2 Vascular endothelial-specific angiogenic factors and their receptors. *Ang-1,* angiopoietin-1; *Ang-2,* angiopoietin-2; *PGF,* placental growth factor; *Tie1* and *Tie2,* receptors for the angiopoietins; *VEGF,* vascular endothelial growth factor; *VEGFR-1, VEGFR-2, VEGR-3,* receptors for VEGF and PGF. (A functional role for Tie1 has not been definitively identified.) (Modified from Gale, N. W., and Yancopoulos, G. D. (1999). Growth factors acting via endothelial cell-specific receptor tyrosine kinases: VEGFs, Angiopoietins, and ephrins in vascular development. *Genes Dev.* 13, 1055.) (See color plate.)

Figure 18.2 for an illustration of the involvement of these molecules in the angiogenic process.)

Biology

VEGF/VPF is a 45 kDa basic, heparin-binding, homodimeric glycoprotein that binds specifically to receptors on endothelial cells. The human VEGF gene has been localized to chromosome 6p21.3 and consists of eight exons separated by seven introns. Five VEGF forms have been identified in mammals, resulting from alternative splicing of the single VEGF gene: $VEGF_{121}$, $VEGF_{145}$, $VEGF_{165}$, $VEGF_{189}$, and $VEGF_{206}$, [1, 15–17]. $VEGF_{121}$ is a weakly acidic polypeptide that does not bind to heparin, whereas $VEGF_{189}$ and $VEGF_{206}$ are more basic and bind to heparin with greater affinity than $VEGF_{165}$ [15]. $VEGF_{121}$ and $VEGF_{145}$ appear to be secreted. $VEGF_{165}$, the predominant isoform, is also secreted; however, a significant fraction remains bound to the cell surface and the extracellular matrix. In contrast, $VEGF_{189}$ and $VEGF_{206}$ are sequestered in the extracellular matrix [16].

VEGF is a potent mitogen for endothelial cells [18]. It has the ability to induce endothelial cell proliferation as well as migratory and sprouting activity and promotes endothelial cell tubule-like structures [19, 20]. VEGF is critical for the earliest stages of vasculogenesis and angiogenesis, is secreted by peraendothelial cells, and acts in a paracrine fashion to modulate activities in adjacent vascular endothelium [21, 22].

VEGF is also known as *VPF* because of its ability to induce vascular leakage [23]. Permeability (leakiness) has been attributed to highly active angiogenesis and vascular remodeling, but the structural basis and mechanisms of development of leakiness remain to be completely elucidated [6, 24–26]. VEGF/VPF induces fenestrations in endothelial cells of small venules and capillaries [27]. An increase in microvascular permeability is a crucial step in angiogenesis. The induction of plasma protein leakage by VEGF during angiogenesis results in the formation of an extravascular fibrin gel, a substrate for endothelial and tumor cell growth. Therefore steady-state physiological properties of blood vessels, including vascular permeability, are determined by the local microenvironment, rather than by only the initial angiogenic stimulus [28].

VEGF-A exerts its effects by binding with high affinity to at least three endothelial cell-specific tyrosine kinase receptors VEGFR-1/Flt (*fms*-like-tyrosine kinase)-1, VEGFR-2/KDR (*k*inase *d*omain *r*egion)/Flk-1, and VEGR-3/F1t-4 [1] (Figure 18.1). Angiogenesis is stimulated by activating the KDR receptor [1]. The null mutation of KDR results in defects in differentiation of hemangioblasts to form angioblastic and hematopoietic cell lineages [29], whereas Flt-1 appears to have a later role, because mouse embryos lacking Flt-1 develop angioblasts, but blood vessel assembly and tube formation are impaired [30]. Flt-1 and KDR have different signal transduction pathways. In transfected cells expressing the KDR receptor, chemotaxis and mitogenic activity have been found in response to VEGF-A. In contrast, transfected cells expressing Flt-1 lack such responses [30]. KDR undergoes strong ligand-dependent tyrosine phosphorylation in intact cells, whereas phosphorylation of Flt-1 is weak [30]. Deletion of Flt-1 tyrosine kinase domains permitted normal embryonic development [31], indicating that Flt-1 might function as an inert "decoy" by binding VEGF-A and thereby regulating the availability of VEGF for activation of KDR [32].

Vascular Endothelial Growth Factor Expression during Folliculogenesis

Reverse transcription-polymerase chain reaction (RT-PCR) demonstrated that among the various VEGF isoforms, messenger ribonucleic acid (mRNA) encoding $VEGF_{165}$ and $VEGF_{121}$ were dominant in normal human ovaries [33, 34].

In situ hybridization studies in female rats have shown that VEGF mRNA is expressed in the interstitial tissue and thecal layers of preantral and small antral follicles (Table 18.1). VEGF receptors were detectable on endothelial cells interspersed in the stroma and on capillaries in the peripheral thecal layers of growing follicles. Thus it appears that the primary target of VEGF, which is found along the path of capillary extension toward growing follicles, is the endothelium. Furthermore, expression of VEGF mRNA in the thecal layers, and not in the inner granulosa, suggests that the locally secreted protein may target capillary extension to the periphery of the follicle [35].

Concomitantly with further follicular growth and maturation, an additional compartment expresses VEGF mRNA: the cumulus cells that engulf the oocyte. In the granulosa cells, high levels of VEGF mRNA were detectable only at the immediate preovulatory stage. Shortly after ovulation, the predominant sites of VEGF mRNA expression were the lutein cells [35, 35a] (Figure 18.3). Thus the dynamic pattern of VEGF mRNA expression parallels gonadotropin stimulation (LH) and likely steroid production. However, Hazzard et al. [36] found that VEGF mRNA expression by granulosa cells in vivo did not change after human chorionic gonadotropin (hCG) stimulation or 3β-hydroxysteroid dehydrogenase inhibition (Trilostane) alone or Trilostane plus progestin in the periovulatory interval of macaque monkeys.

In the reproductive age ovary, the primordial and primary follicles do not demonstrate immunohistochemical staining for VEGF. Positive immunostaining for VEGF protein is observed in the cytoplasm of the granulosa and thecal cells of the antral and preovulatory follicles. The immunohistochemical staining of granulosa cells is weak compared with that in the theca interna of the developing

TABLE 18.1 Localization of Vascular Endothelial Growth Factor and its Receptor (VEGFR1, Flt-1) in Rats

Stage of Folliculogenesis		Primordial/ Primary	Preantral/ Small Antral	Preovulatory	Corpus Luteum	Corpus Luteum Regression	Early Pregnancy
VEGF	**mRNA**	NA	TCs	TCs GCs EC	GLs	NA	NA
	Protein	No	GCs TCs	TCs GCs	GLs TLs	No	GLs TLs
VEGF-R	**mRNA**	NA	EC	NA	NA	NA	NA
	Protein (Flt-1)	NA	NA	GCs TCs EC	GLs TLs	NA	GLs TLs

EC, Endothelial cell; *GCs,* granulosa cells; *GLs,* granulosa-lutein cells; *NA,* data not available; *TCs,* thecal cells; *TLs,* thecal-lutein cells; *VEGF,* vascular endothelial growth factor; *VEGF-R,* vascular endothelial growth factor receptor.

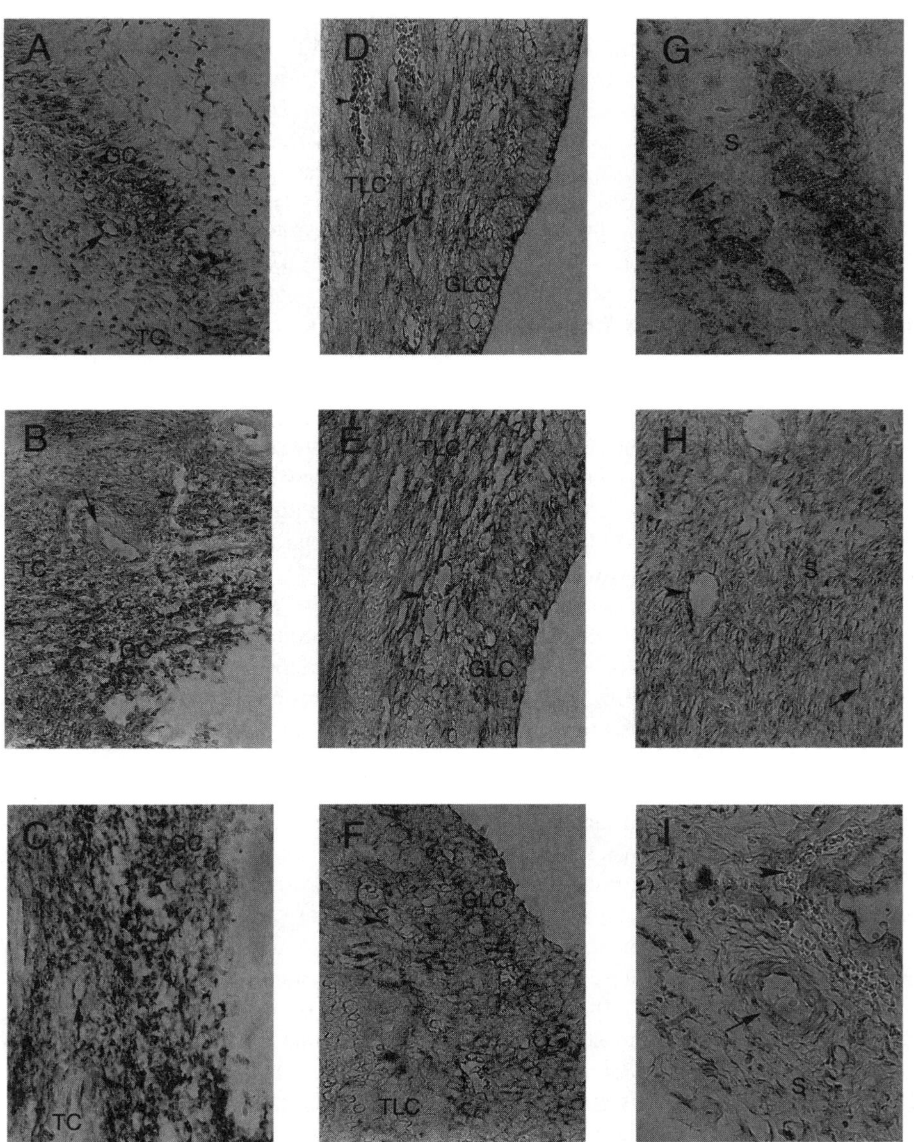

FIGURE 18.3 Localization of VEGF-A, Ang-1, and Ang-2 mRNA in pre- and postmenopausal human ovaries. **A–C,** VEGF-A (**A**), Ang-1 (**B**), and Ang-2 (**C**) hybridization signal in the follicular phase, localized principally in the granulosa cell layer (GC) and vascular endothelial cells and to a lesser degree in the thecal cell layer (TC). **D–F,** In luteal phase ovaries, VEGF-A (**D**), Ang-1 (**E**), and Ang-2 (**F**) mRNA expression was detected mainly in the granulosa-lutein cell layer (GLC) and to a lesser degree in the thecal-lutein cell layer (TLC) and endothelial cells. **G–I,** In postmenopausal ovaries, VEGF-A (**G**), Ang-1 (**H**), and Ang-2 (**I**) mRNA expression was localized in the perivascular stromal cells (S) and vascular endothelial cells. Original magnification × 400. Arrow = artery; arrowhead = vein.

follicle, suggesting that paracrine secretion of VEGF may be essential for follicular angiogenesis [37].

In the corpus luteum, luteinized granulosa and thecal cells exhibit staining for VEGF. However, with further maturation, lutein cell staining for VEGF protein becomes more variable. Theca-lutein cell staining is less intense than exhibited by most granulosa-lutein cells. VEGF protein is not found in atretic follicles or degenerating corpora lutea. In early pregnancy, the intensity of staining in the gestational corpus luteum is stronger than in the luteal phase [34, 38, 39].

Immunostaining for Flt-1 is detected in the cytoplasm of thecal cells and to a lesser degree in the granulosa cells of preovulatory follicles, whereas the endothelial cells stain faintly for Flt-1. In the lutein cells, Flt-1 is detected during the luteal phase and early pregnancy, whereas there is weak staining in endothelial cells of the microvessels. The intensity of staining for Flt-1 is more intense in thecal lutein cells than in granulosa lutein cells [38].

In primordial follicles, small antral follicles and preovulatory follicles, the oocytes stain weakly for VEGF [35a, 38].

Functional Implications of Vascular Endothelial Growth Factor Secretion

Follicular Selection. Based on the preferential accumulation of gonadotropins within the dominant follicle, it has been suggested that differential vascular permeability is involved in, and may mediate, follicular selection [40]. VEGF in the thecal cell layer likely modulates vascular permeability. This modulation may be one mechanism by which differential gonadotropin accumulation is achieved. Thus the richly vascularized thecal cell layer is probably critical for gonadotropin-dependent growth of the follicle and for access of estrogen, produced in the avascular granulosa cell layer by aromatization of thecal androgens, to the systemic circulation. Despite the apparent production of VEGF by granulosa cells, this layer remains largely avascular before ovulation in women, implying that the follicular basement membrane separating the thecal and granulosa cells plays a key role in inhibiting granulosa vascularization.

As VEGF receptors are expressed on endothelial cells participating in angiogenesis [35], as well as in quiescent endothelium [41], it appears that locally released VEGF, controlled by gonadotropins and in a paracrine and/or autocrine manner by ovarian steroids, regulates endothelial cell growth by creating a microenvironment that supports the proliferation of nearby endothelial cells. Moreover, the expression of VEGF mRNA in neovascularized tissue suggests an additional role of VEGF in maintenance of the ovarian vasculature and/or in controlling permeability.

Vascular Permeability. Microvessels associated with the developing corpus luteum, in contrast to those of the ovarian stroma, are usually permeable to plasma and plasma proteins. The developing follicle is characterized by a substantial increase in the number and permeability of thecal blood vessels. At ovulation, variable amounts of blood and plasma extravasate into the follicular cavity where they form a fibrin clot that extends spokelike projections peripherally among groups of granulosa cells. The correlation between VEGF secretion and extravascular fibrin deposition suggests that VEGF plays a role in the process of fibrin accumulation by rendering thecal blood vessels hyperpermeable to plasma fibrinogen [34].

Corpus Luteum Support. Ferrara et al. demonstrated the essential role of VEGF for corpus luteum angiogenesis in vivo [42]. After hormonally induced ovulation, female rats treated with truncated soluble Flt-1 receptors had virtually complete suppression of corpus luteum angiogenesis. In situ hybridization demonstrated that VEGF mRNA was upregulated in the hypoxic luteal cells surrounding the necrotic cores. Immunohistochemical staining for 3β-hydroxysteroid dehydrogenase was normal in the few corpora lutea that developed in the Flt-IgG-treated animals, except in the necrotic core. These findings are consistent with the hypothesis that suppression of progesterone production following soluble VEGF receptor administration was secondary to a defective vascular supply rather than inhibition of luteal cell differentiation.

Vascular Endothelial Growth Factor Regulation

Gonadotropins. Several studies suggest that luteinizing hormone (LH) and hCG modulate expression of VEGF [33, 34, 37]. Analysis of cultured granulosa-lutein cells, obtained at oocyte retrieval for in vitro fertilization, treated with hCG, recombinant human follicle-stimulating hormone (r-hFSH), prostaglandin E_2 (PGE_2), 8-bromo-cAMP (all of which activate the protein kinase A-dependent signaling pathway), and 12-*O*-tetradecanoylphorbol 13-acetate (which activates the protein kinase C-dependent signaling pathway), stimulate VEGF mRNA expression in a concentration-dependent manner [43]. Therefore both follicle-stimulating hormone (FSH) and LH/hCG receptor-activated pathways can induce VEGF mRNA levels in human granulosa cells. The observation that 8-bromo-cAMP and 12-*O*-tetradecanoylphorbol 13-acetate induce VEGF gene transcription is consistent with the potential activating protein-1 and -2 binding sites in the human VEGF gene promoter sequence. The increase in VEGF mRNA by PGE_2 may be mediated through a protein kinase A-dependent signaling pathway, as PGE_2 increases cAMP levels in granulosa cells [43].

In rhesus monkeys studied during the periovulatory phase in vivo, follicular fluid VEGF concentrations increased sixfold by 12 hours after the administration of an ovulatory stimulus with hCG and remained elevated at 36 hours, while no changes in VEGF mRNA were observed at any time point [36]. These observations support the concept that the midcycle gonadotropin surge promotes posttranscriptional regulation of VEGF production by gonadotropins in luteinizing granulosa cells.

Steroid Regulation of VEGF. Recently, Mueller et al. [44] demonstrated that estrogen has a direct effect on VEGF gene transcription through both estrogen receptor α (ERα) (3.2-fold) and estrogen receptor β (ERβ) (2.3-fold) in a model cell system. That both granulosa and thecal cells express VEGF (see Table 18.1) and estrogen receptors [45], suggests that estrogen plays a regulatory role in VEGF expression during folliculogenesis.

In contrast, contradictory studies related to the role of progesterone in VEGF expression have been published. Whereas progesterone increases VEGF expression in vitro in breast cancer cells [46] and epithelial cells [47], progesterone-independent VEGF expression has been found in the periovulatory period in vivo [36].

Pathophysiological Aspects of Vascular Endothelial Growth Factor

Aging. Follicular fluid VEGF from women of later reproductive age (38 to 46 years) is elevated compared with that of younger women. It has been suggested that VEGF concentrations increase because of the hypoxic environment within follicles of older women [48].

Polycystic Ovary Syndrome. In women with polycystic ovarian syndrome (PCOS), increased serum concentrations of VEGF were found during in vitro fertilization (IVF) treatment. Doppler blood flow velocities within ovarian stromal vessels rose in parallel with rising serum VEGF levels [49, 50]. These findings may underlie the increased ovarian stromal vascularity in women with PCOS [51] and may explain the higher risk of ovarian hyperstimulation syndrome (OHSS) in these women.

Increased expression of VEGF mRNA was found in the hyperthecotic stroma of women with PCOS. Interestingly, VEGF immunoreactivity was elevated in the granulosa and thecal cell layers [34]. The increase in granulosa cell VEGF production in women with PCOS may be the result of the elevated LH and/or estradiol associated with this disorder. One of the mechanisms that underpins the unifollicular response of the normal ovary is diversion of the blood flow within the ovaries from cohort follicles to the dominant follicle. This results in diversion of FSH away from the cohort follicles, resulting in atresia. Therefore widespread distribution of VEGF in the ovaries of women with PCOS prevents this diversion of blood flow, leaving a substantial number of small and intermediate-sized follicles in "suspended animation" and ready to respond to gonadotropin stimulation. The distribution of VEGF in ovaries of women with PCOS might explain one of the fundamental features of PCOS: the loss of the intraovarian autoregulatory mechanism that permits unifollicular ovulation to occur [52].

Ovarian Hyperstimulation Syndrome. Sex steroids are known to modulate angiogenic activity (see previous discussion and [53]). OHSS is a potentially life-threatening complication of ovulation induction with gonadotropins. VEGF is a potent inducer of vascular permeability. Increased VEGF expression, mediated by increased levels of gonadotropins and/or estrogen, can lead to excessive vascular permeability [54]. Ovulation induction may induce increased levels of VEGF in multiple follicles and corpora lutea, resulting in increased vascular permeability. Increased vascular leakage leads to extravasation of protein-rich fluid from the intravascular space. The signs of OHSS include accumulation of peritoneal and pleural fluid, edema, and hypovolemia with hyperconcentration, which leads to anuria, hypotension, a hypercoagulable state, adult respiratory distress syndrome, and even death in the most severe form [55].

Serum and follicular levels of VEGF are higher in IVF patients who develop severe OHSS following ovulation induction than those who do not [56]. However, VEGF concentrations before starting gonadotropin treatment in high-risk patients are not predictive of the subsequent development of OHSS [57]. VEGF plasma concentrations are positively correlated with the syndrome [58] but provide no additional diagnostic information for the further course of the disease [59].

Elevated serum estradiol concentrations have been associated with high responders to ovulation induction with gonadotropins and have been suggested as a possible predictive marker for development of OHSS [55]. These high estradiol levels may contribute to the pathophysiology of OHSS by increasing VEGF gene transcription [44].

Permeability in OHSS ascites fluid was reduced by 70% after incubation with hVEGF antiserum [60]. Levin et al. [61] showed that follicular fluid from women undergoing ovulation induction significantly increased endothelial cell permeability, which correlated with the extent of oocyte production. They demonstrated that the follicular fluid factor responsible for increased endothelial cell permeability is VEGF and that the follicular fluid-induced endothelial cell permeability was 98% reversed by VEGF antibody. Moreover, they demonstrated that VEGF disrupts endothelial cell tight junctions and increases permeability by rearrangement of the actin cytoskeleton and disruption of ZO-1 protein.

Several studies suggest that LH and hCG modulate expression of VEGF [43, 62, 63]. Moreover, the severity of the syndrome greatly increases when pregnancy supervenes and is minimized if hCG is not administered, allowing follicles to regress spontaneously. Taken together, these data suggest that LH/hCG serves as a stimulus for VEGF production in the human ovary.

Benign Ovarian Neoplasms. Immunohistochemical studies in ovaries from postmenopausal women revealed VEGF staining in epithelial inclusion cysts and in serous cystadenomas. The VEGF protein was demonstrated only in the epithelial layers of the cysts and the pericytes of the ovarian hilar vessels [37], suggesting that VEGF in benign serous neoplasms may be responsible for cystic fluid accumulation by a transudative mechanism. Moreover, if epithelial ovarian cancer (EOC) originates within epithelial inclusion cysts [64], VEGF within these cysts may represent one means by which a developing neoplasm can induce the formation of an increased vascular supply [37].

Epithelial Ovarian Cancer. Ovarian cancer is the fifth leading form of cancer in women, with approximately 23,000 new cases and 14,000 deaths each year in the United States alone, and is the most lethal gynecologic malignancy. The pathophysiology of ovarian neoplasms (both benign and malignant) remains poorly understood. A leading cause of death in patients with EOC is bowel obstruction resulting from diffuse peritoneal carcinomatosis. Many patients progress to advanced disease (stage III), which includes ascites and peritoneal metastases [65].

VEGF plays a pivotal role in tumor angiogenesis. VEGF mRNA is markedly upregulated in the vast majority of solid tumors, including those of the ovary ($VEGF_{165}$ and $VEGF_{121}$ isoforms), [33, 66]. The extent of VEGF expression has been correlated with the degree of malignancy and vascularity [67]. VEGF mRNA is expressed in tumor cells but not in endothelial cells, whereas mRNA for Flt-1 and KDR are upregulated in endothelial cells. VEGF protein has been localized to the tumor and vessels [68]. Thus the tumor cells (and the stroma) secrete VEGF, which accumulates in the target vascular endothelial cells, bind to VEGF receptor and act in a paracrine manner, mediating changes in vascular permeability associated with tumor growth and ascites formation [69], a common finding in women with advanced EOC.

The increased expression of VEGF in EOC cells, which results in abnormal morphologic appearance of tumor vessels [26], might be regulated by one or more of the following pathways:

1. hypoxia-inducible factor (HIF)-1 [35, 70];
2. cytokines and growth factors, including insulin-like growth factor 1 (IGF-1) [71], epidermal growth factor (EGF), transforming growth factor (TGF)-α and TGF-β, platelet derived growth factor (PDGF), basic fibroblast growth factor (bFGF), tumor necrosis factor (TNF)-β, interleukin (IL)-1β, and IL-6 [1];
3. lysophosphatidic acid [72];
4. a mutated form of p53 [73], *ras* [74], and von Hippel-Lindau tumor suppressor gene [75].

VEGF in ovarian neoplasms using in situ hybridization, and quantitative real-time polymerase chain reaction (qRt-PCR) to determine the extent of expression relative to the normal ovary, demonstrated that VEGF expression was confined to the epithelial and endothelial cells [76]. VEGF mRNA expression was high in ovarian cancer relative to normal pre- and postmenopausal ovaries and borderline tumors further supporting a role for elevated VEGF in ascites formation, characteristic of EOC (Figure 18.4).

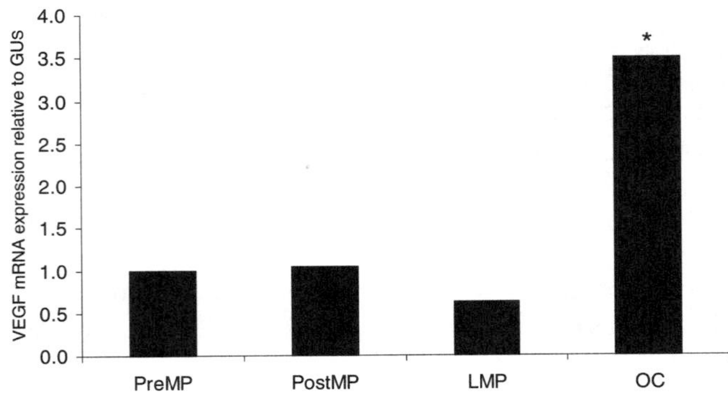

FIGURE 18.4 Real-time quantitative PCR expression of VEGF mRNA, relative to β-glucuronidase (GUS) used as a constitutive contrast in low malignant potential tumors (LMP) and EOC relative to the benign premenopausal (PreMP) and postmenopausal (PostMP) ovary.

EOC, like most solid tumors, is dependent on the development of a new blood supply. Without neovascularization, tumors do not grow beyond 1 to $3\,mm^3$ [69]. Thus preventing vascularization of peritoneal metastases should inhibit tumor growth and improve survival. The association of VEGF with a number of malignancies, including EOC, has resulted in studies to assess the possible use of specific anti-VEGF monoclonal antibodies in the treatment of cancer. Immunoneutralization of VEGF in an athymic, immunodeficient mouse model of EOC with ascites inhibits ascites formation [77] and, when combined with paclitaxel, markedly decreases tumor burden [78]. However, the precise mechanisms involved in new tumor vessel formation and the nature of the vessels so-formed, as well as the mechanisms involved in vascular permeability, remain to be elucidated completely. In a related study, inhibition of a molecule involved in the signaling pathway of VEGF, phosphatidylinositol 3-kinase (PI3-K) [79], inhibits both ascites formation and tumor burden in a mouse model of ovarian cancer, and when the PI3-K inhibitor is combined with paclitaxel this inhibition is further increased [80]. Thus inhibition of VEGF or molecules involved in its signaling pathway are a potentially clinically useful treatment for EOC and associated ascites.

Angiopoietins

More recently, a second family of VEGFs was identified, the angiopoietins (Angs). Angs act in a complementary and coordinated manner with VEGF-A, principally during the later stages of angiogenesis. Ang-1 and Ang-2 are the two members of the family that have been studied most extensively to date. The human Ang-1 and Ang-2 genes are located on chromosome 8 and encode 498- and 496-amino acid glycoproteins, respectively, with 60% homology [81, 82].

Ang-1 binds specifically to and activates the Tie2 (*t*yrosine kinase, *i*mmunoglobulin, and *e*pidermal growth factor) receptor by inducing tyrosine phosphorylation [83]. Whereas Ang-2 binding affinity to the Tie2 receptor is similar, it is unable to phosphorylate the receptor in vitro. Furthermore, high concentrations of Ang-2 substantially block Ang-1 activity. Therefore Ang-2 represents a naturally occurring antagonist of Ang-1/Tie2.

Disruption of mouse Ang-1 or Tie2 receptor genes or overexpression of Ang-2 results in embryonic lethality at 9.5 to 12.5 days as a result of abnormal angiogenesis, demonstrating an essential role for the Angs in early development [2]. Ang-1 is expressed in a wide variety of tissues, whereas Ang-2 appears limited to the female reproductive tract (placenta, ovary, and uterus) under physiologic conditions [82]. In contrast to VEGF-A, which induces capillary sprouting, Ang-1 possesses only weak endothelial cell mitogenic activity, suggesting that Ang-1 may not exert the classical actions of other endothelial growth factors but may play a later role, in a coordinated fashion with VEGF-A, in endothelial maturation and vascular stabilization in its surrounding tissue. Ang-2 may act in a complementary manner with VEGF-A at the front of the invading vascular sprouts by blocking constitutive stabilization and maturation of vessels, allowing them to remain in a more plastic state in which they may be more responsive to a sprouting signal provided by VEGF-A [82]. Thus the opposing actions of Ang-1 and Ang-2 on the activation state of the Tie2 receptor may regulate the plasticity of endothelial cells, thereby modifying their requirement for, and responsivity to, VEGF-A.

Ang-1 is regulated differently than VEGF during the process of angiogenesis. Neither hypoxia nor VEGF induce an Ang-1 or Tie2 response in endothelial cells [83], whereas fetal calf serum, PDGF, EGF, and TGF-β down-regulate Ang-1 mRNA expression. The mechanism of Ang-2 regulation is different from that of Ang-1. In endothelial cells, Ang-2 mRNA expression is decreased by Ang-1, Ang-2, and TGF-β1. However, Ang-2 mRNA levels are increased by hypoxia, VEGF, and bFGF. Similar to VEGF, hypoxia increases Ang-2 mRNA expression directly.

Angiopoietin Expression during Folliculogenesis

Ang-1 transcripts are associated with blood vessels and appear to follow or coincide with, rather than precede, vessel ingrowth into the early corpus luteum. This is consistent with the hypothesis that Ang-1 has a later role in angiogenesis than VEGF. Whereas Ang-2 is present in late preovulatory follicles and associated with blood vessels in the theca interna, in the developing corpus luteum Ang-2 transcripts are abundant at the front of invading vessels, suggesting that Ang-2 may collaborate with VEGF at the front of the invading vessels and revert them to a plastic state in which they may be more responsive to a sprouting signal provided by VEGF [82]. In the atretic follicle and aged corpus luteum, VEGF mRNA is either not detectable or detectable only in small amounts, whereas Ang-2 mRNA is present in a uniformly large amount, especially within the granulosa cell layer. Thus, in the presence of VEGF, Ang-2 may promote vessel sprouting by blocking the Ang-1 signal. In the absence of VEGF, Ang-2 may contribute to vessel regression by inhibition of Ang-1 [84]. Consistent with this interpretation, Ang-2 modulates VEGF-induced neovascularization [85]. The circumference and length of the vessels cooperatively induced by Ang-2 and VEGF are significantly increased compared with VEGF alone or VEGF plus Ang-1. Moreover, histological examination reveals isolated migrating endothelial cells at the leading tip of the capillaries. These findings suggest that the function of Ang-2 on VEGF-induced neovascularization is to promote vascular destabilization and sprouting required to initiate neovascularization. Therefore, in the normal adult, the opposing actions of Ang-1 and Ang-2 on the Tie2 receptor may regulate the plasticity of endothelial cells and thereby modify their requirement for, and responsiveness to, VEGF [85].

VEGF, Ang-1 and -2 mRNA are differentially expressed and localized in the ovaries of pre- and postmenopausal women. In the follicular phase (preovulatory) ovary of premenopausal women, VEGF, Ang-1, and Ang-2 mRNA expression was localized by in situ hybridization principally in the granulosa cell layer and vascular endothelial cells and to a lesser degree in the thecal cell layer [35a] (see Figure 18.3). In luteal phase ovaries, VEGF, Ang-1, and Ang-2 mRNA expression was detected primarily in the granulosa-lutein cell layer and to a lesser degree in the theca-lutein cell layer and in endothelial cells. However, expression was absent in atretic follicles and in an isolated degenerating corpus luteum. In contrast, Wulff et al. [86] found no differences in Ang-1 or Ang-2 mRNA expression between the granulosa and thecal cell layers in the human corpus luteum. The highest Ang-1 concentration was detected in the early luteal phase, whereas Ang-2 mRNA expression was present at lower levels throughout the corpus luteum. Expression of Ang-1 and Ang-2 increased in a corpus luteum obtained following hCG administration. The Ang-2 to Ang-1 ratio increased fivefold from the early to late luteal phase. Interestingly, VEGF-A mRNA expressed in granulosa-lutein cells decreased during the luteal phase and increased following hCG administration. In ovaries from postmenopausal women, VEGF, Ang-1, and Ang-2 mRNA expression was localized in the perivascular stromal cells and vascular endothelial cells. No expression of these angiogenic genes was detected in the corpus albicans.

In subhuman primates, Ang-1 mRNA is gonadotropin-dependent in the early periovulatory stage and progesterone-dependent in the later stage of the periovulatory period, whereas Ang-2 transcription might be mediated by other hormonally (e.g., IGF, activin) or nonhormonally (e.g., hypoxia) dependent mechanisms [35, 36].

Angiopoietin Expression in Ovarian Neoplasms

In low malignant potential ovarian carcinoma (borderline) and frank epithelial ovarian tumor, Ang-1 and Ang-2 mRNA expression was localized principally in the epithelial and vascular endothelial cells [87] (Figure 18.4). Furthermore, whereas VEGF transcription significantly increases in specimens from epithelial cancer, Ang-1 mRNA expression significantly decreases. These observations may reflect the pathobiology of ovarian cancer, and Ang-2 expression in malignant carcinoma cells may facilitate tumor angiogenesis in the presence of higher VEGF levels.

CONCLUSION

Current data indicate that Angs play a critical role in the cyclic angiogenic waves in the ovary. They may participate in follicular growth, selection of the dominant follicle, steroid production, and corpus luteum maintenance and regression. Abnormal expression may predispose to anovulation, corpus luteum insufficiency, ovarian hyperstimulation syndrome, and the development of ovarian neoplasms.

Ovarian angiogenesis requires tight orchestration of vascular endothelial cell-specific growth factors (VEGF, Ang-1, Ang-2, and likely the newly described endocrine gland-derived vascular endothelial growth factor [EG-VEGF]) [88], which are controlled by gonadotropins and/or by locally produced steroids via endocrine and paracrine/autocrine mechanisms, as well as by a variety of other growth factors, cytokines, and environmental factors such as hypoxia. Lack of appropriate integration of one or more of these factors may adversely affect ovarian folliculogenesis, ovulation, corpus luteum function, ovarian hyperstimulation, and benign and malignant neoplasms.

Although speculative at the time of this writing, manipulation of angiogenic gene transcription, translation, or bioactivity [89–91] may prove to be an important means of treating ovarian neoplasms.

References

1. Ferrara, N., and Davis-Smyth, T. (1997). The biology of vascular endothelial growth factor. *Endocr. Rev.* 18, 4–25.
2. Yancopoulos, G. D., Davis, S., Gale, N. W., Rudge, J. S., Wiegand, S. J., and Holash, J. (2000). Vascular-specific growth factors and blood vessel formation. *Nature* 407, 242–248.
3. Folkman, J., and Klagsbrun, M. (1987). Angiogenic factors. *Science* 23, 442–447.
4. Risau, W. (1997). Mechanism of angiogenesis. *Nature* 386, 671–674.
5. Gordon, J. D., Shifren, J. L., Foulk, R. A., Taylor, R. N., and Jaffe, R. B. (1995). Angiogenesis in the human female reproductive tract. *Obstet. Gynecol. Surv.* 50, 688–697.
6. Shay-Salit, A., Shushy, M., Wolfovitz, E., Yahav, H., Breviario, F, Dejana, E., and Resnick, N. (2002). VEGF receptor 2 and the adherens junction as a mechanical transducer in vascular endothelial cells. *Proc. Natl. Acad. Sci. USA* 99, 9462–9467.
7. Reynolds, L. P., Killilea, S. D., and Redmer, D. A. (1992). Angiogenesis in the female reproductive system. *FASEB J.* 6, 886–892.
8. Findlay, J. K. (1986). Angiogenesis in reproductive tissues *J. Endocr.* 111, 357–366.
9. Augustin, H. G., Braun, K., Telemenakis, I., Modlich, U., and Kuhn, W. (1995). Ovarian angiogenesis. Phenotypic characterization of endothelial cells in a physiological model of blood vessel growth and regression. *Am. J. Pathol.* 147, 339–351.
10. Goede, V., Schmidt, T., Kimmina, S., Kozian, D., and Augustin, H. G. (1998). Analysis of blood vessel maturation processes during cyclic ovarian angiogenesis. *Lab. Invest.* 78, 1385–1394.
11. Greenwald, G. S. (1989). Temporal and topographic changes in DNA synthesis after induced follicular atresia. *Biol. Reprod.* 41, 175–178.
12. Dharmarajan, A. M., Bruce, N. W., and Meyer, G. T. (1985). Quantitative ultrastructural characteristics relating to transport between luteal cell cytoplasm and blood in the corpus luteum of the pregnant rat. *Am. J. Anat.* 172, 87–99.
13. Reynolds, L. P. (1986). Utero-ovarian interactions during early pregnancy: Role of conceptus-induced vasodilation. *J. Anim. Sci.* 62, 47–61.
14. Jones, G. S., Maffezzoli, R. D., Strott, C. A., Ross, G. T., and Kaplan, G. (1970). Pathophysiology of reproductive failure after clomiphene-induced ovulation. *Am. J. Obstet. Gynecol.* 108, 847–867.
15. Houck, K. A., Leung, D. W., Rowland, A. M., Winer, J., and Ferrara, N. (1992). Dual regulation of vascular endothelial growth factor bioavailability by genetic and proteolytic mechanisms. *J. Biol. Chem.* 267, 26031–26037.
16. Park, J. E., Keller, G. A., and Ferrara, N. (1993). The vascular endothelial growth factor (VEGF) isoforms: Differential deposition into the subepithelial extracellular matrix and bioactivity of extracellular matrix-bound VEGF. *Mol. Biol. Cell.* 4, 1317–1326.
17. Geva, E. and Jaffe, R. B. (2000). The role of vascular endothelial growth factor (VEGF) in ovarian physiology and pathology. *Fertil. Steril.* 74, 429–438.
18. Leung, D. W., Cachianes, G., Kuang, W. J., Goeddel, D. V., and Ferrara, N. (1989). Vascular endothelial growth factor is a secreted angiogenic mitogen. *Science* 246, 1306–1309.
19. Pepper, M. S., Ferrara, N., Orci, L., and Montesano, R. (1992). Potent synergism between vascular endothelial growth factor and basic fibroblast growth factor in the induction of angiogenesis in vitro. *Biochem. Biophys. Res. Commun.* 189, 824–831.

20. Nicosia, R. F., Nicosia, S. V., and Smith, M. (1994). Vascular endothelial growth factor, platelet-derived growth factor, and insulin-like growth factor-1 promote rat aortic angiogenesis in vitro. *Am. J. Pathol.* 145, 1023–1029.

21. Breier, G., Albrecht, U., Sterrer, S., and Risau, W. (1992). Expression of vascular endothelial growth factor during embryonic angiogenesis and endothelial cell differentiation. *Development* 114, 521–532.

22. Shifren, J. L., Doldi, N., Ferrara, N., Mesiano, S., and Jaffe, R. B. (1994). In the human fetus, vascular endothelial growth factor is expressed in epithelial cells and myocytes, but not vascular endothelium: Implications for mode of action. *J. Clin. Endocrinol. Metab.* 79, 316–322.

23. Senger, D. R., Galli, S. J., Dvorak, A. M., Perruzzi, C. A., Harvey, V. S., and Dvorak, H. F. (1983). Tumor cells secrete a vascular permeability factor that promotes accumulation of ascites fluid. *Science* 219, 983–985.

24. Hanahan, D. (1997) Signaling vascular morphogenesis and maintenance. *Science* 277, 48–50.

25. Jain, R. K., and Munn, L. L. (2000). Leaky vessels? Call Ang-1! *Nat. Med.* 6, 131–132.

26. Hashizume, H., Baluk, P., Morikawa, S., McLean, J. W., Thurston, G., Roberge, S., Jain, R. K., and McDonald, D. M. (2000). Openings between defective endothelial cells explain tumor vessel leakiness. *Am. J. Pathol.* 156, 1363–1380.

27. Roberts, W. G., and Palade, G. E. (1995). Increased microvascular permeability and endothelial fenestration induced by vascular endothelial growth factor. *J. Cell. Sci.* 108, 2369–2379.

28. Dellian, M., Witwer, B. P., Salehi, H. A., Yuan, F., and Jain, R. K. (1996). Quantitation and physiological characterization of angiogenic vessels in mice: Effect of basic fibroblast growth factor, vascular endothelial growth factor/vascular permeability factor, and host microenvironment. *Am. J. Pathol.* 149, 59–71.

29. Shalaby, F., Rossant, J., Yamaguchi, T. P., Gertsenstein, M., Wu, X. F., Breitman, M. L., and Schuh, A. C. (1995). Failure of blood-island formation and vasculogenesis in Flk-1-deficient mice. *Nature* 376, 62–66.

30. Fong, G. H., Rossant, J., Gertsenstein, M., and Breitman, M. L. (1995). Role of the Flt-1 receptor tyrosine kinase in regulating the assembly of vascular endothelium. *Nature* 376, 66–70.

31. Hiratsuka, S., Minowa, O., Kuno, J., Noda, T., and Shibuya, M. (1998). Flt-1 lacking the tyrosine kinase domain is sufficient for normal development and angiogenesis in mice. *Proc. Natl. Acad. Sci. USA* 95, 9349–9354.

32. Carmeliet, P., Moons, L., Luttun, A., Vincenti, V., Compernolle, V., De Mol, M., Wu, Y., Bono, F., Devy, L., Beck, H., Scholz, D., Acker, T., DiPalma, T., Dewerchin, M., Noel, A., Stalmans, I., Barra, A., Blacher, S., Vandendriessche, T., Ponten, A., Eriksson, U., Plate, K. H., Foidart, J. M., Schaper, W., Charnock-Jones, D. S., Hicklin, D. J., Herbert, J. M., Collen, D., and Persico, M. G. (2001). Synergism between vascular endothelial growth factor and placental growth factor contributes to angiogenesis and plasma extravasation in pathological conditions. *Nat. Med.* 7, 575–583.

33. Fujimoto, J., Sakaguchi, H., Hirose, R., Ichigo, S., and Tamaya, T. (1998). Biologic implications of expression of vascular endothelial growth factor subtypes in ovarian carcinoma. *Cancer* 83, 2528–2533.

34. Kamat, B. R., Brown, L. F., Manseau, E. J., Senger, D. R., and Dvorak, H. F. (1995). Expression of vascular permeability factor/vascular endothelial growth factor by human granulosa and theca lutein cells. Role in corpus luteum development. *Am. J. Pathol.* 46, 157–165.

35. Shweiki, D., Itin, A., Soffer, D., and Keshet, E. (1992). Vascular endothelial growth factor induced by hypoxia may mediate hypoxia-initiated angiogenesis. *Nature* 359, 843–845.

35a. Geva, E., Byrne, A., Zaloudek, C., and Jaffe, R. B., unpublished.

36. Hazzard, T. M., Molskness, T. A., Chaffin, C. L., and Stouffer, R. L. (1999). Vascular endothelial growth factor (VEGF) and angiopoietin regulation by gonadotrophin and steroids in macaque granulosa cells during the periovulatory interval. *Mol. Hum. Reprod.* 5, 1115–1121.

37. Gordon, J. D., Mesiano, S., Zaloudek, C. J., and Jaffe, R. B. (1996). Vascular endothelial growth factor localization in human ovary and fallopian tubes: Possible role in reproductive function and ovarian cyst formation. *J. Clin. Endocrinol. Metab.* 81, 353–359.

38. Otani, N., Minami, S., Yamoto, M., Shikone, T., Otani, H., Nishiyama, R., Otani, T., and Nakano, R. (1999). The vascular endothelial growth factor/fms-like tyrosine kinase system in human ovary during the menstrual cycle and early pregnancy. *J. Clin. Endocrinol. Metab.* 84, 3845–3851.

39. Yamamoto, S., Konishi, I., Tsuruta, Y., Nanbu, K., Mandai, M., Kuroda, H., Matsushita, K., Hamid, A. A., Yura, Y., and Mori, T. (1997). Expression of vascular endothelial growth factor (VEGF) during folliculogenesis and corpus luteum formation in the human ovary. *Gynecol. Endocrinol.* 11, 371–381.

40. Zeleznik, A. J., Schuler, H. M., and Reichert, L. J. (1981). Gonadotropin-binding sites in the rhesus monkey ovary: Role of the vasculature in the selective distribution of human chorionic gonadotropin to the preovulatory follicle. *Endocrinology* 109, 356–362.

41. Jakeman, L. B., Winer, J., Bennett, G. L., Altar, C. A., and Ferrara, N. (1992). Binding sites for vascular endothelial growth factor are localized on endothelial cells in adult rat tissues. *J. Clin. Invest.* 89, 244–253.

42. Ferrara, N., Chen, H., Davis-Smyth, T., Gerber, H. P., Nguyen, T. N., Peers, D., Chisholm, V., Hillan, K. J., and Schwall, R. H. (1998). Vascular endothelial growth factor is essential for corpus luteum angiogenesis. *Nat. Med.* 4, 336–340.

43. Laitinen, M., Ristimaki, A., Honkasalo, M., Narko, K., Paavonen, K., and Ritvos, O. (1997). Differential hormonal regulation of vascular endothelial growth factors VEGF, VEGF-B, and VEGF-C messenger ribonucleic acid levels in cultured human granulosa-luteal cells. *Endocrinology* 138, 4748–4756.

44. Mueller, M. D., Jean-Louis, V., Minchenko, A., Lebovic, D. I., Leitman, D. C., and Taylor, R. N. (2000). Regulation of vascular endothelial growth factor (VEGF) gene transcription by estrogen receptors α and β. *Proc. Natl. Acad. Sci. USA* 97, 10972–10977.

45. Palter, S. F., Tavares, A. B., Hourvitz, A., Veldhuis, J. D., and Adashi, E. Y. (2001). Are estrogens of import to

primate/human ovarian folliculogenesis? *Endocr. Rev.* 22, 389–424.
46. Hyder, S. M., Murthy, L., and Stancel, G. M. (1998). Progestin regulation of vascular endothelial growth factor in human breast cancer cells. *Cancer Res.* 58, 392–395.
47. Sone, H., Okuda, Y., Kawakami, Y., Kondo, S., Hanatani, M., Matsuo, K., Suzuki, H., and Yamashita, K. (1996). Progesterone induces vascular endothelial growth factor on retinal pigment epithelial cells in culture. *Life Sci.* 59, 21–25.
48. Friedman, C. I., Danforth, D. R., Herbosa-Encarnacion, C., Arbogast, L., Alak, B. M., and Seifer, D. B. (1997). Follicular fluid vascular endothelial growth factor concentrations are elevated in women of advanced reproductive age undergoing ovulation induction. *Fertil. Steril.* 68, 607–612.
49. Agrawal, R., Conway, G., Sladkevicius, P., Tan, S. L., Engmann, L., Payne, N., Bekir, J., Campbell, S., and Jacobs, H. (1998). Serum vascular endothelial growth factor and Doppler blood flow velocities in in vitro fertilization: Relevance to ovarian hyperstimulation syndrome and polycystic ovaries. *Fertil. Steril.* 70, 651–658.
50. Agrawal, R., Sladkevicius, P., Engmann, L., Conway, G. S., Payne, N. N., Bekis, J., Tan, S. L., Campbell, S., and Jacobs, H. S. (1998). Serum vascular endothelial growth factor concentrations and ovarian stromal blood flow are increased in women with polycystic ovaries. *Hum. Reprod.* 13, 651–655.
51. Adams, J., Franks, S., Polson, D. W., Mason, H. D., Abdulwahid, N., Tucker, M., Morris, D. V., Price, J., and Jacobs, H. S. (1985). Multifollicular ovaries: Clinical and endocrine features and response to pulsatile gonadotropin releasing hormone. *Lancet* 2, 1375–1379.
52. Balen, A. (2000). In vitro fertilization and the patient with polycystic ovaries. In Polycystic Ovary Syndrome, 1st ed., 159–182. Cambridge, England: Cambridge University Press.
53. Folkman, J., and Ingber, D. E. (1987). Angiostatic steroids. Method of discovery and mechanism of action. *Ann. Surg.* 206, 374–383.
54. Neulen, J., Yan, Z., Raczek, S., Weindel, K., Keck, C., Weich, H. A., Marme, D., and Breckwoldt, M. (1995). Human chorionic gonadotropin-dependent expression of vascular endothelial growth factor/vascular permeability factor in human granulosa cells: Importance in ovarian hyperstimulation syndrome. *J. Clin. Endocrinol. Metab.* 80, 1967–1971.
55. Whelan, J. G., and Vlahos, N. F. The ovarian hyperstimulation syndrome. (2000). *Fertil. Steril.* 73, 883–896.
56. Krasnow, J. S., Berga, S. L., Guzick, D. S., Zeleznik, A. J., and Yeo, K. T. (1996). Vascular permeability factor and vascular endothelial growth factor in ovarian hyperstimulation syndrome: A preliminary report. *Fertil. Steril.* 65, 552–555.
57. D'Ambrogio, G., Fasciani, A., Monti, M., Cattani, R., Genazzani, A. R., and Artini, P. G. (1999). Serum vascular endothelial growth factor levels before starting gonadotropin treatment in women who have developed moderate forms of ovarian hyperstimulation syndrome. *Gynecol. Endocrinol.* 13, 311–315.
58. Abramov, Y., Barak, V., Nisman, B., and Schenker, J. G. (1997). Vascular endothelial growth factor plasma levels correlate to the clinical picture in severe ovarian hyperstimulation syndrome. *Fertil. Steril.* 67, 261–265.
59. Ludwig, M., Bauer, O., Lopens, A., Jelkmann, W., and Diedrich, K. (1998). Serum concentration of vascular endothelial growth factor cannot predict the course of severe ovarian hyperstimulation syndrome. *Hum. Reprod.* 13, 30–32.
60. McClure, N., Healy, D. L., Rogers, P. A., Sullivan, J., Beaton, L., Haning, Jr., R. V., Connolly, D. T., and Robertson, D. M. (1994). Vascular endothelial growth factor as capillary permeability agent in ovarian hyperstimulation syndrome. *Lancet* 344, 235–236.
61. Levin, E. R., Rosen, G. F., Cassidenti, D. L., Yee, B., Meldrum, D., Wisot, A., and Pedram, A. (1998). Role of vascular endothelial cell growth factor in ovarian hyperstimulation syndrome. *J. Clin. Invest.* 102, 1978–1985.
62. Ravindranath, N., Little-Ihrig, L., Phillips, H. S., Ferrara, N., and Zeleznik, A. J. (1992). Vascular endothelial growth factor messenger ribonucleic acid expression in the primate ovary. *Endocrinology* 131, 254–260.
63. Neulen, J., Yan, Z., Raczek, S., Weindel, K., Keck, C., Weich, H. A., Marme, D., and Breckwoldt, M. (1995). Human chorionic gonadotropin-dependent expression of vascular endothelial growth factor/vascular permeability factor in human granulosa cells: Importance in ovarian hyperstimulation syndrome. *J. Clin. Endocrinol. Metab.* 80, 1967–1971.
64. Perez, R. P., Godwin, A. K., Hamilton, T. C., and Ozols, R. F. (1991). Ovarian cancer biology. *Semin. Oncol.* 18, 186–204.
65. Olson, T. A., Mohanraj, D., Carson, L. F., and Ramakrishnan, S. (1994). Vascular permeability factor gene expression in normal and neoplastic human ovaries. *Cancer Res.* 54, 276–280.
66. Viglietto, G., Romano, A., Maglione, D., Rambaldi, M., Paoletti, I., Lago, C. T., Califano, D., Monaco, C., Mineo, A., Santelli, G., Manzo, G., Botti, G., Chiappetta, G., and Persico, M. G. (1996). Neovascularization in human germ cell tumors correlates with a marked increase in the expression of the vascular endothelial growth factor but not the placenta-derived growth factor. *Oncogene* 13, 577–587.
67. Brown, L. F., Berse, B., Jackman, R. W., Tognazzi, K., Manseau, E. J., Senger, D. R., and Dvorak, H. F. (1993). Expression of vascular permeability factor (vascular endothelial growth factor) and its receptors in adenocarcinomas of the gastrointestinal tract. *Cancer Res.* 53, 4727–4735.
68. Dvorak, H. F., Nagy, J. A., Feng, D., Brown, L. F., and Dvorak, A. M. (1999). Vascular permeability factor/vascular endothelial growth factor and the significance of microvascular permeability in angiogenesis. *Curr. Top. Microbiol. Immunol.* 237, 97–132.
69. Folkman, J. (1992). The role of angiogenesis in tumor growth. *Semin. Cancer Biol.* 3, 65–71.
70. Popovici, R. M., Irwin, J. C., Giaccia, A. J., and Giudice, L. C. (1999). Hypoxia and cAMP stimulate vascular endothelial growth factor (VEGF) in human endometrial stromal cells: Potential relevance to menstruation and endometrial regeneration. *J. Clin. Endocrinol. Metab.* 84, 2245–2248.
71. Warren, R. S., Yuan, H., Matli, M. R., Ferrara, N., and Donner, D. B. (1996). Induction of vascular endothelial growth factor by insulin-like growth factor 1 in colorectal carcinoma. *J. Biol. Chem.* 271, 29483–29488.
72. Hu, Y. L., Tee, M. K., Goetzl, E. J., Auersperg, N., Mills, G. B., Ferrara, N., and Jaffe, R. B. (2001). Lysophosphatidic acid induction of vascular endothelial growth factor expression

in human ovarian cancer cells. *J. Natl. Cancer Inst.* 93, 762–768.

73. Kieser, A., Weich, H. A., Brandner, G., Marme, D., and Kolch, W. (1994). Mutant p53 potentiates protein kinase C induction of vascular endothelial growth factor expression. *Oncogene* 9, 963–969.
74. Grugel, S., Finkenzeller, G., Weindel, K., Barleon, B., and Marme, D. (1995). Both v-Ha-Ras and v-Raf stimulate expression of the vascular endothelial growth factor in NIH 3T3 cells. *J. Biol. Chem.* 270, 25915–25919.
75. Siemeister, G., Weindel, K., Mohrs, K., Barleon, B., Martiny-Baron, G., and Marme, D. (1996). Reversion of deregulated expression of vascular endothelial growth factor in human renal carcinoma cells by von Hippel-Lindau tumor suppressor protein. *Cancer Res.* 56, 2299–2301.
76. Byrne, A. T., Geva, E., Zaloudek, C., Yanacopoulos, G., and Jaffe, R. B. (2001). In Angiogenesis and cancer: From basic mechanisms to therapeutic applications. Abstract in *Expression and Quantitation of Angiopoietin-1 and -2 mRNA in the Normal Postmenopausal Ovary and Progressive Stages Leading to Ovarian Carcinoma.* Proceedings, *Amer. Assn. Cancer Res.* 42, 721.
77. Mesiano, S., Ferrara, N., and Jaffe, R. B. (1999). Role of vascular endothelial growth factor in ovarian cancer: Inhibition of ascites formation by immunoneutralization. *Am. J. Pathol.* 153, 1249–1255.
78. Hu, L., Hofmann, J., Zaloudek, C., Ferrera, N., Hamilton, T., and Jaffe, R. B. (2002). VEGF immunoneutralization plus paclitaxel markedly reduces tumor burden and ascites in athymic mouse model of ovarian cancer. *Am. J. Pathol.* 161, 1917–1924.
79. Hu, L., Zaloudek, C., Mills, G. B., Gray, J., and Jaffe, R. B. (2000). In vivo and in vitro carcinoma growth inhibition by PI3 kinase inhibitor (LY294002). *Clin. Cancer Res.* 6, 880–886.
80. Hu, L., Hofmann, J., Lu, Y., Mills, G. B., and Jaffe, R. B. (2002). Inhibition of phosphatidylinositol 3'-kinase increases efficacy of paclitaxel in in vitro and in vivo ovarian cancer models. *Cancer Res.* 62, 1087–1092.
81. Davis, S., Aldrich, T. H., Jones, P. F., Acheson, A., Compton, D. L., Jain, V., Ryan, T. E., Bruno, J., Radziejewski, C., Maisonpierre, P. C., and Yancopoulos, G. D. (1996). Isolation of angiopoietin-1, a ligand for the TIE2 receptor, by secretion-trap expression cloning. *Cell* 27, 1161–1169.
82. Maisonpierre, P. C., Suri, C., Jones, P. F., Bartunkova, S., Wiegand, S. J., Radziejewski, C., Compton, D., McClain, J., Aldrich, T. H., Papadopoulos, N., Daly, T. J., Davis, S., Sato, T. N., and Yancopoulos, G. D. (1997). Angiopoietin-2, a natural antagonist for Tie2 that disrupts in vivo angiogenesis. *Science* 277, 55–60.
83. Geva, E., and Jaffe, R. B. (2000). Role of angiopoietins in reproductive tract angiogenesis. *Obstet. Gynecol. Surv.* 55, 511–519.
84. Asahara, T., Chen, D., Takahashi, T., Fujikawa, K., Kearney, M., Magner, M., Yancopoulos, G. D., and Isner, J. M. (1998). Tie2 receptor ligands, angiopoietin-1 and angiopoietin-2, modulate VEGF-induced postnatal neovascularization. *Circ. Res.* 83, 233–240.
85. Lobov, I. B., Brooks, P. C., and Lang, R. A. (2002). Angiopoietin-2 displays VEGF-dependent modulation of capillary structure and endothelial cell survival in vivo. *Proc. Natl. Acad. Sci. USA* 99, 11205–11210.
86. Wulff, C., Wilson, H., Largue, P., Duncan, W. C., Armstrong, D. G., and Fraser, H. M. (2000). Angiogenesis in the human corpus luteum: Localization and changes in angiopoietins, tie-2, and vascular endothelial growth factor messenger ribonucleic acid. *J. Clin. Endocrinol. Metab.* 85, 4302–4309.
87. Byrne, A. T., Geva, E., Zaloudek, C., Yancoupolos, G., and Jaffe, R. B. (2001). Abstract in *Expression and Quantitation of Angiopoietin-1 and -2 mRNA in the Normal Postmenopausal Ovary and Progressive Stages Leading to Ovarian Carcinoma.* Proceedings, *Amer. Assn. Cancer Res.* 42, 3872.
88. LeCouter, J., Lin, R., and Ferrara, N. (2002). Endocrine gland-derived VEGF and the emerging hypothesis of organ-specific regulation of angiogenesis. *Nat. Med.* 8, 913–917.
89. Fraser, H. M., Dickson, S. E., Lunn, S. F., Wulff, C., Morris, K. D., Carroll, V. A., and Bicknell, R. (2000). Suppression of luteal angiogenesis in the primate after neutralization of vascular endothelial growth factor. *Endocrinology* 141, 995–1000.
90. Wulff, C., Wilson, H., Rudge, J. S., Wiegand, S. J., Lunn, S. F., and Fraser, H. M. (2001). Luteal angiogenesis: Prevention and intervention by treatment with vascular endothelial growth factor trap (A40). *J. Clin. Endocrinol. Metab.* 86, 3377–3386.
91. Wulff, C., Wilson, H., Wiegand, S. J., Rudge, J. S., and Fraser, H. M. (2002). Prevention of thecal angiogenesis, antral follicular growth, and ovulation in the primate by treatment with vascular endothelial growth factor Trap R1R2. *Endocrinology* 143, 2797–2807.

PART V

Cyclic Ovarian Cell Death

CHAPTER **19**

Apoptosis in Ovarian Development, Function, and Failure

JONATHAN L. TILLY, JAMES K. PRU, AND BO R. RUEDA

ABSTRACT

Apoptosis, a form of cell death responsible for eliminating cells from the body that are damaged, senescent, potentially harmful, or no longer useful, plays a significant role in almost all aspects of ovarian development and function in vertebrate and invertebrate species. Through the years, studies of laboratory animal models and human tissues have begun to assimilate a molecular blueprint of the hormones, genes, and pathways that modulate apoptosis in ovarian germ cells and somatic cells, leading to the prospects of developing new treatments for improving reproductive health and fertility in women. In addition, significant progress has been made in elucidating a central, and perhaps somewhat surprising, role for the physiological cell death program of apoptosis in mediating pathological ovarian damage caused by exposure of women to a host of environmental, occupational, and clinical insults. However, a considerable number of the observations published to date with respect to the regulation of apoptosis in the ovary are based on correlative gene expression analyses or on the provision of single agents to isolated ovarian cells or follicles cultured in vitro. We know comparatively little of the hormones, genes, and pathways that are functionally relevant to the modulation of ovarian cell death in vivo, or of how these hormones, genes, and pathways interact to coordinate things such as granulosa cell apoptosis during follicle atresia and oocyte depletion during fetal and postnatal life. These concepts and a broad overview of the apoptosis program and its control are presented in this chapter.

INTRODUCTION

During the past two decades, efforts to understand how cells die have made the study of apoptosis, or programmed cell death (PCD), one of the fastest growing fields in the biological and clinical sciences [1]. It is now well established that the body uses apoptosis as part of its developmental program to remove vestigial structures and sculpt new organs [2, 3]. In addition, apoptosis continues to play a prominent role in postnatal life, serving to maintain tissue homeostasis and to remove senescent, damaged, or potentially harmful cells [4, 5]. In many adult tissues, such as muscle or connective tissue, the occurrence of PCD under normal physiological conditions is minimal. However, cells in these tissues can be induced to die on exposure to specific environmental toxicants, chemotherapy, irradiation, oxidative stress, hypoxia, or inflammation. Other tissues, particularly those consisting of hematopoietic or epithelial cell lineages, have a substantially higher rate of normal cellular turnover in which nearly continuous mitosis is countered by a roughly equivalent level of apoptosis. Examples of these tissues include organs of the immune system, the small intestine, the uterus, and the ovary.

Before embarking on further discussions, however, it should be pointed out that the term *programmed cell death* has been used by cell and developmental biologists, physiologists, anatomists, and pathologists to generically describe various "forms" of cell death that may share some or all of the characteristic features of cells dying by apoptosis. To complicate matters further, at least six different forms of cell death have been described to date under in vitro and in vivo conditions. These include apoptosis [6], autoschizis [7], anoikis [8], paraptosis [9], autophagocytosis [10], and necrosis [11]. This chapter focuses primarily on apoptosis, because this form of cell death is most often reported in studies of the ovary under physiological, and many pathological, situations. In addition, we believe that controversies about which form(s) of cell death do or do not play a part in affecting some aspect of ovarian function is of little consequence because clear overlaps exist in the biochemical pathways that mediate the different forms of cell death [12]. Thus our approach to this topic focuses more on identifying functionally significant, nonredundant regulatory genes and signaling pathways that mediate cell death in the ovary rather than on subtle morphological differences in how cells look when dying or dead.

With that said, the following sections of this chapter summarize what is currently known about apoptosis in the ovary, with particular focus on vertebrate species.

However, some reference is given to invertebrate species including *Caenorhabditis elegans* and *Drosophila*, which have traditionally provided the genetic foundation for the study of apoptosis in evolutionarily higher organisms [13–15]. In the following section, a broad overview of the general apoptotic program serves as a source of background information pertinent for the remaining sections. With this general framework for the regulation of apoptosis in mind, the sections entitled "Apoptosis in Ovarian Somatic Cells" and "Female Germ Cell Apoptosis" consider and integrate experimental results from many studies identifying the occurrence, control, and possible significance of apoptosis in ovarian somatic cells and germ cells, respectively. What is known of the basic biology of apoptosis in the ovary is subsequently used in the section entitled "Selected Examples of the Clinical Significance of Apoptosis in the Ovary" to provide several examples of novel therapeutic strategies—that are being developed from the study of cell death. Finally, concluding remarks and speculations are offered in the spirit of stimulating additional research interest in the biological and clinical significance of apoptosis in the ovary.

GENERAL CONCEPTS IN APOPTOSIS

Apoptotic Stimuli and Signal Transduction

The extracellular signals responsible for triggering apoptosis in various cell types can be either physiological or pathological [16–21]. For example, in normal tissue development and function, deprivation of key survival-promoting growth factors or the presence of "death ligands" are mechanisms used by the body to eliminate unwanted, damaged, or senescent cells via apoptosis. However, a number of noxious insults including chemotherapeutic drugs, radiation, oxidative stress, and environmental toxicants have been shown to elicit tissue damage via the inappropriate activation of apoptotic cell death as well [19, 22–27]. As one would therefore imagine, cataloging the number of different signaling pathways that lead to apoptosis—aside from deciphering the interactions amongs many of these pathways—is one of the most challenging aspects of the apoptosis field. Moreover, many of these signals are viewed differently by different cell types or by the same cell type at different stages of development, adding an additional level of complexity to understanding how cells interpret cues from their environment that signal for their demise. The following two sections provide an introductory overview of "death receptor"-mediated apoptosis and highlight selected signal transduction pathways that have emerged as prominent links between receipt of the initial apoptotic signal and engagement of the intracellular machinery required to execute apoptosis.

DEATH RECEPTORS AND COGNATE LIGANDS

Cell surface "death receptors" constitute a subfamily within the 26-member tumor necrosis factor receptor superfamily (TNFrsf) that harbor a cytoplasmic death domain necessary for the activation of apoptosis [28]. Members of this family in mammals include tumor necrosis factor-α (TNF-α) receptor-I (TNFRI, TNFrsf1a), p75 neurotrophin receptor (p75^{NTR}), Fas (APO-1, CD95, TNFrsf6), TNF-α-related apoptosis-inducing ligand (TRAIL) receptor (TNFrsf10a, death receptor-4/DR4), death receptor-3 (DR3, TNFrsf12, TRAMP), death receptor-5 (DR5, TNFrsf10B, KILLER), and death receptor-6 (DR6, TNFrsf21). In most cases, activation of death receptors by their cognate ligands causes receptor trimerization and formation of a death-inducing signaling complex (DISC) at the cytoplasmic surface of the plasma membrane [29–31]. The death domains of the trimerized receptors then coordinate a homophilic interaction of the cytoplasmic portion of each receptor with an adapter protein termed *FADD* (Fas-associated death domain-containing protein; also called *MORT1*). The zymogen form of the proapoptotic cysteine protease, caspase-8, is subsequently recruited by FADD to complete the DISC. Autoprocessing of procaspase-8 to its active form is then thought to occur by an induced proximity model, leading to the rapid initiation of cell death.

However, two mechanisms apparently cause formation of the DISC, which then initiates apoptosis [32]. In "type I" cells, sufficient levels of activated caspase-8 are generated at the DISC to simply cleave, and thus activate, other procaspase enzymes that function as the final executioners of apoptosis (Figure 19.1). In "type II" cells, apoptosis signaling by low levels of caspase-8 produced at the DISC is amplified via mitochondrial destabilization—involving caspase-8 mediated cleavage of the proapoptotic Bid protein—which then leads to a rapid activation of downstream caspases that execute apoptosis (see Figure 19.1). Trimerized death receptors have also recently been shown to oligomerize and relocate to a single pole on the cell surface [33]. This event, called *capping* and probably mediated by ceramide, is thought to facilitate procaspase-8 autocatalysis and thus may function as a signal amplification step for the initiation of apoptosis [33]. Despite death receptor activation serving as a primary mechanism for apoptosis induction under physiological and pathological conditions in vertebrates, no ligands or receptors of the TNF superfamily have been identified in *C. elegans*. Only recently was the *Drosophila* TNFRI homolog, Eiger, cloned and shown to act as a potent inducer of apoptosis [34].

Of final note in this section, many of the ligands that bind and activate death receptors are well known for their cell type- and time-dependent pleiotropic actions independent of apoptosis. How can a single ligand, such as TNF-α, instigate such a broad range of events encompassing proliferation, apoptosis, immune cell activation, or inflammation? One explanation is that the specific protein-protein interactions that occur at or near the cytoplasmic domain(s) of death receptors ultimately dictate the biological outcome of a ligand-activated death receptor [35–37]. For example, the adapter protein, TRAF2 (for TNF-α receptor-associated factor 2), mediates signal transduction of TNFRI by activating either prosurvival (e.g., NFκB) or proapoptotic (e.g., *c*-Jun N-terminal kinase [JNK]) pathways [38]. The sphingolipid-metabolizing enzyme, sphingosine kinase, was recently shown to interact with TRAF2 in HEK 293T cells, an interaction that is apparently necessary for the activation of NFκB, but not of JNK, as well as the prevention of TNFα-induced cell death [39]. Accordingly, the absence or presence of ancillary proteins such as sphingosine kinase probably dictate the response of a given cell to TNF-α. To complicate matters further, TNF-α signaling is influenced by a wide spectrum of other signal transduction pathways that are activated by diverse stimuli [40–42].

Protein Kinases

Mitogen-Activated Protein Kinases. The mitogen-activated protein kinases (MAPK) superfamily has been linked to apoptosis in a large number of publications, serving to both inhibit and activate cell death [36, 43–47]. This group of proteins consists of essentially three subfamilies: the prosurvival extracellular signal-regulated kinases (ERK), the proapoptotic or stress-activated p38 MAPK, and the proapoptotic or stress-activated JNK [47, 48]. Activation of each subfamily stems from a phosphorylation cascade that, in turn, results in phosphorylation-mediated posttranslational modification of target molecules, changes in gene expression, or both. Because of space limitations, this section focuses on the JNK subfamily of MAPK and its role as proximal mediators of apoptosis. The JNK subfamily has received considerable attention in the apoptosis field because almost all cell types studied to date—from yeast to man—respond to diverse forms of stress by activating this class of signaling proteins [49]. However, it should be noted that the role of JNK activation in apoptosis is cell type-specific and stimulus-dependent. Indeed, it has been proposed that the effect of JNK activation on apoptosis is reliant on the activity of other signaling pathways, such as other MAPKs (e.g., ERKs) or NFκB, suggesting that JNK signaling facilitates but does not necessarily initiate apoptosis [50].

Redundancy in mammals has made it difficult to dissect JNK function with regard to apoptosis, because three genes encoding 10 JNK messenger ribonucleic acid (mRNA) splice variants have been identified thus far. Furthermore, the upstream kinases that phosphorylate, and thus activate, JNK are almost as plentiful [48]. Nonetheless, one example reports that caspases have catalyzed cleavage of upstream kinases in the JNK pathway, a mechanism that may enhance apoptosis [51]. Association of the adapter protein, Daxx, with activated Fas also initiates JNK activation during apoptosis [52]. Moreover, JNK signaling has been reported to stabilize p53 [53], a tumor suppressor protein known to function in a proapoptotic capacity in many cell types [20]. However, the significance of these events to apoptosis—that is, whether or not apoptosis in these models requires JNK—has not been clarified. Targeted gene knockout experiments with individual JNK genes failed to show any overt defects in apoptosis. However, double-knockout mice lacking JNK1 and JNK2 die during embryogenesis because of defects in neuronal apoptosis [54]. Furthermore, murine embryonic fibroblasts (MEFs) deficient in JNK1 and JNK2 show resistance to stress-induced but not death receptor-mediated apoptosis [55]. It was further demonstrated that JNK1/JNK2-null MEFs are defective in the release of cytochrome *c* from destabilized mitochondria, a pivotal step in stress-induced cell death that can be by-passed in "type I" death receptor-induced apoptosis.

Whereas the role of JNK signaling in apoptosis in vertebrates is somewhat clouded, a clearer picture has emerged in flies, providing evidence that JNK signaling is essential for death receptor-mediated apoptosis [34]. This finding comes with the recent cloning of the *Drosophila* TNFRI ortholog, Eiger. Unlike, its mammalian counterparts, ligand-activated Eiger does not cause formation of a DISC, but it does appear to be essential for death receptor-mediated apoptosis through a linear pathway that does not require mitochondrial perturbation as an amplification step. However, Eiger-induced cell death is dependent on core components of the *Drosophila* cell death machinery (e.g., the caspase-9-like protease, Dronc, and the Apaf-1-like protein, Dark/Dapaf-1). In 2002 Moreno et al. [34] demonstrated that JNK signaling leads to Dronc activation by suppressing the function of a class of proteins called *inhibitors-of-apoptosis proteins (IAPs)* (see Figure 19.1). Specifically, the Eiger/JNK pathway was shown to be essential for transcriptional upregulation of two key proapoptotic genes in flies—*hid* and *reaper*. As depicted in Figure 19.1, Hid and Reaper bind and functionally inactivate the *Drosophila* IAPs (DIAPs), allowing for apoptosis to proceed. It remains to be determined, however, whether this sort of linear JNK signaling is retained in evolutionarily advanced organisms such as mammals, or if this pathway is a dispensable rudimentary feature of apoptosis signaling that coevolved with TNF receptors during the expansion of this receptor superfamily.

Phosphatidylinositol 3′-kinase (PI3-K) and Akt. A key cell survival pathway linked to either growth factor receptors (e.g., tyrosine kinase-coupled receptors [56]) or other cell survival signaling pathways (e.g., protein kinase A, NFκB [57]) is the phosphatidylinositol 3′-kinase (PI3-K)/Akt phosphorylation cascade [58]. A number of studies have confirmed that PI3-K becomes activated when

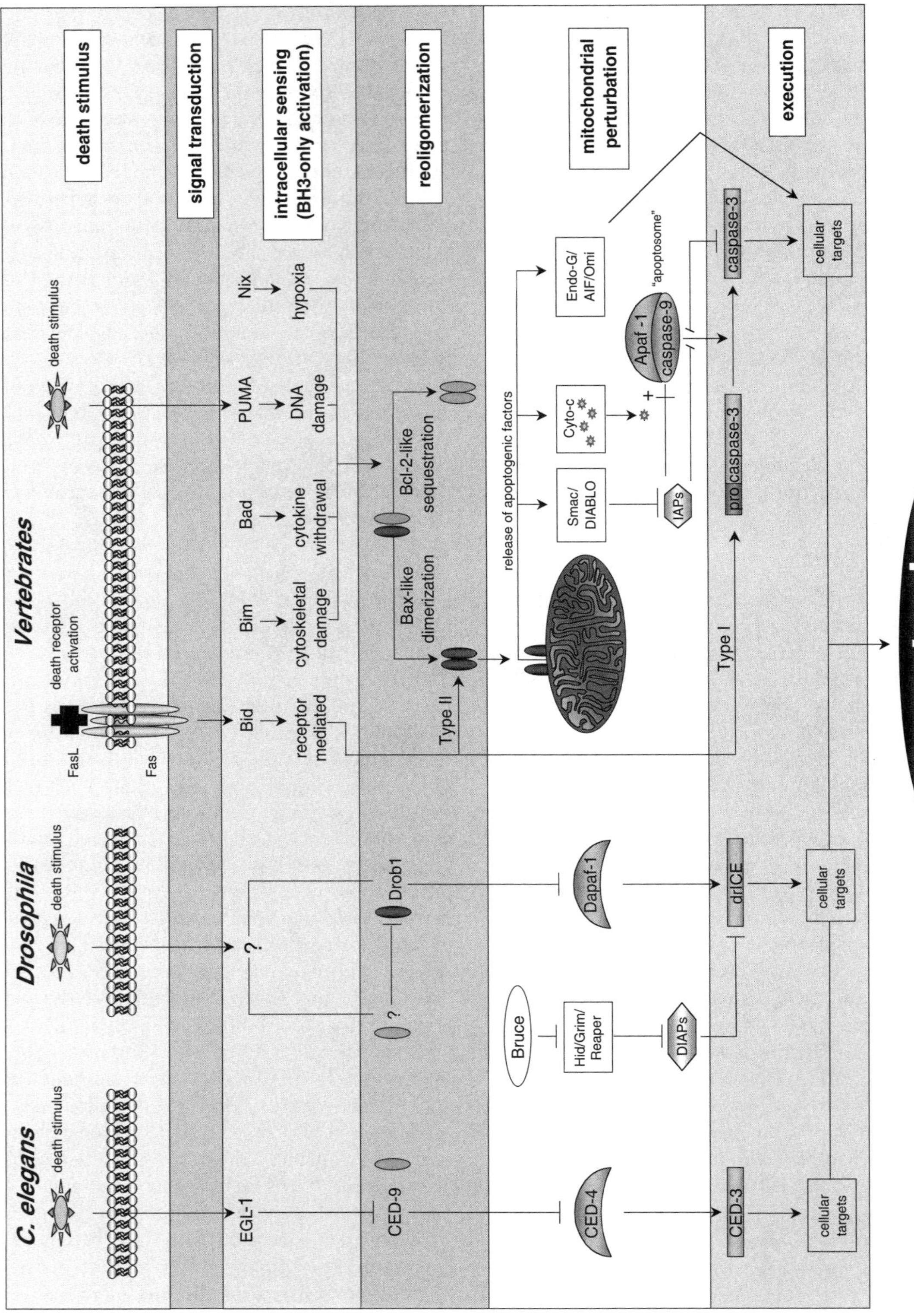
C. elegans
Drosophila
Vertebrates
death stimulus
death receptor activation
FasL
Fas
signal transduction
intracellular sensing (BH3-only activation)
realigomerization
mitochondrial perturbation
execution
EGL-1
CED-9
CED-4
CED-3
cellular targets
?
Drob1
Bruce
Hid/Grim/Reaper
DIAPs
Dapaf-1
drICE
Bid
receptor mediated
Bim
cytoskeletal damage
Bad
cytokine withdrawal
PUMA
DNA damage
Nix
hypoxia
Type II
Bax-like dimerization
Bcl-2-like sequestration
release of apoptogenic factors
Smac/ DIABLO
Cyto-c
Endo-G/ AIF/Omi
IAPs
Apaf -1
caspase-9
"apoptosome"
Type I
pro caspase-3
caspase-3
apoptosis

recruited to the cytoplasmic surface of the plasma membrane following ligand activation of growth factor receptors, or by direct interaction with the Ras proto-oncogene [59]. Activated PI3-K catalyzes the formation of 3′-phosphorylated phosphoinositides from phospholipid stores in the plasma membrane. These lipid molecules are then bound by, and consequently activate, the serine/threonine kinase, 3′-phosphoinositide-dependent kinase-1 (PDK-1) [60], which serves as a pivotal enzyme capable of activating a broad spectrum of downstream kinases, including Akt. Under homeostatic conditions, growth factor-activated Akt serves to phosphorylate, and thereby regulate, proteins that function in maintaining the basic needs of cells, such as the transport and oxidation of glucose for energy production. For example, activation of the insulin-like growth factor-1 (IGF-1) receptor by its cognate ligand induces Akt-mediated phosphorylation of glycogen synthase kinase-3 to increase levels of glucose for catabolism [61]. In addition, the phosphorylation of glucose transporter (Glut)-4 by Akt results in the translocation of Glut-4 to the cell surface where it rapidly moves glucose into the cell for oxidative phosphorylation and energy production [62].

Disruption of Akt signaling often swings cell fate from homeostasis to favor apoptosis by inhibiting vital metabolic processes (e.g., cellular respiration) and activating components of the apoptotic machinery. As discussed in more detail below, stress-related signaling initiated by damage to the cell or a loss of growth factor support can attenuate or completely inhibit Akt signaling through a variety of mechanisms. Whereas the consequences of Akt signaling inhibition are cell type- and stimulus-specific, several laboratories have demonstrated that diverse apoptosis-regulatory proteins are affected by Akt activity at the transcriptional and posttranslational levels. For example, members of the Forkhead family of transcription factors, when phosphorylated by Akt, remain bound to other cytosolic proteins (e.g., 14-3-3 proteins). However, in the absence of Akt-mediated phosphorylation, Forkhead transcription factors can translocate to the nucleus and increase the expression of proapoptotic regulatory genes such as Fas ligand [63].

As another example, activity of the proapoptotic BH3-only protein, Bad, is regulated by its phosphorylation status [64]. In cells supported by an appropriate level of growth factors, activation of Akt leads to a phosphorylation-dependent sequestration of Bad by 14-3-3 proteins [65]. However, loss of Akt signaling or increased phosphatase activity results in the release of Bad [58], making it free to interact with other members of the Bcl-2 family in such a way that facilitates apoptosis. Akt also directly interacts with, and phosphorylates, procaspase-9 [66]. The exact mechanism by which caspase-9 becomes inactivated through phosphorylation by Akt is uncertain, but it has been proposed that the catalytic activity of caspase-9 is directly inhibited. Interestingly, consensus Akt phosphorylation sites (RXRXXS/T) have been identified in other apoptosis-regulatory proteins at each major level of the apoptotic cascade (e.g., caspase-8, Bcl-2, Apaf-1, IAP, and caspase-7 [58]), suggesting that apoptosis can be averted by Akt-mediated phosphorylation of a large cassette of constitutivcly expressed proteins.

The Sphingomyelin Pathway

Whereas sphingolipids are traditionally viewed as structural components of lipid bilayers, the dynamic process of sphingolipid metabolism, which results in the formation of ceramide, sphingosine, and sphingosine-1-phosphate (S1P) as principal metabolites, is now known to coordinate diverse cellular processes [67]. Ceramide, a second messenger that directs cell cycle arrest and apoptosis [68], can be produced in cells by sphingomyelinase-catalyzed breakdown of membrane sphingomyelin or by de novo synthesis. Ceramide can be further modified by ceramidases to generate sphingosine, a second messenger capable of suppressing protein kinase C activity as well as promoting apoptosis [69]. In contrast to the death-inducing functions

FIGURE 19.1 Evolutionarily conserved apoptotic cascades in vertebrate and invertebrate species. Apoptosis is initiated when cells become stressed (e.g., death stimuli such as growth factor deprivation, hypoxia, irradiation) or when death receptors (e.g., Fas) become activated by their ligands (Fas ligand/FasL). Such death stimuli are amplified through activation of a number of signal transduction pathways, which results in posttranslational modification or transcriptional induction of BH3-only proteins as an intracellular "sensing" step. Most BH3-only proteins (e.g., Bim, Bad, PUMA, Nix; EGL-1 orthologs) oligomerize with antiapoptotic Bcl-2-like proteins (CED-9 orthologs), thus liberating proapoptotic multidomain Bcl-2 family members (Bax-like; Drobl orthologs) for mitochondrial insertion following reoligomerization. Some BH3-only proteins (e.g., Bid) directly oligomerize with Bax-like proteins to facilitate their insertion into mitochondria. Mitochondrial perturbation then releases a number of apoptogenic factors, including Smac/DIABLO, cytochrome *c* (Cyto-c), endonuclease G (Endo-G), apoptosis inducing factor (AIF), and Omi into the cytosol. Smac/DIABLO (Hid, Grim and Reaper ortholog) neutralizes inhibitors-of-apoptosis proteins (IAPs) (DIAP orthologs); Endo-G cleaves deoxyribonucleic acid (DNA); and AIF and Omi hydrolyze proteins and/or catalyze DNA breakdown. Release of cytochrome *c* facilitates formation of the "apoptosome," a multimeric protein complex consisting of Apaf-1 (CED-4/Dapaf-1 ortholog) and the initiator caspase, caspase-9. In the absence of a lethal stimulus, IAPs block apoptosome formation and caspase-3 activity. If the apoptosome forms, the complex activates effector procaspases (CED-3 and drICE orthologs) such as procaspase-3 to form active enzymes that cleave protein targets throughout the cell, completing the execution phase of apoptosis. Two models exist in vertebrate species to explain how effector caspases become activated following death receptor ligation. In some cells, mitochondrial perturbation serves as an amplification step to facilitate the execution phase through formation of the apoptosome (Type II cells), whereas in other cells this step is not needed (Type I cells). (See color plate.)

of ceramide and sphingosine, S1P, which is generated by the phosphorylation of sphingosine via sphingosine kinases, is now well established as a signaling molecule for cellular proliferation, growth, and survival [70, 71].

Several mechanisms have been identified by which ceramide accumulation results in apoptosis or growth arrest, with two of these involving cross talk with the MAPK and PI3-K/Akt signaling pathways. For example, ceramide, generated in response to diverse stress signals such as ligand-bound cytokine receptors or irradiation, has been shown to activate the stress-activated protein kinase (SAPK)/JNK phosphorylation cascade [72]. Furthermore, ceramide can also directly antagonize the PI3-K/Akt cell survival pathway [68, 73, 74], possibly by activation of a protein phosphatase [75] or by functional sequestration of prosurvival kinases in lipid microdomains [76–79]. Ceramide appears to also induce the proteolytic degradation of Akt [80]. As discussed earlier, the loss of PI3-K/Akt activity, as a result of any or all of these actions of ceramide, would lead to decreased phosphorylation and the subsequent activation of several key apoptosis-regulatory proteins [58]. Conversely, overexpression of Akt can decrease ceramide generation and block ceramide-induced apoptosis [81].

The proapoptotic actions of ceramide may also target mitochondria by destabilizing membranes or causing the release of "apoptogenic" factors from this organelle. Indeed, ceramide can enhance Bax-induced mitochondrial permeability transition [82] and can form pores sufficient in size to release mitochondrial ions and even small proteins such as cytochrome *c* [83, 84]. Although these nonspecific ceramide pores probably do not directly induce cytochrome *c* release, it is highly likely that they contribute to outer mitochondrial membrane permeabilization during the process of apoptosis. In a final example of how ceramide can trigger apoptosis, Cremesti et al. [33] demonstrated that ceramide generated in the outer leaflet of the plasma membrane causes polar redistribution and oligomerization, or "capping," of the death receptor Fas. In this way, a super-catalytic domain is created on the cytoplasmic surface of the cell that may serve as a signal transduction amplification step necessary for Fas-mediated apoptosis [33].

Although ceramide is an important determinant of the apoptotic stress response, it also serves as a precursor for the synthesis of the antiapoptotic signaling lipid, S1P [85]. The metabolic conversion of ceramide to S1P is thought to serve as a molecular switch, lowering cell death susceptibility. Despite our understanding of how ceramide can promote apoptosis, comparatively little is known of the mechanisms of action of S1P in preventing cell death. Deciphering how S1P functions to block apoptosis is complicated by the fact that this lipid may signal from both inside and outside of the cell. From the outside, S1P acts as a ligand for endothelial differentiation gene (EDG) receptors, a family of G-protein coupled receptors expressed on the plasma membrane of most cells [67, 86]. Five EDG receptors that bind S1P with high affinity have been identified and include EDG1/S1P_1, EDG5/S1P_2, EDG3/S1P_3, EDG6/S1P_4, and EDG8/S1P_5 [86]. Alternatively, S1P has been shown to act as an intracellular second messenger to block apoptosis [85]. Although there is little information regarding the mechanisms by which S1P accomplishes this latter function, some important findings have recently surfaced. First, S1P has been shown to interact with, or directly activate, prosurvival signaling pathways (e.g., NFκB, ERKs) [87, 88]. Second, treatment of lymphocytes with S1P decreases the expression of the proapoptotic Bcl-2 family member, Bax, with a concomitant reduction in apoptosis [89]. Third, S1P may exert some of its antiapoptotic actions by preventing stress-induced mitochondrial perturbation (e.g., S1P inhibits the release of cytochrome *c* and Smac/DIABLO from mitochondria, thereby preventing activation of the caspase cascade [90]. Finally, S1P has been reported to block apoptosis in endothelial cells by increasing the production of nitric oxide [91].

In closing this section, Hannun and Obeid have recently suggested that an understanding of sphingolipid metabolizing enzymes and a careful assessment of the levels of endogenous bioactive sphingolipids in cells—now collectively termed *"lipidomics"*—is imperative, because these second messengers serve as key switches in regulating many aspects of cell function and fate [92]. Indeed, assuming that ceramide and S1P exist in cells in a rheostat that dictates death and survival decisions, respectively, recent studies have provided evidence that it may be possible to favorably manipulate this rheostat for the therapeutic goal of preserving ovarian function and fertility (see section called Preservation of Fertility with S1P-Based Therapies).

The Bcl-2 Family

Bcl-2 Family Members

Whereas other cellular organelles such as the nucleus or endoplasmic reticulum are thought to principally serve as sites for cellular damage to trigger apoptosis activation [93], the mitochondrion remains at the center of the cell death decision-making process [93–97]. In many paradigms of apoptosis, mitochondrial membrane potential becomes disrupted, leading to the formation of reactive oxygen species and the release of "apoptogenic" factors that serve as signals for activation of the final or "effector" phase of apoptosis. The exact mechanism(s) by which the mitochondrial membrane becomes permeabilized is still controversial, and several models have been proposed [96]. Most models, however, include the involvement of the B-cell leukemia/lymphoma-2 (Bcl-2) family of apoptosis-regulatory proteins, which act either autonomously or in association with other mitochondrial proteins (e.g., adenine nucleotide translocator [ANT], voltage-dependent anion channel [VDAC]) to disrupt mitochondrial homeostasis [96, 98].

From an evolutionary perspective, orthologs of mammalian Bcl-2 family members have been identified in *C. elegans* (EGL-1, CED-9 [13]) and *Drosophila* (Drob-1/Debcl/dBorg-1/Dbok, dBorg-2/Buffy [99]). In invertebrate species, as in mammals, these proteins function as key regulators of apoptosis [14, 100]. Similar to many other gene families, *bcl-2* and related genes have expanded extensively over time from invertebrate to vertebrate species via adaptive radiation (i.e., gene duplication and modifications with descent), possibly to contend with an increase in the number of cell types and physiological complexities during evolution. In vertebrates, this family consists of two opposing groups: antiapoptotic proteins (e.g., Bcl-2, Bcl-x_{long}, Bcl-w, Bcl-B, Mcl-1, A1/Bfl-1) and proapoptotic proteins [101–105]. This latter group can be further subdivided based on the number of, and/or which, Bcl-2 homology (BH) domains each protein contains. Importantly, and as will be discussed in more detail below, those that contain two or more (up to four) BH domains—the so-called *multidomain members* (e.g., Bax, Bak, Mtd/Bok, Boo/Diva, Bcl-rambo, Bcl-x_{short})—function differently than those that contain only the BH3 domain (e.g., Bad, Bid, Bik/NBK, Bim, Blk, Bmf-1, Hrk/DP5, Map-1, Nix, Nip3, Noxa, PUMA).

It was initially thought that Bcl-2 and like proteins functioned as a rheostat, such that the absolute levels of antiapoptotic versus proapoptotic Bcl-2 family members in a given cell dictated that cell's fate [106, 107]. However, it is now clear that the regulation of apoptosis by Bcl-2 family members is much more complicated, involving a rheostat that is governed by anti- and proapoptotic multidomain family members with stimulus-specific modification via BH3-only family members (Figures 19.1 and 19.2) [108]. In many cases, the BH3-only proteins serve as intracellular "sensors" that can be activated either transcriptionally (e.g., Nip3, Nix, PUMA, Noxa, Hrk) or posttranslationally (e.g., Bad, Bid, Bik, Blk, Map-1, Bmf, Bim) through a multitude of signal transduction pathways (Figure 19.2). Once activated, BH3-only proteins form evolutionarily conserved functional interactions with their multidomain counterparts [97, 98, 105]. Depending on the BH3-only protein, these interactions either facilitate the insertion of proapoptotic multidomain Bcl-2 family members into mitochondrial membranes—thereby disrupting membrane integrity and the voltage potential necessary for oxidative phosphorylation [98]—or hinder the function of antiapoptotic Bcl-2 family members.

From a regulatory standpoint, BH3-only proteins that are induced via de novo gene expression appear to be capable of interacting with multidomain Bcl-2 family members without further posttranslational modification. By comparison, those BH3-only family members that are present but inactive in healthy cells are recruited into action by phosphorylation/dephosphorylation reactions, proteolysis, or cytoskeletal alterations, resulting in conformational changes or exposure of structural domains in the protein (see Figure 19.2). With the exception of the gene encoding 2′–5′ oligoadenylate synthase (OAS), which is reportedly induced by interferon-β (IFNβ) [109], most transcriptionally-regulated BH3-only genes are expressed as a consequence of cellular damage initiated by hypoxia, DNA damage, or cytokine deprivation (see Figure 19.2). Once activated, the amphipathic α-helix of many BH3-only proteins interacts with a hydrophobic groove on antiapoptotic Bcl-2 family members, causing their "reoligomerization" and subsequent dissociation from proapoptotic multidomain family members (see Figures 19.1 and 19.2) [95, 104]. In this way, BH3-only proteins serve as intracellular "ligands" to bind and functionally sequester antiapoptotic Bcl-2-like proteins, thus allowing proapoptotic multidomain members like Bax and Bak to destabilize mitochondria and trigger apoptosis [110].

BH3-Only Proteins

Despite their significant role in coordinating life and death decisions in cells, fewer than a dozen reports have been published regarding BH3-only gene expression or function in the ovary. Nonetheless, in the following paragraphs we focus on a few selected BH3-only proteins, in anticipation of work to come from the study of these proteins in the female gonads [111]. In the first of four examples, Bim [112] and Bmf [113] are two of the posttranslationally modified, proapoptotic BH3-only family members. These proteins are functionally sequestered in healthy cells by being tethered to the microtubule-associated dynein motor complex and the myosin V actin motor complex, respectively. The signals that initiate the release of Bim or Bmf from the cytoskeleton are diverse and include cytokine withdrawal, anoikis (i.e., loss of cell-to-cell contact), microtubule-disrupting chemicals (e.g., paclitaxel [Taxol]), or ultraviolet irradiation [105, 112]. Like most other BH3-only proteins, Bim and Bmf become activated by a caspase-independent means, suggesting that BH3-only proteins generally function upstream of the caspase cascade. It should be noted, however, that in addition to posttranslational activation, *bim* gene expression is transcriptionally increased by growth factor withdrawal in neurons [114] and hematopoietic cells [115]. Furthermore, *bim* is transcribed in some cell types as three different isoforms (Bim_{EL}, Bim_{L}, Bim_{s}) from the same gene [105, 112]. The potential importance of this is that one isoform may serve as the "killer" while the other isoforms either act as dominant negatives or are less effective at cell killing. Accordingly, changes in the expression of these isoforms, and subsequent protein abundance within cells, could have profound effects on cell death susceptibility [116]. Unfortunately, the notion that different isoforms of any given Bcl-2 family member—except perhaps for Bcl-x splice variants—play divergent roles within the cell has received little attention.

The second example is Bad, a BH3-only protein that has been shown to facilitate oligomerization and inactivation

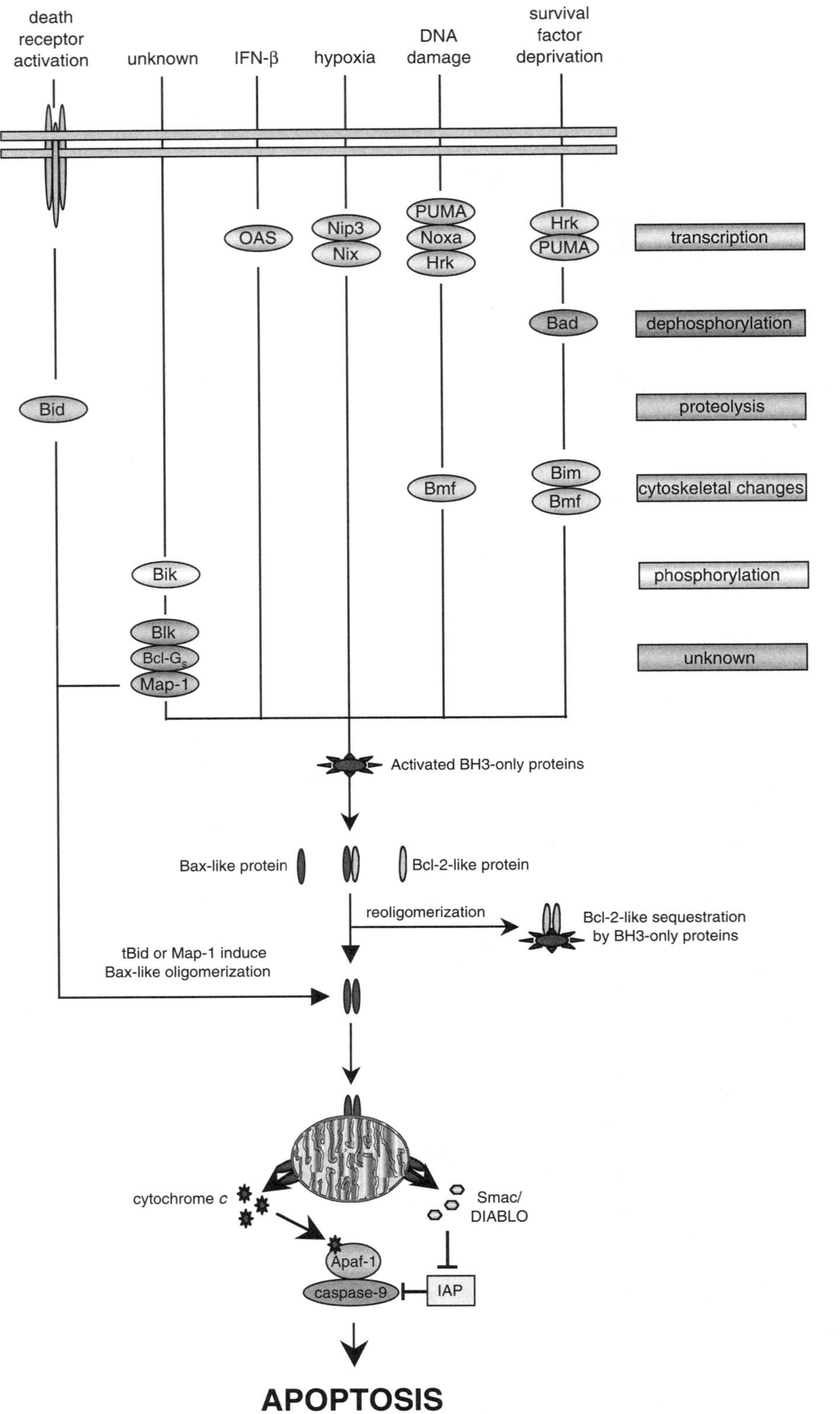

Figure 19.2 BH3-only proteins as intracellular sensors of death stimulation. BH3-only members of the Bcl-2 family are thought to coordinate an intracellular message center that dictates whether or not a cell undergoes apoptosis in response to a potential death stimulus (e.g., death receptor activation, interferon-β [IFN-β], hypoxia, DNA damage, or survival factor deprivation). The mechanisms of BH3-only activation are diverse and include transcription, phosphorylation/dephosphorylation, proteolysis, and cytoskeletal changes. Most BH3-only proteins serve to sequester antiapoptotic Bcl-2-like proteins (*yellow ovals*), thus preventing their inhibitory interaction with proapoptotic multidomain members of the family, such as Bax (*red ovals*). Only Bid and Map-1 have been show to directly interact with proapoptotic Bax-like proteins to facilitate their insertion into mitochondrial membranes. In either case, the actions of BH3-only proteins lead to mitochondrial destabilization and release of a number of apoptogenic factors that activate or amplify the execution phase of apoptosis. (See color plate.)

of antiapoptotic Bcl-2-like proteins. The activity of Bad is modulated by the presence of survival factors in such a way that when growth factor support is provided, Bad becomes phosphorylated via the P13-k/Akt signaling pathway and is then sequestered by 14-3-3 proteins [64]. Conversely, in the absence of sufficient survival factor support, dephosphorylation of Bad results in its release from 14-3-3 proteins and its shuttling to mitochondria, where it interferes with Bcl-2 and/or Bcl-x_{long} function (see Figure 19.2) [58].

The third example is Bid, a BH3-only protein that is proximally linked to activated death domain-containing cell surface receptors such as Fas (see Figure 19.1). Like Bim, Bmf, and Bad, Bid is regulated posttranslationally; however, in this case, activation of Bid occurs via proteolytic cleavage of the protein to produce a truncated form (tBid) that then becomes N-myristoylated for mitochondrial targeting. Once translocated to mitochondria, tBid interacts with proapoptotic multidomain Bcl-2 family members (e.g., Bax and/or Bak) to facilitate their insertion into the mitochondrial membrane [117]. With the exception of Map-1 [118], Bid is thought to be the only other BH3-only protein that functions by interaction with proapoptotic, rather than antiapoptotic, multidomain members of the Bcl-2 family (see Figure 19.2).

The fourth and final example provides an opportunity to emphasize the important role that transcriptional regulation plays in the activation of some BH3-only proteins. The p53-upregulated modulator of apoptosis (*puma*) gene encodes multiple splice variants that are induced in many cell types following p53 activation in response to genomic damage [119]. Like many of the other BH3-only proteins, PUMA isoforms bind Bcl-2-like proteins, localize to mitochondria to induce the release of cytochrome *c*, and activate the rapid and efficient initiation of cell death. In addition to PUMA, Noxa represents yet another BH3-only protein induced during, and implicated in mediating, p53-driven cell death through the mitochondrial pathway [120]. Nix and bNip3 offer additional examples of transcriptionally regulated BH3-only family members, although transcriptional control of these genes is apparently directed by hypoxia-inducible factor-1α under conditions of limited oxygen availability to the cell [121].

Proapoptotic Proteins Released by Destabilized Mitochondria

Mitochondrial perturbation by proapoptotic Bcl-2 family members unleashes a host of mitochondrial intermembrane proteins that act and interact to orchestrate the execution phase of apoptosis [95–97, 100]. Interestingly, several of these proteins appear to have mitochondrial functions as chaperones or reduction-oxidation reaction intermediates in healthy cells, but when released into the cytosol, these proteins change function to one associated with apoptosis commitment [95]. Some released proteins such as AIF, Omi, and Endo-G exhibit nucleolytic or proteolytic activity that contributes directly to cell death (see Figure 19.1). For example, AIF was originally identified as a highly conserved polypeptide that induces chromatin condensation and high molecular weight (>50 kb) DNA fragmentation independently of caspases [122]. Inactivation of the gene encoding AIF in mice has demonstrated that the protein is required for the first wave of cell death associated with embryonic morphogenesis and cavitation [123]. The serine endoprotease, Omi, is a novel proapoptotic protein recently shown to interact with the X-linked inhibitor of apoptosis protein (XIAP) and other IAPs [124, 125] as a means to permit full activation of the death effector caspase cascade. Interestingly, Omi can also induce cell death in the presence of pan-caspase inhibitors, a feature attributed to its N-terminal serine protease catalytic domain [124, 125]. Endo-G, also of mitochondrial origin, relocates to the nucleus after release where it catalyzes high molecular weight DNA cleavage and oligonucleosomal DNA breakdown in a caspase-independent fashion [126]. Other proteins released from mitochondria during the initiation and execution of apoptosis serve as either cofactors or components of a multimeric protein structure termed the *apoptosome*. Examples of these, which will be discussed later, include cytochrome *c*, Smac/DIABLO, and caspase-9 [127].

Postmitochondrial Checkpoint before Cell Death Committal

As would be expected, the commitment to apoptosis is not a decision made without built-in checkpoints to ensure that the cell should be deleted. One possible mechanism to avert cell death is to prevent activation of the caspase cascade. The antiapoptotic IAP proteins, which consist of survivin, livin, Bruce, neuronal IAP (NIAP), XIAP, IAP1, and IAP2 in mammals and DIAP in *Drosophila* (to date, no IAP orthologs have been identified in *C. elegans*), are thought to serve in this capacity through their ability to bind and inactivate certain caspases [128, 129]. Each IAP harbors at least two independent functional motifs called *baculovirus IAP repeat (BIR) domains*. Among the known IAPs, XIAP is unique in that it can selectively bind and inactivate caspase-9 via its BIR3 domain [130]; however, it can also bind and squelch caspase-3 activity through a linker region between BIR domains 1 and 2 [131]. The significance of this is that apoptosis can thus be averted, at least temporarily, at (caspase-9) or distal to (caspase-3) the apoptosome.

However, in cells that have met an apoptosis threshold, the IAP hurdle is removed by at least two mechanisms [132]. First, a protein referred to as *Smac* (for second mitochondrial activator of caspases [133])—also referred to as

DIABLO (for direct IAP binding protein with low isoelectric point; [134])—interacts with the BIR domains of IAPs through its N-terminus. By binding IAPs, Smac/DIABLO either displaces activated caspases or prevents association of IAPs with active caspases, thus perpetuating caspase-mediated proteolysis and cell death commitment. For example, it has been shown that Smac/DIABLO binds to XIAP and prevents it from interacting with processed caspase-9, leading to rapid apoptosis following ultraviolet (UV) irradiation [135]. These antiapoptotic checkpoint proteins can also be eliminated from cells by the ubiquitin-proteosomal pathway [128]. Interestingly, some of the catalytic machinery required for this process appears to be inherent in the IAPs themselves, because certain IAPs exhibit E3 ubiquitin ligase activity and thus become autoubiquitinylated before degradation [128].

Although no *C. elegans* Smac/DIABLO orthologs have been cloned, *Drosophila* appears to express three such proteins, termed Reaper, Grim, and Hid (see Figure 19.1). Structural and functional features of these proteins are similar to Smac/DIABLO in that the N-terminus of each possesses an IAP binding domain. At yet another level of apoptosis regulation, Vernooy et al. recently demonstrated that *Drosophila* Bruce, a large BIR domain-containing protein (BIRP) with E2 ubiquitin-conjugating activity, can potently suppress Reaper- and Grim-dependent, but not Hid-dependent, cell death [136] (see Figure 19.1). Of note, mammals [137] and *C. elegans* [138] also express BIRPs and, as with their *Drosophila* counterpart, each appears to possess a unique function that is unrelated to apoptosis. Finally, studies using mutant mice deficient in IAP1, IAP2, or XIAP have not revealed any significant requirement for IAPs in maintaining cell survival in vivo [128, 129]. However, this may be explained by overlaps in the functions of IAP family members. For example, Harlin et al. [139] determined that cells obtained from XIAP-deficient mice expressed higher levels of IAP1 and IAP-2, suggesting that a compensatory up-regulation in the expression of other IAP family members occurs when XIAP expression is lost.

Unlike deletion of other IAP genes, elimination of survivin results in embryonic lethality on day 4.5 of development. This phenotype stems from disrupted microtubule formation, resulting in polyploidy and defective cytokinesis [140]. Interestingly, mammalian survivin, like several other apoptosis-regulatory proteins, exhibits duel functions. Whereas loss of its IAP-like function may be compensated for by other IAP proteins, the functional domain of survivin that controls microtubule formation and cell cycle progression is necessary for cell survival and cannot be compensated for by other proteins. Thus whether the antiapoptotic function of IAPs actually serves in a postmitochondrial checkpoint to allow damaged cells to recover before committing to apoptosis, or simply prevents unsolicited caspase activity in the absence of potentially cell-lethal stimulus, remains to be determined.

The Apoptosome

The exact role of cytochrome *c* release from mitochondria became apparent when the vertebrate CED-4 ortholog, Apaf-1 (for *a*poptotic *p*rotease-*a*ctivating *f*actor-1), was cloned and functionally characterized as part of a trimeric protein complex consisting of Apaf-1, Apaf-2, (i.e., cytochrome *c*), and Apaf-3 (i.e., procaspase-9) [141] (see Figure 19.1). It is now established that the induction of cytochrome *c* release from mitochondria by proapoptotic Bcl-2 family members causes a conformational change in Apaf-1, exposing a caspase recruitment domain (CARD). The Apaf-1 CARD then forms a homophilic interaction with the CARD of an unprocessed caspase-9 zymogen. The resulting interaction generates procaspase-9 oligomers that, in turn, form a proteolytic complex, via auto- and transcatalysis [142], referred to as the *apoptosome* [94, 143] (see Figure 19.1). On processing and full activation, caspase-9 then serves as the apical enzyme in a proteolytic cascade involving the activation of more downstream or effector caspases that execute apoptosis. In this way, the significance of Apaf-1 in vertebrates, as well as that of CED-4 in *C. elegans* and Dark/Dapaf-1 in *Drosophila*, is to link the function of Bcl-2 family members with the activation of caspases. The latter proteins then attack and degrade key cellular target proteins required for normal cell function and homeostasis. The fundamental importance of the apoptosome to cell death in vertebrates is evident in caspase-9 or Apaf-1 gene knockout mice, in which most homozygous-null fetuses die during gestation because of a lack of apoptosis during critical developmental stages [144, 145].

Execution of Apoptosis and Degradation of Cellular Targets: The Caspases

In mammals at least 14 CED-3 orthologs have been identified based on functional and structural features, most of which have been shown to contribute to the apoptotic process [146, 147]. These orthologs, referred to as *caspases* (for *c*ysteine *asp*artic acid-specific prote*ases*; caspases 1–14), are translated as inactive zymogens that must be proteolytically activated. The mechanisms by which caspases become activated divide these enzymes into two distinct categories. The first, which include caspases-2, -8, -9, and -10, are referred to as *initiator caspases*. These enzymes harbor unique structural domains that facilitate autocatalysis, a process that generally requires the assembly of multiple proteins into a complex [94, 142]. For example, caspase-8 and -10 each contain an N-terminal death-effector domain that allows these caspases to interact with death domain-containing receptors (e.g., Fas or TNFRI) via the adapter protein FADD. Alternatively, initiator caspase-2 and -9 each possess a CARD motif. As discussed earlier, caspase-9 interacts with Apaf-1 during apoptosis, a process mediated by the release of cytochrome *c* from mitochondria. This homophilic interaction occurs through the CARD sequence present in both caspase-9 and Apaf-1. Caspase-12, another initiator caspase, has recently been shown to become activated in a mitochondria- and Apaf-1-independent manner in response to damage or stress induced at the level of the endoplasmic reticulum [148]. However, the specific details of how this protease becomes activated are currently unknown.

Once processed, the now active initiator caspase(s) in turn activates the second category of enzymes in this family, termed *effector caspases*—represented primarily by caspase-3, -6, and -7. The active effector caspases selectively hydrolyze a broad spectrum of polypeptide targets including protein kinases, signal transduction proteins, cytoskeletal components, and inhibitors of deoxyribonucleases [149]. Accordingly, activation of the effector caspase cascade not only disables the cell in terms of functional homeostasis but also facilitates the breakdown and packaging of the cell into small, membrane-bound bodies for phagocytosis—the end step in cellular elimination via apoptosis [150, 151]. As with many other apoptosis gene families, redundancies have been identified in caspase function. For example, Zheng et al. used an in vivo death receptor model to demonstrate that whereas caspase-9 and -3 become activated in hepatocytes during Fas-induced apoptosis, deletion of either of these caspases through gene targeting merely delays hepatocyte death [152]. Immunoblot analysis of various caspase family members revealed that caspase-2, -6, and -7 were activated only in extracts prepared from cells lacking caspase-9 or -3. It was therefore concluded from this study that the mitochondrial pathway of caspase activation (i.e., apoptosome formation and caspase-9 activation) could involve and/or result in the simultaneous activation of alternative initiator and effector caspases as needed to ensure the efficient removal of a cell targeted for elimination via apoptosis.

APOPTOSIS IN OVARIAN SOMATIC CELLS

With this general information on apoptosis and its control as a foundation, this section and the following section called "Female Germ Cell Apoptosis" provide overviews of the current status of work toward elucidating the roles and regulation of apoptosis in ovarian somatic cells and germ cells, respectively. Of note concerning this section, several reviews on apoptosis in granulosa cells [153–157] and corpora lutea [18, 153] are available for additional details, concepts, and references not covered herein.

Granulosa Cell Death during Follicular Atresia

Background and Models

The somatic cells of the ovarian follicle provide a powerful model to investigate hormone-, growth factor-, and cytokine-regulated effects on cellular fate. Within the follicle the most obvious cell type undergoing apoptosis associated with maturing follicle atresia is the granulosa cell. There are, however, some species that exhibit theca cell apoptosis during follicular aresia (i.e., pig, chicken, rat), although the onset of apoptosis in the theca occurs much later than that in the granulosa [158–161]. The significance of this is yet to be determined; however, it is believed that theca cells perform some type of antiapoptotic function for the adjacent granulosa cells [157]. In support of this, bovine granulosa cells derived from small follicles were found to be less likely to undergo apoptosis in response to serum withdrawal when they were cocultured with theca cells [162].

Over the years, many investigators have attempted to design, adapt, and optimize in vitro and in vivo model systems to elucidate the mechanisms responsible for regulating apoptosis in the follicle. The most used and well-characterized in vivo models include the gonadotropin-primed prepubertal rodent (i.e., mouse, rat) (for examples, see [163–165]) and the adult hen of avian species (i.e., chicken, quail) [157]. Many in vitro studies, based on serum withdrawal or treatment of cultured granulosa cells or isolated follicles with various proapoptotic agents, have also served an important role in identifying potential regulators and mediators of apoptosis during atresia [154–157, 166]. Collectively, these types of model systems have enabled investigators to determine that granulosa (and in some studies, theca) cell apoptosis can be inhibited with various growth factors, progesterone, estrogen, or gonadotropins. Conversely, proapoptotic functions for various cytokines, androgens, and gonadotropin-releasing hormone (Gn-RH) have been proposed. Although this chapter could easily expand on each of these factors in greater detail, further comments are restricted to death receptors and atresia because of space constraints and to maintain the theme of previous discussions in this chapter.

Death Receptors and Atresia

It has long been known that cytokines play a significant role in the development, function, and demise of the somatic cells of the follicle. The more notable cytokines include TNF-α and Fas ligand (FasL), whose general actions in apoptosis have been previously described in detail. Within the ovary, bioactive TNF-α is present in the follicular fluid of small and large follicles of several species and is found in the medium of isolated granulosa cells cultured in vitro [167, 168]. In addition, treatment of granulosa cells with TNF-α can reduce levels of steroid acute regulatory (StAR) protein [169] and induce apoptosis [167, 169, 170]. The disruption of steroidogenesis was noticed earlier than the increased rate and extent of apoptosis [169], suggesting that there are independent mechanisms for TNF-α-dependent regulation of steroidogenesis and apoptosis. However, it is well recognized that mitochondria play a critical role in initiating and executing apoptosis. Therefore the ability of TNF-α to affect the levels of a key mitochondrial protein in steroidogenic cells may be indicative of early effects on mitochondrial destabilization that are not readily detectable by conventional assays.

Fas ligand is another of the more recognized members of the TNF superfamily present within the ovary. Fas ligand and its receptor are known to be expressed by follicular cells of mice, rats, cows, pigs, chickens, and humans [171–182]. In the human female, granulosa cells of antral follicles express Fas during the early stages of atresia, and the levels of Fas expression increase as atresia progresses [172]. By comparison, Fas is not evident in theca cells until the later stages of atresia [172]. Consistent with these data implicating the Fas/FasL system in atresia, treatment of cultured granulosa cells with Fas ligand or Fas-activating antibody can induce apoptosis in vitro, and treatment of female mice in vivo with Fas-activating antibody elevates granulosa cell apoptosis and follicular atresia [171, 173, 174, 179]. The importance of the Fas/FasL system is further supported by evidence derived from mutant mouse models. For example, *lpr/lpr* mice exhibit reduced or no expression of Fas (depending on the tissue examined), whereas *gld/gld* mice lack functional FasL. Females of either mutant mouse line display irregular estrous cycles, and *lpr/lpr* females show an increase in the number of secondary follicles. In addition, the *gld/gld* and *lpr/lpr* mutant mice have an increased incidence of ovarian cysts [174].

Although limited studies have been conducted on the possible role of death receptor family members other than TNFRI and Fas in the ovary, there are a few reports that should be mentioned. Expression of the TRAIL-decoy receptor-1 (DcR1) was recently documented in porcine granulosa cells, and the levels of DcR1 were shown to be lower in atretic, compared with healthy, follicles [183]. Interestingly, elimination of the DcR1 in granulosa cells by cleavage of its glycophospholipid anchor followed by treatment with TRAIL increased apoptosis, providing evidence that DcR1 may serve an antiapoptotic role in the follicle during development [183]. In the domestic hen ovary, expression of the avian ortholog of DR6 has been identified in granulosa cells, and elevated levels of DR6 mRNA and protein correlate with follicular atresia. Avian TVB, another member of the death receptor family similar to DR5 in mammals, is also expressed in hen granulosa cells; however, its role, if any, in granulosa cell function or apoptosis is unknown [184].

Signal Transduction in Granulosa Cell Apoptosis

When considering how various hormones, growth factors, and cytokines interact with their cognate receptors to modulate apoptosis in follicular somatic cells, many of the signal transduction pathways outlined earlier have been the subjects of investigation. For example, using the gonadotropin-primed immature rat model, it was reported that JNK activity increases during apoptosis in granulosa cells; however, the increase in JNK activity was detected after biochemical evidence of apoptosis, suggesting that JNK may help to facilitate or amplify, rather than initiate, the cell death process [185]. On the other hand, a loss of ERK signaling was detected long before any evidence of apoptosis in granulosa cells, indicating that a reduction in the activity of prosurvival signal transduction networks may be of greater importance to the initiation of apoptosis in granulosa cells [185]. Such a hypothesis is supported by studies of the role of PI3-K/Akt in regulating granulosa cell survival [186, 187]. This signaling pathway is activated by a number of growth factors, including IGF-1, epidermal growth factor, and basic fibroblast growth factor [188–190], all of which have been reported to prevent apoptosis in granulosa cells cultured in vitro [186, 191–194] or in granulosa cells of intact follicles incubated in vitro [195].

It has been further demonstrated that treatment of granulosa cells with IGF-1 stimulates the activities of PI3-K and Akt, with IGF-1-driven phosphorylation and activation of Akt occurring in a time- and concentration-dependent manner [186]. Moreover, the increase in phosphorylation and activity of Akt, and the corresponding inhibition of apoptosis, in granulosa cells resulting from IGF-1 treatment can be attenuated by either of two PI3-K inhibitors, LY294002 or wortmannin [186]. Similar findings have been reported from studies of avian granulosa cells cultured in vitro in that IGF-1 and TGF-α were shown to induce a rapid phosphorylation of Akt that could be prevented by cotreatment with LY294006 [196]. The ability of LY294006 to antagonize the actions of IGF-1 were not restricted to Akt phosphorylation because the PI3-K inhibitor also abolished the survival-promoting effects of the growth factor in granulosa cells. Interestingly, apoptosis resulting from PI3-K inhibition could be overcome by treatment of the cells with either luteinizing hormone (LH) or a cAMP analog, suggesting that protein kinase A can fully compensate for the loss of PI3-K in maintaining granulosa cell viability [196]. The complexity of signal transduction networks responsible for relaying information from the environment is further exemplified by observations that ERK phosphorylation is also induced by IGF-1 and TGF-α in avian granulosa cells; however, treatment with MAPK kinase inhibitors (i.e., U0126 or PD98059), although capable of completely blocking ERK phosphorylation, did not result in apoptosis [196].

The sphingomyelin pathway, or at least ceramide, has also been studied in the context of granulosa cell death in various species. The first report demonstrated that short-chain ceramide analogs capable of passing the plasma membrane, or pathological manipulations known to stimulate endogenous ceramide production (e.g., chemotherapeutic drugs or UV irradiation), causes a rapid induction of apoptosis in avian granulosa cells cultured in vitro [197]. Moreover, pretreating the cells with the ceramide synthase inhibitor, fumonisin-B1 (FB1), could prevent apoptosis initiated as a result of exposure to the cytotoxic drug, daunorubicin. However, FB1 conveyed no protective effect in avian granulosa cells exposed to UV irradiation, suggesting that different external stresses may stimulate the production of ceramide in granulosa cells by different processes, all of which can lead to apoptosis [197]. Such a proposal is in agreement with earlier data identifying a requirement for acid sphingomyelinase (ASMase), rather than ceramide synthase, in ceramide generation required for radiation-induced apoptosis in lung endothelial cells [198] and in UV-induced activation of JNK [199]. Similar studies with rat ovarian follicles cultured in vitro have shown that short-chain ceramide analogs antagonize gonadotropin-promoted follicular cell survival [200].

Bcl-2 Family Members as Determinants of Granulosa Cell Fate

Historically, much of the research emphasis on the role of Bcl-2 and related proteins in atresia was initially placed on the more "high profile" members of the family. However, recent studies have expanded this work, so the list now includes several antiapoptotic (Bcl-2, Bcl-x_{long}, Mcl-1), proapoptotic multidomain (Bax, Bak, Mtd/Bok, Boo/Diva), and BH3-only (Bad, Bim/Bod) proteins. Initial studies showed that gonadotropin-mediated inhibition of apoptosis in rat granulosa cells results in an alteration in the ratio of *bax* to *bcl-2* and *bcl-*x_{long} expression favoring cellular survival [164]. These changes in gene expression in granulosa cells correspond with shifts in the levels of Bax, Bcl-2, and Bcl-x_{long} proteins as well [185, 201]. In support of these gene expression studies, inactivation of the bax gene in mice results in the accumulation of abnormal follicles in the ovary, possessing atrophic granulosa cells that presumably fail to undergo apoptosis as the follicles attempt to progress through atresia [202]. These data, coupled with findings of elevated Bax protein in atretic follicles of the human [203] and quail [204] ovary, collectively indicate that Bax probably functions as a key modulator of granulosa cell fate in diverse species.

Additional studies of the avian ovary have shown that expression of Bcl-2 and Bcl-x_{long} are markedly higher in granulosa cells of hierarchal follicles selected for ovulation when compared with granulosa cells of prehierarchal follicles that retain the capacity to undergo atresia. In addition, expression of NR-13, an antiapoptotic Bcl-2-like protein in avian species, is only observed in preovulatory follicles [170, 205, 206]. The increased expression of several antiapoptotic Bcl-2 family members in preovulatory follicles correlates with increased resistance of the corresponding granulosa cells to undergo apoptosis in vitro, and the lack of evidence of follicular atresia at the corresponding stages of follicle development in vivo [170, 205, 206]. Mcl-1 is yet another antiapoptotic member of the Bcl-2 family that has been reported to function as a regulator of granulosa cell survival [207]. In this study, Northern blot analysis showed that *mcl-1* is expressed in the rat ovary and transiently inducible by pregnant mare serum gonadotropins (PMSG) priming. Moreover, in situ hybridization studies demonstrated that the mRNA encoding Mcl-1 is evident and regulated in the granulosa and theca cell compartments of growing follicles [208].

In addition to Bax, expression of Mtd/Bok, a multidomain Bcl-2 family member with a relatively limited tissue expression pattern [209, 210], has been identified in the rat ovary [209]. In situ hybridization studies verified the presence of Mtd/Bok message in granulosa of antral follicles with minimal expression of the gene noted in theca-interstitial cells [209]. It was also shown that the levels of mRNA encoding Bok are elevated in rat granulosa cells undergoing apoptosis in vitro [209]. Diva/Boo, a Bcl-2 family member whose function in apoptosis remains controversial [211, 212], is also highly expressed in granulosa cells of the ovary and appears to be correlated with atresia [211]. However, inactivation of the Diva/Boo gene in mice causes no obvious abnormalities in the ovary or in fertility [213], leaving unanswered the question of the importance of Diva/Boo in the granulosa cell death program. The BH3-only family member, Bad, is expressed in granulosa cells and theca-interstitial cells of the rat ovary, and although the levels of *bad* mRNA in granulosa cells remain unchanged after exposure to an apoptotic stimulus, overexpression of Bad in rat granulosa cells induces apoptosis [214]. Furthermore, a reduction in the phosphorylated (inactive) form of Bad has been correlated with the initiation of apoptosis in rat granulosa cells during follicular atresia in vivo [185]. Finally, the BH3-only family member, Bim (renamed Bod in the rat for unknown reasons), is known to be expressed in the rat and human ovary [215], although the cell type(s) that express the gene and the function, if any, of Bim in follicular atresia remain to be elucidated.

The Apoptosome and Caspases in Granulosa Cell Death

As discussed earlier, formation of the apoptosome requires release of cytochrome *c* from destabilized mitochondria—an event triggered by the actions of proapoptotic Bcl-2 family members—and the presence of Apaf-1 and procaspase-9. In murine granulosa cells induced to undergo apoptosis by serum starvation in vitro, the first step in apoptosome formation, that being mitochondrial release of cytochrome *c*, has been documented [216]. In the same study, expression of Apaf-1 at the mRNA and protein level was identified in the mouse ovary, with elevated levels of Apaf-1 in granulosa cells being correlated with the onset of follicular atresia in vivo [216]. Although a direct interaction between cytochrome *c* and Apaf-1 in granulosa cells is yet to be demonstrated, the consequences of such an interaction—processing and activation of caspase-9 and effector caspases such as caspase-3—have been reported [216, 217]. Moreover, preliminary studies have shown that inactivation of the *caspase-9* gene in mice results in defective granulosa cell apoptosis and follicular atresia in vivo [217], collectively indicating that the apoptosome in fact forms and functions in granulosa cells during apoptosis.

Assuming this to be the case, one would envision a critical role for effector caspases in carrying out the process of follicular atresia. Many of the caspases identified in vertebrates to date are expressed within the ovary [218], and recent studies have provided evidence of important roles for at least caspase-3, and perhaps caspase-6 and -7, in executing granulosa cell apoptosis. For example, previous findings have established the existence of an inverse correlation between caspase-3 expression (mRNA and protein) and apoptosis in granulosa cells of the rodent [165, 219, 220] and human [165] ovary. Furthermore, procaspase-3 processing and caspase-3-like enzymatic activity have been detected in murine granulosa cells during apoptosis [216], and cell-permeable peptide inhibitors selective for caspase-3 (e.g., zDEVD-fmk) suppress granulosa cell death in cultured ovarian follicles of the mouse [221]. A central role for caspase-3 in executing granulosa cell death has been solidified by studies of caspase-3-deficient mice, in which the mutant females were shown to possess numerous aberrant atretic follicles containing granulosa cells that failed to undergo apoptosis [165]. These in vivo findings were supported by a number of in vitro studies—using isolated granulosa cells and intact follicles maintained in serum-free cultures—demonstrating an absence of key biochemical markers of apoptosis in mutant granulosa cells or follicles when compared with wild-type granulosa cells or follicles cultured in parallel [165]. Interestingly, however, granulosa cells lacking caspase-3 still eventually succumb to apoptosis, probably via the compensatory induction of caspase-7, which has also been correlated with granulosa cell apoptosis in mouse and human ovaries [165]. Lastly, studies of the avian ovary have proposed a similar role for caspase-3, as well as for caspase-6, in mediating granulosa cell death during follicular atresia [222].

Apoptosis and Luteal Regression

Background and Models of Luteal Cell Apoptosis

The role and regulation of apoptosis in luteal regression has recently been reviewed in detail [18], and thus only highlights of a number of findings will be provided in the following subsections. In brief, apoptosis has been identified during structural involution of the corpus luteum (CL) in the mouse [223, 224], rat [225–228], hamster [229, 230], rabbit [231, 232], sheep [233–236], cow [237–239], pig [240], and primate [241–243]. In general, however, the study of apoptosis during luteal regression has been complicated by many factors [18]. First, whether or not apoptosis is responsible for disrupting steroidogenesis associated with luteal regression remains to be clarified and may be dependent on the stimulus. In addition, many studies of luteal regression have relied on administration of exogenous compounds to initiate luteolysis, which may alter the sequential mechanistic events observed normally during a menstrual or estrous cycle. Moreover, the use of CL derived from pregnant or pseudopregnant animals probably offers another level of complexity because CL collected from these types of models differs considerably from CL of the normal menstrual/estrous cycle [18].

Despite these hurdles, to date a number of in vivo models have been described to investigate the role of apoptosis in luteal regression, including work in rodents (rat, mouse, hamster), rabbits, domestic farm animals (pigs, cows, sheep), nonhuman primates, and humans [18]. Given the heterogeneous nature of the CL with respect to cell lineages present, in vitro models, although invaluable for testing the effects of specific agents on the various cell types, often produce data that are difficult to interpret or extrapolate back to the in vivo situation. For example, $PGF_{2\alpha}$ is often considered "the" luteolytic agent, yet it is not cytotoxic in vitro to luteal cells [18]. There are also examples of medium from cultured luteal cells containing increased levels of progesterone despite an increased incidence of apoptosis [244]. Finally, $PGF_{2\alpha}$, while implicated as an underlying catalyst for luteolysis and consequently the induction of apoptosis in many mammalian species, clearly does not act alone in triggering luteal cell death [18, 245, 246].

Cytokines, Death Receptors, and Signal Transduction in Luteal Cell Apoptosis

There is increasing evidence that members of the death receptor family and their ligands are involved in multiple aspects of luteal regression, including disruption of steroidogenesis and involution of the structure itself. For example, the temporal and spatial expression of Fas and its ligand in the human, bovine, rat, and mouse CL are associated with luteal regression [172, 174, 228, 247]. Similar to that observed in cultured granulosa cells, FasL or Fas-activating antibody induces apoptosis in cultured luteal cells derived from the mouse, rat, cow, and human [171, 223, 228, 244, 248, 249]. In addition, intravenous or intraperitoneal administration of Fas-activating antibody causes luteolysis in the mouse [174]. The activation of Fas in luteal cells has been shown to alter activity of a number of MAPK family members [250]; however, the significance of these signaling pathways to luteal function and demise is not completely understood. Fas-mediated cell death results in the activation of caspase-3 [251], and studies of mice lacking this apoptosis executioner have supported its central role in luteolysis [251]. The functional importance of the Fas/FasL system in luteolysis has also been reinforced by studies of mutant mice lacking Fas (*lpr/lpr*) or FasL (*gld/gld*), which display irregular estrous cycles attributed to defects in follicle development and luteal demise [174].

TNF-α has also been implicated in luteal regression. Although typically thought to be derived from monocytes or macrophages, a significant amount of TNF-α is found within the endothelial cell component of the CL [252, 253]. Expression of TNF-α has been demonstrated in the CL of the rat, rabbit, pig, cow, and human [252–256]. Although the levels of mRNA encoding TNF-α do not change in the CL during the estrous cycle in the cow [256, 257], the levels of TNF-α protein are low in the early to midluteal phase, increase dramatically during the late luteal phase, and decline after regression [256]. Similarly, in the ewe TNF-α mRNA is not detectable by Northern blot analysis; however, TNF-α bioactivity increases after progesterone levels decline during luteal regression [258]. The majority of what has been published with respect to TNF-α receptor subtypes within the CL has focused on TNFRI [255, 256, 259, 260]. Furthermore, TNF-α binding sites in the CL have been identified in multiple species [256, 261, 262] and are present throughout the luteal phase in the cow [256]. From a functional standpoint, TNF-α has been implicated as a luteotropic and a luteolytic agent. The differences are likely luteal phase- or species-dependent [18]. In vitro, TNF-α is cytotoxic to cultured endothelial cells derived from the bovine CL [250, 259], and TNF-α can augment IFNγ-induced cell death in steroidogenic luteal cells derived from the cow [247, 263, 264]. The signaling mechanism(s) by which TNF-α elicits its proapoptotic effect remains to be elucidated; however, it is known that TNF-α activates stress-related signaling pathways [18, 265], as well as the sphingomyelin pathway [250]. Finally, additional evidence for the involvement of TNF-α in CL function has been provided by Roby et al. [266], who demonstrated that TNFRI-deficient mice become "locked" in a diestrous (luteal) phase and thus fail to progress through the estrous cycle. Similar results were found by Bukovsky et al. [267], who reported that rats injected with antithymocyte antiserum to inhibit immune function failed to progress past the diestrous phase. Although this latter study does not directly implicate TNF-α, it does support the role of the immune system as a modulator of luteal regression.

Bcl-2 Family Members as Regulators of Luteal Cell Apoptosis

Rodger et al. were the first to provide evidence of expression of Bcl-2 and Bax in the human CL [268, 269]. Bcl-2 was localized in the granulosa-lutein, theca-lutein, and endothelial cells of some blood vessels. However, no difference in the levels of Bcl-2 or Bax protein was evident during the luteal phase [268, 269]. More recent studies have provided evidence indicating that Bcl-2 expression may in fact be regulated in the human CL during the menstrual cycle, early pregnancy, and in response to human chorionic gonadotropin (hCG) [270, 271]. Similarly, recent work has shown that Bax levels are low in the midluteal phase CL and increase during luteal regression and that Bax is absent in the CL of pregnancy [270]. Unfortunately, few published reports exist on the expression or role(s) played by the Bcl-2 family in the CL or whether the various apoptosis gene mutant mice studied in the context of granulosa cell or oocyte apoptosis exhibit comparable defects in luteal cell apoptosis.

The Apoptosome and Caspases as Executioners of Luteal Regression

The change in the ratio of Bax to Bcl-2 may not be as important as the change in their intracellular location. For example, Bax is known to be translocated to mitochondria following exposure of the cell to a death stimulus [272]. Although mitochondria are thus considered pivotal players in the apoptotic cell death process, for steroidogenic cells these organelles serve an equally important role in the production of steroid hormones. Ultrastructural changes in mitochondria during luteolysis were described as early as 1966 [273]. It was reported that the mitochondria swelled and underwent matrix rarefication, preceding the decline in progesterone production in sheep luteal cells. These characteristics of the mitochondria are strikingly similar to those used today to describe mitochondria in a cell undergoing apoptosis. However, it remains to be established if these changes in mitochondria lead to apoptosome formation and activity in luteal cells of any species.

Although published data for apoptosome function in luteolysis are lacking, there are a number of observations supporting a key role for effector caspases in luteal regression. For example, caspase-3, probably the best studied effector caspase, is present in the rat and human CL [220, 274] and is activated in response to $PGF_{2\alpha}$-induced luteal regression in the rat and ewe [220, 275]. The importance of caspase-3 to luteal regression has been solidified by recent studies using *caspase-3* mutant mice [276]. Whereas cells within CL derived from wild-type mice undergo apoptosis within 24 hours of culture in serum-free medium, cells within CL from caspase-3-deficient mice show a markedly delayed occurrence of apoptosis when cultured in parallel. These data, along with findings of a delayed onset of structural involution in CL of *caspase-3* mutant mice when compared with wild-type mice during a gonadotropin-induced luteal phase, strongly support a role for this effector caspase in mediating the structural aspects of luteal regression [276].

FEMALE GERM CELL APOPTOSIS

Given that this subject has recently been reviewed in detail [17], a brief overview of this topic, along with a more in-depth discussion of relevant publications that have followed this recent review, are presented in the following subsections. Furthermore, the significance of postnatal oocyte apoptosis as a driving force behind atresia of the immature follicle pool and ovarian senescence with age [17, 277] is addressed in a subsequent section of this chapter. For the following discussions, the occurrence and regulation of apoptosis in female germ cells is divided into two broad categories: (1) that which occurs as a normal part of ovarian development and (2) that which occurs as a response to a pathophysiological insult.

Germ Loss during Fetal Ovarian Development

Hormones and Signal Transduction Pathways in Ovarian Germ Cells

Significant progress has been made in elucidating the mechanisms underlying developmental oocyte deletion, principally through the study of gene knockout mice lacking key apoptosis regulators and through the use of fetal ovarian organ cultures. For example, mouse fetal ovaries removed at embryonic day 13.5—a time corresponding to the initiation of meiosis and just before the onset of fetal ovarian germ cell apoptosis—and cultured in vitro without serum or growth factors exhibit a time-dependent onset of apoptosis in the germ cells, with only 10% of the starting germ cell population remaining after 72 hours [278, 279]. Consistent with results from studies of isolated primordial germ cells in culture [280], the addition of stem cell factor (SCF), leukemia inhibitory factor (LIF), and IGF-I to the culture medium prevents germ cell loss in cultured fetal ovaries through mechanisms involving the PI3-K signaling pathway [278].

Related studies showed that germ cell loss in tropic factor-deprived mouse fetal ovaries maintained in vitro requires the presence of the ceramide-generating enzyme, ASMase, suggesting that the cellular stress caused by serum starvation not only shuts down growth factor-dependent PI3-K signaling but also triggers the production of ceramide as a mediator of the apoptotic response [281]. Such a conclusion was reinforced by parallel findings that comparable levels of germ cell survival could be achieved in serum-starved mouse fetal ovaries cultured in vitro by either ASMase deficiency or by provision of the ceramide antagonist, S1P, to wild-type fetal ovaries [281]. Moreover, these in vitro findings were confirmed in vivo in that ASMase-deficient female mice were shown to possess a significantly larger reserve of primordial follicles shortly after birth compared with wild-type sisters, collectively substantiating a central role for ASMase-generated ceramide in deleting fetal ovarian germ cells [281]. Interestingly, the findings that PI3-K and ceramide potentially serve opposing roles in controlling the fate of developing female germ cells is in keeping with reports from somatic cell types showing that ceramide directly suppresses PI3-K and Akt activities [73, 74, 282], whereas overexpression of Akt can block ceramide generation and protect cells from ceramide-induced apoptosis [81].

Role of Bcl-2 Family Members in Determining Oocyte Fate

Downstream of PI3-K and ceramide, several Bcl-2 family members have been implicated in either suppressing (Bcl-2, Bcl-x_L, Bcl-w) or activating (Bax) apoptosis in fetal ovarian germ cells [283]. Immunocytochemical studies of mouse fetal oocytes have shown the accumulation of Bax protein in degenerating germ cells, with low levels of the protein detected in healthy appearing oocytes [284]. In addition, whereas the levels of Bcl-2 in fetal oocytes are extremely low and remain unchanged irrespective of oocyte health status [284], studies of mice lacking Bcl-2 have shown that mutant females do in fact possess a smaller cohort of primordial follicles in young adult life [285]. However, the impact of Bcl-2 deficiency on postnatal oocyte numbers is not dramatic, suggesting that other antiapoptotic Bcl-2 family members may be more critical to female germ cell development. Indeed, in a study of mice with reduced expression of Bcl-x in the germline, it was reported that the mutant females were born with a significantly compromised reserve of primordial follicles caused by excessive germ cell apoptosis during fetal development [286]. Of further interest, simultaneous inactivation of the *bax* gene restored female germ cell numbers to wild-type levels in neonatal *bcl-x* mutant females, providing proof-of-concept in vivo that a Bcl-x_L:Bax rheostat functions as a key determinant of oocyte fate during development [286].

Mitochondrial Events and Caspases in Female Germ Cell Apoptosis

Unfortunately, little is known of the perimitochondrial events with respect to apoptosis signaling in female germ cells, including the importance of the apoptosome presumably formed following Bax (and/or another proapoptotic Bcl-2 family member)-driven cytochrome *c* release. Studies have shown that Apaf-1 is expressed in female germ cells [216] and that mitochondria play a critical role in controlling the activation of apoptosis in oocytes [287]. Moreover, preliminary investigations of caspase-9 deficient female mice have revealed that apoptosis is indeed defective in developing germ cells of mutant females [217], although comparable studies of oocytes in Apaf-1 deficient mice are not available. Evaluations of mutant mice lacking caspase-2 have shown that this caspase family member is essential for the activation of apoptosis in fetal ovarian germ cells caused by cytokine insufficiency [288]. Interestingly, however, loss of female germ cells because of meiotic defects associated with inactivation of the *ataxia telangiectasia-mutated* (*Atm*) gene is not dependent on the presence of caspase-2 [288], suggesting that multiple and stimulus-specific pathways exist for the developmental deletion of oocytes before birth.

Genetic Modifiers of Germ Cell Survival

Finally, recent studies of several different strains of mice have built on an earlier report [289] to establish the existence of genetic modifiers of primordial follicle endowment, early follicular development, and atresia [290]. In examining differences in primordial and total immature (primordial, primary, preantral) follicle numbers from neonatal to young adult life in one outbred and five inbred strains of mice, Canning and colleagues identified nearly two-fold differences in the size of the primordial follicle reserve among the strains, as well as striking strain-dependent differences in the rate of immature follicle atresia [290]. Although the identity of the gene(s) responsible for conveying these effects in the ovary remains to be determined, the known importance of apoptosis to the endpoints evaluated—namely oocyte endowment and immature follicle atresia [17]—suggests that the gene(s) are linked either directly or indirectly to the control of germ cell apoptosis. In addition, these experiments add to previous studies of genetic modifier effects on other aspects of female reproductive function in mice, including germ cell susceptibility to the cytotoxic effects of certain environmental chemicals [291], as well as gonadotropin-induced ovulation rates [292]. Accordingly, these types of investigations may lay the groundwork for the discovery of new genes that influence several key aspects of ovarian function, including apoptosis.

Germ Cell Loss as a Consequence of Pathophysiological Insults

Female germ cells are exquisitely sensitive to a wide-spectrum of chemical and radiological agents, and studies from an increasing number of laboratories have begun to shed light on the importance of apoptosis to various paradigms of pathophysiological oocyte depletion [293, 294]. Given the large number of insults capable of depleting oocytes, however, this section focuses on two examples of toxicant-induced ovarian failure, which are among the best characterized. In addition, mechanisms underlying the ability of anticancer therapies—in the form of either cytotoxic drugs or radiation—to accelerate oocyte depletion, as well as current therapeutic strategies being developed to combat this outcome, are addressed in a subsequent section of this chapter.

Polycyclic Aromatic Hydrocarbons and Oocyte Death

The first class of toxicants to be discussed are polycyclic aromatic hydrocarbons (PAH), including benzo[*a*]pyrene (BaP), 9,10-dimethylbenz[*a*]anthracene (DMBA), and 3-methylcholanthrene (for details on PAH, see the Agency for Toxic Substances and Disease Registry of the Centers for Disease Control at *www.atsdr.cdc.gov/tfacts69.html*). These chemicals are produced primarily as a by-product of the combustion of organic matter, including the burning of fossil fuels and tobacco. Volcanoes and forest fires also generate substantial amounts of airborne PAH. In addition, significant levels of PAH are produced by road and roof tarring operations, as well as by coal tar and aluminum production plants. Thus, given the likelihood of human exposure, through either unintentional (environmental or occupational) or "intentional" (tobacco smoking) means, PAH are considered potentially serious human health hazards. For more than 20 years it has been established that PAH are potent ovotoxicants, causing a rapid destruction of the immature follicle pool following in vivo exposure of female mice to these chemicals [291, 295–297].

In addition, extensive germ cell loss via apoptosis occurs in female fetuses of pregnant mice injected with either BaP [298] or DMBA [299] during gestation. In humans, a link between maternal cigarette smoking during pregnancy and reduced fecundity of female offspring exposed to cigarette smoke-derived chemicals in utero has been reported [300]. These findings, taken with data underscoring a link between smoking and early menopause in women [297, 301], indicate that chemicals present in cigarette smoke impair fetal oogenesis and destroy preexisting germ cells within the postnatal ovaries. Although tobacco smoke contains numerous toxic chemicals in addition to PAH, the animal data discussed earlier along with recent research findings discussed later, strongly implicate PAH as partly responsible for these epidemiological observations.

From a mechanistic standpoint, PAH are intriguing in that they can act as "unnatural" ligands for an orphan transcription factor referred to as the *aromatic hydrocarbon receptor (AHR)* [302, 303]. The AHR is a member of the Per-Arnt-Sim (PAS) family of transcriptional regulators, which are known to modulate a wide spectrum of physiological functions in the body. Although the natural ligand(s) for the AHR remains to be conclusively identified, gene knockout studies have shown that AHR loss of function in the absence of toxicant exposure causes a number of phenotypic abnormalities [304, 305], including a significant enlargement of the primordial follicle reserve at birth caused by defective apoptosis in fetal ovarian germ cells [306]. In subsequent studies using AHR-deficient mice, it was demonstrated that this transcription factor is required for PAH to destroy immature follicles in the postnatal mouse ovary [27]. Accordingly, computer-based searches of known apoptosis-regulatory genes were performed, which revealed that the promoter of the proapoptotic *bax* gene harbors a tandem AHR response element (AHRE). That the *bax* gene is a bona fide target for transcriptional regulation by the PAH-activated AHR in oocytes was subsequently documented by promoter activity analysis and by endogenous gene expression studies in mouse oocytes [27]. More importantly, inactivation of the *bax* gene was shown to completely protect female germ cells from the cytotoxic actions of PAH in vitro [27] and in vivo [299]. Using a human ovarian-mouse xenograft model, it was further shown that PAH induce Bax accumulation followed by apoptosis in oocytes of human primordial and primary follicles in vivo [27], collectively defining a novel and evolutionarily conserved cell death signaling pathway responsible for mediating the pathophysiological depletion of female germ cells caused by PAH exposure.

Follicle Depletion Caused by 4-Vinylcyclohexene Diepoxide

The second class of toxicants to be discussed includes 4-vinylcyclohexene (VCH) and its metabolite, 4-vinylcyclohexene diepoxide (VCD). Unlike PAH, which are generated from natural and man-made processes, VCH is produced essentially as an industrial by-product in the manufacture of plastics, rubber, flame-retardants, and pesticides [307]. Although no data exist with respect to the effects of VCH or VCD in humans, studies with female rodents have shown that VCD exposure in vivo destroys the immature follicle pool [307] through a process involving apoptosis [308]. Subsequent studies have shown that immature follicles in the ovaries of rats exposed to VCD exhibit elevated levels of *bax* mRNA [309], as well as a redistribution of Bax protein from the cytosolic to the mitochondrial compartment [310]. Importantly, gene knockout studies have confirmed the functional requirement for Bax in VCD-induced loss of primordial and primary follicles in mice, although it was noted that there is also a Bax-independent component to ovarian damaged caused by VCD [311].

Additional work has provided evidence of the involvement of initiator (caspase-8 and -9) and effector (caspase-3) caspases in VCD-induced follicle depletion [312], although the timing of caspase-9 activation and the onset of apoptosis following repeated VCD exposure raises questions as to the role of caspase-9, if any, in follicle destruction under these experimental conditions. In contrast, increased activity of caspase-8 and -3 were temporally linked to the onset of VCD-induced follicle degeneration [312], suggesting that these two enzymes may serve as the principal initiator/effector caspases in this model. As with Bax, gene knockout studies have supported a role for caspase-3 in the loss of primary follicles following VCD exposure; however, the absence of caspase-3 affords no protective effect for primordial follicles in VCD-treated mice [311]. The reason(s) behind this remains to be elucidated, although the possibility that another caspase family member plays a role in the execution of apoptosis in VCD-exposed follicles has been tested in parallel studies of *caspase-2* mutant mice. Like caspase-3 deficient animals, the extent of primary follicle destruction in female mice lacking caspase-2 is lower than that observed in VCD-treated wild-type females; however, primordial follicle loss in response to VCD dosing is comparable irrespective of genotype [311]. Such findings would be consistent with one of at least three possibilities. First, the destruction of follicles caused by VCD exposure requires the concerted actions of a number of effector caspases, such that the absence of one enzyme causes only minimal or no defects in the ability of the cells within the follicles to execute apoptosis. Second, a compensatory induction of other caspases in the absence of either caspase-2 or caspase-3 may occur, analogous to that recently described for the livers of mice lacking caspase-3 [152]. Finally, it may be that a caspase-independent mechanism(s) of cell death—similar to those identified in other nonovarian cell types [313]—plays a prominent role in VCD-induced follicle destruction.

SELECTED EXAMPLES OF THE CLINICAL SIGNIFICANCE OF APOPTOSIS IN THE OVARY

Understanding the basic biology of apoptosis and its control in ovarian somatic cells and germ cells has opened numerous avenues to explore with respect to clinical application of these data in the form of apoptosis-based diagnostic tests or therapeutic agents. Although the vast majority of these studies are still in the developmental stages—that is, years from the clinic—the potential significance of these investigations for improving human reproductive health and fertility is clear. The following sections have been designed to provide selected examples of current strategies being pursued, using apoptosis as the principal endpoint, to possibly one day improve the outcome of assisted reproductive technologies, to postpone the natural timing of menopause in women, and to prevent ovarian damage and infertility in female cancer patients.

Granulosa-Lutein Cell Apoptosis and Assisted Reproductive Technologies

In 1997 a nonrandom prospective study of 129 normally ovulating women undergoing in vitro fertilization-embryo transfer (IVF-ET) concluded that the incidence of mural granulosa-lutein cell apoptosis in follicular aspirates was significantly higher in those patients that failed to become pregnant when compared with those women achieving a successful pregnancy [314]. Although there were several caveats with this initial work—including the use of pooled follicular aspirates in the analysis—subsequent studies that compared on a follicle-by-follicle basis the incidence of granulosa-lutein cell apoptosis in the aspirates to oocyte quality and IVF outcome produced the same overall conclusion [315]. This work has since been followed by other reports identifying a consistent inverse relationship between the apoptotic index in granulosa cells and pregnancy outcome [316, 317]. In fact, in one study of 73 women undergoing IVF-ET, those patients who became pregnant showed a reduced incidence of granulosa-lutein cell apoptosis when compared with the nonpregnant group in the absence of any concomitant differences in the patients' age, basal serum follicle-stimulating hormone (FSH) concentrations, serum estradiol concentrations, hCG day, number of oocytes retrieved, fertilization rates, or number of embryos transferred between the two groups [317]. In light of these and other data, the authors proposed that a granulosa-lutein cell apoptotic index of 6.14% or below could be used to predict a successful pregnancy with a sensitivity of 87.5% and a specificity of 73.7% [317].

In related studies, Kaneko and colleagues showed that the type of ovarian stimulation protocol used also significantly affects the incidence of granulosa-lutein cell apoptosis, with the highest levels seen in those patients given a Gn-RH agonist in addition to human menopausal gonadotropins (hMG) and hCG compared with those patients given hMG plus hCG alone or natural cycle patients given hCG only [318]. That a Gn-RH agonist elevates apoptosis in granulosa-lutein cells of follicular aspirates is perhaps not surprising, in light of reports that Gn-RH directly induces apoptosis in cultured granulosa cells of the rat and pig and in human granulosa-lutein cells from IVF patients [319–321]. Importantly, the amount of Gn-RH agonist required to stimulate apoptosis in these reports is considerably lower than that given to patients undergoing controlled ovarian stimulation, suggesting that the use of Gn-RH agonists in assisted reproductive technology programs could both help and hinder the ultimate goal of achieving a successful pregnancy.

Extending Ovarian Function Past the Current Time of Menopause

One of the more intriguing biological questions being asked with respect to the potential usefulness of manipulating apoptosis to benefit human health is rooted in the idea of prolonging normal ovarian function in women as they age. Conceptually, this has been tested in mice based on the assumption that suppressing the rate at which the immature follicle pool is lost from the ovaries via atresia would result in a corresponding lengthening of ovarian life span. The approach taken was to eliminate the function of the proapoptotic protein, Bax, through a gene-targeting strategy. Comparative studies of wild-type and *bax*-null female mice revealed that loss of Bax function does not affect the size of the follicle reserve at birth but significantly reduces the rate of primordial and primary follicle atresia [322]. The end result was in fact a dramatic prolongation of ovarian life span into advanced chronological age. In vivo mating trials revealed that aged *bax*-mutant females fail to become pregnant when housed with young wild-type males, because of the fact that the mutant females, although fully capable of generating large antral follicles, show no evidence of ovulation (i.e., lack of corpora lutea). These findings, which suggest that aging of the hypothalamic-pituitary axis had occurred in these mice, were supported by observations that exogenous gonadotropin injections could be used to complete preovulatory follicle maturation and ovulation, with the ensuing formation of histologically normal corpora lutea. Moreover, some of the oocytes retrieved from aged *bax*-null females by superovulation were competent for fertilization and preimplantation embryogenesis in vitro [322]. Whereas the eventual application, if any, of this type of work in the clinic will be surrounded by controversies—ranging from the possibility of increasing a woman's risk for steroid-dependent cancers to a prolongation of fertile life span into more advanced ages—the availability of an animal model that fails to exhibit ovarian senescence with age has finally provided an opportunity to dissect out the contribution of ovarian aging versus chronological aging to the development of a wide spectrum of health problems known to arise in postmenopausal women.

Preservation of Fertility with S1P-Based Therapies

Although research efforts discussed earlier to control the timing of normal ovarian senescence in women are probably many years away from any practical application in the clinic, studies to understand and alleviate premature ovarian failure and infertility that often occur as a consequence of anticancer treatments may be much closer to clinical trial development. The American Cancer Society has estimated that as many as 1 in 52 women between birth and age 39—that is, the prereproductive and reproductive years—are diagnosed with cancer per year [323]. Although some of these patients will be treated by curative surgery, the majority will be treated using chemotherapeutic drugs, radiotherapy, or a combination of the two. Thus the number of lives affected by this common side effect of anticancer therapy is enormous. Whereas the need for tumor eradication in these patients is clear, the long-term consequences of chemotherapy and radiation on nontarget tissues, such as the ovaries where large numbers of germ cells (oocytes) are also killed, are substantial. Unfortunately, attempts to preserve fertility and ovarian function in female cancer patients have met with little success, caused by a lack of understanding of the mechanisms responsible for ovarian failure [324, 325].

In recent studies we showed that mouse oocytes exposed to doxorubicin, a widely prescribed chemotherapeutic drug, did not degenerate in a pathological fashion but rather initiated apoptosis [22]. That is, the bystander destruction of oocytes caused by anticancer therapies occurs via the same basic mechanism that is deemed clinically desirable in tumor cells. As a consequence, a potential new therapeutic approach to combat premature ovarian failure and infertility in female cancer patients was conceived—target key components of the oocyte death pathway needed for apoptosis to occur [326]. Indeed, using a combination of inhibitor-based approaches and genetically manipulated mice, we subsequently reported that several discrete signaling molecules, including ceramide (generated via ASMase), Bax, and caspases (specifically, caspase-2), are required for the induction of apoptosis in oocytes exposed to this chemotherapeutic drug in vitro [22, 281, 327]. Furthermore, Bax-deficient female mice were shown to be resistant to the ovotoxic effects of doxorubicin treatment in vivo [22].

Despite the mechanistic insight provided by these investigations into how oocytes respond to anticancer therapies, a major hurdle remained before clinical application could be considered a realistic possibility—therapeutic methods designed to protect female germ cells had to be technically feasible for eventual human use. Accordingly, two approaches were initiated: one based on gene therapy and the other on small molecule therapy. In the first study, the promoter of an oocyte-specific gene (*zona pellucida-3 [ZP3]*) was used to direct overexpression of the Bax antagonist, Bcl-2, in transgenic mice [328]. As anticipated, expression of the transgene product was detected only in oocytes. More importantly, the excess Bcl-2 protein in oocytes prevented follicular atresia and conveyed resistance to doxorubicin-induced apoptosis [328].

The second approach, which is clearly more amenable to therapeutic development, was based on our previous work showing that S1P suppresses apoptosis in mouse oocytes exposed to chemotherapeutic drugs in vitro [22]. Previous studies have shown the antiapoptotic effects of S1P in oocytes are pertussis toxin-insensitive [281], indicating that at least $G_{i/o}$-coupled EDG receptor activation was not involved. Moreover, dihydro-S1P, which binds to all S1P receptors identified thus far, does not mimic the antiapoptotic effects of S1P in oocytes [281]. Assuming that S1P would function similarly in vivo, we then tested the efficacy of S1P in preventing radiotherapy-induced ovarian failure in mice [281]. Results from this study showed that the massive oocyte destruction caused by irradiation of young adult female mice could be completely prevented by prior treatment with S1P delivered into the bursal cavity surrounding each ovary. Furthermore, the "protected" oocytes remained fully competent for maturation, fertilization, and preimplantation embryonic development in vitro [281].

It is important to emphasize that the selection of S1P as a therapeutic molecule for these experiments was based not only on data derived from studying its antiapoptotic actions in doxorubicin-exposed oocytes in vitro [22, 281] but also on the intracellular site presumably targeted by S1P [85]. Specifically, previous work had established that suppressing caspase activity in at least some models of Bax-driven apoptosis eventually activates a default pathway of cell death more akin to primary necrosis [329], probably because the mitochondria are still "damaged" by Bax in a caspase-independent manner. In light of studies showing that oocyte death induced by anticancer therapy is Bax-dependent [22], caspases were ruled out as a possible therapeutic target despite the fact that caspase inhibitors can at least temporarily suppress oocyte death induced by chemotherapeutic drugs [22]. Accordingly, to achieve the optimum therapeutic benefit of suppressing apoptosis in oocytes, a "pre-Bax" or "premitochondrial" step in the death program was chosen—use S1P to inhibit the actions of the stress-transducing, proapoptotic molecule ceramide.

In retrospect, such a decision turned out to be important, based on observations from in vivo mating trials conducted recently [26]. In this study, adult female mice irradiated without or with S1P pretreatment were mated with nonirradiated males beginning 2 months postirradiation and thereafter at approximately 2-month intervals, for a total of four matings. Only 50% of vehicle-treated irradiated females delivered litters during the first mating trial, which dropped to 12.5% by the fourth trial. In contrast, all of the S1P-treated irradiated females initially delivered litters, and even after 1 year, 75% of these mice remained fertile [26]. To next determine if the preservation of ovarian function and fertility in irradiated females might result in propagation of genomic damage to the progeny, all F_1 offspring derived from S1P-treated irradiated females were first mated with nonirradiated animals to obtain a colony of F_2 animals. No gross phenotypic or behavioral abnormalities were detected in nearly 500 F_1 and F_2 offspring. Furthermore, no gross histological or biochemical abnormalities were found in F_1 animals euthanized at 18 to 20 months of age or F_2 animals euthanized at 12 to 16 months of age [26].

Nevertheless, it remained possible that subclinical damage had occurred that might be transmitted between generations. To first test for DNA damage in the germline of the F_0 (originally irradiated) females, female mice were examined 8 weeks after treatment with ionizing radiation for evidence of DNA abnormalities in oocytes. There was no significant increase in the percentage of the oocyte population manifesting DNA damage—either chromosomal breaks or nonhomologous chromosome pairing—in S1P-treated irradiated females when compared with vehicle-treated irradiated mice [26], despite the fact that S1P essentially protects the entire oocyte pool from apoptotic death following radiotherapy [281]. These data, which suggest that S1P-treated irradiated female mice retain a much larger reserve of undamaged oocytes for procreation, are in keeping with the fact that the vehicle-treated, but not S1P-treated, irradiated females have compromised fertility. To then evaluate the possibility of transgenerational transmission of DNA damage, the frequency of micronuclei was used as a sensitive indicator of the extent of propagated genomic damage [330–332]. There was no significant difference in the frequency of micronuclei in vehicle-treated versus S1P-treated irradiated mice. Even more important, the frequency of micronuclei in the F_1 and F_2 progeny of the S1P-treated irradiated mothers was similar to that observed in age-matched controls from nonirradiated mothers [26]. Although additional work is needed before a clinical trial can be realistically envisioned, these studies collectively demonstrate that, at least in mice, S1P-based protection of the female germline from radiotherapy does not propagate any discernible genomic damage at the anatomical, histological, biochemical, or cytogenetic level.

Other Strategies for Fertility Preservation in Female Cancer Patients

It should be noted that alternative approaches to preserve fertility in female cancer patients are also being pursued by many laboratories. Most, but not all, of these efforts focus on autotransplantation of frozen-banked ovarian tissue—a procedure first successfully documented in rodents, followed by work in sheep and most recently in humans [294, 325]. However, it is critical to stress that ovarian tissue cryopreservation and grafting has two principal limitations. First, the procedure is designed to provide a short-term restoration of fertility, rather than long-term preservation of ovarian function. In other words, these patients will still suffer from a premature onset of menopause and all of the health complications associated with ovarian failure. Second, in those patients with blood cell-borne cancers, the risk of reintroducing the cancer cells back into the patient posttherapy by ovarian tissue autotransplantation is of concern.

In separate studies, the possibility that Gn-RH agonists could be used to inhibit chemotherapy (cyclophosphamide)-induced ovarian failure in humans has been pursued [324, 325], spurred on by the success of earlier studies conducted with rodents [333, 334] and rhesus monkeys [335]. However, whether or not Gn-RH agonists truly convey any fertility sparing effect in women treated for cancer remains unclear because of the small size and the heterogeneous nature (e.g., wide age range, different chemotherapy protocols) of the patients studied in the limited published trials that exist (for reviews, see [324, 336–339]). Thus comprehensive clinical trials are still needed to determine the efficacy of Gn-RH agonist therapy in preserving fertility and long-term ovarian function following chemotherapy. Furthermore, the protective effect of Gn-RH agonists in the ovaries of females exposed to cytotoxic chemicals does not appear to be a generalized phenomenon, because Gn-RH agonists afford little if any protection to the germline in females exposed to radiotherapy [340]. Whatever the case, it may be that combined therapies using a "cocktail" of S1P and a Gn-RH agonist will ultimately prove to be the most efficacious with respect to broad, long-term protection of the female gonads from the destructive side-effects of chemotherapeutic drugs and radiation.

CONCLUSION

Since the initial identification of apoptosis in the ovary more than 120 years ago [341], tremendous progress has been made in the study of cell death in the female gonads. However, much of what has been described to date with respect to the genes and pathways that regulate ovarian cell death remains correlative, and thus more work is needed to identify those gene products and signaling molecules whose presence and function serves an indispensable role in germ cell, granulosa cell, or luteal cell apoptosis. Although examples of these types of studies already exist—most provided by evaluations of apoptosis gene mutant mice [283]—a lot of work remains to also establish the relevance of data obtained from the study of animal models to human female reproductive function and disease. Nonetheless, the examples cited in this chapter offer hope that this work will indeed have its payoffs, both in terms of a better understanding of the basic biology of human ovarian function and the development of new therapies to combat ovarian failure and infertility. When exactly clinical medicine will benefit from such work is impossible to predict—it has taken more than a decade since the "modern era" of studying apoptosis in the ovary was launched [158, 163, 342] to get to where we are today—but it will happen.

ACKNOWLEDGMENTS

We would like to thank the many past and current members of our laboratories and a long list of colleagues and collaborators for their collective efforts in making this chapter possible. Work we conducted and cited herein was supported by research grants from the National Institutes of Health (R01-AG12279, R01-ES06999, R01-ES08430, R01-HD34226, R01-HD35934) and the U.S. Army Department of Defense (DAMD17-00-1-0567). In addition, we are grateful to the Steven and Michele Kirsch Foundation, the Advanced Medical Research Foundation, the Lalor Foundation, the Sunfield Foundation, and the Vincent Memorial Hospital Board of Trustees for their generous support through the years.

References

1. Melino, G. (2002). The meaning of death. *Cell Death Differ.* 9, 347–348.
2. Jacobson, M. D., Weil, M., and Raff, M. C. (1997). Programmed cell death in animal development. *Cell* 88, 347–354.
3. Baehrecke, E. H. (2002). How death shapes life during development. *Nat. Rev. Mol. Cell. Biol.* 3, 779–787.
4. Rudin, C. M., and Thompson, C. B. (1997). Apoptosis and disease: Regulation and clinical relevance of programmed cell death. *Annu. Rev. Med.* 48, 267–281.
5. Reed, J. C. (1999). Dysregulation of apoptosis in cancer. *J. Clin. Oncol.* 17, 2941–2953.
6. Kerr, J. F., Wyllie, A. H., and Currie, A. R. (1972). Apoptosis: A basic biological phenomenon with wide-ranging implications in tissue kinetics. *Br. J. Cancer* 26, 239–257.
7. Jamison, J. M., Gilloteaux, J., Taper, H. S., Calderon, P. B., and Summers, J. L. (2002). Autoschizis: A novel cell death. *Biochem. Pharmacol.* 63, 1773–1783.

8. Frisch, S. M., and Screaton, R. A. (2001). Anoikis mechanisms. *Curr. Opin. Cell Biol.* 13, 555–562.
9. Chen, Y., Douglass, T., Jeffes, E. W., Xu, Q., Williams, C. C., Arpajirakul, N., Delgado, C., Kleinman, M., Sanchez, R., Dan, Q., Kim, R. C., Wepsic, H. T., and Jadus, M. R. (2002). Living T9 glioma cells expressing membrane macrophage colony-stimulating factor produce immediate tumor destruction by polymorphonuclear leukocytes and macrophages via a "paraptosis"-induced pathway that promotes systemic immunity against intracranial T9 gliomas. *Blood* 100, 1373–1380.
10. Bursch, W. (2001). The autophagosomal-lysosomal compartment in programmed cell death. *Cell Death Differ.* 8, 569–581.
11. McConkey, D. J. (1998). Biochemical determinants of apoptosis and necrosis. *Toxicol. Lett.* 99, 157–168.
12. Bursch, W., Ellinger, A., Gerner, C., Frohwein, U., and Schulte-Hermann, R. (2000). Programmed cell death (PCD). Apoptosis, autophagic PCD, or others? *Ann. N. Y. Acad. Sci.* 926, 1–12.
13. Liu, Q. A., and Hengartner, M. O. (1999). The molecular mechanism of programmed cell death in *C. elegans. Ann. N. Y. Acad. Sci.* 887, 92–104.
14. Tittel, J. N., and Steller, H. (2000). A comparison of programmed cell death between species. *Genome Biol.* 1, Review S0003.
15. Richardson, H., and Kumar, S. (2002). Death to flies: *Drosophila* as a model system to study programmed cell death. *J. Immunol. Methods* 265, 21–38.
16. Martimbeau, S., and Tilly, J. L. (1997). Physiological cell death in endocrine-dependent tissues: An ovarian perspective. *Clin. Endocrinol. (Oxf.)* 46, 241–254.
17. Tilly, J. L. (2001). Commuting the death sentence: How oocytes strive to survive. *Nat. Rev. Mol. Cell. Biol.* 2, 838–848.
18. Davis, J. S., and Rueda, B. R. (2002). The corpus luteum: An ovarian structure with maternal instincts and suicidal tendencies. *Front. Biosci.* 7, d1949–d1978.
19. Billis, W., Fuks, Z., and Kolesnick, R. (1998). Signaling in and regulation of ionizing radiation-induced apoptosis in endothelial cells. *Rec. Prog. Hormone Res.* 53, 85–92.
20. Schuler, M., and Green, D. R. (2001). Mechanisms of p53-dependent apoptosis. *Biochem. Soc. Trans.* 29, 684–688.
21. Mor, G., Straszewski, S., and Kamsteeg, M. (2002). Role of the Fas/Fas ligand system in female reproductive organs: Survival and apoptosis. *Biochem. Pharmacol.* 64, 1305–1315.
22. Perez, G. I., Knudson, C. M., Leykin, L., Korsmeyer, S. J., and Tilly, J. L. (1997). Apoptosis-associated signaling pathways are required for chemotherapy-mediated female germ cell destruction. *Nat. Med.* 3, 1228–1232.
23. Zhou, L., Yuan, R., and Serggio, L. (2003). Molecular mechanisms of irradiation-induced apoptosis. *Front. Biosci.* 8, d9–d19.
24. Fleury, C., Mignotte, B., and Vayssiere, J. L. (2002). Mitochondrial reactive oxygen species in cell death signaling. *Biochimie* 84, 131–141.
25. Kim, R., Tanabe, K., Uchida, Y., Emi, M., Inoue, H., and Toge, T. (2002). Current status of the molecular mechanisms of anticancer drug-induced apoptosis. The contribution of molecular-level analysis to cancer chemotherapy. *Cancer Chemother. Pharmacol.* 50, 343–352.
26. Paris, F., Perez, G. I., Fuks, Z., Haimovitz-Friedman, A., Nguyen, H., Bose, M., Ilagan, A., Hunt, P. A., Morgan, W. F., Tilly, J. L., and Kolesnick, R. (2002). Sphingosine 1-phosphate preserves fertility in irradiated female mice without propagating genomic damage in offspring. *Nat. Med.* 8, 901–902.
27. Matikainen, T., Perez, G. I., Jurisicova, A., Pru, J. K., Schlezinger, J. J., Ryu, H. Y., Laine, J., Sakai, T., Korsmeyer, S. J., Casper, R. F., Sherr, D. H., and Tilly, J. L. (2001). Aromatic hydrocarbon receptor-driven *Bax* gene expression is required for premature ovarian failure caused by biohazardous environmental chemicals. *Nat. Genet.* 28, 355–360.
28. Johnson, A. L., Bridgham, J. T., Wilder, J. A., Hollocher, H., and Johnson, A. L. (2003). All in the family: Evolutionary and functional relationships among vertebrate death receptors. *Cell Death Differ.* 10, 19–25.
29. Ashkenazi, A., and Dixit, V. M. (1999). Apoptosis control by death and decoy receptors. *Curr. Opin. Cell Biol.* 11, 255–260.
30. Nagata, S. (1997). Apoptosis by death factor. *Cell* 88, 355–365.
31. Krammer, P. H. (2000). CD95's deadly mission in the immune system. *Nature* 407, 789–795.
32. Scaffidi, C., Fulda, S., Srinivasan, A., Friesen, C., Li, F., Tomaselli, K. J., Debatin, K. M., Krammer, P. H., and Peter, M. E. (1998). Two CD95 (APO-1/Fas) signaling pathways. *EMBO J.* 17, 1675–1687.
33. Cremesti, A., Paris, F., Grassme, H., Holler, N., Tschopp, J., Fuks, Z., Gulbins, E., and Kolesnick, R. (2001). Ceramide enables fas to cap and kill. *J. Biol. Chem.* 276, 23954–23961.
34. Moreno, E., Yan, M., and Basler, K. (2002). Evolution of TNF signaling mechanisms: JNK-dependent apoptosis triggered by Eiger, the Drosophila homolog of the TNF superfamily. *Curr. Biol.* 12, 1263–1268.
35. Zhou, T., Mountz, J. D., and Kimberly, R. P. (2002). Immunobiology of tumor necrosis factor receptor superfamily. *Immunol. Res.* 26, 323–336.
36. Gupta, S. (2003). Molecular signaling in death receptor and mitochondrial pathways of apoptosis. *Int. J. Oncol.* 22, 15–20.
37. Wajant, H., Pfizenmaier, K., and Scheurich, P. (2003). Nonapoptotic Fas signaling. *Cytokine Growth Factor Rev.* 14, 53–66.
38. Chung, J. Y., Park, Y. C., Ye, H., and Wu, H. (2002). All TRAFs are not created equal: Common and distinct molecular mechanisms of TRAF-mediated signal transduction. *J. Cell. Sci.* 115, 679–688.
39. Xia, P., Wang, L., Moretti, P. A., Albanese, N., Chai, F., Pitson, S. M., D'Andrea, R. J., Gamble, J. R., and Vadas, M. A. (2002). Sphingosine kinase interacts with TRAF2 and dissects tumor necrosis factor-alpha signaling. *J. Biol. Chem.* 277, 7996–8003.
40. Paludan, S. R. (2000). Synergistic action of pro-inflammatory agents: Cellular and molecular aspects. *J. Leukoc. Biol.* 67, 18–25.
41. Arzt, E., Kovalovsky, D., Igaz, L. M., Costas, M., Plazas, P., Refojo, D., Paez-Pereda, M., Reul, J. M., Stalla, G., and Holsboer, F. (2000). Functional cross-talk among cytokines,

T-cell receptor, and glucocorticoid receptor transcriptional activity and action. *Ann. N. Y. Acad. Sci.* 917, 672–677.
42. McKay, L. I., and Cidlowski, J. A. (1998). Cross-talk between nuclear factor-kappa B and the steroid hormone receptors: Mechanisms of mutual antagonism. *Mol. Endocrinol.* 12, 45–56.
43. Harper, S. J., and LoGrasso, P. (2001). Signalling for survival and death in neurones: The role of stress-activated kinases, JNK and p38. *Cell Signal.* 13, 299–310.
44. Peyssonnaux, C., and Eychene, A. (2001). The Raf/MEK/ERK pathway: New concepts of activation. *Biol. Cell* 93, 53–62.
45. Ballif, B. A., and Blenis, J. (2001). Molecular mechanisms mediating mammalian mitogen-activated protein kinase (MAPK) kinase (MEK)-MAPK cell survival signals. *Cell Growth Differ.* 12, 397–408.
46. Weston, C. R., Lambright, D. G., and Davis, R. J. (2002). Signal transduction. MAP kinase signaling specificity. *Science* 296, 2345–2347.
47. Davis, R. J. (2000). Signal transduction by the JNK group of MAP kinases. *Cell* 103, 239–252.
48. Ichijo, H. (1999). From receptors to stress-activated MAP kinases. *Oncogene* 18, 6087–6093.
49. Basu, S., and Kolesnick, R. (1998). Stress signals for apoptosis: Ceramide and c-Jun kinase. *Oncogene* 17, 3277–3285.
50. Lin, A. (2003). Activation of the JNK signaling pathway: Breaking the brake on apoptosis. *Bioessays* 25, 17–24.
51. Cardone, M. H., Salvesen, G. S., Widmann, C., Johnson, G., and Frisch, S. M. (1997). The regulation of anoikis: MEKK-1 activation requires cleavage by caspases. *Cell* 90, 315–323.
52. Yang, X., Khosravi-Far, R., Chang, H. Y., and Baltimore, D. (1997). Daxx, a novel Fas-binding protein that activates JNK and apoptosis. *Cell* 89, 1067–1076.
53. Fuchs, S. Y., Adler, V., Pincus, M. R., and Ronai, Z. (1998). MEKK1/JNK signaling stabilizes and activates p53. *Proc. Natl. Acad. Sci. USA* 95, 10541–10546.
54. Kuan, C. Y., Yang, D. D., Samanta Roy, D. R., Davis, R. J., Rakic, P., and Flavell, R. A. (1999). The Jnk1 and Jnk2 protein kinases are required for regional specific apoptosis during early brain development. *Neuron* 22, 667–676.
55. Tournier, C., Hess, P., Yang, D. D., Xu, J., Turner, T. K., Nimnual, A., Bar-Sagi, D., Jones, S. N., Flavell, R. A., and Davis, R. J. (2000). Requirement of JNK for stress-induced activation of the cytochrome c-mediated death pathway. *Science* 288, 870–874.
56. Burgering, B. M., and Coffer, P. J. (1995). Protein kinase B (c-Akt) in phosphatidylinositol-3-OH kinase signal transduction. *Nature* 376, 599–602.
57. Robinson-White, A., and Stratakis, C. A. (2002). Protein kinase A signaling: "Cross-talk" with other pathways in endocrine cells. *Ann. N. Y. Acad. Sci.* 968, 256–270.
58. Datta, S. R., Brunet, A., and Greenberg, M. E. (1999). Cellular survival: A play in three Akts. *Genes Dev.* 13, 2905–2927.
59. Cantley, L. C. (2002). The phosphoinositide 3-kinase pathway. *Science* 296, 1655–1657.
60. Toker, A., and Newton, A. C. (2000). Cellular signaling: Pivoting around PDK-1. *Cell* 103, 185–188.
61. Cross, D. A., Alessi, D. R., Cohen, P., Andjelkovich, M., and Hemmings, B. A. (1995). Inhibition of glycogen synthase kinase-3 by insulin mediated by protein kinase B. *Nature* 378, 785–789.
62. Kohn, A. D., Summers, S. A., Birnbaum, M. J., and Roth, R. A. (1996). Expression of a constitutively active Akt Ser/Thr kinase in 3T3-L1 adipocytes stimulates glucose uptake and glucose transporter 4 translocation. *J. Biol. Chem.* 271, 31372–31378.
63. Brunet, A., Bonni, A., Zigmond, M. J., Lin, M. Z., Juo, P., Hu, L. S., Anderson, M. J., Arden, K. C., Blenis, J., and Greenberg, M. E. (1999). Akt promotes cell survival by phosphorylating and inhibiting a Forkhead transcription factor. *Cell* 96, 857–868.
64. Zha, J., Harada, H., Yang, E., Jockel, J., and Korsmeyer, S. J. (1996). Serine phosphorylation of death agonist BAD in response to survival factor results in binding to 14–3-3 not BCL-X(L). *Cell* 87, 619–628.
65. Zhou, X. M., Liu, Y., Payne, G., Lutz, R. J., and Chittenden, T. (2000). Growth factors inactivate the cell death promoter BAD by phosphorylation of its BH3 domain on Ser155. *J. Biol. Chem.* 275, 25046–25051.
66. Cardone, M. H., Roy, N., Stennicke, H. R., Salvesen, G. S., Franke, T. F., Stanbridge, E., Frisch, S., and Reed, J. C. (1998). Regulation of cell death protease caspase-9 by phosphorylation. *Science* 282, 1318–1321.
67. Ohanian, J., and Ohanian, V. (2001). Sphingolipids in mammalian cell signalling. *Cell. Mol. Life Sci.* 58, 2053–2068.
68. Ruvolo, P. P. (2001). Ceramide regulates cellular homeostasis via diverse stress signaling pathways. *Leukemia* 15, 1153–1160.
69. el Bawab, S., Mao, C., Obeid, L. M., and Hannun, Y. A. (2002). Ceramidases in the regulation of ceramide levels and function. *Subcell. Biochem.* 36, 187–205.
70. Cuvillier, O., Pirianov, G., Kleuser, B., Vanek, P. G., Coso, O. A., Gutkind, S., and Spiegel, S. (1996). Suppression of ceramide-mediated programmed cell death by sphingosine-1-phosphate. *Nature* 381, 800–803.
71. Spiegel, S. (1999). Sphingosine 1-phosphate: A prototype of a new class of second messengers. *J. Leukoc. Biol.* 65, 341–344.
72. Verheij, M., Bose, R., Lin, X. H., Yao, B., Jarvis, W. D., Grant, S., Birrer, M. J., Szabo, E., Zon, L. I., Kyriakis, J. M., Haimovitz-Friedman, A., Fuks, Z., and Kolesnick, R. N. (1996). Requirement for ceramide-initiated SAPK/JNK signalling in stress-induced apoptosis. *Nature* 380, 75–79.
73. Zundel, W., and Giaccia, A. (1998). Inhibition of the anti-apoptotic PI(3)K/Akt/Bad pathway by stress. *Genes Dev.* 12, 1941–1946.
74. Summers, S. A., Garza, L. A., Zhou, H., and Birnbaum, M. J. (1998). Regulation of insulin-stimulated glucose transporter GLUT4 translocation and Akt kinase activity by ceramide. *Mol. Cell. Biol.* 18, 5457–5464.
75. Salinas, M., Lopez-Valdaliso, R., Martin, D., Alvarez, A., and Cuadrado, A. (2000). Inhibition of PKB/Akt1 by C2-ceramide involves activation of ceramide-activated protein phosphatase in PC12 cells. *Mol. Cell. Neurosci.* 15, 156–169.
76. Dobrowsky, R. T. (2000). Sphingolipid signalling domains floating on rafts or buried in caves? *Cell Signal.* 12, 81–90.
77. Cremesti, A. E., Goni, F. M., and Kolesnick, R. (2002). Role of sphingomyelinase and ceramide in modulating rafts: Do

biophysical properties determine biologic outcome? *FEBS Lett.* 531, 47–53.

78. Waugh, M. G., Minogue, S., Anderson, J. S., dos Santos, M., and Hsuan, J. J. (2001). Signalling and non-caveolar rafts. *Biochem. Soc. Trans.* 29, 509–511.
79. Kolesnick, R. N., Goni, F. M., and Alonso, A. (2000). Compartmentalization of ceramide signaling: Physical foundations and biological effects. *J. Cell. Physiol.* 184, 285–300.
80. Martin, D., Salinas, M., Fujita, N., Tsuruo, T., and Cuadrado, A. (2002). Ceramide and reactive oxygen species generated by H2O2 induce caspase-3-independent degradation of Akt/protein kinase B. *J. Biol. Chem.* 277, 42943–42952.
81. Goswami, R., Kilkus, J., Dawson, S. A., and Dawson, G. (1999). Overexpression of Akt (protein kinase B) confers protection against apoptosis and prevents formation of ceramide in response to pro-apoptotic stimuli. *J. Neurosci. Res.* 57, 884–893.
82. Pastorino, J. G., Tafani, M., Rothman, R. J., Marcinkeviciute, A., Hoek, J. B., Farber, J. L., and Marcineviciute, A. (1999). Functional consequences of the sustained or transient activation by Bax of the mitochondrial permeability transition pore. *J. Biol. Chem.* 274, 31734–31739.
83. Ghafourifar, P., Klein, S. D., Schucht, O., Schenk, U., Pruschy, M., Rocha, S., and Richter, C. (1999). Ceramide induces cytochrome c release from isolated mitochondria. Importance of mitochondrial redox state. *J. Biol. Chem.* 274, 6080–6084.
84. Siskind, L. J., Kolesnick, R. N., and Colombini, M. (2002). Ceramide channels increase the permeability of the mitochondrial outer membrane to small proteins. *J. Biol. Chem.* 277, 26796–26803.
85. Payne, S. G., Milstien, S., and Spiegel, S. (2002). Sphingosine-1-phosphate: Dual messenger functions. *FEBS Lett.* 531, 54–57.
86. Hla, T. (2001). Sphingosine 1-phosphate receptors. *Prostaglandins* 64, 135–142.
87. Siehler, S., Wang, Y., Fan, X., Windh, R. T., and Manning, D. R. (2001). Sphingosine 1-phosphate activates nuclear factor-kappa B through Edg receptors. Activation through Edg-3 and Edg-5, but not Edg-1, in human embryonic kidney 293 cells. *J. Biol. Chem.* 276, 48733–48739.
88. Spiegel, S., and Milstien, S. (2002). Sphingosine 1-phosphate, a key cell signaling molecule. *J. Biol. Chem.* 277, 25851–25854.
89. Goetzl, E. J., Kong, Y., and Mei, B. (1999). Lysophosphatidic acid and sphingosine 1-phosphate protection of T cells from apoptosis in association with suppression of Bax. *J. Immunol.* 162, 2049–2056.
90. Cuvillier, O., Nava, V. E., Murthy, S. K., Edsall, L. C., Levade, T., Milstien, S., and Spiegel, S. (2001). Sphingosine generation, cytochrome c release, and activation of caspase-7 in doxorubicin-induced apoptosis of MCF7 breast adenocarcinoma cells. *Cell Death Differ.* 8, 162–171.
91. Kwon, Y. G., Min, J. K., Kim, K. M., Lee, D. J., Billiar, T. R., and Kim, Y. M. (2001). Sphingosine 1-phosphate protects human umbilical vein endothelial cells from serum-deprived apoptosis by nitric oxide production. *J. Biol. Chem.* 276, 10627–10633.
92. Hannun, Y. A., and Obeid, L. M. (2002). The ceramide-centric universe of lipid-mediated cell regulation: Stress encounters of the lipid kind. *J. Biol. Chem.* 277, 25847–25850.
93. Ferri, K. F., and Kroemer, G. (2001). Mitochondria—the suicide organelles. *Bioessays* 23, 111–115.
94. Shi, Y. (2002). Apoptosome: The cellular engine for the activation of caspase-9. *Structure (Camb.)* 10, 285–288.
95. van Loo, G., Saelens, X., van Gurp, M., MacFarlane, M., Martin, S. J., and Vandenabeele, P. (2002). The role of mitochondrial factors in apoptosis: A Russian roulette with more than one bullet. *Cell Death Differ.* 9, 1031–1042.
96. Kroemer, G., and Reed, J. C. (2000). Mitochondrial control of cell death. *Nat. Med.* 6, 513–519.
97. Ravagnan, L., Roumier, T., and Kroemer, G. (2002). Mitochondria, the killer organelles and their weapons. *J. Cell. Physiol.* 192, 131–137.
98. Schendel, S. L., Montal, M., and Reed, J. C. (1998). Bcl-2 family proteins as ion-channels. *Cell Death Differ.* 5, 372–380.
99. Igaki, T., Kanuka, H., Inohara, N., Sawamoto, K., Nunez, G., Okano, H., and Miura, M. (2000). Drob-1, a Drosophila member of the Bcl-2/CED-9 family that promotes cell death. *Proc. Natl. Acad. Sci. USA* 97, 662–667.
100. Shi, Y. (2001). A structural view of mitochondria-mediated apoptosis. *Nat. Struct. Biol.* 8, 394–401.
101. Gross, A., McDonnell, J. M., and Korsmeyer, S. J. (1999). BCL-2 family members and the mitochondria in apoptosis. *Genes Dev.* 13, 1899–1911.
102. Reed, J. C. (2000). Mechanisms of apoptosis. *Am. J. Pathol.* 157, 1415–1430.
103. Antonsson, B. (2001). Bax and other pro-apoptotic Bcl-2 family "killer-proteins" and their victim the mitochondrion. *Cell Tissue Res.* 306, 347–361.
104. Adams, J. M., and Cory, S. (2001). Life-or-death decisions by the Bcl-2 protein family. *Trends Biochem. Sci.* 26, 61–66.
105. Puthalakath, H., and Strasser, A. (2002). Keeping killers on a tight leash: Transcriptional and post-translational control of the pro-apoptotic activity of BH3-only proteins. *Cell Death Differ.* 9, 505–512.
106. Korsmeyer, S. J., Shutter, J. R., Veis, D. J., Merry, D. E., and Oltvai, Z. N. (1993). Bcl-2/Bax: A rheostat that regulates an anti-oxidant pathway and cell death. *Semin. Cancer Biol.* 4, 327–332.
107. Zamzami, N., Brenner, C., Marzo, I., Susin, S. A., and Kroemer, G. (1998). Subcellular and submitochondrial mode of action of Bcl-2-like oncoproteins. *Oncogene* 16, 2265–2282.
108. Huang, D. C., and Strasser, A. (2000). BH3-only proteins-essential initiators of apoptotic cell death. *Cell* 103, 839–842.
109. Castelli, J. C., Hassel, B. A., Maran, A., Paranjape, J., Hewitt, J. A., Li, X. L., Hsu, Y. T., Silverman, R. H., and Youle, R. J. (1998). The role of 2′-5′ oligoadenylate-activated ribonuclease L in apoptosis. *Cell Death Differ.* 5, 313–320.
110. Zong, W. X., Lindsten, T., Ross, A. J., MacGregor, G. R., and Thompson, C. B. (2001). BH3-only proteins that bind pro-survival Bcl-2 family members fail to induce apoptosis in the absence of Bax and Bak. *Genes Dev.* 15, 1481–1486.
111. Kim, M. R., Pru, J. K., and Tilly, J. L. (2002). Characterization of BH3-only Bcl-2 family members in the mouse ovary by gene array and northern blot analysis. *Proceedings of the 84th Annual Meeting of the Endocrine Society,* San Francisco, 419.

112. Strasser, A., Puthalakath, H., Bouillet, P., Huang, D. C., O'Connor, L., O'Reilly, L. A., Cullen, L., Cory, S., and Adams, J. M. (2000). The role of Bim, a proapoptotic BH3-only member of the Bcl-2 family in cell-death control. *Ann. N. Y. Acad. Sci.* 917, 541–548.
113. Puthalakath, H., Villunger, A., O'Reilly, L. A., Beaumont, J. G., Coultas, L., Cheney, R. E., Huang, D. C., and Strasser, A. (2001). Bmf: a proapoptotic BH3-only protein regulated by interaction with the myosin V actin motor complex, activated by anoikis. *Science* 293, 1829–1832.
114. Whitfield, J., Neame, S. J., Paquet, L., Bernard, O., and Ham, J. (2001). Dominant-negative c-Jun promotes neuronal survival by reducing BIM expression and inhibiting mitochondrial cytochrome c release. *Neuron* 29, 629–643.
115. Shinjyo, T., Kuribara, R., Inukai, T., Hosoi, H., Kinoshita, T., Miyajima, A., Houghton, P. J., Look, A. T., Ozawa, K., and Inaba, T. (2001). Downregulation of Bim, a proapoptotic relative of Bcl-2, is a pivotal step in cytokine-initiated survival signaling in murine hematopoietic progenitors. *Mol. Cell. Biol.* 21, 854–864.
116. Pru, J. K., and Tilly, J. L. (2002). Genomic plasticity in cell death susceptibility. *Cell Death Differ.* 9, 96–98.
117. Zha, J., Weiler, S., Oh, K. J., Wei, M. C., and Korsmeyer, S. J. (2000). Posttranslational N-myristoylation of BID as a molecular switch for targeting mitochondria and apoptosis. *Science* 290, 1761–1765.
118. Tan, K. O., Tan, K. M., Chan, S. L., Yee, K. S., Bevort, M., Ang, K. C., and Yu, V. C. (2001). MAP-1, a novel proapoptotic protein containing a BH3-like motif that associates with Bax through its Bcl-2 homology domains. *J. Biol. Chem.* 276, 2802–2807.
119. Nakano, K., and Vousden, K. H. (2001). PUMA, a novel proapoptotic gene, is induced by p53. *Mol. Cell* 7, 683–694.
120. Wu, X., and Deng, Y. (2002). Bax and BH3-domain-only proteins in p53-mediated apoptosis. *Front. Biosci.* 7, d151–d156.
121. Chen, G., Cizeau, J., Vande Velde, C., Park, J. H., Bozek, G., Bolton, J., Shi, L., Dubik, D., and Greenberg, A. (1999). Nix and Nip3 form a subfamily of pro-apoptotic mitochondrial proteins. *J. Biol. Chem.* 274, 7–10.
122. Zamzami, N., Susin, S. A., Marchetti, P., Hirsch, T., Gomez-Monterrey, I., Castedo, M., and Kroemer, G. (1996). Mitochondrial control of nuclear apoptosis. *J. Exp. Med.* 183, 1533–1544.
123. Joza, N., Susin, S. A., Daugas, E., Stanford, W. L., Cho, S. K., Li, C. Y., Sasaki, T., Elia, A. J., Cheng, H. Y., Ravagnan, L., Ferri, K. F., Zamzami, N., Wakeham, A., Hakem, R., Yoshida, H., Kong, Y. Y., Mak, T. W., Zuniga-Pflucker, J. C., Kroemer, G., and Penninger, J. M. (2001). Essential role of the mitochondrial apoptosis-inducing factor in programmed cell death. *Nature* 410, 549–554.
124. Hegde, R., Srinivasula, S. M., Zhang, Z., Wassell, R., Mukattash, R., Cilenti, L., DuBois, G., Lazebnik, Y., Zervos, A. S., Fernandes-Alnemri, T., and Alnemri, E. S. (2002). Identification of Omi/HtrA2 as a mitochondrial apoptotic serine protease that disrupts inhibitor of apoptosis protein-caspase interaction. *J. Biol. Chem.* 277, 432–438.
125. Suzuki, Y., Imai, Y., Nakayama, H., Takahashi, K., Takio, K., and Takahashi, R. (2001). A serine protease, HtrA2, is released from the mitochondria and interacts with XIAP, inducing cell death. *Mol. Cell* 8, 613–621.
126. Li, L. Y., Luo, X., and Wang, X. (2001). Endonuclease G is an apoptotic DNase when released from mitochondria. *Nature* 412, 95–99.
127. Susin, S. A., Lorenzo, H. K., Zamzami, N., Marzo, I., Brenner, C., Larochette, N., Prevost, M. C., Alzari, P. M., and Kroemer, G. (1999). Mitochondrial release of caspase-2 and -9 during the apoptotic process. *J. Exp. Med.* 189, 381–394.
128. Martin, S. J. (2002). Destabilizing influences in apoptosis: Sowing the seeds of IAP destruction. *Cell* 109, 793–796.
129. Salvesen, G. S., and Duckett, C. S. (2002). IAP proteins: Blocking the road to death's door. *Nat. Rev. Mol. Cell. Biol.* 3, 401–410.
130. Sun, C., Cai, M., Meadows, R. P., Xu, N., Gunasekera, A. H., Herrmann, J., Wu, J. C., and Fesik, S. W. (2000). NMR structure and mutagenesis of the third BIR domain of the inhibitor of apoptosis protein XIAP. *J. Biol. Chem.* 275, 33777–33781.
131. Takahashi, R., Deveraux, Q., Tamm, I., Welsh, K., Assa-Munt, N., Salvesen, G. S., and Reed, J. C. (1998). A single BIR domain of XIAP sufficient for inhibiting caspases. *J. Biol. Chem.* 273, 7787–7790.
132. Verhagen, A. M., and Vaux, D. L. (2002). Cell death regulation by the mammalian IAP antagonist DIABLO/Smac. *Apoptosis* 7, 163–166.
133. Du, C., Fang, M., Li, Y., Li, L., and Wang, X. (2000). Smac, a mitochondrial protein that promotes cytochrome c-dependent caspase activation by eliminating IAP inhibition. *Cell* 102, 33–42.
134. Verhagen, A. M., Ekert, P. G., Pakusch, M., Silke, J., Connolly, L. M., Reid, G. E., Moritz, R. L., Simpson, R. J., and Vaux, D. L. (2000). Identification of DIABLO, a mammalian protein that promotes apoptosis by binding to and antagonizing IAP proteins. *Cell* 102, 43–53.
135. Ekert, P. G., Silke, J., Hawkins, C. J., Verhagen, A. M., and Vaux, D. L. (2001). DIABLO promotes apoptosis by removing MIHA/XIAP from processed caspase 9. *J. Cell. Biol.* 152, 483–490.
136. Vernooy, S. Y., Chow, V., Su, J., Verbrugghe, K., Yang, J., Cole, S., Olson, M. R., and Hay, B. A. (2002). *Drosophila* Bruce can potently suppress Rpr- and Grim-dependent but not Hid-dependent cell death. *Curr. Biol.* 12, 1164–1168.
137. Verhagen, A. M., Coulson, E. J., and Vaux, D. L. (2001). Inhibitor of apoptosis proteins and their relatives: IAPs and other BIRPs. *Genome Biol.* 2, S3009.
138. Fraser, A. G., James, C., Evan, G. I., and Hengartner, M. O. (1999). *Caenorhabditis elegans* inhibitor of apoptosis protein (IAP) homologue BIR-1 plays a conserved role in cytokinesis. *Curr. Biol.* 9, 292–301.
139. Harlin, H., Reffey, S. B., Duckett, C. S., Lindsten, T., and Thompson, C. B. (2001). Characterization of XIAP-deficient mice. *Mol. Cell. Biol.* 21, 3604–3608.
140. Uren, A. G., Wong, L., Pakusch, M., Fowler, K. J., Burrows, F. J., Vaux, D. L., and Choo, K. H. (2000). Survivin and the inner centromere protein INCENP show similar cell-cycle localization and gene knockout phenotype. *Curr. Biol.* 10, 1319–1328.
141. Li, P., Nijhawan, D., Budihardjo, I., Srinivasula, S. M., Ahmad, M., Alnemri, E. S., and Wang, X. (1997). Cytochrome c and dATP-dependent formation of Apaf-1/caspase-9 complex initiates an apoptotic protease cascade. *Cell* 91, 479–489.

142. Salvesen, G. S., and Dixit, V. M. (1999). Caspase activation: The induced-proximity model. *Proc. Natl. Acad. Sci. USA* 96, 10964–10967.
143. Cain, K., Bratton, S. B., and Cohen, G. M. (2002). The Apaf-1 apoptosome: A large caspase-activating complex. *Biochimie* 84, 203–214.
144. Kuida, K., Haydar, T. F., Kuan, C. Y., Gu, Y., Taya, C., Karasuyama, H., Su, M. S., Rakic, P., and Flavell, R. A. (1998). Reduced apoptosis and cytochrome c-mediated caspase activation in mice lacking caspase 9. *Cell* 94, 325–337.
145. Cecconi, F., Alvarez-Bolado, G., Meyer, B. I., Roth, K. A., and Gruss, P. (1998). Apaf1 (CED-4 homolog) regulates programmed cell death in mammalian development. *Cell* 94, 727–737.
146. Shi, Y. (2002). Mechanisms of caspase activation and inhibition during apoptosis. *Mol. Cell* 9, 459–470.
147. Zheng, T. S., Hunot, S., Kuida, K., and Flavell, R. A. (1999). Caspase knockouts: Matters of life and death. *Cell Death Differ.* 6, 1043–1053.
148. Rao, R. V., Castro-Obregon, S., Frankowski, H., Schuler, M., Stoka, V., del Rio, G., Bredesen, D. E., and Ellerby, H. M. (2002). Coupling endoplasmic reticulum stress to the cell death program. An Apaf-1-independent intrinsic pathway. *J. Biol. Chem.* 277, 21836–21842.
149. Harvey, N. L., and Kumar, S. (1998). The role of caspases in apoptosis. *Adv. Biochem. Eng. Biotechnol.* 62, 107–128.
150. Conradt, B. (2002). With a little help from your friends: Cells don't die alone. *Nat. Cell. Biol.* 4, E139–E143.
151. Franc, N. C. (2002). Phagocytosis of apoptotic cells in mammals, *Caenorhabditis elegans* and *Drosophila melanogaster*: Molecular mechanisms and physiological consequences. *Front. Biosci.* 7, d1298–d1313.
152. Zheng, T. S., Hunot, S., Kuida, K., Momoi, T., Srinivasan, A., Nicholson, D. W., Lazebnik, Y., and Flavell, R. A. (2000). Deficiency in caspase-9 or caspase-3 induces compensatory caspase activation. *Nat. Med.* 6, 1241–1247.
153. Tilly, J. L. (1996). The molecular basis of ovarian cell death during germ cell attrition, follicular atresia, and luteolysis. *Front. Biosci.* 1, d1–d11.
154. Tilly, J. L. (1996). Apoptosis and ovarian function. *Rev. Reprod.* 1, 162–172.
155. Amsterdam, A., and Selvaraj, N. (1997). Control of differentiation, transformation, and apoptosis in granulosa cells by oncogenes, oncoviruses, and tumor suppressor genes. *Endocr. Rev.* 18, 435–461.
156. Asselin, E., Xiao, C. W., Wang, Y. F., and Tsang, B. K. (2000). Mammalian follicular development and atresia: Role of apoptosis. *Biol. Signals Recept.* 9, 87–95.
157. Johnson, A. L. (2000). Granulosa cell apoptosis: Conservation of cell signaling in an avian ovarian model system. *Biol. Signals Recept.* 9, 96–101.
158. Tilly, J. L., Kowalski, K. I., Johnson, A. L., and Hsueh, A. J. (1991). Involvement of apoptosis in ovarian follicular atresia and postovulatory regression. *Endocrinology* 129, 2799–2801.
159. Tilly, J. L., Kowalski, K. I., Schomberg, D. W., and Hsueh, A. J. (1992). Apoptosis in atretic ovarian follicles is associated with selective decreases in messenger ribonucleic acid transcripts for gonadotropin receptors and cytochrome P450 aromatase. *Endocrinology* 131, 1670–1676.
160. Palumbo, A., and Yeh, J. (1994). In situ localization of apoptosis in the rat ovary during follicular atresia. *Biol. Reprod.* 51, 888–895.
161. Foghi, A., Ravandi, A., Teerds, K. J., Van Der Donk, H., Kuksis, A., and Dorrington, J. (1998). Fas-induced apoptosis in rat thecal/interstitial cells signals through sphingomyelin-ceramide pathway. *Endocrinology* 139, 2041–2047.
162. Tajima, K., Orisaka, M., Hosokawa, K., Amsterdam, A., and Kotsuji, F. (2002). Effects of ovarian theca cells on apoptosis and proliferation of granulosa cells: Changes during bovine follicular maturation. *Biol. Reprod.* 66, 1635–1639.
163. Hughes, Jr., F. M., and Gorospe, W. C. (1991). Biochemical identification of apoptosis (programmed cell death) in granulosa cells: Evidence for a potential mechanism underlying follicular atresia. *Endocrinology* 129, 2415–2422.
164. Tilly, J. L., Tilly, K. I., Kenton, M. L., and Johnson, A. L. (1995). Expression of members of the *bcl-2* gene family in the immature rat ovary: Equine chorionic gonadotropin-mediated inhibition of granulosa cell apoptosis is associated with decreased *bax* and constitutive *bcl-2* and $bcl\text{-}x_{long}$ messenger ribonucleic acid levels. *Endocrinology* 136, 232–241.
165. Matikainen, T., Perez, G. I., Zheng, T. S., Kluzak, T. R., Rueda, B. R., Flavell, R. A., and Tilly, J. L. (2001). *Caspase-3* gene knockout defines cell lineage specificity for programmed cell death signaling in the ovary. *Endocrinology* 142, 2468–2480.
166. Markstrom, E., Svensson, E., Shao, R., Svanberg, B., and Billig, H. (2002). Survival factors regulating ovarian apoptosis—dependence on follicle differentiation. *Reproduction* 123, 23–30.
167. Basini, G., Mainardi, G. L., Bussolati, S., and Tamanini, C. (2002). Steroidogenesis, proliferation and apoptosis in bovine granulosa cells: Role of tumour necrosis factor-alpha and its possible signalling mechanisms. *Reprod. Fertil. Dev.* 14, 141–150.
168. Roby, K. F., and Terranova, P. (1989). Localization of tumor necrosis factor (TNF) in rat and bovine ovary using immunocytochemistry and cell blot: Evidence for granulosal production. In *Growth Factors and the Ovary,* ed. A. N. Hirshfield, 273–278. New York: Plenum Press.
169. Sasson, R., Winder, N., Kees, S., and Amsterdam, A. (2002). Induction of apoptosis in granulosa cells by TNF alpha and its attenuation by glucocorticoids involve modulation of Bcl-2. *Biochem. Biophys. Res. Commun.* 294, 51–59.
170. Johnson, A. L., Bridgham, J. T., Witty, J. P., and Tilly, J. L. (1996). Susceptibility of avian ovarian granulosa cells to apoptosis is dependent upon stage of follicle development and is related to endogenous levels of $bcl\text{-}x_{long}$ gene expression. *Endocrinology* 137, 2059–2066.
171. Quirk, S. M., Cowan, R. G., Joshi, S. G., and Henrikson, K. P. (1995). Fas antigen-mediated apoptosis in human granulosa/luteal cells. *Biol. Reprod.* 52, 279–287.
172. Kondo, H., Maruo, T., Peng, X., and Mochizuki, M. (1996). Immunological evidence for the expression of the Fas antigen in the infant and adult human ovary during follicular regression and atresia. *J. Clin. Endocrinol. Metab.* 81, 2702–2710.
173. Hakuno, N., Koji, T., Yano, T., Kobayashi, N., Tsutsumi, O., Taketani, Y., and Nakane, P. K. (1996). Fas/APO-1/CD95 system as a mediator of granulosa cell apoptosis in ovarian follicle atresia. *Endocrinology* 137, 1938–1948.

174. Sakamaki, K., Yoshida, H., Nishimura, Y., Nishikawa, S., Manabe, N., and Yonehara, S. (1997). Involvement of Fas antigen in ovarian follicular atresia and luteolysis. *Mol. Reprod. Dev.* 47, 11–18.
175. Guo, M. W., Xu, J. P., Mori, E., Sato, E., Saito, S., and Mori, T. (1997). Expression of Fas ligand in murine ovary. *Am. J. Reprod. Immunol.* 37, 391–398.
176. Peng, X., Maruo, T., Matsuo, H., Takekida, S., and Deguchi, J. (1998). Serum deprivation-induced apoptosis in cultured porcine granulosa cells is characterized by increased expression of p53 protein, Fas antigen and Fas ligand and by decreased expression of PCNA. *Endocr. J.* 45, 247–253.
177. Kim, J. M., Boone, D. L., Auyeung, A., and Tsang, B. K. (1998). Granulosa cell apoptosis induced at the penultimate stage of follicular development is associated with increased levels of Fas and Fas ligand in the rat ovary. *Biol. Reprod.* 58, 1170–1176.
178. Vickers, S. L., Cowan, R. G., Harman, R. M., Porter, D. A., and Quirk, S. M. (2000). Expression and activity of the Fas antigen in bovine ovarian follicle cells. *Biol. Reprod.* 62, 54–61.
179. Quirk, S. M., Porter, D. A., Huber, S. C., and Cowan, R. G. (1998). Potentiation of Fas-mediated apoptosis of murine granulosa cells by interferon-gamma, tumor necrosis factor-alpha, and cycloheximide. *Endocrinology* 139, 4860–4869.
180. Porter, D. A., Vickers, S. L., Cowan, R. G., Huber, S. C., and Quirk, S. M. (2000). Expression and function of Fas antigen vary in bovine granulosa and theca cells during ovarian follicular development and atresia. *Biol. Reprod.* 62, 62–66.
181. Quirk, S. M., Harman, R. M., and Cowan, R. G. (2000). Regulation of Fas antigen (Fas, CD95)-mediated apoptosis of bovine granulosa cells by serum and growth factors. *Biol. Reprod.* 63, 1278–1284.
182. Bridgham, J. T., and Johnson, A. L. (2001). Expression and regulation of Fas antigen and tumor necrosis factor receptor type I in hen granulosa cells. *Biol. Reprod.* 65, 733–739.
183. Wada, S., Manabe, N., Nakayama, M., Inou, N., Matsui, T., and Miyamoto, H. (2002). TRAIL-decoy receptor 1 plays inhibitory role in apoptosis of granulosa cells from pig ovarian follicles. *J. Vet. Med. Sci.* 64, 435–439.
184. Bridgham, J. T., and Johnson, A. L. (2002). Avian TVB (DR5-like) death receptor expression in hen ovarian follicles. *Biochem. Biophys. Res. Commun.* 291, 226–232.
185. Gebauer, G., Peter, A. T., Onesime, D., and Dhanasekaran, N. (1999). Apoptosis of ovarian granulosa cells: Correlation with the reduced activity of ERK-signaling module. *J. Cell. Biochem.* 75, 547–554.
186. Westfall, S. D., Hendry, I. R., Obholz, K. L., Rueda, B. R., and Davis, J. S. (2000). Putative role of the phosphatidylinositol 3-kinase-Akt signaling pathway in the survival of granulosa cells. *Endocrine* 12, 315–321.
187. Taylor, C. C. (2000). Platelet-derived growth factor activates porcine thecal cell phosphatidylinositol-3-kinase-Akt/PKB and ras-extracellular signal-regulated kinase-1/2 kinase signaling pathways via the platelet-derived growth factor-beta receptor. *Endocrinology* 141, 1545–1553.
188. LeRoith, D., Werner, H., Beitner-Johnson, D., and Roberts, Jr., C. T. (1995). Molecular and cellular aspects of the insulin-like growth factor I receptor. *Endocr. Rev.* 16, 143–163.
189. Coffer, P. J., Jin, J., and Woodgett, J. R. (1998). Protein kinase B (c-Akt): A multifunctional mediator of phosphatidylinositol 3-kinase activation. *Biochem. J.* 335 (Pt 1), 1–13.
190. Peterson, R. T., and Schreiber, S. L. (1998). Translation control: Connecting mitogens and the ribosome. *Curr. Biol.* 8, R248–R250.
191. Tilly, J. L., Billig, H., Kowalski, K. I., and Hsueh, A. J. (1992). Epidermal growth factor and basic fibroblast growth factor suppress the spontaneous onset of apoptosis in cultured rat ovarian granulosa cells and follicles by a tyrosine kinase-dependent mechanism. *Mol. Endocrinol.* 6, 1942–1950.
192. Luciano, A. M., Pappalardo, A., Ray, C., and Peluso, J. J. (1994). Epidermal growth factor inhibits large granulosa cell apoptosis by stimulating progesterone synthesis and regulating the distribution of intracellular free calcium. *Biol. Reprod.* 51, 646–654.
193. Trolice, M. P., Pappalardo, A., and Peluso, J. J. (1997). Basic fibroblast growth factor and N-cadherin maintain rat granulosa cell and ovarian surface epithelial cell viability by stimulating the tyrosine phosphorylation of the fibroblast growth factor receptors. *Endocrinology* 138, 107–113.
194. Guthrie, H. D., Garrett, W. M., and Cooper, B. S. (1998). Follicle-stimulating hormone and insulin-like growth factor-I attenuate apoptosis in cultured porcine granulosa cells. *Biol. Reprod.* 58, 390–396.
195. Chun, S. Y., Billig, H., Tilly, J. L., Furuta, I., Tsafriri, A., and Hsueh, A. J. (1994). Gonadotropin suppression of apoptosis in cultured preovulatory follicles: Mediatory role of endogenous insulin-like growth factor I. *Endocrinology* 135, 1845–1853.
196. Johnson, A. L., Bridgham, J. T., and Swenson, J. A. (2001). Activation of the Akt/protein kinase B signaling pathway is associated with granulosa cell survival. *Biol. Reprod.* 64, 1566–1574.
197. Witty, J. P., Bridgham, J. T., and Johnson, A. L. (1996). Induction of apoptotic cell death in hen granulosa cells by ceramide. *Endocrinology* 137, 5269–5277.
198. Santana, P., Pena, L. A., Haimovitz-Friedman, A., Martin, S., Green, D., McLoughlin, M., Cordon-Cardo, C., Schuchman, E. H., Fuks, Z., and Kolesnick, R. (1996). Acid sphingomyelinase-deficient human lymphoblasts and mice are defective in radiation-induced apoptosis. *Cell* 86, 189–199.
199. Huang, C., Ma, W., Ding, M., Bowden, G. T., and Dong, Z. (1997). Direct evidence for an important role of sphingomyelinase in ultraviolet-induced activation of c-Jun N-terminal kinase. *J. Biol. Chem.* 272, 27753–27757.
200. Kaipia, A., Chun, S. Y., Eisenhauer, K., and Hsueh, A. J. (1996). Tumor necrosis factor-alpha and its second messenger, ceramide, stimulate apoptosis in cultured ovarian follicles. *Endocrinology* 137, 4864–4870.
201. Yang, M. Y., and Rajamahendran, R. (2000). Involvement of apoptosis in the atresia of nonovulatory dominant follicle during the bovine estrous cycle. *Biol. Reprod.* 63, 1313–1321.
202. Knudson, C. M., Tung, K. S., Tourtellotte, W. G., Brown, G. A., and Korsmeyer, S. J. (1995). Bax-deficient mice with lymphoid hyperplasia and male germ cell death. *Science* 270, 96–99.
203. Kugu, K., Ratts, V. S., Piquette, G. N., Tilly, K. I., Tao, X. J., Martimbeau, S., Aberdeen, G. W., Krajewski, S., Reed, J. C., Pepe, G. J., Albrecht, E. D., and Tilly, J. L. (1998). Analysis

of apoptosis and expression of *bcl-2* gene family members in the human and baboon ovary. *Cell Death Differ.* 5, 67–76.

204. Van Nassauw, L., Tao, L., and Harrisson, F. (1999). Distribution of apoptosis-related proteins in the quail ovary during folliculogenesis: BCL-2, BAX and CPP32. *Acta. Histochem.* 101, 103–112.
205. Johnson, A. L., Bridgham, J. T., Witty, J. P., and Tilly, J. L. (1997). Expression of *bcl-2* and *nr-13* in hen ovarian follicles during development. *Biol. Reprod.* 57, 1096–1103.
206. Johnson, A. L., Bridgham, J. T., and Jensen, T. (1999). Bcl-X_{LONG} protein expression and phosphorylation in granulosa cells. *Endocrinology* 140, 4521–4529.
207. Johnson, A. L. (1999). Mcl-1—just another antiapoptotic Bcl-2 Homolog? *Endocrinology* 140, 5465–5468.
208. Leo, C. P., Hsu, S. Y., Chun, S. Y., Bae, H. W., and Hsueh, A. J. (1999). Characterization of the antiapoptotic Bcl-2 family member myeloid cell leukemia-1 (Mcl-1) and the stimulation of its message by gonadotropins in the rat ovary. *Endocrinology* 140, 5469–5477.
209. Hsu, S. Y., Kaipia, A., McGee, E., Lomeli, M., and Hsueh, A. J. (1997). Bok is a pro-apoptotic Bcl-2 protein with restricted expression in reproductive tissues and heterodimerizes with selective anti-apoptotic Bcl-2 family members. *Proc. Natl. Acad. Sci. USA* 94, 12401–12406.
210. Inohara, N., Ekhterae, D., Garcia, I., Carrio, R., Merino, J., Merry, A., Chen, S., and Nunez, G. (1998). Mtd, a novel Bcl-2 family member activates apoptosis in the absence of heterodimerization with Bcl-2 and Bcl-XL. *J. Biol. Chem.* 273, 8705–8710.
211. Inohara, N., Gourley, T. S., Carrio, R., Muniz, M., Merino, J., Garcia, I., Koseki, T., Hu, Y., Chen, S., and Nunez, G. (1998). Diva, a Bcl-2 homologue that binds directly to Apaf-1 and induces BH3-independent cell death. *J. Biol. Chem.* 273, 32479–32486.
212. Song, Q., Kuang, Y., Dixit, V. M., and Vincenz, C. (1999). Boo, a novel negative regulator of cell death, interacts with Apaf-1. *EMBO J.*18, 167–178.
213. Russell, H. R., Lee, Y., Miller, H. L., Zhao, J., and McKinnon, P. J. (2002). Murine ovarian development is not affected by inactivation of the Bcl-2 family member diva. *Mol. Cell. Biol.* 22, 6866–6870.
214. Kaipia, A., Hsu, S. Y., and Hsueh, A. J. (1997). Expression and function of a proapoptotic Bcl-2 family member Bcl-X_L/Bcl-2-associated death promoter (BAD) in rat ovary. *Endocrinology* 138, 5497–5504.
215. Hsu, S. Y., Lin, P., and Hsueh, A. J. (1998). BOD (Bcl-2-related ovarian death gene) is an ovarian BH3 domain-containing proapoptotic Bcl-2 protein capable of dimerization with diverse antiapoptotic Bcl-2 members. *Mol. Endocrinol.* 12, 1432–1440.
216. Robles, R., Tao, X. J., Trbovich, A. M., Maravel, D. V., Nahum, R., Perez, G. I., Tilly, K. I., and Tilly, J. L. (1999). Localization, regulation and possible consequences of apoptotic protease-activating factor-1 (Apaf-1) expression in granulosa cells of the mouse ovary. *Endocrinology* 140, 2641–2644.
217. Moriyama, T., Maravei, D. V., Kuida, K., and Tilly, J. L. (2002). Role of caspase-9 in programmed cell death execution in the ovary. *Proceedings of the 84th Annual Meeting of the Endocrine Society,* San Francisco, 418–419.
218. Johnson, A. L., and Bridgham, J. T. (2002). Caspase-mediated apoptosis in the vertebrate ovary. *Reproduction* 124, 19–27.
219. Flaws, J. A., Kugu, K., Trbovich, A. M., DeSanti, A., Tilly, K. I., Hirshfield, A. N., and Tilly, J. L. (1995). Interleukin-1 beta-converting enzyme-related proteases (IRPs) and mammalian cell death: Dissociation of IRP-induced oligonucleosomal endonuclease activity from morphological apoptosis in granulosa cells of the ovarian follicle. *Endocrinology* 136, 5042–5053.
220. Boone, D. L., and Tsang, B. K. (1998). Caspase-3 in the rat ovary: Localization and possible role in follicular atresia and luteal regression. *Biol. Reprod.* 58, 1533–1539.
221. Maravei, D. V., Trbovich, A. M., Perez, G. I., Tilly, K. I., Talanian, R. V., Banach, D., Wong, W. W., and Tilly, J. L. (1997). Cleavage of cytoskeletal proteins by caspases during ovarian cell death: Evidence that cell-free systems do not always mimic apoptotic events in intact cells. *Cell Death Differ.* 4, 707–712.
222. Johnson, A. L., and Bridgham, J. T. (2000). Caspase-3 and -6 expression and enzyme activity in hen granulosa cells. *Biol. Reprod.* 62, 589–598.
223. Quirk, S. M., Harman, R. M., Huber, S. C., and Cowan, R. G. (2000). Responsiveness of mouse corpora luteal cells to Fas antigen (CD95)-mediated apoptosis. *Biol. Reprod.* 63, 49–56.
224. Hasumoto, K., Sugimoto, Y., Yamasaki, A., Morimoto, K., Kakizuka, A., Negishi, M., and Ichikawa, A. (1997). Association of expression of mRNA encoding the $PGF_{2\alpha}$ receptor with luteal cell apoptosis in ovaries of pseudopregnant mice. *J. Reprod. Fertil.* 109, 45–51.
225. Bowen, J. M., Towns, R., Warren, J. S., and Landis Keyes, P. (1999). Luteal regression in the normally cycling rat: Apoptosis, monocyte chemoattractant protein-1, and inflammatory cell involvement. *Biol. Reprod.* 60, 740–746.
226. Tanaka, M., Miyazaki, T., Tanigaki, S., Kasai, K., Minegishi, K., Miyakoshi, K., Ishimoto, H., and Yoshimura, Y. (2000). Participation of reactive oxygen species in $PGF_2\alpha$-induced apoptosis in rat luteal cells. *J. Reprod. Fertil.* 120, 239–245.
227. Guo, K., Wolf, V., Dharmarajan, A. M., Feng, Z., Bielke, W., Saurer, S., and Friis, R. (1998). Apoptosis-associated gene expression in the corpus luteum of the rat. *Biol. Reprod.* 58, 739–746.
228. Roughton, S. A., Lareu, R. R., Bittles, A. H., and Dharmarajan, A. M. (1999). Fas and Fas ligand messenger ribonucleic acid and protein expression in the rat corpus luteum during apoptosis-mediated luteolysis. *Biol. Reprod.* 60, 797–804.
229. McCormack, J. T., Friederichs, M. G., Limback, S. D., and Greenwald, G. S. (1998). Apoptosis during spontaneous luteolysis in the cyclic golden hamster: Biochemical and morphological evidence. *Biol. Reprod.* 58, 255–260.
230. Gaytan, F., Morales, C., Bellido, C., Aguilar, R., and Sanchez-Criado, J. E. (2001). The fate of corpora lutea in the cyclic golden hamster. *Gen. Comp. Endocrinol.* 121, 104–113.
231. Goodman, S. B., Kugu, K., Chen, S. H., Preutthipan, S., Tilly, K. I., Tilly, J. L., and Dharmarajan, A. M. (1998). Estradiol-mediated suppression of apoptosis in the rabbit corpus luteum is associated with a shift in expression of *bcl-2* family

members favoring cellular survival. *Biol. Reprod.* 59, 820–827.

232. Dharmarajan, A. M., Hisheh, S., Singh, B., Parkinson, S., Tilly, K. I., and Tilly, J. L. (1999). Antioxidants mimic the ability of chorionic gonadotropin to suppress apoptosis in the rabbit corpus luteum in vitro: A novel role for superoxide dismutase in regulating *bax* expression. *Endocrinology* 140, 2555–2561.
233. O'Shea, J. D., Nightingale, M. G., and Chamley, W. A. (1977). Changes in small blood vessels during cyclical luteal regression in sheep. *Biol. Reprod.* 17, 162–177.
234. Sawyer, H. R., Niswender, K. D., Braden, T. D., and Niswender, G. D. (1990). Nuclear changes in ovine luteal cells in response to PGF2 alpha. *Domest. Anim. Endocrinol.* 7, 229–237.
235. Murdoch, W. J. (1995). Temporal relationships between stress protein induction, progesterone withdrawal, and apoptosis in corpora lutea of ewes treated with prostaglandin $PGF_{2\alpha}$. *J. Anim. Sci.* 73, 1789–1792.
236. Rueda, B. R., Wegner, J. A., Marion, S. L., Wahlen, D. D., and Hoyer, P. B. (1995). Internucleosomal DNA fragmentation in ovine luteal tissue associated with luteolysis: In vivo and in vitro analyses. *Biol. Reprod.* 52, 305–312.
237. Juengel, J. L., Garverick, H. A., Johnson, A. L., Youngquist, R. S., and Smith, M. F. (1993). Apoptosis during luteal regression in cattle. *Endocrinology* 132, 249–254.
238. Zheng, J., Fricke, P. M., Reynolds, L. P., and Redmer, D. A. (1994). Evaluation of growth, cell proliferation, and cell death in bovine corpora lutea throughout the estrous cycle. *Biol. Reprod.* 51, 623–632.
239. Rueda, B. R., Tilly, K. I., Hansen, T. R., Hoyer, P. B., and Tilly, J. L. (1995). Expression of superoxide dismutase, catalase and glutathione peroxidase in the bovine corpus luteum: Evidence supporting a role for oxidative stress in luteolysis. *Endocrine* 3, 227–232.
240. Bacci, M. L., Barazzoni, A. M., Forni, M., and Costerbosa, G. L. (1996). In situ detection of apoptosis in regressing corpus luteum of pregnant sow: Evidence of an early presence of DNA fragmentation. *Domest. Anim. Endocrinol.* 13, 361–372.
241. Shikone, T., Yamoto, M., Kokawa, K., Yamashita, K., Nishimori, K., and Nakano, R. (1996). Apoptosis of human corpora lutea during cyclic luteal regression and early pregnancy. *J. Clin. Endocrinol. Metab.* 81, 2376–2380.
242. Young, F. M., Illingworth, P. J., Lunn, S. F., Harrison, D. J., and Fraser, H. M. (1997). Cell death during luteal regression in the marmoset monkey (*Callithrix jacchus*). *J. Reprod. Fertil.* 111, 109–119.
243. Young, F. M., Illingworth, P. J., and Fraser, H. M. (1998). Ubiquitin and apoptosis in the corpus luteum of the marmoset monkey (*Callithrix jacchus*). *J. Reprod. Fertil.* 114, 163–168.
244. Pru, J. K., Hendry, I. R., Davis, J. S., and Rueda, B. R. (2002). Soluble Fas ligand activates the sphingomyelin pathway and induces apoptosis in luteal steroidogenic cells independently of stress-activated $p38^{MAPK}$. *Endocrinology* 143, 4350–4357.
245. McCracken, J. A., Custer, E. E., and Lamsa, J. C. (1999). Luteolysis: A neuroendocrine-mediated event. *Physiol. Rev.* 79, 263–323.
246. Niswender, G. D., Juengel, J. L., Silva, P. J., Rollyson, M. K., and McIntush, E. W. (2000). Mechanisms controlling the function and life span of the corpus luteum. *Physiol. Rev.* 80, 1–29.
247. Taniguchi, H., Yokomizo, Y., and Okuda, K. (2002). Fas-fas ligand system mediates luteal cell death in bovine corpus luteum. *Biol. Reprod.* 66, 754–759.
248. Kuranaga, E., Kanuka, H., Furuhata, Y., Yonezawa, T., Suzuki, M., Nishihara, M., and Takahashi, M. (2000). Requirement of the Fas ligand-expressing luteal immune cells for regression of corpus luteum. *FEBS Lett.* 472, 137–142.
249. Kuranaga, E., Kanuka, H., Bannai, M., Suzuki, M., Nishihara, M., and Takahashi, M. (1999). Fas/Fas ligand system in prolactin-induced apoptosis in rat corpus luteum: Possible role of luteal immune cells. *Biochem. Biophys. Res. Commun.* 260, 167–173.
250. Pru, J. K., Lynch, M. P., Davis, J. S., and Rueda, B. R. (2003). Signaling mechanisms in tumor necrosis factor alpha-induced death of microvascular endothelial cells of the corpus luteum. *Reprod. Biol. Endocrinol.* 1, 17.
251. Carambula, S. F., Pru, K. K., Lynch, M. P., Matikainen, T., Goncalves, P. B. D., Flavell, R. A., Tilly, J. L., and Rueda, B. R. (2003). Prostaglandin $PGF_{2\alpha}$- and FAS-activating antibody-induced regression of the corpus luteum involves caspase-8 and is defective in caspase-3 deficient mice. *Reprod. Biol. Endocrinol.* 1, 15.
252. Zhao, Y., Burbach, J. A., Roby, K. F., Terranova, P. F., and Brannian, J. D. (1998). Macrophages are the major source of tumor necrosis factor alpha in the porcine corpus luteum. *Biol. Reprod.* 59, 1385–1391.
253. Hehnke-Vagnoni, K. E., Clark, C. L., Taylor, M. J., and Ford, S. P. (1995). Presence and localization of tumor necrosis factor alpha in the corpus luteum of nonpregnant and pregnant pigs. *Biol. Reprod.* 53, 1339–1344.
254. Bagavandoss, P., Kunkel, S. L., Wiggins, R. C., and Keyes, P. L. (1988). Tumor necrosis factor-α (TNF-α) production and localization of macrophages and T lymphocytes in the rabbit corpus luteum. *Endocrinology* 122, 1185–1187.
255. Okuda, K., Sakumoto, R., Uenoyama, Y., Berisha, B., Miyamoto, A., and Schams, D. (1999). Tumor necrosis factor alpha receptors in microvascular endothelial cells from bovine corpus luteum. *Biol. Reprod.* 61, 1017–1022.
256. Sakumoto, R., Berisha, B., Kawate, N., Schams, D., and Okuda, K. (2000). Tumor necrosis factor-alpha and its receptor in bovine corpus luteum throughout the estrous cycle. *Biol. Reprod.* 62, 192–199.
257. Petroff, M. G., Petroff, B. K., and Pate, J. L. (1999). Expression of cytokine messenger ribonucleic acids in the bovine corpus luteum. *Endocrinology* 140, 1018–1021.
258. Ji, I., Slaughter, R. G., Ellis, J. A., Ji, T. H., and Murdoch, W. J. (1991). Analyses of ovine corpora lutea for tumor necrosis factor mRNA and bioactivity during prostaglandin-induced luteolysis. *Mol. Cell. Endocrinol.* 81, 77–80.
259. Friedman, A., Weiss, S., Levy, N., and Meidan, R. (2000). Role of tumor necrosis factor alpha and its type I receptor in luteal regression: Induction of programmed cell death in bovine corpus luteum-derived endothelial cells. *Biol. Reprod.* 63, 1905–1912.
260. Miyamoto, Y., Sakumoto, R., Sakabe, Y., Miyake, M., Okano, A., and Okuda, K. (2002). Tumour necrosis factor-alpha

receptors are present in the corpus luteum throughout the oestrous cycle and during the early gestation period in pigs. *Reprod. Domest. Anim.* 37, 105–110.

261. Sakumoto, R., Murakami, S., and Okuda, K. (2000). Tumor necrosis factor-alpha stimulates prostaglandin $F_{2\alpha}$ secretion by bovine luteal cells via activation of mitogen-activated protein kinase and phospholipase A_2 pathways. *Mol. Reprod. Dev.* 56, 387–391.
262. Richards, R. G., and Almond, G. W. (1994). Tumour necrosis factor-alpha differentially alters progesterone and prostaglandin $F_{2\alpha}$ production by porcine luteal cells. *J. Endocrinol.* 143, 75–83.
263. Suter, J., Hendry, I. R., Ndjountche, L., Obholz, K., Pru, J. K., Davis, J. S., and Rueda, B. R. (2001). Mediators of interferon gamma-initiated signaling in bovine luteal cells. *Biol. Reprod.* 64, 1481–1486.
264. Benyo, D. F., and Pate, J. L. (1992). Tumor necrosis factor-alpha alters bovine luteal cell synthetic capacity and viability. *Endocrinology* 130, 854–860.
265. Rueda, B. R., Hendry, I. R., Ndjountche, L., Suter, J., and Davis, J. S. (2000). Stress-induced mitogen-activated protein kinase signaling in the corpus luteum. *Mol. Cell. Endocrinol.* 164, 59–67.
266. Roby, K. F., Son, D. S., and Terranova, P. F. (1999). Alterations of events related to ovarian function in tumor necrosis factor receptor type I knockout mice. *Biol. Reprod.* 61, 1616–1621.
267. Bukovsky, A., Presl, J., Krabec, Z., and Bednarik, T. (1977). Ovarian function in adult rats treated with antithymocyte serum. *Experientia* 33, 280–281.
268. Rodger, F. E., Fraser, H. M., Krajewski, S., and Illingworth, P. J. (1998). Production of the proto-oncogene BAX does not vary with changing in luteal function in women. *Mol. Hum. Reprod.* 4, 27–32.
269. Rodger, F. E., Fraser, H. M., Duncan, W. C., and Illingworth, P. J. (1995). Immunolocalization of Bcl-2 in the human corpus luteum. *Hum. Reprod.* 10, 1566–1570.
270. Sugino, N., Suzuki, T., Kashida, S., Karube, A., Takiguchi, S., and Kato, H. (2000). Expression of Bcl-2 and Bax in the human corpus luteum during the menstrual cycle and in early pregnancy: Regulation by human chorionic gonadotropin. *J. Clin. Endocrinol. Metab.* 85, 4379–4386.
271. Devoto, L., Vega, M., Kohen, P., Castro, O., Carvallo, P., and Palomino, A. (2002). Molecular regulation of progesterone secretion by the human corpus luteum throughout the menstrual cycle. *J. Reprod. Immunol.* 55, 11–20.
272. Godlewski, M. M., Motyl, M. A., Gajkowska, B., Wareski, P., Koronkiewicz, M., and Motyl, T. (2001). Subcellular redistribution of BAX during apoptosis induced by anticancer drugs. *Anticancer Drugs* 12, 607–617.
273. Deane, H. W., Hay, M. F., Moor, R. M., Rowson, L. E., and Short, R. V. (1966). The corpus luteum of the sheep: Relationships between morphology and function during the oestrous cycle. *Acta. Endocrinol. (Copenh.)* 51, 245–263.
274. Krajewski, S., Gascoyne, R. D., Zapata, J. M., Krajewska, M., Kitada, S., Chhanabhai, M., Horsman, D., Berean, K., Piro, L. D., Fugier-Vivier, I., Liu, Y. J., Wang, H. G., and Reed, J. C. (1997). Immunolocalization of the ICE/Ced-3-family protease, CPP32 (Caspase-3), in non-Hodgkin's lymphomas, chronic lymphocytic leukemias, and reactive lymph nodes. *Blood* 89, 3817–3825.
275. Rueda, B. R., Hendry, I. R., Tilly, J. L., and Hamernik, D. L. (1999). Accumulation of caspase-3 messenger ribonucleic acid and induction of caspase activity in the ovine corpus luteum following prostaglandin $F_{2\alpha}$ treatment in vivo. *Biol. Reprod.* 60, 1087–1092.
276. Carambula, S. F., Matikainen, T., Lynch, M. P., Flavell, R. A., Goncalves, P. B., Tilly, J. L., and Rueda, B. R. (2002). Caspase-3 is a pivotal mediator of apoptosis during regression of the ovarian corpus luteum. *Endocrinology* 143, 1495–1501.
277. Morita, Y., and Tilly, J. L. (1999). Oocyte apoptosis: Like sand through an hourglass. *Dev. Biol.* 213, 1–17.
278. Morita, Y., Manganaro, T. F., Tao, X. J., Martimbeau, S., Donahoe, P. K., and Tilly, J. L. (1999). Requirement for phosphatidylinositol-3'-kinase in cytokine-mediated germ cell survival during fetal oogenesis in the mouse. *Endocrinology* 140, 941–949.
279. Morita, Y., and Tilly, J. L. (1999). Segregation of retinoic acid effects on fetal ovarian germ cell mitosis versus apoptosis by requirement for new macromolecular synthesis. *Endocrinology* 140, 2696–2703.
280. De Felici, M. (2000). Regulation of primordial germ cell development in the mouse. *Int. J. Dev. Biol.* 44, 575–580.
281. Morita, Y., Perez, G. I., Paris, F., Miranda, S. R., Ehleiter, D., Haimovitz-Friedman, A., Fuks, Z., Xie, Z., Reed, J. C., Schuchman, E. H., Kolesnick, R. N., and Tilly, J. L. (2000). Oocyte apoptosis is suppressed by disruption of the *acid sphingomyelinase* gene or by sphingosine-1-phosphate therapy. *Nat. Med.* 6, 1109–1114.
282. Zhou, H., Summers, S. A., Birnbaum, M. J., and Pittman, R. N. (1998). Inhibition of Akt kinase by cell-permeable ceramide and its implications for ceramide-induced apoptosis. *J. Biol. Chem.* 273, 16568–16575.
283. Pru, J. K., and Tilly, J. L. (2001). Programmed cell death in the ovary: Insights and future prospects using genetic technologies. *Mol. Endocrinol.* 15, 845–853.
284. DeFelici, M., Carlo, A. D., Pesce, M., Iona, S., Farrace, M. G., and Piacentini, M. (1999). *bcl-2* and Bax regulation of apoptosis in germ cells during prenatal oogenesis in mouse embryos. *Cell Death Differ.* 6, 908–915.
285. Ratts, V. S., Flaws, J. A., Kolp, R., Sorenson, C. M., and Tilly, J. L. (1995). Ablation of *bcl-2* gene expression decreases the numbers of oocytes and primordial follicles established in the post-natal female mouse gonad. *Endocrinology* 136, 3665–3668.
286. Rucker, III, E. B., Dierisseau, P., Wagner, K. U., Garrett, L., Wynshaw-Boris, A., Flaws, J. A., and Hennighausen, L. (2000). Bcl-x and Bax regulate mouse primordial germ cell survival and apoptosis during embryogenesis. *Mol. Endocrinol.* 14, 1038–1052.
287. Perez, G. I., Trbovich, A. M., Gosden, R. G., and Tilly, J. L. (2000). Mitochondria and the death of oocytes. *Nature* 403, 500–501.
288. Morita, Y., Maravei, D. V., Bergeron, L., Wang, S., Perez, G. I., Tsutsumi, O., Taketani, Y., Asano, M., Horai, R., Korsmeyer, S. J., Iwakura, Y., Yuan, J., and Tilly, J. L. (2001). Caspase-2 deficiency prevents programmed germ cell death resulting from cytokine insufficiency but not meiotic defects

caused by loss of *ataxia telangiectasia-mutated* (*Atm*) gene function. *Cell Death Differ.* 8, 614–620.

289. Jones, E. C., and Krohn, P. L. (1961). The relationship between age, numbers of oocytes and fertility in virgin and multiparous mice. *J. Endocrinol.* 21, 469–495.
290. Canning, J., Takai, Y., and Tilly, J. L. (2003). Evidence for genetic modifiers of ovarian follicular endowment and development from studies of five inbred mouse strains. *Endocrinology* 144, 9–12.
291. Mattison, D. R., and Thorgeirsson, S. S. (1977). Genetic differences in mouse ovarian metabolism of benzo[*a*]pyrene and oocyte toxicity. *Biochem. Pharmacol.* 26, 909–912.
292. Spearow, J. L., Nutson, P. A., Mailliard, W. S., Porter, M., and Barkley, M. (1999). Mapping genes that control hormone-induced ovulation rate in mice. *Biol. Reprod.* 61, 857–872.
293. Tilly, J. L. (2000). Apoptosis in female reproductive toxicology. In *Apoptosis in Toxicology,* ed. R. Roberts, 95–116. London: Taylor & Francis.
294. Gosden, R., and Nagano, M. (2002). Preservation of fertility in nature and ART. *Reproduction* 123, 3–11.
295. Mattison, D. R., and Thorgeirsson, S. S. (1978). Smoking and industrial pollution and their effects on menopause and ovarian cancer. *Lancet* 1, 187–188.
296. Mattison, D. R. (1980). Morphology of oocyte and follicle destruction by polycyclic aromatic hydrocarbons in mice. *Toxicol. Appl. Pharmacol.* 53, 249–259.
297. Mattison, D. R., Plowchalk, D. R., Meadows, M. J., Miller, M. M., Malek, A., and London, S. (1989). The effect of smoking on oogenesis, fertilization and implantation. *Sem. Reprod. Health* 7, 291–304.
298. MacKenzie, K. M., and Angevine, D. M. (1981). Infertility in mice exposed in utero to benzo(*a*)pyrene. *Biol. Reprod.* 24, 183–191.
299. Matikainen, T. M., Moriyama, T., Morita, Y., Perez, G. I., Korsmeyer, S. J., Sherr, D. H., and Tilly, J. L. (2002). Ligand activation of the aromatic hydrocarbon receptor transcription factor drives Bax-dependent apoptosis in developing fetal ovarian germ cells. *Endocrinology* 143, 615–620.
300. Weinberg, C. R., Wilcox, A. J., and Baird, D. D. (1989). Reduced fecundability in women with prenatal exposure to cigarette smoking. *Am. J. Epidemiol.* 129, 1072–1078.
301. Jick, H., and Porter, J. (1977). Relation between smoking and age of natural menopause. Report from the Boston Collaborative Drug Surveillance Program, Boston University Medical Center. *Lancet* 1, 1354–1355.
302. Denison, M. S., Pandini, A., Nagy, S. R., Baldwin, E. P., and Bonati, L. (2002). Ligand binding and activation of the Ah receptor. *Chem. Biol. Interact.* 141, 3–24.
303. Hahn, M. E. (2002). Aryl hydrocarbon receptors: Diversity and evolution. *Chem. Biol. Interact.* 141, 131–160.
304. Gonzalez, F. J., and Fernandez-Salguero, P. (1998). The aryl hydrocarbon receptor: Studies using the AHR-null mice. *Drug Metab. Dispos.* 26, 1194–1198.
305. Lahvis, G. P., and Bradfield, C. A. (1998). Ahr null alleles: Distinctive or different? *Biochem. Pharmacol.* 56, 781–787.
306. Robles, R., Morita, Y., Mann, K. K., Perez, G. I., Yang, S., Matikainen, T., Sherr, D. H., and Tilly, J. L. (2000). The aryl hydrocarbon receptor, a basic helix-loop-helix transcription factor of the PAS gene family, is required for normal ovarian germ cell dynamics in the mouse. *Endocrinology* 141, 450–453.
307. Hoyer, P. B., Devine, P. J., Hu, X., Thompson, K. E., and Sipes, I. G. (2001). Ovarian toxicity of 4-vinylcyclohexene diepoxide: A mechanistic model. *Toxicol. Pathol.* 29, 91–99.
308. Springer, L. N., McAsey, M. E., Flaws, J. A., Tilly, J. L., Sipes, I. G., and Hoyer, P. B. (1996). Involvement of apoptosis in 4-vinylcyclohexene diepoxide-induced ovotoxicity in rats. *Toxicol. Appl. Pharmacol.* 139, 394–401.
309. Springer, L. N., Tilly, J. L., Sipes, I. G., and Hoyer, P. B. (1996). Enhanced expression of *bax* in small preantral follicles during 4-vinylcyclohexene diepoxide-induced ovotoxicity in the rat. *Toxicol. Appl. Pharmacol.* 139, 402–410.
310. Hu, X., Christian, P., Sipes, I. G., and Hoyer, P. B. (2001). Expression and redistribution of cellular Bad, Bax, and Bcl-X_L protein is associated with VCD-induced ovotoxicity in rats. *Biol. Reprod.* 65, 1489–1495.
311. Takai, Y., Canning, J., Perez, G. I., Pru, J. K., Schlezinger, J. J., Sherr, D. H., Kolesnick, R. N., Yuan, J., Flavell, R. A., Korsmeyer, S. J., and Tilly, J. L. (2003). Bax, caspase-2, and caspase-3 are required for ovarian follicle loss caused by 4-vinylcyclohexene diepoxide exposure of female mice in vivo. *Endocrinology* 144, 69–74.
312. Hu, X., Christian, P. J., Thompson, K. E., Sipes, I. G., and Hoyer, P. B. (2001). Apoptosis induced in rats by 4-vinylcyclohexene diepoxide is associated with activation of the caspase cascades. *Biol. Reprod.* 65, 87–93.
313. Jaattela, M. (2002). Programmed cell death: Many ways for cells to die decently. *Ann. Med.* 34, 480–488.
314. Nakahara, K., Saito, H., Saito, T., Ito, M., Ohta, N., Sakai, N., Tezuka, N., Hiroi, M., and Watanabe, H. (1997). Incidence of apoptotic bodies in membrana granulosa of the patients participating in an in vitro fertilization program. *Fertil. Steril.* 67, 302–308.
315. Nakahara, K., Saito, H., Saito, T., Ito, M., Ohta, N., Takahashi, T., and Hiroi, M. (1997). The incidence of apoptotic bodies in membrana granulosa can predict prognosis of ova from patients participating in in vitro fertilization programs. *Fertil. Steril.* 68, 312–317.
316. Oosterhuis, G. J., Michgelsen, H. W., Lambalk, C. B., Schoemaker, J., and Vermes, I. (1998). Apoptotic cell death in human granulosa-lutein cells: A possible indicator of in vitro fertilization outcome. *Fertil. Steril.* 70, 747–749.
317. Suh, C. S., Jee, B. C., Choi, Y. M., Kim, J. G., Lee, J. Y., Moon, S. Y., and Kim, S. H. (2002). Prognostic implication of apoptosis in human luteinized granulosa cells during IVF-ET. *J. Assist. Reprod. Genet.* 19, 209–214.
318. Kaneko, T., Saito, H., Takahashi, T., Ohta, N., Saito, T., and Hiroi, M. (2000). Effects of controlled ovarian hyperstimulation on oocyte quality in terms of the incidence of apoptotic granulosa cells. *J. Assist. Reprod. Genet.* 17, 580–585.
319. Yano, T., Yano, N., Matsumi, H., Morita, Y., Tsutsumi, O., Schally, A. V., and Taketani, Y. (1997). Effect of luteinizing hormone-releasing hormone analogs on the rat ovarian follicle development. *Horm. Res.* 48 (Suppl 3), 35–41.
320. Takekida, S., Deguchi, J., Samoto, T., Matsuo, H., and Maruo, T. (2000). Comparative analysis of the effects of gonadotropin-releasing hormone agonist on the proliferative activity, apoptosis, and steroidogenesis in cultured porcine granulosa cells at varying stages of follicular growth. *Endocrine* 12, 61–67.

321. Zhao, S., Saito, H., Wang, X., Saito, T., Kaneko, T., and Hiroi, M. (2000). Effects of gonadotropin-releasing hormone agonist on the incidence of apoptosis in porcine and human granulosa cells. *Gynecol. Obstet. Invest.* 49, 52–56.
322. Perez, G. I., Robles, R., Knudson, C. M., Flaws, J. A., Korsmeyer, S. J., and Tilly, J. L. (1999). Prolongation of ovarian lifespan into advanced chronological age by *Bax*-deficiency. *Nat. Genet.* 21, 200–203.
323. Greenlee, R. T., Murray, T., Bolden, S., and Wingo, P. A. (2000). Cancer statistics, 2000. *CA Cancer J. Clin.* 50, 7–33.
324. Meirow, D., and Nugent, D. (2001). The effects of radiotherapy and chemotherapy on female reproduction. *Hum. Reprod. Update* 7, 535–543.
325. Revel, A., and Laufer, N. (2002). Protecting female fertility from cancer therapy. *Mol. Cell. Endocrinol.* 187, 83–91.
326. Reynolds, T. (1999). Cell death genes may hold clues to preserving fertility after chemotherapy. *J. Natl. Cancer Inst.* 91, 664–666.
327. Bergeron, L., Perez, G. I., Macdonald, G., Shi, L., Sun, Y., Jurisicova, A., Varmuza, S., Latham, K. E., Flaws, J. A., Salter, J. C., Hara, H., Moskowitz, M. A., Li, E., Greenberg, A., Tilly, J. L., and Yuan, J. (1998). Defects in regulation of apoptosis in caspase-2-deficient mice. *Genes Dev.* 12, 1304–1314.
328. Morita, Y., Perez, G. I., Maravei, D. V., Tilly, K. I., and Tilly, J. L. (1999). Targeted expression of Bcl-2 in mouse oocytes inhibits ovarian follicle atresia and prevents spontaneous and chemotherapy-induced oocyte apoptosis in vitro. *Mol. Endocrinol.* 13, 841–850.
329. Xiang, J., Chao, D. T., and Korsmeyer, S. J. (1996). BAX-induced cell death may not require interleukin 1 beta-converting enzyme-like proteases. *Proc. Natl. Acad. Sci. USA* 93, 14559–14563.
330. Hayashi, M., Morita, T., Kodama, Y., Sofuni, T., and Ishidate, Jr., M. (1990). The micronucleus assay with mouse peripheral blood reticulocytes using acridine orange-coated slides. *Mutat. Res.* 245, 245–249.
331. Manti, L., Jamali, M., Prise, K. M., Michael, B. D., and Trott, K. R. (1997). Genomic instability in Chinese hamster cells after exposure to X rays or alpha particles of different mean linear energy transfer. *Radiat. Res.* 147, 22–28.
332. Trott, K. R., Jamali, M., Manti, L., and Teibe, A. (1998). Manifestations and mechanisms of radiation-induced genomic instability in V-79 Chinese hamster cells. *Int. J. Radiat. Biol.* 74, 787–791.
333. Montz, F. J., Wolff, A. J., and Gambone, J. C. (1991). Gonadal protection and fecundity rates in cyclophosphamide-treated rats. *Cancer Res.* 51, 2124–2126.
334. Ataya, K., and Ramahi-Ataya, A. (1993). Reproductive performance of female rats treated with cyclophosphamide and/or LHRH agonist. *Reprod. Toxicol.* 7, 229–235.
335. Ataya, K., Rao, L. V., Lawrence, E., and Kimmel, R. (1995). Luteinizing hormone-releasing hormone agonist inhibits cyclophosphamide-induced ovarian follicular depletion in rhesus monkeys. *Biol. Reprod.* 52, 365–372.
336. Blumenfeld, Z., Avivi, I., Linn, S., Epelbaum, R., Ben-Shahar, M., and Haim, N. (1996). Prevention of irreversible chemotherapy-induced ovarian damage in young women with lymphoma by a gonadotrophin-releasing hormone agonist in parallel to chemotherapy. *Hum. Reprod.* 11, 1620–1626.
337. Blumenfeld, Z., Shapiro, D., Shteinberg, M., Avivi, I., and Nahir, M. (2000). Preservation of fertility and ovarian function and minimizing gonadotoxicity in young women with systemic lupus erythematosus treated by chemotherapy. *Lupus* 9, 401–405.
338. Recchia, F., Sica, G., De Filippis, S., Saggio, G., Rosselli, M., and Rea, S. (2002). Goserelin as ovarian protection in the adjuvant treatment of premenopausal breast cancer: A phase II pilot study. *Anticancer Drugs* 13, 417–424.
339. Blumenfeld, Z., Dann, E., Avivi, I., Epelbaum, R., and Rowe, J. M. (2002). Fertility after treatment for Hodgkin's disease. *Ann. Oncol.* 13 (Suppl 1), 138–147.
340. Ataya, K., Pydyn, E., Ramahi-Ataya, A., and Orton, C. G. (1995). Is radiation-induced ovarian failure in rhesus monkeys preventable by luteinizing hormone-releasing hormone agonists? Preliminary observations. *J. Clin. Endocrinol. Metab.* 80, 790–795.
341. Flemming, W. (1885). Über die bildung von richtungsfiguren in säugethiereiern beim untergang Graaf'scher follikel. Archiv fur Anatomie und Entwickelungsgeschichte. *Archiv. Anat. Physiol.* 221–244.
342. Zeleznik, A. J., Ihrig, L. L., and Bassett, S. G. (1989). Developmental expression of Ca^{++}/Mg^{++}-dependent endonuclease activity in rat granulosa and luteal cells. *Endocrinology* 125, 2218–2220.

CHAPTER **20**

Reactive Oxygen Species and Ovarian Function

JESSICA A. BERTOUT, NEAL G. MAHUTTE, SANDRA L. PRESTON, AND HAROLD R. BEHRMAN

INTRODUCTION

Reactive oxygen species are produced in all aerobic cells and are the partially reduced products of oxygen. Interestingly, they can be beneficial to organisms as cell regulators, but in high doses, they become cytotoxic, often leading to cell death. This chapter summarizes the nature, origins, actions, defenses, and medical implications of reactive oxygen species in the ovary. It details recent findings concerning the effects of reactive oxygen species in the follicle, oocyte, and the corpus luteum, as well as during the processes of ovulation and luteal regression. The sources of reactive oxygen species appear to include both immune system and ovarian cells. Prostaglandins, cytokines, hormones, and antioxidant molecules modulate their production and effects, but many of the mechanisms involved remain to be clarified.

REACTIVE OXYGEN SPECIES

Nature and Interactions

The principal reactive oxygen species (ROS) are the superoxide anion (O_2^-), hydrogen peroxide (H_2O_2), hypochlorous acid (HClO), the hydroxyl radical (OH·), lipid hydroperoxides, singlet oxygen (O_2^1), and the peroxynitrite radical (NOO^-). Addition by oxidase of a single electron to oxygen renders O_2^-, which is quickly transformed by superoxide dismutase (SOD) into H_2O_2 with the addition of another single electron. Alternatively, O_2^- can interact with nitric oxide (NO) to generate the reactive peroxynitrite radical. Catalase and glutathione peroxidase convert H_2O_2 to water and oxygen. Otherwise, H_2O_2 will react with ferrous or cuprous ions by the Fenton reaction, producing the highly reactive hydroxyl radical (OH·). O_2^- reduces ferric and cupric ions to ferrous and cuprous ions, supporting a continuous production of OH· by the Haber-Weiss reaction [1]. Polyunsaturated fatty acids are oxidized into lipid peroxides by OH·, NOO^-, and HClO and by H_2O_2-activated peroxidases in the absence of their usual secondary substrate (Figure 20.1).

Other members of the ROS family include hypohalous acids, like HClO, or pseudohalous acids, like HSCNO, which are produced by leukocyte myeloperoxidases in the presence of H_2O_2 [29]. Chloramines, formed by hypochlorous acid reacting with amino groups, can act as secondary oxidants [18]. Photoexcitation or chemoexcitation produce singlet oxygen, a very potent reactive oxygen species [19]. Finally, NO is a gas radical that plays important roles in signal transduction processes [30], but it is actually a weak reducing rather than oxidizing agent. As mentioned earlier, O_2^- interacts with NO to produce the highly reactive peroxinitrite. NO is produced from arginine by nitric oxide synthase and is an endothelium-derived relaxation factor (EDRF) of blood vessels, leukocytes, and other cells [7, 8]. Interestingly, in the presence of suboptimal concentrations of L-arginine or H_4biopterin, NO synthase is modified to act as a calcium/calmodulin-dependent generator of H_2O_2 rather than NO [31, 32]. Myeloperoxidase destroys NO in an ascorbic acid-dependent manner, which is thought to be the basis for neutrophil-induced vasoconstriction in inflammation [33].

All ROS are short-lived. For example, OH· has a half-life of 1 nanosecond. The presence of ROS is usually determined by the effects produced by these agents rather than by direct analysis.

Origins

ROS reside in all cellular compartments that metabolize oxygen. A major site of O_2^- formation is mitochondria [13]. O_2^- is converted into H_2O_2 probably in the flavomononucleotide (FMN) group of complex I of the mitochondrial electron transport chain [34, 35]. Another source of H_2O_2 is monoamine oxidase, associated with the outer membrane of mitochondria [5].

Major sources of ROS in animals are phagocytic leukocytes, the thyroid, and the endothelium. In phagocytic cells, ROS protect the organism against invading pathogens [4, 36]; in the thyroid, H_2O_2 participates in the synthesis of thyroid hormone [37, 38]; whereas in the endothelium, ischemia results in the formation of oxygen radicals after reperfusion [39].

Phagocytes are components of the immune system and accumulate during inflammation. It has been shown that this aggregation is caused by chemoattractants such as bacterial chemotactic peptides, the C5a fragment of comple-

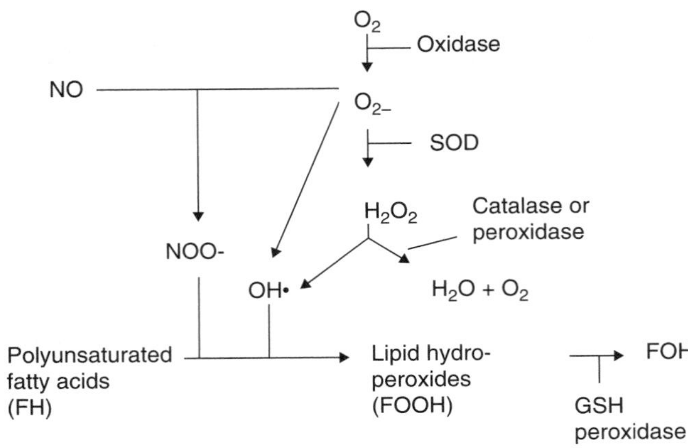

FIGURE 20.1 Oxygen metabolism.

ment, or leukotriene B_4, which are produced locally during inflammation. Epithelioid cells in the rat kidney produce a cytokine-induced neutrophil chemoattractant called *CINC/gro* [40], suspected of functioning as a chemoattractant for neutrophils in lipopolysacchaside (LPS)-induced inflammation in rats and acting like interleukin-8 (IL-8) in human cells [41].

In phagocytes, O_2^- is formed by the reduction of oxygen by nicotinamide-adenine-dinucleotide phosphate (NADPH) oxidase. This enzyme complex consists of several cytosolic and membrane proteins that come together and increase oxidase activity [4]. It is possible that the mechanism used by phagocytes and the thyroid to produce ROS via NADPH oxidase is also used by other cells such as endothelial and B cells [42], fibroblasts [43], adipocytes [44], sperm [45, 46], and oocytes [47].

Cellular Effects of Reactive Oxygen Species

It is well established that ROS can cause damage to many different biomolecules: they induce lipid peroxidation, protein damage, and deoxyribonucleic acid (DNA) strand breaks and are thereby mutagenic. They also inhibit protein and ribonucleic acid (RNA) synthesis, disrupt membrane ion gradients, inhibit protein cross-linking, impair hormone-adenylate cyclase coupling, and deplete adenosine triphosphate concentrations in the cell.

Lipid peroxidation results from the oxidation of polyunsaturated fatty acids into peroxy-fatty acids that then cause structural alterations in cell membranes. A free radical removes a hydrogen atom from the fatty acid, which then becomes a lipid radical. The latter is quickly oxidized into a lipid peroxy radical that then abstracts a hydrogen atom from a neighboring fatty acid. A chain reaction is thus initiated, leading eventually to fluidity changes in the membrane and ultimately to membrane breakdown if the propagation is not stopped by chain-breaking antioxidants such as vitamin E. Oxidation of these membrane phospholipids leads to the impairment of receptor binding, the inhibition of carrier-mediated transport, and changes in the activity of enzymes such as adenylate cyclase [48]. It was also suggested that NADPH-dependent lipid peroxidation in the human placenta might play an important role in the modulation of progesterone biosynthesis via the degradation of cytochrome P450. Cytochrome P450 is a component of the NADPH-cytochrome P450-linked monooxygenase system of mitochondria, and it is required for progesterone synthesis in the placenta. Cytochrome P450 releases O_2^-, initiating lipid peroxidation, which then seems to degrade the cytochrome [49] and inactivate the essential actor in cholesterol side-chain cleavage [50].

By disrupting the sugar moieties or the bases of DNA, ROS cause DNA strands to break [51]. DNA repair mechanisms such as poly-ADP-ribose polymerase become activated, depleting cell levels of nicotinamide-adenine dinucleoitde (NAD) and consequently adenosine triphosphate (ATP), which often leads to apoptosis or cell death [52]. Cells exposed chronically to ROS show increased rates of mutation, probably because of the less-than-perfect DNA repair mechanism set up in response to strand breaks [53]. ROS also inhibit protein synthesis in some cells, probably as a result of impaired ribosomal function and the inhibition of messenger ribonucleic acid (mRNA) synthesis coupled to increased mRNA degradation [54, 55].

Protection from Reactive Oxygen Species

ROS are normal by-products of respiratory metabolism. O_2^- in particular is produced continuously by mitochondria and plasma membranes of immune cells and other cells. There are several mechanisms of protection against ROS used by cells: specific degradative enzymes, antioxidant vitamins, other radical scavengers, and cellular repair mechanisms.

SOD converts O_2^- to H_2O_2. Cu/Zn-SODs are cytosolic and extracellular metalloenzymes [56], whereas Mn-SOD is a mitochondrial metalloenzyme. Mn-SOD seems to respond most effectively to oxidative stress [57]. Catalase and glutathione peroxidase degrade H_2O_2. Catalase is present in most tissues and is highly specific for H_2O_2, whereas glutathione peroxidase also degrades lipid hydroperoxides and H_2O_2.

The ovary contains conspicuously high levels of many antioxidant vitamins such as vitamin C (ascorbic acid) or vitamin E (α-tocopherol), lipid-soluble carotenoids such as lutein [58–60], and many other natural antioxidants including HClO-scavenging amines [18, 28], urea, and bilirubin [61]. Vitamin C is a water-soluble, first-line scavenger of free radicals that accumulates in cells via a specific energy-dependent transporter [62, 63]. Vitamin E is a hydrophobic molecule present at high concentrations in cell membranes and other lipid-rich environments. It is also present in blood, mainly as lipoprotein complexes; it is then transported into cells via the lipoprotein receptor

[64, 65]. Vitamin E protects against oxygen radicals and helps terminate the domino effect of lipid peroxidation. After reacting with oxygen radicals, vitamin E is recycled to its reduced form by ascorbic acid.

Repair processes can be called on to remove cellular components damaged by oxidative stress. For example, phospholipase A2 and acyltransferases replace peroxidized fatty acids of membrane phospholipids, and poly-ADP-ribose polymerase can be activated to repair DNA [66].

Pharmacology of Reactive Oxygen Species

Table 20.1 presents the agents that influence the production, action, or degradation of ROS. These are often used to determine the presence and activity of different reactive species because their ephemeral nature does not allow easy direct measurement. Table 20.1 separates the agents into activators and inhibitors of ROS enzymes and direct generators or inhibitors of ROS.

REACTIVE OXYGEN SPECIES IN THE FOLLICLE AND OOCYTE

In the Follicle and during Ovulation

It has been suggested that ROS may play a regulatory role in follicular steroidogenesis and might mediate ovulation

Table 20.1 Pharmacology of Reactive Oxygen Species

Reactive Oxygen Species Enzymes	Activators/Inducers	Inhibitors
NADPH oxidase [2–4]	LTB_4, FMLP, C_{5a}, PAF, IL-8, LPS, IL-1, TNF-α, IFN-γ, phorbol, A-23187	DPI, immunosuppression, adenosine
Monoamine oxidase [5]	Benzylamine, β-phenylethylamine, tyramine	Pargyline, clorgyline, pyruvate + malate, isocitrate
Xanthine oxidase [6]	Ischemia, protease, FMLP, TNF-α, C_{5a}, hyp, xan, SH-oxidation	Allopurinol, oxypurinol
NO synthase [2, 7–9]	IFN-γ, A-23187, LPS, arginine, bradykinin, acetylcholine	DPI, TFP, N-methul-arginine, N-nitro-arginine, hemoglobin
SOD [10–12]	Oxidative stress, LPS, IL-1, IL-6, TNF-α, IFN-γ, Mn-SOD	DDC, hydrogen peroxide, CN^-, Mn-SOD
Catalase [2, 13–15]	Oxidative stress	3-AT, azide, CN^-, ethanenitronate
GSH peroxidase [13, 16, 17]	Lipid peroxidation, GSH	Se-deficiency, sulfoxamines
Myeloperoxidase [18–22]	LTB_4, FMLP, C_{5a}, LPS, IL-1, TNF-α, phorbol, A-23187, estrogens	Catalase, hydrogen peroxide, HClO, azide, CN^-, vitamin C, GSH, ceruloplasmin
Reactive Oxygen Species	**Generators**	**Inhibitors**
O_2^- [23]	Oxidases (NADPH and xanthine), reducing agents + Fe, Fe + catechol, paraquat, adriamycin, menadione	SOD, ascorbate, GSH, TNM
H_2O_2 [13, 23]	SOD, Fe + reducing agents, glucose oxidase, XO + SOD, monoamine oxidase	Catalase
OH^- [13, 24]	$O_2^- + Fe^{3+} \rightarrow Fe^{2+} + H_2O_2 \rightarrow OH\cdot$ radiation	Alcohols, DMSO, vitamins E and C, MPG, Fe/Cu chelators
Lipid peroxide [25]	$OH\cdot$, O_2^1, HOCl, R·	GSH peroxidase, vitamin E, antioxidants, 17-β-oestradiol, 4-hydroxytamoxifen, tamoxifen
O_2^1 [10, 18, 19, 26, 27]	Ultraviolet light, photosensitive dyes $H_2O_2 + HOCl \rightarrow O_2^1$	Imidazoles, azide, carotenoids, bilirubin
HClO [18, 20, 28]	Myeloperoxidase + $H_2O_2 + Cl^- \rightarrow HClO$, $NaOCl + H^+ \rightarrow HClO$	Taurine, aminosalicylic acid, vitamins A and C, amino acids
NO [2, 7, 13]	SIN-1	Hemoglobin, O_2^-, methylene blue

3-AT, Aminotriazole; *A-23187*, ionophore; *C_{5a}*, complement factor; *CN^-*, cyanide; *DDC*, diethyldithiocarbamate; *DMSO*, dimethylsulfoxide; *DPI*, diphenylene iodonium; *FMLP*, formylmethionyleucylphenylalanine; *GSH*, *hyp*, hypoxanthine; *IFN*, interferon; *IL*, interleukin; *LPS*, lipopolysaccharide; *LTB_4*, leukotriene B_4; *MPG*, mercaptopropionyl-glycine; *PAF*, platelet-activating factor; *SIN-1*, morpholino-sydnonimine; *TFP*, trifluoperazine; *TNF*, tumor necrosis factor; *TNM*, tetranitromethane; *xan*, xanthine; *XO*, xanthine oxidase.

in mammals. In perfused rabbit ovaries, SOD or a combination of SOD and catalase reduced the number of large follicles that ovulated in response to human chorionic gonadotropin (hCG) [67]. Ovulation resembles acute inflammation in many ways, including the observed increase in ovarian blood flow, vasodilation [68], increased vascular permeability [69], and leukocyte infiltration [70].

Reactive Oxygen Species and Prostaglandins

ROS influence follicular function, notably in nonmammalian species. In mollusks the addition of H_2O_2 to sea water induces spawning in male and female abalones. The eggs are fully competent for normal fertilization, producing hatched free-swimming planktonic larvae [71]. Catalase, mercaptoethanol, or aspirin block this effect. H_2O_2 might have acted by stimulating the production of prostaglandins, which have generally been considered to be the principal group of eicosanoids necessary for ovulation [72].

Recruited Leukocytes: Reactive Oxygen Species Producers

Leukocytes are known to produce ROS, and the possible involvement of ROS in ovulation might explain why leukocyte supplementation increases luteinizing hormone (LH)-induced ovulation in the in vitro perfused rat ovary [72a]. Moreover, neutrophil-depleted rats show decreased rates of ovulation [73], and preovulatory follicles in the rat produce O_2^- by a protein kinase C (PKC)-mediated pathway, probably involving cytokine-induced chemoattraction and activation of a leukocytic NADPH oxidase producer [74].

Leukocytes are recruited by the follicle before ovulation [75–77]. Chemokines such as IL-8, CINC/gro, monocyte chemotactic protein-1 (MCP-1), and numerous other members of the four known chemokine families are expressed in the ovaries and might play important roles in this mechanism. An 18-fold increase in MCP-1 6 hours after administration of hCG was associated with leukocyte influx after the midcycle LH surge [77]. CINC/gro, a protein immunohistochemically recognized within the theca layer of the preovulatory follicle, is a rat neutrophil chemoattractant. CINC/gro levels increased 25-fold after hCG treatment, following increases in IL-1β and TNF-α levels, indicating that CINC/gro plays a major role in rat ovulation by attracting neutrophils [75, 77].

IL-8 and Groα were identified in human follicular fluid, and their production was enhanced by hCG [78, 79]. In rabbits, depletion of ovarian IL-8 decreased the rate of ovulation and suppressed neutrophil accumulation and activation in the ovary [80]. Finally, ovarian intrabursal injection of IL-8 increased the rate of ovulation in the rat, suggesting that IL-8 might play an important role in ovulation by chemoattracting neutrophils in and around preovulatory follicles [81]. Many would agree that leukocytes may not be essential for ovulation, but they facilitate the ovulatory process [82], possibly acting in cooperation with other blood-derived cells and their products.

Cytokines: Promoters of Reactive Oxygen Species Production

Cytokines are intracellular signaling proteins secreted by lymphohemopoietic cells, among others. They bind to cell-surface receptors on specific cell types and regulate ovarian functions such as steroidogenesis, prostaglandin production, and gonadotropin receptor induction [83] during the processes of follicular atresia [84], ovulation [85], and luteolysis [86]. It is thought that the regulatory role of cytokines on ovulation might be mediated in part by their stimulatory effect on ROS. Inflammation reactions are usually initiated by a release of cytokines, and cytokines have been localized to follicular fluid [87] and ovarian tissue [88]. The rat ovary was found to secrete copious amounts of IL-6 and granulocyte-macrophage colony–stimulating factor (GM-CSF), with low but detectable levels of TNF-α and IL-1.

GM-CSF is a glycoprotein cytokine that recruits and activates granulocytes, macrophages, and mast cells in peripheral tissues. Several cell types present in the ovary including fibroblasts, endothelial cells, T lymphocytes, macrophages, and mast cells produce GM-CSF [89]. Ovarian output of this cytokine appears to peak with ovulation, suggesting that GM-CSF might play an important role in mediating this event [90]. IL-6 can induce acute phase proteins [91] and appears to have a role in steroidogenesis [92]. It is released at a constant rate by the ovary throughout the ovulatory cycle [90]. IL-1 is capable of producing free radicals and is probably secreted by somatic ovarian cells and macrophages [93]. The IL-1 peak coincides with neutrophil and macrophage infiltration [94]. It has been suggested that granulosa cells of ovarian tissue may also be a source of TNF-α [95], which seems to be involved in follicular atresia, by stimulating thecal progesterone production [84], inhibiting LH-stimulated androgen production by theca cells [96], and inhibiting follicle-stimulating hormone (FSH)-stimulated aromatase activity in the granulosa [97]. Both IL-1 and TNF-α have been shown to promote ovulation in the in vitro perfused rat ovary [85]. The following paradigm has been suggested: LH induces production of TNF-α and IL-1, facilitating leukocyte adhesion to endothelial cells and inducing GM-CSF release by fibroblasts and endothelial cells. Monocytes and granulocytes are then recruited and activated by the latter to secrete eicosanoids, more cytokines, ROS, and other ovulation-associated factors [90].

Xanthine-Xanthine Oxidase: Superoxide Producer

Another possible source of ROS in the follicle might be xanthine oxidase, the O_2^--producing system. Allopurinol, an inhibitor of this enzyme, reduced ovulation in the rabbit

[98]. However, the activity of xanthine oxidase is not increased at ovulation in the rat, and allopurinol did not inhibit ovulation in that species [99].

In Follicular Atresia

ROS are probably involved in follicular atresia. Macrophages were identified in follicular fluids of several species [100, 101], including the human [102]. They have the ability to produce oxidative products: NO, O_2^-, and H_2O_2 [103]. DNA damage, such as that initiated by oxidative free radicals, has been proposed as the possible mechanism for the activation of the apoptotic cascade in atretic follicles [104]. The appearance of macrophages within granulosa cells associated with the onset of apoptosis indicates that macrophages are involved in atresia in rats [105].

Cytochrome P450 is a component of the cytochrome P450-linked monooxygenase system, which is involved in hormonogenesis. After the LH surge, or after hCG treatment, a decrease in microsomal cytochrome P450 was observed in ovarian follicles. It is believed that this inactivation could be caused by oxidative stress because ascorbic acid eliminated this effect in a time-dependent manner [106]. Moreover, in the presence of low levels of H_2O_2, granulosa cells rapidly stop responding to FSH and LH and steroidogenesis is blocked in the rat [107]. FSH also seems to magnify the inhibitory effects of extracellular SOD on granulosa cell aromatase independently of the H_2O_2 pathway, possibly by increasing cell levels of cyclic GMP, a second messenger involved in inhibiting aromatase activity [108]. The exact mechanism of cyclic GMP function is unknown, and the same is true of SOD effects on cyclic guanosine monophosphate (GMP) production. However, NO might be involved in cyclic GMP control, because NO is a potent activator of guanylate cyclase and SOD is known to augment NO-stimulated cyclic GMP levels, whereas NO inhibits human granulosa-luteal cell steroidogenesis [109].

In the Oocyte

Oocyte maturation requires the presence of oxygen, preferably in low concentrations. Glucose and oxidative phosphorylation for the generation of ATP are also necessary for maturation [110, 111]. ROS are probable participants in maturation [112] and meiosis resumption. In fact, antioxidants block the spontaneous resumption of meiosis [113, 114].

NO also seems to play an important role in ovulation and oocyte maturation because endothelial NO synthase knockouts and NO synthase inhibitors impaired these events in mice. Fewer oocytes from knockout mice reached metaphase II, the first polar body was often unusually large, and some oocytes contained two polar bodies [115, 116]. Recent evidence links NO as an inhibitor of meiosis resumption [117]. O_2^- may possibly induce the resumption of meiosis because of its well-known action to reduce NO levels, as described earlier.

In metazoan eggs such as the sea urchin and in teleost fish, ROS are essential for fertilization. In these species, the fertilization envelope, a hard barrier impermeable to sperm, blocks polyspermy. It is formed a few minutes after fertilization and is dependent on ROS. An NADPH oxidase present in the egg plasma membrane releases H_2O_2 into the extracellular matrix. A unique ovoperoxidase is secreted simultaneously in the same area to cross-link tyrosyl moieties of proteins derived from cortical granules that are deposited on the vitelline membrane. Dityrosyl cross-linking produces the hard, almost indestructible fertilization envelope that surrounds the egg. Ovothiols, a family of mercaptoimidazoles, protect the egg from oxidative products generated within the egg by the respiratory burst [47, 118].

The concentration of H_2O_2 in mouse oocytes is usually low, but it increases after fertilization with a peak at the mid two-cell stage [119]. It is suggested that ROS might block embryo development at the two-cell stage in this species, because it had been shown earlier that activated ROS may arrest normal cell division [120]. This suggestion was confirmed by observations that free radical scavengers ameliorate the two-cell block in mouse embryos [121].

Protection against Reactive Species

Of the follicles developing in the ovary, only 1% ovulate, whereas the other 99% undergo atresia. The main event in follicular atresia is apoptosis, which may be a consequence of oxidative stress. Protective mechanisms against oxidative stress are involved in the process of follicular selection. For example, FSH, SOD, ascorbic acid, and N-acetyl L-cysteine (a free radical scavenger) block apoptosis in follicle cells in vitro and a gonadotropin treatment in vivo was associated with increased levels of secreted SOD mRNAs and Mn-SOD mRNA [122].

It has been demonstrated that O_2^-, present in ovarian tissue [123] causes damage to cell membranes and DNA, whereas O_2^- also inactivates many enzymes. There is an inverse correlation between levels of O_2^- and SOD in ovarian cells throughout the estrous cycle [123]. SOD has been shown to inhibit hCG-induced ovulation in isolated perfused rabbit ovaries [124].

Further research using SOD knockout mice showed an essential role for Cu/Zn-SOD in ovarian function, whereas Mn-SOD-deficient ovaries were transplanted to the bursa of wild-type mice without effects on fertility. Cu/Zn-SOD-deficient mice showed low levels of LH and FSH, implying that Cu/Zn-SOD might influence LH and FSH levels thereby affecting fertility [125]. Moreover, levels of Cu/Zn-SOD in human female and male genital organs are high, suggesting an important role for the SOD in protection against inflammation. Cyclic changes of Cu/Zn-SOD localization and intensity in endometria and ovarian follicles suggest a hormonally dependent expression of SOD and its possible participation in steroid biosynthesis [126]. No or weak Cu/Zn-SOD activity was observed in the nonantral follicle of the human ovary, but once the follicle began to form the antral cavity, theca interna cells exhibited intensive SOD activity. Cu/Zn-SOD in the theca interna appears to play a role in protecting the developing oocyte from oxygen radicals, acting as a blood-follicular barrier during follicular maturation [127].

Ascorbic acid and α-tocopherol are also highly concentrated in ovarian interstitial tissue [128, 129]. Ascorbic acid accumulates in large amounts within the granulosa, thecal, and luteal cell layers [130] thanks to a Na^+- and energy-dependent transporter that is regulated by hormones and involves many second messengers [62, 63]. Granulosa cells also take up dehydroascorbic acid (the oxidized form of ascorbic acid), via an endocrine-mediated insulin-insensitive glucose-transporter. This ability might be valuable for maintaining adequate ascorbate levels in the cell [131]. Ascorbic acid has been associated with fertility [132] and is used in cows to treat infertility [133]. LH depletes ascorbic acid in the ovary and preovulatory follicles [134]. Uptake of the vitamin is blocked and the tissue levels are depleted as the cell begins to produce higher amounts of progesterone in response to LH [135]. The depletion of ascorbic acid in the preovulatory follicle coincides with the rise in ROS before follicular rupture and resumption of meiosis. Moreover, agents that deplete ascorbic acid induce oocyte maturation. The exact mechanism by which ascorbic acid depletion affects the onset of meiosis is unclear: ascorbic acid could be inhibiting meiosis, or its depletion could be a result of an increase in ROS [136]. Oocytes in atretic follicles resume meiosis before their degeneration.

In addition, ascorbic acid has been implicated in collagen biosynthesis. Lack of ascorbic acid causes degeneration of follicle membranes [137, 138]. Follicular cultures from the late preantral to the Graafian stages showed that ascorbic acid is necessary for the remodeling of the basement membrane. Ascorbic acid also reduced the degree of apoptosis in follicles that were subjected in vitro to oxidative stress, suggesting that ascorbic acid plays an important role in follicle survival and dominant follicle selection [139].

Glutathione (GSH), the cofactor for lipid hydroperoxide detoxifying enzyme, glutathione peroxidase, is another important mediator of antioxidant protection in the ovary [140]. This intracellular thiol is capable of altering the generation of free radicals following exposure to radiation or cyclophosphamide. GSH can also bind and thereby reduce the effectiveness of several chemotherapeutic agents [141–143]. Glutathione-S-transferase (GST) is a group of cytoplasmic enzymes that catalyze the conjugation of GSH with various electrophiles and plays an important role in the protection of germ cells from xenobiotics [144].

GSH is synthesized during oocyte maturation in many species [145–147]. GSH, with the possible collaboration of cumulus cells in porcine oocytes [148], appears to play an important role in protecting the cell against oxidative damage [16, 149]. Improved development of 6- to 8-cell bovine embryos to the blastocyst stage is associated with increased intracellular GSH [147], and high GSH concentrations are necessary for overcoming the in vitro development arrest in mice and rats [150]. Depletion of GSH in mature hamster oocytes results in irreversible disruption of spindle microtubules and chromosome clumping, inducing aneuploidy and impaired embryo development [151].

With age, free radical levels appear to acquire progressively a relative predominance over the antioxidative scavenger system in the human ovary and H_2O_2 causes a dose-dependent decrease in aromatase activity in vitro [152]. Loss of antioxidant-oxidant balance could explain the decrease in estrogen production, but the exact mechanisms involved are still unclear.

REACTIVE OXYGEN SPECIES IN THE CORPUS LUTEUM AND LUTEOLYSIS

In the Corpus Luteum

Neutrophils are major producers of ROS in the rat corpus luteum, because activation of neutrophils block luteal function in a catalase-sensitive manner [153]. Mononuclear phagocytes that generate ROS when activated are also present in the corpus luteum. Progesterone might play an important role in luteal function by inhibiting O_2^- production by mononuclear phagocytes in pseudopregnant rats [103]. During regression, phagocytes are activated to produce O_2^- in the corpus luteum, but the mechanism by which this occurs is unclear. Low concentrations of progesterone, ischemia-reperfusion, or the activity of prostaglandin $F_{2\alpha}$ ($PGF_{2\alpha}$) could be some possibilities [103].

It is known, however, that low levels of H_2O_2 inhibit progesterone production immediately in the rat. This action of H_2O_2 is mediated by OH·, which induces DNA damage, inhibits protein synthesis, and depletes ATP [154]. LH may induce SOD leading to the conversion of O_2^- to H_2O_2 that then activates peroxidase [123, 155]. Low levels of H_2O_2 stimulate progesterone secretion in midluteal cells in the human [156]. In the same way, low doses of LH or xanthine-xanthine oxidase (an in vitro O_2^--generating system) promote an increase in progesterone secretion [155]. Thus, in certain species, low levels of some ROS might be beneficial to progesterone secretion in the corpus luteum.

During Luteal Arrest

Progesterone synthesis and secretion are terminated with the initiation of luteal regression or luteal arrest. The LH receptor dissociates from the adenylate complex and cyclic adenosine monophosphate (cAMP) levels fall, inhibiting progesterone synthesis. $PGF_{2\alpha}$ has been shown to cause the onset of luteal regression and the structural involution of the corpus luteum in many species [157–159]. Within an hour of treatment with $PGF_{2\alpha}$, progesterone secretion decreases in vivo in the rat [160]. $PGF_{2\alpha}$ treatment of luteal cell cultures induces the uncoupling of the LH receptor complex [157, 160, 161]. LH receptor and steroidogenic enzyme concentrations decrease in late luteal arrest [162]. It is well established that O_2^- [163], H_2O_2 [164], and lipid peroxides [165] are all generated during luteal regression after $PGF_{2\alpha}$, but their cellular origin is still unclear. As detailed below, immune cells infiltrate during luteal arrest, implicating these cells in the generation of ROS.

Mechanism of $PGF_{2\alpha}$ Action

Xanthine oxidase (XO) treatment in vitro causes loss of membrane fluidity because of lipid peroxidation and phospholipid breakdown and inhibits LH-stimulated progesterone secretion in vitro in rat luteal cells. These effects are similar to those of $PGF_{2\alpha}$ and suggest that $PGF_{2\alpha}$ and XO action might be mediated by ROS. Moreover, ascorbic acid concentrations are depleted shortly after $PGF_{2\alpha}$ treatment in the rat corpus luteum implying that ROS may mediate this response [166]. It is probable that O_2^-, produced both with $PGF_{2\alpha}$ and in vitro with XO treatment, leads to the formation of other ROS that play roles in regression, activating phospholipases and producing lipid peroxides. Catalase inhibits the effects of XO, demonstrating that it is H_2O_2 and not O_2^- that mediates the luteolytic actions of XO and possibly also $PGF_{2\alpha}$. It should be noted however that XO has been discounted as a major ROS-producer in the rat ovary [99].

Evidence of Superoxide Presence and Effects

O_2^-, along with H_2O_2 and lipid peroxides, is generated shortly following $PGF_{2\alpha}$ treatment [48, 164]. The ovarian O_2^--generator is probably an NADPH/NADH oxidase with a flavoprotein component [167]. Although the generator and mechanism of O_2^- production is unknown, $PGF_{2\alpha}$-induced O_2^- is produced by several subcellular components, including the plasma membrane, mitochondria, and cytosol. The O_2^- burst is first observed in the mitochondria, followed by a peak in the plasma membrane [168]. It is accompanied by a significant decrease in membrane fluidity that precedes the fall in serum progesterone levels characteristic of functional luteolysis [168, 169]. Eventually, lipid peroxidation and structural involution leads to apoptosis [170].

Lipid Peroxidation

Lipid peroxidation, detected as malondialdehyde, is a consequence of ROS production. Malondialdehyde levels increase significantly after $PGF_{2\alpha}$-induced luteolysis in the rat [171]. Lipid hydroperoxides inhibit LH-sensitive cAMP accumulation and progesterone production, suggesting a possible role for lipid hydroperoxides in functional luteolysis [172].

Hydrogen Peroxide in the Corpus Luteum

In vivo generation of H_2O_2 increases in rat luteal tissue within 2 hours of $PGF_{2\alpha}$ treatment, whereas serum progesterone levels drop. H_2O_2 was found to have an important role in mediating luteal arrest in rats treated with $PGF_{2\alpha}$ [164]. $PGF_{2\alpha}$ inhibits the stimulation of adenylate cyclase by LH [157]. However, H_2O_2 does not appear to act by blocking LH-receptor binding in the rat [154], whereas it did in the human [156]. In the rat, it could be interfering with G protein-dependent activation of adenylate cyclase [107, 154]. H_2O_2 inhibits cAMP-dependent progesterone synthesis by interrupting cAMP-dependent cholesterol transport to the inner membrane of the mitochondria [173]. This may be mediated by the deactivation of certain gonadotropin-dependent and cAMP-dependent inducible proteins responsible for directing cholesterol translocation into the mitochondria, because H_2O_2 is an inhibitor of protein synthesis in luteal cells [174]. Moreover, whereas LH-sensitive cAMP accumulation is partially reversible, inhibition of cAMP-dependent steroidogenesis is irreversible [175].

Cell levels of ATP also decrease significantly within minutes of H_2O_2 treatment, probably in response to the initiation of DNA repair mechanisms. Whereas H_2O_2 might be cytotoxic rather than luteolytic, there is no evidence of cell death after 24 hours with H_2O_2 treatment [154, 175].

The Hydroxyl Radical

H_2O_2 inactivates certain enzymes by oxidizing specific sulfhydryl groups, but otherwise, it is not considered a very reactive molecule. Rather it is the potential conversion of H_2O_2 to more reactive groups that are highly cytotoxic that is more significant. H_2O_2 reacts with iron atoms by the Fenton reaction to produce OH·. Orthophenanthrolene, a cell-permeable iron chelator, blocks the effect of H_2O_2 in luteal cells, suggesting that OH· mediates some of its effects, causing DNA and RNA damage, depleting ATP, and inhibiting protein synthesis [176]. H_2O_2 is also an essential substrate for peroxidases that generate the highly toxic HClO.

Leukocytes

Whereas ovarian cells probably play an important role in luteolysis, immune cells produce ROS that are also essential in luteal arrest. The number of macrophages and neutrophils present in the theca increases five- to eightfold during ovulation [83] and migrate into the forming corpora lutea [177]. Moreover, activation of phagocytic leukocytes increases O_2^- production [167]. It was suggested that neutrophils resident in luteinized ovaries produce O_2^- via protein kinase C-activation after $PGF_{2\alpha}$ treatment. ROS in ovarian tissue were shown to mediate leukocyte-endothelium interaction and neutrophil infiltration [178], thereby attracting more neutrophils. The accumulated neutrophils then produce more O_2^-, causing increased oxidative stress.

Monocytes, macrophages, and neutrophils release myeloperoxidase that generates HClO, which in turn, can cause DNA damage and lipid peroxidation. Eosinophils infiltrate the corpus luteum during regression so their specific HSCNO-generating peroxidase [179] might also play a role in luteal arrest. HClO and H_2O_2 interact to form the highly reactive O_2^1, another potential actor in luteal arrest. The presence of O_2^1 might explain the high luteal concentrations of lutein, an O_2^1 scavenger. Finally, macrophages present in the corpus luteum [102, 180] accumulate during regression [94, 181]. The activity of certain products of macrophages such as TNFα [182] increases during late luteal regression, possibly inhibiting endothelial cell proliferation, inhibiting gonadotropin-supported progesterone production, or stimulating prostaglandin production in certain species [87, 183, 184]. Cytokines such as TNFα and IFNγ, as well as ROS and prostaglandins, stimulate the synthesis of heat shock proteins (HSP), thereby reducing progesterone synthesis in human-granulosa luteal cells [185]. HSP-70 is strongly induced during natural and $PGF_{2\alpha}$–mediated luteolysis, and it was shown to block hormone-sensitive steroidogenesis in rat luteal cells, probably by interfering with the translocation of cholesterol into the mitochondria [186, 187]. Interestingly, physiological and pharmacological inhibitors of LH-dependent steroidogenesis induced HSP-70 in rat luteal cells, further suggesting that the latter might be an early mediator of luteal regression [188].

It is believed that the first step for O_2^- generation must involve steroidogenic luteal cells that have $PGF_{2\alpha}$ receptors, because leukocytes lack such receptors. As a consequence, a chemoattractant is produced to increase neutrophil infiltration and subsequent O_2^- generation [189]. In the rat ovary, the cytokine-induced neutrophil chemoattractant CINC/gro was localized to the theca layer of the preantral follicle [75]. MCP-1 expression is increased during luteal regression and associated with an accumulation of immune cells in the corpus luteum of the cow. However, this may be a result rather than a source of ROS [77, 190, 191]. Recent results show that $PGF_{2\alpha}$-treatment induces CINC/gro in the rat corpus luteum, increasing the protein's expression within 1 hour of treatment [191a].

Despite the uncertainty that still clouds the mechanisms of ROS production induced by $PGF_{2\alpha}$, it is well established that O_2^- is generated in large amounts after an hour of $PGF_{2\alpha}$ treatment in vivo, and this increase in O_2^- accompanies the fall in progesterone levels. As was suggested earlier, it is likely that H_2O_2 or its metabolites serve as the mediator of $PGF_{2\alpha}$ action rather than O_2^- directly.

Antioxidant Action in the Corpus Luteum

Ascorbic acid is present in the corpus luteum in high concentrations [128]; vitamin E and carotenoids show their highest concentrations in the corpus luteum and adrenal gland [60]. Accumulation of ascorbic acid by the corpus luteum and luteal cells is ensured by an energy and sodium-dependent process [192, 193], whereas dehydroascorbic acid is transported into rat luteal cells in an endocrine-regulated and glucose-sensitive manner [194].

After LH or $PGF_{2\alpha}$ treatment in the rat, ascorbic acid is depleted in luteal cells, accompanied by an increase in lipid peroxidation [135, 195] and a suppression of serum progesterone levels [171]. Depletion is mediated both by the oxidation of ascorbic acid as well as the secretion of the antioxidant by luteal cells after $PGF_{2\alpha}$ or LH treatment [192], but the reaction to $PGF_{2\alpha}$ is much faster than to LH, because $PGF_{2\alpha}$ can also inhibit ascorbic acid uptake by the cells [192]. Ascorbic acid has been reported to play a cytoprotective role during the respiratory burst after $PGF_{2\alpha}$ by interacting with leukocyte peroxidases and thereby detoxifying H_2O_2 in the extracellular milieu [196].

Vitamin E levels, on the other hand, increase dramatically after functional regression of the rat corpus luteum [171]. An acute injection of LH causes a significant increase in luteal vitamin E levels, whereas the levels were not altered by $PGF_{2\alpha}$. Lipoprotein receptors mediate plasma transport of vitamin E, and lipoproteins that mediate vitamin E uptake increase in response to LH along with vitamin E uptake [171]. Moreover, the decline in progesterone levels observed in natural luteal regression is not directly affected by addition of vitamin E to ovine corpora lutea treated with $PGF_{2\alpha}$, but the corpora lutea rebounded within 3 days, recovering previous levels and avoiding terminal involution [197]. The increase in vitamin E levels following functional regression may be a consequence of diminished consumption by ROS rather than an increase in uptake of the antioxidant [198].

Glutathione levels increase during the follicular phase until midpregnancy, after which they fall gradually in the rat [195]. Antioxidant levels in the ovary appear to fluctuate with the cycle, suggesting that they are endocrine regulated and play a role in controlling or allowing the structural changes mediated by ROS that lead to apoptosis.

The corpus luteum expresses both Cu/Zn-SOD and Mn-SOD. Prolactin, along with prolactin-like hormones, protects the structure against oxygen radicals by stimulating the expression of these two SOD enzymes both in vitro and in vivo in the rat. The protection enables continual progesterone secretion, usually inhibited by ROS [199]. Following gonadotropin treatment to induce follicular growth, rat theca interna cell levels of Mn-SOD mRNA increases markedly whereas Mn-SOD activity decreases [200, 200a], and the ovarian activity of Mn-SOD is positively correlated with progesterone production throughout pseudopregnancy and during natural regression in rabbits [201, 202]. These results strongly suggest an important role for SOD, and more specifically for Mn-SOD, in luteal steroidogenesis.

The activity of SOD increases until midpregnancy in the rat [202] and pig [203] and decreases gradually thereafter as progesterone secretion drops [202]. The control of SOD is poorly understood, although cytokines appear to have a regulatory role over Mn-SOD. TNFα induces Mn-SOD expression in vitro [204] and in vivo [205], whereas lipopolysaccharide, IL-1α, IL-β, and IL-6 also caused an increase in Mn-SOD mRNA levels. Testosterone, along with other placental luteotropins, also seems to have a stimulatory effect on Mn-SOD expression and progesterone production [206]. However, Cu/Zn-SOD was not affected by these cytokines, hormones, or LPS. Therefore the two SOD are probably regulated differently. They must therefore also have different regulatory roles in the corpus luteum [205, 206]. Cu/Zn-SOD encompasses 80% of total SOD in the corpus luteum, and ROS are increased as Cu/Zn-SOD and progesterone levels decrease in tandem, suggesting that this SOD plays an essential role in protection, but its regulation and role remain poorly understood [202].

The activity of catalase was also shown to fluctuate throughout the ovarian cycle, with a fivefold increase in rat peroxisomes after pregnant mare serum gonadotropins (PMSG)-hCG treatment. A similar increase was observed in pig granulosa cells [207]. Because it parallels an increase in cytochrome P450 concentration, the elevation of catalase might be a protection-mechanism against lipid peroxidation by products of H_2O_2.

Along with these antioxidant enzymes, it was suggested that apoptosis regulatory molecules of the bcl-2 family might also be involved in luteal regression. For example, bax, a proapoptotic bcl-2 family member, promotes apoptosis by inducing mitochondrial release of ROS in the bovine corpus luteum [208]. An inverse relationship was found between the expression of bcl-x and bax mRNA levels in the rabbit corpus luteum throughout pseudopregnancy and regression, with bcl-x mRNA levels being highest until the onset of regression, when bax mRNA becomes predominant. SOD was found to regulate the expression of these genes in an in vitro model, suggesting a novel role for SOD in cell protection [209].

The defense mechanism set up by the luteal cell appears to involve antioxidant enzymes, vitamins, and the suppression of prooxidant factors. The intricate system is overwhelmed when luteotropic support is removed and the redox-balance is lost. ROS then predominate, cause damage to cell membranes, decrease ATP levels, and inhibit progesterone synthesis. The final result is luteal regression and apoptosis.

MEDICAL IMPLICATIONS OF REACTIVE OXYGEN SPECIES IN THE OVARY

In women, ovarian cancer represents 4% of cancers and 6% of cancer deaths. This mortality rate is higher than for cervical and endometrial cancer combined. Survival of ovarian cancer patients has not really improved during the past decades and only 5% to 15% of patients with advanced disease survive 5 years or longer. Therefore research on the mechanisms involved in ovarian cancer and the discovery of better treatments is essential. ROS have been implicated in many medical problems [23], including ovarian cancer. Nulliparous women are at higher risk of contracting ovarian cancer compared with women with one or two children, whereas contraceptives reduce the risk of ovarian cancer [210]. It has been hypothesized that the trauma associated with each cyclic ovulation culminates in unrestrained proliferation and neoplasia [211]. High gonadotropin concentrations experienced at menopause might also aggravate the risk of ovarian cancer [210]. Moreover, ROS generated in the ovary at each cycle damage cell membranes and DNA and also increase mutagenesis [51]. They may therefore contribute to ovarian cancer. Furthermore, it has been suggested that the LH surge associated with each ovulation stimulates ROS production, inducing increased tissue damaging and resulting in higher tumor risks [210].

Oophoritis, usually associated with other ovarian inflammations, is suspected of generating high levels of ROS in the ovary. ROS and other radicals destroy oocytes [212] and could therefore be a central cause of infertility or premature menopause. ROS are produced during immune responses and have been linked to autoimmune diseases in many organs, pointing to the possibility of similar effects on the ovary. ROS are also produced during inflammation and endometriosis, encouraging the formation of pelvic adhesions [213], another cause of infertility. Endometriomas are common in the ovary and can produce high levels of ROS, leading to infertility and gonadotropin resistance. This was observed in isolated human ovarian cells incubated with H_2O_2 [175]. The production and effects of ROS are essential for understanding the causes of infertility and cancer and in the search for cures.

References

1. Fridovich, I. (1986). Biological effects of the superoxide radical. *Arch. Biochem. Biophys.* 247, 1–11.
2. Schmidt, H. H. W., Warner, T. D., Ishii, K., Sheng, H., and Murad, F. (1992). Insulin secretion from pancreatic B cells

caused by L-arginine-derived nitrogen oxides. *Science* 255, 721–723.

3. Schuman, E. M., and Madison, D. V. (1991). A requirement for the intracellular messenger nitric oxide in long-term potentiation. *Science* 254, 1503–1506.
4. Morel, F., Doussiere, J., and Vignais, P. V. (1991). The superoxide-generating oxidase of phagocytic cells. *Eur. J. Biochem.* 201, 523–546.
5. Sandri, G., Panfili, E., and Ernster, L. (1990). Hydrogen peroxide production by monoamine oxidase in isolated rat-brain mitochondria: Its effect on glutathione levels and Ca2+ efflux. *Biochim. Biophys. Acta* 1035, 300–305.
6. Friedl, H. P., Till, G. O., Ryan, U. S., and Ward, P. A. (1988). Mediator-induced activation of xanthine oxidase in endothelial cells. *FASEB J.* 3, 2512–2518.
7. Palmer, R. M. J., Ferrige, A. G., and Moncada, S. (1987). Nitric oxide accounts for the biological activity of endothelium-derived relaxing factor. *Nature* 327, 524–526.
8. Stuehr, D. J., Fasehun, O. A., Kwon, N. S., Gross, S. S., Gonzalez, J. A., Levi, R., and Nathan, C. F. (1991). Inhibition of macrophage and endothelial cell nitric oxide synthase by diphenyleneiodonium and its analogs. *FASEB J.* 5, 98–103.
9. Gryglewski, R. J., Palmer, R. M., and Moncada, S. (1986). Superoxide anion is involved in the breakdown of endothelium-derived vascular relaxing factor. *Nature* 320, 454–456.
10. Hodgson, E. K., and Fridovich, I. (1975). The interaction of bovine erythrocyte superoxide dismutase with hydrogen peroxide: Inactivation of the enzyme. *Biochemistry* 14, 5294–5298.
11. Harris, C. A., Derbin, K. S., Hunte-McDonough, B., Krauss, M. R., Chen, K. T., Smith, D. M., and Epstein, L. B. (1991). Manganese superoxide dismutase is induced by IFN-g in multiple cell types Synergistic induction by IFN-g and tumor necrosis factor or IL-1. *J. Immunol.* 147, 149–154.
12. Dougall, W. C., and Nick, H. S. (1991). Manganese superoxide dismutase: A hepatic acute phase protein regulated by interleukin-6 and glucocorticoids. *Endocrinology* 129, 2376–2384.
13. Chance, B., Sies, H., and Boveris, A. (1979). Hydroperoxide metabolism in mammalian organs. *Physiol. Rev.* 59, 527–605.
14. Porter, D. J. T., and Bright, H. J. (1987). Ethanenitronate is a peroxide-dependent suicide substrate for catalase. *J. Biol. Chem.* 262, 9608–9614.
15. Aebi, H. E. (1983). Catalase. In *Methods of Enzymatic Analysis*, Vol. 3, ed. E. Bergmeyer, 273–286. *Verlag Chem, Weinheim.*
16. Meister, A., and Anderson, M. E. (1983). Glutathione. *Ann. Rev. Biochem.* 52, 711–760.
17. Toyoda, H., Himeno, S-I, and Imura, N. (1990). Regulation of glutathione peroxidase mRNA level by dietary selenium manipulation. *Biochim. Biophys. Acta* 1049, 213–215.
18. Test, S. T., and Weiss, S. J. (1986). The generation of utilization of chlorinated oxidants by human neutrophils. *Adv. Free Radic. Biol. Med.* 2, 91–116.
19. Uehara, K., Hori, K., Nakano, M., and Koga, S. (1991). Highly sensitive chemiluminescence method for determining myeloperoxidase in human polymorphonuclear leukocytes. *Anal. Biochem.* 199, 191–196.
20. Stelmaszynska, T., Kukovetz, E., Egger, G., and Schaur, R. J. (1992). Possible involvement of myeloperoxidase in lipid peroxidation. *Int. J. Biochem.* 24, 121–128.
21. Dularay, B., Elson, C. J., Clements-Jewery, S., Damais, C., and Lando, D. (1990). Recombinant human interleukin-1 beta primes human polymorponuclear leukocytes for stimulus-induced myeloperoxidase release. *J. Leuk. Biol.* 47, 158–163.
22. Jansson, G. (1991). Oestrogen-induced enhancement of myeloperoxidase activity in human polymorphonuclear leukocytes—A possible cause of oxidative stress in inflammatory cells. *Free Radic. Res. Commun.* 14, 195–208.
23. Halliwell, B. (1987). Oxidants and human disease: Some new concepts. *FASEB J.* 1, 358–364.
24. Tsao, P. S., Aoki, N., Lefer, D. J., Johnson, III, G., and Lefer, A. M. (1990). Time course of endothelial dysfunction and myocardial injury during myocardial ischemia and reperfusion in the cat. *Circulation* 82, 1402–1412.
25. Halliwell, B., and Gutteridge, J. M. C. (1988). *Free Radicals in Biology and Medicine.* Oxford: Oxford University Press.
26. DiMascio, P., Kaiser, S. P., Thomas, J., Devasagayam, P. A., and Sies, H. (1990). Biological significance of active oxygen species: In vitro studies on singlet oxygen-induced DNA damage and on the singlet oxygen quenching ability of carotenoids, tocopherols and thiols. In *Biological Reactive Intermediates*, Vol. IV, ed. C. M. Witmer, 71–77. New York: Plenum Press.
27. Hartman, P. E., Hartman, Z., and Ault, K. T. (1990). Scavenging of singlet molecular oxygen by imidazole compounds: High and sustained activities of carboxy terminal histidine dipeptides and exceptional activity of imidazole-4-acetic acid. *Photochem. Photobiol.* 51, 59–66.
28. Dallegri, F., Ottonello, L., Ballestrero, A., Bogliolo, F., Ferrando, F., and Patrone, F. (1990). Cytoprotection against neutrophil derived hypochlorous acid: A potential mechanism for the therapeutic action of 5-aminosalicyclic acid in ulcerative colitis. *Gut.* 31, 184–186.
29. Aune, T. M., and Thomas, E. L. (1977). Accumulation of hypothiocyanite ion during peroxidase-catalyzed oxidation of thiocyanate ion. *Eur. J. Biochem.* 80, 209–214.
30. Stryer, L. (2000). *Biochemistry*, 4th ed. New York: W. H. Freeman and Co.
31. Heinzel, B., John, M., Klatt, P., Bohme, E., and Mayer, B. (1992). Ca2+/calmodulin-dependent formation of hydrogen peroxide by brain nitric oxide synthase. *Biochem. J.* 281, 627–630.
32. Mayer, M., John, M., Heinzel, B., Werner, E. R., Wachter, H., Schultz, G., and Bohme, E. (1991). Brain nitric oxide synthase is a biopterin- and falvin-containing multifunctional oxido-reductase. *Fed. Eur. Biochem. Soc.* 288, 187–191.
33. Eiserich, J. (2002). Myeloperoxidase, a leukocyte-derived vascular NO oxidase. *Science* 296, 2391–2394.
34. Boveris, A., and Chance, B. (1973). The mitochondrial generation of hydrogen peroxide general properties and effect of hyperbaric oxygen. *Biochem. J.* 134, 707–716.
35. Liu, Y., Fiskum, G., and Schubert, D. (2002). Generation of reactive oxygen species by the mitochondial electron transport chain. *J. Neurochem.* 180, 780.

36. Halliwell, B., and Gutteridge, J. M. C. (1988). *Free Radicals in Biology and Medicine*, 2d ed. Oxford: Clarendon Press.
37. Nunez, J., and Pommier, J. (1982). Formation of thyroid hormones. *Vitam. Horm.* 39, 175–229.
38. Dupuy, C., Kaniewski, J., Deme, D., Pommier, J., and Virion, A. (1988). NADPH-dependent H_2O_2 generation catalyzed by thyroid plasma membranes. Studies with electron scavengers. *Eur. J. Biochem.* 185, 597–603.
39. Zweier, J. L., Kuppusamy, P., and Lutty, G. A. (1988). Measurement of endothelial cell free radical generation: Evidence for a central mechanism of free radical injury in postischemic tissues. *Proc. Natl. Acad. Sci. USA* 85, 4046–4050.
40. Watanabe, K., Kinoshita, S., and Nakagawa, H. (1988). Purification and characterization of cytokine-induced neutrophil chemoattractant produced by epithelioid cell line of normal rat kidney (NRK-52E cell). *Biochem. Biophys. Res. Commun.* 161, 1093–1099.
41. Iida, M., Watanabe, K., Tsurufuji, M., Takaishi, K., Iizuki, W., and Tsurufuji, S. (1992). Level of neutrophil chemotactic factor CINC/gro, a member of the interleukin-8 family, associated with lipopolysaccharide-induced inflammation in rats. *Infect. Immun.* 60, 1268–1272.
42. Maly, F-E. (1990). The B lymphocyte: A newly recognized source of reactive oxygen species with immunoregulatory potential. *Free Radic. Res. Commun.* 8, 143–148.
43. Meier, B., Cross, A. R., Hancock, J. T., Kaup, F. J., and Jones, O. T. G. (1991). Identification of a superoxide-generating NADPH oxidase system in human fibroblasts. *Biochem. J.* 275, 241–245.
44. Krieger-Brauer, H. I., and Kather, H. (1992). Human fat cells possess a plasma membrane-bound H_2O_2-generating system that is activated by insulin via a mechanism bypassing the receptor kinase. *J. Clin. Invest.* 89, 1006–1013.
45. Alvarez, J. G., Touchstone, J. C., Blasco, L., and Storey, B. T. (1987). Spontaneous lipid peroxidation and production of hydrogen peroxide and superoxide in human spermatozoa: Superoxide dismutase as major enzyme protectant against oxygen toxicity. *J. Androl.* 8, 338–348.
46. Aitken, R. J., Clarkson, J. S., and Fishel, S. (1988). Generation of reactive oxygen species, lipid peroxidation, and human sperm function. *Biol. Reprod.* 40, 183–197.
47. Shapiro, B. M. (1991). The control of oxidant stress at fertilization. *Science* 252, 533–536.
48. Sawada, M., and Carlson, J. C. (1991). Rapid plasma membrane changes in superoxide radical formation, fluidity, and phospholipase A2 activity in the corpus luteum of the rat during induction of luteolysis. *Endocrinology* 128, 2992–2998.
49. Klimek, J. (1992). The influence of NADPH-dependent lipid peroxidation on the progesterone biosynthesis in human placental mitochondria. *J. Steroid Biochem. Molec. Biol.* 42, 729–736.
50. Simpson, E. R. (1979). Cholesterol side-chain cleavage, cytochrome P450, and the control of steroidogenesis. *Mol. Cell. Endocrinol.* 13, 213–227.
51. Halliwell, B., and Aruoma, O. I. (1991). DNA damage by oxygen-derived species. *FEBS* 281, 9–19.
52. Schraufstatter, I. U., Hinshaw, D. B., Hyslop, P. A., Spragg, R. G., and Cochrane, C. G. (1986). Oxidant injury of cells. DNA strand-breaks activate polyadenosine diphosphate-ribose polymerase and lead to depletion of nicotinamide adenine dinucleotide. *J. Clin. Invest.* 77, 1312–1320.
53. Imlay, J. A., and Linn, S. (1988). DNA damage and oxygen radical toxicity. *Science* 240, 1302–1309.
54. Schraufstatter, I. U., Hinshaw, D. B., Hyslop, P. A., Spragg, R. G., and Cochrane, C. G. (1986). Oxidant injury of cells. DNA stand-breaks activate polyadenosine diphosphate-ribose polymerase and lead to depletion of nitotinamide adenine dinucleotide. *J. Clin. Invest.* 77, 1312–1320.
55. Jornot, L., Petersen, H., and Junod, A. F. (1991). Differential protective effects of O-phenanthroline and catalase on H_2O_2-induced DNA damage and inhibition of protein synthesis in endothelial cells. *J. Cell. Physiol.* 149, 408–413.
56. McCord, J. M., and Fridovich, I. (1988). Superoxide dismutase: An enzymic function for erythrocuprein (hemocuprein). *J. NIH Res.* 1, 111–120.
57. Visner, G. A., Dougall, W. C., Wilson, J. M., Burr, I. A., and Nick, H. S. (1990). Regulation of manganese superoxide dismutase by lipopolysaccharide, interleukin-1, and tumor necrosis factor. *J. Biol. Chem.* 265, 2856–2864.
58. Yuting, C., Rongliang, Z., Zhongjian, J., and Yong, J. (1990). Flavonoids as superoxide scavengers and antioxidants. *Free Radic. Biol. Med.* 9, 19–21.
59. Krinsky, N. I. (1988). Antioxidant functions of carotenoids. *Free Radic. Biol. Med.* 7, 617–635.
60. Bendich, A., and Olson, J. A. (1988). Biological actions of carotenoids. *FASEB J.* 3, 1927–1932.
61. Smith, L. L. (1991). Another cholesterol hypothesis: Cholesterol as antioxidant. *Free Radic. Biol. Med.* 11, 47–61.
62. Behrman, H. R., Preston, S. L., Aten, R. F., Rinaudo, P., and Zreik, T. G. (1996). Hormone induction of ascorbic acid transport in immature granulosa cells. *Endocrinology* 137, 4316–4321.
63. Zreik, T. G., Kodaman, P. H., Jones, E. E., Olive, D. L., and Behrman, H. R. (1999). Identification and characterization of an ascorbic acid transporter in human granulosa-lutein cells. *Mol. Hum. Reprod.* 5, 299–302.
64. Drevon, C. A. (1991). Absorption, transport and metabolism of vitamin E. *Free Radic. Res. Commun.* 14, 229–246.
65. Traber, M. G., and Kayden, H. J. (1984). Vitamin E is delivered to cells via the high affinity receptor for low-density lipoprotein. *Am. J. Clin. Nutr.* 40, 747–751.
66. Schraufstetter, I. U., Hyslop, P. A., Hinshaw, D. B., Spragg, R. G., Sklar, L. A., and Cochrane, C. G. (1986). Hydrogen peroxide-induced injury of cells and its prevention by inhibitors of poly(ADP-ribose) polymerase. *Proc. Natl. Acad. Sci. USA* 83, 4908–4912.
67. Miyazaki, T., Suioka, K., Dharmarajan, A. M., Atlas, S. J., Bulkley, G. B., and Wallach, E. E. (1991). Effect of inhibition of oxygen free radical on ovulation and progesterone production by the in vitro perfused rabbit ovary. *J. Reprod. Fert.* 91, 207–212.
68. Kranzfelder, D., Reich, R., Abisogun, A. O., and Tsafriri, A. (1992). Preovulatory changes in the perifollicular capillary network in the rat: Role of eicosanoids. *Biol. Reprod.* 46, 379–385.
69. Abisogun, A. O., Daphna-Iken, D., Reich, R., Kranzfelder, D., and Tsafriri, A. (1988). Modulatory role of eicosanoids

in vascular changes during the preovulatory period in the rat. *Biol. Reprod.* 38, 756–762.
70. Gerdes, U., Gafvels, M., Bergh, A., and Cajander, S. (1992). Localized increases in ovarian permeability and leucocyte accumulation after induced ovulation in rabbits. *J. Reprod. Fertil.* 95, 539–550.
71. Morse, D. E., Duncan, H., Hooker, N., and Morse, A. (1977). Hydrogen peroxide induces spawning in mollusks, with activation of prostaglandin endoperoxide synthetase. *Science* 196, 298–300.
72. Hamada, Y., Wright, K., and Wallach, E. (1987). Studies of the mechanism(s) of mammalian ovulation. *Fertil. Steril.* 47, 22–34.
72a. Hellberg, (1991). #707.
73. Brannstrom, M., Bonello, N., Norman, R. J., and Robertson, S. A. (1995). Reduction of ovulation rate in the rat by administration of a neutrophil-depleting monoclonal antibody. *J. Reprod. Immunol.* 29, 265–270.
74. Kodaman, P. H., and Behrman, H. R. (2001). Endocrine-regulated and protein kinase C-dependent generation of superoxide by rat preovulatory follicles. *Endocrinology* 142, 687–693.
75. Ushigoe, K. I. M., Fukumochi, M., Kamada, M., and Aono, T. (2000). Production and regulation of cytokine-induced neutrophil chemoattractant in rat ovulation. *Biol. Reprod.* 63, 121–126.
76. Murdoch, W. J., and McCormick, R. J. (1988). Production of low molecular weight chemoattractants for leukocytes by periovulatory ovine follicles. *Biol. Reprod.* 40, 86–90.
77. Wong, K., Negishi, H., and Adashi, E. Y. (2002). Expression, hormonal regulation, and cyclic variation of chemokines in the rat ovary: Key determinants of the intraovarian residence of representatives of the white blood cell series. *Endocrinology* 143, 784–791.
78. Arici, A., Oral,, E., Bukulmez, O., Buradagunta, S., Engin, O., and Olive, D. L. (1996). Interleukin-8 expression and modulation in human preovulatory follicles and ovarian cells. *Endocrinology* 137, 3762–3769.
79. Oral, E., Seli, E., Bahtiyar, M. O., Jones, E. E., and Arici, A. (1997). Growth-regulated a expression in human preovulatory follicles and ovarian cells. *Am. J. Reprod. Immunol.* 38, 19–25.
80. Ujioka, T., Matsukawa, A., Tanaka, N., Matsuura, K., Yoshinaga, M., and Okamura, H. (1998). Interleukin-8 as an essential factor in the human chorionic gonadotropin-induced rabbit ovulatory process: Interleukin-8 induces neutrophil accumulation and activation in ovulation. *Biol. Reprod.* 58, 526–530.
81. Pehlivan, T., Mulayim, N., Preston, S., and Arici, A. (1998). The effect of interleukin-8 (IL-8) on ovulation rate in a rodent model. *Am. Soc. Reprod. Med.* 70 (Suppl 1), S68.
82. Chun, S-Y, Daphna-Iken, D., Calman, D., and Tsafriri, A. (1993). Severe leukocyte depletion does not affect follicular rupture in the rat. *Biol. Reprod.* 48, 905–909.
83. Adashi, E. Y. (1990). The potential relevance of cytokines to ovarian physiology: The emerging role of resident ovarian cells of the white blood cell series. *Endocr. Rev.* 11, 454–464.
84. Roby, K. F., and Terranova, P. F. (1990). Effects of tumor necrosis factor-a on in vitro steroidogenesis of healthy and atretic follicles of the rat: Theca as a target. *Endocrinology* 126, 2711–2718.
85. Brannstrom, M., Wang, L., and Norman, R. J. (1993). Ovulatory effect of interleukin-1B on the perfused rat ovary. *Endocrinology* 132, 399–404.
86. Bagavandoss, P., Wiggins, R. C., Kunkel, S. L., Remick, D. G., and Keyes, P. L. (1990). Tumor necrosis factor production and accumulation of inflammatory cells in the corpus luteum of pseudopregnancy and pregnancy in rabbits. *Biol. Reprod.* 42, 367–376.
87. Wang, L. J., Brannstrom, M., Robertson, S. A., and Norman, R. J. (1992). Tumor necrosis factor-a in the human ovary: Presence in follicular fluid and effects on cell proliferation and protaglandin production. *Fertil. Steril.* 58, 934–940.
88. Hurwitz, A., Ricciarelli, E., Botero, L., Rohan, R. M., Hernandez, R., and Adashi, E. Y. (1991). Endocrine- and autocrine-mediated regulation of rat ovarian (theca-interstitial) interleukin-1b gene expression: Gonadotropin-dependent preovulatory acquisition. *Endocrinology* 129, 3427–3429.
89. Gaytan, F., Aceitero, J., Bellido, C., Sanchez-Criado, J. E., and Aguilar, E. (1991). Estrous cycle-related changes in mast cell numbers in several ovarian compartments in the rat. *Biol. Reprod.* 45, 27–33.
90. Brannstrom, M., Norman, R. J., Seamark, R. F., and Robertson, S. A. (1994). Rat ovary produces cytokines during ovulation. *Biol. Reprod.* 50, 88–94.
91. Van Snick, J. (1990). Interleukin-6: An overview. *Ann. Rev. Immunol.* 8, 253–278.
92. Gorospe, W. C., Highes, Jr., F. M., and Spangelo, B. L. (1992). Interleukin-6: Effects on and production by rat granulosa cells in vitro. *Endocrinology* 130, 1750–1752.
93. Dinarello, C. (1988). Biology of interleukin-1. *FASEB J.* 2, 108–115.
94. Brannstrom, M., Mayrhofer, G., and Robertson, S. A. (1993). Localization of leukocyte subsets in the rat ovary during the periovulatory period. *Biol. Reprod.* 48, 277–286.
95. Sancho-Tello, M., Perez-Roger, I., Imakawa, K., Tilzer, L., and Terranova, P. F. (1992). Expression of tumor necrosis factor-a in the rat ovary. *Endocrinology* 130, 1359–1364.
96. Hurwitz, A., Payne, D. W., Packman, J. N., Andreani, C. L., Resnick, C. E., Hernandez, E. R., and Adashi, E. Y. (1991). Cytokine-mediated regulation of ovarian function: Interleukin-1 inhibits gonadotropin-induced androgen biosynthesis. *Endocrinology* 129, 1250–1256.
97. Adashi, E. Y., Resnick, C. E., Croft, C. S., and Payne, D. W. (1988). Tumor necrosis factor inhibits gonadotrophin hormonal action in nontransformed ovarian granulosa cells. *J. Biol. Chem.* 264, 11591–11597.
98. Miyazaki, T., Kuo, T-C, Dharmarajan, A. M., Atlas, S. J., and Wallach, E. E. (1988). In vivo administration of allopurinol affects ovulation and early embryonic development in rabbits. *Am. J. Obstet. Gynecol.* 161, 1709–1714.
99. Margolin, Y., and Behrman, H. R. (1992). Xanthine oxidase and dehydrogenase activities in rat ovarian tissues. *Am. J. Physiol.* 262, E173–E178.
100. Fukuoka, M., Yasuda, K., Taii, S., Takakura, K., and Mori, T. (1988). Interleukin-1 stimulates growth and inhibits progesterone secretion in cultures of porcine granulosa cells. *Endocrinology* 124, 884–890.

101. Gottschall, P. E., Katsuura, G., Hoffmann, S. T., and Arimura, A. (1988). Interleukin 1: An inhibitor of luteinizing hormone receptor formation in cultured rat granulosa cells. *FASEB J.* 2, 2492–2496.
102. Loukides, J. A., Loy, R. A., Edwards, R., Honig, J., Visintin, I., and Polan, M. L. (1990). Human follicular fluids contain tissue macrophages. *J. Clin. Endocrinol. Metab.* 71, 1363–1367.
103. Sugino, N., Shimamura, K., Tamura, H., Ono, M., Nakamura, Y., Ogino, K., and Kato, H. (1996). Progesterone inhibits superoxide radical production by mononuclear phagocytes in pseudopregnant rats. *Endocrinology* 137, 749–754.
104. Gougeon, A. (1996). Regulation of ovarian follicular development in primates: Facts and hypotheses. *Endocr. Rev.* 17, 121–155.
105. Gaytan, F., Morales, C., Bellido, C., Aguilar, E., and Sanchez-Criado, J. E. (1998). Ovarian follicle macrophages: Is follicular atresia in the immature rat a macrophage-mediated event? *Biol. Reprod.* 58, 52–59.
106. Suzuki, K., and Tamaoki, B-I. (1987). In vitro decrease of lyase activity in rat ovarian cells during incubation: Effect of hCG. *Steroids* 49, 341–353.
107. Margolin, Y., Aten, R. F., and Behrman, H. R. (1990). Antigonadotropic and antisteroidogenic actions of peroxide in rat granulosa cells. *Endocrinology* 127, 245–250.
108. LaPolt, P. S., and Hong, L-S. (1995). Inhibitory effects of superoxide dismutase and cyclic guanosine 3',5'-monophosphate on estrogen production in cultured rat granulosa cells. *Endocrinology* 136, 5533–5539.
109. Van Voorhis, B. J., Dunn, M. S., Snyder, G. D., and Weiner, C. P. (1994). Nitric oxide: An autocrine regulator of human granulosa-luteal cell steroidogenesis. *Endocrinology* 135, 1799–1806.
110. Hashimoto, S., Minami, N., Takakura, R., and Yamada, M. (2000). Low oxygen tension during in vitro maturation is beneficial for supporting the subsequent development of bovine cumulus-oocyte complexes. *Mol. Reprod. Develop.* 57, 353–360.
111. Zeilmaker, G. H., and Verhamme, C. M. P. M. (1974). Observations on rat oocyte maturation in vitro: Morphology and energy requirements. *Biol. Reprod.* 11, 145–152.
112. Guraya, S. (1985). *The Biology of Ovarian Follicles in Mammals.* New York: Springer-Verlag.
113. Takami, M., Preston, S. L., Toyloy, V. A., and Behrman, H. R. (1999). Antioxidants reversibly inhibit the spontaneous resumption of meiosis. *Am. J. Physiol.* 276, E684–E688.
114. Takami, M., Preston, S. L., and Behrman, H. R. (2000). Eicosatetranoic and eicosatrynoic acids, lipoxygenase inhibitors, block meiosis via antioxidant action. *Am. J. Cell Physiol.* 278, C646–C650.
115. Jablonka-Shariff, A., and Olson, L. M. (1998). The role of nitric oxide in ooyte meiotic maturation and ovulation: Meiotic abnormalities of endothelial nitric oxide synthase knock-out mouse oocytes. *Endocrinology* 139, 2944–2954.
116. Jablonka-Shariff, A., Basuray, R., and Olson, L. M. (1999). Inhibitors of nitric oxide synthase influence oocytes maturation in rats. *J. Soc. Gynecol. Invest.* 6, 95–101.
117. Nakamura, Y., Yamamoto, Y., Sugino, N., Takayama, H., and Kato, H. (2002). Nitric oxide inhibits oocyte meiotic maturation. *Biol. Reprod.* 67, 1592–2002.
118. Holler, T. P., and Hopkins, P. B. (1990). Ovothiols as free-radical scavengers and the mechanism of ovothiol-promoted NAD(P)H-O_2 oxidoreductase activity. *Biochemistry* 29, 1953–1961.
119. Nasr-Esfahani, M. H., Aitken, J. R., and Johnson, M. H. (1990). Hydrogen peroxide levels in mouse oocytes and early cleavage stage embryos developed in vitro or in vivo. *Development* 109, 501–507.
120. Oberley, L. W., Oberley, T. D., and Buettner, G. R. (1981). Cell division in normal and transformed cells: The possible role of superoxide and hydrogen peroxide. *Med. Hyp.* 7, 21–42.
121. Legge, M., and Sellens, M. H. (1991). Free radical scavengers ameliorate the 2-cell block in mouse embryo culture. *Hum. Reprod.* 6, 867–871.
122. Tilly, J. L., and Tilly, K. I. (1995). Inhibitors of oxidative stress mimic the ability of follicle-stimulating hormone to suppress apoptosis in cultured rat ovarian follicles. *Endocrinology* 136, 242–252.
123. Laloraya, M., Kumar, G. P., and Laloraya, M. M. (1988). Changes in the levels of superoxide anion radical and superoxide dismutase during the estrous cycle of rattus norvegicus and induction of superoxide dismutase in rat ovary by lutropin. *Biochem. Biophys. Res. Comm.* 157, 146–153.
124. Miyazaki, T., Sueoka, K., Dharmarajan, A. M., Atlas, S. J., Bulkley, G. B., and Wallach, E. E. (1988). The role of oxygen free radicals in ovulation in the in vitro perfused rabbit ovary. *44th Annual Meeting of the American Fertility Society*, S3.
125. Matzuk, M. M., Dionne, L., Guo, Q., Kumar, T. R., and Lebovitz, R. M. (1998). Ovarian function in superoxide dismutase 1 and 2 knockout mice. *Endocrinology* 139, 4008–4011.
126. Narimoto, K., Noda, Y., Shiotani, M., Mori, T., and Ogawa, K. (1993). Review: Immunohistochemical assessment of CuZn-superoxide dismutase in the human genital organs. *Acta Histochem. Cytochem.* 26, 75–83.
127. Shiotani, M., Noda, Y., Narimoto, K., Imai, K., Mori, T., Fujimoto, K., and Ogawa, K. (1991). Immunohistochemical localization of superoxide dismutase in the human ovary. *Hum. Reprod.* 6, 1349–1353.
128. Lutwak-Mann, C. (1962). The influence of nutrition on the ovary. In *The Ovary*, Vol. II, ed. S. Zuckerman, 291–315. New York: Academic Press.
129. Kaseki, H., Kim, E. Y., Whisler, R. L., and Cornwell, D. G. (1986). Effect of an oral dose of vitamin E on the vitamin E and cholesterol content of tissues of the vitamin E-deficient rat. *J. Nutr.* 116, 1631–1639.
130. Deane, H. W. (1952). Histochemical observations on the ovary and oviduct of the albino rat during the estrous cycle. *Am. J. Anat.* 91, 363–393.
131. Kodaman, P. H., and Behrman, H. R. (1999). Hormone-regulated and glucose-sensitive transport of dehydroascorbic acid in immature rat granulosa cells. *Endocrinology* 140, 3659–3665.
132. Luck, M. R., Jeyaseelan, I., and Scholes, R. A. (1995). Ascorbic acid and fertility. *Biol. Reprod.* 52, 262–266.
133. Phillips, P. H., Lardy, H. A., Boyer, P. D., and Werner, G. M. (1941). The relationship of ascorbic acid to reproduction in the cow. *J. Dairy Science* 24, 153–158.

134. Guarnaccia, M. M., Takami, M., Jones, E. E., Preston, S. L., and Behrman, H. R. (2000). LH depletes ascorbic acid in preovulatory rat follicles. *Fertil. Steril.* 74, 959–963.
135. Parlow, A. F. (1972). Influence of difference in the persistence of luteinizing hormones in blood on their potency in the ovarian ascorbic acid depletion bioassay. *Endocrinology* 91, 1109–1112.
136. Behrman, H. R., Preston, S. L., Kodaman, P. H., Takami, M., Rossi, M. J., and Jones, E. E. (2000). Oxidants and antioxidants in follicle/oocyte function. In *Ovulation: Evolving Scientific and Clinical Concepts*, ed. E. Y. Adashi, 255–265. New York: Springer-Verlag.
137. Kramer, M. M., Harman, M. T., and Brill, A. K. (1933). Disturbances of reproduction and ovarian changes in the guinea-pig in relation to vitamin C deficiency. *Am. J. Physiol.* 106, 611–622.
138. Espey, L., and Coons, P. (1976). Factors which influence ovulatory degradation of rabbit ovarian follicles. *Biol. Reprod* 14, 233–245.
139. Murray, A. A., Molinek, M., Baker, S., Kojima, F., Smith, M., Hillier, S. G., and Spears, N. (2001). Role of ascorbic acid in promoting follicle integrity and survival in intact mouse ovarian follicle in vitro. *Reproduction* 121, 89–96.
140. Mattison, D. R., Shiromizu, K., Pendergrass, J. A., and Thorgeirsson, S. S. (1983). Ontogeny of ovarian glutathione and sensitivity to primordial oocyte destruction by cyclophosphamide. *Pediatr. Pharmacol.* 3, 49–55.
141. Crook, T. R., Souhami, R. L., Whyman, G. D., and McLean, A. E. M. (1986). Glutathione depletion as a determinant of sensitivity of human leukemia cells to cyclophosphamide. *Cancer Res.* 46, 5035–5038.
142. Lee, F. Y., Vessey, A. R., and Siemann D. W. (1988). Glutathione as a determinant of cellular response to doxorubicin. *Natl. Cancer Inst. Canada Monogr.* 6, 211–215.
143. Jarrell, J. F., Sevcik, M., and Stuart, G. (1992). Regulation of total ovarian glutathione content in the rat. *Reprod. Toxicol.* 6, 133–135.
144. Fukai, F., Ohtaki, H., Ueda, T., and Katayama, T. (1992). A possible role of glutathione S-transferase in rat ovary and testes. *J. Clin. Biochem. Nutr.* 12, 93–107.
145. Calvin, H., Grosshana, K., and Blake, E. (1986). Estimation and manipulation of glutathione levels in prepubertal mouse ovaries and ova: Relevance to sperm nucleus transformation in the fertilized egg. *Gamete Res.* 14, 265–275.
146. Yoshida, M. (1993). Role of glutathione in the maturation and fertilization of pig oocytes in vitro. *Mol. Reprod. Dev.* 35, 76–81.
147. deMatos, D. G., Furnus, C. C., Moses, D. F., and Bladassarre, H. (1995). Effect of cystamine on glutathione level and developmental capacity of bovine oocyte matured in vitro. *Mol. Reprod. Dev.* 42, 432–436.
148. Tatemoto, H., Sakurai, N., and Muto, N. (2000). Protection of porcine oocytes against apoptotic cell death caused by oxidative stress during in vitro maturation: Role of cumulus cells. *Biol. Reprod.* 65, 805–810.
149. de Matos, D., Furnus, C. C., and Moses, D. F. (1997). Glutathione synthesis during in vitro maturation of bovine oocytes: Role of cumulus cells. *Biol. Reprod.* 57, 1420–1425.
150. Abeydeera, L. R., Wang, W. H., Cantley, T. C., Rieke, A., and Day, B. N. (1998). Coculture with follicular shell pieces can enhance the developmental competence of pig oocytes after in vitro fertilization: Relevance to intracellular glutathione. *Biol. Reprod* 58, 213–218.
151. Zuelke, K. A., Jones, D. P., and Perreault, S. D. (1997). Glutathione oxidation is associated with altered microtubule function and disrupted fertilization in mature hamster oocytes. *Biol. Reprod.* 57, 1413–1419.
152. Okatani, Y., Morioka, N., Wakatsuki, A., Nakano, Y., and Sagara, Y. (1993). Role of the free radical-scavenger system in aromatase activity of the human ovary. *Horm. Res.* 39, 22–27.
153. Pepperell, J. R., Wolcott, K., and Behrman, H. R. (1992). Luteolytic effect of neutrophils in rat luteal cells. *Endocrinology* 130, 1001–1008.
154. Behrman, H. R., and Preston, S. L. (1988). Luteolytic actions of peroxide in rat ovarian cells. *Endocrinology* 124, 2895–2900.
155. Sawada, M., and Carlson, J. C. (1996). Intracellular regulation of progesterone secretion by the superoxide radical in the rat corpus luteum. *Endocrinology* 137, 1580–1584.
156. Vega, M., Carrasco, I., Castillo, T., Troncoso, J. L., and Videla, L. A. (1995). Functional luteolysis in response to hydrogen peroxide in human luteal cells. *J. Endocrinol.* 147, 177–182.
157. Thomas, J. P., Dorflinger, L. J., and Behrman, H. R. (1978). Mechanism of the rapid antigonadotropic action of prostaglandins in cultured luteul cells. *Proc. Natl. Acad. Sci. USA* 75, 1344–1348.
158. Arici, A., Behrman, H. R., and Keefe, D. L. (1999). Prostaglandins and prostaglandin-like products in reproduction: Eicosanoids, peroxides, and oxygen radicals. In *Reproductive Endocrinology*, 4th ed., eds. S. S. C. Yen, R. B. Jaffe, and R. L. Barbieri, 134–152. Philadelphia: W.B. Saunders Co.
159. Behrman, H. R., Grinwich, D. L., and Hichens, M. (1976). Studies on the mechanism of PGF2a and gonadotropin interactions on LH receptor function in corpora lutea during luteolysis. In *Advances in Prostaglandin and Thromoboxane Research*, Vol. 2, eds. B. Samuelsson and R. Paoletti, 665–666. New York: Raven Press.
160. Jordan, A. W. (1981). Effects of prostaglandin F_{2a} treatment on LH and dibutyryl cyclic AMP-stimulated progesterone secretion by isolated rat luteal cells. *Biol. Reprod.* 25, 327–331.
161. Luborsky, J. L., Dorflinger, L. J., Wright, K., and Behrman, H. R. (1984). PGF2a inhibits LH-induced increases in LH receptor binding to isolated rat luteal cells. *Endocrinology* 115, 2210–2216.
162. Behrman, H. R. (1979). Prostaglandins in hypothalamo-pituitary and ovarian function. *Ann. Rev. Physiol.* 41, 685–700.
163. Sawada, M., and Carlson, J. C. (1988). Superoxide radical production in plasma membrane samples from regressing corpora lutea. *Can. J. Physiol. Pharmacol.* 67, 465–471.
164. Riley, J. C. M., and Behrman, H. R. (1991). In vivo generation of hydrogen peroxide in the rat corpus luteum during luteolysis. *Endocrinology* 128, 1749–1753.
165. Sawada, M., and Carlson, J. C. (1985). Association of lipid peroxidation during luteal regression in the rat and natural aging in the rotifer. *Exp. Gerontol.* 20, 179–186.

166. Aten, R. F., Duarte, K. M., and Behrman, H. R. (1992). Regulation of ovarian antioxidant vitamins, reduced glutathione, and lipid peroxidation by luteinizing hormone and prostaglandin F2a. *Biol. Reprod.* 46, 401–407.

167. Aten, R. F., Kolodecik, T. R., Rossi, M. J., Debusscher, C., and Behrman, H. R. (1998). Prostaglandin F2a treatment in vivo, but not in vitro, stimulates protein kinase C-activated superoxide production by nonsteroidogenic cells of the rat corpus luteum. *Biol. Reprod.* 59, 1069–1076.

168. Sawada, M., and Carlson, J. C. (1994). Studies on the mechanism controlling generation of superoxide radical in luteinized rat ovaries during regression. *Endocrinology* 135, 1645–1650.

169. Riley, J. C. M., Cziraki, S. E., and Carlson, J. C. (1988). The effects of prolactin and prostaglandin F2a on plasma membrane changes during luteolysis in the rat. *Endocrinology* 124, 1564–1570.

170. McCormack, J. T., Friederichs, M. G., Limback, S. D., and Greenwald, G. S. (1998). Apoptosis during spontaneous luteolysis in the cyclic golden hamster: Biochemical and morphological evidence. *Biol. Reprod.* 58, 255–260.

171. Aten, R. F., Duarte, K. M., and Behrman, H. R. (1992). Regulation of ovarian antioxidant vitamins, reduced glutathione, and lipid peroxidation by luteinizing hormone and prostaglandin F_{2a}. *Biol. Reprod.* 46, 401–407.

172. Kodaman, P. H., Aten, R. F., and Behrman, H. R. (1994). Lipid hydroperoxides evoke antigonadotropic and antisteroidogenic activity in rat luteal cells. *Endocrinology* 135, 2723–2730.

173. Behrman, H. R., and Aten, R. F. (1991). Evidence that hydrogen peroxide blocks hormone-sensitive cholesterol transport into mitochondria of rat luteal cells. *Endocrinology* 128, 2958–2966.

174. Musicki, B. M., Aten, R. F., Wang, F., and Behrman, H. R. (1991). Hydrogen peroxide: A physiological regulator of protein synthesis and steroidogenesis in rat ovarian cells. (Abstract). *Am. Soc. Cell. Biol.*

175. Endo, T., Aten, R. F., Leykin, L., and Behrman, H. R. (1993). Hydrogen peroxide evokes antisteroidogenic and antigonadotropic actions in human granulosa lutein cells. *J. Clin. Endocrinol. Met.* 76, 337–342.

176. Musicki, B., and Behrman, H. R. (1993). Metal chelators reverse the action of hydrogen peroxide in rat luteal cells. *Mol. Cell. Endocrinol.* 92, 215–220.

177. Hehnke, K. E., Christenson, L. K., Ford, S. P., and Taylor, M. (1994). Macrophage infiltration into the porcine corpus luteum during prostaglandin F2a-induced luteolysis. *Biol. Reprod.* 50, 10–15.

178. Minegishi, K., Miyazaki, T., Kiyokawa, Y., Ishimoto, H., and Yoshimura, Y. (2000). Reactive oxidants mediate leukocyte-endothelium interactions in prostaglandin F_{2a}-induced luteolysis in rats. *J. Soc. Gynecol. Investig.* (Suppl 1) 7, 439.

179. Slungaard, A., and Mahoney, Jr., J. R. (1991). Thiocyanate is the major substrate for eosinophil peroxidase in physiologic fluids. *J. Biol. Chem.* 266, 4903–4910.

180. Bulmer, D. (1964). The histochemistry of ovarian macrophages in the rat. *J. Anat. Lond.* 98, 313–319.

181. Norman, R. J., and Brannstrom, M. (1994). White cells and the ovary—incidental invaders or essential effectors? *J. Endocrinol.* 140, 333–336.

182. Zhao, Y., Burbach, J. A., Roby, K. F., Terranova, P F., and Brannian, J. D. (1998). Macrophages are the major source of tumor necrosis factor a in the porcine corpus luteum. *Biol. Reprod.* 59, 1385–1391.

183. Adashi, E. Y., Resnick, C. E., Packman, J. N., Hurwitz, A., and Payne, D. W. (1990). Cytokine-mediated regulation of ovarian function: Tumor necrosis factor a inhibits gonadotropin-supported progesterone accumulation by differentiating and luteinized granulosa cells. *Am. J. Obstet. Gynecol.* 162, 889–899.

184. Benyo, D. F., and Pate, J. L. (1992). Tumor necrosis factor-a alters bovine luteal cell synthetic capacity and viability. *Endocrinology* 130, 854–860.

185. Kim, A. H., Khanna, A., Aten, R. F., Olive, D. L., and Behrman, H. R. (1996). Cytokine induction of heat shock protein in human granulosa-luteal cells. *Mol. Hum. Reprod.* 2, 549–554.

186. Khanna, A., Aten, R. F., and Behrman, H. R. (1994). Heat shock protein induction blocks hormone-sensitive steroidogenesis in rat luteal cells. *Steroids* 59, 4–9.

187. Khanna, A., Aten, R. F., and Behrman, H. R. (1995). Heat shock protein-70 induction mediates luteal regression in the rat. *Mol. Endocrinology* 9, 1431–1440.

188. Khanna, A., Aten, R. F., and Behrman, H. R. (1995). Physiological and pharmacological inhibitors of luteinizing hormone-dependent steroidogenesis induce heat shock protein-70 in rat luteal cells. *Endocrinology* 136, 1775–1781.

189. Murdoch, W. J. (1987). Treatment of sheep with prostaglandin F2a enhances production of a luteal chemoattractant for eosinophils. *Am. J. Reprod. Immunol.* 15, 52–56.

190. Townson, D. H., Warren, J. S., Flory, C. M., Naftalin, D. M., and Keyes, P. L. (1996). Expression of monocyte chemoattractant protein-1 in the corpus luteum of the rat. *Biol. Reprod.* 54, 513–520.

191. Xu, Y., Rojkind, M., and Czaja, M. J. (1996). Regulation of monocyte chemoattractant protein 1 by cytokines and oxygen free radicals in rat hepatic fat-storing cells. *Gastroenterology* 110, 1870–1877.

191a. Behrman, et al.

192. Musicki, B., Kodaman, P. H., Aten, R. F., and Behrman, H. R. (1996). Endocrine regulation of ascorbic acid transport and secretion in luteal cells. *Biol. Reprod.* 54, 399–406.

193. Stansfield, D. A., and Flint, A. P. (1967). The entry of ascorbic acid into the corpus luteum in vivo and in vitro and the effect of luteinizing hormone. *J. Endocr.* 39, 27–35.

194. Kodaman, P. H., Aten, R. F., and Behrman, H. R. (1998). Accumulation of ascorbate by endocrine-regulated and glucose-sensitive transport of dehydroascorbic acid in luteinized rat ovarian cells. *Biol. Reprod.* 58, 407–413.

195. Shimamura, K., Sugino, N., Yoshida, Y., Nakamura, Y., Ogino, K., and Kato, H. (1995). Changes in lipid peroxide and antioxidant enzyme activities in corpora lutea during pseudopregnancy in rats. *J. Reprod. Fertil.* 105, 253–257.

196. Kolodecik, T. R., Aten, R. F., and Behrman, H. R. (1998). Ascorbic acid-dependent cytoprotection of ovarian cells by leukocyte and nonleukocyte peroxidases. *Biochem. Pharmacol.* 55, 1497–1503.

197. Vierk, J. E., Hansen, T. R., Austin, K. J., Van Kirk, E. A., Hess, B. W., and Murdoch, W. J. (1998). Inhibition by

tocopherol of prostaglandin-induced apoptosis in ovine corpora lutea. *Prostagl. Lipid Mediat.* 56, 265–276.

198. Aten, R. F., Kolodecik, T. R., and Behrman, H. R. (1994). Ovarian vitamin E accumulation: Evidence for a role of lipoproteins. *Endocrinology* 135, 533–539.

199. Sugino, N., Hirosawa-Takamori, M., Zhong, L., Telleria, C. M., Shiota, K., and Gibori, G. (1998). Hormonal regulation of copper-zinc superoxide dismutase and manganese superoxide dismutase messenger ribonucleic acid in the rat corpus luteum: Induction by prolactin and placental lactogens. *Biol. Reprod.* 59, 599–605.

200. Sasaki, J., Sato, E. F., Nomura, T., Mori, H., Watanabe, S., Kanda, S., Watanabe, H., Utsumi, K., and Inoue, M. (1994). Detection of manganese superoxide dismutase mRNA in the theca interna cells of rat ovary during the ovulatory process by in situ hybridization. *Histochemistry* 102, 173–176.

200a. Nomura, (1996). #3519.

201. Hesla, J. S., Miyzaki, T., Dasko, L. M., Wallach, E. E., and Dharmarajan, A. M. (1992). Superoxide dismutase activity, lipid peroxide production and corpus luteum steroidogenesis during natural luteolysis and regression induced by oestradiol deprivation of the ovary in pseudopregnant rabbits. *J. Reprod. Fertil.* 95, 915–924.

202. Sugino, M., Nakamura, Y., Takeda, O., Ishimatsu, M., and Kato, H. (1993). Changes in activities of superoxide dismutase and lipid peroxide in corpus luteum during pregnancy in rats. *J. Reprod. Fertil.* 97, 347–351.

203. Eliasson, M., Bostrom, M., and DePierre, J. W. (1999). Levels and subcellular distributions of detoxifying enzymes in the ovarian *corpus luteum* of the pregnant and non-pregnant pig. *Biochem. Pharmcol.* 58, 1287–1292.

204. Wong, G. H. W., and Goeddel, D. V. (1988). Induction of manganous superoxide dismutase by tumor necrosis factor: Possible protective mechanism. *Science* 242, 941–944.

205. Sugino, N., Telleria, C. M., and Gibori, G. (1998). Differential regulation of copper-zinc superoxide dismutase and manganese superoxide dismutase in the rat corpus luteum: Induction of manganese superoxide dismutase messenger ribonucleic acid by inflammatory cytokines. *Biol. Reprod.* 59, 208–215.

206. Takiguchi, S., Sugino, N., Kashida, S., Yamagata, Y., Makamura, Y., and Kato, H. (2000). Rescue of the corpus luteum and an increase in luteal superoxide dismutase expression induced by placental luteotropins in the rat: Action of testosterone without conversion to estrogen. *Biol. Reprod.* 62, 398–403.

207. Peterson, S. L., and Stevenson, P. M. (1992). Changes in catalase activity and concentration during ovarian development and differentiation. *Biochim. Biophys. Acta* 1135, 207–214.

208. Rueda, B. R., Tilly, K. I., Botros, I. W., Jolly, P. D., Hansen, T. R., Hoyer, P. B., and Tilly, J. L. (1997). Increased bax and interleukin-1b-converting enzyme messenger ribonucleic acid levels coincide with apoptosis in the bovine corpus luteum during structural regression. *Biol. Reprod.* 56, 186–193.

209. Dharmarajan, A. M., Hisheh, S., Singh, B., Parkinson, S., Tilly, K. I., and Tilly, J. L. (1999). Antioxidants mimic the ability of chorionic gonadotropin to suppress apoptosis in the rabbit corpus luteum *in vitro*: A novel role for superoxide dismutase in regulating *bax* expression. *Endocrinology* 140, 2555–2561.

210. Rao, B. R., and Slotman, B. J. (1991). Endocrine factors in common epithelial ovarian cancer. *Endocr. Rev.* 12, 14–26.

211. Casagrande, J. T., Louie, E. W., Pike, M. C., Roy, S., Ross, R. K., and Henderson, B. E. (1979). "Incessant ovulation" and ovarian cancer. *Lancet* 2, 170–173.

212. Shiromizu, K., Thorgeirsson, S. S., and Mattison, D. R. (1984). Effect of cyclophosphamide on oocyte and follicle number in Sprague-Dawley rats, C57BL/6N and DBA/2N mice. *Pediatr. Pharmacol.* 4, 213–221.

213. Portz, D. M., Elkins, T. E., White, R., Warren, J., Adadevoh, S., and Randolph, J. (1991). Oxygen free radicals and pelvic adhesion formation: I Blocking oxygen free radical toxicity to prevent adhesion formation in an endometriosis model. *Int. J. Fertil.* 36, 39–42.

CHAPTER **21**

Follicle Selection in Mammalian Ovaries: Regulatory Mechanisms of Granulosa Cell Apoptosis during Follicular Atresia

NOBORU MANABE, NAOKE INOUE, TAKASHI MIYANO, KAZUHIRO SAKAMAKI, MIKI SUGIMOTO, AND HAJIME MIYAMOTO

INTRODUCTION

In most species of fish, a tremendous number of eggs are produced and ovulated during each ovarian cycle. The ovulated eggs are fertilized, and younglings are born. Some types of anadromous fish (e.g., chum salmon [*Oncorhynchus keta*]) spawn once in their lifetime and die, and then huge alevins hatch and swim to the sea. On the other hand, the ovaries of mammals, including human and farm animals, release a constant small number of oocytes at appropriate intervals during the fertile years of the organism, and the duration of the ovulatory process is species specific. Moreover, during growth and development of the oocytes, a small number of oocytes are selected and the remainder are removed. For example, in humans, the number of oocytes is 7 million/ovary at gestation week –20; 2 million/ovary at birth; 400,000/ovary at puberty; and 0/ovary at postmenopause. The maximum ovulated oocytes will be less than 500/woman. Thus more than 99.9% of oocytes disappear during a mammal's lifetime [1, 2]. The total number of ovulations, which is genetically regulated, is called the *ovulation rate.* The ovulation rate is an important parameter of the reproductive efficiency in farm animals. Although ovulation rate is a major limiting factor in determining the number of offspring born, numerous additional factors act on the uterus and conceptuses throughout gestation and contribute to the number of healthy fetuses that develop to term [3]. Many researchers have studied which factors directly or indirectly regulate and modulate the ovulation rate and how many follicles grow or die during atresia [4–7]. Morphological characteristics of follicular atresia shown in most mammalian ovaries are as follows: first, scattered pyknotic nuclei, apoptotic bodies are seen in the granulosa layer [8]. Then detachment of the granulosa layer from the follicular basement membrane is observed [9], and then fragmentation of the basal membrane [9, 10] and cell debris and macrophages in the antrum of the follicle are seen [11, 12]. In atretic follicles, granulosa cells have a reduced synthesis of deoxyribonucleic acid (DNA) [13] and protein [4], but the amount of synthesized ribonucleic acid (RNA) is unchanged, although changes in expression of some messenger ribonucleic acids (mRNAs) are detected [14]. In contrast to the morphological changes in granulosa cells, endocrine cells in the theca interna layers of the rat, human, and rabbit undergo hypertrophy at the earliest stage of atresia [15]. At the early stage of atresia, the oocyte undergoes meiosis-like changes, followed by oocyte fragmentation and disruption of the oocyte-cumulus connection [16]. These morphological characteristics of granulosa cells in atretic follicles have been shown to be caused by an apoptotic pathway; moreover, biochemical characteristics (e.g., DNA fragmentation multiples of 185 to 200 bp) are also a hallmark of apoptosis [17–19]. However, there are species-specific differences in detailed characteristics of granulosa cell apoptosis, for instance, in the localization of apoptotic cells in granulosa and theca interna layers during atresia.

Viviparity is a newly discovered characteristic of reproduction in mammals, and there is a wide variety of ovarian functions (e.g., follicular growth, development and selection, ovulation, luteinization and luteolysis, fertilization, implantation, and embryonic development). This chapter mainly focuses on the follicle selection that is regulated by discriminating atresia of growing follicles and describes regulation factors that affect the follicular atresia. A brief description of how some factors might regulate atresia or follicular development is discussed. This review also discusses some recent observations from our laboratory that suggest a novel cell-death receptor and decoy receptor in regulating follicle selection in porcine ovaries.

FOLLICULAR GROWTH AND DEVELOPMENT

Follicular Development in Mammals

During embryogenesis, primordial germ cells migrate from the yolk sac through the dorsal mesentery of the hindgut to the genital ridge. The germ cells undergo extensive proliferation, and somatic cells derived from the mesenchyme of the genital ridge proliferate. Then the somatic cells, called *follicular epithelial cells* or *granulosa cells*, enclose the germ cells to form the primordial ovarian follicles. After mitotic division, meiosis begins in the germ cells, called *primary oocytes*. The primary oocytes become arrested in the diplotene stage of the first meiotic division, where they stay until their surrounding follicle leaves the primordial stage and starts to grow to reach ovulation. In both ovaries of newborn mammals, there are more than a million primordial follicles. For example, approximately 5 million primordial follicles are present in both ovaries 10 days after birth in sows, 1.2 million in cows, 1.1 million in sheep, 4 million in women, and 1 million in mice [1–5, 20]. During fertile life in humans, a maximum of 500 oocytes of the 14 million oocytes that entered meiosis will ovulate, and all others will disappear [1, 2]. Such a low success rate is considered the result of an important selection for quality oocytes.

In adult women, primordial follicles in this population are not stimulated to grow and develop at the same time, and only a small number of follicles, which are genetically determined, begin their development, whereas the remainder remain quiescent. Initiation of follicular growth involves endocrinological actions, mainly follicle-stimulating hormone (FSH) and local modulating factors from granulosa cells and endocrine cells of the theca internal layer and from the growing oocytes [5, 21]. The early growth stage of secondary follicles is characterized by a dramatic increase in proliferation of granulosa cells, resulting in a rapid increase in volume and size. Subsequently, granulosa cells separate from each other resulting in the formation of follicular antrum. Such antral follicles are called *tertiary follicles*. Primary oocyte with germinal vesicle (GV) is surrounded by cumulus cells, which are differentiated from granulosa cells [22]. Because of a large increase in proliferation of granulosa cells and an increase in size of the antrum, growth rates of tertiary follicles show an exponential curve [23]. In the oocyte, meiosis restarts, GV disappear (called a *GV breakdown [GVB]*), and then the first polar body is divided. This is called a *secondary oocyte*. Finally, selected follicles burst, and the secondary oocytes are ovulated. However, in dogs and foxes, exceptional cases, primary oocytes are ovulated and fertilized in the oviduct. Only 1 dominant follicle is ovulated in cows, sheep, and humans; 5 to 10 follicles in rodents; and approximately 10 follicles in sows.

Early studies using experimental animals with hypophysectomy, and more recently experiments using knockout mice lacking a functional gene for FSH receptor (FSHR) [24], indicated that FSH is essential for antrum formation and postantral follicular development. Many investigators have studied the detailed relations among FSH secretion and responsiveness to FSH and follicular growth, differentiation, and functions. Researchers have shown that FSH acts as an accelerator and a survival factor for the follicles [3]. In gilts and matured sows, FSH administration increases the ovulation rate [25, 26]. In prepubertal gilts, FSH treatment induces follicular recruitment in a dose-dependent manner [27]. Active immunization against inhibin, which is produced by follicular granulosa cells and inhibits FSH excretion, causes increased FSH levels in peripheral blood and the number of ovulations in gilts [28, 29]. Thus the number of recruited follicles might dominantly depend on FSH levels or on the number of follicles responsive to FSH present at the time of recruitment. Unfortunately, we have insufficient knowledge of the number of FSH-responsive follicles related to some endocrinological event occurring before recruitment, or what other factors might influence it, and how follicles are selected during follicular growth and development.

FOLLICULAR ATRESIA

Follicular Growth, Development, and Atresia in Porcine Ovaries

Before describing the cell-death ligand and its receptor systems in ovaries, the following provides a brief description of the growth, development, and atresia of follicles [3, 23, 30–35]. In porcine ovaries, primary follicles require 84 days to grow to tertiary stage and an additional 19 days to grow to ovulatory size (i.e., 10 mm in diameter) [33]. The process of follicle selection during the tertiary stage probably takes place continuously from days 13 to 14 of the estrous cycle to ovulation (day 21) [30, 34]. During this final maturation stage, the growth rate of tertiary follicles from 3 to 10 mm in diameter is 1.14 mm/day [35], and the cells of the theca and granulosa layers secrete significant amounts of steroid hormones, peptide hormones, prostaglandins, and other physiologically active substances, which participate locally in follicular growth, development, and atresia and act as a coordinator of the hypothalamic-hypophysial-ovarian axis. On day 16, approximately 80 to 100 tertiary follicles are present in both ovaries [23], and then 70 to 90 follicles degenerate and disappear from the ovaries through the process of atresia [32]. Atresia may occur at any time during growth and development of follicles, but most follicles disappear during the transition of growth before reaching 6 mm in diameter in sows [23, 33–35]. On day 21, secondary oocytes are ovulated from 10 follicles selected.

Within each mammalian species, the ovulation rate is regulated within a relatively narrow range. Changes in rates of follicular atresia may alter the number of ovulated follicles. The Meishan sow, a traditional Chinese breed that has a large number of piglets (maximum 30), has a higher ovulation rate than conventional European breeds. For instance, Large White sows have 10 less ovulated oocytes than Meishan sows. Miller et al. [36] showed that on day 16, Meishan sows have more tertiary follicles than Large White sows, and the number of follicles that disappear from days 16 to 19 is larger in Large White sows than in Meishan sows. Thus greater ovulation rates in the Meishan breed is related to differences in both follicular recruitment and atresia.

Apoptotic Cell Death

As described earlier, more than 99% of follicles selectively disappear during follicular growth and development. In sows, FSH acts as an inhibitor of atresia in granulosa cells [3]. In most mammals including pigs, follicular atresia is primarily induced by granulosa cell apoptosis [6, 32, 37], which is characterized by internucleosomal DNA fragmentation, cell shrinkage, plasma membrane blebbing, and formation of apoptotic bodies. Although considerable progress has been made in understanding the regulation mechanisms of apoptotic cell death during atresia, the description of the apoptotic pathway in granulosa cells has not been completed [38]. Apoptotic stimuli and intracellular signal transduction pathways involved in granulosa cell apoptosis remain to be determined; therefore many investigators have been studying which trigger molecules induce granulosa cell apoptosis and how intercellular apoptotic signals are transmitted in the granulosa cells [6, 7, 32, 38–40].

Over the past decade, researchers in the fields of immunology and cancer therapy have found cell-specific death receptors, which are cell-surface proteins that transmit cell death signals initiated by cell-death ligands and play critical roles in apoptosis [41–48]. Biochemical studies have delineated the major intracellular signaling pathway (caspase-cascades) leading from ligand binding death receptor to initiation of apoptosis [49–52]. Each death receptor activates a specific caspase-cascade within seconds of ligand binding, causing apoptotic cell death within hours. In the following sections, we describe the cell-death ligand and receptor systems in mammalian follicles. However, their precise roles on the regulation of follicle selection have yet to be determined.

Granulosa Cell Apoptosis during Follicular Atresia

During the last decade, many findings have suggested that apoptosis, originally described in 1972 by Kerr et al. [53], is the mechanism underlying ovarian follicular atresia [6, 7, 54–57]. Specific apoptosis-related genes such as caspase-3 and apoptotic protease activating factor-1 express in granulosa cells of atretic follicles [58, 59] specific changes in glycoconjugates of cell surface membrane-glycoprotein, which act as regulators for phagocytosis in neighboring granulosa cells in atretic follicles, are demonstrated [60, 61]. Expression levels of kinase cascades, which regulate regulating entry into cell death and proliferation in granulosa cells, changes during atresia [62, 63]. In 1885 Flemming [64] first observed apoptotic cell death of granulosa cells of rabbit tertiary follicles with atresia, calling it *chromatolysis*. However, the physiological roles of chromatolysis in granulosa cells of atretic follicles have been not well understood.

Recently, Tilly, Hsueh, and their colleagues reported that the degeneration of atretic follicles in mammalian ovaries can be explained, at least in part, by apoptotic cell death of granulosa cells and endocrine cells of the theca interna layer [7, 14, 18, 37–39, 54, 55]. However, the degenerating changes in cumulus cells during follicular atresia had not been investigated in detail, so we examined them histologically, cytologically, and biochemically in porcine ovaries and confirmed that apoptosis occurs in granulosa cells but not cumulus cells or oocytes in tertiary follicles in the early stage of atresia, where no macrophages were detected [40, 56, 65]. Briefly, in situ analysis of DNA fragmentation was performed on histological sections of follicles using the terminal deoxynucleotidyl transferase-mediated biotinylated deoxyuridine triphosphate nick end-labeling (TUNEL) method, and conventional transmission electron microscopic (TEM) analysis was also performed (Figure 21.1, *A* and *B*, respectively). In healthy follicles, no apoptotic cells were observed among granulosa or cumulus cells or the cells in internal or external theca layers or oocytes [12, 40, 56, 65, 66].

In the early stage of atresia, apoptosis was detected in scattered granulosa cells located on the inner surface of the follicular wall but not in cumulus cells, oocytes, or the cells of internal or external theca layers. TEM observation revealed that typical apoptotic features such as condensed nuclei were seen in the scattered granulosa cells in the follicles in the early stage of atresia, but cumulus cells or oocytes with normal ultrastructure were seen in the same follicles [12].

In the late stage of atresia, granulosa cells scattered on the inner surface of the follicular wall began to undergo apoptosis, but no TUNEL-positive cells were detected among the cumulus cells or oocytes. Finally, in follicles in the progressed stage of atresia, many apoptotic cells were located in the abutting area of the basement membrane. The basement membrane was broken, and many macrophages had invaded the follicular antrum and ingurgitated the apoptotic granulosa cells and cell debris [9]. Moreover, no activity of the neutral Ca^{2+}/Mg^{2+}-dependent endonuclease, neutral Ca^{2+}-dependent endonuclease, neutral Mg^{2+}-dependent endonuclease, or acidic cation-independent endonuclease was detected in granulosa or cumulus cells prepared from healthy follicles [19]. In granulosa cell apoptosis of the atretic follicles, only the neutral Ca^{2+}/Mg^{2+}-dependent endonuclease was involved. No endonuclease activity was detected in cumulus cells

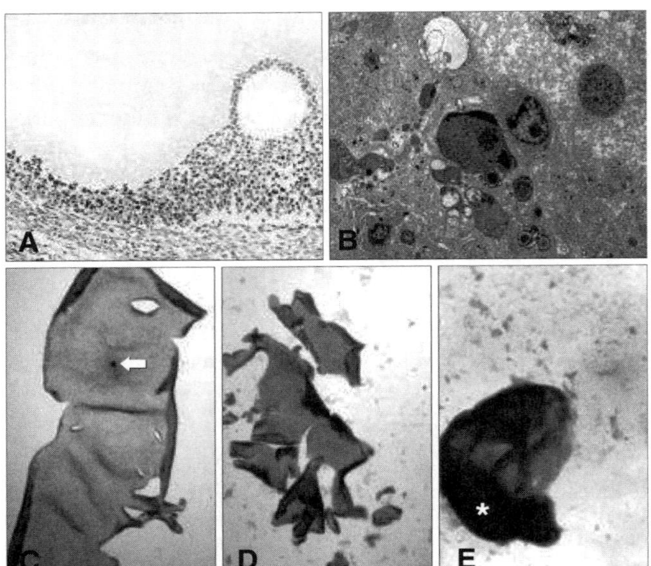

FIGURE 21.1 **A,** Representative section of porcine tertiary follicle in the early stage of follicular atresia was stained for in situ detection of apoptosis by the TUNEL technique. Scattered granulosa cells with condensed nuclei *(arrow)* were observed on the inner side of the follicle. **B,** Transmission electron micrographs of granulosa of the tertiary follicle in the early stage of atresia. Apoptotic nuclear condensation was observed in granulosa cells scattered on the inner surface of the follicular wall. Representative photographs of granulosa layer removed from healthy (**C**), early atretic (**D**), and progressed atretic (**E**) tertiary follicles dissected from porcine ovary under a dissecting microscope. Oocyte-cumulus cell complex *(arrow in* **A***)* tightly contacted with the granulosa layer in healthy follicles. Suspending granulosa cells and follicular walls containing theca interna and externa layers *(asterisk in* **C***)* were seen in progressed atretic follicle. (Magnification: *A*, ×200; *B*, ×6000; *C–E*, ×40.)

prepared from the same atretic follicles. Interestingly, our comparative studies of the progression of granulosa cell apoptosis during follicular atresia revealed that there are species-specific differences in the apoptotic process in granulosa cells [40, 66].

Briefly, as mentioned earlier, in porcine ovaries, granulosa cells located on the inner surface of the granulosa layer appeared to undergo apoptosis in the first stage of atresia, followed by neighboring granulosa cells. In contrast, in bovine ovaries, granulosa cells located on the outer surface of the follicular wall appeared to undergo apoptosis at the first stage. In ovaries of rodents, randomly scattered apoptotic cells were observed in granulosa layers of follicles at the first stage [66, 67]. In the ovaries of these species, detachment and degeneration of the granulosa layer and fragmentation of basement membrane occurred in the follicles in the advanced stage of atresia. In these ovaries, the cells of the theca interna layers were still intact during early atresia, and then apoptotic cells, mainly endocrine cells, appeared in the late to final stages. No apoptotic cells were observed in the theca externa layers during early to middle stages of atresia. These histochemical findings confirm that apoptosis occurring in granulosa cells is an initial symptom of atresia in mammalian ovaries and that the initiation areas of granulosa cell apoptosis are different among the species, indicating that local mechanisms of regulation of granulosa cell apoptosis, in particular apoptotic stimuli induction mechanism, may be different among mammalian species. However, we have insufficient information on the regulation and induction mechanisms of granulosa cell apoptosis (i.e., those of follicular atresia or follicle selection).

Many researchers have revealed a hormonally controlled apoptotic pathway that regulates follicular atresia through peptide hormones, gonadotropins, inhibin, activin, follistatin, gonadotropin-releasing hormone, insulin-like growth factor-1, insulin-like growth factor binding protein, and interleukin-1β [68–77], as well as steroid hormones, 17β-estradiol, and progesterone [78–83]. It seems to be difficult to explain the locally regulated mechanism of granulosa cell apoptosis by a hormonally controlled system, which can well explain general regulation of follicular growth and development [84–90]. Because the cell-death ligand and receptor system is considered an appropriate system for understanding local cell-to-cell regulation mechanisms, we have examined the roles of the cell-death ligand and receptor system in granulosa cell apoptosis during follicular atresia and described here the physiological roles of them in porcine ovaries.

We selected porcine ovaries for examination because (1) they are mammals with a complete estrus cycle, (2) they are easily collected at local slaughterhouses, (3) their stages of follicular development are easily evaluated by measurement of 17β-estradiol and progesterone levels in follicular fluid [32, 79, 80, 83], and most importantly, (4) it is easy to accurately isolate and manipulate each component of follicles, oocytes, cumulus cells, granulosa cells, and thecal layers from each follicle under a surgical microscope (Figure 21.1, *C–E*). In the past, many investigators used the ovaries of rodents, which have an incomplete estrus cycle, but it is impossible to accurately isolate each component of rodent follicles and to evaluate the stages of follicular development.

Other Apoptotic Cell Death in the Ovary

In mammals the luteal body synthesizes and secretes progesterone to provide uterine quiescence for the establishment and maintenance of pregnancy. However, in the absence of pregnancy, the luteal body has a limited life span. Functional and structural regressions of luteal bodies are necessary to maintain estrous-cyclicity and to avoid accumulation of nonfunctional luteal tissue within the ovary. Luteal cell apoptosis occurs during structural luteolysis. As described earlier, apoptosis is triggered by various stimuli, and many molecular pathways have been identified. In luteolysis, most researchers suggest that the Fas ligand and Fas system is major machinery for regulation of luteal cell apoptosis [91–98].

Spontaneous oocyte apoptosis has been reported, but detailed molecular processes of the oocyte apoptosis have not been well explained [21, 90]. Recently, Hsueh and his colleagues [38, 99] reported that targeted expression of bcl-2, a major antiapoptotic protein, in mouse oocytes inhibits ovarian follicular atresia and prevents spontaneous and chemotherapy-induced oocyte apoptosis, indicating that oocytes play important roles in the control of granulosa cell apoptosis in murine ovaries.

CELL-DEATH LIGAND AND RECEPTOR SYSTEM IN GRANULOSA CELLS

Fas Ligand and Fas System

Apoptosis eliminates individual cells when they are no longer needed or have become seriously damaged. Mammals have developed a signaling mechanism that actively directs cells to die by apoptosis; this process, referred to as *instructive apoptosis*, is critical particularly in the immune system [44]. The most studied paradigm for instructive apoptosis is that of Fas ligand (FasL; also called *Apo1L* or *CD95L*) and Fas (*Apo1* or *CD95*) [41–48]. FasL belongs to a family of proteins that have structural homology to tumor necrosis factor (TNF). FasL and TNF-α define a subset of TNF-family members that have apoptosis-inducing activity. FasL is predominantly expressed in activated T lymphocytes and natural killer cells and in several immune-privileged tissues and induces apoptosis in target cells through Fas. Fas, a transmembrane glycoprotein, belongs to the TNF/nerve growth factor (NGF) receptor family and mediates apoptosis. Ligation of cell-surface Fas by FasL delivers an apoptotic signal that rapidly commits the cell to apoptotic cell-death. In vitro studies show that FasL is critical for T-cell apoptosis. Furthermore, in mice or humans carrying spontaneous mutations in the genes encoding FasL or Fas, and in Fas gene knockout mice, accumulated lymphocytes resulting in a massive, lethal enlargement of lymph nodes have been observed. The main biological role of FasL and Fas system is to signal instructive apoptosis during peripheral deletion of lymphocytes. In addition, FasL and Fas-mediated apoptosis contributes to elimination of virus-infected cells and cancer cells by cytotoxic lymphocytes.

Recently, many researchers in this field have elucidated the intracellular signaling pathways that mediate instructive apoptosis. Interestingly, their findings reveal that certain components of the instructive cell-death pathway have roles not only in apoptosis but also in embryonic development, as well as in control of antigen-induced lymphocyte proliferation in the adult animal. Moreover, Fas mRNA expression was detected in the thymus, liver, heart, lung, and ovary, but the physiological and pathological roles of the FasL and Fas system in the ovaries are not accurately understood. Immunohistochemical staining of rat ovaries revealed intense positive immunostaining for FasL and Fas in granulosa cells of small and medium antral follicles with atresia, and intense FasL staining was evident in the theca interna cells of healthy, small, antral follicles [100]. In *lps* mice with hereditary abnormality of Fas, extreme accumulation of follicles and luteal bodies was seen [95]. Fas is expressed abundantly in surface epithelial cells, mediates apoptosis of the surface epithelial cells, and is involved with luteolysis in luteal bodies of rodents, which contain luteal cells, stromal cells, endothelial cells, fibroblasts, and surface epithelial cells [91–98]. In rodent ovaries the FasL and Fas system may regulate granulosa cell apoptosis in ovarian follicle atresia and luteal cell degeneration [92, 95, 100–104]. However, it has not been determined whether the FasL and Fas system mediates apoptosis in the ovaries of other species including pigs.

Our preliminary experiment indicated that constitutive expression of mRNAs of FasL and Fas estimated by reverse transcription-polymerase chain reaction (RT-PCR) method and FasL and Fas proteins assessed by Western blotting were detected in granulosa cells of both healthy and atretic follicles of porcine ovaries (Figure 21.2). However, immunohistochemical staining for these proteins showed Fas localized in the cytoplasmic region but

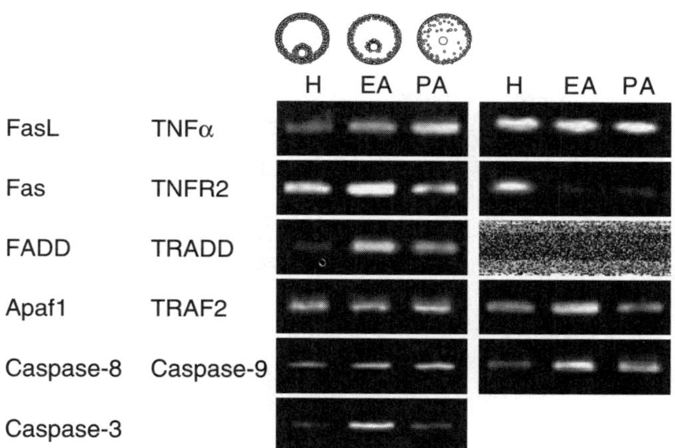

FIGURE 21.2 Representative photographs of RT-PCR products for FasL; TNF-α; Fas; TNF receptor 2 (TNFR2); Fas-associated death domain-containing protein (FADD); TNF receptor-associated death domain protein (TRADD); apoptotic protease-activating factor-1 (Apaf-1); TNF-α receptor-associated factor 2 (TRAF2); and Caspase-8, Caspase-9, and Caspase-3 mRNAs in granulosa cells prepared from healthy *(H)*, early atretic *(EA)*, and progressed atretic *(PA)* tertiary follicles of porcine ovaries.

not in the cell-surface in granulosa cells of both healthy and atretic follicles (unpublished data). We presume that the FasL and Fas system does not play a considerable role in granulosa cell apoptosis during follicular atresia in porcine ovaries.

TNF-α and TNF-Receptor System

TNF-α can induce both cell death and cell proliferation and exerts its effects by binding to either TNF receptor (TNFR) 1 or 2 [105, 106]. TNF-α induces apoptosis in a variety of tumor cells, and the death signal pathway has been suggested to be as follows [107, 108]: (1) TNF-α binds to the extracellular domain of TNFR1, which contains an intracellular death domain (DD); (2) the intracellular DD of the receptor interacts with the DD of the adaptor protein (TNF receptor-associated death domain protein [TRADD]); (3) the DD of TRADD binds with the DD of another adaptor protein (Fas-associated death domain protein [FADD]; also called *MORT1*); (4) FADD activates initiator caspase (procaspase-8); and (5) the caspase cascade is activated for intracellular transduction of the apoptotic signal (named *TNFR1-TRADD-FADD-caspase-8 signaling axis*).

In contrast, when TNF-α acts as survival/antiapoptotic factor, (1) TNF-α binds to the extracellular domain of TNFR1, (2) the intracellular DD of the receptor interacts with the DD of TRADD, (3) the DD of TRADD binds with the DD of receptor interacting protein (RIP) [109], (4) RIP interacts with TNF receptor-associated factors (TRAF) 2, and (5) TRAF2 mediates the physical interaction of the TNFR1-signaling complex with the nuclear factor (NF)-κB-inducing inhibitor of κB kinase (IKK) and inhibitor of apoptosis proteins (cIAP) 1 (named *TNFR1-TRADD-RIP-TRAF2 signaling axis*), and consequently expression of survival/antiapoptotic genes is upregulated. Thus TRADD-RIP are key proteins at the point of divergence of cell death and cell proliferation in the TNFR1 signaling process, and TRAF2 is a good indicator of TNF-α-dependent cell proliferation. Although TRAF2 cannot bind directly to TNFR1 as described earlier, it can interact directly with TNFR2, which is a non–DD-containing TNF receptor. TNFR2 can induce gene transcription for cell survival, growth, and differentiation, and therefore TNFR2 is involved in the antiapoptotic effect of TNF-α [106, 110, 111].

Briefly, (1) TNF-α binds to the extracellular domain of TNFR2, (2) activated TNFR2 interacts with TRAF2, (3) NF-κB is activated, and (4) consequently expression of survival genes is upregulated and apoptosis induced by TNF-α is prevented [107–111]. Thus when TNF-α-bound TNFR2 interacts with TRAF2, expression of survival/antiapoptotic genes is upregulated. TRAF2 expression is considered a good indicator of TNF-α-dependent cell proliferation in both TNFR1 and TNFR2 signaling cascades.

Prange-Kiel et al. [112] showed that TNF-α induced both cell proliferation and cell death in primary cultured granulosa cells prepared from large, antral follicles of pig ovaries. However, there has been no in vivo confirmed evidence of whether TNF-α acts as an apoptotic factor or as a survival/antiapoptotic factor in porcine ovarian follicles. Recently, to determine the physiological roles of TNF-α and its receptor system in granulosa cell apoptosis, we histochemically analyzed the changes in localization of TNF-α and TRAF2 in granulosa cells during follicular atresia in pig ovaries and examined the changes in localization and levels of expression of TNF-α and TRAF2 mRNAs by in situ hybridization and by RT-PCR [113]. The changes in expression of TNFR2 in granulosa cells during follicular atresia were examined by Western blotting analysis. In healthy follicles, intense signals for TNF-α and TRAF2 and their mRNAs were demonstrated in the outer zone of the granulosa layer, where many proliferating cells and no apoptotic cells were seen. In the follicles in the early atretic stage, decreased or trace staining for TRAF2 and its mRNA and decreased expression of TNFR2 were observed in the granulosa layer, where apoptotic cells were seen (see Figure 21.2). These findings indicated that TNF-α acts as a survival factor in granulosa cells during follicular atresia in porcine ovaries. Although the biological roles of the TNF-α and its receptor system in ovarian tissues are largely unknown, TNF-α and the TNFR2 system may dominantly contribute to the selective survival of necessary cells under physiological conditions [105, 106]. Our findings suggest that the TNF-α and its receptor system, TNFR2, but not TNFR1, dominantly detected in ovarian tissue, play crucial roles in induction of survival/proliferating signals in granulosa cells during follicular growth in porcine ovaries. Further studies are necessary to determine which molecular system regulates the disappearance of TNF-α receptor-associated proteins in granulosa cells in the early stage of atresia and which intracellular signal transduction pathway dominantly causes granulosa cell survival.

TNF-α-Related Apoptosis-Inducing Ligand (TRAIL) and TRAIL-Receptor System

In 1995, through the screening of DNA databases for expressed sequence tags similar to TNF-α, TNF-α-related apoptosis-inducing ligand (TRAIL; also called *Apo2L*), a novel cell-death ligand, was identified [114–116]. The complementary DNA (cDNA) sequence of TRAIL is similar to that of FasL, and in vitro functions of TRAIL are also like those of FasL. TRAIL mRNA is expressed constitutively in many tissues. TRAIL interacts with receptors that belong to the TNFR family [45, 117–128]. The receptors in the TNFR family have several cysteine-rich domains in their N-terminal region. The cytoplasmic sequence divides the TNFR family into two subgroups that either possess or lack a DD. The DD-containing receptors (called *death receptors [DRs]*) include TNFR1, Fas, DR3 (also called *Apo3*, *WSL-1*, *TRAMP*, or *LARD*), DR4 (*TRAILR1*), DR5 (*TRAILR2*, *TRICK2* or *KILLER*), and DR6 [45–48]. The DD couples each receptor to caspase-cascades that induce apoptosis or to kinase-cascades that turn on proliferating-gene expression through NF-κB and activating protein-1 (AP-1).

Recently, an interesting subgroup of TNFR-homologues was found and named as *decoy receptor* (*DcR*), which acts as an inhibitor, rather than a transducer of apoptotic signaling. The DcRs include DcR1 (*TRAILR3*, *TRID*, or *LIT*) [122–126], DcR2 (*TRAILR4* or *TRUNDD*) [125, 127], osteoprotegerin (OPG) [129], and DcR3 [130]. DcR1 and DcR2 are cell-membrane proteins, and OPG and DcR3 are secreted-soluble proteins. Four of the novel cellular receptors (DR4, DR5, DcR1, and DcR2) bind to TRAIL and are structurally related [130]. Each has two extracellular cysteine-rich domains and shows closer homology to the other TRAIL receptors than to the rest of the TNFR superfamily, and TRAIL bind to all of these receptors with equivalent high affinities. DR4 and DR5 have cytoplasmic DDs. DcR1 lacks a cytoplasmic region and appears to be attached to the cell surface through a glycosylphosphatidylinositol (GPI) anchor. DcR1-bearing cells pretreated with phosphatidylinositol-specific phospholipase C (PI-PLC), which cleaves the GPI anchor and leads to removal of DcR1 from the cell surface, showed a marked increase in apoptosis induced by TRAIL, indicating that DcR1 has an inhibitory effect on TRAIL-induced apoptosis [122–126]. DcR2 is also a cell-surface receptor and has a cytoplasmic DD, but this is two-thirds shorter than a typical DD and does not signal apoptosis [125, 127]. The extracellular domains of DcR1 or DcR2 compete with those of DR4 or DR5 for ligand binding. In vitro studies show that cell transfection with DcR1 or DcR2 inhibits apoptosis induction by TRAIL. Thus DcR1 and DcR2 compete with those of DR4 and DR5 for ligand binding and can act as decoys for DR4 and DR5 that prevent TRAIL from inducing apoptosis through DR4 and DR5. Hence, cells that express DcR1 and/or DcR2 at high levels relative to DR4 or DR5 may use the decoys as protection against cytotoxic action of TRAIL [47, 48].

Unlike the limited localization of FasL, which is produced only by immune cells, TRAIL is more abundantly expressed in many normal tissues [44–48, 114, 128, 131–135]. Moreover, DR4, DR5, DcR1, and DcR2 transcripts are also widely expressed in normal tissues. Although the biological functions of the TRAIL and TRAIL-receptor system are largely unknown, this system has been suggested to contribute to the selective abolishment of un-necessary cells under physiological conditions [136]. Interestingly, in vitro studies have shown that TRAIL can induce both apoptotic cell-death and cell-proliferation [44–48, 137–139]. The cell-death signal pathway has been suggested to be as follows: (1) TRAIL binds to the extracellular domain of DR4 and/or DR5; (2) intracellular DD of the receptor interacts with the DD of adaptor proteins (TRADD or RIP); (3-apoptotic [app]) DD of TRADD binds with DD of another adaptor protein, FADD; (4-app) FADD activates initiator caspase (procaspase-8); and thereby (5-app) the caspase-cascade is activated for intracellular transduction of the apoptotic signal. (3-servival [srv]) When the DD of RIP binds to the DD of the receptor, NK-κB is activated, and (4-srv) consequently expression of survival and cell-proliferation genes is upregulated [137, 138]. Thus TRADD and RIP are key proteins at the diverging point of cell-death and cell-proliferation, and TRADD expression is a good indicator of TRAIL-dependent apoptosis.

Our experiments were to determine the physiological roles of TRAIL and receptor system on granulosa cell apoptosis during follicular atresia in porcine ovaries. Firstly, we histochemically examined the localization of TRAIL and its receptors in porcine ovaries [140]. A marked reduction in the expression of DcR1, which has high affinity for TRAIL, was demonstrated in granulosa cells of atretic follicles, but no marked differences were seen in expression of TRAIL, DR4, or DR5 in granulosa cells between healthy and atretic follicles. No positive reaction against DcR2 was detected. Secondly, we examined the changes in expression and localization of mRNA of TRADD, which transmits the death signal from receptors to intracellular components, in granulosa cells during follicular atresia [141]. RT-PCR and in situ hybridization analyses revealed increased mRNA expression of TRADD in granulosa cells, which is demonstrated only in atretic follicles (see Figure 21.2). Finally, to confirm the inhibitory activity of DcR1 in granulosa cells, primary cultured granulosa cells prepared from healthy follicles of porcine ovaries were treated with the enzyme (PI-PLC) to cleave GPI anchor of DcR1 and to remove DcR1 from the cell surface and then incubated with TRAIL [142]. PI-PLC treatment increased the number of apoptotic cells induced by TRAIL. Our findings indicate that TRAIL and its receptors (DR4, DR5, and DcR1) are involved in induction of apoptosis in granulosa cells during atresia and that DcR1 plays an inhibitory role in granulosa cell apoptosis, at least in porcine ovaries.

Novel Cell-Death Receptor and Decoy Receptor System

We prepared monoclonal antibodies against granulosa cells prepared from porcine ovarian follicles, and some of them recognized a novel cell-death receptor and decoy receptor [143–147]. Briefly, individual preovulatory tertiary follicles, 3 mm to 5 mm in diameter, were dissected from porcine ovaries under a surgical dissecting microscope (see Figure 21.1, *C–E*). Because the progesterone/estradiol-17β ratio of follicular fluid in each follicle provides a good index of follicular atresia in sows [32, 79, 80, 83], when the progesterone/estradiol-17β ratio of follicular fluid quantified using (^{125}I)-RIA kits was less than 15, the follicle was classified as healthy. The granulosa layers were removed from the follicles and incubated in Ca^{2+}/Mg^{2+}-free Hanks' balanced salt solution containing 10 mM ethylenediaminetetraacetic acid disodium salt and 6.8 mM ethyleneglycol-*bis*-tetraacetic acid for 15 minutes at 22°C, and then granulosa cells were isolated using a pipette. Female BALB/c mice were immunized intravenously with the isolated granulosa cells (10^6 cells/mouse, biweekly). The spleen cells from immunized mice, which produced antigranulosa cell antibodies, were fused with Sp2/O-Ag14 mouse myeloma cells by standard hybridization techniques. The hybridoma cells were selected by hypoxanthine-aminopterin-thymidine and hypoxanthine-thymidine method [148]. Then, the hybridoma cells producing antibodies against the granulosa cells were screened by immunofluorescence staining using frozen sections of porcine ovaries, and antibody class was determined by enzyme-linked immunosorbent assay (ELISA). Three hybridoma cell lines were selected and cloned twice by limiting dilution. PFG-5, PFG-6, and PFG-7 clones produced immunoglobulin M (IgM), immunoglobulin G (IgG), and IgG antibodies to porcine granulosa cell-surface components, respectively. Female BALB/c mice, which were pretreated with 2, 6, 10, 14-tetramethylpentadecane, received intraperitoneal injection of PFG-5, PFG-6, or PFG-7 hybridoma cells (1×10^7 cells/mouse). Two weeks after injection, ascites were obtained from the mice and each antibody was purified using ultrafiltration equipment and a preparative high-performance liquid chromatography.

The characteristics of the monoclonal antibodies produced by the hybridoma cell clones were immunohistochemically determined. Briefly, frozen serial sections of porcine ovaries were cut on a cryostat, mounted on glass slides precoated with 3-aminopropyltriethoxysilane, and fixed with precooled acetone for 5 minutes at −80°C. After preincubation with normal goat serum, the sections were incubated with each purified monoclonal antibody, washed and incubated with fluorescein isothiocyanate (FITC)-conjugated goat antimouse IgM or IgG antibody. After washing, the sections were examined with a confocal laser scanning microscope. PFG-5 and PFG-7 showed strong FITC-staining on granulosa cells of healthy and atretic follicles (Figure 21.3). PFG-6 antibody was reactive with granulosa cells of healthy follicles. These antibodies did not label the theca interna or externa cells, basement membrane, or ovarian stroma cells in either healthy or atretic follicles. Moreover, they showed neither specific binding to the luteal body, oviduct, uterus, testis, liver, kidney, adrenal gland, pancreas, stomach, small intestine, large intestine, spleen, thymus, brain, heart, lung, or skeletal muscle.

To determine the antigen profiles, we performed conventional Western blotting and two-dimensional (2D)-

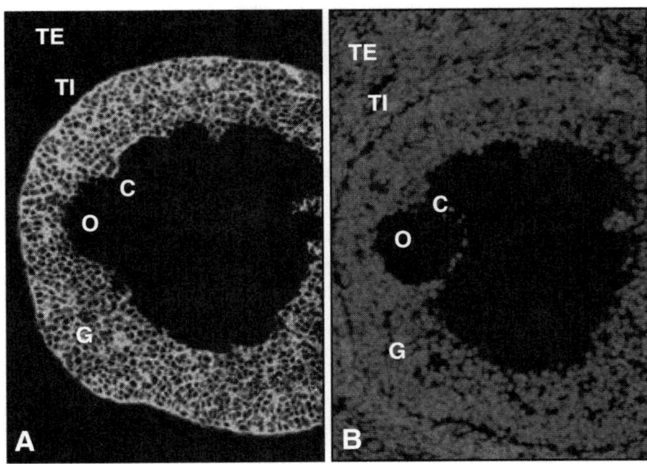

FIGURE 21.3 Composite confocal image of follicular section of porcine ovary. The frozen section was stained with PFG-5 antibody and with FITC-conjugated antimouse IgM to show the distribution of granulosa cell membrane antigens (**A**), and then stained with Hoechst 33258 to visualize the cell nuclei (**B**). The follicle was optically sectioned at 0.5 μm, and five serial images were generated using the confocal laser microscope. PFG-5 antibody showed strong fluorescent staining on granulosa cells (G). No immunostaining of cumulus cells (**C**), oocyte (O), theca interna (TI), or theca externa (TE) layers was observed. (Magnification: ×200.)

Western blotting. Briefly, homogenized samples of ovarian tissues (granulosa cells, cumulus cells, oocytes, and luteal bodies) and other organs were separated by sodium dodecyl sulfate-polyacrylamide gel electrophoresis (SDS-PAGE). Cell membrane samples prepared from isolated granulosa cells of healthy and atretic follicles were separated by 2D-PAGE. After electrophoresis, the proteins were transferred onto nitrocellulose-membranes. The membranes were incubated with each monoclonal antibody, and then immunological reaction products were visualized using a commercial staining kit. On conventional Western blotting, PFG-5, PFG-6, and PFG-7 antibodies only reacted with granulosa cells but not with any other ovarian tissues or organs. On 2D-Western blotting analysis for cell membrane fractions of the granulosa cells prepared from healthy and atretic follicles, the two specific spots (molecular weight 42 kD and isoelectric point pI 5.2, and 55 kD, pI 5.9; named *PFG-6* and *PFG-5 antigens*, respectively) of PFG-5 antibody were seen in the samples from healthy follicles, and only one specific spot of PFG-5 antigen was detected in those from atretic follicles (Figure 21.4, *C* and *D*). Abundant PFG-6 antigen expression was noted in the granulosa cells of healthy follicles. PFG-6 antibody recognized only PFG-6 antigen (Figure 21.4, *E* and *F*), and PFG-7 antibody recognized PFG-5 antigen (Figure 21.4, *G* and *H*).

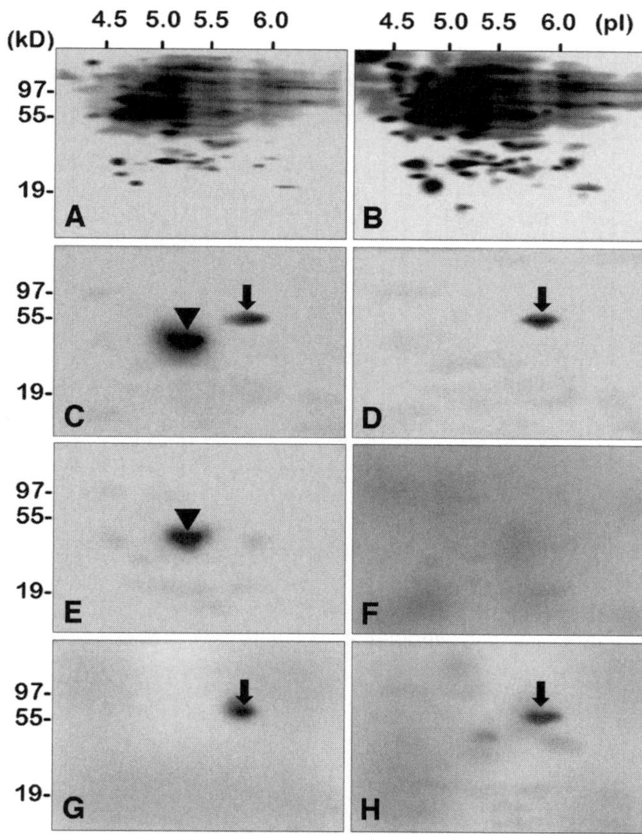

FIGURE 21.4 Representative results of two-dimensional Western blotting analysis of granulosa cell-membrane antigens recognized by PFG-5, PFG-6, and PFG-7. Granulosa cell membrane fractions were separated from granulosa cells of healthy (**A, C, E,** and **G**) and early atretic (**B, D, F,** and **H**) follicles and analyzed by two-dimensional Western blotting. Separated protein spots in gels were visualized by silver staining (**A** and **B**). After electrophoresis, the proteins were transferred onto nitrocellulose sheets and the granulosa cell antigens were visualized by labeling with PFG-5 (**C** and **D**), PFG-6 (**E** and **F**), and PFG-7 (**G** and **H**). Specific 42 kD, pI 5.2 spot (*arrowheads*: PFG-6 antigen) and 55 kD, pI 5.9 spot (*arrows*: PFG-5 antigen) were detected.

We identified the cell-killing activity of IgM PFG-5 antibody but not IgG PFG-6 and PFG-7 antibodies. Briefly, freshly isolated granulosa cells prepared from healthy follicles were cultured in tissue culture medium containing antibody (0.00001 to 1000 μg/ml of PFG-5, PFG-6, and/or PFG-7) for 1 to 72 hours at 37° C. Cell-killing activity was determined by a commercial kit for apoptotic cell determination. After incubation, cultured granulosa cells were stained by TUNEL method using a commercial kit to determine the apoptotic cells, and the nuclei of cultured cells were stained with Hoechst 33258 to observe their morphology. After staining, the cells were examined with a fluorescence microscope. Moreover, DNA samples prepared from cultured granulosa cells were electrophoresed to assess the DNA fragmentation. No TUNEL-positive apoptotic cells were detected in the granulosa cells cultured with vehicle or with PFG-6 or PFG-7 antibodies, whereas many TUNEL-positive round nuclei and small condensed nuclear fractions (apoptotic bodies; a morphological hallmark of apoptotic cell death) were observed in the cells cultured with at least 0.01 μg/ml PFG-5 antibody for more than 6 hours (Figure 21.5, *A* and *B*). PFG-5 antibody-incubated DNA sample displayed a ladder pattern on electrophoresis (biochemical hallmark of apoptosis), whereas DNA samples of the granulosa cells cultured with vehicle or with PFG-6 or PFG-7 antibodies displayed no ladder pattern. Thus in vitro granulosa cell apoptosis mediated by the PFG-5 antibody was confirmed by assessment of TUNEL staining, nuclear morphology, and DNA electrophoretic analysis. Interestingly, when the cells were cultured in medium containing both PFG-5 and PFG-6 antibodies (PFG-6 antibody added first), an extremely low dose of PFG-5 antibody (0.0001 μg/ml) could induce apoptosis, indicating that PFG-6 antibody binds to PFG-6 antigen and to block the binding activity of PFG-5 antibody to PFG-6 antigen. When the cells were cultured in medium containing both PFG-5 and PFG-7 antibodies (PFG-7 antibody added first), no apoptotic cell was seen, indicating inhibitory effect of PFG-7 on PFG-5 antibody-inducible apoptosis.

The molecular weights of well-known apoptosis-mediating receptors, Fas and TNFR1, are 45 to 46 [149, 150] and 65 kD [151], respectively, and the molecular weights of the granulosa cell-surface antigens, PFG-5 and PFG-6 antigens, were 55 and 42 kD, respectively. Fas was immunohistochemically detected in the granulosa cells and luteal cells of both healthy and atretic follicles in rodent ovaries and in the thymus, liver, heart, and lung [44, 95], but TNFR1 was not detected in ovarian follicles or luteal bodies [113]. However, both PFG-5 and PFG-6 antigens were only detected in the granulosa cells but not in luteal cells or other organs. Furthermore, PFG-5 antibody but not PFG-6 or PFG-7 antibodies could induce the apoptotic cell death in primary cultured granulosa cells. Interestingly, the apoptosis-inducing ability of PFG-5 antibody was heightened by pretreatment of PFG-6 antibody, which was added first into culture medium. The cultured granulosa cells were not killed by PFG-5 antibody in the presence of PFG-7 antibody, which was added first into culture medium. Abundant expression of PFG-6 antigen was noted in granulosa cells of healthy follicles, and no expression was demonstrated in granulosa cells of atretic follicles. Based on the biochemical and immunochemical findings, PFG-5 and PFG-6 antigens are different from the known apoptosis-mediating receptors, Fas or TNFR1. We hypothesize that PFG-5 antigen acts as a cell-death receptor specifically expressed on the granulosa cells and that PFG-6 antigen acts as a decoy receptor for PFG-5 antigen and inhibits apoptotic signals through PFG-5 antigen. A cell-surface mechanism exists for the regulation of cellular responsive-

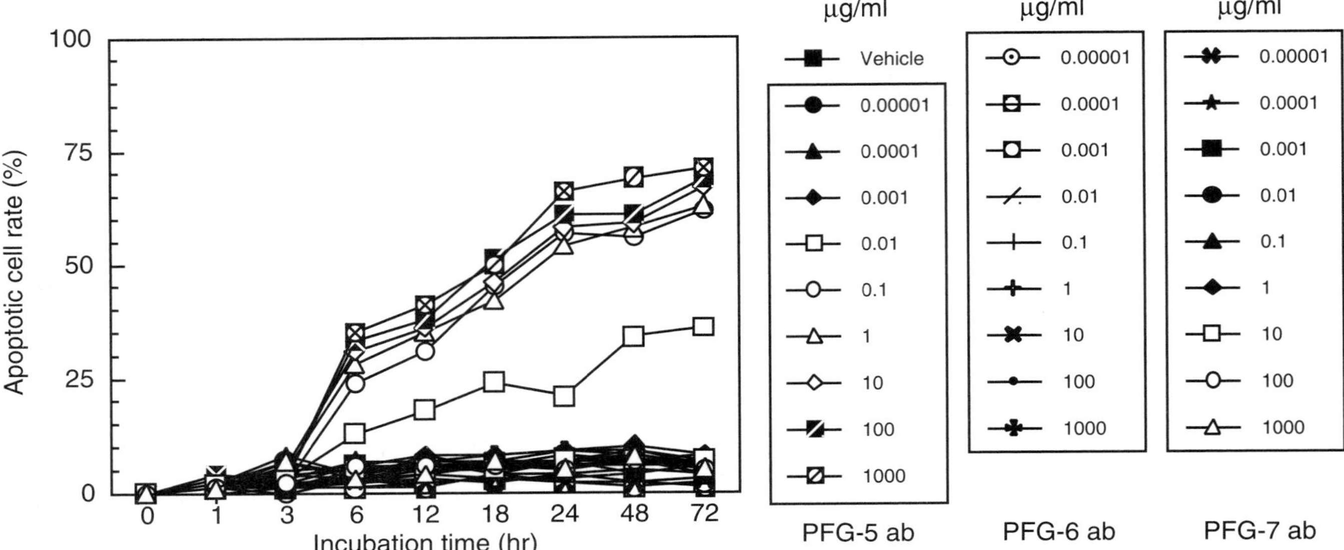

FIGURE 21.5 Time-course and dose-dependency in granulosa cell apoptosis induced by PFG-5 antibody. The isolated granulosa cells prepared from healthy follicles were cultured with each antibody (0.00001 to 1000 μg/ml of PFG-5, PFG-6, or PFG-7) for 72 hours.

ness to proapoptotic stimuli [47, 48]. Cell-death receptor transmits an apoptotic signal, and decoy receptor acts as a modulator of death receptor; both are expressed on the same granulosa cells. It is considered that overexpression of the decoy receptor on the surface of granulosa cells inhibits an apoptotic signal induced by ligand for apoptosis inducing receptor. Unfortunately, we have no data on the natural ligand for the novel cell-death receptor, and the physiological properties of these receptor systems are not well understood. These antibodies will be useful and require sensitive probes to investigate the unique cell-death receptor on the granulosa cell membrane and their natural ligand to elucidate cell surface mechanisms for the regulation of apoptosis and to define the intercellular pathway of apoptotic signal transduction in granulosa cells of porcine ovaries.

Moreover, we demonstrated caspases and related proteins, and their mRNAs are expressed in porcine granulosa cells [147] (see Figure 21.2). Expression levels of Apaf-1 and FADD were decreased during follicular atresia, but those of activated caspase-3, caspase-8, and caspase-9 were increased. No changes in expression levels of FasL or Fas during atresia were noted. It is believed that these caspase-cascade components, which locate the downstream of cell-death ligand and receptor system, transduce the intracellular apoptotic signal. However, detailed mechanisms of signal transduction have not been identified, and so further studies are needed to understand the molecular mechanisms responsible for granulosa cell apoptosis.

Other Cell-Death Ligand and Receptor Systems

Recently, in vitro studies demonstrated that other receptors (angiotensin II type 2 receptor, Gn-RH receptor, etc.) may mediate follicular atresia [152, 153], but the in vivo physiological roles of these receptors in selection of atretic folliculus have not been determined.

As in TRAIL findings, the screening of DNA databases for expressed sequence tags with similarity to TNF-α revealed a novel cell-death ligand (Apo3L or TWEAK) [154, 155]. The cDNA sequence of Apo3L is similar to that of TNF-α. Apo3L, which binds to death receptor 3 (DR3), activates apoptosis in certain tumor cell lines and also activates NF-κB [47, 48]. As described earlier, mRNA of TNF-α showed restricted expression in activated lymphoid and endothelial cells, but expression of Apo3L mRNA is found in many tissues. However, our preliminary experiments showed no expression of Apo3L- or DR3-mRNA in follicular cells of porcine ovaries (unpublished data).

Caspase-cascade acts as an intracellular signal transducer of granulosa cell apoptosis as in lymphocytes and some tumor cells [58, 147]. Some members of the bcl-2 family, which regulate apoptosis, interact with the cascade pathway and some of them have been shown to be functional in granulosa cells [38, 147]. Bok [156], Bod [157], and Boo [158] restrictively express in reproductive tissues. The expression of Boo, a novel antiapoptotic member of the bcl-2 family, was highly restricted to the ovary and epi-

Table 21.1 Apoptosis-Signaling Pathways of Cell-Death Ligand and Receptor System in Mammalian Cells

Each pathway shares essential molecular components with those of other apoptotic stimuli, but the specific components of each pathway are different. For example, Fas, TNFR1, and the cell-death receptors DR3 and DR4 act as sensors for apoptotic stimulation by the ligands. DcR1 and DcR2, which are decoy receptors that bind to TRAIL, and DcR3, which is also decoy receptor that binds to FasL, modulate apoptosis-induction by diverting specific death ligands from their death receptors. FADD, which acts as adaptor, couples Fas to caspase-8 and also couples TNFR1 to caspase-8. However, DR4 can transduce apoptotic signals without FADD. Caspase-3, which is one of the downstream components of caspase-8, acts as an effector.

Incentive	Sensor	Adaptor	Initiator	Effector	Outcome
TRAIL	DR4, DR5 DcR1, DcR2			Caspase-3	Apoptosis
FasL	Fas DcR3	FADD	Caspase-8	Caspase-3	Apoptosis
TNF-α	TNFR1	TRADD/FADD	Caspase-8	Caspase-3	Apoptosis
Apo3L	DR3	TRADD/FADD			
	DR6	TRADD			
	PFG-5		Caspase-8	Caspase-3	Apoptosis
	PFG-6				
UV dexamethasone		Apaf1	Caspase-9	Caspase-3	Apoptosis

didymis in mice, implying that it is in the control of ovarian atresia and sperm maturation. Boo homodimerizes or heterodimerizes with some cell death-promoting and/or cell death-suppressing bcl-2 family members, interacts with Apaf-1 to form a multimeric protein complex with Apaf-1 and caspase-9, and inhibits apoptosis. We found that Boo-like proteins expressed in granulosa cells of healthy follicles in porcine ovaries (unpublished data), indicating bcl-2 members with restrictive expression in granulosa cells, may contribute to the regulation of granulosa cell apoptosis. We are currently conducting further studies to reveal the intracellular regulation mechanism of granulosa cell apoptosis.

CONCLUSION

Biochemical and genetic studies have unraveled many of the signaling mechanisms that mediate induction of instructive apoptosis by cell-death ligand and receptor, such as the FasL and Fas system. Recently, genome sequencing has revealed some new death ligands, death receptors, and decoy receptors, which are categorized into the TNF ligand and receptor superfamilies. It is likely that some novel cell-death ligands and receptors use similar intracellular pathways to the FasL and Fas system, although the molecular details of this are still unknown. Although many researchers in the field of immunology and oncology have revealed the unique biological roles of the ligand-receptor systems and the molecular mechanisms that integrate their functions in the immune system, biological roles and molecular mechanisms of the ligand-receptor systems in the reproductive system are still unknown (Table 21.1).

Apoptosis, an active form of cell suicide, plays a key role in the demise of a majority of mammalian gonadal cells (follicular granulosa and luteal cells in ovaries and germ cells in testes) during reproductive life. In mammalian ovaries, a balance of cell proliferation and apoptosis in granulosa cells is maintained in a healthy follicle and any imbalance of the two processes can lead to atretic change in follicles. Recent studies have indicated the crucial role of the cell-death ligand and receptor system as a survival factor and/or apoptotic factor in follicular granulosa cells, which acts as an inducer of follicular atresia. Based on our findings in porcine ovaries, we presume that the TNF-α and TNFR2 system acts as a survival factor in granulosa cells, that the FasL and Fas system may control luteal cell death during luteolysis but not granulosa cell death during atresia, and that TRAIL and receptors (DR4, DR5, and DcR1) and unknown ligand(s) and receptors (PFG-5 and PFG-6) contribute to selective cell death of granulosa cells during atresia. Furthermore, it is believed that intracellular factors, which locate downstream of the cell-surface ligand and receptor complex, modulate cell-death signal transducing from the receptors and that intragonadal survival factors in the ovary (estrogens, insulin-like growth factor-1, epidermal growth factor, basic fibroblast growth factor, interleukin-1β, and nitrogen monoxide) and apoptotic factors (androgens, Gn-RH-like peptide and interleukin-6) interact with the cell-death ligand and receptor systems. We have no detailed knowledge of the interaction between survival and apoptotic factors and cell-death ligand and receptor systems, and such interaction may be important in regulating the induction of the death of ovarian follicles. Because our knowledge of the regulation mechanism of follicular selection is limited, further studies are essential to understand the cellular and molecular mechanisms responsible for follicular selection—in other words, granulosa cell apoptosis. We hope that the mechanism will be clarified and lead to an integrated understanding of the regulation mechanism.

ACKNOWLEDGMENTS

Our works were supported by a Grant-in-Aid for Creative Scientific Research (13GS0008) and by a Grant-in-Aid for Special Research A (13027241) to Noboru Manabe from the Ministry of Education, Sports, and Culture in Japan. We are grateful to Dr. Seishiro Katoh (Fukuyama University, Fukuyama, Japan) for advice on the determination of healthy and atretic follicles and on the evaluation of isolated porcine granulosa cells.

References

1. Baker, T. G. (1963). A quantitative and cytological study of germ cells in the human ovaries. *Proc. Roy. Soc. Lond.* 158, 417–433.
2. Braw, R. H., Byskov, A. G., Peters, H., and Faber, M. (1976). Follicular atresia in the human infant ovary. *J. Reprod. Fertil.* 46, 55–59.
3. Cárdenas, H., and Pope, W. F. (2002). Control of ovulation rate in swine. *J. Anim. Sci.* 80, 36–46.
4. Byskov, A. G. S. (1979). Atresia. In *Ovarian Follicular Development and Function*, eds. A. R. Midgley and W. A. Sadler, 41–57.New York: Raven Press.
5. Hirshfield, A. N. (1991). Development of follicles in the mammalian ovary. *Int. Rev. Cytol.* 124, 43–101.
6. Herwitz, A., and Adashi, E. Y. (1993). Ovarian follicular atresia as an apoptotic process. In *The Ovary*, 1st ed., eds. E. Y. Adashi, and P. C. K. Leung, 473–485. New York, Raven Press.
7. Tilly, J. L. (1998). Cell death and species propagation: Molecular and genetic aspects of apoptosis in the vertebrate female gonad. In *When Cells Die*, eds. R. A. Lockshin, Z. Zakeri, and J. L. Tilly, 431–452. New York: Wiley-Liss, Inc.
8. Hirshfield, A. N. (1989). Rescue of atretic follicles *in vitro* and *in vivo*. *Biol. Reprod.* 40, 181–190.
9. Imai, Y., Manabe, N., Uchio, K., Kinoshita, A., Kimura, Y., Nakayama, M., Nishihara, S., Wada, S., Sugimoto, M., and Miyamoto, H. (1999). Interactions of apoptosis and extracellular matrices in granulosa cells of atretic follicles in porcine ovaries. *J. Mamm. Ova. Res.* 16, 59–66.
10. Bagavandoss, P., Midgley, A. R., and Wicha, M. (1983). Developmental changes in the ovarian follicular basal lamina detected by immunofluorescence and electron microscopy. *J. Histochem. Cytochem.* 31, 633–640.
11. Hay, M. F., Cran, D. G., and Moor, R. M. (1976). Structural changes occurring during atresia in sheep ovarian follicles. *Cell Tissue Res.* 169, 515–529.
12. Sugimoto, M., Manabe, N., Kimura, Y., Myomoto, A., Imai, Y., Ohno, H., and Miyamoto, H. (1998). Ultrastructural changes in granulosa cells in porcine antral follicles undergoing atresia indicate apoptotic cell death. *J. Reprod. Dev.* 44, 7–14.
13. Greenwald, G. S. (1989). Temporal and topographic changes in DNA synthesis after induced follicular atresia. *Biol. Reprod.* 40, 175–181.
14. Tilly, L. J., Kowalski, K. I., Schomberg, D. W., and Hsueh, A. J. W. (1992). Apoptosis in atretic ovarian follicles is associated with selective decrease in messenger ribonucleic acid transcripts for gonadotropin receptors and cytochrome P450 aromatase. *Endocrinology* 131, 1670–1676.
15. Erickson, G. F., Magoffin, D. A., Dyer, C. A., and Hofeditz, C. (1985). The ovarian androgen producing cells: A review of structure/function relationship. *Endocr. Rev.* 6, 371–399.
16. Tsafriri, A., and Braw, R. H. (1984). Experimental approach to atresia in mammals. *Oxf. Rev. Reprod. Biol.* 6, 226–265.
17. Zeleznik, A. J., Ihrig, L. L., and Bassett, S. G. (1989). Development expression on Ca^{++}/Mg^{++}-dependent endonuclease activity in rat granulosa and luteal cells. *Endocrinology* 125, 2218–2220.
18. Tilly, J. L., Kowalski, K. I., Johnson, A. L., and Hsueh, A. J. W. (1991). Involvement of apoptosis in ovarian follicular atresia and postovulatory regression. *Endocrinology* 129, 2799–2801.
19. Manabe, N., Imai, Y., Kimura, Y., Myoumoto, A., Sugimoto, M., Miyamoto, H., Okamura, Y., and Fukumoto, M. (1996). Ca^{2+}/Mg^{2+}-dependent endonuclease but not Ca^{2+}-dependent, Mg^{2+}-dependent or cation-independent endonuclease is involved in granulosa cell apoptosis of pig atretic follicles. *J. Reprod. Dev.* 42, 247–253.
20. Black, J. L., and Erickson, B. H. (1968). Oogenesis and ovarian development in the prenatal pig. *Anat. Rec.* 161, 45–55.
21. Picton, H., Briggs, D., and Gosden, R. (1998). The molecular basis of oocyte growth and development. *Mol. Cell. Endocrinol.* 145, 27–37.
22. Zamboni, L. (1974). Fine morphology of the follicle wall and follicle cell-oocyte association. *Biol. Reprod.* 10, 125–149.
23. Grant, S. A., Hunter, M. G., and Foxcroft, G. R. (1989). Morphological and biochemical characteristics during ovarian follicular development in the pig. *J. Reprod. Fertil.* 86, 171–183.
24. Dierich, A., Sairam, M. R., Monaco, L., Fimia, G. M., Gunsmuller, A., LeMeur, M., and Sassoni-Corsi, P. (1998). Impairing follicle-stimulating hormone (FSH) signaling *in vivo*: Targeted disruption of the FSH receptor leads to aberrant gametogenesis and hormonal imbalance. *Proc. Natl. Acad. Sci. USA* 95, 13612–13617.

25. Hunter, R. H. F. (1979). Ovarian follicular responsiveness and oocyte quality after gonadotrophic stimulation in mature pigs. *Ann. Biol. Biochem. Biophys.* 5, 1511–1520.
26. Guthrie, H. D., Pursel, V. G., and Wall, R. J. (1997). Porcine follicle stimulating hormone treatment of gilts during an altrenogest-synchronized follicular phase: Effects on follicle growth, hormone secretion, ovulation and fertilization. *J. Anim. Sci.* 75, 3246–3254.
27. Paterson, A. M. (1982). The controlled induction of puberty. In *Control of Pig Reproduction*, eds. D. J. Cole and G. R. Foxcroft, 139–159. London: Butterworth Scientific.
28. Brown, R. W., Hungerford, J. W., Greenwood, P. E., Bloor, R. J., Evans, D. F., Tsonis, C. G., and Forage, G. (1990). Immunization against recombinant bovine inhibin alpha subunit causes increased ovulation rate in gilts. *J. Reprod. Fertil.* 90, 199–205.
29. King, B. F., Britt, J. H., Esbenshade, K. L., Flowers, W. L., Sesti, L. A. C., Martin, T. L., and Ireland, J. J. (1993). Ovulatory and endocrine responses after active immunization of gilts against a synthetic fragment of bovine inhibin. *J. Anim. Sci.* 71, 975–982.
30. Foxcroft, G. R., and Hunter, M. G. (1985). Basic physiology of follicular maturation in the pig. *J. Reprod. Fertil.* 33, 1–19.
31. Fortune, J. E. (1994). Ovarian follicular growth and development in mammals. *Biol. Reprod.* 50, 225–232.
32. Guthrie, H. D., Grimes, R. W., Cooper, B. S., and Hammond, J. M. (1995). Follicular atresia in pigs: Measurement and physiology. *J. Anim. Sci.* 73, 2834–2844.
33. Morbeck, D. E., Esbenshade, K. L., Flowers, W. L., and Britt, J. H. (1992). Kinetics of follicle growth in the prepuberal gilt. *Biol. Reprod.* 47, 485–491.
34. Clark, J. R., Brazier, S. G., Wiginton, L. M., Stevenson, G. R., and Tribble, L. F. (1982). Time of ovarian follicle selection during the porcine estrous cycle. *Theriogenology* 18, 697–709.
35. Dailey, R. A., Clark, J. R., Staigmiller, R. B., First, N. L., Chapman, A. B., and Casida, L. E. (1976). Growth of new follicles following electrocautery in four genetic groups of swine. *J. Anim. Sci.* 43, 175–183.
36. Miller, A. T., Picton, H. M., Craigon, J., and Hunter, M. G. (1998). Follicle dynamics and aromatase activity in high-ovulating Meisha sows and in Large-White hybrid contemporaries. *Biol. Reprod.* 58, 1372–1378.
37. Kaipia, A., and Hsueh, A. J. W. (1997). Regulation of ovarian follicle atresia. *Ann. Rev. Physiol.* 59, 349–363.
38. Hsu, S. Y., and Hsueh, A. J. W. (2000). Tissue-specific Bcl2-protein partners in apoptosis: An ovarian paradigm. *Physiol. Rev.* 80, 593–614.
39. Tilly, J. L. (1993). Ovarian follicular atresia: A model to study the mechanisms of physiological cell death. *Endocrinol. J.* 1, 67–72.
40. Manabe, N., Kimura, Y., Myoumoto, A., Matsushita, H., Tajima, C., Sugimoto, M., and Miyamoto, H. (1998). Role of granulosa cell apoptosis in ovarian follicle atresia. In *Apoptosis: Its Roles and Mechanism*, eds. T. Yamada and Y. Hashimoyto, 97–111. Tokyo: Academic Societies Japan.
41. Yonehara, S., Ishii, A., and Yonehara, M. A. (1989). Cell-killing monoclonal antibody (anti-Fas) to a cell surface antigen co-downregulated with the receptor of tumor necrosis factor. *J. Exp. Med.* 169, 1747–1756.
42. Ellis, R. E., Yuan, J. Y., and Horvitz, H. R. (1991). Mechanisms and functions of cell death. *Annu. Rev. Cell. Biol.* 663–698.
43. Steller, H. (1995). Mechanisms and genes of cellular suicide. *Science* 267, 1445–1449.
44. Nagata, S. (1997). Apoptosis by death factor. *Cell* 88, 355–365.
45. Golstein, P. (1997). Cell death: TRAIL and its receptors. *Curr. Biol.* 7, 750–753.
46. Schulze-Osthoff, K., Ferrari, D., Los, M., Wesselborg, S., and Peter, M. E. (1998). Apoptosis signaling by death receptors. *Eur. J. Biochem.* 254, 439–459.
47. Ashkenazi, A., and Dixit, V. M. (1998). Death receptors: Signaling and modulation. *Science* 281, 1305–1308.
48. Ashkenazi, A., and Dixit, V. M. (1999). Apoptosis control by death and decoy receptors. *Curr. Opin. Cell. Biol.* 11, 255–260.
49. Cohen, G. M. (1997). Caspases: The executioners of apoptosis. *Biochem. J.* 326, 1–16.
50. Nicholson, D. W., and Thornberry, N. A. (1997). Caspases: Killer proteases. *Trend. Biochem. Sci.* 22, 299–306.
51. Thornberry, N. A., and Lazebnik, Y. (1998). Caspases: Enemies within. *Science* 281, 1312–1316.
52. Grutter, M. G. (2000). Caspases: Key players in programmed cell death. *Curr. Opin. Struc. Biol.* 10, 649–655.
53. Kerr, J. F. R., Wyllie, A. H., and Currie, A. R. (1972). Apoptosis: A basic biological phenomenon with wide ranging implication in tissue kinetics. *Br. J. Cancer* 26, 239–257.
54. Tilly, J. L., and Hsueh, A. J. W. (1992). Apoptosis as the basis of ovarian follicular atresia. In *Gonadal Development and Function*, ed. S. G. Hillier, 157–165. New York: Raven Press.
55. Tilly, J. L. (1996). Apoptosis and ovarian function. *Rev. Reprod.* 1, 162–172.
56. Manabe, N., Imai, Y., Ohno, H., Takahagi, Y., Sugimoto, M., and Miyamoto, H. (1996). Apoptosis occurs in granulosa cells but not cumulus cells in the atretic antral follicles in the pig ovaries. *Experientia* 52, 647–651.
57. Hsueh, A. J. W., and Kaipia, A. (1997). Regulation of ovarian follicle atresia. *Annu. Rev. Physiol.* 59, 349–363.
58. Izawa, M., Nguyen, P. H., Kim, H. H., and Yeh, J. (1998). Expression of the apoptosis-related genes, caspase-1, caspase-3, DNA fragmentation factor, and apoptotic protease activating factor-1, in human granulosa cells. *Fertil. Steril.* 70, 549–552.
59. Robles, R., Tao, X-J, Trbovich, A. M., Maravel, D. V., Nahum, R., Perez, G. I., Tilly, K. I., and Tilly, J. L. (1999). Localization, regulation and possible consequences of apoptotic protease-activating factor-1 (Apaf-1) expression in granulosa cells of the mouse ovary. *Endocrinology* 140, 2641–2644.
60. Kimura, Y., Manabe, N., Nishihara, S., Matsushita, H., Tajima, C., Wada, S., and Miyamoto, H. (1999). Up-regulation of the α2,6-sialyltransferase messenger ribonucleic acid increases glycoconjugates containing □2,6-linked sialic acid residues in granulosa cells during follicular atresia of porcine ovaries. *Biol. Reprod.* 60, 1475–1482.
61. Tajima, C., Manabe, N., Inoue, N., Matsui, T., Hondo, E., and Miyamoto, H. (2002). Monoclonal antibody recognizes follicular granulosa cell antigens in porcine ovaries. *J. Reprod. Dev.* 48, 567–572.
62. Anderson, P. (1997). Kinase cascades regulating entry into apoptosis. *Microbiol. Mol. Biol. Rev.* 61, 33–46.

63. Okamura, Y., Myoumoto, A., Manabe, N., Tanaka, N., Okamura, H., and Fukumoto, M. (2001). Protein tyrosine kinase expression in the porcine ovary. *Mol. Human Reprod.* 7, 723–729.
64. Flemming, W. (1885). Über die Bildung von Richtungsfiguren in Säugethiereiern beim Untergang Graaf'scher Follikel. *Arch. Anat. EntGesch.* 221–244.
65. Manabe, N., Imai, Y., Myoumoto, A., Kimura, Y., Sugimoto, M., Okamura, Y., Fukumoto, M., Sakamaki, K., and Miyamoto, H. (1997). Apoptosis occurs in granulosa cells but not cumulus cells in the atretic graafian follicles in multiparous pig ovaries. *Acta. Histochem. Cytochem.* 30, 85–92.
66. Nakayama, M., Manabe, N., Nishihara, S., and Miyamoto, H. (2000). Species specific differences in apoptotic cell localization in granulosa and theca interna cells during follicular atresia in porcine and bovine ovaries. *J. Reprod. Dev.* 46, 147–156.
67. Palumbo, A., and Yeh, J. (1994). *In situ* localization of apoptosis in the rat ovary during follicular atresia. *Biol. Reprod.* 51, 888–895.
68. Hernandez, E. R., Roberts, C. T. J., LeRoith, D., and Adashi, E. Y. (1989). Rat ovarian insulin-like growth factor I (IGF-I) gene expression is granulosa cell-selective: 5′-untranslated mRNA variant representation and hormonal regulation. *Endocrinology* 136, 2770–2775.
69. Dhanasekaran, N., and Moudgal, N. R. (1989). Studies on follicle atresia: Role of gonadotropins and gonadal steroids in regulating cathepsin-D activity of preovulatory follicles in the rat. *Endocrinology* 63, 133–142.
70. Findlay, J. K. (1993). An update on the roles of inhibin, activin and follistatin as local regulators of folliculogenesis. *Biol. Reprod.* 48, 15–23.
71. Yoshimura, Y. (1998). Insulin-like growth factors and ovarian physiology. *J. Obstet. Gynecol. Res.* 24, 305–323.
72. Billig, H., Furuta, I., and Hsueh, A. J. W. (1994). Gonadotropin-releasing hormone directly induces apoptotic cell death in the rat ovary: Biochemical and *in situ* detection of deoxyribonucleic acid fragmentation in granulosa cells. *Endocrinology* 134, 245–251.
73. Chun, S. Y., Billig, H., Tilly, J., Furuta, I., Tsafriri, A., and Hsueh, A. J. W. (1994). Gonadotropin suppression of apoptosis in cultured preovulatory follicles: Mediatory role of endogenous IGF-I. *Endocrinology* 135, 1845–1853.
74. Eisenhauer, K. M., Chun, S. Y., Billig, H., and Hsueh, A. J. W. (1995). Growth hormone suppression of ovarian follicle apoptosis and partial neutralization by insulin-like growth factor binding protein (IGFBP). *Biol. Reprod.* 53, 13–20.
75. Chun, S. Y., Eisenhauer, K. M., Kubo, M., and Hsueh, A. J. W. (1995). Interleukin-1β suppresses apoptosis in rat ovarian follicles by increasing nitric oxide production. *Endocrinology* 136, 3120–3127.
76. Chun, S. Y., Eisenhauer, K. M., Minami, S., Billig, H., Perlas, E., and Hsueh, A. J. W. (1996). Hormonal regulation of apoptosis in early antral follicles: Follicle-stimulating hormone as a major survival factor. *Endocrinology* 137, 1447–1456.
77. McGee, E., Spears, N., Minami, S., Hsu, S. Y., Chun, S. Y., Billig, H., and Hsueh, A. J. W. (1997). Preantral ovarian follicles in serum-free culture: Suppression of apoptosis after activation of the cGMP pathway and stimulation of growth and differentiation by FSH. *Endocrinology* 138, 2417–2424.
78. Ingram, D. L. (1959). The effect of oestrogen on the atresia of ovarian follicles. *J. Endocrinol.* 19, 123–125.
79. Maxson, W. S., Haney, A. F., and Schomberg, D. W. (1985). Steroidogenesis in porcine atretic follicles: Loss of aromatase activity in isolated granulosa and theca. *Biol. Reprod.* 33, 495–501.
80. Babaloa, G. O., and Shapiro, H. (1988). Correlation of follicular steroid hormone profiles with ovarian cyclicity in sows. *J. Reprod. Fertil.* 84, 79–87.
81. Billig, H., Furuta, I., and Hsueh, A. J. W. (1993). Estrogens inhibit and androgens enhance ovarian granulosa cell apoptosis. *Endocrinology* 133, 2204–2212.
82. Coley, A. J., Howard, H. J., Slanger, W. D., and Ford, J. J. (1994). Steroidogenesis in the preovulatory porcine follicle. *Biol. Reprod.* 51, 655–661.
83. Guthrie, H. D., Cooper, B. S., Welch, G. R., Zakaria, A. D., and Johnson, L. A. (1995). Atresia in follicles grown after ovulation in the pig: Measurement of increased apoptosis in granulosa cells and reduced follicular fluid estradiol-17β. *Biol. Reprod.* 52, 920–927.
84. Hsueh, A. J. W., Billig, H., and Tsafriri, A. (1994). Ovarian follicle atresia: A hormonally controlled apoptotic pathway. *Endocr. Rev.* 15, 1–18.
85. Billig, H. (1996). Follicle apoptosis. *Gynecol. Endocrinol.* 10, 7–8.
86. Billig, H., Chun, S. Y., Eisenhauer, K., and Hsueh, A. J. W. (1996). Gonadal cell apoptosis: Hormone-regulated cell demise. *Human Reprod. Update* 2, 103–117.
87. Hsueh, A. J. W., Eisenhauer, K., Chun, S. Y., Hsu, S. Y., and Billig, H. (1996). Gonadal cell apoptosis. *Rec. Prog. Hormone Res.* 51, 433–456.
88. Gougeon, A. (1996). Regulation of ovarian follicular development in primates: Facts and hypotheses. *Endocr. Rev.* 17, 121–155.
89. Chun, S. Y., and Hsueh, A. J. W. (1998). Paracrine mechanisms of ovarian follicle apoptosis. *J. Reprod. Immunol.* 39, 63–75.
90. Driancourt, M. A., and Thuel, B. (1998). Control of oocyte growth and maturation by follicular cells and molecules present in follicular fluid. *Reprod. Nutr. Dev.* 38, 345–362.
91. Juengel, J. L., Garverick, H. A., Johnson, A. L., Youngquist, R. S., and Smith, M. F. (1993). Apoptosis during luteal regression in cattle. *Endocrinology* 132, 249–254.
92. Quirk, S. M., Cowan, R. G., Joshi, S. G., and Henrikson, K. P. (1995). Fas antigen-mediated apoptosis in human granulosa/luteal cells. *Biol. Reprod.* 52, 279–287.
93. Rueda, B. R., Wegner, J. A., Marion, S. L., Wahlen, D. D., and Hoyer, P. B. (1995). Internucleosomal DNA fragmentation in ovine luteal tissue associated with luteolysis: *In vivo* and *in vitro* analyses. *Biol. Reprod.* 52, 305–312.
94. Shikone, T., Yamamoto, M., Kokawawa, K., Yamashita, K., Nishimori, K., and Nakano, R. (1996). Apoptosis of human corpora lutea during cyclic luteal regression and early pregnancy. *J. Clin. Endocrinol. Metab.* 81, 2376–2380.
95. Sakamaki, K., Yoshida, H., Nishimura, Y., Nishikawa, S. I., Manabe, N., and Yonehara, S. (1997). Involvement of Fas antigen in ovarian follicular atresia and luteolysis. *Mol. Reprod. Dev.* 47, 11–18.
96. Bowen, J. M., Towns, R., Warren, J. S., and Keyes, P. L. (1999). Luteal regression in the normally cycling rat: Apoptosis,

monocyte chemoattractant protein-1, and inflammatory cell involvement. *Biol. Reprod.* 60, 740–746.

97. Roughton, S. A., Lareu, R. R., Bittles, A. H., and Dharmarajan, A. M. (1999). Fas and Fas ligand messenger ribonucleic acid and protein expression in the rat corpus luteum during apoptosis-mediated luteolysis. *Biol. Reprod.* 60, 797–804.
98. Quirk, S. M., Harman, R. M., Huber, S. C., and Cowan, R. G. (2000). Responsiveness of mouse corpora luteal cells to Fas antigen (CD95)-mediated apoptosis. *Biol. Reprod.* 63, 49–56.
99. Morita, Y., Perez, G. I., Maravei, D. V., Tilly, K. I., and Tilly, J. L. (1999). Targeted expression of Bcl-2 in mouse oocytes inhibits ovarian follicle atresia and prevents spontaneous and chemotherapy-induced oocyte apoptosis *in vitro*. *Mol. Endocrinol.* 13, 841–850.
100. Hakuno, N., Koji, T., Yano, T., Kobayashi, N., Tsutsumi, O., Taketani, Y., and Nakane, P. K. (1996). Fas/APO-1/CD95 system as a mediator of granulosa cell apoptosis in ovarian follicle atresia. *Endocrinology* 137, 1938–1948.
101. Quirk, S. M., Cowan, R. G., and Huber, S. H. (1997). Fas antigen-mediated apoptosis of ovarian surface epithelial cells. *Endocrinology* 138, 4558–4566.
102. Kim, J. M., Boone, D. L., Auyeung, A., and Tsang, B. K. (1998). Granulosa cell apoptosis induced at the penultimate stage of follicular development is associated with increased levels of Fas and Fas ligand in the rat ovary. *Biol. Reprod.* 58, 1170–1176.
103. Xu, J. P., Li, X., Mori, E., Guo, M. W., and Mori, T. (1998). Aberrant expression and dysfunction of Fas antigen in MRL/MpJlpr/lpr murine ovary. *Zygote* 6, 359–367.
104. Kim, J. M., Yoon, Y. D., and Tsang, B. K. (1999). Involvement of the Fas/Fas ligand system in p53-mediated granulosa cell apoptosis during follicular development and atresia. *Endocrinology* 140, 2307–2317.
105. Hsu, H., Xiong, J., and Goeddel, D. V. (1995). The TNF receptor 1-associated protein TRADD signals cell death and NF-κB activation. *Cell* 81, 495–504.
106. Boldin, M. P., Varfolomeev, E. E., Pancer, Z., Mett, I. L., Camonis, J. H., and Wallach, D. (1995). A novel protein that interacts with the death domain of Fas/APO1 contains a sequence motif related to the death domain. *J. Biol. Chem.* 270, 7795–7798.
107. Inoue, J., Ishida, T., Tsukamoto, N., Kobayashi, N., Naito, A., Azuma, S., and Yamamoto, T. (2000). Tumor necrosis factor receptor-associated factor (TRAF) family: Adapter proteins that mediate cytokine signaling. *Exp. Cell. Res.* 254, 14–24.
108. Wajant, H., and Scheurich, P. (2001). Tumor necrosis factor receptor-associated factor (TRAF) 2 and its role in TNF signaling. *Int. J. Biochem. Cell. Biol.* 33, 19–32.
109. Stanger, B. Z., Leder, P., Lee, T. H., Kim, E., and Seed, B. (1995). RIP: A novel protein containing a death domain that interacts with Fas/APO-1 (CD95) in yeast and causes cell death. *Cell* 81, 513–523.
110. Shu, H. B., Takeuchi, M., and Goeddel, D. V. (1996). The tumor necrosis factor receptor 2 signal transducers TRAF2 and c-IAP1 are components of the tumor necrosis factor receptor 1 signaling complex. *Proc. Natl. Acad. Sci. USA* 93, 13973–13978.
111. Arch, R. H., Gedrich, R. W., and Thompson, C. B. (1998). Tumor necrosis factor receptor-associated factors (TRAFs): A family of adapter proteins that regulates life and death. *Genes Dev.* 12, 2821–2830.
112. Prange-Kiel, J., Kreutzkamm, C., Wehrenberg, U., and Rune, G. M. (2001). Role of tumor necrosis factor in preovulatory follicles of swine. *Biol. Reprod.* 65, 928–935.
113. Nakayama, M., Manabe, N., Inoue, N., Matsui, T., and Miyamoto, H. (2003). Changes in the expression of tumor necrosis factor (TNF) α, TNFα receptor (TNFR) 2 and TNFR-associated factor 2 in granulosa cells during atresia in pig ovaries. *Biol. Reprod.* 68, 530–535.
114. Wiley, S. R., Schooley, K., Smolak, P. J., Din, W. S., Huang, C. P., Nicholl, J. K., Sutherland, G. R., Smith, T. D., Rauch, C., Smith, C. A., and Goodwin, R. G. (1995). Identification and characterization of a new member of the TNF family that induces apoptosis. *Immunity* 3, 673–682.
115. Pitti, R. M., Marsters, S. A., Ruppert, S., Donahue, C. J., Moore, A., and Ashkenazi, A. (1996). Induction of apoptosis by Apo-2 ligand, a new member of the tumor necrosis factor cytokine family. *J. Biol. Chem.* 271, 12687–12690.
116. Marsters, S. A., Pitti, R. M., Donahue, C., Ruppert, S., Bauer, K., and Ashkenazi, A. (1996). Activation of apoptosis by Apo-2 ligand is independent of FADD but blocked by CrmA. *Curr. Biol.* 6, 750–752.
117. Pan, G., O'Rourke, K., Chinnaiyan, A. M., Gentz, R., Ebner, R., Ni, J., and Dixit, V. M. (1997). The receptor for the cytotoxic ligand TRAIL. *Science* 276, 111–113.
118. McFarlane, M., Ahmad, M., Srinivasula, S. M., Fernandes-Alnemri, T., Choen, G. M., and Alnemri, E. S. (1997). Identification and molecular cloning of two novel receptors for the cytotoxic ligand TRAIL. *J. Biol. Chem.* 272, 25417–25420.
119. Schneider, P., Bodmer, J. L., Thome, M., Hofman, K., Hohller, N., and Tschopp, J. (1997). Characterization of two receptors for TRAIL. *FEBS Lett.* 416, 329–334.
120. Marsters, S. A., Sheridan, J. P., Pitti, R. M., Huang, A., Skubatch, M., Baldwin, D., Yuan, J., Gurney, A., Godowski, P., and Ashkenazi, A. (1997). A novel receptor for Apo2L/TRAIL contains a truncated death domain. *Curr. Biol.* 7, 1003–1006.
121. Walczak, H., Degli-Esposti, M. A., Johonson, R. S., Smolak, P. J., Waugh, J. Y., Boiani, N., Timour, M. S., Gerhart, M. J., Schooley, K. A., and Smith, C. A. (1997). TRAIL-R2: A novel apoptosis-mediating receptor for TRAIL. *EMBO J.* 16, 5386–5397.
122. Pan, G., Ni, J., Wei, Y-F, Yu, G-L, Gentz, R., and Dixit, V. M. (1997). An antagonist decoy receptor and a death domain-containing receptor for TRAIL. *Science* 277, 815–818.
123. Sheridan, J. P., Marsters, S. A., Pitti, R. M., Gerney, A., Skubatch, M., Baldwin, D., Ramakrishnan, L., Gray, C. L., Baker, K., Wood, W. I., Goddard, A. D., Godowski, P., and Ashkenazi, A. (1997). Control of TRAIL-induced apoptosis by a family of signaling and decoy receptors. *Science* 277, 818–821.
124. Degli-Esposti, M. A., Smolak, P. J., Walczak, H., Waugh, J. Y., Huang, C. P., Dubose, R. F., Goodwin, R. G., and Smith, C. A. (1997). Cloning and characterization of TRAIL-R3, a novel member of the emerging TRAIL receptor family. *J. Exp. Med.* 186, 1165–1170.
125. Degli-Esposti, M. A., Dougall, W. C., Smolak, P. J., Waugh, J. Y., Smith, C. A., and Goodwin, R. G. (1997). The novel recep-

tor TRAIL-R4 induces NF-κB and protects against TRAIL-mediated apoptosis, yet retrains an incomplete death domain. *Immunity* 7, 813–820.

126. Mongkolsapaya, J., Cowper, A., Xu, X. N., Morris, G., McMichael, A., Bell, J. I., and Screaton, G. R. (1998). Lymphocyte inhibitor of TRAIL: A new receptor protecting lymphocytes from the death ligand TRAIL. *J. Immunol.* 160, 3–6.
127. Pan, G., Ni, J., Yu, L., Wei, Y-F, and Dixit, V. M. (1998). TRUNDD, a new member of the TRAIL receptor family that antagonizes TRAIL signaling. *FEBS Lett.* 424, 41–45.
128. Degli-Esposti, M. A. (1999). To die or not to die—the quest of the TRAIL receptors. *J. Leukoc. Biol.* 65, 535–542.
129. Emery, J. G., McDonnell, P., Burke, M. B., Deen, K. C., Lyn, S., Silverman, C., Dul, E., Appelbaum, E. R., Eichman, C., Diprinzio, R., Dodds, R. A., James, I. E., Rosenberg, M., Lee, J. C., and Young, P. R. (1998). Osteoprotegerin is a receptor for the cytotoxic ligand TRAIL. *J. Biol. Chem.* 273, 14363–14367.
130. Truneh, A., Sharma, S., Silverman, C., Khandekar, S., Reddy, M. P., Deen, K. C., Mclaughlin, M. M., Srinivasula, S. M., Livi, G. P., Marshall, L. A., Alnemri, E. S., Williams, W. V., and Doyle, M. L. (2000). Temperature-sensitive differential affinity of TRAIL for its receptors. DR5 is the highest affinity receptor. *J. Biol. Chem.* 275, 23319–23325.
131. Cleveland, J. L., and Ihle, J. N. (1995). Contenders in FasL/TNF death signaling. *Cell* 81, 479–482.
132. Lynch, D., Ramsdell, F., and Alderson, M. R. (1995). Fas and FasL in the homeostatic regulation of immune responses. *Immunol. Today* 16, 569–573.
133. Nagata, S., and Golstein, P. (1995). The Fas death factor. *Science* 267, 1449–1456.
134. Walczak, H., and Krammer, P. H. (2000). The CD95 (APO-1/Fas) and the TRAIL (APO-2L) apoptosis systems. *Exp. Cell. Res.* 256, 58–66.
135. Ozoren, N., Fisher, M. J., Kim, K., Liu, C. X., Genin, A., Shifman, Y., Dicker, D. T., Spinner, N. B., Lisitsyn, N. A., and EI-Deiry, W. S. (2000). Homozygous deletion of the death receptor DR4 gene in a nasopharyngeal cancer cell line is associated with TRAIL resistance. *Int. J. Oncol.* 16, 917–925.
136. Zhang, X. D., Nguyen, T., Thomas, W. D., Sanders, J. E., and Hersey, P. (2000). Mechanisms of resistance of normal cells to TRAIL induced apoptosis vary between different cell types. *FEBS Lett.* 482, 193–199.
137. Chaudhary, P. M., Eby, M., Jasmin, A., Bookwalter, A., Murray, J., and Hood, L. (1997). Death receptor 5, a new member of the TNFR family, and DR4 induce FADD-dependent apoptosis and activate the NF-κB pathway. *Immunity* 7, 812–830.
138. Schneider, P., Thome, M., Burns, K., Bodmer, J. L., Hofmann, K., Kataoka, T., Holler, N., and Tschopp, J. (1997). TRAIL receptors 1 (DR4) and 2 (DR5) signal FADD-dependent apoptosis and activate NF-κB. *Immunity* 7, 831–836.
139. Kischkel, F. C., Lawrence, D. A., Chuntharapai, A., Schow, P., Kim, J., and Ashkenazi, A. (2000). Apo2L/TRAIL-dependent recruitment of endogenous FADD and caspase-8 to death receptors 4 and 5. *Immunity* 12, 611–620.
140. Wada, S., Manabe, N., Inoue, N., Nakayama, M., Matsui, T., and Miyamoto, H. (2002). TRADD is involved in apoptosis induction in granulosa cells during atresia in pig ovaries. *J. Reprod. Dev.* 48, 175–181.
141. Wada, S., Manabe, N., Inoue, N., Nakayama, M., Matsui, T., and Miyamoto, H. (2002). TRAIL-decoy receptor-1 disappears in granulosa cells of atretic follicles in porcine ovaries. *J. Reprod. Dev.* 48, 167–173.
142. Wada, S., Manabe, N., Nakayama, M., Inoue, N., Matsui, T., and Miyamoto, H. (2002). TRAIL-decoy receptor 1 plays inhibitory role in apoptosis of granulosa cells from pig ovarian follicules. *J. Vet. Med. Sci.* 64, 435–439.
143. Myoumoto, A., Manabe, N., Imai, Y., Kimura, Y., Sugimoto, M., Okamura, Y., Fukumoto, M., Sakamaki, K., Niwano, Y., and Miyamoto, H. (1997). Monoclonal antibodies against pig ovarian follicular granulosa cells induce apoptotic cell death in cultured granulosa cells. *J. Vet. Med. Sci.* 59, 641–649.
144. Manabe, N., Kimura, Y., Uchio, K., Tajima, C., Matsushita, H., Nakayama, M., Sugimoto, M., and Miyamoto, H. (1999). Regulatory mechanisms of granulosa cell apoptosis in ovarian follicle atresia: Role of granulosa cell apoptosis in porcine ovarian follicle atresia. In *Animal Cell Technology*, eds. K. Iikura, M. Nagao, S. Masuda, and R. Sasaki, 343–347. Dordrecht, The Netherlands: Kluwer Academic.
145. Manabe, N., Myoumoto, A., Tajima, C., Fukumoto, M., Nakayama, M., Uchio, K., Yamaguchi, M., and Miyamoto, H. (2000). Immunochemical characteristics of a novel cell death receptor and a decoy receptor on granulosa cells of porcine ovarian follicles. *Cytotechnology* 33, 189–201.
146. Manabe, N., Myoumoto, A., Tajima, C., Nakayama, M., Yamaguchi, M., Yamada-Uchio, K., and Miyamoto, H. (2001). Monoclonal antibodies recognize a novel cell death receptor and a decoy receptor on granulosa cells of porcine ovarian follicles. *J. Mamm. Ova. Res.* 18, 1–13.
147. Manabe, N., Sugimoto, M., Nakayama, M., Inoue, N., Matsui, T., Yamaguchi, M., Yamada-Uchio, K., and Miyamoto, H. (2001). Histological and biochemical profiles of granulosa cell apoptosis in follicular atresia of porcine ovaries. In *Reproductive Biotechnology*, eds. H. Miyamoto and N. Manabe, 61–72. Kyoto, Japan: Hokuto Publications.
148. Oi, V. T., and Herzenberg, L. A. (1980). Immunoglobulin producing hybrid cell lines. In *Selected Methods in Cellular Immunology*, eds. B. B. Mishell and S. M. Shiiji, 351–372. San Francisco: Freeman Publications.
149. Itoh, N., Yonehara, S., Ishii, A., Yonehara, M., Mizushima, S-I, Sameshima, M., Hase, A., Seto, Y., and Nagata, S. (1991). The polypeptide encoded by the cDNA for human cell surface antigen Fas can mediate apoptosis. *Cell* 66, 233–243.
150. Yoo, J., Stone, R. T., and Beattie, C. W. (1996). Cloning and characterization of the bovine Fas. *DNA Cell Biol.* 15, 227–234.
151. Stauber, G. B., Aiyer, R. A., and Aggatwal, B. B. (1988). Human tumor necrosis factor-alpha receptor. purification by immunoaffinity chromatography and initial characterization. *J. Biol. Chem.* 263, 190–198.
152. Murdoch, W. J. (1995). Immunolocalization of a gonadotropin-releasing hormone receptor site in murine endometrium that mediates apoptosis. *Cell Tissue Res.* 282, 527–529.
153. Yamada, T., Horiuchi, M., and Dzau, V. J. S. O. (1996). Angiotensin II type 2 receptor mediates programmed cell death. *Proc. Natl. Acad. Sci. USA* 93, 156–160.
154. Chicheportiche, Y., Bourdon, P. R., Xu, H., Hsu, Y. M., Scott, H., Hession, C., Garcia, I., and Brownin, J. L. (1997).

TWEAK, a new secreted ligand in the tumor necrosis factor family that weakly induces apoptosis. *J. Biol. Chem.* 272, 32401–32410.

155. Marsters, S. A., Sheridan, J. P., Pitti, R. M., Brush, J., Goddard, A., and Ashkenazi, A. (1998). Identification of a ligand for the death-domain-containing receptor Apo3. *Curr. Biol.* 8, 525–528.
156. Hsu, S. Y., Kaipia, A., McGee, E., Lomeli, M., and Hsueh, A. J. W. (1997). Bok is a pro-apoptotic Bcl-2 protein with restricted expression in reproductive tissues and heterodimerizes with selective antiapoptotic Bcl-2 family members. *Proc. Natl. Acad. Sci. USA* 94, 12401–12406.
157. Hsu, S. Y., and Hsueh, A. J. (1998). Bod (Bcl-2-related ovarian death gene) is an ovarian BH3 domain containing proapoptotic Bcl-2 protein capable of dimerization with diverse antiapoptotic Bcl-2 members. *Mol. Endocrinol.* 12, 1432–1440.
158. Song, Q., Kuang, Y., Dixit, V. M., and Vincenz, C. (1999). Boo, a novel negative regulator of cell death, interacts with Apaf-1. *EMBO J.* 18, 167–178.

PART VI

Novel Experimental Models

CHAPTER **22**

Generation and Application of Ovarian Steroidogenic Cell Lines

ABRAHAM AMSTERDAM AND R. SASSON

ABSTRACT

Primary granulosa cells of mammals such as rats, mice, and humans can be immortalized by transfecting them with oncogenes and mutated tumor suppressor genes. The established cell lines preserve their potential to undergo differentiation and luteinization under stimulation by substances elevating intracellular levels of cyclic adenosine monophosphate (cAMP). Moreover, if these cells are cotransfected with plasmids coding for the rat or human luteinizing hormone (LH), human chorionic gonadotropin (hCG), or follicle-stimulating hormone (FSH) receptors, they respond to gonadotropin stimulation by activation of hormone sensitive adenylate cyclase followed by *de novo* formation of steroid acute regulatory (StAR) protein; the cytochrome P450 side chain cleavage enzyme system; and subsequent formation of pregnenolone, progesterone, and 20α dihydroprogesterone. These cells also respond to gonadotropin/cAMP stimulation, elevating intracellular communication via gap junctions (GJs) and forming typical ovarian paracrine factors such as follistatin. This immortalized granulosa cell system is valuable for the study of mechanisms of apoptosis induced by serum deprivation, p53, and tumor necrosis factor-α (TNF-α), as well as the prevention of apoptosis by tyrosine kinase growth factors (e.g., basic fibroblast growth factor [bFGF]) and steroid hormones (e.g., glucocorticoids). Most recently, this cell system has become a useful tool to study genomic function modulated by gonadotropic hormones. The advantage of this cell system is its homogenous population of cells because each cell line is monoclonal. Thus endocrinological, biochemical, and molecular studies on the entire cell population can be applied to an individual cell type.

INTRODUCTION

Ovarian function can be studied on in vivo or in in vitro levels. The in vitro models include perfusion of the intact ovary, culture of intact ovarian follicles or strips of ovarian theca, or transplantation of ex vivo ovarian tissues to other mammalian species, such as mice, after the immune system has been drastically weakened by genetic manipulation or x irradiation to avoid rejection of the ovarian transplant by the host. To study the behavior of single cells, in situ immuno-cytochemistry, high resolution radioautography, and in situ hybridization were applied to visualize specific proteins, hormone receptors, and messenger ribonucleic acid (mRNA) located in the intact organ (for review, see [1]). Cell suspension after tissue dissociation or primary cultures have also been used for the past few decades (for reviews, see [2, 3]). Although these systems are useful tools for the study of ovarian cell function, they suffer from three disadvantages: (1) the life span of primary cells is limited; (2) primary cultures gradually loose their gonadotropic response; and (3) primary cultures do not represent a homogenous population of cells, even if they are derived from the same follicle. It was demonstrated earlier that there is a centripetal gradient of differentiation among the granulosa cell layers in respect to their content of LH and hCG receptors and the cytochrome p450 side cleavage chain enzyme (p450scc) system, based on their proximity to the basement membrane, which engulfs the follicle [4] (for reviews, see [2, 3, 5]). Nevertheless, valuable information concerning the mechanism of steroidogenesis and cooperation between granulosa and theca cells in steroid hormone formation and metabolism was obtained using such systems [6, 7]. Insights into the mechanism of FSH/cAMP induction of LH receptors, the establishment of cell contact and intercellular communication among granulosa and theca cells, and the interactions between these two distinct populations of steroidogenic cells were gained by intensive studies of primary cultures [8–10]. More recently, the effects of extracellular matrix (ECM) on granulosa cell viability and modulation of steroidogenesis has been studied on ECM-coated tissue culture plates [11–14], leading to a better understanding of the cellular and molecular mechanism of basement membrane components on the induction of follicular growth, differentiation, and protection against apoptosis.

GENERATION OF STEROIDOGENIC OVARIAN CELL LINES

Granulosa Cell Lines Responding to Cyclic Adenosine Monophosphate Stimulation

The discovery of oncogenes and oncoviruses opened the possibility to immortalize primary cells. However, early attempts to use SV40, which express the T antigen, to immortalize rat and mouse granulosa cells yielded cell lines that were considerably undifferentiated, showing only modest steroidogenesis with no or weak response to gonadotropin. Using a temperature-sensitive mutant of T antigen did not dramatically improve the steroidogenic capacity of the cells and no consistent remaining response to gonadotropin could be observed [15–17].

The use of a combination of oncogenes to immortalize granulosa cells gave surprising results: Cotransfection of primary rat granulosa cells, either from preantral or preovulatory follicles with SV40 DNA (PSV Bam) and a plasmid coding for Ha-Ras (pEJ 6.6), yielded immortalized granulosa cells that were highly tumorgenic and metastatic when injected into nude mice [18]. Nevertheless, by elevating levels of intracellular cAMP, their proliferation was attenuated and they produced pregnenolone, progesterone, and 20α dihydroprogesterone in appreciable levels, compared with the primary cells from which they were derived [19, 20]. Interestingly, the potential for steroidogenesis could be preserved in the immortalized granulosa cells similarly to the potential of the primary cells from which they were derived at specific critical points of folliculogenesis: Immortalized granulosa cells from preovulatory follicles can yield much higher amounts of progesterone compared with lines derived from preantral follicles [19, 21]. Attempts to immortalize granulosa cells from day 12 rats were also successful, and a response to forskolin in progesterone production was already achieved in cell lines derived from the early stage of follicular development [15].

USE OF MUTANT p53 FOR IMMORTALIZATION OF STEROIDOGENIC GRANULOSA CELLS

Since the discovery that a mutated p53 tumor suppressor gene can act as a dominant negative repressor of the natively expressed p53, a temperature-sensitive mutant of p53 has been used in the creation of immortalized rat and human granulosa cells [22–24]. As a source of human cells, primary granulosa cells were obtained from women undergoing in vitro fertilization (IVF). Rat cell lines obtained following SV40-Ras-p53 triple transfection are highly steroidogenic on cAMP stimulation, whereas human cells are slow growing and loose their steroidogenic capacity following extensive transfers. Because the immortalized cells express 135 valine p53, which behaves like an oncogenic p53 at 37° C (does not bind to deoxyribonucleic acid [DNA]) and as a tumor suppressor gene (binds to DNA) at 32° C, shifting the temperature of growth from 37° C to 32° C induces massive apoptosis in these cells [23, 24]. Recent attempts successfully preserved FSH responsiveness through immortalization of human granulosa cells obtained from IVF patients by cotransfecting them with a temperature-sensitive mutant of p53 and Ha-Ras without SV40. Although a pronounced response to FSH stimulation can be obtained, these cells loose their gonadotropin and cAMP response following extensive passages [25].

Another study reported that long-term growth and steroidogenic potential of human granulosa-lutein cells could be conferred by immortalization with large T antigen [26]. These cell lines showed responsiveness to cAMP, but no consistent response to hCG or FSH could be demonstrated [27]. In another attempt, human granulosa cells were transformed with the E6 and E7 regions of human papillomavirus [27]. Another line established from a metastatic granulosa cell carcinoma seemed to display synthesis of 17β-estradiol and modest response to LH or FSH even at high concentration of the hormones [28], suggesting that immortalization of steroidogenic human granulosa cells responding to gonadotropic hormones had not yet been achieved.

ESTABLISHMENT OF IMMORTALIZED GRANULOSA CELL LINES EXPRESSING GONADOTROPIN RECEPTORS

Because receptors for gonadotropin are generally lost on cell transformation, immortalized nonsteroidogenic cells, such as CHO and embryonic kidney cells, have been transfected with plasmids expressing either the LH/hCG or FSH receptors. However, only the initial interaction between gonadotropins and their receptors and coupling to adenylate cyclase could be studied because such cells do not express regulatory proteins and steroidogenic enzymes [29–32].

Spontaneous immortalization of granulosa cells has been demonstrated [33, 34]. Repeated subculture of primary bovine granulosa cells at high density yielded cell lines that responded weakly to FSH [33] by estradiol synthesis. In another attempt, mouse granulosa cell lines were obtained by transfection with v-myc oncogene [35]). These cell lines, in addition to their modest response to LH and FSH by progesterone production, were able to express and release transferin, activin and activin receptor, inhibin, transforming growth factor-β (TGF-β, transforming growth factor-α TGF-α, insulin growth factor-2 (IGF-2), basic fibroblast growth factor (bFGF), platelet derived growth factor (PDGF), and interleukin-6 [36]. However, increased progesterone secretion was evident only in the presence of high concentrations of gonadotropins [36].

To restore fully the steroidogenic response to gonadotropins in immortalized cells, LH/hCG or FSH receptor expression plasmids have been prepared by introducing the complete coding region of LH/hCG or FSH receptor cDNAs [37, 38] into an SV40 early promoter-based eukaryotic expression vector. Granulosa cells from rat preovulatory follicles transfected with gonadotropin receptor expression plasmid, together with SV40 DNA and Ha-Ras oncogene [39, 40], expressed about 10 times more receptors than primary rat granulosa cells from preovulatory follicles. The recombinant rat LH or FSH receptor molecules expressed in these cells exhibit affinities to their hormones, similar to parental granulosa cells [39, 40]. These cell lines responded well to LH or FSH stimulation by cAMP formation as well as progesterone and 20α-dihydroprogesterone biosynthesis. The LH-responsive cell lines responded well to both hLH and hCG but not to FSH [39], These cells showed a dose-dependent increase of both progesterone and 20α-dihydroprogesterone in response to hCG. The FSH-responsive cell lines responded well to rat, ovine, and bovine FSH but not to LH or hCG [40]. The steroidogenic response of these cell lines was found to be comparable with that of primary granulosa cells and thus could provide a useful system for gonadotropin bioassay in human sera [41]. Luteinized granulosa cell lines have been established also from transgenic mice produced by targeting the expression of SV40 large T antigen into gonads using inhibin α-subunit promoter [42]. These cells possessed high-affinity LH receptor and secreted progesterone and estrogen in response to hCG and FSH respectively.

Theca Cells

Theca cells provide structural integrity for the follicle and are in close proximity to the basement membrane, which surround the mural granulosa cells. A critical intrafollicular interaction involves the biosynthesis of androgens by theca cells for aromatization in granulosa cells [43]. It has been suggested that thecal p45017α activity and hence androgen production is regulated by paracrine factors from granulosa cells [44, 45]. Thus insulin and IGF were found to augment LH-stimulated androgen production in rat and human theca-interstitial cells [44–48]. Only a few attempts have been successful in immortalizing theca cells. One of the most successful was the transfection of theca-interstitial primary cells of hypophysectomized 28-day-old immature female rats with pSV Bam containing the entire SV40 genome, pEJ 6 encoding activated human Ha-Ras oncogene, and PSV-LH/hCG-R containing the complete coding region of LH receptor cDNA. The cell lines obtained were able to respond to LH/hCG stimulation with progesterone production and, more significantly, production of androstenedione as in primary theca cells [49].

Ovarian Epithelial Cells

Isolated ovarian epithelial cells can be cultured as monolayers and can achieve restricted cycles of divisions. Cells transfected with SV40 DNA can yield nonsteroidogenic cell lines (for review, see [17]). Moreover, isolation and cloning of nonsteroid cell lines originated from ovarian carcinoma serve as a useful model for in vitro studies of the characteristics and sensitivity to chemotherapeutic drugs such as cisplatin [50]. Interestingly, transformation of rat ovarian granulosa cells and the developmentally related, but nonsteroidogenic, ovarian surface epithelial cells with Ki-Ras yielded steroidogenic cell lines that responded modestly to FSH and cAMP stimulation [51, 52]. Both these cell lines expressed keratin despite the fact that primary granulosa cells were keratin negative whereas the ovarian surface epithelial cells were keratin positive [52]. However, mesodermally derived cells from other sources failed to express these differentiation-related changes in response to transformation [17].

MECHANISM OF INDUCTION OF DIFFERENTIATION IN ONCOGENE-TRANSFORMED CELLS

Induction of differentiation and steroidogenesis in the mammalian ovary involves a sequential change in the expression of specific genes such as those coding for adrenal 4-binding protein/steroidogenic factor-1 (Ad4BP/SF-1), StAR protein, and the steroidogenic enzymes of the p450scc enzyme system [53–55]. Because induction of steroidogenesis and luteinization in the normal ovary is not homogenous throughout the follicle population and not even among the different granulosa cells of the same follicle [4], it is sometimes difficult to correlate the cellular and the molecular events with biochemical analysis of steroidogenesis.

One advantage of the immortalized granulosa cells is that they are a homogeneous population of cells in which induction of steroidogenesis and other differentiation processes can be synchronized [20, 56]. Therefore such cells can serve as a useful tool to study the regulation of steroidogenic granulosa cells. The main characteristic of the SV40 transformed granulosa cell line is the rapid dedifferentiation process caused by the antidifferentiation activity of the T antigen [22]. These cells express low levels, if any, of steroidogenic hormones; however, they express constitutively the peripheral benzodiazepine receptor (PBR), which is believed to play a role in cholesterol transport into the mitochondria [57]. In contrast, granulosa cells cotransfected with SV40 and Ha-Ras express an entire cascade of steroidogenesis genes including the transcription factor Ad4BP/SF-1, the cholesterol carrier protein 2 (SCP2), StAR, and the steroidogenic enzymes: adrenodoxin reductase (ADR), adrenodoxin (ADX), p450scc, 3β-hydroxysteroid dehydrogenase (3β-HSD) and 17β-hydroxysteroid dehydrogenase (17β-HSD), converting progesterone to 20α dihydroprogesterone as well as PBR.

This is probably caused by the counteractivity of Ras against the dedifferentiating activity of the T antigen expressed by the SV40 genome [22]. The unstimulated cells demonstrate low steroidogenic activity; on gonadotropin/cAMP stimulation, they synthesize *de novo* cholesterol carrier proteins StAR and SCP2 and the steroidogenic enzymes, whereas Ad4BP/SF-1 and PBR are constitutively expressed. Because the amplification of expression of steroidogenic factors and steroidogenic enzymes is many fold, this system provides a useful experimental model to examine systematically modulation in expression of proteins associated with the steroidogenic apparatus as well as other specific markers of differentiation of granulosa cells (for review, see [58]).

Expression of Adrenal 4-Binding Protein/Steroidogenic Factor-1

The promoter regions of all steroidogenic p450 genes contain regulatory elements that have a similar AGGTCA nucleotide sequence. These motifs interact with a common DNA binding protein, alternatively designated Ad4BP or SF1 [59–66]. A 51-kDa protein, which binds to the Ad4 site, has been purified and the corresponding cDNA clone isolated [61, 67, 68]. The nucleotide sequence of the cDNA revealed that this protein, which has a zinc finger domain and a putative ligand binding/dimerization domain, is an orphan member of the steroid/thyroid hormone receptor superfamily [69]. All steroidogenic tissues examined (adrenal, ovary, testis, placenta, adipocyte, and brain) express Ad4BP/SF-1 mRNA [67, 68]. In situ hybridization [70] and immunohistochemical staining [71, 72] of the adrenal glands, testes, and ovaries of adult rats or mice localized Ad4BP/SF-1 expression to the specific steroid hormone-producing cells in the tissues (i.e., adrenocortical cells in the adrenal gland, Leydig's cells in the testis, and granulosa and theca cells in the ovary). Expression of Ad4BP/SF-1 was reported in human granulosa-lutein cells [73]. Several studies suggest a role for Ad4BP/SF1 in regulating genes essential for gonadal development and sexual differentiation in mammalian embryos [72, 74–76]. In these studies, expression of Ad4BP/SF1 in cells of the steroidogenic tissues was found to precede the expression of the steroidogenic p450scc enzyme system.

It was shown that only steroidogenic granulosa cell lines cotransfected with SV40 and Ha-Ras express Ad4BP/SF1, whereas nonsteroidogenic granulosa cell lines (transfected by SV40 alone) have completely lost the expression of this transcription factor [77]. Moreover, in lines that demonstrate cAMP-induced steroidogenesis, the level of Ad4BP/SF1 expression is maximal even in nonstimulated cells that proliferate rapidly while exhibiting only traces of steroidogenic activity. This correlates well with the constitutive expression of Ad4BP/SF1 in human granulosa-lutein cells [73]. The data support the view that Ad4BP/SF1 expression is an intrinsic, specific property of a cell that determines its steroidogenic ability. Furthermore, the data suggest that Ad4BP/SF1 expression is required, but not sufficient, for active steroidogenesis in granulosa cells and probably also in other steroidogenic cells.

Expression of Sterol Carrier Protein 2 and the Peripheral Benzodiazepine Receptor

Efficient steroidogenesis is believed to be dependent not only on the amount and activity of the steroidogenic enzymes but also on the availability of the substrate, cholesterol, to the intramitochondrial steroidogenic enzymes. Sterol carrier protein 2 (SCP2; also named *nonspecific lipid-transfer protein*) is a 13.2-kDa basic protein that is believed to play an important role in the intracellular movement of cholesterol in steroidogenic cells [78, 79]. In the rat ovary, SCP2 mRNA expression was found in granulosa and thecal cells and in corpora lutea. Gonadotropins, which promote follicular growth and luteinization, increased the ovarian content of SCP2 mRNA along with an increase in cytochrome pP450scc mRNA [80]. Using the steroidogenic rat granulosa cells cotransfected with SV40 and the Ha-Ras oncogene, 8-Br-cAMP has been found to increase SCP2 mRNA and protein levels within 24 hours of treatment [80]. The cAMP analog also increased SCP2 mRNA levels in a nonsteroidogenic rat granulosa cell line transfected with SV40 DNA alone [80]. Thus it seems that stimulation of SCP2 expression in ovarian cells is mediated, at least in part, by cAMP in a mechanism requiring ongoing RNA and protein synthesis. SCP2 gene expression, however, does not shown obligatory coupling to steroidogenic activity, because cAMP analogs can increase SCP2 mRNA in transformed ovarian granulosa cell lines incapable of synthesizing steroid hormones [80].

PBR has been shown to be expressed in steroidogenic cells of the adrenal medulla [81–83] and MA-10 Leydig tumor cells [84]. It was suggested that the receptor molecules are localized mainly in the mitochondrial outer membrane [81]. This receptor may stimulate cholesterol import into mitochondria [82] and thus accelerate the conversion of cholesterol to pregnenolone, the limiting step in the biosynthesis of steroid hormones. In the ovary, both central and peripheral receptor types exist in tissue homogenates of normal and cancerous tissues [85, 86].

A high content of the PBR has been found in SV40/Ha-Ras transformed granulosa cells, and a lower content has been found in granulosa cells transformed with SV40 alone [57]. The number of PBR molecules increased in cAMP-stimulated cells. It was also demonstrated that, both in normal and transformed steroidogenic granulosa cells, a benzodiazepine agonist dramatically elevates progesterone production [57]. These data support a possible role of the PBR in ovarian steroidogenesis. Because the expression of SCP2 [80] and PBR [57] were evident both in SV40-transformed cells and SV40/Ha-Ras-transformed cells, it can be concluded that the expression of these proteins is less sensitive to SV40 transformation than the expression of Ad4BP/SF1 [77], StAR [87], and p450scc enzymes [20, 56], which are not expressed in cells that have been transformed with SV40 DNA alone.

Expression of Steroidogenic Acute Regulatory Protein

Regulation of Steroidogenic Acute Regulatory Protein Biosynthesis. The rate-limiting enzymatic step in adrenal and gonadal steroid production, in response to trophic hormone stimulation, is the conversion of cholesterol to pregnenolone [88, 89]. This reaction is catalyzed by the cytochrome p450scc (CSCC) system and its ancillary electron transport proteins, ADX and ADR, located on the matrix side of the inner mitochondrial membrane [90, 91]. Mobilization of the substrate cholesterol in the inner mitochondrial membrane and the CSCC system is a crucial step in this process [92, 93]. In addition, the acute production of steroid hormones depends on a rapidly synthesized, cycloheximide-sensitive, and highly labile protein that appears in response to trophic hormones and transfers cholesterol to the inner mitochondrial membrane [94–98].

A protein of 30 kDa has been observed to be synthesized in response to trophic hormones or cAMP analogs in adrenal [99, 100], ovary [101], and MA-10 mouse Leydig tumor cells [102]. This protein is derived from a larger 37-kDa precursor in all the steroidogenic cell types [102, 103] and may require phosphorylation on a threonine residue for its activity [104]. 30-kDa protein was purified and its cDNA was cloned from MA-10 cells [105]. A cDNA for StAR isolated from a human adrenal library showed a deduced amino acid sequence that was 87% identical to the mouse sequence [106]. Coexpression of StAR cDNA with the CSCC system in COSl cells resulted in an eight-fold increase in pregnenolone production with cholesterol as a substrate, whereas the mutant StAR was inactive; the need for StAR activity could be circumvented by using freely diffusible 20α-hydroxycholesterol as a substrate for steroidogenesis [107]. Therefore StAR appears to play a key role in cholesterol delivery to the inner mitochondrial membrane for the enzymatic action of the CSCC system, which is the rate-limiting enzymatic step in steroidogenesis [55].

It was demonstrated that StAR mRNA is expressed in rat granulosa cells, transformed by SV40 DNA and Ha-Ras oncogene, which preserve their steroidogenic potential [87]. In contrast, cells transformed with SV40 DNA alone that lost their steroidogenic capacity did not express the StAR message. This implies that expression of the StAR gene is obligatory to the steroidogenic activity not only in normal steroidogenic cells [55, 107, 108] but also in oncogene-transformed cells. In addition, it is possible that Ras protein is important for the preservation of differentiation in immortalized granulosa cells.

Using immortalized granulosa cells expressing receptors to LH/hCG, FSH, or the β_2-adrenergic receptor [109], it was demonstrated that expression of StAR mRNA, and its regulation by effectors elevating cAMP levels, such as catecholamines, gonadotropins, and forskolin, can be preserved in transformed rat granulosa cells [87]. The sequence of cDNA isolated from a granulosa cell line expressing FSH receptor demonstrated a high degree of homology with the corresponding region of StAR sequence from the mouse and human cDNA. Such systems can serve as a useful tool for studying the regulation of the StAR gene by endocrine factors as well as by the oncogenes used to immortalize these cells, which could also play an important role in ovarian malignancies.

Regulation of Steroid Acute Regulatory Protein Degradation. The 37-kDa protein is believed to be the active form of StAR, and it is thought that the C-terminus of the protein acts on the outer mitochondrial membrane to promote cholesterol translocation [110]. The import of the cytosolic preprotein into the mitochondria is consequently thought to be the event that terminates StAR's steroidogenic activity. Because the 37-kDa preprotein has a short half-life, it must be produced continuously if steroidogenesis is to be maintained. The upregulation of StAR by gonadotropin/cAMP signaling has been studied in detail [87, 111]; however, little is known about its degradation. Proteasomes catalyze the degradation of nuclear and cytoplasmic proteins and peptide hormones including NF-κB [112], p53 [113], ornithine decarboxylase [114], and gonadotropin releasing hormone (Gn-RH) [115]. Moreover, it has been recently documented that sperm mitochondria are degraded by the ubiquitin-proteasome system following penetration of the sperm into the egg during fertilization [116]. Thus proteasomes participate in the catabolism of proteins in a number of subcellular compartments.

To determine whether proteasomes participate in the turnover of StAR, both rat and human immortalized granulosa cells were incubated in the presence of MG132, a specific inhibitor of proteasome catalysis. This treatment caused accumulation of StAR in unstimulated cells [117]. Moreover, incubation of the cells with MG132 in the presence of forskolin, LH/hCG, or FSH augmented the accumulation of the 37 kDa cytoplasmic protein and the 30 kDa mature mitochondrial protein compared to cells incubated with forskolin (FK) or gonadotropic hormones alone. The increase of 37 kDa StAR protein was already evident after 15 min and proceeded with the increase in the intermediate mitochondrial 32 kDa protein and the 30kDa mature protein. These data were also confirmed in primary rat and human granulosa cells and suggest that StAR protein is either directly or indirectly degraded by the proteasome; this may explain, in part, its short half-life [117]. Moreover, it seems that the cytosolic 37 kDA protein, which is responsible for the steroidogenic activity of StAR, is the primary proteasomal substrate and that the inhibition of its degradation of MG132 causes the upregulation of progesterone production [117].

Induction of Steroidogenesis in the Immortalized Granulosa Cell Lines

The classical and the main avenue to control ovarian steroidogenesis is by gonadotropin/cAMP stimulated steroidogenesis. The homogeneous population of the immortalized granulosa cells and their high responses provide the researcher with a system for detailed studies on the precise kinetics of inducible steroidogenesis and its tuning up by a variety of paracrine and endocrine factors, such as bFGF, glucocorticoids (GC), leptin, TNF-α, and nonphysiological substances stimulating distinct signaling pathways such as the phorbol ester, 12-0-tetradecanorl phorbol-13-acetate (TPA) the classical activator of kinase C. Possible cross talk between the various signal transduction pathways these factors stimulate can also be studied systematically (for reviews, see [58, 118]).

Kinetics of Induction

One of the characteristics of granulosa cells transformed with ras together with SV40DNA and/or a TS mutant of p53 is that when cultured in the absence of stimulants that elevate intracellular cAMP, they proliferate rapidly, showing low expression of the steroidogenic enzymes and releasing small quantities of progesterone. In contrast, on stimulation with gonadotropic hormones, after a lag period of 6 to 12 hours, the cells produce high levels of progesterone. Steroid hormone production in response to gonadotropin/cAMP is 100 times higher than in nonstimulated cells, in the range of progesterone production of highly luteinized primary cells. This unique feature of the cells permits a detailed analysis of the induction kinetics of the steroidogenic enzymes in a homogeneous cell system, compared with the heterogeneous population of the granulosa cells in the intact follicle or in primary cultures [15, 20]. Such studies showed that the induction of p450scc is significantly slower than that of ADX [15, 20]. Nevertheless, the individual components of the SCC system (i.e., the cytochrome p450scc, ADX, and ADR) are uniformly incorporated into all mitochondria of the steroidogenic cells and localized in the inner face of the mitochondrial cristae [20, 39, 40].

Glucocorticoids

GC, such as hydrocortisone and dexamethasone (DEX), enhance cAMP induced progesterone production dramatically in the immortalized steroidogenic granulosa cells, without elevation of intracellular cAMP [119, 120]. These data accord with early observation of Adashi et al. on enhancement of cAMP-dependent induced steroid production in preantral follicles by GC [121]. Increase in progesterone production by GC has been demonstrated recently in LH/hCG-, FSH-, and FK-stimulated granulosa cell of both primary preovulatory and immortalized rat and human granulosa cells. This modulation involves an upregulation of the electron carrier ADX and cytochrome p450scc along with attenuation of StAR expression [25, 120, 122].

These data are in line with recent observations that DEX decreases StAR expression in intact preovulatory follicles [123]. The observations suggest that the rate of steroidogenesis is determined not by the absolute amounts of either StAR or cytochrome p450scc but by the ratio between these factors. Moreover, in view of these findings of the involvement of GC in inducible steroidogenesis in granulosa cells, the effect of GC in ovarian malfunction should be investigated in depth.

Leptin

One of the first demonstrations of ovarian leptin receptors was accomplished in immortalized steroidogenic granulosa cells [124]. The attenuation of GC enhancement of steroidogenesis by leptin was first described in the immortalized rat and human granulosa cells. Leptin suppresses ovarian steroid synthesis in these cells costimulated by FSH/cAMP and DEX. Production of pregnenolone, progesterone, and 20 alpha-hydroxy-4-pregnen-3 one is inhibited by leptin. This inhibition is caused, at least in part, by a reduced expression of the cytochrome p450scc enzyme system whereas the intracellular levels of cAMP are not affected [124]. Interestingly, leptin induces Jun expression and attenuates the transcriptional activity of the glucocorticoid receptor (GR), which possibly leads to the attenuation of steroidogenesis. These data have been confirmed in primary preovulatory granulosa cells. Considering these data together with the inhibiting effect of leptin on insulin, IGF-1 [125, 126], and estradiol [127] enhancement of gonadotropin/cAMP stimulation of steroidogenesis in primary granulosa cells suggests that a direct action of leptin on the ovary is an additional element in the homeostasis of steroid production.

It would be of great interest to determine the general effect of leptin on GR activity, because it may impinge on the transcription of many other genes and give new insights into the endocrine role of leptin.

Activation of Protein Kinase C and Steroidogenesis

Activation of protein kinase C (PKC) by the phorbol ester TPA can partially block gonadotropin/cAMP-induced steroidogenesis but the mechanism is not clear. TPA attenuates dramatically cAMP-sensitive steroidogenesis despite upregulating intracellular levels of cAMP in Ras-SV40 immortalized granulosa cells [19]. It may well be that activation of PKC may upregulate Jun D, which negates cAMP signaling for steroidogenesis.

Attenuation of Steroidogenesis by Basic Fibroblast Growth Factor

Primary granulosa cells express receptors for bFGF. Incubating SV40-Ras-p53 transformed cells and Ras-p53 transformed cells with FSH/cAMP, in the presence of this growth factor, attenuates markedly steroidogenesis, compared with cells stimulated with FSH/cAMP alone [24, 25]. The inhibition of progesterone production by bFGF involves a clear attenuation in the expression of ADX, p450scc, and StAR protein. The attenuation of StAR intracellular levels by bFGF may be caused by the activation of mitogen-activated protein kinase (MAPK) by bFGF. Activation of MAPK was recently demonstrated in FSH and LH/hCG responsive cell lines to downregulate StAR expression [128]. The decrease in the cytochrome 450scc system in the presence of bFGF is still unclear and subject to future research. bFGF exerts a paradoxical effect on granulosa cell growth and differentiation: at early stages of folliculogenesis its effect is mitogenic, whereas at the preovulatory stage it enhances steroidogenesis mainly by increasing the levels of StAR [13]. Therefore it seems that the immortalized steroidogenetic granulosa cells may exhibit an early stage of differentiation. Alternatively, transfection of granulosa cells with oncogenes could modify the intracellular signaling of bFGF toward proliferation rather than differentiation. Transfection of granulosa cells with different oncogenes could shed light on the essential shift from proliferation to differentiation of granulosa cells during follicular maturation.

Tumor Necrosis Factor-α Modulation of Steroidogenesis

TNF-α is a modulator of steroid hormone production induced by gonadotropins in bovine, rat, porcine, and human granulosa cells [54, 129–132]. TNF-α enhances the production of progesterone in cultured intact follicles [133]. In recent studies, it has been suggested that the luteolytic effects of TNF-α may be mediated by inhibition of StAR expression, a key regulatory protein in inducible steroidogenesis [107], or by indirectly decreasing LH receptor expression in addition to stimulation of the luteolytic prostaglandin PGF_{α} production [107, 134]. Use of TNF-α type 1 receptor knockout mice strongly suggests that the mechanism of TNF-α mediated modulation of steroidogenesis is most likely via TNF-α type 1 receptor [133]. However, the exact mechanism by which TNF-α exerts its effect on ovarian steroidogenesis is not completely understood.

Using immortalized human granulosa cells, it was possible to demonstrate that TNF-α attenuates progesterone production stimulated by cAMP, and this attenuation involves downregulation of the intracellular levels of StAR. Similar observations were obtained in primary granulosa cells stimulated by LH/hCG or forskolin. Interestingly, the inhibitory effect of TNF-α on inducible steroidogenesis could be partially blocked by inhibiting MAPK activation by specific inhibitors, suggesting a role of the MAPK cascade in attenuation of steroidogenesis [122].

ANALYSIS OF SIGNAL TRANSDUCTION STIMULATED BY GONADOTROPINS IN STEROIDOGENIC GRANULOSA CELLS LINE TRANSFECTED WITH GONADOTROPIN RECEPTORS

Desensitization to gonadotropin hormones, which can occur in vivo and in vitro, is essential for prevention of overstimulation of the gonadal cells. The long-term process of desensitization to the gonadotropic hormones is probably mediated, in part, by extensive clustering and internalization of the hormone-receptor complex [10, 135].

However, because gonadotropin-induced desensitization could be demonstrated in isolated follicular membrane preparations, internalization may not be a crucial step in this process [136, 137]. It has also been demonstrated in primary rat granulosa cells that desensitization to the hormone preceded internalization of the hormone-receptor complex [135]. Thus the molecular and biochemical mechanisms that underlie the desensitization phenomenon are far from being completely understood.

Desensitization via Receptor Phosphorylation

Establishment of FSH- and LH/hCG-responsive granulosa cell lines, which constitutively express approximately 20 times more gonadotropin receptors than primary granulosa cells, permitted a more detailed analysis of the mechanism of stimulation followed by desensitization to the gonadotropic hormone. In these cells FSH or LH/hCG can stimulate cAMP formation 10- to 20-fold within 20 minutes [15, 39, 40]. A potent kinase inhibitor, staurosporine, is able to enhance the hormone-sensitive cAMP accumulation [138]. It has also been demonstrated that FSH can induce rapid desensitization during a continuous stimulation and that staurosporine can dramatically block this desensitization. This alkaloid can induce rapid resensitization, following induction of refractoriness by the gonadotropic hormone [138]. In addition, it has been shown that the enhancement of the cAMP response to FSH in staurosporine-treated GFSHR-17 cells is correlated with a significant reduction in receptor phosphorylation, whereas stimulation of the cells with FSH, for a period that is sufficient to induce desensitization, results in a pronounced enhancement of receptor phosphorylation [139]. Because staurosporine is known to be a potent inhibitor of protein phosphorylation, it seems likely that cycles of phosphorylation-dephosphorylation of the FSH receptor or G stimulatory coupled protein (Gs) play an important regulatory role in the coupling of the receptor system to the adenylate cyclase system.

Desensitization via Mitogen-Activated Protein Kinase and Extracellular Signal-Regulated Kinase Activation

The response of granulosa cells to LH and FSH is mediated mainly by cAMP/protein kinase A (PKA) signaling. Notably, the activity of the extracellular signal-regulated kinase (Erk) signaling cascade (for review, see [140]) is elevated in response to these stimuli as well [141]. Activation of Erk cascade in LH- and FSH-induced steroidogenesis was studied in two granulosa-derived cell lines, rLHR-4 and rF-SHR-17 [128], and in primary preovulatory rat granulosa cell [140a, b]. It was found that stimulation of these cells, with the appropriate gonadotropin, induced Erk activation and progesterone production, downstream of PKA. Inhibition of Erk activity enhanced gonadotropin-stimulated progesterone production, which correlated with an increased expression of StAR protein [128]. Therefore it is likely that gonadotropin-stimulated progesterone formation is regulated by a pathway that includes PKA and StAR, and this process is downregulated by Erk because of its attenuation of StAR expression. These results suggest that activation of PKA signaling by gonadotropins not only induces steroidogenesis but also activates downregulation machinery involving the Erk cascade. The activation of Erk by gonadotropins and by other substances such as growth factors or cytokines may be a key mechanism for the modulation of gonadotropin-induced steroidogenesis, including desensitization to the hormone.

The involvement of PKA in gonadotropin-dependent Erk activation has been demonstrated both by pharmacological means using the PKA inhibitor H89 and by genetic means (i.e., transfection of cells with a plasmid encoding for protein kinase inhibitor [PKI]) [128]. The data using both methods are in agreement with the notion that PKA plays a role in transducing gonadotropin signaling toward Erk. Nevertheless, it should be noted that although PKI completely suppressed forskolin-induced Erk activation, it did not completely inhibit the gonadotropin-induced Erk activation. Therefore it is possible that the gonadotropin receptors use other G proteins or the Gβr subunits of Gs protein to activate the Erk cascade, as was observed for other receptors and cell types [142, 143]. Interestingly, it was recently discovered that bFGF suppresses progesterone production in granulosa cell lines [24], which suggests that there may be gonadotropin and cAMP-independent pathways in these cells that suppress steroidogenesis via the Erk cascade. It is possible that the negative regulation of StAR expression occurs at the level of the transcription factor dosage-sensitive sex reversal adrenal hypoplasia congenita (DAX-1) [144] or some other unidentified transcription factors. Alternatively, StAR expression could be controlled by induction of potent phosphatases that abolish both the PKA and Erk phosphorylation of steroidogenic factor-1 (SF-1) or induce a proteolytic system that reduces the half-life of the StAR [110, 117, 145]. It is also possible that reductions in StAR levels could be caused by increased turnover by proteasomes [117, 145].

Recently, there has been more supportive evidence on the upregulation of DAX-1, which is known to negate SF-1 activity and downregulate SF-1 intracellular levels in granulosa cells; this may suggest the involvement of both transcription factors in MAPK suppression of StAR expression.

In summary, the recent studies using LH and FSH responsive granulosa cell lines show that activation of cAMP/PKA signaling by gonadotropins not only induces steroidogenesis but also activates a downregulation machinery that involves the Erk cascade. This potent downregulation machinery inhibits the gonadotropin-induced steroidogenic pathway by mechanisms that are different from the well-characterized receptor desensitization mechanisms. Activation of the Erk cascade downstream of PKA in turn regulates the levels of StAR expression, which is probably the key participant in these downregulation processes. Thus PKA not only mediates gonadotropic-induced steroidogenesis but also activates the downregulation mechanism that can silence steroidogenesis under certain conditions. Moreover, these findings raise the possibility that activation or inhibition of Erk by other pathways could be an important mechanism for diminution or amplification of gonadotropin-stimulated steroidogenesis. This could contribute to functional luteolysis, a process in which luteinized granulosa cells show reduced sensitivity to LH, despite maintenance of LH receptor, or to upregulation of the steroidogenic machinery during luteinization of granulosa cells (for review, see [146]).

INTRACELLULAR COMMUNICATION IN STEROIDOGENIC GRANULOSA CELLS

In the ovary, follicular development is under the tight control of FSH. Depending on the presence of FSH receptors, antral follicles have the potential to grow if FSH is present [147]. However, only a few follicles mature and ovulate; most undergo atresia [118]. What regulates the fate of an individual follicle is not clear, but compartmentalization in theca and granulosa cells and intercellular communication via gap junctions (GJs) within these compartments are thought to be crucial for the mediation of signals initiating growth and/or atresia respectively (for reviews, see [1, 58]).

Properties of Follicular Gap Junctions

GJs connect adjacent cells and enable them to communicate by exchanging inorganic ions and molecules with a molecular weight less than 1000 Da. The GJ channels consist of two hemichannels (i.e., connexons) that are built from six radially arranged transmembrane proteins called connexins (Cx). End-to-end attachment of two Cx from adjacent cells results in one intercellular channel. Once a GJ is formed, the degree of intercellular communication can be controlled by diverse gating mechanisms and initiated by changes in pH, free Ca^{2+}, and phosphorylation of Cx molecules [148)]. To date, 16 different forms of Cx have been described. They are classified according to their expected molecular weight. Most ovarian Cx are restricted to defined locations, such as Cx-40 in the endothelia of blood vessels or Cx-37 in the oocyte [149]. In contrast, Cx-43 is the most abundant ovarian Cx and is expressed by several endocrine ovarian cells, including granulosa, theca, and luteal cells [148, 150, 151]. Recent evidence from the organ culture of ovaries from Cx-43 knockout mice underlines the pivotal role of Cx-43 in follicular development and reproductive function [152].

Despite this well-documented presence and indispensability of Cx-43, little is known regarding how Cx and GJ intercellular communication of granulosa cells or theca cells are regulated. Treatment of rats with hCG increase levels of Cx-43 in the ovary and shortly before ovulation, downregulation of Cx-43 in granulosa cells by LH has been shown to be vitally important in the granulosa cell layers for preparation of ovulation [153, 154]. What regulates Cx-43 and GJ communication in granulosa cells of the follicle during follicular development and before ovulation is not known. However, results of immunocytochemical analysis [155], Western blotting [156], Northern blotting [157], and in situ hybridization [158] indicate an enhanced Cx-43 protein and mRNA expression in larger follicles compared with smaller ones, suggesting an upregulation of Cx-43 gene expression during follicular growth [150]. Although these observations give circumstantial evidence for a stimulatory direct and/or indirect role of FSH on Cx-43, its precise effect on GJ formation and communication has not yet been examined.

Plasticity of Gap Junctions in Steroidogenic Cell Lines

Establishment by cotransfection with SV40 and the oncogene Ha-Ras of immortalized granulosa cells that can be stimulated toward steroidogenesis by 8-bromo-cAMP, or substances elevating cAMP, such as forskolin, gave the opportunity to examine the formation of GJs in transformed cells. Whereas the incidence of GJs in nonstimulated cells is low, stimulation by forskolin enhances the appearance of GJs in these cells, suggesting that stimulation of steroidogenesis is tightly coupled to the formation of GJs both in the normal and in the transformed cells [159].

Cx-43 and GJs are more abundant in large antral follicles than in small antral and preantral follicles [160]. The establishment of steroidogenic granulosa cells expressing FSH receptors permitted a direct analysis of the effect of FSH on granulosa cell intercellular communication (Figure 22.1). Stimulation of the FSH receptor lead to rounding of the cells, reduced cellular proliferation and stimulation of progesterone production concomitantly with an increase of Cx-43 mRNA levels during 6 to 9 hours of incubation with the hormone. These effects are preceded by a change in GJ communication, observed within seconds. Using a single -cell/whole-cell patch clamp technique, it has been shown that FSH rapidly and reversibly enhances electrical cell coupling of GFSHR-17 cells. Increased GJ communication is associated with a decrease in phosphorylation of Cx-43, which has been observed within 10 minutes after FSH stimulation (see Figure 22.1). The results demonstrate, for the first time, that FSH acutely and directly stimulates intercellular communication of GFSHR-17 cells through existing GJs and increases levels of Cx-43 mRNA. These changes are associated with a reduced proliferation and an enhanced differentiation of GFSHR-17 cells [161]. In vivo factors in addition to FSH may be involved in the regulation of GJ communication between granulosa cells in the follicle, but these results suggest that improved cell-to-cell coupling, enhanced Cx-43 gene expression, and, possibly, formation of new GJs are direct consequences of FSH receptor activation and may precede and/or initiate the pivotal effects of FSH on granulosa cells.

Cross Talk in Modulation of Gap Junctions

It has been previously demonstrated that steroid hormones such as estrogens affect the development of ovarian GJs in vivo [162]. Because steroidogenic hormones such as hydrocortisone and DEX enhance steroidogenesis in human and rat immortalized granulosa cells, the effects of DEX on the development of GJ in these cells has been analyzed recently [162a]. DEX by itself can enhance the formation of GJs, as demonstrated by Western blotting and quantitative immunochemistry. Moreover, DEX synergizes with forskolin to stimulate GJ formation. A similar phenomenon has been observed in primary human granulosa cells; DEX enhances formation of GJs in the absence or in the presence of gonadotropin/cAMP stimulation [159]. Interestingly, a high level of cAMP, although it elevates the synthesis of Cx-43, leads to breakdown and internalization of GJ. This would, at least in part, explain the termination of the communication between oocyte and granulosa cells

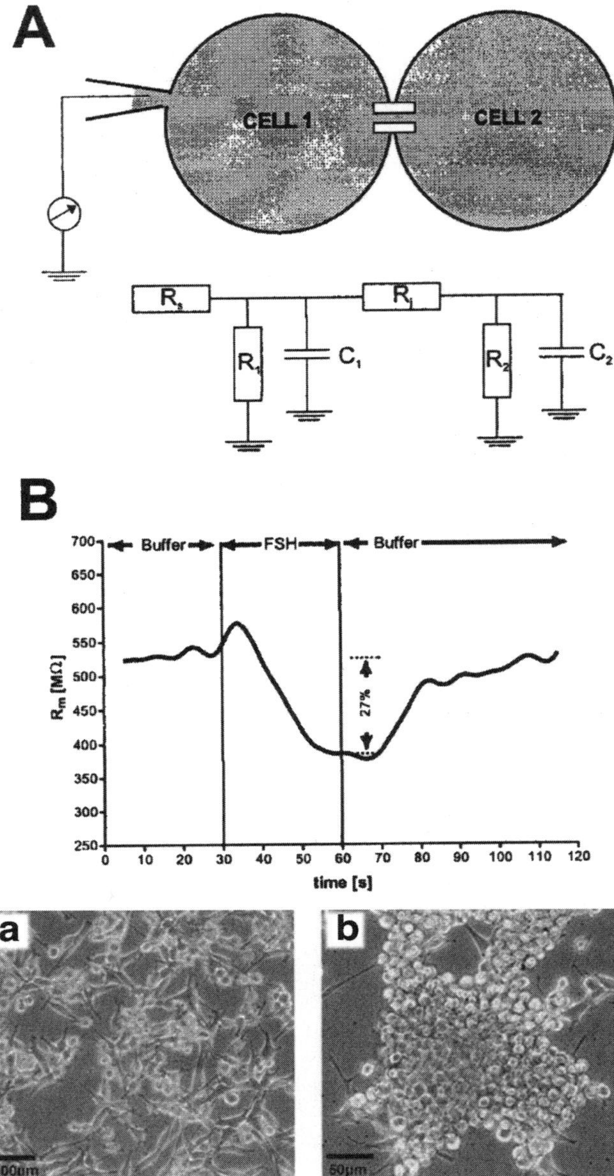

FIGURE 22.1 Rapid effects of FSH on cellular coupling. **A,** Schematic of the electrical circuit required for recording in the whole cell mode. Two adjacent cells, each with its specific membrane resistance (R_1 and R_2) and capacitance (C_1 and C_2), are coupled via GJ channels that can be described as junctional resistance (R_j). Within this system, a sine pulse, consisting of an offset of 260 mV and an amplitude of 20 mV, is administered to a single patched cell. The subsequent changes in the current amplitude, phase, and offset are measured, and serial resistance (R_s), total membrane resistance (R_m), and total membrane capacitance (Cm) are calculated. Simulation of the electrical circuit shows that changes in R_m and Cm reflect changes in R_j. **B,** A typical observation of the progression of R_m measured in a cell pair in response to FSH. In this case, administration of FSH caused a small, transient increase in R_m that was followed by a large, reversible decrease in R_m. Similar results could be reproduced in eight independent experiments. **C,** FSH affects cell morphology of GFSHR-17 cells. Phase-contrast microscopic view of GFSHR-17 cells without *(1)* and after *(2)* addition of FSH (0.5 IU/ml for 3 hours). Note that the cells responded to FSH by rounding up and forming cell clusters. This process starts within a few minutes following hormonal stimulation. (Modified from Ref. [158].)

during the LH surge that initiates the process of ovulation. This includes resumption of meiosis and follicular rupture, which may lead to apoptosis of some follicular cells. Indeed, granulosa cell apoptosis occurs in primary cultures of rat preovulatory granulosa cells in response to high doses of cAMP as well as in the immortalized cells [23, 159, 163]. In conclusion, the immortalized cell system can lend itself to study the effect of autocrine, paracrine, and endocrine factors that may affect intracellular communication in the intact ovary.

OVARIAN CELL DEATH

Ovarian cell death is an essential process for the homeostasis of ovarian function in human and other mammalian species. It ensures the selection of the dominant follicle and the demise of excess follicles. In turn, this process minimizes the possibility of multiple embryo development during pregnancy and assures the development of few but healthy embryos. Degeneration of the old corpora lutea in each estrous/menstrual cycle by programmed cell death is essential to maintain the normal cyclicity of ovarian steroidogenesis. Although there are multiple pathways that can determine cell death or survival (Figure 22.2), cross talk among endocrine, paracrine, and autocrine factors and among protooncogenes, tumor suppressor genes, survival genes, and death genes play an important role in determining the fate of ovarian somatic and germ cells (for review, see [118]). The establishment of immortalized rat and human steroidogenic granulosa cell lines and the investigation of pure populations of granulosa cells allows systematic studies of the mechanisms that control steroidogenesis and apoptosis of granulosa cells. Follicular atresia, or apoptosis, often starts in the inner layers of the membrane granulosa; therefore the investigation of the mechanisms of granulosa cell apoptosis may shed light on the initiation of this process in the intact follicle.

p53-Induced Apoptosis

The tumor suppressor gene p53 is implicated in ovarian cell death, but the mechanism is not clear (for review, see [118]). Establishment of immortalized rat and human granulosa cell lines expressing a TS mutant of p53 that behaves as a tumorigenic protein at 37° C and as a tumor suppressor and inducer of apoptosis at 32° C allows the study of the characteristics of p53-induced apoptosis in granulosa cells [23, 24]. Moreover, it allows the study of possible cross talk between p53-induced apoptosis and other effectors such as bFGF and native ECM, which are considered survival factors, and between TNF-α and high levels of cAMP, which are considered proapoptotic in ovarian cells [24, 122]. Because the cells express GR and respond to GC by enhanced steroidogenesis, the possible role of the steroid

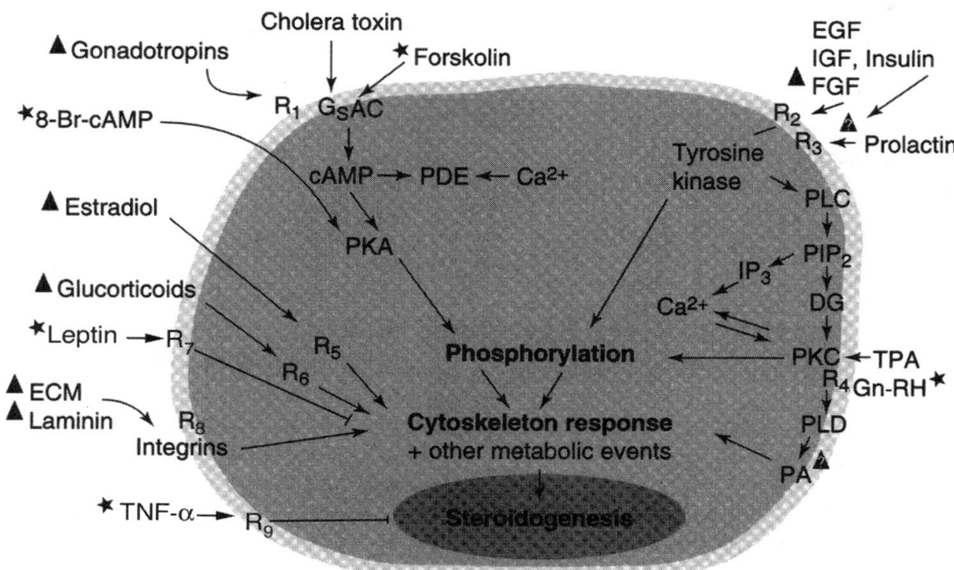

FIGURE 22.2 Signal transduction pathways and possible cross talk among signals that control steroidogenesis and programmed cell death in mature ovarian granulosa cells and in immortalized steroidogenic granulosa cells. Stars indicate signals that might lead to both steroidogenesis and apoptosis; triangles indicate signals that might function as survival factors. The increased level of tyrosine phosphorylation [198] induced either by growth factors or by inhibiting tyrosine phosphatases (Pase) via vanadate was found to synergize with cAMP-generated signals in the induction of progesterone production [199]. Synergism in progesterone production between Gn-RH stimulation, mediated at least in part by phospholipase D (PLD), and cAMP-generated signals was also reported recently [200]. Culturing of granulosa cells on extracellular matrix, in the form of a native basement membrane, enhanced progesterone production by itself and augmented cAMP-induced steroidogenesis [11, 13, 14, 201] in primary cells, while it attenuated cAMP-induced steroidogenesis in the immortalized cells. *Cytoskeleton response* refers to the rearrangement of the actin cytoskeleton, which occurs during both luteinization [3], [202]) and apoptosis of granulosa cells [58, 118, 183]. *Other metabolic events* refers to upregulation of the steroidogenic enzymes, sterol carrier protein 2 (SCP2), the steroidogenic transcription factor SF-1/Ad4-binding protein, and the StAR protein (for review, see [58]). *AC*, Adenylate cyclase Gs, G-stimulatory protein; *DG*, diacylglycerol; *EGF*, epidermal growth factor; *FGF*, fibroblast growth factor; *IGF*, insulin-like growth factor; *IP_3*, inositol 1,4,5-trisphosphate; *PA*, phosphatidic acid; *PDE*, phosphodiesterase; *PIP2*, phosphatidylinositol 4,5-bisphosphate; *PKA*, protein kinase A; *PKC*, protein kinase C; *PLC*, phospholipase C; *R*, receptor; *TPA*, 12-O-tetradecanoylphorbol-13-acetate. (Modified from Ref. [118].)

hormones in controlling apoptosis could be studied in detail [122].

Cyclic Adenosine Monophosphate and Basic Fibroblast Growth Factor Generated Signals: Cross Talk with p53-Induced Apoptosis

It was found that although changing the culture temperature from 37° C to 32° C is sufficient to induce moderate but significant apoptosis in these TS cells, only stimulation with cAMP at 32° C induces massive apoptosis, suggesting a novel type of cross talk between cAMP- and p53-generated signals. Indeed, one of the early target genes for p53, MDM2, which can neutralize p53 activity, is down-regulated in the presence of cAMP [24]. In contrast, bFGF, which has been shown to protect cells from p53-induced apoptosis, is able to upregulate MDM2 expression (for reviews, see [24, 118]). Thus MDM2 might play a pivotal role in the control of granulosa cell apoptosis.

The Antiapoptotic Effect of Glucocorticoids

It has been proposed that locally activated GC production could play a role in limiting ovarian tissue damage and in mediating repair/remodeling after human ovulation (for reviews, see [164, 165]). Support for this idea comes from the finding that just before follicular rupture, there is an elevation of total cortisol concentration in follicular fluid in comparison with the concentration in serum [165]. Additionally, the proinflammatory cytokines, TNF-α and interleukin-1β, have been recently reported to stimulate the expression of 11β-hydroxysteroid dehydrogenase type 1 (11β-HSD1) mRNA in glomerular mesangial cells [166] and rat granulosa cells [167] in vitro. Because 11β-HSD1 promotes reversible formation of cortisol from cortisone, it has been suggested that the proinflammatory cascade that leads to ovulation induces a compensatory antiinflammatory response in the ovary, which includes upregulation of 11β-HSD1 and increased local availability of cortisol [168]. It has been proposed therefore that the developmental increase of 11β-HSD1 expression before follicular rupture could serve to raise the intrafollicular cortisol levels. Because ovulation is an inflammatory process and GCs are antiinflammatory [169, 170], the locally increased cortisol level may serve to minimize inflammatory tissue damage and encourage rapid healing of the ovarian surface in anticipation of the next ovulatory cycle (for review, see [164]).

The role of GCs in ovarian steroidogenesis and apoptosis in immortalized human granulosa cells expressing a TS mutant of p53 has been recently studied in detail [120]. DEX and hydrocortisone synergize with gonadotropin to increase progesterone production. In addition, these GCs almost completely inhibit apoptosis caused by serum deprivation, activation of the tumor suppressor gene p53, or TNF-α stimulation [120, 122]. This protective effect coincides with an increased expression of cadherins and connexins, the major building blocks of the adherence and GJs. This would suggest that GR and p53 act as opposing forces in the decision between cell death and survival. GCs also increase in granulosa cell lines the network formation of the actin cytoskeleton without affecting the de novo synthesis of actin [122]. Most pertinently, GCs increase intracellular levels of the antiapoptotic gene protein bcl-2 [120, 122]. These observations have been confirmed in primary cultures of human and rat preovulatory granulosa cells [122, 159]. It is therefore suggested that protection of granulosa cells from apoptosis by GCs is achieved by enhancement of cell contacts and intercellular communication, stabilization of the actin cytoskeleton, and upregulation of bcl-2 expression. This protection of granulosa cells may contribute to the antiinflammatory reaction thought to take place following follicular rupture (for reviews, see [164, 171]) by minimizing the damage to the follicular tissue and by stimulating postovulatory steroidogenesis [171]. Moreover, it suggests that GCs could serve as a potential drug to overcome specific cases of ovarian failure.

Tumor Necrosis Factor-α-Induction of Apoptosis and Cross Talk with Survival Factors

TNF-α is one of the most potent modulators of apoptosis in rat and bovine ovaries [172] and in cultured mouse, hen, and human granulosa cells [173–175]. Many of the biological effects of soluble TNF-α are mediated via type 1 TNF-α receptor, which contains a cytoplasmic death domain involved in signal transduction and apoptosis [176, 177]. Expression of type 1 TNF-α receptor has been characterized recently in bovine and porcine corpora lutea and in bovine and hen granulosa cells [175, 178–180]. The exact mechanism of how TNF-α affects apoptosis in the ovary is not fully characterized. Induction of apoptosis and suppression of steroidogenesis by TNF-α in human granulosa cells immortalized by mutated p53 has been determined. DEX and hydrocortisone efficiently suppress TNF-α-induced apoptosis in granulosa cells. TNF-α reduces dramatically the intracellular levels of bcl-2, whereas DEX abrogates this reduction. TNF-α reduces considerably intracellular levels of StAR protein, a key regulator factor in steroidogenesis. This reduction can be explained only in part by elimination of cells through apoptosis, because loss of steroidogenic capacity is much higher and faster than the rate and the extent of loss of cell viability induced by TNF-α, suggesting independent mechanisms for TNF-α̃induction of apoptosis and TNF-α̃suppression of steroidogenesis. Essentially similar results have been obtained in primary cultures of human and rat preovulatory granulosa cells, emphasizing the potential of the steroidogenic ovarian cell lines in studying cross talk among survival and death signals that control ovarian cell death [159]. Moreover, they provide a useful model for studying the interrelationships between modulation of steroidogenesis and apoptosis in a well-defined homogenous cell system.

Interrelationships between Steroidogenesis and Apoptosis of Steroidogenic Ovarian Cells

Early studies suggested that the induction of ovarian apoptosis is accompanied by a rise in plasma levels of progesterone [181]. It has been found that during the first few hours after induction of apoptosis in primary and in immortalized granulosa cells, progesterone production increases rather than decreases [23, 163]. Both immunofluorescence studies of cells stained with antibodies for the p450scc enzyme system and electron microscopic studies of ultrathin sections indicate that the mitochondria preserve their integrity and their fine structure [23, 163]. Translocation of mitochondria to the perinuclear region, and their absence from apoptotic blebs, suggests that as long as the biochemical apparatus responsible for conversion of cholesterol to pregnenolone remains intact, steroidogenic activity is uninterrupted. Moreover, clustering of the mitochondria and lipid droplets in the apoptotic cells might increase the efficiency of the steroidogenic process. The preservation of mitochondria during the early stages of apoptosis is unusual, because in other cellular systems, rapid destruction of mitochondria and leakage of cytochrome C into the cytoplasm has been documented [182]. Nevertheless, there is still the possibility that transmission of an apoptotic signal in granulosa cells can bypass mitochondrial destruction.

To investigate the mechanism by which compartmentalization of steroidogenic organelles is achieved, apoptotic cells were costained with antiadrenodoxin and with rhodamine-conjugated phalloidin, which stains actin filaments.

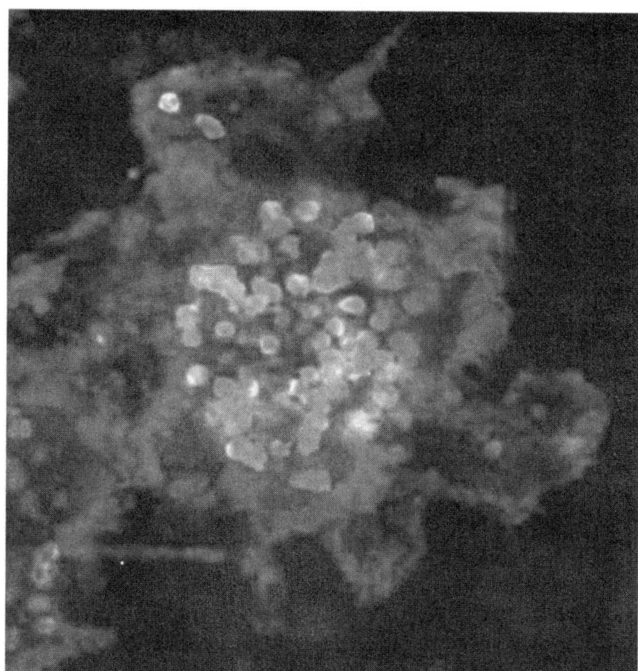

FIGURE 22.3 Apoptotic granulosa cells doubly stained with antiadrenodoxin for steroidogenic mitochondria *(green)* and rhodamin-falloidin, staining the actin cytoskeleton *(red)*. Whereas the actin cytoskeleton is partially disrupted in the apoptotic blebs at the circumference of the cells, the majority of the mitochondria centered in the main bulk of the cytoplasm appears intact. Laser confocal microscopy. (Magnification × 3000.) (See color plate.)

Confocal laser microscopy revealed that the actin cytoskeleton acquired a new conformation, a spherelike structure, that separated the apoptotic blebs from the main bulk of the cell containing lipid droplets, mitochondria, and smooth endoplasmic reticulum [23, 58, 183]. At a later stage of apoptosis, there is a collapse and intensive depolymerization of actin, possibly because of the cleavage of another actin-binding protein, gelsolin, that serves as a cross-linking molecule between adjacent actin filaments [184, 185]. This rearrangement of the actin cytoskeleton during apoptosis has been confirmed in both primary and immortalized granulosa cells (Figure 22.3). It can be concluded that steroidogenesis and apoptosis can exist in the same cells [118]. However, the local effectors that prevent the dominant follicle from undergoing apoptosis in situ are not yet fully characterized. What can be learned from the modulation of apoptosis in the immortalized steroidogenic granulosa cell lines is that because growth factors and steroid hormones can prevent apoptosis, it may well be that the local high concentration of these survival factors rescues the dominant follicle from undergoing apoptosis.

MECHANISMS OF SECRETION OF PARACRINE FACTORS IN IMMORTALIZED STEROIDOGENIC CELLS

Immortalized granulosa cells can secrete various factors and cytokines [36] as primary granulosa cells. A detailed study on the regulation of follistatin gene expression was undertaken in four different rat granulosa cell lines, transfected with SV40 DNA alone, or with SV40 DNA and Ha-Ras oncogene, which lacked or expressed LH or FSH receptors [186]. All the cell lines expressed follistatin mRNA, which could be regulated by forskolin. In cell lines expressing either LH or FSH receptors, follistatin was elevated by stimulation of the appropriate gonadotropins [186]. Activation of PKC by phorbol ester also stimulated follistatin mRNA, as in primary granulosa cells [186–188]. This suggests that follistatin gene expression is regulated by multiple signal transduction pathways in granulosa cells. Moreover, follistatin expression, which is typical in normal granulosa cells, is often maintained after oncogenic transformation and therefore can serve as a potential marker of granulosa cell tumors.

USE OF CELLS FOR IN VITRO BIOASSAY OF GONADOTROPINS

The immortalized stable steroidogenic granulosa cells, which express 20 times more LH/hCG or FSH receptors than primary cells, can serve as a useful tool for biological assay and radio receptor assay (RRA) for these hormones [139]. It was found that stimulation of cells expressing LH/hCG receptor or FSH receptor with increasing doses of gonadotropins results in a dose-dependent increase of cAMP and progesterone [39] [40]. The dose-response data serves as a calibration curve for measuring the gonadotropin bioactivity in biological specimens, such as human sera or pituitary extracts in normal and pathological situation [189]. Close correlation between enzyme immunoassay (EIA) and the in vitro bioassay has been found in the normal cycle, menopausal and pregnant women, and normal adult men. In addition, a RRA for gonadotropins has been developed using an enriched cell membrane fraction from the appropriate cell lines. In vitro bioassay of gonadotropic hormones can serve as a useful tool for a more comprehensive set of assays, which will determine not only the amount but also the possible modulation in bioactivity of gonadotropins associated with gonadal failure and miscarriage [139].

FUTURE RESEARCH

Creation of stable immortalized steroidogenic ovarian cells that represent a homogenous cell population can be used for a number of research directions that may shed light on unknown functions of the granulosa cells [190] and that may reveal the following novel mechanisms regulating ovarian physiology:

- Research may lead to the discovery of novel proteins and genes modulated by gonadotropins and steroid hormones, growth factors, cytokines, and other factors with which these cells preserve their physiological response.
- The cells can serve as a useful platform for insertion of novel genes in a simple manner, such as transfection with plasmids coding for the putative genes. On the other hand, activity of specific genes could be shut down using the antisense mRNA technique.
- The improvement of techniques of immortalization of primary cells, which preserve their potential to differentiate, opens the possibility to study ovarian malfunction in a homogenous cell population taken from patients suffering from ovarian malfunction such as polycystic ovarian syndrome and to immortalize these cells for detailed studies of their function.

Discovery of New Proteins

The immortalized steroidogenic granulosa cells have enabled the discovery of several proteins not known to be expressed in granulosa cells or to be regulated by FSH. For example, synaptosome-associated protein of 25k Da (SNAP 25) has been discovered to be expressed in parallel in oocytes and steroid-producing cells of the rat and human ovary [191, 191a], and it has been confirmed as well in human immortalized granulosa cells [190]. This protein is a key element of the molecular machinery required for regulated exocytosis of neurotransmitters. Interestingly, it participates in regulated exocytosis of hormones by endocrine cells derived from the neuroectoderm. Examples are hormone secretion by the anterior pituitary [192], catecholamine release by chromaffin cells of the adrenal medulla [193], histamine secretion by enterochromaffin-like cells in the stomach [194], and insulin secretion by beta cells of the pancreatic islet [195]. However, the function of this protein in the ovary has not yet been explored. Immortalized human granulosa cells in another study showed expression of muscarinic receptor types M1R, M3R, and M5R mRNA as well as the capacity or synthesis of non-neuronal acetylcholine [196]. In parallel, in the same study the primate ovary is expressed the same as MR as well as the production of acetylcholine. This study supports the concept of a novel muscarinergic regulatory system in the ovary, involving local acetylcholine production and the action via MRs differentially expressed in the ovary, which may participate in regulation of cell proliferation in developing follicles and in the modulation of steroid production [197]. Proteomic analysis of stimulated vs nonstimulated cells has the potential for a comprehensive analysis of the spectrum of modulation of proteins in the steroidogenic granulosa cells.

ACKNOWLEDGMENTS

We thank Drs. A. M. Kaye and G. V. Frajese for their critical review of this chapter. We also thank all of our students and research associates who have contributed significantly to the development and characterization of immortalized steroidogenic granulosa cells. Our research work was supported by a grant from the Israel Scientist Foundation, Jerusalem, and the Center for Scientific Excellence at the Weizmann Institute of Science, Rehovot, Israel. This chapter partially fulfills the postdoctoral work of R. Sasson at the Weizmann Institute of Science. A. Amsterdam is the incumbent of the Joyce and Ben. B. Eisenberg Professor of Molecular Endocrinology and Cancer Research.

References

1. Amsterdam, A., and Rotmensch, S. (1987). Structure-function relationships during granulosa cell differentiation. *Endocr. Rev.* 8, 309–337.
2. Amsterdam, A., Rotmensch, S., and Ben-Ze'ev, A. (1989). Structure-function relationships in the differentiating granulosa cell. *Prog. Clin. Biol. Res.* 296, 121–130.
3. Amsterdam, A., Rotmensch, S., and Ben-Ze'ev, A. (1989). Coordinated regulation of morphological and biochemical differentiation in a steroidogenic cell: The granulosa cell model. *Trends Biochem. Sci.* 14, 377–382.
4. Amsterdam, A., Koch, Y., Lieberman, M. E., and Lindner, H. R. (1975). Distribution of binding sites for human chorionic gonadotropin in the preovulatory follicle of the rat. *J. Cell. Biol.* 67, 894–900.
5. Lindner, H. R., Amsterdam, A., Salomon, Y., et al. (1977). Intraovarian factors in ovulation: Determinants of follicular response to gonadotrophins. *J. Reprod. Fertil.* 51, 215–235.
6. Amsterdam, A., Plehn-Dujowich, D., and Suh, B. S. (1992). Structure-function relationships during differentiation of normal and oncogene-transformed granulosa cells. *Biol. Reprod.* 46, 513–522.
7. Hsueh, A. J., Adashi, E. Y., Jones, P. B., and Welsh, Jr., T. H. (1984). Hormonal regulation of the differentiation of cultured ovarian granulosa cells. *Endocr. Rev.* 5, 76–127.
8. Amsterdam, A., Kohen, F., Nimrod, A., and Lindner, H. R. (1979). Lateral mobility and internalization of hormone receptors to human chorionic gonadotropin in cultured rat granulosa cells. *Adv. Exp. Med. Biol.* 112, 69–75.
9. Amsterdam, A., Berkowitz, A., Nimrod, A., and Kohen, F. (1980). Aggregation of luteinizing hormone receptors in granulosa cells: A possible mechanism of desensitization to the hormone. *Proc. Natl. Acad. Sci. USA* 77, 3440–3444.
10. Amsterdam, A., Knecht, M., and Catt, K. J. (1981). Hormonal regulation of cytodifferentiation and intercellular communication in cultured granulosa cells. *Proc. Natl. Acad. Sci. USA* 78, 3000–3004.

11. Furman, A., Rotmensch, S., Dor, J., et al. (1986). Culture of human granulosa cells from an in vitro fertilization program: Effects of extracellular matrix on morphology and cyclic adenosine 3′,5′ monophosphate production. *Fertil. Steril.* 46, 514–517.
12. Ben-Ze'ev, A., and Amsterdam, A. (1986). Regulation of cytoskeletal proteins involved in cell contact formation during differentiation of granulosa cells on extracellular matrix. *Proc. Natl. Acad. Sci. USA* 83, 2894–2898.
13. Aharoni, D., Meiri, I., Atzmon, R., Vlodavsky, I., and Amsterdam, A. (1997). Differential effect of components of the extracellular matrix on differentiation and apoptosis. *Curr. Biol.* 7, 43–51.
14. Amsterdam, A., Rotmensch, S., Furman, A., Venter, E. A., and Vlodavsky, I. (1989). Synergistic effect of human chorionic gonadotropin and extracellular matrix on in vitro differentiation of human granulosa cells: Progesterone production and gap junction formation. *Endocrinology* 124, 1956–1964.
15. Amsterdam, A., Keren-Tal, I., Dantes, A., Matityahou, A., and Plehn-Dujowich, D. (1993). Generation of ovarian steroidogenic cell lines. In *The Ovary*, 1st ed., eds. E. Y. Adashi, and P. C. K. Leung, 487–500. New York: Academic Press.
16. Lie, B. L., Leung, E., Leung, P. C., and Auersperg, N. (1996). Long-term growth and steroidogenic potential of human granulosa-lutein cells immortalized with SV40 large T antigen. *Mol. Cell. Endocrinol.* 120, 169–176.
17. Auersperg, N., Wong, A. S., Choi, K. C., Kang, S. K., and Leung, P. C. (2001). Ovarian surface epithelium: Biology, endocrinology, and pathology. *Endocr. Rev.* 22, 255–288.
18. Suh, B. S., Eisenbach, L., and Amsterdam, A. (1992). Adenosine 3′,5′-monophosphate suppresses metastatic spread in nude mice of steroidogenic rat granulosa cells transformed by simian virus-40 and Ha-ras oncogene. *Endocrinology* 131, 526–532.
19. Suh, B. S., and Amsterdam, A. (1990). Establishment of highly steroidogenic granulosa cell lines by cotransfection with SV40 and Ha-ras oncogene: Induction of steroidogenesis by cyclic adenosine 3′-5′-monophosphate and its suppression by phorbol ester. *Endocrinology* 127, 2489–2500.
20. Hanukoglu, I., Suh, B. S., Himmelhoch, S., and Amsterdam, A. (1990). Induction and mitochondrial localization of cytochrome P450scc system enzymes in normal and transformed ovarian granulosa cells. *J. Cell. Biol.* 111, 1373–1381.
21. Amsterdam, A., Zauberman, A., Meir, G., Pinhasi-Kimhi, O., Suh, B. S., and Oren, M. (1988). Cotransfection of granulosa cells with simian virus 40 and Ha-RAS oncogene generates stable lines capable of induced steroidogenesis. *Proc. Natl. Acad. Sci. USA* 85, 7582–7586.
22. Michalovitz, D., Amsterdam, A., and Oren, M. (1989). Interactions between SV40 and cellular oncogenes in the transformation of primary rat cells. *Curr. Top. Microbiol. Immunol.* 144, 63–75.
23. Keren-Tal, I., Suh, B. S., Dantes, A., Lindner, S., Oren, M., and Amsterdam, A. (1995). Involvement of p53 expression in cAMP-mediated apoptosis in immortalized granulosa cells. *Exp. Cell. Res.* 218, 283–295.
24. Hosokawa, K., Aharoni, D., Dantes, A., et al. (1998). Modulation of Mdm2 expression and p53-induced apoptosis in immortalized human ovarian granulosa cells. *Endocrinology* 139, 4688–4700.
25. Tajima, K., Hosokawa, K., Yoshida, Y., et al. (2002). Establishment of FSH-responsive cell lines by transfection of pre-ovulatory human granulosa cells with mutated p53 (p53val135) and Ha-ras genes. *Mol. Hum. Reprod.* 8, 48–57.
26. Lie, B. L., Leung, E., Leung, P. C., and Auersperg, N. (1996). Long-term growth and steroidogenic potential of human granulosa-lutein cells immortalized with SV40 large T antigen. *Mol. Cell. Endocrinol.* 120, 169–176.
27. Rainey, W. H., Sawetawan, C., Shay, J. W., et al. (1994). Transformation of human granulosa cells with the E6 and E7 regions of human papillomavirus. *J. Clin. Endocrinol. Metab.* 78, 705–710.
28. Nishi, Y., Yanase, T., Mu, Y., et al. (2001). Establishment and characterization of a steroidogenic human granulosa-like tumor cell line, KGN, that expresses functional follicle-stimulating hormone receptor. *Endocrinology* 142, 437–445.
29. Gudermann, T., Birnbaumer, M., and Birnbaumer, L. (1992). Evidence for dual coupling of the murine luteinizing hormone receptor to adenylyl cyclase and phosphoinositide breakdown and Ca2+ mobilization. Studies with the cloned murine luteinizing hormone receptor expressed in L cells. *J. Biol. Chem.* 267, 4479–4488.
30. Hipkin, R. W., Sanchez-Yague, J., and Ascoli, M. (1993). Agonist-induced phosphorylation of the luteinizing hormone/chorionic gonadotropin receptor expressed in a stably transfected cell line. *Mol. Endocrinol.* 7, 823–832.
31. Minegishi, T., Igarashi, S., Nakamura, K., et al. (1994). Functional expression of the recombinant human FSH receptor. *J. Endocrinol.* 141, 369–375.
32. Quintana, J., Hipkin, R. W., Sanchez-Yague, J., and Ascoli, M. (1994). Follitropin (FSH) and a phorbol ester stimulate the phosphorylation of the FSH receptor in intact cells. *J. Biol. Chem.* 269, 8772–8779.
33. Bernath, V. A., Muro, A. F., Vitullo, A. D., Bley, M. A., Baranao, J. L., and Kornblihtt, A. R. (1990). Cyclic AMP inhibits fibronectin gene expression in a newly developed granulosa cell line by a mechanism that suppresses cAMP-responsive element-dependent transcriptional activation. *J. Biol. Chem.* 265, 18219–18226.
34. Stein, L. S., Stoica, G., Tilley, R., and Burghardt, R. C. (1991). Rat ovarian granulosa cell culture: A model system for the study of cell-cell communication during multistep transformation. *Cancer Res.* 51, 696–706.
35. Briers, T. W., van de Voorde, A., and Vanderstichele, H. (1993). Characterization of immortalized mouse granulosa cell lines. *In Vitro Cell. Dev. Biol. Anim.* 29A, 847–854.
36. Vanderstichele, H., Delaey, B., de Winter, J., et al. (1994). Secretion of steroids, growth factors, and cytokines by immortalized mouse granulosa cell lines. *Biol. Reprod.* 50, 1190–1202.
37. McFarland, K. C., Sprengel, R., Phillips, H. S., et al. (1989). Lutropin-choriogonadotropin receptor: An unusual member of the G protein-coupled receptor family. *Science.* 245, 494–499.
38. Sprengel, R., Braun, T., Nikolics, K., Segaloff, D. L., and Seeburg, P. H. (1990). The testicular receptor for follicle

stimulating hormone: Structure and functional expression of cloned cDNA. *Mol. Endocrinol.* 4, 525–530.

39. Suh, B. S., Sprengel, R., Keren-Tal, I., Himmelhoch, S., and Amsterdam, A. (1992). Introduction of a gonadotropin receptor expression plasmid into immortalized granulosa cells leads to reconstitution of hormone-dependent steroidogenesis. *J. Cell. Biol.* 119, 439–450.
40. Keren-Tal, I., Dantes, A., Sprengel, R., and Amsterdam, A. (1993). Establishment of steroidogenic granulosa cell lines expressing follicle stimulating hormone receptors. *Mol. Cell. Endocrinol.* 95, R1-R10.
41. Selvaraj, N., Dantes, A., Limor, R., Golander, A., and Amsterdam, A. (1996). Establishment of an in vitro bioassay and radio receptor assay for LH/hCG in human sera using immortalized granulosa cells transfected with LH/hCG receptor. *Endocrine* 5, 275–283.
42. Kananen, K., Markkula, M., Rainio, E., Su, J. G., Hsueh, A. J., and Huhtaniemi, I. T. (1995). Gonadal tumorigenesis in transgenic mice bearing the mouse inhibin alpha-subunit promoter/simian virus T-antigen fusion gene: Characterization of ovarian tumors and establishment of gonadotropin-responsive granulosa cell lines. *Mol. Endocrinol.* 9, 616–627.
43. Gore-Langton, R., and Armstrong, D. (1994). Follicular steroidogenesis and its control. In *The Physiology of Reproduction*, eds. E. Knobil, and J. D. Neill, 571–627. New York: Raven Press.
44. Smyth, C. D., Miro, F., Whitelaw, P. F., Howles, C. M., and Hillier, S. G. (1993). Ovarian thecal/interstitial androgen synthesis is enhanced by a follicle-stimulating hormone-stimulated paracrine mechanism. *Endocrinology* 133, 1532–1538.
45. Smyth, C. D., Miro, F., Howles, C. M., and Hillier, S. G. (1995). Effect of luteinizing hormone on follicle stimulating hormone-activated paracrine signalling in rat ovary. *Hum. Reprod.* 10, 33–39.
46. Hsueh, A. J., Dahl, K. D., Vaughan, J., et al. (1987). Heterodimers and homodimers of inhibin subunits have different paracrine action in the modulation of luteinizing hormone-stimulated androgen biosynthesis. *Proc. Natl. Acad. Sci. USA* 84, 5082–5086.
47. Nahum, R., Thong, K. J., and Hillier, S. G. (1995). Metabolic regulation of androgen production by human thecal cells in vitro. *Hum. Reprod.* 10, 75–81.
48. Hillier, S., Miro, F., Mather, J., and Thong, K. (1997). Comparison of the effects of inhibin-A and inhibin-B on androgen production by human theca cells. In *FSH Action and Intraovarian Regulation*, ed. B. C. J. M. Fauser, 137–144. New York: The Parthenon Publishing Group.
49. Solovyeva, E. V., Hayashi, M., Margi, K., et al. (2000). Growth differentiation factor-9 stimulates rat theca-interstitial cell androgen biosynthesis. *Biol. Reprod.* 63, 1214–1218.
50. Yoshida, Y., Hosokawa, K., Dantes, A., Kotsuji, F., Kleinman, H. K., and Amsterdam, A. (2001). Role of laminin in ovarian cancer tumor growth and metastasis via regulation of Mdm2 and Bcl-2 expression. *Int. J. Oncol.* 18, 913–921.
51. Pan, J., Roskelley, C. D., Luu-The, V., Rojiani, M., and Auersperg, N. (1992). Reversal of divergent differentiation by ras oncogene-mediated transformation. *Cancer Res.* 52, 4269–4272.
52. Pan, J., Roskelley, C. D., and Auersperg, N. (1995). Influence of cell type on the steroidogenic potential and basal cyclic AMP levels of ras-oncogene-transformed rat cells. *Differentiation* 58, 321–328.
53. Richards, J. S. (1994). Hormonal control of gene expression in the ovary. *Endocr. Rev.* 15, 725–751.
54. Omura, T., and Morohashi, K. (1995). Gene regulation of steroidogenesis. *J. Steroid. Biochem. Mol. Biol.* 53, 19–25.
55. Stocco, D. M., and Clark, B. J. (1996). Regulation of the acute production of steroids in steroidogenic cells. *Endocr. Rev.* 17, 221–244.
56. Amsterdam, A., Hanukoglu, I., Suh, B., et al. (1992). Oncogene-transformed granulosa cells as a model system for the study of steroidogenic processes. *J. Steroid. Biochem. Mol. Biol.* 43, 875–884.
57. Amsterdam, A., and Suh, B. S. (1991). An inducible functional peripheral benzodiazepine receptor in mitochondria of steroidogenic granulosa cells. *Endocrinology* 129, 503–510.
58. Amsterdam, A., and Selvaraj, N. (1997). Control of differentiation, transformation, and apoptosis in granulosa cells by oncogenes, oncoviruses, and tumor suppressor genes. *Endocr. Rev.* 18, 435–461.
59. Honda, S., Morohashi, K., and Omura, T. (1990). Novel cAMP regulatory elements in the promoter region of bovine P-450(11 beta) gene. *J. Biochem. (Tokyo).* 108, 1042–1049.
60. Rice, D. A., Mouw, A. R., Bogerd, A. M., and Parker, K. L. (1991). A shared promoter element regulates the expression of three steroidogenic enzymes. *Mol. Endocrinol.* 5, 1552–1561.
61. Morohashi, K., Honda, S., Inomata, Y., Handa, H., and Omura, T. (1992). A common trans-acting factor, Ad4-binding protein, to the promoters of steroidogenic P-450s. *J. Biol. Chem.* 267, 17913–17919.
62. Nomura, M., Morohashi, K., and Kirita, S., et al. (1993). Three forms of rat CYP11B genes: 11 beta-hydroxylase gene, aldosterone synthase gene, and a novel gene. *J. Biochem. (Tokyo).* 113, 144–152.
63. Lynch, J. P., Lala, D. S., Peluso, J. J., Luo, W., Parker, K. L., and White, B. A. (1993). Steroidogenic factor 1, an orphan nuclear receptor, regulates the expression of the rat aromatase gene in gonadal tissues. *Mol. Endocrinol.* 7, 776–786.
64. Fitzpatrick, S. L., and Richards, J. S. (1993). Cis-acting elements of the rat aromatase promoter required for cyclic adenosine 3′,5′-monophosphate induction in ovarian granulosa cells and constitutive expression in R2C Leydig cells. *Mol. Endocrinol.* 7, 341–354.
65. Clemens, J. W., Lala, D. S., Parker, K. L., and Richards, J. S. (1994). Steroidogenic factor-1 binding and transcriptional activity of the cholesterol side-chain cleavage promoter in rat granulosa cells. *Endocrinology* 134, 1499–1508.
66. Michael, M. D., Kilgore, M. W., Morohashi, K., and Simpson, E. R. (1995). Ad4BP/SF-1 regulates cyclic AMP-induced transcription from the proximal promoter (PII) of the human aromatase P450 (CYP19) gene in the ovary. *J. Biol. Chem.* 270, 13561–13566.
67. Lala, D. S., Rice, D. A., and Parker, K. L. (1992). Steroidogenic factor I, a key regulator of steroidogenic enzyme

expression, is the mouse homolog of fushi tarazu-factor I. *Mol. Endocrinol.* 6, 1249–1258.

68. Honda, S., Morohashi, K., Nomura, M., Takeya, H., Kitajima, M., and Omura, T. (1993). Ad4BP-regulating steroidogenic P-450 gene is a member of steroid hormone receptor superfamily. *J. Biol. Chem.* 269, 7494–7502.
69. Evans, R. M. (1988). The steroid and thyroid hormone receptor superfamily. *Science* 240, 889–895.
70. Ikeda, Y., Lala, D. S., Luo, X., Kim, E., Moisan, M. P., and Parker, K. L. (1993). Characterization of the mouse FTZ-F1 gene, which encodes a key regulator of steroid hydroxylase gene expression. *Mol. Endocrinol.* 7, 852–860.
71. Morohashi, K., Iida, H., Nomura, M., et al. (1994). Functional difference between Ad4BP and ELP, and their distributions in steroidogenic tissues. *Mol. Endocrinol.* 8, 643–653.
72. Hatano, O., Takayama, K., Imai, T., et al. (1994). Sex-dependent expression of a transcription factor, Ad4BP, regulating steroidogenic P-450 genes in the gonads during prenatal and postnatal rat development. *Development* 120, 2787–2797.
73. Breckwoldt, M., Selvaraj, N., Aharoni, D., et al. (1996). Expression of Ad4-BP/cytochrome P450 side chain cleavage enzyme and induction of cell death in long-term cultures of human granulosa cells. *Mol. Hum. Reprod.* 2, 391–400.
74. Luo, X., Ikeda, Y., and Parker, K. L. (1995). The cell-specific nuclear receptor steroidogenic factor 1 plays multiple roles in reproductive function. *Philos. Trans. R. Soc. Lond. B. Biol. Sci.* 350, 279–283.
75. Shen, W. H., Moore, C. C., Ikeda, Y., Parker, K. L., and Ingraham, H. A. (1994). Nuclear receptor steroidogenic factor 1 regulates the mullerian inhibiting substance gene: A link to the sex determination cascade. *Cell* 77, 651–661.
76. Nomura, M., Bartsch, S., Nawata, H., Omura, T., and Morohashi, K. (1995). An E box element is required for the expression of the ad4bp gene, a mammalian homologue of ftz-f1 gene, which is essential for adrenal and gonadal development. *J. Biol. Chem.* 270, 7453–7461.
77. Keren-Tal, I., Dantes, A., Plehn-Dujowich, D., and Amsterdam, A. (1997). Association of Ad4BP/SF-1 transcription factor with steroidogenic activity in oncogene-transformed granulosa cells. *Mol. Cell. Endocrinol.* 127, 49–57.
78. Yamamoto, R., Kallen, C. B., Babalola, G. O., Rennert, H., Billheimer, J. T., and Strauss, III, J. F. (1991). Cloning and expression of a cDNA encoding human sterol carrier protein 2. *Proc. Natl. Acad. Sci. USA* 88, 463–467.
79. Seedorf, U., and Assmann, G. (1991). Cloning, expression, and nucleotide sequence of rat liver sterol carrier protein 2 cDNAs. *J. Biol. Chem.* 266, 630–636.
80. Rennert, H., Amsterdam, A., Billheimer, J. T., and Strauss, III, J. F. (1991). Regulated expression of sterol carrier protein 2 in the ovary: A key role for cyclic AMP. *Biochemistry* 30, 11280–11285.
81. Anholt, R. R., Pedersen, P. L., De Souza, E. B., and Snyder, S. H. (1986). The peripheral-type benzodiazepine receptor. Localization to the mitochondrial outer membrane. *J. Biol. Chem.* 261, 576–583.
82. Yanagibashi, K., Ohno, Y., Nakamichi, N., et al. (1989). Peripheral-type benzodiazepine receptors are involved in the regulation of cholesterol side chain cleavage in adrenocortical mitochondria. *J. Biochem. (Tokyo).* 106, 1026–1029.
83. Mukhin, A. G., Papadopoulos, V., Costa, E., and Krueger, K. E. (1989). Mitochondrial benzodiazepine receptors regulate steroid biosynthesis. *Proc. Natl. Acad. Sci. USA* 86, 9813–9816.
84. Papadopoulos, V., Mukhin, A. G., Costa, E., and Krueger, K. E. (1990). The peripheral-type benzodiazepine receptor is functionally linked to Leydig cell steroidogenesis. *J. Biol. Chem.* 265, 3772–3779.
85. Fares, F., Bar-Ami, S., Brandes, J. M., and Gavish, M. (1988). Changes in the density of peripheral benzodiazepine binding sites in genital organs of the female rat during the oestrous cycle. *J. Reprod. Fertil.* 83, 619–625.
86. Katz, Y., Ben-Baruch, G., Kloog, Y., Menczer, J., and Gavish, M. (1990). Increased density of peripheral benzodiazepine-binding sites in ovarian carcinomas as compared with benign ovarian tumours and normal ovaries. *Clin. Sci. (Lond.).* 78, 155–158.
87. Selvaraj, N., Israeli, D., and Amsterdam, A. (1996). Partial sequencing of the rat steroidogenic acute regulatory protein message from immortalized granulosa cells: Regulation by gonadotropins and isoproterenol. *Mol. Cell. Endocrinol.* 123, 171–177.
88. Simpson, E. R. (1979). Cholesterol side-chain cleavage, cytochrome P450, and the control of steroidogenesis. *Mol. Cell. Endocrinol.* 13, 213–227.
89. Miller, W. L. (1988). Molecular biology of steroid hormone synthesis. *Endocr. Rev.* 9, 295–318.
90. Mitani, F., Shimizu, T., Ueno, R., et al. (1982). Cytochrome P-45011 beta and P-450scc in adrenal cortex: Zonal distribution and intramitochondrial localization by the horse-radish peroxidase-labeled antibody method. *J. Histochem. Cytochem.* 30, 1066–1074.
91. Farkash, Y., Timberg, R., and Orly, J. (1986). Preparation of antiserum to rat cytochrome P-450 cholesterol side chain cleavage, and its use for ultrastructural localization of the immunoreactive enzyme by protein A-gold technique. *Endocrinology* 118, 1353–1365.
92. Crivello, J. F., and Jefcoate, C. R. (1980). Intracellular movement of cholesterol in rat adrenal cells. Kinetics and effects of inhibitors. *J. Biol. Chem.* 255, 8144–8151.
93. Jefcoate, C. R., DiBartolomeis, M. J., Williams, C. A., and McNamara, B. C. (1987). ACTH regulation of cholesterol movement in isolated adrenal cells. *J. Steroid. Biochem.* 27, 721–729.
94. Arthur, J. R., and Boyd, G. S. (1974). The effect of inhibitors of protein synthesis on cholesterol side-chain cleavage in the mitochondria of luteinized rat ovaries. *Eur. J. Biochem.* 49, 117–127.
95. Krueger, R. J., and Orme-Johnson, N. R. (1983). Acute adrenocorticotropic hormone stimulation of adrenal corticosteroidogenesis. Discovery of a rapidly induced protein. *J. Biol. Chem.* 258, 10159–10167.
96. Epstein, L. F., and Orme-Johnson, N. R. (1991). Acute action of luteinizing hormone on mouse Leydig cells: Accumulation of mitochondrial phosphoproteins and stimulation of testosterone synthesis. *Mol. Cell. Endocrinol.* 81, 113–126.

97. Stocco, D. M., and Chen, W. (1991). Presence of identical mitochondrial proteins in unstimulated constitutive steroid-producing R2C rat Leydig tumor and stimulated nonconstitutive steroid-producing MA-10 mouse Leydig tumor cells. *Endocrinology* 128, 1918–1926.
98. Stevens, V. L., Xu, T., and Lambeth, J. D. (1993). Cholesterol trafficking in steroidogenic cells. Reversible cycloheximide-dependent accumulation of cholesterol in a pre-steroidogenic pool. *Eur. J. Biochem.* 216, 557–563.
99. Alberta, J. A., Epstein, L. F., Pon, L. A., and Orme-Johnson, N. R. (1989). Mitochondrial localization of a phosphoprotein that rapidly accumulates in adrenal cortex cells exposed to adrenocorticotropic hormone or to cAMP. *J. Biol. Chem.* 264, 2368–2372.
100. Elliott, M. E., Goodfriend, T. L., and Jefcoate, C. R. (1993). Bovine adrenal glomerulosa and fasciculata cells exhibit 28.5-kilodalton proteins sensitive to angiotensin, other agonists, and atrial natriuretic peptide. *Endocrinology* 133, 1669–1677.
101. Pon, L. A., and Orme-Johnson, N. R. (1986). Acute stimulation of steroidogenesis in corpus luteum and adrenal cortex by peptide hormones. Rapid induction of a similar protein in both tissues. *J. Biol. Chem.* 261, 6594–6599.
102. Stocco, D. M., and Sodeman, T. C. (1991). The 30-kDa mitochondrial proteins induced by hormone stimulation in MA-10 mouse Leydig tumor cells are processed from larger precursors. *J. Biol. Chem.* 266, 19731–19738.
103. Epstein, L. F., and Orme-Johnson, N. R. (1991). Regulation of steroid hormone biosynthesis. Identification of precursors of a phosphoprotein targeted to the mitochondrion in stimulated rat adrenal cortex cells. *J. Biol. Chem.* 266, 19739–19745.
104. Stocco, D. M., and Clark, B. J. (1993). The requirement of phosphorylation on a threonine residue in the acute regulation of steroidogenesis in MA-10 mouse Leydig cells. *J. Steroid. Biochem. Mol. Biol.* 46, 337–347.
105. Clark, B. J., Wells, J., King, S. R., and Stocco, D. M. (1994). The purification, cloning, and expression of a novel luteinizing hormone-induced mitochondrial protein in MA-10 mouse Leydig tumor cells. Characterization of the steroidogenic acute regulatory protein (StAR). *J. Biol. Chem.* 269, 28314–28322.
106. Sugawara, T., Holt, J. A., Driscoll, D., et al. (1995). Human steroidogenic acute regulatory protein: Functional activity in COS-1 cells, tissue-specific expression, and mapping of the structural gene to 8p11.2 and a pseudogene to chromosome 13. *Proc. Natl. Acad. Sci. USA* 92, 4778–4782.
107. Lin, D., Sugawara, T., Strauss, III, J. F., et al. (1995). Role of steroidogenic acute regulatory protein in adrenal and gonadal steroidogenesis. *Science* 267, 1828–1831.
108. Stocco, D. M., and Clark, B. J. (1997). The role of the steroidogenic acute regulatory protein in steroidogenesis. *Steroids* 62, 29–36.
109. Selvaraj, N., Dantes, A., and Amsterdam, A. (2000). Establishment and characterization of steroidogenic granulosa cells expressing beta(2)-adrenergic receptor: Regulation of adrenodoxin and steroidogenic acute regulatory protein by adrenergic agents. *Mol. Cell. Endocrinol.* 168, 53–63.
110. Arakane, F., Kallen, C. B., Watari, H., et al. (1998). The mechanism of action of steroidogenic acute regulatory protein (StAR). StAR acts on the outside of mitochondria to stimulate steroidogenesis. *J. Biol. Chem.* 273, 16339–16345.
111. Strauss, III, J. F., Kallen, C. B., Christenson, L. K., et al. (1999). The steroidogenic acute regulatory protein (StAR): A window into the complexities of intracellular cholesterol trafficking. *Rec. Prog. Hormone Res.* 54, 369–394; discussion 394–395.
112. Orian, A., Gonen, H., Bercovich, B., et al. (2000). SCF(beta)(-TrCP) ubiquitin ligase-mediated processing of NF-kappaB p105 requires phosphorylation of its C-terminus by IkappaB kinase. *EMBO J.* 19, 2580–2591.
113. Oren, M. (1999). Regulation of the p53 tumor suppressor protein. *J. Biol. Chem.* 274, 36031–36034.
114. Bercovich, Z., and Kahana, C. (1993). Involvement of the 20S proteasome in the degradation of ornithine decarboxylase. *Eur. J. Biochem.* 213, 205–210.
115. Leibovitz, D., Koch, Y., Fridkin, M., et al. (1995). Archaebacterial and eukaryotic proteasomes prefer different sites in cleaving gonadotropin-releasing hormone. *J. Biol. Chem.* 270, 11029–11032.
116. Sutovsky, P., Moreno, R. D., Ramalho-Santos, J., Dominko, T., Simerly, C., and Schatten, G. (2000). Ubiquitinated sperm mitochondria, selective proteolysis, and the regulation of mitochondrial inheritance in mammalian embryos. *Biol. Reprod.* 63, 582–590.
117. Tajima, K., Babich, S., Yoshida, Y., Dantes, A., Strauss, III, J. F., and Amsterdam, A. (2001). The proteasome inhibitor MG132 promotes accumulation of the steroidogenic acute regulatory protein (StAR) and steroidogenesis. *FEBS Lett.* 490, 59–64.
118. Amsterdam, A., Gold, R. S., Hosokawa, K., et al. (1999). Crosstalk among multiple signaling pathways controlling ovarian cell death. *Trends Endocrinol. Metab.* 10, 255–262.
119. Hosokawa, K., Dantes, A., Schere-Levy, C., et al. (1998). Induction of Ad4BP/SF-1, steroidogenic acute regulatory protein, and cytochrome P450scc enzyme system expression in newly established human granulosa cell lines. *Endocrinology* 139, 4679–4687.
120. Sasson, R., Tajima, K., and Amsterdam, A. (2001). Glucocorticoids protect against apoptosis induced by serum deprivation, cyclic adenosine 3′,5′-monophosphate and p53 activation in immortalized human granulosa cells: Involvement of Bcl-2. *Endocrinology* 142, 802–811.
121. Adashi, E. Y., Jones, P. B., and Hsueh, A. J. (1981). Synergistic effect of glucocorticoids on the stimulation of progesterone production by follicle-stimulating hormone in cultured rat granulosa cells. *Endocrinology* 109, 1888–1894.
122. Sasson, R., Winder, N., Kees, S., and Amsterdam, A. (2002). Induction of apoptosis in granulosa cells by TNF alpha and its attenuation by glucocorticoids involve modulation of Bcl-2. *Biochem. Biophys. Res. Commun.* 294, 51–59.
123. Huang, T. J., and Shirley Li P. (2001). Dexamethasone inhibits luteinizing hormone-induced synthesis of steroidogenic acute regulatory protein in cultured rat preovulatory follicles. *Biol. Reprod.* 64, 163–170.
124. Barkan, D., Jia, H., Dantes, A., Vardimon, L., Amsterdam, A., and Rubinstein, M. (1999). Leptin modulates the glucocorticoid-induced ovarian steroidogenesis. *Endocrinology* 140, 1731–1738.

125. Spicer, L. J., and Francisco, C. C. (1997). The adipose obese gene product, leptin: Evidence of a direct inhibitory role in ovarian function. *Endocrinology* 138, 3374–3379.
126. Zachow, R. J., and Magoffin, D. A. (1997). Direct intraovarian effects of leptin: Impairment of the synergistic action of insulin-like growth factor-I on follicle-stimulating hormone-dependent estradiol-17 beta production by rat ovarian granulosa cells. *Endocrinology* 138, 847–850.
127. Karlsson, C., Lindell, K., Svensson, E., et al. (1997). Expression of functional leptin receptors in the human ovary. *J. Clin. Endocrinol. Metab.* 82, 4144–4148.
128. Seger, R., Hanoch, T., Rosenberg, R., et al. (2001). The ERK signaling cascade inhibits gonadotropin-stimulated steroidogenesis. *J. Biol. Chem.* 276, 13957–13964.
129. Santana, P., Llanes, L., Hernandez, I., et al. (1995). Ceramide mediates tumor necrosis factor effects on P450-aromatase activity in cultured granulosa cells. *Endocrinology* 136, 2345–2348.
130. Adashi, E. Y., Resnick, C. E., Packman, J. N., Hurwitz, A., and Payne, D. W. (1990). Cytokine-mediated regulation of ovarian function: Tumor necrosis factor alpha inhibits gonadotropin-supported progesterone accumulation by differentiating and luteinized murine granulosa cells. *Am. J. Obstet. Gynecol.* 162, 889–896; discussion 896–899.
131. Spicer, L. J. (1998). Tumor necrosis factor-alpha (TNF-alpha) inhibits steroidogenesis of bovine ovarian granulosa and thecal cells in vitro. Involvement of TNF-alpha receptors. *Endocrine* 8, 109–115.
132. Fukuoka, M., Yasuda, K., Taii, S., and Mori, T. (1992). Synergistic actions of cytokines and growth factors in enhancing porcine granulosa cell growth. *Endocrinol. Jpn.* 39, 277–288.
133. Roby, K. F., and Terranova, P. F. (1990). Effects of tumor necrosis factor-alpha in vitro on steroidogenesis of healthy and atretic follicles of the rat: Theca as a target. *Endocrinology* 126, 2711–2718.
134. Chen, Y. J., Feng, Q., and Liu, Y. X. (1999). Expression of the steroidogenic acute regulatory protein and luteinizing hormone receptor and their regulation by tumor necrosis factor alpha in rat corpora lutea. *Biol. Reprod.* 60, 419–427.
135. Amsterdam, A., Nimrod, A., Lamprecht, S. A., Burstein, Y., and Lindner, H. R. (1979). Internalization and degradation of receptor-bound hCG in granulosa cell cultures. *Am. J. Physiol.* 236, E129–E138.
136. Ezra, E., and Salomon, Y. (1981). Mechanism of desensitization of adenylate cyclase by lutropin. Impaired introduction of GTP into the regulatory site. *J. Biol. Chem.* 256, 5377–5382.
137. Ekstrom, R. C., and Hunzicker-Dunn, M. (1990). Comparison of the luteinizing hormone-sensitive adenylyl cyclase of the pig ovarian follicle and corpus luteum and its susceptibility to in vitro hormone-dependent desensitization. *Endocrinology* 126, 1191–1198.
138. Keren-Tal, I., Dantes, A., and Amsterdam, A. (1996). Activation of FSH-responsive adenylate cyclase by staurosporine: Role for protein phosphorylation in gonadotropin receptor desensitization. *Mol. Cell. Endocrinol.* 116, 39–48.
139. Selvaraj, N., and Amsterdam, A. (1997). Modulation of FSH receptor phosphorylation correlates with hormone-induced coupling to the adenylate cyclase system. *Endocrine* 6, 179–185.
140. Seger, R., and Krebs, E. G. (1995). The MAPK signaling cascade. *FASEB J.* 9, 726–735.
140a. Amsterdam, A., Tajima, K., Frajese, V., Seger, R. (2003). Analysis of signal transduction stimulated by gonadotropins in granulosa cells. *Mol. Cell Endocrinol.* 202(1–2), 77–80.
140b. Tajima, K., Dantes, A., Yao, Z., Sorokina, K., Kotsuji, F., Seger, R., Amsterdam, A. (2003). Down-regulation of steroidogenic response to gonadotropins in human and rat preovulatory granulosa cells involves mitogen-activated protein kinase activation and modulation of DAX-1 and steroidogenic factor-1. *J. Clin. Endocrinol. Metab.* 88(5), 2288–2289.
141. Das, S., Maizels, E. T., DeManno, D., St. Clair, E., Adam, S. A., and Hunzicker-Dunn, M. (1996). A stimulatory role of cyclic adenosine 3′,5′-monophosphate in follicle-stimulating hormone-activated mitogen-activated protein kinase signaling pathway in rat ovarian granulosa cells. *Endocrinology* 137, 967–974.
142. Gutkind, J. S. (1998). Cell growth control by G protein-coupled receptors: From signal transduction to signal integration. *Oncogene* 17, 1331–1342.
143. Naor, Z., Benard, O., and Seger, R. (2000). Activation of MAPK cascades by G-protein-coupled receptors: The case of gonadotropin-releasing hormone receptor. *Trends Endocrinol. Metab.* 11, 91–99.
144. Lalli, E., Melner, M. H., Stocco, D. M., and Sassone-Corsi, P. (1998). DAX-1 blocks steroid production at multiple levels. *Endocrinology* 139, 4237–4243.
145. Granot, Z., Geiss-Friedlander, R., Melamed-Book, N., Eimerl, S., Timberg, R., Weiss, A. M., Hales, K. H., Hales, D. B., Stocco, D. M., Orly, J. (2003). Proteolysis of normal and mutated steroidogenic acute regulatory (StAR) proteins in the mitochondria: the fale of unmanted proteins. *Mol. Endocrinol.* (in press).
146. Zeleznik, A. J., and Somers, J. P. (1999). Regulation of the primate corpus luteum: Cellular and molecular perspectives. *Trends Endocrinol. Metab.* 10, 189–193.
147. McGee, E. A., Perlas, E., LaPolt, P. S., Tsafriri, A., and Hsueh, A. J. (1997). Follicle-stimulating hormone enhances the development of preantral follicles in juvenile rats. *Biol. Reprod.* 57, 990–998.
148. Goodenough, D. A., Goliger, J. A., and Paul, D. L. (1996). Connexins, connexons, and intercellular communication. *Annu. Rev. Biochem.* 65, 475–502.
149. Simon, A. M., Goodenough, D. A., Li, E., and Paul, D. L. (1997). Female infertility in mice lacking connexin 37. *Nature* 385, 525–529.
150. Grazul-Bilska, A. T., Reynolds, L. P., and Redmer, D. A. (1997). Gap junctions in the ovaries. *Biol. Reprod.* 57, 947–957.
151. Khan-Dawood, F. S., Yang, J., and Dawood, M. Y. (1996). Expression of gap junction protein connexin-43 in the human and baboon *(Papio anubis)* corpus luteum. *J. Clin. Endocrinol. Metab.* 81, 835–842.
152. Juneja, S. C., Barr, K. J., Enders, G. C., and Kidder, G. M. (1999). Defects in the germ line and gonads of mice lacking connexin 43. *Biol. Reprod.* 60, 1263–1270.
153. Wiesen, J. F., and Midgley, Jr., A. R. (1993). Changes in expression of connexin 43 gap junction messenger ribonu-

cleic acid and protein during ovarian follicular growth. *Endocrinology* 133, 741–746.
154. Granot, I., and Dekel, N. (1998). Cell-to-cell communication in the ovarian follicle: Developmental and hormonal regulation of the expression of connexin 43. *Hum. Reprod.* 13 (Suppl 4), 85–97.
155. Mayerhofer, A., and Garfield, R. E. (1995). Immunocytochemical analysis of the expression of gap junction protein connexin 43 in the rat ovary. *Mol. Reprod. Dev.* 41, 331–338.
156. Huet, C., Monget, P., Pisselet, C., Hennequet, C., Locatelli, A., and Monniaux, D. (1998). Chronology of events accompanying follicular atresia in hypophysectomized ewes. Changes in levels of steroidogenic enzymes, connexin 43, insulin-like growth factor II/mannose 6 phosphate receptor, extracellular matrix components, and matrix metalloproteinases. *Biol. Reprod.* 58, 175–185.
157. Granot, I., and Dekel, N. (1997). Developmental expression and regulation of the gap junction protein and transcript in rat ovaries. *Mol. Reprod. Dev.* 47, 231–239.
158. Sommersberg, B., Bulling, A., Salzer, U., et al. (2000). Gap junction communication and connexin 43 gene expression in a rat granulosa cell line: Regulation by follicle-stimulating hormone. *Biol. Reprod.* 63, 1661–1668.
159. Sasson, R., and Amsterdam, A. (2002). Stimulation of apoptosis in human granulosa cells from in vitro fertilization patients and its prevention by dexamethasone: Involvement of cell contact and bcl-2 expression. *J. Clin. Endocrinol. Metab.* 87, 3441–3451.
160. Amsterdam, A., Josephs, R., Lieberman, M. E., and Lindner, H. R. (1976). Organization of intramembrane particles in freeze-cleaved gap junctions of rat graafian follicles: Optical-diffraction analysis. *J. Cell. Sci.* 21, 93–105.
161. Sommersberg, B., Bulling, A., Salzer, U., et al. (2000). Gap junction communication and connexin 43 gene expression in a rat granulosa cell line: Regulation by follicle-stimulating hormone. *Biol. Reprod.* 63, 1661–1668.
162. Risek, B., Klier, F. G., Phillips, A., Hahn, D. W., and Gilula, N. B. (1995). Gap junction regulation in the uterus and ovaries of immature rats by estrogen and progesterone. *J. Cell. Sci.* 108, 1017–1032.
162a. Sasson, R., Shinder, V., Dantes, A., Land, A and Amsterdam, A. (2003). Activation of multiple signal transduction pathways by glucocorticoids: protection of ovarian follicular cells against apoptosis. *Biochem. Biophys. Res. Comm.* (in press).
163. Aharoni, D., Dantes, A., Oren, M., and Amsterdam, A. (1995). cAMP-mediated signals as determinants for apoptosis in primary granulosa cells. *Exp. Cell. Res.* 218, 271–282.
164. Hillier, S. G., and Tetsuka, M. (1998). An anti-inflammatory role for glucocorticoids in the ovaries? *J. Reprod. Immunol.* 39, 21–27.
165. Andersen, C. Y., and Hornnes, P. (1994). Intrafollicular concentrations of free cortisol close to follicular rupture. *Hum. Reprod.* 9, 1944–1949.
166. Escher, G., Galli, I., Vishwanath, B. S., Frey, B. M., and Frey, F. J. (1997). Tumor necrosis factor alpha and interleukin 1beta enhance the cortisone/cortisol shuttle. *J. Exp. Med.* 186, 189–198.
167. Tetsuka, M., Haines, L. C., Milne, M., Simpson, G. E., and Hillier, S. G. (1999). Regulation of 11beta-hydroxysteroid dehydrogenase type 1 gene expression by LH and interleukin-1beta in cultured rat granulosa cells. *J. Endocrinol.* 163, 417–423.
168. Yong, P. Y., Thong, K. J., Andrew, R., Walker, B. R., and Hillier, S. G. (2000). Development-related increase in cortisol biosynthesis by human granulosa cells. *J. Clin. Endocrinol. Metab.* 85, 4728–4733.
169. Werb, Z. (1978). Biochemical actions of glucocorticoids on macrophages in culture. Specific inhibition of elastase, collagenase, and plasminogen activator secretion and effects on other metabolic functions. *J. Exp. Med.* 147, 1695–1712.
170. Orth, D., Kovacs, W., and Debold, C. (1992). The adrenal gland. In *Textbook of Endocrinology*, 8th ed., eds. J. D. Wilson, and D. W. Foster, 89–620. London: WB Saunders Company.
171. Amsterdam, A., Tajima, K., and Sasson, R. (2002). Cell-specific regulation of apoptosis by glucocorticoids: Implication to their anti-inflammatory action. *Biochem. Pharmacol.* 64, 843.
172. Kaipia, A., Chun, S. Y., Eisenhauer, K., and Hsueh, A. J. (1996). Tumor necrosis factor-alpha and its second messenger, ceramide, stimulate apoptosis in cultured ovarian follicles. *Endocrinology* 137, 4864–4870.
173. Quirk, S. M., Porter, D. A., Huber, S. C., and Cowan, R. G. (1998). Potentiation of Fas-mediated apoptosis of murine granulosa cells by interferon-gamma, tumor necrosis factor-alpha, and cycloheximide. *Endocrinology* 139, 4860–4869.
174. Matsubara, H., Ikuta, K., Ozaki, Y., et al. (2000). Gonadotropins and cytokines affect luteal function through control of apoptosis in human luteinized granulosa cells. *J. Clin. Endocrinol. Metab.* 85, 1620–1626.
175. Witty, J. P., Bridgham, J. T., and Johnson, A. L. (1996). Induction of apoptotic cell death in hen granulosa cells by ceramide. *Endocrinology* 137, 5269–5277.
176. Grell, M., Becke, F. M., Wajant, H., Mannel, D. N., and Scheurich, P. (1998). TNF receptor type 2 mediates thymocyte proliferation independently of TNF receptor type 1. *Eur. J. Immunol.* 28, 257–263.
177. Grell, M., Wajant, H., Zimmermann, G., and Scheurich, P. (1998). The type 1 receptor (CD120a) is the high-affinity receptor for soluble tumor necrosis factor. *Proc. Natl. Acad. Sci. USA* 95, 570–575.
178. Roby, K. F., and Terranova, P. F. (1990). Effects of tumor necrosis factor-alpha in vitro on steroidogenesis of healthy and atretic follicles of the rat: Theca as a target. *Endocrinology* 126, 2711–2718.
179. Sakumoto, R., Murakami, S., Kishi, H., Iga, K., Okano, A., and Okuda, K. (2000). Tumor necrosis factor-alpha and its receptor in the corpus luteum of pregnant cows. *Mol. Reprod. Dev.* 55, 406–411.
180. Bridgham, J. T., and Johnson, A. L. (2001). Expression and regulation of Fas antigen and tumor necrosis factor receptor type I in hen granulosa cells. *Biol. Reprod.* 65, 733–739.
181. Braw, R. H., Bar-Ami, S., and Tsafriri, A. (1981). Effect of hypophysectomy on atresia of rat preovulatory follicles. *Biol. Reprod.* 25, 989–996.
182. Gross, A., Jockel, J., Wei, M. C., and Korsmeyer, S. J. (1998). Enforced dimerization of BAX results in its translocation,

mitochondrial dysfunction and apoptosis. *EMBO J.* 17, 3878–3885.

183. Pitzer, F., Dantes, A., Fuchs, T., Baumeister, W., and Amsterdam, A. (1996). Removal of proteasomes from the nucleus and their accumulation in apoptotic blebs during programmed cell death. *FEBS Lett.* 394, 47–50.
184. Kothakota, S., Azuma, T., Reinhard, C., et al. (1997). Caspase-3-generated fragment of gelsolin: Effector of morphological change in apoptosis. *Science* 278, 294–298.
185. Kwiatkowski, D. J. (1999). Functions of gelsolin: Motility, signaling, apoptosis, cancer. *Curr. Opin. Cell. Biol. 11*, 103–108.
186. Shukovski, L., Keren-Tal, I., Dantes, A., and Amsterdam, A. (1995). Regulation of follistatin messenger ribonucleic acid in steroidogenic rat granulosa cell lines. *Endocrinology* 136, 2889–2895.
187. Lindsell, C. E., Misra, V., and Murphy, B. D. (1994). Regulation of follistatin gene expression in the ovary and in primary cultures of porcine granulosa cells. *J. Reprod. Fertil.* 100, 591–597.
188. Miyanaga, K., and Shimasaki, S. (1993). Structural and functional characterization of the rat follistatin (activin-binding protein) gene promoter. *Mol. Cell. Endocrinol.* 92, 99–109.
189. Shimon, I., Rubinek, T., Bar-Hava, I., et al. (2001). Ovarian hyperstimulation without elevated serum estradiol associated with pure follicle-stimulating hormone-secreting pituitary adenoma. *J. Clin. Endocrinol. Metab.* 86, 3635–3640.
190. Amsterdam, A. (2003). Novel genes regulated by gonadotropins in granulosa cells: New perspectives on their physiological functions. *Mol. Cell. Endocrinol.* 202, 133–137.
191. Grosse, J., Bulling, A., Brucker, C., et al. (2000). Synaptosome-associated protein of 25 kilodaltons in oocytes and steroid-producing cells of rat and human ovary: Molecular analysis and regulation by gonadotropins. *Biol. Reprod.* 63, 643–650.

191a. Sasson, R., Dantes, A., Tajma, K., Amsterdam, A. Novel genes modulated by FSH in normal and immortalized FSH-responsive cells: new insights into the mechanism of FSH action. *FASEB J.* 17(10), 1256–1266.

192. Masumoto, N., Ikebuchi, Y., Matsuoka, T., Tasaka, K., Miyake, A., and Murata, Y. (1997). Involvement of SNAP-25 in TRH-induced exocytosis in pituitary GH4C1 cells. *J. Endocrinol.* 153, R5-R10.
193. Hohne-Zell, B., and Gratzl, M. (1996). Adrenal chromaffin cells contain functionally different SNAP-25 monomers and SNAP-25/syntaxin heterodimers. *FEBS Lett.* 394, 109–116.
194. Hohne-Zell, B., Galler, A., Schepp, W., Gratzl, M., and Prinz, C. (1997). Functional importance of synaptobrevin and SNAP-25 during exocytosis of histamine by rat gastric enterochromaffin-like cells. *Endocrinology* 138, 5518–5526.
195. Sadoul, K., Lang, J., Montecucco, C., et al. (1995). SNAP-25 is expressed in islets of Langerhans and is involved in insulin release. *J. Cell. Biol.* 128, 1019–1028.
196. Fritz, S., Wessler, I., Breitling, R., et al. (2001). Expression of muscarinic receptor types in the primate ovary and evidence for nonneuronal acetylcholine synthesis. *J. Clin. Endocrinol. Metab.* 86, 349–354.
197. Fritz, S., Grunert, R., Stocco, D. M., Hales, D. B., and Mayerhofer, A. (2001). StAR protein is increased by muscarinic receptor activation in human luteinized granulosa cells. *Mol. Cell. Endocrinol.* 171, 49–51.
198. Peluso, J. J. (1997). Putative mechanism through which N-cadherin-mediated cell contact maintains calcium homeostasis and thereby prevents ovarian cells from undergoing apoptosis. *Biochem. Pharmacol.* 54, 847–853.
199. Aharoni, D., Dantes, A., and Amsterdam, A. (1993). Cross-talk between adenylate cyclase activation and tyrosine phosphorylation leads to modulation of the actin cytoskeleton and to acute progesterone secretion in ovarian granulosa cells. *Endocrinology* 133, 1426–1436.
200. Amsterdam, A., Dantes, A., and Liscovitch, M. (1994). Role of phospholipase-D and phosphatidic acid in mediating gonadotropin-releasing hormone-induced inhibition of preantral granulosa cell differentiation. *Endocrinology* 135, 1205–1211.
201. Furman, A., Rotmensch, S., Kohen, F., Mashiach, S., and Amsterdam, A. (1986). Regulation of rat granulosa cell differentiation by extracellular matrix produced by bovine corneal endothelial cells. *Endocrinology* 118, 1878–1885.
202. Amsterdam, A., and Aharoni, D. (1994). Plasticity of cell organization during differentiation of normal and oncogene transformed granulosa cells. *Microsc. Res. Tech.* 27, 108–124.

CHAPTER 23

The Application of Gene Ablation and Related Technologies to the Study of Ovarian Function

KATHLEEN H. BURNS AND MARTIN M. MATZUK

INTRODUCTION

Our ability to engineer targeted mutations of the mammalian genome is revolutionizing the ways in which we study essential gene functions and has already greatly enhanced our understanding of ovarian development and physiology. When this approach is used to generate a nonfunctional or null allele, it is termed *gene ablation* or *gene "knockout" technology.* Knockout mouse models are being created at an ever-increasing rate, and more than 200 have been reported to date with reproductive phenotypes [1]. This number already surpasses the quantity of naturally occurring mutations associated with identified genes. In this chapter, we review how these models have helped researchers piece together the molecular mechanisms important for female fertility, from those that mediate primordial germ cell survival to those that conduct oocyte and somatic cell functions during folliculogenesis. We also consider postovulatory events contingent on genes expressed in oocytes while still within the ovary.

TARGETING ENDOGENOUS LOCI IN EMBRYONIC STEM CELLS

Embryonic stem (ES) cells, which are derived from the inner cell mass of mouse blastocysts, can be maintained for long periods in pluripotent states in vitro and altered by targeted mutagenesis [2]. Deleting or altering a particular site in the murine genome relies on the endogenous ES cell homologous recombination machinery to mediate crossover exchanges between the locus to be targeted and a "look-alike" targeting vector. Correctly targeted exchanges are typically selected for by a two-step process wherein researchers isolate cells that have integrated the desired sequence (positive selection), while excluding those with random vector incorporation (negative selection). Pluripotent ES cells may then be introduced into blastocysts where they combine with the inner cell mass and randomly give rise to somatic and germ cell lineages in resulting chimeras. When these cells contribute to the germline, the F1 generation will include offspring that carry the mutant allele (Figure 23.1). The goal of many gene targeting experiments is to disrupt a given gene in ES cells and study the resultant phenotype in mice bred to homozygosity for the alteration. These null or knockout mouse models provide compelling demonstrations of gene function in vivo.

GERM CELL DEVELOPMENT AND GONADOGENESIS

Ovarian function in mature females depends on the development and migration of germ cells and their organization into primordial follicles within the putative ovary. Primordial germ cell (PGC) precursors of oocytes are first discernable by alkaline phosphatase staining in the developing mouse at embryonic day 6.5 (E6.5) when they are located in the extraembryonic mesoderm [3]. From E7.5 to E13.5, these cells rapidly proliferate and migrate along the allantois to the embryonic hindgut and then caudally across the dorsal mesentery to the left and right genital ridges [4, 5]. Mitotic divisions of the PGCs are completed between E12.5 and E13.5 in the mouse, and the germ cells then arrest in the dictyate stage of prophase I of meiosis. Complex paracrine signaling pathways are critical for PGC migration and proliferation, and early meiosis must be completed without complication for germ cell survival. Several mouse models have demonstrated roles of particular genes in these processes (Table 23.1).

One of the most well-researched paracrine factors important to PGCs is stem cell factor (kit ligand), which is elaborated by somatic cells along the germ cell migration route. Kit ligand binds to KIT, a tyrosine kinase receptor expressed by the germ cells. Naturally occurring mutations affecting the kit ligand (*Kitl*) and *Kit* loci in Steel (*sl*) and white spotting (*w*) mouse models, respectively, cause failures in proliferation, migration, and survival of the PGCs [6, 7]. Similarly, signaling pathways elicited by members of the TGF-β superfamily are necessary for PGC develop-

1. Electroporation of targeting vector.

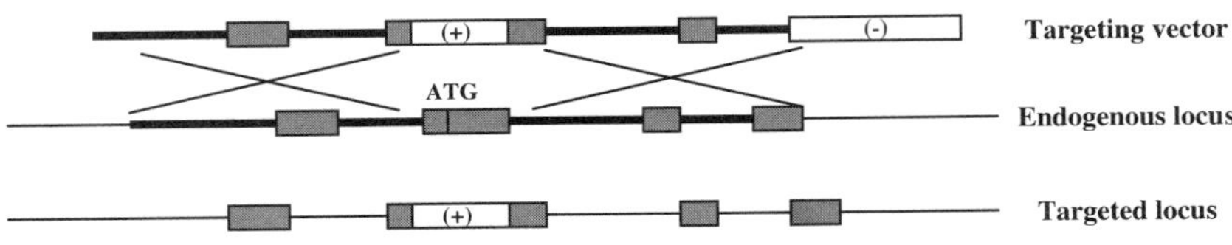

2. ES cell selection and identification of targeted clones.

3. Injection of blastocysts with targeted ES cells. Transfer to pseudopregnant recipient mice.

4. Breed chimeras to obtain heterozygotes.

5. Cross heterozygotes to generate knockout mice.

FIGURE 23.1 Generation of knockout mice by embryonic stem (ES) cell technology. A replacement (?) targeting vector is designed with large regions of homology with the endogenous locus (thick lines). The positive selection cassette (+) replaces a portion of the coding sequence and confers antibiotic resistance, allowing for the selection of ES cell clones that have incorporated the transgene. The (–) cassette, if retained because of random integration, will make cells susceptible to an administered compound. Together, this (+)/(–) strategy allows for the selective survival of ES cells that have undergone homologous recombination at the desired locus. These ES cells are injected into day 3.5 blastocysts. A coat color difference between the ES cell donor strain and the blastocyst donor strain allow for the ready assessment of chimerism. Chimeras with a germline component can generate uniform heterozygote offspring when mated with wild-type mice. Finally, barring effects on development, crosses between heterozygotes are expected to yield knockout mice at the Mendelian frequency of 1:3.

ment and have been implicated in PGC migration and proliferation. Knockout mouse models with mutations in bone morphogenetic protein-4 (*Bmp-4*) [8], *Bmp-8b* [9], Smad1 [10], or Smad5 [11] exhibit complete or nearly complete loss of the PGC population. More recently, double mutant studies generating $Bmp\text{-}2^{+/-}$, $Bmp\text{-}4^{+/-}$ double heterozygotes have revealed cooperative functions of these related molecules in PGC development [12]. Thus multiple TGF-β superfamily ligands (i.e., BMP-2, BMP-4, and BMP-8B), signaling through the intracellular proteins SMAD1 and SMAD5, play key roles in PGC development (for review, see [13]).

Preceding the cessation of meiosis in female germ cells, homologous chromosomes synapse and crossover exchanges then occur between them. Several proteins are known to play key roles between the zygotene and pachytene stages as these chromosomes come together. Defects in early meiosis are evident in knockout mice lacking genes encoding recombination proteins or deoxyribonucleic acid (DNA) repair enzymes [14–18]. $Spo11^{-/-}$, $Msh4^{-/-}$, $Msh5^{-/-}$, $Atm^{-/-}$, and $Dmc1h^{-/-}$ mice exhibit loss of the female germ cell population during embryogenesis or in the perinatal ovary (for reviews, see [1, 19, 20]). Similarly, knockout mice lacking *Cpeb* or *Dazla* genes encoding ribonucleic acid (RNA)-binding proteins have defects evident in early meiosis, though how these gene products regulate meiosis are still not clear [21, 22]. Thus meiosis before the prophase I block requires the cooperative function of many factors and represents a period in oocyte development during which selection mechanisms prevent the progression of abnormal gametes.

Differentiation of somatic ovarian components hinges on the activity of several transcription factors (i.e., EMX2, LHX9, SF-1, and WT-1), as demonstrated by gonadal agenesis in mice lacking each of these proteins [23–26]. Gene expression analyses in knockout embryos have allowed researchers to discern some hierarchical relationships between some of these transcription factors, though ultimate target genes in the genital ridge are not yet obvious. Transgenic mouse models have also identified or verified roles of several genes important in Müllerian duct development to form the oviducts and uterus and in the inhibition of this sequence in males (for reviews, see [27, 28]). Together, these studies underscore the usefulness of mouse models in identifying genes involved in the development of the reproductive system (Table 23.2).

Table 23.1 Germ Cell Development

Mutant Gene	Sex Affected	Reproductive Phenotype	Fertility Status	References
Ataxia telangiectasia (*Atm*)	Both	Germ cells degenerate; disruptions evident in meiosis I	Infertility	[105, 106]
Bone morphogenetic protein-4 (*Bmp-4*)	Both	Absent primordial germ cell (PGC) population; defect in PGC development	Lethal	[8]
Bmp-8b	Both	Reduced or absent PGCs (developmental defect); Postnatal male germ cell proliferation/differentiation defect and spermatocyte apoptosis	Subfertility/ infertility	[107]
Connexin-43 (*Gja1*; Cx-43)	Both	Small ovaries and testes; decreased numbers of germ cells from E11.5	Neonatal lethality	[108]
Cytoplasmic polyadenylation element binding protein (*Cpeb*)	Both	Disrupted germ cell differentiation and meiosis I synaptonemal complex formation	Infertility	[21]
Deleted in azoospermia-like (*Dazl*)	Both	Reduced germ cells; differentiation failure and degeneration of germ cells	Infertility	[22]
Disrupted meiotic cDNA 1 homolog (*Dmc1h*)	Both	Defects in chromosome synapsis in meiosis; female germ cells degenerate during embryogenesis	Infertility	[18, 109]
Kit ligand (*Kitl*)	Both	*Steel* mutation causes defect in PGC migration/survival; *panda* mutation causes blocks in folliculogenesis in females	Infertility	[110, 111]
Kit receptor (*Kit*)	Both	*White spotting* null mutation causes PGC defects	Infertility	[112]
MutL homolog 1 (*Mlh1*)	Both	Meiotic arrest and genomic instability	Infertility	[100, 113]
MutS homolog 4 (*Msh4*)	Both	Prophase I meiotic defects apparent at the zygotene/pachytene stage; germ cells lost within a few days postpartum	Infertility	[15]
MutS homologue 5 (*Msh5*)	Both	Zygotene/pachytene meiotic defects with aberrant chromosome synapsis and apoptosis	Infertility	[16, 114]
Smad1 (MAD homolog 1; [*Madh1*])	Both	Developing embryos lose PGCs	Lethal	[10]
Smad5 (MAD homolog 5; [*Madh5*])	Both	Developing embryos lose PGCs	Lethal	[115]
SPO11 homolog (*Spo11*)	Both	Defects in meiosis; oocytes lost soon after birth	Infertility	[14, 116]
Synaptonemal complex protein 3 (*Sycp3*)	Both	Defects in chromosome synapsis during meiosis; germ cell apoptosis in males; embryonic loss in females caused by aneuploidy	Infertility (M); subfertility (F)	[102, 117]
Cytotoxic granule-associated ribonucleic acid (RNA) binding protein-like 1 (*Tial1*)	Both	PGCs lost by E13.5	Infertility	[118]
Zinc finger protein X-linked (*Zfx*)	Both	Reduced germ cell numbers in both sexes	Subfertility (F)	[119]

APOPTOTIC PROGRAMS IN GERM CELLS AND SOMATIC CELLS

Whereas germ cell populations in the adult male are continually undergoing mitosis, females have finite numbers of oocytes established during embryogenesis. After PGCs complete mitosis, apoptosis then becomes key in controlling the size of the female germ cell reserve. Large quantities of germ cells are normally lost in the perinatal period, and oocyte apoptosis also occurs in adults, both

Table 23.2 Gonadal and Reproductive Tract Development

Mutant Gene	Sex Affected	Reproductive Phenotype	Fertility Status	References
Anti-Müllerian hormone (*Amh*, MIS)	Both	Uteri development in males causes obstruction and secondary infertility; females exhibit early depletion of primordial follicles	Secondary infertility	[120, 121]
Cytochrome P450, 11a, cholesterol side chain cleavage (*Cyp11a*)	Both	Males feminized with female external genitalia, underdeveloped sex organs; gonads degenerate	Lethal	[122]
Empty spiracles homolog 2 (*Emx2*)	Both	Defective development of gonads and urogenital tracts	Lethal	[23]
LIM homeobox gene (*Lhx9*)	Both	Gonadal agenesis in both sexes	Infertility	[24]
Nuclear receptor subfamily 5, group A, member 1 (*Nr5a1*); steroidogenic factor-1 (SF-1)	Both	Gonadal agenesis in both sexes	Lethal	[25]
Steroid acute regulatory protein (*StAR*)	Both	Males have female external genitalia; both sexes die of adrenocortical insufficiency	Lethal	[123]
Wilms tumor homolog (*Wt1*)	Both	Gonadal agenesis	Lethal	[26]
Wingless-related MMTV integration site 4 (*Wnt4*)	Female	Ovaries are depleted of oocytes; Müllerian ducts do not form	Infertility	[124]
Wnt7a	Both	Females show abnormal development of oviducts and uterus; males do not have Müllerian duct regression	Infertility	[125]

Table 23.3 Cell Survival

Mutant Gene	Sex Affected	Reproductive Phenotype	Fertility Status	References
Bcl-2-associated X protein (*Bax*)	Both	Premeiotic arrest of spermatogenesis; increased oocytes and primordial follicles postnatally	Infertility (M)	[31, 126]
Bcl-2	Female	Fewer oocytes/primordial follicles in the postnatal ovary	Subfertility	[35]
Bcl-x (*Bcl-2l*) hypomorph	Both	Primordial germ cells (PGCs) are lost by E15.5	Infertility	[33]
Bclw (Bcl-2l2, *Bcl-2-like 2*)	Both	Late meiotic arrest with loss of germ cells (M) and reduced PGC survival (F)	Infertility (M); subfertility (F)	[127]
Caspase-2 (*Casp-2*)	Female	Decreased apoptosis of female germ cells	Increase fertility	[38]
Caspase-3 (*Casp-3*)	Female	Defects in regression of corpora lutea in unfertilized mice	Not reported	[38]

physiologically and in response to environmental insults. Mouse models have indicated that a functional antagonism between proapoptotic BAX and antiapoptotic factors (BCL-X and BCL-2) regulates programmed cell death in oocytes [29, 30]. Knockout models exhibiting disruptions in this balance or in other aspects of ovarian apoptotic pathways are considered here and listed in Table 23.3.

Bax knockout females demonstrate limited oocyte apoptosis with age, as indicated by a reduction in the postnatal loss of primordial and primary follicles, a threefold increase in the number of primordial follicles at sexual maturity, and an extended life span of ovarian function [31]. Intriguingly, the *Bax* knockout ovarian phenotype is somewhat similar to that of the aryl hydrocarbon receptor (AhR) (*Ahr*) null mice, which exhibit an increased number of primordial follicles within the first few days of postnatal life. These findings substantiate studies linking exposure to environmental polycyclic aromatic hydrocarbons, which bind to AhR, with transcription of *Bax* mRNA and BAX-mediated oocyte apoptosis. This model was also confirmed by the discovery that neither *Ahr–/–* or *Bax–/–* mice exhibit primordial follicle apoptosis after treatment with 9,10-dimethylbenz[*a*]anthracene (DMBA), a potent polycyclic aromatic hydrocarbon, or its metabolite [29, 32]. Thus these models provide us with an indication of the importance of BAX-mediated pathways in both physiological and pathological oocyte atresia.

In contrast, *Bcl-x* hypomorphic mice have been engineered by insertional targeting into the endogenous *Bcl-x* promoter, and this results in depletion of PGCs by E15.5 [33]. Although late embryonic and perinatal oocyte loss is not measurably inhibited in *Bax* knockout mice, BAX is expressed in embryonic PGCs and is involved in loss of PGCs in bcl-x hypomorphic mouse embryos. As evidence for this, the *Bcl-x* hypomorphic PGC loss is corrected in *Bax–/–*, *Bcl-x* double mutants [33]. Interestingly, although BCL-X is also expressed in oocytes and granulosa cells of developing follicles, as well as luteal cells, its deletion in these cell types does not abrogate follicle development or fertility [34]. Like BCL-X, BCL-2 also counters early oocyte apoptotic pathways; *Bcl-2* knockout mice establish fewer primordial follicles, and many of these follicles are devoid of oocytes owing to germ cell degeneration [35]. Conversely, overexpression of *Bcl-2* in oocytes provides a survival signal in two different transgenic mouse models. *Bcl-2* expression driven by the *Kit* promoter increases the numbers of primordial follicles established at birth [36]. *Bcl-2* expression under the *Zp3* promoter increases the nonatretic maturing follicle pool, decreases follicular atresia and spontaneous oocyte loss, and suppresses oocyte apoptosis induced by doxorubicin [37].

Apoptotic pathways converge to initiate cascades of caspase enzyme activity, which in turn cleave specific substrates to execute the morphological changes associated with programmed cell death, including DNA condensation and fragmentation, cell shrinkage, and plasma membrane blebbing. Mouse models lacking caspase-2 (*Casp-2*) or caspase-3 (*Casp-3*) genes indicate important roles for these enzymes in mediating apoptosis in the mammalian ovary. *Casp-2* knockout mice demonstrate decreased germ cell death during development, increased numbers of primordial follicles in the postnatal ovary, and resistance to doxorubicin-induced oocyte apoptosis [38]. *Casp-3–/–* mice emphasize the importance of appropriate programmed cell death in somatic ovarian cells. Corpora lutea cultured ex vivo from unfertilized *Casp-3* knockout females are resistant to apoptosis, and in vivo regressions of corpora lutea in *Casp-3–/–* mice are delayed [39]. Thus knockout mouse models have confirmed important roles for several apoptosis regulatory proteins in diverse aspects of ovarian function.

FOLLICULOGENESIS AND OOCYTE-GRANULOSA CELL COMMUNICATIONS

In the perinatal ovary, oocytes become intimately associated with a single layer of surrounding somatic cells to form quiescent primordial follicles. Intercellular communications ensuing between the oocyte and its companion granulosa cells are then crucial in directing stages of follicle development and are ultimately determinants of oocyte developmental potential. Individual follicles are recruited from the pool of primordial follicles in a measured fashion over the reproductive life span of the female. Recruitment initiates a period of oocyte and granulosa cell growth, and development beyond the primary follicle stage involves a proliferation of the granulosa cell population. Stages of follicle development are illustrated in Figure 23.2; mouse models exhibiting defects in folliculogenesis are listed in Tables 23.4 and 23.5. In this section, we focus on knockout mouse models that have brought to light the interrelatedness of germ cell and somatic cell follicle compartments and the active roles of oocyte-derived factors in directing granulosa cell phenotypes [1, 40].

Oocyte-derived factors direct initial follicle formation in the newborn ovary, and knockout mice lacking factor in the germline α FIGα, an oocyte-specific helix-loop-helix transcription factor, fail to develop primordial follicles [41]. Primordial follicles are continuously allocated to the pool of growing follicles, and this transition represents a commitment to later stages of folliculogenesis. Although no models have been developed with defects in primordial follicle recruitment, several gene products have proved necessary in mice for the progression of follicles beyond the primary follicle stage. For example, *Gdf-9* knockout mice, which lack expression of an oocyte-secreted TGF-β family growth factor, have a defect in follicle development precluding the proliferation of granulosa cells and the formation of secondary follicles (Figure 23.3*A*) [42, 43].

The *Gdf-9* knockout phenotype provided a dramatic in vivo demonstration of the fact that oocytes direct somatic cell function within the ovary, and this proof-of-principle renewed interest in defining the functions of GDF-9 and related oocyte factors throughout folliculogenesis. Studies with recombinant GDF-9 revealed that it induces hyaluronan synthase 2 (*Has2*) and suppresses the expression of the urokinase plasminogen activator (uPA) protease in granulosa cells maintained in vitro, effects that promote mucification of the cumulus granulosa cell mass [44]. Similarly,

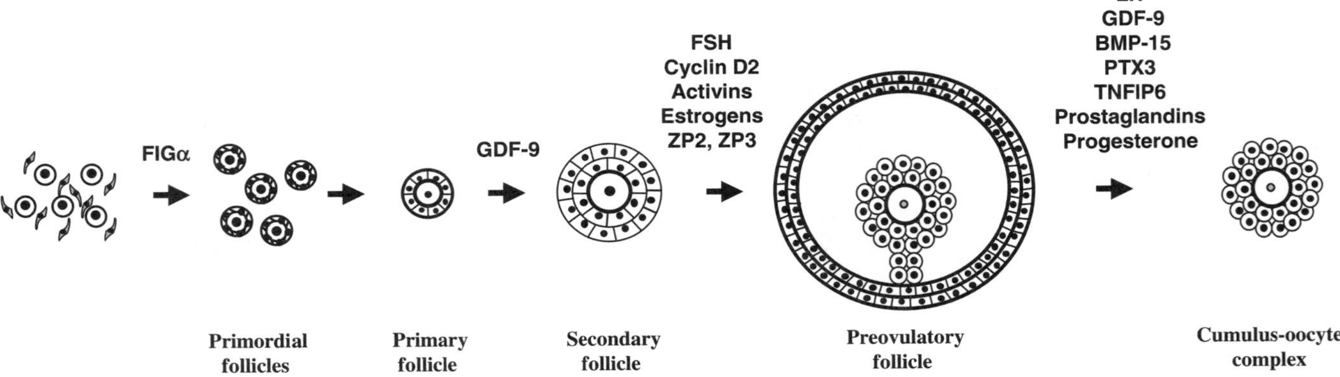

FIGURE 23.2 The progression of folliculogenesis. Communication between oocytes and their associated somatic cells is established with primordial follicle formation in the embryonic ovary. Follicles are recruited from the resting pool of primordial follicles to develop into primary follicles by unknown factors, and this indicates a commitment to further follicle development. Granulosa cells divide during the ensuing stages of folliculogenesis, and factors derived from the oocyte (such as GDF-9) as well as other endocrine/paracrine factors (follicle-stimulating hormone [FSH], activins, and estrogens) are necessary to direct this proliferation. Around the time of the luteinizing hormone (LH) surge and cumulus-oocyte complex (COC) release into the oviduct, oocytes resume meiosis I beginning with the dissolution of the nuclear membrane. Several factors influencing the differentiation of the cumulus granulosa cells and ovulation are listed.

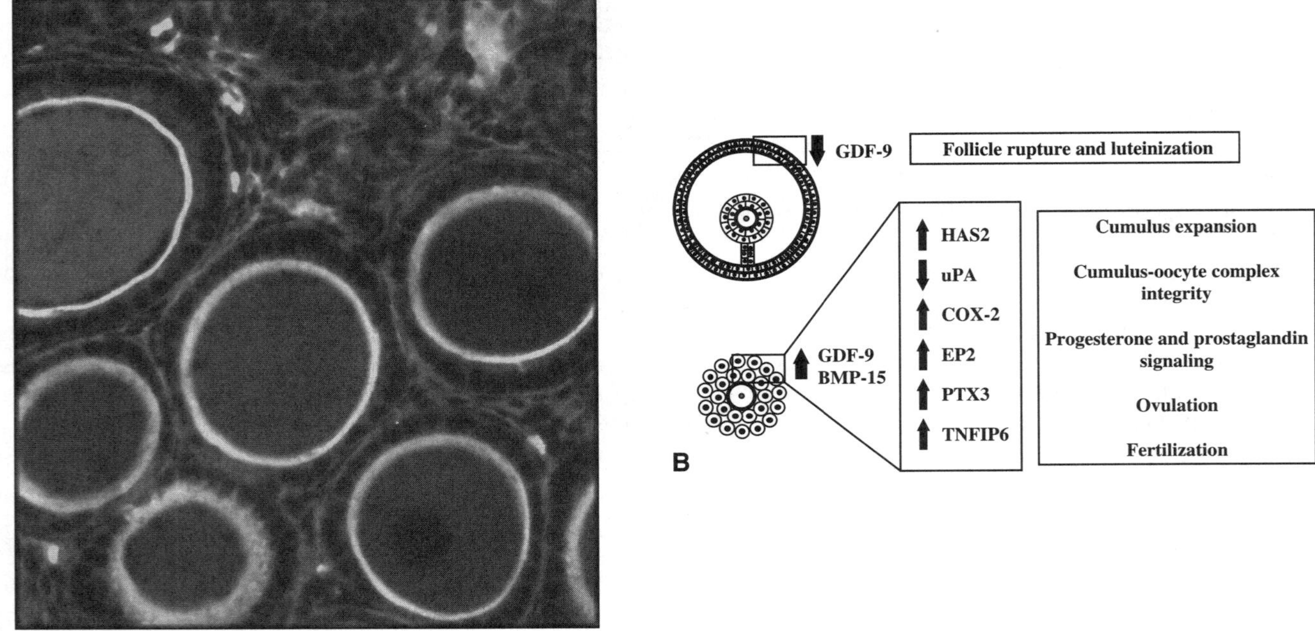

FIGURE 23.3 Effects of GDF-9. **A,** In *Gdf-9* knockout mice, there is a block in follicle development at the primary follicle stage. A deconvolution micrograph shows a cluster of these arrested follicles in which each oocyte is surrounded by its zona pellucida and a single layer of cuboidal granulosa cells. The phenotype provides a dramatic example of the need for oocyte signaling to granulosa cells during follicle development. **B,** This schematic illustrates paracrine roles of GDF-9 and BMP-15 in preovulatory follicles. The mural granulosa cells (above) are exposed to low levels of these oocyte factors, whereas the differentiation of the cumulus cell complex (below) depends heavily on them. A list of gene products upregulated or downregulated in these cells is given.

Table 23.4 Ovarian Folliculogenesis

Mutant Gene	Sex Affected	Female Reproductive Phenotype	Fertility Status	References
Activin receptor-type IIA (*Acvr2*)	Both	Antral follicle block in females because of reduced FSH levels	Infertility (F); subfertility (M)	[74]
A disintegrin-like and metalloprotease with thrombospondin type 1 motif, 1 (*Adamts1*)	Female	Defects in preovulatory follicle development; cystic formations in uteri	Subfertility	[128]
Bone morphogenetic protein (BMP) receptor, type 1B (*Bmpr1b*)	Female	Defects in estrous cyclicity, cumulus expansion, and endometrial gland development	Subfertility	[129]
Cyclic adenosine monophosphate (cAMP)-specific phosphodiesterase type 4 (*Pde4d*)	Female	Diminished sensitivity of granulosa cells to gonadotropins	Subfertility	[130]
Connexin-37 (*Gja4*; Cx-37)	Female	Defects in late folliculogenesis and oocyte meiosis	Infertility	[131]
Cyclin D2 (*Ccnd2*)	Both	Failure of granulosa cell proliferation	Infertility	[90]
Cyclin dependent kinase 4 (*Cdk4*)	Female	Defects in the hypothalamic-pituitary-gonadal axis	Infertility	[132]
Cytochrome P450, 19, aromatase (*Cyp19*)	Both	Folliculogenesis block and ovulation defects	Infertility (F); progressive infertility (M)	[86, 133, 134]
Estrogen receptor α (ERα) (*Esr1*)	Both	Hemorrhagic ovarian cysts and uterine defects, decreased lordosis response	Infertility	[78, 135–137]
Estrogen receptor β (ERβ) (*Esr2*)	Both	Inefficient follicle development	Subfertility	[82]
Fanconi anemia complementation group A (*Fanca*)	Both	Hypogonadism, reduced fertility, more dramatic and progressive in females	Subfertility	[138]
Fanconi anemia complementation group C (*Fancc*)	Both	Hypogonadism, compromised gametogenesis	Subfertility	[139, 140]
Fanconi anemia complementation group G (*Fancg*)	Both	Hypogonadism, compromised gametogenesis	Subfertility	[141]
Figla or FIGα (Factor in the germline α)	Female	No primordial follicles develop at birth and oocytes die	Infertility	[41]
FSH hormone β-subunit (*Fshb*)	Both	Female preantral block in folliculogenesis	Infertility (F)	[59]
FSH receptor (*Fshr*)	Both	Female preantral block in folliculogenesis	Infertility (F)	[60]
γ-Glutamyl transpeptidase (*Ggtp*)	Both	Hypogonadal and infertile; phenotype corrected by feeding mice N-acetylcysteine	Infertility	[142, 143]
Glycoprotein hormone α-subunit (*Cga*)	Both	Hypogonadal caused by FSH and LH deficiency	Infertility	[56]
Growth differentiation factor-9 (*Gdf-9*)	Female	Folliculogenesis arrest at the one-layer follicle stage	Infertility	[42, 43]
Growth hormone receptor (*Ghr*)	Female	Delayed puberty and prolonged pregnancy		[144]
Insulin-like growth factor 1 (*Igf-1*)	Both	Hypogonadal and infertile; impaired antral follicle formation	Infertility	[145]

Table 23.4 (*Continued*)

Mutant Gene	Sex Affected	Female Reproductive Phenotype	Fertility Status	References
Insulin-like hormone 3 (*Insl3*)	Both	Irregular estrous cycles	Subfertility	[146]
Insulin receptor substrate 2 (*Irs2*)	Female	Small, anovulatory ovaries with reduced numbers of follicles	Infertility	[147]
Leptin (*Lep*; *ob/ob*) mutant	Both	Obese with hypogonadotropic hypogonadism	Infertility	[148, 149]
Leptin receptor (*Lepr*; *db/db*) mutant	Both	Obese with hypogonadotropic hypogonadism	Infertility	[150]
Luteinizing hormone receptor (*Lhcgr*)	Both	Underdeveloped sex organs and infertility; preantral folliculogenesis block	Infertility	[63, 64]
Neuronal insulin receptor (NIR)	Both	Hypothalamic hypogonadism; impaired follicle maturation	Infertility	[151]
Orthodenticle homolog 1 (*Otx1*)	Both	Prepubescent dwarfism and hypogonadism; progressive recovery of follicular development and fertility	Delayed fertility	[152]
p57[Kip2] (*Cdkn1c*)	Both	Surviving mice show sexual immaturity	Mostly lethal	[153]
PAC_1; adenylate cyclase activating polypeptide 1 receptor 1 (*Adcyap1r1*)	Female	Prolonged and irregular diestrus phase	Subfertility	[154]
Pituitary specific transcription factor 1 (*Pit1*)	Both	*Snell* dwarf mice have multiple anterior pituitary hormone deficiencies and hypogonadism	Infertility	[155]
Prolactin (*Prl*)	Female	Irregular estrous cycles	Infertility	[156]
Paired like homeodomain factor 1; prophet of *Pit1* (*Prop1*)	Both	*Ames* dwarf mice have multiple anterior pituitary hormone deficiencies and hypogonadism	Infertility	[157]
SH2-B	Both	Females have small, anovulatory ovaries with reduced numbers of developing follicles	Subfertility (M); infertility (F)	[158]
Superoxide dismutase 1 (*Sod1*)	Female	Folliculogenesis defect; failure to maintain pregnancy	Subfertility	[159, 160]
TAF4B RNA polymerase II, TATA box binding protein-associated factor; TAFII105 (*Taf4b*)	Female	Defects in follicular development, oocyte maturation/fertilization	Infertility	[161]
Thyroid stimulating hormone β (*Tshb; hyt/hyt*) mutant	Female	Hypothyroid; females show continuous diestrus and poor response to gonadotropin-induced superovulation	Infertility	[162]
Tumor necrosis factor type 1 receptor (*Tnfrsf1a*)	Female	Enhanced prepubertal response to gonadotropins; early ovarian senescence	Subfertility	[163]
Ubiquitin protein ligase E3A (*Ube3a*; E6-AP ubiquitin protein ligase)	Both	Ovarian hypoplasia, defects in ovulation and uterine development	Subfertility	[164]
Vitamin D receptor (*Vdr*) knockout	Both	Defects in estrogen biosynthesis; elevated serum gonadotropins	Infertility	[165, 166]

GDF-9 induces prostaglandin-endoperoxide synthase 2 (Cox2; *Ptgs2*) and the EP2 prostaglandin E2 receptor (EP2; *Ptgerep2*), upregulating prostaglandin and progesterone signaling pathways important for oocyte release on ovulation [45]. Gene expression profiling of granulosa cells treated with recombinant GDF-9 identified pentraxin 3 (*Ptx3*) and TNF-induced protein 6 (*Tnfip6*) mRNAs as being upregulated [46]. Verifying roles of GDF-9-mediated pathways in the periovulatory period, *Ptx3* knockout females are subfertile, and *Tnfip6* females are infertile because of defects in the formation and integrity of the COC [46, 47]. Knockout mice lacking a second oocyte-secreted TGF-β family protein, BMP-15, exhibit female subfertility [48]. Moreover, studies in *BMP-15–/–, GDF-9+/–* mice demonstrate that BMP-15 functions in a cooperative manner with GDF-9 to optimize ovulation, the resilience of the COC, and fertilization [48]. Thus, in addition to the essential roles of GDF-9 early in follicle development, GDF-9 and BMP-15 signaling are important in directing the final stages of folliculogenesis and contribute to the efficiency of fertilization (Figure 23.3, *B*).

In addition to paracrine factors, growing oocytes produce and secrete components of their circumscribing zona pellucida matrix, forming a physical interface with the surrounding granulosa cells. Knockout mice lacking oocyte-derived zona pellucida protein-3 (ZP3) or ZP2 demonstrate defects in early antral and preovulatory follicle development, COC formation, and ovulation [49, 50], evidence that oocytes influence somatic cell functions at these stages. Blastocysts derived from in vitro maturation and fertilization of eggs from *Zp2* or *Zp3* knockout females are not capable of completing development after transfer to wild-type pseudopregnant recipients, suggesting that zona matrix proteins are important in mediating granulosa cell signals and connections to oocytes that optimize their later developmental potential [50].

GONADOTROPIN HORMONES AND MOUSE MODELS OF HUMAN DISEASE

Intercellular communication within the ovary is critical for all stages of folliculogenesis, but it is not sufficient to promote development beyond the preantral stage when follicles become dependent on the pituitary gonadotropins, FSH and LH. Together, FSH and LH orchestrate antral follicle development, ovarian steroidogenesis, ovulation, and luteinization [51]. In this section, we will consider knockout mice with endocrine phenotypes that impact gonadotropin pathways and compromise ovarian function (for review, see [52]). We will also emphasize the relevance of these research findings to cases of ovarian failure in women.

Production of FSH and LH is regulated by gonadotropin releasing hormone (Gn-RH), which is secreted by the hypothalamus and signals through a G protein-coupled receptor expressed in the anterior pituitary. Gn-RH production and its signaling pathway are essential to maintaining serum gonadotropins and, ultimately, fertility in mammals. In mice, a naturally occurring 33.5 kb deletion truncating the *Gn-RH* gene results in a model of hereditary hypogonadism (*hpg*), which phenocopies clinical cases of hypogonadotropic hypogonadism (HHG) [53]. In humans, causative mutations result in loss-of-function of genes mediating the migration of Gn-RH-releasing cells during neural development (as seen in the *KAL* gene causing Kallman's syndrome) or aspects of Gn-RH processing (as seen in mutations in the *PC1* protein processing enzyme) [54, 55].

FSH and LH are heterodimeric glycoproteins each composed of an α-subunit that is shared between these and other anterior pituitary hormones and a unique β-subunit. Knockout mice have been generated lacking a functional common α-subunit locus; besides reproductive defects, the knockout mouse is hypothyroid and displays proportional dwarfism owing to loss of thyroid-stimulating hormone (TSH) function [56]. No mutations altering the amino acid sequence of the common α-subunit have been described in humans. It has been hypothesized that a deleterious mutation in the human α subunit gene (*GLYCA*) would result in embryonic lethality, because in humans (and not in mice), the α-subunit is also shared with chorionic gonadotropin (hCG) [57]. Placental-derived hCG maintains ovarian luteal cells and is thereby required for pregnancy during the first trimester.

Isolated loss of FSH signaling causes infertility in women, and this condition can be modeled by disrupting either the FSHβ (*Fshb*) or FSH receptor (*Fshr*) loci in mice. Women who are homozygous or compound heterozygous for inactivating ligand (frameshift/truncation and missense) or receptor (missense) mutations exhibit normal preantral follicle development but no antral-stage follicles capable of ovulation form [58]. These patients typically experience primary amenorrhea and sexual infantilism. Both *Fshb* and *Fshr* knockouts in mice phenocopy the human mutations, resulting in female infertility, uterine hypoplasia, and folliculogenesis blocks before antrum formation [59–61]. Interestingly, both ligand and receptor knockout mouse models also exhibit progressive elevation of serum LH with age. It is believed that LH and LH-induced androgen synthesis in the *Fshr* model contribute to the development of ovarian sex-cord stromal tumors, which are seen in 92% of these mice by 12 months of age [62].

Loss of isolated LH function can arise from LH receptor defects in women and in mouse models. Several luteinizing hormone receptor (LHR) mutations have been discovered in patients to be associated with barriers to preovulatory follicle development, ovulation, and luteinization [57]. These conditions are modeled by targeted deletion of the *Lhr* locus in mice; *Lhr* null females demonstrate normal prenatal sexual development but are infertile [63, 64]. These mice have underdeveloped ovaries and uteri, and their ovaries do not contain preovulatory stage follicles or corpora lutea. Thus, the *Lhr*, *Fshb*, and *Fshr* knockouts in female mice very closely model pathologies of women with gonadotropin deficiencies or resistances.

MODELS OF INHIBIN AND ACTIVIN FUNCTION AND VARIATIONS ON KNOCKOUT TECHNOLOGY

We have already briefly described the critical roles of some TGF-β superfamily members in regulating PGC development and oocyte-granulosa cell communication loops. Inhibins (α:βA and α:βB heterodimers) and activins (βA:βA and βB:βB homodimers and βA:βB heterodimers) are additional members of this family important in ovarian function. Inhibins and activins were originally discovered as gonadal factors named for their respective abilities to suppress and enhance pituitary FSH production [65]. In this section, we review the phenotypes of several genetic models that provide insight into the roles of inhibins and activins. In addition to knockout experiments, which demonstrate necessary gene functions, we present two innovative mouse models designed to conduct studies of sufficiency based on bitransgenic and "knockin" strategies.

Knockout mice lacking the inhibin α-subunit (*Inha–/–*), and therefore depleted of the biological effects of inhibins, develop steroidogenic sex-cord stromal tumors with mixed granulosa cell and Sertoli cell-like features in both sexes [66]. Because of the early development and 100% penetrance of these tumors, as well as a concomitant cachexia-like wasting syndrome [67], they have provided an excellent model for identifying genetic modifiers of this pathological granulosa/Sertoli cell proliferation. Double mutant studies have indicated roles for extracellular factors (e.g., the gonadotropins) [68, 69], as well as an intracellular cell cycle regulator ($p27^{Kip1}$) [70] in the process of tumorigenesis. Effects of the inhibin α knockout have demonstrated not only the essential tumor suppressor functions of inhibins but also indicate potential roles for inhibin signaling in conducting ovarian follicle development. Superovulation experiments in young knockout females show that there are defects in late stages of follicle development, and ovarian transplant experiments demonstrate important roles for local inhibins in maintaining the granulosa cell phenotype [71].

In an attempt to engineer an inducible rescue of tumor formation in inhibin α knockout mice, a bitransgenic system was used [71a]. The first transgene used is expressed in the mouse liver and encodes a transcription factor protein product that is activated by mifepristone administration. The second transgene contains a responder operon, which directs transcription of a bicistronic mRNA encoding the inhibin α and βA subunits only in the presence of the active transcription factor. Thus, by giving mifepristone, ectopic inhibin A (α:βA) dimer expression was induced. The system was tested in bitransgenic mice wild-type at the inhibin α locus, and in females this inhibin A expression suppressed FSH levels and led to a block in follicle development at the early antral stage. Surprisingly, though induction of the transgenic system averts tumor formation in inhibin α knockout males, female bitransgenic knockouts still succumb to granulosa cell tumor development. Whether this failure reflects the importance of constitutive inhibin exposure, a nonredundant tumor suppressor function of inhibin B (α:βB) when βB is available for activin formation, or a requirement for locally produced inhibins within the ovary remains unsolved.

Knockout mice lacking a functional activin/inhibin βA locus (*Inhba–/–*) die neonatally because of craniofacial defects that prevent suckling, and until more recently, this had largely precluded in vivo studies pertaining to the role of this activin/inhibin subunit in reproduction. The null phenotype, however, can be partially rescued by replacing the activin/inhibin βA coding sequence with that of the activin/inhibin βB gene, conferring the activin/inhibin βA expression pattern on this related sequence (63% amino acid identity). Knockin mice demonstrate hypogonadism and diminished female fertility, indicating unique functions of the activin/inhibin βA protein product in reproduction [72]. Knockout mice lacking the activin/inhibin βB subunit (*Inhbb–/–*) have compromised female fertility with prolonged gestation times and lactation failure likely caused by defects in oxytocin regulation [73]. Future models, including those that allow tissue-specific gene excision by Cre/*loxP* recombination, can be expected to better delineate the intraovarian functions of the activin/inhibin β-subunits.

Signaling pathways that mediate activin and inhibin effects are complex, and no receptor or downstream signaling protein mutations have been described that phenocopy the mutant models lacking functional ligands. Activin receptor type II (*Acvr2*), however, has been shown to relay activin-mediated induction of FSH, and knockout mice lacking Acvr2 have suppressed FSH levels in the pituitary and serum. *Acvr2* null mice also exhibit gonadal pathologies at least in part because of the lack of FSH. In females, this phenotype includes infertility, follicular atresia, and reduced numbers of corpora lutea [74]. Bioactivities of activin dimers are modulated by their association with a binding protein, follistatin; the interaction is believed to antagonize activin functions in the pituitary [71, 75]. Follistatin knockout mice have numerous embryonic defects and die in the perinatal period [76], but the role of follistatin in controlling FSH levels can be appreciated in part from studies of transgenics overexpressing follistatin under the control of the metallothionein promoter. Lines of mice with widespread expression of the transgene exhibit suppression of serum FSH and defects in gonadal growth and gametogenesis that may be partially ascribed to FSH deficiency and/or local antagonism of gonadal TGFβ superfamily members [77].

KNOCKOUT MOUSE MODELS WITH DEFECTS IN ESTROGEN SYNTHESIS AND SIGNALING

Gonadotropins promote ovarian steroid hormone production by inducing the expression of steroidogenic enzymes, such as aromatase, which produces estrogens from androgen precursors. Knockout mice have been generated lacking the estrogen receptors (ERα and ERβ) and aromatase, and together these models give us a better appreciation for the roles of estrogens in ovarian function and reproductive endocrinology in vivo.

ERα (*Esr1*) knockout females are infertile and develop multilayered, but anovulatory, ovarian follicles [78, 79]. In these mice, *Fshr* and *Lhr* mRNAs are upregulated in the ovary [79], and there is overexpression of gonadotropin subunit mRNAs in the pituitary [80]. Actions of gonadotropin hormones appear to contribute to precocious follicle development in the ERα–/– mice, as well as an onset of hemorrhagic, polycystic ovaries [79, 81]. Dissecting aspects of this phenotype that are caused by the loss of intraovarian ERα verses aberrant gonadotropin regulation remains an area of investigation. In contrast, a targeted null mutation of ERβ (*Esr2*) does not preclude follicle development or fertility in homozygote females, although there is evidence of early-stage follicle atresia, decreased numbers of corpora lutea in ERβ–/– ovaries, and a decreased ovarian response to hCG (an LH agonist used to induce ovulation) [82]. Double knockout females lacking ERα and ERβ exhibit an ovarian phenotype in which granulosa cells take on a Sertoli cell-like morphology [83, 84] and express a number of Sertoli cell markers, namely Müllerian inhibiting substance, sulfated glycoprotein-2, and *Sox9* [83]. These findings indicate that combined estrogen receptor signaling pathways are critical for specifying the granulosa cell phenotype.

Estrogen production is abrogated in the P450 aromatase knockout mouse model, the ovarian phenotype of which resembles that of ERα–/– and ERα–/–, ERβ–/– double knockout mice and is more pronounced when mice are maintained on a phytoestrogen-free diet. Aromatase knockouts have high serum levels of LH and FSH, are infertile owing to a block in follicular development and ovulation defects, and develop hemorrhagic ovarian cysts by 21 to 23 weeks of age [85, 86]. These mice also exhibit an aberrant differentiation of ovarian somatic cells to Sertoli cell-like and Leydig cell-like cells [87]. Interestingly, administration of estrogens can reverse this phenomenon, even after the loss of oocytes, providing the first evidence that in the presence of estrogens, oocytes are not required for maintaining granulosa cell-like somatic cells as opposed to Sertoli cell-like ones.

INTRACELLULAR REGULATORS OF CELL DIVISION WITHIN THE OVARY

Thus far, we have considered a number of paracrine and endocrine-acting factors that provide mitogenic stimuli or differentiation signals to granulosa cells during follicle development. How these extracellular signals interface with intracellular signaling cascades within granulosa cells is an active area of research, which has been furthered by ovarian phenotypes in knockout models lacking cell cycle regulators.

Granulosa cell proliferation in response to FSH is one of the most rapid expansions of a cell population in the adult, and this contrasts strikingly with the abrupt and terminal differentiation of these cells after ovulation in response to LH. Female infertility in knockout models lacking cyclin D2 and the CDK inhibitor protein p27 demonstrate essential roles for these cell cycle regulators during ovarian folliculogenesis and luteinization, respectively (for review, see [88]). Both are key mediators of the G1 to S phase transition. Cyclins complex with cyclin-dependent kinases (CDKs), and the activity of cyclin-CDKs is important in promoting S phase commitment and DNA synthesis. Cyclin-CDKs are countered by CDK inhibitors, such as p27, which limit cell division by down-regulating or restricting CDK-mediated phosphorylation (for review, see [89]).

Cyclin D2 knockout females have a defect in granulosa cell proliferation that results in a block in follicle development before antral follicle formation [90]. Cyclin D2 seems to be a downstream target of FSH signaling; the cyclin D2 and FSHβ or FSHR knockout phenotypes are similar, and cyclin D2 mRNA is upregulated in vitro in response to FSH [90]. It should be noted, however, that even in the absence of FSH, high levels of cyclin D2 mRNA are expressed in granulosa cells [91]. In contrast to the cyclin D2 phenotype, infertility in p27 knockout females is associated with defects in granulosa cell cycle withdrawal and differentiation at luteinization. The enlarged ovaries in these mice are filled with multilayered follicles that progress to form defective corpora lutea with continued cell division [92–94]. Surprisingly, defective luteinization is also a hallmark of knockout mice lacking CDK4. Although these mice exhibit a modest reduction in the numbers of follicles developing to the preovulatory stage in response to gonadotropin administration, CDK4 is clearly not a prerequisite for granulosa cell proliferation [95]. Conceptually, why a failure of cellular differentiation, rather than proliferation, is observed in the absence of a CDK is obscure, and these data argue against CDK4 as the principle kinase acting with cyclin D2 to mediate granulosa cell mitosis. Thus, although cyclin D2, p27, and CDK4 are widely expressed, functional redundancy in most tissues limits the deleterious effects of their loss. In each case, intraovarian expression of the cell cycle regulator is being studied as each functions cell autonomously, though the potential for primary defects in the central endocrine axis remains because of their widespread presence.

MEIOSIS, FERTILIZATION, AND MATERNAL EFFECT GENES

Apart from ovarian endocrine functions that allow for implantation and pregnancy, postovulatory development depends on a number of oocyte factors. Many mRNAs and proteins expressed in the developing oocyte (while within the ovary) serve vital functions in the completion of meiosis, fertilization, and early embryonic development. Thus events contingent on these gene products may be considered extensions of ovarian function, and a number of recent mouse models attest to their importance (Figure 23.4 and Table 23.6).

In the periovulatory period, mammalian oocytes progress through meiosis I and arrest at the metaphase of meiosis II until fertilization, at which time meiosis II is completed and the second polar body is extruded. B-type cyclin proteins have been implicated in directing the commitment to metaphase I and metaphase II as regulatory components of the maturation-promoting factor (MPF) complex. B-type cyclin levels increase before each meiotic metaphase, and their ubiquitin-mediated degradation coincides with the metaphase-anaphase transition. Cyclin B1 is expressed in oocytes in this pattern, and injection of cyclin B1 antisense mRNA causes defects during the completion of meiosis I and in the onset metaphase II [96]. Embryonic lethality in cyclin B1 knockout mice has so far precluded in vivo studies of this protein's function in oocytes [97], though other knockout models have given some insight into the regulation of MPF. Targeted mutation of *Cdc25b*, which encodes an MPF activator, results in female sterility caused by a failure of oocytes to exit prophase I and resume meiosis [98]. In addition to transient MPF activity to establish metaphase, sustained MPF function appears critical to maintenance of the metaphase II block. This is compromised in *Mos* knockout mice lacking the oocyte-expressed MOS kinase, which is a component of the cytostatic factor complex implicated in MPF stabilization. Female *Mos* knockouts are subfertile, and their oocytes are predisposed to parthenogenetic activation with visible abnormalities in chromatin organization after the completion of meiosis I [99]. In addition to direct MPF regulators, two mismatch repair proteins, MLH1 and MLH3, are critical to these stages of meiosis. *Mlh1* or *Mlh3* knockout females are completely sterile. In each case, folliculogenesis is intact, and oocytes ovulate normally, but postfertilization development is blocked, and extrusion to the polar bodies is hampered [100, 101]. More recently, female mice deficient in the synaptonemal complex protein (SYCP3) were found to be subfertile because of loss of early aneuploid embryos, demonstrating an important role of this

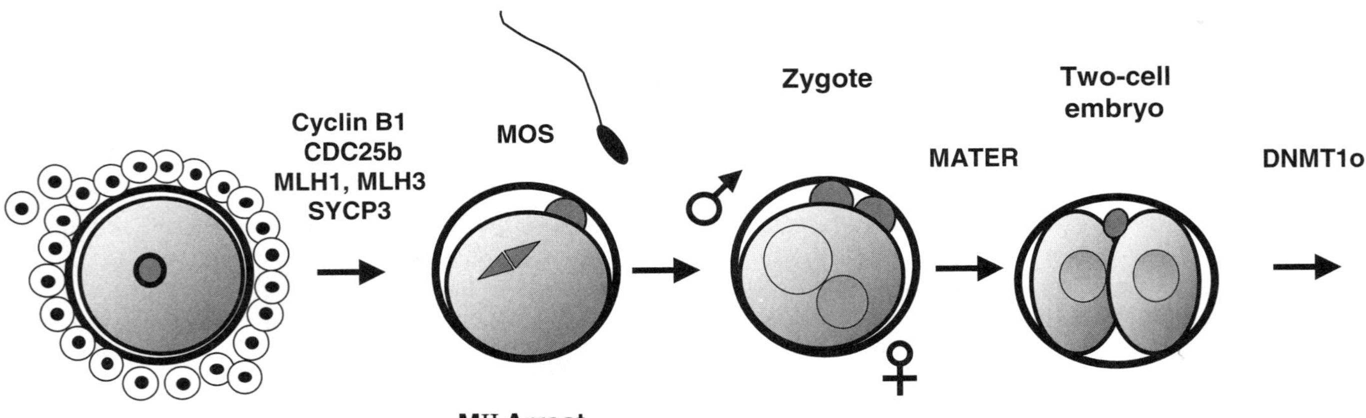

FIGURE 23.4 Postovulatory, preimplantation development. Ovulated oocytes are released from the prophase I meiosis block and progress to arrest at metaphase II. After fertilization, meiosis II is completed and male and female pronuclei undergo chromatin restructuring. Appropriate oocyte development during ovarian folliculogenesis is essential for its competence to resume meiosis, participate in fertilization, and contribute crucial factors to early embryonic development. Several oocyte factors are presented that function during specific stages in this progression, including factors involved in controlling maturation (or M-phase)-promoting factor (MPF) activity (cyclin B1, CDC25b, MOS), and mediating maternal genomic reorganization (MLH1, MLH3, SYCP3), as well as maternal effect gene products important in regulating zygote gene expression (MATER and DNMT1o).

Table 23.5 Meiosis, Ovulation, and Luteinization

Mutant Gene	Sex Affected	Reproductive Phenotype	Fertility Status	References
Alpha 1 microglobulin/ bikunin (*Ambp*; urinary trypsin inhibitor)	Female	Defects in ovulation and cumulus-oocytes complex (COC) integrity	Subfertility	[167]
Bone morphogenetic protein-15 (*Bmp-15*)	Female	Defects in COC formation and ovulation	Subfertility	[48]
Cell division cycle 25 homolog B (*Cdc25b*) (Cdc25b phosphatase)	Female	Oocytes are arrested in meiotic prophase, with defects in maturation promoting factor activity	Infertility	[98]
CCAAT/enhancer-binding protein β (*C/EPBβ*)	Female	Reduced ovulation and block in corpus luteum (CL) differentiation	Infertility	[168]
Connexin-37 (*Gja4*; Cx-37)	Female	Defects in late folliculogenesis and oocyte meiosis	Infertility	[131]
Cyclooxygenase 2 (*Ptgs2*)	Female	Defects in ovulation and implantation	Most infertile	[169, 170]
Cytochrome P450, 19, aromatase (*Cyp19*)	Both	Early spermatogonial arrest, Leydig cell hyperplasia, and defects in sexual behavior (M); folliculogenesis block and ovulation defects (F)	Progressive infertility (M); infertility (F)	[86, 133, 134]
P450 25-hydroxyvitamin D-1ᾶhydroxylase (*Cyp40*)	Female	Uterine hypoplasia and absence of CL	Infertility	[171]
Early growth response 1 (*Egr1*; NGFI-A) targeted *lacZ* insertion	Both	Lack of luteinizing hormone (LH) (M); downregulation of luteinizing hormone receptors (LHR), not remedied with gonadotropin treatment (F)	Infertility	[172]
Early growth response 1 (*Egr1*) targeted *neo* insertion	Female	LH insufficiency; loss of estrous cyclicity, no CL; rescued by treatment with gonadotropins	Infertility	[173]
Insulin receptor substrate 2 (*Irs2*)	Female	Small, anovulatory ovaries with reduced numbers of follicles	Infertility	[147]
Nitric oxide synthase 3, endothelial cell (*Nos3*; eNos)	Female	Compromised ovulation, delayed meiotic progression from metaphase I	Subfertility	[174]
Nuclear receptor corepressor RIP40 (*Nrip1*)	Female	Ovulation defect; ovaries accumulate luteinized, unruptured follicles	Infertility	[175]
$p27^{Kip1}$ (*Cdkn1b*)	Both	CL differentiation failure and granulosa cell hyperplasia (F); males fertile with testicular hyperplasia	Infertility (F)	[93, 94]
Pentraxin 3 (*Ptx3*)	Female	Defects in COC integrity and ovulation	Subfertility	[46]
Progesterone receptor (*Pgr*)	Female	Defects in ovulation, implantation, sexual behavior, and mammary gland development	Infertility	[176]
Prolactin receptor (*Prlr*)	Both	Compromised ovulation, fertilization, and preimplantation development in knockouts (F); defects in maternal behavior in knockouts and heterozygotes (F); variable infertility and subfertility (M)	Infertility (F); subfertility (M)	[177, 178]
Prostaglandin F receptor (*Ptgfr*)	Female	Females do not undergo parturition; failed luteolysis	Infertility	[179]
Puromycin-sensitive aminopeptidase (*Psa*)	Female	Lack of CL formation and prolactin production cause early pregnancy loss	Infertility	[180]
Scavenger receptor, class B1 (*Srb1*)	Female	Defects in oocyte maturation and early embryo development caused by abnormal lipoprotein metabolism	Infertility	[181–183]
SH2-B	Both	Males have small testes and reduced sperm count; females have small, anovulatory ovaries with reduced numbers of developing follicles	Subfertility (M); infertility (F)	[158]
Ubiquitin protein ligase E3A (*Ube3a*; E6-AP ubiquitin protein ligase)	Both	Testicular hypoplasia, defects in spermatogenesis and prostate gland development (M); ovarian hypoplasia, defects in ovulation and uterine development (F)	Subfertility	[164]

Table 23.6 Fertilization and Embryonic Development

Mutant Gene	Sex Affected	Reproductive Phenotype	Fertility Status	References
Basigin (*Bsg*)	Both	Defects in fertilization and implantation (F); block in spermatogenesis at metaphase I (M)	Partial lethality; infertility	[184, 185]
CD9 antigen (*Cd9*)	Female	Sperm-egg binding defect	Subfertility	[186]
Colony stimulating factor (granulocyte-macrophage) (*Csf2*)	Both	Mean litter size decrease with disproportionate loss of males pups (F); maternal effects most pronounced in intercrosses with knockout males	Intercrossing subfertility	[187]
DNA methyltransferase (*Dnmt1o*)	Female	Embryos of knockout females die during gestation because of imprinting defects; maternal effect gene	Subfertility	[104]
H19	Female (Hetero)	Loss of maternal allele in developing embryos causes somatic overgrowth caused by loss of IGF2 imprinting	Maternal effect	[188]
Heatshock transcription factor 1 (*Hsf1*)	Female	Maternal effect gene; pre- and postimplantation defects	Infertility	[189, 190]
Insulin-like growth factor 2 receptor (*Igf2r*); T-associated maternal effect (*Tme*) mutation	Female (Hetero)	Mutation of maternal allele in pups causes developmental defects and embryonic/perinatal death	Lethality; maternal effect	[191]
Maternal antigen that embryos require (*Mater*) knockout	Female	Development beyond the two-cell stage is blocked; maternal effect gene	Infertility	[192]
Nucleoplasmin 2 (*Npm2*)	Female	Post-fertilization embryo loss; defects in heterochromatin formation	Subfertility	[104c]
Postmeiotic segregation increased 2 (*Pms2*)	Both	Abnormal chromosome synapsis in meiosis (M); female knockout zygotes have microsatellite instability in both maternal and paternal genomes; maternal effect gene	Infertility (M)	[193, 194]
Synaptonemal complex protein 3 (*Sycp3*)	Both	Defects in chromosome synapsis during meiosis; germ cell apoptosis in males; embryonic loss in females caused by aneuploidy	Infertility (M); subfertility (F)	[102, 117]
Zygote arrest 1 (*Zar1*)	Female	Post-fertilization embryo loss before 2-cell stage	Infertility	[104b]

protein in the segregation of chromosomes during oocyte meiosis [102].

Until sperm DNA decondensation and reorganization of a diploid nucleus is completed, many events of early embryogenesis cannot rely on *de novo* transcription from either parental genome, and embryonic development must be supported by factors from the oocyte. Disruptions of the maternal genome that cause phenotypes in embryonic development are termed *maternal effect mutations,* and several have been recently identified in mice using knockout technology. In several cases, the gene product normally accumulates in growing oocytes and persists in the early developing embryo. The phenotype affects offspring of homozygous null females, regardless of their genotype or gender. The first maternal effect gene discovered encodes *m*aternal *a*ntigen *t*hat *e*mbryos *r*equire (MATER), which is necessary for development beyond the two-cell stage; MATER has been implicated in establishing embryonic genome transcription patterns [103]. Another maternal effect protein is DNMT1o, an oocyte-specific DNA methyltransferase that maintains genomic imprinting crucial for viability of the developing fetus [104].

Our lab recently described two early-acting maternal effect genes recovered from an ovary cDNA library enriched in oocyte-specific genes by subtractive hybridization [104a]. The first of these, zygote arrest 1 (*Zar1*), encodes an atypical plant homeodomain (PHD) motif-containing protein essential for embryo development to the two-cell and four-cell stage after fertilization [104b]. The null mutation results in complete infertility in female mice. The second, the mammalian nucleoplasmin ortholog, nucleoplasmin 2 (*Npm2*), is important in heterochromatin formation and nucleolar organization in both unfertilized oocyte nuclei and the pronuclei of fertilized eggs [104c]. Presence of NPM2 proves important for efficient progression through mitosis to the two-cell stage, and knockout females are markedly subfertile. The parallel discoveries of *Zar1* and *Npm2* underscore that oocytes are filled with transcripts and proteins that are dispensable for their viability, follicular development, and fertilization, but are crucial to early embryos. In the future, additional oocyte-expressed genes important for embryonic development will likely be appreciated.

CONCLUSION

We are rapidly generating and characterizing new transgenic mouse models, which makes for an especially exciting time in the study of reproductive biology. Researchers can hardly fail to recognize an overt reproductive phenotype during the process of expanding a transgenic line. Thus the list of recognized fertility defects in these models is growing at an outstanding rate. Reviewing the literature allows us to categorize these phenotypes and begin to draw functional associations between gene products. In the future, double mutant studies and variations on transgenic technologies will allow us to pose more pointed questions as to the interrelatedness of particular gene products and the organization of genetic pathways. There are numerous commonalities in human and mouse physiology, and more mouse models recapitulating recognized or idiopathic human reproductive defects are being described. Therefore the future also holds promise for those interested in translational research, the development of contraceptives, and the clinical management of infertility.

ACKNOWLEDGMENTS

Studies in the Matzuk laboratory on fertility pathways have been supported by Wyeth Research and National Institutes of Health grants HD33438, CA60651, HD32067, HD42500, and the Specialized Cooperative Centers Program in Reproduction Research (HD07495).

References

1. Matzuk, M. M., and Lamb, D. J. (2002). Genetic dissection of mammalian fertility pathways. *Nat. Cell Biol.* 4 (S41–49).
2. Bradley, A. (1987). Production and analysis of chimeric mice-teratocarcinomas and embryonic stem cells: A practical approach. In *Production and Analysis of Chimeric Mice,* ed. E. J. Robinson, 113–151. Oxford: IRL, London.
3. Ginsburg, M., Snow, M. H., and McLaren, A. (1990). Primordial germ cells in the mouse embryo during gastrulation. *Development* 110, 521–528.
4. Clark, J. M., and Eddy, E. M. (1975). Fine structural observations on the origin and associations of primordial germ cells of the mouse. *Dev. Biol.* 47, 136–155.
5. Tam, P. P., and Snow, M. H. (1981). Proliferation and migration of primordial germ cells during compensatory growth in mouse embryos. *J. Embryol. Exp. Morphol.* 64, 133–147.
6. Matsui, Y., Zsebo, K. M., and Hogan, B. L. (1990). Embryonic expression of a haematopoietic growth factor encoded by the Sl locus and the ligand for c-kit. *Nature* 347, 667–669.
7. Manova, K., and Bachvarova, R. F. (1991). Expression of c-*kit* encoded at the *W* locus of mice in developing embryonic germ cells and presumptive melanoblasts. *Dev. Biol.* 146, 312–324.
8. Lawson, K. A., Dunn, N. R., Roelen, B. A., Zeinstra, L. M., Davis, A. M., Wright, C. V., Korving, J. P., and Hogan, B. L. (1999). Bmp4 is required for the generation of primordial germ cells in the mouse embryo. *Genes Dev.* 13, 424–436.
9. Ying, Y., Liu, X.-M., Marble, A., Lawson, K. A., and Zhao, G.-Q. (2000). Requirement of *BMP8b* for the generation of primordial germ cells in the mouse. *Mol. Endocrinol.* 14, 1053–1063.
10. Tremblay, K. D., Dunn, N. R., and Robertson, E. J. (2001). Mouse embryos lacking Smad1 signals display defects in extra-embryonic tissues and germ cell formation. *Development* 128, 3609–3621.
11. Chang, H., Huylebroeck, D., Verschueren, K., Guo, Q., Matzuk, M. M., and Zwijsen, A. (1999). Smad5 knockout mice die at mid-gestation due to multiple embryonic and extraembryonic defects. *Development* 126, 1631–1642.
12. Ying, Y., and Zhao, G. Q. (2001). Cooperation of endoderm-derived BMP2 and extraembryonic ectoderm-derived BMP4 in primordial germ cell generation in the mouse. *Dev. Biol.* 232, 484–492.
13. Chang, H., Brown, C. W., and Matzuk, M. M. (2002). Genetic analysis of the mammalian TGF-β supefamily. *Endocr. Rev.* 23, 787–823.
14. Baudat, F., Manova, K., Yuen, J. P., Jasin, M., and Keeney, S. (2000). Chromosome synapsis defects and sexually dimorphic meiotic progression in mice lacking Spo11. *Mol. Cell.* 6, 989–998.
15. Kneitz, B., Cohen, P. E., Avdievich, E., Zhu, L., Kane, M. F., Hou, Jr., H., Kolodner, R. D., Kucherlapati, R., Pollard, J. W., and Edelmann, W. (2000). MutS homolog 4 localization to meiotic chromosomes is required for chromosome pairing during meiosis in male and female mice. *Genes Dev.* 14, 1085–1097.
16. Edelmann, W., Cohen, P. E., Kneitz, B., Winand, N., Lia, M., Heyer, J., Kolodner, R., Pollard, J. W., and Kucherlapati, R. (1999). Mammalian MutS homologue 5 is required for chromosome pairing in meiosis. *Nat. Genet.* 21, 123–127.
17. Barlow, C., Hirotsune, S., Paylor, R., Liyanage, M., Eckhaus, M., Collins, F., Shiloh, Y., Crawley, J. N., Ried, T., Tagle, D., and Wynshaw-Boris, A. (1996). Atm-deficient mice: A paradigm of ataxia telangiectasia. *Cell* 86, 159–171.
18. Pittman, D. L., Cobb, J., Schimenti, K. J., Wilson, L. A., Cooper, D. M., Brignull, E., Handel, M. A., and Schimenti, J. C. (1998). Meiotic prophase arrest with failure of chro-

mosome synapsis in mice deficient for *Dmc1*, a germline-specific RecA homolog. *Mol. Cell.* 1, 697–705.

19. Cohen, P. E., and Pollard, J. W. (2001). Regulation of meiotic recombination and prophase I progression in mammals. *Bioessays* 23, 996–1009.
20. Hunt, P. A., and Hassold, T. J. (2002). Sex matters in meiosis. *Science* 296, 2181–2183.
21. Tay, J., and Richter, J. D. (2001). Germ cell differentiation and synaptonemal complex formation are disrupted in CPEB knockout mice. *Dev. Cell.* 1, 201–213.
22. Ruggiu, M., Speed, R., Taggart, M., McKay, S. J., Kilanowski, F., Saunders, P., Dorin, J., and Cooke, H. J. (1997). The mouse *Dazla* gene encodes a cytoplasmic protein essential for gametogenesis. *Nature* 389, 73–76.
23. Miyamoto, N., Yoshida, M., Kuratani, S., Matsuo, I., and Aizawa, S. (1997). Defects of urogenital development in mice lacking *Emx2*. *Development* 124, 1653–1664.
24. Birk, O. S., Casiano, D. E., Wassif, C. A., Cogliati, T., Zhao, L., Zhao, Y., Grinberg, A., Huang, S., Kreidberg, J. A., Parker, K. L., Porter, F. D., and Westphal, H. (2000). The LIM homeobox gene Lhx9 is essential for mouse gonad formation. *Nature* 403, 909–913.
25. Luo, X., Ikeda, Y., and Parker, K. L. (1994). A cell-specific nuclear receptor is essential for adrenal and gonadal development and sexual differentiation. *Cell* 77, 481–490.
26. Kreidberg, J. A., Sariola, H., Loring, J. M., Maeda, M., Pelletier, J., Housman, D., and Jaenisch, R. (1993). WT-1 is required for early kidney development. *Cell* 74, 679–691.
27. Whitworth, D. J., and Behringer, R. R. (2001). The transgenic mouse in studies of mammalian sexual differentiation. In *Contemporary Endocrinology: Transgenics in Endocrinology*, eds. M. M. Matzuk, C. W. Brown, and T. R. Kumar, 19–39. Totowa, N.J.: Humana Press, Inc.
28. Mishina, Y. (2001). The in vivo function of Mullerian-inhibiting substance during mammalian sexual development. In *Contemporary Endocrinology: Transgenics in Endocrinology,* eds. M. M. Matzuk, C. W. Brown, and T. R. Kumar, 41–59. Totowa, N.J.: Humana Press, Inc.
29. Matzuk, M. M. (2001). Eggs in the balance. *Nat. Genet.* 28, 300–301.
30. Tilly, J. L. (2001). Commuting the death sentence: How oocytes strive to survive. *Nat. Rev. Mol. Cell Biol.* 2, 838–848.
31. Perez, G. I., Robles, R., Knudson, C. M., Flaws, J. A., Korsmeyer, S. J., and Tilly, J. L. (1999). Prolongation of ovarian lifespan into advanced chronological age by *Bax*-deficiency. *Nat. Genet.* 21, 200–203.
32. Matikainen, T., Perez, G. I., Jurisicova, A., Pru, J. K., Schlezinger, J. J., Ryu, H.-Y., Laine, J., Sakai, T., Korsmeyer, S. J., Casper, R. F., Sherr, D. H., and Tilly, J. L. (2001). Aromatic hydrocarbon receptor-driven *Bax* gene expression is required for premature ovarian failure caused by biohazardous environmental chemicals. *Nat. Genet.* 28, 355–360.
33. Rucker, III, E. B., Dierisseau, P., Wagner, K. U., Garrett, L., Wynshaw-Boris, A., Flaws, J. A., and Hennighausen, L. (2000). Bcl-x and Bax regulate mouse primordial germ cell survival and apoptosis during embryogenesis. *Mol. Endocrinol.* 14, 1038–1052.
34. Riedlinger, G., Okagaki, R., Wagner, K. U., Rucker, III, E. B., Oka, T., Miyoshi, K., Flaws, J. A., and Hennighausen, L. (2002). Bcl-x is not required for maintenance of follicles and corpus luteum in the postnatal mouse ovary. *Biol. Reprod.* 66, 438–444.
35. Ratts, V. S., Flaws, J. A., Kolp, R., Sorenson, C. M., and Tilly, J. L. (1995). Ablation of bcl-2 gene expression decreases the numbers of oocytes and primordial follicles established in the post-natal female mouse gonad. *Endocrinology* 136, 3665–3668.
36. Flaws, J. A., Hirshfield, A. N., Hewitt, J. A., Babus, J. K., and Furth, P. A. (2001). Effect of bcl-2 on the primordial follicle endowment in the mouse ovary. *Biol. Reprod.* 64, 1153–1159.
37. Morita, Y., Perez, G. I., Maravei, D. V., Tilly, K. I., and Tilly, J. L. (1999). Targeted expression of Bcl-2 in mouse oocytes inhibits ovarian follicle atresia and prevents spontaneous and chemotherapy-induced oocyte apoptosis in vitro. *Mol. Endocrinol.* 13, 841–850.
38. Bergeron, L., Perez, G. I., Macdonald, G., Shi, L., Sun, Y., Jurisisova, A., Varmuza, S., Latham, K. E., Flaws, J. A., Salter, J. C. M., Hara, H., Moskowitz, M. A., Li, E., Greenberg, A., Tilly, J. L., and Yuan, J. (1998). Defects in regulation of apoptosis in caspase-2-deficient mice. *Genes Dev.* 12, 1304–1314.
39. Carambula, S. F., Matikainen, T., Lynch, M. P., Flavell, R. A., Goncalves, P. B., Tilly, J. L., and Rueda, B. R. (2002). Caspase-3 is a pivotal mediator of apoptosis during regression of the ovarian corpus luteum. *Endocrinology* 143, 1495–1501.
40. Matzuk, M. M., Burns, K., Viveiros, M. M., and Eppig, J. (2002). Intercellular communication in the mammalian ovary: Oocytes carry the conversation. *Science* 296, 2178–2180.
41. Soyal, S. M., Amleh, A., and Dean, J. (2000). FIGα, a germ cell-specific transcription factor required for ovarian follicle formation. *Development* 127, 4645–4654.
42. Dong, J., Albertini, D. F., Nishimori, K., Kumar, T. R., Lu, N., and Matzuk, M. M. (1996). Growth differentiation factor-9 is required during early ovarian folliculogenesis. *Nature* 383, 531–535.
43. Elvin, J. A., Yan, C., Wang, P., Nishimori, K., and Matzuk, M. M. (1999). Molecular characterization of the follicle defects in the growth differentiation factor-9-deficient ovary. *Mol. Endocrinol.* 13, 1018–1034.
44. Elvin, J. A., Clark, A. T., Wang, P., Wolfman, N. M., and Matzuk, M. M. (1999). Paracrine actions of growth differentiation factor-9 in the mammalian ovary. *Mol. Endocrinol.* 13, 1035–1048.
45. Elvin, J. A., Yan, C., and Matzuk, M. M. (2000). Growth differentiation factor-9 stimulates progesterone synthesis in granulosa cells via a prostaglandin E2/EP2 receptor pathway. *Proc. Natl. Acad. Sci. USA* 97, 10288–10293.
46. Varani, S., Elvin, J. A., Yan, C., DeMayo, J., DeMayo, F. J., Horton, H. F., Byrne, M. C., and Matzuk, M. M. (2002). Knockout of pentraxin 3, a downstream target of growth differentiation factor-9, causes female subfertility. *Mol. Endocrinol.* 16, 1154–1167.
47. Fulop, C., Szanto, S., Mukhopadhyay, D., Bardos, T., Kamath, R. V., Rugg, M. S., Day, A. J., Salustri, A., Hascall, V. C., Glant, T. T., and Mikecz, K. (2003). Impaired cumulus mucification and female sterility in tumor necrosis factor-induced protein-6 deficient mice. *Development* 130, 2253–2261.

48. Yan, C., Wang, P., DeMayo, J., DeMayo, F., Elvin, J., Carino, C., Prasad, S., Skinner, S., Dunbar, B., Dube, J., Celeste, A., and Matzuk, M. (2001). Synergistic roles of bone morphogenetic protein 15 and growth differentiation factor 9 in ovarian function. *Mol. Endocrinol.* 15, 854–866.
49. Rankin, T., Familari, M., Lee, E., Ginsberg, A., Dwyer, N., Blanchette-Mackie, J., Drago, J., Westphal, H., and Dean, J. (1996). Mice homozygous for an insertional mutation in the *Zp3* gene lack a zona pellucida and are infertile. *Development* 122, 2903–2910.
50. Rankin, T. L., O'Brien, M., Lee, E., Wigglesworth, K., Eppig, J., and Dean, J. (2001). Defective zonae pellucidae in Zp2-null mice disrupt folliculogenesis, fertility and development. *Development* 128, 1119–1126.
51. Greenwald, G. S., and Roy, S. K. (1994). Follicular development and its control. In *The Physiology of Reproduction,* 2d ed., Vol. 1, eds. E. Knobil, and J. Neill, 629–724. New York: Raven Press, Ltd.
52. Burns, K. H., and Matzuk, M. M. (2002). Genetic models for the study of gonadotropin actions. *Endocrinology* 143, 2823–2835.
53. Mason, A. J., Hayflick, J. S., Zoeller, R. T., Young, W. S., Phillips, H. S., Nikolics, K., and Seeburg, P. H. (1986). A deletion truncating the gonadotropin-releasing hormone gene is responsible for hypogonadism in the *hpg* mouse. *Science* 234, 1366–1371.
54. Franco, B., Guioli, S., Pragliola, A., Incerti, B., Bardoni, B., Tonlorenzi, R., Carrozzo, R., Maestrini, E., Pieretti, M., and Taillon-Miller, P., et al. (1991). A gene deleted in Kallmann's syndrome shares homology with neural cell adhesion and axonal path-finding molecules. *Nature* 353, 529–536.
55. Jackson, R. S., Creemers, J. W., Ohagi, S., Raffin-Sanson, M. L., Sanders, L., Montague, C. T., Hutton, J. C., and O'Rahilly, S. (1997). Obesity and impaired prohormone processing associated with mutations in the human prohormone convertase 1 gene. *Nat. Genet.* 16, 303–306.
56. Kendall, S. K., Samuelson, L. C., Saunders, T. L., Wood, R. I., and Camper, S. A. (1995). Targeted disruption of the pituitary glycoprotein hormone α-subunit produces hypogonadal and hypothyroid mice. *Genes Dev.* 9, 2007–2019.
57. Themmen, A. P. N., and Huhtaniemi, I. T. (2000). Mutations of gonadotropins and gonadotropin receptors: Elucidating the physiology and pathophysiology of pituitary-gonadal function. *Endocr. Rev.* 21, 551–583.
58. Layman, L. C., and McDonough, P. G. (2000). Mutations of follicle stimulating hormone-β and its receptor in human and mouse: Genotype/phenotype. *Mol. Cell. Endocrinol.* 161, 9–17.
59. Kumar, T. R., Wang, Y., Lu, N., and Matzuk, M. M. (1997). Follicle stimulating hormone is required for ovarian follicle maturation but not male fertility. *Nat. Genet.* 15, 201–204.
60. Dierich, A., Sairam, M. R., Monaco, L., Fimia, G. M., Gansmuller, A., LeMeur, M., and Sassone-Corsi, P. (1998). Impairing follicle-stimulating hormone (FSH) signaling *in vivo*: Targeted disruption of the FSH receptor leads to aberrant gametogenesis and hormonal imbalance. *Proc. Natl. Acad. Sci. USA* 95, 13612–13617.
61. Abel, M. H., Wootton, A. N., Wilkins, V., Huhtaniemi, I., Knight, P. G., and Charlton, H. M. (2000). The effect of a null mutation in the follicle-stimulating hormone receptor gene on mouse reproduction. *Endocrinology* 141, 1795–1803.
62. Danilovich, N., Roy, I., and Sairam, M. R. (2001). Ovarian pathology and high incidence of sex cord tumors in follitropin receptor knockout (FORKO) mice. *Endocrinology* 142, 3673–3684.
63. Zhang, F. P., Poutanen, M., Wilbertz, J., and Huhtaniemi, I. (2001). Normal prenatal but arrested postnatal sexual development of luteinizing hormone receptor knockout (LuRKO) mice. *Mol. Endocrinol.* 15, 172–183.
64. Lei, Z. M., Mishra, S., Zou, W., Xu, B., Foltz, M., Li, X., and Rao, C. V. (2001). Targeted disruption of luteinizing hormone/human chorionic gonadotropin receptor gene. *Mol. Endocrinol.* 15, 184–200.
65. Vale, W., Bilezikjian, L. M., and Rivier, C. (1994). Reproductive and other roles of inhibins. In *The Physiology of Reproduction,* 2d ed., Vol. 1, eds. E. Knobil, and J. Neill, 1861–1878. New York: Raven Press, Ltd.
66. Matzuk, M. M., Finegold, M. J., Su, J.-G.J., Hsueh, A. J. W., and Bradley, A. (1992). α-Inhibin is a tumor-suppressor gene with gonadal specificity in mice. *Nature* 360, 313–319.
67. Matzuk, M. M., Finegold, M. J., Mather, J. P., Krummen, L., Lu, H., and Bradley, A. (1994). Development of cancer cachexia-like syndrome and adrenal tumors in inhibin-deficient mice. *Proc. Natl. Acad. Sci. USA* 91, 8817–8821.
68. Kumar, T. R., Wang, Y., and Matzuk, M. M. (1996). Gonadotropins are essential modifier factors for gonadal tumor development in inhibin-deficient mice. *Endocrinology* 137, 4210–4216.
69. Kumar, T. R., Palapattu, G., Wang, P., Woodruff, T. K., Boime, I., Byrne, M. C., and Matzuk, M. M. (1999). Transgenic models to study gonadotropin function: The role of follicle-stimulating hormone in gonadal growth and tumorigenesis. *Mol. Endocrinol.* 13, 851–865.
70. Cipriano, S., Chen, L., Burns, K., Koff, A., and Matzuk, M. (2001). Inhibin and p27 interact to regulate gonadal tumorigenesis. *Mol. Endocrinol.* 15, 985–996.
71. Matzuk, M. M., Kumar, T. R., Shou, W., Coerver, K. A., Lau, A. L., Behringer, R. R., and Finegold, M. J. (1996). Transgenic models to study the roles of inhibins and activins in reproduction, oncogenesis, and development. *Rec. Prog. Hormone Res.* 51, 123–157.
71a. Pierson, T. M., Wang, Y., DeMayo, F. J., Matzuk, M. M., Tsai, S. Y., and O'Malley, B. W. (2000). Regulable expression of inhibin A in wild-type and inhibin α null mice. *Mol. Endo.* 14, 1075–1085.
72. Brown, C. W., Houston-Hawkins, D. E., Woodruff, T. K., and Matzuk, M. M. (2000). Insertion of Inhbβ into the Inhbα locus rescues the Inhbα-null phenotype and reveals new activin functions. *Nat. Genet.* 25, 453–457.
73. Vassalli, A., Matzuk, M. M., Gardner, H. A. R., Lee, K.-F., and Jaenisch, R. (1994). Activin/inhibin βB subunit gene disruption leads to defects in eyelid development and female reproduction. *Genes Dev.* 8, 414–427.
74. Matzuk, M. M., Kumar, T. R., and Bradley, A. (1995). Different phenotypes for mice deficient in either activins or activin receptor type II. *Nature* 374, 356–360.
75. Nakamura, T., Takio, K., Eto, Y., Shibai, H., Titani, K., and Sugino, H. (1990). Activin-binding protein from rat ovary is follistatin. *Science* 247, 836–838.

76. Matzuk, M. M., Lu, H., Vogel, H., Sellheyer, K., Roop, D. R., and Bradley, A. (1995). Multiple defects and perinat death in mice deficient in follistatin. *Nature* 372, 360–363.
77. Guo, Q., Kumar, T. R., Woodruff, T., Hadsell, L. A., DeMayo, F. J., and Matzuk, M. M. (1998). Overexpression of mouse follistatin causes reproductive defects in transgenic mice. *Mol. Endocrinol.* 12, 96–106.
78. Lubahn, D. B., Moyer, J. S., Golding, T. S., Couse, J. F., Korach, K. S., and Smithies, O. (1993). Alteration of reproductive function but not prenatal sexual development after insertional disruption of the mouse estrogen receptor gene. *Proc. Natl. Acad. Sci. USA* 90, 11162–11166.
79. Schomberg, D. W., Couse, J. F., Mukherjee, A., Lubahn, D. B., Sar, M., Mayo, K. E., and Korach, K. S. (1999). Targeted disruption of the estrogen receptor-α gene in female mice: Characterization of ovarian responses and phenotype in the adult. *Endocrinology* 140, 2733–2744.
80. Scully, K. M., Gleiberman, A. S., Lindzey, J., Lubahn, D. B., Korach, K. S., and Rosenfeld, M. G. (1997). Role of estrogen receptor-α in the anterior pituitary gland. *Mol. Endocrinol.* 11, 674–681.
81. Couse, J. F., and Korach, K. S. (1999). Estrogen receptor null mice: What have we learned and where will they lead us? *Endocr. Rev.* 20, 358–417.
82. Krege, J. H., Hodgin, J. B., Couse, J. F., Enmark, E., Warner, M., Mahler, J. F., Sari, M., Korach, K. S., Gustafsson, J.-A., and Smithes, O. (1998). Generation and reproductive phenotypes of mice lacking estrogen receptor β. *Proc. Natl. Acad. Sci. USA* 95, 15677–15682.
83. Couse, J. F., Hewitt, S. C., Bunch, D. O., Sar, M., Walker, V. R., Davis, B. J., and Korach, K. S. (1999). Postnatal sex reversal of the ovaries in mice lacking estrogen receptors α and β. *Science* 286, 2328–2331.
84. Dupont, S., Krust, A., Gansmuller, A., Dierich, A., Chambon, P., and Mark, M. (2000). Effect of single and compound knockouts of estrogen receptors α (ERα) and β (ERβ) on mouse reproductive phenotypes. *Development* 127, 4277–4291.
85. Fisher, C. R., Graves, K. H., Parlow, A. F., and Simpson, E. R. (1998). Characterization of mice deficient in aromatase (ArKO) because of targeted disruption of the *cyp19* gene. *Proc. Natl. Acad. Sci. USA* 95, 6965–6970.
86. Britt, K. L., Drummond, A. E., Cox, V. A., Dyson, M., Wreford, N. G., Jones, M. E. E., Simpson, E. R., and Findlay, J. K. (2000). An age-related ovarian phenotype in mice with targeted disruption of the *Cyp19* (aromatase) gene. *Endocrinology* 141, 2614–2623.
87. Britt, K. L., Kerr, J., O'Donnell, L., Jones, M. E., Drummond, A. E., Davis, S. R., Simpson, E. R., and Findlay, J. K. (2002). Estrogen regulates development of the somatic cell phenotype in the eutherian ovary. *FASEB J.* 16, 1389–1397.
88. Robker, R. L., and Richards, J. S. (1998). Hormone-induced proliferation and differentiation of granulosa cells: A coordinated balance of the cell cycle regulators cyclin D2 and p27KIP1. *Mol. Endocrinol.* 12, 924–940.
89. Sherr, C. J. (1995). D-type cyclins. *Trends Biochem. Sci* 20, 187–190.
90. Sicinski, P., Donaher, J. L., Gene, Y., Parker, S. B., Gardner, H., Park, M. Y., Robker, R. L., Richard, J. S., McGinnis, L. K., Biggers, J. D., Eppig, J. J., Bronson, R. T., Elledge, S. J., and Weinberg, R. A. (1996). Cyclin D2 is an FSH-responsive gene involved in gonadal cell proliferation and oncogenesis. *Nature* 384, 470–474.
91. Burns, K. H., Yan, C., Kumar, T. R., and Matzuk, M. M. (2001). Analysis of ovarian gene expression in follicle-stimulating hormone beta knockout mice. *Endocrinology* 142, 2742–2751.
92. Kiyokawa, H., Kineman, R. D., Manova-Todorova, K. O., Soares, V. C., Hoffman, E. S., Ono, M., Khanam, D., Hayday, A. C., Frohman, L. A., and Koff, A. (1996). Enhanced growth of mice lacking the cyclin-dependent kinase inhibitor function of p27(Kip1). *Cell* 85, 721–732.
93. Nakayama, K., Ishida, N., Shirane, M., Inomata, A., Inoue, T., Shishido, N., Horii, I., Loh, D. Y., and Nakayama, K. (1996). Mice lacking p27(Kip1) display increased body size, multiple organ hyperplasia, retinal dysplasia, and pituitary tumors. *Cell* 85, 707–720.
94. Fero, M. L., Rivkin, M., Tasch, M., Porter, P., Carow, C. E., Firpo, E., Polyak, K., Tsai, L. H., Broudy, V., Perlmutter, R. M., Kaushansky, K., and Roberts, J. M. (1996). A syndrome of multiorgan hyperplasia with features of gigantism, tumorigenesis, and female sterility in p27(Kip1)-deficient mice. *Cell* 85, 733–744.
95. Moons, D. S., Jirawatnotai, S., Tsutsui, T., Franks, R., Parlow, A. F., Hales, D. B., Gibori, G., Fazleabas, A. T., and Kiyokawa, H. (2002). Intact follicular maturation and defective luteal function in mice deficient for cyclin-dependent kinase-4. *Endocrinology* 143, 647–654.
96. Ledan, E., Polanski, Z., Terret, M. E., and Maro, B. (2001). Meiotic maturation of the mouse oocyte requires an equilibrium between cyclin B synthesis and degradation. *Dev. Biol.* 232, 400–413.
97. Brandeis, M., Rosewell, I., Carrington, M., Crompton, T., Jacobs, M. A., Kirk, J., Gannon, J., and Hunt, T. (1998). Cyclin B2-null mice develop normally and are fertile whereas cyclin B1-null mice die in utero. *Proc. Natl. Acad. Sci. USA* 95, 4344–4349.
98. Lincoln, A. J., Wickramasinghe, D., Stein, P., Schultz, R. M., Palko, M. E., De Miguel, M. P., Tessarollo, L., and Donovan, P. J. (2002). Cdc25b phosphatase is required for resumption of meiosis during oocyte maturation. *Nat. Genet.* 30, 446–449.
99. Hashimoto, N., Watanabe, N., Furuta, Y., Tamemoto, H., Sagata, N., Yokoyama, M., Okazaki, K., Nagayoshi, M., Takeda, N., Ikawa, Y., and Aizawa, S. (1994). Parthenogenetic activation of oocytes in c-*mos*-deficient mice. *Nature* 370, 68–71.
100. Edelmann, W., Cohen, P. E., Kane, M., Lau, K., Morrow, B., Bennett, S., Umar, A., Kunkel, T., Cattoretti, G., Chaganti, R., Pollard, J. W., Kolodner, R. D., and Kucherlapati, R. (1996). Meitoic pachytene arrest in MLH1-deficient mice. *Cell* 85, 1125–1134.
101. Lipkin, S. M., Moens, P. B., Wang, V., Lenzi, M., Shanmugarajah, D., Gilgeous, A., Thomas, J., Cheng, J., Touchman, J. W., Green, E. D., Schwartzberg, P., Collins, F. S., and Cohen, P. E. (2002). Meiotic arrest and aneuploidy in MLH3-deficient mice. *Nat. Genet.* 31, 385–390.
102. Yuan, L., Liu, J. G., Hoja, M. R., Wilbertz, J., Nordqvist, K., and Hoog, C. (2002). Female germ cell aneuploidy and embryo death in mice lacking the meiosis-specific protein SCP3. *Science* 296, 1115–1118.

103. Tong, Z. B., Bondy, C. A., Zhou, J., and Nelson, L. M. (2002). A human homologue of mouse mater, a maternal effect gene essential for early embryonic development. *Hum. Reprod.* 17, 903–911.
104. Howell, C. Y., Bestor, T. H., Ding, F., Latham, K. E., Mertineit, C., Trasler, J. M., and Chaillet, J. R. (2001). Genomic imprinting disrupted by a maternal effect mutation in the Dnmt1 gene. *Cell* 104, 829–838.
104a. Diatchenko, L., Lau, Y. F., Campbell, A. P., Chenchik, A., Moqadam, F., Huang, B., Lukyanov, S., Lukyanov, K., Gurskaya, N., Sverdlov, E. D., and Siebert, P. D. (1996). Suppression subtractive hybridization: a method for generating differentially regulated or tissue-specific cDNA probes and libraries. *Proc. Natl. Acad. Sci. USA* 93, 6025–30.
104b. Wu, X., Viveiros, M., Eppig, J., Bai, Y., Fitzpatrick, S., and Matzuk, M. M. (2003). Zygote arrest 1 (Zar1) is a novel maternal-effect gene critical for the oocyte-to-embryo transition. *Nature Genetics* 33, 187–191.
104c. Burns, K., Viveiros, M., Ren, Y., Wang, P., DeMayo, F. J., Frail, D. E., Eppig, J. J., and Matzuk, M. M. (2003). Roles of NPM2 in chromatin and nucleolar organization in oocytes and embryos. *Science* 300, 633–636.
105. Barlow, C., Liyanage, M., Moens, P. B., Tarsounas, M., Nagashima, K., Brown, K., Rottinghaus, S., Jackson, S. P., Tagle, D., Ried, T., and Wynshaw-Boris, A. (1998). *Atm* deficiency results in severe meiotic disruption as early as leptonema of prophase I. *Development* 125, 4007–4017.
106. Xu, Y., Ashley, T., Brainerd, E. E., Bronson, R. T., Meyn, M. S., and Baltimore, D. (1996). Targeted disruption of ATM leads to growth retardation, chromosomal fragmentation during meiosis, immune defects, and thymic lymphoma. *Genes Dev.* 10, 2411–2422.
107. Zhao, G.-Q., Deng, K., Labosky, P. A., Liaw, L., and Hogan, B. L. M. (1996). The gene encoding bone morphogenetic protein 8B is required for the initiation and maintenance of spermatogenesis in the mouse. *Genes Dev.* 10, 1657–1669.
108. Juneja, S. C., Barr, K. J., Enders, G. C., and Kidder, G. M. (1999). Defects in the germ line and gonads of mice lacking connexin 43. *Biol. Reprod.* 60, 1263–1270.
109. Yoshida, K., Kondoh, G., Matsuda, Y., Habu, T., Nishimune, Y., and Morita, T. (1998). The mouse RecA-like gene Dmc1 is required for homologous chromosome synapsis during meiosis. *Mol. Cell* 1, 707–718.
110. Matsui, Y., Zsebo, K. M., and Hogan, B. L. M. (1990). Embryonic expression of a haematopoietic growth factor encoded by the *Sl* locus and the ligand for c-*kit*. *Nature* 347, 667–669.
111. Beechey, C. V., Loutit, J. F., and Searle, A. G. (1986). Panda, a new steel allele. *Mouse News Letter* 74, 92.
112. Manova, K., Nocka, K., Besmer, P., and Bachvarova, R. F. (1990). Gonadal expression of c-*kit* encoded at the *W* locus of the mouse. *Development* 110, 1057–1069.
113. Baker, S. M., Plug, A. W., Prolla, T. A., Bronner, C. E., Harris, A. C., Yao, X., Christie, D.-M., Monell, C., Arnheim, N., Bradley, A., Ashley, T., and Liskay, R. M. (1996). Involvement of mouse Mlh1 in DNA mismatch repair and meiotic crossing over. *Nat. Genet.* 13, 336–341.
114. deVries, S. S., Baart, E. B., Dekker, M., Siezen, A., de Rooij, D. G., de Boer, P., and te Riele, H. (1999). Mouse MutS-like protein Msh5 is required for proper chromosome synapsis in male and female meiosis. *Genes Dev.* 13, 523–531.
115. Chang, H., and Matzuk, M. M. (2001). Smad5 is required for mouse primordial germ cell development. *Mech. Dev.* 104, 61–67.
116. Romanienko, P. J., and Camerini-Otero, R. D. (2000). The mouse Spo11 gene is required for meiotic chromosome synapsis. *Mol. Cell* 6, 975–987.
117. Yuan, L., Liu, J. G., Zhao, J., Brundell, E., Daneholt, B., and Hoog, C. (2000). The murine SCP3 gene is required for synaptonemal complex assembly, chromosome synapsis, and male fertility. *Mol. Cell* 5, 73–83.
118. Beck, A. R. P., Miller, I. J., Anderson, P., and Streuli, M. (1998). RNA-binding protein TIAR is essential for primordial germ cell development. *Proc. Natl. Acad. Sci. USA* 95, 2331–2336.
119. Luoh, S.-W., Bain, P. A., Polakiewicz, R. D., Goodheart, M. L., Gardner, H., Jaenisch, R., and Page, D. C. (1997). *Zfx* mutation results in small animal size and reduced germ cell number in male and female mice. *Development* 124, 2275–2284.
120. Behringer, R. R., Finegold, M. J., and Cate, R. L. (1994). Müllerian-inhibiting substance function during mammalian sexual development. *Cell* 79, 415–425.
121. Durlinger, A. L., Kramer, P., Karels, B., de Jong, F. H., Uilenbroek, J. T., Grootegoed, J. A., and Themmen, A. P. (1999). Control of primordial follicle recruitment by anti-Mullerian hormone in the mouse ovary. *Endocrinology* 140, 5789–5796.
122. Hu, M.-C., Hsu, N.-C., Hadj, N., Pai, C.-I., Chu, H.-P., C-KL, W., and Chung, B.-C. (2002). Steroid deficiency syndromes in mice with targeted disruption of *Cyp11a1*. *Mol. Endocrinol.* 16, 1943–1950.
123. Caron, K. M., Soo, S.-C., Wetsel, W. C., Stocco, D. M., Clark, B. J., and Parker, K. L. (1997). Targeted disruption of the mouse gene encoding steroidogenic acute regulatory protein provides insights into congenital lipoid adrenal hyperplasia. *Proc. Natl. Acad. Sci. USA* 94, 11540–11545.
124. Vainio, S., Heikkila, M., Kispert, A., Chin, N., and McMahon, A. P. (1999). Female development in mammals is regulated by Wnt-4 signalling. *Nature* 397, 405–409.
125. Parr, B. A., and McMahon, A. P. (1998). Sexually dimorphic development of the mammalian reproductive tract requires *Wnt-7a*. *Nature* 395, 707–710.
126. Knudson, C. M., Tung, K. S. K., Tourtellotte, W. G., Brown, G. A. J., and Korsmeyer, A. J. (1995). Bax-deficient mice with lymphoid hyperplasia and male germ cell death. *Science* 270, 96–99.
127. Ross, A. J., Waymire, K. G., Moss, J. E., Parlow, A. F., Skinner, M. K., Russell, L. D., and MacGregor, G. R. (1998). Testicular degeneration in Bclw-deficient mice. *Nat. Genet.* 18, 251–256.
128. Shindo, T., Kurihara, H., Kuno, K., Yokoyama, H., Wada, T., Kurihara, Y., Imai, T., Wang, Y., Ogata, M., Nishimatsu, H., Moriyama, N., Oh-hashi, Y., Morita, H., Ishikawa, T., Nagai, R., Yazaki, Y., and Matsushima, K. (2000). ADAMTS-1: A melloproteinase-disintegrin essential for normal growth, fertility, and organ morphology and function. *J. Clin. Invest.* 105, 1345–1352.
129. Yi, S. E., LaPolt, P. S., Yoon, B. S., Chen, J. Y., Lu, J. K., and Lyons, K. M. (2001). The type I BMP receptor BmprIB is

essential for female reproductive function. *Proc. Natl. Acad. Sci. USA* 98, 7994–7999.

130. Jin, S. L., Richard, F. J., Kuo, W. P., D'Ercole, A. J., and Conti, M. (1999). Impaired growth and fertility of cAMP-specific phosphodiesterase PDE4D-deficient mice. *Proc. Natl. Acad. Sci. USA* 96, 11998–12003.
131. Simon, A. M., Goodenough, D. A., Li, E., and Paul, D. L. (1997). Female infertility in mice lacking connexin 37. *Nature* 385, 525–529.
132. Rane, S. G., Dubus, P., Mettus, R. V., Galbreath, E. J., Boden, G., Reddy, E. P., and Barbacid, M. (1999). Loss of Cdk4 expression causes insulin-deficient diabetes and Cdk4 activation results in β-islet cell hyperplasia. *Nat. Genet.* 22, 44–52.
133. Robertson, K. M., O'Donnell, L., Jones, M. E., Meachem, S. J., Boon, W. C., Fisher, C. R., Graves, K. H., McLachlan, R. I., and Simpson, E. R. (1999). Impairment of spermatogenesis in mice lacking a functional aromatase (cyp 19) gene. *Proc. Natl. Acad. Sci. USA* 96, 7986–7991.
134. Robertson, K. M., Simpson, E. R., Lacham-Kaplan, O., and Jones, M. E. (2001). Characterization of the fertility of male aromatase knockout mice. *J. Androl.* 22, 825–830.
135. Hess, R. A., Bunick, D., Lee, K. H., Bahr, J., Taylor, J. A., Korach, K. S., and Lubahn, D. B. (1997). A role for oestrogens in the male reproductive system. *Nature* 390, 509–512.
136. Ogawa, S., Eng, V., Taylor, J., Lubahn, D. B., Korach, K. S., and Pfaff, D. W. (1998). Roles of estrogen receptor-alpha gene expression in reproduction-related behaviors in female mice. *Endocrinology* 139, 5070–5081.
137. Ogawa, S., Lubahn, D. B., Korach, K. S., and Pfaff, D. W. (1997). Behavioral effects of estrogen receptor gene disruption in male mice. *Proc. Natl. Acad. Sci. USA* 94, 1476–1481.
138. Cheng, N. C., van de Vrugt, H. J., van der Valk, M. A., Oostra, A. B., Krimpenfort, P., de Vries, Y., Joenje, H., Berns, A., and Arwert, F. (2000). Mice with a targeted disruption of the Fanconi anemia homolog Fanca. *Hum. Mol. Genet.* 9, 1805–1811.
139. Chen, M., Tomkins, D. J., Auerbach, W., McKerlie, C., Youssoufian, H., Liu, L., Gan, O., Carreau, M., Auerbach, A., Groves, T., Guidos, C. J., Freedman, M. H., Cross, J., Percy, D. H., Dick, J. E., Joyner, A. L., and Buchwald, M. (1996). Inactivation of *Fac* in mice produces inducible chromosomal instability and reduced fertility reminiscent of Fanconi anaemia. *Nat. Genet.* 12, 448–451.
140. Whitney, M. A., Royle, G., Low, M. J., Kelly, M. A., Axthelm, M. K., Reifsteck, C., Olson, S., Braun, R. E., Heinrich, M. C., Rathbun, R. K., Bagby, G. C., and Grompe, M. (1996). Germ cell defects and hematopoietic hypersensitivity to γ-interferon in mice with a targeted disruption of the fanconi anemia C gene. *Blood* 88, 49–58.
141. Koomen, M., Cheng, N., van de Vrugt, H., Godthelp, B., van der Valk, M., Oostra, A., Zdzienicka, M., Joenje, H., and Arwert, F. (2002). Reduced fertility and hypersensitivity to mitomycin C characterize Fancg/Xrcc9 null mice. *Hum. Mol. Genet.* 11, 273–281.
142. Kumar, T. R., Wiseman, A. L., Kala, G., Kala, S. V., Matzuk, M. M., and Lieberman, M. W. (2000). Reproductive defects in gamma-glutamyl transpeptidase-deficient mice. *Endocrinology* 141, 4270–4277.
143. Lieberman, M. W., Wiseman, A. L., Shi, Z.-Z., Carter, B. Z., Barrios, R., Ou, C.-N., Chevez-Barrios, P., Wang, Y., Habib, G. M., Goodman, J. C., Huang, S. L., Lebovitz, R. M., and Matzuk, M. M. (1996). Growth retardation and cysteine deficiency in γ-glutamyl transpeptidase-deficient mice. *Proc. Natl. Acad. Sci. USA* 93, 7923–7926.
144. Zhou, Y., Xu, B. C., Maheshwari, H. G., He, L., Reed, M., Lozykowski, M., Okada, S., Cataldo, L., Coschigamo, K., Wagner, T. E., Baumann, G., and Kopchick, J. J. (1997). A mammalian model for Laron syndrome produced by targeted disruption of the mouse growth hormone receptor/binding protein gene (the Laron mouse). *Proc. Natl. Acad. Sci. USA* 94, 13215–13220.
145. Baker, J., Hardy, M. P., Zhou, J., Bondy, C., Lupu, F., Bellvé, A. R., and Efstratiadis, A. (1996). Effects of an *Igf1* gene null mutation on mouse reproduction. *Mol. Endocrinol.* 10, 903–918.
146. Nef, S., and Parada, L. F. (1999). Cryptorchidism in mice mutant for Insl3. *Nat. Genet.* 22, 295–299.
147. Burks, D. J., de Mora, J. F., Schubert, M., Withers, D. J., Myers, M. G., Towery, H. H., Altamuro, S. L., Flint, C. L., and White, M. F. (2000). IRS-2 pathways integrate female reproduction and energy homeostasis *Nature* 407, 377–382.
148. Swerdloff, R. S., Batt, R. A., and Bray, G. A. (1976). Reproductive hormonal function in the genetically obese (ob/ob) mouse. *Endocrinology* 98, 1359–1364.
149. Swerdloff, R. S., Peterson, M., Vera, A., Batt, R. A., Heber, D., and Bray, G. A. (1978). The hypothalamic-pituitary axis in genetically obese (ob/ob) mice: Response to luteinizing hormone-releasing hormone. *Endocrinology* 103, 542–547.
150. Chua, Jr., S. C., Chung, W. K., Wu-Peng, X. S., Zhang, Y., Liu, S. M., and Tartaglia, L., Leibel, R. L. (1996). Phenotypes of mouse diabetes and rat fatty due to mutations in the OB (leptin) receptor. *Science* 271, 994–996.
151. Bruning, J. C., Gautam, D., Burks, D. J., Gillette, J., Schubert, M., Orban, P. C., Klein, R., Krone, W., Muller-Wieland, D., and Kahn, C. R. (2000). Role of brain insulin receptor in control of body weight and reproduction. *Science* 289, 2122–2125.
152. Acampora, D., Mazan, S., Tuorto, F., Avantaggiato, V., Tremblay, J. J., Lazzaro, D., di Carlo, A., Mariano, A., Macchia, P. E., Corte, G., Macchia, V., Drouin, J., Brulet, P., and Simeone, A. (1998). Transient dwarfism and hypogonadism in mice lacking Otx1 reveal prepubescent stage-specific control of pituitary levels of GH, FSH and LH. *Development* 125, 1229–1239.
153. Takahashi, K., Kobayashi, T., and Kanayama, N. (2000). p57(Kip2) regulates the proper development of labyrinthine and spongiotrophoblasts. *Mol. Hum. Reprod.* 6, 1019–1025.
154. Jamen, F., Rodriguez-Henche, N., Pralong, F., Jegou, B., Gaillard, R., Bockaert, J., and Brabet, P. (2000). PAC1 null females display decreased fertility. *Ann. N.Y. Acad. Sci. 921*, 400–404.
155. Li, S., Crenshaw, III, E. B., Rawson, E. J., Simmons, D. M., Swanson, L. W., and Rosenfeld, M. G. (1990). Dwarf locus mutants lacking three pituitary cell types result from mutations in the POU-domain gene pit-1. *Nature* 347, 528–533.
156. Horseman, N. D., Zhao, W., Montecino-Rodriguez, E., Tanaka, M., Nakashima, K., Engle, S. J., Smith, F., Markoff,

E., and Dorshkind, K. (1997). Defective mammopoiesis, but normal hematopoiesis, in mice with a targeted disruption of the prolactin gene. *EMBO J.* 16, 6926–6935.

157. Sornson, M. W., Wu, W., Dasen, J. S., Flynn, S. E., Norman, D. J., O'Connell, S. M., Gukovsky, I., Carriere, C., Ryan, A. K., Miller, A. P., Zuo, L., Gleiberman, A. S., Andersen, B., Beamer, W. G., and Rosenfeld, M. G. (1996). Pituitary lineage determination by the Prophet of Pit-1 homeodomain factor defective in Ames dwarfism. *Nature* 384, 327–333.
158. Ohtsuka, S., Takaki, S., Iseki, M., Miyoshi, K., Nakagata, N., Kataoka, Y., Yoshida, N., Takatsu, K., and Yoshimura, A. (2002). SH2-B is required for both male and female reproduction. *Mol. Cell. Biol.* 22, 3066–3077.
159. Matzuk, M. M., Dionne, L., Guo, Q., Kumar, T. R., and Lebovitz, R. M. (1998). Ovarian function in superoxide dismutase 1 and 2 knockout mice. *Endocrinology* 139, 4008–4011.
160. Ho, Y.-S., Gargano, M., Cao, J., Bronson, R. T., Heimler, I., and Hutz, R. J. (1998). Reduced fertility in female mice lacking copper-zinc superoxide dismutase. *J. Biol. Chem.* 273, 7765–7769.
161. Freiman, R. N., Albright, S. R., Zheng, S., Sha, W. C., Hammer, R. E., and Tjian, R. (2001). Requirement of tissue-selective TBP-associated factor TAFII105 in ovarian development. *Science* 293, 2084–2087.
162. Jiang, J. Y., Imai, Y., Umezu, M., and Sato, E. (2001). Characteristics of infertility in female hypothyroid (hyt) mice. *Reproduction* 122, 695–700.
163. Roby, K. F., Son, D. S., and Terranova, P. F. (1999). Alterations of events related to ovarian function in tumor necrosis factor receptor type I knockout mice. *Biol. Reprod.* 61, 1616–1621.
164. Smith, C. L., DeVera, D. G., Lamb, D. J., Nawaz, Z., Jiang, Y. H., Beaudet, A. L., and O'Malley, B. W. (2002). Genetic ablation of the steroid receptor coactivator-ubiquitin ligase, E6-AP, results in tissue-selective steroid hormone resistance and defects in reproduction. *Mol. Cell. Biol.* 22, 525–535.
165. Kinuta, K., Tanaka, H., Moriwake, T., Aya, K., Kato, S., and Seino, Y. (2000). Vitamin D is an important factor in estrogen biosynthesis of both female and male gonads. *Endocrinology* 141, 1317–1324.
166. Johnson, L., and DeLuca, H. (2001). Vitamin D receptor null mutant mice fed high levels of calcium are fertile. *J. Nutr.* 131, 1787–1791.
167. Sato, H., Kajikawa, S., Kuroda, S., Horisawa, Y., Nakamura, N., Kaga, N., Kakinuma, C., Kato, K., Morishita, H., Niwa, H., and Miyazaki, J. (2001). Impaired fertility in female mice lacking urinary trypsin inhibitor. *Biochem. Biophys. Res. Commun.* 281, 1154–1160.
168. Sterneck, E., Tessarollo, L., and Johnson, P. F. (1997). An essential role for C/EBPβ in female reproduction. *Genes Dev.* 11, 2153–2162.
169. Dinchuk, J. E., Car, B. D., Focht, R. J., Johnston, J. J., Jaffee, B. D., Covington, M. B., Contel, N. R., Eng, V. M., Collins, R. J., Czerniak, P. M., Gorry, S. A., and Trzaskos, J. M. (1995). Renal abnormalities and an altered inflammatory response in mice lacking cyclooxygenase II. *Nature* 378, 406–409.
170. Lim, H., Paria, B. C., Das, S. K., Dinchuk, J. E., Langenbach, R., Trzaskos, J. M., and Dey, S. K. (1997). Multiple female reproductive failures in cyclooxygenase 2-deficient mice. *Cell* 91, 197–208.
171. Panda, D. K., Miao, D., Tremblay, M. L., Sirois, J., Farookhi, R., Hendy, G. N., and Goltzman, D. (2001). Targeted ablation of the 25-hydroxyvitamin D 1alpha-hydroxylase enzyme: Evidence for skeletal, reproductive, and immune dysfunction. *Proc. Natl. Acad. Sci. USA* 98, 7498–7503.
172. Topilko, P., Schneider-Maunoury, S., Levi, G., Trembleau, A., Gourdji, D., Driancourt, M. A., Rao, C. V., and Charnay, P. (1998). Multiple pituitary and ovarian defects in Krox-24 (NGFI-A, Egr-1)-targeted mice. *Mol. Endocrinol.* 12, 107–122.
173. Lee, S. L., Sadovsky, Y., Swirnoff, A. H., Polish, J. A., Goda, P., Gavrilina, G., and Milbrandt, J. (1996). Luteinizing hormone deficiency and female infertility in mice lacking the transcription factor NGFI-A (Egr-1). *Science* 273, 1219–1221.
174. Jablonka-Shariff, A., and Olson, L. M. (1998). The role of nitric oxide in oocyte meiotic maturation and ovulation: Meiotic abnormalities of endothelial nitric oxide synthase knockout mouse oocytes. *Endocrinology* 139, 2944–2954.
175. White, R., Leonardsson, G., Rosewell, I., Jacobs, M. A., Milligan, S., and Parker, M. (2000). The nuclear receptor co-repressor nrip1 (RIP140) is essential for female fertility. *Nat. Med.* 6, 1368–1374.
176. Lydon, J. P., DeMayo, F. J., Funk, C. R., Mani, S. K., Hughes, A. R., Montgomery, C. A., Shyamala, G., Conneely, O. M., and O'Malley, B. W. (1995). Mice lacking progesterone receptor exhibit pleiotropic reproductive abnormalities. *Genes Dev.* 9, 2266–2278.
177. Ormandy, C. J., Camus, A., Barra, J., Damotte, D., Lucas, B., Buteau, H., Edery, M., Brousse, N., Babinet, C., Binart, N., and Kelly, P. A. (1997). Null mutation of the prolactin receptor gene produces multiple reproductive defects in the mouse. *Genes Dev.* 11, 167–178.
178. Lucas, B. K., Ormandy, C. J., Binart, N., Bridges, R. S., and Kelly, P. A. (1998). Null mutation of the prolactin receptor gene produces a defect in maternal behavior. *Endocrinology* 139, 4102–4107.
179. Sugimoto, Y., Yamasaki, A., Segi, E., Tsuboi, K., Aze, Y., Nishimura, T., Oida, H., Yoshida, N., Tanaka, T., Katsuyama, M., Hasumoto, K., Murata, T., Ushikubi, F., Negishi, M., Ichikawa, A., and Narumiya, S. (1997). Failure of parturition in mice lacking the prostaglandin F receptor. *Science* 277, 681–683.
180. Osada, T., Watanabe, G., Sakaki, Y., and Takeuchi, T. (2001). Puromycin-sensitive aminopeptidase is essential for the maternal recognition of pregnancy in mice. *Mol. Endocrinol.* 15, 882–893.
181. Rigotti, A., Trigatti, B. L., Penman, M., Rayburn, H., Herz, J., and Krieger, M. (1997). A targeted mutation in the murine gene encoding the high density lipoprotein (HDL) receptor scavenger receptor class B type I reveals its key role in HDL metabolism. *Proc. Natl. Acad. Sci. USA* 94, 12610–12615.
182. Trigatti, B., Rayburn, H., Vinals, M., Braun, A., Miettinen, H., Penman, M., Hertz, M., Schrenzel, M., Amigo, L., Rigotti, A., and Krieger, M. (1999). Influence of the high

density lipoprotein receptor SR-BI on reproductive and cardiovascular pathophysiology. *Proc. Natl. Acad. Sci. USA* 96, 9322–9327.

183. Miettinen, H. E., Rayburn, H., and Krieger, M. (2001). Abnormal lipoprotein metabolism and reversible female infertility in HDL receptor (SR-BI)-deficient mice. *J. Clin. Invest.* 108, 1717–1722.

184. Kuno, N., Kadomatsu, K., Fan, Q.-W., Hagihara, M. N., Senda, T., Mizutani, S., and Muramatsu, T. (1998). Female sterility in mice lacking the *basigin* gene, which encodes a transmembrane glycoprotein belonging to the immunoglobulin superfamily. *Fed. Euro. Biochem. Sciences* 425, 191–194.

185. Igakura, T., Kadomatsu, K., Kaname, T., Muramatsu, H., Fan, Q. W., Miyauchi, T., Toyama, Y., Kuno, N., Yuasa, S., Takahashi, M., Senda, T., Taguchi, O., Yamamura, K., Arimura, K., and Muramatsu, T. (1998). A null mutation in basigin, an immunoglobulin superfamily member, indicates its important roles in peri-implantation development and spermatogenesis. *Dev. Biol.* 194, 152–165.

186. Le Naour, F., Rubinstein, E., Jasmin, C., Prenant, M., and Boucheix, C. (2000). Severely reduced female fertility in CD9-deficient mice. *Science* 287, 319–321.

187. Robertson, S. A., Roberts, C. T., Farr, K. L., Dunn, A. R., and Seamark, R. F. (1999). Fertility impairment in granulocyte-macrophage colony-stimulating factor-deficient mice. *Biol. Reprod.* 60, 251–261.

188. Leighton, P. A., Ingram, R. S., Eggenschwiler, J., Efstratiadis, A., and Tilghman, S. M. (1995). Disruption of imprinting caused by deletion of the H19 gene region in mice. *Nature* 375, 34–39.

189. Xiao, X., Zuo, X., Davis, A. A., McMillan, D. R., Curry, B. B., Richardson, J. A., and Benjamin, I. J. (1999). HSF1 is required for extra-embryonic development, postnatal growth and protection during inflammatory responses in mice. *EMBO J.* 18, 5943–5952.

190. Christians, E., Davis, A. A., Thomas, S. D., and Benjamin, I. J. (2000). Maternal effect of Hsf1 on reproductive success. *Nature* 407, 693–694.

191. Lau, M. M., Stewart, C. E., Liu, Z., Bhatt, H., Rotwein, P., and Stewart, C. L. (1994). Loss of the imprinted IGF2/cation-independent mannose 6-phosphate receptor results in fetal overgrowth and perinatal lethality. *Genes Dev.* 8, 2953–2963.

192. Tong, Z. B., Gold, L., Pfeifer, K. E., Dorward, H., Lee, E., Bondy, C. A., Dean, J., and Nelson, L. M. (2000). Mater, a maternal effect gene required for early embryonic development in mice. *Nat. Genet.* 26, 267–268.

193. Baker, S. M., Bronner, C. E., Zhang, L., Plug, A. W., Robatzek, M., Warren, G., Elliott, E. A., Yu, J., Ashley, T., and Arnheim, N., et al. (1995). Male mice defective in the DNA mismatch repair gene PMS2 exhibit abnormal chromosome synapsis in meiosis. *Cell* 82, 309–319.

194. Gurtu, V. E., Verma, S., Grossmann, A. H., Liskay, R. M., Skarnes, W. C., and Baker, S. M. (2002). Maternal effect for DNA mismatch repair in the mouse. *Genetics* 160, 271–277.

CHAPTER **24**

Bioinformatic Analysis of Ovarian Genes Using an Ovary-Specific Database

IZHAR BEN-SHLOMO AND AARON J. W. HSUEH

INTRODUCTION

In recent years there has been a dramatic increase in the amount of data derived from the sequencing of entire genomes of diverse species ranging from the nematode *Caenorabditis elegans* [1], to the fruit fly *Drosophila melanogaster* [2], the mosquito *Anopheles gambiae* [3], the bony fish *Fugu rubripes* [4], and the human [5]. With the introduction of complementary deoxyribonucleic acid (cDNA) microarray and proteomics technology, profiles of gene transcription (the transcriptomes) and corresponding proteins (proteomes) are also becoming widely available. However, the organizational principles of these massive data are sequence based or organism specific rather than organ specific. If one wishes to understand the physiological roles of individual genes and their interactions in the coordinated regulation of tissue and organ functions, an organ-based approach provides a valuable advantage. Such an organ-based approach can facilitate the analysis of the accumulating data on gene expression in the context of specific functional states of the organ and its specific cell populations.

OVARY-SPECIFIC DATABASE

The embryonic development of the ovary, the cyclic fluctuation of ovarian hormonal production throughout life, and the tight control of follicle maturation, ovulation, and luteinization are regulated by the many genes expressed in the ovary. A sorted and organized arrangement of the accumulating literature and gene sequence information would facilitate innovative research in ovarian physiology. The arrangement of this rapidly expanding data into a categorized searchable database has become a prerequisite for the efficient analysis and understanding of whole organ systems. In September 1999 the Ovarian Kaleidoscope database (OKdb) at *http://ovary.stanford.edu/* was launched as a unified online gateway to store, search, review, and update information about genes expressed in the ovary [6]. The infrastructure of the OKdb was designed to allow searches based on biological function, expression pattern, mutant phenotypes, cellular localization, and hormonal regulation of ovarian genes. The basic structural unit of the OKdb is the single gene page. Each gene page in the OKdb links to other online databases including the Online Mendelian Inheritance in Man (OMIM) at *www.ncbi.nlm.nih.gov/Omim/* and publications in PubMed that are relevant to individual genes. The OMIM website contains text on the genetic basis of human diseases and the general function of individual genes. In addition, OMIM includes links to websites with information on nucleotide and amino acid sequences and chromosomal localization. The current number of gene entries in the OKdb is more than 1400 (as of October 2002) with approximately 9000 links to outside databases.

The field of bioinformatics is the most rapidly expanding area in current biological research. The central themes of this field revolve around the most efficient ways to derive significant new insights and to guide investigative efforts by "mining" the ever increasing data sets. Using the OKdb as an example of organ-specific functional genomic analysis, we herein describe bioinformatic approaches that were made possible as a result of the continuing accumulation of gene pages in the OKdb.

The total number of human genes is estimated to be around 35,000 to 40,000, and the OMIM documents 14,000 individual pages corresponding to 8500 genes with known chromosomal location. Thus more than 60% of genes in our genome remain to be "discovered" in terms of their specific functions. UniGene (*www.ncbi.nlm.nih.gov/UniGene/index.html*) is an experimental system that automatically partitions GenBank sequences into a nonredundant set of gene-oriented clusters. Each UniGene cluster contains sequences that represent a unique gene and information such as the tissue types in which the gene has been expressed. In addition to sequences of well-characterized genes, hundreds of thousands of novel expressed sequence tag (EST) sequences have been included in the UniGene database [7]. The complex reproductive and endocrine functions of the ovary are orchestrated by the interplay of thousands of genes expressed in this organ. Based on information gained from the human oocyte and ovarian gene cDNA libraries, the ovary likely expresses more genes than other organ because of the presence of both somatic and germ cell types. Assuming that the expression of 25% of human genes occurs in the ovary, one can estimate that this percentage represents 10,000 to 15,000 ovarian genes. In addition, a recent study using serial analysis of gene expression (SAGE)-PCR identified 21,000 known genes and ESTs as well as 6000 unknown tags in human oocytes [8]. The high abundance of expressed ovarian genes is in direct contrast to the lower number of expressed genes in several other human tissues (e.g., muscle expresses approximately 5500 genes, the liver expresses approximately 17,000 genes, the prostate expresses approximately 15,000 genes).

OVARIAN "BOTTLENECK" GENES ASSOCIATED WITH INFERTILITY

A valuable approach to the study of infertility is the comparison of mutations of individual human and mouse genes associated with infertility phenotypes. The individual gene page in the OKdb contains information on associated fertility phenotypes sorted by ovarian and nonovarian defects and by subfertility or infertility. If one searches for null mutations (under the subject "mutation type") that cause infertility ("infertile, ovarian defect," under "female fertility status") in mice (under "species"), 44 gene entries are found. The expression of these infertility genes in the oocyte and granulosa cells together with their cellular localization is presented in Figure 24.1. The theca cell genes are not presented because most publications emphasize granulosa cell studies.

It is striking that all five oocyte infertility genes with known nuclear localization have been shown to be involved in DNA repair and mismatch correction, thus emphasizing the importance of this pathway(s) in regulating oocyte function and fertility. Although it is well known that zona pellucida-2 and -3 (ZP2 and ZP3) null mice are infertile, ZP1 null mice are only subfertile. Growth differentiation factor 9 (GDF-9) is an oocyte-secreted protein shown to regulate granulosa cell development. Although the receptor and downstream signaling pathway for GDF-9 are not clear, it is interesting to note that ALK-6 (a TGF-β receptor family member) and Smad2 (an intracellular mediator of BMP/TGF-β) null mice are also infertile. The majority of ovarian infertility genes expressed in granulosa cells are nuclear receptors and other transcription factors. The other prominent group of infertility genes in the granulosa cells are those associated with cell cycle regulation, cyclin D2, and the two cyclin-associated genes, cyclin dependent kinase inhibitor 1B (CDN1B) and cyclin dependent kinase 4 (CDK4).

A search for mice null mutations leading to subfertility retrieved 47 genes. Global analysis of these ovarian infertility and subfertility genes and microarray analysis using a gene pathway approach can allow analysis of upstream and downstream component genes of these pathways. Analysis of DNA microarray studies, obtained under multiple experimental conditions and knockout mice [9], could confirm and expand studies on "bottleneck" genes in key pathways that may underlie human ovarian pathologies.

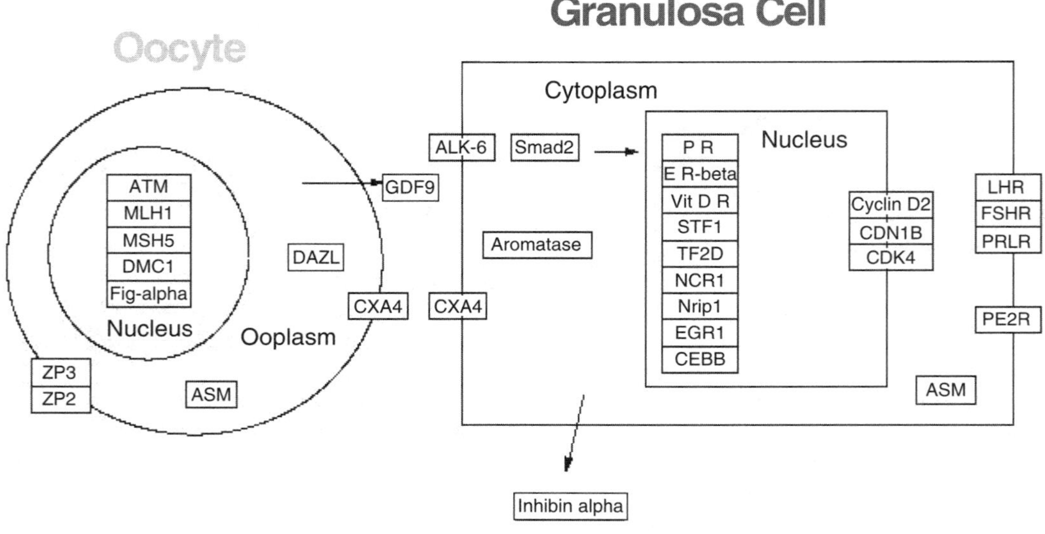

FIGURE 24.1 Cell type expression and cellular localization of infertility genes, based on phenotypes of mutant mice. (See color plate.)

CONSTRUCTION OF GENE PATHWAY MAPS

Protein function is usually accomplished by interactions with other proteins. Gene products in a given cell function in a concerted manner and belong to specific pathways for carrying out unique cellular functions. Although most of the DNA array experiments still focus on the analysis of transcripts with the largest increases or decreases in expression, new attempts have been made to investigate concerted regulation of the expression of genes in individual pathways. With the rapid development in microarray technology and the increasing number of genes that can be simultaneously probed, the GenMapp project has focused on the analysis and presentation of gene pathway maps (*www.genmapp.org*) [10]. This tool provides analogous graphic representation of the relative expression of selected groups of genes categorized by their known positions in physiological pathways. Thus ribonucleic acid (RNA) transcripts for thousands of genes from defined cell populations can be probed for relative abundance based on prearranged maps representing functional pathways. An infertility gene map is being incorporated into the OKdb, and each of the represented genes is linked to its gene page. One may now adapt the map to probe for the expression of infertility genes in ovarian cells under various experimental conditions and view the results in direct connection with the existing text- and sequence-based knowledge of these genes.

Past research efforts focused on key genes within an intracellular pathway, whereas the map tool allows visualization of concomitant changes in the expression of all elements of a given pathway. As it is becoming clear that known signal transduction pathways directly modulate the function of other signal transduction pathways [10], combining different pathway maps will eventually disclose complex networks to allow an integrated perspective on gene regulation in the cells and organs of interest. With a rapid expansion of data on genes in the ovulation pathway [11], integration of results from individual laboratories to construct a pathway map would be fruitful. With the recent implementation of unified standards for DNA microarray experiments [12], one can now share many of the ovarian DNA array data to facilitate more sophisticated bioinformatic analyses.

SORTING OUT CELL-SPECIFIC EXPRESSION OF GENES

In the OKdb, one can retrieve genes based not only on their expression in a given cell type but also in a cell type-specific manner. Currently, there are 398, 182, and 280 genes known to be expressed in the granulosa cell, theca cell, and oocyte, respectively. Whereas in the oocyte 169 (60%) of the listed genes are specific for the germ cell, in theca and granulosa cells only 18 (9%) and 124 (31%) of the listed genes are cell-type specific, respectively (Figure 24.2). It becomes clear that genes expressed in different ovarian somatic cell types overlap to a large extent, whereas the oocyte expresses a fundamentally different set of genes. In the case of cumulus cells, we found 69 expressed genes, of which only 5 were cumulus specific: KE-6 (a 17β-hydroxysteroid dehydrogenase), brain-derived neurotrophic factor, Pentraxin 3, hyaluronan synthase 2, and TNF-α-induced protein 6, of which the latter two are likely important for cumulus expansion. The mismatch between the number of genes found only in one cell type and those defined as specific to that cell type is caused by the omission of genes expressed in luteal, stromal, epithelial, and other cell types in this analysis.

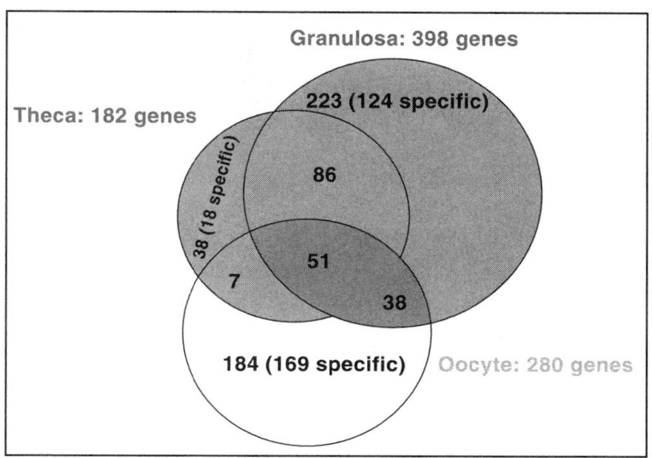

FIGURE 24.2 The distribution of genes in the OKdb by their cellular expression in different ovarian cell types. The genes designated as "specific" are those expressed only in the oocyte or granulosa cells among all ovarian cell types. (See color plate.)

The ability to search and define cell type-specific genes presents an opportunity to use the promoter regions of candidate genes for cell-specific knockout mice experiments [13]. Recently, the Cre/loxP system has been implemented, leading to the deletion of a targeted gene only in the cell type of interest. Using this tissue-specific mutant mouse approach, it was shown that bcl-x is not required for the maintenance of follicles and corpus luteum in the postnatal mouse ovary [14]. In the future, comparison of ovarian genes with genes expressed in other tissues could provide leads to identify ovary-specific genes, mutations of which are likely to be associated with infertility phenotypes.

PROMOTER ANALYSIS OF SYN-EXPRESSED GENES DURING FOLLICULAR DEVELOPMENT, OVULATION, AND LUTEINIZATION

Genes are expressed in a development-, tissue-, and regulation-specific manner. The promoter sequences of all genes contain multiple transcription factor binding sites, and the expression of individual genes is dependent on a combinatorial use of transcription factors at multiple promoter elements. As shown in *S. cerevisiae*, combinatorial analysis of promoter elements could improve our understanding of gene regulation [15]. A critical issue for all large-scale computational approaches to gene regulation is, however, the experimental validation of the physiological significance of the predicted promoter elements [16]. The detailed spatiotemporal expression of ovarian genes, as documented in the OKdb, can serve as the basis for future identification and verification of common regulatory mechanisms of gene expression, including consensus DNA elements and transcriptional factors. The available data in the OKdb can be used to construct microarray queries based on existing knowledge of ovarian gene expression such as genes induced by gonadotropins and growth factors. This approach could facilitate the confirmation and identification of syn-expressed genes for future promoter analysis using bioinformatic methods.

CHROMOSOMAL LOCALIZATION OF GENES: IDENTIFICATION OF MUTANT GENES WITH UNIQUE PHENOTYPES

Completion of the human genome project not only provides information about the sequence of individual genes but specifies their chromosomal location. Extensive genetic analysis has accumulated a vast amount of literature on the chromosomal localization of mutant genes associated with unique phenotypes. The current structure of the OKdb includes a direct link for each listed gene to its chromosomal localization in humans as well as a human chromosomal map of ovarian genes. Whereas in phylogenetically distant animals gene localizations on chromosomes are unrelated, in phylogenetically close animals such as humans, mice, and sheep, the conservation of gene order in chromosome segments (synteny) constitutes a powerful research approach.

Fecundity is a unique trait that has been studied extensively in humans and farm animals. The GDF-9 and GDF-9B (also known as *bone morphogenetic protein-15 [BMP-15]*) signaling pathways play an essential role in follicle development. Loss-of-function mutations in GDF-9 null mice [17] and GDF-9B mutant Inverdale sheep [18] are associated with an arrest of initial follicle recruitment [19]. Paradoxically, the heterozygous female Inverdale sheep exhibited an increase in the number of offspring, presumably caused by an increase in the number of ovulated oocytes. Interestingly, the Booroola FecB mutation in sheep, causing increased fecundity, is phenotypically identical to the heterozygous Inverdale sheep. Cosegregation studies localized the FecB mutation to chromosome 6 in sheep [20], syntenic to the human chromosome 4q [21]. Based on the assumption that similar phenotypes are likely to be found for ligand/receptor pairs, one can search for receptors located at human 4q in the OKdb. Of interest, ALK-6, a family member of the TGF-β receptor family, is localized in this region and represents a candidate receptor for GDF-9 or GDF-9B. One can predict that ALK-6 is a candidate gene for the Booroola sheep mutation. Indeed, a mutation in the intracellular kinase domain of ALK-6 was found in the Booroola sheep [22–24].

Future use of chromosomal locations may reveal candidate ovarian genes responsible for ovarian pathologies. The polycystic ovary syndrome (PCOS), exhibiting hyperandrogenic anovulation, has long intrigued reproductive endocrinologists. One of the promising approaches to the study of this pathology is the cosegregation of genes within affected families. This has led to the identification of several candidate PCOS genes, including CYP11, insulin receptor, and follistatin [25, 26]. However, the genetic approach provides only correlative information and usually maps the genes to a large chromosomal segment. Studies on the chromosomal location of all ovarian genes could facilitate the elucidation of ovarian genes in the pathogenesis of PCOD.

Because the chromosomal localization of most mouse genes are known, a portal for synteny searches has been established by the National Center for Biotechnology Information (*www.ncbi.nlm.nih.gov/Homology/*). With the well-developed technology of gene engineering in mice, future comparisons of human and mouse phenotypes and the elucidation of underlying genes based on chromosomal synteny approaches are valuable.

IDENTIFICATION OF LIGAND-RECEPTOR PAIRS FOR PARACRINE REGULATION

It is becoming clear that all organs are under paracrine control, and autocrine and paracrine regulators for any organ outnumber the endocrine regulators. For example, follicular development is driven by the signaling cascade initiated by follicle-stimulating hormone (FSH) and luteinizing hormone (LH) but is fine-tuned by numerous paracrine and juxtacrine interactions [27]. The ovary, like all other organs, is endowed with a multitude of paracrine networks of ligands and receptors. Although earlier studies clearly documented the importance of insulin-like growth factor-1 [28], interleukin-1 [29], TGF-β/BMPs [30], and kit ligand [31] in ovarian physiology, few attempts have been made to obtain a comprehensive understanding of ovarian paracrine networks.

A prerequisite for paracrine regulation is the expression of both ligands and their cognate receptors in the same organ. The OKdb accumulates literature- and sequence-based information (including ESTs) on gene expression in the ovary. By searching the OKdb, one can identify potential paracrine interacting pairs. The most striking of these are the ovarian expression of one Notch receptor family member and one Notch ligand, four Toll receptor family members and three Toll ligands, and two guanylyl cyclase family receptors with two ligands. Armed with this information, ovarian researchers can further investigate the spatiotemporal relationships of the expression of these genes to uncover their physiological roles. A large-scale study using this approach has been conducted recently on malignant tumors to define the presence of paracrine ligand-receptor pairs likely involved in tumorigenesis [32].

CONCLUSION

In the text-based PubMed database, one can identify 66,500 papers by searching "ovary NOT CHO." The current ovary-specific database uses an "alert" service to provide weekly updates of PubMed publications dealing with ovarian and oocyte genes. The OKdb serves as a foundation for future hypothesis-driven research and for uncovering previously unsuspected relationships among ovarian genes. This database has a unique role in the functional genomics of the ovary by bringing together text- and sequence-based data for the compilation of information on the expression and function of individual ovarian genes, thus allowing an integrated global perspective on gene pathways and networks. Continuing expansion of this database could facilitate ovarian research in the postgenomic era. With increasing use of the bioinformatic approaches for the functional characterization of genes, increasing participation and cooperation of the ovarian community could lead to a faster elucidation of ovarian physiology and the underlying mechanisms responsible for various pathophysiology.

ACKNOWLEDGMENTS

This work was supported by the NICHHD/NIH through Cooperative Agreement U54-HD-31398 as part of the Specialized Cooperative Centers Program in Reproduction Research.

References

1. The *C. elegans* Sequencing Consortium. (1998). Genome sequence of the nematode *C. elegans:* A platform for investigating biology. *Science* 282, 2012–2018.
2. Adams, M. D., Celniker, S. E., Holt, R. A., Evans, C. A., Gocayne, J. D., Amanatides, P. G., Scherer, S. E., Li, P. W., Hoskins, R. A., Galle, R. F., et al. (2000). The genome sequence of *Drosophila melanogaster. Science* 287, 2185–2195.
3. Holt, R. A., Subramanian, G. M., Halpern, A., Sutton, G. G., Charlab, R., Nusskern, D. R., Wincker, P., Clark, A. G., Ribeiro, J. M., Wides, R., et al. (2002). The genome sequence of the malaria mosquito *Anopheles gambiae. Science* 298, 129–149.
4. Aparicio, S., Chapman, J., Stupka, E., Putnam, N., Chia, J. M., Dehal, P., Christoffels, A., Rash, S., Hoon, S., Smit, A., et al. (2002). Whole-genome shotgun assembly and analysis of the genome of *Fugu rubripes. Science* 297, 1301–1310.
5. (2001). The human genome. Science genome map. *Science* 291, 1218.
6. Leo, C. P., Vitt, U. A., and Hsueh, A. J. (2000). The Ovarian Kaleidoscope database: An online resource for the ovarian research community. *Endocrinology* 141, 3052–3054.
7. Schuler, G. D., Boguski, M. S., Stewart, E. A., Stein, L. D., Gyapay, G., Rice, K., White, R. E., Rodriguez-Tome, P., Aggarwal, A., Bajorek, E., et al. (1996). A gene map of the human genome. *Science* 274, 540–546.
8. Neilson, L., Andalibi, A., Kang, D., Coutifaris, C., Strauss, III, J. F., Stanton, J. A., and Green, D. P. (2000). Molecular phenotype of the human oocyte by PCR-SAGE. *Genomics* 63, 13–24.
9. Elvin, J. A., and Matzuk, M. M. (1998). Mouse models of ovarian failure. *Rev. Reprod.* 3, 183–195.
10. Dahlquist, K. D., Salomonis, N., Vranizan, K., Lawlor, S. C., and Conklin, B. R. (2002). GenMAPP, a new tool for viewing and analyzing microarray data on biological pathways. *Nat. Genet.* 31, 19–20.
11. Richards, J. S., Russell, D. L., Ochsner, S., and Espey, L. L. (2002). OVULATION: New dimensions and new regulators of the inflammatory-like response. *Annu. Rev. Physiol.* 64, 69–92.
12. Brazma, A., Hingamp, P., Quackenbush, J., Sherlock, G., Spellman, P., Stoeckert, C., Aach, J., Ansorge, W., Ball, C. A., Causton, H. C., et al. (2001). Minimum information about a microarray experiment (MIAME)-toward standards for microarray data. *Nat. Genet.* 29, 365–371.
13. Sauer, B. (1998). Inducible gene targeting in mice using the Cre/lox system. *Methods* 14, 381–392.
14. Riedlinger, G., Okagaki., R., Wagner, K. U., Rucker, I. E., Oka, T., Miyoshi, K., Flaws, J. A., and Hennighausen, L. (2002). Bcl-x is not required for maintenance of follicles and corpus luteum in the postnatal mouse ovary. *Biol. Reprod.* 66, 438–444.
15. Pilpel, Y., Sudarsanam, P., and Church, G. M. (2001). Identifying regulatory networks by combinatorial analysis of promoter elements. *Nat. Genet.* 29, 153–159.
16. Michelson, A. M. (2002). Deciphering genetic regulatory codes: A challenge for functional genomics. *Proc. Natl. Acad. Sci. USA* 99, 546–548.
17. Dong, J., Albertini, D. F., Nishimori, K., Kumar, T. R., Lu, N., and Matzuk, M. M. (1996). Growth differentiation factor-9 is required during early ovarian folliculogenesis. *Nature* 383, 531–535.
18. Galloway, S. M., McNatty, K. P., Cambridge, L. M., Laitinen, M. P., Juengel, J. L., Jokiranta, T. S., McLaren, R. J., Luiro, K.,

Dodds, K. G., Montgomery, G. W., et al. (2000). Mutations in an oocyte-derived growth factor gene (BMP15) cause increased ovulation rate and infertility in a dosage-sensitive manner. *Nat. Genet.* 25, 279–283.

19. McGee, E. A., and Hsueh, A. J. (2000). Initial and cyclic recruitment of ovarian follicles. *Endocr. Rev.* 21, 200–214.
20. Montgomery, G. W., Lord, E. A., Penty, J. M., Dodds, K. G., Broad, T. E., Cambridge, L., Sunden, S. L., Stone, R. T., and Crawford, A. M. (1994). The Booroola fecundity (FecB) gene maps to sheep chromosome 6. *Genomics* 22, 148–153.
21. Montgomery, G. W., Crawford, A. M., Penty, J. M., Dodds, K. G., Ede, A. J., Henry, H. M., Pierson, C. A., Lord, E. A., Galloway, S. M., Schmack, A. E., et al. (1993). The ovine Booroola fecundity gene (FecB) is linked to markers from a region of human chromosome 4q. *Nat. Genet.* 4, 410–414.
22. Wilson, T., Wu, X. Y., Juengel, J. L., Ross, I. K., Lumsden, J. M., Lord, E. A., Dodds, K. G., Walling, G. A., McEwan, J. C., O'Connell, A. R., et al. (2001). Highly prolific Booroola sheep have a mutation in the intracellular kinase domain of bone morphogenetic protein IB receptor (ALK-6) that is expressed in both oocytes and granulosa cells. *Biol. Reprod.* 64, 1225–1235.
23. Mulsant,, P., Lecerf, F., Fabre, S., Schibler, L., Monget, P., Lanneluc, I., Pisselet, C., Riquet, J., Monniaux, D., Callebaut, I., et al. (2001). Mutation in bone morphogenetic protein receptor-IB is associated with increased ovulation rate in Booroola Merino ewes. *Proc. Natl. Acad. Sci. USA* 98, 5104–5109.
24. Souza, C. J., MacDougall, C., Campbell, B. K., McNeilly, A. S., and Baird, D. T. (2001). The Booroola (FecB) phenotype is associated with a mutation in the bone morphogenetic receptor type 1 B (BMPR1B) gene. *J. Endocrinol.* 169, R1–R6.
25. Urbanek, M., Legro, R. S., Driscoll, D. A., Azziz, R., Ehrmann, D. A., Norman, R. J., Strauss, III, J. F., Spielman, R. S., and Dunaif, A. (1999). Thirty-seven candidate genes for polycystic ovary syndrome: Strongest evidence for linkage is with follistatin. *Proc. Natl. Acad. Sci. USA* 96, 8573–8578.
26. Franks, S., Gharani, N., and McCarthy, M. (2001). Candidate genes in polycystic ovary syndrome. *Hum. Reprod. Update* 7, 405–410.
27. Hsueh, A. J., Adashi, E. Y., Jones, P. B., and Welsh, Jr., T. H. (1984). Hormonal regulation of the differentiation of cultured ovarian granulosa cells. *Endocr. Rev.* 5, 76–127.
28. Adashi, E. Y. (1998). The IGF family and folliculogenesis. *J. Reprod. Immunol.* 39, 13–19.
29. Adashi, E. Y. (1998). The potential role of interleukin-1 in the ovulatory process: An evolving hypothesis. *Mol. Cell. Endocrinol.* 140, 77–81.
30. Elvin, J. A., Yan, C., and Matzuk, M. M. (2000). Oocyte-expressed TGF-beta superfamily members in female fertility. *Mol. Cell. Endocrinol.* 159, 1–5.
31. Driancourt, M. A., Reynaud, K., Cortvrindt, R., and Smitz, J. (2000). Roles of KIT and KIT LIGAND in ovarian function. *Rev. Reprod.* 5, 143–152.
32. Graeber, T. G., and Eisenberg, D. (2001). Bioinformatic identification of potential autocrine signaling loops in cancers from gene expression profiles. *Nat. Genet.* 29, 295–300.

PART VII

Human Ovarian Pathophysiology: Select Aspects

CHAPTER **25**

Gonadotropin Ovulation Induction

NICK S. MACKLON AND BART C. J. M. FAUSER

ABSTRACT

Infertile women suffering from normogonadotropic anovulation (World Health Organization class II [WHO class II]) who remain anovulatory with clomiphene citrate treatment can be successfully treated with gonadotropins. In recent years, preparations of increasing purity have become available, and recombinant gonadotropins are now widely used for ovulation induction. Conventional high-dose treatment regimens are associated with serious complications such as high-order multiple gestation and ovarian hyperstimulation. The currently most widely used low-dose stimulation protocol is the low-dose step-up protocol. Although this regimen provides a relatively simple, effective, and safe approach, it poorly mimics the normal physiology of follicle development and selection. The step-down protocol addresses this and has been established in our clinic as a safe and effective means of inducing monofollicular development. Problems with both of these approaches relate to the individual variability in response to follicle-stimulating hormone (FSH) and the dose required to achieve monofollicular development. Women undergoing the low-dose step-up regimen who have a high-response dose require prolonged treatment, whereas those with a low-response dose who are treated with the step-down regimen may receive excessive stimulation. The ability to predict the individual FSH response dose would individualize treatment and improve efficiency. Moreover, novel adjuvant therapies such as insulin-sensitizing agents may have a role in improving outcomes from gonadotropin ovulation induction.

INTRODUCTION

Exogenous gonadotropins have been widely used for the treatment of anovulatory infertile women since 1958 [1]. The first clinically available gonadotropin preparations contained a mixture of FSH and luteinizing hormone (LH) in a ratio of activity of 1:1 and a large quantity of unidentified urinary proteins. Early production techniques were crude and labor intensive, requiring up to 30 liters of urine to produce enough human menopausal gonadotropin (HMG) for one treatment cycle. Improvements in purification techniques led to increasing relative amounts of the active ingredients, and the first urine-derived preparation containing only FSH (u-FSH) became available in 1983. The development and application of production techniques based on immunoaffinity chromatography with monoclonal antibodies enabled the production of highly purified u-FSH. Although improvements in purity and specific activity were thus achieved, the large quantities of urine required and a massive increase in worldwide demand for FSH compounds for infertility treatment put increasing pressure on production and availability. In the 1980s, recombinant DNA technology led to the development and, later, the clinical introduction of recombinant human FSH (r-hFSH). This advance promised not only unlimited availability but also improved purity and batch-to-batch consistency compared with urinary derived products. Since 1996 r-hFSH has been clinically available in the form of follitropin alfa and follitropin beta. More recently, r-recombinant human LH (r-hLH), recombinant human chorionic gonadotropin (r-hCG), and a long-acting r-hFSH has been added to the clinical arsenal for ovarian stimulation.

The majority of anovulatory patients currently treated with gonadotropin preparations comprise normogonadotropic (i.e., normal serum FSH concentrations, WHO class II) anovulatory infertile women who failed to conceive during previous antiestrogen medication. The aim of this treatment modality is to approach normal conditions as closely as possible (i.e., maturation and ovulation of a single dominant follicle and subsequent singleton pregnancy). This is in contrast to the aim of ovarian stimulation for assisted reproduction, where in most cases ovulatory women are hyperstimulated to produce multiple follicles. To achieve development of a single dominant follicle with exogenous gonadotropins, specific treatment and monitoring protocols are needed. The two most frequently encountered in the literature and in clinical practice are the low-dose step-up and, more recently, step-down protocols.

In recent years the observation that many women with WHO class II anovulation suffer from insulin resistance and compensatory hyperinsulinemia has increased interest in the possible role of insulin-sensitizing drugs such as metformin as an alternative or adjunctive therapy to gonadotropin ovulation induction. Enthusiasm for this approach derives from evidence that elevated circulating insulin concentrations impede ovulation and that weight reduction has been shown to improve ovarian function in some women. Although laser surgery and assisted conception may also have a place in treating anovulatory infertility, in this chapter the theory and practice of gonadotropin ovulation induction is discussed, together with the influence of the different currently available gonadotropin preparations and the possible role of adjunctive therapies such as metformin.

PATHOPHYSIOLOGY OF OVARIAN STIMULATION

The majority of human oocytes are destined to undergo atresia [2, 3]. Only those follicles able to respond to stimulation by FSH at the right time of the cycle will enter the final stage of development and ovulate [4, 5]. Owing to the demise of the corpus luteum and a subsequent decrease in inhibin B and estradiol production, FSH levels increase at the end of the luteal phase of the menstrual cycle [6, 7]. The high FSH levels that occur during the luteo-follicular transition give rise to continued growth of a limited number (or cohort) of follicles that have reached a certain developmental stage [8]. Subsequent development of this cohort during the follicular phase becomes dependent on continued stimulation by gonadotropins [9]. Each growing follicle possesses a threshold requirement for stimulation by circulating FSH [10, 11]. This theshold level should be surpassed to ensure ongoing preovulatory development. In response to negative feedback from rising estradiol and inhibin levels, FSH levels fall in the late follicle phase. In the normoovulatory cycle, only a single follicle will remain responsive to falling FSH levels. This dominant follicle has increased sensitivity to FSH, aquires responsiveness to LH, and continues growing. Those follicles that commence the latter stages of development after FSH levels start to fall undergo atresia (Figure 25.1). The duration of this "FSH window" during which FSH levels are above the threshold required to stimulate ongoing development determines the number of follicles that can develop to the preovulatory stage [1, 12]. Families with dyzygotic twins (where two dominant follicles are selected in natural cycles) should therefore be interesting subjects for the study of mechanisms underlying single dominant follicle selection.

One of the principle roles of the developing follicle is estrogen production. Estrogens play important functional roles in the reproductive system by, among other functions, inducing the midcycle gonadotropin surge, stimulating cervical mucous production, and stimulating endometrial proliferation. During the advanced phase of follicular development, LH has a synergistic action with FSH. Theca cells are stimulated by LH to convert cholesterol into androstenedione (AD) and testosterone (T) by

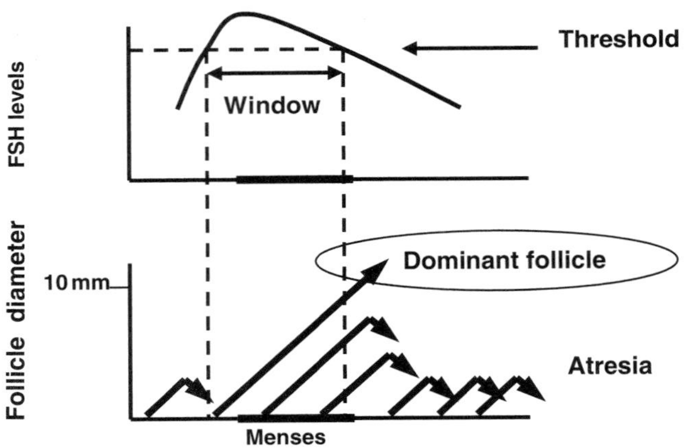

FIGURE 25.1 The intercycle rise in serum FSH concentrations exceeds the threshold for recruitment of a cohort of follicles for further development. The number of follicles recruited is determined by the time ("window") in which the serum FSH is above the threshold at which recruitment occurs. (Modified from Ref. [1].)

cytochrome p450 side chain cleavage oxidases and 3β-hydroxysteroid dehydrogenase. Aromatase activity in the granulosa cells is induced by FSH and converts AD and T into estrone and estradiol (E_2). The involvement of two cell types (granulosa and theca cells) and two hormones (LH and FSH) to produce estrogens from cholesterol has led to the concept of the "two cell, two gonadotropin" theory [1]. In vivo evidence for this concept has grown in recent years. In 1992 Schoot et al. [13] described the effects of recombinant FSH administration on a woman suffering from complete gonadotropin deficiency caused by a previous hypophysectomy. For the first time, the effects of FSH alone could be studied in the absence of endogenous and exogenous LH. Although multiple follicular growth was induced, E_2 levels remained low and no pregnancy ensued. Subsequent case reports confirmed these findings [14, 15].

Recent evidence also points to a central role for LH in monofollicular selection and dominance in the normal ovulatory cycle. As described earlier, despite falling FSH levels in the late follicular phase, the dominant follicle continues to develop. One of the actions of FSH is the induction of LH receptors on granulosa cells. Whereas granulosa cells from early antral follicles respond only to FSH, those from mature follicles, possessing receptors to both gonadotropins, are reponsive to FSH and LH. The maturing dominant follicle may become less dependent on FSH because of the ability to respond to LH levels, which remain relatively constant during the follicular phase [16]. Elegant studies using r-hLH in downregulated women have indicated that although follicles of 14 mm or greater require gonadotropic stimulation for continued estradiol production, they are responsive to either FSH or LH [17]. In contrast, less mature follicles that do not express LH receptors undergo atresia because of falling FSH levels.

GONADOTROPIN PREPARATIONS

The degree to which the type of FSH compound used may influence outcomes in ovulation induction remains the subject of controversy. A metaanalysis comparing the effectiveness of daily urinary FSH with daily HMG for inducing ovulation in women with polycystic ovarian syndrome (PCOS) who had not responded to clomiphene citrate demonstrated no difference in pregnancy rate per treatment cycle [18]. However, the women given FSH were less likely to have moderately severe or severe ovarian hyperstimulation syndrome. Subsequent studies remained consistent with these conclusions [19].

With respect to r-hFSH, a multicenter prospective trial found that the cumulative ovulation rates were comparable with those achieved with purified urinary FSH (95% after three cycles) [20]. The total dose of r-hFSH needed and duration of treatment was less, and the complication rates were similar. Two prospective randomized trials comparing r-hFSH with urinary purified FSH in women having in vitro fertilization were recently reported. One study of 123 women found that the two preparations were equally effective [21]. However, in two larger studies of 981 [22] and 235 women [23], the dose of r-hFSH and the duration of r-hFSH treatment needed to stimulate follicle development were less. More oocytes were recovered, implying greater efficacy for r-hFSH. In a recent metaanalysis of randomized controlled trials comparing r-hFSH with u-FSH for ovulation induction in women with clomiphene citrate resistant PCOS, no significant differences were demonstrated for the ovulation rate (OR 1.19 [95% CI 0.78–1.80]). Moreover, the odds ratios for pregnancy rate (0.95 [95% CI 0.64–1.41]), miscarriage rate (1.26 [95% CI 0.59–2.70], multiple pregnancy rate (0.44 [95% CI 0.16–1.21]), and ovarian hyperstimulation syndrome (1.55 [95% CI 0.50–4.84]) showed no significant difference between r-hFSH and u-FSH [24].

In terms of long-terms risks, u-FSH is associated with a theoretical risk of transmission of prion proteins, which have been identified in human urine [25]. Although infectivity by urine prions in humans and animals has not been reported, and in 40 years of use no such infections have been identified, the risk of prion disease such as new variant Creutzfeldt-Jakob disease has been deemed by some to be sufficient as to advise against the use of u-FSH [26]. However, others consider the risk to be minimal and not in itself a reason to prescribe r-hFSH over u-FSH [27].

The success in clinical studies of pure FSH preparation, increasingly devoid of LH has served to enhance the impression that excess LH is detrimental to oocyte development and chances of pregnancy following therapeutic intervention. However, a number of recent clinical studies, together with an increasing understanding of the function played by LH in oocyte maturation, have begun to redefine the role of LH as a therapeutic agent in anovulatory fertility.

The treatment of hypogonadotropic women with FSH alone leads to follicular development but not pregnancy [13]. Exogenous LH is therefore required to treat this form of anovulatory infertility. Until recently, human menopausal gonadotropin was the only source of exogenous LH for this group of patients. R-hLH now offers the possibility for a more sophisticated and individualized approach to treatment. Recent studies have demonstrated the safety and appropriate dose required to effect follicle development and subsequent pregnancy [28]. It has been established that resting levels of at least 0.5–1.0 IU should be sufficient to provide maximal stimulation to thecal cells [29, 30]. In a recent study of hypogonadotropic women undergoing treatment with r-hFSH and r-hLH, a dose of 75 IU per day of r-hLH was observed to result in follicular development and pregnancy. However, further increases in LH levels above the threshold level needed to gain a response did not appear to induce a greater degree of ovarian stimulation [31].

In normogonadotropic anovulation, endogenous LH does not normally require supplementation. Indeed, the focus on LH in this group of patients has been primarily directed at reducing the potential detrimental effects associated with excessive LH [32]. The improved outcomes referred to earlier following ovulation induction with r-hFSH devoid of LH activity have further supported this view. More recently, however, the demonstration of the importance of LH in optimizing oocyte quality has reopened the debate as to the role of LH in ovulation induction [33]. Supplementation of LH activity may offer advantages in some patients by hastening large follicle development and therefore shortening the duration of treatment [34]. Moreover, the work of Sullivan et al. [17] referred to earlier points to a potential therapeutic role for LH in effecting monofollicular stimulation as part of a sequential ovarian stimulation protocol following initiation with r-hFSH. As the availability of recombinant gonadotropins leads to increasing knowledge of the processes of follicular development and selection, further improvements in the efficacy and safety of ovulation induction may follow.

OVULATION INDUCTION PROTOCOLS

In sharp contrast to ovarian hyperstimulation for assisted reproduction where multiple dominant follicles are sought, the aim of ovulation induction in anovulatory women is the formation and ovulation of a single dominant follicle. To achieve this, specific treatment and monitoring protocols are needed. Whereas several approaches to ovulation induction with gonadotropins have been described, the two currently most often used in clinical practice are the low-dose step-up and the step-down protocols.

The Step-Up Protocol

The initially described "standard" step-up protocol had a starting dose of FSH 150 IU/day [35]. However, this regimen was associated with a high complication rate. Multiple pregnancy rates of up to 36% were reported, while ovarian hyperstimulation occurred in up to 14% of treatment cycles [1]. As a result, this protocol has been largely abandoned.

The concept of the FSH "threshold" proposed by Brown [10] postulated that FSH concentrations must exceed a certain level before follicular development will proceed. Once this level is reached, normal follicular growth requires only a minor further increase above this threshold. Exposure to excessive FSH serum concentrations may lead to excessive follicular development. This experimentally substantiated concept [36] formed the theoretical basis for low-dose step-up regimens for ovulation induction. A low-dose step-up protocol [37] designed to allow the FSH threshold to be reached gradually has now become the most widely used regimen, reducing the risk of excessive stimulation and development of multiple preovulatory follicles. In this protocol, the initial subcutaneous or intramuscular dose of FSH is 50 to 75 IU/day [37]. The dose is increased if after 14 days no response is observed on ultrasonography (and serum estradiol monitoring). Increments of 37.5 IU are then given at weekly intervals up to a maximum of 225 IU/day [37]. The detection of an ovarian response is an indication to continue the current dose until human chorionic gonadotropin (hCG) can be given to stimulate ovulation (Figure 25.2).

In a series describing outcomes using the low-dose step-up regimen, 225 women with PCOS treated for 10 years reported ovulation and pregnancy rates of 72% and 45% respectively [38]. The low-dose step-up protocol is associated with a lower incidence of multiple folliculogenesis and hyperstimulation than the standard protocol [39], and pregnancy rates appear similar [40]. However, the results of the low-dose step-up protocol are negatively influenced by age, obesity, and persistent raised serum LH concentrations [38]. More recent studies focusing on further reducing the starting dose have reported the feasibility of commencing with 50 IU [41] and even 37.5 IU [42]. However, although ovulation can be achieved with this approach, the stimulation period may be further extended [42]. Indeed the sometimes long duration of a treatment cycle before the FSH response dose is achieved remains one of the disadvantages of the low-dose step-up protocol, particularly in women with a high FSH threshold. The ability to determine the individual's FSH response dose threshold would offer the prospect of more efficient application of this protocol.

The Step-Down Protocol

In contrast to the concept of the FSH threshold on which the low-dose step-up protocol is based, the concept of the FSH "window" stresses the significance of the duration of FSH elevation above the threshold level, rather than the magnitude of elevation of FSH for single dominant selection [1, 12]. This concept has recently been substantiated by the demonstration that elevating FSH levels high above the threshold level for a short period in the early follicular phase does not increase the number of dominant follicles [43]. Conversely, when the physiological decrease of FSH in a normal cycle is prevented by administration of FSH in the late follicular phase, the augmented sensitivity for FSH allows several follicles to gain dominance [44]. Moreover,

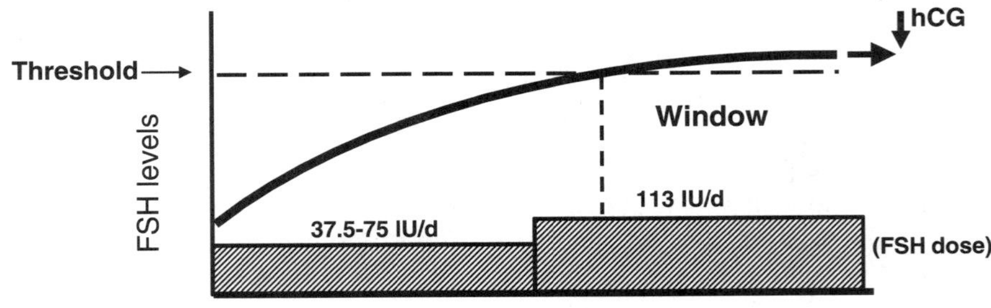

FIGURE 25.2 The low-dose, step-up protocol of gonadotropin administration for ovulation induction. The initial subcutaneous or intramuscular dose of FSH is 37.5 to 75 IU/day; the dose is increased only if, after 14 days, no response is documented on ultrasonography and serum estradiol monitoring. Increments of 37.5 IU then are given at weekly intervals up to a maximum of 225 IU/day. Detection of an ovarian response is an indication to continue the current dose until hCG can be given to stimulate ovulation. (Modified from Ref. [54].)

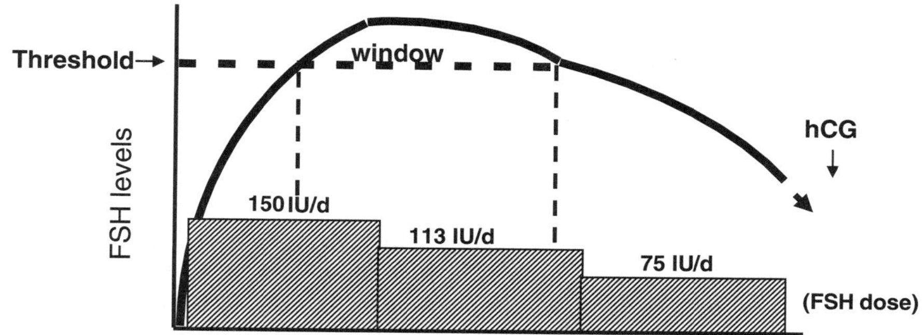

FIGURE 25.3 The step-down protocol of gonadotropin administration is designed to cause monofollicular development. This regimen mimics more closely the physiology of normal cycles. Therapy with FSH at 150 IU/day is started shortly after a spontaneous or progesterone-induced bleed and continued until a dominant follicle (≥10 mm) is seen on transvaginal ultrasonography. The dose is then decreased to 112.5 IU/day followed by a further decrease to 75 IU/day, which is continued until hCG is administered to induce ovulation. (Modified from Ref. [54]).

when the negative feedback effects of estradiol on gonadotropin production are suppressed by administration of anti-estrogens, selection of the preovulatory follicle is overridden [45]. If equal daily doses of FSH are given from the beginning of the follicular phase, steady state serum FSH concentrations are reached after 5 to 7 days [46]. During step-up regimens, elevated FSH serum concentrations may occur during the late follicular phase, which may, in a similar manner, interfere with selection of a single dominant follicle.

Based on these considerations, our group conducted a series of experiments designed to test the hypothesis that a follicle might be stimulated to maturity using a decremental dose regimen, while leading to a reduced number of functionally active follicles (i.e., monofollicular ovarian stimulation). These studies demonstrated that the late follicular phase FSH profile during a step-down regimen closely resembled serum FSH levels in the spontaneous cycle [47, 48]. Moreover, a median daily fall of 5% to 10% in serum FSH levels was observed in all women treated with the step-down regimen, whereas 39% of women treated with a low-dose step-up regimen experienced a reduction[49]. In the majority of women (and consistent with pharmacokinetic studies [50, 51]), the FSH levels remained stable in the late follicular phase.

Further studies on the process of selection of the dominant follicle in the normal cycle have indicated that throughout the cycle, up to 10 nondominant follicles (measuring between 2 and 10 mm in diameter) can be visualiszd by transvaginal ultrasound. The dominant follicle itself can be identified once it has reached a diameter greater than 9 mm [52]. Endocrine studies have confirmed that serum E_2 begins to rise only after a dominant follicle is present [53]. The initial research findings mentioned earlier provided the theoretical basis for developing and monitoring a step-down regimen of ovulation induction.

With the goal of rapidly achieving the FSH threshold for stimulating follicle development, current regimens normally begin therapy with 150 IU/day started shortly after a spontaneous or progesterone-induced bleed. This dose is continued until a dominant follicle (≥10 mm) is observed on transvaginal ultrasonography. The dose is then decreased to 112.5 IU/day followed by a further decrease to 75 IU/day 3 days later, which is continued until hCG is administered to induce ovulation [54] (Figure 25.3).

Should no ovarian response be observed after 3 to 5 days, the FSH dose can be further increased. For some patients, an initial dose of 150 IU/day is too high, reflecting major individual differences in the FSH threshold. The appropriate starting dose may be determined by using the low-dose step-up regimen for the first treatment cycle to assess the individual FSH response dose [55]. Patients who demonstrate good follicular growth with a starting dose of 75 IU/day, the "good responders" who might have been at risk for OHSS with the normal starting dose of the step-down regimen, can thus be identified. Conversely, those who do not respond with ongoing follicle growth to the initial dose should have the daily dosage increased. The second cycle is then initiated as a step-down regimen with a starting dose 37.5 IU above the effective dose in the preceding low-dose step-up cycle.

Experience with the step-down protocol in a series of 82 women suggested that the duration of treatment and total gonadotropin dosage were reduced compared with the low-dose step-up protocol. Moreover, monofollicular growth was more frequently achieved [56]. These findings were subsequently confirmed by a prospective randomized comparison of low-dose step-up and step-down regimens

[49]. The clinical benefits of a more physiological means of stimulating follicle development were reflected in an incidence of monofollicular cycles of 88% compared with 56% observed in women treated with the step-up regimen, presumably reducing the risk of multiple pregnancy and hyperstimulation. Potential health-economic benefits were also apparent because those treated with the step-down regimen required a mean duration of treatment of just 9 days, as opposed to 18 days in women treated with the low-dose step-up regimen.

Other studies assessing outcomes with the step-down protocol have used varied inclusion criteria and treatment protocols. Steinkampf and Banks [57] reported in abstract form a randomized prospective multicenter study comparing a step-down regimen with a step-up regimen. Ovulation and complication rates were equal, but pregnancy rates in the step-down group were significantly reduced. However, the starting dose used was 225 IU hMG/day and therefore may have been excessive [58]. Furthermore, the dose was decreased according to a fixed schedule that did not account for individual differences in the FSH threshold [54]. In a recent randomized study comparing a low-dose step-up with a modified step-down regimen where the starting dose was 300 IU followed by 3 days of no treatment and then r-hFSH 75 IU/day with subsequent stepwise dose increments, monofollicular cycles were more frequently achieved and fewer cycles were cancelled in the step-down group [59].

MONITORING OVULATION INDUCTION

Ovarian response to gonadotropin therapy is monitored using transvaginal ultrasonography to measure follicular diameter. The scans, usually performed every 2 or 4 days, should focus on identifying follicles of intermediate size. hCG (5000 to 10,000 IU) is given intramuscularly on the day that at least one follicle measures greater than 18 mm. If more than three follicles larger than 15 mm are present, stimulation should be stopped, hCG should be withheld, and a barrier contraceptive should be used to prevent multiple pregnancies and ovarian hyperstimulation. Measurements of serum E_2 may also be useful. Preovulatory concentrations far above the normal range (14 to 40 ng/dL [500 to 1500 pmol/L]) may predict the onset of ovarian hyperstimulation syndrome [60], a potentially life-threatening complication characterized by ovarian enlargement, high serum sex steroids, and extravascular fluid accumulation, primarily in the peritoneal cavity. However, it is unclear to what extent E_2 levels add to information generated by ultrasound alone, because large quantities of E_2 can be produced by small or intermediate-sized follicles, particularly in patients with PCOS [47].

PATIENT CHARACTERISTICS AS DETERMINING FACTORS FOR TREATMENT OUTCOME

Experience to date has indicated that the major drawback of the step-down regimen is the risk that the initial starting dose is too high for some patients. In an effort to overcome this problem, sequential low-dose step-up and step-down regimens have been proposed [61]. Starting with a step-up regimen, the FSH dose is reduced when the leading follicle has reached 14 mm in diameter. Comparisons with a group treated with a low-dose step-up regimen showed the incidence of monofollicular cycles to be similar. This approach requires further evaluation and the problem of the large individual variability in the dose of exogenous FSH required for monofollicular development remains to be properly addressed. The associated risks of cycle-to-cycle variability, multifollicular development, OHSS, and multiple pregnancy may be reduced by individualizing the starting dose. This would require the means to reliably predict the dose of FSH at which a given individual will respond by way of monofollicular selection to dominance (i.e., their individual FSH threshold for stimulation). Our group recently developed a prediction model that may be used to determine the individual FSH response dose (which is presumably closely related to the FSH threshold) [55]. Women about to undergo low-dose step-up ovulation induction with recombinant FSH were subject to a standard clinical, sonographic, and endocrine screening. The measured parameters were analyzed for predictors of the FSH dose on the day of ovarian response. In multivariate analysis, body mass index (BMI), ovarian response to preceding clomiphene citrate medication (clomiphene citrate resistant anovulation [CRA], or failure to conceive despite ovulatory cycles), initial free insulin-like growth factor-1 (free IGF-1), and serum FSH levels were included in the final model [55]. Application of this model may enable the administration of the lowest possible daily dose of exogenous gonadotropins to surpass the individual FSH threshold of a given patient and achieve follicular development and subsequent ovulation. In a subsequent analysis of women with PCOS who had undergone ovulation induction with the step-down regimen, a correlation was observed between the predicted individual FSH response dose and the number of treatment days before dominance was observed [62]. The presumption that a static formula can predict the ideal response dose for an individual patient implies that within a certain small range (cycle-to-cycle variation) this dose is constant. However, this model was developed from a first low-dose step-up induction cycle. It should be tested whether this model can also be applied for subsequent induction cycles. Until this is known, fine-tuning of the starting dose in following cycles should be done by sonography. Ongoing prospective studies will further evaluate the value of this individually tailored approach to gonadotropin ovulation induction.

INSULIN SENSITIZERS AS ADJUVANT THERAPY

A number of studies have now been published indicating that metformin can increase menstrual cyclicity, improve spontaneous ovulation, and thus promote fertility by correcting hyperinsulinemia [63–65]. Because women with WHO class II anovulatory infertility frequently demonstrate a hyperstimulatory response to FSH, it has been proposed that metformin may have an adjuvant role to gonadotropin ovulation induction by correcting hyperinsulinemia and hence normalizing the response of the patient to gonadotropin stimulation [65]. In a study of clomiphene citrate-resistant women with PCOS who were randomized to pretreatment with metformin or no pretreatment before ovulation induction with FSH, the incidence of multiple follicular development was reduced in those receiving metformin beforehand [66]. Although these findings suggest that treatment with metformin may reduce the rate of hyperstimulatory response with FSH treatment, few randomized controlled trials of insulin-sensitizing drugs as an adjuvant to gonadotropin ovulation induction have yet been reported, and their role in this context remains uncertain.

CONCLUSION

In appropriately selected women with normogonadotropic clomiphene-resistant anovulatory infertility, induction of ovulation using a step-down gonadotropin dose regimen results in comparable ovulation and pregnancy rates and a much shorter induction period than that required with a low-dose step-up regimen. By offering more ovulations per a given period, health economic benefits are likely to accrue. The more physiological late follicular phase FSH profile and more frequently occurring E_2 levels within the normal preovulatory range have implications for the risk of ovarian hyperstimulation and multiple pregnancy and therefore for the safety and efficacy of gonadotropin ovulation induction. Certain aspects of the step-down protocol require attention before clinical introduction. A starting dose of 150 IU/day may induce an excessive response in some women. Intensive monitoring (every 2 to 3 days) is therefore recommended. Monitoring a step-down regimen requires additional skills, and complications may arise in inexperienced hands. The use of an initial dose-finding step-up cycle may increase safety and efficacy of the step-down regimen. However, reliable prediction of the individual's FSH threshold level may offer an alternative approach.

Further evaluation of health economics of FSH ovulation induction (singleton pregnancies in relation to risks, side effects, complications, and costs) and the possibilities for improvement by developing individually tailored, cumulative pregnancy approaches are required. In this light, current approaches to gonadotropin ovulation induction should also be compared prospectively with weight reduction in obese patients, laser ovarian surgery, and in vitro fertilization.

References

1. Fauser, B. C. J. M., and van Heusden, A. M. (1997). Manipulation of human ovarian function: Physiological concepts and clinical consequences. *Endocr. Rev.* 18, 71–106.
2. Baker, T. C. (1963). A quantitative and cytological study of germ cells in human ovaries. *Proc. R. Soc. Ser. B.* 158, 417–433.
3. Schwartzman, R. A., and Cidlowski, J. A. (1993). Apoptosis: The biochemistry and molecular biology of programmed cell death. *Endocr. Rev.* 14, 133–151.
4. Gougeon, A. (1993). Dynamics of human follicle growth. A morphologic perspective. In *The Ovary*, eds. E. Y. Adashi and P. C. K. Leung, 21–39. New York: Raven Press.
5. Macklon, N. S., and Fauser, B. C. J. M. (1998). Follicle development during the normal menstrual cycle. *Maturitas* 30, 181–188.
6. Roseff, S. J., Bangah, M. L., Kettel, L. M., et al. (1989). Dynamic changes in circulating inhibin levels during the luteo-follicular transition of the human menstrual cycle. *J. Clin. Endocrinol. Metab.* 69, 1033–1039.
7. Le Nestour, E., Marraoui, Lahlou, N., et al. (1993). Role of estradiol in the rise in follicle-stimulating hormone levels during the luteal-follicular transition. *J. Clin. Endocrinol. Metab.* 77, 439–442.
8. Hall, J. E., Schoenfeld, D. A., Martin, K. A., et al. (1992). Hypothalamic gonadotropin-releasing hormone secretion and follicle-stimulating hormone dynamics during the luteal-follicular transition. *J. Clin. Endocrinol. Metab.* 74, 600–607.
9. Macklon, N. S., and Fauser, B. C. J. M. (2001). Follicle-stimulating hormone and advanced follicle development in the human. *Arch. Med. Res.* 32, 595–600.
10. Brown, J. B. (1978). Pituitary control of ovarian function concepts derived from gonadotrophin therapy. *Aust. NZ. J. Obstet. Gynaecol.* 18, 47–54.
11. van der Meer, M., Hompes, P. G. A., Scheele, F., et al. (1994). Follicle stimulating hormone (FSH) dynamics of low dose step-up ovulation induction with FSH in patients with polycystic ovary syndrome. *Hum. Reprod.* 9, 1612–1617.
12. Baird, D. T. (1987). A model for follicular selection and ovulation: Lessons from superovulation. *J. Steroid. Biochem.* 27, 15–23.
13. Schoot, D. C., Coelingh Bennink, H. J. T., Mannaerts, B. M. J. L., Lamberts, S. W. J., Bouchard, P., and Fauser, B. C. J. M. (1992). Human recombinant follicle-stimulating hormone induces growth of preovulatory follicles without concomitant increase in androgen and estrogen biosynthesis in a woman with isolated gonadotropin deficiency. *J. Clin. Endocrinol. Metab.* 75, 1471–1473.

14. Balasch, J., Miro, F., Burzaco, I., et al. (1995). The role of luteinizing hormone in human follicle development and oocyte fertility: Evidence from in vitro fertilization in a woman with long-standing hypogonadotrophic hypogonadism and using recombinant human follicle stimulating hormone. *Hum. Reprod.* 10, 1678–1683.
15. Battaglia, C., Salvatori, M., Regnani, G., et al. (2000). Successful induction of ovulation using highly purified follicle-stimulating hormone in a woman with Kallmann's syndrome. *Fertil. Steril.* 73, 284–286.
16. Zeleznik, A. J., and Hillier, S. G. (1984). The role of gonadotropins in the selection of the preovulatory follicle. *Clin. Obstet. Gynecol.* 27, 927–940.
17. Sullivan, M. W., Stewart-Akers, A., Krasnow, J. S., et al. (1999). Ovarian responses in women to recombinant follicle-stimulating hormone and luteinizing hormone (LH): A role for LH in the final stages of follicular maturation. *J. Clin. Endocrinol. Metab.* 84, 228–232.
18. Hughes, E., Collins, J., and Vanderkerkhove, P. (1996). Ovulation induction with urinary follicle stimulating hormone vs human menopausal gonadotropin for clomiphene-resistant polycystic ovary syndrome. (*Cochrane Review*). In: The Cochrane Library, 2 (2003), Oxford Update Software.
19. Yarali, H., Bukulmez, O., and Gurgan, T. (1999). Urinary follicle-stimulating hormone (FSH) versus recombinant FSH in clomiphene citrate-resistant, normogonadotropic, chronic anovulation: A prospective randomized study. *Fertil. Steril.* 72, 276–281.
20. Coelingh Bennink, H. J., Fauser, B. C., and Out, H. J. for the European Puregon Collaborative Anovulation Study Group. (1998). Recombinant follicle-stimulating hormone (FSH; Puregon) is more efficient than urinary FSH (Metrodin) in women with clomiphene citrate-resistant, normogonadotropic, chronic anovulation: A prospective, multicenter, assessor-blind, randomized, clinical trial. *Fertil. Steril.* 69, 19–25.
21. Recombinant human FSH study group. (1995). Clinical assessment of recombinant human follicle-stimulating hormone in stimulating ovarian follicular development before in vitro fertilization. *Fertil. Steril.* 63, 77–86.
22. Out, H. J., Mannaerts, B. M. J. L., Driessen, S. G. A. J., et al. (1995). A prospective, randomized, assessor-blind, multicentre study comparing recombinant and urinary follicle-stimulating hormone (Puregon vs Metrodin) in in vitro fertilization. *Hum. Reprod.* 10, 2534–2540.
23. Bergh, C., Howles, C. M., Borg, K., et al. (1997). Recombinant human follicle stimulating hormone (rh-FSH; Gonal F) versus highly purified urinary FSH (Metrodin HP): Results of a randomized comparative study in women undergoing assisted reproductive techniques. *Hum. Reprod.* 12, 2133–2139.
24. Bayram, N., van Wely, M., and van der Veen, F. (2002). Recombinant FSH versus urinary gonadotrophins for ovulation induction in subfertility associated with polycystic ovary syndrome.
25. Shaked, G. M., Shaked, Y., Kariv-Inbal, Z., et al. (2001). A protease-resistant prion protein isoform is present in urine of animals and humans affected with prion diseases. *J. Biol. Chem.* 276, 31479–31482.
26. Matorras, R., and Rodriguez-Escudero, F. J. (2002). Bye-bye urinary gonadotrophins? The use of urinary gonadotropins should be discouraged. *Hum. Reprod.* 17, 1675.
27. Balen, A. (2002). Is there a risk of prion disease after the administration of urinary-derived gonadotrophins? *Hum. Reprod.* 17, 1676–1680.
28. The European Recombinant Human LH Study Group. (1998). Recombinant human luteinizing hormone (LH) to support recombinant human follicle stimulating hormone (FSH)-induced follicular development in LH- and FSH-deficient anovulatory women: A dose finding study. *J. Clin. Endocrinol. Metab.* 83, 1507–1514.
29. Kousta, E., White, D. M., Piazzi, A., et al. (1996). Successful induction of ovulation and completed pregnancy using recombinant human luteinizing hormone and follicle stimulating hormone in a woman with Kallmann's syndrome. *Hum. Reprod.* 11, 70–76.
30. Chappel, S. C., and Howles, C. (1991). Reevaluation of the roles of luteinizing hormone and follicle stimulating hormone in the ovulatory process. *Hum. Reprod.* 6, 1206–1212.
31. Burgués, S. (2001). The effectiveness and safety of recombinant human LH to support follicular development induced by recombinant human FSH in WHO group 1 anovulation: Evidence from a multicentre study in Spain. *Hum. Reprod.* 16, 2525–2532.
32. Shoham, Z., Jacobs, H. S., and Insler, V. (1993). Luteinizing hormone: Its role, mechanism of action, and detrimental effects when hypersecreted during the follicular phase. *Fertil. Steril.* 59, 1153–1161.
33. Filicori, M., and Cognigni, G. E. (2001). Roles and novel regimens of luteinizing hormone and follicle-stimulating hormone in ovulation induction. *J. Clin. Endocrinol. Metab.* 86, 1437–1441.
34. Filicori, M., Cognigni, G. E., Taraborrelli, S., et al. (1999). Luteinizing hormone activity supplementation enhances follicle-stimulating hormone efficacy and improves ovulation induction outcome. *J. Clin. Endocrinol. Metab.* 84, 2659–2663.
35. Franks, S., and Hamilton-Fairley, D. (1996). Ovulation induction: Gonadotropins. In *Reproductive Endocrinology, Surgery and Technology*, eds. E. Y. Adashi, J. A. Rock, and Z. Rosenwaks, 1207–1223. Philadelphia: Lipincott Raven.
36. Van Weissenbruch, M. M., Schoemaker, H. C., Drexhage, H. A., et al. (1993). Pharmaco-dynamics of human menopausal gonadotropin (HMG) and follicle-stimulating hormone (FSH). The importance of the FSH concentration in initiating follicular growth in polycystic ovary-like disease. *Hum. Reprod.* 8, 813–821.
37. Franks, S., Mason, H. D., Polson, D. W., et al. (1988). Mechanism and management of ovulation failure in women with polycystic ovary syndrome. *Hum. Reprod.* 3, 531–534.
38. White, D. M., Polson, D. W., Kiddy, D., et al. (1996). Induction of ovulation with low-dose gonadotropins in polycystic ovary syndrome: An analysis of 109 pregnancies in 225 women. *J. Clin. Endocrinol. Metab.* 81, 3821–3824.
39. Buvat, J., Buvat, H. M., Marcolin, G., et al. (1989). Purified follicle-stimulating hormone in polycystic ovary syndrome: Slow administration is safer and more effective. *Fertil. Steril.* 52, 553–557.
40. Shoham, Z., Patel, A., and Jacobs, H. S. (1991). Polycystic ovary syndrome; Safety and effectiveness of a stepwise and low-dose administration of purified FSH. *Fertil. Steril.* 55, 1051–1055.

41. Hayden, C. J., Rutherford, A. J., and Balen, A. H. (1999). Induction of ovulation with the use of a starting dose of 50 units of recombinant human follicle-stimulating hormone (Puregon). *Fertil. Steril.* 71, 106–108.
42. Balasch, J., Fabregues, F., Creus, M., et al. (2000). Recombinant human follicle-stimulating hormone for ovulation induction in polycystic ovary syndrome: A prospective, randomized trial of two starting doses in a chronic low-dose step-up protocol. *J. Assist. Reprod. Genet.* 17, 561–565.
43. Schipper, I., Hop, W. C. J., and Fauser, B. C. J. M. (1998). The follicle-stimulating hormone (FSH) threshold/window concept examined by differential interventions with exogenous FSH during the follicular phase of the normal menstrual cycle: Duration rather than magnitude of FSH increase affects follicle development. *J. Clin. Endocrinol. Metab.* 83, 1292–1298.
44. Hohmann, F., Laven, J. S., de Jong, F. H., Eijkemans, M. J., and Fauser, B. C. J. M. (2001). Low dose exogenous FSH initiated during the early, mid or late follicular phase can induce dominant follicle development. *Hum. Reprod.* 16, 846–854.
45. Zeleznik, A. J. Hutchison, J. S., and Schuler, H. M. (1985). Interference with the gonadotropin-suppressing actions of estradiol in macaques overrides the selection of a single preovulatory follicle. *Endocrinol.* 117, 991–999.
46. Mizunama, H., Takagi, T., Honjyo, S., et al. (1991). Clinical pharmodynamics of urinary follicle-stimulating hormone and its applications for pharmokinetic simulation program. *Fertil. Steril.* 53, 440–445.
47. Schoot, D. C., Hop, W. C., Pache, T. D., de Jong, F. H., and Fauser, B. C. J. M. (1993). Growth of the dominant follicle is similar to normal in patients with gonadotropin-stimulated polycystic ovary syndrome exhibiting monofollicular development during a decremental dose regimen. *Acta. Endocrinol. (Kbh)* 129, 126–129.
48. Van Dessel, H. J. H. M., Schoot, B. C., Schipper, I., et al. (1995). Circulating immunoreactive and bioactive follicle-stimulating hormone concentrations in anovulatory infertile women during gonadotrophin induction of ovulation using a decremental dose regimen. *Hum. Reprod.* 11, 101–108.
49. Van Santbrink, E. J. P., and Fauser, B. C. J. M. (1997). Urinary follicle-stimulating hormone for normogonadotropic clomiphene-resistant infertility: Prospective, randomized comparison between low dose step-up and step-down dose regimens. *J. Clin. Endocrinol. Metab.* 82, 3597–3602.
50. Mannaerts, B. J., Shoham, Z., Schoot, B. S., Bouchard, P., Harlin, J., and Fauser, B. C. J. M. (1993). Single dose pharmacokinetics and pharmacodynamics of recombinant human FSH (Org 32489) in gonadotropin-deficient volunteers. *Fertil. Steril.* 59, 108–114.
51. Van Santbrink, E. J, Hop, W. C., Van Dessel, H. J., de Jong, F. H., and Fauser, B. C. (1995). Decremental follicle-stimulating hormone and dominant follicle development during the normal menstrual cycle. *Fertil. Steril.* 64, 37–43.
52. Pache, T. D., Wladimiroff, J. W., de Jong, F. H., et al. (1990). Growth patterns of non-dominant ovarian follicles during the normal menstrual cycle. *Fertil. Steril.* 54, 638–644.
53. Van Dessel, H. J. H. M., Schipper, I., Pache, T. D., et al. (1996). Normal human follicle development: An evaluation of corelations with oestradiol, androstenedione and progesterone levels in individual follicles. *Clin. Endocrinol. (Oxf).* 36, 565–571.
54. Fauser, B. C. J. M., Donderwinkel, P., and Schoot, D. C. (1993). The step-down principle in gonadotrophin treatment and the role of GnRH analogues. *Bailliéres. Clin. Obstet. Gynaecol.* 7, 309–330.
55. Imani, B., Eijkemans, M., Faessen, G., et al. (2002). Prediction of the individual follicle-stimulating hormone threshold for gonadotropin induction of ovulation in normogonadotropic anovulatory infertility: An approach to increase safety and efficiency. *Fertil. Steril.* 77, 83–90.
56. van Santbrink, E. J. P, Donderwinkel, P. F. J, van Dessel, H. J. H. M., et al. (1995). Gonadotrophin induction of ovulation using a step-down dose regimen: Single center clinical experience in 82 patients. *Hum. Reprod.* 110, 1048–1053.
57. Steinkampf, M. P., and Banks, K. S.(1993). "Stepdown vs conventional FSH treatment in patients with WHO group II amenorrhoea: Results of a U.S. multicenter clinical trial." *Annual meeting American Fertility Society, Montreal, Canada.* Abstract, S21–S22.
58. Schoot, D. C., Pache, T. D., Hop, W. C., de Jong, F. H., and Fauser, B. C. J. M. (1992). Growth patterns of ovarian follicles during induction of ovulation with decreasing doses of HMG following presumed selection in polycystic ovarian syndrome. *Fertil. Steril.* 57, 1117–1120.
59. Balasch, J., Fábregues, F., Creus, M., Puerto, B., Penarrubia, J., and Vanrell, J. A. (2001). Follicular development and hormone concentrations following recombinant FSH administration for anovulation associated with polycystic ovarian syndrome: Prospective, randomized comparison between low-dose step-up and modified step-down regimens. *Hum. Reprod.* 16, 652–656.
60. Haning, R. V., Austin, C. W., Carlston, I. H., Kuzma, D. L., Shapiro, S. S., and Zweibel, W. J. (1983). Plasma estradiol is superior to ultrasound and urinary estriol glucuronide as a predictor of ovarian hyperstimualtion during induction of ovulation with menotropins. *Fertil. Steril.* 40, 31–36.
61. Hugues, J. N., Cédrin-Durnerin, I., Avril, C., et al. (1996). Sequential step-up and step-down dose regimen: An alternative method for ovulation induction with follicle-stimulating hormone in polycystic ovarian syndrome. *Hum. Reprod.* 11, 2581–2584.
62. Van Santbrink, E. J. P., Eijkemans, M. J. C., Macklon, N. S., and Fauser, B. C. J. M. (2002). FSH response-dose can be predicted in ovulation induction for normogonadotropic anovulatory infertility. *Eur. J. Endocrinol.* 147, 1–4.
63. Velazquez, E. M., Mendoza, S, Hamer, T., et al. (1994). Metformin therapy in polycystic ovary syndrome reduces hyperinsulinaemia, insulin resistance, hyperandrogenaemia, and systolic blood pressure, while facilitating normal menses and pregnancy. *Metabolism*, 43, 647–654.
64. Glueck, C. J., Wang, P., Fontaine, R., et al. (1999). Metformin-induced resumption of normal menses in 39 of 43 (91%) previously amenorrheic women with the polycystic ovary syndrome. *Metabolism*, 48, 511–519.
65. Nestler, J. E., Stovall, D., Akhter, N., et al. (2002). Strategies for the use of insulin-sensitizing drugs to treat infertility in women with polycystic ovary syndrome. *Fertil. Steril.* 77, 209–215.
66. De Leo, V., la Marca, A., Ditto, A., et al. (1999). Effects of metformin on gonadotropin-induced ovulation in women with polycystic ovary syndrome. *Fertil. Steril.* 72, 282–285.

CHAPTER **26**

The Role of Gn-RH Antagonists in Supporting Ovarian Hyperstimulation Protocols

NATHALIE CHABBERT-BUFFET, F. OLIVENNES, BART C. J. M. FAUSER, PHILIPPE BOUCHARD, AND RENÉ FRYDMAN

ABSTRACT

Gn-RH antagonists result from multiple amino acid substitutions from the native Gn-RH structure. Gn-RH antagonists are inactive but able to bind to Gn-RH receptors with high affinity. They behave as competitive inhibitors of Gn-RH by binding to its receptors and allow immediate suppression of gonadotropins and sex steroids. Their clinical applications are still being studied, particularly in assisted reproductive technologies (ART) where they are more user-friendly and allow a dramatic improvement in the risk of ovarian hyperstimulation syndrome (OHSS). The main concern of their use is a possible reduction of ongoing pregnancy rates in antagonist treated in vitro fertilization (IVF) cycles when compared with Gn-RH agonist treated cycles [1]. The mechanisms of this difference are still speculative and eventually related to abnormal endometrial maturation. In addition, the necessary learning curve inherent to the use of any new treatment may cause interference. Additional studies are necessary for treatment protocol optimization.

INTRODUCTION

IVF (or IVF combined with intracytoplasmic sperm injection [ICSI]) is the only treatment available for infertile couples with bilateral tubal obstruction or severe oligo/azoospermia. The use IVF/ICSI is now used as treatment for couples with unexplained infertility. The risks of IVF are now well documented, including OHSS (which is sometimes life-threatening) and multiple pregnancy-induced morbidity and mortality. The reduction in the number of transferred embryos could reduce the multiple pregnancy rate, but the procedures of embryo quality assessment are still too weak. Therefore at least two embryos are usually transferred to obtain acceptable pregnancy rates in IVF cycles, although this has an elevated risk of causing multiple pregnancies. Interestingly, a pregnancy rate of 10% per cycle is well accepted by the scientific community for in vivo cycles that use monoovulation induction [2]. Compared with IVF cycles, monoovulation induction cycles are less expensive, less time consuming, and more user-friendly; they also have a reduced risk of OHSS. For IVF cycles a pregnancy rate of approximately 25% per cycle is acceptable because of the risks and costs. In fact, additional IVF costs can go beyond $15,000 per pregnancy when compared with standard care. In addition, in the United States neonatal costs for IVF-associated multiple pregnancies is 36% more than the actual cost of the IVF procedure [2].

The association of Gn-RH analog treatment to gonadotropin stimulation has allowed significant reduction in the risk of OHSS, premature luteinization, and subsequent cycle cancellation. It has also simplified the organization of facilities providing IVF because of improvements to the scheduling of ovarian stimulation. The possible role of Gn-RH antagonists in improving ovarian hyperstimulation management is currently being evaluated and is discussed later.

STRUCTURE AND MECHANISM OF ACTION OF Gn-RH ANALOGS

Following the elucidation of the structure of Gn-RH in 1971 by Schally and coworkers, Gn-RH analogs were synthesized [3]. Several thousand molecules were produced with the initial hope that these analogs would improve fertility. In 1978 it was discovered that repeated administration of Gn-RH superanalogs (Gn-RH agonists) produced a decrease in gonadal function associated with a significant drop in sex steroid levels following an initial increase [4].

Treatment with a Gn-RH agonistic analog results in an initial rise in gonadotropin secretion caused by its binding to Gn-RH receptors and their subsequent activation (Figure 26.1). In relation to the continuous occupation of the receptors, luteinizing hormone (LH) levels decrease whereas follicle-stimulating hormone (FSH) levels also decrease but to a lesser degree because of the desensitization process [5]. If the agonists are administered for a long period (i.e., several months), LH levels remain suppressed

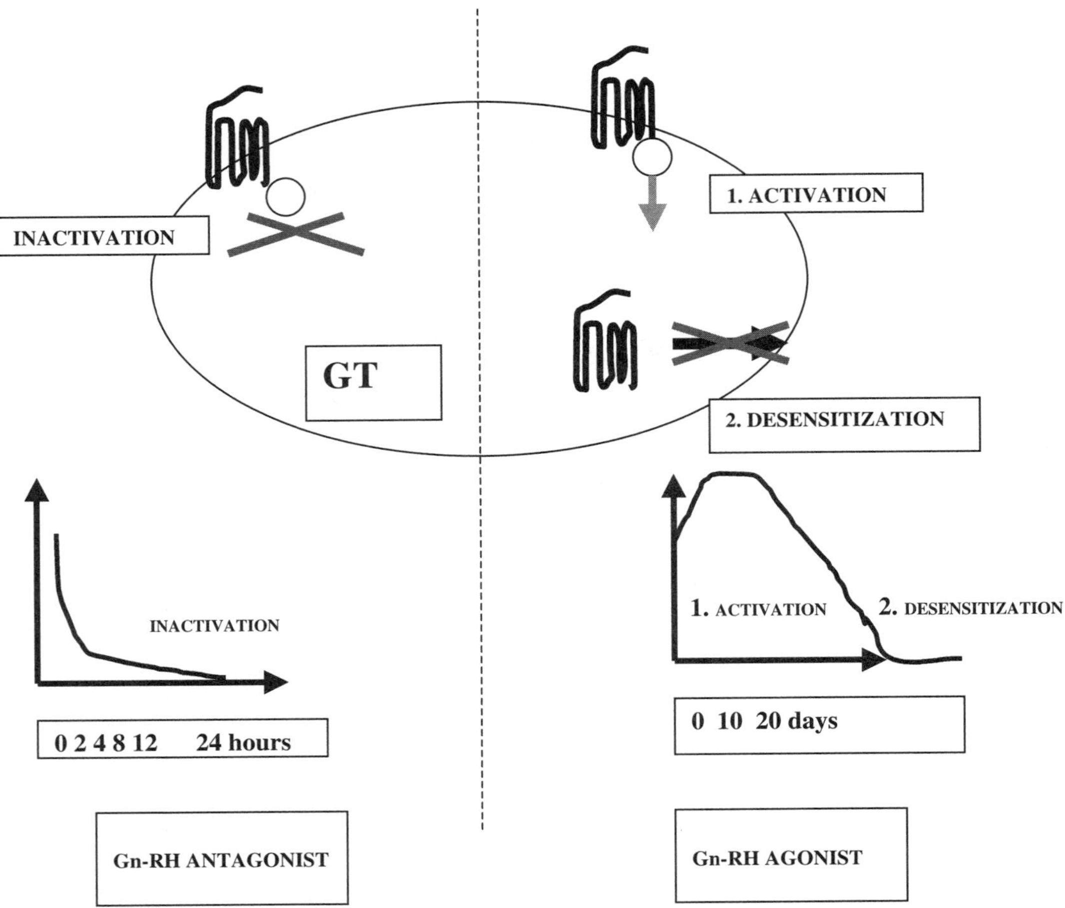

FIGURE 26.1 Mechanisms of action of Gn-RH analogs agonists vs antagonists. (See color plate.)

whereas FSH levels return to normal and eventually may rise to supraphysiological levels [6]. The mechanisms underlying the desensitization and the changes in FSH levels, or even in the α-subunit overproduction, are poorly understood. What is known, however, is that the desensitization is not specific of agonistic analogs and can be observed with continuous administration of Gn-RH itself. In addition, desensitization does not require a decrease in receptor numbers or in Ca++ mediated events [7]. Until recently, the use of Gn-RH analogs has been restricted to Gn-RH agonists. Their indications are now well established and concern the suppression of LH-dependent estradiol/testosterone-dependent disorders. A significant indication is now represented by ART (25% of the agonist market [8]).

Gn-RH antagonists, discovered as early as 1972, have a mechanism of action completely different from agonists because they bind to Gn-RH receptors with high affinity but are unable to activate their transducing capacities because of their inactive nature (see Figure 26.1). They thus behave as competitive inhibitors [9–11]. The first antagonistic analogs are now commercially available (cetrorelix, ganirelix), and their use is thus far restricted to the suppression of the LH surge in ovarian superovulation protocols in ART (e.g., IVF, ICSI) [12, 13]. Gn-RH antagonists result from multiple amino acid substitutions from the native Gn-RH structure, and being inactive but able to bind to Gn-RH receptors with high affinity, they behave as competitive inhibitors of Gn-RH binding to its receptors [11]. The site of binding of Gn-RH antagonists seems to differ from those of agonists [14]. In addition, receptor dimerization that occurs following Gn-RH agonist binding does not seem to occur following antagonist administration [7]. Their subcutaneous administration results in the rapid decrease in bioactive and immunoreactive LH followed by a secondary decrease in FSH levels. The latter effect is significant following several injections of antagonists probably because of the long half-life of FSH [15]. This confirms that there is no differential control for LH and FSH and justifies the terminology of Gn-RH rather than luteinizing hormone-releasing hormone (LH-RH). Some discussion still occurs as to whether Gn-RH receptors decrease following antagonist administration. Schally and colleagues have reported a significant decrease in Gn-RH receptors 3

Table 26.1 Structures of Gn-RH Antagonists

Abarelix*	Ac-DNal-DCpa-DPal-Ser-N-Me Tyr-Dasn-Leu-Ilys-Pro-DAla-NH_2
Acyline†	Ac-DNal-DCpa-DPal-Ser-Aph-Daph(Ac)-Leu-ILys-Pro-DAla-NH_2
Antarelix‡	Ac-DNal-DCpa-DPal-Ser-Tyr-DHci-Leu-ILys-Pro-Dala-NH_2
Iturelix‖	Ac-DNal-DCpa-DPal-Ser-Lys(Nic)-Dlys(Nic)-Leu-Ilys-Pro-Dala-NH_2
Azaline B	Ac-DNal-DCpa-DPal-Ser-Aph(Atz)-DAph(Atz)-Leu-Ilys-Pro-Dala-NH_2
Cetrorelix¶	Ac-DNal-DCpa-DPal-Ser-Tyr-Dcit-Leu-Arg-Pro-DAla-NH_2
Ganirelix#	Ac-DNal-DCpa-DPal-Ser-Tyr-DHArg(Et_2)-Leu-Harg(Et_2)-Pro-Dala-NH_2
Nal-Glu	Ac-DNal-DCpa-DPal-Ser-Arg-Dglu(AA)-Leu-Arg- Pro-Dala-NH_2
FE 200486§	Ac-DNal-DCpa-DPal-Ser-Aph(Hor)-DAph(Cba)-Leu-ILys-Pro-Dala-NH_2

Gn-RHpGlu-His-Trp-Ser-Tyr-Gly-Leu-Arg-Pro-Gly-NH_2

Products in development:

*Praecis Pharmaceuticals: peptide polymer complex for sustained delivery.

†Patent assigned to Salk Institute; developed by the National Institutes of Health.

‡Tavarelix, Lab Asta Medica.

§Lab Ferring.

Products already on the market:

‖Antide, Lab Ares Serono.

¶Cetrotide, Lab Ares Serono.

#Antagon, Orgalutran, Lab Organon, T1/2 = 12.8h single dose; 16.2h multiple dose.

to 6 hours following cetrorelix administration in the rat. This decrease was even higher than what is observed following agonist treatment. Receptor gene transcription is also decreased in a significant manner [16]. The clinical significance of this phenomenon is still unknown because other authors have reported that, regardless of the duration of the treatment with antagonists, a response to exogenous Gn-RH was maintained [17].

Gn-RH antagonists (Table 26.1) are produced by a significant substitution of four to six amino acids for non-natural D amino acids. Since 1972, when the first antagonist was synthesized by removal of the His in position 2 (an amino acid essential for biological action), many antagonists have been produced [11, 18]. Their development was, however, limited because of side effects related to their ability to release histamine from the skin at the site of injection or to eventually provoke systemic reactions [19]. This is especially true with the $DArg^6$ class of antagonists. New generations of Gn-RH antagonists devoid of significant histamine-releasing properties are now available for clinical use [20]. The more advanced compounds include cetrorelix and ganirelix [21, 22]; other antagonists such as abarelix, antarelix (Teverelix), FE 200486, and acyline are in development [23]. Finally, antagonists suppress sex steroids to castration levels at milligram doses. This difference with agonists that require microgram doses for their action is probably because of competitive inhibitors that need to occupy all Gn-RH receptors in a continuous manner. The pharmacokinetic properties of Gn-RH antagonists remain a mystery because plasma half-life may vary from a few hours to more than 30 hours or more in relation to the dose administered and to a gel formation, probably at the site of injection. The gel formation is under the influence of NaCl concentrations. This intrinsic "depot" property of antagonists has been used to manufacture long-acting forms of antagonists. Although many companies claimed to have obtained long-acting preparations, no long-term reproducible data have been produced thus far. However, it remains clear that the antagonists' effect is proportional to their plasma levels.

Finally, Gn-RH receptors have been described on gonadotroph cells (Gn-RHR-I) [24, 25] while the presence of extra pituitary receptors, including the recently cloned, Gn-RH-RII, remains controversial [26, 27]. Thus far, although many studies produced data supporting a role of Gn-RH and its analogs in vitro, no convincing in vivo extra pituitary effects of Gn-RH analogs have been demonstrated [28–32]. Although this is not definitive proof for the lack of extra pituitary effect, there is no reason to believe that antagonists could behave differently than agonists because they share the same receptors.

GN-RH ANTAGONISTS IN OVARIAN HYPERSTIMULATION

In clinical practice, although it is the case in vitro, Gn-RH antagonists do not produce significant desensitization of Gn-RH receptors [33, 34]. As discussed previously, these antagonists can suppress gonadotropin secretion in a rapid and dramatic manner. It is also clear that Gn-RH antagonists are more potent in suppressing LH and FSH than Gn-RH agonists [15]. The suppression of gonadotropin production is observed within hours and lasts from 10 to 100 hours, depending on the dose administered, because antagonists have an intrinsic property for increased half-life in relation to the dose administered. This phenomenon is generally considered to be caused by precipitation of the product and a subsequent depot effect. Obviously there is no flare following antagonist administration and the gonadotropin suppression can be overridden by exogenous administration of native Gn-RH or Gn-RH agonist [34]. In normal women, Gn-RH antagonist administration can postpone the LH surge if administered at the end of the follicular phase before the LH surge or even at the time of the surge [5, 35, 36]. Although it is impossible in humans to directly measure Gn-RH levels in the portal circulation, this effect of antagonist treatment is clearly related to the key role of Gn-RH during the surge as it has been demonstrated in rats, ewes, and nonhuman primates (all species in which the secretion of Gn-RH is accessible to direct determination) [36–42]. The only outstanding controversy concerns the amount of Gn-RH that is secreted at the time of the surge [43]. Recent evidence would support that Gn-RH has a permissive action and that increasing levels are not required to trigger the gonadotropin surge.

Based on this information, it seems likely that Gn-RH antagonists are of interest in circumstances where gonadotropin suppression needs to be profound and immediate. Long-term applications will have to wait until depot preparations are available, provided that the final cost of antagonists remains reasonable.

Clinical applications therefore include controlled ovarian stimulation for IVF, in which one or two injections of Gn-RH antagonist or longer protocols using repeated daily administration prevent LH surges [13, 44–46] (Figure 26.2). The advantage of the first regimen using a single or two injections is in suppressing the LH surge without a long-lasting depletion of endogenous gonadotropins. At the same time, the multiple dose regimen (although using low doses) provides a longer and eventually deeper suppression of LH, which can produce lower estradiol plasma levels that result in reduced endometrial quality when gonadotropin regimens devoid of LH (using recombinant FSH preparations) are used [47].

Single Dose Gn-RH Antagonist Regimen

Initial investigations with cetrorelix used a 5-mg dose administered twice on days 7 and 9 of stimulation. It was observed that the second injection was usually unnecessary because hCG was administered on the same day. It was also concluded that the 5-mg dose induced deep sustained suppression of LH and could be lowered [48]. A single dose protocol using a 3-mg dose of cetrorelix on day 7 of stimulation was studied in a pilot study, which still showed efficient suppression of LH surges [49]. A dose-finding study was then conducted to determine the minimal efficient dose of cetrorelix. The IVF results were identical between the 2- and 3-mg groups [50]. However, the LH suppression with the 2-mg dose was of shorter duration, and LH peaks were observed on day 4 after cetrorelix injection. The single dose 3-mg cetrorelix protocol was thus considered the safer solution, with a protection period of at least four days. The number of human menopausal gonadotropin (hMG) ampoules was also clearly reduced when compared with the long antagonist protocol using a depot preparation [49]. The interruption of the LH rise does not appear to have any deleterious effect on IVF results [36]. The cetrorelix single dose protocol was also compared with the Gn-RH agonist long protocol using a depot formulation of triptorelin [47]. The mean duration of stimulation was significantly reduced in the cetrorelix group, and the mean number of gonadotropins used was higher in the triptorelin group. The efficacy of cetrorelix given in a single 3-mg dose was excellent as well: 18 of the 115 patients (15.6%) in the cetrorelix group experienced an LH surge (up to 10 UI/L or more) on the day of cetrorelix injection, and no patients had an LH surge after cetrorelix injection. In the triptorelin group, one patient had an LH surge. The single dose regimen thus requires more attention in terms of monitoring follicular development or estradiol production but allows the completion of multifollicular growth without the use of high doses of hMG/FSH. The association of the single dose Gn-RH antagonist protocol with

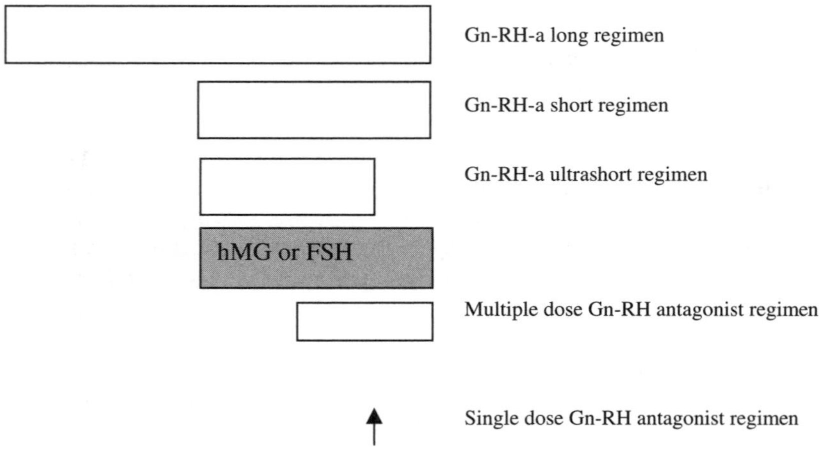

FIGURE 26.2 The most widely used protocols in ART, Gn-RH agonists and antagonists. In the long protocol the Gn-RH agonist is started before stimulation, in the midluteal phase of the pretreatment cycle, whereas gonadotropins are started on day 7 of the subsequent cycle. In short protocols, Gn-RH-a and gonadotropins are started simultaneously on day 7 of the stimulated cycle. Gn-RH antagonists are administered either once on day 7 of stimulation or daily from day 6 of stimulation.

recombinant FSH ovarian stimulation is currently being evaluated in a large multicenter trial.

Multiple Dose Regimen

All studies used 0.25 mg/day of cetrorelix or ganirelix. The opened randomized trial of the European Cetrorelix Study Group [51] compared the multiple dose cetrorelix regimen with a buserelin long protocol. The pregnancy rate was not significantly different, but the duration of gonadotropin stimulation and the incidence of OHSS were both reduced in the group treated with antagonists. The European Orgalutran Study Group [52] compared a multiple dose antagonist regimen with a long protocol buserelin. The duration of gonadotropin treatment, number of ampoules used, and incidence of OHSS were lower in the antagonist group. The number of good quality embryos, the fertilization rate, and the replaced embryos were similar in the two groups. The implantation rate was lower in the antagonist group, but the clinical pregnancy rate per attempt was not significantly different. The North American Ganirelix Study Group [53] compared the multiple dose ganirelix scheme with a long protocol leuprolide desensitization in IVF patients. No differences were observed between the two groups in terms of number of retrieved oocytes and fertilization and implantation rates. Ongoing pregnancy rates were comparable as well (ganirelix = 30.8; leuprolide = 36.4%) with a shorter stimulation duration in the antagonist group. The European and Middle East Orgalutran Study Group [54] compared ganirelix and triptorelin in 337 women. The mean fertilization rate, number of good quality embryos, implantation rates, and ongoing pregnancy rates were comparable.

These trials were included in the Cochrane database system in a metaanalysis [55] that concluded that the multiple dose antagonist protocol allowed a significant reduction of severe OHSS and that the incidence of LH surges was not different. Pooled results from the four studies using multiple dose antagonist protocol [51–54] indicated a significantly lower clinical pregnancy rate when compared with the long agonist protocol, whereas the four trials had shown nonsignificant trends to decreased pregnancy rates in Gn-RH antagonist treated groups when analyzed separately.

The multiple 0.25 mg/day dose antagonist protocol when compared with the long agonist protocol thus seems to offer a safer solution. The main concern is the possible decreased pregnancy rate when compared with Gn-RH antagonists. The incidence of LH surge is low with the multiple dose antagonist regimen, although this might not be observed in poor responders. These data remain to be confirmed, and the mechanism is still uncertain. The 0.25 mg/day dose might be insufficient, particularly in patients with a high body mass index (BMI). A multicenter dose finding study (0.0625 – 2 mg) with ganirelix [56] that examined follicle development showed that increased doses of antagonist lead to decreased levels of estradiol and androstenedione. The follicular growth pattern was not affected. Data on embryos, implantation, or pregnancy were not included.

In a recent study [57], recombinant human FSH (r-hFSH) was administered at a fixed dose of 150 U/day from cycle day 2 (group B) or 5 (group C), whereas the Gn-RH antagonist was initiated when the follicular diameter reached 14 mm. These two groups were compared with a group undergoing a Gn-RH long protocol stimulation cycle. In group C the stimulation was shorter, and although the number of cancelled cycles was higher, the final pregnancy rate was identical to the two other groups because of better quality embryos when compared with groups A and B.

Minimal Stimulation

The possibility of using Gn-RH antagonists in minimal stimulation or in natural (unstimulated) cycles [58, 59] seems promising because women do not receive high doses of gonadotropins and because ICSI can probably improve the efficacy. In a natural cycle, monofollicular development is associated with a high risk of cancellation as a result of premature LH surges. As proposed by Frydman, this can be prevented by the coadministration of an antagonist and a low dose of hMG/FSH at the same time on day 8 or 9 of the follicular phase [58]. The gonadotropin administration would compensate for the decrease in endogenous gonadotropin following antagonist administration. The "minimal stimulation" approach concerns low dose hMG/FSH administration restricted to the mid- to late follicular phase [56]. If the preliminary results obtained with spontaneous cycle and hMG support are confirmed with larger patient numbers, then the repetition of two or three of these "friendly IVF" cycles could lead to acceptable cumulative pregnancy rates. This could thus avoid the potential adverse effects of ovarian stimulation.

Ovulation Triggering with Gn-RH Agonists in Antagonist Treated Cycles

Because of their mechanism of action (that does not include desensitization of Gn-RH receptors), Gn-RH antagonists allow ovulation triggering using the flare effect of Gn-RH analogs. The latter in fact induces an endogenous LH surge that leads to appropriate progesterone secretion [59]. This strategy has been proposed to reduce OHSS because endogenous LH has a lower plasma half-life than hCG [60].

Luteal Phase Support

During the luteal phase, corpus luteum development and survival are dependent on LH. Luteal phase defect in Gn-

Table 26.2 Summary of the Main Prospective Randomized Studies Comparing Gn-RH Agonists and Multiple Dose Antagonists

	Duration of Stimulation (Days)	Implantation Rate (%)	Ongoing Pregnancy per Attempt (%)	Ongoing Pregnancy per Transfer (%)	OHSS (%)
Ganirelix (n = 448) vs Buserelin (n = 224) [52]	9 (6–18) vs 10 (6–19)	15.7 vs 21.8	20.3 vs 25.7	23.3 vs 29	1.0 vs 2.9
Cetrorelix (n = 188) vs Buserelin (n = 85) [51]	10.6 ± 2.3 vs 11.4 ± 1.8	12.2 vs 14.4	19.1 vs 25.9	21.6 vs 29.8	1.1 vs 6.5
Ganirelix (n = 208) vs leuprolide (n = 105) [53]	8 vs 10	21.1 vs 26.1	30.8 vs 36.4	NA	6.1 vs 2.0
Ganirelix (n = 226) vs triptorelin (n = 111) [54]	9 (6–14) vs 11 (7–16)	22.9 vs 22.9	31 vs 33.9	34 vs 38.5	1.8 vs 0.9
Metaanalysis of the four previous [55] antagonists (n = 1211) vs agonist (n = 585)	Significantly shorter in antagonist group	NA	OR 0.77 (95% CI 0.61–0.96)	OR 0.76 (95% CI 0.60–0.97)	RR 0.36 (95% CI 0.16–0.80)

RH agonist treated cycles is well known and related to sustained, profound pituitary suppression [61]. Because of their short-term inhibitory effect on pituitary secretions [35, 62], Gn-RH antagonists were first thought to be devoid of adverse effects on luteal function. However, different studies including Gn-RH antagonist treatment in IVF cycles have shown that the corpus luteum demise occurs prematurely, resulting in a shortened luteal phase and decreased pregnancy rates [56, 63, 64, 65]. Early and mid-luteal phase LH levels remain suppressed [61]. Low LH levels could be responsible for the luteal dysfunction because other possible explanations (follicle puncture induced damage [Hohmann, 2001] or short-loop feedback caused by the late follicular phase hCG administration [65]) are not convincing hypotheses. Luteal phase supplementation thus seems necessary in Gn-RH antagonist treated IVF cycles.

FUTURE PERSPECTIVE

Tailoring of New Protocols and Improvement of Pregnancy Rate in Gn-RH Antagonist Treated Cycles

The use of antagonist analogs in IVF needs additional research, in particular to select new protocols of administration and to determine the patients that can benefit most from this treatment (including patients with polycystic ovarian syndrome [PCOS] and poor responders). Although they allow flexible stimulation procedures, their result until now may appear slightly less than those observed with agonists in some centers. This seems as a result of the need for physicians to learn new procedures and to adapt gonadotropin doses. Also in relation to the potent suppression of LH and FSH, it is possible that the potentially lower results obtained are related to the use of r-hFSH, which might impair estradiol increases and its subsequent impact on the endometrium, in relation to the suppression of LH secretion. This may lead to the necessity of a careful titration of the antagonist. There is no such thing as a standardized procedure; therefore patients should be treated according to their individual characteristics. To this extent, antagonists represent a valuable contribution.

Outstanding questions include the potential direct effects of Gn-RH agonists and antagonists on ovarian function and the endometrium. Although this question is as old as the use of Gn-RH, no data that support a significant deleterious effect of these drugs has been produced. The study of endometrial maturation during Gn-RH antagonist treated cycles has shown that the alterations (advanced endometrial maturation) are correlated to LH levels at the beginning of the cycle and to the duration of stimulation [66]. This suggests that the endometrial effect is secondary to the gonadotropin pattern rather than to the direct effect of Gn-RH antagonists. Interestingly, recent data suggest that frozen embryos obtained from antagonist treated cycles are normal and yield a number of ongoing pregnancies, which is not different from agonist treated cycles [67]. Finally, the question of fetal risk has also been raised, but no answer has been given; however, the risk of malformation appears no different than other ART procedures and the babies appear as healthy as those born from other ART techniques [68, 69].

In addition to the successful use of antagonists in IVF, there may also be favorable effects in gonadotropin ovarian stimulation protocols for intrauterine insemination. This has yet to be studied.

Development of New (Easier) Routes of Administration

Although antagonists are orally active at 1000 times the active dose as when administered subcutaneously or intravenously, orally active antagonists remain to be studied. However, the search for nonpeptidic ligands of the Gn-RH receptor using screening programs for small molecules that bind to the Gn-RH receptors has already begun. No product has thus far reached clinical applications because of difficulties that range from instability to absorption and elimination. Several hits have been obtained on 5000 molecules tested. The current compounds are aryl-quinolone or thienopyridine derivatives and are effective at several mg/kg doses [70]. Two compounds are currently in phase I in Japan and the United States. Acyline is a new compound tested in healthy young men that provides suppression of FSH and LH in an efficient and prolonged way (48h after injection of a 75 µg dose) [71]. Other groups hope to identify the bioactive conformation of Gn-RH antagonists that can be used to design nonpeptide orally active molecules [72]. TAK-013 is the first orally active compound tested in healthy men. A single dose of 10 to 200 mg dose dependently decreased serum LH and testosterone levels [73].

CONCLUSION

Gn-RH antagonists have a specific mechanism of action that includes inactivation of Gn-RH receptors without desensitization. This allows a rapid short-term decrease in gonadotropin levels, which is particularly suitable for the prevention of premature LH surge during IVF cycles. In clinical practice, Gn-RH antagonists allow shorter ovarian stimulation schemes. They can thus improve patient satisfaction and may decrease the costs of direct IVF. They are efficient in preventing OHSS in IVF cycles and could be particularly useful in high-risk patients (e.g., patients with PCOS). Gn-RH antagonists may thus also contribute to reduced IVF risks and indirect costs. The current challenge is to improve the pregnancy rate, which has been shown to be reduced in Gn-RH antagonist treated cycles when compared with Gn-RH analog treated cycles. The growing experience of physicians and the development of new treatment schemes and molecules will possibly lead to the accomplishment of this goal.

References

1. Al-Inany, H., and Aboulghar, M. (2001). Gonadotrophin-releasing hormone antagonists for assisted conception. *Cochrane Database Syst. Rev.* 4.
2. Fauser, B. C., Bouchard, P., Coelingh Bennink, H., Collins, J., Devroey, P., Evers, J., and Van Steirteghem, A. (2002). Alternative approaches in IVF. *Hum. Reprod. Update* 8, 1–9.
3. Baba, Y., Matsuo, H., and Schally, A. V. (1971). Structure of the porcine LH- and FSH-releasing hormone. II. Confirmation of the proposed structure by conventional sequential analyses. *Biochem. Biophys. Res. Commun.* 44, 459–463.
4. Cusan, L., Auclair, C., Belanger, A., Ferland, L., Kelly, P. A., Seguin, C., and F., L. (1979). Inhibitory effects of long term treatment with a luteinizing hormone-releasing hormone agonist on the pituitary-gonadal axis in male and female rats. *Endocrinology* 104, 1369–1376.
5. Leroy, I., d'Acremont, M., Brailly-Tabard, S., Frydman, R., de Mouzon, J., and Bouchard, P. (1994). A single injection of a gonadotropin-releasing hormone (Gn-RH) antagonist (cetrorelix) postpones the luteinizing hormone (LH) surge: Further evidence for the role of Gn-RH during the LH surge. *Fertil. Steril.* 62, 461–467.
6. Santen, R. J., Manni, A., and Harvey, H. (1986). Gonadotropin releasing hormone (Gn-RH) analogs for the treatment of breast and prostatic carcinoma. *Breast Cancer Res. Treat.* 7, 129–145.
7. Conn, P. M., and Crowley, Jr., W. F. (1994). Gonadotropin-releasing hormone and its analogs. *Annu. Rev. Med.* 45, 391–405.
8. Barbieri, R. L., and Hornstein, M. D. (1999). Assisted reproduction-in vitro fertilization success is improved by ovarian stimulation with exogenous gonadotropins and pituitary suppression with gonadotropin-releasing hormone analogues. *Endocr. Rev.* 20, 249–252.
9. Bouchard, P., and Garcia, E. (1987). Comparison of the mechanisms of action of LHRH analogs and steroids in the treatment of endometriosis. *Contrib. Gynecol. Obstet.* 16, 260–265.
10. Bouchard, P., Wolf, J. P., and Hajri, S. (1988). Inhibition of ovulation: Comparison between the mechanism of action of steroids and Gn-RH analogues. *Hum. Reprod.* 3, 503–506.
11. Karten, M. J., and Rivier, J. E. (1986). Gonadotropin-releasing hormone analog design. Structure-function studies toward the development of agonists and antagonists: Rationale and perspective. *Endocr. Rev.* 7, 44–66.
12. Bouchard, P. (1990). Gn-RH antagonists. Therapeutic and practical aspects. *J. Gynecol. Obstet. Biol. Reprod.* 19, 607–608.
13. Bouchard, P., and Fauser, B. C. (2000). Gonadotropin-releasing hormone antagonist: New tools vs old habits. *Fertil. Steril.* 73, 18–20.

14. Zhou, W., Rodic, V., Kitanovic, S., Flanagan, C. A., Chi, L., Weinstein, H., Maayani, S., Millar, R. P., and Sealfon, S. C. (1995). A locus of the gonadotropin-releasing hormone receptor that differentiates agonist and antagonist binding sites. *J. Biol. Chem.* 270, 18853–18857.
15. Pavlou, S. N., Brewer, K., Farley, M. G., Lindner, J., Bastias, M. C., Rogers, B. J., Swift, L. L., Rivier, J. E., Vale, W. W., Conn, P. M., et al. (1991). Combined administration of a gonadotropin-releasing hormone antagonist and testosterone in men induces reversible azoospermia without loss of libido. *J. Clin. Endocrinol. Metab.* 73, 1360–1369.
16. Kovacs, M., Schally, A. V., Csernus, B., and Rekasi, Z. (2001). Luteinizing hormone-releasing hormone (LH-RH) antagonist Cetrorelix down-regulates the mRNA expression of pituitary receptors for LH-RH by counteracting the stimulatory effect of endogenous LH-RH. *Proc. Natl. Acad. Sci. USA* 98, 1829–1834.
17. Gordon, K., Danforth, D. R., Williams, R. F., and GD., H. (1992). New trends in combined use of gonadotropin-releasing hormone antagonists with gonadotropins or pulsatile gonadotropin-releasing hormone in ovulation induction and assisted reproductive technologies. *Curr. Opin. Obstet. Gynecol.* 4, 690–696.
18. Felberbaum, R. E., Ludwig, M., and Diedrich, K. (2000). Clinical application of Gn-RH-antagonists. *Mol. Cell. Endocrinol.* 166, 9–14.
19. Sundaram, K., Didolkar, A., Thau, R., Chaudhuri, M., and Schmidt, F. (1988). Antagonists of luteinizing hormone releasing hormone bind to rat mast cells and induce histamine release. *Agents Actions* 25, 307–313.
20. Felberbaum, R., Ludwig, M., and Diedrich, K. (2001). *Agonists and Antagonists, Formulation and Indication in Gn-RH Analogues.* Philadelphia: W. B. Sauders.
21. Reissmann, T., Schally, A. V., Bouchard, P., Riethmiiller, H., and Engel, J. (2000). The LHRH antagonist cetrorelix: A review. *Hum. Reprod. Update* 6, 322–331.
22. Gillies, P., Faulds, D., Balfour, J., and Perry, C. (2000). Ganirelix. *Drugs* 59, 107–111.
23. Blithe, D. L. (2001). Applications for Gn-RH antagonists. *Trends Endocrinol. Metab.* 12, 238–240.
24. Chi, L., Zhou, W., Prikhozhan, A., Flanagan, C., Davidson, J. S., Golembo, M., Illing, N., Millar, R. P., and Sealfon, S. C. (1993). Cloning and characterization of the human Gn-RH receptor. *Mol. Cell. Endocrinol.* 91, R1–R6.
25. Illing, N., Jacobs, G. F., Becker, II, Flanagan, C. A., Davidson, J. S., Eales, A., Zhou, W., Sealfon, S. C., and Millar, R. P. (1993). Comparative sequence analysis and functional characterization of the cloned sheep gonadotropin-releasing hormone receptor reveal differences in primary structure and ligand specificity among mammalian receptors. *Biochem. Biophys. Res. Commun.* 196, 745–751.
26. Millar, R., Lowe, S., Conklin, D., Pawson, A., Maudsley, S., Troskie, B., Ott, T., Millar, M., Lincoln, G., Sellar, R., Faurholm, B., Scobie, G., Kuestner, R., Terasawa, E., and Katz, A. (2001). A novel mammalian receptor for the evolutionarily conserved type II Gn-RH. *Proc. Natl. Acad. Sci. USA* 98, 9636–9641.
27. Neill, J. D., Duck, L. W., Sellers, J. C., and Musgrove, L. C. (2001). A gonadotropin-releasing hormone (Gn-RH) receptor specific for Gn-RH II in primates. *Biochem. Biophys. Res. Commun.* 282, 1012–1018.
28. Hanssens, R. M., Brus, L., Cahill, D. J., Huirne, J. A., Schoemaker, J., and Lambalk, C. B. (2000). Direct ovarian effects and safety aspects of Gn-RH agonists and antagonists. *Hum. Reprod. Update* 6, 505–518.
29. Mannaerts, B., and Gordon, K. (2000). Embryo implantation and Gn-RH antagonists: Gn-RH antagonists do not activate the Gn-RH receptor. *Hum. Reprod.* 15, 1882–1883.
30. Ortmann, O., and Diedrich, K. (1999). Pituitary and extrapituitary actions of gonadotrophin-releasing hormone and its analogues. *Hum. Reprod.* 14 (Suppl 1), 194–206.
31. Weiss, J. M., Oltmanns, K., Gurke, E. M., Polack, S., Eick, F., Felberbaum, R., Diedrich, K., and Ortmann, O. (2001). Actions of gonadotropin-releasing hormone antagonists on steroidogenesis in human granulosa lutein cells. *Eur. J. Endocrinol.* 144, 677–685.
32. Kang, S. K., Tai, C. J., Nathwani, P. S., Choi, K. C., and Leung, P. C. (2001). Stimulation of mitogen-activated protein kinase by gonadotropin-releasing hormone in human granulosa-luteal cells. *Endocrinology* 142, 671–679.
33. Dubourdieu, S., Charbonnel, B., D'Acremont, M. F., Carreau, S., Spitz, I. M., and Bouchard, P. (1994). Effect of administration of a gonadotropin-releasing hormone (Gn-RH) antagonist (Nal-Glu) during the periovulatory period: The luteinizing hormone surge requires secretion of Gn-RH. *J. Clin. Endocrinol. Metab.* 78, 343–347.
34. Lahlou, N., Delivet, S., Bardin, C. W., Roger, M., Spitz, I. M., and Bouchard, P. (1990). Changes in gonadotropin and alpha-subunit secretion after a single administration of gonadotropin-releasing hormone antagonist in adult males. *Fertil. Steril.* 53, 898–905.
35. Ditkoff, E. C., Cassidenti, D. L., Paulson, R. J., Sauer, M. V., Paul, W. L., Rivier, J., Yen, S. S., and Lobo, R. A. (1991). The gonadotropin-releasing hormone antagonist (Nal-Glu) acutely blocks the luteinizing hormone surge but allows for resumption of folliculogenesis in normal women. *Am. J. Obstet. Gynecol.* 165, 1811–1817.
36. Christin-Maitre, S., Olivennes, F., Dubourdieu, S., Chabbert-Buffet, N., Charbonnel, B., Frydman, R., and Bouchard, P. (2000). Effect of gonadotrophin-releasing hormone (Gn-RH) antagonist during the LH surge in normal women and during controlled ovarian hyperstimulation. *Clin. Endocrinol. (Oxf.)* 52, 721–726.
37. Clarke, I. J. (1993). Variable patterns of gonadotropin-releasing hormone secretion during the estrogen-induced luteinizing hormone surge in ovariectomized ewes. *Endocrinology* 133, 1624–1632.
38. Norman, R. L., Rivier, J., Vale, W., and Spies, H. G. (1986). Inhibition of estradiol-induced gonadotropin release in ovariectomized rhesus macaques by a gonadotropin-releasing hormone antagonist. *Fertil. Steril.* 45, 288–291.
39. Karsch, F. J., Bowen, J. M., Caraty, A., Evans, N. P., and Moenter, S. M. (1997). Gonadotropin-releasing hormone requirements for ovulation. *Biol. Reprod.* 56, 303–309.
40. Caraty, A., Antoine, C., Delaleu, B., Locatelli, A., Bouchard, P., Gautron, J. P., Evans, N. P., Karsch, F. J., and Padmanabhan, V. (1995). Nature and bioactivity of gonadotropin-releasing hormone (Gn-RH) secreted during the Gn-RH surge. *Endocrinology* 136, 3452–3460.
41. Moenter, S. M., Caraty, A., and Karsch, F. J. (1990). The estradiol-induced surge of gonadotropin-releasing hormone in the ewe. *Endocrinology* 127, 1375–1384.

42. Xia, L., Van Vugt, D., Alston, E. J., Luckhaus, J., and Ferin, M. (1992). A surge of gonadotropin-releasing hormone accompanies the estradiol-induced gonadotropin surge in the rhesus monkey. *Endocrinology* 131, 2812–2820.
43. Martin, K. A., Welt, C. K., Taylor, A. E., Smith, J. A., Crowley, Jr., W. F., and Hall, J. E. (1998). Is Gn-RH reduced at the mid-cycle surge in the human? Evidence from a Gn-RH-deficient model. *Neuroendocrinology* 67, 363–369.
44. Diedrich, K., Frydman, R., Devroey, P., Felberbaum, R., Schally, A. V., Reissmann, T., and Engel, J. (2001). Comment on the debate article: Embryo implantation: The Rubicon for Gn-RH antagonists. *Hum. Reprod.* 16, 1305–1306.
45. Diedrich, K., Ludwig, M., and Felberbaum, R. E. (2001). The role of gonadotropin-releasing hormone antagonists in in vitro fertilization. *Semin. Reprod. Med.* 19, 213–220.
46. Frydman, R., Cornel, C., de Ziegler, D., Taieb, J., Spitz, I. M., and Bouchard, P. (1992). Spontaneous luteinizing hormone surges can be reliably prevented by the timely administration of a gonadotrophin releasing hormone antagonist (Nal-Glu) during the late follicular phase. *Hum. Reprod.* 7, 930–933.
47. Olivennes, F., Belaisch-Allart, J., Emperaire, J. C., Dechaud, H., Alvarez, S., Moreau, L., Nicollet, B., Zorn, J. R., Bouchard, P., and Frydman, R. (2000). Prospective, randomized, controlled study of in vitro fertilization—embryo transfer with a single dose of a luteinizing hormone-releasing hormone (LH-RH) antagonist (cetrorelix) or a depot formula of an LH-RH agonist (triptorelin). *Fertil. Steril.* 73, 314–320.
48. Olivennes, F., Cunha-Filho, J. S., Fanchin, R., Bouchard, P., and Frydman, R. (2002). The use of Gn-RH antagonists in ovarian stimulation. *Hum. Reprod. Update* 8, 279–290.
49. Olivennes, F., Fanchin, R., Bouchard, P., Taieb, J., Selva, J., and Frydman, R. (1995). Scheduled administration of a gonadotrophin-releasing hormone antagonist (Cetrorelix) on day 8 of in-vitro fertilization cycles: A pilot study. *Hum. Reprod.* 10, 1382–1386.
50. Olivennes, F., Alvarez, S., Bouchard, P., Fanchin, R., Salat-Baroux, J., and Frydman, R. (1998). The use of a Gn-RH antagonist (Cetrorelix) in a single dose protocol in IVF-embryo transfer: A dose finding study of 3 versus 2 mg. *Hum. Reprod.* 13, 2411–2414.
51. Albano, C., Felberbaum, R., and Smitz, J. E. A. (2000). Ovarian stimulation with HMG: A prospective randomized phase III European study comparing the luteinizing hormone releasing hormone (LHRH) antagonist cetrorelix and the LHRH-agonist buserelin. European Cetrorelix Study Group. *Hum. Reprod.* 15, 526–531.
52. The European Orgalutran Study Group. (2000). Treatment with gonadotropin releasing hormone antagonist cetrorelix in women undergoing ovarian stimulation with recombinant follicle stimulating hormone is effective, safe and convenient: Results of a controlled randomized, multicentre trial. *Hum. Reprod.* 15, 1490–1498.
53. The North American Ganirelix Study Group. (2001). Efficacy and safety of ganirelix acetate vs leuprolide acetate in women undergoing controlled ovarian hyperstimulation. *Fertil. Steril.* 75, 38–45.
54. European and Middle East Orgalutran Study Group. (2001). Comparable clinical outcome using the Gn-RH antagonist ganirelix or a long protocol of the Gn-RH agonist triptorelin for the prevention of premature LH surges in women undergoing ovarian stimulation. *Hum. Reprod.* 16, 644–651.
55. Al-Inany, H., and Aboulghar, M. (2002). Gn-RH antagonist in assisted reproduction: A Cochrane review. *Hum. Reprod.* 17, 874–885.
56. de Jong, D., Macklon, N. S., and Fauser, B. C. (2000). A pilot study involving minimal ovarian stimulation for in vitro fertilization: Extending the "follicle-stimulating hormone window" combined with the gonadotropin-releasing hormone antagonist cetrorelix. *Fertil. Steril.* 73, 1051–1054.
57. Hohmann, F. P., Macklon, N. S., and Fauser, B. C. (2003). A randomized comparison of two ovarian stimulation protocols with gonadotropin-releasing hormone (Gn-RH) antagonist cotreatment for in vitro fertilization commencing recombinant follicle-stimulating hormone on cycle day 2 or 5 with the standard long Gn-RH agonist protocol. *J. Clin. Endocrinol. Metab.* 88, 166–173.
58. Rongieres-Bertrand, C., Olivennes, F., Righini, C., Fanchin, R., Taieb, J., Hamamah, S., Bouchard, P., and Frydman, R. (1999). Revival of the natural cycles in in-vitro fertilization with the use of a new gonadotrophin-releasing hormone antagonist (Cetrorelix): A pilot study with minimal stimulation. *Hum. Reprod.* 14, 683–688.
59. Olivennes, F., Fanchin, R., Bouchard, P., Taieb, J., and Frydman, R. (1996). Triggering of ovulation by a gonadotropin-releasing hormone (Gn-RH) agonist in patients pretreated with a Gn-RH antagonist. *Fertil. Steril.* 66, 151–153.
60. Lewitt, N., Kol, S., Manor, D., and Itskovitz-Eldor, J. (1996). Comparison of Gn-RH analogs and hCG for induction of ovulation and prevention of ovarian hyperstimulation syndrome (OHSS): A case control study. *Hum. Reprod.* 11, 1399–1402.
61. Tavaniotou, A., Albano, C., Smitz, J., and Devroey, P. (2002). Impact of ovarian stimulation on corpus luteum function and embryonic implantation. *J. Reprod. Immunol.* 55, 123–130.
62. Frydman, R., Cornel, C., de Ziegler, D., Taieb, J., Spitz, I. M., and Bouchard, P. (1991). Prevention of premature luteinizing hormone and progesterone rise with a gonadotropin-releasing hormone antagonist, Nal-Glu, in controlled ovarian hyperstimulation. *Fertil. Steril.* 56, 923–927.
63. Albano, C., Grimbizis, G., Smitz, J., Riethmuller-Winzen, H., Reissmann, T., Van Steirteghem, A., and Devroey, P. (1998). The luteal phase of nonsupplemented cycles after ovarian superovulation with human menopausal gonadotropin and the gonadotropin-releasing hormone antagonist Cetrorelix. *Fertil. Steril.* 70, 357–359.
64. Albano, C., Smitz, J., Tournaye, H., Riethmuller-Winzen, H., Van Steirteghem, A., and Devroey, P. (1999). Luteal phase and clinical outcome after human menopausal gonadotrophin/gonadotrophin releasing hormone antagonist treatment for ovarian stimulation in in-vitro fertilization/intracytoplasmic sperm injection cycles. *Hum. Reprod.* 14, 1426–1430.
65. Beckers, N. G. M. (2002). Comparison of the non supplemented luetal phase characteristics after recombinant (r)hCG, rLH, on Gn-RH agonist for oocyte maturation in IVF. *Hum. Reprod.* O-157.
66. Kolibianakis, E., Bourgain, C., Albano, C., Osmanagaoglu, K., Smitz, J., Van Steirteghem, A., and Devroey, P. (2002). Effect of ovarian stimulation with recombinant follicle-stimulating hormone, gonadotropin releasing hormone antagonists, and human chorionic gonadotropin on endometrial maturation on the day of oocyte pick-up. *Fertil. Steril.* 78, 1025–1029.

67. Kol, S. (2000). Embryo implantation and Gn-RH antagonists: Gn-RH antagonists in ART: Lower embryo implantation? *Hum. Reprod.* 15, 1881–1882.
68. Ludwig, M., Riethmuller-Winzen, H., Felberbaum, R. E., Olivennes, F., Albano, C., Devroey, P., and Diedrich, K. (2001). Health of 227 children born after controlled ovarian stimulation for in vitro fertilization using the luteinizing hormone-releasing hormone antagonist cetrorelix. *Fertil. Steril.* 75, 18–22.
69. Olivennes, F., Mannaerts, B., Struijs, M., Bonduelle, M., and Devroey, P. (2001). Perinatal outcome of pregnancy after Gn-RH antagonist (ganirelix) treatment during ovarian stimulation for conventional IVF or ICSI: A preliminary report. *Hum. Reprod.* 16, 1588–1591.
70. Young, J. R., Huang, S. X., Chen, I., Walsh, T. F., DeVita, R. J., Wyvratt, Jr., M. J., Goulet, M. T., Ren, N., Lo, J., Yang, Y. T., Yudkovitz, J. B., Cheng, K., and Smith, R. G. (2000). Quinolones as gonadotropin releasing hormone (Gn-RH) antagonists: Simultaneous optimization of the C(3)-aryl and C(6)-substituents. *Bioorg. Med. Chem. Lett.* 10, 1723–1727.
71. Herbst, K. L., Anawalt, B. D., Amory, J. K., and Bremner, W. J. (2002). Acyline: The first study in humans of a potent, new gonadotropin-releasing hormone antagonist. *J. Clin. Endocrinol. Metab.* 87, 3215–3220.
72. Sasaki, S., Cho, N., Nara, Y., Harada, M., Endo, S., Suzuki, N., Furuya, S., and Fujino, M. (2003). Discovery of a thieno[2,3-d]pyrimidine-2,4-dione bearing a p-methoxyureidophenyl moiety at the 6-position: A highly potent and orally bioavailable non-peptide antagonist for the human luteinizing hormone-releasing hormone receptor. *J. Med. Chem.* 46, 113–124.
73. Suzuki, N., Cho, N., Furuya, S., Harada, M., Urushibara, T., Takakawa, S., Horinouci, A., Clark, E., Onda, H., and Boyce, M. (2002). A novel, potent and orally active nonpeptide antagonist for the human gonadotropin-releasing hormone receptor. *The Endocrine Society 84th Annual meeting*, OR7–OR2.

CHAPTER 27

The Ovarian Factor in Assisted Reproductive Technology

LAUREL STADTMAUER, ESTELLA JONES, AND ROGER GOSDEN

INTRODUCTION

It has now been more than 20 years since the first successful in vitro fertilization (IVF) conception [1] and since the first conception in the United States at the Jones Institute. Assisted reproductive technology (ART) has become increasingly prevalent each year, with more than 360 ART programs available in 1999 and more than 88,000 cycles in the United States alone [2]. In addition, success rates have increased, although outcomes remain age-dependent. The 1999 database generated by the Society for Assisted Reproductive Technology (SART) showed an IVF delivery rate per cycle of 32.4% for women younger than 35 years of age, 26.4% for women aged 35 to –57 years, 18.5% for women aged 38 to 40 years, and only 8.1% for women older than 40 years. In oocyte donor programs, rates were higher with a delivery rate per transfer of 41%, which is consistent with early research that showed higher success rates for older patients using oocytes from young donors [2, 3]. Therefore the most important factor for the success of ART is oocyte quality, which is affected by ovarian age, whereas the age of the endometrium is less important [4]. The biggest challenge continues to be treating women of advanced reproductive age who wish to use their own eggs.

This chapter addresses the role of the ovary in ART, the organ with the largest impact on ART success. We discuss the decline in fertility with age and the relationship between increased aneuploidy and decreased oocyte quality and ovarian reserve. We also discuss ovarian stimulation, specifically the approach to low responders, hyper-responders, and the role of luteinizing hormone (LH) in ovarian stimulation.

DECLINE IN FEMALE FERTILITY WITH AGE

Overview

The decline in female fertility associated with increasing chronological age has been established and is especially evident in the fourth and fifth decades of women's lives. Studies based on IVF, intracytoplasmic sperm injection (ICSI), and other ARTs indicate there is a reduced potential for pregnancy among older women. National data collected by SART, along with other studies, reveal that clinic-specific and national pregnancy success rates for IVF decline markedly with age [2, 5, 6]. The age-related decline in fertility is also seen in patients receiving less aggressive treatments, such as human menopausal gonadotropins (hMG) and IUI [7]. Multiple pregnancy risk in ART cycles also declines with age, which is another indication of reduced fecundity [2]. Fertility starts to decrease at about age 30, with a precipitous decline after 37 to 38 years of age [8]. There is a maternal age-related effect on oocyte quality leading to a decline in the embryo implantation rate and a decline in pregnancy rates. In addition, a decreased ovarian reserve is observed by counting the number of follicles in ovaries from pathology specimens on autopsy, and the steady decline in follicle numbers until 37 to 38 years of age accelerates in the years before menopause [9].

The origin of the age-related decline in egg and embryo quality with advanced maternal age seen in IVF patients is unknown. However, we know that it is not just a decrease in the ability to fertilize oocytes. In addition, it is unlikely that the decline is causally linked to reduced numbers of eggs at retrieval or embryos at transfer because these parameters do not drop in proportion to the pregnancy rates. Instead, it appears to be caused by a decrease in oocyte quality related to nuclear and cytoplasmic abnormalities in oocytes of women with advanced reproductive age. A number of unanswered questions remain. Are abnormalities in nuclear and cytoplasmic components predetermined during oogenesis in fetal life? Do they reflect the impact of adverse environmental factors present at that time? Are ovarian follicles that finally develop gonadotropin responsiveness after years of inactivity unable to interact effectively with the other intraovarian factors required to ensure proper egg maturation? Are oocytes exposed to environmental toxins leading to increased cellular damage? The physiology and cell biology of oocyte formation and maturation will continue to be an exciting area of basic research because the findings could have immediate clinical significance.

The reduction in follicle numbers with advancing age is reflected by rising levels of serum follicle-stimulating hormone (FSH) measured during the early follicular phase [10]. The number of mature follicles and oocytes that can be obtained in response to stimulation using gonadotropins is an index of total ovarian follicular reserve and correlates inversely with FSH levels. Numerous studies have shown that the rates of implantation, pregnancy, and miscarriage are not only related to age but also to FSH levels [11–16]. Moreover, young and reproductively aged women who respond poorly to stimulation share the inherent problem of ovarian aging. Biological aging of the ovaries manifests before high levels of FSH are observed, as a decline of oocyte quality is evident even while FSH levels are still within the normal range of young women [11], and weak responses to gonadotropins can occur at any age. However, young poor responders have higher pregnancy rates than older patients, although the pregnancy rates are lower than age-matched normal responders [17]. Hence, the counseling of patients must involve discussions on the impact on pregnancy rates of their prior history of ovarian response, day 3 FSH levels, and age. This subject is discussed in more detail in Chapter 28, Ovarian Function in Assisted Reproduction.

Age-Related Aneuploidy

Many types of genetic abnormalities have been reported in human oocytes. The most common egg abnormalities result from an error in chromatid segregation during the first meiotic division. The frequency of chromosomally abnormal offspring resulting from errors during female meiosis, such as trisomy, is directly correlated with maternal age. In women older than 40 years, it is estimated that 50% or more of all ovulated oocytes are chromosomally abnormal [18, 19].

In the human female, oocytes enter meiosis during the fetal period and remain suspended in prophase of the first meiotic division at the diplotene stage until ovulation. Possibly, this delay in meiosis contributes to the large increase in aneuploidy, which is not paralleled in spermatogenesis. There is evidence suggesting that the age effect for trisomy is caused by events that occur prenatally at the time of entry into meiosis I [20] or postnatally at the time of reentry into meiosis I [21–23]. The ability to resume and complete the first meiotic division before ovulation is linked to the process of oocyte growth. In the neonate, inactive oocytes are surrounded by a single layer of somatic cells. During the process of folliculogenesis, these primordial follicles undergo significant growth and development to produce a preovulatory follicle containing a mature oocyte.

Recent studies in the mouse have demonstrated that the ability of the oocyte to resume and complete the first meiotic division and the capacity to undergo fertilization and cleavage are acquired by the oocyte in a stepwise fashion during the late stages of folliculogenesis [24]. The importance of the final stages of follicular maturation in the meiotic process suggests that somatic factors may play a role in subsequent meiotic events. Meiotic studies of oocytes from mice with a mutation that causes defects in folliculogenesis demonstrate strikingly similar meiotic defects to those observed in human oocytes from reproductively aged donors [24]. This may not be the best model however for the human, because the mouse does not go through such dramatic ovarian senescence as the human. The control of the female meiotic process may lack a cell cycle checkpoint control mechanism, as is found in mice, to monitor the alignment of chromosomes at metaphase [25]. A lack of checkpoint control may explain the high error frequency in female meiosis and the age-related increased meiotic nondisjunction.

The disappointing success rate for IVF involving women older than 40 years indicates an age-related reduction in the developmental competence of human oocytes, including fertilization, embryo cleavage, and implantation. The age-related reduction of pregnancy and implantation rates is associated with the increase in meiotic chromosome nondisjunction and decline in oocyte quality observed in oocytes and embryos obtained from ovarian stimulation during IVF [18, 26–28]. Munne et al. [27] have concluded that in morphologically and developmentally normal human embryos at cleavage stages, aneuploidy significantly increases with maternal age. Through the use of fluorescent in situ hybridization (FISH), Munne et al. have convincingly demonstrated that more than 40% of apparently normal developing embryos are aneuploid. This is a primary reason for implantation failure in older women. Less surprisingly, the majority of morphologically abnormal oocytes and embryos are aneuploid [19, 29] and 60% of the embryos arresting in the preimplantation stages showed chromosome mosaicism with FISH analysis [30]. However, it is difficult to assess the true number of abnormal oocytes and their relationship with age, although multifluorescent FISH can reveal the karyotype of human oocytes and their polar bodies [31]. Studies in IVF may not be representative of natural fertility because the stimulation of the ovary of infertile patients might influence the rate of meiotic nondisjunction. Moreover, slight alterations in the culture conditions can impact the meiotic process and the rate of aneuploidy may be underestimated by FISH, which gives information only on the chromosomes for which specific probes are available. However, it is certain that polyploidy, aneuploidy, monosomy, and mosaicism are all common in stimulated cycles from women of all ages. It is also becoming apparent that oocytes from unstimulated ovaries have similar levels of aneuploidy [32].

Unfortunately, chromosomal normality and viability are not reliably predicted using the morphological grading system used for selecting embryos [27]. When aneuploidy testing is done using FISH analysis, high numbers of embryos in women older than 40 years undergoing IVF are abnormal despite their "good grades" based on embryo grade. We need a simple, noninvasive way to select embryos that is predictive of euploidy and developmental competence.

Assisted Hatching

Failure of the embryo to implant may also be the result of zona pellucida hardening, which can be caused by culture conditions and perhaps age [33]. Zona hardening may prevent embryos from hatching. Assisted hatching is most commonly performed with an acidified Tyrode's solution on day 3 embryos, although it can also be done with laser [34, 35]. With acidified Tyrode's solution, it is important to reverse the acid quickly after the zona is pierced to avoid the detrimental effects of acid on embryos. In addition, small or narrow gaps may lead to incomplete hatching and possibly increased twinning rates [36].

The benefit of assisted hatching has been demonstrated in a randomized trial in which implantation was studied in more than 100 patients in each group (with or without micromanipulation). The implantation rates were comparable in each group. There was an improvement in the implantation rate of poor prognosis patients, including a subset of women aged 39 or older with thickened zona pellucida and/or elevated FSH levels [34]. In assisted hatching patients, implantation occurred earlier than in patients who did not receive the procedure, and this may also have led to increased implantation rates [37]. Other studies, including prospective randomized studies, have confirmed these results, showing higher pregnancy and delivery rates in selected assisted hatching patients. The benefit was in the poor prognosis patients who were older than 38 years, had elevated FSH levels, and had a history of repeated IVF failure [38–40].

MEIOTIC SPINDLES

Overview

There has been much debate about the influence of the meiotic spindle apparatus on oocyte viability. The oocyte is a highly specialized cell that must undergo many maturational changes in preparation for fertilization and embryonic development. These changes involve nuclear and cytoplasmic events. At ovulation, mammalian oocytes are arrested at metaphase of the second meiotic division with the meiotic spindle apparatus composed of microtubules with maternal chromosomes attached [41]. Microtubules are dynamic components of the cytoskeleton that have important functions in the processes of cell division and motility, morphogenesis, and organelle transport [42]. In addition, they play important roles in the postfertilization events of spindle rotation, polar body formation, pronuclear migration, and cytokinesis [43–44].

The meiotic spindle of mammalian oocytes is sensitive to environmental changes, notably temperature and pH [45]. Exposure of oocytes to adverse conditions such as cryoprotectants and low temperatures has also been shown to disrupt the microtubules [41, 45–46]. Eroglu et al. [47] reported that cryopreservation of mouse oocytes with DMSO does not impair the function of microtubules postfertilization if a brief incubation period follows the thaw process. Similarly, Baka et al. [48] reported, contrary to some claims, that cryopreservation of prophase I human oocytes did not significantly increase abnormalities in the meiotic spindle. The meiotic spindle human oocytes are highly sensitive to temperature changes and depolymerize when exposed to temperatures less than 37°C even for brief periods [45, 49]. In the bovine, effects of cooling and rewarming on the meiotic spindle of in vitro matured bovine oocytes showed that exposure to temperatures as high as only 25°C resulted in damage to the chromosome alignment. However, rewarming to 39°C enabled the spindle to return to normal in most oocytes [50]. Currently we do not know whether advanced maternal age changes the spindle's sensitivity to temperature [49].

In addition to spindle disassembly as a result of temperature and pH fluctuations, damage has been reported in the microtubules of the meiotic spindle during manipulation. In the hamster oocyte, Asada et al. [51] demonstrated that ICSI need not result in significant damage to the meiotic spindle if the polar body is oriented away from the injection site. On the other hand, Blake et al. [52] showed that placement of sperm during ICSI relative to the presumed location of the spindle significantly impacts both fertilization and development. The authors concluded that sperm deposition in the area of the meiotic spindle apparatus should be avoided, but debate continues about the optimal orientation of meiotic spindle apparatus and the first polar body position. In the hamster, the first polar body did not accurately predict the spindle location in 25 out of 30 oocytes [53]. Hardarson et al. [54] reported that in human oocytes the majority of the spindles were found in the same hemisphere as the first polar body. Perhaps the orientation of the spindle in relation to the first polar body will be better resolved using the Polscope. Polarization microscopy reveals birefringence, which is an inherent property of highly ordered molecules like microtubules in the meiotic spindle apparatus [34]. Recently, it was reported [55] that the use of the Polscope was a reliable and noninvasive technique to view the meiotic spindle in the hamster oocyte. Similarly, Wang et al. [56] demonstrated that the Polscope can also be safely used with living human oocytes and found that visualization of a birefringent spindle is predictive of outcome with ICSI, although fertilization and blastocyst formation also occurred in oocytes without visible spindles.

Spindle and Aneuploidy

Age-related aneuploidy may be related to abnormalities in spindle formation and chromosomal alignment in stimulated and unstimulated cycles. Volarcik et al. [32] examined oocytes from unstimulated ovaries by immunofluorescence and FISH to study simultaneously the meiotic stage and the structural aspects of the meiotic spindle apparatus. The overall rate of meiotic maturation after maturation in vitro was only slightly lower among oocytes obtained from donors older than 35 years, but metaphase II (MII)-arrested oocytes showed an age-related increase in defects of the second meiotic metaphase spindle formation and chromosome alignment.

Battaglia et al. [57] described comparable findings in stimulated cycles: 79% of the oocytes from women aged 40 to 45 exhibited abnormal spindle assembly and chromosome alignment compared with only 17% of younger patients. These two studies demonstrated global defects in the meiotic process in oocytes obtained from reproductively aged donors, and Polscope technology may prove useful in human IVF clinics to help diagnose aneuploidy.

OOCYTE MATURATION AND MITOCHONDRIAL DEOXYRIBONUCLEIC ACID

In contrast to the process of nuclear maturation, cytoplasmic changes involved in oocyte maturation are less well understood. In the mouse, the oocyte experiences a stage of rapid growth and metabolic activity following recruitment from the primordial follicle stage. Only fully grown oocytes have the capability to resume meiosis and ovulation, and during this growth period, there are striking changes in the ultra structure of the oocyte, including changes in morphology and number of mitochondria changes in structure and activity of the Golgi apparatus [58]. Recent evidence suggests that physiological factors in the preovulatory follicle can have developmental consequences in the ovary. Factors related to chromosomal normality of the oocyte, embryo cleavage, and embryo transfer outcome include perifollicular vascularity and intrafollicular P02, pH, and biochemistry [59–61]. Van Blerkom et al. [62] investigated the differential mitochondrial distribution in human pronuclear embryos to address the question of what begins to make a good oocyte/embryo. Their findings demonstrated that specific perinuclear mitochondrial aggregation patterns and microtubular organization occur synergistically. Some blastomeres in embryos evidently receive reduced quotas of mitochondria and are therefore prone to diminished adenosine triphosphate (ATP) generation. The authors concluded that this could be an epigenetic basis for the variation in developmental ability observed in morphologically normal IVF cleavage stage embryos. Preexisting oocyte mitochondrial deoxyribonucleic acid (mtDNA) defects or accumulation of age-related mtDNA mutations could result in reduced meiotic competence and ability to fertilize and undergo development [63]. This may explain early pregnancy failure in women of advanced reproductive age [64].

GRANULOSA CELL COMMUNICATION

Ovarian physiology is underpinned by the dynamics of primordial follicle growth, development, and atresia during reproductive life [65]. Ovarian senescence is linked with this decreasing pool of primordial follicles. The follicles develop through successive stages through primary and secondary stages until an antral cavity forms. It is at the antral stage when a dominant ovulatory follicle emerges and most follicles undergo atresia [66]. Endocrine and paracrine factors control the fate of the follicles.

The process of primordial follicle recruitment is independent of gonadotropins, and intraovarian factors determine which follicles grow and when they start. This recruitment process could be because of the release of inhibitory stimuli that maintains the follicles at rest or a stimulatory factor that triggers growth, or a combination of factors. The existence of oocyte factors influencing follicle development has been established. Oocyte-derived factors stimulate the proliferation of granulosa cells but inhibit LH receptor expression [67]. Growth differentiation factor 9 (GDF-9) is a member of the transforming growth factor-β superfamily and a product of the oocyte that has been implicated in the diversification of the granulosa cell phenotypes [68, 69]. Animals deficient in GDF-9 have follicle development arrested at the primary stage [70]. Treatment with recombinant GDF-9, but not FSH, stimulated thymidine incorporation into cultured granulosa cells in early antral and preovulatory follicles [71]. The data suggest that GDF-9 is a proliferative factor for granulosa cells and plays a role in their differentiation. Secondary effects occur in the absence of GDF-9 including the failure of the thecal layer to form and defects in the oocyte, such as abnormal germinal vesicle breakdown, spontaneous parthenogenetic activation, and increased growth rate [72]. Because follicles in knockout mice are blocked at the type 3b stage, GDF-9 is not a principal factor for recruitment of primordial follicles and, so far, research has failed to identify the key triggers/inhibitors. Factor in the germline, alpha, (FIGα) mRNA is required for germ cell development in mice, and the FIGα protein has been implicated in the transcription of zona pellucida genes [73] and is expressed in human oogenesis [73a]. The granulosa cell secreted kit ligand has also been implicated in early follicular development [74]. Driancourt et al. [75] showed that kit-kit ligand interaction is involved in the initiation of follicular growth from the primordial pool and progression beyond the primary follicle stage. The protein controls growth and theca cell differentiation during early folliculargenesis, protects preantral follicles from apoptosis, and is required for antral cavity formation. In large antral follicles, it modulates the ability of the oocyte to undergo cytoplasmic maturation and maximizes thecal androgen output [75].

It is not until the onset of follicle growth and zona pellucida formation that full oocyte-granulosa cell bidirectional exchange of signals occurs. This communication system is facilitated by transzonal projections (TZPs) at the oocyte-granulosa cell boundary [76]. TZPs are follicle cell extensions that transverse the zona pellucida and terminate on the oocyte cell surface. The studies of Motta et al. [77] conducted on human ovarian follicles were the first to indicate that TZPs may facilitate the coordination or exchange of signals between oocyte and follicle cells. These structures mediate directed transport, secretion, and possibly selective uptake of factors secreted by the oocyte and the granulosa cells, as well as provide physical anchorage. The exchange via gap junctions includes small molecules such as amino acids, sugar, and nucleotides [78]. Gap junctions occur at places of close cell contact and allow small molecules (<1000 Da) to pass from cell to cell [79]. Connexin is the fundamental unit of gap junction forming a hemichannel in the membrane. Each connexin is a hexamer of protein subunits called *connexins* [80]. In addition, there is communication via other growth factor–ligand interactions such as oocyte-derived factors (e.g., GDF-9) that affect cumulus mucification [81, 82]. The ovarian follicle is therefore essentially a functional syncytium with the oocyte communicating with the surrounding cumulus cells and the cumulus cells also communicating to the mural cells through gap junctions.

GONADOTROPIN STIMULATION PROTOCOLS

Use of Gonadotropin-Releasing Hormone Agonist or Antagonist

Gonadotropin-releasing hormone (Gn-RH) is decapeptide secreted by the hypothalamus in a pulsatile pattern that binds to a specific receptor in the pituitary cells to regulate the secretion and synthesis of gonadotropins. After binding with the receptor, the Gn-RH-receptor complex forms a microaggregation that leads to the release of pituitary hormones LH and FSH. Gn-RH agonists and antagonists both exert their specific effects via the binding to the transmembrane receptor according to their structure (Figure 27.1). Gn-RH agonists differ from the antagonists in that initially there is a flare response, followed by a long period of downregulation suppression [83]. With the Gn-RH antagonist, there is a competitive block of the receptor leading to a direct blockade of FSH and LH release. Because of the prolonged half-life of FSH and perhaps other factors, the effect on LH is more profound than FSH. Gn-RH agonists have gained popularity because of their convenience on controlling stimulation cycles. In addition, metaanalysis of studies comparing the "long protocol" of midluteal Gn-RH-agonist (Gn-RH-a) suppression followed by hMG treatment compared with hMG treatment alone have shown a twofold increase of the pregnancy rate with the use of the drug [84]. With the long Gn-RH-a/hMG regimen, more follicles and oocytes are produced, and there is an improvement in oocyte quality [85]. The purpose of the Gn-RH-a is to suppress bioactive LH to prevent premature luteinization. In addition, increased pregnancy rates with Gn-RH-a are possible because of a larger number of oocytes and embryos [86]. The disadvantage of its use is the increased length of treatment, the greater amount of gonadotropin needed, and the risk of ovarian hyperstimulation syndrome (OHSS).

Amino Acid Sequence 1to10 of Gn-RH and Gn-RH Antagonists

Pyro Glu	His	Trp	Ser	Tyr	Gly	Leu	Arg	Pro	Gly Nh_2
AcD-Nal	D-4Ci Phe	D-Pal	Ser	Tyr	D-Cit	Leu	Arg	Pro	D-Ala
AcD-Nal	D-4Ci	D-Pal	Ser	Tyr	D-Aph (Et_2)	Leu	L-Aph (Et_2)	Pro	D-Ala

FIGURE 27.1 Specific effects of Gn-RH agonists and antagonists.

It is possible to prevent the LH surge without a desensitization period if Gn-RH antagonists are used. These medications induce an inhibition of LH secretion without a flare-up period. The new antagonists, Citrorelix and ganirelix, are devoid of the histaminergic reactions of the previous medications, and the treatment period is shorter because the antagonist can be added in the middle of the follicular phase when the leading follicle is already between 14 to 16 mm in diameter. Moreover, there is no flare-up and the risk of ovarian cysts is lessened. The disadvantage of the antagonist is that too early administration can lead to FSH suppression as well, and a poor response and late administration can allow a premature LH surge.

There have been several controlled, multicenter, randomized trials with hundreds of patients in Europe and North America comparing treatment regimens with Gn-RH antagonist with the long protocol using Gn-RH-a. Similar numbers of embryos, fertilization rates, and pregnancy rates were obtained for a shorter stimulation duration and fewer side effects with the antagonist protocols in normal responders [87, 88, 89]. Further large-scale studies are now needed for patients with polycystic ovarian syndrome (PCOS) and for patients who are poor responders.

The Role of Follicle-Stimulating Hormone and Luteinizing Hormone on Oocyte and Embryo Quality

The gonadotropins, LH and FSH, play critical roles in follicular development. The rise in serum FSH that occurs during the luteal-follicular transition is a stimulus for follicular recruitment and development of early antral follicles. FSH stimulates estrogen production from the granulosa cells through aromatization of the androgens produced by the thecal cells ("two cell theory"). This increase in estradiol suppresses FSH secretion in the late follicular phase, inhibiting maturation of the less mature follicles. Granulosa cells develop their own LH receptors in the mid- to late follicular phase as a result of FSH action. At this stage, LH can synergize with FSH to sustain follicular development and to prepare it for a midcycle LH surge that triggers ovulation. During the normal menstrual cycle, LH levels rise before ovulation along with estradiol levels. LH is also the stimulus for androgen secretion by the theca cells. A role for androgens and LH in follicle atresia and poor oocyte quality in PCOS patients is suspected.

IVF protocols that involve Gn-RH-a or antagonists in IVF by suppressing the endogenous LH levels can prevent early luteinization in high LH level preparations, such as HMG. The debate continues whether recombinant FSH is on its own sufficient when bioactive LH levels are suppressed. If the increase in LH in the late follicular phase is important for oocyte development, excessive LH suppression might compromise oocyte quality, whereas pure FSH would lead to a poorer stimulation. Addition of a low dose of LH should increase estradiol levels and follicular growth. In hypothalamic-hypogonadotropic patients, Shoham et al. [90] examined the use of recombinant FSH and found fewer developing follicles, lower estradiol levels, and decreased fertilization and embryo survival rates compared with HMG treatment cycles. However, in ovulatory patients, two studies comparing pure FSH with hMG showed no difference in response parameters [91, 92]. Metaanalyses of studies comparing the use of recombinant FSH with urinary HMG have shown little difference between the two. One showed a higher pregnancy rate with pure FSH compared with hMG (odds ratio 1.7), but Gn-RH-a was not consistently used [93]. A second metaanalysis comparing FSH and hMG in women using agonist protocols showed a trend toward higher pregnancy rates with HMG [94]. Patients with decreased LH levels demonstrated lower estradiol production, decreased oocyte yield, and increased days of stimulation [95]. Weston et al. [96] found that the cryopreservation survival and implantation rates of blastocysts decreased when pure FSH was used alone to stimulate oocyte production, perhaps because of poorer cytoplasmic maturation. In contrast, a randomized prospective trial of highly purified FSH compared with FSH plus recombinant LH in a long leuprolide (Lupron) protocol found a trend toward better outcomes in the former group [97]. Patients in this study were less suppressed and had higher baseline LH levels (0.5 mg in the midluteal phase that decreased to 0.25 mg with the initiation of the gonadotropins). Therefore the type and dose of Gn-RH-a may be important when using pure FSH because this will have an effect on the extent of suppression of endogenous LH. In the United States the most common dose of leuprolide (Lupron) has been 1 mg daily subcutaneously until the onset of menses, and then the dose is decreased to 0.5 mg until human chorionic gonadotropin (hCG) is given. This protocol suppresses LH at a higher level than Buserelin, which is the most common agonist used in Europe. There appears to be a threshold level of LH required for adequate follicular development and maturation and oocyte quality, as revealed in patients with hypothalamic hypogonadism with baseline LH levels less than 1 mIU/ml. However, the biological threshold may be extremely low because only 1% of LH receptors need to be occupied for normal steroidogenesis to occur [98]. What the threshold level is and whether endogenous LH is sufficient or should be supplemented is still debatable. Studies are required with a more consistent supplement such as minidoses of hCG or recombinant LH because the role of LH is still controversial.

Stimulation in Patients with Polycystic Ovarian Syndrome

Patients with PCOS have excessive secretion of LH and irregular menstrual cycles, an ovulation and infertility, and an increased frequency of miscarriage. LH-stimulated excessive androgen secretion by the thecal cells may promote more atresia and disruption of the dominant follicle, which may account for the reduced quality of oocytes in PCOS. Excessive LH levels might directly or indirectly influence late follicular phase meiotic maturation, disrupting cumulus-granulosa gap junctions and attenuate oocyte maturation inhibitors, all of which lead to poorer quality oocytes and reduced fertilization potential. Hence, an exaggerated response to gonadotropins is at the heart of the problem of oocyte quality in PCOS. Stimulation with gonadotropins leads to multifollicular development, and super-elevated estradiol levels are reached earlier in the cycle than is appropriate. As a result, the oocytes retrieved are more likely to be immature and will have been exposed to high estradiol levels, exhibiting low fertilization rates and poor embryonic development.

Several groups, including our center, have devised strategies to dampen the response to gonadotropins to improve follicular development, oocyte quality, and embryo quality. This has involved a combination of a step-down protocol and the use of insulin-sensitizing drugs such as metformin during stimulation. Starting with low-dose gonadotropins for all patients with PCOS is not the best strategy, because there is a critical level of FSH stimulation per follicle that is required for the early stages of follicular development, after which the requirement lessens as follicles grow. Coasting or withdrawing gonadotropin treatment can be successfully done when the follicle size is larger than 14 mm and the estradiol levels are higher than 2000 pg/ml [99–101]. Coasting has been shown to decrease the rate of cycle cancellation and the incidence of OHSS. Other options to reduce OHSS include (1) reducing the hCG dose or (2) using Gn-RH antagonist during stimulation and a Gn-RH agonist or recombinant LH to trigger the surge, both of which are more rapidly cleared from the circulation and produce a shorter duration of exposure of the follicular/luteal cells to hCG [102, 103]. The other option is to cryopreserve all the embryos, which should be done for patients with estradiol levels greater than 7000 pg/ml because these patients have lower pregnancy rates. It should also be done for patients with a high risk for developing OHSS.

Suppression of the pituitary gland is achieved with leuprolide (Lupron) (0.5 mg daily subcutaneously) in the luteal phase or, in anovulatory patients, there is an overlap of the oral contraceptive pill (OCP) with the Gn-RH agonist for 1 week with continuation of the agonist until menses. Both the agonist and OCPs suppress the high LH levels in these patients and dampen the response to doses of FSH during the stimulation phase of the cycle. This has lead to an improvement in the stimulation of the ovaries, leading to better egg and embryo quality, higher pregnancy rates, and decreased OHSS. Studies are currently underway to test if the Gn-RH antagonist has any advantage over the agonist in these patients with PCOS. Initial reports with the antagonist reveal a comparable clinical outcome in patients with PCOS [104].

Minimal Ovarian Stimulation and Poor Responders

Minimal ovarian stimulation can be done in selected cases to reduce the cost of treatment and decrease the risk of OHSS (Figure 27.2). Suitable candidates are young, normal ovulatory women with tubal or male factor and poor prognosis patients that consistently produce fewer than five follicles with high dosage gonadotropins. We start with 00 mg clomiphene citrate on day 3 of the cycle, followed by gonadotropins on day 8. The Gn-RH antagonist is used to reduce the risk of a premature LH surge, and, although pregnancy rates are slightly lower than after full stimulation, the cost is reduced, which is an attractive option for some patients.

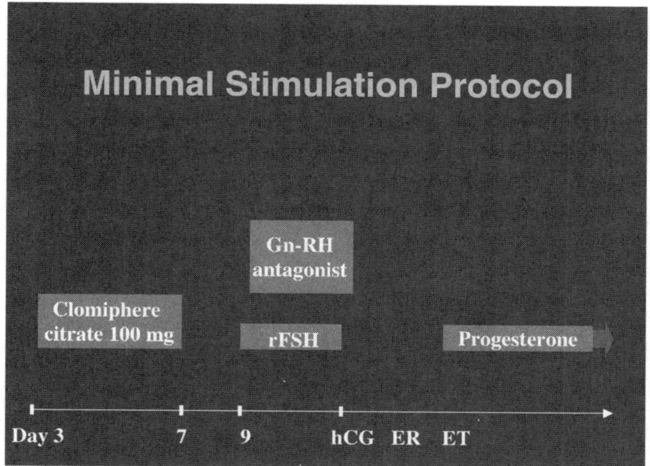

FIGURE 27.2 Minimal ovarian stimulation protocol.

There is no uniform definition of a poor responder; various stimulation protocols have attempted to improve IVF success rates in these patients. We define low responders as those patients with diminished ovarian reserve based on age greater than 40 years, FSH levels on day 3 greater than 15 mIU/ml, or those who consistently have peak estradiol concentrations of less than 500 pg/ml with fewer than five dominant follicles on day of hCG. Reports show that in these poor responders, increasing the dosage of medication may lead to increased numbers of oocytes retrieved and embryos, but the pregnancy rates were equally poor [105]. In addition, poor responders are more likely to fail to respond to gonadotropins following Gn-RH downregulation. Although donor egg treatment is the best option for these patients, many are not emotionally ready for this decision and want to try first with their own eggs. We, along with other researchers, have had some success with other protocols for the low responders that do not involve Gn-RH-a downregulation, including (1) "stop Lupron", (2) "microdose flare," and (3) "Gn-RH antagonist" protocols (summarized in Figures 27.3 to 27.5).

In the "stop Lupron" protocol, Gn-RH agonist (leuprolide [Lupron] 0.5 mg daily subcutaneously) downregulation is initiated in the luteal phase followed by commencement of high dosages of gonadotropins when menses begins (300 IU of pure FSH plus 300 IU of urinary combined FSH and LH). Lupron is stopped at the initiation of gonadotropins, after downregulation [106]. The pro-

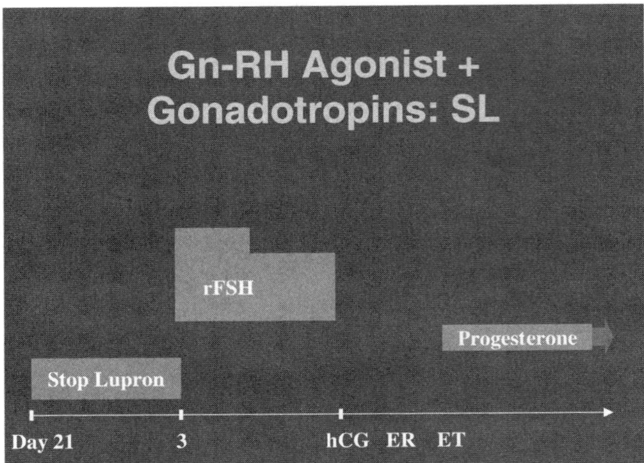

FIGURE 27.3 Stop Lupron protocol.

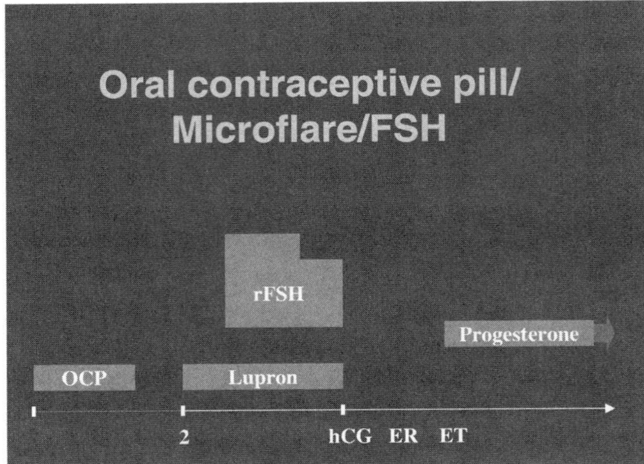

FIGURE 27.4 Microdose flare protocol.

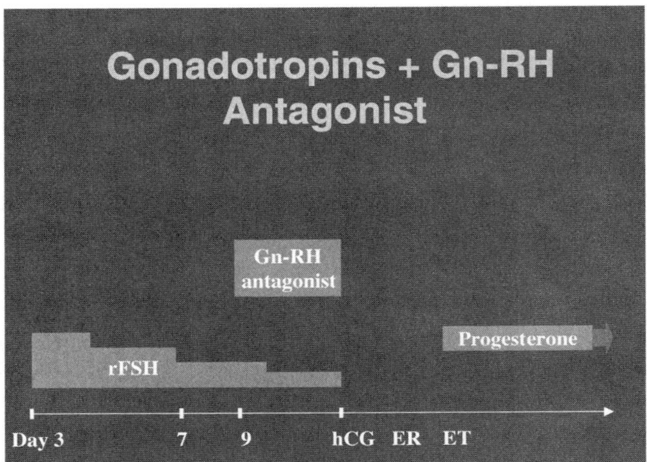

FIGURE 27.5 Gn-RH antagonist protocol.

tocol maximizes the ovarian response without risking a spontaneous, premature LH surge. Faber et al. [106] reviewed 182 low-responder patients treated with this protocol and obtained a clinical pregnancy rate of 32% and cycle cancellation rate of only 12.5%, but there was no control group. Another study showed improved pregnancy rates in poor-responder patients and found a clinical pregnancy rate per cycle of 31.4% [107].

In the "microdose flare" protocol, microdoses of Gn-RH-a and gonadotropins are initiated in the follicular phase after a month of OCPs [108]. On day 3, we use 50 mg Lupron twice daily and start gonadotropin stimulation on day 5. Success is similar to the "stop Lupron" protocol. Studies show no difference in pure FSH compared with FSH/LH in poor-responder protocols, because significant endogenous LH is released. In fact several centers have found a trend toward better outcomes with recombinant FSH alone. The "antagonist protocol" has also been used in poor responders.

Akman et al. [109] compared gonadotropins alone to gonadotropins with Gn-RH antagonist in cycles of poor responders undergoing IVF and found higher implantation, clinical pregnancy rates, and ongoing pregnancy rates in these patients. Studies that compared the Gn-RH antagonist with the microdose flare showed no differences in outcome [110]. However, no large prospective, randomized controlled studies have been done. Each program should evaluate the three protocols in their own poor-responder population. Addition of LH is recommended in the "stop–Lupron" protocol where basal LH levels will be suppressed.

Because oocyte donation is a back-up option and unacceptable to some couples, cytoplasmic or germinal vesicle transfer have been explored experimentally for age-related or poor oocyte quality problems [111, 112]. There was an initial flurry of excitement that these approaches may avoid aneuploidy, perhaps as a result of the younger cytoplasm promoting a healthy spindle and hence allowing normal chromosomal segregation during meiosis. However, the implications of this radical strategy for mitochondrial heteroplasmy and imprinting phenomena have yet to be fully investigated and the risks for the child-to-be are unknown.

References

1. Steptoe, P. C., and Edwards, R. G. (1978). Birth after re-implantation of a human embryo. *Lancet* 2, 366.
2. Society for Assisted Reproductive Technology and the American Society for Reproductive Medicine. Assisted reproductive technology in the United States: 1999 results generated from the American Society for Reproductive

Medicine/Society for Assisted Reproductive Technology Registry. *Fertil. Steril.* 78, 918–928.

3. Sauer, M. V., Paulson, R. J., and Lobo, R. A. (1990). A preliminary report on oocyte donation extending the reproductive potential to women over 40. *N. Engl. J. Med.* 323, 1157–1160.
4. Navot, D., Bergh, P. A., Williams, M. A., Garrisi, G. J., Guzman, I., Sandler, B., and Grunfeld, L. (1991). Poor oocyte quality rather than implantation failure is a cause of age-related decline in female fertility. *Lancet* 337, 1375–1377.
5. Craft, I., Al-Shawaf, T., Lewis, P., Serhal, P., Simons, E., Ah-Moye, M., Fiamanya, W., Robertson, D., Shrivastav, P., and Brinsden, P. (1988). Analysis of 1,071 GIFT procedures: The case for a flexible approach to treatment. *Lancet I.* 1094–1097.
6. Tan, S. L., Royston, P., Campbell, S., Jacobs, H. S., Betts, J., Mason, B., and Edwards, R. G. (1992). Cumulative conception and live birth rates after in-vitro fertilization. *Lancet* 339, 1390–1394.
7. Dickey, R. P., Olar, T. T., Taylor, S. N., Curole, D. N., Rye, P. H., and Matulich, E. M. (1991). Relationship of follicle number, serum estradiol, and other factors to birth rate and multiparity in human menopausal gonadotropin-insemination cycles. *Fertil. Steril.* 56, 89–92.
8. Maroulis, G. B. (1991). Effect of aging on fertility and pregnancy. *Sem. Reprod. Endocrinol.* 9, 165–175.
9. Faddy, M. J., Gosden, R. G., Gougeon, A., Richardson, S. J., and Nelson, J. F. (1992). Accelerated disappearance of ovarian follicles in mid-life: Implications for forecasting menopause. *Hum. Reprod.* 7, 1342–1346.
10. Faddy, M. J., and Gosden, R. G. (1996). A model conforming the decline in follicle numbers to the age of menopause in women. *Hum. Reprod.* 11, 1484–1486.
11. Akande, V. A., Fleming, C. F., Hunt, L. P., Keay, S. D., and Jenkins, J. M. (2002). Biological verses chronological ageing of oocytes, distinguishable by raised FSH levels in relation to the success of IVF treatment. *Hum. Reprod.* 17, 2003–2008.
12. El-Toukhy, T., Khalaf, Y., Hart, R., Taylor, A., and Braude, P. (2002). Young age does not protect against the adverse effects of reduced ovarian reserve—an eight year study. *Hum. Reprod.* 17, 1519–1524.
13. Hull, M. G., Fleming, C. F., Hughes, A. O., and McDermott, A. (1996). The age related decline in female fecundity: A quantitative controlled study of implanting capacity and survival of individual embryos after in vitro fertilization. *Fertil. Steril.* 65, 783–790.
14. Oehninger, S., Veeck, L. O., Lanzendorf, S., Mahoney, M., Toner, J., and Muasher, S. (1995). Intracytoplasmic sperm injection: Achievement of high pregnancy rates in couples with severe male factor infertility is dependent primarily upon female and not male factors. *Fertil. Steril.* 64, 977–981.
15. Muasher, S. J., Oehninger, S., Simonetti, S., Matta, J., Ellis, L. M., Liu, H. C., Jones, G. S., and Roserwaks, Z. (1988). The value of basal and/or stimulated serum gonadotropin levels in prediction of stimulation response and in-vitro fertilization outcome. *Fertil. Steril.* 50, 298–307.
16. Toner, J. P., Philput, C. B., Jones, G. S., and Muasher, S. J. (1991). Basal follicle-stimulating hormone level is a better predictor of in-vitro fertilization performance than age. *Fertil. Steril.* 55, 784–791.
17. Hanoch, J., Lavy, Y., Holzer, H., Hurwitz, A., Simon, A., Revel, A., and Laufer, N. (1998). Young low responders are protected from untoward effects of reduced ovarian response. *Fertil. Steril.* 69, 1001–1004.
18. Hassold, T., Hunt, P. A., and Sherman, S. (1993). Trisomy in humans: Incidence, origin and etiology. *Curr. Opin. Genet. Dev.* 3, 398–403.
19. Magli, M. C., Gianaroli, L., Munne, S., and Ferraretti, A. P. (1998). Incidence of chromosomal abnormalities from a morphologically normal cohort of embryos in poor-prognosis patients. *J. Assist. Reprod. Genet.* 15, 297–301.
20. Henderson, S. A., and Edwards, R. G. (1968). Chiasma frequency and maternal age in mammals. *Nature* 218, 22–28.
21. Warburton, D. (1989). The effect of maternal age on the frequency of trisomy: Change in meiosis or in utero selection? In *Molecular and Cytogenetic Studies of Non-disjunction*, eds. T. G. Hassold and C. J. Epstein, 165–181. New York: Alan R. Liss.
22. Crowley, P., Gulah, D., Hayden, T., et al. (1979). A chiasma-hormonal hypothesis relating Down's syndrome and maternal age. *Nature* 280, 417–418.
23. Tarin, J. J. (1995). Aetiology of age-associated aneuploidy: A mechanism based on the free radical theory of ageing. *Mol. Hum. Reprod.* 1, 1563–1565.
24. Eppig, J. J., Shultz, R. M., O'Brien, M., and Chesnel, F. (1994). Relationship between the developmental programs controlling nuclear and cytoplasmic maturation of mouse oocytes. *Dev. Biol.* 164, 1–9.
25. LeMaire-Adkins, R., Radke, K., and Hunt, P. A. (1997). Lack of checkpoint control at the metaphase-anaphase transition: A mechanism of meiotic non-disjunction in mammalian females. *J. Cell. Biol.* 139, 1611–1619.
26. Munne, S., Alikani, M., Tomkin, G., Grifo, J., and Cohen, J. (1995). Embryo morphology, developmental rates and maternal age are correlated with chromosome abnormalities. *Fertil. Steril.* 64, 382–391.
27. Munne, S., Magli, C., Cohen, J., Morton, P., Sadoy, S., Gianaroli, L., Tucker, M., Marquez, C., Sable, D., Ferraretti, A. P., Massey, J., and Scott, R. (1999). Positive outcome after preimplantation diagnosis of aneuploidy in human embryos. *Hum. Reprod.* 14, 2191–2199.
28. Dailey, T., Dale, B., Cohen, H., and Munne, S. (1996). Association between non-disjunction and maternal age in meiosis-II human oocytes detected by FISH analysis. *Am. J. Hum. Genet.* 59, 176–184.
29. Van Blerkom, J., and Henry, G. (1992). Oocyte dysmorphology and aneuploidy in meiotically mature human oocytes after ovarian stimulation. *Hum. Reprod.* 7, 379–390.
30. Munne, S., Grifo, J., Cohen, J., and Weier, H. U. G. (1994). Chromosome abnormalities in human arrested preimplantation embryos: A multiple-probe FISH study. *Am. J. Hum. Genet.* 55, 150–159.
31. Clyde, J. M., Gosden, R. G., Rutherford, A. J., and Picton, H. M. (2001). Demonstration of a mechanism of aneuploidy in human oocytes using Multifluor fluorescence in situ hybridization. *Fertil. Steril.* 76, 837–840.
32. Volarcik, K., Sheean, L., Goldfarb, J., Woods, L., Abdul-Karim, F. W., and Hunt, P. (1998). The meiotic competence

of in-vitro matured human oocytes is influenced by donor age: Evidence that folliculogenesis is compromised in the reproductively aged ovary. *Hum. Reprod.* 13, 154–160.

33. DeFelici, M., and Siracusa, G. (1982). Spontaneous hardening of the zona pellucida of mouse oocytes during in vitro culture. *Gamete Res.* 6, 107–113.
34. Cohen, J., Alikani, M., Reing, A. M., Ferrara, T. A., Trowbridge, J., and Tucker, M. (1992). Selective assisted hatching of human embryos. *Arc. Of Med.* 21, 565–570.
35. Hsuh, Y. Y., Huang, C. C., Cheng, T. C., Chang, C. C., Tsai, H. D., and Lee, M. S. (2002). Laser-assisted hatching of embryos is better than the chemical method for enhancing the pregnancy rate in women with advanced age. *Fertil. Steril.* 78, 179–182.
36. Alikani, M., Noyes, N., Cohen, J., and Rosenwaks, Z. (1994). Monozygotic twinning in the human is associated with the zona pellucida architecture. *Hum. Reprod.* 8, 1723–1728.
37. Liu, H. C., Cohen, J., Alikani, M., Noyes, N., and Rosenwaks, Z. (1993). Assisted hatching facilitates earlier implantation. *Fertil. Steril.* 60, 871–875.
38. Schoolcraft, W., Schlenker, T., Jones, G., and Jones, H. (1995). In vitro fertilization in women age 40 and over: The impact of assisted hatching. *J. Asst. Reprod.* 12, 581–583.
39. Schoolcraft, W., Schlenker, T., Gee, M., Jones, G., and Jones, H. (1994). Assisted hatching in the treatment of poor prognosis in vitro fertilization candidates. *Fertil. Steril.* 62, 551–554.
40. Stein, A., Rufas, O., Amit, S., Avrech, O., Pinkas, H., Ovadia, H., and Fisch, B. (1995). Assisted hatching by partial zona dissection of human pre-embryos in patients with recurrent implantation failure after in vitro fertilization. *Fertil. Steril.* 63, 838–841.
41. Magistrini, M., and Szollosi, D. (1980). Effects of cold and isopropyl-n-phenylcarbamate on the second meiotic spindle of mouse oocytes. *Eur. J. Cell. Biol.* 22, 699–707.
42. Waterman-Storer, C. M. (1998). Microtubules and microscopes: How the development of light microscopic imaging technologies has contributed to discoveries about microtubule dynamics in living cells. *Mol. Biol. Cell.* 9 (12), 3263–71.
43. Maro, B., Johnson, M. H., Webb, M., and Flach, G. (1986). Mechanism of polar body formation in the mouse oocyte: An interaction between the chromosomes, cytoskeleton and the plasma membrane. *J. Embryol. Exp. Morphol.* 92, 11–32.
44. Schatten, G., Simerly, C., and Schatten, H. (1985). Microtubule configurations during fertilization, mitosis, and early development in the mouse and the requirement for egg microtubule-mediated motility during mammalian fertilization. *Proc. Natl. Acad. Sci. USA.* 82, 152–156.
45. Pickering, S. J., Cant, A., Braude, P. R., Currie, J., and Johnson, M. H. (1990). Transient cooling to room temperature can cause irreversible disruption of the meiotic spindle in the human oocyte. *Fertil. Steril.* 54, 102–108.
46. Johnson, M. H., and Pickering, D. (1987). The effect of dimethylsulfoxide on the microtubular system of the mouse oocyte. *Development* 100, 313–324.
47. Eroglu, A., Toth, T. L., and Toner, M. (1998). Alterations of the cytoskeleton and polyploidy induced by cryopreservation of metaphase II mouse oocytes. *Fertil. Steril.* 69, 944–957.
48. Baka, S. G., Toth, T. L., Veeck, L. L., Jones, H. W., Muasher, S. J., and Lanzendorf, S. E. (1995). Evaluation of the spindle apparatus of in-vitro matured human oocytes following cryopreservation. *Hum. Reprod.* 10, 1816–1820.
49. Almeida, P. A., and Bolton, V. N. (1995). The effect of temperature fluctuations on the cytoskeletal organization and chromosomal constitution of the human oocyte. *Zygote* 3 (4), 357–365.
50. Aman, R. R., and Parks, J. E. (1994). Effects of cooling and rewarming on the meiotic spindle and cultured in vitro matured bovine oocytes. *Biol. Reprod.* 50 (1), 103–110.
51. Asada, Y., Baka, S. G., Hodgen, G. D., and Lanzendorf, S. E. (1995). Evaluation of the meiotic spindle apparatus in oocytes undergoing intracytoplasmic sperm injection. *Fertil. Steril.* 64, 76–381.
52. Blake, M., Garrisi, J., Tomkin, G., and Cohen, J. (2000). Sperm deposition site during ICSI affects fertilization and development. *Fertil. Steril.* 73 (1), 31–37.
53. Silva, C. P., Kommineni, K., Oldenbourg, R., and Keefe, D. L. (1999). The first polar body does not predict accurately the location of the metaphase II meiotic spindle apparatus in mammalian oocytes. *Fertil. Steril.* 71 (4), 719–721.
54. Hardarson, T. H., Lundin, K., and Hamberger, L. (2000). The position of the metaphase II spindle cannot be predicted by the location of the first polar body in human oocyte. *Hum. Reprod.* 15 (6), 1372–1376.
55. Liu, L. (2000). A reliable, noninvasive technique for spindle imaging and enucleation of mammalian oocytes. *Nat. Biotech.* 18 (2), 223–225.
56. Wang, W. H., Meng, L., Hackett, R. J., Odenbourg, R., and Keefe, D. L. (2001). The spindle observation and its relationship with fertilization after intracytoplasmic sperm injection in living human oocyte. *Fertil. Steril.* 75 (2), 348–53.
57. Battaglia, D. E., Goodwin, P., Klein, N. A., and Soules, M. R. (1996). Influence of maternal age on meiotic spindle assembly in oocytes from naturally cycling women. *Hum. Reprod.* 11, 2217–2222.
58. Wasserman, P. M., and Albertini, D. F. (1994). The mammalian ovum. In *The Physiology of Reproduction*, 2d ed., eds. E. Knobil and J. D. Neill, 79–122. New York: Raven Press.
59. Van Blerkom, J. (1997). Can the developmental competence of early human embryos be predicated effectively in the clinical IVF laboratory? *Hum. Reprod.* 12 (8), 1610–1614.
60. Huey, S., Abuhamad, A., Barroso, G., Hsu, M. I., Kolm, P., Mayer, J., and Oehninger, S. (1999). Perifollicular blood flow Doppler indices, but not follicular pO2, pCO2, or pH, predict oocyte developmental competence in in vitro fertilization. *Fertil. Steril.* 72 (4), 707–712.
61. Gregory, L. (1998). Ovarian markers of implantation potential in assisted reproduction. *Hum. Reprod.* 13 (Suppl 4), 117–132.
62. Van Blerkom, J., Davis, P., and Alexander, S. (2000). Differential mitochondrial distribution in human pronuclear embryos leads to disproportional inheritance between blastomeres: Relationship to microtubular organization, ATP content and competence. *Hum. Reprod.* 15 (12), 2621–2633.
63. Keefe, D. L., Niven-Fairchild, T., Powell, S., and Buradaguntas, S. (1995). Mitochondrial deoxyribonucleic acid deletions in oocytes and reproductive aging in women. *Fertil. Steril.* 64 (3), 577–583.

64. Jansen, R. P., and de Boer, K. (1998). The bottleneck: Mitochondrial imperatives in oogenesis and ovarian follicular fate. Review. *Mol. Cell. Endocrinol.* 145 (1–2), 81–88.
65. Gougeon, A. (1996). Regulation of ovarian follicular development in primates: Facts and hypotheses. *Endocr. Rev.* 156 (6), 2282–2293.
66. Hsueh, A. J., Billing, H., and Tsafriri, A. (1994). Ovarian follicular atresia: A hormonally controlled apoptotic process. Review. *Endocr. Rev.* 15 (6), 707–724.
67. Eppig, J. J., Cheshel, F., Hirao, Y., O'Brien, M. J., Pendolaf, L., Watanabe, S., and Wigglesworth, K. (1997). Oocyte control granulosa cell development: How and why. Review. *Hum. Reprod.* 12 (Suppl 11), 127–132.
68. McPherron, A. C., and Lee, S. J. (1993). GDF-3 and GDF-9: Two new members of the transforming growth factor-beta super family containing a novel pattern of cysteines. *J. Biol. Chem.* 268 (5), 3444–3449.
69. McGrath, S. A., Esquela, A. F., and Lee, S. J. (1995). Oocyte specific expression of growth/differentiation factor 9. *Mol. Endocrinol.* 9 (1), 131–136.
70. Dong, J., Albertini, D. F., Nishimori, K., Kumar, T. R., Lu, N., and Matzuk, M. M. (1996). Growth differentiation factor-9 is required during early ovarian folliculogenesis. *Nature* 383 (6600), 531–535.
71. Vitt, U. A., Hayashi, M., Klien, C., and Hsueh, A. J. W. (2000). Growth differentiation factor-9 stimulates proliferation but suppresses the follicular hormone-induced differentiation of cultured granulosa cells from small antral and preovulatory rat follicles. *Biol. Reprod.* 62, 370–377.
72. Carabatsos, M. J., Sellitto, C., Goodenough, D. A., and Albertini, D. F. (2000). Oocyte-granulosa cell heterologous gap junctions are required for the coordination of nuclear and cytoplasmic meiotic competence. *Dev. Biol.* 226 (2), 167–179.
73. Liang, L., Soyal, S. M., and Dean, J. (1997). FIG ALPHA, a germ cell specific transcription factor in the expression of the zona pellucida genes. *Development* 124 (24), 4939–4947.
73a. Huntriss, et al. (2002).
74. Yoshida, H., Takakura, N., Kataoka, H., Kunisada, T., Okamura, H., and Nishikawa, S. (1997). Stepwise requirement of c-kit tyrosine kinase in mouse ovarian follicle development. *Dev. Biol.* 184, 122–137.
75. Driancourt, M. A., Reynaud, K., Cortvrindt, R., and Smitz, J. (2000). Roles of KIT and KIT LIGAND in ovarian function. *Rev. Reprod.* 5, 143–152.
76. Albertini, D. F., Combelles, C. M., Benecchi, E., and Carabatos, M. J. (2001). Cellular basis for paracrine regulation of ovarian follicle development. Review. *Reprod.* 121 (5), 647–653.
77. Motta, P. M., Makabe, S., Naguro, T., and Correr, S. (1994). Oocyte follicle cells association during development of human ovarian follicle. A study by high resolution scanning and transmission electron microscopy. *Arch. Histol. Cyto.* 57 (4), 369–394.
78. Haghighat, N., and Van Winkle, L. J. (1990). Developmental change in follicular cell-enhanced amino acid uptake into mouse oocytes that depends on intact gap, junctions and transport system Gly. *J. Exp. Zool.* 253, 71–82.
79. Bruzzone, R., White, T. W., and Paul, D. L. (1996). Connections with connexins: The molecular basis of direct intercellular signaling. Review. *Eur. J. Biochem.* 238 (1), 1–27.
80. Unger, V. M., Kumar, N. M., Gilula, N. B., and Yeager, M. (1999). Expression two-dimensional cystallization and electron cryo-crystallography of recombinant gap junction membrane channels. *J. Struct. Biol.* 128 (1), 98–105.
81. Buccione, R., Vanderhyden, B. C., Caron, P. J., and Eppig, J. J. (1990). FSH-induced expansion of the mouse cumulus oophorus in vitro is dependent upon a specific factor(s) secreted by the oocyte. *Dev. Biol.* 138, 16–25.
82. Ackert, C. L., Gittens, J. E., O'Brien, M. J., Eppig, J. J., and Kidder, G. M. (2001). Intercellular communication via connexin-43 gap junctions is required for ovarian folliculogenesis in the mouse. *Dev. Biol.* 233 (2), 258–270.
83. Reissmann, T., Felberbaum, R., Diedrich, K., Engel, J., Comaru-Schally, A. M., and Schally, A. V. (1995). Development and applications of luteinizing hormone-releasing hormone antagonists in the treatment of infertility: An overview. *Hum. Reprod.* 10 (8), 1974–1981.
84. Hughes, E. G., Fedorkow, D. M., Daya, S., Sagle, M. A., Van de Koppel, P., and Collins, J. A. (1992). The routine use of gonadotropin-releasing hormone agonists prior to in vitro fertilization and gamete intrafallopian transfer: A meta-analysis of randomized controlled trials. *Fertil. Steril.* 58, 888–896.
85. Ron-El, R., Herman, A., Golan, A., Nachum, H., Soffer, Y., and Caspi, E. (1991). Gonadotropins and combined gonadotropin-releasing hormone agonist-gonadotropins protocols in a randomized prospective study. *Fertil. Steril.* 55, 574–578.
86. Liu, H. C., Lai, Y. M., Davis, O., Berkeley, A. S., Graf, M., Grifo, J., Cohen, J., and Rosenwaks, Z. (1992). Improved pregnancy outcome with gonadotropin releasing hormone agonist (GnRH-a) stimulation is due to the improvement in oocyte quantity rather than quality. *J. Assist. Reprod. Genet.* 9, 338–342.
87. The European Orgalutran Study Group. (Borm, G., and Mannaerts, B.) (2000). Treatment with gonadotrophin-releasing hormone antagonist ganirelix in women undergoing ovarian stimulation with recombinant follicle stimulating hormone is effective, safe and convenient: Results of a controlled, randomized, multicentre trial. *Hum. Reprod.* 15, 1490–1498.
88. The North American Ganirelix Study Group. (2001). Efficacy and safety of ganirelix acetate verses leuprolide acetate in women undergoing controlled ovarian hyperstimulation. *Fertil. Steril.* 75, 38–45.
89. Ludwig, M., Katalinic, A., and Diedrich, K. (2001). Use of GnRH antagonists in ovarian stimulation for ART compared with the long protocol: A meta-analysis. *Arch. Gynecol. Obstet.* 265, 175–182.
90. Shoham, Z., Jacobs, H. S., and Insler, V. (1993). Luteinizing hormone: Its role, mechanism of action, and detrimental effects when hypersecreted during the follicular phase. *Fertil. Steril.* 59, 1153–1161.
91. Bentick, B., Shaw, R. W., Iffland, C. A., Burford, G., and Bernard, A. (1988). A randomized comparative study of purified follicle stimulating hormone and hormone menopausal gonadotropin after pituitary desensitization with Buserelin for superovulation and in vitro fertilization. *Fertil. Steril.* 50, 79–84.

92. Edelstein, M. C., Brzyski, R. G., Jones, G. S., Simonetti, S., and Muasher, S. J. (1990). Equivalency of human menopausal gonadotropin and follicle-stimulating hormone after gonadotropin-releasing hormone suppression. *Fertil. Steril.* 53, 103–106.
93. Daya, S., Gunby, J., Hughes, E. G., Collins, J. A., and Sagle, M. A. (1995). Follicle-stimulating hormone versus human menopausal gonadotropin for in vitro fertilization cycles: A meta analysis. *Fertil. Steril.* 64, 347–354.
94. Agrawal, R., Holmes, J., and Jacobs, H. S. (2000). Follicle-stimulating hormone or human menopausal gonadotropin for ovarian stimulation in in vitro fertilization cycles: A meta- analysis. *Fertil. Steril.* 73, 338–343.
95. Fleming, R., Rehka, P., Deshpande, N., Jamieson, M. E., Yates, R. W., and Lyall, H. (2000). Suppression of LH during ovarian stimulation: Effects differ in cycles stimulated with purified urinary FSH and recombinant FSH. *Hum. Reprod.* 75, 1440–1445.
96. Weston, A. M., Zelinski-Wooten, M. B., Hutchison, J. S., Stouffer, R. L., and Wolf, D. P. (1996). Developmental potential of embryos produced by in-vitro fertilization from gonadotrophin-releasing hormone antagonist-treated macaques stimulated with recombinant human follicle stimulating hormone alone or I combination with luteinizing hormone. *Hum. Reprod.* 11, 608–613.
97. Sills, E. S., Levy, D. P., Moomjy, M., McGee, M., and Rosenwaks, Z. (1999). A prospective randomized comparison of ovulation induction using highly purified follicle-stimulating hormone alone and with recombinant human luteinizing hormone in in-vito fertilization. *Hum. Reprod.* 14, 2230–2235.
98. Chappel, S. C., and Howles, C. (1991). Reevaluation of the roles of luteinizing hormone and follicle stimulating hormone in the ovulatory process. *Hum. Reprod.* 6, 1206–1212.
99. Tortoriello, D. V., McGovern, P. G., Colon, J. M., Skurnick, J. H., Lipetz, K., and Santoro, N. (1998). "Coasting" does not adversely affect cycle outcome in a subset of highly responsive in vitro fertilization patients. *Fertil. Steril.* 69, 454–460.
100. Benadiva, C. A., Davis, O., Kligman, I., Moomjy, M., Liu, H. C., and Rosenwaks, Z. (1997). Withholding gonadotropin administration is an affective alternative for the prevention of ovarian hyperstimulation syndrome. *Fertil. Steril.* 67, 724–727.
101. Stadtmauer, L. A., Toma , S. K., Riehl, R. M., and Talbert, L. M. (2002). Impact of metformin therapy on ovarian stimulation and outcome in coasted patients with polycystic ovary syndrome undergoing in vitro fertilization. *RBMOnline.* 5, 11–116.
102. Ludwig, M., Felberbaum, R. E., Devroey, P., Albano, C., Riethmuller-Winzen, H., Schuler, A., Engel, W., and Diedrich, K. (2000). Significant reduction of the incidence of ovarian hyperstimulation (OHSS) by using the LHRH antagonist Cetrorelix (Cetrotide) in controlled ovarian stimulation for assisted reproduction. *Arch. Gynecol. Obstet.* 264, 29–32.
103. de Jong, D., Macklon, N. S., Mannaerts, B. M., Coelingh Bennink, H. J., and Fauser, B. C. (1988). High dose gonadotropin releasing hormone antagonist (ganirelix) may prevent ovarian hyperstimulation syndrome caused by ovarian stimulation for in-vitro fertilization. *Hum. Reprod.* 13, 573–575.
104. Bracro, N., Jurema, M., Vlahos, N., Kolp, L., and Garcia, J. (2002). Polycystic ovarian syndrome (PCOS) patients have a favorable response to ganirelix acetate during controlled ovarian hyperstimulation (COH) for in vitro fertilization (IVF)-embryo transfer (ET). *Fertil. Steril.* 78 (1001), S149–S150.
105. Stadtmauer, L., Ditkoff, E. C., Session, D., and Kelly, A. (1994). High dosages of gonadotropins are associated with poor pregnancy outcomes after IVT-ET. *Fertil. Steril.* 61, 1058–1064.
106. Faber, B., Mayer, J., Cox, B., Jones, D., Toner, J. P., Oehninger, S., and Muasher, S. J. (1998). Cessation of gondaotrophin-releasing hormone agonist therapy combined with high-dose gonadotrophin stimulation yields favorable pregnancy results in low responders. *Fertil. Steril.* 69, 826–830.
107. Karande, V., and Gleicher, N. (1999). A rational approach to the management of low responders in in-vitro fertilization: Opinion. *Hum. Reprod.* 14, 1744–1748.
108. Frydman, R., Belaisch-Allart, J., Parneix, I., Forman, R., Hazout, A., and Testart, J. (1988). Comparison between flare up and down regulation effects of luteinizing hormone releasing hormone agonists in an in vitro fertilization program. *Fertil. Steril.* 40, 471–475.
109. Akman, M. A., Erden, H. F., Tosun, S. B., Bayazit, N., Aksoy, E., and Bahceci, M. (2000). Addition of GnRH antagonist in cycles of poor responders undergoing in-vitro fertilization. *Hum. Reprod.* 15, 2145–2147.
110. Akman, M. A., Erden, H. F., Tosun, S. B., Bauazit, N., Aksoy, E., and Bahceci, M. (2001). Comparison of agonist flare-up protocol and antagonist multiple dose protocol in ovarian stimulation of poor responders: Results of a prospective randomized trial. *Hum. Reprod.* 16, 868–870.
111. Cohen, J., Scott, R., Schimmel, T., Leuron, J., and Willadsen, S. (1997). Birth of infant after transfer of a nucleate donor cytoplasm into recipient eggs. *Lancet* 350, 186–187.
112. Zhang, J, Wang, C. W., Krey, L., Liu, H., Meng, L., Blaszczyk, A., Adler, A., and Grifo, J. (1999). In vitro maturation of human preovulatory oocytes reconstructed by germinal vesicle transfer. *Fertil. Steril.* 71, 726–731.

CHAPTER **28**

Ovarian Function in Assisted Reproduction

CAROLE GILLING-SMITH AND STEPHEN FRANKS

INTRODUCTION

In this chapter, superovulation regimens used in assisted reproduction technology (ART) and their potential risks are analyzed in terms of their effect on ovarian function. An overview of normal ovarian folliculogenesis is first presented as a prerequisite to analyzing the impact of exogenous gonadotropins, gonadotropin-releasing hormone (Gn-RH) analogs and antagonists, and other drugs used in ART on ovarian response, oocyte quality, and pregnancy outcome.

NORMAL OVARIAN PHYSIOLOGY

At birth the human ovaries contain approximately two million follicles arrested at the primordial stage of development. Most will undergo atresia throughout infancy, childhood, and the reproductive years with only one or two follicles selected in each ovarian cycle to mature and release an oocyte capable of being fertilized. This transformation from primordial to mature graafian follicle is a prolonged process that occurs over several months [1] and can be divided into three stages: initiation, recruitment, and maturation. The strategy of in vitro fertilization (IVF) stimulation regimens is to override the natural process of unifollicular recruitment and maturation (characteristic of the human cycle) by manipulating ovarian exposure to follicle-stimulating hormone (FSH) and luteinizing hormone (LH) during the last 14 days of the ovarian cycle. A good understanding of the natural ovarian cycle is a prerequisite if ART regimens are to be titrated to optimize ovarian response in women with either a poor response or abnormal ovarian function (e.g., polycystic ovary syndrome).

Folliculogenesis

Initiation of folliculogenesis occurs continuously from birth to senescence and is gonadotropin independent. Little is known about local endocrine and paracrine factors that may influence this stage, although growth and maturation of both somatic and germ cells in the follicle appear to be influenced by factors produced by the oocyte and surrounding granulosa cells [2–4]. There are data to suggest that kit ligand produced by the pregranulosa cells of primordial follicles and its receptor c-kit, found in the oocyte, play a role in initiation of growth [5]. In the luteal phase of the cycle preceding that leading to ovulation, follicle growth starts to accelerate. Responsiveness to FSH is only acquired once granulosa cells are formed. FSH acts through membrane-associated receptors to stimulate granulosa cell proliferation and differentiation and is required for antrum formation, which occurs once the follicle diameter reaches 0.25 mm diameter. Growth factors of the transforming growth factor-β (TGF-β) superfamily are involved in the early stages of follicular growth. Oocyte-derived factors that are likely to have an influence on granulosa cell proliferation and follicle growth include growth differentiation factor 9 (GDF-9) and bone morphogenetic protein-15 (BMP-15) [6]. Antimüllerian hormone (AMH) and activin produced by granulosa cells have both autocrine and paracrine effects within the follicle [7]. These findings suggest that both the local ovarian milieu and circulating endocrine factors influence follicle growth and oocyte quality.

FSH and LH play a central role in regulating the second and third stages of folliculogenesis: recruitment and growth. At the onset of menstruation, a cohort of early tertiary (antral) follicles is present in both ovaries, most of which are destined to undergo atresia. Failure of fertilization in the previous cycle results in corpus luteum regression, which is accompanied by a fall in circulating levels of progesterone, estradiol, and inhibin. This removes the negative feedback inhibition of pituitary FSH, which rises in the early follicular phase (days 2 to 4). This rise in serum FSH beyond a critical threshold level is the primary stimulus for follicle recruitment, and several early antral follicles in the cohort at the appropriate stage of maturation start to enlarge. The effect is maximal in the follicle(s) with the lowest threshold requirement for FSH (i.e., the one whose granulosa cells are most responsive). As this follicle starts to enlarge, it secretes increasing amounts of estradiol, which has a negative feedback effect on FSH secretion through the hypothamo-pituitary axis. Serum FSH levels fall to a level too low to sustain follicular growth of those antral follicles with higher FSH threshold requirements, which therefore undergo atresia. The dominant follicle is thus singled out as the one destined to mature and continues to grow under the influence of low levels of FSH. Evidence of a single dominant follicle is usually apparent by days 7 to 8 of the cycle, when its diameter has reached 10 mm.

Two-Cell Two-Gonadotropin Theory

As the follicle develops, granulosa and theca cell layers work in synchrony to produce estradiol, a phenomenon referred to as the two-cell, two-gonadotropin theory [8]. In the early follicular phase, LH receptors are found exclusively on theca cells and FSH receptors exclusively on granulosa cells. Tonic LH levels at this stage in the cycle stimulate theca cell androgen and growth factor production. Rising FSH levels stimulate aromatization of theca cell androgen to estradiol. With further growth of the follicle, FSH induces the development of aromatase-linked LH receptors on granulosa cells [9]. Once follicle recruitment is achieved and FSH levels fall, LH provides the main gonadotropin drive, leading to follicle maturation and oocyte release. It has a direct effect on both theca cell androgen production and granulosa cell aromatization, producing a sharp rise in estradiol levels, which have a positive feedback effect on LH secretion. Thus estradiol levels rise sharply during the late follicular phase, leading to the midcycle surge, once the follicle diameter reaches 17 to 18 mm, and ovulation 36 hours later. The LH surge stimulates a gene cascade in granulosa cells, which leads to protrusion of the follicle onto the ovarian surface followed by rupture. The oocyte surrounded by its cumulus and antral fluid are picked up by the fimbriae of the fallopian tube.

Luteal Function

The LH surge stimulates increased expression of vascular endothelial growth factor (VEGF), an endothelial cell mitogen normally found in ovarian blood vessels. VEGF stimulates the capillary invasion of the basal lamina, leading to vascularization of the granulosa layer. Supplied directly with precursor low-density lipoprotein, luteinized granulosa cells produce large quantities of estradiol and progesterone in response to LH. The peak in progesterone production is reached 7 days post ovulation, unless fertilization occurs when human chorionic gonadotropin (hCG) produced by the developing trophoblast ensures progesterone production by the corpus luteum is maintained until the placenta is fully formed at around 12 weeks' gestation. If fertilization does not take place, luteal regression and a fall in estradiol and progesterone begins. As an endocrine gland, the corpus luteum has one of the highest blood flows per unit mass compared with other glands in the body.

Gonadotropin Structure

The pituitary gonadotropins FSH and LH and hCG produced by the trophoblast are glycoproteins composed of α and β subunits. The α subunit is identical in all three. The α subunit is hormone-specific, differing in both amino acid and carbohydrate composition. The β subunits have considerable amino acid sequence homology, particularly those of LH and hCG, which allows hCG to be used as an LH substitute to trigger ovulation in ART cycles and maintain progesterone secretion by the corpus luteum. Both bind to a common LH/hCG transmembrane receptor in theca and luteinized theca and activate similar postreceptor effects. The cellular effects of FSH, LH, and hCG are all mediated through G –protein-coupled receptors in target cell membranes. Binding stimulates an adenylate cyclase cascade, which activates the phosphorylation of specific proteins, which induce genes encoding enzymes involved in ovarian steroid biosynthesis. This amplification system means that only a small percentage of receptors need to be occupied in order to trigger a significant steroid response. FSH binds to receptors on granulosa cells and increases aromatase activity. In the circulation, FSH has a relatively long plasma half-life (mean: 149 minutes) compared to LH (mean: 30 minutes).

Inhibin and Activin

Inhibin and activin are proteins isolated from ovarian follicular fluid, which have opposing actions on FSH secretion by the pituitary. Inhibin suppresses FSH secretion whereas activin stimulates it. Within the follicle, inhibin augments LH-stimulated theca androgen synthesis in contrast to activin, which inhibits androgen production [10, 11]. Studies of activin messenger ribonucleic acid (mRNA) in nonhuman primates suggests that activin synthesis is induced as the follicle reaches the antral stage. Inhibin production then increases as the follicle matures, which provides a mechanism for selectively enhancing androgen substrate for aromatization before ovulation. Inhibin A is the dominant form of circulating inhibin in the late follicular and luteal phases, while inhibin B is the principal circulating form of inhibin in the early and midfollicular phases.

MODULATING OVARIAN FUNCTION FOR ASSISTED REPRODUCTION

The first pregnancy following IVF, reported by Steptoe and Edwards in 1978 [12], resulted from the laparoscopic recovery of a single preovulatory oocyte and subsequent single embryo transfer. It was soon apparent that this approach was inefficient and that the chances of pregnancy and live birth could be significantly improved with controlled ovarian hyperstimulation (COH) and multiple embryo transfer, a technique that forms the basis of most ART regimens. A few centers still offer natural cycle IVF as an option to patients wishing to avoid some of the risks associated with COH, namely multiple pregnancy and hyperstimulation; to those with moral and ethical objections to multiple embryo creation; or for women with reduced ovarian reserve in whom multiple follicular development would not be feasible.

The pharmacologic approach to COH for IVF has two objectives. The first is to interfere with the process of single dominant follicle selection to induce multiple follicular recruitment and maturation, achieved by administering exogenous FSH alone or FSH/LH combinations from the early follicular phase. The second is to prevent the premature spontaneous LH surge to allow oocyte maturation and recovery to be meticulously timed, achieved by either downregulating pituitary LH secretion with Gn-RH analogs or administering Gn-RH antagonists.

Options for Inhibiting the Luteinizing Hormone Surge

Traditionally, Gn-RH analogs have formed the basis of ART regimens to achieve pituitary downregulation and in combination with exogenous gonadotropins to significantly improve IVF outcome by preventing the premature surge of LH [13, 14]. More recently, Gn-RH antagonists have been developed and appear to achieve comparable oocyte recovery, fertilization, and pregnancy rates.

Gonadotropin Preparations

Urinary-derived human menopausal gonadotropins (hMGs) were the only gonadotropin preparations commercially availably for ovulation induction and COH in IVF for more than 30 years. Derived from postmenopausal women, these contain approximately equal amounts of FSH and LH activity. Despite similar activity levels, the plasma half-life of LH is much shorter than that of FSH such that 24 hours after injection, exogenous FSH is measurable whereas exogenous LH is undetectable [15]. The recognition that FSH was the principal regulator of follicular recruitment prompted research into further urinary purification. By the 1980s, purified FSH with < 1% LH contamination was introduced into practice. By the early 1990s, highly purified FSH with < 0.1% LH contamination was developed and followed soon thereafter by the synthesis of recombinant FSH and LH using DNA technology. Recombinant human FSH (r-hFSH), completely devoid of any LH activity, is well tolerated without significant side effects. Its half-life in serum is similar to that of the native hormone [16, 17], and it compares favorably to early urinary preparations in terms of ovarian response and pregnancy outcome [18]. More recently, recombinant human LH (r-hLH) has been introduced into clinical practice, providing further options for fine-tuning follicular response during COH [19] and generating further fuel to the already existing debate over the relative importance of LH in ART regimens [20, 21].

Is Luteinizing Hormone Necessary?

From our understanding of normal ovarian physiology, and in particular the two-cell two-gonadotropin theory discussed previously, it would seem logical to include both FSH and LH in ovulation induction and COH regimens. FSH is the principle regulator of follicular recruitment, and high doses are needed to effectively lower the minimum threshold required to recruit a larger number of antral follicles from the developing cohort present in the ovary in the early follicular phase. However, both in vitro work and clinical studies provide clear evidence that LH, although not essential for follicle recruitment and subsequent growth to the preovulatory stage, plays a critical role in allowing the follicle to mature and the oocyte to achieve competence. When ovulation is induced in profoundly hypogonadotropic women with Kallman's syndrome or isolated LH deficiency using recombinant or highly purified FSH, follicle recruitment and growth occurs, but serum androstenedione and estradiol levels remain low and a spontaneous surge does not occur. Even when hCG is administered, follicle rupture and luteinization may be incomplete [22]. The addition of LH, either through urinary preparations or r-hLH, allows oocyte maturation and successful pregnancy outcome [23, 24]. Comparing IVF regimens for COH in hypogonadotropic women, administration of recombinant or purified FSH in the absence of LH leads to lower serum and follicular estradiol levels, lower follicular inhibin levels, thinner endometrial thickness, reduced fertilization rates, and lower embryo cryosurvival rates compared to urinary preparation containing LH [17, 24, 25]. Further evidence for the importance of LH comes from a study in a woman with isolated gonadotropin deficiency in which the response to HMG, r-hFSH, and highly purified FSH plus estradiol valerate in three IVF cycles was compared [25]. HMG produced the best result: normal follicular growth, normal estradiol levels, and a 93% fertilization rate. With r-hFSH, follicular growth was normal, but estradiol and inhibin levels were low and fertilization was only 28%. With urinary FSH and estradiol valerate, follicular growth and estradiol and inhibin levels were normal, but again fertilization rate was poor (27%). Adequate estradiol levels during folliculogenesis are important in stimulating granulosa cell differentiation and growth and endometrial proliferation. The introduction of Gn-RH antagonist regimens into ART has provided a further avenue in which to study the relative importance of FSH and LH. High-dose Gn-RH antagonists (Ganarelix 2 mg) mimic profound hypogonadotropic deficiency. COH with r-hFSH in the absence of LH was found to shorten the follicular phase and lead to low estradiol levels and low implantation and pregnancy rates [26].

Optimizing Luteinizing Hormone Levels during Follicle Maturation

The actual amount of LH activity required for normal follicle maturation is unknown but estimated to be between 1 to 10 IU/L as < 1% of LH receptors need to be occupied for a normal steroidogenic response [27]. The necessity for and optimum dose of LH to achieve follicular maturation was elegantly demonstrated in a study of 38 hypogonadotropic hypogonadal women (WHO Group I anovulation) by measuring their response to different r-hLH doses added to supplement a fixed r-hFSH dose to induce ovulation [28]. Patients were randomized to receive 0, 25, 75, or 225 IU/day r-hLH in addition to a fixed dose of r-hFSH of 150 IU/day. They noted that the estradiol and androstenedione responses measured on the last day of FSH administration were related in a dose-dependant fashion to the dose of r-hLH given, that follicular recruitment was higher in the women receiving 75 or 225 IU/day r-hLH, and that the addition of r-hLH was essential for follicular luteinization. Pregnancies were only achieved in the 75 and 225 IU dose groups, and cycles were cancelled in 11 of 15 women in the 0 and 25 IU dose groups. They concluded that the minimum effective daily dose of r-hLH required to achieve optimal follicular development (defined as one or more follicles ≥ 17 mm in diameter with estradiol levels ≥ 400 pmol/L and a midluteal progesterone level ≥ 25 nmol/L) was 75 IU, but they commented that a few patients might require up to 225 IU/day.

Interestingly, serum LH levels in the women on 75 IU r-hLH were undetectable despite optimum effects on follicular maturation. Likewise, in IVF cycles in women on full-dose Gn-RH agonist pituitary suppression, endogenous serum LH levels are sufficient to allow complete follicle and oocyte maturation when stimulation is carried out with either highly purified urinary FSH or r-hFSH [20, 29, 30]. A comparative pilot study of highly purified FSH alone or with r-hLH found no significant difference in length of stimulation, oocyte yield, rate of fertilization, or embryo morphology between the two groups [30], although a higher cancellation rate resulting from poor response was found in the r-hLH group. Some studies have suggested that in some normogonadotropic women, LH is more profoundly suppressed during Gn-RH analog downregulation than in others and that the relative lack of LH in these patients during the mid- to late follicular phase may impair estradiol production, fertilization rates, and pregnancy outcome [31–34]. In a retrospective analysis of 200 consecutive IVF or intracytoplasmic sperm injection (ICSI) cycles in normogonadotropic women using Gn-RH analog pituitary downregulation and r-hFSH stimulation, Westergaard et al. [34] analyzed the impact of low LH concentrations (<0.5 IU/L) versus normal levels (≥0.5 IU/L) on stimulation day 8. Low LH was found in 49% of the women who were otherwise comparable in terms of pretreatment clinical parameters to the normal LH group. Although pregnancy rate was similar in both groups, the low LH group had a five-fold increase in early pregnancy loss. These findings would suggest there is a benefit to adding r-hLH or using hMG in stimulation regimens in those patients found to have low LH levels by day 8 (<0.5 IU/L) during standard Gn-RH analog downregulation. A prospective randomized, controlled trail is awaited.

Not only is the dose of exogenous LH likely to influence response, but timing of administration will be a factor as well. LH receptors are induced on granulosa cells once the follicle reaches 10 to 12 mm in diameter [35], and granulosa become LH responsive by day 7 of the cycle [36]. On that basis, administration of r-hLH from day 7 of FSH stimulation should suffice.

Detrimental Effects of High Luteinizing Hormone Levels

Paradoxically, a recent prospective study suggested a potential detrimental effect of adding r-hLH to stimulation regimens as judged by ovarian response and fertilization. Balasch et al. [37] compared ovarian response and oocyte and embryo yields in women randomized to receive either r-hFSH (n = 13) alone or r-hFSH + r-hLH (n = 15) in a standard step-down protocol, with Gn-RH analogs with LH being given at a standard fixed dose of 75 IU throughout the stimulation phase. The r-hFSH alone group had significantly more metaphase II oocytes and higher fertilization rates than the r-hFSH + r-hLH group, although peak o-estradiol levels on the day of hCG administration were similar. Lower fertilization rates were also noted in the group of women who had previously had ART with FSH alone. The concept of an "LH ceiling" has been suggested to explain these findings [38]. Although LH is essential during folliculogenesis, follicles exposed to excess LH risk undergoing atresia or premature luteinization. Oocyte maturation may also be compromised because high LH levels stimulate resumption of meiosis prematurely. Thus LH levels in the mid- to late follicular phase above a critical level can comprise follicular development and oocyte and embryo quality.

Substantial data suggest that the detrimental effects of excess LH may be more marked in women with polycystic ovaries (PCO) or polycystic ovary syndrome (PCOS). A further discussion of the adverse effects of endogenous LH hypersecretion and potential adverse effects of exogenous LH on oocyte and embryo quality and pregnancy outcome in these women is discussed in detail in the section on PCOS as follows.

OPTIMIZING STIMULATION PROTOCOLS

From the evidence just presented, it would appear that for most "normal" women undergoing COH, a small amount of LH activity is required for optimal oocyte maturation. Ideally, administration of LH should be within the therapeutic window with respect to dose and timing in the cycle to most closely mimic natural folliculogenesis. Different groups of patients exist, such as women with PCO, older women, or those with a high FSH or poor ovarian response in whom requirements for LH may be lower or higher; stimulation protocols in these women merit separate analysis (discussed in following sections).

One of the difficulties in trying to extract information from the IVF literature is that it is swamped with poorly conducted, skewed trails. Patient numbers are often too small to draw statistically valid information, inclusion criteria are varied or poorly defined, and few studies are prospective and correctly randomized. This makes meta-analysis unreliable and should be borne in mind in the ensuing discussion.

Which Gonadotropin-Releasing Hormone Agonist Protocol?

Numerous protocols (e.g., long, short, ultrashort, step-up, step-down) have employed Gn-RH agonists for pituitary downregulation in combination with either urinary-derived or recombinant FSH. The dose of FSH may be fixed, increased, or stepped down once follicular recruitment is evident. The step-down regimen best replicates that found in a natural cycle by mimicking the intercycle rise in FSH. Although the evidence in humans is lacking, studies in primates have shown that the step-down regimen produces better synchronization of follicle growth than conventional step-up regimens [39].

Tan reviewed long, short, and ultrashort protocols and concluded that the long protocol resulted in the highest pregnancy rates in normal responders and conferred the added flexibility over timing of hCG administration [40]. A disadvantage of the long protocol is the increased incidence of functional cyst formation, which in turn can impair stimulation and pregnancy outcome [41]. Cyst formation has been shown to be reduced with prior treatment with the combined oral contraceptive pill [42].

Seven different Gn-RH agonists have been reported in IVF cycles, but only four are commonly used. Short-acting rather than depot preparations are preferable unless prolonged downregulation is required, as in patients with endometriosis. Depot preparations produce prolonged pituitary suppression, which persists for up to 8 weeks after the last injection and consequently may have adverse effects on luteal function. This was demonstrated in a study by Devreker et al. [43], who found lower implantation and live birth rates with depot preparations. There does not appear to be much to choose from between the different short-acting agonists, although the optimum dose to suppress the LH surge but to allow adequate endogenous LH to persist has yet to be determined.

Recombinant or Urinary-Derived Gonadotropins?

This subject has been extensively debated and has been the subject of numerous publications and more recently two meta-analyses [44, 45]. Manassiev analyzed five studies, all randomized prospective trials using Gn-RH agonist long stimulation protocols comparing r-hFSH with either purified or highly purified urinary FSH. All of the studies showed an improvement in clinical pregnancy rate when r-hFSH was used, but none was statistically significant. When analyzed together the combined odds ratio of achieving a pregnancy with r-hFSH as opposed to urinary FSH was 1.36 (95% CI 1.06 to 1.74), which was significant. These results were confirmed in the second, larger meta-analysis of 12 trials on 2875 patients, 1556 treated with r-hFSH and 1319 with urinary FSH [45]. The odds ratio in this analysis for achieving a clinical pregnancy with r-hFSH was 1.2 (95% CI 1.02 to 1.42). Both meta-analyses suggest that r-hFSH is superior to urinary FSH in achieving a pregnancy, but neither of these studies was designed to determine whether the benefit persists if r-hFSH is substituted with highly purified urinary FSH. This topic has been addressed in two studies [46, 47], where no significant difference in pregnancy outcome was found between highly purified FSH and recombinant FSH despite a higher oocyte yield on those treated with r-hFSH.

Gonadotropin-Releasing Antagonists

Gn-RH antagonists administered at pharmacologic doses provide an immediate but completely reversible competitive block of Gn-RH receptors at the pituitary level. The Ganarelix dose-finding study [26] attempted to define the optimum dose of Gn-RH antagonist from a range of 0.0625 mg to 2 mg. All patients were undergoing IVF and prescribed r-hFSH alone. Results are shown in Table 28.1. The highest pregnancy rate and lowest miscarriage rate was seen in the group prescribed the 0.25 mg dose of Gn-RH antagonist; however, antagonist dose did not have a significant effect on oocyte yield and maturation. Other outcomes measured included LH and estradiol levels on the day of hCG. Some residual LH activity was noted in all groups, and as with estradiol, levels fell in an inverse relationship to dose of Ganarelix prescribed. The study was small, with only 60 in each group, weakening any attempt to draw any statistically valid conclusions. In a comparative evaluation of Gn-RH antagonists and agonists in 52 women, oocyte yield, fertilization rate, and pregnancy rate were comparable [48].

TABLE 28.1 Characteristics of 329 Ganirelix-treated patients undergoing IVF treatment with FSH alone (data taken from Ganirelix Dose-Finding Study Group [26])

Daily Dose of Ganirelix (mg)	0.0625	0.125	0.25	0.5	1	2
FSH (mean in IU/L)	9.1	9	9.1	10.2	9.8	8.8
LH on hCG day (mean in IU/L)	3.6	2.5	1.7	1.0	0.6	0.4
Estradiol on hCG day (mean in pg/mL)	1475	1130	1160	823	703	430
Number of oocytes retrieved (mean)	9	9.5	10	8.8	9.3	8.6
Implantation rate (%)	14.2	16.6	21.9	9	8.8	1.5
Early miscarriage rate per transfer (%)	0	3.3	1.6	3.7	8.5	13
Pregnancy rate per transfer (%)	25.9	25	37.1	13	15.3	0

OVARIAN FUNCTION IN POLYCYSTIC OVARY SYNDROME

PCOS is the most common cause of anovulatory infertility for which first-line treatment should be ovulation induction. IVF may be necessary in women who fail to conceive after six or more ovulatory cycles of treatment or in those in whom additional fertility factors exist. The prevalence of PCO on pelvic ultrasound in ovulatory women referred for IVF with either unexplained or tubal infertility is far higher (50%) than in age-matched controls (20%), suggesting that factors other than anovulation alone may compromise ovarian function and lead to problems with maturation of the oocyte and/or endometrium [49].

Ultrasound Diagnosis and Endocrine Features

Correct diagnosis of ovarian morphology, part of the basic workup of any infertility patient, is of paramount importance in ART because women with polycystic ovarian morphology, irrespective of symptoms and/or biochemical abnormalities associated with the syndrome, have an exaggerated response to conventional-dose gonadotropin stimulation, which puts them at high risk of developing ovarian hyperstimulation or forming cysts [50–52]. Basic definition of PCOS rests on ultrasound criteria. Ovaries are described as being polycystic if there are 10 or more (15 if using transvaginal scanning) follicles, 2 to 8 mm in diameter, in one plane distributed either around a dense stroma or scattered throughout an increased amount of stroma [53]. Ovarian volume is characteristically enlarged because of the increase in stroma. By contrast, multifollicular ovaries, found during puberty and in women with hypothalamic hypogonadotropic amenorrhea, are of normal volume, have no increase in stroma, and cysts are fewer and of larger diameter. Color and pulsed Doppler ultrasonography, if available, can improve diagnostic accuracy because polycystic ovaries have increased peak stromal blood flow velocity throughout the cycle [54]. A positive correlation has been demonstrated between ovarian stromal blood flow velocity in both the early follicular phase and after downregulation in normal and polycystic ovaries, supporting the view that increased stromal blood flow in women with PCO may be responsible for the enhanced response to gonadotropin stimulation because a larger quantity of the drug reaches the granulosa cells.

Although it is important to clinically differentiate between women who have PCO alone with no symptoms and those with accompanying symptoms of cycle disturbance and/or hyperandrogenemia, numerous similarities in ovarian function exist in both groups and ART treatment strategies are essentially similar, particularly with respect to the increased risk of ovarian hyperstimulation syndrome. The characteristic endocrine features of PCOS include hypersecretion of LH, characteristically found in association with anovulation, and hypersecretion of androgens found in all groups of women with PCO [55–57]. More recently, a subgroup of women with PCOS have been characterized as having a typical "metabolic syndrome" associated with peripheral insulin resistance and compensatory hyperinsulinemia [58].

Abnormal Intrafollicular Endocrine and Paracrine Signaling in Polycystic Ovary Syndrome

Apart from elevations in circulating LH, androgens, and insulin, which may adversely affect oocyte maturation and subsequent embryo development, there is clear-cut evidence from in vitro work that the hormonal milieu surrounding the maturing oocyte is abnormal in women with PCO. In vitro studies of follicles from these women, particularly in those with anovulation, have identified abnormalities in both theca and granulosa cell function. Theca cells from women with PCO and PCOS hypersecrete androstenedione and progesterone in response to LH [59, 60]. Granulosa cells from anovulatory women with PCOS hypersecrete estradiol and progesterone in response to FSH [61]. In addition, granulosa cells show a premature response to LH [61, 62]. Paradoxically, despite peripheral insulin resistance, ovarian granulosa (and theca) cells remain insulin sensitive [63], and hyperinsulinemia may contribute to the abnormal granulosa cell response. In effect there are significant abnormalities in endocrine and paracrine signaling within the polycystic ovary, and it is not unreasonable to postulate that the process of oocyte maturation and subsequent embryogenesis may be adversely affected. Additional intrinsic abnormalities in the oocyte of these women, such as the abnormal expression of GDF-9, could additionally impair oocyte quality [64].

Oocyte and Embryo Quality in Polycystic Ovaries

The issue of whether oocyte maturation and embryogenesis in women with PCO or PCOS is compromised remains unresolved. Numerous studies have reported reduced fertilization and embryo cleavage rates in PCOS compared to controls [51, 65–69], but this finding is not consistent and may be partly explained by differences in the definition and diagnosis of PCOS [70, 71]. Similar rates of oocyte maturation and embryo scores were noted in a series of women with PCO requiring ICSI compared to normal controls, although the miscarriage rate was significantly in the PCO group [72]. Interestingly, studies of women with PCO on oocyte donation programs report no difference in fertilization and cleavage rates, suggesting little or no impairment of oocyte quality [73, 74]. Fertilization and cleavage rates of oocytes during in vitro maturation (IVM) cycles in women with PCO also compare favorably to those obtained from women with normal ovaries, irrespective of gonadotropin stimulation [75–77], supporting the view that oocyte quality is not significantly impaired in PCO.

Luteinizing Hormone Hypersecretion and Reproductive Outcome

In terms of pregnancy outcome, women with PCO have a higher incidence of early pregnancy loss following both natural conception and ovulation induction compared to age-matched controls [23, 78, 79], which suggests that oocyte maturation and embryogenesis is impaired in some way. There is good evidence that hypersecretion of LH in the midfollicular phase is one of the principle factors that adversely affects oocyte maturation and reproductive outcome. This was first noted by Stanger & Yovich [80], who reported reduced rates of fertilization and cleavage in a series of women who had LH levels at the time of hCG administration one standard deviation above the mean. Subsequent studies measuring urinary LH during assisted conception programs not only confirmed these findings [81, 82] but also demonstrated that miscarriage rates were higher in women with high tonic LH levels. In a prospective study of 193 women planning to become pregnant, Regan et al. [83] found that midfollicular phase LH levels greater than 10 IU/L were associated with a significantly lower conception rate (67% v. 88%) and a higher miscarriage rate (65% v. 12%) compared to controls with normal LH levels.

Two plausible explanations have been proposed to account for the detrimental effect of tonic LH hypersecretion on oocyte maturation and reproductive outcome. First, elevated intrafollicular LH levels prompt a reduction in oocyte maturation factor and the premature resumption of meiosis. Animal studies suggest that there is a species-specific interval between ovulation and fertilization which, if exceeded, leads to the production of poor-quality "prematurely aged" oocytes, which may either not be capable of fertilization or if fertilized lead to abnormal embryogenesis and miscarriage [82] Alternately, or in addition, LH may exert its adverse effect by promoting excess intraovarian (theca cell) androgen production and subsequent follicular atresia. Despite profound suppression of endogenous LH levels with Gn-RH analogs or antagonists, an exaggerated theca cell androgen response to LH previously reported in vitro persists [59, 84] and may have adverse effects on oocyte maturation. Teissier et al. [85] reported a lower proportion of meiotically competent oocytes obtained from follicles with higher testosterone and progesterone concentrations, suggesting that these eggs may have been obtained from prematurely "luteinized" follicles.

The Impact of Hyperinsulinemia and Insulin Resistance

Both in vitro and in vivo work have conclusively shown a direct correlation between elevated insulin levels and increased ovarian androgen biosynthesis. Insulin acts as a co-gonadotroph and both augments LH-stimulated theca cell androgen biosynthesis [86] and leads to inappropriately exaggerated steroidogenesis by granulosa cells [62, 63]. These phenonmena may, in turn, lead to detrimental effects on oocyte maturation. An effect of elevated insulin levels on pregnancy outcome was noted by Cano et al. [87], who studied a series of women with PCO on ultrasound who donated some of their eggs. He found that women with PCO and insulin resistance had lower fertilization and implantation rates following IVF. Obesity, commonly found in women with PCOS, exacerbates the tendency toward hyperinsulinemia and insulin resistance. Even a moderate elevation of body mass index (BMI, >25 kg/m^2) is associated with an increased rate of miscarriage, an effect that is independent of LH [88]. Metformin and other insulin-lowering agents have been evaluated in ovulation induction and IVF either alone or as an adjunct to clomiphene or gonadotrophins. A recent review of 30 published studies comprising 12 randomized, controlled trials and 16 uncontrolled descriptive studies would suggest that metformin, given alone for a period of 3 to 6 months, can restore ovulation in up to 60% of anovulatory women with PCO [89]. There has been only one study analyzing the use of metformin (500 mg twice or three times per day) during 60 IVF cycles in 46 women with PCOS [90]. This was a retrospective cohort study and patients were unselected for BMI (mean BMI: 25 kg/m^2) and had high mean fasting insulin levels. All were treated with Gn-RH agonist on a long protocol with FSH. The metformin group had a higher yield of mature oocytes and better fertilization and pregnancy rates, suggesting that metformin has potential benefit. A larger prospective randomized trial is required to evaluate whether an improvement in live birth rate can be achieved by the co-administration of metformin and FSH.

Superovulation Strategies in Polycystic Ovaries and Polycystic Ovarian Syndrome

From the previous discussion it is evident that superovulation strategies should aim to first correct the abnormal hormonal parameters, notably hypersecretion of LH, androgens, and insulin, and second minimize the tendency to hyperstimulation. The hyperandrogenemia and hyperinsulinemia associated with obesity are difficult to correct, and obese women on IVF programs have compromised fertility. Hence weight reduction in women with elevated BMI (>25 kg/m^2) should be a prerequisite to offering treatment.

To date, there have been no satisfactory large-scale randomized prospective studies of different regimens in the PCO and PCOS population undergoing IVF to direct clinical practice. Numerous small studies have attempted to compare the outcome of different IVF stimulation regimens in patients with PCO against those with normal ovaries and tubal infertility. Interpretation of the literature is confounded by lack of a universal definition of PCOS, patient numbers too small to yield meaningful conclusions, and differing endpoints measured. A general consensus is that women with PCO tend to produce increased numbers of oocytes compared with age-matched controls but have overall similar pregnancy rates [51, 65, 67–70, 91]. In terms of embryo quality, blastocyst cell numbers were found to be significantly higher, following a "titrated" gonadotropin regimen, in women with PCO than in those with tubal infertility [70] (Figure 28.1).

The long protocol using Gn-RH analog pituitary downregulation is favored over the short protocol because it minimizes any adverse effects caused by LH hypersecretion and avoids any sudden surge of gonadotropins, which could increase the risk of ovarian hyperstimulation. A longer period of desensitization has been shown to further reduce the risk of hyperstimulation without affecting pregnancy rate [65]. By the same reasoning, it would seem advisable to use highly purified FSH or r-hFSH rather than protocols involving hMG or r-hLH in women with elevated LH levels. In practice there does not seem to be any advantage in using r-hFSH alone over highly purified FSH or hMG in IVF, almost certainly because the quantities of LH in urinary preparations are too low to produce any significant impact on serum LH levels [92]. The effect of r-hLH in IVF regimens was recently analyzed in a series of 48 clomiphene-resistant women, with PCO assigned to receive either r-hFSH alone or r-hFSH and LH during pituitary downregulation, with and without dexamethasone. LH levels rose to between 1 to 2 IU/L with r-hLH treatment as opposed to <0.5 IU/L on r-hFSH alone; however, no significant differences in estradiol response, follicular recruitment, and pregnancy outcome were noted [93].

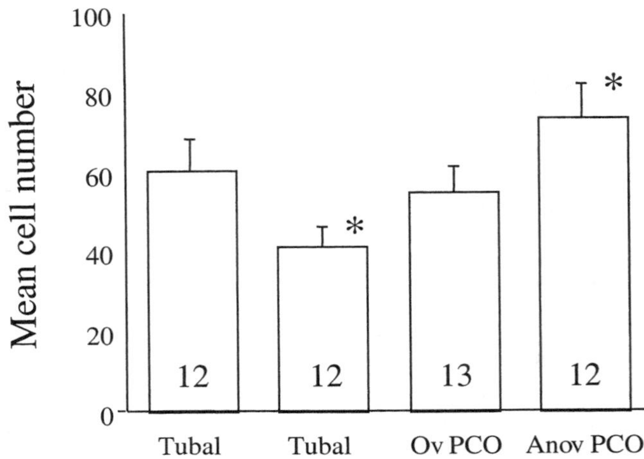

FIGURE 28.1 Mean blastocyst cell number in embryos obtained after superovulation with a standard gonadotropin protocol (column 1) and a lower dose, "titrated" FSH regimen (columns 2 to 4) from women with tubal infertility compared with ovulatory (ovPCO) and anovulatory (anovPCO) women with PCO. Note significantly greater blastocyst cell number in the PCO groups compared with tubal infertility subjects in response to the "titrated" dose of FSH (column 2 v. column 4: $p < 0.05$, Mann-Whitney) (data from Hardy et al. [70]) (Reproduced by permission of the editor and publishers of Reproductive Biomedicine Online).

More important than the gonadotropin preparation itself is the dose used, which should be lower than in women with normal ovaries. In our center, a woman with PCO who is younger than 38 with a normal day 3 FSH (<8 IU/L), would be started on a dose of 150 IU/75 IU on alternate days as opposed to 150 IU daily if she had normal ovaries. Gn-RH antagonist regimens theoretically should allow lower doses of gonadotropins to be used and minimize the risk of ovarian hyperstimulation. Beneficial effects in PCO patients have yet to be established.

Pretreatment with Ovarian Drilling

Laparoscopic ovarian drilling, by laser or diathermy, is now a well-established method of inducing ovulation in anovulatory women with PCO [94]. Current data are insufficient to determine if ovarian drilling could be beneficial to women undergoing IVF by reducing the total dose of gonadotropin required and minimizing the risk of hyperstimulation. In a small prospective study of 23 women with PCOS pretreated with diathermy versus 36 women who were not, ongoing pregnancy rate was significantly higher in the pretreated group [95]. Lower intrafollicular androgen levels noted in the pretreated women may have improved outcome. A larger retrospective study also found improved pregnancy outcome in IVF cycles following ovarian diathermy [96], but a larger prospective randomized trial is needed to validate these findings.

Ovarian Hyperstimulation in Women with Polycystic Ovaries

Several factors in PCO function predispose these women to excessive follicular recruitment in response to standard doses of gonadotropins. The increase in stromal blood flow delivering larger quantities of drug to the follicle has already been mentioned. The cohort of small antral follicles in the early follicular phase, ready to respond to FSH, is increased. Theca cell production of androgens is exaggerated, through an increase in both theca cell number and responsiveness to LH [59], thereby enhancing the substrate supply for granulosa cell estradiol production. In some women this effect is further increased through hypersecretion of LH. Higher estradiol levels in the early follicular phase increase granulosa cell sensitivity to FSH and effectively lower the threshold for follicular recruitment, which enhances multiple follicular development. The effect is even more exaggerated in the subgroup of women with PCO and hyperinsulinemia because insulin acts as a co-gonadotroph and augments LH-driven androgen production by theca and both FSH and LH stimulated estradiol production by granulosa [57, 63].

Increased expression of vascular endothelial growth factor (VEGF), a granulosa cell product, has been reported in theca of women with PCO and PCOS. Serum levels of VEGF are also higher, even when LH levels are downregulated with Gn-RH analog, and correlate with increased ovarian stromal blood flow [97]. Increased ovarian VEGF has two potential implications: (1) follicular blood flow, which has a major influence on oocyte quality, is increased [98]; and (2) VEGF, as an endothelial mitogen, increases vascular permeability and plays a central role in the pathophysiology of ovarian hyperstimulation syndrome (OHSS) [99].

In Vitro Maturation in Polycystic Ovarian Syndrome

IVM is a relatively new technique in which immature oocytes, retrieved from unstimulated ovaries, are matured in vitro. The first successful pregnancy was reported by Trounson et al. [100], and recent reports suggest that for women with PCO or PCOS, IVM represents a safer but equally effective alternative to IVF because the risk of ovarian hyperstimulation is avoided [75, 101–102] without compromising reproductive outcome. Concerns remain, however, about the implications for normal health and development of the embryo following prolonged culture of first oocyte and then embryo before transfer [71]. The minimum follicle diameter required for the oocyte to have reached developmental competence is 5 to 7 mm.

THE IMPACT OF AGE ON OVARIAN FUNCTION

Reproductive potential declines with increasing age, and success rates in IVF programs fall sharply in women older than 40. The impact of age on reproductive outcome is conclusively correlated primarily to oocyte quality and number [103]. Uterine age has been evaluated in donor-recipient programs and by contrast appears to have little influence on implantation and live birth rates. The decline in ovarian number with age is an inevitable exponential fall, which starts at approximately five months in utero, when the maximum oocyte number of 7 million is reached, and continues through to menopause, when the oocyte stock is exhausted. Optimal fertility potential occurs in a woman's twenties, falls in her thirties, and generally ends in her early forties; however, considerable variation exists from this average such that some women show a much faster rate of oocyte depletion and may find themselves infertile through ovarian aging in their late twenties or early thirties. The rate of follicular atresia follows a biphasic pattern, with a second phase of accelerated atresia occurring once the primordial follicle "reserve" reaches 25,000 (mean age: 37.5 years). Increasing numbers of oocytes have meiotic spindle and microtubule abnormalities, follicles contain fewer granulosa cells, and steroid production falls. The rate of aneuploidy rises, increasing the probability of early pregnancy loss. It has been argued that the observed decline in fecundicity with age can be primarily attributed to a higher rate of early (often undetectable) pregnancy losses caused by meiotically incompetent oocytes. In a study of early pregnancy loss in a rural setting (in the absence of widespread contraceptive use), the probability of early fetal loss was estimated at 0.55 for a 20-year-old woman rising to 0.96 for a 40-year-old woman [104].

EVALUATION OF OVARIAN FUNCTION

Several tests of ovarian reserve have been developed to help identify those women with a reduced ovarian reserve and in consequence poor reproductive potential, naturally or with ART. As oocyte quality and quantity decline with age, the size of the antral follicle cohort available for dominant follicle selection in the early follicular phase falls.

This leads to a quantitative fall in inhibin B produced by these follicles and a rise in FSH levels as inhibin B feedback on the pituitary is reduced.

Antral Follicle Count

The number of small antral follicles (diameter: 2 to 10 mm) present in the ovary at the start of any cycle declines with increasing age and is believed to correlate with the number of primordial follicles remaining in the ovary [105]. The antral follicle count correlates directly with the number of oocytes retrieved at egg collection and number of embryos obtained and indirectly with risk of cancellation [106], and has also been found to predict the number of immature oocytes collected in IVM [102]. It appears to be superior in predicting ovarian reserve more than measurement of ovarian volume alone. A recent study found that transvaginal ultrasound measurement of the antral follicle cohort was the single best predictor of poor response [107]. Other markers such as chronologic age, ovarian volume, early follicular FSH, inhibin B and estradiol levels, and various dynamic "challenge" tests, which all indirectly assess the antral follicle count, provide useful additional information and can be combined with antral count to refine the predicted response. Further work is needed to establish whether antral follicle measurements should include total counts (2 to –10 mm), selectable follicles (2 to –5 mm), or selected follicles (5 to 10 mm) and whether three-dimensional scanning is more accurate.

Follicle-Stimulating Hormone and Inhibin B

Early follicular phase levels of FSH start to rise during a woman's late thirties, but this pattern is variable, with a rise noted in much younger women. On this basis it has been proposed that not all women have the same "threshold" FSH value for follicular recruitment. Consequently, elevated basal (day 3) FSH only predict a reduced ovarian response to gonadotropins if the cut-off level is set relatively high [108]. Inhibin B is inversely correlated to FSH levels in the early follicular phase and, although it has been shown to usefully predict oocyte response and pregnancy rate in IVF [109], it confers no advantage over basal FSH screening and is far more expensive [110]. FSH and estradiol changes 24 hours after a dose of Gn-RH agonist given on day 2 (F-G-test) are more sensitive predictors of ovarian reserve than basal FSH and estradiol levels and can be useful in determining IVF drug dosage and regimen [111–112].

POOR OVARIAN RESPONSE

The term poor responder is applied to those patients exhibiting a suboptimal follicular response to exogenous gonadotropins. It is critical to identify potential low responders at an early stage, using some of the tests to evaluate ovarian reserve discussed previously, so that stimulation protocols can be titrated to optimize oocyte yield and to prevent cycle cancellation. Although numerous strategies have been evaluated, there does not appear to be a clear-cut advantage of one stimulation protocol over another. The undisputed fact remains that women with reduced ovarian reserve, irrespective of their age, have a poor prognosis for future IVF cycles. Furthermore, increasing evidence suggests that poor response in IVF cycles predicts earlier menopause [113].

Definition and Endpoint in Evaluation of Poor Response

The overall prevalence of poor responders is estimated at 5% to 20%, but variation in patient selection criteria for entry into an IVF program produces wide differences in prevalence from one center to another [114]. The interpretation of studies comparing stimulation protocols in this group of patients is hampered by a lack of consensus on the definition of a poor responder and endpoint being measured [115–116]. Most series define poor responders on the basis of high gonadotropin requirements, reduced numbers of follicles, low estradiol levels, and poor oocyte yield. Additional criteria include cancellation because of poor follicle recruitment or elevated day 2 to 3 FSH levels [117–119]. In order to reduce sample size, most trials focus on an improvement in estradiol levels and oocyte yield rather than live birth rate. Unfortunately, an increase in oocyte number may have little or no benefit on pregnancy outcome because oocyte quality may be too poor to result in a healthy embryo with normal development potential. As discussed in previous sections, the lack of properly conducted prospective randomized, controlled trials in IVF makes interpreting the literature in this area difficult. Most series studying poor responders compare outcome with previous cycles, an approach that fails to control for the natural variation in response from cycle to cycle [120].

Strategies to Improve Outcome

Based on normal ovarian physiology, the most logical strategy to increase oocyte yield is to increase the dose of gonadotropin administered from the early follicular phase to >300 IU per day. Two early studies suggested that follicular development was improved with higher doses [121, 122], but subsequent studies failed to confirm such a benefit [123, 124]. Nevertheless, a high-dose approach is almost universally adopted in clinical practice. Other approaches that have been studied include reducing the dose and duration of Gn-RH analogs in flare protocols, adding r-hLH or hMG, or using adjuvants such as low-dose aspirin, growth hormone, or dexamethasone. More recently, the role of Gn-RH antagonists has been evaluated [125]. Poor responders represent a heterogeneous population, and it is sometimes a question of trial and error to define an effective protocol for an individual patient.

Some poor responders become refractory to gonadotropins following downregulation with Gn-RH agonists. Gn-RH receptors have been identified in the ovary, and although their precise role is unclear, it is apparent that in these women Gn-RH agonist treatment may interfere with the response to gonadotropins at the ovarian level. Several strategies have been studied. One is to stop Gn-RH analog once downregulation is achieved and gonadotropins are started (Gn-RH agonist stop protocol). Two randomized studies have failed to find this regimen beneficial in terms of pregnancy outcome over a standard long protocol [120]. In the microdose Gn-RH flare protocol, the patient is pretreated with a monophasic combined oral contraceptive for 21 days, and then a very low dose of Gn-RH agonist (2% of the normal dose) is given from day 2. Gonadotropin stimulation starts 48 hours later. Overall, this approach does seem to significantly improve oocyte yield, but this conclusion is drawn from small retrospective trials [117, 121], and a larger prospective study is needed. The recent introduction of Gn-RH antagonists has prompted research into their potential use in poor responders. A prospective randomized trial comparing Gn-RH antagonists with the microdose flare protocol in poor responders found that the microdose protocol was superior in term of peak estradiol concentration and oocyte yield, but that there was no significant difference in pregnancy rates [119]. In a retrospective study comparing gonadotropin stimulation in a series of women older than 40 treated either with or without antagonist, cancellation rates were significantly lower in the antagonist group (16% v. 67%). In those women who went on to have egg retrieval, oocyte yield was higher in those receiving antagonist, but pregnancy rates were similar [125].

Following on from the earlier discussion assessing the role of LH in COH, a preliminary study has addressed the potential benefit of LH in poor responders by measuring the response to r-hFSH + r-hLH during Gn-RH analog downregulation in a long protocol. Twelve women were studied, defined as poor responders on the basis of elevated day 3 FSH (mean: 12.2 IU/L) and requirement for at least 3000 IU r-hFSH in a previous IVF cycle [127]. In this study, 75 IU r-hLH was administered from day 7 of stimulation until day of hCG. There was no difference in total quantity of r-hFSH used, oocyte yield, or embryo morphology, but the addition of r-hLH resulted in a significant increase in fertilization rate and clinical pregnancy rate. This finding is in contrast to the study by Sills et al. [30] of normal responders (mean FSH <7 IU/L), which reported no additional benefit of adding r-hLH. These data suggest a larger randomized prospective study is warranted to analyze the potential role of r-hLH in poor responders.

Growth hormone stimulates insulin-like growth factor 1 (IGF-1) production by the ovary, which augments the effect of FSH and LH. Although early reports suggested clinical benefit in stimulating low responders with gonadotropins and growth hormone or growth hormone-releasing hormone [128, 129], later prospective trials have failed to confirm a significant improvement in either oocyte yield or pregnancy outcome [130, 131].

Other Ways of Manipulating Oocyte Potential in Poor Responders

There is a school of thought that advocates natural cycle IVF in poor responders on the basis that within the reduced cohort of antral follicles, only the naturally selected dominant follicle is chromosomally healthy and capable of achieving maturation.

Assisted zona hatching, a technique whereby an opening is made in the zona pellucida before embryo transfer, has been difficult to evaluate in poor responders because of differences in the technique used to perform assisted hatching and different patient populations studied. A review of the literature leads to conflicting findings, with some studies reporting a benefit in implantation rates and others none [120]. The consensus of opinion at present is that data are insufficient to support performing assisted hatching routinely in poor responders or older women.

IVM is another technique currently under evaluation in poor responders. Early findings are less promising than in women with PCO because the antral follicle cohort is far smaller [132]. It is possible that in the future, in vitro follicle maturation from ovarian cortical biopsies will offer a more useful route for older women with a reduced primordial follicle pool.

Although the decline in oocyte function and quality with age cannot be reversed, recent research has identified potential benefit in ooplasm transfer (i.e., transferring oocyte cytoplasm from a younger healthy donor to the older recipient egg), and children born from this technique are reported as healthy [133]. Another option is aneuploidy screening, which may allow the selection of only chromosomally "normal" embryos for transfer. Both are areas of ongoing research, confounded by ethical issues, which nevertheless offer new direction in trying to maximize the chances of a healthy pregnancy outcome in older women.

CONCLUSION

Increasing knowledge of the physiology of human ovarian function has helped refine treatment regimens for controlled ovarian stimulation in women undergoing assisted reproduction. The emergence of recombinant human gonadotropins for human use and the development of antagonists of Gn-RH has allowed "fine-tuning" of the endocrine environment leading up to egg collection and improved the prospect of better outcome in terms of pregnancy rates and, most important, for both fetal and maternal health. It has also proven possible to control the abnormal endocrine environment in women with polycystic ovary syndrome to lower the risk of ovarian hyperstimulation and to maximize the chances of a successful pregnancy.

References

1. Gougeon, A. (1996). Regulation of ovarian follicular development in primates: Facts and hypotheses. *Endo. Rev.* 17, 121–154.
2. Eppig, J. J. (1991). Intercommunication between mammalian oocytes and companion somatic cells. *Bioessays* 13, 569–574.
3. Eppig, J. J., and Wigglesworth, K. (2000). Development of mouse and rat oocytes in chimeric reaggregated ovaries after interspecific interchange of somatic and germ cell components. *Biol. Reprod.* 63, 1014–1023.
4. Elvin, J. A., Yan, C., and Matzuk, M. M. (2000). Oocyte-expressed TGF-beta superfamily members in female fertility. *Mol. Cell. Endocrinol.* 159, 1–5.
5. Picton, H., Briggs, D., and Gosden, R. (1998). The molecular basis of oocyte growth and development. *Mol. Cell. Endocrinol.* 145, 27–37.
6. Yan, C., Wang, P., DeMayo, J. et al. (2001). Synergistic roles of bone morphogenetic protein 15 and growth differentiation factor 9 in ovarian function. *Mol. Endocrinol.* 15, 854–866.
7. Durlinger, A. L., Gruijters, M. J., Kramer, K. A. et al. (2002). Anti-Mullerian hormone inhibits initiation of primordial follicle growth in the mouse ovary. *Endocrinology* 143, 1076–1084.
8. Hillier, S. G., van den Boogaard, A. M. J., Reichert, L. E. J., and van Hall, E. V. (1980). Intraovarian sex steroid hormone interactions and the regulation of follicular maturation: Aromatization of androgens by human granulosa cells in vitro. *J. Clin. Endocrinol. Metab.* 50, 640–647.
9. Erickson, G. F., Wang, C., and Hsueh, A. J. W. (1979). FSH induction of functional LH receptors in granulosa cells cultured in a chemically defined medium. *Nature* 279, 336–338.
10. Hillier, S. G., Yong, E. L., Illingworthe, P. J. et al. (1991a). Effect of recombinant inhibin on androgen synthesis in cultured human thecal cells. *Mol. Cell. Endocrinol.* 75, R1–R6.
11. Hillier, S. G., Yong, E. L., Illingworth, P. J. et al. (1991b). Effect of recombinant activin on androgen synthesis in cultured human thecal cells. *J. Clin. Endocrinol. Metab.* 72, 1206–1211.
12. Steptoe, P. C., and Edwards, R. G. (1978). Birth after reimplanation of a human embryo. *Lancet* 2, 366.
13. Rutherford, A. J., Subak-Sharpe, R. J., Dawson, K. J. et al. (1988). Improvement of in-vitro fertilization after treatment with buserilin, an agonist of luteinising hormone releasing hormone. *Br. Med. J.* 296, 1765–1768.
14. Barbieri, R. L., and Hornstein, M. D. (1999). Assisted reproduction in-vitro fertilization success is improved by ovarian stimulation with exogenous gonadotrophins and pituitary suppression with gonodotrophin-releasing hormone analogues. *Endocr. Rev.* 20, 249–252.
15. Yen, S. S., llerena, O., Little, B. et al. (1968). Disappearance rates of endogenous luteinizing hormone and chorionic gonadotrophin in man. *J. Clin. Endocrinol. Metab.* 28, 1763–1767.
16. Mannaerts, B., Shoham, Z., Schoot, D. et al. (1993). Single dose pharmacokinetics and pharmacodynamics of recombinant human follicle-stimulating hormone (Org 32489) in gonadotrophin deficient volunteers. *Fertil. Steril.* 59, 108–114.
17. Schoot, D. C., Harlin, J., Shoham, Z. et al. (1994). Recombinant human follicle-stimulating hormone and ovarian response in gonadotrophin-deficient women. *Hum. Reprod.* 9, 1237–1242.
18. Germond, M., Dessole, S., Senn, A. et al. (1992). Successful in-vitro fertilisation and embryo transfer after treatment with recombinant human FSH. *Lancet* 339, 1170.
19. Hull, M., Corrigan, E., Piazzi, A., and Loumaye, E. (1994). Recombinant human luteinizing hormone: an effective new gonadotrophin preparation. *Lancet* 344, 334–335.
20. Levy, D. P., Navarro, J. M., Schattman, G. L. et al. (2000). The role of LH in ovarian stimulation. Exogenous LH: Let's design the future. *Hum. Reprod.* 15, 2258–2265.
21. Balasch, J., Creus, M., Fabregues, F. et al. (2001). The effect of exogenous luteinizing hormone (LH) on oocyte viability: Evidence from a comparative study using recombinant human follicle-stimulating hormone (FSH) alone or in combination with recombinant LH for ovarian stimulation in pituitary-suppressed women undergoing assisted reproduction. *J. Ass. Reprod. Genet.* 18, 250–256.
22. Filicori, M., and Cognigni, G. E. (2001). Roles and novel regimens of luteinizing hormone and follicle-stimulating hormone in ovulation induction. *J. Clin. Endocrinol. Metab.* 86, 1437–1441.
23. Kousta, E., White, D. M., Piazzi, A. et al. (1996). Successful induction of ovulation and completed pregnancy using recombinant luteinizing hormone and follicle stimulating hormone in a woman with Kallman's syndrome. *Hum. Reprod.* 11, 70–71.
24. Shoham, Z., Balen, A., Patel, A. et al. (1991). Results of ovulation induction using human menopausal gonadotrophin or purified follicle-stimulating hormone in hypogonadotrophic hypogonadism patients. *Fertil. Steril.* 56, 1048–1053.
25. Balasch, J., Fabregues, F., Creus, M. et al. (1996). Pure and highly purified follicle-stimulating hormone alone or in combination with human menopausal gonadotrophin for ovarian stimulation after pituitary suppression in in-vitro fertilisation. *Hum. Reprod.* 11, 2400–2404.
26. Ganirelix Dose-Finding Study Group (1998). A double-blind, randomized, dose-finding study to assess the efficacy of the gonadotrophin-releasing hormone antagonist ganirelix (Org 37462) to prevent premature luteinizing hormone surges in women undergoing ovarian stimulation with recombinant follicle stimulating hormone (Puregon). *Hum. Reprod.* 13, 1788–1792.
27. Chapel, S. C., and Howles, C. (1991). Reevaluation of the roles of the luteinizing hormone and follicle-stimulating hormone in the ovulatory process. *Hum. Reprod.* 6, 1206–1212.

28. Recombinant Human LH Study Group (1998). Recombinant human luteinizing hormone (LH) to support recombinant human follicle-stimulating hormone (FSH)-induced follicular development in LH- and FSH- deficient anovulatory women: A dose-finding study. *J. Clin. Endocrinol. Metab.* 83, 1507–1514.
29. Devroey, P., Mannaerts, B., Sith, J. et al. (1994). Clinical outcome of a pilot study on recombinant human follicle stimulating hormone (Org 32489) combined with various gonadotrophin-releasing hormone agonist regimens. *Hum. Reprod.* 9, 1064–1069.
30. Sills, E. S., Levy, D. P., Moomjy, M. et al. (1999). A prospective randomized comparison of ovulation induction using highly purified follicle-stimulating hormone alone and with recombinant human luteinizing hormone in in-vitro fertilisation. *Hum. Reprod.* 14, 2230–2235.
31. Westergaard, L. G., Erb, K., Laursen, S. et al. (1996). The effects of human menopausal gonadotrophin and highly purified, urine-derived follicle stimulating hormone on the outcome of in-vitro fertilization in down-regulated normogonadotrophic women. *Hum. Reprod.* 11, 1209–1213.
32. Flemming, R., Lloyd, F., Herbert, M. et al. (1998). Effects of profound suppression of luteinizing hormone during ovarian stimulation on follicular activity, oocyte and embryo function in cycles stimulated with purified follicle stimulating hormone. *Hum. Reprod.* 13, 1788–1792.
33. Flemming, R., Rehka, P., Deshpande, N. et al. (2000) Suppression of LH during ovarian stimulation: Effects differ in cycles stimulated with purified urinary FSH and recombinant FSH. *Hum. Reprod.* 15, 1440–1445.
34. Westergaard, L. G., Laursen, S. B., and Anderson, C. Y. (2000). Increased risk of early pregnancy loss by profound suppression of luteinizing hormone during ovarian stimulation in normogonadotrophic women undergoing assisted reproduction. *Hum. Reprod.* 15, 1003–1008.
35. Hillier, S. G., Whitelaw, P. F., and Smyth, C. D. (1994). Follicular oestrogen synthesis: The "two-cell, two-gonadotrophin" model revisited. *Mol. Cell. Endocrinol.* 100, 51–54.
36. Yamoto, M., Shima, K., Nakano, R. (1992). Gonadotrophin receptors in human ovarian follicles and corpora lutea throughout the menstrual cycle. *Horm. Res.* 37, 5–11.
37. Balasch, J., Vidal, E., Penarrubia, J. et al. (2001). Suppression of LH during ovarian stimulation: Analysing threshold values and effects on ovarian response and the outcome of assisted reproduction in down-regulated women stimulated with recombinant FSH. *Hum. Reprod.* 16, 1636–1643.
38. Loumaye, E., Engrand, P., Shoham, Z. et al. (2003). Clinical evidence for an LH "ceiling" effect induced by administration of recombinant human LH during the late follicular phase of stimulated cycles in World Health Organization type I and type II anovulation. *Hum. Reprod.* 18, 314–322.
39. Abbasi, R., Kenigsberg, D., Danforth, D. et al. (1987). Cumulative ovulation rate in human menopausal/human chorionic gonadotrophin-treated monkeys: "Step-up" versus "step-down" dose regimens. *Fertil. Steril.* 47, 119–1024.
40. Tan, S. L. (1994). Luteinizing hormone releasing hormone agonists for ovarian stimulation in assisted reproduction. *Curr. Opin. Obstet. Gynaecol.* 6, 166–167.
41. Keltz, M. D., Jones, E. E., Duleba, A. J. et al. (1995). Baseline cyst formation after luteal phase gonadotrophin-releasing hormone agonist administration is linked to poor in vitro fertilization outcome. *Fertil Steril.* 64, 568–572.
42. Biljan, M. M., Mahutte, N. G., Dean, N. et al. ((1998). Pretreatment with an oral contraceptive is effective in reducing the incidence of functional cyst formation during pituitary suppression by gonadotrophin hormone releasing hormone analogues. *J. Assist. Reprod. Genet.* 15, 599–604.
43. Devreker, F., Govaerts, I., Bertrand, E. et al. (1996). The long-acting gonadotrophin-releasing hormone analogues impaired the implantation rate. *Fertil. Steril.* 65, 122–126.
44. Manassiev, N. A., Tenekedjier, K. I., and Collins, J. (1999). Does the use of recombinant follicle stimulating hormone instead of urinary follicle stimulating hormone lead to higher pregnancy rates in in vitro fertilisation-embryo transfer cycles? *Assist. Reprod.* 9, 7–12.
45. Daya, S., and Gunby, J. (1999). Recombinant versus urinary follicle stimulating hormone for ovarian stimulation in assisted reproduction. *Hum. Reprod.* 14, 2207–2215.
46. Bergh, C., Howles, C. M., Borg, K. et al. (1997). Recombinant human follicle stimulating hormone (r-hFSH) versus highly purified urinary FSH (Metrodin HP): Results of a randomized comparative study in women undergoing assisted reproductive techniques. *Hum. Reprod.* 12, 2133–2139.
47. Frydman, R., Avril, C., Camier, B. et al. (1998). A double blind, randomized study comparing the efficacy of recombinant human follicle stimulating hormone (rhFSH-Gonal F) and highly purified urinary FSH (uhFSH/Metrodin HP) in inducing ovulation in women undergoing assisted reproductive techniques. *Hum. Reprod.* 123 (abstract Book 1), 94.
48. Del Gadilloa, J. C., Siebzehnrubl, E., Dittrich, R. et al. (2002). Comparison of GnRH agonists and antagonists in unselected IVF/ICSI patients treated with different controlled ovarian hyperstimulation protocols: A matched study. *Eur. J. Obstet. Gynecol.* 102, 179–183.
49. Kousta, E., White, D. M., Cela, E. et al. (1999). The prevalence of polycystic ovaries in women with infertility. *Hum. Reprod.* 14, 2720–2723.
50. Smitz, J., Camus, M., Devroey, P. et al. (1991). Incidence of severe ovarian hyperstimulation syndrome after gonadotrophin releasing hormone agonist/HMG superovulation for in-vitro fertilization. *Hum. Reprod.* 6, 933–937.
51. MacDougall, M. J., Tan, S. L., Balen, A., and Jacobs, H. S. (1993). A controlled study comparing patients with or without polycystic ovaries undergoing in vitro fertilitzation. *Hum. Reprod.* 8, 233–237.
52. Engmann, L., Maconochie, N., Sladkevicius, P. et al. (1999). The outcome of in vitro fertilisation treatment in women with sonographic evidence of polycystic ovarian morphology. *Hum. Reprod.* 14, 167–171.
53. Adams, J., Polson, D. W., Abdulwahid, N. et al. (1985). Multifollicular ovaries: Clinical and endocrine features and response to pulsatile gonadotrophin releasing hormone. *Lancet* ii, 1375–1378.
54. Zaidi, J., Campbell, S., Pittrof, R. et al. (1995). Ovarian stromal blood flow in women with polycystic ovaries—a possible new marker for diagnosis. *Hum. Reprod.* 10, 1992–1996.
55. Conway, G. S., Honour, J. W., and Jacobs, H. S. (1989). Heterogeneity of the polycystic ovary syndrome: clinical,

endocrine and ultrasound features in 556 patients. *Clin. Endocrin.* 30, 459–470.

56. Balen, A. H., Conway, G. S., Kaltas, G. et al. (1995). Polycystic ovary syndrome: The spectrum of the disorder in 1741 patients. *Hum. Reprod.* 10, 2107–2111.
57. Franks, S. (1995). Polycystic ovary syndrome. *N. Engl. J. Med.* 333, 853–861.
58. Dunaif, A. (1997). Insulin resistance and the polycystic ovary syndrome: mechanisms and implications for pathogenesis. *Endocr. Rev.* 18, 774–800.
59. Gilling-Smith, C., Willis, D. S., Beard, R. W., and Franks, S. (1994). Hypersecretion of androstenedione by isolated thecal cells from polycystic ovaries. *J. Clin. Endocrinol. Metab.* 79, 1158–1165.
60. Nelson, V. L., Legro, R. S., Strauss III, J. F., and McAllister, J. (1999). Augmented androgen production is a stable steroidogeneic phenotype of propagated theca cells from polycystic ovaries. *Mol. Endocrinol.* 13, 946–957.
61. Franks, S., Mason, D., and Willis, D. (2000). Follicular dynamics in the polycystic ovary syndrome. *Mol. Cell. Endocrinol.* 163, 49–52.
62. Willis, D., Watson, H., Mason, H. et al. (1998). Premature responsiveness to luteinizing hormone in granulosa cells from anovulatory women with polycystic ovary syndrome: Relevance to mechanism of anovulation. *J. Clin. Endocrinol. Metab.* 83, 3984–3491.
63. Willis, D., Mason, H., Gilling-Smith, C., and Franks, S. (1996). Modulation by insulin of follicle-stimulating hormone and luteinizing hormone in human granulosa cells from normal and polycystic ovaries. *J. Clin. Endocrinol. Metab.* 81, 302–309.
64. Filho, T., Baracat, E. C., Lee, T. H. et al. (2002). Abberant expression of growth differentiation factor-9 in oocytes of women with polycystic ovary syndrome. *J. Clin. Endocrinol. Metab.* 87, 1343–1344.
65. Salat-Baroux, J., Alvarez, S., Antoine, J. M. et al. (1988). Results of IVF in the treatment of polycystic ovary disease. *Hum. Reprod.* 3, 331–335.
66. Testart, J., Belaisch-Allart, J., Forman, R. et al. (1989). Influence of different stimulation treatments on oocyte characteristics and in vitro fertilization. *Hum. Reprod.* 4, 192–197.
67. Dor, J., Shultnan, A., Levran, D. et al. (1990). The treatment of patients with polycystic ovarian syndrome by in vitro fertilization: A comparison of results with those of patients with tubal infertility. *Hum. Reprod.* 5, 816–818.
68. Dale, P. O., Taribo, T., and Abyholm, T. (1991). In vitro fertilization in infertile women with polycystic ovarian syndrome. *Hum. Reprod.* 6, 238–241.
69. Homburg, R., Levy, T., Berkovitcz, D. et al. (1993). Gonadotrophin releasing hormone agonist reduces the miscarriage rate for pregnancies achieved in women with polycystic ovaries. *Fertil. Steril.* 59, 527–531.
70. Hardy, K., Robinson, F., Paraschos, T. et al. (1995) Normal development and metabolic activity of preimplantation embryos in vitro from patients with polycystic ovaries. *Hum. Reprod.* 10, 2125–2135.
71. Hardy, K., Wright, C. S., Franks, S., and Winston, R. M. L. (2000). In vitro maturation of oocytes. *Br. Med. Bul.* 56, 588–602.
72. Ludwig, M., Finas, D. F., Al-Hassani, S., Diedrich, K., and Ortmann, O. (1999). Oocyte quality and treatment outcome in intracytoplasmic sperm injection cycles of polycystic ovarian syndrome patients. *Hum. Reprod.* 14, 354–358.
73. Remohi, J., Vidal, A., and Pellicer, A. (1989). Oocyte donation in low responders to conventional ovarian stimulation for in vitro fertilization. *Fertil. Steril.* 59, 1208–1215.
74. Ashkenazi, J., Farhi, J., Orvieto, N. R. et al. (1995). Polycystic ovary syndrome patients as oocyte donors: The effect of ovarian stimulation protocol on the implantation rate of the recipient. *Fertil. Steril.* 64, 564–567.
75. Child, T. J., Abdul-Jalil, A. K., Gulekli, B., and Tan, S. L. (2001). In vitro maturation and fertilization of oocytes from unstimulated normal and polycystic ovaries and women with polycystic ovary syndrome. *Fertil. Steril.* 76, 936–942.
76. Mikkelsen, A. L., and Lindenberg, S. (2001). Morphology of in vitro matured oocytes: Impact on fertility potential and embryo quality. *Hum. Reprod.* 16, 1714–1718.
77. Tan, S. L., and Child, T. J. (2002). In-vitro maturation of oocytes from unstimulated polycystic ovaries. *Reprod. Biomed. Online* 4 (Suppl 1), 18–23.
78. Sagle, M., Bishop, K., Alexander, F. M. et al. (1988). Recurrent early miscarriage and polycystic ovaries. *Br. Med. J.* 297, 1027–1028.
79. White, D. M., Polson, D. W., Kiddy, D. et al. (1996). Induction of ovulation with low dose gonadotrophins in polycystic ovary syndrome: An analysis of 109 pregnancies in 225 women. *J. Clin. Endocrinol. Metab.* 81, 1–4.
80. Stanger, J. D., and Yovich, J. L. (1985). Reduced in-vitro fetilisation of human oocyte from patients with raised basal luteinising hormone levels during the follicular phase. *Br. J. Obstet. Gynaecol.* 92, 385–393.
81. Howles, C. M., Macnamee, M. C., Edwards, R. G. et al. (1986). Effect of high tonic levels of luteinising hormone on outcome of in-vitro fertilisation. *Lancet* i, 521–522.
82. Homburg, R., Armar, N. A., Eshel, A. et al. (1988). Influence of serum luteinising hormone concentrations on ovulation, conception and early pregnancy loss in polycystic ovary syndrome. *Br. Med. J.* 297, 1024–1026.
83. Regan, L., Owen, E. J., and Jacobs, H. S. (1990). Hypersecretion of luteinising hormone, infertility and miscarriage. *Lancet* 336, 1141–1144.
84. Gilling-Smith, C., Story, H., Rogers, V., and Franks, S. (1997). Evidence for a primary abnormality of thecal cell steroidogenesis in the polycystic ovary syndrome. *Clin. Endocrinol.* (Oxf) 47, 93–99.
85. Teissier, M. P., Chable, H., Paulhac, S., and Aubard, Y. (2000). Comparison of folliculogenesis from normal and polycystic ovaries in women undergoing IVF. Relationship between steroid concentrations, follicle size, oocyte quality and fecundability. *Hum. Reprod.* 15, 2471–2477.
86. Barbieri, R. L., Makris, A., Randall, R. W. et al. (1986). Insulin stimulates androgen accumulation in incubations of ovarian stroma obtained from women with hyperandrogenism. *J. Clin. Endocrinol. Metab.* 62, 904–910.
87. Cano, F., Garcia-Velasco, J. A., Millet, A. et al. (1997) Oocyte quality in polycystic ovaries revisited: Identification of a particular subgroup of women. *J. Assist. Reprod. Genet.* 14, 254–61.

88. Kiddy, D. S., Hamilton-Fairly, D., Bush, A. et al. (1992). Improvement in endocrine and ovarian function during dietary treatment of obese women with polycystic ovary syndrome. *Clin. Endocrinol.* (Oxf), 36, 105–111.
89. Costello, M. F., and Eden, J. A. (2003). A systematic review of the reproductive system effects of Metformin in patients with polycystic ovary syndrome. *Fertil. Steril.* 79, 1–13.
90. Stadmauer, L. A., Toma, S. K., Riehl, R. M., and Talbert, L. M. (2002). Impact of Metformin therapy on ovarian stimulation and outcome in "coasted" patients with polycystic ovary syndrome undergoing in-vitro fertilization. *Reprod. Biomed. Online* 5, 112–116.
91. Franks, S., Roberts, L. R., and Hardy, K. (2003). Gonadotrophin regimens and oocyte quality in women with polycystic ovaries. *Reprod. Biomed. Online* (in press).
92. Buyalos, R. P., and Lee, C. T. (1996). Polycystic ovary syndrome: Pathophysiology and outcome with IVF. *Fertil. Steril.* 65, 1–10.
93. Cheung, A. P., Pride, S. M., and Yuen, B. H. (2002). In-vivo ovarian androgen responses to recombinant FSH with and without recombinant LH in polycystic ovary syndrome. *Hum. Reprod.* 17, 2540–2547.
94. Armar, N. A., and Lachelin, G. (1993). Laparoscopic ovarian diathermy: An effective treatment for anti-oestrogen resistant anovulatory infertility in women with PCOS. *Br. J. Obstet. Gynaecol.* 100, 161–164.
95. Colacurci, N., Zullo, F., De Franciscis, P. et al. (1997). In vitro fertilization following laparoscopic ovarian diathermy in patients with polycystic ovarian syndrome. *Acta. Obstet. Gynaecol. Scand.* 76, 555–558.
96. Tozer, A. J., Al-Shawaf, T., Zosmer, A. et al. (2001). Does laparoscopic ovarian diathermy affect the outcome of IVF-embryo transfer in women with polycystic ovarian syndrome? A retrospective comparative study. *Hum. Reprod.* 16, 91–95.
97. Agrawal, R., Sladkevicius, P., Engman, L. et al. (1998). Serum vascular endothelial growth factor concentrations and ovarian stromal blood flow are increased in women with polycystic ovaries. *Hum. Reprod.* 13, 651–655.
98. Van Blerkom, J. (2000). Intrafollicular influences on human oocyte developmental competence: Perifollicular vascularity, oocyte metabolism and mitochondrial function. *Hum. Reprod.* 15 (Suppl 2), 173–188.
99. Jacobs, H. S., and Agrawal, R. (1998). Complications of ovarian stimulation. *Ballieres Clin. Obstet. Gynaecol.* 12, 565–579.
100. Trounson, A., Wood, C., and Kausch, A. (1994). In vitro maturation and fertilization and development competence of oocytes recovered from untreated polycystic ovary patients. *Fertil. Steril.* 62, 456–460.
101. Child, T. J., Phillips, S. J., Abdul-Jalil, A. K. et al. (2002). A comparison of in vitro maturation and in vitro fertilisation for women with polycystic ovaries. *Obstet. Gynaecol.* 100, 665–670.
102. Tan, S. L., Child, T. J., and Gulekli, B. (2002). In vitro maturation and fertilization of oocytes from unstimulated ovaries: Predicting the number of immature oocytes retrieved by early follicular phase ultrasonography. *Am. J. Obstet. Gynecol.* 186, 684–689.
103. Battaglia, D. E., Goodwin, P., Klein, N. A., and Soules, M. R. (1996). Influence of maternal age on meiotic spindle assembly in oocytes from naturally cycling women. *Hum. Reprod.* 11, 2217–2222.
104. Holman, D. J., Wood, J. W., and Campbell, K. L. (2000). Age dependent decline of female fecundity is caused by early fetal loss. In *Female Reproductive Aging*, 9th ed., eds. E. R. Te Velde, P. L. Pearson, and F. J. Broekmans, 123–136. London: Parthenon Publishing Group.
105. Scheffer, G. J., Broekmans, F. J., Dorland, M. et al. (1999). Antral follicle counts by transvaginal ultrasound are related to age in women with proven natural fertility. *Fertil. Steril.* 72, 845–851.
106. Chang, M. Y., Chiang, C. H., Hsieh, T. T. et al. (1998). Use of the antral follicle count to predict the outcome of assisted reproductive technologies. *Fertil. Steril.* 69, 505–510.
107. Bancsi, L. F., Broekmans, F. J., Eijkemans, M. J. et al. (2002). Predictors of poor ovarian response in in vitro fertilization: A prospective study comparing basal markers of ovarian reserve. *Fertil. Steril.* 77, 328–336.
108. Te Velde, E. R., Scheffer, G. J., Dorland, M. et al. (1998). Developmental and endocrine aspects of normal ovarian aging. *Mol. Cell. Endocrinol.* 145, 67–73.
109. Seifer, D. B., Lambert-Messerlian, G., Hogan, J. et al. (1997). Day 3 serum inhibin-B is predictive of assisted reproductive technologies outcome. *Fertil. Steril.* 67, 110–114.
110. Creus, M., Penarrubia, J., Fabregues, F. et al. (2000). Day 3 serum inhibin B and FSH and age as predictors of assisted reproduction treatment outcome. *Hum. Reprod.* 15, 2341–2346.
111. Ranieri, D. M., Quinn, F., Makhlouf, A. et al. (1998). Simultaneous evaluation of basal follicle-stimulating hormone and oestradiol response to gonadotrophin-releasing hormone analogue stimulation: An improved predictor of ovarian reserve. *Fertil. Steril.* 70, 227–233.
112. Ranieri, D. M., Phophong, P., Khadum, I. et al. (2001). Simultaneous evaluation of basal FSH and oestradiol response to GnRH analogue (F-G-test) allows effective drug regimen selection for IVF. *Hum. Reprod.* 16, 673–675.
113. Nikolaou, D., Lavery, S., Turner, C. et al. (2002). Is there a link between an extremely poor response to ovarian hyperstimulation and early ovarian failure? *Hum. Reprod.* 17, 1106–1111.
114. Karander, V., and Gleicher, N. (1999). A rational approach to the management of low responders in in-vitro fertilisation. *Hum. Reprod.* 14, 1744–1748.
115. Ben Rafael, Z., and Felberg, D. (1993). The poor responder patient in an in vitro fertilization-embryo transfer program. *J. Assist. Reprod. Genet.* 10, 118–120.
116. Surrey, E. S., and Schoolcraft, W. B. (2000). Evaluating strategies for improving ovarian response of the poor responder undergoing assisted reproductive technology. *Fertil. Steril.* 73, 667–676.
117. Schoolcraft, W., Schlenker, T., Gee, M. et al. (1997). Improved controlled ovarian hyperstimulation in poor responder in vitro fertiidation patients with a microdose follicle stimulating hormone flare, growth hormone protocol. *Fertil. Steril.* 67, 93–97.
118. Garcia-Velasco, J. A., Isaza, V., Requena, A. et al. (2000). High doses of gonadotrophins combined with stop versus non-stop protocol of GnRH analogue administration in low

responder IVF patients: A prospective, randomized, controlled trial. *Hum. Reprod.* 15, 2292–2296.

119. Akman, M. A., Erden, H. F., Tosun, T. B. et al. (2001). Comparison of agonistic flare-up-protocol and antagonistic multiple dose protocol in ovarian stimulation of poor responders: Results of a prospective randomized trial. *Hum. Reprod.* 16, 868–870.
120. Mahutte, N. G., and Arici, A. (2002). Poor responders: Does the protocol make a difference? *Curr. Opin. Obstet. Gynecol.* 14, 275–281.
121. Crosignani, P. G., Ragni, G., Lombroso, G. C. et al. (1989). IVF: Induction of ovulation in poor responsers. *J. Steroid. Biochem.* 32, 171–173.
122. Hofmann, G. E., Toner, J. P., Muasher, S. J. et al. (1989). High-dose follicle-stimulating hormone (FSH) ovarian stimulation in low-responder patients for in-vitro fertilization. *J. In Vitro Fert. Embryo Transfer.* 6, 285–289.
123. Karande, V. C., Jones, G. S., Veeck, L. L. et al. (1990). High-dose follicle stimulating hormone at the onset of the menstrual cycle does not improve the in vitro fertilization outcome in low responder patients. *Fertil. Steril.* 53, 486–489.
124. Land, L. A., Yarmolinskaya, M. I., Dumoulin, J. C. et al. (1996). High-dose human menopausal gonadotrophin stimulation in poor responders does not improve in vitro fertilization outcome. *Fertil. Steril.* 65, 961–965.
125. Chang, P. L., Zeitoun, K. M., Chan, L. K. et al. (2002). GnRH antagonist in older IVF patients. Retrieval rates and clinical outcome. *J. Reprod. Med.* 47, 253–258.
126. Scott, R. T., and Navot, D. (1994). Enhancement of ovarian responsiveness with micro-doses of GnRH-agonist during ovulation induction for in vitro fertilisation. *Fertil. Steril.* 61, 880–885.
127. Lisi, F., Rinaldi, L., Fishel, S. et al. (2001). Use of recombinant FSH and recombinant LH in multiple follicular stimulation for IVF: A preliminary study. *Reproductive BioMedicine Online Webpaper* 3, 190–194
128. Ibrahim, Z. H., Lieberman, B. A., Matson, P. L., and Buck, P. (1991). The use of biosynthetic human growth hormone to augment ovulation induction with buserilin acetate/human menopausal gonadotrophin during controlled ovarian hyperstimulation for in vitro fertilisation in women with a poor ovarian response. *Fertil. Steril.* 55, 202–205.
129. Hughes, J. N., Torresani, T., Herve, F. et al. (1991). Interest in growth hormone-releasing hormone administration for improvement of ovarian responsiveness to gonadotrophins in poor responder women. *Fertil. Steril.* 55, 945–951.
130. Levy, T., Limor, R., Villa, Y. et al. (1993). Another look at co-treatment with growth hormone and human menopausal gonadotrophins in poor ovarian responders. *Hum. Reprod.* 8, 834–839.
131. Howles, C. M., Lourmaye, E., Germond, M. et al. (1999). Does growth hormone-releasing factor assist follicular development in poor responder patients undergoing ovarian stimulation for in-vitro fertilization? *Hum. Reprod.* 14, 1939–1943.
132. Requena, A., Neuspiller, F., Cobo, A. C. et al. (2000). The potential use of maturation in vitro of human oocytes in low responder patients. *J. Assist. Reprod. Genet.* 17, 239–244.
133. Krey, L., Liu, H., Zhang, J. et al. (2001). Fertility and maternal age strategies to improve pregnancy outcome. *Ann. N.Y. Acad. Sci.* 943, 26–33.

CHAPTER **29**

Polycystic Ovarian Syndrome

RICHARD S. LEGRO

ABSTRACT

Polycystic ovarian syndrome (PCOS) is a common endocrinopathy, but it is poorly understood. It is a disorder of unexplained hyperandrogenic chronic anovulation and clearly heterogeneous in etiology; however, many women with PCOS are noted to have profound peripheral resistance to insulin-mediated glucose uptake. Despite evidence of familial clustering, no clear molecular or genetic mechanism has been identified to date to explain the vast majority of cases. Women with PCOS present with infertility, menstrual disorders, and hirsutism. They appear to be at increased risk for diabetes and display multiple risk factors for endometrial cancer and cardiovascular disease. Unfortunately, there are few randomized, controlled trials of any treatment in PCOS to provide us with clear treatment guidelines. Therefore, treatment tends to be symptom based, although lifestyle interventions and pharmaceutical treatments directed at improving insulin sensitivity appear to improve multiple stigmata of the syndrome. For instance, studies with these agents have shown improvements in ovulation and hirsutism.

INTRODUCTION

Polycystic ovarian syndrome (PCOS) is a heterogeneous and still unexplained disorder, whose etiology remains the holy grail of reproductive endocrinologists. It is also one of the most common, if not *the* most common, endocrinopathies in women, affecting 5% of women in the developed world [1]. PCOS was first diagnosed in situ on the basis of enlarged ovaries by pelvic examination combined with a history of amenorrhea and hirsutism [2]. An abnormal morphology was subsequently confirmed by examining histologic sections of the ovary [2]. The ovary was viewed as the prime culprit of the syndrome, and assays confirming increased androgen excretion and circulating levels appeared to validate this belief [3].

The discovery of hyperinsulinemia [4] and decreased sensitivity to insulin in women with PCOS [5] led to a deemphasis on the ovary as a diagnostic criterion. Instead, PCOS was recognized as an endocrinopathy of undetermined etiology. This concept was summarized in a 1990 National Institutes of Health—National Institute of Child and Human Development (NIH-NICHD) consensus conference on PCOS [6] and has been upheld in similar proceedings in recent years. These criteria are hyperandrogenism and/or hyperandrogenemia, oligo-ovulation, and exclusion of other potential causes such as congenital adrenal hyperplasia, Cushing's syndrome, and androgen-secreting tumors [6]. This definition of hyperandrogenic chronic anovulation has also been utilized for several large series describing metabolic sequelae in PCOS [7–11], several seminal clinical trials in PCOS [12–14], and in familial and genetic studies [15], and will be the basis for the definition of PCOS used in this chapter.

DIFFERENTIAL DIAGNOSIS OF POLYCYSTIC OVARIAN SYNDROME

The differential diagnosis of PCOS is found in Table 29.1. It is important to note that PCOS rarely presents with signs of virilization. Virilization includes the common signs of acne and hirsutism but is also accompanied by other peripheral effects such as temporal balding, clitoromegaly, deepening of the voice, breast atrophy, and changes in body contour. In virilization, balding in women tends to present with centripetal balding and frontal recession more characteristic of androgenic alopecia in men as opposed to the more indolent presentation of androgenic alopecia in women with a generalized thinning of the crown region [16]. A deepening of the voice has been reported in women with androgen-secreting tumors or who are undergoing exogenous androgen treatment (often permanent). Increase in the size of the larynx, an androgen-sensitive organ, is one factor in the voice change.

Clitoromegaly, another sign of virilization, is defined as a clitoral index greater than $35\,mm^2$ (the clitoral index is the product of the sagittal and transverse diameters of the glans of the clitoris) [17]. In a normal women these diameters are in the range of 5 mm each. The degree of clitoral enlargement correlates with the degree of androgen excess. Androgens can lead to body composition changes, especially in the upper body, with increased muscle mass

TABLE 29.1 Differential Diagnosis of PCOS in Women

Congenital adrenal hyperplasia (CAH)
Cushing's syndrome
Androgen-producing tumor-ovary or adrenal
Exogenous anabolic/sex steroids
Hyperprolactinemia
Severely insulin-resistant states
Thyroid dysfunction

and decreased fat mass. This is accompanied by breast atrophy.

Androgen-Secreting Tumors

Most commonly, virilization, especially combined with a sudden onset and rapid progression, is caused by a tumor or dysfunctional state of the ovary, and less commonly of the adrenal. The most common androgen-producing tumor in a premenopausal woman is a Sertoli-Leydig cell tumor. Any large ovarian tumor can produce androgens indirectly by causing hyperplasia of the surrounding normal stroma (i.e., benign cystic teratomas, dysgerminomas, epithelial tumors). Most ovarian androgen-secreting tumors are benign. Adrenal tumors are rare, with an estimated incidence of 2 cases per one million persons per year, which are equally divided among adenomas and carcinomas. The age of onset in adults peaks in the fifth decade. Virilization can accompany both tumors primarily producing androgens and tumors primarily producing cortisol (Cushing's syndrome). A long history of symptoms, as in the case with an ovarian tumor, does not exclude the presence of an adrenocortical neoplasm.

Nonclassical Congenital Adrenal Hyperplasia

Nonclassical congenital adrenal hyperplasia (NC-CAH) is a term referring to the milder form of adult-onset congenital adrenal hyperplasia. The CYP21 (21-hydroxylase) gene is the most commonly mutated gene in humans. It is tightly linked to the HLA locus on the short arm of chromosome 6, a frequent site of genetic recombination. Nonetheless, it remains a rare disorder in the larger population. It is estimated to be present in less than 1% of unselected hirsute women [18]. CAH occurs with the highest frequency in the U.S. population among Native Americans in Alaska. Other populations with high carrier status are Ashkenazi Jews (3.7%), Latinos (1.9%), Yugoslavs (1.6%), and Italians (0.3%) [19]. Because of the lack of 21 hydroxylation, 17-hydroxyprogesterone accumulates. Because of the lack of cortisol synthesis, adrenocorticotropic hormone (ACTH) levels increase, resulting in overproduction and accumulation of cortisol precursors. These, in turn, can be shunted to androgen biosynthetic pathways, which causes excessive production of androgens, resulting in virilization. NC-CAH can be screened for with a fasting 17-OHP level in the morning.

A value less than 2 ng/mL is normal, and cutoffs as high as 4 ng/mL have been proposed recently if obtained in the morning and during the follicular phase [20]. Values above the cutoff should be screened with an ACTH stimulation test. This is performed in the early morning by giving 250 μg of Cortrosyn, a synthetic form of ACTH, intravenously after baseline 17-OHP analysis and then obtaining a 1-hour value. Results are interpreted according to the nomogram of New et al. [21]. In affected patients, 1-hour stimulated 17-OHP values are generally >10 ng/mL. Phenotype is largely a result of the amount of functional enzymatic activity of the allelic variants, and those with NC-CAH have 10% to 20% activity [22]. About 70% will have oligomenorrhea, 80% hirsutism, and 40% polycystic ovaries on ultrasound [23]. Patients also appear to lack the insulin resistance of PCOS, and treatment strategies focus primarily on suppression of adrenal function.

Cushing's Syndrome

Like PCOS, Cushing's syndrome or glucocorticoid excess most commonly occurs in the reproductive years and predominantly affects women; however, the prevalence of 2 to 5 cases per million is a fraction of the high prevalence of PCOS [24]. Nevertheless, it must be considered in the differential diagnosis of androgen excess. Coexisting signs of Cushing's syndrome, including a moon facies, buffalo hump, abdominal striae, centripetal fat distribution, and hypertension, should be sought and further screening provided for this cause. Polycystic ovaries are commonly found in women with Cushing's [25]. Most cases of Cushing's syndrome (about 70%) are caused by a pituitary ACTH-secreting tumor (Cushing's disease) [26]. Cortisol excess can be screened with a 24-hour urine for free cortisol (which better quantifies excess cortisol production than random spot blood levels, normal values < 100 μg/24 hours) or an overnight dexamethasone suppression test.

Hyperinsulinemic and/or Insulin-Resistant States

Dysfunctional states of the ovary, primarily hyperthecosis, may also result in marked androgen excess and hyperinsulinemia [27]. In stromal hyperthecosis, most of the ovarian androgen overproduction results from hyperplasia of the ovarian stroma (and not from the accumulation of small follicles as is the case with PCOS). Most women with stromal hyperthecosis have severe hyperinsulinemia, which may be the stimulus for stromal androgen overproduction [28]. It has been reported in both premenopausal and postmenopausal women, often with coexisting sequelae of the insulin-resistance syndrome such as dyslipidemia and glucose intolerance. Surgery, consisting of oophorectomy, usually results in restoration of both normal insulin levels and androgen levels in the acquired late presentations of stromal hyperthecosis.

Extreme elevations in insulin levels occur in individuals with insulin receptor defects. Many such defects have now been identified, although their overall prevalence is low. In such individuals, the elevated insulin levels may stimulate excess ovarian androgen production, resulting in what has been described as the HAIR-AN syndrome, which represents the coexistence of hyperandrogenism, insulin resistance, and acanthosis nigricans [29].

Other Causes

Also in the differential diagnosis of androgen excess in an adult female are the use of exogenous androgens (e.g., anabolic steroids in a body builder) or an overdose of androgens in a postmenopausal women. Severe hirsutism and even virilization that occurs during pregnancy has its own unique differential, including benign ovarian sources such as hyperreactio luteinalis (i.e., gestational ovarian theca-lutein cysts) or luteomas, and extremely rare fetoplacental sources such as aromatase deficiency resulting in androgen excess caused by the placental inability to convert precursor androgens into estrogens. Many texts also recommend screening subjects with menstrual disorders for hyperprolactinemia and thyroid dysfunction, which are also common in this population.

CLINICAL STIGMATA OF POLYCYSTIC OVARIAN SYNDROME AND THEIR EVALUATION

A suggested laboratory evaluation of women with PCOS is provided in Table 29.2, but this remains an area where the cost effectiveness of such an extensive workup should be justified. We will begin with two common stigmata of women with PCOS that do not appear to merit routine evaluation: inappropriate gonadotropin secretion and morphology of the ovary.

Inappropriate Gonadotropin Secretion

Inappropriate gonadotropin secretion (IGS) has been one of the characteristic signs of PCOS since assays were available to characterize it [30]. An excess of luteinizing hormone (LH) in the urine was first noted [31], and urinary studies also supported abnormal, erratic pulses of LH secretion in these women [32]. The availability of plasma assays allowed clear documentation of overproduction of

TABLE 29.2 Tests to Consider in Women with Polycystic Ovary Syndrome

Blood Tests	Normal Range*	Purpose
Total Testosterone (consider also free or bioavailable measures)	<60 ng/dL*	Determine extent of androgen excess
Fasting Blood Tests		
17-hydroxyprogesterone	<2 ng/mL	Evaluate for NC-CAH; use <4 ng/mL for random sample, ACTH stimulation test if abnormal
Prolactin	<20 ng/mL	Evaluate for prolactin excess
Glucose	<126 mg/dL	Screen for diabetes
Insulin	<20 microU/mL*	Screen for insulin resistance
Glucose-to-insulin ratio	>4.5	Screen for insulin resistance
Cholesterol	<200 mg/dL	Identify cardiovascular risk
HDL	>35 mg/dL (and preferably >45 mg/dL)	Identify cardiovascular risk
LDL	<130 mg/dL	Identify cardiovascular risk
Triglycerides	<200 mg/dL	Identify cardiovascular risk
Dynamic Blood Tests		
Oral glucose tolerance test, give 75 g glucose in am after overnight fast	2 h glucose >140 mg/dL—impaired glucose tolerance 2 h glucose >200 mg/dL type 2 diabetes mellitus	Identify or diagnose diabetes, repeat if abnormal

LH, resulting in an elevated LH to follice-stimulating hormone (FSH) ratio [33]. Varying authors have recommended specific cutoff ratios as diagnostic of the syndrome.

These ratios are rarely utilized because of the lack of sensitivity (>50% of women with no detectable gonadotropin abnormality) [34], especially in obese women. Pulse studies with larger numbers of women with PCOS have shown that LH pulse amplitude is inversely related to body mass index (BMI) and percentage body fat, despite an underlying increased pulse frequency of LH that is independent of body fat or composition [35, 36]. The suppression of LH levels by increasing obesity reduces the usefulness of gonadotropin levels as diagnostic criteria in PCOS. Others have criticized that the conventional measure of immunoreactive LH is not as sensitive in detecting women with PCOS, compared to bioactive LH levels; however, the latter are not routinely available [37, 38].

Ovarian Morphology

Others have defined PCOS on the basis of the morphology of the ovary found on ultrasound, with multiple 2- to 8-mm subcapsular preantral follicles forming a "black pearl necklace" sign (Figure 29.1) [39]. Polycystic ovaries are found in a wide variety of unrelated disorders, including in up to 30% of women with normal menses and normal circulating androgens [40–42]. The differential diagnosis of polycystic ovaries is extensive, with some syndromes having little overlap with hyperandrogenic chronic anovulation (Table 29.3).

Reports have suggested that polycystic ovaries per se may identify a group of women with some further stigmata of reproductive and metabolic abnormalities found in the endocrine syndrome of PCOS [43, 44], but the data have not been consistent [45]. It is important to note that not all women with the endocrine syndrome of PCOS have polycystic-appearing ovaries [45], and that polycystic ovaries alone should not be viewed as synonymous with PCOS. Polycystic ovaries appear to be an independent risk factor for ovarian hyperstimulation syndrome after ovulation induction [46], and thus it may make clinical sense to document the morphology of the ovary in infertile patients seeking ovulation induction.

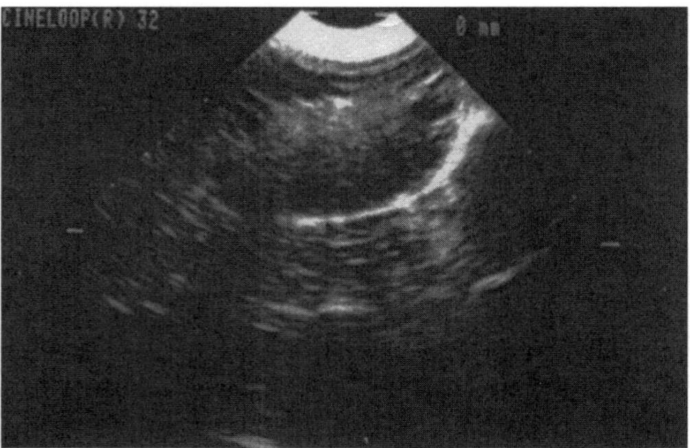

FIGURE 29.1 Transvaginal ultrasound of a polycystic ovary. There are multiple small subcapsular follicles ("pearl necklace") and increased central stroma. There are an absence of preovulatory follicles.

TABLE 29.3 Syndromes or Disease Entities That Have Been Associated with Polycystic Ovaries

Hyperandrogenism
Steroidogenic Enzyme Deficiencies
(CAH, aromatase deficiency, etc.)
Androgen-Secreting Tumors
Ovarian
Adrenal
Exogenous Androgens
Anabolic steroids
Transsexual hormone replacement
Hyperandrogenism and Insulin Resistance
Congenital
Type A syndrome
Type B syndrome
Leprechaunism
Lipoatrophic diabetes
Rabson-Mendenall
Polycystic ovary syndrome(?)
Acquired
Cushing's syndrome
Insulin Resistance
Glycogen storage diseases
Other
Central Nervous System
Trauma/lesions
Hyperprolactinemia
Nonhormonal medications
Valproate
Heriditary Angioedema
Bulimia
Idiopathic
(includes normoandrogenic women with cyclic menses)

Hyperandrogenism

Hyperandrogenism can be documented based on clinical stigmata of androgen excess, such as by the presence of acne, hirsutism, or androgenic alopecia. Others rely on biochemical confirmation of circulating hyperandrogenemia. Ethnic, and presumably underlying genetic, differences in population may result in the presence of hyperandrogenemia without clinical signs of hyperandrogenism [47].

Hyperandrogenemia

Both the adrenal glands and ovaries contribute to the circulating androgen pool in women. The adrenal preferentially secretes weak androgens such as DHEA or its sulfated "depot" form DHEA-S (up to 90% of adrenal origin). These hormones, in addition to androstenedione (often elevated in women with PCOS), may serve as prohormones for more potent androgens such as testosterone or dihydrotestosterone (DHT). The ovary is the preferential source of testosterone, and it is estimated that 75% of circulating testosterone originates from the ovary (mainly through peripheral conversion of prohormones by liver, fat, and skin, but also through direct ovarian secretion). Androstenedione, of both adrenal (50%) and ovarian (50%) origin, is the only circulating androgen that is higher in premenopausal women than in men, yet its androgenic potency is only 10% of testosterone. DHT is the most potent androgen, although it circulates in negligible quantities and results primarily from the intracellular 5α-reduction of testosterone. In the past, measurement of 3α-androstanediol glucuronide, a peripheral metabolite of DHT, was used as a circulating marker of androgen excess in the skin (hirsutism and acne), but its clinical use is negligible.

Thus circulating testosterone levels may be the androgen of choice to measure, and their circulating levels may offer better discrimination between a control population and the affected population with PCOS. A 14% overlap in elevated androgen levels was noted between women with PCOS and a prospectively recruited cohort of cycling control women [15], versus a 20% to 30% overlap of polycystic ovaries in a normal population [40, 41]. A circulating total testosterone level was found to be the best hormonal correlate of the combined syndrome of hyperandrogenic chronic anovulation and polycystic ovaries [34]. Many prefer either a free testosterone or a bioavailable testosterone level because that better reflects the suppressive effects of hyperinsulinemia on sex hormone binding globulin [48]. Assays are reproducible and eliminate any observer bias in identifying women with androgen excess; however, given the interassay variability, it is difficult to assign a uniform and specific level of circulating testosterone, which is the cutoff for diagnosing PCOS [49].

Hirsutism

Hirsutism is defined as excess body hair in undesirable locations, and as such is a subjective phenomenon that makes both diagnosis and treatment difficult. Most commonly, hirsutism as associated with PCOS tends to be an androgen-dependent, midline-predominant hair growth. The pilosebaceous unit (PSU) is the common skin structure that gives rise to both hair follicles and sebaceous glands and is found everywhere on the body except the palms and soles. Before puberty the body hair is primarily fine, unpigmented vellus hair. After puberty and stimulated by the increased androgens, some of these hairs (mainly midline hair) are transformed into coarser, pigmented terminal hairs. A similar mechanism may explain the increase in acne with puberty, with increased sebum production by the sebaceous glands. One of the central paradoxes is that androgens can exert opposite effects (vellus to terminal, terminal to vellus), depending on the site of the hair follicle. It is important to note that factors other than androgen action may contribute to the development of hirsutism. Hyperinsulinemia, which accompanies many benign forms of virilization, can also stimulate the PSU both directly or indirectly by contributing to hyperandrogenemia.

Hirsutism and acne, however, are heterogeneous and common disorders, similar to polycystic ovaries. Only 50% of women with hirsutism may have PCOS [50]. Hirsutism is also not invariably present in a woman with PCOS. There are, for instance, ethnic differences in target tissue sensitivity to circulating androgens and intracellular androgens [51], such that marked androgen excess may not manifest as hirsutism (e.g., in Asians) [47]. Methodology of the assessment of hirsutism and response to treatment has been poorly validated [52].

Hirsutism scores are notoriously subjective [53], and even the most frequently utilized standard of subjective hirsutism scores, the modified Ferriman-Gallwey score, relies excessively on nonmidline, non-androgen-dependent body hair to make the diagnosis [54]. The FDA approval of eflornithine hydrochloride cream for hirsutism was based on a Physician's Global Assessment (PGA) scale, evaluating facial hair 48 hours after shaving on treatment compared to placebo (Vaniqa package insert). In the largest clinical trial to date in PCOS, 50% to 60% of the 400 women prospectively identified to have hyperandrogenemic chronic anovulation had no evidence of hirsutism (Ferriman-Gallwey score <6) [14]. Also, hirsutism is frequently idiopathic and accompanied by normal circulating androgen levels [51], although other studies with more thorough examination have shown idiopathic hirsutism to be rare (<10% of a hirsute population) [55].

Chronic Anovulation

In the broadest definition, PCOS has been identified with the World Health Organization (WHO) type 2 ovulatory dysfunction, or normoestrogenic anovulation. Although chronic anovulation may be the *sine qua non* of the syndrome, only a small percentage of women with PCOS are completely amenorrheic. Most are oligomenorrheic and experience varying intervals of vaginal bleeding. The cause of this vaginal bleeding may be physiologic (postovulatory withdrawal bleed) or pathologic. How infrequent should the menstrual bleeding be to qualify as "chronic anovulation" and how do you classify persistent anovulatory bleeding? There is no consensus here, but general guidelines are 6 to 8 spontaneous episodes of vaginal bleeding per year. The baseline endogenous ovulatory frequency is unknown in an untreated PCOS population, but the ovulation rate in the largest randomized, controlled trial in women with PCOS to date demonstrated an almost 30% ovulatory frequency in the placebo-treated arm, indicating either a significant placebo effect and/or high endogenous rate [14].

Acanthosis Nigricans

Acanthosis nigricans is a dermatologic condition marked by velvety, mossy, verrucous, hyperpigmented skin. It has been noted on the back of the neck, in the axillae, underneath the breasts, and even on the vulva. Originally, it was noted in severe states of insulin resistance, such as the HAIR-AN syndrome (hyperandrogenic insulin-resistant acanthosis nigricans) [56]. These conditions with mutations in the insulin receptor may present in childhood with virilization and wasting (as opposed to obesity); however, like polycystic ovaries, its presence appears to be more a sign of insulin resistance than a distinct disease unto itself. But it can also be present in less severe states of insulin resistance, and most cases of acanthosis nigricans are not associated with mutations of the insulin receptor. There is no accepted grading system for the extent of acanthosis nigricans, as for hirsutism or alopecia. Similar to polycystic ovaries or hirsutism, other pathologic conditions are associated with acanthosis nigricans that must be considered when noted. It also has appeared in association with an insulinoma and malignant disease, especially adenocarcinoma of the stomach. Nonetheless, in most cases, the presence of acanthosis nigricans suggests compensatory hyperinsulinemia caused by an insulin-resistant state.

Insulin Resistance

The decrease of insulin resistance in women with PCOS compared to appropriate controls (~35 to 40 percent) is of a similar magnitude to that seen in type 2 diabetes and is independent of obesity, glucose intolerance, increases in waist-hip-girth ratio, and differences in muscle mass [5]. This synergistic negative effect of obesity and PCOS on hepatic glucose production is an important factor in the pathogenesis of glucose intolerance in PCOS. One of the most common prevailing theories about the etiology of type 2 diabetes proposes that the primary pathogenetic defect is peripheral insulin resistance, resulting in compensatory hyperinsulinemia. Over time there is beta cell dysfunction, leading to inadequate secretion of insulin and ultimately to beta cell exhaustion, and the development of frank type 2 diabetes. There is now a relatively substantial body of literature confirming beta cell dysfunction in PCOS, although as in diabetes, there is still considerable debate regarding the primacy of the defects and their worsening over time [57]. Basal insulin levels are increased, and insulin secretory response to meals has been shown to be reduced in women with PCOS [58]. This dysfunction is also independent of obesity [59].

Detection of Insulin Resistance in Women with Polycystic Ovarian Syndrome

Total body insulin sensitivity can be assessed by the euglycemic glucose clamp technique [60]. Here, exogenous insulin is infused to produce the desired insulin concentration. Glucose is infused simultaneously to maintain euglycemia. At steady state, the amount of glucose infused is equal to the amount of glucose utilized by the tissues and can be used as an index of sensitivity to insulin. The more glucose that is infused, the greater the sensitivity to insulin and vice versa. Total body insulin sensitivity can also be assessed via a modification of the intravenous glucose tolerance test known as frequently sampled intravenous glucose tolerance test (FSIGT) [61]. In this test, a bolus injection of glucose is given and blood is very frequently sampled for glucose and insulin levels. Minimal model analysis is then applied to the glucose and insulin levels obtained, and an insulin sensitivity index is derived. The precision of the model can be improved by enhancing second-phase insulin secretion with an intravenous injection of the insulin secretagogue tolbutamide or of insulin, 20 minutes after the glucose bolus. Minimal model estimates of insulin sensitivity are highly correlated with euglycemic clamp determinations of insulin action [61]. The FSIGT has been well valdiated in women with PCOS [59]. This test is substantially less labor intensive and costly to perform than the euglycemic clamp, but it still remains impractical and expensive in a clinical setting. Both of these tests have little benefit as diagnostic tests to identify insulin resistance in a PCOS population.

Currently, the American Diabetes Association (ADA) does not recommend screening for insulin resistance with fasting measures of insulin or other markers of the insulin-resistance syndrome [62]. Concerns about the utility of screening focus on the insulin assay variability, the lack of predictive value of fasting insulin levels, and the unclear association between hyperinsulinemia and other metabolic sequelae (primarily cardiovascular disease) [62].

Oral Glucose Tolerance Testing

Oral glucose tolerance testing (OGTT) allows for the diagnosis of clinically recognized categories of glucose tolerance, including impaired glucose tolerance and type 2 diabetes. Recent studies have suggested that the prevalence rates of glucose intolerance are as high as 40 percent in women with PCOS when the less stringent WHO [63] (2-hour glucose ≥140 mg/dL) criteria are used [8, 9]. These studies are of interest because they have shown nearly identical rates of impaired glucose tolerance and type 2 diabetes among a diverse cohort, both ethnically and geographically as well as from different investigational groups. This would suggest that these abnormalities may represent a universal characteristic of women with PCOS, at least those diagnosed on the basis of hyperandrogenic chronic anovulation.

Fasting glucose levels are poor predictors of glucose intolerance risks in PCOS because few women with PCOS with impaired glucose tolerance (IGT) had elevated fasting glucose values (Figure 29.2). This is supported by the limited studies of hemoglobin $A1_c$ in women with PCOS, which tend to be normal even in women with PCOS with IGT [64, 65]. Although diagnosing diabetes by fasting glucose using the 1997 ADA criteria may detect a more severe form of diabetes than the WHO criteria [66], this category of women with normal fasting glucoses and glucose intolerance may be exactly the subset of women (young and otherwise healthy) for whom more intensive early intervention can prevent long-term complications, such as the development of diabetes [67].

CLINICAL SEQUELAE OF POLYCYSTIC OVARIAN SYNDROME

Infertility and Chronic Anovulation

The most common reason that women with PCOS present to the gynecologist is because of infertility, caused by chronic anovulation [68]. As a general rule, PCOS women represent one of the most difficult groups in which to induce ovulation both successfully and safely. Many women with PCOS are unresponsive to clomiphene citrate and human menopausal gonadotropins (hMG), and this is exacerbated by the underlying obesity. On the other end

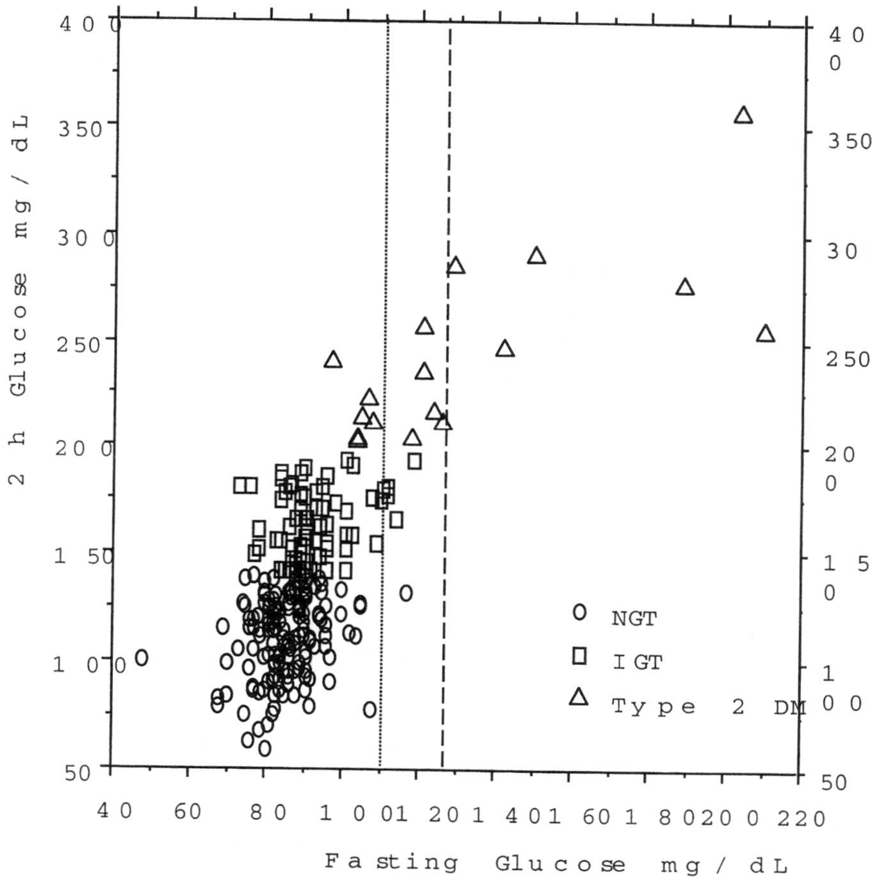

FIGURE 29.2 Scattergram of fasting blood glucose levels versus 2-hour glucose-stimulated levels in 254 women with PCOS. Points on the graph are coded to reflect the World Health Organization (WHO) status based on oral glucose tolerance testing (OGTT). The dotted vertical line is the threshold for impaired fasting glucose (110 mg/dL) by the 1997 American Diabetes Association (ADA) criteria, and the dashed vertical line (126 mg/dL) is the threshold for type 2 diabetes by the same criteria. Most women with PCOS, regardless of WHO OGTT status, have normal fasting glucose levels (Adapted from reference [8]).

of the spectrum are women with PCOS who overrespond to both of these medications. Women with PCOS are at especially increased risks of ovarian hyperstimulation syndrome (OHSS), a syndrome of massive enlargement of the ovaries and transudation of ascites into the abdominal cavity that can lead to rapid and symptomatic enlargement of the abdomen, intravascular contraction, hypercoagulability, and systemic organ dysfunction [69]. They are also at increased risk for multiple pregnancy. In addition, there is emerging evidence that baseline hyperinsulinemia may contribute to the increased OHSS risk [70, 71].

Gynecologic Cancer

Endometrial cancer is the most commonly diagnosed invasive gynecologic cancer in women. Case series have identified women with PCOS at high risk for developing endometrial cancer and often at an early age [72–75]. But there is actually little solid epidemiologic evidence to link PCOS and endometrial cancer. A stronger association between PCOS and endometrial cancer may be possible if we were able to make the diagnosis of PCOS in menopausal women, but a diagnosis based on hyperandrogenic chronic anovulation becomes difficult to make after ovarian failure and cessation of menses [76].

The mechanism by which women with PCOS may be at increased risk for endometrial hyperplasia and endometrial cancer is thought to be chronic stimulation of the endometrium with weak, but bioactive estrogens, combined with the lack of progestin exposure. This condition known as "unopposed estrogen" is perhaps the clearest hormonal risk factor for endometrial cancer [77]. PCOS women have been shown to be normoestrogenic, perhaps even hypoestrogenic with elevated levels of estrone [78]. A Scandinavian study looked at a group of both premenopausal and postmenopausal women with endometrial carcinoma and found hirsutism and obesity in both groups of cases compared to controls [79]. In the younger group, they additionally noted a recent history of anovulation and infertility, two of the most common presenting complaints of women with PCOS (in addition to hirsutism and obesity) [68]. Endometrial hyperplasia has often been noted in association with anovulation and infertility, common symptoms of PCOS [74, 80, 81]. There are no systematic prospective studies of the prevalence of endometrial hyperplasia/neoplasia in a population with PCOS. Other gynecologic cancers have been reported to be more common in women with PCOS, including ovarian cancer [82] and breast cancer [83].

Type 2 Diabetes Mellitus

Retrospective studies looking at diabetes prevalence over time have generally noted an increased prevalence with age in women with PCOS. Studies from Scandinavia have shown increased rates of type 2 diabetes and hypertension compared to controls [84]. This study used a combination of ovarian morphology and clinical criteria to identify women with PCOS and found that 15% had developed diabetes compared to 2.3% of the controls [84]. A case-control study of PCOS in the United States has shown persistent hyperinsulinemia and dyslipidemia as women with PCOS age, although androgen levels tend to decline in older women with PCOS [85]. In a thin Dutch population, although the overall prevalence of self-reported diabetes by telephone survery was 2.3%, in women with PCOS aged 45 to 54 years (n = 32), the prevalence of diabetes was four times higher ($P < 0.05$) than the prevalence of this condition in the corresponding age group of the Dutch female population [86].

Adult women with PCOS have glucose intolerance rates of 40% (as defined by prevalence of either IGT or type 2 diabetes as diagnosed by a 2-hour glucose value after a 75 g OGTT [8, 9]. New data now suggest that adolescents may have soaring rates of glucose intolerance [87], comparable with adults, which appears to be mirrored in the adolescent population with PCOS [88]. Studies of large cohorts of women with PCOS have demonstrated that the prevalence rates of glucose intolerance are as high as 40 percent in women with PCOS when the less stringent WHO criteria are used (see Figure 29.2) [8, 9]. These studies are of interest because they have shown nearly identical rates of impaired glucose tolerance and type 2 diabetes among a diverse cohort, both ethnically and geographically as well as from different investigational groups.

Cardiovascular Disease

Both PCOS and cardiovascular disease (CVD) are common in women, but is cardiovascular disease more common (and at an earlier age) in women with PCOS? The metabolic profile noted in women with PCOS is similar to the insulin-resistance syndrome, a clustering within an individual of hyperinsulinemia, mild glucose intolerance, dyslipidemia, and hypertension [89]. There is a prolific literature identifying obesity, dyslipidemia, glucose intolerance, and diabetes, and occasionally hypertension as risk factors for cardiovascular disease in women with PCOS [11, 90–95].

However, the metabolic syndrome X and PCOS remain distinct. When women with the metabolic syndrome are studied for reproductive stigmata of PCOS, they are no more likely to have polycystic ovaries than are other segments of the population, and less than half have a history of oligomenorrhea [96]. Nor do all women with PCOS have the metabolic syndrome. In some countries most women with PCOS (~80%) are nonobese [97], and as many as 50% of obese women with PCOS may not have documented insulin resistance by intensive testing [98]. There is actually little published evidence supporting a link between PCOS and cardiovascular events, such as increased mortality from CVD, premature mortality from CVD, or an increased incidence of cardiovascular events (stroke and/or myocardial infarction).

Hyperandrogenic Chronic Anovulation and Cardiac Events

A large-scale epidemiologic case-control study from the University of Pittsburgh initiated in 1992 has identified cases with PCOS primarily based on hyperandrogenic chronic anovulation (n > 200) and concurrently recruited community-based controls (n > 200) [7]. Another study from the Czech Republic with a much smaller case group (n = 28) noted a higher prevalence of self-reported coronary heart disease symptoms when compared with age-matched controls (n = 752) (21% of PCOS v. 5.2% of controls, P + 0.001) [99]. This group used diagnostic criteria of both hyperandrogenic chronic anovulation and past histopathologic evidence of PCO to identify cases, but only 28 of 61 cases identified responded to the questionnaire.

Several surrogate markers for atherosclerotic disease, including carotid wall thickness as determined by B-mode ultrasonography, have been studied in women with PCOS. The University of Pittsburgh performed ultrasonography of the carotid arteries on 125 women with PCOS and 142 control women from their original cohort and found a significantly higher prevalence of abnormal carotid plaque index in women with PCOS (7.2% v. 0.7% in controls) [10]. Thus most predominantly premenopausal women with PCOS (93%) had no evidence for subclinical carotid atherosclerosis. No difference was noted in the intima-media thickness between PCOS and controls until the age group 45 to 49, after which the difference increased in the oldest age groups [10].

Polycystic Ovaries and Cardiovascular Events

Despite the periodic discordance between PCO and PCOS, many of the largest, best-designed studies of long-term health risks in women with PCOS have been done using ovarian morphology. In older women presently under study, ovarian morphology during their reproductive years may be retrieved from hospital records (i.e., pathology report, operative notes, etc. from a wedge resection/oophorectomy), and at least is not subject to the recall bias of a menstrual history in establishing a prior phenotype. But this method may also include a treatment bias if this wedge resection resulted in long-term benefits. Many of these women have experienced long-term resolution of their symptoms (e.g., infertility, anovulation, hirsutism) [100]; however, this benefit is not supported by short-term studies of the metabolic effects of partial ovarian destruction, which have shown little effect on insulin sensitivity and dyslipidemia [101].

In a study from the United Kingdom, 800 women diagnosed with PCO, primarily by histopathology at the time of an ovarian wedge resection, were followed for an average of 30 years after the procedure [102]. Observed death rates were compared to expected death rates using standardized mortality ratios. There was no increased death from cardiovascular-related causes, although there was an increased number of deaths caused by complications of diabetes in the PCO group. In a follow-up study by the same investigative group of 345 of these women with PCO and 1060 age-matched control women there was no increased long-term coronary heart disease mortality, although there was evidence of increased stroke-related mortality even after adjustment for BMI [103]. In a cohort of women with proven coronary artery disease (n = 143 and age <60 years), PCO were noted in 42% of the women, and additionally their presence was associated with more severe coronary artery stenosis (odds ratio: 1.7, 95% confidence interval: 1.1 to 2.3 of >50% stenosis with PCO compared to normal ovaries) [92].

Chronic Anovulation and Cardiovascular Events

Despite the heterogeneous nature of anovulation in a reproductive-age population, some of the best epidemiologic studies of menstrual irregularity as a marker for chronic anovulation have shown an increased risk for cardiovascular events. The Dutch breast cancer screening study found a greater incidence of anovulatory cycles during the reproductive years (based on a midluteal urine sample) in women later developing cardiovascular disease [104]. Utilizing a prospective cohort design from the Nurse's Health Study [105], 82,439 female nurses provided information in 1982 on prior menstrual regularity (at ages 20 to 35 years) and were followed through 1996 for cardiovascular events. Incident reports of nonfatal myocardial infarction, fatal CHD, and nonfatal and fatal stroke were made and confirmed by review of medical records.

Compared with women reporting a history of regular menstrual cycles, women reporting usually irregular or very irregular cycles had an increased risk for nonfatal or fatal CHD. This increasing risk with increasing menstrual irregularity suggests a dose-response effect. Increased risks for CHD associated with prior cycle irregularity remained significant after adjustment for BMI and other several potential confounders, including family history of myocardial infarction and personal exercise history. There was a nonsignificant increase in overall stroke risk as well as in ischemic stroke risk associated with very irregular cycles. There was unfortunately no information on clinical or biochemical androgen excess among the study cohort to make the diagnosis of PCOS. The Nurse's Health Study has also identified oligomenorrhea and highly irregular menstrual cycles as risk factors for developing type 2 diabetes, a major risk factor in itself for cardiovascular disease, especially in women [106]. Thus the increased cardiovascular risk ascribed to women with PCOS is still largely inferential, based on risk factors or surrogate markers [91, 95] or epidemiologic studies that focus on isolated stigmata of PCOS, such as PCO or chronic anovulation, that are even more heterogeneous than PCOS.

POLYCYSTIC OVARIAN SYNDROME: A LIFETIME DISORDER?

The concept of PCOS as a reproductive disorder limited to the years between menarche and menopause has been shattered by its association with insulin resistance and its sequelae. This has led to the expansion of PCOS to a lifetime disorder, with premenarchal and postmenopausal phenotypes. In 1962, Neel was the first who argued for the existence of "thrifty" genes, which would have been preferred during human evolution [107]. Thrifty genes promoted an insulin-resistant phenotype, which utilized and stored energy efficiently, a survival benefit in the feast-or-famine world of the hunter/gatherer. The immense resources of the Human Genome Project have led to massive searches for genes that cause type 2 diabetes and obesity. This search is still underway and is hampered by the complex genetic basis of the disorder as well as by gene-environment interactions [108]. Although many candidate genes in type 2 diabetes and obesity have been identified, pundits would claim that the lack of success in identifying specific mutations (except in rare, severe phenotypes) argues against a purely genetic cause for these conditions in the larger population.

This belief has led to the development of the alternate hypothesis, that we are creatures of our environment, with the intrauterine environment exerting the greatest impact on our subsequent metabolic phenotype. The Barker hypothesis proposes that the source of insulin resistance lies in a harsh intrauterine milieu [109]. This milieu environmentally imprints our future metabolic fate. For those exposed to a nutritionally restricted womb, decreased fetal growth and birth weight are the result. The intrauterine famine results in imprinting a thrifty phenotype, where the anabolic effects of growth factors must be blunted in a nutrient-limited environment, one that ceases at birth. For instance, in the skeletal muscle, glucose is shunted to the development of more vital organs. They remain forever resistant to the effects of insulin, forming the basis for developing type 2 diabetes and cardiovascular disease in later life [110]. Studies by the proponents of this theory have shown that adults with low birth weight have an increased prevalence of impaired glucose tolerance and type 2 diabetes [111] and have stigmata of the insulin-resistance syndrome (i.e., glucose intolerance, hypertension, and dyslipidemia) [112].

Premature pubarche, defined as the early appearance of pubic hair (before 8 years in girls and 9 years in boys), has been postulated as an early expression of PCOS in prepubescent girls [113]. Adolescent girls with premature pubarche have been noted to be hyperinsulinemic [114] and to have an increased androgen response to a gonadotropin-releasing hormone (Gn-RH) agonist [115]. Baseline DHEAS and androstenedione levels at diagnosis or premature adrenarche correlated with 17-hydroxyprogesterone (17-OHP) values after Gn-RH agonist stimulation, suggesting that functional ovarian hyperandrogenism is more common in these girls (same gene for CYP17 is expressed in both the adrenal and ovary). This sign of increased CYP17 activity is therefore the first phenotypic manifestation of this abnormality in both glands.

These studies suggest that hyperinsulinemia plays a role in the hyperandrogenism found in premature pubarche and PCOS [116–118]. This hyperinsulinemia has been observed throughout all stages of puberty and cannot be explained by an increase in BMI when compared to normal subjects [119]. In one study, 45% of girls with a history of premature pubarche had ovarian hyperandrogenism [115]. These girls have subsequently developed chronic anovulation at the age of menarche [120]. Further low birth weight among girls with premature pubarche appeared to exacerbate the PCOS phenotype (Figure 29.3) [121].

At the other end of the reproductive spectrum, both menstrual irregularity [122] and hyperandrogenemia [123] appear to normalize as women with PCOS approach their late thirties and early forties. Evidence also suggests that polycystic ovaries may be more prevalent in younger women with PCOS, and that these also resolve with age [45]. Thus many of the reproductive stigmata may resolve before menopause, leading to the difficulty discussed as follows of linking long-term sequelae such as endometrial cancer and cardiovascular disease back to an earlier phenotype.

GENETIC ETIOLOGY

There are several difficulties in conducting family studies in the search for genes that cause or contribute to the PCOS phenotype. PCOS is associated with infertility and low fecundity. Thus it is rare to find large pedigrees with multiple affected women with whom to perform linkage analysis. Assigning phenotypes based on hyperandrogenism or anovulation to premenarchal girls and postmenopausal women is difficult. Although a male phenotype has been postulated, there are no rigorously established clinical or biochemical features that can be

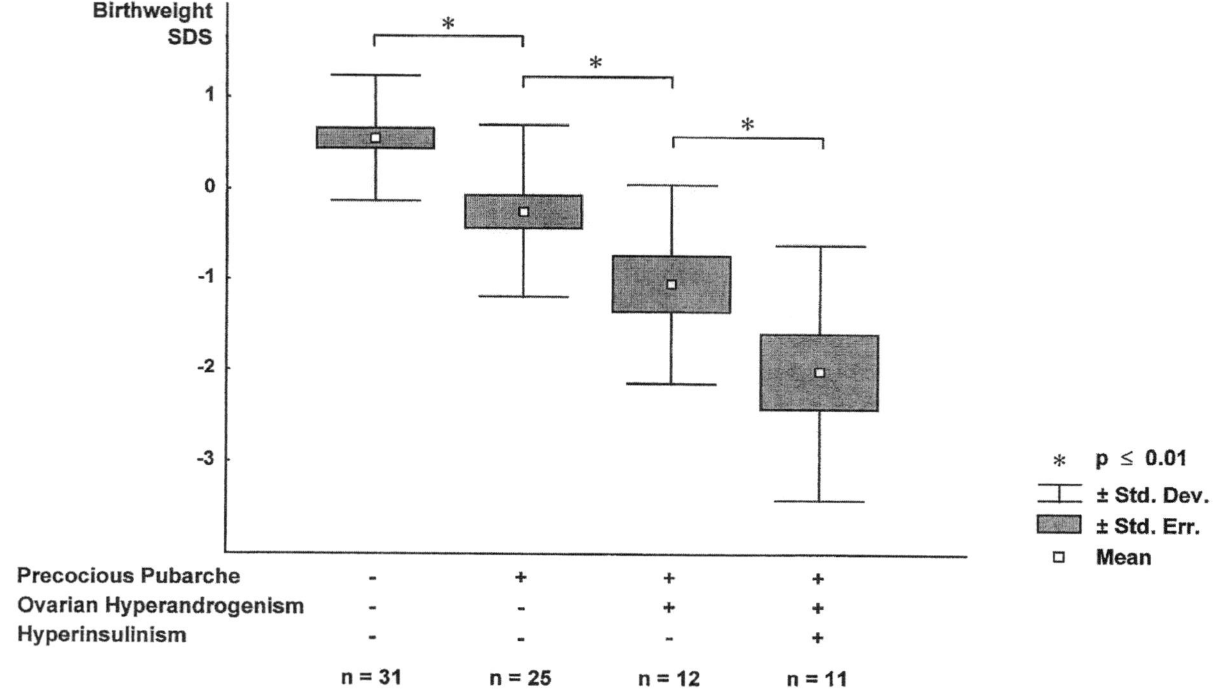

FIGURE 29.3 Birth weight scores of postmenarcheal control girls (–, –, and –) and postmenarcheal girls with a history of precocious pubarche without ovarian hyperandrogenism and without hyperinsulinemia (+, –, and –), with ovarian hyperandrogenism and without hyperinsulinemia (+, +, and –), and with both ovarian hyperandrogenism and hyperinsulinemia (+, +, and +). Adapted from reference [121].

used to identify "PCOS males." This makes formal segregation analysis and genetic linkage studies more difficult. The lack of animals that spontaneously develop a PCOS-like phenotype, especially mice, precludes the use of powerful tools of genetic mapping.

Family Studies

The foundation of genetic studies is the evidence that disease clusters in families. None of the existing family studies of PCOS convincingly establishes a mode of inheritance either, because the number of families studied was too small, the parental phenotypes could not be firmly established, and the male phenotype is uncertain [124–133]. Moreover, the diagnostic criteria used to assign affected status differed among the studies, as did the methods with which the status of first- and second-degree relatives were ascertained. By and large, ovarian morphology determined from tissue biopsy, direct visualization, or diagnostic imaging, in association with menstrual disturbances and evidence for hyperandrogenism, have been used in most studies as the criteria for diagnosing PCOS in probands. Despite the heterogeneity in study design and the inability to obtain comprehensive phenotype information to permit a formal segregation analysis, collectively the existing literature strongly suggests the clustering of PCOS in families, with a mode of inheritance that is not inconsistent with an autosomal-dominant pattern (Table 29.4).

Nearly 50% of sisters of women diagnosed with PCOS had elevated total or bioavailable testosterone levels, suggesting that hyperandrogenemia is a dominant trait (Figure 29.4). The contribution of genetics to blood androgen levels was recently substantiated in a large population study that was not dealing with PCOS per se. The authors concluded that plasma androgen levels are "highly heritable" [134]. Several studies have shown altered and elevated levels of androgens in brothers of women with PCOS [131, 132].

It is surprising that there have been only a few studies of monozygotic twins with PCOS given the power of this approach to disclose the genetic basis of disease. Case reports have described affected sets of female twins [135, 136]. Yet, the largest available twin study did not support a strong genetic component [137]. Both mono- and dizygotic twins were studied with ultrasound, as well as with clinical and biochemical parameters. There was an unusually high incidence of polycystic ovarian morphology on ultrasound, with 50% of the study population being

TABLE 29.4 Summary of Diagnostic Criteria for the Proband in Familial Studies of PCOS and Proposed Mode of Inheritance

Author	Diagnostic Criteria for PCOS	Number Studied	Mode of Inheritance
Cooper et al. (124)	Oligomenorrhea, hirsutism, polycystic ovaries (by culdoscopy, gynecography, or wedge resection)	18 women with PCOS and their first-degree relatives and a control group	Autosomal-dominant with reduced penetrance
Givens et al. (125)	Oligomenorrhea, hirsutism, and polycystic ovaries (examination and surgery)	3 multigeneration kindreds	(?X-linked) dominant
Ferriman and Purdie (126)	Hirsutism and/or oligomenorrhea, 60% with polycystic ovaries (by air-contrast gynecography)	381 women with PCOS and relatives and a control group	Modified dominant
Lunde et al. (127)	Clinical symptoms (menstrual irregularities, hirsutism, infertility, and obesity) and multicystic ovaries on wedge resection	132 women with PCOS and first- and second-degree relatives and a control group	Unclear, most consistent with autosomal-dominant
Hague et al. (128)	Clinical symptoms (menstrual dysfunction, hyperandrogenism, obesity, and infertility) and polycystic ovaries by transabdominal ultrasound	50 women with PCOS and 17 women with CAH and a control group	Segregation ratios exceeded autosomal-dominant pattern
Carey et al. (129)	Polycystic ovaries (by transabdominal ultrasound)	10 kindreds and 62 relatives	Autosomal-dominant with 90% penetrance
Norman et al. (130)	Elevated androgens, decreased SHBG, and polycystic ovaries on ultrasound	5 families with 24 females and 8 males	Not stated
Legro et al. (131)	Elevated testosterone levels combined with oligomenorrhea (≤6 menses/yr)	80 PCOS probands and 115 sisters	Hyperandrogenemia consistent with an autosomal-dominant trait
Govind et al. (132)	Polycystic ovary morphology on ultrasonograpy	29 families with 53 sisters and 18 brothers	Autosomal-dominant
Kahsar-Millar et al. (133)	Oligomenorrhea and either hirsutism or elevated testosterone levels	90 PCOS probands, 50 sisters, 78 mothers	Increased prevalence of symptoms in first-degree relatives suggesting genetic trait

affected. The authors found a high degree of discordance among the available twins for polycystic ovaries and suggested that PCOS might have a more complex inheritance pattern than autosomal-dominant, perhaps X-linked or polygenic; however, there was greater concordance among affected twins with respect to biochemical parameters, including fasting insulin levels and androgens. Hyperinsulinemia has been identified as a familial trait in PCOS families [130] and also appears to track with androgen levels in sisters of women with PCOS [138].

Phenotypes of Polycystic Ovarian Syndrome Cells

Freshly isolated theca cells collected from ovaries of women with PCOS studied in short-term culture [139] and propagated PCOS thecal cells grown through multiple population doublings [140] display greater steroidogenic activity than theca cells collected from normal ovaries (Figure 29.5). The latter studies are of importance because the long-term culture conditions and cell replication would presumably erase any effects of the *in vivo* hormonal milieu. The increased steroidogenic activity is caused by increased transcription of genes encoding steroidogenic enzymes, as reflected by enhanced promoter activities in cultured PCOS theca cells and increased levels of steroidogenic enzyme messenger ribonucleic acid (mRNA) in thecal tissue [140]. The biochemical phenotype displayed by PCOS theca cells is consistent with the findings from family studies, indicating genetic control of androgen production. The *in vitro* studies also demonstrated that the alterations in steroidogenic activity and expression of steroidogenic enzyme genes encompassed increased synthesis of progestins as well as androgens. Thus hyperandrogenemia cannot be attributed to abnormal expression of a single gene encoding a steroidogenic enzyme.

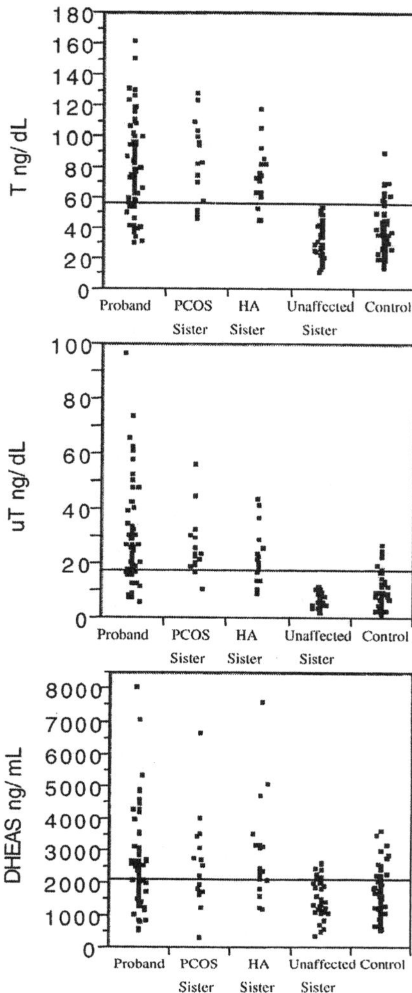

FIGURE 29.4 Distribution of serum androgen levels in control women (control), hyperandrogenemic sisters with regular cycles (HA Sister), unaffected sisters, sisters with PCOS (PCOS Sister), and PCOS probands (Proband). (Adapted from reference [131]).

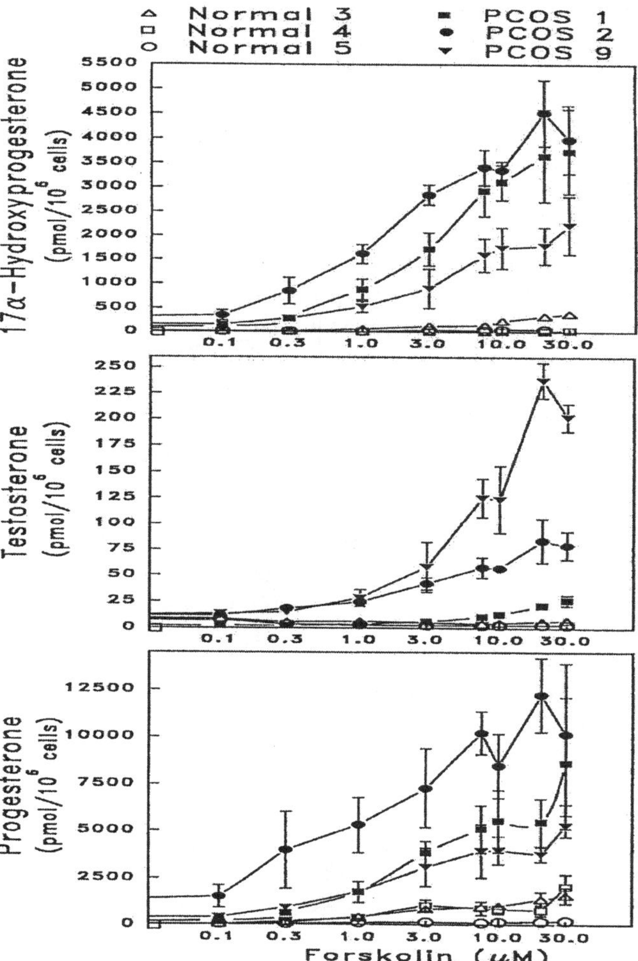

FIGURE 29.5 Accumulation of 17OHP4, P4, and T in the Medium of Normal and PCOS Theca Cell Cultures Grown for 22 to 26 Population Doublings. Long-term cultures of normal and PCOS theca cells were grown until subconfluence and then transferred into SFM containing 5 μg/mL low-density lipoprotein, with increasing concentrations of forskolin (F) for 72 hours. After treatment the media were collected and analyzed by RIA. Results are presented as the means ± SDof steroid levels from quadruplicate theca cell cultures from three normal and three PCOS patients. (Adapted from reference [140]).

Differential patterns of phosphorylation of the β-subunit of the insulin receptor in skeletal muscle cells and fibroblasts from women with PCOS have been identified [141]. Approximately 50% of the sample population of women with PCOS studied showed the increased insulin receptor serine phosphorylation. This finding has been substantiated in ovarian tissue [142]. Although the persistent biochemical/molecular alterations in PCOS cells maintained *in vitro* could possibly be explained by a stable metabolic imprint (epigenetic factor) obtained *in vivo*, the collective observations are more simply explained by genetic differences. Moreover, the fact that several genes show altered patterns of expression suggests that the fundamental genetic abnormality in PCOS affects signal transduction pathways controlling the expression of suites of genes.

Polycystic Ovarian Syndrome Candidate Genes

This conclusion raises to prominence candidate genes that are involved in cell signaling or chromosomal loci in which signal transduction genes reside, rather than candidate genes that are directly involved in steroid hormone synthesis and action, or carbohydrate metabolism and fuel homeostasis, or gonadotropin action and regulation. These genes to date have yielded few clues to the genetics of PCOS [143]. These latter group of candidate genes were selected for study because they could account for certain

PCOS features or because they have been implicated in insulin-resistance syndromes. Although several loci have been proposed as PCOS genes, including *CYP11A* [144], the insulin gene al [145], and a region near the insulin receptor, the evidence supporting linkage is not overwhelming. The strongest case can be made for the region near the insulin receptor gene because it has been identified in two separate studies [146, 147]; however, the responsible gene at chromosome 19p13.3 remains to be identified. Association studies have provided several potential loci with genetic variants that may create or add to a PCOS phenotype, including *Calpain 10* [148], *IRS-1* and *-2* [146, 147], and *SHBG* [149]. These are characterized by their genetic and clinical diversity. Because they are rare and their full impact on the phenotype is incompletely understood, routine screening of women with PCOS or stigmata of PCOS for these genetic variants is not indicated at this time. Currently, the treatment implications for individually identified genetic variants is uncertain and must be addressed on a case-by-case basis.

TREATMENT OF POLYCYSTIC OVARIAN SYNDROME

The treatment section focuses first on therapies designed for generalized treatment of the syndrome and then on treatments directed at specific complaints. We are currently changing from a symptom-oriented treatment approach to PCOS, which often focused alternately on either suppression of the ovaries (for hirsutism and menstrual disorders) or stimulation of the ovaries (for infertility), to one that improves insulin sensitivity and treats a variety of stigmata simultaneously [150]. Multiple studies have shown that improving insulin sensitivity, be it from lifestyle modifications or from pharmacologic intervention, can result in lowered circulating androgens (primarily mediated through increased sex hormone binding globulin and less bioavailable androgen but also through decreased total testosterone), spontaneous ovulation, and spontaneous pregnancy. In other populations this improvement in insulin sensitivity can also result in a lower chance for developing diabetes; however, long-term studies documenting decreases in the incidence of such sequelae as endometrial cancer with improvements in insulin sensitivity are lacking.

GENERALIZED TREATMENTS OF POLYCYSTIC OVARIAN SYNDROME

Lifestyle Modifications

Obesity has become epidemic in our society and contributes substantially to reproductive and metabolic abnormalities in PCOS. Unfortunately, there are no effective treatments that result in permanent weight loss, and it is estimated that 90% to 95% of patients who experience a weight decrease will relapse [151]. For obese patients with hirsutism, weight loss is frequently recommended as a potential benefit. Increases in SHBG through improved insulin sensitivity from weight loss may lower bioavailable androgen levels. In one study, about 50% of these women who lost weight experienced improvement in their hirsutism [152]. There have, unfortunately, been few studies on the effect of exercise alone on insulin action in hyperandrogenic women [153]. It is reasonable to assume that exercise would have the same beneficial effects in women with PCOS as women with type 2 diabetes [154]. There is much hype about the beneficial effects of diets of varying composition on insulin sensitivity, with many popular sources advocating a high-protein diet as the diet of choice for women with PCOS. Few studies support this theory, and there are theoretical concerns about the adverse effects of high protein on renal function in a population at high risk for diabetes, as well as the adverse effects of the increased fat composition of these diets on dyslipidemia.

Ovarian Suppressive Therapies

Women with documented hyperandrogenemia, and stigmata of hirsutism and acne, would theoretically benefit most from this form of therapy. Suppressing the ovary has been achieved with either oral contraceptives, depot progestins, or Gn-RH analog treatment. Oral contraceptives both inhibit ovarian steroid production by lowering gonadotropins and raise SHBG through their estrogen effect, thus further lowering bioavailable testosterone. They may also inhibit dihydrotestosterone binding to the androgen receptor and 5α-reductase activity, and increase hepatic steroid clearance (because of stimulation of the P-450 system). These myriad actions contribute to improving hirsutism [155]. There are theoretical reasons for choosing an oral contraceptive using a less androgenic progestin or one with specific androgen antagonistic properties (such as cyproterone acetate or drospirenone), but few studies show a clinical difference between different types of progestins. Although several oral contraceptive pills, including a triphasic oral contraceptive containing norgestimate, have been shown to improve acne and have received an FDA indication for this treatment, other pills also appear to offer similar results.

A Gn-RH agonist may further lower circulating androgens, but comparative trials against other agents and combined agent trials have been mixed and have not shown a greater benefit of one or the other or combined treatment [156–159]. A Gn-RH agonist given alone results in unacceptable bone loss [159]. Glucocorticoid suppression of the adrenal also offers theoretical benefits, but deterioration in glucose tolerance is problematic for women with PCOS, and long-term effects such as osteoporosis are a significant concern. It may be useful as adjunctive therapy in inducing ovulation with clomiphene citrate.

Surgical Options

The beneficial influence of treatment on sequelae of PCOS, especially destructive ovarian interventions such as wedge resection or ovarian drilling, has been suggested but not proven. Many argue that the best monotherapy results for the endocrine abnormalities of PCOS can be obtained through surgical destructive processes of the ovary, wedge resection or ovarian drilling [160–162]. The value of laparoscopic ovarian drilling as a primary treatment for subfertile patients with anovulation and PCOS is undetermined, according to a Cochrane review [163]. There is insufficient evidence to determine a difference in ovulation or pregnancy rates when compared to gonadotrophin therapy as a secondary treatment for clomiphene-resistant women [163], although a recent study suggested that the pregnancy rates were equivalent [164]. None of the various drilling techniques appear to offer obvious advantages [163]. The results of ovarian drilling may in some cases also be temporary [100]. Surgery, consisting of total abdominal hysterectomy and bilateral salpingo-oophorectomy, is not a usual initial treatment option for androgen excess, but may be indicated in some cases of refractory ovarian hyperandrogenism.

Insulin-Sensitizing Agents

Drugs developed initially to treat type 2 diabetes have also been utilized to treat PCOS. None of these agents are currently FDA approved for the treatment of PCOS or for related symptoms such as anovulation, hirsutism, or acne. These include metformin [165–167], thiazolidinediones, and an experimental insulin sensitizer drug d-*chiro*-inositol [13].

Metformin

Metformin was approved for the treatment of type 2 diabetes by the FDA in 1994 but was used clinically for close to 20 years before that in other parts of the world. Several trials on metformin's effects in women with PCOS have been published, and meta-analyses have begun to appear [168], although there has never been an adequately powered placebo-controlled dose-ranging study. Metformin is a biguanide that works primarily by suppressing hepatic gluconeogenesis, but it also improves insulin sensitivity in the periphery. Metformin has no known human teratogenic risk or embryonic lethality in humans. There have been no reported abnormalities associated with its use during pregnancy in women with diabetes [169–171], or to women with marked hyperandrogenism during pregnancy [172], or to the small number of women with PCOS who have conceived during treatment [173–175]. Some clinicians advocate its use during early pregnancy to reduce the miscarriage rate, but the documentation for this claim is poor [176]. Studies of longer duration with metformin in PCOS suggest long-term improvement in ovulatory function in about half of the patients [177]. Unfortunately, there have been few well-designed studies that test the effect on hirsutism.

Thiazolidinediones

Thiazolidinediones are peroxisome proliferator-activated receptor (PPAR) agonists and are thought to improve insulin sensitivity through a postreceptor mechanism. It is difficult to separate the effects of improving insulin sensitivity from that of lowering serum androgens because any "pure" improvement in insulin sensitivity can raise SHBG and thus lower bioavailable androgen. Given the long onset of action for improving hirsutism, longer periods of observation are needed. In a large multicenter trial, troglitazone has been shown to have a dose-response effect in improving ovulation and hirsutism [14]. This appeared to be mediated through decreases in hyperinsulinemia and decreases in free testosterone levels. Troglitazone has subsequently been removed from the worldwide market because of hepatotoxicity. Newer thiazolidinediones such as rosiglitazone and pioglitazone appear to be safer in terms of hepatotoxicity but have also been associated with embryotoxicity in animal studies (both are pregnancy category C), and little has been published on their effects in women with PCOS.

TREATMENT OF INFERTILITY

Clomiphene Citrate

Clomiphene citrate (CC) has traditionally been the first-line treatment agent for infertility in women with PCOS. It is a nonsteroidal agent and a member of a large family of triphenylethylene derivatives, which includes clorotrianisene and tamoxifen (both of which compare favorably to CC in inducing ovulation). It is a racemic mixture of two isomers, zuclomiphene (longer acting) and enclomiphene (more potent in inducing ovulation) [178]. Clomiphene has a long half-life; only 51% of the oral dose is excreted after 5 days, and the zu isomer can be detected in the serum for up to 1 month after treatment [179]. Clomiphene is thought to work as a selective estrogen receptor modulator (SERM), acting as an estrogen antagonist at the hypothalamic-pituitary axis and stimulating Gn-RH secretion. CC's mixed estrogen agonist/antagonist effects on the lower female genital tract as well as on implantation have been more theoretically antagonist than documented.

A meta-analysis showed CC to be effective in patients with ovulatory dysfunction similar to PCOS [180]. Compared with a placebo, CC was associated with increased ovulation. CC (all doses) was associated with an increased pregnancy rate per treatment cycle (odds ratio: 3.41, 95% confidence interval: 4.23 to 9.48) The odds ratio was better for high doses (50–250 milligrams per day) (odds ratio: 6.82, 95% confidence interval: 3.92 to 11.85) [180].

There are no clear prognostic factors to response, although increasing weight is associated with a larger dose requirement and a greater likelihood for failure [181]. Roughly 50% of women with PCOS do not respond to CC. There is no universal definition of resistance to CC, although in its simplest rendition this would involve failure to ovulate to three progressive dose increases up to 750 mg/cycle. Alternate CC regimens have been developed, including prolonging the period of administration [182] and adding dexamethasone [183], both of which have been shown to improve response in small studies.

Gonadotropins

Gonadotropins are also frequently utilized in both step-up and step-down regimens to induce ovulation in women with PCOS. In one of the largest trials of gonadotropins in women with PCOS to date, women were randomized to a conventional method of ovulation with more aggressive dosing and increases in FSH dosing compared to a low-dose protocol; higher pregnancy rates were achieved with the low-dose protocol (40% v. 20% for the conventional arm) [184]. There were fewer cases of multiple pregnancy and ovarian hyperstimulation in the low-dose arm and a higher percentage of monofollicular ovulation (74% v. 27%) [184]. Low-dose therapy with gonadotropins offers a high rate on monofollicular development (~50% or greater) with a significantly lower risk of OHSS (20% to 25%) leading to cycle cancellation or more serious sequelae [184–188]. A Cochrane review reports a reduction in the incidence of OHSS with FSH compared to hMG in stimulation cycles without the concomitant use of a Gn-RH-a (odds ratio: 0.20, 95% confidence interval: 0.08 to 0.46) and a higher overstimulation rate when a Gn-RH-a is added to gonadotropins (odds ratio: 3.15, 95% confidence interval: 1.48 to 6.70) [189]. Despite theoretical advantages, urinary-derived FSH preparations did not improve pregnancy rates when compared to traditional and cheaper hMG preparations; their only demonstrable benefit was a reduced risk of OHSS in cycles when administered without the concomitant use of a Gn-RH-a. A meta-analysis found no studies of adequate power to confirm the benefit of pulsatile Gn-RH-a to induce ovulation in PCOS [190].

TREATMENT OF HIRSUTISM

Many of the aforementioned generalized treatments are also applicable to the treatment of hirsutism. Most medical methods, while improving hirsutism, do not produce the dramatic results patients desire. In general, combination therapies appear to produce better results than single-agent approaches; responses with medical therapies often take 3 to 6 months to notice improvement; and adjunctive mechanical removal methods are often necessary. However, most women will experience improvement in their hirsutism. There are unfortunately no universally accepted techniques for assessing hirsutism and response to treatment. Trials have been hampered by these methodology concerns as well as by small numbers of subjects. For instance, although spironolactone has had a long and extensive use as an antiandrogen and multiple clinical trials have been published showing a benefit, the overall quality of the trials and small numbers enrolled have limited the ability of a meta-analysis to document its benefit in the treatment of hirsutism [191].

Ornithine Decarboxylase Inhibitors

Ornithine decarboxylase is necessary for the production of polyamines and is also a sensitive and specific marker of androgen action in the prostate [192]. Inhibition of this enzyme limits cell division and function. Recently, a potent inhibitor of this enzyme, eflornithine, has been tested and found to be effective as a facial cream against hirsutism and has been approved by the FDA for this indication. It is given as a 13.9% cream of eflornithine hydrochloride and applied to affected areas twice a day for a minimum of 4 hours each. In clinical trials, 32% of patients showed marked improvement after 24 weeks compared to 8% of those treated with a placebo; benefit was first noted at 8 weeks. It is a pregnancy category C drug that appears to be well tolerated. A variety of adverse skin conditions occurred in 1% of subjects.

Antiandrogens and Androgen Receptor Antagonists

These compounds antagonize the binding of testosterone and other androgens to the androgen receptor and are not approved by the FDA for this indication in women. As a class, therefore, they are teratogenic and pose risk of feminization of the external genitalia in a male fetus if the patient conceives. Spironolactone, a diuretic and aldosterone antagonist, also binds to the androgen receptor with 67% of the affinity of dihydrotestosterone [193]. It has other mechanisms of action, including inhibition of ovarian and adrenal steroidogenesis, competition for androgen receptors in hair follicles, and direct inhibition of 5α-reductase activity. There is a dose-response effect and a long period of onset: 6 months or more. About 20% of treated women will experience increased menstrual frequency, which is one reason for combining this therapy with the oral contraceptive [194]. Because it can cause and exacerbate hyperkalemia, it should be used cautiously in patients with renal impairment. The medication also has potential teratogenicity as an antiandrogen, although exposure has rarely resulted in ambiguous genitalia in male infants [195]. Acne has also been successfully treated with spironolactone [196]. Thus much of the treatment basis is empiric. Cyproterone acetate, not available commercially in the United States, is a progestogen with antiandrogen properties. It is frequently combined in an oral contraceptive. Flutamide is another nonsteroidal antiandrogen that has been shown to be effective against hirsutism [197]. There is a greater risk of teratogenicity with this compound, so contraception should be used.

Antiandrogens: 5α-reductase Inhibitors

There are two forms of the enzyme 5α-reductase: type 1 predominantly found in the skin and type II predominantly found in the prostate and reproductive tissues. Both forms are found in the PSU and may contribute to hirsutism, acne, and balding. Finasteride inhibits both forms. It has been found to be effective for the treatment of hirsutism in women [198, 199]. Finasteride is better tolerated than other antiandrogens but has the highest and clearest risk for teratogenicity in a male fetus, so adequate contraception must be used. Randomized trials have found that spironolactone, flutamide, and finasteride all have similar efficacy in improving hirsutism [200, 201].

OTHER TREATMENTS

There are several, perhaps innumerable other treatments, that have been proposed for PCOS. Many of these have come and gone, and some never arrived. Minoxidil has mild efficacy in increasing hair growth in women with alopecia. Ketoconazole is an inhibitor of the P450 enzyme system and thus inhibits androgen biosynthesis but has hepatotoxicity. Others have given aromatase inhibitors to induce ovulation and lower circulating androgens, although hirsutism has not been the primary focus to date [202].

Mechanical hair removal (e.g., shaving, plucking, waxing, depilatory creams, electrolysis, and laser vaporization) can control hirsutism, and these methods are often the front-line treatment used by women. Laser vaporization is receiving increasing attention. Hair is damaged using the principle of selective photothermolysis with wavelengths of light well absorbed by follicular melanin and pulse durations that selectively thermally damage the target without damaging surrounding tissue. Patients with dark hair and light skin are ideal candidates, and it appears to be most effective during anagen.

CONCLUSION

PCOS is a common endocrinopathy, but it is poorly understood. It is a disorder of unexplained hyperandrogenic chronic anovulation and clearly heterogeneous in etiology; however, many women are noted to have profound peripheral resistance to insulin-mediated glucose uptake. Despite evidence of familial clustering, no clear molecular or genetic mechanism has been identified to date to explain most cases. Women with PCOS present with infertility, menstrual disorders, and hirsutism. They appear to be at increased risk for diabetes and display multiple risk factors for endometrial cancer and cardiovascular disease. Unfortunately, there are few randomized, controlled trials of any treatment in PCOS to provide clear treatment guidelines. Therefore, treatment tends to be symptom based, although lifestyle interventions and pharmaceutical treatments directed at improving insulin sensitivity appear to improve multiple stigmata of the syndrome. For instance, studies with these agents have shown improvements in ovulation and hirsutism.

ACKNOWLEDGMENTS

This work was supported by PHS K24 HD01476, the National Cooperative Program in Infertility Research (NCPIR) U54 HD34449, a GCRC grant MO1 RR 10732 to Pennsylvania State University and K24 HD01476.

References

1. Knochenhauer, E. S., Key, T. J., Kahsar-Miller, M., Waggoner, W., Boots, L. R., and Azziz, R. (1998). Prevalence of the polycystic ovary syndrome in unselected black and white women of the southeastern United States: A prospective study. *J. Clin. Endocrinol. Metab.* 83, 3078–3082.
2. Stein, I. F., and Leventhal, M. L. (1935). Amenorrhea associated with polycystic ovaries. *Am. J. Obstet. Gynecol.* 29, 181–191.
3. Lloyd, C. W., Lobotsky, J., Segre, E. J., Kobayashi, T., Taymor, M. L., and Batt, R. E. (1966). Plasma testosterone and urinary 17-ketosteroids in women with hirsutism and polycystic ovaries. *J. Clin. Endocrinol. Metab.* 26, 314–324.
4. Chang, R. J., Nakamura, R. M., Judd, H. L., and Kaplan, S. A. (1983). Insulin resistance in nonobese patients with polycystic ovarian disease. *J. Clin. Endocrinol. Metab.* 57, 356–359.
5. Dunaif, A., Segal, K. R., Futterweit, W., and Dobrjansky, A. (1989). Profound peripheral insulin resistance, independent of obesity, in polycystic ovary syndrome. *Diabetes* 38, 1165–1174.
6. Zawadski, J. K., and Dunaif, A. (1992). Diagnostic criteria for polycystic ovary syndrome; towards a rational approach. In *Polycystic Ovary Syndrome*, eds. A. Dunaif, J. R. Givens, F. Haseltine, and G. R. Merriam, 377–384. Boston, MA: Blackwell Scientific.

7. Talbott, E., Guzick, D., Clerici, A., Berga, S., Detre, K., Weimer, K., and Kuller, L. (1995). Coronary heart disease risk factors in women with polycystic ovary syndrome. *Arteriosclerosis, Thrombosis Vasc. Biol.* 15, 821–826.
8. Legro, R. S., Kunselman, A. R., Dodson, W. C., and Dunaif, A. (1999). Prevalence and predictors of risk for type 2 diabetes mellitus and impaired glucose tolerance in polycystic ovary syndrome: A prospective, controlled study in 254 affected women. *J. Clin. Endocrinol. Metab.* 84(1), 165–169.
9. Ehrmann, D. A., Barnes, R. B., Rosenfield, R. L., Cavaghan, M. K., and Imperial, J. (1999). Prevalence of impaired glucose tolerance and diabetes in women with polycystic ovary syndrome. *Diabetes Care* 22(1), 141–146.
10. Talbott, E. O., Guzick, D. S., Sutton-Tyrrell, K., McHugh-Pemu, K. P., Zborowski, J. V., Remsberg, K. E., and Kuller, L. H. (2000). Evidence for association between polycystic ovary syndrome and premature carotid atherosclerosis in middle-aged women. *Arteriosclerosis, Thrombosis Vasc. Biol.* 20, 2414–2421.
11. Legro, R. S., Kunselman, A. R., Dunaif, A. (2001). Prevalence and predictors of dyslipidemia in women with polycystic ovary syndrome. *Am. J. Med.* 111, 607–613.
12. Nestler, J. E., and Jakubowicz, D. J. (1996). Decreases in ovarian cytochrome P450C17-alpha activity and serum free testosterone after reduction of insulin secretion in polycystic ovary syndrome. *N. Engl. J. Med.* 335, 617–623.
13. Nestler, J. E., Jakubowicz, D. J., Reamer, P., Gunn, R. D., and Allan, G. (1999). Ovulatory and metabolic effects of d-chiro-inositol in the polycystic ovary syndrome. *N. Engl. J. Med.* 340, 1314–1320.
14. Azziz, R., Ehrmann, D., Legro, R. S., Whitcomb, R. W., Fereshetian, A. G., O'Keefe, M., and Ghazzi, M. N. (2001). Troglitazone improves ovulation and hirsutism in the polycystic ovary syndrome: A multicenter, double-blind, placebo-controlled trial. *J. Clin. Endocrinol. Metab.* 86, 1626–1632.
15. Legro, R. S., Driscoll, D., Strauss III, J. F., Fox, J., and Dunaif, A. (1998). Evidence for a genetic basis for hyperandrogenemia in polycystic ovary syndrome. *Proc. Natl. Acad. Sci. USA* 95(25), 14956–14960.
16. Ludwig, E. (1977). Classification of the types of androgenetic alopecia (common baldness) occurring in the female sex. *Br. J. Dermatol.* 97, 247–254.
17. Tagatz, G. E., Kopher, R. A., Nagel, T. C., and Okagaki, T. (1979). The clitoral index: A bioassay of androgenic stimulation. *Obstet. Gynecol.* 54(5), 562–564.
18. Chetkowski, R. J., DeFazio, J., Shamonki, I., Judd, H. L., and Chang, R. J. (1984). The incidence of late-onset congenital adrenal hyperplasia due to 21-hydroxylase deficiency among hirsute women. *J. Clin. Endocrinol. Metab.* 58(4), 595–598.
19. New, M. I., and Speiser, P. W. (1986). Genetics of adrenal steroid 21-hydroxylase deficiency. [Review] [115 refs]. *Endocr Rev* 7, 331–349.
20. Azziz, R., Hincapie, L. A., Knochenhauer, E. S., Dewailly, D., Fox, L., and Boots, L. R. (1999). Screening for 21-hydroxylase-deficient nonclassic adrenal hyperplasia among hyperandrogenic women: A prospective study. *Fertil. Steril.* 72, 915–925.
21. New, M. I., Lorenzen, F., Lerner, A. J,, Kohn, B., Oberfield, S. E., Pollack, M. S., Dupont, B., Stoner, E., Levy, D. J., Pang, S., and Levine, L. S. (1983). Genotyping steroid 21-hydroxylase deficiency: Hormonal reference data. *J. Clin. Endocrinol. Metab.* 57(2), 320–326.
22. Speiser, P. W., Dupont, J., Zhu, D., Serrat, J., Buegeleisen, M., Tusie-Luna, M. T., New, M. I., and White, P. C. (1992). Disease expression and molecular genotype in congenital adrenal hyperplasia due to 21-hydroxylase deficiency. *J. Clin. Invest.* 90, 584–595.
23. Azziz, R., Dewailly, D., and Owerbach, D. (1994). Clinical review 56: Nonclassic adrenal hyperplasia: Current concepts. *J. Clin. Endocrinol. Metab.* 78(4), 810–815.
24. Cizza, G., and Chrousos, G. P. (1997). Adrenocorticotrophic hormone-dependent Cushing's syndrome. [Review] [50 refs]. *Cancer Treat. Res.* 89, 25–40.
25. Kaltsas, G. A., Korbonits, M., Isidori, A. M., Webb, J. A., Trainer, P. J., Monson, J. P., Besser, G. M., and Grossman, A. B. (2000). How common are polycystic ovaries and the polycystic ovarian syndrome in women with Cushing's syndrome? *Clin. Endocrinol.* 53(4), 493–500.
26. Plotz, C. M., Knowlton, A. L., and Ragan, C. The natural history of Cushing's syndrome. *Am. J. Med.* 13, 597–605.
27. Givens, J. R. (1971). Ovarian hyperthecosis. *N. Engl. J. Med.* 285, 691.
28. Barth, J. H., Jenkins, M., and Belchetz, P. E. (1997). Ovarian hyperthecosis, diabetes and hirsuties in post-menopausal women [see comments]. *Clin. Endocrinol.* 46, 123–128.
29. Barbieri, R. L., Smith, S., and Ryan, K. J. (1988). The role of hyperinsulinemia in the pathogenesis of ovarian hyperandrogenism. [Review]. *Fertil. Steril.* 50, 197–212.
30. Rebar, R., Judd, H. L., Yen, S. S., Rakoff, J., Vandenberg, G., and Naftolin, F. (1976). Characterization of the inappropriate gonadotropin secretion in polycystic ovary syndrome. *J. Clin. Invest.* 57, 1320–1329.
31. Keettel, W. C., Bradbury, J. T., and Stoddard, F. J. (1957). Observations on the PCO syndrome. *Am. J. Obstet. Gynecol.* 73, 954–965.
32. McArthur, J. W., Ingersall, F. M., and Worcester, J. (1958). The urinary excretion of interstitial cell and folicle-stimulating hormone activity by women with diseases of the reproductive system. *J. Clin. Endocrinol. Metab.* 18, 1202–1205.
33. Yen, S. S., Vela, P., and Rankin, J. (1970). Inappropriate secretion of follicle-stimulating hormone and luteinizing hormone in polycystic ovarian disease. *J. Clin. Endocrinol. Metab.* 30, 435–442.
34. Robinson, S., Rodin, D. A., Deacon, A., Wheeler, M. J., and Clayton, R. N. (1992). Which hormone tests for the diagnosis of polycystic ovary syndrome? [see comments]. *Br. J. Obstet. Gynaecol.* 99, 232–238.
35. Arroyo, A., Laughlin, G. A., Morales, A. J., and Yen, S. S. (1997). Inappropriate gonadotropin secretion in polycystic ovary syndrome: Influence of adiposity. *J. Clin. Endocrinol. Metab.* 82, 3728–3733.
36. Taylor, A. E., McCourt, B., Martin, K. A., Anderson, E. J., Adams, J. M., Schoenfeld, D. H. (1997). Determinants of abnormal gonadotropin secretion in clinically defined women with polycystic ovary syndrome. *J. Clin. Endocrinol. Metab.* 82, 2248–2256.
37. Lobo, R. A., Shoupe, D., Chang, S. P., and Campeau, J. (1984). The control of bioactive luteinizing hormone secretion in women with polycystic ovary syndrome. *Am. J. Obstet. Gynecol.* 148, 423–428.

38. Fauser, B. C., Pache, T. D., Hop, W. C., de Jong, F. H., and Dahl, K. D. (1992). The significance of a single serum LH measurement in women with cycle disturbances: Discrepancies between immunoreactive and bioactive hormone estimates. *Clin. Endocrinol.* 37, 445–452.
39. Franks, S. (1995). Polycystic ovary syndrome [published erratum appears in *N. Engl. J. Med.* 1995: 333(21), 1435]. [Review]. *N. Engl. J. Med.* 333, 853–861.
40. Polson, D. W., Adams, J., Wadsworth, J., and Franks, S. (1988). Polycystic ovaries—a common finding in normal women. *Lancet* 1, 870–872.
41. Farquhar, C. M., Birdsall, M., Manning, P., Mitchell, J. M., and France, J. T. (1994). The prevalence of polycystic ovaries on ultrasound scanning in a population of randomly selected women. *Aust. NZ J. Obstet. Gynaecol.* 34, 67–72.
42. Koivunen, R., Laatikainen, T., Tomas, C., Huhtaniemi, I., Tapanainen, J., and Martikainen, H. (1999). The prevalence of polycystic ovaries in healthy women. *Acta Obstetricia Gynecologica Scandinavica* 78(2), 137–141.
43. Chang, P. L., Lindheim, S. R., Lowre, C., Ferin, M., Gonzalez, F., Berglund, L., Carmina, E., Sauer, M. V., and Lobo, R. A. (2000). Normal ovulatory women with polycystic ovaries have hyperandrogenic pituitary-ovarian responses to gonadotropin-releasing hormone-agonist testing. *J. Clin. Endocrinol. Metab.* 85(3), 995–1000.
44. Carmina, E., Wong, L., Chang, L., Paulson, R. J., Sauer, M. V., Stanczyk, F. Z., and Lobo, R. A. (1997). Endocrine abnormalities in ovulatory women with polycystic ovaries on ultrasound. *Hum. Reprod.* 12, 905–909.
45. Loucks, T. L., Talbott, E. O., McHugh, K. P., Keelan, M., Berga, S. L., and Guzick, D. S. (2000). Do polycystic-appearing ovaries affect the risk of cardiovascular disease among women with polycystic ovary syndrome? *Fertil. Steril.* 74(3), 547–552.
46. Enskog, A., Henriksson, M., Unander, M., Nilsson, L., and Brännström, M. (1999). Prospective study of the clinical and laboratory parameters of patients in whom ovarian hyperstimulation syndrome developed during controlled ovarian hyperstimulation for in vitro fertilization. *Fertil. Steril.* 71(5), 808–814.
47. Carmina, E., Koyama, T., Chang, L., Stanczyk, F. Z., and Lobo, R. A. (1992). Does ethnicity influence the prevalence of adrenal hyperandrogenism and insulin resistance in polycystic ovary syndrome? *Am. J. Obstet. Gynecol.* 167, 1807–1812.
48. Nestler, J. E. (1993). Sex hormone-binding globulin: a marker for hyperinsulinemia and/or insulin resistance? [editorial; comment]. *J. Clin. Endocrinol. Metab.* 76, 273–274.
49. Boots, L. R., Potter, S., Potter, D., and Azziz, R. (1998). Measurement of total serum testosterone levels using commercially available kits: High degree of between-kit variability. *Fertil. Steril.* 69(2), 286–92.
50. Moran, C., Tapia, M. C., Hernandez, E., Vazquez, G., and Garcia-Hernandez, E. (1994). Etiological review of hirsutism in 250 patients. *Arch. Med. Res.* 25, 311–314.
51. Lobo, R. A., Goebelsmann, U., and Horton, R. (1983). Evidence for the importance of peripheral tissue events in the development of hirsutism in polycystic ovary syndrome. *J. Clin. Endocrinol. Metab.* 57, 393–397.
52. Barth, J. H. (1996). How robust is the methodology for trials of therapy in hirsute women? *Clin. Endocrinol.* 45, 379–380.
53. Holdaway, I. M., Fraser, A., Sheehan, A., Croxson, M. S., France, J. T., and Ibbertson, H. K. (1985). Objective assessment of treatment response in hirsutism. *Horm. Res.* 22(4), 253–259.
54. Hatch, R., Rosenfield, R. L., Kim, M. H., and Tredway, D. (1981). Hirsutism: Implications, etiology, and management. *Am. J. Obstet. Gynecol.* 140, 815–830.
55. Azziz, R., Waggoner, W. T., Ochoa, T., Knochenhauer, E. S., and Boots, L. R. (1998). Idiopathic hirsutism: An uncommon cause of hirsutism in Alabama. *Fertil. Steril.* 70(2), 274–278.
56. Barbieri, R. L., and Ryan, K. J. (1983). Hyperandrogenism, insulin resistance, and acanthosis nigricans syndrome: A common endocrinopathy with distinct pathophysiologic features. [Review] [70 refs]. *Am. J. Obstet. Gynecol.* 147(1), 90–101.
57. Pimenta, W., Korytkowski, M., Mitrakou, A., Jenssen, T., Yki-Jarvinen, H., Dailey, G., and Gerich, J. (1995). Pancreatic beta-cell dysfunction as the primary genetic lesion in NIDDM. Evidence from studies in normal glucose-tolerant individuals with a first-degree NIDDM relative [see comments]. *JAMA* 273, 1855–1861.
58. O'Meara, N. M., Blackman, J. D., Ehrmann, D. A., Barnes, R. B., Jaspan, J. B., Rosenfield, R. L., and Polonsky, K. S. (1993). Defects in beta-cell function in functional ovarian hyperandrogenism. *J. Clin. Endocrinol. Metab.* 76, 1241–1247.
59. Dunaif, A., and Finegood, D. T. (1996). Beta-cell dysfunction independent of obesity and glucose intolerance in the polycystic ovary syndrome. *J. Clin. Endocrinol. Metab.* 81, 942–947.
60. DeFronzo, R. A., Tobin, J. D., and Andres, R. (1979). Glucose clamp technique: A method for quantifying insulin secretion and resistance. *Am. J. Physiol.* 237(3), E214-E223.
61. Bergman, R. N., Prager, R., Volund, A., and Olefsky, J. M. (1987). Equivalence of the insulin sensitivity index in man derived by the minimal model method and the euglycemic glucose clamp. *J. Clin. Invest.* 79, 790–800.
62. American Diabetic Association. (1998). Consensus Development Conference on Insulin Resistance, November 5–6, 1997. *Diabetes Care* 21, 310–314.
63. Harris, M. I., Hadden, W. C., Knowler, W. C., and Bennett, P. H. (1987). Prevalence of diabetes and impaired glucose tolerance and plasma glucose levels in U.S. population aged 20–74 yr. *Diabetes* 36, 523–534.
64. Golland, I. M., Vaughan Williams, C. A., Shalet, S. M., Million, L. H., and Elstein, M. (1989). Lack of predictive value of HbA1 for impaired glucose tolerance in polycystic ovary syndrome. *Gynecol. Endocrinol.* 3, 229–235.
65. Azziz, R., Ehrmann, D., Legro, R. S., Whitcomb, R. W., Hanley, R., Fereshetian, A. G., O'Keefe, M., and Ghazzi, M. N., PCOS/Troglitazone Study Group. (2001). Troglitazone improves ovulation and hirsutism in the polycystic ovary syndrome: A multicenter, double-blind, placebo-controlled trial. *J. Clin. Endocrinol. Metab.* 86(4), 1626–1632.
66. Harris, M. I., Eastman, R. C., Cowie, C. C., Flegal, K. M., and Eberhardt, M. S. (1997). Comparison of diabetes diagnostic categories in the U.S. population according to 1997 American Diabetes Association and 1980–1985 World Health Organization diagnostic criteria. *Diabetes Care* 20, 1859–1862.

67. Knowler, W. C., Barrett-Connor, E., Fowler, S. E., Hamman, R. F., Lachin, J. M., Walker, E. A., and Nathan, D. M., Diabetes Prevention Program Research Group. (2002). Reduction in the incidence of type 2 diabetes with lifestyle intervention or metformin. *N. Engl. J. Med.* 346, 393–403.
68. Goldzieher, J. W., and Axelrod, L. R. (1963). Clinical and biochemical features of polycystic ovarian disease. *Fertil. Steril.* 14, 631–653.
69. Elchalal, U., and Schenker, J. G. (1997). The pathophysiology of ovarian hyperstimulation syndrome—views and ideas [see comments]. [Review] [103 refs]. *Hum. Reprod.* 12(6), 1129–1137.
70. Fulghesu, A. M., Villa, P., Pavone, V., Guido, M., Apa, R., Caruso, A., Lanzone, A., Rossodivita, A., and Mancuso, S. (1997). The impact of insulin secretion on the ovarian response to exogenous gonadotropins in polycystic ovary syndrome. *J. Clin. Endocrinol. Metab.* 82(2), 644–648.
71. Dale, P. O., Tanbo, T., Haug, E., and Abyholm, T. (1998). The impact of insulin resistance on the outcome of ovulation induction with low-dose follicle stimulating hormone in women with polycystic ovary syndrome. *Hum. Reprod.* 13(3), 567–570.
72. Coulam, C. B., Annegers, J. F., and Kranz, J. S. (1983) Chronic anovulation syndrome and associated neoplasia. *Obstet. Gynecol.* 61, 403–407.
73. Smyczek-Gargya, B., and Geppert, M. (1992). Endometrial cancer associated with polycystic ovaries in young women. *Pathol. Res. Prac.* 188(7), 946–948; discussion 948–50.
74. Ho, S. P., Tan, K. T., Pang, M. W., and Ho, T. H. (1997). Endometrial hyperplasia and the risk of endometrial carcinoma. *Singapore Med. J.* 38(1), 11–15.
75. Jackson, R. L., and Dockerty, M. B. (1957). The Stein-Leventhal syndrome. Analysis of 43 cases with special reference to endometrial cancer. *Am. J. Obstet. Gynecol.* 73, 161–173.
76. Legro, R. S., Spielman, R., Urbanek, M., Driscoll, D., Strauss III, J. F., and Dunaif, A. (1998). Phenotype and genotype in polycystic ovary syndrome. *Recent Progress Horm. Res.* 53, 217–256.
77. Gambrell Jr., R. D., Bagnell, C. A., and Greenblatt, R. B. (1983). Role of estrogens and progesterone in the etiology and prevention of endometrial cancer: Review. *Am. J. Obstet. Gynecol.* 146(6), 696–707.
78. Lobo, R. A., Granger, L., Goebelsmann, U., and Mishell Jr., D. R. (1981). Elevations in unbound serum estradiol as a possible mechanism for inappropriate gonadotropin secretion in women with PCO. *J. Clin. Endocrinol. Metab.* 52, 156–158.
79. Dahlgren, E., Friberg, L. G., Johansson, S., Lindstrom, B., Oden, A., and Samsioe, G. (1991). Endometrial carcinoma; ovarian dysfunction—a risk factor in young women. *Eur. J. Obstet. Gynecol. Reprod. Biol.* 41, 143–150.
80. Aksel, S., Wentz, A. C., and Jones, G. S. (1974). Anovulatory infertility associated with adenocarcinoma and adenomatous hyperplasia of the endometrium. *Obstet. Gynecol.* 43(3), 386–391.
81. Chamlian, D. L., and Taylor, H. B. (1970). Endometrial hyperplasia in young women. *Obstet. Gynecol.* 36(5), 659–666.
82. Schildkraut, J. M., Schwingl, P. J., Bastos, E., Evanoff, A., and Hughes, C. (1996). Epithelial ovarian cancer risk among women with polycystic ovary syndrome. *Obstet. Gynecol.* 88, 554–559.
83. Anderson, K. E., Sellers, T. A., Chen, P. L., Rich, S. S., Hong, C. P., and Folsom, A. R. (1997). Association of Stein-Leventhal syndrome with the incidence of postmenopausal breast carcinoma in a large prospective study of women in Iowa. [Comment]. *Cancer* 79(3), 494–499.
84. Dahlgren, E., Johansson, S., Lindstedt, G., Knutsson, F., Oden, A., Janson, P. O., Crona, N., and Lundberg, P. A. (1992). Women with polycystic ovary syndrome wedge resected in 1956 to 1965: A long-term follow-up focusing on natural history and circulating hormones. *Fertil. Steril.* 57, 505–513.
85. Talbott, E., Clerici, A., Berga, S. L., Kuller, L., Guzick, D., Detre, K., Daniels, T., and Engberg, R. A. (1998). Adverse lipid and coronary heart disease risk profiles in young women with polycystic ovary syndrome: Results of a case-control study. *J. Clin. Epidemiol.* 51(5), 415–422.
86. Elting, M. W., Korsen, T. J., Bezemer, P. D., and Schoemaker, J. (2001). Prevalence of diabetes mellitus, hypertension and cardiac complaints in a follow-up study of a Dutch PCOS population. *Hum. Reprod.* 16(3), 556–560.
87. Sinha, R., Fisch, G., Teague, B., Tamborlane, W. V., Banyas, B., Allen, K., Savoye, M., Rieger, V., Taksali, S., Barbetta, G., Sherwin, R. S., and Caprio, S. (2002). Prevalence of impaired glucose tolerance among children and adolescents with marked obesity. [See comments.] [Erratum appears in *N. Engl. J. Med.* 2002: 346(22), 1756.] [Note: correction of dosage error in abstract.]. *N. Engl. J. Med.* 346(11), 802–810.
88. Palmert, M. R., Gordon, C. M., Kartashov, A., Legro, R. S., Emans, S. J., and Dunaif, A. (2002). Screening for abnormal glucose tolerance in adolescents with polycystic ovary syndrome. *J. Clin. Endocrinol. Metab.* 87, 1017–1023.
89. Reaven, G. M. (1988). Banting lecture 1988. Role of insulin resistance in human disease. *Diabetes* 37, 1595–1607.
90. Wild, R. A., Grubb, B., Hartz, A., Van Nort, J. J., Bachman, W., and Bartholomew, M. (1990). Clinical signs of androgen excess as risk factors for coronary artery disease. *Fertil. Steril.* 54, 255–259.
91. Dahlgren, E., Janson, P. O., Johansson, S., Lapidus, L., and Oden, A. (1992). Polycystic ovary syndrome and risk for myocardial infarction. Evaluated from a risk factor model based on a prospective population study of women. *Acta Obstetricia Gynecologica Scandinavica* 71, 599–604.
92. Birdsall, M. A., Farquhar, C. M., and White, H. D. (1997). Association between polycystic ovaries and extent of coronary artery disease in women having cardiac catheterization. *Ann. Intern. Med.* 126(1), 32–35.
93. Prelevic, G. M., Beljic, T., Balint-Peric, L., and Ginsburg, J. (1995). Cardiac flow velocity in women with the polycystic ovary syndrome. *Clin. Endocrinol.* 43, 677–681.
94. Temple, R. (1999). Are surrogate markers adequate to assess cardiovascular disease drugs? *JAMA* 282(8), 790–795.
95. Wild, R. A. (2002). Polycystic ovary syndrome: a risk for coronary artery disease? [Review] [25 refs]. *Am. J. Obstet. Gynecol.* 186(1), 35–43.
96. Korhonen, S., Hippelainen, M., Niskanen, L., Vanhala, M., and Saarikoski, S. (2001). Relationship of the metabolic syndrome and obesity to polycystic ovary syndrome: A

controlled, population-based study. *Am. J. Obstet. Gynecol.* 184(3), 289–296.

97. Balen, A. H., Conway, G. S., Kaltsas, G., Techatrasak, K., Manning, P. J., and West, C. (1995). Polycystic ovary syndrome: The spectrum of the disorder in 1741 patients. *Hum. Reprod.* 10, 2107–2111.
98. Legro, R. S., Finegood, D., and Dunaif, A. (1998). A fasting glucose to insulin ratio is a useful measure of insulin sensitivity in women with polycystic ovary syndrome. *J. Clin. Endocrinol. Metab.* 83, 2694–2698.
99. Cibula, D., Cifkova, R., Fanta, M., Poledne, R., Zivny, J., and Skibova, J. (2000). Increased risk of non-insulin dependent diabetes mellitus, arterial hypertension and coronary artery disease in perimenopausal women with a history of the polycystic ovary syndrome. *Hum. Reprod.* 15(4), 785–789.
100. Donesky, B. W., and Adashi, E. Y. (1995). Surgically induced ovulation in the polycystic ovary syndrome: wedge resection revisited in the age of laparoscopy. *Fertil. Steril.* 63, 439–463.
101. Lemieux, S., Lewis, G. F., Ben-Chetrit, A., Steiner, G., and Greenblatt, E. M. (1999). Correction of hyperandrogenemia by laparoscopic ovarian cautery in women with polycystic ovarian syndrome is not accompanied by improved insulin sensitivity or lipid-lipoprotein levels. *J. Clin. Endocrinol. Metab.* 84(11), 4278–4282.
102. Pierpoint, T., McKeigue, P. M., Isaacs, A. J., Wild, S. H., and Jacobs, H. S. (1998). Mortality of women with polycystic ovary syndrome at long-term follow-up. *J. Clin. Epidemiol.* 51(7), 581–586.
103. Wild, S., Pierpoint, T., McKeigue, P., and Jacobs, H. (2000). Cardiovascular disease in women with polycystic ovary syndrome at long-term follow-up: A retrospective cohort study. *Clin. Endocrinol.* 52(5), 595–600.
104. Gorgels, W. J., Blankenstein, M. A., Collette, H. J., and Erkelens, D. W. (1997). Urinary sex hormone excretions in premenopausal women and coronary heart disease risk: A nested case-referent study in the DOM-cohort. *J. Clin. Epidemiol.* 50, 275–281.
105. Solomon, C. G., Hu, F. B., Dunaif, A., Rich-Edwards, J. E., Stampfer, M. J., Willett, W. C., Speizer, F. E., and Manson, J. E. (2002). Menstrual cycle irregularity and risk for future cardiovascular disease. *J. Clin. Endocrinol. Metab.* 87(5), 2013–2017.
106. Solomon, C. G., Hu, F. B., Dunaif, A., Rich-Edwards, J., Willett, W. C., Hunter, D. J., Colditz, G. A., Speizer, F. E., and Manson, J. E. (2000). Long or highly irregular menstrual cycles as a marker for risk of type 2 diabetes mellitus. *JAMA* 286(19), 2421–2426.
107. Neel, J. V. (1962). Diabetes mellitus: A "thrifty" genotype rendered detrimental by "progress"? *Am. J. Hum. Genet.* 14, 353–362.
108. Lander, E. S., and Schork, N. J. (1994). Genetic dissection of complex traits [published erratum appears in *Science* 1994: 266(5184), 353]. [Review] [149 refs]. *Science* 265, 2037–2048.
109. Hales, C. N., and Barker, D. J. (1992). Type 2 (non-insulin-dependent) diabetes mellitus: The thrifty phenotype hypothesis. [See comments]. [Review] [78 refs]. *Diabetologia* 35(7), 595–601.
110. Barker, D. J., and Clark, P. M. (1997). Fetal undernutrition and disease in later life. [Review] [64 refs]. *Rev. Reprod.* 2(2), 105–112.
111. Phipps, K., Barker, D. J., Hales, C. N., Fall, C. H., Osmond, C., and Clark, P. M. (1993). Fetal growth and impaired glucose tolerance in men and women [see comments]. *Diabetologia* 36(3), 225–228.
112. Phillips, D. I., and Barker, D. J. (1997). Association between low birthweight and high resting pulse in adult life: Is the sympathetic nervous system involved in programming the insulin resistance syndrome? *Diabetic Med.* 14(8), 673–677.
113. Ibanez, L., Dimartino-Nardi, J., Potau, N., and Saenger, P. (2000). Premature adrenarche—normal variant or forerunner of adult disease? [Review] [323 refs]. *Endocr. Rev.* 21(6), 671–696.
114. Ibanez, L., Potau, N., Zampolli, M., Rique, S., Saenger, P., and Carrascosa, A. (1997). Hyperinsulinemia and decreased insulin-like growth factor-binding protein-1 are common features in prepubertal and pubertal girls with a history of premature pubarche. *J. Clin. Endocrinol. Metab.* 82(7), 2283–2288.
115. Ibanez, L., Potau, N., Virdis, R., Zampolli, M., Terzi, C., Gussinye, M., and Vicens-Calvet, E. (1993). Postpubertal outcome in girls diagnosed of premature pubarche during childhood: Increased frequency of functional ovarian hyperandrogenism. *J. Clin. Endocrinol. Metab.* 76, 1599–1603.
116. Ibanez, L., Hall, J. E., Potau, N., Carrascosa, A., Prat, N., and Taylor, A. E. (1996). Ovarian 17-hydroxyprogesterone hyperresponsiveness to gonadotropin-releasing hormone (GnRH) agonist challenge in women with polycystic ovary syndrome is not mediated by luteinizing hormone hypersecretion: Evidence from GnRH agonist and human chorionic gonadotropin stimulation testing. *J. Clin. Endocrinol. Metab.* 81(11), 4103–4107.
117. Calvo, R. M., Asuncion, M., Sancho, J., San Millan, J. L., and Escobar-Morreale, H. F. (2000). The role of the cag repeat polymorphism in the androgen receptor gene and of skewed x-chromosome inactivation, in the pathogenesis of hirsutism. *J. Clin. Endocrinol. Metab.* 85(4), 1735–1740.
118. Vuguin, P., Linder, B., Rosenfeld, R. G., Saenger, P., and DiMartino-Nardi, J. (1999). The roles of insulin sensitivity, insulin-like growth factor i (IGF-i), and IGF-binding protein-1 and -3 in the hyperandrogenism of African-American and Caribbean Hispanic girls with premature adrenarche. *J. Clin. Endocrinol. Metab.* 84(6), 2037–2042.
119. Potau, N., Ibanez, L., Rique, S., and Carrascosa, A. (1997). Pubertal changes in insulin secretion and peripheral insulin sensitivity. *Horm. Res.* 48(5), 219–226.
120. Ibanez, L., de Zegher, F., and Potau, N. (1999). Anovulation after precocious pubarche: Early markers and time course in adolescence. *J. Clin. Endocrinol. Metab.* 84(8), 2691–2695.
121. Ibanez, L., Potau, N., Francois, I., and de Zegher, F. (1998). Precocious pubarche, hyperinsulinism, and ovarian hyperandrogenism in girls: Relation to reduced fetal growth. *J. Clin. Endocrinol. Metab.* 83(10), 3558–3562.
122. Elting, M. W., Korsen, T. J., Rekers-Mombarg, L. T., and Schoemaker, J. (2000). Women with polycystic ovary syndrome gain regular menstrual cycles when ageing. *Hum. Reprod.* 15, 24–28.
123. Winters, S. J., Talbott, E., Guzick, D. S., Zborowski, J., and McHugh, K. P. (2000). Serum testosterone levels decrease in middle age in women with the polycystic ovary syndrome. *Fertil. Steril.* 73(4), 724–729.

124. Cooper, D. N., and Clayton, J. F. (1988). DNA polymorphism and the study of disease associations. [Review]. *Hum. Genet.* 78, 299–312.
125. Givens, J. R. (1988). Familial polycystic ovarian disease. [Review]. *Endocrinol. Metab. Clin. North. Am.* 17, 771–783.
126. Ferriman, D., and Purdie, A. W. (1979). The inheritance of polycystic ovarian disease and a possible relationship to premature balding. *Clin. Endocrinol.* 11, 291–300.
127. Lunde, O., Magnus, P., Sandvik, L., and Hoglo, S. (1989). Familial clustering in the polycystic ovarian syndrome. *Gynecol. Obstet. Invest.* 28, 23–30.
128. Hague, W. M., Adams, J., Reeders, S. T., Peto, T. E., and Jacobs, H. S. (1988). Familial polycystic ovaries: A genetic disease? *Clin. Endocrinol.* 29, 593–605.
129. Carey, A. H., Chan, K. L., Short, F., White, D., Williamson, R., and Franks, S. (1993). Evidence for a single gene effect causing polycystic ovaries and male pattern baldness. *Clin. Endocrinol.* 38, 653–658.
130. Norman, R. J., Masters, S., and Hague, W. (1996). Hyperinsulinemia is common in family members of women with polycystic ovary syndrome. *Fertil. Steril.* 66, 942–947.
131. Legro, R. S., Driscoll, D., Strauss III, J. F., Fox, J., and Dunaif, A. (1998). Evidence for a genetic basis for hyperandrogenemia in polycystic ovary syndrome. *Proc. Natl. Acad. Sci. USA* 95(25), 14956–14960.
132. Govind, A., Obhrai, M. S., and Clayton, R. N. (1999). Polycystic ovaries are inherited as an autosomal dominant trait: Analysis of 29 polycystic ovary syndrome and 10 control families. *J. Clin. Endocrinol. Metab.* 84(1), 38–43.
133. Kahsar-Miller, M. D., Nixon, C., Boots, L. R., Go, R. C., and Azziz, R. (2001). Prevalence of polycystic ovary syndrome (PCOS) in first-degree relatives of patients with PCOS. *Fertil. Steril.* 75(1), 53–58.
134. Hong, Y., Rice, T., Gagnon, J., Despres, J. P., Nadeau, A., Perusse, L., Bouchard, C., Leon, A. S., Skinner, J. S., Wilmore, J. H., and Rao, D. C. (1998). Familial clustering of insulin and abdominal visceral fat: The heritage family study. *J. Clin. Endocrinol. Metab.* 83(12), 4239–4245.
135. McDonough, P. G., Mahesh, V. B., and Ellegood, J. O. (1972). Steroid, follicle-stimulating hormone, and luteinizing hormone profiles in identical twins with polycystic ovaries. *Am. J. Obstet. Gynecol.* 113, 1072–1078.
136. Hutton, C., and Clark, F. (1984). Polycystic ovarian syndrome in identical twins. *Postgrad. Med. J.* 60, 64–65.
137. Jahanfar, S., Eden, J. A., Warren, P., Seppala, M., and Nguyen, T. V. (1995). A twin study of polycystic ovary syndrome. *Fertil. Steril.* 63, 478–486.
138. Legro, R. S., Bentley-Lewis, R., Driscoll, D., Wang, S. C., and Dunaif, A. (2002). Insulin resistance in the sisters of women with polycystic ovary syndrome: Association with hyperandrogenemia rather than menstrual irregularity. *J. Clin. Endocrinol. Metab.* 87(5), 2128–2133.
139. Gilling-Smith, C., Willis, D. S., Beard, R. W., and Franks, S. (1994). Hypersecretion of androstenedione by isolated thecal cells from polycystic ovaries. *J. Clin. Endocrinol. Metab.* 79, 1158–1165.
140. Nelson, V. L., Legro, R. S., Strauss, J. F. I., and McAllister, J. M. (1999). Augmented androgen production is a stable steroidogenic phenotype of propagated theca cells from polycystic ovaries. *Mol. Endocrinol.* 13, 946–957.
141. Dunaif, A., Xia, J., Book, C. B., Schenker, E., and Tang, Z. (1995). Excessive insulin receptor serine phosphorylation in cultured fibroblasts and in skeletal muscle. A potential mechanism for insulin resistance in the polycystic ovary syndrome. *J. Clin. Invest.* 96, 801–810.
142. Moran, C., Huerta, R., Conway-Myers, B. A., Hines, G. A., and Azziz, R. (2001). Altered autophosphorylation of the insulin receptor in the ovary of a woman with polycystic ovary syndrome. *Fertil. Steril.* 75(3), 625–628.
143. Legro, R. S., and Strauss, J. F. (2002). Molecular progress in infertility: Polycystic ovary syndrome. *Fertil. Steril.* 78(3), 569.
144. Gharani, N., Waterworth, D. M., Batty, S., White, D., Gilling-Smith, C., Conway, G. S., McCarthy, M., Franks, S., and Williamson, R. (1997). Association of the steroid synthesis gene CYP11a with polycystic ovary syndrome and hyperandrogenism. *Hum. Mol. Genet.* 6, 397–402.
145. Waterworth, D. M., Bennett, S. T., Gharani, N., McCarthy, M. I., Hague, S., Batty, S., White, D., Todd, J. A., Franks, S., and Williamson, R. (1997). Linkage and association of insulin gene VNTR regulatory polymorphism with polycystic ovary syndrome. *Lancet* 349, 986–990.
146. Tucci, S., Futterweit, W., Concepcion, E. S., Greenberg, D. A., Villanueva, R., Davies, T. F., and Tomer, Y. (2001). Evidence for association of polycystic ovary syndrome in Caucasian women with a marker at the insulin receptor gene locus. *J. Clin. Endocrinol. Metab.* 86(1), 446–449.
147. Urbanek, M., Legro, R. S., Driscoll, D. A., Azziz, R., Ehrmann, D. A., Norman, R. J., Strauss, J. F. I., Spielman, R. S., and Dunaif, A. (1999). Thirty-seven candidate genes for polycystic ovary sydnrome: Strongest evidence for linkage is with follistatin. *Proc. Natl. Acad. Sci. USA* 96, 8573–8578.
148. Ehrmann, D. A., Schwarz, P. E., Hara, M., Tang, X., Horikawa, Y., Imperial, J., Bell, G. I., and Cox, N. J. (2002). Relationship of calpain-10 genotype to phenotypic features of polycystic ovary syndrome. *J. Clin. Endocrinol. Metab.* 87(4), 1669–1673.
149. Hogeveen, K. N., Cousin, P., Pugeat, M., Dewailly, D., Soudan, B., and Hammond, G. L. (2002). Human sex hormone-binding globulin variants associated with hyperandrogenism and ovarian dysfunction. *J. Clin. Invest.* 109(7), 973–981.
150. Nestler, J. E. (1997). Role of hyperinsulinemia in the pathogenesis of the polycystic ovary syndrome, and its clinical implications. [Review] [91 refs]. *Sem. Reprod. Endocrinol.* 15, 111–122.
151. Rosenbaum, M., Leibel, R. L., and Hirsch, J. (1997). Obesity [see comments]. [Review] [139 refs]. *N. Engl. J. Med.* 337, 396–407.
152. Pasquali, R., Antenucci, D., Casimirri, F., Venturoli, S., Paradisi, R., Fabbri, R., Balestra, V., Melchionda, N., and Barbara, L. (1989). Clinical and hormonal characteristics of obese amenorrheic hyperandrogenic women before and after weight loss. *J. Clin. Endocrinol. Metab.* 68, 173–179.
153. Jaatinen, T. A., Anttila, L., Erkkola, R., Koskinen, P., Laippala, P., Ruutiainen, K., Scheinin, M., and Irjala, K. (1993). Hormonal responses to physical exercise in patients with polycystic ovarian syndrome. *Fertil. Steril.* 60, 262–267.
154. Braun, B., Zimmermann, M. B., and Kretchmer, N. (1995). Effects of exercise intensity on insulin sensitivity in women

with non-insulin-dependent diabetes mellitus. *J. Appl. Physiol.* 78, 300–306.

155. Givens, J. R., Andersen, R. N., Wiser, W. L., Umstot, E. S., and Fish, S. A. (1976). The effectiveness of two oral contraceptives in suppressing plasma androstenedione, testosterone, LH, and FSH, and in stimulating plasma testosterone-binding capacity in hirsute women. *Am. J. Obstet. Gynecol.* 124(4), 333–339.
156. Azziz, R., Ochoa, T. M., Bradley Jr., E. L., Potter, H. D., and Boots, L. R. (1995). Leuprolide and estrogen versus oral contraceptive pills for the treatment of hirsutism: A prospective randomized study [see comments]. *J. Clin. Endocrinol. Metab.* 80, 3406–3411.
157. Heiner, J. S., Greendale, G. A., Kawakami, A. K., Lapolt, P. S., Fisher, M., Young, D., and Judd, H. L. (1995). Comparison of a gonadotropin-releasing hormone agonist and a low-dose oral contraceptive given alone or together in the treatment of hirsutism. *J. Clin. Endocrinol. Metab.* 80(12), 3412–3418.
158. Elkind-Hirsch, K. E., Anania, C., Mack, M., and Malinak, R. (1995) Combination gonadotropin-releasing hormone agonist and oral contraceptive therapy improves treatment of hirsute women with ovarian hyperandrogenism. *Fertil. Steril.* 63, 970–978.
159. Carr, B. R., Breslau, N. A., Givens, C., Byrd, W., Barnett-Hamm, C., and Marshburn, P. B. (1995). Oral contraceptive pills, gonadotropin-releasing hormone agonists, or use in combination for treatment of hirsutism: A clinical research center study. *J. Clin. Endocrinol. Metab.* 80(4), 1169–1178.
160. Katz, M., Carr, P. J., Cohen, B. M., and Millar, R. P. (1978). Hormonal effects of wedge resection of polycystic ovaries. *Obstet. Gynecol.* 51, 437–444.
161. Greenblatt, E., and Casper, R. F. (1987). Endocrine changes after laparoscopic ovarian cautery in polycystic ovarian syndrome. *Am. J. Obstet. Gynecol.* 156, 279–285.
162. Adashi, E. Y., Rock, J. A., Guzick, D., Wentz, A. C., Jones, G. S., and Jones Jr., H. W. (1981). Fertility following bilateral ovarian wedge resection: A critical analysis of 90 consecutive cases of the polycystic ovary syndrome. *Fertil. Steril.* 36, 320–325.
163. Farquhar, C., Vandekerckhove, P., Arnot, M., and Lilford, R. (2000). Laparoscopic "drilling" by diathermy or laser for ovulation induction in anovulatory polycystic ovary syndrome. [Review] [9 refs]. Cochrane Database of Systematic Reviews [computer file] [2], CD001122.
164. Farquhar, C. M., Williamson, K., Gudex, G., Johnson, N. P., Garland, J., Sadler, L. (2002). A randomized controlled trial of laparoscopic ovarian diathermy versus gonadotropin therapy for women with clomiphene citrate-resistant polycystic ovary syndrome. *Fertil. Steril.* 78(2), 404–411.
165. Velazquez, E. M., Mendoza, S., Hamer, T., Sosa, F., and Glueck, C. J. (1994). Metformin therapy in polycystic ovary syndrome reduces hyperinsulinemia, insulin resistance, hyperandrogenemia, and systolic blood pressure, while facilitating normal menses and pregnancy. *Metabolism* 43, 647–654.
166. Nestler, J. E., and Jakubowicz, D. J. (1997). Lean women with polycystic ovary syndrome respond to insulin reduction with decreases in ovarian p450c17 alpha activity and serum androgens. *J. Clin. Endocrinol. Metab.* 82(12), 4075–4079.
167. Nestler, J. E., Jakubowicz, D. J., Evans, W. S., and Pasquali, R. (1998). Effects of metformin on spontaneous and clomiphene-induced ovulation in the polycystic ovary syndrome. *N. Engl. J. Med.* 338(26), 1876–1880.
168. Costello, M. F., and Eden, J. A. (2003). A systematic review of the reproductive system effects of metformin in patients with polycystic ovary syndrome. [Review] [60 refs]. *Fertil. Steril.* 79(1), 1–13.
169. Coetzee, E. J., and Jackson, W. P. (1979). Metformin in management of pregnant insulin-independent diabetics. *Diabetologia* 16(4), 241–245.
170. Callahan, T. L., Hall, J. E., Ettner, S. L., Christiansen, C. L., Greene, M. F., Crowley Jr., W. F. (1994). The economic impact of multiple-gestation pregnancies and the contribution of assisted-reproduction techniques to their incidence [see comments]. *N. Engl. J. Med.* 331(4), 244–249.
171. Coetzee, E. J., and Jackson, W. P. (1980). Pregnancy in established non-insulin-dependent diabetics. A five-and-a-half year study at Groote Schuur Hospital. *South African Med. J.* 58(20), 795–802.
172. Sarlis, N. J., Weil, S. J., and Nelson, L. M. (1999). Administration of metformin to a diabetic woman with extreme hyperandrogenemia of nontumoral origin: Management of infertility and prevention of inadvertent masculinization of a female fetus. *J. Clin. Endocrinol. Metab.* 84(5), 1510–1512.
173. Diamanti-Kandarakis, E., Kouli, C., Tsianateli, T., and Bergiele, A. (1998). Therapeutic effects of metformin on insulin resistance and hyperandrogenism in polycystic ovary syndrome. *Eur. J. Endocrinol.* 138(3), 269–274.
174. Velazquez, E., Acosta, A., and Mendoza, S. G. (1997). Menstrual cyclicity after metformin therapy in polycystic ovary syndrome. *Obstet. Gynecol.* 90, 392–395.
175. Vandermolen, D. T., Ratts, V. S., Evans, W. S., Stovall, D. W., Kauma, S. W., and Nestler, J. E. (2001). Metformin increases the ovulatory rate and pregnancy rate from clomiphene citrate in patients with polycystic ovary syndrome who are resistant to clomiphene citrate alone. *Fertil. Steril.* 75(2), 310–315.
176. Glueck, C. J., Phillips, H., Cameron, D., Sieve-Smith, L., and Wang, P. (2001). Continuing metformin throughout pregnancy in women with polycystic ovary syndrome appears to safely reduce first-trimester spontaneous abortion: A pilot study. *Fertil. Steril.* 75(1), 46–52.
177. Moghetti, P., Castello, R., Negri, C., Tosi, F., Perrone, F., Caputo, M., Zanolin, E., and Muggeo, M. (2000). Metformin effects on clinical features, endocrine and metabolic profiles, and insulin sensitivity in polycystic ovary syndrome: A randomized, double-blind, placebo-controlled 6-month trial, followed by open, long-term clinical evaluation. *J. Clin. Endocrinol. Metab.* 85(1), 139–146.
178. Glasier, A. F., Irvine, D. S., Wickings, E. J., Hillier, S. G., and Baird, D. T. (1989). A comparison of the effects on follicular development between clomiphene citrate, its two separate isomers and spontaneous cycles. *Hum. Reprod.* 4(3), 252–256.
179. Mikkelson, T. J., Kroboth, P. D., Cameron, W. J., Dittert, L. W., Chungi, V., and Manberg, P. J. (1986). Single-dose pharmacokinetics of clomiphene citrate in normal volunteers. *Fertil. Steril.* 46(3), 392–396.

180. Hughes, E., Collins, J., and Vandekerckhove, P. (2000). Clomiphene citrate for ovulation induction in women with oligo-amenorrhoea. [Review] [4 refs]. Cochrane Database of Systematic Reviews [computer file] [2], CD000056.
181. Shepard, M. K., Balmaceda, J. P., and Leija, C. G. (1979). Relationship of weight to successful induction of ovulation with clomiphene citrate. *Fertil. Steril.* 32(6), 641–645.
182. Lobo, R. A., Granger, L. R., Davajan, V., and Mishell Jr., D. R. (1982). An extended regimen of clomiphene citrate in women unresponsive to standard therapy. *Fertil. Steril.* 37, 762–766.
183. Lobo, R. A., Paul, W., March, C. M., Granger, L., and Kletzky, O. A. (1982). Clomiphene and dexamethasone in women unresponsive to clomiphene alone. *Obstet. Gynecol.* 60, 497–501.
184. Homburg, R., Levy, T., and Ben-Rafael, Z. (1995). A comparative prospective study of conventional regimen with chronic low-dose administration of follicle-stimulating hormone for anovulation associated with polycystic ovary syndrome. *Fertil. Steril.* 63, 729–733.
185. Ergur, A. R., Yergok, Y. Z., Ertekin, A., Kucuk, T., Mungen, E., and Tutuncu, L. (1998). Clomiphene citrate-resistant polycystic ovary syndrome. Preventing multifollicular development. *J. Reprod. Med.* 43(3), 185–190.
186. Dale, O., Tanbo, T., Lunde, O., and Abyholm, T. (1993). Ovulation induction with low-dose follicle-stimulating hormone in women with the polycystic ovary syndrome. *Acta Obstetricia Gynecologica Scandinavica* 72, 43–46.
187. Strowitzki, T., Seehaus, D., Korell, M., and Hepp, H. (1994). Low-dose follicle stimulating hormone for ovulation induction in polycystic ovary syndrome. *J. Reprod. Med.* 39, 499–503.
188. Sagle, M. A., Hamilton-Fairley, D., Kiddy, D. S., and Franks, S. (1991). A comparative, randomized study of low-dose human menopausal gonadotropin and follicle-stimulating hormone in women with polycystic ovarian syndrome. *Fertil. Steril.* 55, 56–60.
189. Nugent, D., Vandekerckhove, P., Hughes, E., Arnot, M., and Lilford, R. (2000). Gonadotrophin therapy for ovulation induction in subfertility associated with polycystic ovary syndrome. Cochrane Database of Systematic Reviews, Issue 4.
190. Bayram, N., van Wely, M., Vandekerckhove, P., Lilford, R., and van Der Veen, F. (2000). Pulsatile luteinising hormone releasing hormone for ovulation induction in subfertility associated with polycystic ovary syndrome. [Review] [4 refs]. Cochrane Database of Systematic Reviews [computer file] [2], CD000412.
191. Lee, O., Farquhar, C., Toomath, R., and Jepson, R. (2000). Spironolactone versus placebo or in combination with steroids for hirsutism and/or acne. [Review] [5 refs]. Cochrane Database of Systematic Reviews [computer file] [2], CD000194.
192. McCann, P. P., and Pegg, A. E. (1992). Ornithine decarboxylase as an enzyme target for therapy. [Review] [128 refs]. *Pharmacol. Therap.* 54(2), 195–215.
193. Eil, C., and Edelson, S. K. (1984). The use of human skin fibroblasts to obtain potency estimates of drug binding to androgen receptors. *J. Clin. Endocrinol. Metab.* 59(1), 51–55.
194. Helfer, E. L., Miller, J. L., and Rose, L. I. (1988). Side-effects of spironolactone therapy in the hirsute woman. *J. Clin. Endocrinol. Metab.* 66(1), 208–211.
195. Groves, T. D., and Corenblum, B. (1995). Spironolactone therapy during human pregnancy [letter] [see comments]. *Am. J. Obstet. Gynecol.* 172(5), 1655–1656.
196. Muhlemann, M. F., Carter, G. D., Cream, J. J., and Wise, P. (1986). Oral spironolactone: An effective treatment for acne vulgaris in women. *Br. J. Dermatol.* 115(2), 227–232.
197. Fruzzetti, F., De Lorenzo, D., Ricci, C., and Fioretti, P. (1993). Clinical and endocrine effects of flutamide in hyperandrogenic women. *Fertil. Steril.* 60, 806–813.
198. Moghetti, P., Castello, R., Magnani, C. M., Tosi, F., Negri, C., Armanini, D., Bellotti, G., and Muggeo, M. (1994). Clinical and hormonal effects of the 5 alpha-reductase inhibitor finasteride in idiopathic hirsutism. *J. Clin. Endocrinol. Metab.* 79(4), 1115–1121.
199. Fruzzetti, F., de Lorenzo, D., Parrini, D., and Ricci, C. Effects of finasteride, a 5 alpha-reductase inhibitor, on circulating androgens and gonadotropin secretion in hirsute women. *J. Clin. Endocrinol. Metab.* 79(3), 831–835.
200. Moghetti, P., Tosi, F., Tosti, A., Negri, C., Misciali, C., Perrone, F., Caputo, M., Muggeo, M., and Castello, R. (2000). Comparison of spironolactone, flutamide, and finasteride efficacy in the treatment of hirsutism: A randomized, double blind, placebo-controlled trial. *J. Clin. Endocrinol. Metab.* 85(1), 89–94.
201. Wong, I. L., Morris, R. S., Chang, L., Spahn, M. A., Stanczyk, F. Z., and Lobo, R. A. (1995). A prospective randomized trial comparing finasteride to spironolactone in the treatment of hirsute women. *J. Clin. Endocrinol. Metab.* 80, 233–238.
202. Mitwally, M. F., and Casper, R. F. (2001). Use of an aromatase inhibitor for induction of ovulation in patients with an inadequate response to clomiphene citrate. *Fertil. Steril.* 75(2), 305–309.

CHAPTER **30**

The Role of the Ovary in the Genesis of Hyperandrogenism

DENIS A. MAGOFFIN

ABSTRACT

The ovary is the principal source of circulating androstenedione and testosterone in hyperandrogenic women. The androgen-producing cells in the theca interna are increased in both functional capacity and number in the ovaries of hyperandrogenic women. The increased capacity for androgen biosynthesis is directly related to overexpression of steroidogenic enzyme and regulatory genes in the theca cells. The theca cells appear to be hyperstimulated, but the specific causes of the hyperstimulation remain uncertain. A variety of secreted hormones and growth and differentiation factors may contribute to thecal hyperstimulation, notably luteinizing hormone (LH) and insulin, but the nature of the interactions between specific regulatory molecules and their intracellular effectors is unclear. Defining the molecular mechanisms regulating ovarian androgen biosynthesis and the mechanisms by which excessive androgen concentrations cause pathology are active areas of current investigation.

THE OVARIAN CONTRIBUTION TO CIRCULATING ANDROGEN CONCENTRATIONS IN HYPERANDROGENIC WOMEN

Hyperandrogenism is a fundamental symptom of polycystic ovarian syndrome (PCOS), the leading endocrine cause of female infertility. Within the infertile population, approximately three-quarters of women with anovulatory infertility have PCOS, thus accounting for approximately one-third of women with secondary amenorrhea and approximately 90% of women with oligomenorrhea [1].

In hyperandrogenic women, there are elevated serum concentrations of androstenedione and testosterone and, in up to 50% of women, dehydroepiandrosterone sulfate [2]. There are two principal sources of circulating androgens in women: the ovary and the adrenal gland. Selective venous catheterization and the use of ovarian and adrenal stimulation and suppression tests have failed to unambiguously determine the glandular source of elevated androgen production, but the use of long-acting gonadotropin-releasing hormone agonists (Gn-RH-a) to selectively suppress ovarian androgen secretion has resolved the controversy. In the presence of Gn-RH-a treatment, ovarian androgen production is eliminated and only adrenal androgen production remains. The results of these studies indicate that the ovary is the source of excessive androstenedione and testosterone [3]. Furthermore, it appears that in hyperandrogenic women who do not have congenital adrenal hyperplasia involving 3β-hydroxysteroid dehydrogenase (3β-HSD), 21-hydroxylase, or 11-hydroxylase deficiency, up to 50% have both ovarian and adrenal hyperandrogenism and the remainder have exclusively ovarian hyperandrogenism [2, 4, 5]. Thus it is clear that the ovary is the source of excessive androstenedione and testosterone production in hyperandrogenic women and that the ovary plays a major, but not exclusive, role in female hyperandrogenism.

CHARACTERIZATION OF THE OVARIAN PHENOTYPE IN HYPERANDROGENIC WOMEN

It is clear that the source of androgens in the human ovary is the theca interna. The theca cells are capable of *de novo* production of androstenedione and dehydroepiandrosterone (DHEA). Therefore, to understand the role of the ovary in the genesis of hyperandrogenism, it is essential to understand how theca cell differentiation and function are regulated. There are two major contributing factors to the ovarian capacity for androgen secretion: (1) the total number of theca cells in the ovary and (2) the steroidogenic capability of each theca cell. In hyperandrogenic women there are not only more theca cells in the ovarian follicles, but the theca cells are also capable of producing more androgens on a per-cell basis than are theca cells from euandrogenic women.

Morphology/Thecal Hyperplasia

In hyperandrogenic women the ovary has either a polycystic morphology or less frequently, hyperthecosis. The polycystic ovary differs from the normal ovary in that there is an accumulation of small antral follicles 3 to 7 mm in diameter, forming the classic "string of pearls" morphology (Figure 30.1). Therefore, the ovaries in most hyperandrogenic women contain more small antral follicles than ovaries from regularly cycling women. Many follicles in polycystic ovaries contain a hypertrophied theca interna. Instead of the normal three to five layers of theca cells, there can be many more layers of differentiated androgen-producing cells in follicles from polycystic ovaries (Figure 30.2). Although women with hyperthecosis do not have polycystic ovaries, a similar increase in the number of theca cells is present.

The factors regulating theca cell proliferation (Table 30.1) are poorly understood. Much of what is known comes from studies in animals. Luteinizing hormone (LH) or human chorionic gonadotropin (hCG) is a potent stimulator of theca cell steroidogenesis, but long-term treatment also causes marked and selective proliferation of theca cells [6–8]. In addition to LH, evidence supports a role for growth factors in stimulating theca cell proliferation, including activin [9], epidermal growth factor (EGF)/transforming growth factor-α (TGF-α) [10, 11], insulin and insulin-like growth factor 1 (IGF-1) [12], stem cell factor (SCF)/kit ligand (KL) [13], and tumor necrosis factor-α (TNF-α) [14]. Although insulin and IGF-1 may stimulate human theca proliferation *in vitro* [15], the degree to which these findings are applicable to healthy women remains to be proven. Whether any of these regulatory mechanisms plays a significant role in ovarian hyperandrogenism and PCOS is an area for future investigation.

Overexpression of Steroidogenic Enzyme and Regulatory Genes

Not only is there an increase in the number of theca cells in polycystic ovaries (see Figure 30.2), but the theca cells overexpress messenger ribonucleic acid (mRNAs) for LH

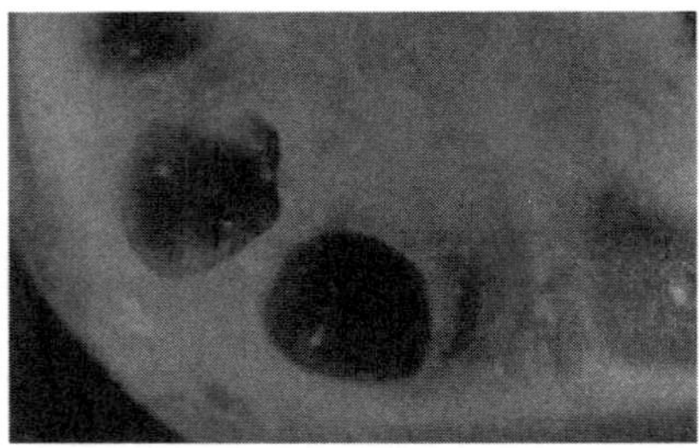

FIGURE 30.1 Morphology of the polycystic ovary. Polycystic ovaries are characterized by accumulation of numerous subcapsular 5 to 7 mm follicles in a classic "string of pearls" pattern. Also characteristic of polycystic ovaries is the thickened and fibrous capsule and stroma. Note the absence of large antral developing follicles.

TABLE 30.1 Regulatory Factors Stimulating Theca Cell Proliferation

Factor	Origin	Mode of Regulation
LH	Pituitary	Endocrine
Insulin	Pancreas	Endocrine
IGF-1	Granulosa cells	Paracrine
Activin	Granulosa cells	Paracrine
TGF-α	Theca cells	Autocrine
SCF	Granulosa cells	Paracrine
TNF-α	Oocyte/Granulosa cells/ Resident Ovarian Macrophages	Paracrine

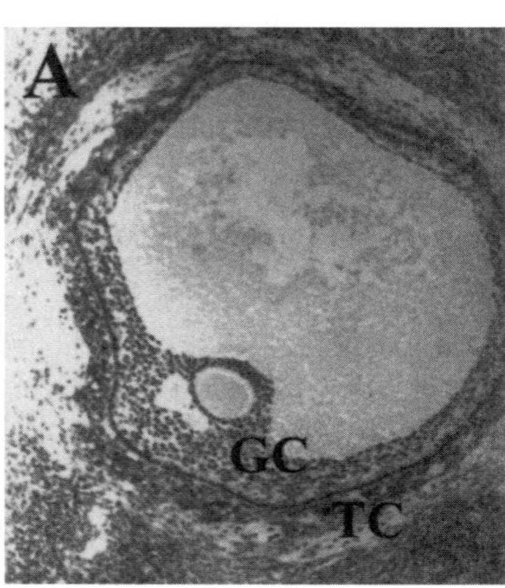

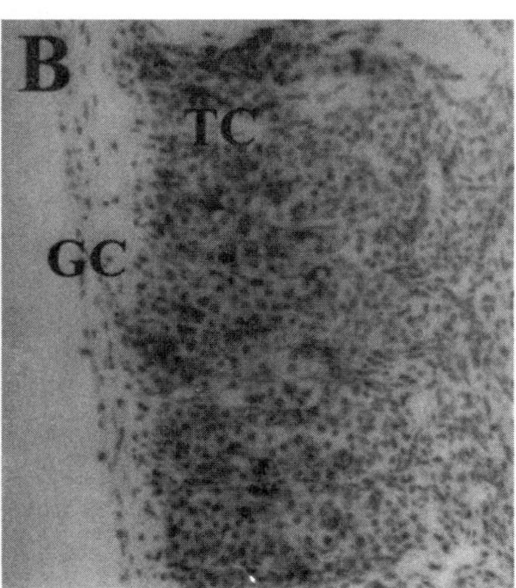

FIGURE 30.2 Hypertrophy of the theca interna in polycystic ovaries. **A,** In follicles from regularly cycling ovaries, the theca interna is composed of three to four layers of cells (TC) adjacent to the basal lamina. The granulosa layer (GC) in this healthy developing follicle is four to five cell layers thick. **B,** In follicles from polycystic ovaries, the theca interna consists of more than 10 layers of cells with the capacity to produce androgens. The darkly staining cells (TC) are immunohistochemically stained for CYP17, the key enzyme required for androgen biosynthesis. The granulosa cell layer (GC) consists of three to four layers of cells.

receptor, steroid acute regulatory protein (StAR), CYP17, and CYP11A on a per-cell basis compared with theca from control women [16]. When theca cells are removed from their follicular microenvironment and are cultured *in vitro*, the overexpression of these key mRNAs persists and the cells continue to exhibit increased 17α-hydroxylase activity [17]. These data suggest that the theca cells are hyperstimulated in PCOS relative to regularly cycling women. The observation that theca cells from polycystic ovaries have an increased rate of CYP17 gene transcription [18] indicates that the stimulus regulates not only acute androgen production but also theca cell differentiation. There are a host of regulatory molecules with the potential to contribute to hyperstimulation of theca cell differentiation and androgen production in hyperandrogenic women.

REGULATION OF THECA CELL DIFFERENTIATION AND STEROIDOGENESIS

Luteinizing Hormone

The myriad *in vivo* and *in vitro* studies demonstrating the stimulatory effects of LH on theca cells reveal that LH is the principal hormone regulating theca cell differentiation and function [19, 20]. The trophic actions of LH on theca cell steroidogenesis are mediated through activation of the cyclic adenosine monophosphate (cAMP)/protein kinase A (PKA) signaling pathway. Studies in isolated rat theca-interstitial cells (TICs) have shown that activation of either type I or type II PKA stimulates expression of steroidogenic enzyme mRNAs [21]. LH stimulates the expression of cholesterol side-chain cleavage cytochrome P450 (CYP11A), 3β-hydroxysteroid dehydrogenase (3β-HSD), and 17α-hydroxylase/C_{17-20} lyase cytochrome P450 (CYP17) mRNAs and translation of the mRNAs into functional proteins [22–24]. Although there is evidence that LH also stimulates inositol phosphate formation in granulosa [25, 26] and luteal cells [27, 28], LH has not been shown to activate the inositol phosphate signaling pathway in theca cells. Evidence demonstrates that direct activation of PKC with other ligands such as angiotensin II sensitizes TIC to LH [29] and that depletion of PKC with long-term phorbol ester treatment inhibits the ability of LH to stimulate steroidogenesis [30]; however, the role, if any, of PKC in mediating the effects of LH on theca cell steroidogenesis remains unclear. LH stimulates marked increases in progesterone and androgen production in differentiated theca cells [19, 31] from all mammalian species, including rats, mice, sheep, swine, cows, horses, nonhuman primates, and women. Thus LH is a key regulator that must be accounted for when attempting to understand the genesis of ovarian hyperandrogenism.

TABLE 30.2 Regulatory Factors Affecting Ovarian Androgen Production

Factor	Origin	Mode of Regulation
Inhibitory regulators		
Activin	Granulosa cells	Paracrine
TGF-α	Theca cells	Autocrine
TGF-β	Granulosa/Theca cells	Paracrine/Autocrine
bFGF	Granulosa cells	Paracrine
HGF	Theca cells	Autocrine
KGF	Theca cells	Autocrine
TNF-α	Oocyte/Granulosa cells/ Resident Ovarian Macrophages	Paracrine
IL-1β	Granulosa cells/Resident Ovarian Macrophages	Paracrine
Stimulatory regulators		
LH	Pituitary	Endocrine
Insulin	Pancreas	Endocrine
IGF-1	Granulosa cells	Paracrine
Inhibin	Granulosa cells	Paracrine
NGF	Theca cells	Autocrine
GDF-9	Oocyte	Paracrine

Intraovarian Modulators

In addition to the primary effects of LH, an increasing number of stimulatory and inhibitory factors (Table 30.2) can modulate the steroidogenic capacity of the theca cells (for review, see [31, 32]). Of the modulatory factors known to influence ovarian thecal androgen biosynthesis, a relatively small number have been investigated with respect to their potential roles in PCOS.

The Transforming Growth Factor Family

Members of the transforming growth factor-β (TGF-β family of proteins, including TGF-β inhibin, activin, bone morphogenetic protein-4 (BMP-4), and growth differentiation factor-9 (GDF-9), as well as related molecules such as follistatin, have received considerable attention with respect to the genesis of ovarian hyperandrogenism. Both TGF-β1 and TGF-β2 are produced within the human ovary. TGF-β1 is present in both theca and granulosa cells, whereas TGF-β2 has been localized only in theca cells [33]. Each of the inhibin subunits (α, $β_A$, and $β_B$) are produced in human follicles [34, 35]; however, there is no evidence that follistatin is produced in the ovary [34]. GDF-9 is produced exclusively by the oocyte [36].

In vitro studies demonstrated that TGF-β inhibits StAR protein expression in human theca tumor cells [37] and blocks LH-dependent androgen production in rat theca cells [38] through a direct noncompetitive inhibition of

CYP17 activity [39]. Activin is also an inhibitor of thecal androgen production [40, 41] and CYP17 mRNA expression [41], whereas inhibin is a stimulator of thecal androgen production [41,42] and CYP17 mRNA expression [41]. BMP-4 inhibits androgen production and CYP17 mRNA expression in human theca tumor cells [43]. GDF-9 promotes the growth of theca cells and has been reported to inhibit androgen production [44]. Thus the members of the TGF-β family can have direct stimulatory and inhibitory effects on thecal androgen biosynthesis independent of their effects on gonadotropin secretion.

There is general agreement that circulating inhibin B concentrations are not abnormal in women with PCOS as a group [45–47]; however, it appears that lean women with PCOS may have increased circulating inhibin B concentrations, whereas obese women with PCOS do not [48]. This is apparently related to a negative effect of obesity on inhibin B concentrations independent of PCOS per se [49]. Furthermore, the pulsatile pattern of inhibin B secretion present in regularly cycling women appears to be absent in PCOS [50]. Differences in circulating activin A concentrations are controversial: one group reporting a decrease [46] and another no change [51]. A similar pattern was found in follicular fluid. Neither inhibin B nor activin A were altered in follicles from PCOS; however, inhibin A decreased in PCOS follicles compared to similar-sized follicles in regularly cycling women [52]. Follistatin appears to be increased in PCOS [46, 51] regardless of whether the women were lean or obese [51]. The increased circulating follistatin concentrations are not reflected in the follicular fluid, where there were comparable concentrations in control and PCOS follicles [53]. Taken together, these data indicate that differences in inhibin and activin are not likely to play a major role in causing ovarian hyperandrogenism.

There is evidence that GDF-9 is decreased in polycystic ovaries [36]. The significance of this finding remains to be defined because of the conflicting effects of GDF-9 relative to the PCOS phenotype. The possibility exists that GDF-9 may have stage-dependent effects on theca cell proliferation and differentiation, with proliferation predominating in preantral follicles and inhibition of androgen biosynthesis dominating in small antral follicles. A decrease in GDF-9 would be consistent with hyperandrogenism in small antral follicles, but is inconsistent with the theca hypertrophy that is present in many follicles in polycystic ovaries. Further research is necessary to determine if GDF-9 plays an important role in the genesis of ovarian hyperandrogenism.

Transforming Growth Factor-α

Transforming growth factor-α (TGF-α) is an inhibitor of thecal androgen biosynthesis that is present in both theca cells and granulosa cells in growing human follicles [54]. Potentially, abnormal production of TGF-α could play a role in ovarian hyperandrogenism. The concentrations of TGF-α in follicular fluid are variable but always less than 1 ng/mL [55–57]. There are no differences in TGF-α concentrations in follicular fluid from polycystic ovaries, and the production of TGF-α *in vitro* is comparable between tissues from polycystic ovaries and control ovaries [56]. Therefore, the evidence does not support a role for abnormal TGF-α production in the genesis of ovarian hyperandrogenism.

Tumor Necrosis Factor-α

In addition to growth factors produced by ovarian cells, it has become apparent that immune system cells also play a regulatory role during follicle development and ovulation. Tumor necrosis factor-α (TNF-α) is a well-characterized cytokine that exerts potent inhibitory effects on LH-dependent androgen production by theca cells [58]. Studies have shown that TNF-α is not present in theca cells, and it is uncertain as to whether granulosa cells synthesize TNF-α; however, TNF-α is produced by oocytes and resident ovarian macrophages [59]. Serum concentrations of TNF-α increase with increasing obesity in both control and women with PCOS [60]. When matched for weight, serum TNF-α concentrations are elevated in PCOS. In contrast, there are no differences in follicular fluid TNF-α concentrations between women with PCOS and regularly cycling controls [61]. TNF-α secretion by human ovarian tissues *in vitro* was undetectable [61]. Thus the evidence does not support a role for intra-ovarian effects of TNF-α in the genesis of ovarian hyperandrogenism.

Insulin

The most actively studied regulator of ovarian androgen biosynthesis related to ovarian hyperandrogenism and PCOS is insulin. The observation that insulin resistance is associated with the androgen excess of PCOS [62] has prompted researchers to seek the mechanism by which insulin regulates thecal androgen biosynthesis. There is a moderate compensatory increase in circulating insulin levels when a woman is insulin resistant. Although blood glucose concentrations are controlled within normal levels, the increased fasting insulin-to-glucose ratio has been shown to correlate well with the degree of insulin resistance in women with PCOS [63].

A significant body of evidence supports a causal link between the modest hyperinsulinemia and the increased ovarian androgen synthesis characteristic of PCOS [64, 65]. There is an abundance of receptors for insulin and insulin-like growth factors in the human ovary [66–69], providing a basis for the hypothesis that insulin excess can contribute to excessive ovarian androgen production. In addition to the enhanced basal androgen secretion by cultured theca cells from polycystic ovaries [70, 71], the stimulatory effect of insulin on thecal steroidogenesis is also augmented in polycystic ovaries [72], suggesting an ovarian hyperresponsiveness to insulin action in PCOS. Thus there is a paradox: How can thecal androgen production be hyperresponsive to insulin in an insulin-resistant woman [73]? If a woman is insulin resistant, the compensatory hyperinsulinemia should only be sufficient to compensate for the insulin resistance, not hyperstimulate the ovary.

One hypothesis proposed to explain the apparent paradox is that the excess insulin produced as compensation for peripheral insulin resistance exerts its ovarian effect by activating the type 1 IGF receptor that is present in theca cells [68]. The evidence does not support this hypothesis, however, because the effects of insulin on thecal androgen synthesis in PCOS are mediated by the insulin receptor [74] and blocking the type 1 IGF receptor with neutralizing antibodies failed to prevent insulin stimulation of androgen production [75]. Although insulin is known to bind to and activate type 1 IGF receptors, the binding affinity is considerably lower than for its cognate receptor [76]. Consequently, supraphysiologic concentrations of insulin are required to initiate signaling through the type 1 IGF receptor. In most women with insulin resistance and PCOS, the modest increase in insulin concentrations is too small to cause a significant activation of the type 1 IGF receptor [77].

It remains unclear whether hyperinsulinemia per se contributes to ovarian hyperandrogenism or if alterations in ovarian insulin signaling play a role (Figure 30.3). The finding that inhibition of insulin secretion by treatment with diazoxide caused a decline in circulating ovarian androgen concentrations supports the conclusion that the hyperinsulinemia directly stimulates androgen concentrations [78]. Thus it appears that the increased circulating insulin of insulin-resistant women can act directly through ovarian insulin receptors to enhance the ability of endogenous LH to stimulate androgen biosynthesis by the theca cells.

Clinical studies using insulin-sensitizing agents such as troglitazone [79] and metformin [80] have demonstrated the importance of insulin resistance to the genesis of PCOS. The disubstituted biguanide, metformin, reduces fasting plasma glucose levels and increases oral glucose tolerance in PCOS [81], decreases plasma insulin and improves insulin sensitivity in type 2 diabetic patients and their first-degree relatives [82], and improves insulin-stimulated glucose transport in skeletal muscle from patients with type 2 diabetes [83]. Most recent studies agree that metformin improves peripheral insulin sensitivity, attenuates hyperandrogenemia in both lean and obese women with PCOS, and can restore menses in approximately one-third of previously amenorrheic women [84–86].

Troglitazone, a member of the thiazolidenedione class of insulin-sensitizing agents, is a ligand for the nuclear peroxisomal proliferator-activated receptor-γ (PPAR-γ) that is

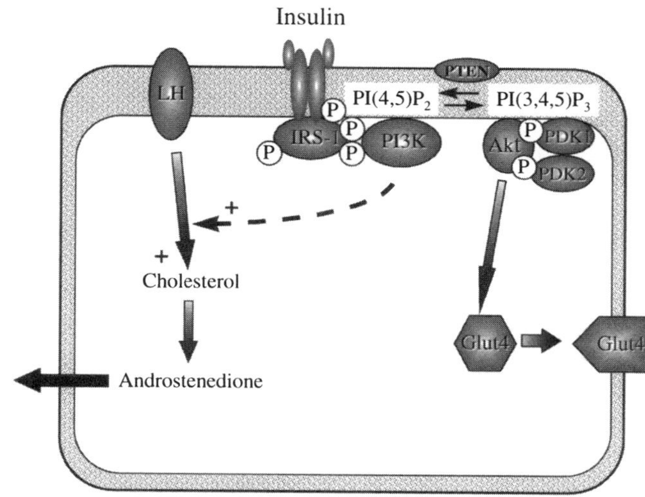

FIGURE 30.3 Insulin regulation of glucose transport and androgen production in ovarian theca cells. Insulin stimulation of glucose transport is mediated by an intracellular signaling cascade involving insulin-receptor association with and phosphorylation of insulin-receptor substrates (IRS-1), recruitment of phosphatidylinositol-3-kinase (PI3-K) to the membrane and generation of phosphatidylinositol trisphosphate. Activation of the protein kinase Akt leads to translocation of glucose transporter 4 (glut 4) to the plasma membrane to facilitate glucose uptake into the cell. Insulin regulation of androgen production appears to involve the same proximal insulin signaling steps up to the recruitment of PI3-K. By mechanisms yet unclear, PI3-K activates effector molecules that converge with the LH/cAMP signaling pathway to augment the conversion of cholesterol to androstenedione. The apparent divergence of the intracellular signaling pathways may explain why androgen production can be hyperstimulated in theca cells from insulin-resistant women.

involved in stimulating transcription of factors that assist in glucose disposal in skeletal muscle [87]. In subjects with type 2 diabetes, troglitazone decreases hyperglycemia [88, 89] and improves glucose uptake in skeletal muscle [90]. Troglitazone treatment in women with PCOS dramatically reduced androgen excess and insulin resistance, while improving both metabolic and reproductive endocrine dysfunction [79, 91]. In addition to its effects on insulin sensitivity, troglitazone—but not metformin—has direct inhibitory effects on thecal androgen production that do not appear to involve activation of PPAR-γ [92].

Conversely, therapies designed to reduce excessive androgen concentrations modestly improved but did not abolish the insulin resistance. No significant improvement in peripheral insulin resistance occurred following long-term treatment of women with PCOS with gonadotropin-releasing hormone analogs [93–95]. Similarly, antiandrogens were unable to normalize insulin sensitivity in women with PCOS [85, 96, 97]. Thus amelioration of hyperandrogenemia has little effect on insulin resistance, implying that hyperandrogenemia is secondary to the hyperinsulinemia that appears to be a fundamental metabolic problem in a significant proportion of women with PCOS.

Obesity-Related Factors

Leptin

Obesity is commonly associated with hyperandrogenism in infertile women. The observation that leptin plays an important role in fertility regulation in the mouse led to speculation regarding its potential role in promoting hyperandrogenism in women [98]. A strong positive correlation exists between circulating leptin concentrations and the amount of body fat in humans [99–102], demonstrating that obesity is associated with high circulating leptin levels. The concentration of leptin in human follicular fluid is equivalent to that in the plasma, demonstrating that the ovarian follicle is exposed to high leptin concentrations in obese women; however, there is less leptin binding in follicular fluid than in plasma [103]. Analysis of the circulating leptin concentrations in women with PCOS reveals that the leptin in PCOS is not altered apart from that caused by obesity alone [104].

Multiple splice variants of leptin receptor mRNA are expressed in the human ovary, providing the basis for direct regulation of ovarian steroidogenesis by leptin [98, 105, 106]. In human theca cells, leptin alone has no effect on LH-stimulated androstenedione production [105], but at physiologic concentrations leptin inhibits the synergistic effect IGF-1 has on LH-stimulated androstenedione production. There are also direct effects of leptin in human granulosa cells [105]. Although leptin has no effect on basal estradiol production and follicle-stimulating hormone (FSH)-stimulated aromatase activity, physiologic concentrations of leptin commonly found in obese women completely blocked the ability of IGF-1 to augment FSH-stimulated estradiol production. The inhibitory effect of leptin was specific to aromatase activity because there was no effect on progesterone production [105].

Taken together, the available data demonstrate direct inhibitory actions of leptin on both androstenedione synthesis by the theca cells and aromatization of androstenedione by granulosa cells. In obese women with PCOS this combination of effects may contribute to ovarian hyperandrogenism, but leptin does not appear to be a primary cause of ovarian hyperandrogenism.

Resistin

Resistin is a recently discovered member of a family of proteins with tissue-specific expression patterns [107]. Although two other members of this family known as resistin-like molecules (RELM) and found in inflamatory zone (FIZZ) proteins have been described, resistin is the only family member secreted by adipocytes. In mice, resistin has been linked to insulin resistance. Administration of recombinant resistin impaired insulin action and glucose tolerance, while administration of antiresistin antibodies improved insulin action [108]. Because of the potential role of resistin in regulating insulin sensitivity, it is reasonable to speculate that resistin may play a role in ovarian hyperandrogenism.

A human homolog of resistin has been detected in fat tissue [107]. The human resistin gene shows 53% homology to murine resistin and lies on chromosome 19p13.3, a region not previously implicated in the susceptibility to obesity, insulin resistance, or diabetes. The evidence linking resistin to type 2 diabetes in humans is inconsistent. Two groups were unable to detect significant levels of resistin mRNA in human adipose tissue [109, 110], and a third study indicated no clear relationship between resistin mRNA expression and adiposity [111]. In contrast, a recent study has convincingly demonstrated that resistin is localized in isolated adipose cells and that both resistin mRNA and protein are expressed and secreted by human adipose tissue [112]. The role of resistin in ovarian hyperandrogenism remains to be investigated.

CONCLUSION

Convincing evidence shows that the ovary contributes most circulating androstenedione and testosterone in hyperandrogenic women and that ovarian hyperandrogenism is a cause of infertility and polycystic ovarian syndrome. A considerable amount of information is known about mechanisms regulating ovarian androgen production from both an endocrine and intraovarian perspective, but few of the regulators examined are likely to play a significant role in causing ovarian hyperandrogenism.

The details of the interactions between individual regulatory molecules and their signaling systems are unclear. Furthermore, it is highly likely that additional, presently unrecognized, hormones and effector molecules play key roles in regulating ovarian androgen biosynthesis.

Although there is a considerable amount of information concerning the mechanisms regulating ovarian androgen biosynthesis, the mechanisms by which excessive concentrations of androgens cause their associated pathologies are essentially unknown. Thus there is fertile ground for future research into the causes and consequences of ovarian hyperandrogenism.

References

1. Franks, S., and White, D. M. (1993). Prevalence of and etiological factors in polycystic ovarian syndrome. *Ann. N.Y. Acad. Sci.* 687, 112–114.
2. Hoffman, D. I., Klove, K., and Lobo, R. A. (1984). The prevalence and significance of elevated dehydroepiandrosterone sulfate levels in anovulatory women. *Fertil. Steril.* 42, 76–81.

3. Chang, R. J., Laufer, L. R., Meldrum, D. R., DeFazio, J., Lu, J. K., Vale, W. W., Rivier, J. E., and Judd, H. L. (1983). Steroid secretion in polycystic ovarian disease after ovarian suppression by a long-acting gonadotrpoin-releasing hormone agonist. *J. Clin. Endocrinol. Metab.* 56, 897–903.
4. Rittmaster, R. S., and Thompson, D. L. (1990). Effect of leuprolide and dexamethasone on hair growth and hormone levels in hirsute women: The relative importance of the ovary and the adrenal in the pathogenesis of hirsutism. *J. Clin. Endocrinol. Metab.* 70, 1096–1102.
5. Siegel, S. F., Finegold, D. N., Lanes, R., and Lee, P. A. (1990). ACTH stimulation tests and plasma dehydroepiandrosterone sulfate levels in women with hirsutism. *N. Engl. J. Med.* 323, 849–854.
6. Selye, H., Collip, J. B., and Thomson, D. L. (1933). On the effect of the anterior pituitary-like hormone on the ovary of the hypophysectomized rat. *Endocrinology* 17, 494–500.
7. Selye, H., and Collip, J. B. (1933). Production of exclusively thecal luteinization and continuous oestrus with anterior-pituitary-like hormone. *Proc. Soc. Exp. Biol. Med.* 30, 647–649.
8. Selye, H., Collip, J. B., and Thomson, D. L. (1933). Further studies on production of thecal luteinization by means of A.P.L. *Proc. Soc. Exp. Biol. Med.* 30, 780–783.
9. Duleba, A. J., Pehlivan, T., Carbone, R., and Spaczynski, R. Z. (2001). Activin stimulates proliferation of rat ovarian theca-interstitial cells. *Biol. Reprod.* 65, 704–709.
10. Roberts, A. J., and Skinner, M. K. (1991). Transforming growth factor-α and -β differentially regulate growth and steriodogenisis of bovine thecal cells during antral follicle development. *Endocrinology* 129, 2041–2048.
11. Pehlivan, T., Mansour, A., Spaczynski, R. Z., and Duleba, A. J. (2001). Effects of transforming frowth factors-α and -β on proliferation and apoptosis of rat theca-interstitial cells. *J. Endocrinol.* 170, 639–645.
12. Duleba, A. J., Spaczynski, R. Z., Olive, D. L., and Behrman, H. R. (1997). Effecs of insulin and insulin-like growth factors on proliferation of rat ovarian theca-interstitial cells. *Biol. Reprod.* 56, 891–897.
13. Parrott, J. A., and Skinner, M. K. (1997). Direct actions of kit-ligand on theca cell growth and differentiation during follicle development. *Endocrinology* 138, 3819–3827.
14. Spaczynski, R. Z., Arici, A., and Duleba, A. J. (1999). Tumor necrosis factor-α stimulates proliferation of rat ovarian theca-interstitial cells. *Biol. Reprod.* 61, 993–998.
15. Duleba, A. J., Spaczynski, R. Z., and Olive, D. L. (1998). Insulin and insulin-like growth factor I stimulate the proliferation of human ovarian theca-interstitial cells. *Fertil. Steril.* 69, 335–340.
16. Jakimiuk, A. J., Weitsman, S. R., Navab, A., and Magoffin, D. A. (2001). Luteinizing hormone receptor, steroidogenesis acute regulatory protein and steroidogenic enzyme messenger ribonucleic acids are over-expressed in theca and granulosa cells from polycystic ovaries. *J. Clin. Endocrinol. Metab.* 86, 1318–1323.
17. Nelson, V. L., Legro, R. S., Strauss III, J. F., and McAllister, J. M. (1999). Augmented androgen production is a stable steroidogenic phenotype of propagated theca cells from polycystic ovaries. *Mol. Endocrinol.* 13, 946–957.
18. Wickenheisser, J. K., Quinn, P. G., Nelson, V. L., Legro, R. S., Strauss III, J. F., and McAllister, J. M. (2000). Differential activity of the cytochrome P450 17α-hydroxylase and steroidogenic acute regulatory protein gene promoters in normal and polycystic ovary syndrome theca cells. *J. Clin. Endocrinol. Metab.* 58, 2304–2311.
19. Erickson, G. F., Magoffin, D. A., Dyer, C. A., and Hofeditz, C. (1985). The ovarian androgen producing cells: a review of structure/function relationships. *Endocr. Rev.* 6, 371–399.
20. Magoffin, D. A. (1991). Regulation of differentiated functions in ovarian theca cells. *Sem. Reprod. Endocrinol.* 9, 321–331.
21. Magoffin, D. A. (1989). Evidence that luteinizing hormone-stimulated differentiation of purified ovarian thecal-interstitial cells is mediated by both type I and type II adenosine 3′,5′-monophosphate-dependent protein kinases. *Endocrinology* 125, 1464–1473.
22. Magoffin, D. A., and Weitsman, S. R. (1993). Differentiation of ovarian theca-interstitial cells in vitro: Regulation of 17α-hydroxylase messenger ribonucleic acid expression by luteinizing hormone and insulin-like growth factor-I. *Endocrinology* 132, 1945–1951.
23. Magoffin, D. A., and Weitsman, S. R. (1993). Insulin-like growth factor-I stimulates the expression of 3β-hydroxysteroid dehydrogenase messenger ribonucleic acid in ovarian theca-interstitial cells. *Biol. Reprod.* 48, 1166–1173.
24. Magoffin, D. A., and Weitsman, S. R. (1993). Effect of insulin-like growth factor-I on cholesterol side chain cleavage cytochrome P450 messenger ribonucleic acid expression in ovarian theca-interstitial cells stimulated to differentiate in vitro. *Mol. Cell. Endocrinol.* 96, 45–51.
25. Davis, J. S., Weakland, L. L., West, L. A., and Farese, R. V. (1986). Luteinizing hormone stimulates the formation of inositol triphosphate and cyclic AMP in rat granulosa cells. *Biochem. J.* 238, 597–604.
26. Dimino, M. J., Snitzer, J., and Brown, K. M. (1987). Inositol phosphates accumulation in ovarian granulosa after stimulation by luteinizing hormone. *Biol. Reprod.* 37, 1129–1134.
27. Allen, R. B., Su, H. C., Snitzer, J., and Dimino, M. J. (1988). Rapid decreases in phosphatidylinositol in isolated luteal plasma membranes after stimulation by luteinizing hormone. *Biol. Reprod.* 38, 79–83.
28. Davis, J. S., Weakland, L. L., Farese, R. V., and West, L. A. (1987). Luteinizing hormone increases inositol triphosphate and cytosolic free Ca^{2+} in isolated bovine luteal cells. *J. Biol. Chem.* 262, 8515–8521.
29. Magoffin, D. A. (1991). LH stimulation of ovarian thecal-interstitial cell differentiation: Sensitizing effect of angiotensin II. In *Signaling Mechanisms and Gene Expression in the Ovary*, ed. G. Gibori, 417–422. Norwell, MA: Serono Symposia.
30. Hofeditz, C., Magoffin, D. A., and Erickson, G. F. (1988). Evidence for protein kinase C regulation of ovarian theca-interstitial cell androgen biosynthesis. *Biol. Reprod.* 39, 873–881.
31. Magoffin, D. A. (2001). The ovarian androgen-producing cells: A 2001 perspective. *Rev. Endocr. Metab. Dis.* 3, 47–53.
32. Zachow, R. J., Weitsman, S. R., and Magoffin, D. A. (1996). Ovarian androgen biosynthesis: Autocrine/paracrine

regulation. In *Androgen Excess Disorders in Women*, eds. R. Azziz, D. Dewailly, and J. E. Nestler. Philadelphia: Lippincott-Raven 333–345.

33. Chegini, N., and Flanders, K. C. (1992). Presence of transforming growth factor-β and their selective cellular localization in human ovarian tissue of various reproductive stages. *Endocrinology* 130, 1707–1715.
34. Roberts, V. J., Barth, S., El-Roeiy, A., and Yen, S. S. C. (1994). Expression of inhibin/activin system messenger ribonucleic acids and proteins in ovarian follicles from women with polycystic ovarian syndrome. *J. Clin. Endocrinol. Metab.* 79, 1434–1439.
35. Pangas, S. A., Rademaker, A. W., Fishman, D. A., and Woodruff, T. K. (2002). Localization of the activin signal transduction components in normal human ovarian follicles: Implications for autocrine and paracrine signaling in the ovary. *J. Clin. Endocrinol. Metab.* 87, 2644–2657.
36. Teixeira Filho, F. L., Baracat, E. C., Lee, T. H., Suh, C. S., Matsui, M., Chang, R. J., Shimasaki, S., and Erickson, G. F. (2002). Aberrant expression of growth differentiation factor-9 in oocytes of women with polycystic ovary syndrome. *J. Clin. Endocrinol. Metab.* 87, 1337–1344.
37. Attia, G. R., Dooley, C. A., Rainey, W. E., and Carr, B. R. (2000). Transforming growth factor beta inhibits steroidogenic acute regulatory (StAR) protein expression in human ovarian thecal cells. *Mol. Cell. Endocrinol.* 170, 123–129.
38. Hernandez, E. R., Hurwitz, A., Payne, D. W., Dharmarajan, A. M., Purchio, A. F., and Adashi, E. Y. (1990). Transforming growth factor-β1 inhibits ovarian androgen production: Gene expression, cellular localization, mechanism(s), and site(s) of action. *Endocrinology* 127, 2804–2811.
39. Fournet, N., Weitsman, S. R., Zachow, R. J., and Magoffin, D. A. (1996). Transforming growth factor-β inhibits ovarian 17α-hydroxylase activity by a direct non-competitive mechanism. *Endocrinology* 137, 166–174.
40. Hillier, S. G., Yong, E. L., Illingworth, P. J., Baird, D. T., Schwall, R. H., and Mason, A. J. (1991). Effect of recombinant activin on androgen synthesis in cultured human thecal cells. *J. Clin. Endocrinol. Metab.* 72, 1206–1211.
41. Sawetawan, C., Carr, B. R., McGee, E. A., Bird, I. M., Hong, T. L., and Rainey, W. E. (1996). Inhibin and activin differentially regulate androgen production and 17α-hydroxylase expression in human ovarian thecal-like tumor cells. *J. Endocrinol.* 148, 213–221.
42. Hillier, S. G., Yong, E. L., Illingworth, P. J., Baird, D. T., Schwall, R. H., and Mason, A. J. (1991). Effect of recombinant inhibin on androgen synthesis in cultured human thecal cells. *Mol. Cell. Endocrinol.* 75, R1–R6.
43. Dooley, C. A., Attia, G. R., Rainey, W. E., and Carr, B. R. (2000). Bone morphogenetic protein inhibits ovarian androgen production. *J. Clin. Endocrinol. Metab.* 85, 3331–3337.
44. Yamamoto, N., Christenson, L. K., McAllister, J. M., and Strauss III, J. F. (2002). Growth differentiation factor-9 inhibits 3′5′-adenosine monophosphate-stimulated steroidogenesis in human granulosa and theca cells. *J. Clin. Endocrinol. Metab.* 87, 2849–2856.
45. Lambert-Messerlain, G. M., Hall, J. E., Sluss, P. M., Taylor, A. E., Martin, K. A., Groome, N. P., Crowley, W. F., and Schneyer, A. L. (1994). Relatively low levels of dimeric inhibin circulate in men and women with polycystic ovarian syndrome using a specific two-site enzyme-linked immunosorbent assay. *J. Clin. Endocrinol. Metab.* 79, 45–50.
46. Norman, R. J., Milner, C. R., Groome, N. P., and Robertson, D. M. (2001). Circulating follistatin concentrations are higher and activin concentrations are lower in polycystic ovarian syndrome. *Hum. Reprod.* 16, 668–672.
47. Laven, J. S., Imani, B., Eijkemans, M. J., De Jong, F. H., and Fauser, B. C. (2001). Absent biologically relevant associations between serum inhibin B concentrations and characteristics of polycystic ovary syndrome in normogonadotrophic anovulatory infertility. *Hum. Reprod.* 16, 1359–1364.
48. Pigny, P., Cortet-Rudelli, C., Decanter, C., Deroubaix, D., Soudan, B., Duhamel, A., and Dewailly, D. (2000). Serum levels of inhibins are differentially altered in patients with polycystic ovary syndrome: Effects of being overwieght and relevance to hyperandrogenism. *Fertil. Steril.* 73, 972–977.
49. Cortet-Rudelli, C., Pigny, P., Decanter, C., Leroy, M., Maunoury-Lefebvre, C., Thomas-Desrousseaux, P., and Dewailly, D. (2002). Obesity and serum luteinizing hormone level have an independent and opposite effect on the serum inhibin B level in patients with polycystic ovary syndrome. *Fertil. Steril.* 77, 281–287.
50. Lockwood, G. M., Muttukrishna, S., Groome, N. P., Matthews, D. R., and Ledger, W. L. (1998). Mid-follicular phase pulses of inhibin B are absent in polycystic ovarian syndrome and are initiated by successful laparoscopic ovarian diathermy: A possible mechanism regulating emergence of the dominant follicle. *J. Clin. Endocrinol. Metab.* 83, 1730–1735.
51. Eldar-Geva, T., Spitz, I. M., Groome, N. P., Margalioth, E. J., and Homburg, R. (2001). Follistatin and activin A serum concentrations in obese and non-obese patients with polycystic ovary syndrome. *Hum. Reprod.* 16, 2552–2556.
52. Magoffin, D. A., and Jakimiuk, A. J. (1998). Inhibin A, inhibin B and activin A concentrations in follicular fluid from women with polycystic ovary syndrome. *Hum. Reprod.* 13, 2693–2698.
53. Erickson, G. F., Chung, D.-G., Sit, A., DePaolo, L. V., Shimasaki, S., and Ling, N. (1995). Follistatin concentrations in follicular fluid of normal and polycystic ovaries. *Hum. Reprod.* 10, 2120–2124.
54. Daya, A., Gunby, J., Hughes, E. G., Collins, J. A., and Sagle, M. A. (1995). Follicle-stimulating hormone versus human menopausal gonadotropin for in vitro fertilization cycles: A meta-analysis. *Fertil. Steril.* 64, 347–354.
55. Eden, J. A., Jones, J., Carter, G. D., and Alaghband-Zadeh, J. (1990). Follicular fluid concentrations of insulin-like growth factor 1, epidermal growth factor, transforming growth factor-alpha and sex-steroids in volume matched normal and polycystic human follicles. *Clin. Endocrinol.* 32, 395–405.
56. Mason, H. D., Carr, L., Leake, R., and Franks, S. (1995). Production of transforming growth factor-α by normal and polycystic ovaries. *J. Clin. Endocrinol. Metab.* 80, 2053–2056.
57. Reeka, N., Berg, F. D., and Brucker, C. (1998). Presence of transforming growth factor alpha and epidermal growth factor in human ovarian tissue and follicular fluid. *Hum. Reprod.* 13, 2199–2205.
58. Zachow, R. J., Tash, J. S., and Terranova, P. F. (1993). Tumor necrosis factor-α attenuation of luteinizing hormone-

stimulated androstenedione production by ovarian theca-interstitial cells: Inhibition at loci with the adenosine 3′,5′-monophosphate-dependent signaling pathway. *Endocrinology* 133, 2269–2276.

59. Chen, H., Marcinkiewicz, J. L., Sancho-Tello, M., Hunt, J. S., and Terranova, P. F. (1993). Tumor necrosis factor-α gene expression in mouse oocytes and follicular cells. *Biol. Reprod.* 48, 707–714.
60. Gonzalea, F., Thusu, K., Abdel-Rahman, E., Prabhala, A., Tomani, T., and Dandona, P. (1999). Elevated serum levels of tumor necrosis factor-alpha in normal-weight women with polycystic ovary syndrome. *Metabolism* 48, 437–441.
61. Jasper, M., and Norman, R. J. (1995). Immunoreactive interleukin-I beta and tumour necrosis factor-alpha in thecal, stromal and granulosa cell cultures from normal and polycystic ovaries. *Hum. Reprod.* 10, 1352–1354.
62. Burghen, G. A., Givens, J. R., and Kitabchi, A. E. (1980). Correlation of hyperandrogenism with hyperinsulinism in polycystic ovarian disease. *J. Clin. Endocrinol. Metab.* 50, 113–116.
63. Legro, R. S., Finegood, D., and Dunaif, A. (1998). A fasting glucose to insulin ratio is a useful measure of insulin sensitivity in women with polycystic ovary syndrome. *J. Clin. Endocrinol. Metab.* 83, 2694–2698.
64. Ehrmann, D. A., Sturis, J., Byrne, M. M., Karrison, T., Rosenfield, R. L., and Polonsky, K. S. (1995). Insulin secretory defects in polycystic ovary syndrome. Relationship to insulin sensitivity and family history of non-insulin-dependent diabetes mellitus. *J. Clin. Invest.* 96, 520–527.
65. Dunaif, A. (1997). Insulin resistance and the polycystic ovary syndrome: Mechanism and implications for pathogenesis. *Endocr. Rev.* 18, 774–800.
66. Barbieri, R. L., Smith, S., and Ryan, K. J. (1988). The role of hyperinsulinemia in the pathogenesis of ovarian hyperandrogenism. *Fertil. Steril.* 50, 197–212.
67. Bergh, C., Carlsson, B., Olsson, J.-H., Selleskog, U., and Hillensjo, T. (1993). Regulation of androgen production in cultured human thecal cells by insulin-like growth factor I and insulin. *Fertil. Steril.* 59, 323–331.
68. El-Roeiy, A., Chen, X., Roberts, V. J., Shimasaki, A., Ling, N., LeRoith, D., Roberts, C. T., and Yen, S. S. C. (1994). Expression of the genes encoding the insulin-like growth factors (IGF-I and II), the IGF and insulin receptors, and IGF-binding proteins-1–6 and the localization of their gene products in normal and polycystic ovary syndrome ovaries. *J. Clin. Endocrinol. Metab.* 78, 1488–1496.
69. Franks, S., Gilling-Smith, C., Watson, H., and Willis, D. (1999). Insulin action in the normal and polycystic ovary. *Endocrinol. Metab. Clin. North Am.* 28, 361–378.
70. Gilling-Smith, C., Story, H., Rogers, V., and Franks, S. (1997). Evidence for a primary abnormality of thecal cell steroidogenesis in the polycystic ovary syndrome. *Clin. Endocrinol.* (Oxf) 47, 93–99.
71. Gilling-Smith, C., Willis, D. S., Beard, R. W., and Franks, S. (1994). Hypersecretion of androstenedione by isolated thecal cells from polycystic ovaries. *J. Clin. Endocrinol. Metab.* 79, 1158–1165.
72. Barbieri, R. L., Makris, A., Randall, R. W., Daniels, G., Kistner, R. W., and Ryan, K. J. (1986). Insulin stimulates androgen accumulation in incubations of ovrian stroma obtained from women with hyperandrogenism. *J. Clin. Endocrinol. Metab.* 62, 904–910.
73. Poretsky, L. (1991). On the paradox of insulin-induced hyperandrogenism in insulin-resistant states. *Endocr. Rev.* 12, 3–13.
74. Nestler, J. E., Jakubowicz, D. J., de Vargas, A. F., Brik, C., Quintero, N., and Medina, F. (1998). Insulin stimulates testosterone biosynthesis by human thecal cells from women with polycystic ovary syndrome by activating its own receptor and using inositol glycan mediators as the signal transduction system. *J. Clin. Endocrinol. Metab.* 83, 2001–2005.
75. Willis, D., and Franks, S. (1995). Insulin action in human granulosa cells from normal and polycystic ovaries is mediated by the insulin receptor and not the type-I insulin-like growth factor receptor. *J. Clin. Endocrinol. Metab.* 80, 3788–3790.
76. Froesch, E. R., and Zapf, J. (1985). Insulin-like growth factors and insulin: Comparative aspects. *Diabetologia* 28, 485–493.
77. LeRoith, D., Werner, H., Neuenschwander, S., Kalebic, T., and Helman, L. J. (1995). The role of the insulin-like growth factor-I receptor in cancer. *Ann. N.Y. Acad. Sci.* 766, 402–408.
78. Nestler, J. E., and Jakubowicz, D. J. (1996). Decreases in ovarian cytochrome P450c17 alpha activity and serum free testosterone after reduction of insulin secretion in polycystic ovary syndrome. *N. Engl. J. Med.* 335, 617–623.
79. Dunaif, A., Scott, D., Finegood, D., Quintana, B., and Whitcomb, R. (1996). The insulin-sensitizing agent troglitazone improves metabolic and reproductive abnormalities in the polycystic ovary syndrome. *J. Clin. Endocrinol. Metab.* 81, 3299–3306.
80. Acbay, O., and Gundogdu, S. (1996). Can metformin reduce insulin resistance in polycystic ovary syndrome? *Fertil. Steril.* 65, 946–949.
81. Sattar, N., Hopkinson, Z. E., and Greer, I. A. (1998). Insulin-sensitizing agents in polycystic ovary syndrome. *Lancet* 351, 305–307.
82. Widen, E. I., Eriksson, J. G., and Groop, L. C. (1992). Metformin normalizes nonoxidative glucose metabolism in insulin-resistant normoglycemic first-degree relatives of patients with NIDDM. *Diabetes* 41, 354–358.
83. Galuska, D., Nolte, L. A., Zierath, J. R., and Wallberg-Henriksson, H. (1994). Effect of metformin on insulin-stimulated glucose transport in isolated skeletal muscle obtained from patients with NIDDM. *Diabetologia* 37, 826–832.
84. Nestler, J. E., and Jakubowicz, D. J. (1997). Lean women with polycystic ovary syndrome respond to insulin reduction with decreases in ovarian P450c17 alpha activity and serum androgens. *J. Clin. Endocrinol. Metab.* 82, 4075–4079.
85. Diamanti-Kandarakis, E., Mitrakou, A., Raptis, S., Tolis, G., and Duleba, A. J. (1998). The effect of a pure antiandrogen receptor blocker, flutamide, on the lipid profile in the polycystic ovary syndrome. *J. Clin. Endocrinol. Metab.* 83, 2699–2705.
86. La Marca, A., Egbe, T. O., Morgante, G., Paglia, T., Ciani, A., and de Leo, V. (2000). Metformin treatment reduces ovarian cytochrome P-450c17 response to human chorionic gonadotrophin in women with insulin resistance-polycystic ovary syndrome. *Hum. Reprod.* 15, 21–23.

87. Saltiel, A. R., and Olefsky, J. M. (1996). Thiazolidinediones in the treatment of insulin resistance and type II diabetes. *Diabetes* 45, 1661–1669.
88. Buse, J. B., Gumbiner, B., Mathias, N. P., Nelson, D. M., Faja, B. W., and Whitcomb, R. W. (1998). Troglitazone use in insulin-treated type 2 diabetic patients. *Diabetes Care* 21, 1455–1461.
89. Fonseca, V. A., Valiquett, T. R., Huang, S. M., Ghazzi, M. N., and Whitcomb, R. W. (1998). Troglitazone monotherapy improves glycemic control in patients with type 2 diabetes mellitus: A randomized, controlled study. The troglitazone study group. *J. Clin. Endocrinol. Metab.* 83, 3169–3176.
90. Park, K. S., Ciaraldi, T. P., Abrams-Carter, L., Mudaliar, S., Nikoulina, S. E., and Henry, R. R. (1998). Troglitazone regulation of glucose metabolism in human skeletal muscle cultures from obese, type II diabetic subjects. *J. Clin. Endocrinol. Metab.* 83, 1636–1643.
91. Hasegawa, I., Murakawa, H., Suzuki, M., Yamamoto, Y., Kurabayashi, T., and Tanaka, K. (1999). Effect of troglitazone on endocrine and ovulatory performance in women with insulin resistance-related polycystic ovary syndrome. *Fertil. Steril.* 71, 323–327.
92. Arlt, W., Auchus, R. J., and Miller, W. L. (2001). Thiazolidinediones but not metformin directly inhibit the steroidogenic enzymes P450c17 and 3beta-hydroxysteroid dehydrogenase. *J. Biol. Chem.* 276, 16767–16771.
93. Geffner, M. E., Kaplan, S. A., Bersch, N., Golde, D. W., Landaw, E. M., and Chang, R. J. (1986). Persistence of insulin resistance in polycystic ovarian disease after inhibition of ovarian steroid secretion. *Fertil. Steril.* 45, 327–333.
94. Dunaif, A., Green, G., Futterweit, W., and Dobrjansky, A. (1990). Suppression of hyperandrogenism does not improve peripheral or hepatic insulin resistance in the polycystic ovarian syndrome. *J. Clin. Endocrinol. Metab.* 70, 699–704.
95. Lasco, A., Cucinotta, D., Gigante, A., Denuzzo, G., Pedulla, M., Trifiletti, A., and Frisina, N. (1995). No changes of peripheral insulin resistance in polycystic ovary syndrome after long-term reduction of endogenous androgens with leuprolide. *Eur. J. Endocrinol.* 133, 718–722.
96. Diamanti-Kandarakis, E., Mitrakou, A., Hennes, M. M., Platanissiotis, D., Kaklas, N., Spina, J., Georgiadou, E., Hoffman, R. G., Kissebah, A. H., and Raptis, S. (1995). Insulin senstivity and antiandrogenic therapy in women with polycystic ovary syndrome. *Metabolism* 44, 525–531.
97. Vidal-Puig, A., Munoz-Torres, M., Garcia-Calvente, C., Jodar-Gimeno, E., Lardelli, P., Ruiz-Requena, M. E., and Escobar-Jiminez, F. (1994). Reduction of endogenous, ovarian and adrenal androgens with ketoconazole does not alter insulin response in the polycystic ovary syndrome. *J. Endocrinol. Invest.* 17, 647–652.
98. Ezzell, C. (1996). The molecular link between fat and female fertility. *J. NIH Res.* 8, 24–25.
99. Caro, J. F., Sinha, M. K., Kolaczynski, J. W., Zhang, P. L., and Considine, R. V. (1996). Leptin: The tale of an obesity gene. *Diabetes* 45, 1455–1462.
100. Maffei, M., Halaas, J., Ravussin, E., Pratley, R. E., Lee, G. H., Zhang, Y., Fei, H., Kim, S., Lallone, R., Ranganathan, S., Kern, P. A., and Friedman, J. M. (1995). Leptin levels in human and rodent: Measurement of plasma leptin and ob RNA in obese and weight-reduced subjects. *Nature Med.* 1, 1155–1161.
101. Considine, R. V., Sinha, M. K., Heiman, M. L., Kriauciunas, A., Stephens, T. W., Nyce, M. R., Ohannesian, J. P., Marco, C. C., McKee, L. J., Bauer, T. L., and Caro, J. F. (1996). Serum immunoreactive-leptin concentrations in normal-weight and obese humans. *N. Engl. J. Med.* 334, 292–295.
102. Dagogo-Jack, S., Fanelli, C., Paramore, D., Brothers, J., and Landt, M. (1996). Plasma leptin and insulin relationships in obese and nonobese humans. *Diabetes* 45, 695–698.
103. Fedorcsak, P., Toreng, R., Ale, P. O., Anbo, T., Orjesen, P., Rbancsek, J., and Byholm, T. (2000). Leptin and leptin binding activity in the preovulatory follicle of polycystic ovary syndrome patients. *Scand. J. Clin. Lab. Invest.* 60, 649–655.
104. Magoffin, D. A., Duggal, P. S., and Norman, R. J. (2003). The role of leptin in polycystic ovary syndrome. In *Leptin and Reproduction*, eds. M. C. Henson and V. D. Castracane. New York: Kluwer Academic/Plenum Publishers (in press).
105. Agarwal, S. K., Vogel, K., Weitsman, S. R., and Magoffin, D. A. (1999). Leptin antagonizes the insulin-like growth factor-I augmentation of steroidogenesis in granulosa and theca cells of the human ovary. *J. Clin. Endocrinol. Metab.* 84, 1072–1076.
106. Karlsson, C., Lindell, K., Svensson, E., Bergh, C., Lind, P., Billig, H., Carlsson, L. M. S., and Carlsson, B. (1997). Expression of functional leptin receptors in the human ovary. *J. Clin. Endocrinol. Metab.* 82, 4144–4148.
107. Steppan, C. M., Brown, E. J., Wright, C. M., Bhat, S., Banerjee, R. R., Dai, C. Y., Enders, G. H., Silberg, D. G., Wen, X., Wu, G. D., and Lazar, M. A. (2001). A family of tissue-specific resistin-like molecules. *Proc. Natl. Acad. Sci. USA* 98, 502–506.
108. Steppan, C. M., Bailey, S. T., Bhat, S., Brown, E. J., Banerjee, R. R., Wright, C. M., Patel, H. R., Ahima, R. S., and Lazar, M. A. (2001). The hormone resistin links obesity to diabetes. *Nature* 409, 307–312.
109. Savage, D. B., Sewter, C. P., Klenk, E. S., Segal, D. G., Vidal-Puig, A., Considine, R. V., and O'Rahilly, S. (2001). Resistin/FIZZ3 expression in relation to obesity and peroxisome proliferator-activated receptor-gamma action in humans. *Diabetes* 50, 2199–2202.
110. Nagaev, I., and Smith, U. (2001). Insulin resistance and type 2 diabetes are not related to resistin expression in human fat cells or skeletal muscle. *Biochem. Biophys. Res. Commun.* 285, 561–564.
111. Janke, J., Engeli, S., Gorzelniak, K., Luft, F. C., and Sharma, A. M. (2002). Resistin gene expression in human adipocytes is not related to insulin resistance. *Obes. Res.* 10, 1–5.
112. McTernan, P. G., McTernan, C. L., Chetty, R., Jenner, K., Fisher, F. M., Lauer, M. N., Crockeer, J., Barnett, A. H., and Kumar, S. (2002). Increased resistin gene and protein expression in human abdominal adipose tissue. *J. Clin. Endocrinol. Metab.* 87, 2407–2410.

CHAPTER **31**

Luteal Dysfunction

REBECCA S. USADI, AND MARC A. FRITZ

INTRODUCTION

Luteal phase deficiency (LPD) is a disorder classically described as a delayed or otherwise abnormal pattern of secretory endometrial development caused by inadequate corpus luteum (CL) progesterone production [1]. Subfertility and early pregnancy loss commonly are regarded as reproductive consequences of LPD, presumably resulting from failed implantation or a premature luteal-placental shift, but the pathophysiology of the disorder has remained elusive. Moreover, controversies regarding the methods for diagnosis and even the very existence of LPD have persisted. This chapter outlines the requirements for normal corpus luteum function, considers the causes of LPD and the pathophysiologic mechanisms by which the disorder may adversely affect reproductive performance, reviews the diagnosis and treatment of LPD, and discusses recent investigations that offer new perspectives on this enigmatic and controversial disorder.

HISTORICAL PERSPECTIVE

As early as 1929, studies of CL physiology performed by Allen and Corner led them to hypothesize that progesterone deficiency might predispose to pregnancy loss [2]. Rock and Bartlett first suggested the potential significance of changes in endometrial morphology across the secretory phase of the cycle in 1937 [1]. Jones's hypothesis that delayed endometrial maturation might be a cause of infertility and early pregnancy loss followed in 1949 [3]. The seminal work of Noyes, Hertig, and Rock was published in 1950 and established histologic endometrial "dating" criteria [4] that have endured as the gold standard against which all other methods for assessing the quality of luteal function are compared. In the more than 50 years since that work was published, a great deal of effort has been directed toward better defining and understanding corpus luteum physiology. Nevertheless, the mechanisms that govern corpus luteum function and regression remain largely unknown. Many clinical investigations have focused on LPD and its clinical consequences. Few would dispute that LPD is real and that the disorder contributes to reproductive failure; however, the extent to which LPD adversely affects fertility and pregnancy outcome, the prevalence of the disorder, diagnostic criteria, and treatment all remain controversial.

REQUIREMENTS FOR NORMAL CORPUS LUTEUM FUNCTION

The quality of CL function depends largely on the quality of preovulatory follicular development because the size and functional capacity of the CL relate directly to the number of luteal cells that derive from the granulosa and theca cells of the follicle. Simply put, normal preovulatory follicular development is a likely prerequisite for normal luteal function. Ovarian follicular development is driven by pituitary gonadotropins that, in turn, are secreted in a pattern influenced by the frequency and amplitude of hypothalamic gonadotropin-releasing hormone (Gn-RH) secretion. Any disturbance in this highly coordinated and delicately balanced hypothalamic-pituitary-ovarian axis may adversely affect the progress or quality of follicular development. If not severe enough to cause frank anovulation, that disturbance may still prevent complete follicular maturation and, consequently, compromise the quality or duration of CL function. In this context, LPD may be viewed as a subtle form of ovulatory dysfunction. At midcycle, the luteinizing hormone (LH) surge triggers ovulation and also luteinizes and reorganizes the follicle to form the CL. After ovulation, angiogenic factors, including vascular endothelial growth factor (VEGF), promote rapid development of a rich neovascular network in the developing CL. Capillaries that now penetrate the basement membrane ensure that another requirement for normal luteal function is met—ample supplies of low-density lipoproteins (LDLs), which serve as steroidogenic substrate for progesterone synthesis [5].

Numerous lines of evidence indicate that the life span and functional capacity of the CL further depend on at least tonic levels of pituitary LH secretion. In nonhuman primates, treatment with an LH antiserum in the early luteal phase results in a prompt decline in circulating progesterone levels and early onset of menses [6]. Whereas a pulsatile infusion of exogenous Gn-RH can restore gonadotropin secretion and induce ovulation in monkeys with hypothalamic lesions that eliminate endogenous Gn-RH production, discontinuation of that infusion during the luteal phase brings about a prompt fall in progesterone levels and onset of menses [7]. Similar observations have been made in normal women when luteal phase LH secretion is inhibited by use of a Gn-RH antagonist [8]. A short luteal phase and low levels of progesterone production follow ovulation induction in hypophysectomized women, unless further exogenous gonadotropin support is provided [9]. Studies involving frequent blood sampling in both nonhuman primates [10] and women [11] have demonstrated that the CL secretes progesterone in distinct pulses that closely correlate with pulses in pituitary LH secretion. These observations indicate that LH plays not just a supportive role but is also an acute regulator of CL function.

Given the similar structure and actions of LH and human chorionic gonadotropin (hCG), it is easy to envision how rapidly rising levels of hCG serve to "rescue" the CL in a conception cycle. Why the CL regresses in the first place, when there is no dramatic fall in endogenous luteal phase LH levels, is less clear. Current evidence suggests that luteolysis represents a form of programmed cell death associated with a progressive decrease in sensitivity to LH stimulation. Consequently, CL regression is inevitable without the progressive increases in stimulation that the early and exponential rise of hCG in conception cycles provides. In the fertile cycle, hCG first appears at a time that coincides exactly with the peak in CL development and function. Evidence indicates that this temporal association may be crucial to a successful rescue of the CL. Studies in the nonhuman primate demonstrate that the patterns and amounts of estrogen and progesterone secretion that accompany a course of incremental exogenous hCG vary significantly with the postovulatory age of the CL [12, 13]. The steroidogenic response to hCG is modest in the early luteal phase, greatest at midluteal phase, and decreases again in the late luteal phase. Very similar results have been observed in women [14]. These observations suggest that timely implantation and hCG production are necessary to ensure that the CL can provide the requisite level and duration of steroidogenic support until the developing trophoblast is sufficiently mature to assume that responsibility.

PATHOPHYSIOLOGY

LPD is best viewed not as a single distinct entity, but rather as a final common pathway with a variety of predisposing factors or causes. Inadequate luteal function naturally implicates the ovary; however, evidence indicates that LPD most often results from pituitary or hypothalamic dysfunction. Moreover, the endometrial consequences of inadequate progesterone production are likely to be the proximate cause of any adverse effects the disorder may have on reproductive function.

Abnormalities of Pituitary Gonadotropin Secretion

As suggested earlier, functional deficiencies of the CL might be simply the natural consequence of abnormal follicular phase endocrine dynamics or poor preovulatory folliculogenesis. Given that the pace and quality of follicular development are governed largely by the levels and sequence of pituitary gonadotropin stimulation, it is logical to anticipate that abnormalities of luteal function might be associated with abnormal patterns of gonadotropin secretion earlier in the cycle. Evidence indicates that even subtle abnormalities in gonadotropin secretion during the follicular phase can compromise the quality and duration of luteal function [15].

Early studies in women having a naturally occurring short luteal phase demonstrated that such cycles often exhibit lower follicular phase follicle-stimulating hormone (FSH)/LH ratios and decreased LH surge amplitude when compared to normal cycles [16]. Others have shown that low luteal phase estradiol and progesterone concentrations or delayed secretory endometrial maturation often are associated with decreased FSH levels during the early or midfollicular phase [17, 18]. The inferences drawn from these early observations have been confirmed by direct experiment in both nonhuman primates and women. In monkeys, selective suppression of follicular phase FSH secretion (achieved by infusion of porcine follicular fluid, a rich source of inhibin) results in lower preovulatory estradiol levels, a decrease in luteal cell mass, and reduced luteal phase progesterone concentrations [15, 19]; simultaneous treatment with exogenous human menopausal gonadotropins (FSH : LH, 3 : 1) restores normal luteal function. In women, treatment with a long-acting Gn-RH agonist for a brief interval during the early follicular phase decreases midfollicular phase FSH levels and yields an abnormally short luteal phase, in which both estradiol and progesterone concentrations are clearly low [20]. These observations clearly suggest that abnormally low follicular phase FSH levels predispose to poor luteal function; however, careful studies in women indicate that low follicular phase FSH concentrations are not characteristic of LPD in general [21]. Other abnormalities of gonadotropin secretion observed in LPD cycles include decreased concentrations of both immunoactive and bioactive LH during the midcycle surge and reduced LH bioactivity during the luteal phase [22]. Given that the LH surge is the stimulus for luteinization and that LH subsequently drives CL progesterone secretion during the luteal phase, any such decreases in LH stimulation clearly might result in poor luteal function. In fact, evidence indicates that the characteristically low circulating levels of luteal phase progesterone observed in LPD cycles result from a decreased amplitude of each pulse of progesterone secretion from the CL progesterone that occurs in response to rhythmic pulses in pituitary LH release [21].

Abnormalities in Pulsatile Hypothalamic Gonadotropin-Releasing Hormone Secretion

The pulsatile pattern of pituitary gonadotropin release correlates closely with that of hypothalamic Gn-RH secretion. The frequency of Gn-RH pulses also influences the relative quantities of LH and FSH that are released. Consequently, the abnormalities in follicular phase gonadotropin concentrations observed in cycles having a short or otherwise inadequate luteal phase might result from aberrant patterns of pulsatile Gn-RH secretion. Clinical and experimental evidence suggests that normal follicular development and luteal function require a Gn-RH pulse frequency within a relatively narrow range. Young women with LPD associated with exercise and dieting exhibit a decreased LH (and by inference, Gn-RH) pulse frequency, lower follicular phase estradiol levels, and a blunted rise in FSH during the luteal-follicular transition, compared to normal women [23–25]. An abnormally rapid endogenous LH pulse frequency has also been observed in women with LPD [26]. Imposition of a supraphysiologic exogenous Gn-RH pulse rhythm during the follicular phase in normal ovulatory women results in increased follicular phase plasma LH/FSH ratios, decreased luteal phase immunoactive and bioactive LH concentrations, decreased luteal phase progesterone levels, and a grossly short luteal phase duration [27]. Given that the Gn-RH pulse frequency is modulated both by feedback signals from the periphery and by input from higher centers in response external stimuli, these observations illustrate that a wide variety of factors, both intrinsic and extrinsic, may cause LPD via their influence on the output of the Gn-RH pulse generator or the pituitary response to Gn-RH secretion.

Endocrinopathies Associated with Abnormal Luteal Function

Thyroid and prolactin disorders, their metabolic consequences, or the homeostatic mechanisms they trigger may disrupt the hypothalamic-pituitary-ovarian axis and predispose to LPD. Both hypothyroidism and hyperthyroidism are relatively common in reproductive-age women. In both disorders, changes in sex hormone–binding globulin concentrations and in the metabolic clearance rate of estrogen yield elevated total and free estrogen levels that may result in increased feedback inhibition of gonadotropin secretion [28]. Primary hypothyroidism may also result in a secondary hyperprolactinemia though several interrelated mechanisms. Increased hypothalamic thyrotropin-releasing hormone (TRH) secretion stimulates pituitary lactotropes directly. Increased circulating estrogens further stimulate prolactin production by activating gene transcription, interfering with the inhibitory action of hypothalamic dopamine, and upregulating the TRH receptor. Furthermore, the metabolic clearance of prolactin is reduced in individuals with hypothyroidism. Hyperprolactinemia is often associated with abnormalities of the menstrual cycle. Whereas marked hyperprolactinemia often results in anovulation or even amenorrhea, the adverse effects of modest prolactin elevations may be more subtle and include LPD. Observations of cycle characteristics after discontinuation of bromocriptine treatment in hyperprolactinemic women suggest that inadequate luteal function may be one of the earliest clinical manifestations of an emerging prolactin disorder or mild hyperprolactinemia. As prolactin levels progressively rise again, a short luteal phase is first observed and followed, in sequence, by recurrent galactorrhea, anovulation, and finally amenorrhea [29]. Numerous studies have demonstrated that hyperprolactinemic women often exhibit a short or otherwise inadequate luteal phase and that hyperprolactinemia is commonly observed in subfertile women with documented LPD [30–34].

Several lines of evidence suggest that prolactin may have direct effects on CL function. Prolactin receptors are present in the human CL [35]. Progesterone production by luteinized granulosa cells in vitro declines when prolactin in culture medium is neutralized, but also when prolactin is added to yield abnormally high concentrations [36]. In normal cycling women, dopamine agonist treatment lowers both prolactin concentrations and luteal phase progesterone production in a dose-dependent fashion [37]. Conversely, experimental metaclopramide-induced hyperprolactinemia in normal ovulatory women results in smaller preovulatory follicles, an attenuated midcycle LH surge, and lower luteal phase progesterone levels [38]. These data suggest that whereas physiologic concentrations of prolactin may support the CL, abnormally high or low levels may adversely affect luteal function.

Other evidence indicates that hyperprolactinemia may adversely affect luteal function via central actions that disturb or inhibit pulsatile hypothalamic Gn-RH or pituitary gonadotropin secretion rather than from local effects on the CL. The decreased LH pulse frequency observed in hyperprolactinemic women suggests that supraphysiologic prolactin concentrations inhibit pulsatile Gn-RH secretion. Experiments in nonhuman primates have provided compelling evidence to support this notion. After menstrual cycles are restored by pulsatile exogenous Gn-RH treatment in female monkeys bearing hypothalamic lesions that eliminate endogenous Gn-RH secretion, luteal function is normal regardless of whether serum prolactin levels are markedly elevated or even undetectable [39].

The mechanism by which hyperprolactinemia may inhibit hypothalamic Gn-RH secretion may involve increased hypothalamic dopamine and opioid peptide levels, both being inhibitory neuromodulators of Gn-RH release, or direct effects exerted via prolactin receptors on Gn-RH neurons [40, 41]. The weight of available evidence supports a causal relationship between hyperprolactinemia and luteal dysfunction and indicates that elevated prolactin levels may adversely affect luteal function directly, or indirectly by inhibiting Gn-RH or gonadotropin secretion; however, most women with documented LPD do not exhibit hyperprolactinemia or abnormal patterns of prolactin secretion [42].

Endometrial Consequences of Inadequate Corpus Luteum Progesterone Production

Progesterone is critical to the development of a receptive endometrium. Under its influence, proliferating endometrial cells undergo a characteristic secretory transformation and begin synthesis and secretion of proteins now thought to play a vital role in the implantation process [43–45]. Over the course of the luteal phase, continued high levels of progesterone stimulation again transform the secretory endometrial stroma into the decidua, a highly specialized tissue compartment that produces extracellular matrix, cytokines, and growth factors that both facilitate and limit invasion of the trophoblast.

One important feature of progesterone action is that the hormone selectively downregulates its own progesterone receptor (PR); as the luteal phase advances, epithelial PR concentrations decline in epithelial cells but remain high in the deciduas [46–48]. This is arguably a key event in endometrial development because it represents a shift from epithelial activity to stromal/decidual function. At least in theory, inadequate progesterone production might cause a delay in epithelial PR downregulation and result in altered patterns of protein expression that render the endometrium unreceptive to embryo implantation.

Numerous studies have attempted to define the patterns of endometrial estrogen receptor (ER) and PR expression in women with normal cycles and women with LPD, but results have been conflicting. Lower, normal, and even higher PR concentrations have been reported in women with abnormally delayed endometrial maturation [49–55]. These widely varying observations suggest that the endometrial consequences of LPD may involve more than a single mechanism; however, given the temporally dependent and dynamic changes in PR levels and the differing patterns of PR expression in endometrial glands and stroma across the secretory phase, differences in study design and methods are more likely responsible. Immunohistochemical studies of PR expression *in situ* have revealed that delayed endometrial maturation is associated with a delay in epithelial PR downregulation and that both abnormalities can be corrected with appropriate treatment [56].

Given that progesterone drives secretory endometrial maturation, delayed preimplantation endometrial development might logically result from inadequate levels of CL progesterone production. Not surprisingly, delayed secretory endometrial histological development has become the *sine qua non* of LPD, a morphological abnormality presumed to have an important functional consequence—a decrease or loss of endometrial receptivity [57]. The relevance of delayed endometrial maturation derives from observations indicating that the "window of implantation" spans a relatatively narrow interval of time. Data from careful studies using highly sensitive assays for hCG suggest that implantation occurs between cycle days 20 and 24 (6 to 10 days after ovulation) [58]. These data are consistent with earlier observations from studies of hysterectomy specimens obtained in conception cycles, which revealed that embryos were uniformly unattached before cycle day 19 and always attached after cycle day 21 [59].

From the embryo's perspective, the absolute concentrations of circulating progesterone are of little importance; whatever level or pattern of progesterone secretion effectively prepares the endometrium for its arrival is sufficient. Abnormalities of endometrial maturation have been identified even when progesterone concentrations are not clearly low [60, 61]. In one large study, delayed endometrial development was observed in 13.5% of infertile women and in 32.5% of women with history of recurrent pregnancy loss, although serum progesterone concentrations were within the normal range in 86% overall [60]. In another more recent study, abnormal preimplantation endometrial development was observed nearly five times more often in women with unexplained infertility than in fertile women, even though progesterone concentrations were again normal in all but a few [62]. Whether it results from lower-than-normal levels of progesterone production or from endometrial dysfunction that delays or prevents a normal response to progesterone, delayed endometrial maturation has been considered the proximate cause of subfertility in women with LPD.

Ultimately, abnormalities in the expression of necessary cell surface adhesion molecules (integrins) may be the most important endometrial consequence of LPD. Evidence indicates that three specific integrins (i.e., $\alpha v\beta 3$, $\alpha 1\beta 1$, and $\alpha 4\beta 1$) are conspicuously coexpressed in endometrial epithelium only during an interval that coincides with the putative implantation window. Deviations from the characteristic patterns of epithelial integrin expression, in association with both normal and delayed endometrial maturation, have been observed in infertile women [63]. These observations suggest that poor luteal function may have important functional endometrial consequences, but they do not establish a causal link between LPD and subfertility or recurrent early pregnancy loss.

Abnormalities of Luteal Function in Early Pregnancy

The mechanisms responsible for the subfertility and recurrent pregnancy loss associated with LPD are different, but also related, and probably represent only different points on a pathophysiologic continuum (Figure 31.1). In theory, if an arriving embryo is greeted by an endometrium that is not yet receptive or prepared to receive it, implantation may be delayed or even fail altogether. Profound delays in endometrial maturation may postpone implantation until the embryo is no longer able to attach or even viable. Less severe delays in endometrial maturation that do not prevent implantation may still adversely affect the ability of the embryo to synthesize the levels of hCG necessary to rescue and support the CL or compromise its longer-term developmental potential. Even minor delays in endometrial maturation and implantation may still yield a tardy hCG rescue signal that arrives only after regression of the CL has already begun. The regressing CL will still respond, but a decreased amplitude and duration of steroidogenic response can be expected. Progesterone production may then be insufficient to provide the level or length of support required until pregnancy becomes independent of luteal function and self-supporting.

The importance of luteal function to the success of early pregnancy was first revealed in classic studies of the effects of lutectomy performed in women planning elective termination of pregnancy [64]. Lutectomy before seven weeks' gestation (five weeks after conception) uniformly resulted in declining serum progesterone concentrations, followed by spontaneous abortion. Beyond nine weeks' gestation, progesterone levels declined transiently after lutectomy, but pregnancy continued normally. Subsequent studies demonstrated that exogenous progesterone treatment could prevent spontaneous abortion after lutectomy at seven weeks' gestation [65]. More recent studies in successful oocyte donation cycles have confirmed the inferences drawn from these early observations and provided new insights into the endocrine dynamics of the luteal-placental shift. [66, 67]. Placental steroid hormone production begins at approximately five weeks' gestation (three weeks after conception), but serum concentrations of estradiol and progesterone do not rise significantly

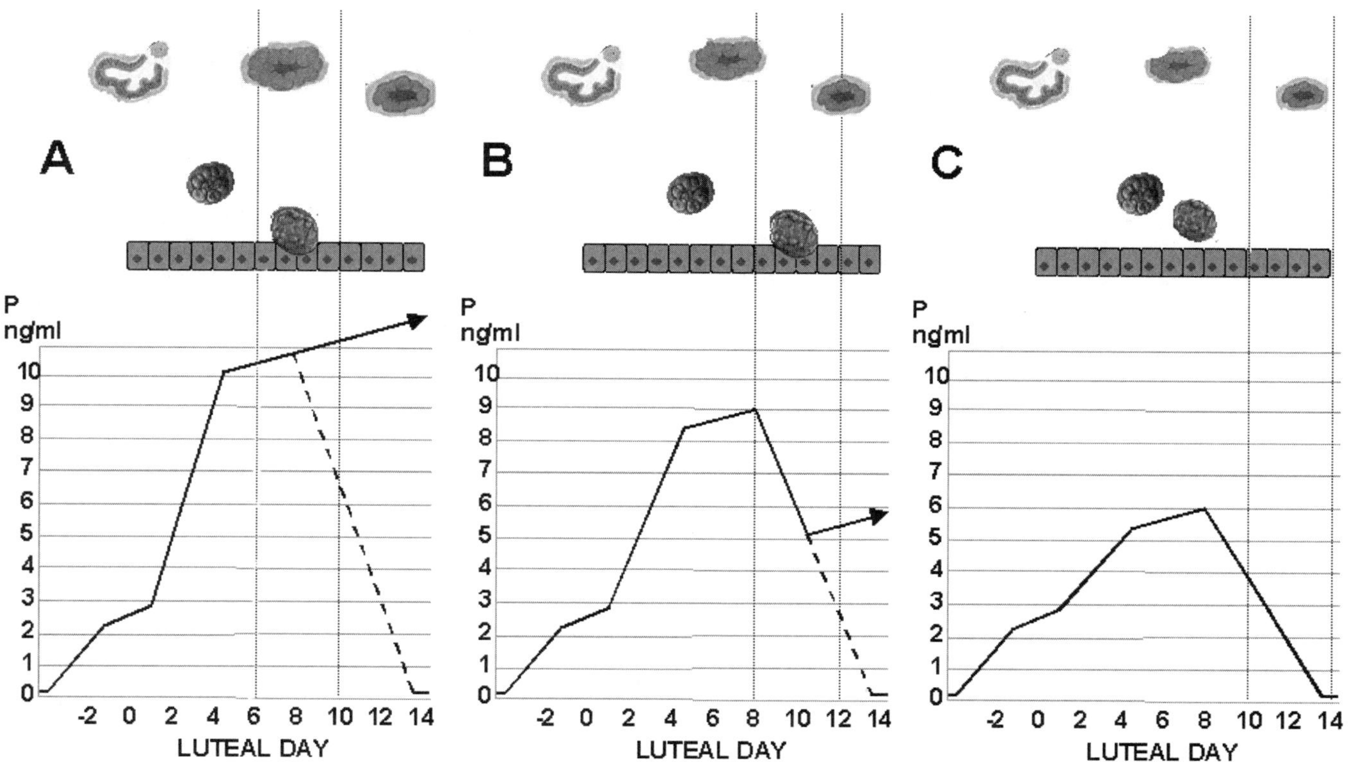

FIGURE 31.1 Pathophysiologic mechanisms of luteal deficiency that may result in subfertility or predispose to pregnancy loss. **A,** Normal luteal function resulting in normal endometrial maturation, timely implantation, and effective CL rescue. **B,** Mild luteal deficiency resulting in delayed endometrial maturation, late implantation of an embryo that may have decreased functional or developmental potential, and ineffective CL rescue because of inadequate or late hCG stimulation. **C,** Severe luteal deficiency resulting in markedly delayed endometrial maturation and failed implantation. Paired dotted lines indicate the implantation window. Dashed lines indicate progesterone concentrations when conception does not occur.

above the stable levels achieved by treatment with a constant exogenous hormone replacement regimen until seven weeks' gestation [68]. These data indicate that luteal function must be maintained until at least seven weeks' gestation. Thereafter, increasing placental hormone production compensates for declining luteal function. Ultimately, pregnancy becomes independent of the CL, but premature luteal regression jeopardizes the conceptus and predisposes to early pregnancy loss.

DIAGNOSIS OF LUTEAL PHASE DEFICIENCY

The various methods used to assess the quality of luteal function in women with infertility or a history of recurrent early spontaneous abortion have been previously reviewed [69, 70]. Unfortunately, there is no one uniformly accepted diagnostic criterion. The differing methods correlate poorly and thus have yielded widely varying estimates of the prevalence of LPD, generally ranging from 3% to 32% of infertile women [71, 72], but as high as 60% in some studies [73]. No one method is clearly superior to all others. Each has its proponents, advantages, disadvantages, and pitfalls.

Short Luteal Phase

In normal ovulatory women, the luteal phase has a mean duration of 14.13 ± 1.41 days [74]. Consequently, a luteal phase duration less than approximately 13 days is abnormally short, presumably reflecting premature luteolysis from whatever cause. Luteal phase duration may be determined by basal body temperature (BBT) monitoring, or more precisely by detection of the midcycle LH surge, using any one of the many commercially available home urine test kits.

BBT monitoring is a time-honored test of ovulatory function, based on the "thermogenic" properties of progesterone. As progesterone levels rise after ovulation, BBT also increases, and after CL regression, progesterone levels and BBT fall again to baseline levels. The thermogenic effects of progesterone are to some extent concentration dependent, but more qualitative than quantitative; any progesterone level above approximately 3 ng/mL will raise BBT. The progesterone-induced increase in BBT is subtle but most often distinct; generally occurs 1 to 2 days after the midcycle LH surge; and is relatively easy to detect when BBT is carefully monitored on a daily basis [75]. Given that temporal relationship, temperature elevations of less than 11 days (onset of menses less than 12 days after the rise in BBT) indicate an abnormally short luteal phase. A gradual, staggered rise in BBT may be another indication of poor luteal function. Not surprisingly, the first diagnostic criterion for LPD was based on BBT [3].

As a method for the diagnosis of LPD, the BBT is both noninvasive and relatively inexpensive. Unfortunately, when judged by its correlation with abnormally delayed histologic endometrial maturation or low integrated serum progesterone concentrations, the short luteal phase also lacks sensitivity and specificity. A short temperature elevation or other abnormal BBT pattern has been observed in 30% to 80% of infertile women with histologically documented LPD [76, 77]. A short luteal phase certainly suggests LPD, but also may be observed in fertile women whose luteal function is normal by any other measure [77, 78]. Only 14% of cycles with abnormally low integrated luteal phase progesterone concentrations exhibit a short luteal phase by BBT criteria [79]. Conversely, progesterone concentrations are low in 74% of cycles in which the luteal phase is abnormally short in duration [79]. These observations suggest that the short luteal phase may be useful for detecting gross but not subtle deficiencies of luteal function; however, even when most accurately defined by detection of the midcycle LH surge, a short luteal phase has been observed with equal frequency in fertile and infertile women.

Serum Progesterone Concentrations

Quite obviously, the amount of progesterone produced by the CL is perhaps the most valid measure of its functional capacity. Not surprisingly, serum progesterone concentrations are often used to assess luteal function [80–82]. Integrated serum progesterone concentrations (the sum of daily luteal phase determinations) generally correlate well with the quality of secretory endometrial development [78, 79, 83], but daily serum progesterone determinations clearly are neither practical nor cost effective in clinical practice. As a compromise, some have proposed serial but less frequent measurements for diagnostic purposes—a sum of three midluteal phase progesterone determinations totaling greater than 15 ng/mL [84] or 30 ng/mL [79] has been recommended. Others have suggested that a single midluteal phase serum progesterone determination is adequate, but recommended threshold values (3 to 10 ng/mL) have varied considerably [78, 84–86]. Unfortunately, there is no consensus on the minimum midluteal phase progesterone concentration that might be confidently interpreted as adequate. A judgment based on a single test, no matter how well timed, has numerous pitfalls and, for several reasons, cannot reliably define the quality of luteal function.

Serum progesterone concentrations observed in normal and abnormal cycles and in conception and nonconception cycles in both fertile and infertile women vary widely and overlap considerably [87]. One explanation for such observations is that CL progesterone secretion has a varying circadian rhythm [88] and is distinctly pulsatile in nature. Careful studies in both nonhuman primates [89] and women [90] have clearly demonstrated that progesterone levels fluctuate widely during the luteal phase, closely correlating with distinct pulses in pituitary LH release. Progesterone levels as low as 2 and as high as 40 ng/mL may be observed within an interval of only hours [11]. Consequently, a single random serum progesterone concentration defies confident interpretation [91]. Some have suggested that sampling during the morning hours, when concentrations generally are highest and less erratic, may minimize the influence of pulsatile progesterone secretion [92]. These observations question the use of serum progesterone concentrations as a reliable gauge of luteal function.

Histologic Endometrial Dating

The histologic features of the secretory endometrium change with the duration of progesterone exposure, in a classical sequence first described by Noyes, Hertig, and Rock [4]. The predictable progression of endometrial maturation is the basis for endometrial "dating," an estimate of the number of days since ovulation occurred. Given that endometrial maturation reflects both the functional capacity of the CL and the end organ tissue response, histologic endometrial dating has been regarded as a bioassay of luteal function.

For diagnostic purposes, the observed histologic "date" (based on the most advanced maturational features observed in the tissue specimen) is compared to the expected date (based on the known day of sampling). Traditionally, the day of biopsy and expected histologic date are defined by counting backward from onset of the next menstrual period, assuming that menses uniformly begins on the 14th postovulatory day [93]. A histologic endometrial date "out of phase" with the expected date suggests maturation delay resulting from inadequate luteal function.

Based on observations of delayed endometrial maturation, LPD has been identified more often in women with endometriosis or unexplained infertility than in those with tubal or male factor infertility or in normally fertile women [73]. The abnormality has also been observed more commonly in women with primary infertility than in those who have conceived before and more frequently in women with a history of recurrent early pregnancy loss than in those with a normal obstetrical history [94]; however, these observations must be interpreted cautiously because the methods and criteria for diagnosis of LPD have varied among studies.

Traditionally, biopsy for evaluation of endometrial maturation is performed in the late luteal phase, at a time when sampling might best reflect the total impact and overall quality of luteal function [93]. Late luteal phase sampling also allows dating to be based on a larger number of histologic features and may yield a more reliable interpretation [95]. Others have argued that midluteal phase tissue sampling, coinciding with the time of implantation, is more relevant. Studies involving both midluteal and late luteal phase biopsies in infertile women suggest that biopsy during the implantation window can identify abnormalities of endometrial maturation that might otherwise go undetected [96]; however, results of midluteal phase endometrial sampling generally have correlated only modestly with integrated luteal phase progesterone concentrations [97] or urinary excretion of estrogen and progesterone metabolites [98].

Whereas most have considered any discrepancy between observed and expected histologic dates less than three days as insignificant, others have defined LPD as a maturation delay of only two days or more. Some have required only a single abnormal result for diagnosis. Acknowledging that delayed endometrial development may also be observed in normal fertile women [73, 99, 100], others require abnormal results in two separate, preferably consecutive cycles. These differences in diagnostic criteria can have profound effects on the observed and reported prevalence of LPD in any study or patient population. For example, serial endometrial sampling over the course of a year has revealed that the incidence of LPD in normal women may range from 7% to 50%, depending on which diagnostic criteria are applied [101].

Although long regarded as the "gold standard" method for diagnosis of LPD, endometrial dating has become highly controversial in recent years, for several reasons. First, the dating criteria used as the normal standard were based on examinations of tissue specimens obtained not from normal parous women, but from infertile women. Second, the postovulatory day on which those specimens were obtained was not accurately and specifically defined because it was based on the onset of the next menses, ignoring any effect that biopsy may have on when menses next begins or when it is perceived to start. Moreover, subsequent studies in normal cycling women have shown that the correlation between observed and expected histologic dates is generally poor (65%) when the day of biopsy is defined by onset of menses. Correlation is much improved when the time of sampling (days since ovulation and the expected histologic date) is defined prospectively, using the midcycle LH surge (85%) or ultrasound observations of follicular collapse (96%) as a reference point [102]. Third, histologic endometrial dating is quite subjective and results can vary widely among different pathologists [103, 104], or even when a single tissue specimen is reexamined by the same pathologist [105]. Differences in interpretation within and among pathologists are great enough to affect diagnosis and management in 20% to 40% of women [103, 105]. Last, and perhaps most important, observations of normal or delayed endometrial maturation in conception cycles or in previous cycles do not correlate with pregnancy outcome in fertile or infertile women [106]. Given the many controversies and pitfalls of histologic endometrial dating, even this method for diagnosis of LPD has fallen out of favor.

Other Methods

Still other methods have been proposed for the diagnosis of LPD. These include serial sonograms to evaluate follicular development or measure endometrial thickness [107] and hysteroscopic inspection [108]. Color-flow Doppler ultrasound has been used to examine characteristics of blood flow into and around the CL [109] and the endometrium [110]. Measurements of urinary pregnanediol (the principal metabolite of progesterone), salivary progesterone, and serum placental protein-14 concentrations [111] represent other alternatives that have been investigated in the search for a simple and reliable method for the diagnosis of LPD. Newly identified biochemical markers of endometrial receptivity, such as osteopontin and pinopods, represent yet another possibility but will require careful additional study and validation before they can be applied in clinical practice.

TREATMENT

The results of early uncontrolled and nonrandomized studies suggested that treatment improves cycle fecundity in women with LPD [77, 112]. Several different treatment strategies have been proposed, reflecting the many potential causes of LPD, but evidence for their efficacy remains relatively weak [113]. Treatment in most forms is empiric, except when LPD is associated with a thyroid or prolactin disorder for which specific therapy is indicated. Empirical treatment options include clomiphene citrate (CC) or gonadotropin stimulation, progesterone supplementation, and hCG.

Clomiphene Citrate

CC is the drug used most frequently for ovulation induction and is often chosen for the treatment of LPD. Given its mechanism of action, CC may be particularly useful in women with a short luteal phase because such cycles frequently exhibit abnormally low follicular phase FSH concentrations [16, 17].

Structural similarity to estrogen allows CC to bind to estrogen receptors (ER) throughout the reproductive system; however, in contrast to estrogen, CC binds nuclear ER for an extended period and ultimately depletes ER concentrations by interfering with the normal process of ER replenishment [114]. At the hypothalamic level, depletion of ER prevents correct interpretation of circulating estrogen levels. The resulting decrease in estrogen negative feedback triggers normal compensatory mechanisms that alter pulsatile hypothalamic Gn-RH secretion to stimulate increased pituitary gonadotropin release, which, in turn, stimulates ovarian follicular activity [115]. Given that the CL derives from the ovulatory follicle and that its functional capacity partly depends on the quality of preovulatory follicle development, CC is a logical treatment option for women with LPD [116]. Progesterone levels are typically higher after CC treatment than in spontaneous cycles, reflecting improved preovulatory follicle and CL development [117] or multifollicular ovulation and the combined hormone production of more than one CL [118].

Paradoxically, some have observed a high incidence of LPD (diagnosis based on histologic endometrial dating) in ovulatory women treated with CC [119]. Systemic CC treatment certainly does have the potential to interfere with estrogen-mediated actions at other levels of the reproductive system, including the endometrium and the ovary. Limited endometrial proliferation has been observed in some CC-treated patients [120], but the effect is minor or not at all evident in the largest majority of women [121, 122]. Although some studies have suggested that fecundity may relate to endometrial thickness, others have failed to demonstrate any significant correlation. CC has been shown to inhibit steroid hormone production by cultured avian [123], ovine [124], and human granulosa/luteal cells [125, 126], but estrogen and progesterone levels in CC-induced cycles are typically significantly higher, not lower, than in spontaneous cycles. Adverse effects of CC on mouse ovum fertilization and embryo development have been demonstrated in vitro [127], but clinical studies have revealed that circulating levels of CC never reach the concentrations required to produce these effects, even after several consecutive treatment cycle [128]. Available evidence and accumulated clinical experience suggest that any adverse antiestrogenic effects that CC may have present no significant obstacle in the largest majority of treated women.

Evidence indicates that CC treatment can be effective in infertile women with LPD as might be diagnosed by histologic endometrial dating [118, 129, 130] or observation of a short luteal phase [116]. More aggressive stimulation with exogenous gonadotropins may be considered for those in whom treatment fails to improve luteal function [131, 132].

Progesterone Therapy

Exogneous progesterone supplementation is a logical and common treatment for poor luteal function. Inadequate endogenous progesterone can be supplemented in a variety of ways, including vaginal suppositories [77, 133] or gel [134], oral micronized progesterone [135–137], and intramuscular injections [138]. Even nasal [139] and sublingual [140] routes of administration have been described, but experience with them is limited, and their efficacy for raising serum progesterone concentrations has not been established. Transdermal therapy is not practical because of the relatively large surface areas required to achieve physiologic serum concentrations. Normal luteal phase progesterone concentrations generally can be achieved easily via the vaginal or intramuscular routes of administration [141]. Evidence suggests that vaginal progesterone treatment is associated with a "first uterine pass effect" that may result in greater intrauterine concentrations or effects than other forms of treatment at similar serum concentrations [134, 142].

Supplemental progesterone treatment has been reported to correct the histologic endometrial maturation delay observed in women with LPD [77] and to increase endometrial thickness [143]. One of the few randomized, controlled trials to examine the effects of treatment in women with LPD found that progesterone supplementation improved cycle fecundity when compared to no treatment [144]. Trials comparing the efficacy of progesterone supplementation and clomiphene treatment suggest that the two are equally effective [145, 146].

When supplementation is indicated, only pure progesterone should be used. Although concerns have lingered, the results of numerous prospective cohort studies involving thousands of women indicate that the doses and durations of progesterone therapy commonly used to treat LPD or to provide luteal support in the assisted reproductive technologies do not pose any significant teratogenic risk. Treatment during early pregnancy with synthetic nortestosterone-derived progestational agents may have virilizing effects on a female fetus and therefore should be avoided [147].

Human Chorionic Gonadotropin

Exogenous hCG stimulates the CL directly and represents another effective alternative to CC treatment or exogenous progesterone supplementation for the treatment of LPD. Supplemental hCG may be used empirically or as specific treatment when an abnormally low-amplitude midcycle LH surge or inadequate luteal phase LH secretion can be identified. Recommendations regarding the dosage of exogenous hCG range widely [93, 148]. Some clinicians advocate administration of 5000 to 10,000 IU at the time of ovulation followed by an additional 5000 IU 5 to 7 days later. Alternately, smaller doses (2500 IU) may be offered at more frequent intervals (every 3 to 4 days after ovulation) [149]. Disadvantages of such treatment include menstrual delay, false-positive pregnancy tests, and an increased risk of ovarian hyperstimulation syndrome in cycles stimulated with exogenous gonadotropins [138].

Supplemental exogenous hCG during early pregnancy has also been used in efforts to reduce the risk of spontaneous abortion in women with histories of recurrent early pregnancy loss. Early reports suggested that such treatment might reduce the risk of recurrent abortion [150–152], but convincing evidence of its efficacy is lacking.

Dopamine Agonists

Given the established association between hyperprolactinemia and LPD [29, 153–155], treatment with bromocriptine or other dopamine agonists (cabergoline) is logical when elevated prolactin levels are observed. Hyperprolactinemia is common in infertile women, and treatment clearly appears to improve fecundity reatment with bromocriptine [156]. Dopamine agonists lower prolactin production via a direct action on pituitary lactotrophs and are the drug of choice for LPD associated with hyperprolactinemia [157–160].

Adverse effects of dopamine agonists include gastrointestinal upset and orthostatic hypotension. Starting with small doses at bedtime and increasing in increments as needed or vaginal administration reduces the incidence and severity of side effects. Treatment at the doses required to restore euprolactinemia generally should continue until pregnancy is achieved. Given the evidence that abnormally low prolactin levels may also compromise luteal function [36, 37], oversuppression of prolactin levels is best avoided [161]. Although large-scale follow-up studies of pregnancies conceived during bromocriptine treatment have revealed no evidence of increased risk of congenital malformations [162], there is no indication to continue treatment once pregnancy is documented and fetal heart activity is observed.

CHOICE OF THERAPY FOR TREATMENT OF LUTEAL PHASE DEFICIENCY

Given the numerous pathophysiologic mechanisms that might result in poor luteal function and the difficulty of defining which might be operating in any given individual woman (except perhaps in those with hyperprolactinemia), treatment for LPD is largely empiric. Moreover, in the absence of any well-established and generally accepted criteria for the clinical diagnosis of LPD, it is difficult to validate the effectiveness of any form of treatment for the disorder.

Clomiphene citrate or exogenous gonadotropin-induced ovarian follicular stimulation, luteal phase progesterone supplementation, and postovulatory hCG stimulation all can effectively increase luteal phase serum progesterone concentrations; however, comparative studies of outcomes have been rare [145, 146, 163, 164]. None have been strictly randomized controlled trials, two were retrospective cohort studies subject to selection bias [146, 164], all have lacked sufficient power, and any

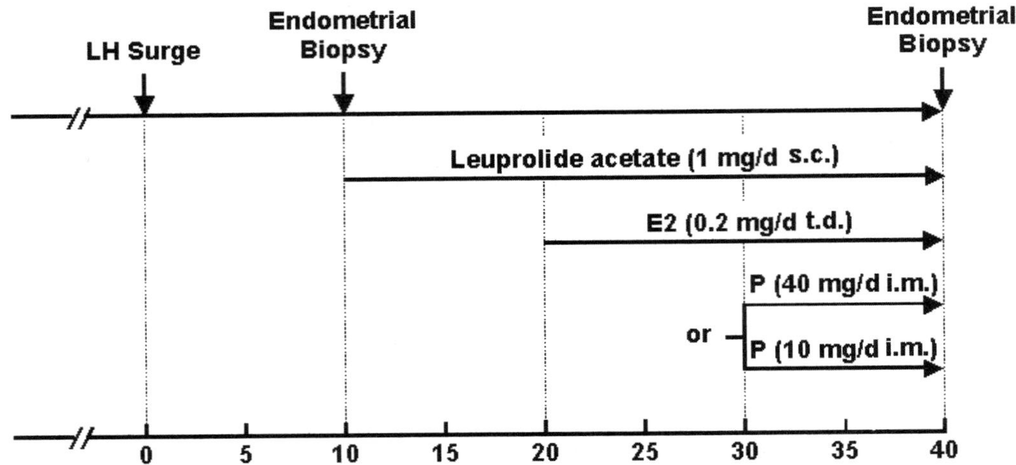

FIGURE 31.2 Study Design. E2, estradiol; P, progesterone in oil; s.c., subcutaneous; t.d., transdermal; i.m., intramuscular

differences observed were not significant. Numerous other studies have described the results of treatment with progestational agents (50% to 70% pregnancy rates) [77, 165, 166], clomiphene citrate (19% to 88% pregnancy rates) [116, 130, 167–169], follicle-stimulating hormone (33% to 40% pregnancy rates) [170–172], or varying treatments (36% to 81% pregnancy rates) [78, 173]. In general, because pregnancies may result from biologic variation or be treatment-independent, descriptive studies do not allow causal inferences. Before any confident conclusions can be drawn, a clear definition of LPD must be established, and more rigorous clinical studies with larger sample sizes must be conducted.

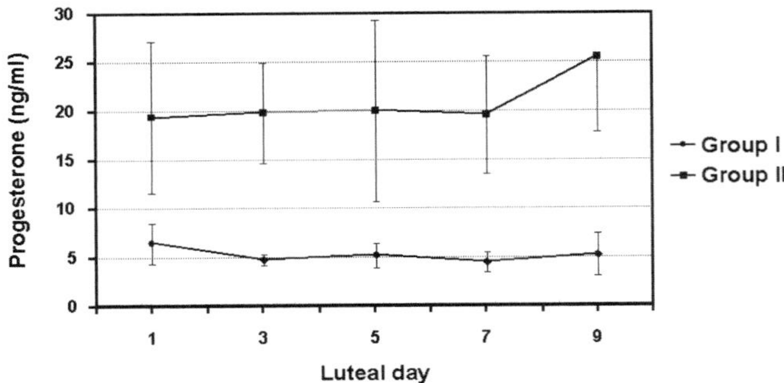

FIGURE 31.3 Mean progesterone concentrations in Group I (progesterone 10 mg/d i.m.) and Group II (progesterone 40 mg/d i.m.)

NEW DATA AND NEW PERSPECTIVES

The foundation for the concept of LPD is that inadequate CL progesterone production results in delayed or otherwise abnormal secretory endometrial development that predisposes to delayed or failed embryo implantation. Surprisingly, despite more than 50 years having elapsed since the concept was first suggested and the histologic endometrial dating criteria were first described, no study has tested this pathophysiologic concept directly, until very recently.

We studied a group of normally cycling young women with demonstrated normal patterns of endometrial histologic maturation in tissue specimens obtained 10 days after detection of the midcycle LH surge in a spontaneous menstrual cycle. Subjects were then suppressed with a long-acting Gn-RH agonist (leuprolide acetate, 0.2 mg/d s.c.; serum estradiol <40 pg/mL), treated with a fixed physiologic dose of transdermal estradiol (0.2 mg/d; serum estradiol 134.9 ± 71.2 pg/mL), and randomized to receive progesterone replacement at physiologic (40 mg/day i.m.; serum progesterone 21.6 ± 10.0 ng/mL [Figure 31.2]) or subphysiologic (10 mg/day i.m.; serum progesterone 5.0 ± 1.4 ng/mL) levels before repeat biopsy on the 10th day of combined hormone replacement (Figure 31.3). Surprisingly, the patterns of endometrial histologic maturation observed in the two groups were indistinguishable. Although preliminary, these observations clearly challenge the traditional concept that abnormally low levels of progesterone production result in delayed histologic endometrial maturation. They further suggest that the secretory endometrium tolerates wide variations in serum progesterone concentrations and that the characteristic histologic features of maturation may relate more to the duration than to the level of progesterone exposure.

The results of another very recent study that sought to more rigorously define the histologic characteristics of normal secretory endometrial maturation and to address the many controversies regarding the utility of traditional dating criteria have provided additional new insights. We

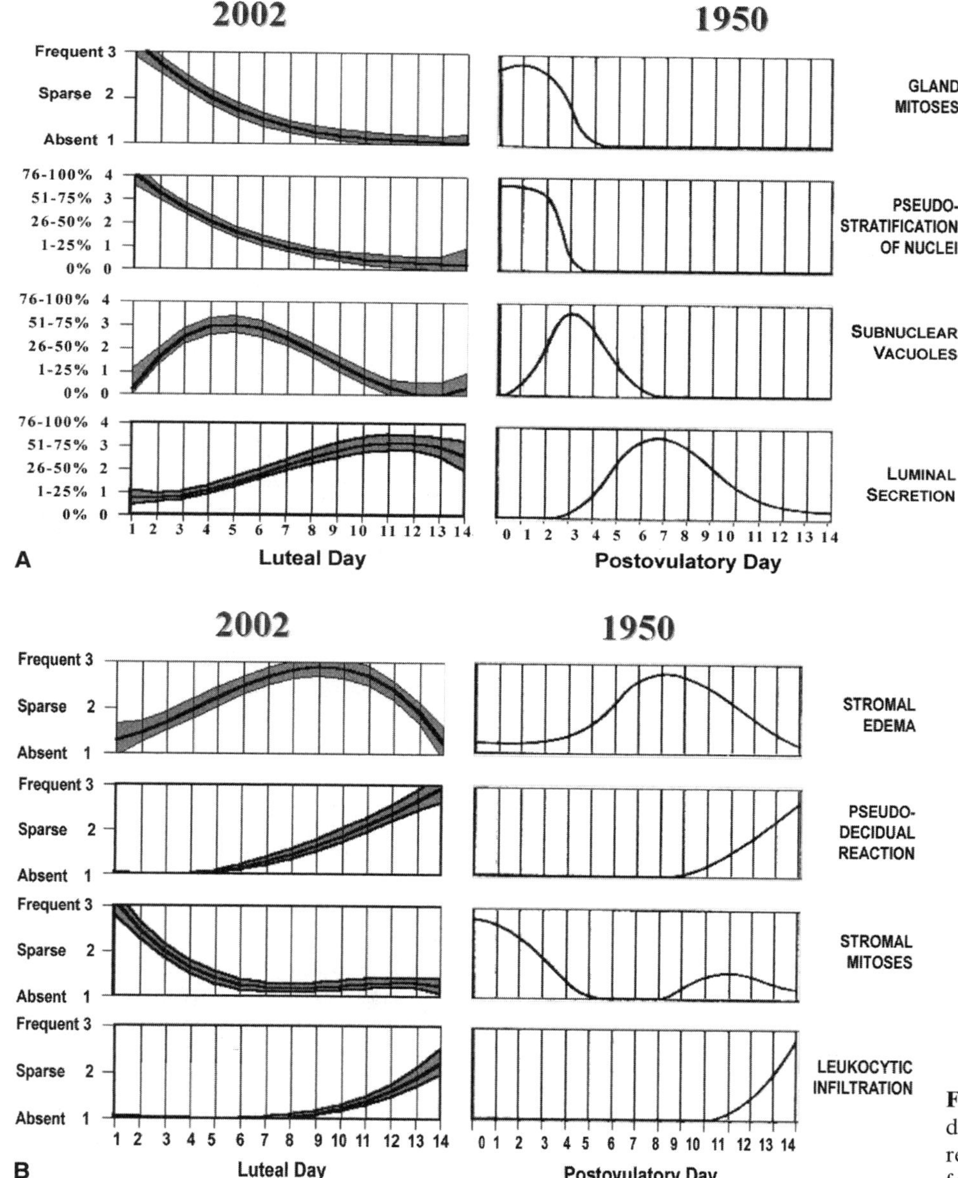

FIGURE 31.4A, B Comparison of traditional histologic dating criteria [4] with results of randomized controlled trial in fertile women.

recruited 130 normally cycling women (age 20 to 35 years) with proven fertility in whom we identified the midcycle LH surge (luteal day 0) and performed endometrial biopsies on randomly assigned days across the secretory phase of spontaneous menstrual cycles. Adjacent sections of tissue specimens were examined by three independent gynecologic pathologists masked to the day of sampling and scored for 32 different histologic features that were defined before initiation of the study (Figure 31.4a and b). For each histologic feature, mean scores and the extent of between-tissue and inter-observer variation were determined for each luteal day (1 to 14). Features were ranked according to the strength of correlation with luteal day, score range (maximum minus minimum), and inter-observer variation, and a final rank order was established giving the three performance measures equal weight.

Our observations were in many ways consistent with the classical description, but in others, very different (Figure 31.4a and b). Whereas some of the traditional histologic dating criteria were among the features exhibiting the best overall performance in our objective analysis, others clearly were not. We found that the characteristics of secretory phase endometrial histology exhibit greater individual variations than indicated in the classical description. Whereas the most dramatic, consistent, and discriminating changes in score for the best-performing features were observed during the putative implantation window (luteal days 6 to 10), we were unable to identify any one or combination of histologic features that could effectively define a specific luteal day. These observations challenge directly the validity of traditional histologic endometrial dating and therefore also challenge the conclusions of studies using those criteria to define a population of women with LPD or to evaluate the effect of treatment.

CONCLUSIONS

Despite years of basic and clinical investigation, our understanding of CL physiology and pathophysiology is still rudimentary. The weight of available evidence indicates that LPD is a real disorder characterized by abnormally low levels of CL progesterone production, most likely representing a subtle form of ovulation dysfunction as one point on a spectrum ranging from anovulation to normal ovulatory function. The disorder is relatively common in cycling hyperprolactinemic women, is often a symptom of deteriorating ovulatory function in women under nutritional or physical stress, and is often observed as regular cycles resume in previously anovulatory or ammenorheic women. LPD may be identified in otherwise normally cycling infertile women, and plausible pathophysiologic mechanisms suggest that the disorder may cause subfertility or reproductive failure, when it is a consistent phenomenon. LPD also occurs, at least sporadically, in women with normal reproductive histories. The true prevalence of LPD, in subfertile and fertile women, is unknown and cannot be determined without a properly validated or even uniformly accepted diagnostic criterion.

Diagnosis of LPD is most clearly established by demonstration of abnormally low integrated luteal phase progesterone concentrations. This criterion is useful for investigational purposes but impractical in clinical practice. Alternative methods for diagnosis of LPD have numerous pitfalls. Inconsistent diurnal variations and the pulsatile nature of CL progesterone secretion prevent confident interpretation of random or even timed single or serial serum progesterone concentrations. The utility of traditional histologic endometrial dating criteria has been effectively undermined by wide variations in interpretation among different observers, poor correlation with integrated luteal phase serum progesterone concentrations, and other legitimate challenges to their validity. Paradoxically, the oldest and least sophisticated diagnostic criterion, consistent observation of grossly short luteal phase duration, remains the most objective and reliable diagnostic standard for clinical practice. For diagnostic purposes, luteal phase duration is most accurately defined as the interval from detection of the midcycle LH surge to onset of the subsequent menses.

Any of the described clinical treatments for LPD, including the use of CC or exogenous gonadotropins to stimulate improved or multiple follicular development and luteal phase progesterone supplementation or exogenous hCG stimulation, can increase luteal phase progesterone concentrations. Results of the few comparative clinical trials and numerous descriptive studies have been inconclusive. Consequently, a choice among treatments is entirely empiric, and no one treatment can be considered superior. Specific treatment is possible only when LPD is associated with a thyroid disorder or hyperprolactinemia. The outcome to be expected from any form of treatment for LPD is and will remain speculative until the disorder is clearly defined and rigorous clinical studies based on that definition are conducted.

References

1. Rock, J., and Bartlett, M. K. (1937). Biopsy studies of human endometrium: criteria of dating and information about amenorrhea, menorrhagia, and time of ovulation. *JAMA* 108(24), 2022–2028.
2. Allen, W. M., and Corner, G. W. (1929). Physiology of the corpus luteum III. Normal growth and implantation of embryos after very early ablation of the ovaries, under the influence of extracts of the corpus luteum. *Am. J. Physiol.* 88, 340–346.
3. Jones, G. E. S. (1949). Some newer aspects of management of infertility. *JAMA* 141, 1123.
4. Noyes, R. W., Hertig, A. T., and Rock, J. P. (1950). Dating the endometrial biopsy. *Fertil. Steril.* 1, 3.
5. Carr, B. R., MacDonald, P. C., and Simpson, E. (1982). The role of lipoproteins in the regulation of progesterone secretion by the human corpus luteum. *Fertil. Steril.* 38, 303.
6. Baird, D. T., Backstrom, T., McNeilly, A. S., Smith, S. K., and Wathen, C. G. (1984). Effect of enucleation of the corpus luteum at different stages of the luteal phase of the human menstrual cycle on subsequent follicular development. *J. Reprod. Fertil.* 70(2), 615–624.
7. Belchetz, P. E., Plant, T. M., Nakai, Y., Keogh, E. J., and Knobil, E. (1978). Hypophysial responses to continuous and intermittent delivery of hypopthalamic gonadotropin-releasing hormone. *Science* 202(4368), 631–633.
8. Mais, V., Kazer, R. R., Cetel, N. S., Rivier, J., Vale, W., and Yen, S. S. (1986). The dependency of folliculogenesis and corpus luteum function on pulsatile gonadotropin secretion in cycling women using a gonadotropin-releasing hormone antagonist as a probe. *J. Clin. Endocrinol. Metab.* 62(6), 1250–1255.
9. Van de Wiele, R. L., Bogumil, J., Dyrenfrith, I., Ferin, M., Jewelewicz, R., Warren, M., Rizkallah, T., and Mikhail, G. (1971). Mechanisms regulating the menstrual cycle in women. *Rec. Prog. Hormone Res.* 26, 63–82.
10. Ellinwood, W. E., Norman, R. L., and Spies, H. G. (1984). Changing frequency of pulsatile luteinizing hormone and progesterone secretion during the luteal phase of the menstrual cycle of rhesus monkeys. *Biol. Reprod.* 31(4), 714–722.
11. Filicori, M., Butler, J. P., and Crowley, Jr. W. F. (1984). Neuroendocrine regulation of the corpus luteum in the human. Evidence for pulsatile progesterone secretion. *J. Clin. Invest.* 73(6), 1638–1647.

12. Wilks, J. W., and Noble, A. S. (1983). Steroidogenic responsiveness of the monkey corpus luteum to exogenous chorionic gonadotropin. *Endocrinol.* 112(4), 1256–1266.
13. Dhont, M., VandeKerckhove, D., Vermeulen, A., and Vandeweghe, M. (1974). Daily concentrations of plasma LH, FSH, estradiol, estrone and progesterone throughout the menstrual cycle. *Eur. J. Obstet. Gynecol. Reprod. Biol.* 4 (Suppl 1), S153–S159.
14. Fritz, M. A., Hess, D. L., and Patton, P. E. (1992). Influence of corpus luteum age on the steroidogenic response to exogenous human chorionic gonadotropin in normal cycling women. *Am. J. Obstet. Gynecol.* 167(3), 709–716.
15. DiZerega, G. S., and Hodgen, G. D. (1981). Luteal phase dysfunction infertility: A sequel to aberrant folliculogenesis. *Fertil. Steril.* 35, 489.
16. Strott, C. A., Cargille, C. M., Ross, G. T., and Lipsett, M. B. (1970). The short luteal phase. *J. Clin. Endocrinol. Metab.* 30(2), 246–251.
17. Sherman, B. M., and Korenman, S. G. (1974). Measurement of plasma LH, FSH, estradiol and progesterone in disorders of the human menstrual cycle: The short luteal phase. *J. Clin. Endocrinol. Metabol.* 38, 89.
18. Cook, C. L., Rao, C. W. V., and Yussman, M. A. (1983). Plasma gonadotropin and sex steroid hormone levels during early, midfollicular and midluteal phases of women with luteal phase defects. *Fertil. Steril.* 40, 45.
19. Stouffer, R. L., and Hodgen, G. D. (1980). Induction of luteal phase defects in rhesus monkeys by follicular fluid administration at the onset of the menstrual cycle. *J. Clin. Endocrinol. Metabol.* 51, 669.
20. Sheehan, K. L., Casper, R. F., and Yen, S. S. C. (1982). Luteal phase defects induced by an agonist of luteinizing hormone-releasing factor: A model for fertility control. *Science* 215, 170.
21. Soules, M. R., Clifton, D. K., Cohen, N. L., Bremner, W. J., and Steiner, R. A. (1989). Luteal phase deficiency: Abnormal gonadotropin and progesterone secretion patterns. *J. Clin. Endocrinol. Metabol.* 69(4), 813–820.
22. Soules, M. R., McLachlan, R. I., Ek, M., Dahl, K. D., Cohen, N. L., and Bremner, W. J. (1989). Luteal phase deficiency: Characterization of reproductive hormones over the menstrual cycle. *J. Clin. Endocrinol. Metabol.* 69(4), 804–812.
23. De Souza, M. J., Miller, B. E., Loucks, A. B., Luciano, A. A., Pescatello, L. S., Campbell, C. G., and Lasley, B. L. (1998). High frequency of luteal phase deficiency and anovulation in recreational women runners: Blunted elevation in follicle-stimulating hormone observed during luteal-follicular transition. *J. Clin. Endocrinol. Metabol.* 83(12), 4220–4232.
24. Pirke, K. M., Schweiger, U., Strowitzki, T., Tuschl, R. J., Laessle, R. G., Broocks, A., Huber, B., and Middendorf, R. (1989). Dieting causes menstrual irregularities in normal weight young women through impairment of episodic luteinizing hormone secretion. *Fertil. Steril.* 51(2), 263–268.
25. Loucks, A. B., Mortola, J. F., Girton, L., and Yen, S. S. (1984). Alterations in the hypothalamic-pituitary-ovarian and the hypothalamic-pituitary-adrenal axes in athletic women. *J. Clin. Endocrinol. Metab.* 68(2), 402–411.
26. Soules, M. R., Steiner, R. A., Clifton, D. K., and Bremner, W. J. (1984). Abnormal patterns of pulsatile luteinizing hormone in women with luteal phase deficiency. *Obstet. Gynecol.* 63(5), 626–629.
27. Soules, M. R., Clifton, D. K., Bremner, W. J., and Steiner, R. A. (1987). Corpus luteum insufficiency induced by a rapid gonadotropin-releasing hormone-induced gonadotropin secretion pattern in the follicular phase. *J. Clin. Endocrinol. Metab.* 65(3), 457–464.
28. Burrow, G. N. (1999). The thyroid gland and reproduction. In *Reproductive Endocrinology*, eds. S. C. C. Yen and R. B. Jaffe, 413–435.
29. Seppala, M., Ranta, T., and Hirvonen, E. (1976). Hyperprolactinaemia and luteal insufficiency. *Lancet* 1(7953), 229–230.
30. Franks, S., Murray, M. A., Jequier, A. M., Steele, S. J., Nabarro, J. D., and Jacobs, H. S. (1975). Incidence and significance of hyperprolactinaemia in women with amenorrhea. *Clin. Endocrinol.* 4(6), 597–607.
31. Corenblum, B., Pairaudeau, N., and Shewchuk, A. B. (1976). Prolactin hypersecretion and short luteal phase defects. *Obstet. Gynecol.* 47(4), 486–488.
32. Spark, R. F., Pallotta, J., Naftolin, F., and Clemens, R. (1976). Galactorrhea-amenorrhea syndromes: Etiology and treatment. *Ann. Intern. Med.* 84(5), 532–537.
33. Bahamondes, L., Saboya, W., Tambascia, M., and Trevisan, M. (1979). Galactorrhea, infertility, and short luteal phases in hyperprolactinemic women: Early stage of amenorrhea-galactorrhea? *Fertil. Steril.* 32(4), 476–477.
34. del Pozo, E., Wyss, H., Tollis, G., Alcaniz, J., Campana, A., and Naftolin, F. Prolactin and deficient luteal function. *Obstet. Gynecol.* 53(3), 282–286.
35. McNeilly, A. S., Kerin, J., Swanston, I. A., Bramley, T. A., and Baird, D. T. (1980). Changes in the binding of human chorionic gonadotrophin/luteinizing hormone, follicle-stimulating hormone and prolactin to human corpora lutea during the menstrual cycle and pregnancy. *J. Endocrinol.* 87(3), 315–325.
36. McNatty, K. P., Sawers, R. S., and McNeilly, A. S. (1974). A possible role for prolactin in control of steroid secretion by the human Graafian follicle. *Nature* 250(468), 653–655.
37. Schulz, K. D., Geiger, W., del Pozo, E., and Kunzig, H. J. (1978). Pattern of sexual steroids, prolactin, and gonadotropic hormones during prolactin inhibition in normally cycling women. *Am. J. Gynecol.* 132(5), 561–566.
38. Kauppila, A., Leinonen, P., Vihko, R., and Ylostalo, P. (1982). Metoclopramide-induced hyperprolactinemia impairs ovarian follicle maturation and corpus luteum function in women. *J. Clin. Endocrinol. Metab.* 54(5), 955–960.
39. Richardson, D. W., Goldsmith, L. T., Pohl, C. R., Schallenberger, E., and Knobil, E. (1985). The role of prolactin in the regulation of the primate corpus luteum. *J. Clin. Endocrinol. Metab.* 60(3), 501–504.
40. Moult, P. J., Rees, L. H., and Besser, G. M. (1982). Pulsatile gonadotrophin secretion in hyperprolactinaemic amenorrhoea an the response to bromocriptine therapy. *Clin. Endocrinol.* 16(2), 153–162.
41. Milenkovi, L., D'Angelo, G., Kelly, P. A., and Weiner, R. I. (1994). Inhibition of gonadotropin hormone-releasing hormone release by prolactin from neuronal cell lines through prolactin receptors. *Proc. Natl. Acad. Sci.* 91(4), 1244–1247.

42. Soules, M. R., Bremner, W. J., Steiner, R. A., and Clifton, D. K. (1991). Prolactin secretion and corpus luteum function in women with luteal phase deficiency. *J. Clin. Endocrinol. Metab.* 72(5), 986–992.
43. Fazleabas, A. T., Hild-Petito, S., and Verhage, H. G. (1994). Secretory proteins and growth factors of the baboon (Papio anubis) uterus: Potential roles in pregnancy. *Cell. Biol. Int.* 18(12), 1145–1153.
44. Joshi, S. G., Rao, R., Henriques, E. E., Raikar, R. S., and Gordon, M. (1986). Luteal phase concentrations of a progestagen-associated endometrial protein (PEP) in the serum of cycling women with adequate or inadequate endometrium. *J. Clin. Endocrinol. Metab.* 63(5), 1247–1249.
45. Ilesanmi, A. O., Hawkins, D. A., and Lessey, B. A. (1993). Immunohistochemical markers of uterine receptivity in the human endometrium. *Microsc. Res. Tech.* 25(3), 208–222.
46. Lessey, B. A., Killam, A. P., Metzger, D. A., Haney, A. F., Greene, G. L., and McCarty, Jr. K. S. (1988). Immunohistochemical analysis of human uterine estrogen and progesterone receptors throughout the menstrual cycle. *J. Clin. Endocrinol. Metab.* 67(2), 334–340.
47. Garcia, E., Bouchard, P., De Brux, J., Berdah, J., Frydman, R., Schaison, G., Milgrom, E., and Perrot-Applanat, M. (1988). Use of immunocytochemistry of progesterone and estrogen receptors for endometrial dating. *J. Clin. Endocrinol. Metab.* 67(1), 80–87.
48. Press, M. F., Udove, J. A., and Greene, G. L. (1988). Progesterone receptor distribution in the human endometrium. Analysis using monoclonal antibodies to the human progesterone receptor. *Am. J. Pathol.* 131(1), 112–124.
49. Gautray, J. P., de Brux, J., Tajchner, G., Robel, P., and Mouren, M. (1981). Clinical investigation of the menstrual cycle. III. Clinical, endometrial, and endocrine aspects of luteal defect. *Fertil. Steril.* 35(3), 296–303.
50. Gravanis, A., Zorn, J. R., Tanguy, G., Nessmann, C., Cedard, L., and Robel, P. (1984). The "dysharmonic luteal phase" syndrome: Endometrial progesterone receptor and estradiol dehydrogenase. *Fertil. Steril.* 42(5), 730–736.
51. Laatikainen, T., Andersson, B., Karkkainen, J., and Wahlstrom, T. (1983). Progestin receptor levels in endometria with delayed or incomplete secretory changes. *Obstet. Gynecol.* 62(5), 592–595.
52. Saracoglu, O. F., Aksel, S., Yeoman, R. R., and Wiebe, R. H. (1985). Endometrial estradiol and progesterone receptors in patients with luteal phase defects and endometriosis. *Fertil. Steril.* 43(6), 851–855.
53. Spirtos, N. J., Yurewicz, E. C., Moghissi, K. S., Magyar, D. M., Sundareson, A. S., and Bottoms, S. F. (1985). Pseudocorpus luteum insufficiency: A study of cytosol progesterone receptors in human endometrium. *Obstet. Gynecol.* 65(4), 535–540.
54. Levy, C., Robel, P., Gautray, J. P., De Brux, J., Verma, U., Descomps, B., and Baulieu, E. E. (1980). Estradiol and progesterone receptors in human endometrium: Normal and abnormal menstrual cycles and early pregnancy. *Am. J. Obstet. Gynecol.* 136(5), 646–651.
55. McRae, M. A., Blasco, L., and Lyttle, C. R. (1984). Serum hormones and their receptors in women with normal and inadequate corpus luteum function. *Fertil. Steril.* 42(1), 58–63.
56. Lessey, B. A., Yeh, I., Castelbaum, A. J., Fritz, M. A., Ilesanmi, A. O., Korzeniowski, P., Sun, J., and Chwalisz, K. (1996). Endometrial progesterone receptors and markers of uterine receptivity in the window of implantation. *Fertil. Steril.* 65(3), 477–483.
57. Lessey, B. A., Damjanovich, L., Coutifaris, C., Castelbaum, A., Albelda, S. M., and Buck, C. A. (1992). Integrin adhesion molecules in the human endometrium. Correlation with the normal and abnormal menstrual cycle. *J. Clin. Invest.* 90(1), 188–195.
58. Bergh, P. A., and Navot, D. (1992). The impact of embryonic development and endometrial maturity on the timing of implantation. *Fertil. Steril.* 58(3), 537–542.
59. Hertig, A. T., Rock, J., and Adams, E. C. (1956). A description of 34 human ova within the first 17 days of development. *Am. J. Anat.* 98, 435–493.
60. Balasch, J., and Vanrell, J. A. (1986). Luteal phase deficiency: An inadequate endometrial response to normal hormone stimulation. *Intl. J. Fertil.* 31(5), 368–371.
61. Grunfeld, L., Sandler, B., Fox, J., Boyd, C., Kaplan, P., and Navot, D. (1989). Luteal phase deficiency after completely normal follicular and periovulatory phases. *Fertil. Steril.* 52(6), 919–923.
62. Batista, M. C., Cartledge, T. P., Zellmer, A. W., Merino, M. J., Nieman, L. K., Loriaux, D. L., and Merriam, G. R. (1996). A prospective controlled study of luteal and endometrial abnormalities in an infertile population. *Fertil. Steril.* 65(3), 495–502.
63. Lessey, B. A., Castelbaum, A. J., Sawin, S. W., and Sun, J. (1995). Integrins as markers of uterine receptivity in women with primary unexplained infertility. *Fertil. Steril.* 63(3), 535–542.
64. Csapo, A. I., Pulkkinen, M. O., Ruttner, B., Sauvage, J. P., and Wiest, W. G. (1972). The significance of the human corpus luteum in pregnancy maintenance. I. Preliminary studies. *Am. J. Obstet. Gynecol.* 112(8), 1061–1067.
65. Csapo, A. I., Pulkkinen, M. O., and Wiest, W. G. (1973). Effects of lutectomy and progesterone replacement therapy in early pregnant patients. *Am. J. Obstet. Gynecol.* 115(6), 759–765.
66. Navot, D., Laufer, N., Kopolovic, J., Rabinowitz, R., Birkenfeld, A., Lewin, A., Granat, M., Margalioth, E. J., and Schenker, J. G. (1986). Artificially induced endometrial cycles and establishment of pregnancies in the absence of ovaries. *N. Engl. J. Med.* 314(13), 806–811.
67. Scott, R., Navot, D., Liu, H. C., and Rosenwaks, Z. (1991). A human in vivo model for the luteoplacental shift. *Fertil. Steril.* 56(3), 481–484.
68. Devroey, P., Camus, M., Palermo, G., Smitz, J., Van Waesberghe, L., Wisanto, A., Wijbo, I., and Van Steirteghem, A. C. (1990). Placental production of estradiol and progesterone after oocyte donation in patients with primary ovarian failure. *Am. J. Obstet. Gynecol.* 162(1), 66–70.
69. Gibson, M. (1990). Clinical evaluation of luteal function. *Sem. Reprod. Endocrinol.* 8, 130–141.
70. Somkuti, S., Appenzeller, M. F., and Lessey, B. A. (1995). Advances in the assessment of endometrial function. *Infert. Reprod. Med. Clin. North Am.* 6, 303–308.
71. Jones, G. S. (1976). The luteal phase defect. *Fertil. Steril.* 27, 351.

72. Noyes, R. W. (1959). The underdeveloped secretory endometrium. *Am. J. Obstet. Gynecol.* 77(5), 929–945.
73. Li, T., Dockery, P., and Cooke, I. (1991). Endometrial development in the luteal phase of women with various types of infertility: Comparison with women of normal fertility. *Hum. Reprod.* 6, 325.
74. Lenton, E. A., Landgren, B. M., and Sexton, L. (1984). Normal variation in the length of the luteal phase of the menstrual cycle: Identification of the short luteal phase. *Br. J. Obstet. Gynaecol.* 91(7), 685–689.
75. Luciano, A. A., Peluso, J., Koch, E. I., Maier, D., Kuslis, S., and Davison, E. (1990). Temporal relationship and reliability of the clinical, hormonal, and ultrasonographic indices of ovulation in infertile women. *Obstet. Gynecol.* 75, 412–416.
76. Downs, K. A., and Gibson, M.(1983). Basal body temperature graph and the luteal phase defect. *Fertil. Steril.* 40(4), 466–468.
77. Soules, M. R., Wiebe, R. H., Aksel, S., and Hammond, C. B. (1977). The diagnosis and therapy of luteal phase deficiency. *Fertil. Steril.* 28(10), 1033–1037.
78. Annos, T., Thompson, I. E., and Taymor, M. L. (1980). Luteal phase deficiency and infertility: Difficulties encountered in diagnosis and treatment. *Obstet. Gynecol.* 55(6), 705–710.
79. Jordan, J., Craig, K., Clifton, D. K., and Soules, M. R. (1994). Luteal phase defect: The sensitivity and specificity of diagnostic methods in common clinical use. *Fertil. Steril.* 62(1), 54–62.
80. Soules, M. R., McLachlan, R. I., Ek, M., Dahl, K. D., Cohen, N. L., and Bremner, W. J. (1989). Luteal phase deficiency: Characterization of reproductive hormones over the menstrual cycle. *J. Clin. Endocrinol. Metabol.* 69(4), 804–812.
81. Hecht, B. R., Bardawil, W. A., Khan-Dawood, F. S., and Dawood, M. Y. (1990). Luteal insufficiency: Correlation between endometrial dating and integrated progesterone output in clomiphene citrate-induced cycles. *Am. J. Obstet. Gynecol.* 163, 1986–1991.
82. Shepard, M. K., and Senturia, Y. D. (1977). Comparison of serum progesterone and endometrial biopsy for confirmation of ovulation and evaluation of luteal function. *Fertil. Steril.* 28(5), 541–548.
83. Li, T. C., Lenton, E. A., Dockery, P., and Cooke, I. D. (1990). A comparison of some clinical and endocrinological features between cycles with normal and defective luteal phases in women with unexplained infertility. *Hum. Reprod.* 5(7), 805–810.
84. Abraham, G. E., Maroulis, G. B., and Marshall, J. R. (1974). Evaluation of ovulation and corpus luteum function using measurements of plasma progesterone. *Obstet. Gynecol.* 44(4), 522–525.
85. Hull, M. G., Savage, P. E., Bromham, D. R., Ismail, A. A., and Morris, A. F. (1982). The value of a single serum progesterone measurement in the midluteal phase as a criterion of a potentially fertile cycle ("ovulation") derived form treated and untreated conception cycles. *Fertil. Steril.* 37(3), 355–360.
86. Wathen, N. C., Perry, L., Lilford, R. J., and Chard, T. (1984). Interpretation of single progesterone measurement in diagnosis of anovulation and defective luteal phase: Observations on analysis of the normal range. *Br. Med. J. Clin. Res. Ed.* 288(6410), 7–9.
87. Rosenfeld, D. L., Chudow, S., and Bronson, R. A. (1980). Diagnosis of luteal phase inadequacy. *Obstet. Gynecol.* 56(2), 193–196.
88. Fujimoto, V. Y., Clifton, D. K., Cohen, N. L., and Soules, M. R. (1990). Variability of serum prolactin and progesterone levels in normal women: The relevance of single hormone measurements in the clinical setting. *Obstet. Gynecol.* 76(1), 71–78.
89. Ellinwood, W. E., Norman, R. L., and Spies, H. G. (1984). Changing frequency of pulsatile luteinizing hormone and progesterone secretion during the luteal phase of the menstrual cycle of rhesus monkeys. *Biol. Reprod.* 31(4), 714–722.
90. Filicori, M., Butler, J. P., and Crowley, Jr. W. F. (1984). Neuroendocrine regulation of the corpus luteum in the human. Evidence for pulsatile progesterone secretion. *J. Clin. Invest.* 73(6), 1638–1647.
91. Soules, M. R., Clifton, D. K., Steiner, R. A., Cohen, N. L., and Bremner, W. J. (1988). The corpus luteum: Determinants of progesterone secretion in the normal menstrual cycle. *Obstet. Gynecol.* 71(5), 659–666.
92. Syrop, C. H., and Hammond, M. G. (1987). Diurnal variations in midluteal serum progesterone measurements. *Fertil. Steril.* 47(1), 67–70.
93. Wentz, A. C. (1979). Physiologic and clinical considerations in luteal phase defects. *Clin. Obstet. Gynecol.* 22(1), 169–185.
94. Fritz, M. A. (1988). Inadequate luteal function and recurrent abortion: Diagnosis and treatment of luteal phase deficiency. *Semin. Reprod. Endocrinol.* 6, 129–144.
95. Wentz, A. C. (1980). Endometrial biopsy in the evaluation of infertility. *Fertil. Steril.* 33(2), 121–124.
96. Castelbaum, A. J., Wheeler, J., Coutifaris, C. B., Mastroianni, Jr. L., and Lessey, B. A. (1994). Timing of the endometrial biopsy may be critical for the accurate diagnosis of luteal phase deficiency. *Fertil. Steril.* 61(3), 443–447.
97. Batista, M. C., Cartledge, T. P., Merino, M. J., Axiotis, C., Platia, M. P., Merriam, G. R., Loriaux, D. L., and Nieman, L. K. (1993). Midluteal phase endometrial biopsy does not accurately predict luteal function. *Fertil. Steril.* 59(2), 294–300.
98. Santoro, N., Goldsmith, L. T., Heller, D., Illsley, N., McGovern, P., Molina, C., Peters, S., Skurnick, J. H., Forst, C., and Weiss, G. (2000). Luteal progesterone relates to histological endometrial maturation in fertile women. *J. Clin. Endocrinol. Metab.* 85(11), 4207–4211.
99. Batista, M. C., Cartledge, T. P., Zellmer, A. W., Merino, M. J., Nieman, L. K., Loriaux, D. L., and Merriam, G. R. (1996). A prospective controlled study of luteal and endometrial abnormalities in an infertile population. *Fertil. Steril.* 65(3), 495–502.
100. Aksel, S. (1980). Sporadic and recurrent luteal phase defects in cyclic women: Comparison with normal cycles. *Fertil. Steril.* 33(4), 372–377.
101. Davis, O. K., Berkeley, A. S., Naus, G. J., Cholst, I. N., and Freedman, K. S. (1989). The incidence of luteal phase defect in normal, fertile women, determined by serial endometrial biopsies. *Fertil. Steril.* 51(4), 582–586.
102. Shoupe, D., Mishell, Jr. D. R., Lacarra, M., Lobo, R. A., Horenstein, J., d'Ablaing, G., and Moyer, D. (1989). Correlation of endometrial maturation with four methods of estimating day of ovulation. *Obstet. Gynecol.* 73(1), 88–92.

103. Scott, R. T., Snyder, R. R., Strickland, D. M., Tyburski, C. C., Bagnall, J. A., Reed, K. R., Adair, C. A., and Hensley, S. B. (1988). The effect of interobserver variation in dating endometrial histology on the diagnosis of luteal phase defects. *Fertil. Steril.* 50(6), 888–892.
104. Duggan, M. A., Brashert, P., Ostor, A., Scurry, J., Billson, V., Kneafsey, P., and Difrancesco, L. (2001). The accuracy and interobserver reproducibility of endometrial dating. *Patholology* 33(3), 292–297.
105. Scott, R. T., Snyder, R. R., Bagnall, J. W., Reed, K. D., Adair, C. F., and Hensley, S. D. (1993). Evaluation of the impact of intraobserver variability on endometrial dating and the diagnosis of luteal phase defects. *Fertil. Steril.* 60(4), 652–657.
106. Balasch, J., Fabregues, F., Creus, M., and Vanrell, J. A. (1992). The usefulness of endometrial biopsy for luteal phase evaluation in infertility. *Hum. Reprod.* 7(7), 973–977.
107. Grunfeld, L., Walker, B., Bergh, P. A., Sandler, B., Hofmann, G., and Navot, D. (1991). High-resolution endovaginal ultrasonography of the endometrium: A noninvasive test for endometrial adequacy. *Obstet. Gynecol.* 78(2), 200–204.
108. Sakumoto, T., Inafuku, K., Miyara, M., Takamiyagi, N., Miyake, A., Shinkawa, T., and Nakayama, M. (1992). Hysteroscopic assessment of midsecretory-phase endometrium, with special reference to the luteal-phase defect. *Horm. Res.* 37 (Suppl 1), 48–52.
109. Glock, J. L., and Brumsted, J. R. (1995). Color flow pulsed Doppler ultrasound in diagnosing luteal phase defect. *Fertil. Steril.* 64(3), 500–504.
110. Steer, C. V., Tan, S. L., Dillon, D., Mason, B. A., and Campbell, S. (1995). Vaginal color Doppler assessment of uterine artery impedance correlates with immunohistochemical markers of endometrial receptivity required for the implantation of an embryo. *Fertil. Steril.* 63(1), 101–108.
111. McRae, M. A., Galle, P. C., and Joshi, S. G. (1991). The role of measurement of progestagen-associated endometrial protein in predicting adequate endometrial differentiation. *Hum. Reprod.* 6(6), 761–765.
112. DeVane, G. W., and Guzick, D. S. (1986). Bromocriptine therapy in normoprolactinemic women with unexplained infertility and galactorrhea. *Fertil. Steril.* 46(6), 1026–1031.
113. Karamardian, L. M., and Grimes, D. A. (1992). Luteal phase deficiency: Effect of treatment on pregnancy rates. *Am. J. Obstet. Gynecol.* 167(5), 1391–1398.
114. Markaverich, B. M., Upchurch, S., McCormack, S. A., Glasser, S. R., and Clark, J. H. (1981). Differential stimulation of uterine cells by nafoxidine and clomiphene: Relationship between nuclear estrogen receptors and type II estrogen binding sites and cellular growth. *Biol. Reprod.* 24(1), 171–181.
115. Kerin, J. F., Liu, J. H., Phillipou, G., and Yen, S. S. (1985). Evidence for a hypothalamic site of action of clomiphene citrate in women. *J. Clin. Endocrinol. Metab.* 61(2), 265–268.
116. Quagliarello, J., and Weiss, G. (1979). Clomiphene citrate in the management of infertility associated with shortened luteal phases. *Fertil. Steril.* 31(4), 373–377.
117. Dodson, K. S., MacNaughton, M. C., and Coutts, J. R. (1975). Infertility in women with apparently ovulatory cycles. II. The effects of clomiphene treatment on the profiles of gonadotrophin and sex steroid hormones in peripheral plasma. *Br. J. Obstet. Gynecol.* 82(8), 625–633.
118. Guzick, D. S., and Zeleznik, A. (1990). Efficacy of clomiphene citrate in the treatment of luteal phase deficiency: Quantity versus quality of preovulatory follicles. *Fertil. Steril.* 54(2), 206–210.
119. Cook, C. L., Schroeder, J. A., Yussman, M. A., and Sanfilippo, J. S. (1984). Induction of luteal phase defect with clomiphene citrate. *Am. J. Obstet. Gynecol.* 149(6), 613–616.
120. Dickey, R. P., Olar, T. T., Taylor, S. N., Curole, D. N., and Matulich, E. M. (1993). Relationship of endometrial thickness and pattern to fecundity in ovulation induction cycles: Effect of clomiphene citrate alone and with human menopausal gonadotropin. *Fertil. Steril.* 59(4), 756–760.
121. Eden, J. A., Place, J., Carter, G. D., Jones, J., Alaghband-Zadeh, J., and Pawson, M. E. (1989). The effect of clomiphene citrate on follicular phase increase in endometrial thickness and uterine volume. *Obstet. Gynecol.* 73(2), 187–190.
122. Randall, J. M., and Templeton, A. (1991). Transvaginal sonographic assessment of follicular and endometrial growth in spontaneous and clomiphene citrate cycles. *Fertil. Steril.* 56(2), 208–212.
123. Sgarlata, C. S., Mikhail, G., and Hertelendy, F. (1984). Clomiphene and tamoxifen inhibit progesterone synthesis in granulosa cells: Comparison with estradiol. *Endocrinolology* 114(6), 2032–2038.
124. Opsahl, M. S., Fitz, T. A., Rexroad, Jr. C. E., and Fritz, M. A. (1996). Effects of enclomiphene and zuclomiphene on basal and gonadotrophin-stimulated progesterone secretion by isolated subpopulations of small and large ovine luteal cells. *Hum. Reprod.* 11(6), 1250–1255.
125. Olsson, J. H., Dennefors, B., and Nilsson, L. (1986). Influence of clomiphene citrate in vivo on subsequent steroid formation and gonadotropic responsiveness in vitro of isolated human follicular cells. *Acta. Obstet. Gynecol. Scand.* 65(2), 115–119.
126. Olsson, J. H., and Granberg, S. (1990). Effect of clomiphene isomers on oestradiol synthesis in cultured human granulosa cells. *Hum. Reprod.* 5(8), 928–932.
127. Schmidt, G. E., Kim, M. H., Mansour, R., Torello, L., and Friedman, C. I. (1986). The effects of enclomiphene and zuclomiphene citrates on mouse embryos fertilized in vitro and in vivo. *Am. J. Obstet. Gynecol.* 154(4), 727–736.
128. Young, S. L., Opsahl, M. S., and Fritz, M. A. (1999). Serum concentrations of enclomiphene and zuclomiphene across consecutive cycles of clomiphene citrate therapy in anovulatory infertile women. *Fertil. Steril.* 71(4), 639–644.
129. Daly, D. C., Walters, C. A., Soto-Albors, C. E., and Riddick, D. H. (1983). Endometrial biopsy during treatment of luteal phase defects is predictive of therapeutic outcome. *Fertil. Steril.* 40(3), 305–310.
130. Downs, K. A., and Gibson, M. (1983). Clomiphene citrate therapy for luteal phase defect. *Fertil. Steril.* 39(1), 34–38.
131. Balasch, J., Jove, I. C., Marquez, M., and Vanrell, J. A. (1990). Early follicular phase follicle-stimulating hormone treatment of endometrial luteal phase deficiency. *Fertil. Steril.* 54(6), 1004–1007.
132. Li, T. C., Ding, S. H., Anstie, B., Tuckerman, E., Wood, K., and Laird, S. (2001). Use of human menopausal gonadotropins in the treatment of endometrial defects associated with

recurrent miscarriage: preliminary report. *Fertil. Steril.* 75(2), 434–437.

133. Rosenberg, S. M., Luciano, A. A., and Riddick, D. H. (1980). The luteal phase defect: The relative frequency of, and encouraging response to, treatment with vaginal progesterone. *Fertil. Steril.* 34(1), 17–20.
134. de Ziegler, D., and Fanchin, R. (2000). Progesterone and progestins: Applications in gynecology. *Steroids* 65(10–11), 671–679.
135. Maxson, W. S., and Hargrove, J. T. (1985). Bioavailability of oral micronized progesterone. *Fertil. Steril.* 44(5), 622–626.
136. Frishman, G. N., Klock, S. C., Luciano, A. A., and Nulsen, J. (1995). Efficacy of oral micronized progesterone in the treatment of luteal phase defects. *J. Reprod. Med.* 40(7), 521–524.
137. McAuley, J. W., Kroboth, F. J., and Kroboth, P. D. (1996). Oral administration of micronized progesterone: A review and more experience. *Pharmacotherapy* 16(3), 453–457.
138. Pritts, E. A., and Atwood, A. K. (2002). Luteal phase support in infertility treatment: A meta-analysis of the randomized trials. *Hum. Reprod.* 17(9), 2287–2299.
139. Steege, J. F., Rupp, S. L., Stout, A. L., and Bernhisel M. (1986). Bioavailability of nasally administered progesterone. *Fertil. Steril* 46(4), 727–729.
140. Stovall, D. W., Van Voorhis, B. J., Mattingly, K. L., Sparks, A. E., Chapler, F. K., and Syrop, C. H. (1996). The effectiveness of sublingual progesterone administration during cryopreserved embryo transfer cycles: Results of a matched follow-up study. *Fertil. Steril.* 65(5), 986–991.
141. Nillius, S. J., and Johansson, E. D. (1971). Plasma progesterone levels after intramuscular or rectal administration of progesterone. *Acta. Obstet. Gynecol. Scand.* 9 (Suppl 9), 46.
142. Bulletti, C., De Ziegler, D., Giacomucci, E., Polli, V., Rossi, S., Alfieri, S., and Flamigni, C. (1997). Vaginal drug delivery: The first uterine pass effect. *Ann. N.Y. Acad. Sci.* 828, 285–290.
143. Segal, S., and Casper, R. F. (1992). Progesterone supplementation increases luteal phase endometrial thickness and oestradiol levels in in-vitro fertilization. *Hum. Reprod.* 7(9), 1210–1213.
144. Balasch, J., Vanrell, J. A., Marquez, M., Burzaco, I., and Gonzalez-Merlo, J. (1982). Dehydrogesterone versus vaginal progesterone in the treatment of the endometrial luteal phase deficiency. *Fertil. Steril.* 37(6), 751–754.
145. Huang, K. E. (1986). The primary treatment of luteal phase inadequacy: Progesterone versus clomiphene citrate. *Am. J. Obstet. Gynecol.* 155(4), 824–828.
146. Murray, D. L., Reich, L., and Adashi, E. Y. (1989). Oral clomiphene citrate and vaginal progesterone suppositories in the treatment of luteal phase dysfunction: A comparative study. *Fertil. Steril.* 51(1), 35–41.
147. Simpson, J. L., and Kaufman, R. H. (1998). Fetal effects of estrogens, progestogens and diethylstilbestrol. In *Estrogens and Progestogens in Clinical Practice*, ed. I. S. Fraser, 533–553. London: Harcourt, Brace & Co.
148. Jones, G. S. (1986). Editorial comment. *Obstet. Gynecol. Survey* 41, 706–709.
149. Blumenfeld, Z., and Nahhas, F. (1988). Luteal dysfunction in ovulation induction: The role of repetitive human chorionic gonadotropin supplementation during the luteal phase. *Fertil. Steril.* 50(3), 403–407.
150. Quenby, S., and Farquharson, R. G. (1994). Human chorionic gonadotropin supplementation in recurring pregnancy loss: A controlled trial. *Fertil. Steril.* 62(4), 708–••.
151. Pearce, J. M., and Hamid, R. I. (1994). Randomised controlled trial of the use of human chorionic gonadotrophin in recurrent miscarriage associated with polycystic ovaries. *Br. J. Obstet. Gynaecol.* 101(8), 685–688.
152. Harrison, R. F. (1985). Treatment of habitual abortion with human chorionic gonadotropin: Results of open and placebo-controlled studies. *Eur. J. Obstet. Gynecol. Reprod. Biol.* 20(3), 159–168.
153. del Pozo, E., Wyss, H., Tollis, G., Alcaniz, J., Campana, A., and Naftolin, F. (1979). Prolactin and deficient luteal function. *Obstet. Gynecol.* 53(3), 282–286.
154. Muhlenstedt, D., Bohnet, H. G., Hanker, J. P., and Schneider, H. P. (1978). Short luteal phase and prolactin. *Intl. J. Fertil.* 23(3), 213–218.
155. Fredricsson, B., Bjork, G., and Carlstrom, K. (1977). Short luteal phase and prolactin. *Lancet* 1(8023), 1210.
156. Daly, D. C. (1983). The endometrium and the luteal defect. *Semin. Reprod. Endocrinol.* 1, 237–234.
157. Andersen, A. N., Larsen, J. F., Eskildsen, P. C., Knoth, M., Micic, S., Svenstrup, B., and Nielsen, J. (1979). Treatment of hyperprolactinemic luteal insufficiency with bromocriptine. *Acta. Obstet. Gynecol. Scand.* 58(4), 379–383.
158. Lehtovirta, P., Arjomaa, P., Ranta, T., Laatikainen, T., Hirvonen, E., and Seppala, M. (1979). Prolactin levels and bromocriptine treatment of short luteal phase. *Intl. J. Fertil.* 24(1), 57–60.
159. Saunders, D. M., Hunter, J. C., Haase, H. R., and Wilson, G. R. (1979). Treatment of luteal phase inadequacy with bromocriptine. *Obstet. Gynecol.* 53(3), 287–289.
160. Borenstein, R., Katz, Z., Lancet, M., Caspi, B., and Ben-David, M. (1980). Bromocriptine treatment of hyperprolactinemic infertility with ovulatory disturbances. *Intl. J. Gynaecol. Obstet.* 18(3), 195–199.
161. Bohnet, H. G., Muhlenstedt, D., Hanker, J. P., and Schneider, H. P. (1977). Prolactin oversuppression. *Arch. Gynakol.* 223(3), 173–178.
162. Griffith, R. W., Turkalj, I., and Braun, P. (1979). Pituitary tumours during pregnancy in mothers treated with bromocriptine. *Br. J. Clin. Pharmacol.* 7(4), 393–396.
163. Balasch, J., Vanrell, J. A., Marquez, M., Burzaco, I., and Gonzalez-Merlo, J. (1982). Dehydrogesterone versus vaginal progesterone in the treatment of the endometrial luteal phase deficiency. *Fertil. Steril.* 37(6), 751–754.
164. Wentz, A. C., Herbert, C. M., Maxson, W. S., and Garner, C. H. (1984). Outcome of progesterone treatment of luteal phase inadequacy. *Fertil. Steril.* 41(6), 856–862.
165. Check, J. H., and Adelson, H. G. (1987). The efficacy of progesterone in achieving successful pregnancy: II. In women with pure luteal phase defects. *Intl. J. Fertil.* 32(2), 139–141.
166. Rosenberg, S. M., Luciano, A. A., and Riddick, D. H. (1980). The luteal phase defect: the relative frequency of, and encouraging response to, treatment with vaginal progesterone. *Fertil. Steril.* 34(1), 17–20.
167. Hammond, M. G., and Talbert, L. M. (1982). Clomiphene citrate therapy of infertile women with low luteal phase progesterone levels. *Obstet. Gynecol.* 59(3), 275–279.

168. Garcia, J., Jones, G. S., and Wentz, A. C. (1977). The use of clomiphene citrate. *Fertil. Steril.* 28(7), 707–717.
169. Echt, C. R., Romberger, F. T., and Goodman, J. A. (1969). Clomiphene citrate in the treatment of luteal phase defects. *Fertil. Steril.* 20(4), 564–571.
170. Balasch, J., Jove, I. C., Marquez, M., and Vanrell, J. A. (1990). Early follicular phase follicle-stimulating hormone treatment of endometrial luteal phase deficiency. *Fertil. Steril.* 54(6), 1004–1007.
171. Minassian, S. S., Wu, C. H., Groll, M., Gocial, B., and Goldfarb, A. F. (1988). Urinary follicle stimulating hormone treatment for luteal phase defect. *J. Reprod. Med.* 33(1), 11–16.
172. Huang, K. E., Muechler, E. K., and Bonfiglio, T. A. (1984). Follicular phase treatment of luteal phase defect with follicle-stimulating hormone in infertile women. *Obstet. Gynecol.* 64(1), 32–36.
173. Daly, D. C., Walters, C. A., Soto-Albors, C. E., and Riddick, D. H. (1983). Endometrial biopsy during treatment of luteal phase defects is predictive of therapeutic outcome. *Fertil. Steril.* 40(3), 305–310.

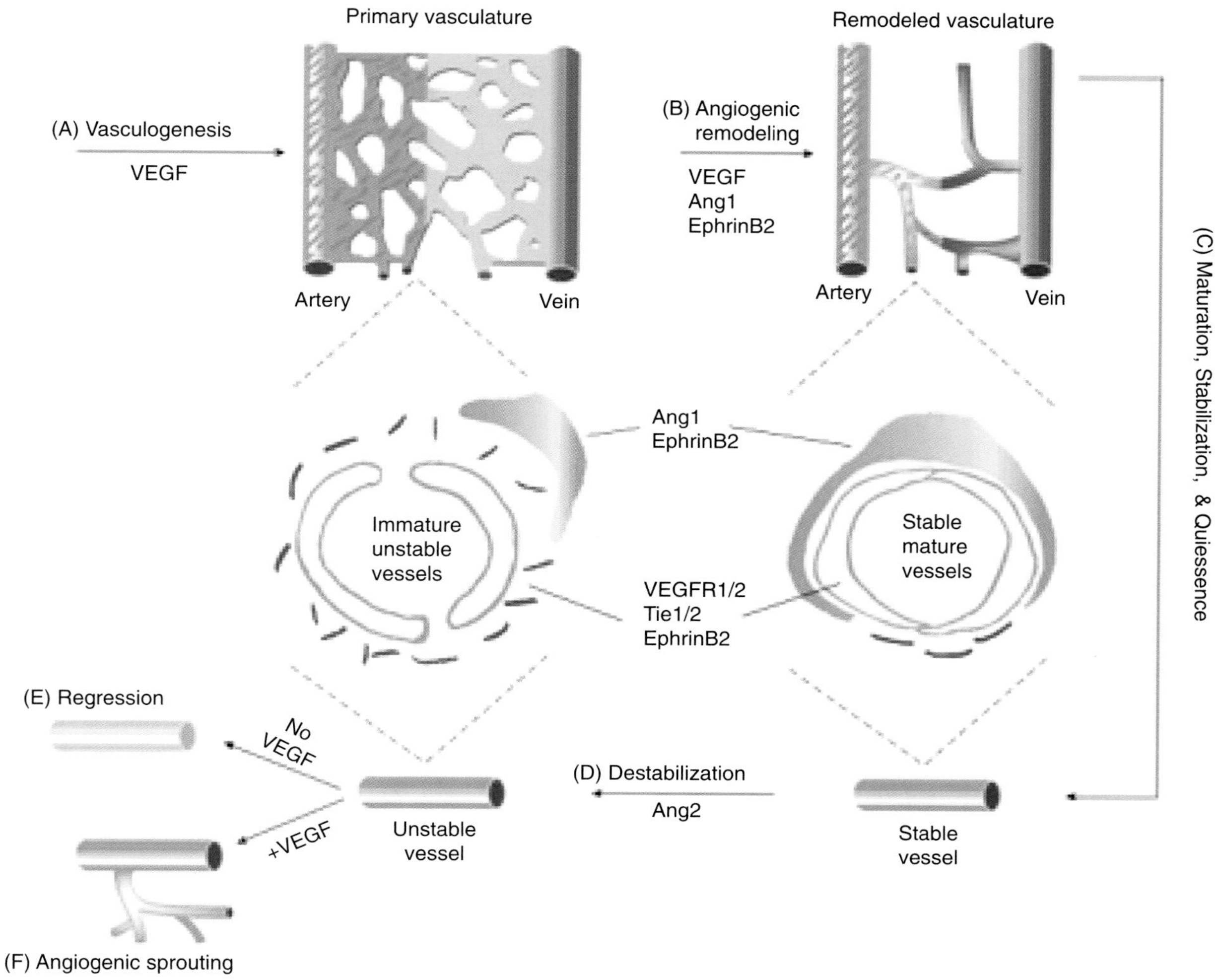

Primary vasculature
Remodeled vasculature
(A) Vasculogenesis
VEGF
(B) Angiogenic remodeling
VEGF
Ang1
EphrinB2
Artery
Vein
Artery
Vein
(C) Maturation, Stabilization, & Quiessence
Ang1
EphrinB2
Immature unstable vessels
Stable mature vessels
VEGFR1/2
Tie1/2
EphrinB2
(E) Regression
No VEGF
+VEGF
(D) Destabilization
Ang2
Unstable vessel
Stable vessel
(F) Angiogenic sprouting

FIGURE 18.1 Stages of angiogenesis and roles of VEGF, angiopoietin (Ang) -1 and -2, and their receptors in the angiogenic process. Ephrin and its receptor are not discussed in the text. (From Ref. [2].)

PlGF VEGF-A VEGF-B VEGF-C VEGF-D
Ang1 Ang2 Ang3 Ang4
?
?
VEGFR-1 (Flt-1)
VEGFR-2 (KDR/Flk-1)
VEGFR-3 (Flt-4)
Tie1
Tie2
KEY: Ig-Like EGF-Like FN3III-Like Cystein Rich Kinase

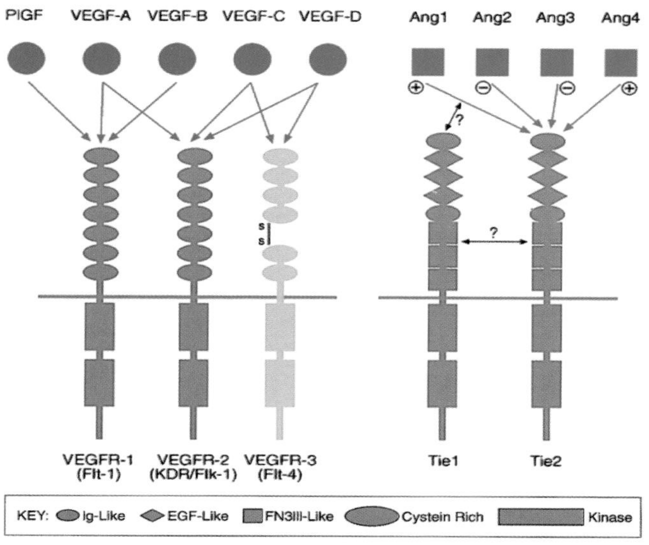

FIGURE 18.2 Vascular endothelial-specific angiogenic factors and their receptors. *Ang-1,* angiopoietin-1; *Ang-2,* angiopoietin-2; *PGF,* placental growth factor; *Tie1* and *Tie2,* receptors for the angiopoietins; *VEGF,* vascular endothelial growth factor; *VEGFR-1, VEGFR-2, VEGR-3,* receptors for VEGF and PGF. (A functional role for Tie1 has not been definitively identified.) (Modified from Gale, N. W., and Yancopoulos, G. D. (1999). *Genes Dev.* 13, 1055.)

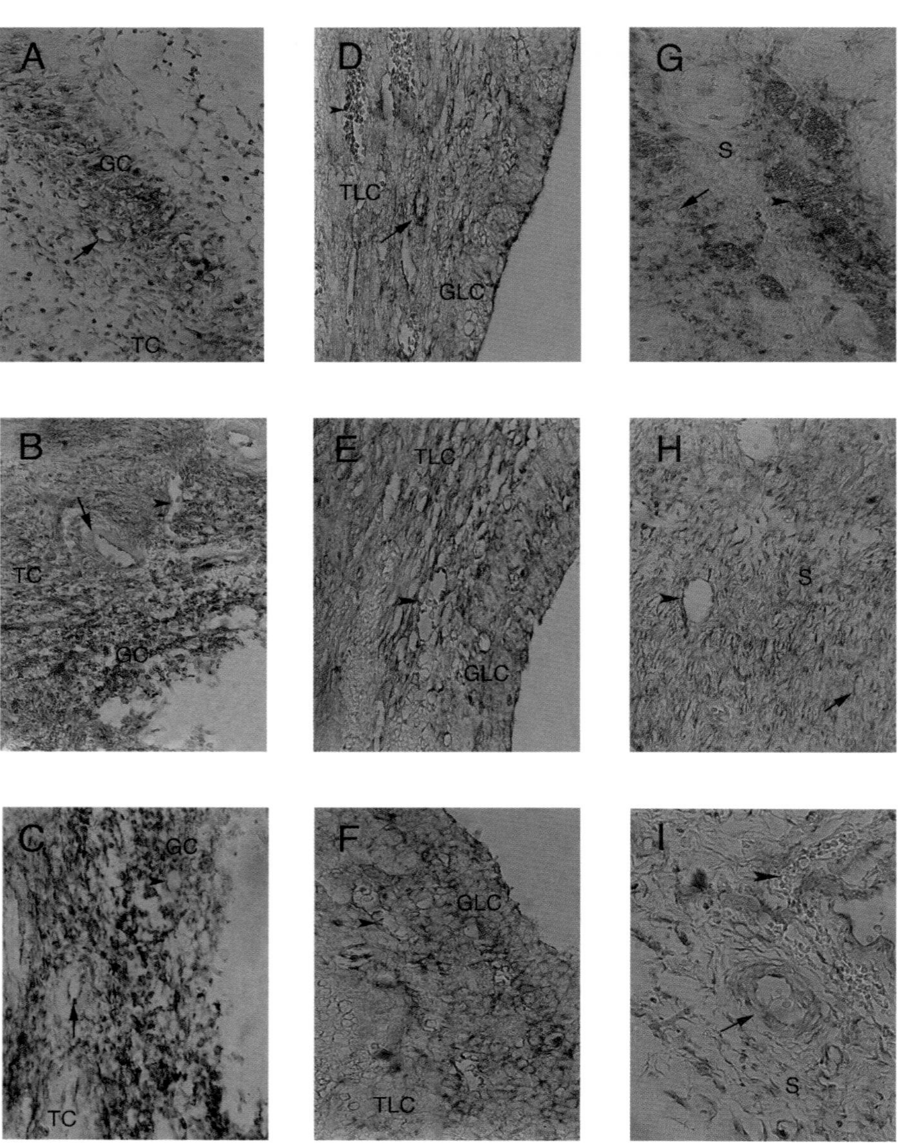

FIGURE 18.3 Localization of VEGF-A, Ang-1, and Ang-2 mRNA in pre- and postmenopausal human ovaries. **A–C,** VEGF-A (**A**), Ang-1 (**B**), and Ang-2 (**C**) hybridization signal in the follicular phase, localized principally in the granulosa cell layer (GC) and vascular endothelial cells and to a lesser degree in the thecal cell layer (TC). **D–F,** In luteal phase ovaries, VEGF-A (**D**), Ang-1 (**E**), and Ang-2 (**F**) mRNA expression was detected mainly in the granulosa-lutein cell layer (GLC) and to a lesser degree in the thecal-lutein cell layer (TLC) and endothelial cells. **G–I,** In postmenopausal ovaries, VEGF-A (**G**), Ang-1 (**H**), and Ang-2 (**I**) mRNA expression was localized in the perivascular stromal cells (S) and vascular endothelial cells. Original magnification × 400. Arrow = artery; arrowhead = vein.

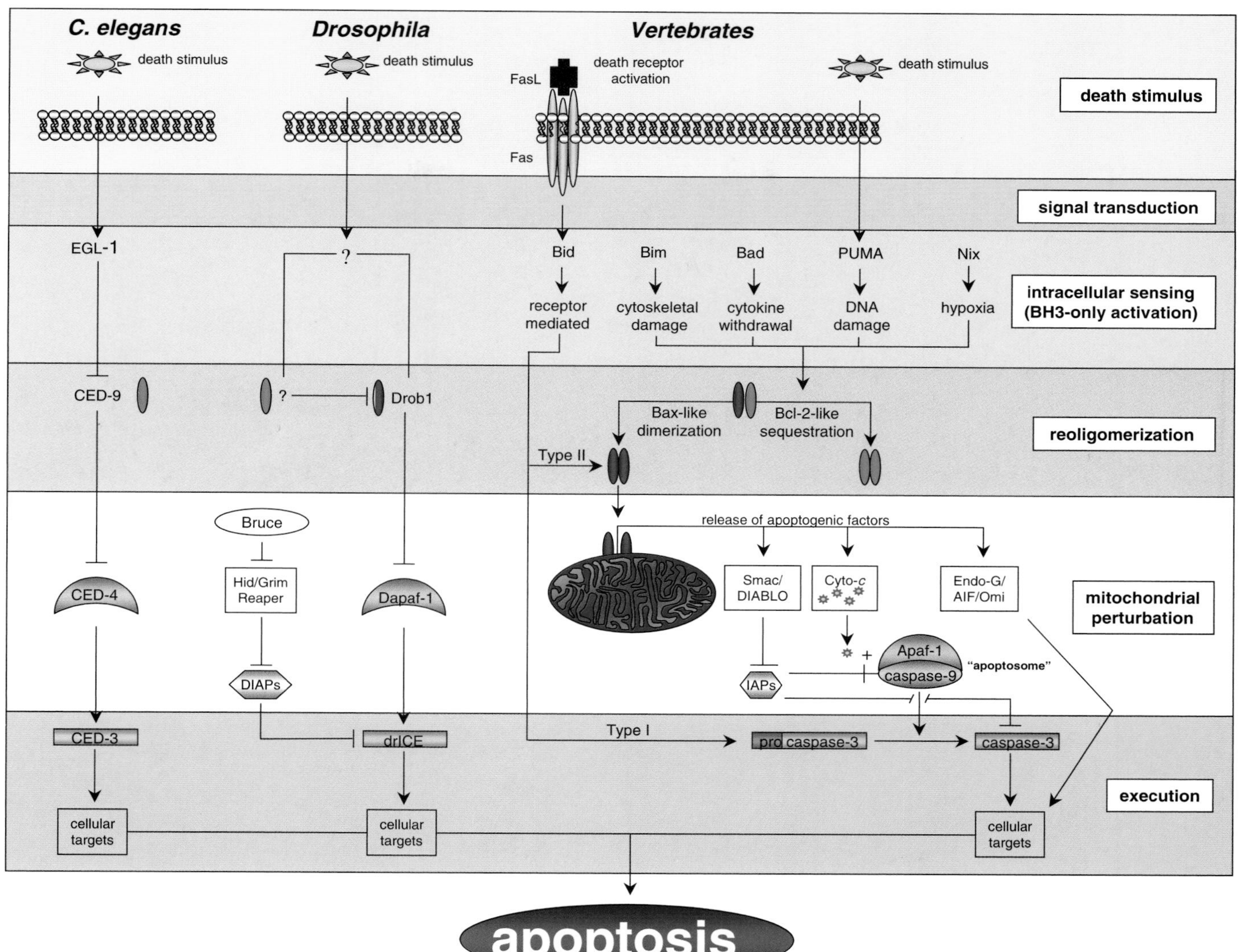

FIGURE 19.1 Evolutionarily conserved apoptotic cascades in vertebrate and invertebrate species. Apoptosis is initiated when cells become stressed (e.g., death stimuli such as growth factor deprivation, hypoxia, irradiation) or when death receptors (e.g., Fas) become activated by their ligands (Fas ligand/FasL). Such death stimuli are amplified through activation of a number of signal transduction pathways, which results in posttranslational modification or transcriptional induction of BH3-only proteins as an intracellular "sensing" step. Most BH3-only proteins (e.g., Bim, Bad, PUMA, Nix; EGL-1 orthologs) oligomerize with antiapoptotic Bcl-2-like proteins (CED-9 orthologs), thus liberating proapoptotic multidomain Bcl-2 family members (Bax-like; Drob1 orthologs) for mitochondrial insertion following reoligomerization. Some BH3-only proteins (e.g., Bid) directly oligomerize with Bax-like proteins to facilitate their insertion into mitochondria. Mitochondrial perturbation then releases a number of apoptogenic factors, including Smac/DIABLO, cytochrome *c* (Cyto-c), endonuclease G (Endo-G), apoptosis inducing factor (AIF), and Omi into the cytosol. Smac/DIABLO (Hid, Grim and Reaper ortholog) neutralizes inhibitors-of-apoptosis proteins (IAPs) (DIAP orthologs); Endo-G cleaves deoxyribonucleic acid (DNA); and AIF and Omi hydrolyze proteins and/or catalyze DNA breakdown. Release of cytochrome *c* facilitates formation of the "apoptosome," a multimeric protein complex consisting of Apaf-1 (CED-4/Dapaf-1 ortholog) and the initiator caspase, caspase-9. In the absence of a lethal stimulus, IAPs block apoptosome formation and caspase-3 activity. If the apoptosome forms, the complex activates effector procaspases (CED-3 and drICE orthologs) such as procaspase-3 to form active enzymes that cleave protein targets throughout the cell, completing the execution phase of apoptosis. Two models exist in vertebrate species to explain how effector caspases become activated following death receptor ligation. In some cells, mitochondrial perturbation serves as an amplification step to facilitate the execution phase through formation of the apoptosome (Type II cells), whereas in other cells this step is not needed (Type I cells). (See color plate.)

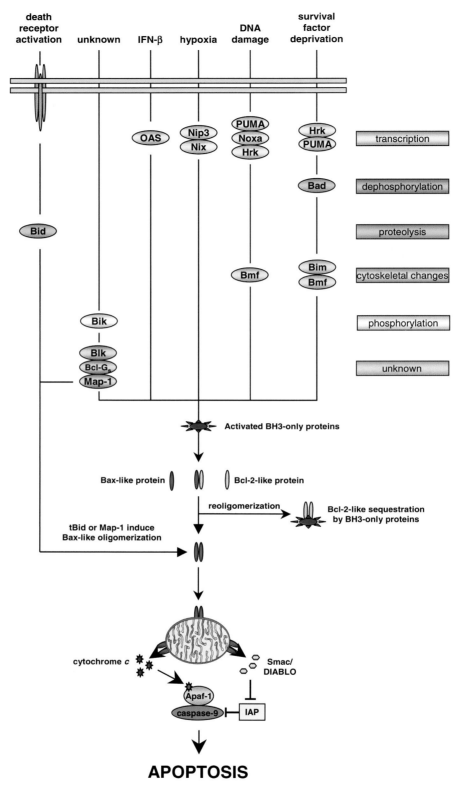

Figure 19.2 BH3-only proteins as intracellular sensors of death stimulation. BH3-only members of the Bcl-2 family are thought to coordinate an intracellular message center that dictates whether or not a cell undergoes apoptosis in response to a potential death stimulus (e.g., death receptor activation, interferon-β [IFN-β], hypoxia, DNA damage, or survival factor deprivation). The mechanisms of BH3-only activation are diverse and include transcription, phosphorylation/dephosphorylation, proteolysis, and cytoskeletal changes. Most BH3-only proteins serve to sequester antiapoptotic Bcl-2-like proteins (*yellow ovals*), thus preventing their inhibitory interaction with proapoptotic multidomain members of the family, such as Bax (*red ovals*). Only Bid and Map-1 have been show to directly interact with proapoptotic Bax-like proteins to facilitate their insertion into mitochondrial membranes. In either case, the actions of BH3-only proteins lead to mitochondrial destabilization and release of a number of apoptogenic factors that activate or amplify the execution phase of apoptosis. (See color plate.)

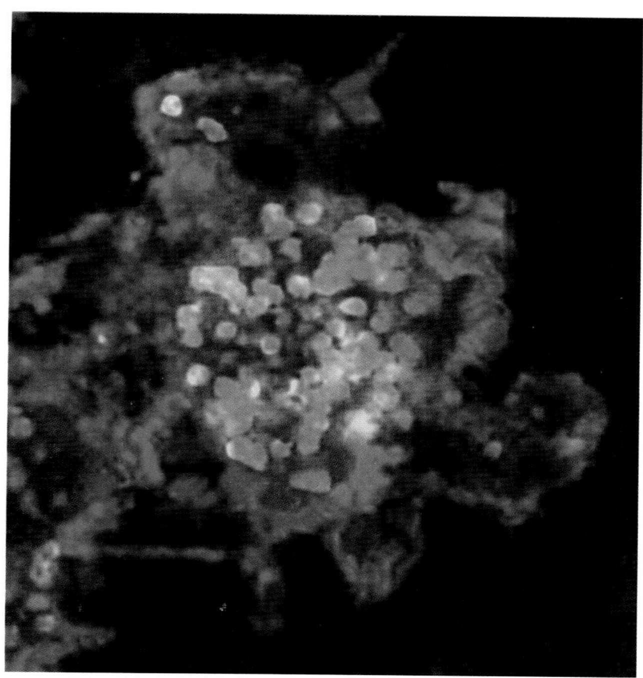

FIGURE 22.3 Apoptotic granulosa cells doubly stained with anti-adrenodoxin for steroidogenic mitochondria *(green)* and rhodamin-falloidin, staining the actin cytoskeleton *(red)*. Whereas the actin cytoskeleton is partially disrupted in the apoptotic blebs at the circumference of the cells, the majority of the mitochondria centered in the main bulk of the cytoplasm appears intact. Laser confocal microscopy. (Magnification × 3000.)

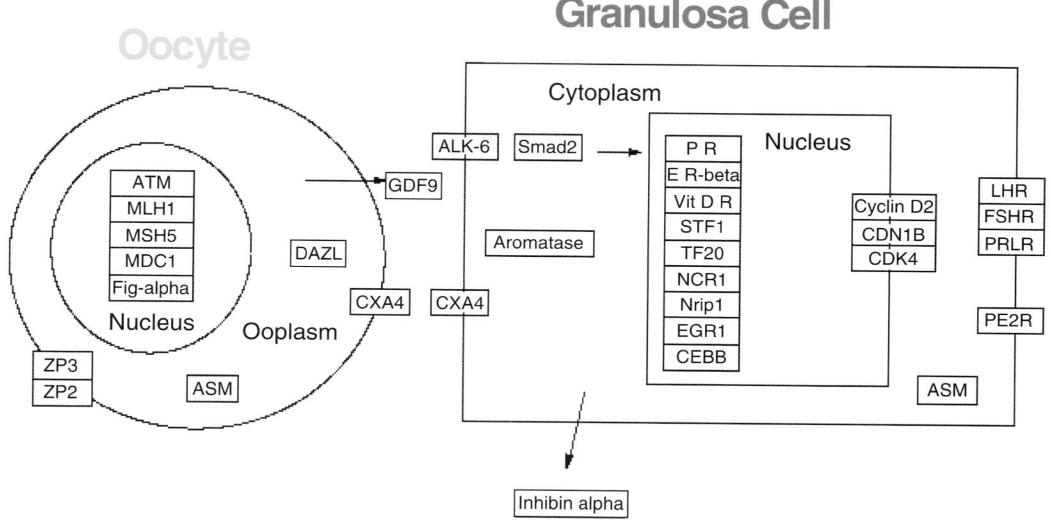

FIGURE 24.1 Cell type expression and cellular localization of infertility genes, based on phenotypes of mutant mice.

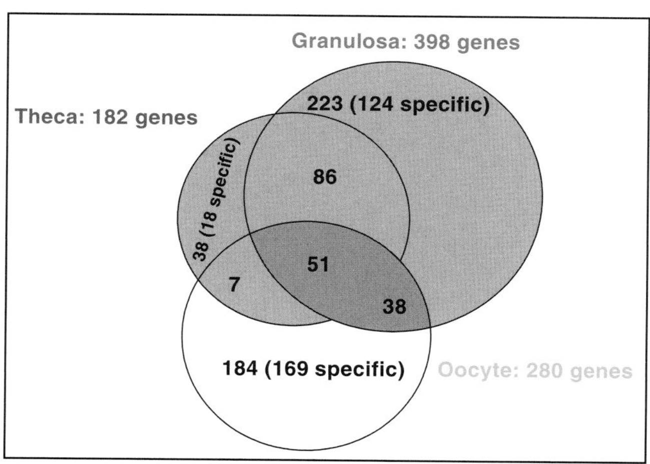

FIGURE 24.2 The distribution of genes in the OKdb by their cellular expression in different ovarian cell types. The genes designated as "specific" are those expressed only in the oocyte or granulosa cells among all ovarian cell types.

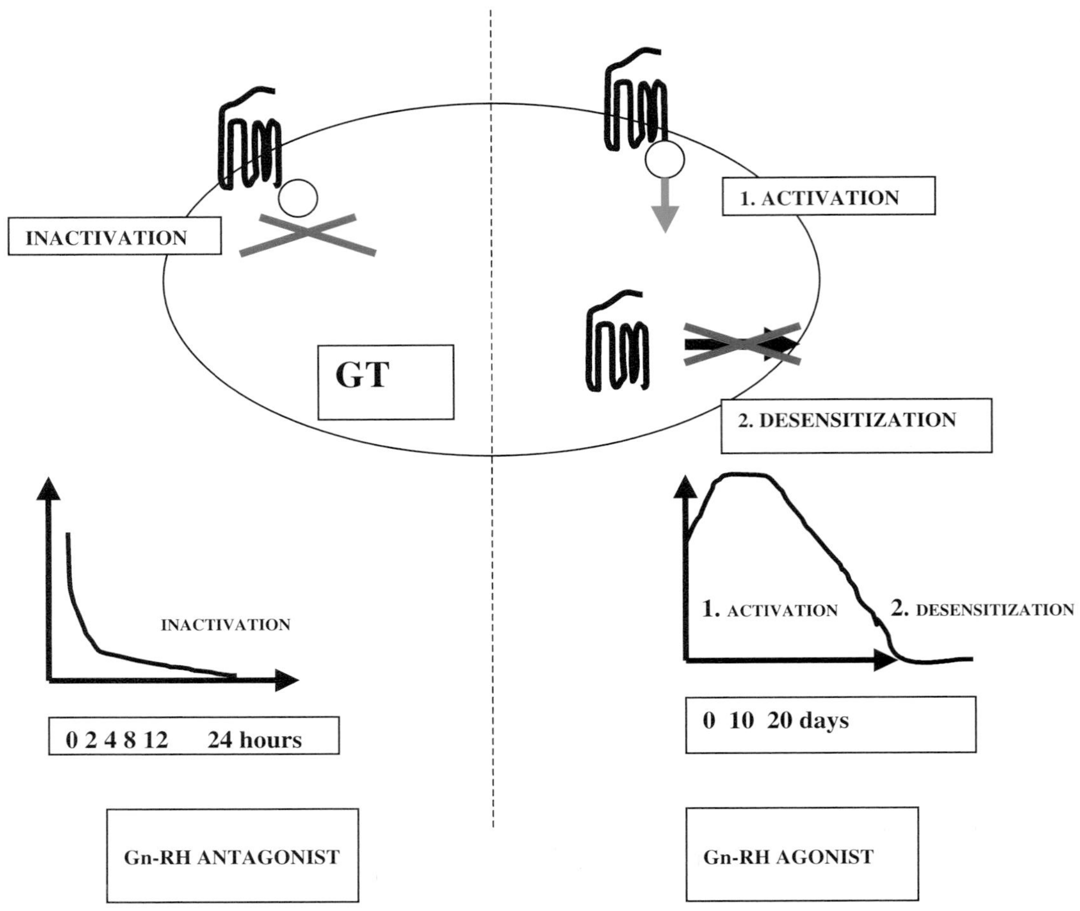

FIGURE 26.1 Mechanisms of action of Gn-RH analogs agonists vs antagonists.

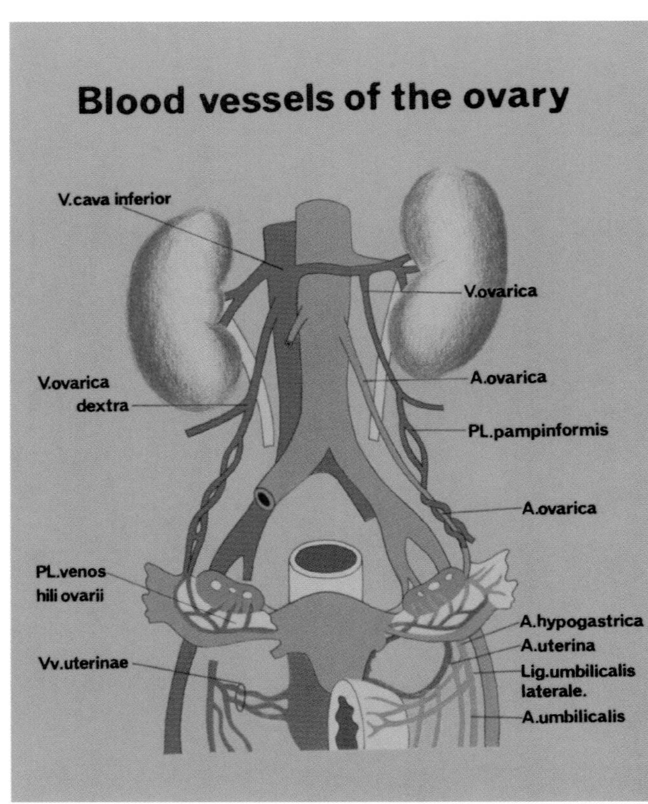

FIGURE 33.7 Blood supply to ovary. The ovarian artery and the uterine artery anastomose in the broad ligament.

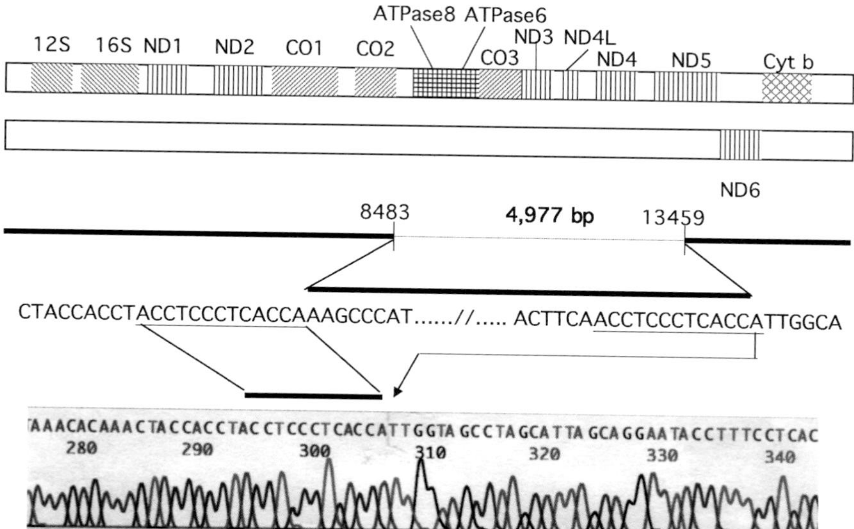

FIGURE 34.1 The relationship between defective mtDNA gene expression in oocytes with common 4977 bp deletion.

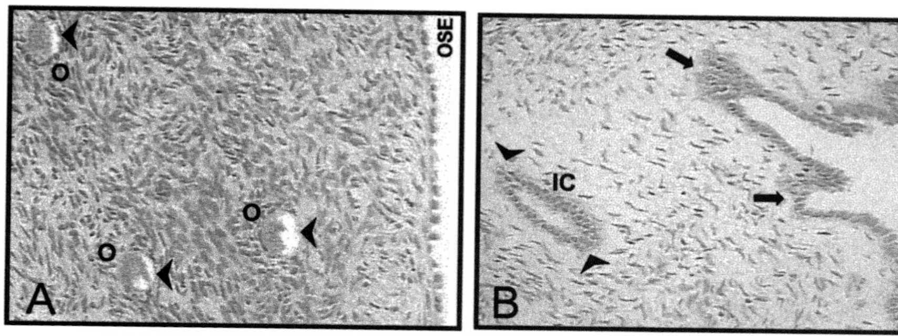

FIGURE 36.4 Immunohistochemical detection of kit expression in normal human ovaries. Kit is expressed in epithelial invaginations (*arrows*) and inclusion cysts (*arrowheads; b*), but not in ovarian surface epithelium (OSE; *a*). O indicates oocytes. Figure was originally presented in Tonary et al. (2000) published by Wiley-Liss, Inc.

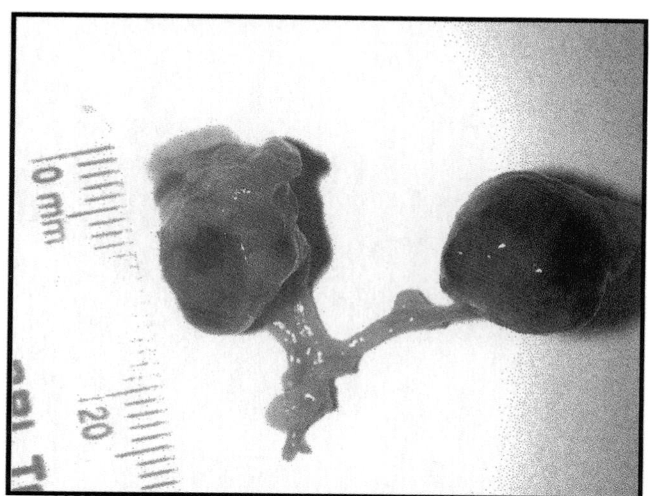

FIGURE 36.5 Development of ovarian tumors following injection of OVCA429 ovarian cancer cells under the bursal membrane of nude mouse ovaries. This xenograft model allows significant growth of tumors (more than 10 times normal diameter along the greatest length) within the ovarian environment.

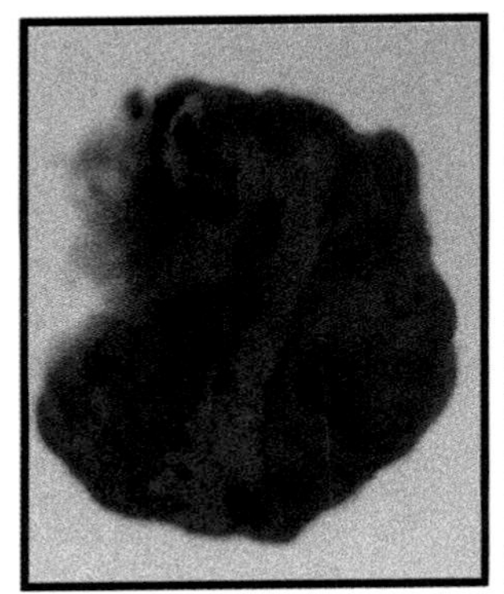
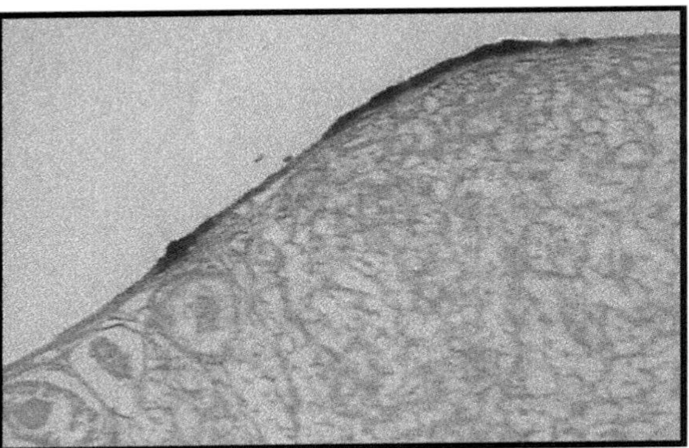

FIGURE 36.6 Confirmation that mouse ovarian surface epithelium (OSE) cells will take up and express adenoviral genes. Adenovirus expressing lacZ was injected under the bursa surrounding mouse ovaries, and ovaries were subsequently removed and stained for expression of β-galactosidase.

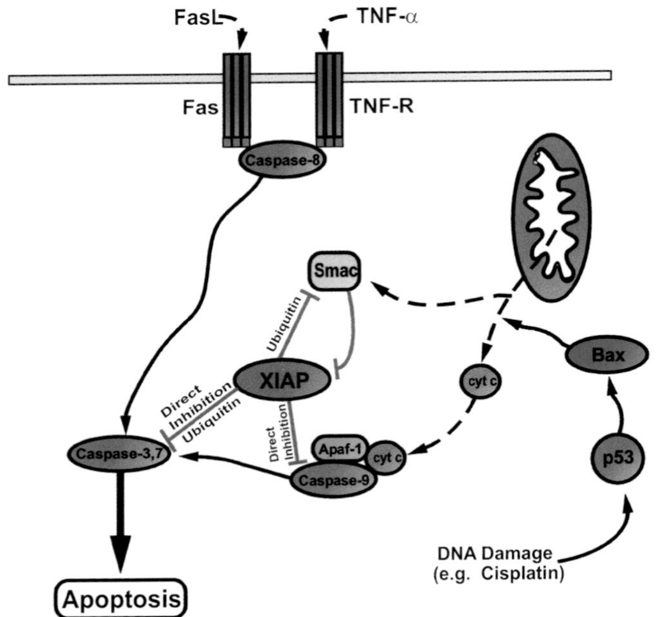

FIGURE 37.1 Classical Mechanisms of XIAP Action. XIAP is known to elicit its antiapoptotic effects by several distinct mechanisms (1) XIAP is a direct inhibitor of caspase-3. XIAP can also ubiquitinate caspase-3, and thus cause its degradation through the proteosome; (2) XIAP inhibits the activation of caspase-9; and (3) XIAP is known to ubiquitinate and cause the degradation of its endogenous inhibitor, Smac/DIABLO. Thus XIAP can inhibit both the mitochondrial- (caspase-9 activation of caspase-3) and death receptor- (caspase-8 activation of caspase-3) mediated apoptosis pathways.

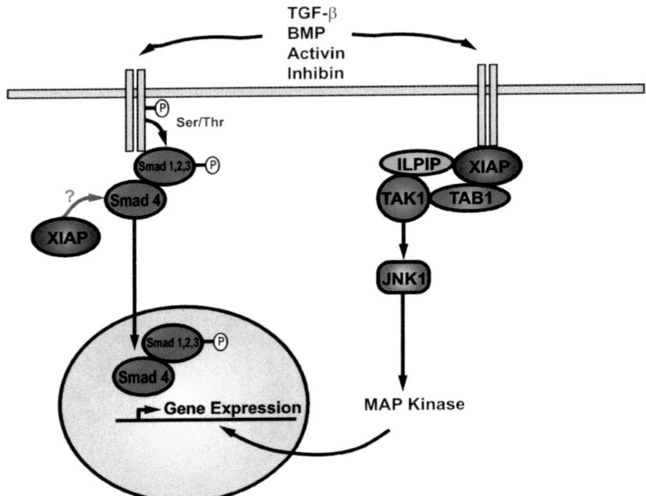

FIGURE 37.2 XIAP interacts with the TGF-β/BMP and MAP kinase pathways. XIAP has been shown to interact with the TGF-β/BMP signaling pathway member TAB1, as well as the BMP Type I and II receptors, and the TGF-β Receptor Type I. TAB1 is involved in activation of TAK1, which in turn is upstream of the MAP kinase JNK1. Signaling through JNK1 is known to activate genes implicated in cell survival and growth. An XIAP binding protein, ILPIP, has been shown to facilitate this function of XIAP. Moreover, XIAP may interact with Smad 4, which is intimately involved in TGF-β signaling to the nucleus.

CHAPTER **32**

Germ Cell Failure and Ovarian Resistance: Human Genes and Disorders

JOE LEIGH SIMPSON AND ALEKSANDAR RAJKOVIC

INTRODUCTION

Ovarian failure and ovarian resistance in humans have a variety of causes. Failure may be complete or premature, occurring earlier (younger than 35 or 40 years) than the expected age of menopause. Either complete or premature ovarian failure have long been deduced to result from either deletions of the X chromosome or Mendelian causes; however, only rarely is the actual gene known. In this discussion, we shall systematically survey the known disorders of ovarian failure and ovarian resistance in humans. This chapter inevitably reflects our previous publications [1–3].

EMBRYOLOGY OF OVARIAN DEVELOPMENT: NATURE OF GENES TO BE POSTULATED

Primordial germ cells originate in the endoderm of the yolk sac and migrate to the genital ridge to form the indifferent gonad. 46,XY and 46,XX gonads are initially indistinguishable. Indifferent gonads develop into testes if the embryo, or more specifically the gonadal stroma, is 46,XY. Testes become morphologically identifiable 7 to 8 weeks following conception (9 to 10 weeks gestational or menstrual weeks). Ovaries become identifiable thereafter.

In the absence of a Y chromosome, the indifferent gonad develops into an ovary. Transformation into fetal ovaries begins at 50 and 55 days of embryonic development. It is debatable whether female (ovarian) differentiation is truly a default (constitutive) pathway, or whether a specific gene product directs primary ovarian differentiation. At one time the default hypothesis seemed most plausible [4, 5], but more recently a primary directive role in ovarian differentiation has been proposed anew. Previously, an attractive candidate gene for this role was DAX-1 (dosage-sensitive sex reversal/adrenal hypoplasia critical region X). DAX-1 was attractive because it was shown to be encoded in the region of the X short arm (Xp21), which could redirect 46,XY embryos into female differentiation when duplicated [6]. The mouse homologue for human AHC was Ahch. If Ahch (DAX1) were to play a pivotal role in primary ovarian differentiation, Ahch should be upregulated in the XX mouse ovary [7]. This did occur, and transgenic XY mice overexpressing Ahch developed as females, at least in the presence of a relatively weak Sry [8, 9]; however, XX mice lacking Ahch unexpectedly showed ovarian differentiation, ovulated, and were even fertile [10]! Thus Ahch cannot be responsible for primary ovarian differentiation in mice, nor presumably is DAX1 in (AHC) humans.

Irrespective of the aforementioned uncertainty, the key observation—clinically and genetically—is that germ cells are present in 45,X embryos [11]. This can be deduced by the presence of germ cells in 45,X abortuses, which account for 10% of all first-trimester spontaneous abortions. The pathogenesis of germ-cell absence in 45,X adults thus involves atresia, occurring at a rate more rapid than that occurring in normal 46,XX embryos. Pathogenesis does not involve failure of germ-cell formation. In fact, germ cells are present in virtually all monosomy X mammals (e.g., mice), and often adults as well. If two intact X chromosomes are required to prevent human 45,X ovarian follicles from degenerating prematurely, it follows that the second X chromosome in humans must be responsible for ovarian maintenance, rather than primary ovarian differentiation.

OVARIAN FAILURE AS A RESULT OF HAPLO-INSUFFICIENCY FOR THE X CHROMOSOME (X-MONOSOMY AND X-DELETIONS)

Nomenclature

The first group of subjects with ovarian failure was recognized in 1938 by Turner [12]. These women had not only ovarian failure but also short stature and other now well-known somatic anomalies. For many years, the term *Turner syndrome* was applied to all women with ovarian failure.

Yet Turner syndrome is a broad term, and we prefer to apply the term *gonadal dysgenesis* to women with streak gonads and reserve the term *Turner stigmata* for those having short stature and certain somatic anomalies (Table 32.1). By itself, Turner stigmata as defined would not imply the presence of streak gonads. The term *Turner syndrome* would be applied to those individuals with streak gonads, Turner stigmata, and a 45,X or X-deletion complement.

Monosomy X

Monosomy X explains perhaps 50% of hypergonadotrophic hypogonadism. In 80% of 45,X cases, the X is maternal (X^m) in origin. In the remaining 20%, the remaining X is paternal (X^p) in origin [13, 14]. That 45,X individuals show streak gonads as adults is not as obvious as might be expected because relatively normal ovarian development occurs in many other mammals (e.g., mice) with monosomy X. The presumptive explanation is that pivotal genes on the heterochromatic (inactive) X are not inactivated. Of the some 2000 genes on the X, perhaps 5% escape inactivation [15]. Most of these genes are on the X short arm (Xp), clustered in selected euchromatic regions. Candidate genes for ovarian maintenance genes probably lie in these euchromatic regions, although studies have not truly addressed this obvious postulate.

Not all 45,X patients show complete ovarian failure. Approximately 3% to 5% of adult 45,X patients menstruate spontaneously. Fertile patients have been reported, as reviewed by Abir and colleagues [16] and Hovatta [17]. An undetected 46,XX cell line (i.e., 45,X/46,XX mosaicism) should be suspected in menstruating 45,X patients, which seems especially plausible in some reports. Magee and colleagues [18] observed seven pregnancies in one ostensibly 45,X woman; however, it is not unexpected that some 45,X individuals could be fertile, inasmuch as germ cells are present in 45,X embryos.

X Short-Arm Deletions and Ovarian Failure

Several different terminal deletions of the short arm of the X chromosome exist, showing varying amounts of persisting Xp. Determining precise breakpoints and disrupted genes is necessary, but still not often pursued. Few studies have reexamined cases ascertained before the modern molecular era.

Pooling morphologically similar terminal deletions has long shown that the most common breakpoint for terminal deletions is Xp11.2 → 11.4. Again, the actual molecular breakpoint could and probably is different in literally every case. Overall, however, in 46,X,del(X)(p11) only proximal Xp remains; the del(Xp) chromosome thus appears acrocentric or telocentric. Distal (telomeric) breakpoints are also reported and include Xp21, 22.1, 22.2, and 22.3. Sequencing and analysis with polymorphic

TABLE 32.1 Somatic Features Associated with the 45,X Chromosomal Complement

Growth
Decreased birth weight
Decreased adult height (141 to 146 cm)

Intellectual function
Verbal IQ > performance IQ
Cognitive deficits (space-form blindness)
Immature personality, probably secondary to short stature

Cranofacial
Premature fusion sphenoccipital and other sutures, producing brachycephaly
Abnormal pinnae
Retruded mandible
Ptosis
Hypertelorism
Epicanthal folds (25%)
High-arched palate (36%)
Abnormal dentition
Visual anomalies, usually strabismus (22%), amblyopia
Hypernetropia auditory deficits; sensorineural or secondary to middle ear infection

Neck
Pterygium colli (46%)
Short, broad neck (74%)
Low nuchal hair (71%)

Chest
Rectangular contour (shield chest) (35%)
Apparent widely spaced nipples
Tapered lateral ends of clavicle

Cardiovascular
Coarctation of aorta or ventricular septal defect (10% to 16%)

Renal (38%)
Horseshoe kidneys
Unilateral renal aplasia
Duplication ureters

Gastrointestinal
Telangiectasias

Skin and Lymphatics
Pigmented nevi (63%)
Lymphadema (38%), generalized, due to hypoplasia superficial vessels; puffy hands and feet

Nails
Hypoplasia and malformation (66%)

Skeletal
Cubitus valgus (54%)
Radial tilt of articular surface of trochlear
Clinodactyly V
Short metacarpals, usually IV (48%)
Decreased carpal arch (mean angle 117°)
Deformities of medical tibial condyle

Dermatoglyphics
Increased total digital ridge count
Increased distance between palmar triradii a and b
Distal axial triradius in position t'

Percentage affected reflect tabulation of Simpson [145].

DNA markers are beginning to identify breakpoints [19–22].

Approximately half of 46,X,del(Xp)(p11) cases show primary amenorrhea and gonadal dysgenesis. In one tabulation by the author 15 years ago, 12 of 27 reported del(X)(p11.2 → 11.4) individuals menstruated spontaneously; however, menstruation was rarely normal [4]. More recent calculations have not materially altered this conclusion [1, 2, 23]. Figure 32.1 shows our compilation of cases through 1999. To date, molecular analyses have yielded conclusions similar to those derived on the basis of phenotypic-karyotypic correlations [19, 20, 24, 25].

Women with more distal deletions [del(X)(p.21.1 to p22.122)] menstruate more often, but many are still infertile or show secondary amenorrhea. Ovarian failure (menopause) is more likely to occur prematurely (younger than 35 or 40 years of age, depending on definition). Thus loci in regions Xp21, 22.1 or 22.2 are probably less pivotal for ovarian development than those nearer the centromere (Xp11) [1, 23]. Deletion of only the most telomeric portion of Xp (Xp22.3 → Xpter) does not result in amenorrhea [26]. Zinn and colleagues [19] and Zinn and Ross [20] concluded only that the relatively large region Xp11.3 → 22.1 was pivotal. Cases with an interstitial deletion will ideally help narrow the region of interest [19, 20].

Familial cases of X short-arm deletions have been observed, namely mother and daughter having either the same terminal Xp-deletion [21, 27] or the same X/autosome translocations. Among 10 del(Xp) cases studied by James and colleagues [28] were two mother-daughter pairs. Thomas and Huson [25] reported 25 females with *de novo* deletions of Xp and four familial Xp deletions. Familial cases have involved deletions at Xp11 as well as Xp22–12 [19, 29].

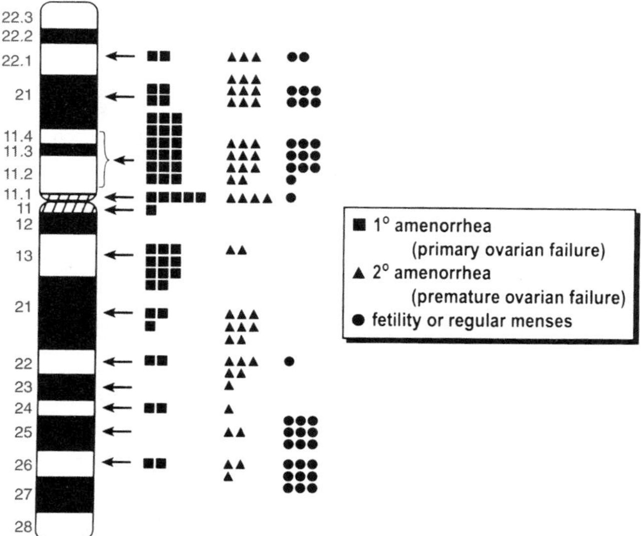

FIGURE 32.1 Schematic diagram of the X chromosome showing ovarian function as a function of nonmosaic terminal deletions [2].

Almost all reported 46,i(Xq) patients show streak gonads and short stature, and Turner stigmata have long been accepted as almost universal [30]. Only rarely do 46,X,i(Xq) patients menstruate. The frequency of gonadal failure in 46,X,i(Xq) individuals is greater than in 46,X,del(Xp11) individuals, about half of whom menstruate or develop breasts. In turn, isochromosome for the X long arm [i(Xq)] differs from terminal deletion of Xp in that not just the terminal portion but all of the Xp is deleted. This finding further suggests the existence of gonadal determinants at several different locations on Xp. If so, a locus near the centromere could be deleted in i(Xq) yet retained in del(X)(p11).

Candidate Genes for Xp Gonadal Determinants

Several candidate genes for Xp gonadal determinants have been proposed. Zinn and colleagues [19] proposed ZFX, a DNA binding protein; a homologous gene exists on the Y (ZFY). Jones and colleagues [31] proposed DFRX, located on XP11.4 and homologous to a locus on Yq11.2. DFRX (or USP9X) targets proteins for degradation by the ubiquitan pathway. USP9X is homologous to the Drosophila gene fat facets (faf). Both DFRX (USP9X) and ZFX escaped inactivation in two human *de novo* (X)(p11.2) deletions; however, after observing ovarian function in two cases despite haplo-insufficiency, James and colleagues [32] concluded that DFRX was an unlikely candidate. On the other hand, neither of these cases were categorically normal clinically; therefore, a role for DFRX in gonadal development is not completely excluded. Studying an interstitial deletion of Xp11.2–11.4, Zinn and colleagues [19] hypothesized three Xp candidate genes: DFRX (USP9X), UBE1 (another ubiquitan pathway enzyme), and BMP15 (a member of the transforming growth factor-β [TGF-β] family of signaling compounds). Mutations in BMP15 cause primary ovarian failure in X-linked recessive fashion in Inverdale sheep [33]. BMP15 is structurally similar to GDF9 and probably interacts with GDF9 *in vivo* [34].

Other candidate X-ovarian genes are reviewed by Bione and Toniolo [35], Zinn [36], and Zinn and Ross [20]. In addition, many other candidate genes can be deduced from homologues in the mouse. (See Simpson and Rajkovic [2] and Matzuk and Lamb [37].) The latter provided an overview of murine genes causing germ-cell abnormalities in males and females; however, in the mouse most of these genes are autosomal. Thus perhaps better candidate genes could be proposed for the disorders of human XX gonadal dysgenesis to premature ovarian failure (POF). Irrespective, determining which human homologues of these mouse genes are pertinent will be the future direction.

X Long-Arm Deletions

Deletions of the X long arm (Xq) vary in composition, as do those involving the X short arm. The most extensive deletions originate at Xq13 and are associated invariably with primary amenorrhea, lack of breast development, and complete ovarian failure [1, 2, 23, 32, 38]. Xq13 must be a pivotal region for ovarian maintenance. That this region contains the human X-inactivation center (XIC) may or may not be the explanation. The abnormal phenotype associated with del(Xq13) could reflect perturbation of XIC and loss of the gene product Xist rather than loss of an ovarian gene per se. Irrespective, key loci must lie no more distal than proximal Xq21, given that menstruation occurs in deletions of breakpoints Xq21 or beyond (see Figure 32.1). Menstruating del(X)(q21) women might have retained a region containing an ovarian maintenance gene, whereas del(X)(q13 or 21) cases with primary amenorrhea could have lost such a locus.

In more distal Xq deletions, the phenotype is usually not primary amenorrhea but rather premature ovarian failure [2, 39, 40]. Distal Xq is thus less pivotal for ovarian maintenance than proximal Xq, although the former still contains regions important for ovarian maintenance. Although there is no stepwise demarcation into discrete breakpoint regions, it is heuristically useful to stratify terminal deletions in this fashion: Xq13 → 21,Xq22–25, and Xq26–28. In 1995, Ogata and Matsuo [38] correlated ovarian function using such stratification and arrived at conclusions similar to our own.

Molecular mapping of the regions of Xq integral for ovarian development has begun [40], but to date views on locations and the nature of Xq ovarian determinants have not changed substantively from those derived on the basis of phenotypic-karyotopic correlations. Sala and colleagues [41] studied seven X/autosome translocations involving Xq21–22, five of which had primary amenorrhea. A region of Xq spanning 15 mb encompassed breakpoints in all seven cases. Breakpoints in four other X-autosome translocations studied by Philippe and colleagues [42] were localized to the same region, extending from DXS233 to DXS1171 (most of Xq21) [6]. If the breakpoints associated with ovarian failure truly spanned the entire Xq21 region, it would be unlikely that only a single gene in this region is responsible for ovarian failure. Alternatively, ovarian failure associated with these translocations could be the result not of perturbation of any specific gene but rather of generalized cytologic (meiotic) instability. Incidentally, the official nomenclature designates genes causing POF as POF1 and POF2, based on presumptive order of discovery. Thus the Xq25–26 region is POFl, whereas the more pivotal Xq13 region is officially POF2.

Distal Xq deletions may be familial, such as del(Xp). Some of these familial aggregates are derivative of Xq/autosome translocations, but aggregating with terminal deletions exist as well [21, 29, 42–45]. Ovarian function may vary among different family members having the same deletion.

Candidate Genes for Xq Gonadal Determinants

A popular candidate for genes causing ovarian failure on the X long arm is the human homologue of the *Drosophila melanogaster* gene diaphanous (dia). Drosophila dia is a member of a family of proteins that establish cell polarity, govern cytokinesis, and organize the cytoskeleton mutation of the dia gene, which causes sterility in male and female flies [46]. Sequence comparisons between dia and the human EST (expressed sequence tag) DRE25 show significant homology. In turn, DRE25 maps to human Xq21 [46], a region we have already noted to be important for ovarian maintenance. Studying an Xq21/autosome translocation originally reported by Philippe and colleagues [42], Sala and colleagues [41] found DRE25 [40] to be disrupted in women with ovarian failure.

Another candidate gene is XPNPEP2, which encodes the Xaa-Pro aminopeptidase (metalloprotease) that hydrolyzes proline bonds. XPNPEP2 is ubiquitously expressed in many tissues and can influence a host of biologically active peptides that could include regulations of ovarian function. XPNPEP2 was disrupted in an Xq translocation that involved Xq25 [35, 36, 47], and several other Xq candidate genes were considered.

Other human candidate POF genes were suggested by Davison and colleagues [22] after analysis of a 46,X,del(X)(q26) case associated with the fragile X premutation phenotype. Based on the deleted chromosomal region, three candidate genes were identified by NIX and BLAST analysis: (1) heparan-sulfate-6-transferase (HS6ST), (2) an E2F-related transcription factor, and (3) some gene(s) in the region in which LINE 1 elements (long interspersed nuclear elements) were found. LINE 1 elements are retrotransposons that are potentially mutagenic and capable of interfering with transcription or gene expression. Davison and colleagues [22] considered HS6ST, which showed 82% nucleotide and 65% amino acid homology to the purported human locus, to be the most likely candidate gene. Sulfated proteoglycans are involved in regulation of cell proliferation and migration, and in Drosophila are known to influence oocyte polarity. E2F, which showed 75% homology with the deleted Xq candidate sequence, is known to regulate somatic cell cycles and can imitate apoptosis. Other genes in the E2F family are active in mammalian embryos, including oocytes. The deleted candidate sequences were also homologous to LINE 1 elements (97% homology).

OVARIAN FAILURE AS A RESULT OF MENDELIAN CAUSES

Phenotypic females with normal chromosomal complements (46,XX) may have gonadal failure and display ovarian failure identical to that of 45,X gonadal dysgenesis (Turner syndrome). Applying the general term *XX gonadal dysgenesis* implies that a coexisting 45,X line does not exist. A wide spectrum of disorders falls under this rubric (Table 32.2). In this section we discuss those disorders of ovarian failure whose etiology is either known to be caused by autosomal genes or which seems likely to be caused by such.

TABLE 32.2 The Spectrum of XX Gonadal Dysgenesis

XX gonadal dysgenesis without somatic anomalies
XX gonadal dysgenesis with neurosensory deafness (Perrault syndrome)
XX gonadal dysgenesis with cerebellar ataxia (hetereogeneous)
XX gonadal dysgenesis in malformation syndrome (Table 32.3)
XX gonadal dysgenesis as one component of pleiotropic Mendelian disorders (Table 32.4)
FSH receptor mutations (FSHR)
LH receptor mutations (LHR)
Blepharophimosis-ptosis-epicanthus (FOXL2)
Germ cell absence in both sexes (46,XX)
No somatic anomalies
Hypertension and deafness
Alopecia
Microcephaly and short stature
Adrenal and ovarian biosynthetic defects
17α-hydroxylase (CYP17)
Aromatase
Agonadia (46,XX cases)
Inborn errors of metabolism
Galactosemia
Carbohydrate-deficient glycoprotein (Phosphomannomutase deficiency, PMM2)
Dynamic mutations (triplet repeat)
Fragile X (FRAXA)
Myotonic dystrophy (uncommon cause)
Ovarian-specific autoimmunity
Polyglandular autoimmune syndrome (Premature ovarian failure)
Autosomal trisomies
Trisomy 13
Trisomy 18

In some conditions, premature ovarian failure is observed as well [3].

XX Gonadal Dysgenesis without Somatic Anomalies

This category implies a diagnosis of exclusion for those 46,XX gonadal dysgenesis cases not associated with somatic anomalies. Overall, these cases are most often inherited in autosomal-recessive fashion. Affected individuals are normal in stature (mean height, 165 cm) [30], and somatic features of Turner stigmata are absent. Consanguinity pointed to autosomal-recessive inheritance decades ago, and segregation analysis by the author and colleagues later revealed the segregation ratio to be 0.16 for female sibs [48]. That is, two-thirds of gonadal dysgenesis in 46,XX individuals is genetic. Nongenetic phenocopies could be caused by infection, infarction, infiltrative, or autoimmune phenomena.

Of clinical relevance is variable expressivity in XX gonadal dysgenesis. In some families one sib had streak gonads, whereas another had primary amenorrhea and extreme ovarian hypoplasia (presence of a few oocytes) [30, 48–52]. If the mutant gene responsible for XX gonadal dysgenesis were capable of variable expression, it follows that that gene may be responsible for some sporadic cases of POF.

By definition, the "entity" discussed in this section is heterogeneous. It can be expected that many distinct entities will be elucidated. Many causative genes will be discovered, probably soon. These can be expected to act in different ways, as is already evident in the mouse. Genes preferentially expressed in ovaries represent candidate genes for nonsyndronic POF and gonadal dysgenesis [53]. Transcriptional factors such as Obox and Nobox are oocyte-specific and potentially critical in human oogenesis [54, 55]. Concerted efforts to identify genes exclusively expressed in ovaries via different molecular and genomic methodologies will provide a plethora of candidate genes for XX gonadal dysgenesis without somatic anomalies [53]. In addition, any abnormality in meiosis, organ-specific (ovary) or not, could be manifested as ovarian failure and infertility in otherwise normal women. It remains only to search for perturbations in the human homologues of the many attractive genes being identified in animal models.

Perrault Syndrome (XX Gonadal Dysgenesis with Neurosensory Deafness)

XX gonadal dysgenesis associated with neurosensory deafness is called Perrault syndrome [56]. Perrault syndrome is inherited in autosomal-recessive fashion [30, 57–60]. Endocrine features seem identical to XX gonadal dysgenesis without deafness. Candidate genes include the connexin family, given that gene knockout for connexin 37 results in ovulation defect in mice [61].

Cerebellar Ataxia and XX Gonadal Dysgenesis

XX gonadal dysgenesis can be found in association with a heterogeneous group of cerebellar ataxias. The hereditary ataxias are confusing nosologically, principally because of ill-defined diagnostic criteria and lack of direct access to the cerebellum. Forms of ataxia characterized by *hypo*gonadotrophic hypogonadism also exist but are not relevant here.

The association between hypergonadotrophic hypogonadism and ataxia was first reported by Skre and colleagues [62]. In one family, a 16-year-old girl was affected. In the other family, three sisters were affected. In the one sporadic case and in one of the three affected sibs, ataxia was manifested shortly after birth; in the two other sibs, age of onset occurred later in childhood. Cataracts were present in all individuals described by Skre and colleagues [62].

Hypergonadotropic hypogonadism and ataxia were subsequently reported by De Michele and colleagues [63], Linssen and colleagues [64], Gottschalk and colleagues [65], Fryns and colleagues [66], Nishi and colleagues [60], and Amor and colleagues [67]. In these various reports, the clinical features of ataxia and other neurologic abnormalities varied (e.g., being either progressive versus nonprogressive). (See Simpson and Elias [3] for further discussion.)

XX Gonadal Dysgenesis in Other Unique Malformation Syndromes

Among other pleiotropic genes causing XX gonadal dysgenesis and distinctive somatic features are several that have been reported in only a single family. Table 32.3 lists these syndromes: XX gonadal dysgenesis, microcephaly, and arachnodactyly [68]; XX gonadal dysgenesis, cardiomyopathy, blepharoptosis, and broad nasal bridge [67, 69]; XX gonadal dysgenesis and epibulbar dermoid [70]; XX gonadal dysgenesis, short stature, and metabolic acidosis [71]. If Mendelian, these disorders are presumably autosomal recessive; however, subtle chromosomal rearrangements cannot be excluded.

In these syndromes and others that doubtless will be reported in the future, the key underlying biologic question is whether the ostensibly pleiotropic gene(s) causes both somatic anomalies and ovarian failure. If so, do the purported genes play roles in normal ovarian differentiation, or does their perturbation merely cause ovarian failure secondary to generalized somatic disturbance? Alternatively, could the somatic and gonadal phenotypes merely reflect closely linked genes (i.e., a contiguous gene syndrome)?

Pleiotropic Mendelian Disorders Showing Ovarian Failure

Primary ovarian failure is observed in several well-established and not necessarily uncommon Mendelian disorders. These are well known to geneticists and relevant to clinical specialists. All are characterized by distinct somatic features (Table 32.4).

Of special note are Denys-Drash syndrome and Frasier syndrome, both of which are caused by mutations in the WT-1 (Wilms' tumor-1) gene. WT-1 mutations can cause either 46,XY gender reversal or 46,XY genital ambiguity. One 46,XX individual with Frasier syndrome has been reported [72]. This woman manifested not only the renal parenchymal disease characteristic of Frasier syndrome, but also primary amenorrhea and ovarian failure. Gonadal failure in 46,XX Frasier syndrome could easily pass

TABLE 32.3 Malformation Syndromes with 46,XX Gonadal Dysgenesis [3]

Somatic Features	Etiology (Gene)
Cerebellar ataxia, sensorineural deafness, other somatic features [67,62]	Autosomal recessive, heterogeneous
Microcephaly, arachnodactyly [68]	Autosomal recessive
Epibulbar dermoids [70]	Autosomal recessive
Short stature and metabolic acidosis [71,146]	Autosomal recessive
Blepharophimosis-ptosis-epicanthus [147,117]	Autosomal dominant (FOXL2)
Renal parenchypud disease, ovarian failure (46,XX Frasier syndrome) [72], Wilms' tumor and genital ambiguity (Denys-Drash syndrome) due to different perturbation of same gene (WT1).	Autosomal dominant (WT1)
Dilated cardiomyopathy, mental retardation, bleparoptosis (Malouf syndrome) [69,148]	Autosomal recessive

TABLE 32.4 Autosomal-Recessive Disorders in Which the Phenotype is Predominately Somatic, but Showing Ovarian Failure [3]

Disorder	Somatic Features	Ovarian Anomalies	Etiology
Ataxia–telangiectasia	Cerebella ataxia, multiple telangiectasias (eyes, ears, flexa surface of extremities), immunodeficiency, chromosomal breakage, malignancy, x-ray hypersensitivity	"Complete absence of ovaries", "absence of primary follicles" [149,150]	
Carbohydrate-deficient glycoprotein syndrome, Type 1 (PMM2) [91]	Neurologic abnormalities (e.g., unscheduled eye movements), ataxia, hypotonial/hyporeflexia strokes, joint cartractures	Ovarian failure (hypogonadism) [89]	Autosomal recessive
Cockayne Syndrome [151]	Dwarfism, microcephaly, mental retardation, pigmentary retinopathy and photosensitivity, premature senility. Sensitivity to ultraviolet light	Ovarian atrophy and fibrosis [152]	Autosomal recessive
Galactosemia (galactose-1-phosphate uridyl transferase deficiency) (GALT)	Hepatic failure with cirrhosis, renal failure, cataracts, cardiac failure	Ovarian failure with streak gonads [82–84]	Autosomal recessive
Martsolf Syndrome [153]	Short stature, microbrachycephaly, cataracts, abnormal facies with relative prognathism due to maxillary hypoplasia	"Primary hypogonadism" [154,155]	Autosomal recessive
Nijmegen Syndrome [156]	Chromosomal instability, immunodeficiency, hypersensity to ionizing radiation, malignancy	Ovarian failure (primary) [157,158]	Autosomal recessive
Rothmund-Thompson Syndrome [159]	Skin abnormalities (telangiectasia, erythrema irregular pigmentation), short statue, cataracts, sparse hair, small hands and feet, mental retardation, osteosarcoma	Ovarian failure (primary hypogonadism or delayed puberty) [160]	Autosomal recessive
Werner Syndrome [161]	Short stature, premature senility, skin changes (scleroderma)	Ovarian failure [161]	Autosomal recessive

unappreciated if the primary amenorrhea were assumed secondary to azotemia.

Germ-Cell Failure in Male (46,XY) and Female (46,XX) Sibs

In several sibships, male (46,XY) and female (46,XX) sibs have each shown germ-cell failure. Affected 46,XX females showed streak gonads, whereas 46,XY males showed germ-cell aplasia (Sertoli-cell-only syndrome). In two families, parents were consanguineous, and in each there were no somatic anomalies [73, 74]. In three other families, characteristic somatic anomalies suggested distinct entities. Hamet and colleagues [75] observed germ-cell failure, hypertension, and deafness; Al-Awadi and colleagues [76] found germ-cell failure and alopecia; Mikati and colleagues [77] reported germ-cell failure, microcephaly, and short stature.

In each of these families, a single autosomal gene is presumed to deleteriously affect germ-cell development in both sexes. This gene(s) could act either at a specific site common to early germ-cell development or exert its effect through meiotic breakdown. Elucidating such genes could help explain normal germ cell development. A variety of attractive candidate genes exist in mouse and Drosophila. An example of attractive candidate genes is *gcd*, the mouse mutant that causes germ cells to be deficient in both males and females. A novel gene, proliferation of germ cells (POG), was shown to be disputed in *gcd* mice and presumably is responsible for the observed phenotype. POG is one of the few genes known to specifically affect primordial germ-cell proliferation at the time of their entry into the developing genital ridge [78]. Several other genes are known to affect germ-cell proliferation and migration. Tyrosine kinase receptor (kit) and its ligand (kit-ligand) are required for the proliferation, survival, and migration of the germ cells [79]. Mice lacking the Wilm's tumor associated gene, WT-1, show normal germ-cell migration, but the urogenital ridge fails to develop, leading to kidney and gonadal agenesis [80]. Lack of steroidogenic factor-1 (SF-1) also leads to complete gonadal agene [81].

Galactosemia

Galactosemia is caused by deficiency of galactose I-phosphate uridyl transferase (GALT), encoded by a gene on 9p. Somatic features included renal, hepatic, and ocular defects. Kaufman and colleagues [82] reported POF in 12 of 18 galactosemic women, and Waggoner and colleagues [83] observed ovarian failure in 8 of 47 galactosemic women. Pathogenesis is presumed to involve galactose toxicity during infancy or childhood; elevated fetal levels of toxic metabolites should be cleared rapidly *in utero* by maternal enzymes. Consistent with this hypothesis, a neonate with galactosemia showed normal ovarian histology [84].

Given the necessity for dietary treatment during childhood to prevent mental retardation, it seems highly unlikely that previously undiagnosed galactosemia would prove to be the cause of ovarian failure in women presenting solely with primary amenorrhea or POF. Of greater relevance to gynecology, therefore, was a report in 1989 by Cramer and colleagues [85] that GALT heterozygotes were at increased risk for POF; however, Kaufman and colleagues [86] failed to confirm the observation of Cramer et al. [85], and even Cramer and colleagues [85] later failed to confirm perturbations of GALT abnormalities in a later study of women with early menopause. Moreover, not all homozygotes for human galactosemia are abnormal, nor are transgenic mice in which GALT is inactivated [87].

Carbohydrate-Deficient Glycoprotein (Phosphomannomutase Deficiency)

In type 1 carbohydrate-deficient glycoprotein (CDG) deficiency, mannose-6-phosphate cannot be converted to mannose-1-phosphate. These lipid-linked mannose-containing oligosaccharides are also needed because secretory glycoproteins are lacking. Lacking these glycoproteins, the phenotype is ovarian failure characterized by ovaries devoid of follicular activity [88, 89]. The molecular pathogenesis in the CDG gene located on 16p13 is usually a missense mutation [90].

Neurologic abnormalities coexist, encompassing hypotonia, hyperreflexia, unprovoked eye movements, ataxia, joint contractions, epilepsy, and stroke-like episodes [91] subcutaneous fat deposits, hepatomegaly, cardiomyopathy, pericardial effusion, and factor XI (clotting) deficiency.

Deficiency of 17α-Hydroxylase/17,20-Desmolase Deficiency (CYP17)

Sex steroid synthesis requires intact adrenal and gonadal biosynthetic pathways. Various gene products (enzymes) are required to convert cholesterol to testosterone and androstenedione and, hence, estrogens. The various enzyme blocks in the adrenal/gonadal biosynthetic pathways have varying but predictable consequences, depending on their site in the biosynthetic pathway (see Figure 32.1). The most common adrenal biosynthetic problem involves deficiency of 21- or 11β-hydroxylase, either of which causes pseudohermaphroditism. These disorders cause genital ambiguity because of virilization, but need not be considered in the differential diagnosis of XX gonadal dysgenesis. Perturbations of CYP17 and CYP19 (aromatase), however, may cause gonadal abnormalities without accompanying genital abnormalities.

If the cytochrome P450 enzyme 17α-hydroxylase/17–20-lyase is deficient, pregnenolone cannot be converted to 17α-hydroxypregnenolone. If the enzyme defect were complete, cortisol, androstenedione, testosterone, and estrogens could not be synthesized; however, 11-deoxycorticosterone and corticosterone could. With compensatory increase in adrenocorticotropic hormone (ACTH secretion), 11-deoxycorticosterone and corticosterone increase to result in hypernatremia, hypokalemia, and hypervolemia. Hypertension occurs. Aldosterone is decreased, presumably because hypervolemia suppresses the renin-angiotensin system.

Like most enzyme defects, 17α-hydroxylase deficiency is inherited in autosomal-recessive fashion. Females (46,XX) with 17α-hydroxylase deficiency have normal external genitalia, but at puberty they fail to undergo normal secondary sexual development (primary amenorrhea). Affected males (46,XY) usually have genital ambiguity (male pseudohermaphroditism) because partial expression of the gene can produce some androgens. Affected females are ordinarily encountered in the differential diagnosis of XX gonadal dysgenesis. Usually, hypertension is the major distinguishing feature. Oocytes appear incapable of spontaneously exceeding a diameter greater than 2.5 mm [92], but ovaries nonetheless respond to exogenous gonadotropins [93].

The CYP17 gene is located on 10q24–25, and its gene product is a cytochrome P450 enzyme. More than 20 different mutations have been identified, scattered among the 8 exons. Mutations include missense mutations, duplications, deletions, and premature protein truncation [94]. Most mutations have been observed in only a single family, yet another example of molecular hetereogeneity. An exception exists in Mennonites of Dutch origin, where a 4-base duplication in exon 8 accounts for most cases [95]. This founder mutation originated in Friesland.

A single gene (and enzyme) is responsible for both 17α-hydroxylase and 17,20-desmolase (lyase) actions (see Figure 32.2). A few patients having deficiency of both 17α-hydroxylase and 17,20 lyase activities have been analyzed, with mutations differing in those showing only deficient 17α-hydroxylase or showing both hydroxylase and desmo-

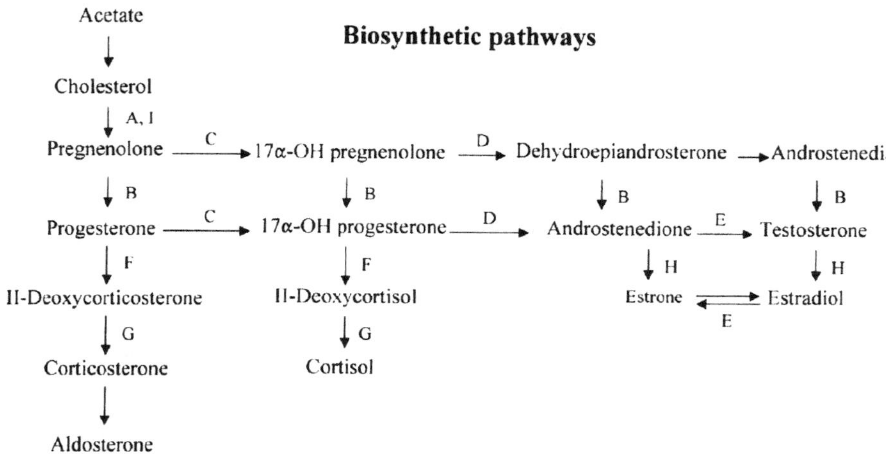

FIGURE 32.2 Pivotal adrenal and gonadal biosynthetic pathways. Letters designate enzymes or activities required for the appropriate conversions. **A,** 20-hydroxylase and 20,22-desmolase; **B,** 3β-ol-dehydrogenase; **C,** 17α-hydroxylase; **D,** 17,20-desmolase; **E,** 17-ketosteroid reductase; **F,** 21-hydroxylase; **G,** 11-hydroxylase; **H,** aromatase. In addition to these enzymes, **S**teroid **A**cute **R**egulatory protein (StAR), designated **I,** is responsible for transporting cholesterol to the site of steroid biosynthesis. Finally, 17α-hydroxylase (C) and 17,20-desmolase (D) activities are actually governed by a single gene. (Redrawn from [3]).

lase defects [96, 97]. Site-directed mutagenesis in the rat gene indicates that mutations closer to the 5⁻ end are more deleterious [98].

Aromatase Mutations (CYP 19)

Conversion of androgens (Δ4-androstenedione) to estrogens (estrone) requires cytochrome P-450 aromatase, an enzyme product of a 40-kb gene located on chromosome 15q21.1 [99]. Deficiency of the aromatase enzyme in 46,XX individuals can be associated with clitoral hypertrophy or genital ambiguity, but 46,XX aromatase deficiency may be recognized as primary amenorrhea in otherwise normal females.

Ito and colleagues [100] reported aromatase mutation (CYP19) in an 18-year-old 46,XX Japanese woman having primary amenorrhea and cystic ovaries. Compound heterozygosity existed for two point mutations in exon 10. The mutant protein had no activity. Conte and colleagues [101] reported aromatase deficiency in a 46,XX woman presenting with primary amenorrhea, elevated gonadatropins, and ovarian cysts. Compound heterozygosity also existed for two mutations in exon 10. One mutation was C1303T (cysteine rather than arginine); the other was G1310A (tyrosine rather than cysteine).

Clitoral enlargement at puberty was reported by Mullis and colleagues [102]. No breast development occurred. Follicle-stimulating hormone (FSH) was elevated; estrone and estradiol were decreased. Multiple ovarian follicular cysts were evident. Compound heterozygosity existed in the CYP19 locus.

46,XX Agonadia

In 46,XY agonadia, gonads are completely absent, not represented by a fibrous streak. Agonadia usually occurs in 46,XY individuals but, rarely, 46,XX cases exist. In agonadia (XY or XX) external genitalia are abnormal but female-like; no more than rudimentary Mullerian *or* wolffian derivatives are present. External genitalia usually consist of a phallus about the size of a clitoris, underdeveloped labia majora, and nearly complete fusion of labioscrotal folds. Thus external genitalia are usually female-like in appearance, albeit not normal. Somatic anomalies coexist in approximately one-half of cases: craniofacial anomalies, vertebral anomalies, and mental retardation.

Sporadic 46,XX agonadia cases were reported by Duck [103] and Levinson [104]. Mendonca and colleagues [105] reported agonadia without somatic anomalies in phenotypic sibs having unlike chromosomal complements (46,XY and 46,XX). Kennerknecht and colleagues [106] reported agonadism, hypoplasia of the pulmonary artery and lung, and dextrocardia in discordant sex sibs (XX and XY).

Fragile X Syndrome and Expansion of Triplet Nucleotide Repeats (CGG)

A molecular perturbation seemingly relevant to ovarian failure is expansion of triplet nucleotide repeats (CGG). The prototype is the fragile X syndrome, caused by mutation of the FMRI gene on Xq27. "Fragile" refers to a tendency toward chromosomal breakage when affected cells are cultured in folic acid–deficient media. Various fragile sites exist in humans, but FRAXA and FRAXE are relevant to the present discussion.

The molecular basis of FRAXA involves repetition of the triplet repeat CGG $(CGG)^n$ 230 times or more at a given site on the X long arm (Xq17) (Figure 32.3). Ordinarily, the normal number of CGG repeats in males is only 6 to 50. Males with CGG expansion show mental retardation, characteristic facial features, and large testes. Heterozygous females having 50 to 200 repeats are said to have a *premutation*. During female (but not male) meiosis, the number of triplet repeats may increase (expand). Thus a

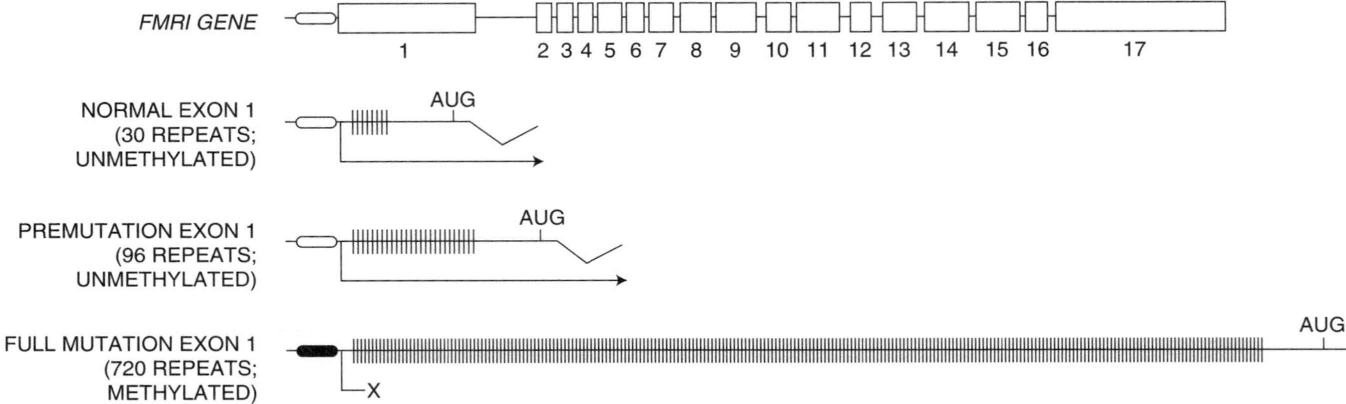

FIGURE 32.3 Diagram of the FMR1 gene (also called FRAYA) and the first exon in normal, premutation, and full mutation alleles. The oval immediately to the left of the start site of transcription represents the promoter region of the FMR1 gene. The open symbol represents active transcription, and the black symbol, silenced transcription. The vertical lines indicate CGG trinucleotides upstream of the methionine codon (AUG) at the translocational start site. (Reprinted with permission from [162]).

woman with a FRAXA premutation may have an affected son if the number of CGG repeats on the X she transmits to her offspring were to expand during meiosis to more than 230. These molecular changes are readily detectable by straightforward molecular studies. Females may also be affected (50% likelihood) if CGG expansion occurs, but the phenotype is less severe than in affected males.

Females with the FRAXA premutation may show POF. Schwartz and colleagues [107] reported that fragile X carrier females (premutation) more often showed oligomenorrhea than noncarrier female relatives (38% versus 6%). Murray and colleagues [108] analyzed 1268 controls, 50 familial POF cases, and 244 sporadic POF cases. Of familial cases, 16% showed a FRAXA premutation; among sporadic cases, only 1.6% showed POF. In the same sample, POF was not increased in FRAXE. An international collaborative survey [109] of 395 premutation carriers revealed that 63 (16%) underwent menopause at younger than 40 years of age; only 0.4% of controls did. Consistent with these findings are observations that heterozygous FRAXA women respond poorly to ovulation-inducing agents, producing fewer oocytes and fewer embryos in assisted reproductive technologies (ART) [110]. Surprisingly, however, frequency of POF was not increased in 128 FRAXA cases having a full mutation.

Although the consensus is that FRAXA is associated with POF, Kenneson and colleagues [111] do not agree. They argue that data are best explained by a contiguous gene syndrome (i.e., two separate but closely linked loci). That Xq27–28 contains both FMR-1 (FRAXA) and a region important for ovarian maintenance is consistent with, but does not prove, this hypothesis.

Myotonic Dystrophy and Expansion of Triplet Repeats (CTG)

Myotonic dystrophy (MD) is an autosomal-dominant disorder characterized by muscle wasting (head, neck, extremities), frontal balding, cataracts, and male hypogonadism (80%) caused by testicular atrophy. The pathogenesis of MD involves nucleotide expansion of CTG in the 3′ untranslated region of a gene located on chromosome 19. Normally, there are 5 to 27 CTG repeats. Heterozygotes usually have at least 50 repeats; severely affected individuals show 600 or more. Female hypogonadism is much less common than male hypogonadism. Despite frequent citations in texts, ovarian failure actually seems not to be well documented.

Nonetheless, as in FRAXA, there is a poor response to ovulation induction regions. Sermon and colleagues [112] report fewer embryos per cycle than in standard ART; thus pregnancy rates in preimplantation genetic diagnosis are decreased.

Blepharophimosis-Ptosis-Epicanthus (FOXL2)

Blepharophimosis-Ptosis-Epicanthus syndrome I (BPES-Type 1) is an autosomal-dominant multiple-malformation syndrome long known to be associated with ovarian failure. POF is the usual clinical manifestation, rather than complete ovarian failure [69, 113]. In one unusual case, Fraser and colleagues [114] reported that the ovaries of an affected individual were unresponsive to gonadatropins.

Sib-pair analysis using polymorphic DNA variants [115] initially localized the gene to chromosome 3 (3q22→24)

[116]. Positional cloning revealed mutation in the winged helix/forkhead transcription factor gene (FOXL2), a truncated protein in each of four cases [117]. Reported mutations include three cases with stop codons and one with 17-bp duplication causing a frameshift and, hence, the truncated gene product. This indicates that the mechanism of gene action is haplo-insufficiency.

The FOXL2 gene is expressed in mesenchyma of mouse eyelids and in granulosa cells of adult ovarian follides, consistent with the phenotype observed in perturbation of the human homologue BPE. Mutations in FOXL2 can lead to POF without eyelid abnormalities, although this seemingly accounts for only a small number of ostensibly non-syndrome POF cases [118–120]. De Baere et al. [119] tabulate all FOXL2 mutations detected to date and offer genotype-phenotype correlations. The authors predict that a protein truncated before the poly-Ala tract will lead to POF.

Autosomal-Dominant Premature Ovarian Failure

Familial tendencies reminiscent of autosomal-dominant inheritance have long been recognized in cytogenetically normal women who have POF but no other clinical abnormalities. Dominant tendencies are especially associated with multiple-system autoimmune abnormalities (ovarian, adrenal, thyroid); however, families with dominantly transmitted POF exist with no autoimmune problems. This is further distinct from familial transmission of terminal deletions of Xp or Xq. Thus Coulam and colleagues [121] reported POF in sibs who had an affected mother and aunt. Affected individuals in more than one generation were reported by Starup and Sele [122] and Austin and colleagues [123].

Dominant gene(s) causing POF may be more common than once believed. Testa and colleagues [124] and Vegetti and colleagues [125] are systematically studying women with POF (menopause at younger than 40 years of age) who were ascertained in the northern Italian population. After excluding 10 cases with known etiologies (5 chromosomal, 3 prior ovarian surgery, 1 prior chemotherapy, 1 galactosemia), there remained 71 probands. Of the 71, 22 (31%) had other affected relatives. A later report by the authors encompassed 130 cases, 28.5% familial [125]. Patterns of inheritance observed were consistent with either autosomal or X-linked dominant inheritance; transmission through both maternal and paternal lineage was observed. Of 30 other women experiencing early menopause (40 to 50 years) but not POF per se, half showed other affected relatives. Thus POF and early menopause (40 to 50 years) may constitute the same phenomena. The two different phenotypes have been observed within a single kindred transmission through either a paternal or maternal relative.

POLYGENIC FACTORS IN PREMATURE OVARIAN FAILURE: NORMAL CONTINUATIONS VARIATION AS A CAUSE OF HERITABLE EARLY MENOPAUSE

Oocyte number (reservoir) could be low in some women simply on statistical (stochastic) grounds. A normal distribution exists for essentially all anatomic traits (e.g., height) and physiologic (e.g., blood pressure) traits, and this principle surely applies to oocyte number and reservoir. Rodent strains show characteristic breeding duration, implying genetic control over either the rate of oocyte depletion or the number of oocytes initially present. That a normal distribution of germ-cell number exists in ostensibly normal females is difficult to prove in humans, but some ostensibly normal (menstruating) women can be expected to have decreased oocyte reservoir or increased oocyte attrition on a genetic basis. This genetic basis is presumably not a single gene but polygenic (see Simpson and Elias [3]).

Age at human menopause is heritable. Cramer and colleagues [126] took appropriate confounders (e.g., hysterectomy) into account in a case-control study of 10,606 U.S. women. Women with early menopause (40 to 45 years) were age-matched with controls who were either still menstruating or who had experienced menopause after age 46. Of 129 early menopause cases, 37.5% had a similarly affected mother, sister, aunt, or grandmother. Only 9% of controls had such a relative (odds ratio after adjustment: 6.1, 95% confidence interval [CI]: 3.9 to 9.4). The odds ratio was greatest (9.1) for sisters and greater when menopause occurred before 40 years. Results of Cramer and colleagues [126] were confirmed by Torgerson and colleagues [127], who studied women undergoing menopause during the 5-year centile ages 45 to 49 years. The likelihood was increased that menopause would occur in a similar 5-year centile in their daughters.

Twin studies also confirmed heritability of age at menopause [128]. Snieder and colleagues [129] studied 275 monozygotic (MZ) and 353 dizygotic (DZ) U.K. twin pairs. Correlation *(r)* for age at menopause was 0.58 for MZ and 0.39 DZ twins; heritability (h2) was calculated to be 63%. Treloar and colleagues [130] studied 466 MZ and 262 DZ Australian twin pairs. For age at menopause, correlation *(r)* was 0.49 to 0.57 for MZ and 0.31 to 0.33 for DZ twin pairs. Differences between MZ and DZ held when iatrogenic causes of menopause were taken into account.

OVARIAN RESISTANCE

Ovarian resistance implies that the genes necessary for ovarian differentiation are intact, but the ovary is unable to respond to nonovarian stimuli (e.g., FSH, LH). Only a few disorders of ovarian resistance are known. Many of the disorders discussed in the previous section could be the result not of ovarian failure per se but of ovarian resistance. The phenotype example occurs in XX gonadal dysgenesis without somatic anomalies, one form of which proved to result from a mutation in the FSH receptor gene.

XX Gonadal Dysgenesis Due to Follicle-Stimulating Hormone Receptor Gene Mutation (C566T)

In Finland, Aittomaki and colleagues [51, 131] have identified this condition as the primary cause of XX gonadal dysgenesis. A nationwide search identified 75 patients fulfilling these diagnostic criteria: primary or secondary amenorrhea, serum FSH > 40 IU/mL. These 75 cases included 57 sporadic cases and 18 cases having one or more affected relative (7 different families). A preponderance of cases resided in north central Finland, a more sparsely populated part of the country. The frequency was 1 per 8300 liveborn Finnish females; the relatively high incidence was attributed to a founder effect. Segregation ratio of 0.23 for female sibs was consistent with autosomal-recessive inheritance, as was the high consanguinity rate (12%).

In the initial analysis of Aittomaki and colleagues [51, 131] a specific mutation was found in Val566Ala of the FSHR gene, in six families [51, 131]. This cytosine-thymidine transition (C566T) was later found in additional families [131, 132].

The C566T mutation has only rarely been detected in women with 46,XX ovarian failure who reside outside Finland. In the United States, Layman and colleague [133] found no FSHR mutations in 35 46,XX women having hypergonadotropic hypogonadism (15 with primary amenorrhea, 20 with secondary amenorrhea). Liu and colleagues [134] found no FSHR anomalies in one multigenerational POF family, four sporadic POF cases, and two other hypergonadotropic hypogonadism cases. No cases were found in 46,XX POF or primary amenorrhea cases from Germany [135], Brazil [136], and Mexico [137]. The last report analyzed all exons of FSHR. Similarly, Jiang et al. [138] failed to detect C566T in 1100 normal Danish or 540 normal Singaporean individuals (v. 1% in the general Finnish population); 1 in 1200 in Switzerland showed C566T heterozygosity).

Comparing the phenotype of C566T XX gonadal dysgenesis (Val566Ala) with non-Val566Ala XX gonadal dysgenesis, Aittomaki and colleagues [132] showed the former to be more likely to have ovarian follicles on ultrasound examination. Thus C566T XX gonadal dysgenesis showed some of the features gynecologists have long predicted for a gonadotropin-resistant disorder (Savage syndrome), although in general the phenotype of streak gonads found by Aittomaki [51] was not expected. FSHR (knockout) mice similarly show failure of oogenesis; however, the necessity of FSH for progression of oogenesis is clear. [139]

Inactivating Luteinizing Hormone Receptor Defect (46,XX)

Another trophic hormone receptor gene whose perturbation causes XX gonadal dysgenesis is lutenizing hormone receptor (LHR), 75 kd in length and consisting of 17 exons. Located on 2p near FSHR, the first 10 exons of LHR are extracellular; the last 6 are intracellular; the 11th, transmembrane.

LHR mutations have been reported predominantly in 46,XY individuals, where the phenotype may extend to complete LH resistance and XY gender reversal (female). 46,XX cases are less common than 46,XY cases, for reasons that are unclear. The only reported cases have occurred in sibships in which an affected 46,XY male had Leydig cell hypoplasia.

46,XX women with LHR mutations show oligomenorrhea or, less often, primary amenorrhea. Ovulation does not occur, although gametogenesis proceeds until the preovulatory stage, but not beyond. This is consistent with findings in the mouse knockout model [140, 141].

Mutations in human LHR are molecularly heterogeneous, but most have been found in the transmembrane domain (exon 11). Latronico and colleagues [142] reported primary amenorrhea in a 22-year-old woman (46,XX) who had three affected male sibs (46,XY). Like her sibs, the 46,XX female was homozygous for a nonsense mutation at codon 554 (Arg554ter). The resulting stop codon produced a truncated protein. The affected 46,XX female showed breast development, but only experienced a single episode of menstrual bleeding at age 20 years; LH was 37 mIU/mL, FSH 9 mIU/mL. The mutation reduced signal transduction activity of the LHR gene.

Toledo and colleagues [143] studied a 46,XX female whose two 46,XY affected sibs had been previously reported by Cramer and colleagues [126]. The sister showed elevated gonadotropins but anatomically normal ovaries. The mutation was Ala593Pro. Two sisters reported by Laue and colleagues [144] showed the nonsense mutation cys545ter in exon 11; the father but not the mother had the mutation. The authors postulated a dominant negative effect, but more likely a mutant allele was also transmitted from the probably heterozygous mother but not recognized.

References

1. Simpson, J. L. (2000). Genetic programming in ovarian development and oogenesis. In *Menopause Biology and Pathobiology*, eds. R. A. Lobo and J. M. R. Kelsey, 77–94. London: Academic Press.
2. Simpson, J. L., and Rajkovic, A. (1999). Ovarian differentiation and gonadal failure. *Am. J. Med. Genet.* 89, 186–200.

3. Simpson, J. L., and Elias, S. (2003). *Genetics in Obstetrics and Gynecology*, 3rd ed. Philadelphia: W.B. Saunders.
4. Simpson, J. L. (1987). Phenotypic-karyotypic correlations of gonadal determinants: Current status and relationship to molecular studies. In *Human Genetics (Proceedings of the Seventh International Congress, Berlin)*, ed. K. V. F. Sperling. Heidelberg: Springer-Verlag.
5. German, J. (1988). Gonadal dimorphism explained as a dosage effect of a locus on the sex chromosomes, the gonad-differentiation locus (GDL). *Am. J. Hum. Genet.* 42, 414–421.
6. Bardoni, B., Zanaria, E., Guioli, S. et al. (1994). A dosage sensitive locus at chromosome Xp21 is involved in male to female sex reversal. *Nat. Genet.* 7, 497–501.
7. Swain, A., Zanaria, E., Hacker, A., Lovell-Badge, R., and Camerino, G. (1996). Mouse Dax1 expression is consistent with a role in sex determination as well as in adrenal and hypothalamus function. *Nat. Genet.* 12, 404–409.
8. Simpson, J. L. (2003). Male pseudohermaphroditism, true hermaphroditism and XY sex reversal. In *Reproductive Medicine: Molecular Cellular and Genetic Fundamentals*, vol. 2, eds. Fauser, B. C. J. M. 541–563. London: The Parthenon publishing Group.
9. Swain, A., Narvaez, V., Burgoyne, P., Camerino, G., and Lovell-Badge, R.. (1998). Dax1 antagonizes Sry action in mammalian sex determination. *Nature* 391, 761–767.
10. Yu, R. N., Ito, M., Saunders, T. L., Camper, S. A., and Jameson, J. L. (1998). Role of Ahch in gonadal development and gametogenesis. *Nat. Genet.* 20, 353–357.
11. Jirasek, J. (1976). Principles of reproductive embryology. In *Disorders of Sexual Differentiation:Etiology and Clinical Delineation*, ed. J. L. Simpson, 51–110. San Diego: Academic Press.
12. Turner, H. H. (1938). A syndrome of infantilism, congenital webbed neck, and cubitus valgus. *Endocrinology* 23, 566.
13. Mathur, A., Stekol, L., Schatz, D. et al. (1991). The parental origin of the single X chromosome in Turner syndrome: Lack of correlation with parental age or clinical phenotype. *Am. J. Hum. Genet.* 48, 682–686.
14. Cockwell, A., MacKenzie, M., Youings, S., and Jacobs, P. (1991). A cytogenetic and molecular study of a series of 45,X fetuses and their parents. *J. Med. Genet.* 28, 152–155.
15. Willard, H. F. (2001). The sex chromosomes and X chromosome inactivation. In *The Metabolic and Molecular Bases of Inherited Disease*, vol. 1, eds. C. R. Scriver, A. L. Beaudet, W. S. Sly, and D. Valle, 1191–1211. New York: McGraw-Hill.
16. Abir, R., Fisch, B., Nitke, S. et al. (2001). Morphological study of fully and partially isolated early human follicles. *Fertil. Steril.* 75, 141–146.
17. Hovatta, O. (1999). Pregnancies in women with Turner's syndrome. *Ann. Med.* 31, 106–110.
18. Magee, A. C., Nevin, N. C., Armstrong, M. J., McGibbon, D., and Nevin, J. (1998). Ullrich-Turner syndrome: Seven pregnancies in an apparent 45,X woman. *Am. J. Med. Genet.* 75, 1–3.
19. Zinn, A. R., Tonk, V. S., Chen, Z. et al. (1998). Evidence for a Turner syndrome locus or loci at Xp11.2-p22.1. *Am. J. Hum. Genet.* 63, 1757–1766.
20. Zinn, A. R., and Ross, J. L. (2001). Molecular analysis of genes on Xp controlling Turner syndrome and premature ovarian failure (POF). *Semin. Reprod. Med.* 19, 141–146.
21. Tharapel, A. T., Anderson, K. P., Simpson, J. L. et al. (1993). Deletion (X)(q26.1→q28) in a proband and her mother: Molecular characterization and phenotypic-karyotypic deductions. *Am. J. Hum. Genet.* 52, 463–471.
22. Davison, R. M., Fox, M., and Conway, G. S. (2000). Mapping of the POF1 locus and identification of putative genes for premature ovarian failure. *Mol. Hum. Reprod.* 6, 314–318.
23. Simpson, J. L. (1998). Genetics of female infertility. In *Proceedings of the Conference, Treatment of Infertility: The New Frontiers*, eds. M. Filicori and C. Flamigni, 37–52. Boca Raton, FL: Communications Media for Education, Inc.
24. Wandstrat, A. E., Conroy, J. M., Zurcher, V. L. et al. (2000). Molecular and cytogenetic analysis of familial Xp deletions. *Am. J. Med. Genet.* 94, 163–169.
25. Thomas, N. S., and Huson, S. M. (2001). Atypical phenotype in a female with a large Xp deletion. *Am. J. Med. Genet.* 104, 81–83.
26. Thomas, N. S., Sharp, A. J., Browne, C. E. et al. (1999). Xp deletions associated with autism in three females. *Hum. Genet.* 104, 43–48.
27. Fraccaro, M., Maraschio, P., Pasquali, F., and Scappaticci, S. (1977). Women heterozygous for deficiency of the (p21 leads to pter) region of the X chromosome are fertile. *Hum. Genet.* 39, 283–292.
28. James, R. S., Dalton, P., Gustashaw, K. et al. (1997). Molecular characterization of isochromosomes of Xq. *Ann. Hum. Genet.* 61 (Part 6), 485–490.
29. Massa, G., Vanderschueren-Lodeweyckx, M., and Fryns, J. P. (1992). Deletion of the short arm of the X chromosome: a hereditary form of Turner syndrome. *Eur. J. Pediatr.* 151, 893–894.
30. Simpson, J. L. (1979). Gonadal dysgenesis and sex chromosome abnormalities. Phenotypic/karyotypic correlations. In *Genetic Mechanisms of Sexual Development*, eds. H. L. Vallet and I. H. Perter, 365–405. New York: Academic Press.
31. Jones, M. H., Furlong, R. A., Burkin, H. et al. (1996). The Drosophila developmental gene fat facets has a human homologue in Xp11.4 which escapes X-inactivation and has related sequences on Yq11.2. *Hum. Mol. Genet.* 5, 1695–1701.
32. James, R. S., Coppin, B., Dalton, P. et al. (1998). A study of females with deletions of the short arm of the X chromosome. *Hum. Genet.* 102, 507–516.
33. Galloway, S. M., McNatty, K. P., Cambridge, L. M. et al. (2000). Mutations in an oocyte-derived growth factor gene (BMP15) cause increased ovulation rate and infertility in a dosage-sensitive manner. *Nat. Genet.* 25, 279–283.
34. Yan, C., Wang, P., DeMayo, J. et al. (2001). Synergistic roles of bone morphogenetic protein 15 and growth differentiation factor 9 in ovarian function. *Mol. Endocrinol.* 15, 854–866.
35. Bione, S., and Toniolo, D. (2000). X chromosome genes and premature ovarian failure. *Semin. Reprod. Med.* 18, 51–57.
36. Zinn, A. R. (2001). The X chromosome and the ovary. *J. Soc. Gynecol. Investig.* 8, S34–S36.
37. Matzuk, M. M., and Lamb, D. J. (2002). Genetic dissection of mammalian fertility pathways. *Nat. Cell. Biol.* 4 (Suppl), s41–s49.

38. Ogata, T., and Matsuo, N. (1995). Turner syndrome and female sex chromosome aberrations: deduction of the principal factors involved in the development of clinical features. *Hum. Genet.* 95, 607–629.
39. Susca, F., Aoam, R., Vucubim, M., Louerro, G., and Guanti, G. (1999). Xq deletion and premature ovarian failure. [abstract]. *Hum. Reprod.* 14, 236.
40. Bione, S., Sala, C., Manzini, C. et al. (1998). A human homologue of the Drosophila melanogaster diaphanous gene is disrupted in a patient with premature ovarian failure: Evidence for conserved function in oogenesis and implications for human sterility. *Am. J. Hum. Genet.* 62, 533–541.
41. Sala, C., Arrigo, G., Torri, G. et al. (1997). Eleven X chromosome breakpoints associated with premature ovarian failure (POF) map to a 15-Mb YAC contig spanning Xq21. *Genomics* 40, 123–131.
42. Philippe, C., Arnould, C., Sloan, F. et al. (1995). A high-resolution interval map of the q21 region of the human X chromosome. *Genomics* 27, 539–543.
43. Krauss, C. M., Turksoy, R. N., Atkins, L. et al. (1987). Familial premature ovarian failure due to an interstitial deletion of the long arm of the X chromosome. *N. Engl. J. Med.* 317, 125–131.
44. Veneman, T. F., Beverstock, G. C., Exalto, N., and Mollevanger, P. (1991). Premature menopause because of an inherited deletion in the long arm of the X-chromosome. *Fertil. Steril.* 55, 631–633.
45. Brown, S., Yu, C., Lanzano, P. et al. (1998). A de novo mutation (Gln2Stop) at the 5′ end of the SRY gene leads to sex reversal with partial ovarian function. *Am. J. Hum. Genet.* 62, 189–192.
46. Castrillon, D. H., and Wasserman, S. A. (1994). Diaphanous is required for cytokinesis in Drosophila and shares domains of similarity with the products of the limb deformity gene. *Development* 120, 3367–3377.
47. Prueitt, R. L., Ross, J. L., and Zinn, A. R. (2000). Physical mapping of nine Xq translocation breakpoints and identification of XPNPEP2 as a premature ovarian failure candidate gene. *Cytogenet. Cell Genet.* 89, 44–50.
48. Meyers, C. M., Boughman, J. A., Rivas, M., Wilroy, R. S., and Simpson, J. L. (1996), Gonadal (ovarian) dysgenesis in 46,XX individuals: Frequency of the autosomal recessive form. *Am. J. Med. Genet.* 63, 518–524.
49. Simpson, J. L., Christakos, A. C., Horwith, M., and Silverman, F. S. (1971). Gonadal dysgenesis in individuals with apparently normal chromosomal complements: tabulation of cases and compilation of genetic data. *Birth Defects Orig. Artic. Ser.* 7(6), 215–228.
50. Boczkowski, K. (1970). Pure gonadal dysgenesis and ovarian dysplasia in sisters. *Am. J. Obstet. Gynecol.* 106, 626–628.
51. Aittomaki, K. (1994). The genetics of XX gonadal dysgenesis. *Am. J. Hum. Genet.* 54, 844–851.
52. Portuondo, J. A., Neyro, J. L., Benito, J. A., de los, R. A., and Barral, A. (1987). Familial 46,XX gonadal dysgenesis. *Intl. J. Fertil.* 32, 56–58.
53. Rajkovic, A., and Matzuk, M. M. (2002). Functional analysis of oocyte-expressed genes using transgenic models. *Mol. Cell. Endocrinol.* 187, 5–9.
54. Rajkovic, A., Yan, C., Yan, W., Klysik, M., and Matzuk, M. M. (2002). Obox, a family of homeobox genes preferentially expressed in germ cells. *Genomics* 79, 711–717.
55. Suzumori, N., Yan, C., Matzuk, M. M., and Rajkovic, A. (2002). Nobox is a homeobox-encoding gene preferentially expressed in primordial and growing oocytes. *Mech. Dev.* 111, 137–141.
56. Perrault, M., Klotz, P., and Housset, E. (1951). Deux cas de syndrome de Turner avec surdi-mutite dans une meme fratrie. *Bull. Soc. Med. Hop. Paris.* 67, 79.
57. Christakos, A. C., Simpson, J. L., Younger, J. B., and Christian, C. D. (1969). Gonadal dysgenesis as an autosomal recessive condition. *Am. J. Obstet. Gynecol.* 104, 1027–1030.
58. Pallister, P. D., and Opitz, J. M. (1979). The Perrault syndrome: Autosomal recessive ovarian dysgenesis with facultative, non-sex-limited sensorineural deafness. *Am. J. Med. Genet.* 4, 239–246.
59. McCarthy, D. J., and Opitz, J. M. (1985). Perrault syndrome in sisters. *Am. J. Med. Genet.* 22, 629–631.
60. Nishi, Y., Hamamoto, K., Kajiyama, M., and Kawamura, I. (1988). The Perrault syndrome: Clinical report and review. *Am. J. Med. Genet.* 31, 623–629.
61. Simon, A. M., Goodenough, D. A., Li, E., and Paul, D. L. (1997). Female infertility in mice lacking connexin 37. *Nature* 385, 525–529.
62. Skre, H., Bassoe, H. H., Berg, K., and Frovig, A. G. (1976). Cerebellar ataxia and hypergonadotropic hypogonadism in two kindreds. Chance concurrence, pleiotropism or linkage? *Clin. Genet.* 9, 234–244.
63. De Michele, G., Filla, A., Striano, S., Rimoldi, M., and Campanella, G. (1993). Heterogeneous findings in four cases of cerebellar ataxia associated with hypogonadism (Holmes' type ataxia). *Clin. Neurol. Neurosurg.* 95, 23–28.
64. Linssen, W. H., Van den Bent, M. J., Brunner, H. G., and Poels, P. J. (1994). Deafness, sensory neuropathy, and ovarian dysgenesis: A new syndrome or a broader spectrum of Perrault syndrome? *Am. J. Med. Genet.* 51, 81–82.
65. Gottschalk, M. E., Coker, S. B., and Fox, L. A. (1996). Neurologic anomalies of Perrault syndrome. *Am. J. Med. Genet.* 65, 274–276.
66. Fryns, J. P., Van Lingen, C., Devriendt, K., Legius, E., and Raus, P. (1998). Two adult females with a distinct familial mental retardation syndrome: Non-progressive neurological symptoms with ataxia and hypotonia, similar facial appearance, hypergonadotrophic hypogonadism, and retinal dystrophy. *J. Med. Genet.* 35, 333–335.
67. Amor, D. J., Delatycki, M. B., Gardner, R. J., and Storey, E. (2001). New variant of familial cerebellar ataxia with hypergonadotropic hypogonadism and sensorineural deafness. *Am. J. Med. Genet.* 99, 29–33.
68. Maximilian, C., Ionescu, B., and Bucur, A. (1970). Two sisters with major gonadal dysgenesis, dwarfism, microcephaly, arachnodactyly, and normal karyotype 46, XX. *J. Genet. Hum.* 18, 365–378.
69. Malouf, J., Alam, S., Kanj, H., Mufarrij, A., and Der, K. V. (1985). Hypergonadotropic hypogonadism with congestive cardiomyopathy: An autosomal-recessive disorder? *Am. J. Med. Genet.* 20, 483–489.
70. Quayle, S. A., and Copeland, K. C. (1991). 46,XX gonadal dysgenesis with epibulbar dermoid. *Am. J. Med. Genet.* 40, 75–76.

71. Pober, B. R., Zemel, S., and Hisama, F. M. (1998). 46,XX gonadal dysgenesis, short stature and recurrent metabolic acidosis in two sisters. [abstract]. *Am. J. Hum. Genet.* 63, A117.
72. Bailey, W. A., Zwingman, T. A., Reznik, V. M. et al. (1992). End-stage renal disease and primary hypogonadism associated with a 46,XX karyotype. *Am. J. Dis. Child.* 146, 1218–1223.
73. Smith, A., Fraser, I. S., and Noel, M. (1979). Three siblings with premature gonadal failure. *Fertil. Steril.* 32, 528–530.
74. Granat, M., Amar, A., Mor-Yosef, S., Brautbar, C., and Schenker, J. G. (1983). Familial gonadal germinative failure: Endocrine and human leukocyte antigen studies. *Fertil. Steril.* 40, 215–219.
75. Hamet, P., Kuchel, O., Nowaczynski, W. et al. (1973). Hypertension with adrenal, genital, renal defects, and deafness. A new familial syndrome. *Arch. Intern. Med.* 131, 563–569.
76. Al Awadi, S. A., Farag, T. I., Teebi, A. S. et al. (1985). Primary hypogonadism and partial alopecia in three sibs with mullerian hypoplasia in the affected females. *Am. J. Med. Genet.* 22, 619–622.
77. Mikati, M. A., Najjar, S. S., Sahli, I. F. et al. (1985). Microcephaly, hypergonadotropic hypogonadism, short stature, and minor anomalies: A new syndrome. *Am. J. Med. Genet.* 22, 599–608.
78. Agoulnik, A. I., Lu, B., Zhu, Q. et al. (2002). A novel gene, Pog, is necessary for primordial germ cell proliferation in the mouse and underlies the germ cell deficient mutation, gcd. *Hum. Mol. Genet.* 11, 3047–3053.
79. Besmer, P., Manova, K., Duttlinger, R. et al. (1993). The kit-ligand (steel factor) and its receptor c-kit/W: Pleiotropic roles in gametogenesis and melanogenesis. *Dev. Suppl.* (105), 125–137.
80. Kreidberg, J. A., Sariola, H., Loring, J. M. et al. (1993). WT-1 is required for early kidney development. *Cell* 74, 679–691.
81. Luo, X., Ikeda, Y., and Parker, K. L. (1994). A cell-specific nuclear receptor is essential for adrenal and gonadal development and sexual differentiation. *Cell* 77, 481–490.
82. Kaufman, F. R., Kogut, M. D., Donnell, G. N. et al. (1981). Hypergonadotropic hypogonadism in female patients with galactosemia. *N. Engl. J. Med.* 304, 994–998.
83. Waggoner, D. D., Buist, N. R., and Donnell, G. N. (1990). Long-term prognosis in galactosaemia: Results of a survey of 350 cases. *J. Inherit. Metab. Dis.* 13, 802–818.
84. Levy, H. L., Driscoll, S. G., Porensky, R. S., and Wender, D. F. (1984). Ovarian failure in galactosemia. *N. Engl. J. Med.* 310, 50.
85. Cramer, D. W., Harlow, B. L., Barbieri, R. L., and Ng, W. G. (1989). Galactose-1-phosphate uridyl transferase activity associated with age at menopause and reproductive history. *Fertil. Steril.* 51, 609–615.
86. Kaufman, F. R., Devgan, S., and Donnell, G. N. (1993). Results of a survey of carrier women for the galactosemia gene. *Fertil. Steril.* 60, 727–728.
87. Leslie, N. D., Yager, K., and Bai, S. (1995). A mouse model for transferase deficiency galactosemia. [abstract]. *Am. J. Hum. Genet.* 57, 191.
88. de Zegher, F., and Jaeken, J. (1995). Endocrinology of the carbohydrate-deficient glycoprotein syndrome type 1 from birth through adolescence. *Pediatr. Res.* 37, 395–401.
89. Kristiansson, B., Stibler, H., and Wide, L. (1995). Gonadal function and glycoprotein hormones in the carbohydrate-deficient glycoprotein (CDG) syndrome. *Acta Paediatr.* 84, 655–659.
90. Bjursell, C., Stibler, H., Wahlstrom, J. et al. (1997). Fine mapping of the gene for carbohydrate-deficient glycoprotein syndrome, type I (CDG1): Linkage disequilibrium and founder effect in Scandinavian families. *Genomics* 39, 247–253.
91. Matthijs, G., Schollen, E., Pardon, E. et al. (1997). Mutations in PMM2, a phosphomannomutase gene on chromosome 16p13, in carbohydrate-deficient glycoprotein type I syndrome (Jaeken syndrome). *Nat. Genet.* 16, 88–92.
92. Araki, S., Chikazawa, K., Sekiguchi, I. et al. (1987). Arrest of follicular development in a patient with 17 alpha-hydroxylase deficiency: Folliculogenesis in association with a lack of estrogen synthesis in the ovaries. *Fertil. Steril.* 47, 169–172.
93. Rabinovici, J., Blankstein, J., Goldman, B. et al. (1989). In vitro fertilization and primary embryonic cleavage are possible in 17 alpha-hydroxylase deficiency despite extremely low intrafollicular 17 beta-estradiol. *J. Clin. Endocrinol. Metab.* 68, 693–697.
94. Yanase, T. (1995). 17 alpha-Hydroxylase/17,20-lyase defects. *J. Steroid. Biochem. Mol. Biol.* 53, 153–157.
95. Imai, T., Yanase, T., Waterman, M. R., Simpson, E. R., and Pratt, J. J. (1992). Canadian Mennonites and individuals residing in the Friesland region of The Netherlands share the same molecular basis of 17 alpha-hydroxylase deficiency. *Hum. Genet.* 89, 95–96.
96. Miura, K., Yasuda, K., Yanase, T. et al. (1996). Mutation of cytochrome P-45017 alpha gene (CYP17) in a Japanese patient previously reported as having glucocorticoid-responsive hyperaldosteronism: With a review of Japanese patients with mutations of CYP17. J Clin Endocrinol Metab. 81, 3797–3801.
97. Kaneko, S., Oshio, S., Kobayashi, T., Iizuka, R., and Mohri, H. (1984). Human X- and Y-bearing sperm differ in cell surface sialic acid content. *Biochem. Biophys. Res. Commun.* 124, 950–955.
98. Buczko, E., Koh, Y. C., Miyagawa, Y., and Dufau, M. L.(1995). The rat 17 alpha-hydroxylase-17,20-desmolase (CYP17) active site: Computerized homology modeling and site directed mutagenesis. *J. Steroid. Biochem. Mol. Biol.* 52, 209–218.
99. Simpson, E. R. (1998). Genetic mutations resulting in estrogen insufficiency in the male. *Mol. Cell. Endocrinol.* 145, 55–59.
100. Ito, Y., Fisher, C. R., Conte, F. A., Grumbach, M. M., and Simpson, E. R. (1992). Molecular basis of aromatase deficiency in an adult female with sexual infantilism and polycystic ovaries. *Proc. Natl. Acad. Sci. USA* 90, 11673–11677.
101. Conte, F. A., Grumbach, M. M., Ito, Y., Fisher, C. R., and Simpson, E. R. (1994). A syndrome of female pseudohermaphrodism, hypergonadotropic hypogonadism, and multicystic ovaries associated with missense mutations in the gene encoding aromatase (P450arom). *J. Clin. Endocrinol. Metab.* 78, 1287–1292.
102. Mullis, P. E., Yoshimura, N., Kuhlmann, B. et al. (1997). Aromatase deficiency in a female who is compound heterozy-

gote for two new point mutations in the P450arom gene: Impact of estrogens on hypergonadotropic hypogonadism, multicystic ovaries, and bone densitometry in childhood. *J. Clin. Endocrinol. Metab.* 82, 1739–1745.

103. Duck, S. C., Sekhon, G. S., Wilbois, R., Pagliara, A. S., and Weldon, V. V. (1975). Pseudohermaphroditism, with testes and a 46,XX karyotype. *J. Pediatr.* 87, 58–62.
104. Levinson, G., Zarate, A., Guzman-Toledano, R., Canales, E. S., and Jimenez, M. (1976). An XX female with sexual infantilism, absent gonads, and lack of Mullerian ducts. *J. Med. Genet.* 13, 68–69.
105. Mendonca, B. B., Barbosa, A. S., Arnhold, I. J. et al. (1994). Gonadal agenesis in XX and XY sisters: evidence for the involvement of an autosomal gene. *Am. J. Med. Genet.* 52, 39–43.
106. Kennerknecht, I., Sorgo, W., Oberhoffer, R. et al. (1993). Familial occurrence of agonadism and multiple internal malformations in phenotypically normal girls with 46,XY and 46,XX karyotypes, respectively: A new autosomal recessive syndrome. *Am. J. Med. Genet.* 47, 1166–1170.
107. Schwartz, C. E., Dean, J., Howard-Peebles, P. N. et al. (1994). Obstetrical and gynecological complications in fragile X carriers: A multicenter study. *Am. J. Med. Genet.* 51, 400–402.
108. Murray, A., Webb, J., Grimley, S., Conway, G., and Jacobs, P. (1998). Studies of FRAXA and FRAXE in women with premature ovarian failure. *J. Med. Genet.* 35, 637–640.
109. Allingham-Hawkins, D. J., Babul-Hirji, R., Chitayat, D. et al. (199). Fragile X premutation is a significant risk factor for premature ovarian failure: The International Collaborative POF in Fragile X study—preliminary data. *Am. J. Med. Genet.* 83, 322–325.
110. Black, S. H., Levinson, G., Harton, G. L. et al. (1995). Preimplanatation genetic testing (PGT) from fragile X (fraxX). [abstract]. *Am. J. Hum. Genet.* 57, A31.
111. Kenneson, A., Cramer, D. W., and Warren, S. T. (1997). Fragile X premutations are not a major cause of early menopause. *Am. J. Hum. Genet.* 61, 1362–1369.
112. Sermon, K., De Vos, A., Van, D. V. et al. (1998). Fluorescent PCR and automated fragment analysis for the clinical application of preimplantation genetic diagnosis of myotonic dystrophy (Steinert's disease). *Mol. Hum. Reprod.* 4, 791–796.
113. Panidis, D., Rousso, D., Vavilis, D., Skiadopoulos, S., and Kalogeropoulos, A. (1994). Familial blepharophimosis with ovarian dysfunction. *Hum. Reprod.* 9, 2034–2037.
114. Fraser, I. S., Shearman, R. P., Smith, A., and Russell, P. (1988). An association among blepharophimosis, resistant ovary syndrome, and true premature menopause. *Fertil. Steril.* 50, 747–751.
115. Harrar, H. S., Jeffery, S., and Patton, M. A. (1995). Linkage analysis in blepharophimosis-ptosis syndrome confirms localisation to 3q21-24. *J. Med. Genet.* 32, 774–777.
116. Amati, P., Gasparini, P., Zlotogora, J. et al. (1996). A gene for premature ovarian failure associated with eyelid malformation maps to chromosome 3q22-q23. *Am. J. Hum. Genet.* 58, 1089–1092.
117. Crisponi, L., Deiana, M., Loi, A. et al. (2001). The putative forkhead transcription factor FOXL2 is mutated in blepharophimosis/ptosis/epicanthus inversus syndrome. *Nat. Genet.* 27, 159–166.
118. De Baere, E., Lemercier, B., Christin-Maitre, S., Durval, D., Messiaen, L., Fellous, M. et al. (2002). FOXL2 mutation screening in a large panel of POF patients and XX males. *J. Med. Genet.* 39, e43.
119. De Baere, E., Beysen, D., Oley, C. et al. (2003). FOXL2 and BPES: Mutational hotspots, phenotypic variability, and revision of the genotype-phenotype correlation. *Am. J. Hum. Genet.* 72, 478–487.
120. Harris, S. E., Chand, A. L., Winship, I. M. et al. (2002). Identification of novel mutations in FOXL2 associated with premature ovarian failure. *Mol. Hum. Reprod.* 8, 729–733.
121. Coulam, C. B., Stringfellow, S., and Hoefnagel, D. (1983). Evidence for a genetic factor in the etiology of premature ovarian failure. *Fertil. Steril.* 40, 693–695.
122. Starup, J., and Sele, V. (1983). Premature ovarian failure. *Acta Obstet. Gynecol. Scand.* 52, 259–268.
123. Austin, G. E., Coulam, C. B., and Ryan, R. J. (1979). A search for antibodies to luteinizing hormone receptors in premature ovarian failure. *Mayo Clin. Proc.* 54, 394–400.
124. Testa, G., Vegetti, W., Tibiletti, M. C., Dalpra, L., De Lauretis, L., Lalia, M. et al. (1997). Pattern of inheritance in familial premature ovarian failure. *Hum. Reprod.* 12, P-174, 202.
125. Vegetti, W., Marozzi, A., Manfredini, E. et al. (2000). Premature ovarian failure. *Mol. Cell. Endocrinol.* 161, 53–57.
126. Cramer, D. W., Xu, H., and Harlow, B. L. (1995). Family history as a predictor of early menopause. *Fertil. Steril.* 64, 740–745.
127. Torgerson, D. J., Thomas, R. E., and Reid, D. M. (1997). Mothers and daughters menopausal ages: Is there a link? *Eur. J. Obstet. Gynecol. Reprod. Biol.* 74, 63–66.
128. Treloar, S. A., Do, K. A., and Martin, N. G. (1998). Genetic influences on the age at menopause. *Lancet* 352, 1084–1085.
129. Snieder, H., MacGregor, A. J., and Spector, T. D. (1998). Genes control the cessation of a woman's reproductive life: A twin study of hysterectomy and age at menopause. *J. Clin. Endocrinol. Metab.* 83, 1875–1880.
130. Treloar, S. A., Martin, N. G., and Heath, A. C. (1998). Longitudinal genetic analysis of menstrual flow, pain, and limitation in a sample of Australian twins. *Behav. Genet.* 28, 107–116.
131. Aittomaki, K., Lucena, J. L., Pakarinen, P. et al. (1995). Mutation in the follicle-stimulating hormone receptor gene causes hereditary hypergonadotropic ovarian failure. *Cell* 82, 959–968.
132. Aittomaki, K., Herva, R., Stenman, U. H. et al. (1996). Clinical features of primary ovarian failure caused by a point mutation in the follicle-stimulating hormone receptor gene. *J. Clin. Endocrinol. Metab.* 81, 3722–3726.
133. Layman, L. C., Amde, S., Cohen, D. P., Jin, M., and Xie, J. (1998). The Finnish follicle-stimulating hormone receptor gene mutation is rare in North American women with 46,XX ovarian failure. *Fertil. Steril.* 69, 300–302.
134. Liu, J. Y., Gromoll, J., Cedars, M. I., and La Barbera, A. R. (1998). Identification of allelic variants in the follicle-stimulating hormone receptor genes of females with or without hypergonadotropic amenorrhea. *Fertil. Steril.* 70, 326–331.
135. Simoni, M., Gromoll, J., and Nieschlag, E. (1997). The follicle-stimulating hormone receptor: biochemistry, molecular

biology, physiology, and pathophysiology. *Endocr. Rev.* 18, 739–773.

136. da Fonte Kohek, M. B., Batista, M. C., Russell, A. J., Vass, K., Giacaglia, L. R., Mendonca, B. B. et al. (1998). No evidence of the inactivating mutation (C566T) in the follicle-stimulating hormone receptor gene in Brazilian women with premature ovarian failure. *Fertil. Steril.* 70, 565–567.
137. de la Chesnaye, E., Canto, P., Ulloa-Aguirre, A., and Mendez, J. P. (2001). No evidence of mutations in the follicle-stimulating hormone receptor gene in Mexican women with 46,XX pure gonadal dysgenesis. *Am. J. Med. Genet.* 98, 125–128.
138. Jiang, X., Morland, S. J., Hitchcock, A., Thomas, E. J., and Campbell, I. G. (1998). Allelotyping of endometriosis with adjacent ovarian carcinoma reveals evidence of a common lineage. *Cancer Res.* 58, 1707–1712.
139. Burns, K.H., DeMayo, F.J., Matzuk, M. (2003) Transgenic technology, cloning and germ cell transplantation. In *Reproductive Medicine: Molecular, Cellular and Genetic Fundamentals*, vol. 2, eds. Fauser, B.C.J.M. 169–195. London: The Parthenon Publishing Group.
140. Lei, Z. M., Mishra, S., Zou, W. et al. (2001). Targeted disruption of luteinizing hormone/human chorionic gonadotropin receptor gene. *Mol. Endocrinol.* 15, 184–200.
141. Zhang, F. P., Poutanen, M., Wilbertz, J., and Huhtaniemi, I. (2001). Normal prenatal but arrested postnatal sexual development of luteinizing hormone receptor knockout (LuRKO) mice. *Mol. Endocrinol.* 15, 172–183.
142. Latronico, A. C., Anasti, J., Arnhold, I. J. et al. (1996). Brief report: Testicular and ovarian resistance to luteinizing hormone caused by inactivating mutations of the luteinizing hormone-receptor gene. *N. Engl. J. Med.* 334, 507–512.
143. Toledo, S. P., Brunner, H. G., Kraaij, R. et al. (1996). An inactivating mutation of the luteinizing hormone receptor causes amenorrhea in a 46,XX female. *J. Clin. Endocrinol. Metab.* 81, 3850–3854.
144. Laue, L., Wu, S. M., Kudo, M. et al. (1995). A nonsense mutation of the human luteinizing hormone receptor gene in Leydig cell hypoplasia. *Hum. Mol. Genet.* 4, 1429–1433.
145. Simpson, J. L. (1975). Gonadal dysgenesis and abnormalities of the human sex chromosomes: Current status of phenotypic-karyotypic correlations. *Birth Defects Orig. Artic. Ser.* 11 (4), 23–59.
146. Hisama, F. M., Zemel, S., Cherniske, E. M., Vladutiu, G. D., and Pober, B. R. (2001). 46,XX gonadal dysgenesis, short stature, and recurrent metabolic acidosis in two sisters. *Am. J. Med. Genet.* 98, 121–124.
147. Zlotogora, J., Sagi, M., and Cohen, T. (1983). The blepharophimosis, ptosis, and epicanthus inversus syndrome: Delineation of two types. *Am. J. Hum. Genet.* 35, 1020–1027.
148. Narahara, K., Kamada, M., Takahashi, Y. et al. (1992). Case of ovarian dysgenesis and dilated cardiomyopathy supports existence of Malouf syndrome. *Am. J. Med. Genet.* 44, 369–373.
149. Zadik, Z., Levin, S., Prager-Lewin, R., and Laron, Z. (1978). Gonadal dysfunction in patients with ataxia telangiectasia. *Acta Paediatr. Scand.* 67, 477–479.
150. Waldmann, T. A., Misiti, J., Nelson, D. L., and Kraemer, K. H. (1983). Ataxia-telangiectasis: A multisystem hereditary disease with immunodeficiency, impaired organ maturation, x-ray hypersensitivity, and a high incidence of neoplasia. *Ann. Intern. Med.* 99, 367–379.
151. Nance, M. A., and Berry, S. A. (1992). Cockayne syndrome: Review of 140 cases. *Am. J. Med. Genet.* 42, 68–84.
152. Sugarman, G. I., Landing, B. H., and Reed, W. B. (1977). Cockayne syndrome: Clinical study of two patients and neuropathologic findings in one. *Clin. Pediatr.* (Phila.) 16, 225–232.
153. Martsolf, J. T., Hunter, A. G., and Haworth, J. C. (1978). Severe mental retardation, cataracts, short stature, and primary hypogonadism in two brothers. *Am. J. Med. Genet.* 1, 291–299.
154. Harbord, M. G., Baraitser, M., and Wilson, J. (1989). Microcephaly, mental retardation, cataracts, and hypogonadism in sibs: Martsolf's syndrome. *J. Med. Genet.* 26, 397–400.
155. Hennekam, R. C., van de Meeberg, A. G., van Doorne, J. M., Dijkstra, P. F., and Bijlsma, J. B. (1988). Martsolf syndrome in a brother and sister: Clinical features and pattern of inheritance. *Eur. J. Pediatr.* 147, 539–543.
156. Weemaes, C. M., Hustinx, T. W., Scheres, J. M. et al. (1981). A new chromosomal instability disorder: The Nijmegen breakage syndrome. *Acta Paediatr. Scand.* 70, 557–564.
157. Conley, M. E., Spinner, N. B., Emanuel, B. S., Nowell, P. C., and Nichols, W. W. (1986). A chromosomal breakage syndrome with profound immunodeficiency. *Blood* 67, 1251–1256.
158. Chrzanowska, K. H., Kleijer, W. J., Krajewska-Walasek, M. et al. (1995). Eleven Polish patients with microcephaly, immunodeficiency, and chromosomal instability: The Nijmegen breakage syndrome. *Am. J. Med. Genet.* 57, 462–471.
159. Hall, J. G., Pallister, P. D., Clarren, S. K. et al. (1980). Congenital hypothalamic hamartoblastoma, hypopituitarism, imperforate anus and postaxial polydactyly—a new syndrome? Part I: Clinical, causal, and pathogenetic considerations. *Am. J. Med. Genet.* 7, 47–74.
160. Starr, D. G., McClure, J. P., and Connor, J. M. (1985). Non-dermatological complications and genetic aspects of the Rothmund-Thomson syndrome. *Clin. Genet.* 27, 102–104.
161. Goto, M., Tanimoto, K., Horiuchi, Y., and Sasazuki, T. (1994). Family analysis of Werner's syndrome: A survey of 42 Japanese families with a review of the literature. *Clin. Genet.* 19, 8–15.
162. Warren, S. T., and Nelson, D. L. (1994). Advances in molecular analysis of fragile X syndrome. *JAMA* 271, 536–542.

CHAPTER **33**

Ovarian Function and Survival of Patients with Cervical Carcinoma Treated with Radical Hysterectomy and Ovarian Transposition

KAZUHIRA OKAMOTO, NORIAKI SAKURAGI, AND SEIICHIRO FUJIMOTO

INTRODUCTION

Although the gynecologist's ultimate aim in treating a woman with a malignant tumor is to cure her, her normal ovaries should not be needlessly sacrificed. In the treatment of cervical cancer, gynecologists should make an effort to maintain the quality of life (QOL) of patients by maximally preserving the physiologic functions of the pelvic organs while pursuing a cure of the disease. Bilateral oophorectomy and resultant loss of ovarian function in young patients will cause climacteric-like symptoms, decrease in bone mineral density, hypercholesterolemia, increased risk of ischemic heart disease, and adverse psychological effects. In cervical cancer, especially in squamous cell carcinoma, risk of ovarian metastasis is quite low [1–4]. There are several reports [1–2, 5–6] of ovarian metastasis in adenocarcinoma of the cervix.

In order to avoid the adverse effects of loss of ovarian function in young women, preservation of ovary at the time of radical hysterectomy (RH) has been attempted since the 1950s [7]. Postoperative whole-pelvis radiation therapy is often employed for patients who have risk factors for recurrence, such as lymph node metastasis, deep cervical stromal invasion, parametrium involvement, and lymph-vascular space invasion. The ovary is an extremely radiosensitive organ, and it loses its hormonal function if the ovarian dose is more than 300 cGy [8]. To prevent radiation-induced loss of ovarian function, ovaries must be transposed to beyond or outside of the radiation field at the time of surgery [9–11]. Only a few reports focus on the long-term sequelae of the endocrine function of transposed ovaries [12–14], and the effect of ovarian preservation on patient survival in cervical carcinoma has not been sufficiently investigated.

The objectives of this chapter are to investigate the long-term prognosis of the physiologic function of transposed ovaries in patients with cervical cancer and the risk factors of impairment of ovarian function after RH, and to analyze the survival of patients treated with RH with ovarian transposition. We prospectively followed up the hormonal function of transposed ovaries and survival of patients treated with RH and ovarian transposition in cervical carcinoma.

PATIENTS AND METHODS

A total of 260 patients with stage IB, IIA, and IIB cervical cancer at the age of 55 years or younger underwent RH from 1982 to 2000 at the Hokkaido University Hospital (Table 33.1). At least one ovary was preserved, under the conditions of that patient was 45 years old or less with normal ovarian function, no family history of ovarian carcinoma or breast cancer in the first- and second-degree relatives, tumor not extending to the uterine corpus, and intraoperative frozen-section diagnosis of wedge-resected ovary revealing no metastasis. In some cases of adenocarcinoma (n = 12) and adenosquamous carcinoma (n = 11), we preserved ovaries with a more careful preoperative indication criteria: the tumor size is small and has well-differentiated histology, and there is no definite lymph-vascular space invasion on the biopsy or conization specimen. More recently, we exclude the cases with adeno-/adenosquamous carcinomas from the indication of ovarian preservation if the tumor forms a clear mass on magnetic resonance imaging (MRI).

In 101 women, one or both ovaries were transposed either to the subcutaneous adipose tissue in the flank or to the paracolic gutters outside the pelvic radiation field (Group 1). As shown in Table 33.1, in 159 patients, because of age advancement, postmenopausal status, bulky tumor, or apparent corpus invasion, bilateral salpingo-oophorectomy (BSO) was performed (Group 2).

In Group 1, the median age of patients was 36.8 years old (range: 26 to 46), with 40 patients 35 years or younger, 32 between 36 and 40 years, and 29 from 41 to 45 years of

TABLE 33.1 Characteristics of patients with Stage I/II Cervical Carcinoma

	Group 1 RH with ovarian transposition (n = 101)	Group 2 RH with BSO (n = 159)	p-value
Age	36.8 (26–46)	44.9 (24–55)	p < 0.0001
FIGO stage			
IB	57 (56.4%)	89 (56.0%)	NS
IA	3 (3.0%)	8 (5.0%)	
IIB	41 (40.6%)	62 (39.0%)	
Histologic type			
Squamous cell carcinoma	78 (77.2%)	113 (71.1%)	NS
Adenocarcinoma	12 (11.9%)	29 (18.2%)	
Adenosquamous carcinoma	11 (10.9%)	17 (10.7%)	
Retroperitoneal lymphnode metastasis			
Negative	83 (82.2%)	121 (76.1%)	NS
Positive	18 (17.8%)	38 (23.9%)	
Adjuvant therapy			
None	47 (46.5%)	91 (57.2%)	NS
Radiation (whole pelvis 45–50GY)	45 (44.6%)	54 (34.0%)	
Chemotherapy	9 (9.0%)	14 (8.8%)	
Follow-up period (mean and range)	79 (8–187) months	78 (11–173) months	NS

RH: radical hysterectomy, BSO: bilateral salpingo-oophorectomy.

age. Fifty-seven had stage IB tumors, 3 had stage IIA, and 41 had stage IIB. Histologic type included 78 squamous cell carcinomas, 12 pure adenocarcinomas, and 11 adenosquamous carcinomas. Ovaries were transposed to the flank in 47 patients and to the paracolic gutters in 54 patients. In 82 patients, both ovaries were preserved. In 19 patients, the unilateral ovary was transposed because of benign ovarian diseases, such as simple cyst and endometrial cyst, or ovarian vessel injury during the operation. Retroperitoneal lymph node metastasis was observed in 18 of 101 (17.8%) patients in Group 1. Forty-seven (46.5%) patients did not receive any postoperative adjuvant therapy. Forty-five (44.6%) received whole-pelvis postoperative radiation therapy (45–50 Gy), and 9 (9.0%) received cisplatin-based adjuvant chemotherapy because of histopathologic findings of deep cervical stromal invasion, lymph node metastasis, parametrial involvement, and/or lymph-vascular space involvement. Median follow-up duration was 79 months (range: 8 to 187 months). One patient developed mucinous cystadenoma 7 years after the operation in the preserved ovary transposed to the subcutaneous tissue in the flank.

In Group 2, the median age of the patients was 44.9 years old (range: 24 to 55), and 89 were stage IB, 8 had stage IIA, and 62 had stage IIB. Histologic type included 113 squamous cell carcinomas, 29 pure adenocarcinomas, and 17 adenosquamous carcinomas. Ninety-one (57.2%) patients did not receive any postoperative adjuvant therapy. Fifty-four (34.0%) patients received postoperative whole-pelvis radiation therapy (45–50 Gy), and 14 (8.8%) received cisplatin-based adjuvant chemotherapy. Median follow-up duration was 78 months (range: 11 to 173 months). In this group of patients, the rate of retroperitoneal lymph node metastasis was 23.9% (38/159), as depicted in Table 33.1.

At the time of operation, we inspected abdominal cavity and ovaries as to whether there were any abnormal findings. Fallopian tubes were removed, and wedge resection of ovaries was carried out even when they looked macroscopically normal. If any adverse conditions, such as endometriosis or benign ovarian cyst, were present, ovarian transposition was not carried out. The wedge-resected specimens were intraoperatively sent to the Pathology Department to examine the presence or absence of ovarian metastasis. Para-aortic lymphadenectomy at least to the level of the inferior mesenteric artery was performed. When the hysterectomy and systematic retroperitoneal lymphadenectomy were completed, we separated ovarian vessels from the mesocolon and freed ovarian vessel pedicle, obtaining a length of about 15 cm. The ovaries were then transposed to the subcutaneous tissue of the flank or paracolic gutter. We paid meticulous attention to avoid torsion and extension of ovarian vessels, which may deteriorate blood supply to the ovaries.

Until 1987, we fixed the ovaries in the subcutaneous adipose tissue at the flank; however, patients often complained of a painful cystic mass during the periovulatory period. Since 1987, we have transposed ovaries to paracolic gutters in the abdominal cavity. In the case of transposing the ovaries to the paracolic gutter, they were fixed to the

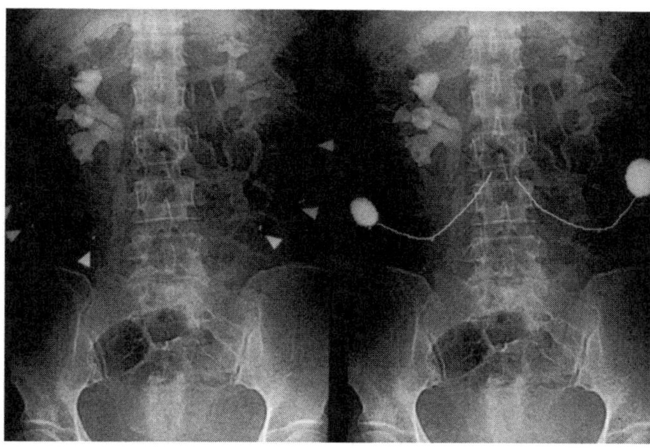

FIGURE 33.1 X-ray photograph of metal clips fixed to the upper and lower poles of ovaries transposed to paracolic gutters and to the lowest end of the ovarian vessel loop. The location of ovaries and ovarian vessels are schematically shown on the right photograph.

retroperitoneum, keeping them in the peritoneal cavity. Two hemoclips were placed at both poles of the ovary, and one at the lowest end of the ovarian vessel loop, identified by X-ray as an aid for shielding ovaries and ovarian vessels from scattered radiation beam. The position of the transposed ovaries was intended to be at the level of the kidneys (Figure 33.1). The surgical technique described here was created independently by our clinical team, which is almost equivalent to the technique described by Belinson et al. [9].

We analyzed the duration of the endocrine function of transposed ovaries in relation to patient age at the time of operation and the mode of adjuvant therapy. Ovarian function was endocrinologically analyzed in 94 of 101 cases, excluding 6 deceased cases and one case in which the record for ovarian function after treatment was not available. We divided the patients into three groups according to age: 35 years or younger, 36 to 40 years, and 41 years and older. Ovarian function was considered to remain if the patient's basal body temperature (BBT) chart showed a biphasic pattern, or serum E2 level was higher than 30 pg/mL. The cessation of ovarian function was diagnosed by serum follicle-stimulating hormone (FSH) level of higher than 40 mIU/mL and/or serum E2 level below 10 pg/mL. When the hormone levels fell between these criteria, the assay was repeated for further confirmation of the cessation of ovarian hormonal function.

When patients had prognostic risk factors for carcinoma recurrence, such as lymph node metastasis, deep cervical stromal invasion, parametrium involvement, or lymph-vascular space invasion, whole-pelvis radiation therapy (45 to 50 Gy) was employed. In pure adenocarcinoma or adenosquamous carcinoma, or squamous cell carcinomas with evident lymph-vascular space invasion, three to six courses of cisplatin-based chemotherapy were employed.

Estimated duration of hormonal function of the transposed ovaries and survival curves for patients were obtained using the Kaplan-Meier method. Kaplan-Meier curves were compared by log-rank test. Prognostic factors were analyzed using Cox's proportional hazards model. Statistical significance level was set to $p < 0.05$. Statistical analyses were performed using the Statistica™ software package (Statsoft, Tulsa, OK).

RESULTS

The Influence of Ovarian Preservation on Patient Survival

Clinicopathologic characteristics for patients in Groups 1 and 2 showed no difference (see Table 33.1). In Group 1, six patients died (five died of disease and one died of intercurrent disease); however, there was no metastatic recurrence in the transposed ovary. Ten-year overall survival rates were 93% for Group 1 and 80% for Group 2 patients as determined by the Kaplan-Meier method (Figure 33.2). The survival of patients with ovarian preservation was significantly better than that of patients whose ovaries had been removed ($p = 0.022$). Because the patients who underwent bilateral oophorectomy had more frequent adverse prognostic factors, such as corpus invasion, large tumor size, and others, it is not certain whether ovarian preservation confers survival benefit. By Cox regression analysis, only lymph node metastasis and parametrial invasion were, respectively, independent prognostic risk factors for patients with stage I/II cervical carcinoma in this study (Table 33.2). Ovarian preservation did not adversely affect patient survival.

The Influence of Patient's Age on the Function of Preserved Ovary in Cases Having Undergone No Adjuvant Therapy

We analyzed the hormonal function of transposed ovaries in patients without adjuvant therapy, according to the three age groups. In patients 35 years or younger ($n = 18$), ovarian function was preserved 100% with a median follow-up period of 54 months (range: 22 to 104); however, the preservation rate of ovarian function decreased with the advance of patient's age. Three-year, 5-year, and 10-year survival rates of ovarian function were 86%, 70%, and 54% in patients 36 to 40 years old ($n = 10$), and 60%, 43%, and 0% in patients 41 years and older ($n = 15$), respectively. The preservation rates of endocrine function of the ovaries of patients 36 to 40 years old were higher than those of patients 41 years and older ($p = 0.0098$; Figure 33.3).

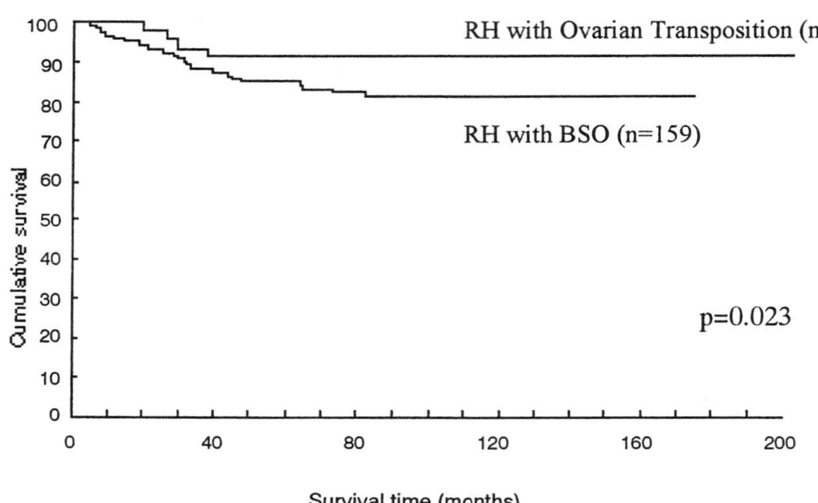

FIGURE 33.2 Overall survival of patients with stage I/II cervical carcinoma according to preservation of ovaries. RH: radical hysterectomy, BSO: bilateral salpingo-oophorectomy

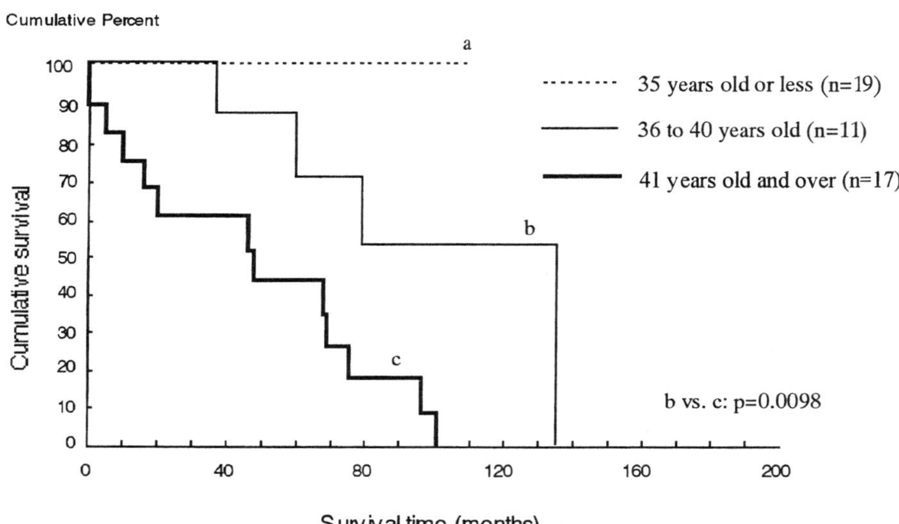

FIGURE 33.3 Kaplan-Meier curves for ovarian function in patients without adjuvant therapy.

TABLE 33.2 Cox Regression Analysis of Prognostic Factors for Patients with Stage I/II Cervical Carcinoma

Factor	Univariate analysis p-value	Multivariate analysis p-value
FIGO Stage (I vs. II)	$p = 0.032$	N.S.
Lymph node metastasis (Negative vs. Positive)	$p < 0.0001$	$p = 0.0039$
Parametrium invasion (Negative vs. Positive)	$p < 0.0001$	$p = 0.018$
Ovarian transposition (With vs. Without)	$p = 0.022$	N.S.
Hystological type (SCC vs. Adeno/Adenosquamous)	N.S.	N.S.

SCC: squamous cell carcinoma.

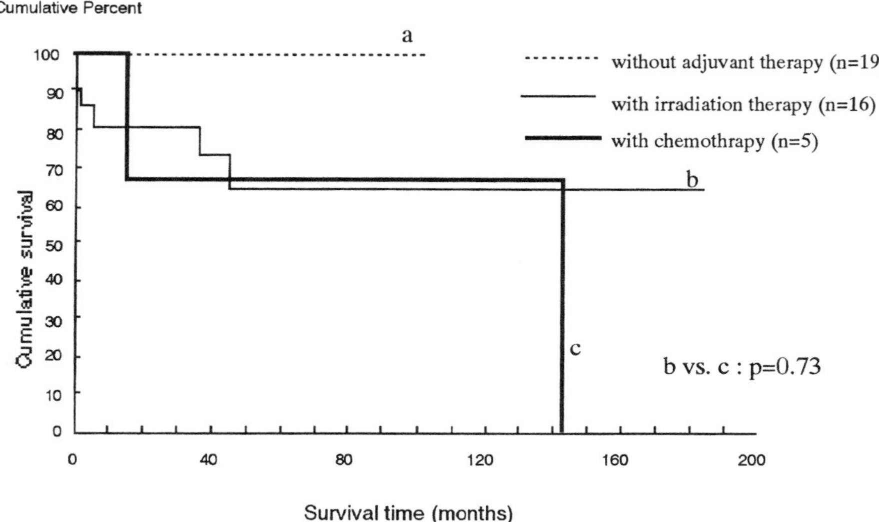

FIGURE 33.4 Kaplan-Meier curves for ovarian function in patients 35 years or younger.

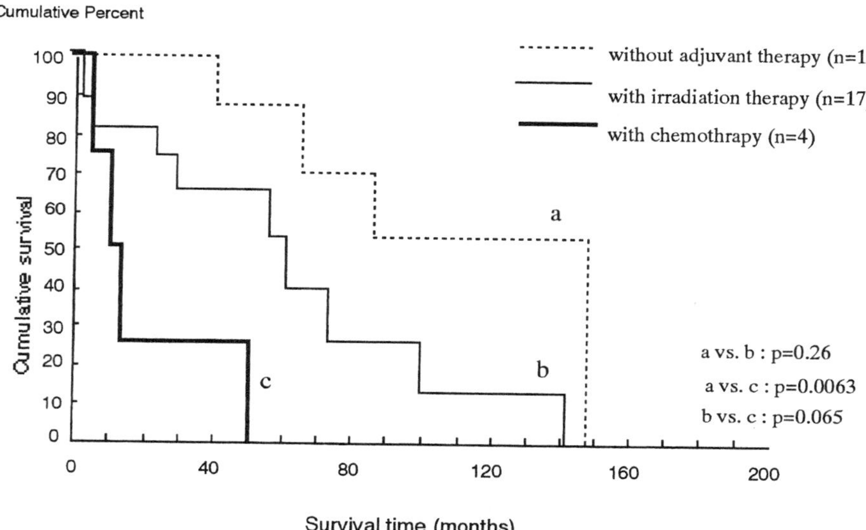

FIGURE 33.5 Kaplan-Meier curves for ovarian function in patients 36 to 40 years old.

The Influence of Modality of Adjuvant Therapy on Endocrine Function of Preserved Ovary

We analyzed ovarian function according to the mode of adjuvant therapy in each age group. Although the number of cases was very limited in each mode of adjuvant therapy and age group, the following data were obtained.

In patients 35 years or younger, only few patients undergoing postoperative radiation therapy lost ovarian function early, but more than 60% of patients maintained ovarian function for more than 10 years. A 66% rate of preservation of ovarian function in the patients undergoing cisplatin-based adjuvant chemotherapy was maintained for about 10 years. Ovarian transposition seemed to be effective for preserving ovarian hormonal function for a long time in patients younger than 35 years who received adjuvant therapy (Figure 33.4).

In patients 36 to 40 years old, the 3-year, 5-year, and 10-year preservation rates of ovarian function by adjuvant therapy were 66%, 39%, and 17%, respectively, with radiation, and 26%, 0%, and 0%, respectively, with chemotherapy. Durations of ovarian function in patients undergoing radiation therapy and in patients undergoing chemotherapy were significantly shorter than that in patients without adjuvant therapy ($p = 0.026$ and $p = 0.0063$, respectively; Figure 33.5).

In patients 41 years and older, duration of preserving ovarian function in those having undergone radiation therapy tended to be shorter than that in patients not having undergone any adjuvant therapy, but it was not significant ($p = 0.16$; Figure 33.6).

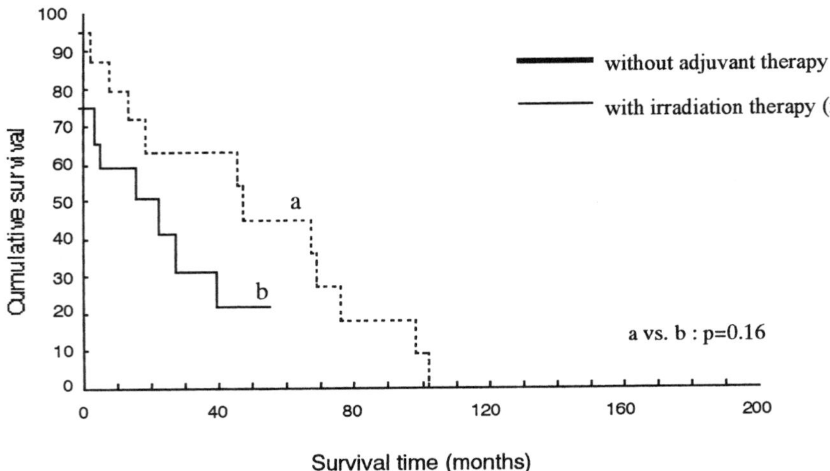

FIGURE 33.6 Kaplan-Meier curves for ovarian function in patients 41 years and older.

TABLE 33.3 Ovarian Metastasis in Cervical Adenocarcinoma by FIGO Stage: Literature Review

	Stage IB	Stage II	Stage III	Total
Tabata et al. (1987) [1]	2/26 (7.7%)	2/15 (13.3%)	2/7 (28.6%)	6/48 (12.5%)
Brown et al. (1990) [5]	1/25 (4.0%)			1/25 (4.0%)
Toki et al. (1991) [2]	0/26 (0%)	2/10 (20%)		2/36 (5.5%)
Sutton et al. (1992) [3]	2/121 (1.7%)			2/121 (1.7%)
Natsume et al. (1999) [6]	1/40 (2.5%)	8/42 (19.0%)		9/82 (11.0%)

Resection of Preserved Ovary Because of Its Adverse Condition

We had to remove the transposed ovary in only one patient in this series because of mucinous cystadenoma occurring in the subcutaneous tissue of the flank 7 years after transposition.

DISCUSSION

In the treatment of cancer, it is important to preserve physiologic function and maintain QOL while pursuing a radical cure of the disease. We have been attempting to preserve the functions of ovarian endocrines and the pelvic autonomic nerves during RH. Ovarian metastasis from cervical squamous cell carcinoma is rare (0% to 0.5%) [1–4]. Ovarian metastasis has been suggested to be related to bulky tumor, corpus extension, lymph-vascular space involvement, and parametrium invasion, and it is often associated with lymph node metastasis [1–4]. Therefore, the prognosis for patients with ovarian metastasis has been reported to be extremely poor. Ovarian metastasis in adenocarcinoma of the uterine cervix is more frequent than in squamous cell carcinoma (Table 33.3) [1–3, 5–6]. Whether ovarian preservation should be attempted in RH for adenocarcinoma of the cervix is controversial. Because the rate of ovarian metastasis rises in stage II adenocarcinoma, preservation of the ovary should be limited to stage I adenocarcinoma. Investigations of stage I patients who had ovarian metastasis showed that most of those patients had adverse prognostic factors such as lymph-vascular space invasion (LVSI) and lymph node metastasis [6–7, 15–17].

As shown in Table 33.4, we previously reported that blood vessel invasion, parametrial invasion, and histology (adeno-/adenosquamous) were significantly related to ovarian metastasis as determined by multivariate analysis [17]. We currently consider that the cases of adeno-/adenosquamous carcinoma with parametrial invasion and/or LVSI should not undergo ovarian preservation. The tumor size is closely related to parametrial involvement and LVSI. Therefore, only small-sized adeno-/adenosquamous carcinoma without LVSI that has been confirmed by the preoperative procedures of MRI and conization is recommended as an indication for ovarian conservation.

There are few available data regarding survival impact of ovarian preservation in the surgical treatment of cervical carcinoma. Ovarian preservation has been reported not

TABLE 33.4 Logistic Regression Analysis of Risk Factors for Ovarian Metastasis

	Univariate analysis		Multivariate analysis	
Variables	**Odds Ratio**	**p-value**	**Odds Ratio**	**p-value**
Histology	17.8	<0.0005	46.6	<0.0005
Corpus Invasion	35.8	<0.0025		NS
Parametrial Invasion	31.4	<0.001	49.7	<0.0025
Lymph Vessel Invasion	4.8	<0.025		NS
Blood Vessel Invasion	40.1	<0.001	12.2	<0.05

NS: not significant.

Histology: squamous vs. adeno/adenosquamous, lymph vessel invasion: nil/minimal vs. prominent, blood vessel invasion: negative vs. positive, corpus invasion: negative vs. positive, parametrial invasion: negative vs. positive.

TABLE 33.5 Clinical Features of Transposed Ovary According to the Location of Transposition

Location of Transposed Ovary	Tactility of Transposed Ovary	Cyst Formation	Blood flow Impediment	Shift from the Original Location
Breast	+	+/–	+	–
Flank	+	+/–	+/–	–
Paracolic Gutter	–	–	–	+/–

to adversely affect patient survival [18]. In this study, survival of patients with ovarian transposition was superior to that of patients who underwent oophorectomy, although ovarian preservation was not an independent prognostic factor in multivariate analysis. Our previous results lead us to conclude that ovarian preservation in situ is not likely to have an adverse effect on survival of patients with adenocarcinoma of the cervix, if the patients are operated by simple hysterectomy on FIGO stage 0 and IA. For the patient with pure or mixed adenocarcinoma of the cervix on FIGO stage IB and II without ovarian metastasis, ovaries could be left laterally in transposition. The recurrence of cancer in the preserved ovaries may occur [19–21]. The reported recurrent cases were associated with either bulky adenosquamous tumor [19] or bulky adenocarcinoma [20], or extensive lymphatic permeation [21].

Adverse complications of ovarian transposition include benign functional cyst formation, especially when transposed laterally to the subcutaneous tissue of the flank. Chambers et al. [13] reported that the rate of ovarian cyst formation was 24% in patients treated with RH with ovarian transposition. Before 1987, we fixed ovaries in the subcutaneous adipose tissue in the flank. This technique had an advantage in that we could easily palpate the transposed ovary and confirm its function in terms of its regular, cyclic swelling. By this method, transposed ovaries were surely placed beyond the pelvic radiation field. But patients often complained of painful sensation resulting from the swelling (functional cyst) of subcutaneous ovaries during the periovulatory period. After 1987, ovaries were fixed in the paracolic gutters so that ovaries were exposed in the peritoneal cavity. Patients' complaints of painful swelling of the ovary or other subjective complaints were not reported since then (Table 33.5).

The purpose of ovarian transposition is to preserve ovarian endocrine function for patients who would undergo external radiotherapeutical treatment following RH. Only a few of the previous reports regarding the function of the transposed ovaries have included more than 20 cases having undergone postoperative radiation therapy and with a follow-up period of more than 30 months [8, 14, 22]. Anderson et al. [8] reported that 4 of 82 (17%) patients with radiation had maintained ovarian hormonal function. In their series, transposition was not successful in preserving ovarian function, and they so far concluded that ovarian preservation was not indicative. Later, the same group described the efficacy of preserving ovarian hormonal function in the same series of patients after a further prolonged follow-up period [19]. When radiation was added, only 48% of the patients retained ovarian function for a mean of 43 months and a mean age at menopause of 36.6 years, while 98% of the patients without radiation therapy retained ovarian function for a mean of 125 months.

A Cox proportional hazards model found that advancing age at diagnosis and initiation of the treatment was a significant independent predictor of early menopause or early cessation of ovarian endocrine function. In contrast, Feeney et al. [22] reported a 50% preservation rate of ovarian function in patients treated with RH and ovarian transposition receiving postoperative radiation therapy. Morice et al. [14] concluded that ovarian transposition was a safe and effective procedure for preserving ovarian hormonal function, with 60% preservation rate in patients treated with RH and radiation therapy who were younger than 40 years with small invasive cervical cancer (<3 cm). Other reports containing smaller numbers of patients reported preservation rates of hormonal function from 17% to 88% [23–26].

The procedure of a simple abdominal hysterectomy, in which blood supply from the ascending branch of the uterine artery to the ovary (Figure 33.7) is interrupted, may cause earlier ovarian failure than in cases who had not undergone hysterectomy [27]. This suggests that hormonal function is vulnerable to decreased blood flow. We found that ovarian transposition did not influence ovarian function in young patients. In the present study, all patients 35 years and younger without adjuvant therapy maintained ovarian hormonal function for more than 10 years. But as the patient's age exceeded 35 years, duration of ovarian function preservation became shorter. This can be regarded as natural because the likelihood of the survival of hormonal function of the ovary becomes shorter as the patient's age advances.

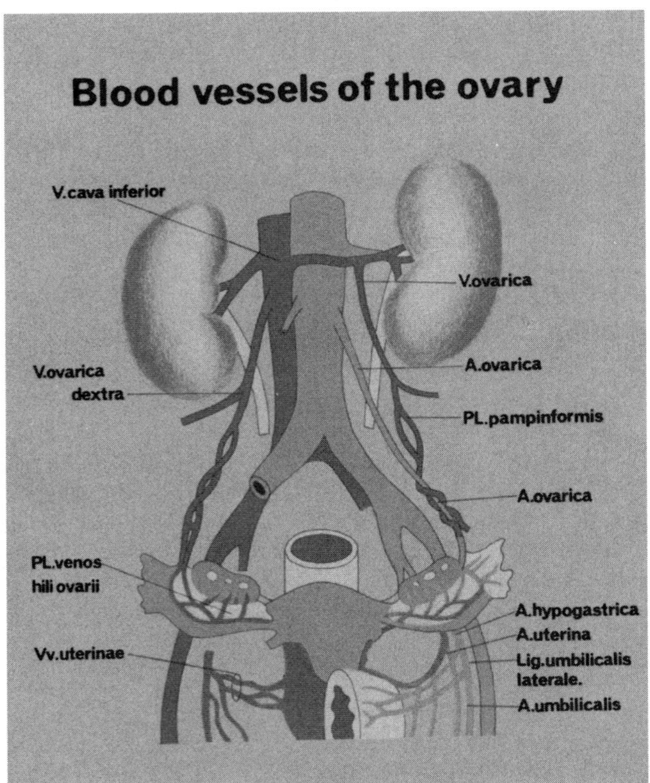

FIGURE 33.7 Blood supply to ovary. The ovarian artery and the uterine artery anastomose in the broad ligament. (See color plate.)

The vulnerability of ovaries in older patients may be caused by a smaller number of ovum reservoirs and may be associated with the aging of the ovarian blood vessel. For the same reason, ovaries in older patients were more vulnerable to scattered radiation beams, and patients 36 years and older may have lost ovarian endocrine function more often than patients 35 years and younger. To avoid receiving scattered irradiation, ovaries should be transposed to a position as distant as possible from the radiation field. The influence of irradiation on ovarian function varies with age as well as ovarian dose [28]. A dose of 400 cGy of radiation may cause 30% sterility in young women, but in women older than 40 years, it results in 100% sterility. It has been reported that the ovarian dose was about 400 cGy at 2 to 3 cm beyond the external radiation field and 300 cGy at 4 to 5 cm beyond the radiation field for cervical carcinoma [9].

In a study of cervical cancer, median ovarian dose in lateral transposition was 120 cGy (range: 16 to 229) with brachytherapy, and 280 cGy (range: 21 to 1340) with external radiation therapy plus brachytherapy [14]. If radiation dose to the ovary can be limited to 300 cGy or less, more than approximately 90% of patients will retain ovarian endocrine function [13]. Radiation induces apoptosis in microvascular endothelial cells [29] and may cause a decrease in blood supply in tissues in combination with scar formation. Scattered radiation to the ovarian vessels as well as to the ovary should be avoided. To this end, we place a clip around the lowest ranking point of the ovarian vessel in order to create a reference point for shielding parenchymal tissue of the ovary and ovarian vessel from scattered radiation (see Figure 33.1).

In regard to the influence of chemotherapy on ovarian function as seen in this study, more than 60% of patients 35 years and younger maintained ovarian function for a long time, but patients 36 years and older lost ovarian function earlier following adjuvant chemotherapy. The ovaries of aged patients are not tolerant to the toxicity of an anticancer agent and to a decrease in blood supply. Careful observation regarding the occurrence of premature ovarian failure is necessary in patients 36 years and older when chemotherapy is added.

CONCLUSION

We conclude that ovarian preservation is safe in stage I to II squamous cell carcinoma and stage I small adenocarcinoma without LVSI. Ovarian transposition at the time of RH is beneficial for preventing radiation-induced ovarian failure in young women with invasive cervical cancer.

Although we evaluate the virtues of hormone replacement therapy for patients oophorectomized during RH, we believe that the ovaries should not be needlessly sacrificed when ovarian conservation is pathologically safe for the patient. Ovarian preservation may obviate the necessity for long-term hormone replacement therapy and will thus ensure a better QOL, even emotionally, for younger patients with cervical carcinoma.

In conclusion, ovarian preservation can be safely performed in patients with stage IB to IIB squamous cell carcinoma and small stage I adenocarcinoma of the uterine cervix without adversely affecting patient survival. Ovarian transposition at the time of RH is beneficial for preventing radiation-induced ovarian hormonal failure in young women with invasive cervical cancer.

References

1. Tabata, M., Ichinoe, K., Sakuragi, N. et al. (1987). Incidence of ovarian metastasis in patients with cancer of the uterine cervix. *Gynecol. Oncol.* 28, 255–361.
2. Toki, N., Tsukamoto, N., Kaku, T. et al. (1991). Microscopic ovarian metastasis of the uterine cervical cancer. *Gynecol. Oncol.* 41, 46–51.
3. Sutton, G. P., Bundy, B. N., Delgado, G. et al. (1992). Ovarian metastases in stage IB carcinoma of the cervix: A Gynecologic Oncology Group study. *Am. J. Obstet. Gynecol.* 166, 50–53.
4. Wu, H. S., Yen, M. S., Lai, C. R. et al. (1997). Ovarian metastasis from cervical carcinoma. *Int J. Gynaecol. Obstet.* 57, 173–178.
5. Brown, J. V., Fu, Y. S., and Berek, J. S. (1990). Ovarian metastases are rare in stage I adenocarcinoma of the cervix. *Obstet. Gynecol.* 76, 623–626. Review.
6. Natsume, N., Aoki, Y., Kase, H. et al. (1999). Ovarian metastasis in stage IB and II cervical adenocarcinoma. *Gynecol. Oncol.* 74, 255–258.
7. McCall, M. L., Keaty, E. C., Thompson, J. D. (1958). Conservation of ovarian tissue in the treatment of carcinoma of the cervix with radical surgery. *Am. J. Obstet. Gynecol.* 75, 590–602.
8. Anderson, B., LaPolla, J., Turner, D. et al. (1993). Ovarian transposition in cervical cancer. *Gynecol. Oncol.* 49, 206–214.
9. Belinson, J. L., Doherty, M., and McDay, J. B. (1984). A new technique for ovarian transposition. *Surg. Gynecol. Obstet.* 159, 157–160.
10. Krebs, C., and Blixenkrome-Moller, N. (1958). Ovarian function after combined surgical and radiologic treatment of early cervical cancer. *Acta Radiol.* 49, 128–136.
11. Kovacev, M. (1966). Exteriorization of ovaries under the skin of young women operated upon for cancer of the cervix. *Am. J. Obstet. Gynecol.* 101, 756–759.
12. Buekers, T. E., Anderson, B., Sorosky, J. I. et al. (2001). Ovarian function after surgical treatment for cervical cancer. *Gynecol. Oncol.* 80, 85–88.
13. Chambers, S. K., Chambers, J. T., Kier, R. et al. (1991). Sequelae of lateral ovarian transposition in irradiated cervical cancer patients. *Intl. J. Radiat. Oncol. Biol. Physiol.* 20, 1305–1308.
14. Morice, P., Juncker, L., Rey, A. et al. (2000). Ovarian transposition for patients with cervical carcinoma treated by radiosurgical combination. *Fertil. Steril.* 74, 743–748.
15. Mann, W. J., Chumas, J., Amalfitano, T. et al. (1987). Ovarian metastases from stage IB adenocarcinoma of the cervix. *Cancer* 60, 1123–1126.
16. Bouma, J., and Hollema, H. (1989). Ovarian metastasis from squamocellular cervical cancer, stages IB and IIA. *Acta Obstet. Gynecol. Scand.* 68, 471–473.
17. Sakuragi, N., Takeda, N., Hareyama, H. et al. (2000). A multivariate analysis of blood vessel and lymph vessel invasion as predictors of ovarian and lymph node metastases in patients with cervical carcinoma. *Cancer* 88, 2578–2583.
18. Windbichler, G. H., Muller-Holzner, E., Nicolussi-Leck, G. et al. (1999). Ovarian preservation in the surgical treatment of cervical carcinoma. *Am. J. Obstet. Gynecol.* 180, 963–969.
19. Shigematsu, T., Ohishi, Y., Fujita, T. et al. (2000). Metastatic carcinoma in a transposed ovary after radical hysterectomy for a stage 1 B cervical adenosquamous cell carcinoma. Case report. *Eur. J. Gynaecol. Oncol.* 21, 383–386.
20. Nguyen, L., Brewer, C. A., and DiSaia, P. J. (1998). Ovarian metastasis of stage IB1 squamous cell cancer of the cervix after radical parametrectomy and oophoropexy. *Gynecol. Oncol.* 68, 198–200.
21. Parham, G., Heppard, M. C., and DiSaia, P. J. (1994). Metastasis from a stage IB cervical adenocarcinoma in a transposed ovary: A case report and review of the literature. *Gynecol. Oncol.* 55, 469–472. Review.
22. Feeney, D. D., Moore, D. H., Look, K. Y. et al. (1995). The fate of the ovaries after radical hysterectomy and ovarian transposition. *Gynecol. Oncol.* 56, 3–7.
23. Van Beurden, M., Schuster-Uitterhoeve, A. L., and Lammes, F. B. (1990). Feasibility of transposition of the ovaries in the surgical and radiotherapeutical treatment of cervical cancer. *Eur. J. Surg. Oncol.* 16, 141–146.
24. Owens, S., Roberts, W. S., Fiorica, J. V. et al. (1989). Ovarian management at the time of radical hysterectomy for cancer of the cervix. *Gynecol. Oncol.* 35, 349–351.
25. Bidzinski, M., Lemieszczuk, B., and Zielinski, J. (1993). Evaluation of the hormonal function and features of the ultrasound picture of transposed ovary in cervical cancer patients after surgery and pelvic irradiation. *Eur. J. Gynaecol. Oncol.* 14 (Suppl), 77–80.
26. Hadar, H., Loven, D., Herskovitz, P. et al. (1994). An evaluation of lateral and medial transposition of the ovaries out of radiation fields. *Cancer* 74, 774–779.
27. Siddle, N., Sarrel, P., and Whitehead, M. (1987). The effect of hysterectomy on the age at ovarian failure: Identification of a subgroup of women with premature loss of ovarian function and literature review. *Fertil. Steril.* 47, 94–100. Review.
28. Ash, P. (1980). The influence of radiation on fertility in man. *Br. J. Radiol.* 53, 271–278. Review.
29. Korner, G., Deutsch, V. R., Vlodavsky, I. et al. (1993). Effects of ionizing irradiation on endothelial cell transglutaminase. *FEBS Lett.* 330, 41–45.

CHAPTER **34**

The Role of Mitochondria in the Aging Ovary

RONG-HONG HSIEH, HENG-KIEN AU, RUEY-SHENG WANG, PENG-SHENG YANG, AND CHII-RUEY TZENG

INTRODUCTION

Human mitochondrial deoxyribonucleic acid (mtDNA) is a maternally inherited double-stranded circular DNA molecule, which is involved in respiratory and oxidative phosphorylation. The human metaphase II oocyte is estimated to have 100,000 mitochondria; however, there is only one mitochondrial genome per organelle. The mtDNA is not protected by histones and is exposed in high concentrations of reactive oxygen species (ROS) and free radicals in the matrix of mitochondria. Thus the aged oocytes are very vulnerable to oxidative damage and mtDNA mutation. The current study demonstrates that mtDNA 4977 bp deletions in compromised human oocytes may range from 56.3% when maternal age is younger than 32 up to 73% when maternal age is older than 37. Most nondisjunction and aneuplodies take place during meiosis, which are highly energy-intensive, and increase exponentially with maternal age. Mitochondria in oocyte and early embryos are structurally immature. They are round or ovoid, with few cristae. They become more elongated with numerous transverse cristae at the blastocyst stage. Nevertheless, after ovulation the multiplication of mitochondria and the replication of mtDNA are not resumed until the gastrulation stage.

The transcript levels from mtDNA ND2, COI, COII, ATPase 6, COIII, ND3, ND6, and Cytb genes were remarkably more decreased in unfertilized oocytes than in arrested embryos. In conclusion, the antioxidant enzymes including Mn-superoxide dismutase (Mn-SOD), catalase, and glutathione peroxidase decrease with age, whereas the production of ROS gradually increases as maternal age advances. The mutant mtDNA will accumulate in the mitochondria, leading to defective respiratory enzymes. As a result, the increased oxidative stress will impair adenosine triphosphate (ATP) production and hamper meiotic and mitotic spindle formation in the growing oocyte. The adverse effect will compromise the fertility potential of aging women.

MITOCHONDRIAL DNA

Human mtDNA is a circular, histone-free molecule composed of 16.6 kb of DNA, present in one or more copies in every mitochondrion. It encodes 13 protein subunits out of a total of about 80 constituting the oxidative phosphorylation system, the remainder being encoded by nuclear genes, which are imported into the mitochondrion. Human mtDNA also encodes two ribosome RNAs and 22 transfer RNAs. All of them are components of the OXPHOS system: seven subunits of NADH: ubiquinone oxidoreductase (complex I; ND1–6 and ND4L), one subunit of ubiquinone: cytochrome oxidoreductase (complex III; Cyt b), three subunits of cytochrome c oxidase (complex IV; COI–III), and two subunits of ATP synthase (complex V; ATPase 6 and 8). The oxidative phosphorylation capacity of mitochondria is determined by the interplay between nuclear and mitochondrial genes. While mtDNA encodes 13 polypeptides that are components of the respiratory system, nuclear DNA encodes most respiratory chain proteins and all of the proteins and enzymes that regulate replication and transcription of mtDNA.

The nuclear-encoded proteins are translated in cytoplasmic ribosomes and imported into their final organelle compartment by translocases, which are located in the outer and inner mitochondrial membranes [1]. The mitochondrial genome is replicated and transcribed within the organelle. Both mtDNA replication and transcription have been characterized mainly in mammals, where the *cis*-elements responsible for regulating these processes are mostly located within a small noncoding DNA fragment, the D-loop region. The two strands of mammalian mtDNA are replicated asynchronously and asymmetrically. DNA synthesis begins with the origin of replication of the heavy strand located in the D-loop region and proceeds unidirectionally until the origin of replication of the light strand, located two-thirds of the way around the genome, is reached [2, 3].

The free radical theory, first proposed by Harman [4], is one of the most comprehensive theories of aging. It suggests that living organisms age because of accumulation of oxygen radical–induced cellular damage, and that mtDNA is a possible target of free radical attack during the aging process. In humans, germ-line cells are derived from primordial cells, which are conspicuous in the developing zygote by the third week after conception. Following sexual differentiation, the number of germ cells increases through mitotic division from a few hundred to several million, reaching its peak in humans at 20 weeks of gestational age [5]. Quiescent primordial follicles might not enter meiotic division for a period of up to 40 years, and therefore they have been postulated to accumulate considerable mtDNA mutations.

MITOCHONDRIA AND OOGENESIS

The morphology of mitochondria in oocytes is different from oogenesis through embryogenesis. In mature human oocytes, mitochondria are the prominent organelle. The mitochondria are rounded and accumulate electron-dense material in the mitochondrial matrix [6]. Mitochondrial cristae have an arched shape and are located in the mitochondria periphery. The mitochondria begin to form transverse cristae during early embryogenesis; however, a decreased number of mitochondria are also observed. An elongated mitochondrial morphology similar to that of somatic cells is established after implantation [7]. The dynamic cristae may be bound to the inner mitochondrial membrane as a result of proteins mediating electron transport and oxidative phosphorylation. The varied crista structures represent mitochondria maturation from the arrested to the active state following embryo development. A relationship between energy production and crista area has been shown in different studies. A proportional increase in respiratory chain enzymes and crista surface areas has been observed [8].

The high energy demand of cells is supported by an increase in the surface area of cristae [9]. Crista differentiation may provide an efficient energy power supply for embryo development. Mitochondrial cristae change from a vesicular pattern in primordial germ cells (PGCs) to rounded mitochondria with tubo/vesicular profiles in oogonia, which are then differentiated into a spare, lamellar configuration primary oocyte [10]. Throughout oogenesis to early embryogenesis, despite crista changes, mitochondrial morphology also differentiates into various shapes to fit the energy requirements of different developmental stages. Mitochondria vary considerably in size and structure depending on their source and metabolic state.

It is reported that mature mammalian oocytes have about the same number of mitochondria as they have mtDNA, indicating that mtDNA is haploid in oocytes [11–13]. Most human somatic cells contain about 1000 mitochondria, and each mitochondrion consists of 2 to 10 copies of mtDNA [14]. There is a higher copy number of mtDNA in mature oocytes, but just one mtDNA molecule per organelle [12]. The mtDNA copy number of a bovine oocyte was estimated to be 260,000, which is about 100 times higher than that of somatic cells in animals [13]. The number of mtDNA in a mouse oocyte was approximately 92,000 [12], and that of the human oocyte was estimated to be about 100,000 [12].

Recently, two reports have quantified the mtDNA copy number in unfertilized human oocytes obtained from in vitro fertilization (IVF) failure patients using real-time polymerase chain reaction (PCR) [15, 16]. The former study found an average of 314,000 mtDNA copies in 18 oocytes, and the latter found an average of 193,000 mtDNA copies in 113 unfertilized oocytes. Steuerwald et al. [15] reported that there was no correlation between the mtDNA concentrations in either polar bodies or cytoplasmic samples and their corresponding oocyte. In contrast, the average mtDNA copy number was significantly lower in cohorts with fertilization failure compared to cohorts with a normal rate of fertilization [16].

In previous studies, Piko and Taylor [12] reported that mouse mitochondrial DNA does not replicate during preimplantation development but is transcribed actively from the two-cell stage. There is about a 30-fold rise during cleavage through the blastocyst stage [17]. The important role of mitochondria in embryonic development has been described by experiments with mice, whose mitochondrial transcription factor A gene was disrupted by the gene knockout technique [18]. Heterozygous knockout mice displayed a reduced mtDNA copy number and respiratory chain deficiency in the heart. Homozygous knockout embryos exhibited severe mtDNA depletion with defects in oxidative phosphorylation and had abundant enlarged mitochondria with abnormal cristae. That study suggested that the maternal contribution of functional mitochondria was sufficient to maintain oxidative phosphorylation during early embryonic development. Unknown factors causing unfertilized oocytes and arrested embryo development may be caused by cytoplasmic defects of the oocytes. In particular, the organization and continued metabolic activity of mitochondria are necessary features of cytoplasmic maturation and resumption of meiosis [19, 20]. Accumulation of mtDNA rearrangements, decreased mtDNA copy numbers, and decreased mtRNA expression, all reflecting mitochondrial defects, may compromise the maturation of oocytes.

MITOCHONDRIA AND REPRODUCTIVE AGING

mtDNA may play a specific role in female reproductive aging as well as in general aging processes in tissues and human organs [10, 21–23]. Many reports describe the relationship between the aging processes and mutant mtDNA accumulations in human oocytes [24–28]. These mtDNA mutations include large-scale mtDNA deletions and point mutations. A "common deletion" occurring in patients of Kearns-Sayre syndrome (KSS), as well as normal tissue of aging subjects, is the 4977-bp mtDNA deletion, which is flanked by two 13-bp direct repeats beginning at positions 8470 and 13,447, respectively [29, 30]. The removal of major

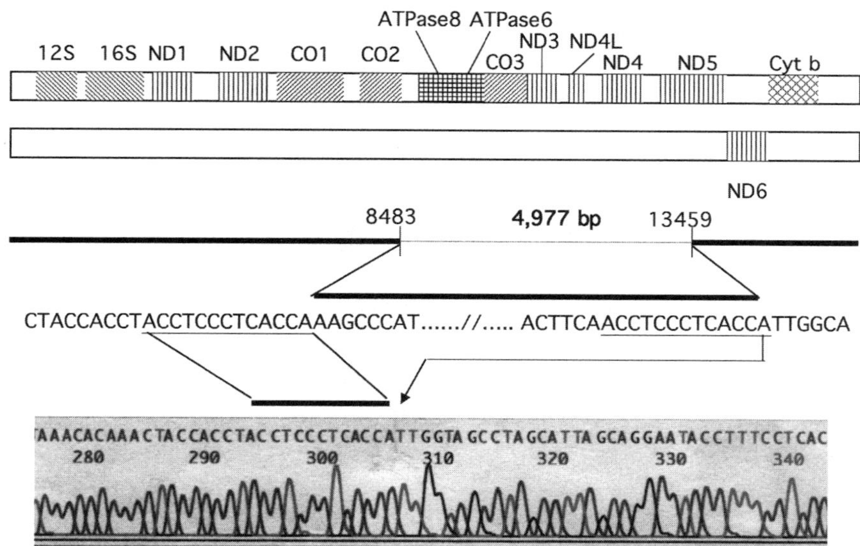

FIGURE 34.1 The relationship between defective mtDNA gene expression in oocytes with common 4977 bp deletion. (See color plate.)

structural genes containing F_0-F_1-ATPase (ATPase 6 and 8), cytochrome oxidase (CO III), and NADH-CoQ oxidoreductase (ND3, ND4, ND4L and ND5) (Figure 34.1) also creates a chimeric gene, which fuses the 5′-proportion of ATPase 8 and the 3′-proportion of ND5 genes. Therefore, the deleted or truncated genes in this rearranged mtDNA may result in impaired gene expression by decreasing expression of the deleted genes or by producing transcripts of fused genes.

In 1995, Chen et al. [24] first demonstrated that rearranged mtDNA exists in human oocytes; they also quantified that the mtDNA content in a single human oocyte is about 100,000 copies. A nested PCR strategy amplifying mtDNA and detecting minor quantities of rearranged mtDNA has also been used to study human oocytes and embryos [28, 31]. Those authors found the rearrangements from 33% to 66% in oocytes, decreasing significantly to 8% to 35% in embryos. Multiple PCR fragments, with lengths shorter than expected, were observed after PCR amplification of deleted mtDNA. Thirteen mtDNA rearrangements were identified, and the deletion junction was determined by direct sequencing of the PCR products.

Table 34.1 shows the length of deletions, deletion junctions, and primers used to characterize the 13 established mtDNA deletions [28]. These deletions may be grouped into two classes: (1) type I deletion, which is the dominant one bearing the same nucleotide sequences flanking the breakpoints at the 5′ and 3′ ends of the deletion; and (2) type II deletion, which does not harbor such direct repeat sequences. The occurrence of multiple mtDNA deletions was 77.9% in unfertilized oocytes, 38.2% in arrested and fragmented embryos, and 26.3% in tripronucleate (3PN) embryo (Table 34.2).

When comparing deleted mtDNA interference with oocyte fertilization and embryo development, there were no significant differences between younger women and older women except in a study done by Keefe et al. [25]; however, there was statistical significance between oocytes and embryos. This suggests that detrimental mtDNA may retard the fertilization capacity of oocytes. Injection of the donated cytoplasm from 3PN embryos of younger patients may enhance the clinical pregnancy rate in patients with repeated implantation failure in an IVF program. The intracytoplasmic sperm injection (ICSI) procedure assumes that only a single spermatozoon is microinjected in each oocyte, but sometimes some zygotes show three pronuclei instead of the expected two by 16 to 18 hours after ICSI [32–35].

The most probable hypothesis to explain the existence of 3PN would be normal fertilization by a single injected spermatozoon, along with the nonextrusion of a second polar body [33, 34]. There are no reports indicating that cytoplasmic or mitochondrial dysfunction will cause formation of 3PN zygotes. Decreased proportions of the 4977 bp deletion in 3PN embryos may also show that fewer mutant defective mitochondria do not retard the normal growth rates of 3PN zygotes. This strongly implies the contributory role for mtDNA in determining oocyte fertilizability and embryo development. It seems that a defective energy supply from oocytes with deleted mtDNA may compromise oocyte fertilization. Schon et al. [36] also postulated that the observation of an increasing aging-trisomy curve of maternal gametes may be caused by defective mitochondrial function in oocytes and the surrounding follicular somatic cells in aging women of reproductive age. The general ovarian levels of mtDNA deletions increase in patients reaching menopause [37, 38].

TABLE 34.1 Types of Mitochondrial DNA Rearrangements in Human Oocytes and Embryos and Primers Used to Characterize These Deleted mtDNAs

Deletion Type	Deleted Length	Primer Pairs	PCR Product	Deletion Junction	Direct Repeat Sequence
I (13/13)*	4977	H1 + L1	389	8470–13446	ACCTCCCTCACCA
I (12/12)	7436	H1 + L4	690	8637–16072	CATCAACAACCG
I (12/12)	4237	H3 + L2	702	9486–13722	TTCGCAGGATTT
I (10/10)	4642	H3 + L2	297	9431–14072	CCAAAAAGGC
I (9/9)	4365	H3 + L2	574	9579–13943	AATCCCCTA
I (7/7)	7150	H1 + L3	462	8581–15730	GCCGCAG
I (7/7)	5228	H1 + L2	633	8771–13998	CTAACCT
I (6/7)	6130	H2 + L3	986	9189–15318	CCT(A)GCA
I (6/7)	5007	H1 + L2	854	8987–13993	TAG(C)CCT
II	4921	H1 + L1	445	8503–13423	
II	7276	H1 + L4	850	8712–15987	
II	6827	H2 + L3	289	8810–15636	
II	4036	H3 + L2	903	9697–13732	

The type I deletion bears direct repeats flanking the breakpoints at the 5′ and 3′ ends of the deletion. The type II deletion contains no such feature.

*Nucleotide number of the direct repeat.

(Reprinted with permission from R. H. Hsieh, N. H. Tsai, H. K. Au, S. J. Chang, Y. H. Wei, and C. R. Tzeng. [2002]. Multiple rearrangements of mitochondrial DNA in unfertilized human oocytes. *Fertil. Steril.* 77, 1012–1017. Copyright: American Society for Reproductive Medicine.)

TABLE 34.2 Frequency of Deleted mtDNA in Human Oocytes, Embryos, and 3 PN Embryos by Nested PCR

	No. analyzed	No. amplified	No. deletions	Frequency (%)
Oocytes	124	109	85	77.9*,†
Embryos	98	89	34	38.2*
3PN	42	38	10	26.3†

*,†Statically significant difference ($p < 0.001$) by χ^2 analysis.

(Reprinted with permission from R.H. Hsieh, N. H. Tsai, H. K. Au, S. J. Chang, Y. H. Wei, and CR Tzeng. [2002]. Multiple rearrangements of mitochondrial DNA in unfertilized human oocytes. *Fertil. Steril.* 77, 1012–1017. Copyright: American Society for Reproductive Medicine.)

It has also been reported that increased proportions of mtDNA rearrangements are related to maternal age older than 38 years [25]. Age-related protein synthesis and mitochondrial function are crucial in increased aneuploidy rates through altered maturation kinetics and spindle formation [39]. In addition, ATP contents in oocytes were also correlated with fertilization capacity. It has been suggested that impaired mtDNA, which affects metabolic capacity, may be a proximal cause of failure of oocyte maturation, fertilization, and early embryonic development. The mitochondrial membrane potential appears to influence the level of certain mitochondrial activities, including ATP liberation and ionic fluxes. The measurements were determined using a mitochondria-specific fluorescence dye and a confocal microscope [40, 41]. They observed that asymmetrical mitochondrial distributions at the pronuclear stage resulted in some proportion of blastomeres having reduced mitochondrial inheritance and diminished ATP-generating capacity.

The mitochondria with high membrane potential may occur in the subplasmalemmal cytoplasm, where intercellular contact is absent. These two studies proposed that highly polarized (high membrane potential) pericortical mitochondria may have a putative role in the acquisition of oocyte competence and the regulation of early developmental processes. A wide range of ATP contents has been detected in meiotically mature oocytes from IVF patients, and a higher potential for continued embryogenesis and further implantation is correlated with oocytes with higher ATP concentrations [19]. Mitochondria participate in the regulation of early developmental processes, which may be associated with elevated metabolism or intracellular signaling through calcium-induced calcium release pathways.

At birth, approximately 2 million primordial follicles still remain in the ovaries. During reproductive life, follicle depletion occurs at a rate of approximately 1000 per month, increasing in rate after the age of 35 years until menopause, when the stock of follicles is exhausted. In females of many species, more than half of the oocyte population dies by apoptosis before birth [42]. Krakauer et al. [43] reported this death of germ cells as a developmental solution to the accumulation of mutations in mitochondria, suggesting that prenatal oocyte apoptosis effectively removes oocytes carrying mutant mitochondria. It is noteworthy that mitochondria influencing the fate of oocytes has also been proven by microinjecting small numbers of mitochondria into mouse oocytes, which prevents these oocytes with inherently high rates of apoptosis from undergoing programmed cell death [44].

CONCLUSION

It is well documented that at least five different types of mtDNA mutations have been found to be age-related: (1) large-scale deletion, (2) point mutation, (3) insertion, (4) small tandem duplication in the D-loop region, and (5) DNA rearrangement. The frequency of those age-related mutant mtDNA are quite low (1% to 4%) compared with the disease-associated mutant mtDNA of affected tissues, which are generally higher than 80%. The occurrence of the mutation is commonly presented and accumulated in the postmitotic tissues with high energy demand, including muscle, heart, and brain [45]. In contract, the oocyte has the propensity to be fertilized, cleave, and turns out to be a fetus. The paucity of intact mtDNA-encoded protein subunits, which are responsible for oxidative phosphorylation and sufficient ATP production, may jeopardize the fertilization potential of the aging oocyte. Unfortunately, the production of ROS, which includes superoxide anion, hydrogen peroxide, and hydroxyl radical, in mitochondria increases with age, while antioxidant enzymes including Mn-SOD, catalase, and glutathione peroxidase, all the free radical scavengers, decrease with age [46].

These age-related toxic by-products will inevitably lead to enhancing the lipid peroxidation of encoded protein subunits and oxidative modification of mtDNA in the inner membrane of mitochondria. The mutant or modified mtDNA will accumulate in the aging process. As a result, the impaired respiratory enzymes will lose energy conservation capability and generate more ROS and free radicals, which in turn will aggravate the oxidative stress and damages to mtDNA in the aging ovary. The meiotic or mitotic spindles of the microtubule in growing oocytes are vulnerable to ROS caused by accumulated mutant mtDNA and modified respiratory enzymes [47–49]. In addition, quantitation of the transcript levels from the mtDNA ND2, COI, COII, ATPase 6, COIII, ND3, ND6, and Cytb genes in oocytes and embryos revealed that the transcript levels were remarkably more decreased in unfertilized oocytes than in arrested embryos and 3PN embryos. Besides, the 4977 bp deletion was the most common deletion in human oocytes and embryos.

About 66.1% of unfertilized oocytes, 34.8% of arrested or fragmented embryos, and 21.1% of 3PN embryos harbored the 4977 bp deletion of mtDNA [50]. The frequency of occurrence of 4977 bp mtDNA rearrangements in unfertilized oocytes increase from 56.3% when maternal age is younger than 32, up to 73% if maternal age is older than 37. The further quantitative rather than qualitative measurement will clarify the association between maternal age and the oocyte quality [28]. It has been reported that the activity of mitochondria in metaphase II oocyte was negatively correlated with maternal age. This trend was obvious when analyzing mitochondrial activity, which was strongly correlated with the rate of embryo development on day 3 after fertilization [51].

In conclusion, because of peculiar properties of histones less and single copy of mtDNA in each mitochondria organelle, the oxidative stress induced by accumulation of impaired or mutant mtDNA, will thereby damage the functional and structural integrity of mtDNA-encoded protein subunits in the ovary of the woman of advanced maternal age. This mtDNA mutation is generally estimated to be 10 to 20 times higher than that of nuclear DNA [52–54]. The changes are amenable to deteriorate oocyte quality and compromise the fertility potential in an aging woman.

References

1. Taanman, J. D. (1999). The mitochondrial genome: Structure, transcription, translation and replication. *Biochem. Biophys. Acta.* 1410, 103–123.
2. Clayton, D. A. (1982). Replication of animal mitochondrial DNA. *Cell* 28,693–705.
3. Clayton, D. A. (1987). Nuclear gene products that function in mitochondrial DNA replication. *Philos. Trans. R. Soc. Lond. B. Biol. Sci.* 317, 473–482.
4. Harman, D. (1972). The biological clock: The mitochondria? *J. Am. Geriatr. Soc.* 20, 145–147.
5. Baker, T. G. (1963). A quantitative and cytological study of germ cells in human ovaries. *Proc. Roy. Soc. B. Biol. Med. (London)* 158, 417–433.

6. Hertig, A. T., and Adams, E. C. (1967). Studies on the human oocyte and its follicle. I. Ultrastructural and histochemical observations on the primordial follicle stage. *J.Cell. Biol.* 34, 647–675.
7. Smith, L. C., and Alcivar, A. A. (1993). Cytoplasmic inheritance and its effects on development and performance. *J. Reprod. Fertil.* 48 (Suppl.), 31–43.
8. Nicholls, D. G., and Budd, S. L. (2000). Mitochondria and neuronal survival. *Physiol. Rev.* 80, 315–360.
9. Gosslau, A., Dittrich, W., Willig, A., and Jaros, P. P. (2001). Cytological effects of platelet-derived growth factor on mitochondrial ultrastructure in fibroblasts. *Comp. Biochem. Physiol. A. Mol. Integr. Physiol.* 128, 241–249.
10. Jansen, R. P., and de Boer, K. (1998). The bottleneck: Mitochondrial imperatives in oogenesis and ovarian follicular fate. *Mol. Cell. Endocrinol.* 145, 81–88.
11. Piko, L., and Matsumoto, L. (1976). Number of mitochondria and some properties of mitochondrial DNA in the mouse egg. *Dev. Biol.* 49, 1–10.
12. Piko, L., and Taylor, K. D. (1987). Amounts of mitochondrial DNA and abundance of some mitochondrial gene transcripts in early mouse embryos. *Dev. Biol.* 123, 364–374.
13. Michaels, G. S., Hauswirth, W. W. and Laipis, P. J. (1982). Mitochondrial DNA copy number in bovine oocytes and somatic cells. *Dev. Biol.* 94, 246–251.
14. Giles, R. E., Blanc, H., Cann, H. M., and Wallace, D. C. (1980). Maternal inheritance of human mitochondrial DNA. *Proc. Natl. Acad. Sci. USA* 77, 6715–6719.
15. Steuerwald, N., Barritt, J. A., Adler, R., Malter, H., Schimmel, T., Cohen, J., and Brenner, C. A. (2000). Quantification of mtDNA in single oocytes, polar bodies and subcellular components by real-time rapid cycle fluorescence monitored PCR. *Zygote* 8, 209–215.
16. Reynier, P., May-Panloup, P., Chretien, M. F., Morgan, C. J., Jean, M., Savagner, F., Barriere, P., and Malthiery, Y. (2001). Mitochondrial DNA content affects the fertilizability of human oocytes. *Mol. Hum. Reprod.* 7, 425–429.
17. Taylor, K. D., and Piko, L. (1995). Mitochondrial biogenesis in early mouse embryos: expression of the mRNAs for subunits IV, Vb, and VIIc of cytochrome c oxidase and subunit 9 (P1) of H(+)-ATP synthase. *Mol. Reprod. Dev.* 40, 29–35.
18. Larsson, N. G., Wang, J., Wilhelmsson, H., Oldfors, A., Rustin, P., Lewandoski, M., Barsh, G. S., and Clayton, D. A. (1998). Mitochondrial transcription factor A is necessary for mtDNA maintenance and embryogenesis in mice. *Nat. Genet.* 18, 231–236.
19. Van Blerkom, J., Davis, P. W., and Lee, J. (1995). ATP content of human oocytes and developmental potential and outcome after in-vitro fertilization and embryo transfer. *Hum. Reprod.* 10, 415–424.
20. Cummins, J. (1998). Mitochondrial DNA in mammalian reproduction. *Rev. Reprod.* 3, 172–182.
21. Jansen, R. P. (1995). Older ovaries: Ageing and reproduction. *Med. J. Aust.* 162, 623–624.
22. Janny, L., and Menezo, Y. J. (1996). Maternal age effect on early human embryonic development and blastocyst formation. *Mol. Reprod. Dev.* 45, 31–37.
23. Kirkwood, T. B. (1998). Ovarian ageing and the general biology of senescence. *Maturitas* 30, 105–111.
24. Chen, X., Prosser, R., Simonetti, S., Sadlock, J., Jagiello, G., and Schon, E. A. (1995). Rearranged mitochondrial genomes are present in human oocytes. *Am. J. Hum. Genet.* 57, 239–247.
25. Keefe, D. L., Niven-Fairchild, T., Powell, S., and Buradagunta, S. (1995). Mitochondrial deoxyribonucleic acid deletions in oocytes and reproductive aging in women. *Fertil. Steril.* 64, 577–583.
26. Brenner, C. A., Wolny, Y. M., Barritt, J. A., Matt, D. W., Munne, S., and Cohen J. (1998). Mitochondrial DNA deletion in human oocytes and embryos. *Mol. Hum. Reprod.* 4, 887–892.
27. Barritt, J. A., Brenner, C. A., Willadsen, S., and Cohen, J. (2000). Spontaneous and artificial changes in human ooplasmic mitochondria. *Hum. Reprod.* 15 (Suppl. 2), 207–217.
28. Hsieh, R. H., Tsai, N. M., Au, H. K., Chang, S. J., Wei, Y. H., and Tzeng, C. R. (2002). Multiple rearrangements of mitochondrial DNA in unfertilized human oocytes. *Fertil. Steril.* 77, 1012–1017.
29. Moraes, C. T., DiMauro, S., Zeviani, M., Lombes, A., Shanske, S., Miranda, A. F., Nakase, H., Bonilla, E., Werneck, L. C., and Servidei, S. (1989). Mitochondrial DNA deletions in progressive external ophthalmoplegia and Kearns-Sayre syndrome. *N. Engl. J. Med.* 320, 1293–1299.
30. Rotig, A., Cormier, V., Koll, F., Mize, C. E., Saudubray, J. M., Veerman, A., Pearson, H. A., and Munnich, A. (1991). Site-specific deletions of the mitochondrial genome in the Pearson marrow-pancreas syndrome. *Genomics* 10, 502–504.
31. Barritt, J. A., Brenner, C. A., Cohen, J., and Matt, D. W. (1999). Mitochondrial DNA rearrangements in human oocytes and embryos. *Mol. Hum. Reprod.* 5, 927–933.
32. Huang, C. C., Cheng, T. C., Chang, H. H., Chang, C. C., Chen, C. I., Liu, J., and Lee, M. S. (1999). Birth after the injection of sperm and the cytoplasm of tripronucleate zygotes into metaphase II oocytes in patients with repeated implantation failure after assisted fertilization procedures. *Fertil. Steril.*72, 702–706.
33. Van Steirteghem, A. C., Nagy, Z., Joris, H., Liu, J., Staessen, C., Smitz, J., Wisanto, A., and Devroey, P. (1993). High fertilization and implantation rates after intracytoplasmic sperm injection. *Hum. Reprod.* 8, 1061–1066.
34. Macas, E., Imthurn, B., Rosselli, M., and Keller, P. J. (1996). The chromosomal complements of multipronuclear human zygotes resulting from intracytoplasmic sperm injection. *Hum. Reprod.* 11, 2496–2501.
35. Grossmann, M., Calafell, J. M., Brandy, N., Vanrell, J. A., Rubio, C., Pellicer, A., Egozcue, J., Vidal, F., and Santalo, J. (1997). Origin of tripronucleate zygotes after intracytoplasmic sperm injection. *Hum. Reprod.* 12, 2762–2765.
36. Schon, E. A., Kim, S. H., Ferreira, J. C., Magalhaes, P., Grace, M., Warburton, D., and Gross, S. J. (2000). Chromosomal non-disjunction in human oocytes: Is there a mitochondrial connection? *Hum. Reprod.* 15 (Suppl. 2), 160–172.
37. Kitagawa, T., Suganuma, N., Nawa, A., Kikkawa, F., Tanaka, M., Ozawa, T., and Tomoda, Y. (1993). Rapid accumulation of deleted mitochondrial deoxyribonucleic acid in postmenopausal ovaries. *Biol. Reprod.* 49, 730–736.
38. Suganuma, N., Kitagawa, T., Nawa, A., and Tomoda, Y. (1993). Human ovarian aging and mitochondrial DNA deletion. *Horm. Res.* 39 (Suppl. 1), 16–21.
39. Eichenlaub-Ritter, U. (1998). Genetics of oocyte ageing. *Maturitas* 30, 143–169.

40. Van Blerkom, J., Davis, P., and Alexander, S. (2000). Differential mitochondrial distribution in human pronuclear embryos leads to disproportionate inheritance between blastomeres: Relationship to microtubular organization, ATP content and competence. *Hum. Reprod.* 15, 2621–2633.
41. Van Blerkom, J., Davis, P., Mathwig, V., and Alexander, S. (2002). Domains of high-polarized and low-polarized mitochondria may occur in mouse and human oocytes and early embryos. *Hum. Reprod.* 17, 393–406.
42. Morita, Y., and Tilly, J. L. (1999). Oocyte apoptosis: Like sand through an hourglass. *Dev. Biol.* 213, 1–17.
43. Krakauer, D. C., and Mira, A. (1999). Mitochondria and germ-cell death. *Nature* 400, 125–126.
44. Perez, G. I., Trbovich, A. M., Gosden, R. G., and Tilly, J. L. (2000). Mitochondria and the death of oocytes. *Nature* 403, 500–501.
45. Wei, Y. H. (1998). Oxidative stress and mitochndrial DNA mutation in human aging. *Proc. Soc. Exp. Bio. Med.* 21, 53–56.
46. Wei, Y. H., Ma, Y. S., Lee, H. C., Lee, C. F., and Lu, C. Y. (2001). Mitochondrial theory of aging matures: Roles of mtDNA mutation and oxidative stress in human aging. *Chin. Med. J.* (Taipei) 64, 259–270.
47. Simmoneti, S., Chen, X., DiMaturo, S., and Schon, E. A. (1992). Accumulation of deletions in human mitochondrial DNA during normal aging: Analysis by quantitative PCR. *Biochim. Biophys. Acta.* 1180, 113–122.
48. Wei, Y. H., Pang, C. Y., You, B. J., and Lee, H. C. (1996). Tandem duplications and large-scale deletions of mitochondrial DNA are early molecular events of human aging process. *Ann. N.Y. Acad. Sci.* 786, 82–101.
49. Ames, B. N., Shigenaga, M. K., and Hagen, T. M. (1993). Oxidants, antioxidants, and the degenerative diseases of aging. *Proc. Natl. Acad. Sci. USA* 90, 7915–7922.
50. Heish, R., Tsai, N., Au, H., Chang, S., Cheng, Y., and Tzeng, C. (2001). Multiple rearragements of mitochondrial DNA and defective oxidative phosphorylation gene expression in unfertilized human oocytes. *Fertil. Steril.* 76 (Suppl. 1), S8 abstracts.
51. Wilding, M., Dale, B., Marino, M., Matteo, L., Alviggi, C., Pisaturo, M. L., Lombardi, L., and Placido, G. (2001). Mitochondrial aggregation patterns and activity in human oocytes and preimplantation embryos. *Hum. Reprod.* 16, 909–917.
52. Merriwether, D. A., Clark, A. G., Ballinger, S. W., Schutt, T. G., Soodyall, I. I., Ienkins, T., Sheny, S. T., and Wallaee, D. C. (1991). The structure of human mitochondrial DNA variation. *J. Mol. Evol.* 33, 543–555.
53. Richter, C., Park, J. W., and Ames, B. N. (1998). Normal oxidative damage to mitochondrial and nuclear DNA is extensive. *Proc. Natl. Acad. Sci. USA* 85, 6465–6467.
54. Wallaee, D. C. (1994). Mitochondrial DNA sequence variation in human evolution and disease. *Pro. Natl. Acad. Sci. USA* 91, 8739–8746.

PART VIII

Human Ovarian Surface Epithelium and Neoplasia

CHAPTER 35

Development and Differentiation of Ovarian Surface Epithelium: Cues for the Basis of its Malignant Potential

NELLY AUERSPERG AND MICHELLE M. M. WOO

ABSTRACT

The human ovarian surface epithelium (OSE), which is the source of the most common and most lethal ovarian carcinomas, is a simple mesothelium overlying the ovary. In contrast to the extraovarian pelvic peritoneum, the OSE remains uncommitted and multipotential in the adult. Its multipotential nature is reflected in the plasticity of the OSE phenotype *in vivo* and *in vitro*, and by its capacity to differentiate along several pathways. These include epithelio-mesenchymal transition (EMT) under physiologic conditions, and the acquisition of complex characteristics of the Müllerian duct–derived oviductal, endometrial, and endocervical epithelia in metaplasia and with neoplastic progression. This chapter summarizes developmental influences that may be responsible for the unique characteristics of OSE and outlines its capacity to exist in several forms with different potentials for growth, differentiation, and malignant progression.

INTRODUCTION

The ovarian surface epithelium (OSE), also referred to in the literature as normal ovarian epithelium [1] or ovarian mesothelium (OM) [2, 3], is the part of the pelvic peritoneum that covers the ovary [4] (Figure 35.1). It is an inconspicuous tissue with no known major function, but it is of great importance in gynecologic pathology because it is the source of the most common and most lethal form of human ovarian malignancies—the epithelial ovarian carcinomas. Opportunities for animal studies of these neoplasms are limited because ovarian tumors in most species other than human do not arise in the OSE but, rather, in stromal, granulosa, or germ cells. Furthermore, model systems to study human OSE in culture have been established only relatively recently. Clinically, such carcinomas are almost invariably detected in late stages, after they have spread beyond the ovary. Consequently, the etiology and early events in ovarian epithelial carcinogenesis are among the least understood of all major human malignancies, and the prognosis of women with this disease is dismal.

This review addresses the question of whether specific aspects in the development and differentiation of OSE contribute to the tendency of this simple epithelium to undergo malignant transformation and to create cancers that are structurally and functionally among the most complex of all human neoplasms.

EMBRYONIC DEVELOPMENT

Early in embryonic development, the future OSE forms from part of the coelomic epithelium, which is the mesodermally derived epithelial lining of the intraembryonic coelom. It overlies the presumptive gonadal area and, by proliferation and differentiation, gives rise to part of the gonadal blastema. The coelomic epithelium undergoes numerous changes during prenatal development and is considered a pleuripotent epithelium because it can give rise to several epithelial tissues. Most of the developmental changes of this epithelium occur during the embryonic and fetal periods and thus will be the focus of this section, but important changes also occur during adulthood, and will be discussed later in the section, "Differentiation in the Adult."

During embryonic development, the zygote, a totipotent stem cell with the ability to become all the different cell types in the body, divides many times and progressively transforms into a multicellular human being through cell division, migration, growth, apoptosis, and differentiation. The zygote reaches the uterine cavity, and implantation occurs before the end of the first week of gestation. At the end of the second week of embryonic life, the human embryo is bilaminar, with two germ layers (dorsal epiblast

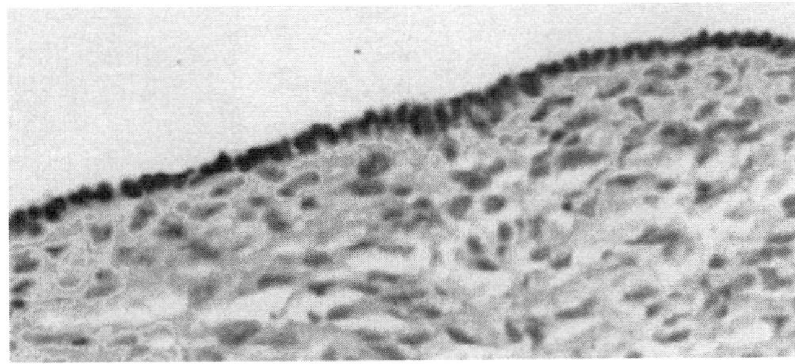

FIGURE 35.1 Histologic appearance of normal human ovarian surface epithelium (OSE). The epithelium appears as a simple mesothelium covering the ovarian surface. Hematoxylin and Eosin ×120.

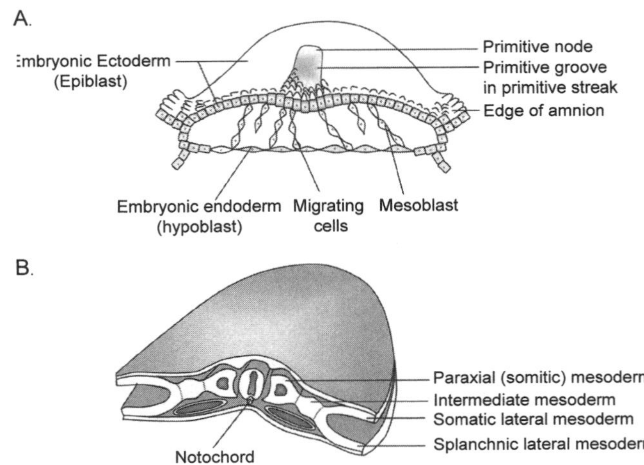

FIGURE 35.2 Early developmental stages of the presumptive gonads and coelomic epithelium. **A**, During the third week of embryonic development, gastrulation occurs and epiblastic cells from the primitive streak migrate between the epiblast and hypoblast to form mesoblast or mesenchyme that soon organizes to form the intraembryonic mesoderm. **B**, Depending on the region from which the epiblastic cells migrated, the embryonic mesoderm can be subdivided into three layers: the paraxial, intermediate, and lateral plate mesoderm. The urogenital system is derived from the intermediate mesoderm, where the somatic and splanchnic mesoderm diverge, and the overlying mesoderm becomes the ovarian surface epithelium.

and ventral hypoblast) [5, 6]. During the third week of development, the mesodermal cells that give rise to the future OSE develop as an invagination of epiblastic cells from the primitive streak (Figure 35.2). These cells give rise to mesenchymal cells, which migrate between the epiblast and hypoblast and form a layer known as the intraembryonic mesoderm.

Depending on the region from which the epiblastic cells migrated, the mesodermal cells form the paraxial, intermediate, and lateral mesoderm. The coelomic epithelium is derived from the lateral mesoderm, where isolated coelomic spaces or vesicles begin to form, which eventually coalesce to form a single cavity. As lateral folding of the embryo occurs, the intraembryonic coelom is formed. This cavity separates the lateral mesoderm into two layers: (1) a somatic or parietal layer and (2) a splanchnic or visceral layer. The parietal mesoderm layer surrounding the developing intraembryonic coelom is the primordium for the mesothelium (peritoneum) of the peritoneal and pleural cavities. In the region where the parietal and splanchnic mesoderm diverge, the underlying intermediate mesoderm develops into the urogenital system and the overlying mesoderm becomes OSE [5] (see Figure 35.2).

Mesothelial cells have epithelium-like properties but have differentiated from the underlying mesenchymal cells. This raises the possibility of a more intimate biologic relationship between epithelium and stroma in mesodermal tissues than is the case where ectodermal or endodermal epithelia are supported by mesodermal stroma. This may be an important aspect of epithelio-mesenchymal conversion observed in adult OSE (see the following section, "Differentiation in the Adult"). By the fourth week of gestation, gastrulation is complete, and the embryonic mesodermal germ layer, which gives rise to the coelomic epithelium, has been formed.

In the four-week embryo, the first sign of gonadal development is detectable. The first signs of differentiation of the intermediate mesoderm are in the most cranial regions, where the remnants of the earliest form of the kidney, the pronephros, briefly appear. In the latter part of the fourth week, a longitudinal prominence, the pronephric duct, appears on each side of the embryo in the lateral region of the intermediate mesoderm [2, 7]. This duct is important in organizing the development of much of the adult urogenital system, which forms largely from cells of the caudal portions of the intermediate mesoderm. Development of the duct begins cranially and extends caudally toward the developing mesonephros. The gonads arise from an elongated region of steroidogenic mesoderm along the ventromedial border of the mesonephros. Thus gonadal development is closely associated with the mesonephros, which participates in gonad formation, in the gonad itself, and in association with the Müllerian duct.

Transcriptional factors that are important regulators of gonadal and kidney development include steroidogenic factor 1 (SF-1) and the Wilm's tumor suppressor gene (WT-1). SF-1 is expressed in embryos from the earliest stages of gonadogenesis, when the intermediate mesoderm condenses to form the urogenital ridge [8]. SF-1 can direct pleuripotential embryonic stem cells to differentiate, at least partly, down the steroidogenic pathway, activating expression of the cholesterol side-chain cleavage enzyme [9, 10]. WT-1 is widely expressed in the coelomic epithelium, the subjacent mesenchyme, and in mesonephric structures, in accordance with a role in gonadal and renal morphogenesis [11]. WT-1 appears to regulate the transformation from mesenchyme to epithelium during early development of the urogenital system: the differentiation of the metanephric mesenchyme to nephrons, the formation of the mesothelium from the mesenchyme lining the coelom, and the production of sex cords from the mesenchyme of the primitive gonad [12]. In the adult ovaries, the expression of WT-1 becomes restricted to the granulosa and theca cells [10].

Another factor that appears to be important in urogenital development is Wnt-4, a member of the Wnt family of locally acting secreted signaling glycoproteins. During development, it is expressed in the mesonephros and in the coelomic epithelium in the region of the presumptive gonad [13]. Interestingly, it has been suggested that estrogens can regulate Wnt-4 expression in the adult and thus may also be important in regulation of fetal OSE development [14]. In addition, several other genes such as SOX9, DAX-1, GATA-4, and Lhx9 may also play key developmental roles in gonadal differentiation [15–19].

Just before and during the arrival of primitive germ cells in the urogenital ridge, starting at about five weeks of development, the coelomic epithelial cells covering the primitive gonad undergo marked proliferation, and some of the cells penetrate the underlying mesenchyme, which produces a bulge in the coelomic cavity, the genital ridge (Figure 35.3). The germinal component of the ovary (oocytes) in the adult derives from primordial germ cells, which appear first in the wall of the endoderm yolk sac. By week five, the urogenital ridge consists of several different kinds of somatic cells, a proliferating coelomic epithelium covering the developing gonad, and an underlying compartment containing mesenchymal cells, blood vessels, and cells of the neighboring mesonephros [2, 7].

In the six-week embryo, the paramesonephric or Müllerian ducts begin to develop on each side from invaginations of Wnt-4 expressing coelomic epithelium, in the mesonephric region [13, 20]. The edges of these invaginations approach each other and fuse together to form the Müllerian ducts. Once formed, the Müllerian duct epithelium expresses the transcriptional regulator Pax8, as well as Wnt-7a, a second Wnt family member, which appears to be maintained in the Müllerian duct derivatives throughout life, consistent with a function of Wnt-7a signaling in both fetal and adult ductal development. Wnt-4 becomes localized to the mesenchyme cells underlying the newly formed Müllerian duct. The epithelial-derived Wnt-7a signal might function by regulating gene expression in the adjacent mesenchyme. Thus Wnt-4 signaling is required for the initial stages of ductal morphogenesis, while Wnt-7a functions as an epithelial-to-mesenchymal signal, possibly by regulating the Müllerian-inhibiting substance receptor expressed by underlying mesenchymal cells [20].

The cranial ends of the ducts open into the coelomic cavity as funnel-shaped structures, which later develop into the fallopian tubes. The paramesonephric ducts also run caudally and approach each other in the future pelvic region of the embryo, where they fuse together to form a Y-shaped structure. This crossing and ultimate meeting in the midline are caused by the medial swinging of the entire urogenital ridge. The region of midline fusion of the paramesonephric ducts ultimately becomes the uterus and endocervix, while the ridge tissue that is carried along with the paramesonephric ducts forms the broad ligament of the uterus [5]. Thus the coelomic epithelium in the vicinity

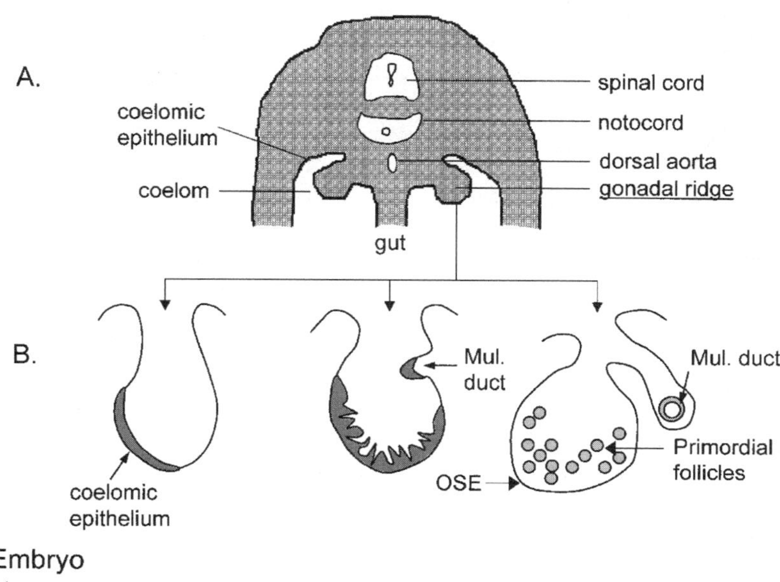

FIGURE 35.3 Schematic representation of the development of the coelomic epithelium in the gonadal ridge region. **A,** cross section through the dorsal part of a 13-mm human embryo; **B,** sequential changes in the gonadal ridge, which is covered by modified coelomic epithelium (shaded). This epithelium proliferates and forms cords, which penetrate into the ovarian cortex and give rise to the granulosa cells in the primordial follicles. The follicles become separated from the overlying ovarian surface epithelium (OSE) by stroma. The Müllerian ducts (Mul. duct) develop as invaginations of the coelomic epithelium dorsolaterally from the gonadal ridges. (Reproduced with permission from N. Auersperg, A. S. T. Wong, K. C. Choi, S. K. Kang, and P. C. K. Leung. [2001]. Ovarian surface epithelium: Biology, Endocrinology and Pathology, *Endocr. Rev.* 22(2), 255–288. Copyright 2001 by the Endocrine Society.)

of the presumptive gonads has the competence to create the Müllerian ducts (i.e., the primordia for the epithelia of the oviduct, endometrium, and endocervix). Interestingly, although the coelomic epithelium is the precursor of OSE, extraovarian peritoneum (EP), and Müllerian epithelia, the differentiation marker CA-125 is expressed in the adult in EP and Müllerian epithelia, but not in the OSE [21]. It has been suggested that this difference is evidence of divergent differentiation between OSE and EP, which leads to the cessation of CA125 production by OSE before birth [21]. An alternative interpretation is that the part of the coelomic epithelium that gives rise to OSE never reaches the stage of differentiation where CA125 is expressed, which is attained by the other epithelia in the first trimester of gestation.

At later stages of development, some of the germ cells have migrated to the urogenital ridge and are intermingling with the surface epithelial cells. A delicate basal lamina with scanty collagen fibrils separates these cells from the underlying mesenchyme. The coelomic epithelium continues to proliferate and forms a multistratified, papillary epithelium overlying a basal lamina and in some areas a nascent tunica albuginea. The tunica albuginea in the future ovary is a collagenous connective tissue layer that separates the OSE from the underlying ovarian stroma. As shown by electron microscopy, continued growth of the coelomic epithelium into the underlying mesenchyme gives rise to finger-like epithelial cortical cords, which subsequently break up into isolated cell clusters, each surrounding one or more primitive germ cells [2, 7, 22]. These surrounding epithelial cells are the follicular or pregranulosa cells of the primordial follicles. Therefore, the fetal OSE is also likely a progenitor of the ovarian granulosa cells (see Figure 35.3) [23].

During the late stages of fetal development, the coelomic epithelium reverts to one layer in the now elongated, lobular ovary. Common features on the apical surface of the epithelial cells now include microvilli, blebs, ruffles, and solitary cilia. The tunica albuginea is well developed. It is composed of bundles of collagen fibers and elongated fibroblasts. The germ cells (oogonia or oocytes), now surrounded by a single layer of flattened pregranulosa cells, detach themselves from the finger-like epithelial cords to form isolated primordial and primary developing follicles [7].

In summary, during development of the coelomic epithelium, the fetal OSE changes from a flat-to-cuboidal simple epithelium with a fragmentary basement membrane to a multistratified, papillary epithelium on a well-defined basement membrane. Subsequently, it reverts to a monolayer of cuboidal cells covering the ovary. Thus the coelomic epithelium in and near the gonadal area represents an embryonic field with the competence or capacity to differentiate along many different pathways. In addition to its likely role as a progenitor of granulosa cells, the coelomic epithelium in the gonadal region can also differentiate along Müllerian duct epithelial lines. The factors involved in the development and differentiation of the coelomic epithelium are not fully understood. This phenotypic plasticity of the coelomic epithelium during development appears to be retained in the adult OSE because it can alter its state of differentiation under physiologic and pathologic conditions.

DIFFERENTIATION IN THE ADULT

Ovarian Surface Epithelium as Part of the Pelvic Peritoneum

In the mature woman, the pelvic peritoneum, including the OSE, is a simple epithelium with secretory and transporting functions [4]. It is characterized by keratin, simple desmosomes, apical microvilli, occasional cilia, and a basal lamina. In distinction from epithelia of ectodermal or endodermal origin as found, for example, in the breast and intestine, the peritoneum retains a mixed epithelio-mesenchymal phenotype, which reflects its mesodermal origin. For example, the cytoskeleton contains not only the epithelial type of intermediate filament, keratin, but also vimentin, which is the intermediate filament form typical of mesenchymal cells [24]. Furthermore, OSE and the extraovarian peritoneum (EP) have the capacity to secrete the stromal collagens type I and type III [24].

Although the OSE and the EP are contiguous, have many common features, and are both embryologically derived from the coelomic epithelium, they differ in adult women phenotypically and give rise to different malignancies. These phenotypic differences, some of which may predispose the OSE to cancer, must arise during embryonic development as a result of tightly regulated inductive events. The exact nature of such developmental events is poorly understood, but it is likely that the differentiation of the fetal OSE is influenced by exposure to local factors that are produced by the adjacent developing ovary. Some molecular mechanisms that may be involved in these interactions are discussed in a previous section of this chapter.

In the adult, two major factors differentially influence OSE and EP as a consequence of their anatomic locations: First, the OSE but not EP is exposed to monthly ruptures at the sites of ovulation, followed by wound repair. Currently, the most popular hypothesis to explain the propensity of the OSE to undergo neoplastic progression is that the cell proliferation which is part of the postovulatory repair process provides an opportunity for the accumulation of mutations that may contribute to the carcinogenic process [25]. Second, the OSE is located near the source of ovarian hormones and growth factors and is exposed to some of them cyclically at high concentrations. OSE cells have receptors for estrogens, androgens, progestins, and gonadotropin-releasing hormone (Gn-RH) I and II and for several growth factors, all of which are produced by the ovary (see other chapters in this book). The effects of these agents on OSE physiology and pathology are only incompletely defined, and there are conflicting reports about the responsiveness of the OSE in terms of growth regulation [26, 27]; however, ovarian hormones and growth factors undoubtedly modulate the OSE phenotype, whereas the EP is differently or not at all affected by these agents.

The following are examples of differences between normal adult OSE and EP and their implications:

- OSE, but not EP, in adult women has the peculiar property of being so loosely attached to underlying structures that it is easily removed from the ovarian surface by wiping or handling the ovary. Furthermore, it is separated from the ovarian stroma, and thus from the circulation, by a substantial collagen layer, the tunica albuginea. These features strongly suggest that the access to local and systemic regulatory factors and metabolic exchanges by OSE is reduced compared to EP, and also compared to other parts of the ovary. Recently, there has been increasing interest in the influence of hypoxia on cellular metabolism and signal transduction [28, 29]. The likelihood that OSE on the ovarian surface exists in a hypoxic, acidic, and metabolically deficient environment is particularly interesting for two reasons: (1) because it suggests that these cells may normally be adapted to conditions that invasive and metastatic tumor cells often find themselves in; and (2) because when OSE cells form epithelial inclusion cysts within the ovarian cortex where access to local and systemic metabolites and regulatory factors is improved, they show an increased tendency for metaplastic and neoplastic changes.
- The profile of receptors to hormones and growth factors differs between OSE and EP. For example, the Met receptor for hepatocyte growth factor (HGF), which is a major regulator of growth and cell migration and is overexpressed in ovarian cancer [4, 30, 31], is present in normal OSE but not in EP; furthermore, follicle-stimulating hormone (FSH) and human chorionic gonadotropin (hCG)/luteinizing hormone (LH) are mitogens for OSE [32–36], but receptors for these hormones in EP have not been demonstrated.
- The ovarian tumor- and differentiation-marker CA125 [37] is secreted by EP and also by the epithelia of the oviduct, endometrium, and other derivatives of the coelomic epithelium, but not by OSE. This difference in the adult is evidence of divergent differentiation between OSE and EP [21] during development and may indicate that the part of the coelomic epithelium that gives rise to the OSE does not reach the stage of differentation where CA125 is expressed in other coelomic epithelial derivatives. Such an interpretation is in keeping with the idea that adult OSE is less mature and less committed to a mesothelial phenotype than the EP.
- The growth potential of OSE is greater than that of EP. For example, in our laboratory, under identical culture conditions, freshly explanted adult human OSE will undergo 12 to 18 population doublings, whereas EP cells senesce after only 4 to 8 population doublings.
- In contrast to adult EP, which is committed to the mesothelial phenotype and forms mesotheliomas when undergoing malignant transformation, normal adult OSE remains pleuripotential, as shown by its capacity for Müllerian (oviductal, endometrial, and endocervical) epithelial differentiation in the course of neoplastic progression and inclusion cyst formation [38].

The lack of CA125 expression, the greater growth potential, and the pleuripotential nature of OSE are all in keeping with the concept that OSE is developmentally less mature than peritoneum in other sites and that its development is arrested at a progenitor stage. Many investigators have suggested that this is a major factor that renders OSE more prone to neoplastic transformation.

Endocrine Differentiation

The OSE secretes and has receptors for ovarian and extraovarian hormones, growth factors, and cytokines with growth- and differentiation regulatory capabilities [36, 39–44). Although the secretion of, and responsiveness to, these different agents are normal OSE functions, their recruitment into autocrine loops appears to contribute to neoplastic progression [45–48]. Human OSE cells have receptors for FSH [32], which supports the hypothesis that the high FSH levels in peri- and postmenopausal women may play a promoting role in ovarian carcinogenesis [49]. hCG, which is secreted by normal and neoplastic human OSE [33], and LH stimulate the proliferation of human and rabbit OSE, indicating that these cells express LH receptors [34–36] and that their regulation may be in part autocrine. Receptors for estrogen, progesterone, androgens, and corticosteroids are found at the mRNA and/or protein level in human OSE [27, 50]. Reports of direct effects of some of these steroids on OSE proliferation have been controversial [26, 27, 51, 52], but there is evidence for indirect actions: for example, estrogen reduces the expression of the receptor for Gn-RH in OSE and modulates levels of HGF and epidermal growth factor (EGF), both of which are mitogens for OSE [53, 54]. Reports of corticosteroid effects on OSE proliferation are controversial, but combinations of EGF and hydrocortisone are among the most potent mitogens for cultured human OSE [44, 52, 55].

Growth factors, many of which are synthesized within the ovarian stroma or follicles, affect ovarian tissues including OSE directly and indirectly. EGF inhibits FSH effects and induction of LH receptors [56], inhibits estrogen production [57] and theca differentiation [58], and stimulates progestin biosynthesis [59]. Factors that stimulate OSE growth directly through mesenchymal-epithelial interactions include HGF [60], basic fibroblast growth factor (bFGF) [61], platelet-derived growth factor (PDGF) [62], tumor necrosis factor-α (TNF-α) [63–65], and keratinocyte growth factor (KGF) [66].

HGF action on human OSE has been studied in detail and illustrates the complex influence of growth factors on derivatives of the coelomic epithelium. In general, HGF is produced primarily by mesenchymal and stromal cells and acts on epithelial cells through its receptor tyrosine kinase encoded by the *c-met* protooncogene. It stimulates growth, motility, scattering, and morphogenesis of many epithelia [67]. In the adult ovary, Met is expressed by the OSE and granulosa cells, while the stroma and theca cells produce HGF [68]. The Müllerian duct–derived epithelia and renal epithelium also express Met [31, 69]. In contrast, extraovarian mesothelial cells lack HGF and Met [67, 70], suggesting that expression of the Met receptor is a feature specifically characteristic of coelomic epithelial derivatives in the urogenital ridge region. The physiologic influence of HGF on OSE may also depend on basement membrane components. For example, HGF induces apoptosis of rat OSE cells if they are cultured on plastic but is mitogenic when these cells grow on a fibronectin-like extracellular matrix [71, 72]. Although the responsiveness to growth factors and hormones by OSE differs among species [73], similar modulations may regulate the contributions of OSE to follicular rupture before ovulation and to postovulatory repair. HGF also affects, and is affected by, the action of various hormones [54, 72, 74].

Several agents inhibit OSE growth, including Gn-RH, which is an autocrine growth inhibitor for normal OSE [42], and several members of the TGF-β family of growth factors [75–77]. Interestingly, 5α-dihydrotestosterone downregulates the expression of mRNA for the TGF-β receptors I and II in ovarian carcinoma lines [78], suggesting that it might also counteract growth inhibition of OSE by TGF-β.

The Multipotential Nature of Ovarian Surface Epithelium

The adult human OSE retains the potential to differentiate along several pathways. These include conversion to mesenchymal (stromal) phenotypes under physiologic conditions, and the assumption of characteristics of the Müllerian duct–derived oviductal, endometrial, and endocervical epithelia, which are closely related to OSE developmentally, in metaplasia, and in the course of neoplastic progression.

Epithelio-Mesenchymal Transition

After ovulation ruptures the ovarian surface, OSE cells adjacent to the ovulatory defect flatten, assume mesenchymal shapes, and become migratory, but retain some epithelial characteristics, such as polarization and intercellular contact [2, 3]. They also remain epithelial on fibrin clots, which they encounter in the process of repair [79]. In contrast, preliminary evidence suggests that OSE cells can assume mesenchymal characteristics if they are dispersed within the ovarian cortex: sections through newly formed corpora lutea in postovulatory human ovaries have revealed fibroblast-like cells that contain keratin, identifying them as OSE [4].

When explanted into culture, OSE cells at first form keratin-positive epithelial monolayers, but concurrently initiate synthesis of the stromal collagen type III [80]. Subsequently, they modulate to more mesenchymal phenotypes, which are characterized by anterior-posterior polarity, reduced intercellular cohesion, gel contraction, secretion of collagen types I and III, and loss of epithelial markers (Figure 35.4) [4]. Epithelio-mesenchymal transition (EMT) in response to the culture environment also occurs in other mesodermally derived epithelia (e.g., kidney epithelium and endothelial cells). In general, cells respond to explantation into culture as they would to wounding. In analogy, the response of OSE to culture may mimic its response *in vivo* to ovulatory rupture and other forms of injury.

EMT by cultured OSE does not take place in every case, suggesting that this process requires undefined factors in the culture environment that are not always present. They might depend on the physiologic state and composition of the original ovarian biopsy specimen. We and others have found that several factors that are present in or near the corpus luteum near the time of ovulation cause morphologic EMT of OSE cells in culture (see Figure 35.4) [61]. These include the growth factors EGF/TGF-α, bFGF, PDGF [2, 3, 52, 62], and ascorbate [81, 82]. EGF and PDGF are not present in large amounts in plasma [83], but they are released from platelets during the clotting process. Therefore, high levels of EGF and PDGF are present at ovulation because of the hemorrhage that occurs during follicular rupture [84].

In addition, TGF-α, which binds to the EGF receptor, is found in high concentrations in follicular fluid [85]. The resulting localized stimulation of OSE by these growth factors likely contributes to its rapid postovulatory proliferation, but perhaps also to EMT of OSE cells trapped within the ruptured follicle. bFGF is a multifunctional growth factor found in, among other tissues, endothelial, granulosa, and luteal cells. It is angiogenic, modifies extracellular matrix, delays senescence, maintains differentiation and viability, and enhances motility in a variety of cells [61, 86]. In culture, bFGF is a mitogen for many types of mesoderm-derived cells, including OSE, and causes morphologic EMT of OSE cells [87]. Ascorbate is present in very high concentrations in ovarian luteal cells and follicular fluid [81, 82]. It also induces morphologic EMT in

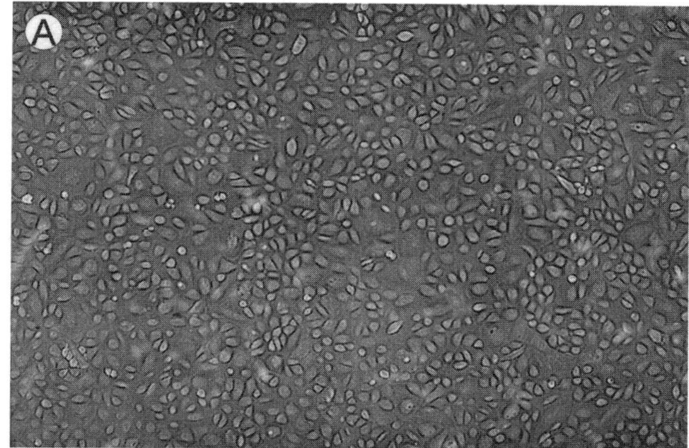

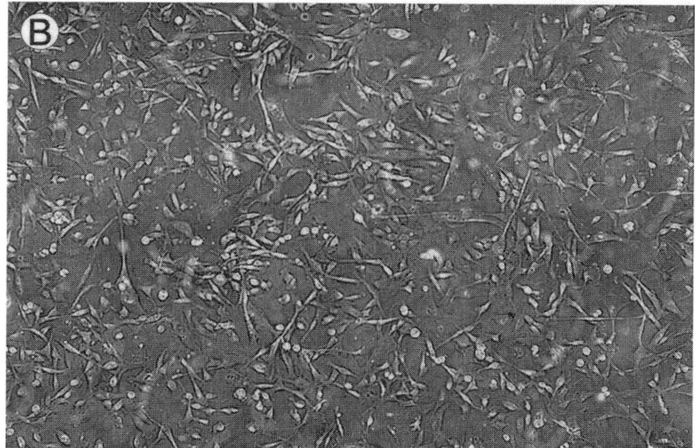

FIGURE 35.4 Epithelio-mesenchymal transition (EMT) of cultured ovarian surface epithelium. **A**, Culture in passage 3, maintained in medium 199/105 with 10% fetal bovine serum. The cells form compact, epithelial monolayers. **B**, Cells derived from the same culture as those in **A**, after growth with 10 ng/mL of epidermal growth factor and 1 μg/mL of hydrocortisone for 12 days (passage 4). The OSE cells have undergone EMT as indicated by fibroblast-like shapes and growth pattern. Such cells are initially keratin-positive but tend to lose keratin with time and passages in culture [52, 80]. Phase microscopy ×80.

cultured OSE. Among its many functions, ascorbate plays a prominent supportive role in the synthesis and secretion of collagens and, therefore, likely contributes to the production of stromal collagen by OSE undergoing EMT. The collagenous extracellular matrix, in turn, would be expected to influence cellular functions via integrins. HGF is produced *in vivo* by the ovarian stroma and may function as a paracrine mitogen and survival factor for OSE. HGF is a potent mitogen for cultured OSE, but in contrast to its effect on many other epithelia, it causes neither scattering nor EMT of OSE [47].

We recently proposed the hypothesis that EMT may serve as a homeostatic mechanism to accomodate OSE that has been displaced from the ovarian surface into the ovarian cortex (see Figure 3 in reference [4]). Fragments of OSE may be trapped in the ovarian cortex by two mechanisms: (1) at the time of ovulation, as a result of rupture and repair of the ovarian surface, or (2) as a result of conformational changes of the ovary, which lead to entrapment of the OSE within invaginations (clefts) that can become separated from the surface. If such trapped OSE cells survive within the stroma, they may undergo EMT as a form of homeostasis, which leads to their integration into the ovarian connective tissues as normal, functional stromal cells. Alternatively, they may fail to undergo EMT, in which case they would remain epithelial and form epithelial inclusion cysts. OSE lining inclusion cysts and clefts is prone to metaplasia and to neoplastic transformation, as indicated by the high proportion of early (pre)neoplastic lesions that arise in inclusion cysts and by the increased number of inclusion cysts in ovaries of women who are prone to develop ovarian cancer [88–90]. Importantly, the capacity of OSE to undergo EMT is greatly reduced with malignant progression and, to a lesser degree, in women with a genetic predisposition to develop ovarian cancer [24, 91]. It would, therefore, seem of great importance to define the mechanisms that lead to EMT by OSE cells and the reasons for their failure to do so.

MÜLLERIAN DIFFERENTIATION

On the ovarian surface, OSE normally exists as a simple nonproliferative mesothelium, where the cells undergo reversible shape changes to accomodate alterations in the contours of the ovary and bursts of localized proliferation to repair ovulatory damage. In contrast, OSE that is physically removed from the ovarian surface but retains its epithelial phenotype as the lining of inclusion cysts and surface clefts (invaginations) frequently undergoes metaplastic changes, which are most commonly of a tubal (oviductal) type. Early neoplastic changes with the potential to progress to carcinomas also appear preferentially in epithelial inclusion cysts. The basis for the propensity of OSE to undergo such changes when removed from the ovarian surface is unknown, but it is tempting to speculate that this propensity is related to the improved blood supply and exposure to paracrine stromal influences within the ovarian cortex.

An unusual aspect of epithelial ovarian carcinogenesis are the changes in differentiation that accompany neoplastic progression. Whereas normal OSE is a simple epithelium with some stromal features, it acquires characteristics of the Müllerian duct–derived (oviductal, endometrial, and endocervical) epithelia in the course of tumorigenesis (Figure 35.5). Like these epithelia, differentiated ovarian carcinomas lack the stromal markers of normal OSE and are more highly differentiated, as shown, for example, by high-molecular-weight keratins, mucus, cilia, and the formation of glands and papillae. Thus, in contrast to other epithelia where neoplastic progression

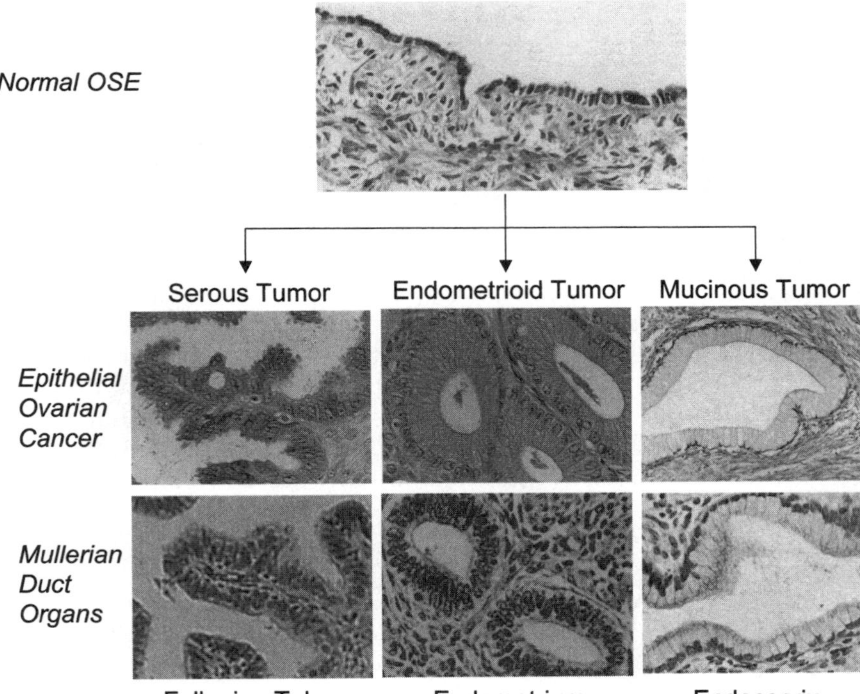

FIGURE 35.5 Histologic appearance of normal ovarian surface epithelium (OSE), epithelial ovarian carcinomas derived from OSE, and normal epithelia derived from the Müllerian ducts. OSE is a simple mesothelium overlying the ovary. With neoplastic transformation, it frequently assumes the complex epithelial characteristics of either the fallopian tube, endometrium, or endocervix. The resulting carcinomas are classified as serous, endometrioid, and mucous, respectively. Note the resemblance of the carcinomas to the normal Müllerian duct–derived tissues and their complex architecture compared to OSE. Hematoxylin and Eosin ×200.

results in loss of differentation, OSE progresses to a more highly differentiated phenotype, which is lost again only in late stages [4, 38]. Furthermore, neoplastic OSE cells become firmly committed to such epithelial phenotypes and less responsive to signals that induce EMT. Inappropriate expression of Müllerian differentiation by OSE in the course of neoplastic progression occurs so frequently and consistently as to suggest that it may confer a selective advantage on the transforming cells, perhaps in the form of altered responses to their environment.

CONCLUSION

The adult OSE represents a relatively uncommitted epithelium with the capacity to alter its state of differentiation. It appears to have retained the pleuripotential nature of its mesodermal embryonic precursor, the coelomic epithelium. The pleuripotential nature of OSE is reflected in culture by the exquisite plasticity of the OSE phenotype, which modulates in response to environmental variables that include hormones, growth factors, and extracellular matrix. There is only limited information about the relationship of these modulations to physiologic or pathologic events *in vivo.* Preliminary data suggest that epithelio-mesenchymal transition may be a means of maintaining homeostasis of OSE that is displaced into the ovarian cortex, whereas a loss of the capacity to undergo this conversion may contribute to the development of pathologic changes.

Under pathologic conditions, and in particular with metaplasia or neoplastic progression, the OSE undergoes Müllerian differentiation, which leads to increasingly stable and complex epithelial characteristics resembling the Müllerian duct–derived epithelia. Thus the close developmental relationship between the Müllerian epithelia and OSE is an important aspect of ovarian carcinogenesis. During development, various transcriptional factors present at specific times, and specific cell types appear to regulate the divergence in differentiation of the coelomic epithelial cells in the urogenital region into either OSE or Müllerian ducts. It is tempting to speculate that the factors involved in the induction of coelomic epithelial differentiation may also be involved in ovarian neoplastic progression. Understanding the embryologic development of OSE may provide us with clues about the etiology of epithelial ovarian cancers.

ACKNOWLEDGMENTS

Part of this work was supported by grants to N.A. from the National Cancer Institute of Canada through the Canadian Cancer Society and from the B.C. Foundation for Non-

Animal Research. M.M.M. Woo is the recipient of a studentship from the B.C. Research Institute.

References

1. Bast, R. C., Xu, F., Yu, Y., Fang, X. J., Wiener, J., and Mills, G. B. (1998). Overview: The molecular biology of ovarian cancer. In *Ovarian Cancer 5*, eds. F. Sharp, T. Backett, J. Berek, and R. Bast, 87–97. Oxford, United Kingdom: Isis Medical Media Publishers.
2. Nicosia, S. V., Saunders, B. O., Acevedo-Duncan, M. E., Setrakian, S., and Degregorio, R. (1991). Biopathology of ovarian mesothelium. In *Ultrastructure of the Ovary*, eds. G. Familiari, S. Makabe, and P. M. Motta, 287–310. Boston, MA: Kluwer Academic Publishers.
3. Nicosia, S. V., Ku, N. K., Oliveros-Saunders, B., Giacomini, G., Pierro, E., Mayer, J., and Nicosia, R. F. (1997). Ovarian mesothelium (surface epithelium) in normal, pathological and experimental conditions. In *Recent Advances in Microscopy of Cells, Tissues, and Organs*, ed. P. M. Motta, 509–517. Rome, Italy: Antonio Delfino Editore.
4. Auersperg, N., Wong, A. S., Choi, K. C., Kang, S. K., and Leung, P. C. (2001). Ovarian surface epithelium: Biology, endocrinology, and pathology. *Endocr. Rev.* 22, 255–288.
5. Moore, K. L., and Persaud, T. V. N. (1998). *The Developing Human. Clinically Oriented Embryology.* Philadelphia, PA: W.B. Saunders Company.
6. Dye, F. J. (2000). *Human Life Before Birth.* Amsterdam, Netherlands: Harwood Academic Publishers.
7. Byskov, A. G. (1986). Differentiation of mammalian embryonic gonad. *Physiol. Rev.* 66, 71–117.
8. Ikeda, Y., Shen, W. H., Ingraham, H. A., and Parker, K. L. (1994). Developmental expression of mouse steroidogenic factor-1, an essential regulator of the steroid hydroxylases. *Mol. Endocrinol.* 8, 654–662.
9. Crawford, P. A., Sadovsky, Y., and Milbrandt, J. (1997). Nuclear receptor steroidogenic factor 1 directs embryonic stem cells toward the steroidogenic lineage. *Mol. Cell. Biol.* 17, 3997–4006.
10. Parker, K. L., and Schimmer, B. P. (1997). Steroidogenic factor 1: A key determinant of endocrine development and function. *Endocr. Rev.*18, 361–377.
11. Kreidberg, J. A., Sariola, H., Loring, J. M., Maeda, M., Pelletier, J., Housman, D., and Jaenisch, R. (1993). WT-1 is required for early kidney development. *Cell* 74, 679–691.
12. Pritchard-Jones, K., Fleming, S., Davidson, D., Bickmore, W., Porteous, D., Gosden, C., Bard, J., Buckler, A., Pelletier, J., Housman, D., van Heyningen, V., and Hastie, N. (1990). The candidate Wilms' tumour gene is involved in genitourinary development. *Nature* 346, 194–197.
13. Vainio, S., Heikkila, M., Kispert, A., Chin, N., and McMahon, A. P. (1999). Female development in mammals is regulated by Wnt-4 signalling. *Nature* 397, 405–409.
14. Miller, C., Pavlova, A., and Sassoon, D. A. (1998). Differential expression patterns of Wnt genes in the murine female reproductive tract during development and the estrous cycle. *Mech. Dev.* 76, 91–99.
15. Sinclair, A. H. (1998). Human sex determination. *J. Exp. Zool.* 281, 501–505.
16. Morais da Silva, S., Hacker, A., Harley, V., Goodfellow, P., Swain, A., and Lovell-Badge, R. (1996). Sox9 expression during gonadal development implies a conserved role for the gene in testis differentiation in mammals and birds. *Nat. Genet.* 14, 62–68.
17. Pelliniemi, L. J., Frojdman, K., Sundstrom, J., Pollanen, P., and Kuopio, T. (1998). Cellular and molecular changes during sex differentiation of embryonic mammalian gonads. *J. Exp. Zool.* 281, 482–493.
18. Birk, O. S., Casiano, D. E., Wassif, C. A., Cogliati, T., Zhao, L., Zhao, Y., Grinberg, A., Huang, S., Kreidberg, J. A., Parker, K. L., Porter, F. D., and Westphal, H. (2000). The LIM homeobox gene Lhx9 is essential for mouse gonad formation. *Nature* 403, 909–913.
19. Oreal, E., Mazaud, S., Picard, J. Y., Magre, S., and Carre-Eusebe, D. (2002). Different patterns of anti-Mullerian hormone expression, as related to DMRT1, SF-1, WT1, GATA-4, Wnt-4, and Lhx9 expression, in the chick differentiating gonads. *Dev. Dyn.* 225, 221–232.
20. Parr, B. A., and McMahon, A. P. (1998). Sexually dimorphic development of the mammalian reproductive tract requires Wnt-7a. *Nature* 395, 707–710.
21. Kabawat, S. E., Bast Jr., R. C., Bhan, A. K., Welch, W. R., Knapp, R. C., and Colvin, R. B. (1983). Tissue distribution of a coelomic-epithelium-related antigen recognized by the monoclonal antibody OC125. *Int. J. Gynecol. Pathol.* 2, 275–285.
22. Gondos, B. (1975). Surface epithelium of the developing ovary. Possible correlation with ovarian neoplasia. *Am. J. Pathol.* 81, 303–321.
23. Pan, J., Roskelley, C. D., Luu-The, V., Rojiani, M., and Auersperg, N. (1992). Reversal of divergent differentiation by ras oncogene-mediated transformation. *Cancer Res.* 52, 4269–4272.
24. Auersperg, N., Maines-Bandiera, S. L., Dyck, H. G., and Kruk, P. A. (1994). Characterization of cultured human ovarian surface epithelial cells: Phenotypic plasticity and premalignant changes. *Lab. Invest.* 71, 510–518.
25. Auersperg, N., Edelson, M. I., Mok, S. C., Johnson, S. W., and Hamilton, T. C. (1998). The biology of ovarian cancer. *Semin. Oncol.* 25, 281–304.
26. Syed, V., Ulinski, G., Mok, S. C., Yiu, G. K., and Ho, S. M. (2001). Expression of gonadotropin receptor and growth responses to key reproductive hormones in normal and malignant human ovarian surface epithelial cells. *Cancer Res.* 61, 6768–6776.
27. Karlan, B. Y., Jones, J., Greenwald, M., and Lagasse, L. D. (1995). Steroid hormone effects on the proliferation of human ovarian surface epithelium in vitro. *Am. J. Obstet. Gynecol.* 173, 97–104.
28. Blaschke, F., Stawowy, P., Goetze, S., Hintz, O., Grafe, M., Kintscher, U., Fleck, E., and Graf, K. (2002). Hypoxia activates beta(1)-integrin via ERK 1/2 and p38 MAP kinase in human vascular smooth muscle cells. *Biochem. Biophys. Res. Commun.* 296, 890–896.
29. Nishi, H., Nishi, K. H., and Johnson, A. C. (2002). Early Growth Response-1 gene mediates up-regulation of epidermal growth factor receptor expression during hypoxia. *Cancer Res.* 62, 827–834.
30. Di Renzo, M. F., Narsimhan, R. P., Olivero, M., Bretti, S., Giordano, S., Medico, E., Gaglia, P., Zara, P., and Comoglio, P. M.

(1991). Expression of the Met/HGF receptor in normal and neoplastic human tissues. *Oncogene* 6, 1997–2003.

31. Huntsman, D., Resau, J. H., Klineberg, E., and Auersperg, N. (1999). Comparison of c-met expression in ovarian epithelial tumors and normal epithelia of the female reproductive tract by quantitative laser scan microscopy. *Am. J. Pathol.* 155, 343–348.
32. Zheng, W., Magid, M. S., Kramer, E. E., and Chen, Y. T. (1996). Follicle-stimulating hormone receptor is expressed in human ovarian surface epithelium and fallopian tube. *Am. J. Pathol.* 148, 47–53.
33. Blaustein, A., Kaganowicz, A., and Wells, J. (1982). Tumor markers in inclusion cysts of the ovary. *Cancer* 49, 722–726.
34. Osterholzer, H. O., Streibel, E. J., and Nicosia, S. V. (1985). Growth effects of protein hormones on cultured rabbit ovarian surface epithelial cells. *Biol. Reprod.* 33, 247–258.
35. Elliott, W. M., and Auersperg, N. (1993). Growth of normal human ovarian surface epithelial cells in reduced- serum and serum-free media. *In Vitro Cell Dev. Biol.* 29A, 9–18.
36. Parrott, J. A., Doraiswamy, V., Kim, G., Mosher, R., and Skinner, M. K. (2001). Expression and actions of both the follicle stimulating hormone receptor and the luteinizing hormone receptor in normal ovarian surface epithelium and ovarian cancer. *Mol. Cell. Endocrinol.* 172, 213–222.
37. Bast Jr., R. C., Xu, F. J., Yu, Y. H., Barnhill, S., Zhang, Z., and Mills, G. B. (1998). CA 125: The past and the future. *Int. J. Biol. Markers* 13, 179–187.
38. Young, R. H., Clement, P. B., and Scully, R. E. (1989). The ovary. In *Diagnosis in Surgical Pathology*, ed. S.S. Sternberg, 1655–1734. New York: Raven Press.
39. Choi, K. C., Auersperg, N., and Leung, P. C. (2001). Expression and antiproliferative effect of a second form of gonadotropin-releasing hormone in normal and neoplastic ovarian surface epithelial cells. *J. Clin. Endocrinol. Metab.* 86, 5075–5078.
40. Choi, K. C., Kang, S. K., Nathwani, P. S., Cheng, K. W., Auersperg, N., and Leung, P. C. (2001). Differential expression of activin/inhibin subunit and activin receptor mRNAs in normal and neoplastic ovarian surface epithelium (OSE). *Mol. Cell. Endocrinol.* 174, 99–110.
41. Johnson, G. R., Saeki, T., Auersperg, N., Gordon, A. W., Shoyab, M., Salomon, D. S., and Stromberg, K. (1991). Response to and expression of amphiregulin by ovarian carcinoma and normal ovarian surface epithelial cells: Nuclear localization of endogenous amphiregulin. *Biochem. Biophys. Res. Commun.* 180, 481–488.
42. Kang, S. K., Choi, K. C., Cheng, K. W., Nathwani, P. S., Auersperg, N., and Leung, P. C. (2000). Role of gonadotropin-releasing hormone as an autocrine growth factor in human ovarian surface epithelium. *Endocrinology* 141, 72–80.
43. Kohler, M., Bauknecht, T., Grimm, M., Birmelin, G., Kommoss, F., and Wagner, E. (1992). Epidermal growth factor receptor and transforming growth factor alpha expression in human ovarian carcinomas. *Eur. J. Cancer* 28A, 1432–1437.
44. Rodriguez, G. C., Berchuck, A., Whitaker, R. S., Schlossman, D., Clarke-Pearson, D. L., and Bast Jr., R. C. (1991). Epidermal growth factor receptor expression in normal ovarian epithelium and ovarian cancer. II. Relationship between receptor expression and response to epidermal growth factor. *Am. J. Obstet. Gynecol.* 164, 745–750.
45. Berchuck, A., Rodriguez, G. C., Kamel, A., Dodge, R. K., Soper, J. T., Clarke-Pearson, D. L., and Bast Jr., R. C. (1991). Epidermal growth factor receptor expression in normal ovarian epithelium and ovarian cancer. I. Correlation of receptor expression with prognostic factors in patients with ovarian cancer. *Am. J. Obstet. Gynecol.* 164, 669–674.
46. Kacinski, B. M., Carter, D., Mittal, K., Yee, L. D., Scata, K. A., Donofrio, L., Chambers, S. K., Wang, K. I., Yang-Feng, T., and Rohrschneider, L. R.(1990). Ovarian adenocarcinomas express fms-complementary transcripts and fms antigen, often with coexpression of CSF-1. *Am. J. Pathol.* 137, 135–147.
47. Wong, A. S., Pelech, S. L., Woo, M. M., Yim, G., Rosen, B., Ehlen, T., Leung, P. C., and Auersperg, N. (2001). Coexpression of hepatocyte growth factor-Met: An early step in ovarian carcinogenesis? *Oncogene* 20, 1318–1328.
48. Ziltener, H. J., Maines-Bandiera, S., Schrader, J. W., and Auersperg, N. (1993) Secretion of bioactive interleukin-1, interleukin-6, and colony- stimulating factors by human ovarian surface epithelium. *Biol. Reprod.* 49, 635–641.
49. te Velde, E. R., Scheffer, G. J., Dorland, M., Broekmans, F. J., and Fauser, B. C. (1998). Developmental and endocrine aspects of normal ovarian aging. *Mol. Cell. Endocrinol.* 145, 67–73.
50. Lau, K. M., Mok, S. C., and Ho, S. M. (1999). Expression of human estrogen receptor-alpha and -beta, progesterone receptor, and androgen receptor mRNA in normal and malignant ovarian epithelial cells. *Proc. Natl. Acad. Sci. USA* 96, 5722–5727.
51. Ivarsson, K., Sundfeldt, K., Brännström, M., and Janson, P. O. (2001). Production of steroids by human ovarian surface epithelial cells in culture: Possible role of progesterone as growth inhibitor. *Gynecol. Oncol.* 82, 116–121.
52. Siemens, C. H., and Auersperg, N. (1988) Serial propagation of human ovarian surface epithelium in tissue culture. *J. Cell. Physiol.* 134, 347–356.
53. Kang, S. K., Choi, K. C., Tai, C. J., Auersperg, N., and Leung, P. C. (2001). Estradiol regulates gonadotropin-releasing hormone (GnRH) and its receptor gene expression and antagonizes the growth inhibitory effects of GnRH in human ovarian surface epithelial and ovarian cancer cells. *Endocrinology* 142, 580–588.
54. Liu, Y., Lin, L., and Zarnegar, R. (1994). Modulation of hepatocyte growth factor gene expression by estrogen in mouse ovary. *Mol. Cell. Endocrinol.* 104, 173–181.
55. Berchuck, A., Kohler, M. F., Boente, M. P., Rodriguez, G. C., Whitaker, R. S., and Bast Jr., R. C. (1993). Growth regulation and transformation of ovarian epithelium. *Cancer* 71, 545–551.
56. Mondschein, J. S., and Schomberg, D. W. (1981). Growth factors modulate gonadotropin receptor induction in granulosa cell cultures. *Science* 211, 1179–1180.
57. Hsueh, A. J., Welsh, T. H., and Jones, P. B. (1981). Inhibition of ovarian and testicular steroidogenesis by epidermal growth factor. *Endocrinology* 108, 2002–2004.
58. Erickson, G. F., and Case, E. (1983). Epidermal growth factor antagonizes ovarian theca-interstitial cytodifferentiation. *Mol. Cell. Endocrinol.* 31, 71–76.

59. Knecht, M., and Catt, K. J. (1983). Modulation of cAMP-mediated differentiation in ovarian granulosa cells by epidermal growth factor and platelet-derived growth factor. *J. Biol. Chem.* 258, 2789–2794.
60. Parrott, J. A., and Skinner, M. K. (2000). Expression and action of hepatocyte growth factor in human and bovine normal ovarian surface epithelium and ovarian cancer. *Biol. Reprod.* 62, 491–500.
61. Pierro, E., Nicosia, S. V., Saunders, B., Fultz, C. B., Nicosia, R. F., and Mancuso, S. (1996). Influence of growth factors on proliferation and morphogenesis of rabbit ovarian mesothelial cells in vitro. *Biol. Reprod.* 54, 660–669.
62. Dabrow, M. B., Francesco, M. R., McBrearty, F. X., and Caradonna, S. (1998). The effects of platelet-derived growth factor and receptor on normal and neoplastic human ovarian surface epithelium. *Gynecol. Oncol.* 71, 29–37.
63. Wu, S., Rodabaugh, K., Martinez-Maza, O., Watson, J. M., Silberstein, D. S., Boyer, C. M., Peters, W. P., Weinberg, J. B., Berek, J. S., and Bast Jr., R. C. (1992). Stimulation of ovarian tumor cell proliferation with monocyte products including interleukin-1, interleukin-6, and tumor necrosis factor-alpha. *Am. J. Obstet. Gynecol.* 166, 997–1007.
64. Wu, S., Boyer, C. M., Whitaker, R. S., Berchuck, A., Wiener, J. R., Weinberg, J. B., and Bast Jr., R. C. (1993). Tumor necrosis factor alpha as an autocrine and paracrine growth factor for ovarian cancer: monokine induction of tumor cell proliferation and tumor necrosis factor alpha expression. *Cancer Res.* 53, 1939–1944.
65. Marth, C., Zeimet, A. G., Herold, M., Brumm, C., Windbichler, G., Muller-Holzner, E., Offner, F., Feichtinger, H., Zwierzina, H., and Daxenbichler, G. (1996). Different effects of interferons, interleukin-1beta and tumor necrosis factor-alpha in normal (OSE) and malignant human ovarian epithelial cells. *Int. J. Cancer* 67, 826–830.
66. Parrott, J. A., Kim, G., Mosher, R., and Skinner, M. K. (2000). Expression and action of keratinocyte growth factor (KGF) in normal ovarian surface epithelium and ovarian cancer. *Mol. Cell. Endocrinol.* 167, 77–87.
67. To, C. T., and Tsao, M. S. (1998). The roles of hepatocyte growth factor/scatter factor and met receptor in human cancers (Review). *Oncol. Rep.* 5, 1013–1024.
68. Parrott, J. A., Vigne, J. L., Chu, B. Z., and Skinner, M. K. (1994). Mesenchymal-epithelial interactions in the ovarian follicle involve keratinocyte and hepatocyte growth factor production by thecal cells and their action on granulosa cells. *Endocrinology* 135, 569–575.
69. Matsumoto, K., and Nakamura, T. (2002) Renotropic role and therapeutic potential of HGF in the kidney. *Nephrol. Dial. Transplant* 17 (Suppl. 9), 59–61.
70. Klominek, J., Baskin, B., Liu, Z., and Hauzenberger, D. (1998). Hepatocyte growth factor/scatter factor stimulates chemotaxis and growth of malignant mesothelioma cells through c-met receptor. *Int. J. Cancer* 76, 240–249.
71. Gulati, R., and Peluso, J. J. (1997). Opposing actions of hepatocyte growth factor and basic fibroblast growth factor on cell contact, intracellular free calcium levels, and rat ovarian surface epithelial cell viability. *Endocrinology* 138, 1847–1856.
72. Hess, S., Gulati, R., and Peluso, J. J. (1999). Hepatocyte growth factor induces rat ovarian surface epithelial cell mitosis or apoptosis depending on the presence or absence of an extracellular matrix. *Endocrinology* 140, 2908–2916.
73. Auersperg, N., Ota, T., and Mitchell, G. W. (2002) Early events in ovarian epithelial carcinogenesis: progress and problems in experimental approaches. *Int. J. Gynecol. Cancer* 12, 691–703.
74. Negami, A. I., Sasaki, H., Kawakami, Y., Kamitani, N., Kotsuji, F., Tominaga, T., and Nakamura, T. (1995). Serum human hepatocyte growth factor in human menstrual cycle and pregnancy: A novel serum marker of regeneration and reconstruction of human endometrium. *Horm. Res.* 44 (Suppl. 2), 42–46.
75. Taipale, J., Saharinen, J., and Keski-Oja, J. (1998). Extracellular matrix-associated transforming growth factor-beta: Role in cancer cell growth and invasion. *Adv. Cancer Res.* 75, 87–134.
76. Berchuck, A., Rodriguez, G., Olt, G., Whitaker, R., Boente, M. P., Arrick, B. A., Clarke-Pearson, D. L., and Bast Jr., R. C. (1992). Regulation of growth of normal ovarian epithelial cells and ovarian cancer cell lines by transforming growth factor-beta. *Am. J. Obstet. Gynecol.* 166, 676–684.
77. Vigne, J. L., Halburnt, L. L., and Skinner, M. K. (1994). Characterization of bovine ovarian surface epithelium and stromal cells: Identification of secreted proteins. *Biol. Reprod.* 51, 1213–1221.
78. Evangelou, A., Jindal, S. K., Brown, T. J., and Letarte, M. (2000). Down-regulation of transforming growth factor beta receptors by androgen in ovarian cancer cells. *Cancer Res.* 60, 929–935.
79. Kruk, P. A., Uitto, V. J., Firth, J. D., Dedhar, S., and Auersperg, N. (1994). Reciprocal interactions between human ovarian surface epithelial cells and adjacent extracellular matrix. *Exp. Cell Res.* 215, 97–108.
80. Dyck, H. G., Hamilton, T. C., Godwin, A. K., Lynch, H. T., Maines-Bandiera, S., and Auersperg, N. (1996). Autonomy of the epithelial phenotype in human ovarian surface epithelium: Changes with neoplastic progression and with a family history of ovarian cancer. *Int. J. Cancer* 69, 429–436.
81. Kodaman, P. H., Aten, R. F., and Behrman, H. R. (1998). Accumulation of ascorbate by endocrine-regulated and glucose-sensitive transport of dehydroascorbic acid in luteinized rat ovarian cells. *Biol. Reprod.* 58, 407–413.
82. Cassano, E., Tosto, L., Balestrieri, M., Zicarelli, L., and Abrescia, P. (1999). Antioxidant defense in the follicular fluid of water buffalo. *Cell Physiol. Biochem.* 9, 106–116.
83. Oka, Y., and Orth, D. N. (1983). Human plasma epidermal growth factor/beta-urogastrone is associated with blood platelets. *J. Clin. Invest.* 72, 249–259.
84. Gillet, J. Y., Maillet, R., and Gautier, C. (1980). Blood supply and lymph supply of the ovary. In *Biology of the Ovary*, eds. P. M. Motta and E. S. E. Makabe, 86–98. Boston, MA: Martinus Nijhoff Publishers.
85. Reeka, N., Berg, F. D., and Brucker, C. (1998). Presence of transforming growth factor alpha and epidermal growth factor in human ovarian tissue and follicular fluid. *Hum. Reprod.* 13, 2199–2205.
86. Song, S., Wientjes, M. G., Gan, Y., and Au, J. L. (2000). Fibroblast growth factors: An epigenetic mechanism of broad spectrum resistance to anticancer drugs. *Proc. Natl. Acad. Sci. USA* 97, 8658–8563.

87. Salamanca, C., Hu, Y., Ota, T., and Auersperg, N. (2001). *Influence of Growth Factors on Human Ovarian Surface Epithelium.* Whistler, Canada: The 47th Annual Meeting, Canadian Fertility and Andrology Society.
88. Scully, R. E. (1995). Early de novo ovarian cancer and cancer developing in benign ovarian lesions. *Int. J. Gynaecol. Obstet.* 49 (Suppl.), S9–S15.
89. Scully, R. E. (1995). Pathology of ovarian cancer precursors. *J. Cell. Biochem. Suppl.* 23, 208–218.
90. Salazar, H., Godwin, A. K., Daly, M. B., Laub, P. B., Hogan, W. M., Rosenblum, N., Boente, M. P., Lynch, H. T., and Hamilton, T. C. (1996). Microscopic benign and invasive malignant neoplasms and a cancer-prone phenotype in prophylactic oophorectomies. *J. Natl. Cancer. Inst.* 88, 1810–1820.
91. Wong, A. S., Maines-Bandiera, S. L., Rosen, B., Wheelock, M. J., Johnson, K. R., Leung, P. C., Roskelley, C. D., and Auersperg, N. (1999). Constitutive and conditional cadherin expression in cultured human ovarian surface epithelium: influence of family history of ovarian cancer. *Int. J. Cancer* 81, 180–188.

CHAPTER **36**

Ovarian Carcinogenesis

BARBARA C. VANDERHYDEN, TANYA J. SHAW, KENNETH GARSON, AND ANGELA M. TONARY

ABSTRACT

Ovarian cancer is the fifth leading cause of all female cancer-related deaths in North America, and it is the most lethal of all gynecologic cancers. Most ovarian cancers arise from the surface epithelium, a single layer of cells that covers the surface of the ovary. These epithelial cells are thought to play a role in ovulation and are responsive to hormones, growth factors, and cytokines, but the cellular and molecular events associated with ovarian carcinogenesis are poorly understood. This chapter addresses the etiology of ovarian cancer, with particular emphasis on the wide range of factors that have been implicated in the initiation and/or progression of ovarian cancer. These factors include ovulation, gonadotropic and steroid hormones, germ-cell depletion, oncogenes and tumor suppressor genes, growth factors, cytokines, and environmental carcinogens. The ability to culture ovarian surface epithelial cells from a variety of species has lead to attempts to transform these cells *in vitro*, with some success. Ovarian cancer research is limited significantly by the lack of appropriate animal models. This chapter describes some of the experimental models, both *in vivo* and *in vitro*, that are being used to investigate the early events associated with neoplastic transformation of the ovarian surface epithelium.

INTRODUCTION

Ovarian cancer is the fifth leading cause of all female cancer-related deaths in the Western world, and it is the most prevalent and lethal of all gynecologic cancers. The disease carries a 1-in-70 lifetime risk for women in North America [1], and approximately 60% of the women who develop ovarian cancer will die from their disease. Despite improved knowledge of the etiology of the disease, aggressive cytoreductive surgery, and modern combination chemotherapy, mortality statistics have changed only slightly over the last 30 years. Lack of an adequate screening test for early disease detection, coupled with rapid progression to chemoresistance, has prevented appreciable improvements in the five-year survival rate of patients with ovarian cancer. Although ovarian cancer can arise from any of the cell types found in the ovary, including oocytes, granulosa cells, theca-interstitial cells, and surface epithelium, almost 90% are derived from the ovarian surface epithelium (OSE) [2]. Recent characterization and genetic manipulation of OSE cells have formed a patchy foundation for our current understanding of the neoplastic events involved in ovarian tumorigenesis. This chapter focuses on epithelial ovarian carcinogenesis, with particular emphasis on the cellular and molecular events that appear to contribute to the development of ovarian cancer, and the experimental models that will undoubtedly be helpful in defining these events both *in vitro* and *in vivo*.

THE OVARIAN SURFACE EPITHELIUM

The OSE covers the entire ovarian surface and varies morphologically from simple squamous to cuboidal to low pseudostratified columnar [3, 4]. Embryologically derived from the mesodermal epithelium of the gonadal ridges, OSE cells are continuous with the flattened mesothelium of the peritoneum [5] and are separated from the underlying stromal compartment of the ovary by a basement membrane and a dense collagenous connective tissue referred to as the tunica albuginea. OSE cells are joined laterally by desmosomes and gap and tight junctions [6, 7], and they have numerous apical microvilli and endocytic vesicles that allow for ready absorption of fluid and particulate matter [8]. They are loosely adherent to the basement membrane and can be removed easily by scraping or brushing the surface of the ovary [9, 10].

Immunohistochemical staining has shown that OSE cells express cytokeratin, desmoplakin, transforming growth factor-α (TGF-α), and receptors for estrogen, progesterone, and epidermal growth factor (EGF) [11–16]. Although epithelial in morphology in the resting ovary, human OSE cells exhibit several mesenchymal characteristics that reflect their mesodermal origin, including expression of the intermediate filament protein vimentin, stromal collagens, and matrix-degrading proteases. In the normal adult ovary, OSE cells can be distinguished from the extraovarian mesothelium by their differential expression of mucin, cilia, 17β-hydroxysteroid dehydrogenase, and several antigenic markers [4, 17–21]. One of these antigens, CA125, is a cell surface glycoprotein that is not expressed in OSE cells, but is normally expressed by oviductal, endometrial, and endocervical epithelia and peritoneal mesothelium. Ovarian epithelial carcinomas, however, express CA125 in sufficient levels that it is commonly used as a tumor marker for ovarian cancer [22, 23].

Despite their rather unremarkable appearance *in vivo*, it is believed that OSE cells actively participate in the ovulatory process. It has been suggested that OSE cells become activated upon contact with gonadotropin-stimulated preovulatory follicles, which triggers the release of proteolytic enzymes that degrade the tunica albuginea and the underlying apical follicular wall, weakening the ovarian surface to the point of rupture [24]. The OSE cells directly over the point of rupture undergo apoptotic cell death and are shed from the ovarian surface before ovulation [25]. The wound created at the ovarian surface is repaired by rapid proliferation of OSE cells from the perimeter of the ruptured follicle [26]. Furthermore, the OSE cells are capable of depositing and restructuring the extracellular matrix of the underlying tunica albuginea following ovulation [27, 28]. The squamous form of OSE cells may represent cells that have undergone postovulatory proliferation to repair the wound in the ovarian surface [29].

Although the ovarian surface is generally smooth in early reproductive life, with aging the ovary becomes more convoluted. Invaginations of the epithelium result in crypts or glands that can become pinched off to form epithelial inclusion cysts within the underlying stromal compartment (Figure 36.1; [30]). This may occur following the postovulatory proliferation of OSE, follicular attrition, and/or from inflammation caused by carcinogens or chemical irritants such as talcum powder [31]. These cysts are usually lined by a single layer of columnar epithelium and are most commonly located in the superficial ovarian cortex.

Although inclusion cysts can be found in ovaries from all age groups, including infants and adolescents [32, 33], their incidence increases with advancing age such that they are common in postmenopausal women. Although common and generally benign in nature, these epithelial rearrangements are widely thought to be the potential origin of many epithelial cancers. The more frequent appearance of epithelial invaginations and inclusion cysts in women with hereditary risk of ovarian cancer has strengthened this hypothesis. In addition, some microscopic borderline and malignant tumors have been observed to arise directly within these sites, and they are often associated with dysplasia in similar sites elsewhere in the same or contralateral ovary [34–36]. Tubal metaplasia of epithelial inclusion cysts in ovaries contralateral to those containing epithelial ovarian cancers is significantly more common than in control ovaries, suggesting that Müllerian differentiation may be an early step in tumorigenesis [35, 37, 38].

ETIOLOGY OF EPITHELIAL OVARIAN CANCER

There is evidence that epithelial ovarian cancer arises by clonal expansion from a single transformed progenitor cell [39, 40]. Unlike other cancers, however, the series of events involved in the initiation, progression, and metastasis of ovarian cancer is not yet established. It is not clear if malignancies arise from benign or borderline tumors or if they develop *de novo* from the surface epithelium or inclusion cysts, as there is evidence for both [41]. The incidence of

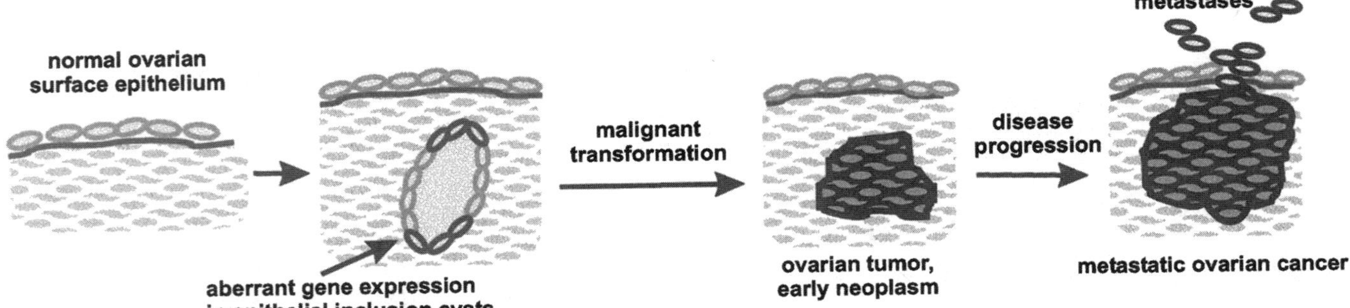

FIGURE 36.1 Model for ovarian tumorigenesis. Ovarian surface epithelium (OSE) cells form a single layer of simple epithelium attached to a basement membrane on the surface of the ovary. Following ovulation, the wound on the ovarian surface is repaired by the proliferation of these cells. The healing process can lead to the formation of crypts or OSE-lined structures enclosed in the stromal compartment. Expression of a number of genes is induced in epithelial invaginations and in inclusion cysts, rendering these structures more epithelial in character and potentially more susceptible to neoplastic transformation. Under conditions that are not yet defined, these structures can lead to tumor development. Although the diagram portrays a progression to metastatic disease, it is equally possible that more aggressive malignancies arise independently.

ovarian cancer climbs dramatically in women around the age at which they reach menopause. The reason for this timing is not clear, but there are at least three distinct differences between pre- and postmenopausal women that result from changes in the ovary: (1) the depletion of oocytes or germ cells, which is the underlying cause of menopause; (2) a reduction in circulating estrogen levels that results from the loss of follicle development; and (3) a significant increase in the pituitary's production of the gonadotropic hormones, follicle-stimulating hormone (FSH) and luteinizing hormone (LH), which arises as a consequence of the reduced estrogen levels. In addition to the loss of germ cells and the associated alterations in hormone levels, which normally occur at menopause, several nonmenopausal factors have been shown to have physiologic relevance in epithelial ovarian tumorigenesis, including ovulation, growth factors and cytokines, and environmental carcinogens. Each of these factors is discussed in the context of its potential role in the initiation and/or progression of ovarian cancer.

Ovulation

The "incessant ovulation hypothesis" proposes that continuous ovulation, with its successive rounds of surface rupture and OSE cell mitosis to repair the wound, renders the cells susceptible to malignant transformation [42]. Anecdotal support for this hypothesis comes from the observation that intensive egg-laying domestic hens frequently develop peritoneal carcinomata that is presumably of ovarian origin [43]. Epidemiologic studies indicate that circumstances that decrease the number of ovulations (i.e., pregnancy, oral contraceptive usage, duration of lactation, and early menopause) all substantially reduce the risk of ovarian cancer [44, 45]. Furthermore, although still controversial, some investigators have found an increased risk of developing ovarian cancer among women treated with ovulation-inducing drugs in assisted reproduction programs [reviewed in 46].

Inherent in the incessant ovulation hypothesis for ovarian cancer risk is the premise that repetitive damage of the OSE at ovulation and/or the subsequent mitotic repair (wound repair) following ovulation increases the risk of developing ovarian cancer. Ovulation-induced DNA damage in ovarian surface epithelial cells at the periphery of the ovulatory site has been reported in sheep [47]. Experimental evidence to support the susceptibility of OSE cells to mutagenic events during mitosis is provided by studies showing that primary cultures of normal rat and mouse OSE cells, which have been repeatedly subcultured to maintain continued proliferation, acquire features associated with malignant transformation, including loss of contact inhibition, substrate-independent growth, and ability to form tumors in nude mice [48, 49].

In addition to enhanced opportunities for DNA damage and/or inadequate repair, the risk generated by incessant ovulation may also be associated with the formation of epithelial cell—lined inclusion cysts that are often found in the ovarian stroma of perimenopausal women (see Figure 36.1). As noted previously, these inclusion cysts may form as a result of the process of ovulation and the pinching off of deep clefts [42]. In mice, the lifetime total number of ovulations is associated with a marked increase in OSE invagination and stratification [50], although the incidence of inclusion cysts was more related to age than to number of ovulations. Under normal circumstances, these cysts are thought to be eliminated through TGF-β—induced transformation of epithelial cells into mesenchymal cells [51] and/or apoptosis. The persistence of these cysts could represent a preneoplastic event in the development of ovarian cancer because they are characteristically found in prophylactically removed ovaries from women carriers of germline *BRCA1* mutations [52].

Ovulation involves dramatic changes in not only the OSE cells, but also the underlying basement membrane, tunica albuginea, and stromal cells. Extracellular matrix components change significantly during the periovulatory period [53], and it is well established that OSE cell behaviors, including proliferation and morphology, are dramatically affected by extracellular matrix (Figure 36.2; [28]). It has been proposed that loss of the underlying basement membrane in epithelial invaginations and inclusion cysts

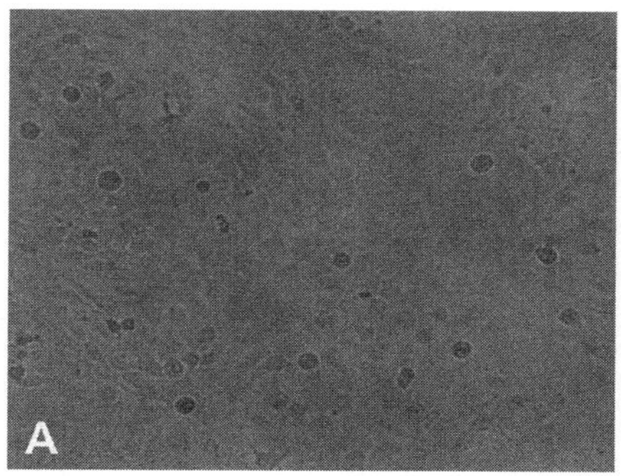

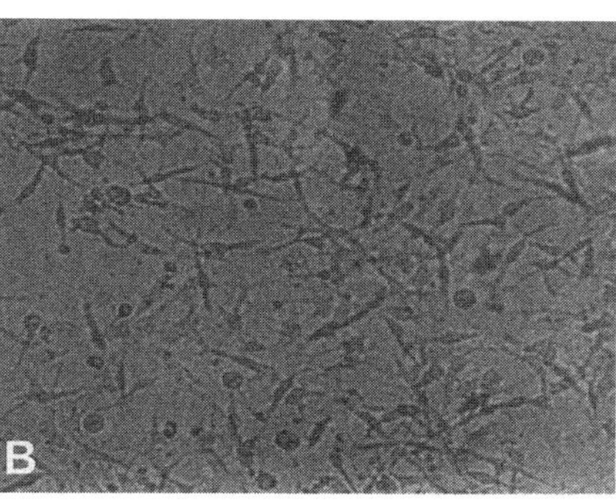

FIGURE 36.2 Morphology of human ovarian surface epithelium (OSE) cells cultured on plastic (*left*) and collagen I (*right*). The cells, which were immortalized by transfection with SV40 T antigen but are not tumorigenic, show typical cobblestone epithelial morphology on plastic, but rapidly adopt a more mesenchymal appearance when cultured on collagen I.

may contribute to premalignant OSE cell transformation by removing components that are important for positional organization of the OSE cells [54]. Thus ovulation may be a risk factor for ovarian cancer not only because of direct consequences on OSE cells, but also indirectly through the dramatic alteration of the extracellular/stromal environment in which the OSE cells reside.

Gonadotropins

An alternative, but not mutually exclusive, hypothesis for the mechanism of ovarian carcinogenesis proposes that the development of ovarian tumors is related to excessive gonadotropin production associated with the onset of menopause or premature ovarian failure [55]. The median age for epithelial ovarian cancer is 60 to 65 years, with only 10% to 15% of the tumors appearing in premenopausal women [56]. Serum FSH and LH levels reach their peak during perimenopausal and postmenopausal years and remain elevated thereafter [57, 58]. These elevated gonadotropin levels are caused by the loss of follicular estrogen and an age-related decreased sensitivity, at the level of the hypothalamus and pituitary, to negative feedback normally mediated by follicular estrogen [reviewed in 59]. In fact, both gonadotropic and steroid hormones of the hypothalamic-pituitary-ovarian axis have been implicated in ovarian tumorigenesis, including gonadotropin-releasing hormone (Gn-RH), FSH, LH/human chorionic gonadotropin (hCG), estrogen, progesterone, and androgen.

High circulating levels of pituitary gonadotropins may increase the risk of ovarian cancer by stimulating the growth of ovarian epithelial cells. Normal human OSE cells and epithelial inclusions have been found to express receptors for FSH (FSHR; [60]) and LH/hCG (LHR; [61]). Enhanced cell proliferation in response to FSH and/or LH/hCG has been reported for primary rabbit [62], mouse [63], and human [61] but not rhesus macaque OSE cells [64]. Treatment of primary human OSE cells with hCG prevents apoptosis induced by serum deprivation [61].

FSHR and LHR have been identified on benign and malignant ovarian tumor cells [65–69]. Enhanced cell proliferation in response to FSH and/or LH/hCG treatment has been demonstrated for primary ovarian cancer cell cultures [70, 71] and ovarian carcinoma cell lines [70, 72]. In one report, hCG did not affect the proliferation of two ovarian carcinoma cell lines, but its addition significantly suppressed cisplatin-induced apoptosis in one of the lines [73]. Additionally, Schiffenbauer and colleagues [74] found that human epithelial ovarian cancers progressed faster in ovariectomized mice as a result of elevated FSH and LH levels, which promoted increased vascular endothelial growth factor (VEGF) expression and tumor neovascularization. Interestingly, Zheng et al. [75] recently found that the growth of two FSHR- and LHR-expressing ovarian carcinoma cell lines was stimulated by FSH but not by LH, and that the FSH-stimulated growth was actually opposed by simultaneous treatment with LH, providing a possible explanation for why high postmenopausal gonadotropin levels or ovulation-induction drugs do not always correlate with increased ovarian cancer risk.

Thus numerous studies have implicated gonadotropins in ovarian tumorigenesis. Zheng et al. [75] found FSHR expression in 100% of epithelial inclusions (n = 20) and benign tumors (n = 12), 94% of LMP tumors (n = 18), but in only 60% of the carcinomas (n = 30), suggesting that FSH may be more important in early tumorigenesis. Recent evidence indicates that FSH induces growth stimulation in human OSE cells through activation of the mitogen-activated protein (MAP) kinase signaling pathway [76]. It should be noted that some of the activities that suppress ovulation and were found to be protective against ovarian cancer (e.g., oral contraceptive use, pregnancy) also reduce levels of gonadotropins, suggesting an additional mechanism by which these protective activities may be effective.

In contrast to the pituitary gonadotropins, Gn-RH action on OSE cells is generally growth inhibitory. Normal human OSE cells have been found to express both forms of Gn-RH and their receptor, and treatment of the cells with Gn-RH agonists causes decreased proliferation [77, 78]. Similarly, Gn-RH agonists have been shown to inhibit the growth of ovarian carcinoma cells [79, 80] and human ovarian tumor xenografts in nude mice [79, 81, 82]. In ovarian cancer cell lines, decreased proliferation in response to Gn-RH analogs was associated with a G_0/G_1 phase block in the cell cycle [79] and hypophosphorylation of the retinoblastoma protein, pRB [80]. Conversely, Yano and colleagues [83] have reported that treatment of athymic mice bearing human epithelial ovarian cancer xenografts with a Gn-RH antagonist resulted in decreased tumor growth. Perhaps not surprisingly, clinical studies using a single Gn-RH agonist for treatment of advanced ovarian cancer and in combination with cisplatin have demonstrated conflicting results [84–86].

Steroid Hormones

In the developing fetal ovary, marked OSE cell proliferation occurs at 16 to 20 weeks of gestation, coincident with the appearance of steroid-producing cells in the ovarian cortex [87]. Adult human OSE cells express receptors for estrogen (ER), progesterone (PR), and androgens (AR) [88, 89], and human OSE cell proliferation can be stimulated by androgens [90]. In contrast, human OSE cells in culture are reportedly unaffected by estradiol or progesterone [88], which would suggest that these steroid hormones do not have a significant role in ovarian tumorigenesis; however, continuous exposure to estradiol stimulates sheep [91] and rabbit OSE cell proliferation and results in the formation of a papillary ovarian surface resembling human serous neoplasms of low malignant potential [92]. In addition, a recent study has found that menopausal women who have taken hormone replacement therapy using only estrogen are at an increased risk of ovarian cancer [93]. The mechanisms by which estrogen may contribute to ovarian cancer risk are unknown, but may be indirect, because estrogen reduces Gn-RH receptor expression in both OSE and ovarian cancer cells, thereby suppressing the growth inhibitory effects of Gn-RH [94]. Estrogen also modulates levels of hepatocyte growth factor (HGF), which stimulates OSE cell growth [95].

In contrast to the effects of estrogen, the evidence available indicates that progesterone may decrease ovarian cancer risk. Specifically, progesterone can inhibit proliferation of some primary cultures of human OSE [10]. Although the mechanism by which oral contraceptives have a protective effect against ovarian cancer is unknown, one study that administered oral contraceptives of various compositions to cynomolgus macaques found that the progesterone component in the hormone composition caused an increase in the proportion of apoptotic OSE cells [96]. Similarly, pregnancy reduces the risk of ovarian cancer, and because progesterone levels are significantly higher during this period, elevated progesterone may represent an additional mechanism of protection during pregnancy that is independent of the suppression of ovulation. In a case-control study of 4000 women born between 1925 and 1960, and diagnosed with either invasive ovarian cancers (i.e., epithelial, stromal, germ-cell, or nonclassified) or tumors of borderline malignant potential, Adami et al. [97] found that increasing parity was consistent with a decreased relative risk of all invasive ovarian cancers, and that the risk of developing ovarian cancer decreased by 10% for each 5-year increment in age for first childbirth. Because the incessant ovulation and elevated serum gonadotropin hypotheses do not readily explain these findings, it has been proposed that in pregnant women cells that have undergone malignant transformation are cleared from the ovaries, thus reducing the risk of ovarian cancer. This hypothesis has been strengthened by the more recent demonstration that progesterone can enhance OSE cell apoptosis [96].

Steroid hormone receptors (i.e., ER, PR, and AR) have been detected, with varying levels of expression and activity, in ovarian tumors [66, 98, 99] and ovarian carcinoma cell lines [66, 100–103]. Although there does not appear to be any correlation between the level of expression of ER or PR and tumor stage [104], ER expression has been reported to be higher in well-differentiated malignant tumors [105] and less highly expressed in metastatic tumors relative to the primary tumor [106]. It is perhaps not surprising then that high tumor ER- and PR-positivity has been associated with better patient survival [107, 108].

Treatment with estradiol or progesterone is generally associated with enhanced proliferation of many ovarian carcinoma cell lines [103, 109–115]. In some ovarian carcinoma cells, the mitogenicity in response to estradiol and progesterone has been associated with increased TGF-α production [114, 115] and rapid transcriptional induction of c-*myc* [116]. Estradiol also upregulates *bcl-2* expression in transformed OSE cells [117], and ER binding to the estrogen response element in the H-*ras* gene has been demonstrated in ovarian tumors [118]. In contrast, exposure of some ovarian cancer cell lines to estradiol or progesterone has resulted in antiproliferative effects, including apoptosis and upregulation of the tumor suppressor gene p53 [70, 119], suggesting that therapies based on disruption of hormone action may be contraindicated in some patients. Nevertheless, modest patient response rates to synthetic progestins, antiestrogens (e.g., tamoxifen), and antiandrogens have been reported [120].

In addition to being responsive to estrogen and progesterone, ovarian cancer cells can also produce these hormones, providing the opportunity for autocrine stimulation. Heinonen and colleagues [121] measured elevated levels of progesterone in patients with epithelial ovarian cancer, particularly in those patients with mucinous tumors. Endogenous steroid production by both human OSE cells [10] and ovarian tumors has been documented [122], and it would appear that estradiol production can be modulated, because aromatase expression in human OSE cells is regulated through protein kinase C- and protein kinase A-mediated mechanisms [123].

Several studies, largely epidemiologic, support the hypothesis that androgens are involved in ovarian carcinogenesis. Although 50% to 60% of ovarian tumors express ER and/or PR, up to 95% of tumors express AR [101, 124, 125], and androgens are the main steroids produced by the postmenopausal ovary [126]. An increased risk of ovarian cancer was found in women with elevated circulating levels of androgens [127]. Polycystic ovarian syndrome (PCOS), a disease that is characterized in part by elevated circulating levels of androgens, has also been associated with an increased risk of ovarian cancer [128]. Testosterone-stimulated growth of OSE cells in guinea pigs caused the formation of benign epithelial ovarian neoplasms [129]. The proliferation of several ovarian carcinoma cell lines is inhibited by antiandrogens [90, 130], and the synthetic androgen, mibolerone, stimulates DNA synthesis in 55% of primary cultures of human OSE cells [131]. In support of these findings, Evangelou et al. [132] demonstrated that treatment of ovarian carcinoma cells with the androgen 5α-dihydrotestosterone caused down-regulation of TGF-β receptors. Thus androgens may promote ovarian cancer progression in part by decreasing TGF-β receptor levels, thereby allowing ovarian cancer cells to escape TGF-β growth inhibition.

Germ-Cell Deficiency/Depletion

Aging and hereditary risk are associated with the more frequent incidence of epithelial invaginations and inclusion cysts, putative preneoplastic precursor lesions, but the underlying mechanism for these epithelial-stromal rearrangements is unknown. OSE cell hyperplasia with stromal invasion has been reported in a diverse array of experimental situations, all of them involving loss of germ cells and consequent failure of follicle development. For example, mutations at the *W* (*Kit*) or *Sl* (*Kitl*) loci result in sterility by preventing the normal proliferation of germ cells during fetal development [133]. Germ cell deficiency *in vivo*, as is found in W^x/W^v mice, results in bilateral ovarian tubular adenomas in more than 95% of the animals by 5 months of age [134, 135]. The tumors arise from interstitial cell hyperplasia, with proliferation and invasion of the OSE into the stromal compartment of the ovary. Invasive epithelial tubules are also found in Sl/Sl^t germ cell–deficient mice by 7 months of age [136]. Likewise, female mice that are homozygous for the germ cell–deficient (*gcd*) mutation enter reproductive senescence prematurely because of a dearth of germ cells arising in embryonic development. The ovaries of young *gcd/gcd* animals are atrophic, composed of little more than stromal cells in a connective tissue matrix. By 1 year of age, 56% of homozygotes have developed ovarian tubulostromal adenomas, while 100% of wild-type and heterozygous littermates are phenotypically normal [137].

Experimental ovarian tumorigenesis has been investigated in inbred and hybrid strains of mice and induced by a diversity of mechanisms, including X-irradiation, oocytotoxic xenobiotic chemicals, ovarian grafting to ectopic or orthotopic sites, neonatal thymectomy, genetic defects reducing germ-cell populations, and aging [reviewed in 138]. Although germ-cell deficiency seems to be a required element for the development of epithelially derived adenomas, the mechanism by which germ-cell loss contributes to tumorigenesis in these models remains unclear. Ovarian follicles do not develop in the absence of oocytes, indicating that the oocyte directs the development of follicles. The importance of the oocyte as a necessary element for normal follicular development and function has been demonstrated *in vitro* [139, 140], and recent studies have identified some of the specific oocyte-secreted factors (e.g., growth differentiation factor-9; GDF-9) that are required for follicle development [141]. These oocyte factors are likely to be important for human fertility as well, because aberrant expression of GDF-9 has been found in the oocytes of women with PCOS [142]. Therefore, germ cells, by promoting normal follicular morphology and function, are important for ovarian health, and oocyte depletion, similar to that which occurs naturally by the time of menopause, may be a contributing factor to the oncogenic behavior of the surface epithelial cells. Pathogenetic factors that prematurely destroy or diminish the numbers of germ cells thus lead to failure in follicle development and a resulting decrease in sex steroid hormone secretion (notably estradiol), leading to a compensatory overproduction of pituitary gonadotropins (particularly LH), which places the ovary at an increased risk to develop tumors.

The intense proliferation of OSE and stromal (interstitial) cells with the development of unique tubular adenomas in response to sterility seems to require both the lack of germ cells/follicles and the increased production of gonadotropins. Oocyte destruction by gamma irradiation in hypogonadal mice that are deficient in gonadotropins did not result in the development of tubular adenomas [143], suggesting that both oocyte loss/destruction and elevated gonadotropins are necessary for tumor formation. Similarly, the suppression of gonadotropin levels in W^x/W^v mice was sufficient to prevent the development of ovarian tubular adenomas from the surface epithelium [144].

It is therefore well established in animal models that premature ovarian failure resulting from loss or depletion of germ cells consistently results in OSE cell hyperplasia and stromal invasion. It is not yet clearly established whether premature ovarian failure in women increases the risk of ovarian cancer. Galactose metabolism differs between women with and without a family history of ovarian cancer and has been proposed to be a genetic risk caused by galactose-induced oocyte toxicity [145]; however, other known oocytotoxic agents such as busulphan, which is known to cause severe and persistent ovarian failure [146], have not yet been evaluated for their impact on the risk of ovarian cancer.

Genetics

Many ovarian cancers exhibit aneuploidy, and several studies have shown that ploidy is an independent prognostic variable for patient survival [reviewed in 147]. More specifically, genetic alterations involving oncogenes, tumor suppressor genes, and several signaling molecules that have critical roles in normal cell growth and survival have been found to be important in ovarian tumorigenesis. Although many potential candidates have been studied in this regard [reviewed in 148, 149], only the genes best characterized for their involvement in ovarian cancer are discussed here.

Oncogenes

The three members of the *ras* oncogene family, H-, K-, and N-*ras*, encode $p21^{ras}$ G proteins that are involved in promoting cell growth. K-*ras* mutations have correlated most frequently with the mucinous ovarian tumor subtype, having been detected in 11% to 75% of mucinous versus

5% to 36% of nonmucinous tumors [reviewed in 150]. Tumor cells with *ras* mutations demonstrated resistance to chemotherapy and radiotherapy [151, 152], suggesting a reason why K-*ras* mutation in human ovarian tumors correlated with a shorter patient survival in one study [153]. Stable expression of the H-*ras* oncogene in immortalized rat OSE cells (ROSE 199 cells) resulted in malignant transformation of the cells, as evidenced by loss of contact inhibition and growth in soft agar *in vitro*, and the ability to form invasive tumors when injected subcutaneously into immunocompetent rats; however, these *ras*-transformed OSE cells generated sarcomas rather than tumors resembling ovarian carcinomas [154].

The HER-2/*neu* (*erbB*-2) gene encodes a transmembrane glycoprotein with tyrosine kinase activity, which belongs to a family of growth factor receptors that includes the epidermal growth factor receptor (EGFR). Normal human OSE cells express little or no HER-2/*neu* [155, 156], but amplification and/or overexpression of HER-2/*neu* has been reported in 19% to 59% of epithelial ovarian cancers [reviewed in 150] and some ovarian carcinoma cell lines [157]. No relationship between HER-2/*neu* amplification and histologic tumor grade has been found [158], but a correlation between HER-2/*neu* overexpression and poor prognosis has been reported in approximately half of the studies [reviewed in 150]. In other cell systems, HER-2/*neu* overexpression has been associated with taxol resistance [159] and metastasis [160]. Notably, overexpression of activated HER-2/*neu* in ROSE 199 cells resulted in highly tumorigenic cells that grew as solid tumors when injected into immunocompetent rat ovaries, with peritoneal seeding and ascites formation; however, like the *ras*-transformed ROSE 199 cells, ROSE 199-*neu* tumors possessed sarcomatous morphology [161].

The c-*myc* oncogene encodes a transcription factor that regulates cell proliferation via effects on the cell cycle. Amplification and overexpression of the c-*myc* gene has been detected in ovarian cancer cell lines [162] and in 26% to 37% of epithelial ovarian cancers [reviewed in 150]. C-*myc* overexpression is more common in malignant serous ovarian tumors and is associated with stage III disease, suggesting a role in disease progression [163]. Although no correlation has been observed between c-*myc* overexpression and patient survival [reviewed in 150], one study did demonstrate poor prognosis if c-*myc* overexpression was associated with high levels of HER-2/*neu* and $p21^{ras}$ [164].

Tumor Suppressor Genes

The most widely used approach to identify where tumor suppressor genes may reside is by examination for loss of heterozygosity (LOH). Studies have shown LOH for chromosomes 1p, 3p, 4p, 5q, 6q, 7p, 7q, 8q, 9p, 11p, 11q, 12p, 12q, 13q, 14q, 16p, 16q, 17p, 17q, 18q, 19p, 22q, Xp, and Xq in ovarian tumor specimens [reviewed in 148, 149]. Although the identification of most of these genetic loci remains to be determined, loss and/or inactivation of a few tumor suppressor genes have been correlated with poor patient survival.

Mutations in two tumor suppressor genes, *BRCA1* and *BRCA2*, form the basis for most cases of familial ovarian cancer. The *BRCA1* protein is involved in DNA damage repair via interaction with RAD51 [165, 166] and may also be involved in gene transcription because it can associate with RNA polymerase II holoenzyme [167]. *BRCA1* is considered to be a tumor suppressor gene because retroviral infection of the gene into ovarian and breast cancer cells suppresses their growth *in vitro* and tumorigenicity *in vivo* [168]. Mutations in *BRCA1* are found in 34% to 58% of hereditary ovarian cancer families of North America and European origin [reviewed in 150]. In general, mutations in the *BRCA1* gene account for approximately 78% of site-specific ovarian cancers and 92% of breast/ovarian cancer syndrome cases [169]. The risk among first-degree relatives (i.e., mother, sister, daughter) of developing ovarian cancer can be as high as 50% [1]; however, it is not clear whether *BRCA1* mutation actually affects ovarian cancer patient survival. Although 80% of ovarian cancers show LOH at the *BRCA1* gene locus, suggesting that inactivation of the *BRCA1* gene is related not only to familial ovarian cancer cases but also to sporadic cases, the estimated proportion of sporadic ovarian cancer caused by *BRCA1* mutation is 5% or less [170–172].

The *BRCA2* protein is very similar in structure and function to *BRCA1*, and it is estimated that 7% to 14% of ovarian cancer families harbor *BRCA2* mutations [reviewed in 150]. In one study, *BRCA2* mutations were detected in 9% of 119 families, but the authors found no evidence for differences in survival of the women [173]. Like *BRCA1* gene mutations, *BRCA2* mutations occur in only about 5% of sporadic ovarian cancer cases [174, 175].

The p53 tumor suppressor gene is the most commonly mutated gene in human neoplasms. The p53 protein is a transcription factor that regulates the cell cycle via transactivation of genes involved in cell cycle arrest or apoptosis. Mutations and/or overexpression of p53 have been described in 26% to 62% of ovarian cancers, particularly serous ovarian carcinomas [reviewed in 150]. A genomic polymorphism of the p53 gene that contains a 16 bp insertion in intron 3 (called PIN3) has been found to be associated with an increased risk of developing ovarian cancer [175]. Correlation between p53 alteration and poor patient survival has been reported in about 50% of the studies [reviewed in 150]. Adenovirus-mediated gene transfer of wild-type p53 into ovarian cancer cells containing a mutated p53 gene has been shown to inhibit tumor growth [176, 177] and enhance sensitivity to chemotherapy and radiotherapy, resulting in increased apoptosis [178, 179].

Several other tumor suppressor genes are less well characterized but appear to play a role in ovarian carcinogenesis. PTEN is mutated in a significant number of endometrioid ovarian cancers [180], and expression of the putative tumor suppressor NOEY2 is reduced in breast and ovary carcinomas [181]. Expression of Disabled-2/DOC-2, a protein thought to be involved in positional organization of epithelial cells, is also lost in the transition from normal OSE to ovarian cancer [182, 183].

Thus molecular biological studies are providing valuable information regarding alterations in these and other genes in the hopes of identifying genetic models of epithelial ovarian cancers that could be exploited in the diagnosis and treatment of ovarian cancer. Several Phase I gene therapy clinical trials have been initiated to restore wild-type p53 or *BRCA1* gene function or to downregulate HER-2/*neu* overexpression [184].

Growth Factors and Cytokines

Several growth factors and cytokines have been shown to regulate the proliferation of both normal human OSE cells and ovarian cancer cells and, therefore, have been implicated in epithelial ovarian tumorigenesis. Normal OSE cells express EGFR [185], and EGF has been shown to be a potent mitogen for these cells in tissue culture (Figure 36.3; [21, 186]). TGF-α, which resembles EGF structurally and functionally and can bind to and activate the EGFR [187], is also produced by normal human OSE cells and stimulates their proliferation [188]. Like normal OSE cells, most ovarian carcinoma cells are also stimulated to proliferate in the presence of either EGF or TGF-α [70, 114, 188, 189], and the growth of ovarian carcinoma cells in serum-free tissue culture can be inhibited by treatment with anti-TGF-α neutralizing antibodies [189].

EGF has been shown to significantly reduce the levels of HER-2/*neu* protein in ovarian carcinoma cells [190],

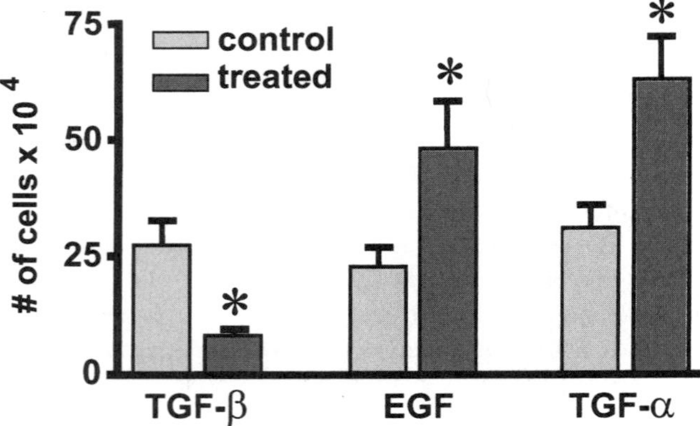

FIGURE 36.3 Growth of primary cultures of rat ovarian surface epithelium (OSE) cells in the presence of 10 ng/mL various growth factors for 4 days.

whereas TGF-α–stimulated growth of ovarian carcinoma cells has been associated with upregulation of its own mRNA expression [20] and c-*myc* gene expression [191]. Tumor EGFR status was found to have no independent prognostic or predictive significance in advanced disease (n = 185; [192]). Perhaps as a consequence of enhanced activity of growth factor receptors, phosphatidylinositol 3′-kinase (PI3K) and its downstream effector, AKT2, have been shown to be overexpressed in a proportion of ovarian cancers [193, 194]. These may be early events in tumorigenesis because PI3K expression is elevated in neoplastic OSE compared with normal OSE cells [195].

TGF-β is a powerful growth inhibitor in many cell types, including epithelial cells (see Figure 36.3; [196]). Normal human OSE cells produce TGF-β, which acts as an autocrine growth inhibitor [197, 198]. The proliferation of various ovarian cancer cells has also been demonstrated to be inhibited by exogenous TGF-β, including primary ovarian cancer cells from solid tumors and patients' ascites [198, 199], as well as ovarian carcinoma cell lines [197, 200]. Many of these ovarian cancer cells also produce endogenous TGF-β [197, 199]. In conjunction with its growth suppression of ovarian cancer cells, TGF-β has been shown to induce apoptosis [198, 201] and to downregulate expression of TGF-α [20], c-*myc* [200], and the antiapoptotic gene *bcl*-2 [201]; however, it should be noted that some ovarian cancer cells, despite appropriate TGF-β–induced Smad signaling [202], were resistant to the growth-inhibitory effects of TGF-β and/or did not produce TGF-β [197, 199], pointing to a mechanism for escape from the negative growth regulation by TGF-β during tumor progression.

Normal OSE cells also secrete bioactive cytokines, including interleukin (IL)-1 and IL-6, granulocyte colony–stimulating factor (G-CSF), macrophage (M)-CSF, GM-CSF [203], and kit ligand (KL; [204–206]). Almost all of these factors are also produced by ovarian cancer cells and stimulate their proliferation [207]. Both the KL and M-CSF receptors are expressed by many malignant ovarian cancers but not by normal OSE cells [205, 207], suggesting that KL and M-CSF secreted by normal OSE may act in a paracrine manner but subsequently become autocrine regulatory factors with malignant progression. The ability of ovarian cancer cells to invade has been correlated with high endogenous M-CSF production [208].

Hepatocyte growth factor (HGF) is produced primarily by mesenchymal and stromal cells and acts on epithelial cells through Met, a receptor tyrosine kinase [209, 210]. Although HGF can be mitogenic for bovine, rat, and human OSE cells [210, 211], its effects are strongly influenced by the presence of extracellular matrix components [211]. The stimulatory effects of hCG on OSE cell proliferation are mediated by upregulation of HGF expression [211]. c-*Met* is overexpressed in a significant proportion of well-differentiated ovarian carcinomas [212], and recombinant HGF increases migration and proliferation of Met-expressing ovarian cancer cells [213, 214]. As a key mediator of mesenchymal-epithelial interactions, it can be speculated that this ligand-receptor system may play an important role in the transitional events that arise during epithelial invagination and formation of inclusion cysts.

Environmental Carcinogens, Infectious Agents, and Inflammation

Although the more established hypotheses that have been proposed to explain increased risk of developing ovarian cancer are related to the number of ovulations or to increased hormone levels, several additional risk factors have been identified, some of which have no apparent link to these two factors. Weak correlations have been made between alcohol and coffee usage and high-fat diets and increased risk of developing ovarian cancer [215]. Use of perineal talc has also been identified as a risk factor, possibly because of its ability to ascend the genital tract and affect the ovarian surface [216]. Direct exposure of rat ovaries to talc results in focal areas of papillary change in the OSE [217]. Infections that may lead to premature ovarian failure (e.g., mumps virus) have been related to increased ovarian cancer risk [218], and it has been proposed that sexually transmitted disease organisms may underlie the increased risk associated with infertility [219]. Cigarette smoking appears to be a risk factor for mucinous ovarian tumors [220], and exposure of rhesus and cynomolgus monkeys to the environmental pollutant hexachlorobenzene results in both reproductive failure and notable alterations in the size, shape, and degree of stratification of the OSE [221–223]. More recent studies have shown that the insecticide methoxychlor also modifies the height of the OSE in exposed mice [224].

The mechanisms by which environmental carcinogens or infectious agents enhance the risk of ovarian cancer is unknown; however, Ness and Cottreau [225] have proposed that a common mechanism underlying many of the risk factors is inflammation. Inflammation leads to cell damage, rapid DNA turnover, oxidative stress, and increased cytokine levels, all of which can be mutagenic [225, 226]. Inflammatory cytokines, growth factors, and chemokines have been found in ovarian tumors [227, 228]. This hypothesis is consistent with the known protective effects of tubal ligation and hysterectomy on ovarian cancer risk, because they disrupt the pathway by which irritants may reach the OSE cells.

MALIGNANT TRANSFORMATION OF NORMAL OVARIAN SURFACE EPITHELIUM

Despite the evidence to support the various etiologies of epithelial ovarian cancer, the precise sequence of events, notably the early events, that result in malignant transformation of OSE cells is uncertain. In this regard, an increased commitment to an epithelial phenotype appears to be one of the earliest changes in the process of ovarian tumorigenesis. Normal OSE cells express both epithelial (e.g., keratin) and mesenchymal (e.g., collagen type III) markers *in vivo* [19, 229] and *in vitro* [230, 231], but in OSE-lined inclusion cysts, epithelial differentiation predominates, often in conjunction with Müllerian metaplasia [52, reviewed in 232]. Ovarian epithelial cancers have been classified into serous, mucinous, and endometrioid adenocarcinomas based mainly on their histologica similarities to tumors arising from organs that are embryologically derived from Müllerian ducts, which include the fallopian tubes, endocervix, and endometrium, respectively. Because tumors morphologically identical to ovarian carcinomas can be found outside the ovary, Dubeau has argued that remnants of the Müllerian system are potential sites for the origins of epithelial ovarian tumorigenesis [233].

Normal human OSE cells do not express the epithelial cell adhesion molecule E-cadherin; however, OSE cells lining inclusion cysts do express E-cadherin [234]. Similarly, in contrast to normal surface OSE, epithelial cells in inclusion cysts secrete the glycoprotein CA125, and express HOXA7, *HER-2/neu*, and the KIT tyrosine kinase receptor (Figure 36.4; [23, 205, 235, 236]). Although the formation of inclusion cysts is associated with alterations

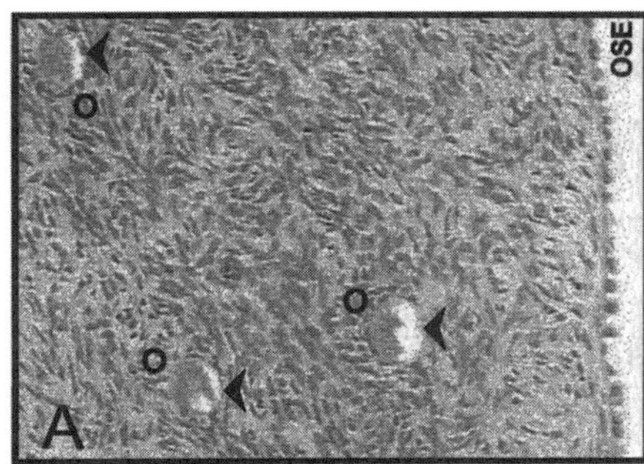

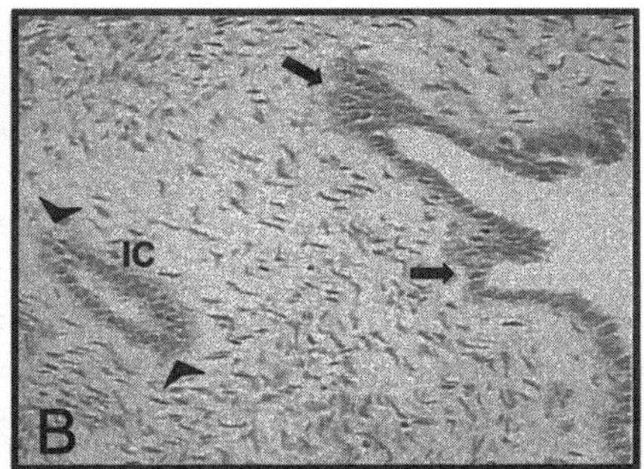

FIGURE 36.4 Immunohistochemical detection of KIT expression in normal human ovaries. KIT is expressed in epithelial invaginations (*arrows*) and inclusion cysts (*arrowheads; b*), but not in ovarian surface epithelium (OSE; *a*). O indicates oocytes. Figure was originally presented in Tonary et al. (2000) published by Wiley-Liss, Inc. (See color plate).

in gene expression, it is not clear whether these changes contribute to cyst formation or whether they are a consequence of the altered environment when the OSE cells become entirely embedded within stromal tissue; however, the infrequent or low levels of expression of these factors in OSE and the frequent and/or elevated levels of expression of all of these factors in ovarian carcinomas are consistent with the hypothesis that the epithelium in inclusion cysts may represent preneoplastic lesions.

Ovarian cancers are distinctly epithelial with expression of keratin, CA125, E-cadherin, cilia, and the formation of papillae and glands [229, 234, 237]. In primary culture, ovarian cancer cells retain this epithelial phenotype [238]. Interestingly, OSE cells cultured from the ovaries of women with strong family histories of ovarian cancer contained more CA125–expressing cells, more keratin and E-cadherin, and less collagen type III compared with overtly normal OSE cells from patients with no family history [239–241]. Constitutive expression of E-cadherin in SV40-immortalized human OSE cells has been shown to induce epithelial differentiation [242], and the cells formed adenocarcinomas when injected into severe combined immunodeficiency (SCID) mice [243], suggesting that a causal relationship may exist between E-cadherin expression and neoplastic progression of human OSE.

EXPERIMENTAL MODELS TO STUDY OVARIAN SURFACE EPITHELIUM CELL TRANSFORMATION AND OVARIAN CANCER

Experimental models for human diseases are of crucial importance not only to understand the biologic and genetic factors that influence the phenotypic characteristics of the disease but also to utilize as a basis for developing rational intervention strategies. Ovarian cancer cell lines derived from ascites or primary ovarian tumors have been used extensively and can be very effective for studying the processes controlling growth regulation and chemosensitivity; however, our limited knowledge of the initiating events of ovarian cancer has restricted the development of models in which the early pathogenic events for ovarian cancer can be studied. Some of the models that have been developed to investigate OSE cell transformation *in vitro* and *in vivo* are described here.

Ovarian Surface Epithelium Cell Transformation *In Vitro*

Although OSE cells have been implicated as the cell of origin for most ovarian cancers based primarily on histologic and immunohistochemical analyses of patient samples, several recent experimental models manipulating these cells *in vitro* have provided additional support for this concept. Primary culture of human OSE was first reported by Auersperg et al. in 1984 [230], and her group has since contributed substantially to our knowledge of the characteristics of human OSE. As the methods that can be used to isolate and culture OSE cells and the biologic characteristics of these cells in culture have been comprehensively described by Auersperg and colleagues in a recent review [232], they are addressed only minimally here.

OSE cells have been studied in primary cultures using several different systems that allow characterization of the responsiveness of these cells to a wide variety of hormones and growth factors. To address the three-dimensional nature of inclusion cysts, OSE have been cultured in collagen gels, organoids, Matrigel, and Spongostan, a collagenous sponge [reviewed in 232]. In most of these culture systems, the OSE cells demonstrate a propensity to convert to mesenchymal phenotypes, which can also occur in two-dimensional cultures and which may reflect their normal behavior during epithelial wound repair following ovulation. Because epithelial carcinogenesis is associated with increased commitment to the epithelial phenotype, however, it remains to be seen if these culture systems can be modified to allow OSE cells to acquire more epithelial characteristics.

In vitro models of ovarian epithelial carcinogenesis that have been developed as a consequence of the establishment of methods to culture OSE cells include the use of SV40 T antigen early genes to induce immortalization of OSE cells, which delays, but does not prevent, the senescence that normally occurs after a few passages [244]. Introduction of E-cadherin into these immortalized cells yielded cells that were anchorage-independent and formed transplantable, invasive adenocarcinomas in SCID mice [243]. In contrast to SV40-immortalized cells, introduction of the human papilloma virus E6 and E7 genes into human OSE cells resulted in the spontaneous progression from a benign to invasive phenotype [245].

Unlike human OSE, rat and mouse OSE do not senesce. Rat OSE cells that have spontaneously immortalized but are not tumorigenic (e.g., ROSE 199 cells; [246]) have been used in a variety of experiments, including some to characterize the cellular features when SV40 T antigen or H-*ras* is introduced into immortalized cells [154]. Repeated subculture of rat and mouse OSE cells to maintain continued proliferation results in spontaneous malignant transformation, as characterized by loss of contact inhibition, substrate-independent growth, and the ability to form tumors in nude mice [48, 49]. Recently, Orsulic and colleagues introduced oncogenes into mouse OSE *ex vivo* using retroviral infection and determined the malignant potential of the transformed cells following their reintroduction into nude or syngeneic animals [247]. Although these models allow an evaluation of oncogenes whose activation may contribute to the development of epithelial ovarian cancer, this approach does not allow investigation of the early events in ovarian tumorigenesis inherent in mice when the tumors arise *in situ*.

The establishment of *in vitro* models of normal and transformed OSE cells has provided the opportunity to use molecular approaches such as microarray or suppression subtractive hybridization to identify differential gene expression patterns that can distinguish normal OSE and ovarian cancer cells [248–250]. These data will be useful for the elucidation of molecular events associated with OSE cell transformation.

Animal Models

The gonadotropin theory of ovarian tumorigenesis suggests that elevated gonadotropin concentrations contribute to the development of ovarian tumors. This theory is based on the initial observation of Biskind and Biskind in 1944 [251], who reported that transplantation of ovaries into the splenic pulp of adult rats led to the development of ovarian tumors. The tumorigenesis was attributed to inactivation of estrogen in the liver and the consequent elevation of gonadotropin levels caused by the lack of steroid feedback on the pituitary. Several transgenic or knockout animal models in which gonadotropin levels are elevated also result in ovarian tumorigenesis. For example, when inhibin, the ovarian factor that inhibits the production of FSH, is made deficient in mice, gonadal stromal tumors arise [252].

Transgenic mice generated to have chronic LH hypersecretion develop granulosa cell tumors or luteomas, depending on the background strain [253, 254]. Mice with disruption of the FSH receptor are acyclic and sterile, with very small, underdeveloped ovaries; they exhibit hypergonadotropic-hypogonadism with high levels of circulating FSH similar to the postmenopausal state in women. By 12 months, more than 92% of these animals developed various kinds of ovarian pathology, including neoplasms of sex cord–stromal type as well as cysts, suggesting that FSH receptor insensitivity in the face of prolonged elevated levels of gonadotropins may contribute to the development of ovarian granulosa or stromal tumors [255]. As noted in the section "Germ-Cell Deficiency/Depletion," the development of tubular adenomas derived by epithelial invasion into the ovarian stroma in germ cell–deficient mice is also highly dependent on elevated gonadotropins. Although most models with hormonally induced ovarian tumors involve elevated levels of gonadotropins, formation of benign epithelial tumors has been reported in guinea pigs treated with testosterone [129].

Few animal models develop ovarian tumors spontaneously. Hens maintained under intensive egg-laying conditions develop ovarian adenocarcinomas; however, such tumors are uncommon in hens less than 2 years of age [43]. Ovarian tumors will also arise with age in some strains of mice [256]; however, the low incidence and the length of time required for the appearance of tumors in both of these models renders them poorly feasible for studies of ovarian carcinogenesis.

The ideal model to investigate the pathogenic events associated with early ovarian tumorigenesis would be a mouse model in which the tumor arises directly from the OSE cells. This model would differ from current xenograft models in that transgenic mice with defined genetic lesions could be studied at various stages as they inevitably develop ovarian cancer *in situ*. In addition, the development of a genetic model would permit the direct testing of oncogenes and tumor suppressors for their contribution to the initiation and progression of overt malignancies in the mouse ovary. Finally, several different factors could be altered, such as the genetic background of the mouse strain, the frequency of ovulation, and the levels of various hormones, to determine their impact on the development of tumors in the susceptible transgenic mouse line.

The major impediment to the development of a mouse model of ovarian cancer is the lack of specific promoters able to direct gene expression to OSE cells. Previous models of ovarian cancer have resulted in granulosa cell tumors using promoters active in this cell type to drive the expression of the large T antigen of SV40 [257, 258]. In the absence of an ovarian epithelial cell-specific promoter, other strategies are being employed to generate mouse models of ovarian cancer. Xenograft models, in which ovarian cancer cells have been injected either subcutaneously or into the peritoneal cavity, have been used extensively to test novel therapeutics or modified regimens for administration of standard chemotherapeutic drugs [259–261].

Mouse models currently in development take advantage of the presence of a bursa, a sac-like structure that envelops rodent ovaries. For decades, researchers have used the intrabursal space for transplants of xenografted ovaries or to facilitate direct exposure of the ovary to various factors, including hormones, growth factors, drugs, antisense oligonucleotides, and sperm [262–264]. For the generation of mouse models of ovarian cancer, the injection of ovarian cancer cells into the intrabursal space results in tumor formation that can perhaps be viewed as more physiologic, because the cancer cells are placed directly into the environment where ovarian tumors normally arise (Figure 36.5). As an alternative, the OSE readily takes up and expresses genes delivered by intrabursal injection of adenoviruses (Figure 36.6), rendering this an effective method for manipulating gene expression in these cells. This method has the potential advantage of mimicking somatic mutations that contribute to early ovarian tumorigenesis. The generation of animal models in which OSE cells undergo neoplastic transformation *in vivo* will provide much-needed opportunities to investigate the cellular and molecular changes associated with the initiation of OSE cell transformation, as well as provide models in which diagnostic, screening, and prevention strategies can be developed.

CONCLUSION

Ovarian cancer is known as "the disease that whispers" because few specific symptoms are associated with early-stage disease. Yet early detection is the key to saving women's lives, because 90% of women are cured by surgery alone if the diagnosis is made at stage I [1]. Symptoms of ovarian cancer include many pelvic or abdominal disturbances, which often indicate ascites accumulation and widespread metastases of advanced-stage disease [1]; only 24% of all cases are detected when the disease is confined to the ovary [265].

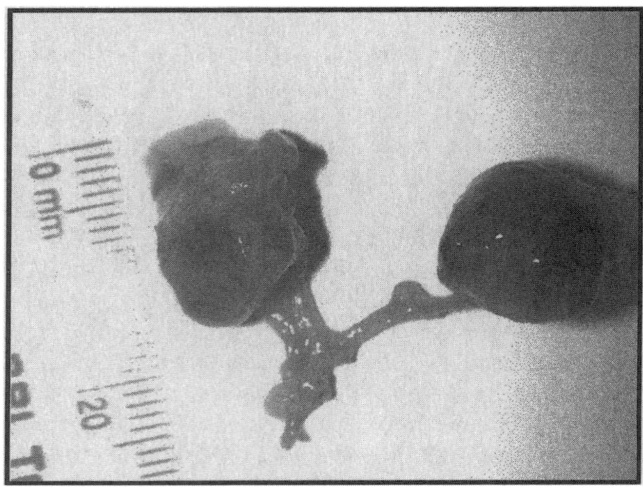

FIGURE 36.5 Development of ovarian tumors following injection of OVCA429 ovarian cancer cells under the bursal membrane of nude mouse ovaries. This xenograft model allows significant growth of tumors (more than 10 times normal diameter along the greatest length) within the ovarian environment. (See color plate.)

To date, there is no single, reliable, specific screening method for detecting ovarian cancer. If appraisal of a woman's risk using medical, reproductive, and family cancer histories warrants careful observation, there are currently three main screening procedures [266]: (1) measurement of tumor-associated antigens (notably CA125); (2) regular transvaginal ultrasonography; and/or (3) determination of *BRCA1* gene mutations.

The two most pressing problems in the management of ovarian cancer are the lack of adequate diagnostic or screening strategies and the recurrence of disease that is often chemoresistant. In part, the deficiency in diagnostic tools is a result of the lack of markers to detect preneoplastic or early neoplastic changes in the OSE cells, which reflects our rather poor understanding of this process. As knowledge of the cellular and molecular events involved in ovarian epithelial carcinogenesis improves, candidate approaches for the development of strategies for the prevention, screening, and diagnosis of ovarian cancer will become evident.

ACKNOWLEDGMENTS

The authors wish to thank Dr. Douglas Gray for his critical review of this chapter, Manon Prevost for contributing the data for Figure 36.3, and Dr. Andrew Godwin, Fox Chase Cancer Center, for providing human immortalized OSE cells. We also gratefully acknowledge the excellent technical assistance provided by Kerri Dawson. Research was supported by grants from the National Cancer Institute of Canada (BCV) and the National Institutes of Health (BCV; Dr. Thomas Hamilton, Fox Chase Cancer Center, Principal Investigator), a scholarship from the Canadian Institutes of Health Research (TJS), and an Ontario Graduate Scholarship (AMT).

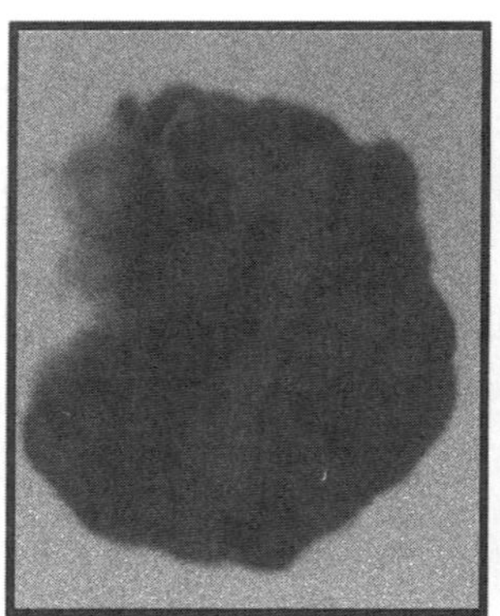

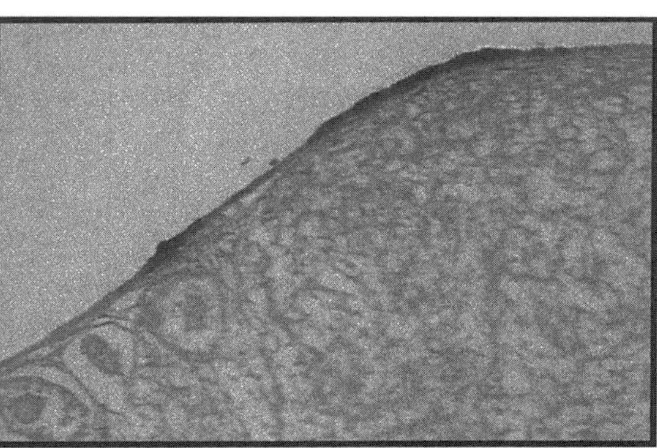

FIGURE 36.6 Confirmation that mouse ovarian surface epithelium (OSE) cells will take up and express adenoviral genes. Adenovirus expressing lacZ was injected under the bursa surrounding mouse ovaries, and ovaries were subsequently removed and stained for expression of β-galactosidase. (See color plate.)

References

1. Murdoch, W. J. (1996). Ovarian surface epithelium, ovulation and carcinogenesis. *Biol. Rev. Camb. Philos. Soc.* 71, 529–543.
2. Weiss, N. S., Homonchuk, T., and Young, J. L. J. (1977). Incidence of the histologic types of ovarian cancer: The U.S. Third National Cancer Survey, 1969–1971. *Gynecol. Oncol.* 5, 161–167.
3. Papadaki, L., and Beilby, J. O. (1971). The fine structure of the surface epithelium of the human ovary. *J. Cell Sci.* 8, 445–465.
4. Blaustein, A., and Lee, H. (1979). Surface cells of the ovary and pelvic peritoneum: A histochemical and ultrastructure comparison. *Gynecol. Oncol.* 8, 34–43.
5. Moore, K. L. (1992). The pelvis and perineum. In *Clinically oriented anatomy*, eds. T. S. Satterfield, L. Napora, and K. Lumpkin, 281–289. Baltimore: Williams & Williams.
6. Espey, L. L. (1967). Ultrastructure of the apex of the rabbit graafian follicle during the ovulatory process. *Endocrinology* 81, 267–276.
7. Ribeiro, A. F., Ferronha, M. H., and David-Ferreira, J. F. (1983). Freeze-fracture study of the hamster ovary surface epithelium intercellular junctions. *J. Submicrosc. Cytol.* 15, 415–423.
8. Perez, R. P., Godwin, A. K., Hamilton, T. C., and Ozols, R. F. (1991). Ovarian cancer biology. *Semin. Oncol.* 18, 186–204.
9. Auersperg, N., and Maines-Bandiera, S. L. (2000). Culture and characterization of human ovarian surface epithelium. In *Ovarian Cancer: Methods and Protocols*, ed. J. M. S. Bertlett, Humana Press: Totowa, NJ, 169–173.
10. Ivarsson, K., Sundfeldt, K., Brännström, M., and Janson, P. O. (2001). Production of steroids by human ovarian surface epithelial cells in culture: Possible role of progesterone as growth inhibitor. *Gynecol. Oncol.* 82, 116–121.
11. Benjamin, E., Law, S., and Bobrow, L. G. (1987). Intermediate filaments cytokeratin and vimentin in ovarian sex cord-stromal tumours with correlative studies in adult and fetal ovaries. *J. Pathol.* 152, 253–263.
12. Isola, J., Kallioniemi, O. P., Korte, J. M., Wahlstrom, T., Aine, R., Helle, M., and Helin, H. (1990). Steroid receptors and Ki-67 reactivity in ovarian cancer and in normal ovary: Correlation with DNA flow cytometry, biochemical receptor assay, and patient survival. *J. Pathol.* 162, 295–301.
13. Czernobilsky, B., Moll, R., Levy, R., and Franke, W. W. (1985). Co-expression of cytokeratin and vimentin filaments in mesothelial, granulosa and rete ovarii cells of the human ovary. *Eur. J. Cell Biol.* 37, 175–190.
14. Jindal, S. K., Ishii, E., Letarte, M., Vera, S., Teerds, K., and Dorrington, J. H. (1995). Regulation of transforming growth factor-α gene expression in an ovarian surface epithelial cell line derived from a human carcinoma. *Biol. Reprod.* 52, 1027–1037.
15. Rodriguez, G. C., Berchuck, A., Whitaker, R. S., Schlossman, D., Clarke-Pearson, D. L., and Bast, R. C. J. (1991). Epidermal growth factor receptor expression in normal ovarian epithelium and ovarian cancer. II. Relationship between receptor expression and response to epidermal growth factor. *Am. J. Obstet. Gynecol.* 164, 745–750.
16. Miettinen, M., Lehto, V. P., and Virtanen, I. (1983). Expression of intermediate filaments in normal ovaries and ovarian epithelial, sex cord-stromal, and germinal tumors. *Int. J. Gynecol. Pathol.* 2, 64–71.
17. Nicosia, S. V., and Johnson, J. H. (1984). Surface morphology of ovarian mesothelium (surface epithelium) and of other pelvic and extrapelvic mesothelial sites in the rabbit. *Int. J. Gynecol. Pathol.* 3, 249–260.
18. Blaustein, A., Kaganowicz, A., and Wells, J. (1982). Tumor markers in inclusion cysts of the ovary. *Cancer* 49, 722–726.
19. van Niekerk, C. C., Boerman, O. C., Ramaekers, F. C., and Poels, L. G. (1991). Marker profile of different phases in the transition of normal human ovarian epithelium to ovarian carcinomas. *Am. J. Pathol.* 138, 455–463.
20. Zeimet, A. G., Offner, F. A., Muller-Holzner, E., Widschwendter, M., Abendstein, B., Fuith, L. C., Daxenbichler, G., and Marth, C. (1998). Peritoneum and tissues of the female reproductive tract as physiological sources of CA-125. *Tumour Biol.* 19, 275–282.
21. Nicosia, S. V., and Nicosia R. F. (1988). Neoplasms of the ovarain mesothelium. In *Path of Human Neoplasms*, ed. H. A. Azar, 435–486. New York: Raven Press.
22. Jacobs, I., and Bast Jr., R. C. (1989). The CA 125 tumour-associated antigen: A review of the literature. *Hum. Reprod.* 4, 1–12.
23. Kabawat, S. E., Bast Jr., R. C., Bhan, A. K., Welch, W. R., Knapp, R. C., and Colvin, R. B. (1983). Tissue distribution of a coelomic-epithelium-related antigen recognized by the monoclonal antibody OC125. *Int. J. Gynecol. Pathol.* 2, 275–285.
24. Bjersing, L., and Cajander, S. (1974). Ovulation and the mechanism of follicle rupture. V. Ultrastructure of tunica albuginea and theca externa of rabbit graafian follicles prior to induced ovulation. *Cell Tissue Res.* 153, 15–30.
25. Ackerman, R. C., and Murdoch, W. J. (1993). Prostaglandin-induced apoptosis of ovarian surface epithelial cells. *Prostaglandins* 45, 475–485.
26. Osterholzer, H. O., Johnson, J. H., and Nicosia, S. V. (1985). An autoradiographic study of rabbit ovarian surface epithelium before and after ovulation. *Biol. Reprod.* 33, 729–738.
27. Kruk, P. A., and Auersperg, N. (1992). Human ovarian surface epithelial cells are capable of physically restructuring extracellular matrix. *Am. J. Obstet. Gynecol.* 167, 1437–1443.
28. Kruk, P. A., Uitto, V. J., Firth, J. D., Dedhar, S., and Auersperg, N. (1994). Reciprocal interactions between human ovarian surface epithelial cells and adjacent extracellular matrix. *Exp. Cell Res.* 215, 97–108.
29. Gillett, W. R., Mitchell, A., and Hurst, P. R. (1991). A scanning electron microscopic study of the human ovarian surface epithelium: Characterization of two cell types. *Hum. Reprod.* 6, 645–650.
30. Nicosia, S. V. (1987). The aging ovary. *Med. Clin. North Am.* 71, 1–9.
31. Hamilton, T. C. (1992). Ovarian cancer, Part I: Biology. *Curr. Probl. Cancer* 16, 1–57.
32. Blaustein, A. (1981). Surface cells and inclusion cysts in fetal ovaries. *Gynecol. Oncol.* 12, 222–233.
33. Blaustein, A., Kantius, M., Kaganowicz, A., Pervez, N., and Wells, J. (1982). Inclusions in ovaries of females aged day 1–30 years. *Int. J. Gynecol. Pathol.* 1, 145–153.

34. Deligdisch, L., and Gil, J. (1989). Characterization of ovarian dysplasia by interactive morphometry. *Cancer* 63, 748–755.
35. Bell, D. A., and Scully, R. E. (1994). Early de novo ovarian carcinoma. A study of fourteen cases. *Cancer* 73, 1859–1864.
36. Scully, R. E. (1995). Early de novo ovarian cancer and cancer developing in benign ovarian lesions. *Int. J. Gynaecol. Obstet.* 49 (Suppl), S9–S15.
37. Mittal, K. R., Zeleniuch-Jacquotte, A., Cooper, J. L., and Demopoulos, R. I. (1993). Contralateral ovary in unilateral ovarian carcinoma: a search for preneoplastic lesions. *Int. J. Gynecol. Pathol.* 12, 59–63.
38. Resta, L., Russo, S., Colucci, G. A., and Prat, J. (1993). Morphologic precursors of ovarian epithelial tumors. *Obstet. Gynecol.* 82, 181–186.
39. Jacobs, I. J., Kohler, M. F., Wiseman, R. W., Marks, J. R., Whitaker, R., Kerns, B. A., Humphrey, P., Berchuck, A., Ponder, B. A., and Bast, R. C. J. (1992). Clonal origin of epithelial ovarian carcinoma: analysis by loss of heterozygosity, p53 mutation, and X-chromosome inactivation. *J. Natl. Cancer Inst.* 84, 1793–1798.
40. Mok, C. H., Tsao, S. W., Knapp, R. C., Fishbaugh, P. M., and Lau, C. C. (1992). Unifocal origin of advanced human epithelial ovarian cancers. *Cancer Res.* 52, 5119–5122.
41. Scully, R. E., Young, R. H., and Clement, P. B. (1996). *Tumors of the Ovary, Maldeveloped Gonads, Fallopian Tube, and Broad Ligament.* Washington, DC: Armed Forces Institute of Pathology.
42. Fathalla, M. F. (1971). Incessant ovulation: A factor in ovarian neoplasia? *Lancet* 2, 163.
43. Fredrickson, T. N. (1987). Ovarian tumors of the hen. *Environ. Health Perspect.* 73, 35–51.
44. Whittemore, A. S., Harris, R., and Itnyre, J. (1992). Characteristics relating to ovarian cancer risk: collaborative analysis of 12 US case-control studies. IV. The pathogenesis of epithelial ovarian cancer. Collaborative Ovarian Cancer Group. *Am. J. Epidemiol.* 136, 1212–1220.
45. La Vecchia, C., and Franceschi, S. (1999). Oral contraceptives and ovarian cancer. *Eur. J. Cancer Prev.* 8, 297–304.
46. Burmeister, L., and Healy, D. L. (1998). Ovarian cancer in infertility patients. *Ann. Med.* 30, 525–528.
47. Murdoch, W. J., Townsend, R. S., and McDonnel, A. C. (2001). Ovulation-induced DNA damage in ovarian surface epithelial cells of ewes: Prospective regulatory mechanisms of repair/survival and apoptosis. *Biol. Reprod.* 65, 1417–1424.
48. Godwin, A. K., Testa, J. R., Handel, L. M., Liu, Z., Vanderveer, L. A., Tracey, P. A., and Hamilton, T. C. (1992a). Spontaneous transformation of rat ovarian surface epithelial cells: Association with cytogenetic changes and implications of repeated ovulation in the etiology of ovarian cancer. *J. Natl. Cancer Inst.* 84, 592–601.
49. Roby, K. F., Taylor, C. C., Sweetwood, J. P., Cheng, Y., Pace, J. L., Tawfik, O., Persons, D. L., Smith, P. G., and Terranova, P. F. (2000). Development of a syngeneic mouse model for events related to ovarian cancer. *Carcinogenesis* 21, 585–591.
50. Clow, O. L., Hurst, P. R., and Fleming, J. S. (2002). Changes in the mouse ovarian surface epithelium with age and ovulation number. *Mol. Cell Endocrinol.* 191, 105–111.
51. Miettinen, P. J., Ebner, R., Lopez, A. R., and Derynck, R. (1994). TGF-beta induced transdifferentiation of mammary epithelial cells to mesenchymal cells: Involvement of type I receptors. *J. Cell Biol.* 127, 2021–2036.
52. Salazar, H., Godwin, A. K., Daly, M. B., Laub, P. B., Hogan, W. M., Rosenblum, N., Boente, M. P., Lynch, H. T., and Hamilton. T. C. (1996). Microscopic benign and invasive malignant neoplasms and a cancer-prone phenotype in prophylactic oophorectomies. *J. Natl. Cancer Inst.* 88, 1810–1820.
53. Silvester, L. M., and Luck, M. R. (1999). Distribution of extracellular matrix components in the developing ruminant corpus luteum: A wound repair hypothesis for luteinization. *J. Reprod. Fertil.* 116, 187–198.
54. Capo-Chichi, C. D., Smith, E. R., Yang, D. H., Roland, I. H., Vanderveer, L., Cohen, C., Hamilton, T. C., Godwin, A. K., and Xu, X. X. (2002). Dynamic alterations of the extracellular environment of ovarian surface epithelial cells in premalignant transformation, tumorigenicity, and metastasis. *Cancer* 95, 1802–1815.
55. Cramer, D. W., and Welch, W. R. (1983). Determinants of ovarian cancer risk. II. Inferences regarding pathogenesis. *J. Natl. Cancer Inst.* 71, 717–721.
56. Sell, A., Bertelsen, K., Andersen, J. E., Stroyer, I., and Panduro, J. (1990). Randomized study of whole-abdomen irradiation versus pelvic irradiation plus cyclophosphamide in treatment of early ovarian cancer. *Gynecol. Oncol.* 37, 367–373.
57. Chakravarti, S., Collins, W. P., Forecast, J. D., Newton, J. R., Oram, D. H., and Studd, J. W. (1976). Hormonal profiles after the menopause. *Br. Med. J.* 2, 784–787.
58. Scaglia, H., Medina, M., Pinto-Ferreira, A. L., Vazques, G., Gual, C., and Perez-Palacios, G. (1976). Pituitary LH and FSH secretion and responsiveness in women of old age. *Acta Endocrinol. (Copenh.)* 81, 673–679.
59. Richardson, S. J. (1993). The biological basis of the menopause. In *Baillier's clinical endocrinology and metabolism*, vol. 7: The menopause, ed. H. G. Burger, 1–16. Toronto: Baillere Tindall.
60. Zheng, W. X., Magid, M. S., Kramer, E. E., and Chen, Y. T. (1996). Follicle-stimulating hormone receptor is expressed in human ovarian surface epithelium and fallopian tube. *Am. J. Pathol.* 148, 47–53.
61. Konishi, I., Kuroda, H., and Mandai, M. (1999). Review: Gonadotropins and development of ovarian cancer. *Oncology* 57 (Suppl. 2), 45–48.
62. Osterholzer, H. O., Streibel, E. J., and Nicosia, S. V. (1985). Growth effects of protein hormones on cultured rabbit ovarian surface epithelial cells. *Biol. Reprod.* 33, 247–258.
63. Davies, B. R., Finnigan, D. S., Smith, S. K., and Ponder, B. A. (1999). Administration of gonadotropins stimulates proliferation of normal mouse ovarian surface epithelium. *Gynecol. Endocrinol.* 13, 75–81.
64. Wright, J. W., Toth-Fejel, S., Stouffer, R. L., and Rodland, K. D. (2002). Proliferation of rhesus ovarian surface epithelial cells in culture: lack of mitogenic response to steroid or gonadotropic hormones. *Endocrinology* 143, 2198–2207.
65. Kammerman, S., Demopoulos, R. I., Raphael, C., and Ross, J. (1981). Gonadotropic hormone binding to human ovarian tumors. *Hum. Pathol.* 12, 886–890.
66. Kobayashi, F., Monma, C., Nanbu, K., Konishi, I., Sagawa, N., and Mori, T. (1996). Rapid growth of an ovarian clear cell

carcinoma expressing LH/hCG receptor arising from endometriosis during early pregnancy. *Gynecol. Oncol.* 62, 309–313.

67. Mandai, M., Konishi, I., Kuroda, H., Fukumoto, M., Komatsu, T., Yamamoto, S., Nanbu, K., Rao, C. V., and Mori, T. (1997). Messenger ribonucleic acid expression of LH/hCG receptor gene in human ovarian carcinomas. *Eur. J. Cancer* 33, 1501–1507.
68. Emons, G., Ortmann, O., Pahwa, G. S., Hackenberg, R., Oberheuser, F., and Schulz, K. D. (1992). Intracellular actions of gonadotropic and peptide hormones and the therapeutic value of GnRH-agonists in ovarian cancer. *Acta Obstet. Gynecol. Scand. Suppl.* 155, 31–38.
69. Godwin, A. K., Perez, R. P., Johnson, S. W., Hamaguchi, K., and Hamilton, T. C. (1992). Growth regulation of ovarian cancer. *Hematol. Oncol. Clin. North Am.* 6, 829–841.
70. Wimalasena, J., Dostal, R., and Meehan, D. (1992). Gonadotropins, estradiol, and growth factors regulate epithelial ovarian cancer cell growth. *Gynecol. Oncol.* 46, 345–350.
71. Kurbacher, C. M., Jager, W., Kurbacher, J. A., Bittl, A., Wildt, L., and Lang, N. (1995). Influence of human luteinizing hormone on cell growth and CA 125 secretion of primary epithelial ovarian carcinomas in vitro. *Tumour Biol.* 16, 374–384.
72. Simon, W. E., Albrecht, M., Hansel, M., Dietel, M., and Holzel, F. (1983). Cell lines derived from human ovarian carcinomas: growth stimulation by gonadotropic and steroid hormones. *J. Natl. Cancer Inst.* 70, 839–845.
73. Kuroda, H., Mandai, M., Konishi, I., Yura, Y., Tsuruta, Y., Hamid, A. A., Nanbu, K., Matsushita, K., and Mori, T. (1998). Human chorionic gonadotropin (hCG) inhibits cisplatin-induced apoptosis in ovarian cancer cells: possible role of up-regulation of insulin-like growth factor-1 by hCG. *Int. J. Cancer* 76, 571–578.
74. Schiffenbauer, Y. S., Abramovitch, R., Meir, G., Nevo, N., Holzinger, M., Itin, A., Keshet, E., and Neeman, M. (1997). Loss of ovarian function promotes angiogenesis in human ovarian carcinoma. *Proc. Natl. Acad. Sci. USA* 94, 13203–13208.
75. Zheng, W., Lu, J. J., Luo, F., Zheng, Y., Feng, Y., Felix, J. C., Lauchlan, S. C., and Pike, M. C. (2000). Ovarian epithelial tumor growth promotion by follicle-stimulating hormone and inhibition of the effect by luteinizing hormone. *Gynecol. Oncol.* 76, 80–88.
76. Choi, K. C., Kang, S. K., Tai, C. J., Auersperg, N., and Leung, P. C. (2002). Follicle-stimulating hormone activates mitogen-activated protein kinase in preneoplastic and neoplastic ovarian surface epithelial cells. *J. Clin. Endocrinol. Metab.* 87, 2245–2253.
77. Kang, S. K., Choi, K. C., Cheng, K. W., Nathwani, P. S., Auersperg, N., and Leung, P. C. (2000). Role of gonadotropin-releasing hormone as an autocrine growth factor in human ovarian surface epithelium. *Endocrinology* 141, 72–80.
78. Choi, K. C., Auersperg, N., and Leung, P. C. (2001). Expression and antiproliferative effect of a second form of gonadotropin-releasing hormone in normal and neoplastic ovarian surface epithelial cells. *J. Clin. Endocrinol. Metab.* 86, 5075–5078.
79. Kim, J. H., Park, D. C., Kim, J. W., Choi, Y. K., Lew, Y. O., Kim, D. H., Jung, J. K., Lim, Y. A., and Namkoong, S. E. (1999). Antitumor effect of GnRH agonist in epithelial ovarian cancer. *Gynecol. Oncol.* 74, 170–180.
80. Kimura, A., Ohmichi, M., Kurachi, H., Ikegami, H., Hayakawa, J., Tasaka, K., Kanda, Y., Nishio, Y., Jikihara, H., Matsuura, N., and Murata, Y. (1999). Role of mitogen-activated protein kinase/extracellular signal-regulated kinase cascade in gonadotropin-releasing hormone-induced growth inhibition of a human ovarian cancer cell line. *Cancer Res.* 59, 5133–5142.
81. Peterson, C. M., Jolles, C. J., Carrell, D. T., Straight, R. C., Jones, K. P., Poulson, A. M. J., and Hatasaka, H. H. (1994). GnRH agonist therapy in human ovarian epithelial carcinoma (OVCAR-3) heterotransplanted in the nude mouse is characterized by latency and transience. *Gynecol. Oncol.* 52, 26–30.
82. Manetta, A., Gamboa-Vujicic, G., Paredes, P., Emma, D., Liao, S., Leong, L., Asch, B., and Schally, A. (1995). Inhibition of growth of human ovarian cancer in nude mice by luteinizing hormone-releasing hormone antagonist Cetrorelix (SB-75). *Fertil Steril* 63, 282–287.
83. Yano, T., Pinski, J., Halmos, G., Szepeshazi, K., Groot, K., and Schally, A. V. (1994). Inhibition of growth of OV-1063 human epithelial ovarian cancer xenografts in nude mice by treatment with luteinizing hormone-releasing hormone antagonist SB-75. *Proc. Natl. Acad. Sci. USA* 91, 7090–7094.
84. Van der Vange, N., Greggi, S., Burger, C. W., Kenemans, P., and Vermorken, J. B. (1995). Experience with hormonal therapy in advanced epithelial ovarian cancer. *Acta Oncol.* 34, 813–820.
85. Emons, G., Ortmann, O., Teichert, H. M., Fassl, H., Löhrs, U., Kullander, S., Kauppila, A., Ayalon, D., Schally, A., and Oberheuser, F. (1996). Luteinizing hormone-releasing hormone agonist triptorelin in combination with cytotoxic chemotherapy in patients with advanced ovarian carcinoma: A prospective double blind randomized trial. *Cancer* 78, 1452–1460.
86. Falkson, C. I., Falkson, H. C., and Falkson, G. (1996). Cisplatin versus cisplatin plus D-Trp-6-LHRH in the treatment of ovarian cancer: A pilot trial to investigate the effect of the addition of a GnRH analogue to cisplatin. *Oncology* 53, 313–317.
87. Gondos, B. (1975). Surface epithelium of the developing ovary. Possible correlation with ovarian neoplasia. *Am. J. Pathol.* 81, 303–321.
88. Karlan, B. Y., Jones, J., Greenwald, M., and Lagasse, L. D. (1995). Steroid hormone effects on the proliferation of human ovarian surface epithelium in vitro. *Am. J. Obstet. Gynecol.* 173, 97–104.
89. Lau, K. M., Mok, S. C., and Ho, S. M. (1999). Expression of human estrogen receptor-alpha and -beta, progesterone receptor, and androgen receptor mRNA in normal and malignant ovarian epithelial cells. *Proc. Natl. Acad. Sci. USA* 96, 5722–5727.
90. Hamilton, T. C., Davies, P., and Criffiths, K. (1983). Steroid hormone receptor status of the normal and neoplastic ovarian surface germinal epithelium. In *Factors Regulating Ovarian Function*, eds. G. S. Greenwald and P. F. Terranova, 81–85. New York: Raven Press.
91. Murdoch, W. J., and Van Kirk, E. A. (2002). Steroid hormonal regulation of proliferative, p53 tumor suppressor, and

apoptotic responses of sheep ovarian surface epithelial cells. *Mol. Cell Endocrinol.* 186, 61–67.

92. Bai, W., Oliveros-Saunders, B., Wang, Q., Acevedo-Duncan, M. E., and Nicosia, S. V. (2000). Estrogen stimulation of ovarian surface epithelial cell proliferation. *In Vitro Cell Dev. Biol. Anim.* 36, 657–666.
93. Lacey Jr., J. V., Mink, P. J., Lubin, J. H., Sherman, M. E., Troisi, R., Hartge, P., Schatzkin, A., and Schairer, C. (2002). Menopausal hormone replacement therapy and risk of ovarian cancer. *JAMA* 288, 334–341.
94. Kang, S. K., Choi, K. C., Tai, C. J., Auersperg, N., and Leung, P. C. (2001). Estradiol regulates gonadotropin-releasing hormone (GnRH) and its receptor gene expression and antagonizes the growth inhibitory effects of GnRH in human ovarian surface epithelial and ovarian cancer cells. *Endocrinology* 142, 580–588.
95. Liu, Y., Lin, L., and Zarnegar, R. (1994). Modulation of hepatocyte growth factor gene expression by estrogen in mouse ovary. *Mol. Cell Endocrinol.* 104, 173–81.
96. Rodriguez, G. C., Walmer, D. K., Cline, M., Krigman, H., Lessey, B. A., Whitaker, R. S., Dodge, R., and Hughes, C. L. (1998). Effect of progestin on the ovarian epithelium of macaques: Cancer prevention through apoptosis? *J. Soc. Gynecol. Investig.* 5, 271–276.
97. Adami, H. O., Hsieh, C. C., Lambe, M., Trichopoulos, D., Leon, D., Persson, I., Ekbom, A., and Janson, P. O. (1994). Parity, age at first childbirth, and risk of ovarian cancer. *Lancet* 344, 1250–1254.
98. Kommoss, F., Pfisterer, J., Thome, M., Schafer, W., Sauerbrei, W., and Pfleiderer, A. (1992). Steroid receptors in ovarian carcinoma: Immunohistochemical determination may lead to new aspects. *Gynecol. Oncol.* 47, 317–322.99.
99. Brandenberger, A. W., Tee, M. K., and Jaffe, R. B. (1998). Estrogen receptor alpha (ER-alpha) and beta (ER-beta) mRNAs in normal ovary, ovarian serous cystadenocarcinoma and ovarian cancer cell lines: Down-regulation of ER-beta in neoplastic tissues. *J. Clin. Endocrinol. Metab.* 83, 1025–1028.
100. Hamilton, T. C., Young, R. C., McKoy, W. M., Grotzinger, K. R., Green, J. A., Chu, E. W., Whang-Peng, J., Rogan, A. M., Green, W. R., and Ozols, R. F. (1983). Characterization of a human ovarian carcinoma cell line (NIH:OVCAR-3) with androgen and estrogen receptors. *Cancer Res.* 43, 5379–5389.
101. Kuhnel, R., de Graaff, J., Rao, B. R., and Stolk, J. G. (1987). Androgen receptor predominance in human ovarian carcinoma. *J. Steroid Biochem.* 26, 393–397.
102. Grenman, S. E., Klemi, P., Toikkanen, S., Kaihola, H. L., Laippala, P., Maenpaa, J., Makinen, J., and Gronroos, M. (1994). Steroid hormone receptors and flow cytometric DNA ploidy in ovarian carcinoma. *Ann. Chir. Gynaecol. Suppl.* 208, 15–19.
103. Baldwin, W. S., Curtis, S. W., Cauthen, C. A., Risinger, J. I., Korach, K. S., and Barrett, J. C. (1998). BG-1 ovarian cell line: An alternative model for examining estrogen-dependent growth in vitro. *In Vitro Cell Dev. Biol. Anim.* 34, 649–654.
104. Vihko, R., Isotalo, H., Kauppila, A., and Vierikko, P. (1983). Female sex steroid receptors in gynecological malignancies: Clinical correlates. *J. Steroid Biochem.* 19, 827–832.
105. Iversen, O. E., Skaarland, E., and Utaaker, E. (1986). Steroid receptor content in human ovarian tumors: Survival of patients with ovarian carcinoma related to steroid receptor content. *Gynecol. Oncol.* 23, 65–76.
106. Quinn, M. A., Rome, R. M., Cauchi, M., and Fortune, D. W. (1988). Steroid receptors and ovarian tumors: Variation within primary tumors and between primary tumors and metastases. *Gynecol. Oncol.* 31, 424–429.
107. Slotman, B. J., Nauta, J. J., and Rao, B. R. (1990). Survival of patients with ovarian cancer. Apart from stage and grade, tumor progesterone receptor content is a prognostic indicator. *Cancer* 66, 740–744.
108. Kieback, D. G., McCamant, S. K., Press, M. F., Atkinson, E. N., Gallager, H. S., Edwards, C. L., Hajek, R. A., and Jones, L. A. (1993). Improved prediction of survival in advanced adenocarcinoma of the ovary by immunocytochemical analysis and the composition adjusted receptor level of the estrogen receptor. *Cancer Res.* 53, 5188–5192.
109. Nash, J. D., Ozols, R. F., Smyth, J. F., and Hamilton, T. C. (1989). Estrogen and anti-estrogen effects on the growth of human epithelial ovarian cancer in vitro. *Obstet. Gynecol.* 73, 1009–1016.
110. Langdon, S. P., Hawkes, M. M., Lawrie, S. S., Hawkins, R. A., Tesdale, A. L., Crew, A. J., Miller, W. R., and Smyth, J. F. (1990). Oestrogen receptor expression and the effects of oestrogen and tamoxifen on the growth of human ovarian carcinoma cell lines. *Br. J. Cancer* 62, 213–216.
111. Langdon, S. P., Ritchie, A., Young, K., Crew, A. J., Sweeting, V., Bramley, T., Hillier, S., Hawkins, R. A., Tesdale, A. L., and Smyth, J. F. (1993). Contrasting effects of 17 beta-estradiol on the growth of human ovarian carcinoma cells in vitro and in vivo. *Int. J. Cancer* 55, 459–464.
112. Wimalasena, J., Meehan, D., Dostal, R., Foster, J. S., Cameron, M., and Smith, M. (1993). Growth factors interact with estradiol and gonadotropins in the regulation of ovarian cancer cell growth and growth factor receptors. *Oncol Res.* 5, 325–337.
113. Langdon, S. P., Hirst, G. L., Miller, E. P., Hawkins, R. A., Tesdale, A. L., Smyth, J. F., and Miller, W. R. (1994). The regulation of growth and protein expression by estrogen in vitro: A study of 8 human ovarian carcinoma cell lines. *J. Steroid Biochem. Mol. Biol.* 50, 131–135.
114. Simpson, B. J., Langdon, S. P., Rabiasz, G. J., Macleod, K. G., Hirst, G. L., Bartlett, J. M., Crew, A. J., Hawkins, R. A., Macineira-Perez, P. P., Smyth, J. F., and Miller, W. R. (1998). Estrogen regulation of transforming growth factor-alpha in ovarian cancer. *J. Steroid Biochem. Mol. Biol.* 64, 137–145.
115. Ridderheim, M., Stendahl, U., and Backstrom, T. (1994). Progesterone and estradiol stimulate release of epidermal growth factor/transforming growth factor alpha by ovarian tumours in vitro. *Anticancer Res.* 14, 2763–2768.
116. Chien, C.-H., Wang, F.-F., and Hamilton, T. C. (1994). Transcriptional activation of c-*myc* proto-oncogene by estrogen in human ovarian cancer cells. *Mol. Cell Endocrinol.* 99, 11–19.
117. Choi, K. C., Kang, S. K., Tai, C. J., Auersperg, N., and Leung, P. C. (2001). Estradiol up-regulates antiapoptotic Bcl-2 messenger ribonucleic acid and protein in tumorigenic ovarian surface epithelium cells. *Endocrinology* 142, 2351–2360.

118. Zachos, G., Varras, M., Koffa, M., Ergazaki, M., and Spandidos, D. A. (1996). Glucocorticoid and estrogen receptors have elevated activity in human endometrial and ovarian tumors as compared to the adjacent normal tissues and recognize sequence elements of the H-*ras* proto-oncogene. *Jpn. J. Cancer Res.* 87, 916–922.
119. Bu, S. Z., Yin, D. L., Ren, X. H., Jiang, L. Z., Wu, Z. J., Gao, Q. R., and Pei, G. (1997). Progesterone induces apoptosis and up-regulation of p53 expression in human ovarian carcinoma cell lines. *Cancer* 79, 1944–1950.
120. Rao, B. R., and Slotman, B. J. (1991). Endocrine factors in common epithelial ovarian cancer. *Endocr. Rev.* 12, 14–26.
121. Heinonen, P. K., Koivula, T., and Pystynen, P. (1985). Elevated progesterone levels in serum and ovarian venous blood in patients with ovarian tumors. *Acta Obstet. Gynecol. Scand.* 64, 649–652.
122. Abrahamsson, G., Janson, P. O., and Kullander, S. (1997). Steroid release from two human epithelial ovarian tumors: Evidence for an intrinsic production in vitro. *Gynecol. Oncol.* 64, 99–104.
123. Okubo, T., Mok, S. C., and Chen, S. (2000). Regulation of aromatase expression in human ovarian surface epithelial cells. *J. Clin. Endocrinol. Metab.* 85, 4889–4899.
124. Chadha, S., Rao, B. R., Slotman, B. J., Van Vroonhoven, C. C. J., and Van der Kwast, T. H. (1993). An immunohistochemical evaluation of androgen and progesterone receptors in ovarian tumors. *Hum. Pathol.* 24, 90–95.
125. Ilekis, J. V., Connor, J. P., Prins, G. S., Ferrer, K., Niederberger, C., and Scoccia, B. (1997). Expression of epidermal growth factor and androgen receptors in ovarian cancer. *Gynecol. Oncol.* 66, 250–254.
126. Adashi, E. Y. (1994). The climacteric ovary as a functional gonadotropin-driven androgen-producing gland. *Fertil. Steril.* 62, 20–27.
127. Helzlsouer, K. J., Alberg, A. J., Gordon, G. B., Longcope, C., Bush, T. L., Hoffman, S. C., and Comstock, G. W. (1995). Serum gonadotropins and steroid hormones and the development of ovarian cancer. *JAMA* 274, 1926–1930.
128. Schildkraut, J. M., Schwingl, P. J., Bastos, E., Evanoff, A., and Hughes, C. (1996). Epithelial ovarian cancer risk among women with polycystic ovary syndrome. *Obstet. Gynecol.* 88, 554–559.
129. Silva, E. G., Tornos, C., Fritsche, H. A. J., el-Naggar, A., Gray, K., Ordonez, N. G., Luna, M., and Gershenson, D. (1997). The induction of benign epithelial neoplasms of the ovaries of guinea pigs by testosterone stimulation: A potential animal model. *Mod. Pathol.* 10, 879–883.
130. Slotman, B. J., and Rao, B. R. (1989). Response to inhibition of androgen action of human ovarian cancer cells in vitro. *Cancer Lett.* 45, 213–220.
131. Edmondson, R. J., Monaghan, J. M., and Davies, B. R. (2002). The human ovarian surface epithelium is an androgen responsive tissue. *Br. J. Cancer* 86, 879–885.
132. Evangelou, A., Jindal, S. K., Brown, T. J., and Letarte, M. (2000). Down-regulation of transforming growth factor beta receptors by androgen in ovarian cancer cells. *Cancer Res.* 60, 929–935.
133. Mintz, B., and Russell, E. S. (1957). Gene-induced embryological modifications of primordial germ cells in the mouse. *J. Exp. Zool.* 134, 207–237.
134. Murphy, E. D. (1972). Hyperplastic and early neoplastic changes in the ovaries of mice after genic deletion of germ cells. *J. Natl. Cancer Inst.* 48, 1283–1295.
135. Murphy, E. D., and Beamer, W. G. (1973). Plasma gonadotropin levels during early stages of ovarian tumorigenesis in mice of the *Wx/Wv* genotype. *Cancer Res.* 33, 721–723.
136. Ishimura, K., Matsuda, H., Tatsumi, H., Fujita, H., Terada, N., and Kitamura, Y. (1986). Ultrastructural changes in the ovaries of *Sl/Slt* mutant mice, showing developmental deficiency of follicles and tubular adenomas. *Arch. Histol. Jpn.* 49, 379–389.
137. Duncan, M. K., and Chada, K. K. (1993). Incidence of tubulostromal adenoma of the ovary in aged germ cell-deficient mice. *J. Comp. Pathol.* 109, 13–19.
138. Capen, C. C., Beamer, W. G., Tennent, B. J., and Stitzel, K. A. (1995). Mechanisms of hormone-mediated carcinogenesis of the ovary in mice. *Mutat. Res.* 333, 143–151.
139. Vanderhyden, B. C., Caron, P. J., Buccione, R., and Eppig, J. J. (1990). Developmental pattern of the secretion of cumulus expansion-enabling factor by mouse oocytes and the role of oocytes in promoting granulosa cell differentiation. *Dev. Biol.* 140, 307–317.
140. Vanderhyden, B. C., Telfer, E. E., and Eppig, J. J. (1992). Mouse oocytes promote proliferation of granulosa cells from preantral and antral follicles *in vitro*. *Biol. Reprod.* 46, 1196–1204.
141. Dong, J., Albertini, D. F., Nishimori, K., Kumar, T. R., Lu, N., and Matzuk, M. M. (1996). Growth differentiation factor-9 is required during early ovarian folliculogenesis. *Nature* 383, 531–535.
142. Teixeira Filho, F. L., Baracat, E. C., Lee, T. H., Suh, C. S., Matsui, M., Chang, R. J., Shimasaki, S., and Erickson, G. F. (2002). Aberrant expression of growth differentiation factor-9 in oocytes of women with polycystic ovary syndrome. *J. Clin. Endocrinol. Metab.* 87, 1337–1344.
143. Tennent, B. J., and Beamer, W. G. (1986). Ovarian tumors not induced by irradiation and gonadotropins in hypogonadal (hpg) mice. *Biol. Reprod.* 34, 751–760.
144. Blaakaer, J., Baeksted, M., Micic, S., Albrectsen, P., Rygaard, J. and Bock, J. (1995). Gonadotropin-releasing hormone agonist suppression of ovarian tumorigenesis in mice of the *Wx/Wv* genotype. *Biol. Reprod.* 53, 775–779.
145. Cramer, D. W., Muto, M. G., Reichardt, J. K., Xu, H., Welch, W. R., Valles, B., and Ng, W. G. (1994). Characteristics of women with a family history of ovarian cancer. I. Galactose consumption and metabolism. *Cancer* 74, 1309–1317.
146. Teinturier, C., Hartmann, O., Valteau-Couanet, D., Benhamou, E., and Bougneres, P. F. (1998). Ovarian function after autologous bone marrow transplantation in childhood: High-dose busulfan is a major cause of ovarian failure. *Bone Marrow Transplant.* 22, 989–994.
147. Friedlander, M. L. (1998). Prognostic factors in ovarian cancer. *Semin. Oncol.* 25, 305–314.
148. Auersperg, N., Edelson, M. I., Mok, S. C., Johnson, S. W., and Hamilton, T. C. (1998). The biology of ovarian cancer. *Semin. Oncol.* 25, 281–304.

149. Lynch, H. T., Casey, M. J., Lynch, J., White, T. E., and Godwin, A. K. (1998). Genetics and ovarian carcinoma. *Semin. Oncol.* 25, 265–280.
150. Aunoble, B., Sanches, R., Didier, E., and Bignon, Y.-J. (2000). Major oncogenes and tumor suppressor genes involved in epithelial ovarian cancer. *Int. J. Oncol.* 16, 567–576.
151. Sklar, M. D. (1988). Increased resistance to cis-diamminedichloroplatinum(II) in NIH 3T3 cells transformed by ras oncogenes. *Cancer Res.* 48, 793–797.
152. Sklar, M. D. (1988). The ras oncogenes increase the intrinsic resistance of NIH 3T3 cells to ionizing radiation. *Science* 239, 645–647.
153. Scambia, G., Masciullo, V., Benedetti, P. P., Marone, M., Ferrandina, G., Todaro, N., Bellacosa, A., Jain, S. K., Neri, G., Piffanelli, A., and Mancuso, S. (1997). Prognostic significance of ras/p21 alterations in human ovarian cancer. *Br. J. Cancer* 75, 1547–1553.
154. Hoffman, A. G., Burghardt, R. C., Tilley, R., and Auersperg, N. (1993). An *in vitro* model of ovarian epithelial carcinogenesis: Changes in cell-cell communication and adhesion occuring during neoplastic progression. *Int. J. Cancer* 54, 828–838.
155. Berchuck, A., Kamel, A., Whitaker, R., Kerns, B., Olt, G., Kinney, R., Soper, J. T., Dodge, R., Clarke-Pearson, D. L., and Marks, P. (1990). Overexpression of HER-2/neu is associated with poor survival in advanced epithelial ovarian cancer. *Cancer Res.* 50, 4087–4091.
156. Gordon, A. W., Pegues, J. C., Johnson, G. R., Kannan, B., Auersperg, N., and Stromberg, K. (1995). mRNA phenotyping of the major ligands and receptors of the EGF supergene family in human ovarian epithelial cells. *Cancer Lett.* 89, 63–71.
157. Ruler, B. L., Carter, D., Foellmer, H. G., and Kacinski, B. M. (1992). Neu proto-oncogene amplification and expression in ovarian adenocarcinoma cell lines. *Am. J. Pathol.* 140, 23–31.
158. Zheng, J. P., Robinson, W. R., Ehlen, T., Yu, M. C., and Dubeau, L. (1991). Distinction of low grade from high grade human ovarian carcinomas on the basis of losses of heterozygosity on chromosomes 3, 6, and 11 and HER-2/neu gene amplification. *Cancer Res.* 51, 4045–4051.
159. Yu, D. H., Liu, B. L., Tan, M., Li, J. Z., Wang, S. S., and Hung, M. C. (1996). Overexpression of c-erbB-2/*neu* in breast cancer cells confers increased resistance to Taxol via *mdr*-1-independent mechanisms. *Oncogene* 13, 1359–1365.
160. Yu, D., Wang, S. S., Dulski, K. M., Tsai, C. M., Nicolson, G. L., and Hung, M. C. (1994). c-erbB-2/neu overexpression enhances metastatic potential of human lung cancer cells by induction of metastasis-associated properties. *Cancer Res.* 54, 3260–3266.
161. Davies, B. R., Auersperg, N., Worsley, S. D., and Ponder, B. A. (1998). Transfection of rat ovarian surface epithelium with erb-B2/neu induces transformed phenotypes in vitro and the tumorigenic phenotype in vivo. *Am. J. Pathol.* 152, 297–306.
162. Yasue, H., Takeda, A., and Ishibashi, M. (1987). Amplification of the c-myc gene and the elevation of its transcripts in human ovarian tumor lines. *Cell Struct. Funct.* 12, 121–125.
163. Tashiro, H., Miyazaki, K., Okamura, H., Iwai, A., and Fukumoto, M. (1992). c-myc over-expression in human primary ovarian tumours: its relevance to tumour progression. *Int. J. Cancer* 50, 828–833.
164. Katsaros, D., Theillet, C., Zola, P., Louason, G., Sanfilippo, B., Isaia, E., Arisio, R., Giardina, G., and Sismondi, P. (1995). Concurrent abnormal expression of *erb*B-2, *myc* and *ras* genes is associated with poor outcome of ovarian cancer patients. *Anticancer Res.* 15, 1501–1510.
165. Scully, R., Chen, J., Plug, A., Xiao, Y., Weaver, D., Feunteun, J., Ashley, T., and Livingston, D. M. (1997). Association of BRCA1 with Rad51 in mitotic and meiotic cells. *Cell* 88, 265–275.
166. Chen, J. J., Silver, D., Cantor, S., Livingston, D. M., and Scully, R. (1999). BRCA1, BRCA2, and Rad51 operate in a common DNA damage response pathway. *Cancer Res.* 59, 1752s–1756s.
167. Scully, R., Anderson, S. F., Chao, D. M., Wei, W., Ye, L., Young, R. A., Livingston, D. M., and Parvin, J. D. (1997). BRCA1 is a component of the RNA polymerase II holoenzyme. *Proc. Natl. Acad. Sci. USA* 94, 5605–5610.
168. Holt, J. T., Thompson, M. E., Szabo, C., Robinson-Benion, C., Arteaga, C. L., King, M. C., and Jensen, R. A. (1996). Growth retardation and tumour inhibition by BRCA1. *Nat. Genet.* 12, 298–302.
169. Narod, S. A., Ford, D., Devilee, P., Barkardottir, R. B., Lynch, H. T., Smith, S. A., Ponder, B. A. J., Weber, B. L., Garber, J. E., Birch, J. M., Cornelis, R. S., Kelsell, D. P., Spurr, N. K., Smyth, E., Haites, N., Sobol, H., Bignon, Y.-J., Chang-Claude, J., Hamann, U., Lindblom, A., Borg, A., Piver, M. S., Gallion, H. H., and Struewing, J. P. (1995). An evaluation of genetic heterogeneity in 145 breast-ovarian cancer families. *Am. J. Hum. Genet.* 56, 254–264.
170. Futreal, P. A., Liu, Q., Shattuck-Eidens, D., Cochran, C., Harshman, K., Tavtigian, S., Bennett, L. M., Haugen-Strano, A., Swensen, J., Miki, Y., Eddington, K., McClure, M., Frye, C., Weaver-Feldhaus, J., Ding, W., Gholami, Z., Söderkvist, P., Terry, L., Jhanwar, S., Berchuck, A., Iglehart, J. D., Marks, J., Ballinger, D. G., Barrett, J. C., Skolnick, M. H., Kamb, A., and Wiseman, R. (1994). *BRCA1* mutations in primary breast and ovarian carcinomas. *Science* 266, 120–122.
171. Merajver, S. D., Pham, T. M., Caduff, R. F., Chen, M., Poy, E. L., Cooney, K A., Weber, B. L., Collins, F. S., Johnston, C., and Frank, T. S. (1995). Somatic mutations in the *BRCA1* gene in sporadic ovarian tumours. *Nature Genet.* 9, 439–443.
172. Takahashi, H., Behbakht, K., McGovern, P. E., Chiu, H.-C., Couch, F. J., Weber, B. L., Friedman, L. S., King, M.-C., Furusato, M., LiVolsi, V. A., Menzin, A. W., Liu, P. C., Benjamin, I., Morgan, M. A., King, S. A., Rebane, B. A., Cardonick, A., Mikuta, J. J., Rubin, S. C., and Boyd, J. (1995). Mutation analysis of the *BRCA1* gene in ovarian cancers. *Cancer Res.* 55, 2998–3002.
173. Pharoah, P. D., Easton, D. F., Stockton, D. L., Gayther, S., and Ponder, B. A. (1999). Survival in familial, BRCA1-associated, and BRCA2-associated epithelial ovarian cancer. United Kingdom Coordinating Committee for Cancer Research (UKCCCR) Familial Ovarian Cancer Study Group. *Cancer Res.* 59, 868–871.
174. Foster, K. A., Harrington, P., Kerr, J., Russell, P., DiCioccio, R. A., Scott, I. V., Jacobs, I., Chenevix-Trench, G., Ponder, B. A. J., and Gayther, S. A. (1996). Somatic and germline muta-

tions of the *BRCA2* gene in sporadic ovarian cancer. *Cancer Res.* 56, 3622–3625.

175. Runnebaum, I. B., Tong, X. W., Konig, R., Zhao, H., Korner, K., Atkinson, E. N., Kreienberg, R., Kieback, D. G., and Hong, Z. (1995). p53-based blood test for p53PIN3 and risk for sporadic ovarian cancer. *Lancet* 345, 994.
175. Takahashi, H., Chiu, H. C., Bandera, C. A., Behbakht, K., Liu, P. C., Couch, F. J., Weber, B. L., LiVolsi, V. A., Furusato, M., Rebane, B. A., Cardonick, A., Benjamin, I., Morgan, M. A., King, S. A., Mikuta, J. J., Rubin, S. C., and Boyd, J. (1996). Mutations of the BRCA2 gene in ovarian carcinomas. *Cancer Res.* 56, 2738–2741.
176. Santoso, J. T., Tang, D. C., Lane, S. B., Hung, J., Reed, D. J., Muller, C. Y., Carbone, D. P., Lucci, J. A., Miller, D. S., and Mathis, J. M. (1995). Adenovirus-based p53 gene therapy in ovarian cancer. *Gynecol. Oncol.* 59, 171–178.
177. Mujoo, K., Maneval, D. C., Anderson, S. C., and Gutterman, J. U. (1996). Adenoviral-mediated p53 tumor suppressor gene therapy of human ovarian carcinoma. *Oncogene* 12, 1617–1623.
178. Gallardo, D., Drazan, K. E., and McBride, W. H. (1996). Adenovirus-based transfer of wild-type *p53* gene increases ovarian tumor radiosensitivity. *Cancer Res.* 56, 4891–4893.
179. Nielsen, L. L., Lipari, P., Dell, J., Gurnani, M., and Hajian, G. (1998). Adenovirus-mediated p53 gene therapy and paclitaxel have synergistic efficacy in models of human head and neck, ovarian, prostate, and breast cancer. *Clin. Cancer Res.* 4, 835–846.
180. Obata, K., Morland, S. J., Watson, R. H., Hitchcock, A., Chenevix-Trench, G., Thomas, E. J., and Campbell, I. G. (1998). Frequent PTEN/MMAC mutations in endometrioid but not serous or mucinous epithelial ovarian tumors. *Cancer Res.* 58, 2095–2097.
181. Yu, Y., Xu, F., Peng, H., Fang, X., Zhao, S., Li, Y., Cuevas, B., Kuo, W. L., Gray, J. W., Siciliano, M., Mills, G. B., and Bast Jr., R. C. (1999). NOEY2 (ARHI), an imprinted putative tumor suppressor gene in ovarian and breast carcinomas. *Proc. Natl. Acad. Sci. USA* 96, 214–219.
182. Fazili, Z., Sun, W., Mittelstaedt, S., Cohen, C., and Xu, X. X. (1999). Disabled-2 inactivation is an early step in ovarian tumorigenicity. *Oncogene* 18, 3104–3113.
183. Mok, S. C., Chan, W. Y., Wong, K. K., Cheung, K. K., Lau, C. C., Ng, S. W., Baldini, A., Colitti, C. V., Rock, C. O., and Berkowitz, R. S. (1998). DOC-2, a candidate tumor suppressor gene in human epithelial ovarian cancer. *Oncogene* 16, 2381–2387.
184. Tong, X. W., Kieback, D. G., Ramesh, R., and Freeman, S. M. (1999). Molecular aspects of ovarian cancer. Is gene therapy the solution? *Hematol. Oncol. Clin. North Am.* 13, 109–133.
185. Berchuck, A., Rodriguez, G. C., Kamel, A., Dodge, R. K., Soper, J. T., Clarke-Pearson, D. L., and Bast Jr., R. C. (1991). Epidermal growth factor receptor expression in normal ovarian epithelium and ovarian cancer. I. Correlation of receptor expression with prognostic factors in patients with ovarian cancer. *Am. J. Obstet. Gynecol.* 164, 669–674.
186. Siemens, C. H., and Auersperg, N. (1988). Serial propagation of human ovarian surface epithelium in tissue culture. *J. Cell Physiol.* 134, 347–356.
187. Salomon, D. S., Kim, N., Saeki, T., and Ciardiello, F. (1990). Transforming growth factor-alpha: An oncodevelopmental growth factor. *Cancer Cells* 2, 389–397.
188. Jindal, S. K., Snoey, D. M., Lobb, D. K., and Dorrington, J. H. (1994). Transforming growth factor-α localization and role in surface epithelium of normal human ovaries and in ovarian carcinoma cells. *Gynecol. Oncol.* 53, 17–23.
189. Stromberg, K., Collins IV, T. J., Gordon, A. W., Jackson, C. L., and Johnson, G. R. (1992). Transforming growth factor-α acts as an autocrine growth factor in ovarian carcinoma cell lines. *Cancer Res.* 52, 341–347.
190. Marth, C., Lang, T., Cronauer, M. V., Doppler, W., Zeimet, A. G., Bachmair, F., Ullrich, A., and Daxenbichler, G. (1992). Epidermal growth factor reduces HER-2 protein level in human ovarian carcinoma cells. *Int. J. Cancer* 52, 311–316.
191. Park, H. Y. (1997). Inhibition of the proliferative effect of transforming growth factor-alpha by c-myc antisense DNA in human ovarian cancer cells. *Biochem. Mol. Biol. Int.* 43, 1015–1022.
192. Baekelandt, M., Kristensen, G. B., Trope, C. G., Nesland, J. M., and Holm, R. (1999). Epidermal growth factor receptor expression has no independent prognostic significance in advanced ovarian cancer. *Anticancer Res.* 19, 4469–4474.
193. Shayesteh, L., Lu, Y., Kuo, W. L., Baldocchi, R., Godfrey, T., Collins, C., Pinkel, D., Powell, B., Mills, G. B., and Gray, J. W. (1999). PIK3CA is implicated as an oncogene in ovarian cancer. *Nat. Genet.* 21, 99–102.
194. Bellacosa, A., de Feo, D., Godwin, A. K., Bell, D. W., Cheng, J. Q., Altomare, D. A., Wan, M., Dubeau, L., Scambia, G., Masciullo, V., Ferrandina, G., Panici, P. B., Mancuso, S., Neri, G., and Testa, J. R. (1995). Molecular alterations of the AKT2 oncogene in ovarian and breast carcinomas. *Int. J. Cancer* 22, 280–285.
195. Wong, A. S., Kim, S. O., Leung, P. C., Auersperg, N., and Pelech, S. L. (2001). Profiling of protein kinases in the neoplastic transformation of human ovarian surface epithelium. *Gynecol. Oncol.* 82, 305–311.
196. Lyons, R. M., and Moses, H. L. (1990). Transforming growth factors and the regulation of cell proliferation. *Eur. J. Biochem* 187, 467–473.
197. Berchuck, A., Rodriguez, G., Olt, G., Whitaker, R., Boente, M. P., Arrick, B. A., Clarke-Pearson, D. L., and Bast Jr., R. C. (1992). Regulation of growth of normal ovarian epithelial cells and ovarian cancer cell lines by transforming growth factor-β. *Am. J. Obstet. Gynecol.* 166, 676–684.
198. Havrilesky, L. J., Hurteau, J. A., Whitaker, R. S., Elbendary, A., Wu, S., Rodriguez, G. C., Bast Jr., R. C., and Berchuck, A. (1995). Regulation of apoptosis in normal and malignant ovarian epithelial cells by transforming growth factor β. *Cancer Res.* 55, 944–948.
199. Hurteau, J., Rodriguez, G. C., Whitaker, R. S., Shah, S., Mills, G., Bast, R. C., and Berchuck, A. (1994). Transforming growth factor-beta inhibits proliferation of human ovarian cancer cells obtained from ascites. *Cancer* 74, 93–99.
200. Kim, J. W., Lee, C. G., Lyu, M. S., Kim, H. K., Rha, J. G., Kim, D. H., Kim, S. J., and Namkoong, S. E. (1997). A new cell line from human undifferentiated carcinoma of the ovary: Establishment and characterization. *J. Cancer Res. Clin. Oncol.* 123, 82–90.

201. Lafon, C., Mathieu, C., Guerrin, M., Pierre, O., Vidal, S., and Valette, A. (1996). Transforming growth factor beta 1-induced apoptosis in human ovarian carcinoma cells: Protection by the antioxidant N-acetylcysteine and bcl-2. *Cell. Growth Differ.* 7, 1095–1104.
202. Dunfield, L. D., Dwyer, E. J., and Nachtigal, M. W. (2002). TGF beta-induced Smad signaling remains intact in primary human ovarian cancer cells. *Endocrinology* 143, 1174–1181.
203. Ziltener, H. J., Maines-Bandiera, S., Schrader, J. W., and Auersperg, N. (1993). Secretion of bioactive interleukin-1, interleukin-6, and colony-stimulating factors by human ovarian surface epithelium. *Biol. Reprod.* 49, 635–641.
204. Ismail, R. S., Cada, M., and Vanderhyden, B. C. (1999). Transforming growth factor-beta regulates Kit ligand expression in rat ovarian surface epithelial cells. *Oncogene* 18, 4734–4741.
205. Tonary, A. M., Macdonald, E. A., Faught, W., Senterman, M. K., and Vanderhyden, B. C. (2000). Lack of expression of c-KIT in ovarian cancers is associated with poor prognosis. *Int. J. Cancer* 89, 242–250.
206. Parrott, J. A., Kim, G., and Skinner, M. K. (2000). Expression and action of kit ligand/stem cell factor in normal human and bovine ovarian surface epithelium and ovarian cancer. *Biol. Reprod.* 62, 1600–1609.
207. Berchuck, A., Kohler, M. F., Boente, M. P., Rodriguez, G. C., Whitaker, R. S., and Bast Jr., R. C. (1993). Growth regulation and transformation of ovarian epithelium. *Cancer* 71 (Suppl.), 545–551.
208. Chambers, S. K., Wang, Y., Gertz, R. E., and Kacinski, B. M. (1995). Macrophage colony-stimulating factor mediates invasion of ovarian cancer cells through urokinase. *Cancer Res.* 55, 1578–1585.
209. Huntsman, D., Resau, J. H., Klineberg, E., and Auersperg, N. (1999). Comparison of c-met expression in ovarian epithelial tumors and normal epithelia of the female reproductive tract by quantitative laser scan microscopy. *Am. J. Pathol.* 155, 343–348.
210. Parrott, J. A., and Skinner, M. K. (2000). Expression and action of hepatocyte growth factor in human and bovine normal ovarian surface epithelium and ovarian cancer. *Biol. Reprod.* 62, 491–500.
211. Hess, S., Gulati, R., and Peluso, J. J. (1999). Hepatocyte growth factor induces rat ovarian surface epithelial cell mitosis or apoptosis depending on the presence or absence of an extracellular matrix. *Endocrinology* 140, 2908–2916.
212. Di Renzo, M. F., Olivero, M., Katsaros, D., Crepaldi, T., Gaglia, P., Zola, P., Sismondi, P., and Comoglio, P. M. (1994). Overexpression of the Met/HGF receptor in ovarian cancer. *Int. J. Cancer* 58, 658–662.
213. Corps, A. N., Sowter, H. M., and Smith, S. K. (1997). Hepatocyte growth factor stimulates motility, chemotaxis and mitogenesis in ovarian carcinoma cells expressing high levels of c-met. *Int. J. Cancer* 73, 151–155.
214. Ueoka, Y., Kato, K., Kuriaki, Y., Horiuchi, S., Terao, Y., Nishida, J., Ueno, H., and Wake, N. (2000). Hepatocyte growth factor modulates motility and invasiveness of ovarian carcinomas via Ras-mediated pathway. *Br. J. Cancer* 82, 891–899.
215. Shu, X. O., Gao, Y. T., Yuan, J. M., Ziegler, R. G., and Brinton, L. A (1989). Dietary factors and epithelial ovarian cancer. *Br. J. Cancer* 59, 92–96.
216. Gertig, D. M., Hunter, D. J., Cramer, D. W., Colditz, G. A., Speizer, F. E., Willett, W. C., and Hankinson, S. E. (2000). Prospective study of talc use and ovarian cancer. *J. Natl. Cancer Inst.* 92, 249–252.
217. Hamilton, T. C., Fox, H., Buckley, C. H., Henderson, W. J., and Griffiths, K. (1984). Effects of talc on the rat ovary. *Br. J. Exp. Pathol.* 65, 101–106.
218. Menczer, J., Modan, M., Ranon, L., and Golan, A. (1979). Possible role of mumps virus in the etiology of ovarian cancer. *Cancer* 43, 1375–1379.
219. Hardiman, P., Nieto, J. J., and MacLean, A. B. (1999). Infertility and ovarian cancer [editorial]. *Gynecol. Oncol.* 76, 1–2.
220. Modugno, F., Ness, R. B., and Cottreau, C. M. (2002). Cigarette smoking and the risk of mucinous and nonmucinous epithelial ovarian cancer. *Epidemiology* 13, 467–471.
221. Iatropoulos, M. J., Hobson, W., Knauf, V., and Adams, H. P. (1976). Morphological effects of hexachlorobenzene toxicity in female rhesus monkeys. *Toxicol. Appl. Pharmacol.* 37, 433–444.
222. Babineau, K. A., Singh, A., Jarrell, J. F., and Villeneuve, D. C. (1991). Surface epithelium of the ovary following oral administration of hexachlorobenzene to the monkey. *J. Submicrosc. Cytol. Pathol.* 23, 457–464.
223. Sims, D. E., Singh, A., Donald, A., Jarrell, J., and Villeneuve, D. C. (1991). Alteration of primate ovary surface epithelium by exposure to hexachlorobenzene: A quantitative study. *Histol. Histopathol.* 6, 525–529.
224. Borgeest, C., Symonds, D., Mayer, L. P., Hoyer, P. B., and Flaws, J. A. (2002). Methoxychlor may cause ovarian follicular atresia and proliferation of the ovarian epithelium in the mouse. *Toxicol. Sci.* 68, 473–478.
225. Ness, R. B., and Cottreau, C. (1999). Possible role of ovarian epithelial inflammation in ovarian cancer. *J. Natl. Cancer Inst.* 91, 1459–1467.
226. Ness, R. B., Grisso, J. A., Cottreau, C., Klapper, J., Vergona, R., Wheeler, J. E., Morgan, M., and Schlesselman, J. J. (2000). Factors related to inflammation of the ovarian epithelium and risk of ovarian cancer. *Epidemiology* 11, 111–117.
227. Negus, R. P., Stamp, G. W., Relf, M. G., Burke, F., Malik, S. T., Bernasconi, S., Allavena, P., Sozzani, S., Mantovani, A., and Balkwill, F. R. (1995). The detection and localization of monocyte chemoattractant protein-1 (MCP-1) in human ovarian cancer. *J. Clin. Invest.* 95, 2391–2396.
228. Naylor, M. S., Stamp, G. W., Foulkes, W. D., Eccles, D., and Balkwill, F. R. (1993). Tumor necrosis factor and its receptors in human ovarian cancer. Potential role in disease progression. *J. Clin. Invest.* 91, 2194–2206.
229. van Niekerk, C. C., Ramaekers, F. C., Hanselaar, A. G., Aldeweireldt, J., and Poels, L. G. (1993). Changes in expression of differentiation markers between normal ovarian cells and derived tumors. *Am. J. Pathol.* 142, 157–177.
230. Auersperg, N., Siemens, C. H., and Myrdal, S. E. (1984). Human ovarian surface epithelium in primary culture. *In Vitro* 20, 743–755.
231. van Niekerk, C. C., Jap, P. H., Thomas, C. M., Smeets, D. F., Ramaekers, F. C., and Poels, L. G. (1989). Marker profile of mesothelial cells versus ovarian carcinoma cells. *Int. J. Cancer* 43, 1065–1071.

232. Auersperg, N., Wong, A. S., Choi, K. C., Kang, S. K., and Leung, P. C. (2001). Ovarian surface epithelium: Biology, endocrinology, and pathology. *Endocr. Rev.* 22, 255–288.
233. Dubeau, L. (1999). The cell of origin of ovarian epithelial tumors and the ovarian surface epithelium dogma: Does the emperor have no clothes? *Gynecol. Oncol.* 72, 437–442.
234. Sundfeldt, K., Piontkewitz, Y., Ivarsson, K., Nilsson, O., Hellberg, P., Brännström, M., Janson, P. O., Enerback, S., and Hedin, L. (1997). E-cadherin expression in human epithelial ovarian cancer and normal ovary. *Int. J. Cancer* 74, 275–280.
235. Wang, D. P., Konishi, I., Koshiyama, M., Nanbu, Y., Iwai, T., Nonogaki, H., Mori, T., and Fujii, S. (1992). Immunohistochemical localization of c-erbB-2 protein and epidermal growth factor receptor in normal surface epithelium, surface inclusion cysts, and common epithelial tumours of the ovary. *Virchows. Arch. A. Pathol. Anat. Histopathol.* 421, 393–400.
236. Naora, H., Montz, F. J., Chai, C. Y., and Roden, R. B. (2001). Aberrant expression of homeobox gene HOXA7 is associated with mullerian-like differentiation of epithelial ovarian tumors and the generation of a specific autologous antibody response. *Proc. Natl. Acad. Sci. USA* 98, 15209–15214.
237. Maines-Bandiera, S. L., and Auersperg, N. (1997). Increased E-cadherin expression in ovarian surface epithelium: An early step in metaplasia and dysplasia? *Int. J. Gynecol. Pathol.* 16, 250–255.
238. Auersperg, N., Maines-Bandiera, S. L., Dyck, H. G., and Kruk, P. A. (1994). Characterization of cultured human ovarian surface epithelial cells: Phenotypic plasticity and premalignant changes. *Lab. Invest.* 71, 510–518.
239. Auersperg, N., Maines-Bandiera, S., Booth, J. H., Lynch, H. T., Godwin, A. K., and Hamilton, T. C. (1995). Expression of two mucin antigens in cultured human ovarian surface epithelium: Influence of a family history of ovarian cancer. *Am. J. Obstet. Gynecol.* 173, 558–565.
240. Dyck, H. G., Hamilton, T. C., Godwin, A. K., Lynch, H. T., Maines-Bandiera, S., and Auersperg, N. (1996). Autonomy of the epithelial phenotype in human ovarian surface epithelium: Changes with neoplastic progression and with a family history of ovarian cancer. *Int. J. Cancer* 69, 429–436.
241. Wong, A. S., Maines-Bandiera, S. L., Rosen, B., Wheelock, M. J., Johnson, K. R., Leung, P. C., Roskelley, C. D., and Auersperg, N. (1999). Constitutive and conditional cadherin expression in cultured human ovarian surface epithelium: Influence of family history of ovarian cancer. *Int. J. Cancer* 81, 180–188.
242. Auersperg, N., Pan, J., Grove, B. D., Peterson, T., Fisher, J., Maines-Bandiera, S., Somasiri, A., and Roskelley, C. D. (1999). E-cadherin induces mesenchymal-to-epithelial transition in human ovarian surface epithelium. *Proc. Natl. Acad. Sci. USA* 96, 6249–6254.
243. Ong, A., Maines-Bandiera, S. L., Roskelley, C. D., and Auersperg, N. (2000). An ovarian adenocarcinoma line derived from SV40/E-cadherin-transfected normal human ovarian surface epithelium. *Int. J. Cancer* 85, 430–437.
244. Leung, E. H., Leung, P. C., and Auersperg, N. (2001). Differentiation and growth potential of human ovarian surface epithelial cells expressing temperature-sensitive SV40 T antigen. *In Vitro Cell Dev. Biol. Anim.* 37, 515–521.
245. Gregoire, L., Rabah, R., Schmelz, E. M., Munkarah, A., Roberts, P. C., and Lancaster, W. D. (2001). Spontaneous malignant transformation of human ovarian surface epithelial cells in vitro. *Clin. Cancer Res.* 7, 4280–4287.
246. Adams, A. T., and Auersperg, N. (1985). A cell line, ROSE 199, derived from normal rat ovarian surface epithelium. *Exp. Cell Biol.* 53, 181–188.
247. Orsulic, S., Li, Y., Soslow, R. A., Vitale-Cross, L. A., Gutkind, J. S., and Varmus, H. E. (2002). Induction of ovarian cancer by defined multiple genetic changes in a mouse model system. *Cancer Cell* 1, 53–62.
248. Tonin, P. N., Hudson, T. J., Rodier, F., Bossolasco, M., Lee, P. D., Novak, J., Manderson, E. N., Provencher, D., and Mes-Masson, A. M. (2001). Microarray analysis of gene expression mirrors the biology of an ovarian cancer model. *Oncogene* 20, 6617–6626.
249. Roberts, D., Williams, S. J., Cvetkovic, D., Weinstein, J. K., Godwin, A. K., Johnson, S. W., and Hamilton, T. C. (2002). Decreased expression of retinol-binding proteins is associated with malignant transformation of the ovarian surface epithelium. *DNA Cell Biol.* 21, 11–19.
250. Ono, K., Tanaka, T., Tsunoda, T., Kitahara, O., Kihara, C., Okamoto, A., Ochiai, K., Takagi, T., and Nakamura, Y. (2000). Identification by cDNA microarray of genes involved in ovarian carcinogenesis. *Cancer Res.* 60, 5007–5011.
251. Biskind, M. S., and Biskind, G. S. (1944). Development of tumors in the rat ovary after transplantation into the spleen. *Proc. Soc. Exp. Biol. Med.* 55, 176–179.
252. Matzuk, M. M., Finegold, M. J., Su, J. G., Hsueh, A. J., and Bradley, A. (1992). Alpha-inhibin is a tumor-suppressor gene with gonadal specificity in mice. *Nature* 360, 313–319.
253. Nilson, J. H., Abbud, R. A., Keri, R. A., and Quirk, C. C. (2000). Chronic hypersecretion of luteinizing hormone in transgenic mice disrupts both ovarian and pituitary function, with some effects modified by the genetic background. *Recent Prog. Horm. Res.* 55, 69–89.
254. Keri, R. A., Lozada, K. L., Abdul-Karim, F. W., Nadeau, J. H., and Nilson, J. H. (2000). Luteinizing hormone induction of ovarian tumors: Oligogenic differences between mouse strains dictates tumor disposition. *Proc. Natl. Acad. Sci. USA* 97, 383–387.
255. Danilovich, N., Roy, I., and Sairam, M. R. (2001). Ovarian pathology and high incidence of sex cord tumors in follitropin receptor knockout (FORKO) mice. *Endocrinology* 142, 3673–3684.
257. Kananen, K., Markkula, M., Rainio, E., Su, J. G., Hsueh, A. J., and Huhtaniemi, I. T. (1995). Gonadal tumorigenesis in transgenic mice bearing the mouse inhibin alpha-subunit promoter/simian virus T-antigen fusion gene: Characterization of ovarian tumors and establishment of gonadotropin-responsive granulosa cell lines. *Mol. Endocrinol.* 9, 616–627.
258. Dutertre, M., Gouedard, L., Xavier, F., Long, W. Q., di Clemente, N., Picard, J. Y., and Rey, R. (2001). Ovarian granulosa cell tumors express a functional membrane receptor for anti-Mullerian hormone in transgenic mice. *Endocrinology* 142, 4040–4046.

259. Ward, B. G., and Wallace, K. (1987). Localization of the monoclonal antibody HMFG2 after intravenous and intraperitoneal injection into nude mice bearing subcutaneous and intraperitoneal human ovarian cancer xenografts. *Cancer Res.* 47, 4714–4718.
260. Hamilton, T. C., Young, R. C., Louie, K. G., Behrens, B. C., McKoy, W. M., Grotzinger, K. R., and Ozols, R. F. (1984). Characterization of a xenograft model of human ovarian carcinoma which produces ascites and intraabdominal carcinomatosis in mice. *Cancer Res.* 44, 5286–5290.
261. Massazza, G., Tomasoni, A., Lucchini, V., Allavena, P., Erba, E., Colombo, N., Mantovani, A., D'Incalci, M., Mangioni, C., and Giavazzi, R. (1989). Intraperitoneal and subcutaneous xenografts of human ovarian carcinoma in nude mice and their potential in experimental therapy. *Int. J. Cancer* 44, 494–500.
262. Lee, W. S., Otsuka, F., Moore, R. K., and Shimasaki, S. (2001). Effect of bone morphogenetic protein-7 on folliculogenesis and ovulation in the rat. *Biol. Reprod.* 65, 994–999.
263. Van der Hoek, K. H., Maddocks, S., Woodhouse, C. M., van Rooijen, N., Robertson, S. A., and Norman, R. J. (2000). Intrabursal injection of clodronate liposomes causes macrophage depletion and inhibits ovulation in the mouse ovary. *Biol. Reprod.* 62, 1059–1066.
264. Sato, M., and Kimura, M. (2001). Intrabursal transfer of spermatozoa (TS): A new route for artificial insemination of mice. *Theriogenology* 55, 1881–1890.
265. Landis, S. H., Murray, T., Bolden, S., and Wingo, P. A. 1998. Cancer statistics, 1998. *CA Cancer J. Clin.* 48, 6–29.
266. Collins, W. P., Bourne, T. H., and Campbell, S. (1998). Screening strategies for ovarian cancer. *Curr. Opin. Obstet. Gynecol.* 10, 33–39.

CHAPTER **37**

The Role of X-Linked Inhibitor of Apoptosis Protein in Chemoresistant Ovarian Cancer

MICHAEL FRASER AND BENJAMIN K. TSANG

INTRODUCTION

Although our understanding of the fundamental cellular and molecular defects that underlie human cancer has increased significantly in recent years, the overall incidence of ovarian cancer, with a lifetime risk of 1 in 70 (1.4%), has remained relatively unchanged during the past decade [1], and the disease is the most lethal of the gynecologic malignancies. In the United States alone, it was responsible for nearly 14,000 deaths in 2001 [2]. Inherent with the problem is our limited understanding of the fundamental biological lesions giving rise to the ovarian disease. Most ovarian cancers are not detected until stage III or IV, by which time the prognosis is often very poor. The five-year survival rate for patients with stage III ovarian cancer is approximately 20% [3].

The current therapeutic regimens for ovarian cancer are largely ineffective in terms of long-term treatment. Although chemotherapy is the preferred treatment option, with cisplatin and paclitaxel (Taxol) as first-line chemotherapeutic agents [4], chemoresistance remains a major therapeutic hurdle. Moreover, the mechanisms that underlie chemoresistance are not completely understood. This review will address some of the most recent studies that have provided insight into the novel mechanisms leading to the development of chemoresistant ovarian cancer. Although previously reported mechanisms of chemoresistance are discussed, the specific focus is on several related intracellular signaling pathways that have recently been implicated in chemoresistance.

MECHANISMS OF CHEMORESISTANCE

The success of chemotherapy depends on at least two cellular events. First, the drug must be taken up by the cancer cells, and remain therein long enough to elicit its pharmacologic action. Second, the drug must reach its target site within the cell and perform its desired effect. Because cisplatin enters the cell primarily by passive diffusion through the plasma membrane [5], drug influx is not of primary concern, although cellular retention of cisplatin is critical to its efficacy. Furthermore, as the action of cisplatin is mediated through the formation of DNA-platinum adducts [6], its effects are modulated by factors that positively influence DNA repair. In this regard, decreased drug accumulation and increased DNA repair are important factors in resistance of cancer cells to the cytotoxic actions of cisplatin.

Increased drug efflux and/or decreased drug influx can reduce the net accumulation of cisplatin in cancer cells. Several genes, including *MDR1, MRP1, MRP2*, and *LRP*, are responsible for drug transport [7–9]. *MDR1* and *MRP1* play a role in drug efflux [10, 11], while *MRP2* has been found to be overexpressed in a number of cisplatin-resistant cell lines [12, 13] and involved in drug efflux. The 110-kDa *LRP* plays an important role in nuclear-cytoplasmic drug transport and is frequently elevated in cells displaying multidrug resistance [14]. Moreover, LRP expression in advanced ovarian carcinoma indicates poor response to cisplatin [15]. Recently, the copper-transporting P-type adenosine triphosphatase (*ATP7B*) gene has been reported to be responsible for cisplatin resistance in human prostate cancer [16] and in ovarian carcinoma [17] cells.

The formation of DNA-platinum adducts is accompanied by an increase in the expression of pro-apoptotic genes such as *Fas*, *FasL*, and *p53*, and downregulation of antiapoptotic proteins such as Xiap [18, 19]; however, the effects of cisplatin are modulated by endogenous DNA repair mechanisms, which act to excise platinum-DNA adducts. Repair of platinum adducts occurs primarily via the nucleotide excision repair (NE) pathway [20, 21], by which bulky and helix-distorting DNA adducts are removed. Cisplatin-resistant cell lines display increased DNA repair, as measured by the loss of platinum adducts [22, 23] and reactivation of cisplatin-damaged plasmid DNA [24, 25]. Normal cells repair cisplatin interstrand crosslinks preferentially in transcriptionally active genes, whereas resistant cells show further increases in this repair [26].

Multiple genes are involved in the NE pathway. Among them is *ERCC1*, which encodes a protein containing a helix-turn-helix motif characteristic of DNA-binding proteins. This protein may be involved in the recognition of cisplatin damage and serves as an excision nuclease. *ERCC1* is expressed 2.6-fold higher in clinically resistant tumors than in sensitive tumors [27]. Another DNA repair gene, *ERCC2*, encodes the xeroderma pigmentosum group D (XPD) protein, a helicase component of transcription factor TFIIH [28]. Mutations of XPD protein can alter the repair capacity of a cancer cell [29]. In addition, xeroderma pigmentosum group E binding protein (XPE-BF), another DNA repair protein, is elevated 5-fold in some cisplatin-resistant tumor cell lines [25].

Thus alterations in cellular drug retention and in DNA repair can significantly influence the ability of chemotherapeutic agents to elicit their antitumor effects; however, our recent demonstration of XIAP as a novel determinant of cisplatin responsiveness of human ovarian cancer cells not only shed new light into the complex mechanism of chemoresistance, but also offers potentially a new strategy for therapeutic targeting in cisplatin-resistant ovarian cancer.

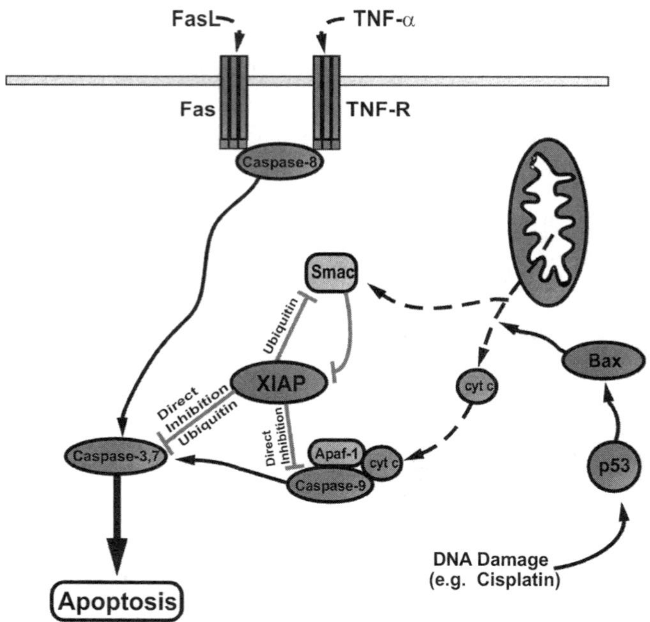

FIGURE 37.1 Classical Mechanisms of XIAP Action. XIAP is known to elicit its antiapoptotic effects by several distinct mechanisms (1) XIAP is a direct inhibitor of caspase-3. XIAP can also ubiquitinate caspase-3, and thus cause its degradation through the proteosome; (2) XIAP inhibits the activation of caspase-9; and (3) XIAP is known to ubiquitinate and cause the degradation of its endogenous inhibitor, Smac/DIABLO. Thus XIAP can inhibit both the mitochondrial- (caspase-9 activation of caspase-3) and death receptor- (caspase-8 activation of caspase-3) mediated apoptosis pathways. (See color plate.)

X-LINKED INHIBITOR OF APOPTOSIS PROTEIN

The IAP Family of Proteins

The inhibitor of apoptosis proteins (IAPs), originally identified in baculovirus, are potent endogenous inhibitors of programmed cell death. The family currently consists of six members: neuronal apoptosis inhibitory protein (NAIP), X-linked inhibitor of apoptosis protein (XIAP; also known as cIAP-3 or hILP), human inhibitor of apoptosis protein-1 and human inhibitor of apoptosis protein-2 (HIAP-1 and HIAP-2, also known as cIAP-2 and cIAP-1, respectively), survivin, and livin [30]. Although the exact mechanism by which each IAP inhibits cell death varies greatly, they all share certain structural characteristics that contribute to their antiapoptotic effects. HIAP-1 and -2 contain a **ca**spase **r**ecruitment **d**omain (CARD) and, with the exception of NAIP and survivin, all IAPs contain at least one NH_2-terminal **b**aculovirus **i**nhibitor of apoptosis **r**epeat (BIR) domain, responsible for direct inhibition of caspases, and a COOH-terminal RING/Zinc finger domain, which is believed to play a role in protein–protein and protein–nucleic acid interactions. HIAP-1 and HIAP-2 inhibit tumor necrosis factor (TNF) receptor signaling by binding to and inhibiting TNF-receptor associated factor (TRAF) [31]. XIAP is a direct inhibitor of caspase-3 and -7, and suppresses the mitochondrial apoptotic pathway by inhibiting caspase-9 [32]. Moreover, XIAP contains E3 ubiquitin ligase activity, which is involved in the autoubiquitination and subsequent proteasomal degradation of XIAP. Furthermore, XIAP can ubiquitinate other targets such as members of the caspase family [33], and Smac/DIABLO, an endogenous inhibitor of IAP function [34]. These recently discovered properties of XIAP offer new insight into the cellular mechanisms by which XIAP interacts with cell death pathways in the maintenance of cell survival (Figure 37.1).

XIAP and Chemoresistance in Human Ovarian Cancer

We have recently examined the role of the IAP family on chemoresistance in human ovarian surface epithelial cancer and have demonstrated that XIAP is a key determinant in the ability of the cancer cell to respond to cisplatin. XIAP expression in human ovarian cancer cells was found to be highest in proliferative, but not apoptotic cells [35]. Expression of the other IAP family members, such as HIAP-1 and -2 and NAIP, are relatively low in these cells. Treatment of cisplatin-sensitive ovarian cancer cells with cisplatin decreased XIAP protein content, an effect that was not observed in cisplatin-resistant variant cells [35]. Moreover, downregulation of XIAP in cisplatin-resistant human ovarian cancer cells using an adenoviral vector containing a XIAP antisense cDNA not only activated procaspase-3 and -9 and induced apoptosis, but also sensitized these cells to the cytotoxic action of cisplatin [4]. The decrease in XIAP protein content induced by cisplatin is not accompanied by a change in XIAP mRNA abundance, suggesting that *XIAP* gene expression is not affected by cisplatin [36]. In contrast, expression of XIAP sense cDNA renders cisplatin-sensitive human ovarian cancer cells resistant to cisplatin treatment [35]. These data suggest that XIAP plays an important role in determining cellular response to cisplatin. Furthermore, in ovarian cancer samples taken from patients during surgical debulking, immunolocalization of XIAP was inversely correlated with apoptosis [35]. Taken together, these data suggest that XIAP is an important regulator of cell survival and a key determinant of cisplatin sensitivity in human ovarian cancer.

INTERACTIONS BETWEEN XIAP AND CELLULAR SIGNALING PATHWAYS

Recent evidence has challenged the notion that XIAP prevents apoptosis solely through modulation of caspase function. We and others have recently investigated the possibility that XIAP elicits its antiapoptotic effects through interactions with various cellular signaling pathways [36]. Cell fate is determined through a set of signaling pathways, each of which respond to a different subset of intra- and extracellular stimuli. Interaction of growth factors with their specific receptors induces a host of downstream events that are mediated, for the most part, through protein–protein interactions and protein modifications. The pathway activated is a function of both receptor specificity and ligand abundance. Because any given ligand may bind to one or more receptors, and any given receptor may activate several signaling cascades, the ability of the cell to transduce messages from its surroundings must be tightly coordinated. Although cross talk between signaling pathways are complex, each of these pathways has mechanisms of activation that are increasingly well defined. The role of XIAP in some of these pathways will be elucidated in the following sections.

XIAP and the TGF-β/BMP Signaling Pathway

Members of the transforming growth factor-β (TGF-β) superfamily are significant regulators of cell growth and differentiation. TGF-β signals are induced through heteromeric type I and type II Ser/Thr kinase receptors. The TGF-β family includes such diverse ligands as TGF-β, the bone morphogenic proteins (BMPs), and the activins/inhibins [37]. Following ligand binding, the type II receptor recruits and phosphorylates the type I receptor, which activates downstream signaling events, including phosphorylation of Smad1, Smad2, or Smad3, depending on ligand identity and cell type [38]. Phosphorylated Smads dimerize with Smad4, and the complex translocates to the nucleus, where it functions as a co-activator of gene expression [38].

Other pathways have also been implicated in TGF-β signaling. For instance, TAK1, a member of the mitogen-activated protein (MAP) 3-kinase family, has been shown to participate in BMP4 and TGF-β1 signaling [39]; however, the mechanism by which TAK1 is activated by these factors is not clear. A recent study has shown that TAB1, a known activator of TAK1, is required for BMP4- or TGF-β1—mediated activation of the MAP kinase pathway, although the mechanism by which TAB1 and TAK1 are activated by the receptors is not clear [16].

Recent evidence suggests that XIAP may play a key role in this pathway by binding to TAB1 and to BMP type I and II receptors, suggesting that XIAP is the intracellular docking protein in the activation of the MAP kinase cascade by BMP and TGF-β [38]. XIAP is known to interact with several members of the type I class of TGF-β receptor superfamily, including TSR1, activin RIb, and TGF-β RI, and this interaction is not contingent upon receptor activation. Moreover, XIAP can activate transcription from TGF-β-responsive promoters, an effect ablated by removal of the C-terminal RING finger of XIAP [13]. Interestingly, this effect depends on Smad4, but not TAK1, suggesting that the interaction of XIAP with the TGF-β pathways is broader than originally believed. XIAP does not appear to potentiate TGF-β—induced gene expression through direct interaction with Smad4, nor is Smad4 or TAK1 involved in its inhibitory action on caspases.

XIAP and the MAP Kinase Cascade

The interaction of XIAP with the TGF-β signaling pathway results in activation of the MAP kinase JNK1. JNK1 is activated by the MAP kinase family member MKK4, which, in turn, is activated by MEKK1 [40]. Recent evidence suggests that JNK1 may also be activated by TAK1 [38]. Interestingly, XIAP has been shown to activate JNK1 [40]. Its ability to inhibit interleukin-converting enzyme (ICE)—induced apoptosis depends on its ability to activate the MAP kinase cascade through JNK1. This effect is independent of the MEKK1/MKK4 pathway, suggesting a novel mechanism of JNK1 activation. Because XIAP can interact with TAB1, a direct activator of the MAP 3-kinase TAK1 [38], and because JNK1 and XIAP cannot be coprecipitated, a possible mechanism of XIAP-mediated activation of JNK1 has been suggested. Sanna et al. showed that TAK1 was essential for the XIAP-mediated activation of JNK1 and protection from TNFα- and ICE-induced apoptosis [41]. TAK1 was not required for XIAP-mediated caspase inhibition. Recently, a novel antiapoptotic protein, termed hILP-interacting protein (ILPIP), which enhances XIAP-mediated induction of JNK1 activity, has been reported [42]. ILPIP potentiates the action of XIAP on JNK1 activity, a phenomenon blocked by expression of a TAK1 inactive mutant. In addition, both ILPIP and XIAP can be coprecipitated with TAK1, suggesting an interaction between ILPIP, TAK1, and XIAP in JNK1 activation.

The aforementioned findings suggest that the antiapoptotic effects of XIAP are not restricted to inhibition of caspases (Figure 37.2). Because XIAP has been implicated in the development of chemoresistance in ovarian cancer, they suggest a novel mechanism by which XIAP may influence the cellular response to chemotherapy; however, the precise relationship between the TGF-β pathway, JNK1 activation, and XIAP in chemoresistant ovarian cancer remains to be elucidated. Because many immortalized human ovarian cancer cell lines lose the ability to respond to TGF-β [43–49], it may prove difficult to ascertain the role of TGF-β in XIAP-mediated chemoresistance using traditional *in vitro* methods, such as manipulation of cell lines.

THE PI3K/Akt PATHWAY

Phosphatidylinositol 3-kinase (PI3-K) is a lipid kinase, activated in response to growth factors or cytokines. It is composed of a p85-regulatory subunit and a p110-catalytic subunit. PI3-K phosphorylates inositol lipids at the 3′ position of the inositol ring. There are currently three cloned PI3-K isoforms: p85α, p85β, and p85γ, and p110α, p110β, and p110γ. Type III PI3-Ks synthesize phosphatidylinositol-3-phosphate (PtdIns-3-P), the levels of which are constitutively present in all cells and are not affected by receptor activation. On the other hand, type I and II PI3-Ks synthesize PtdIns-3,4-P2 and PtdIns-3,4,5-P3, which are normally undetectable in most cells. Their formation results in the activation of downstream molecules containing pleckstrin homology (PH) domains, such as Akt, phosphatidylinositol-dependent kinase-1 (PDK-1), and integrin-linked kinase (ILK) [50].

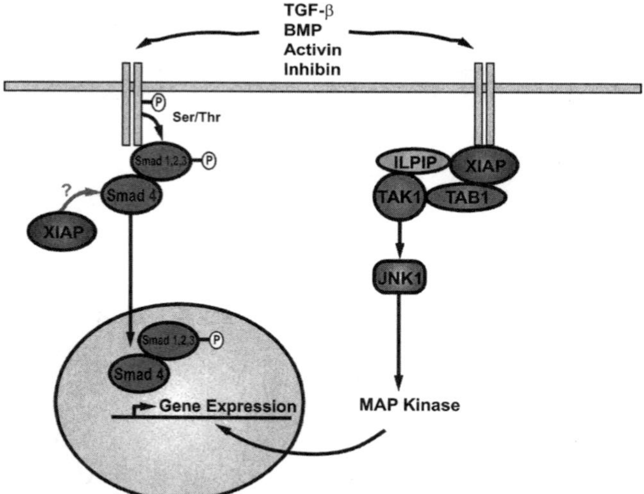

FIGURE 37.2 XIAP interacts with the TGF-β/BMP and MAP kinase pathways. XIAP has been shown to interact with the TGF-β/BMP signaling pathway member TAB1, as well as the BMP Type I and II receptors, and the TGF-β Receptor Type I. TAB1 is involved in activation of TAK1, which in turn is upstream of the MAP kinase JNK1. Signaling through JNK1 is known to activate genes implicated in cell survival and growth. An XIAP binding protein, ILPIP, has been shown to facilitate this function of XIAP. Moreover, XIAP may interact with Smad 4, which is intimately involved in TGF-β signaling to the nucleus. (See color plate.)

Several studies have implicated Akt as a major downstream target of PI3-K activation [51]. Akt, also known as protein kinase B (PKB), is a serine/threonine protein kinase originally identified as the cellular counterpart of the v-Akt transforming protein of a retrovirus that caused T-cell lymphomas in mice [52]. Three Akt isoforms have been identified: Akt/AKT1/PKBα, AKT2/PKBβ, and AKT3/PKBγ. The overall homology between isoforms is more than 85%. They share a similar structure, which contains an N-terminal PH domain, a central kinase domain, and a C-terminal rich in serines and threonines. The integrity of the PH domain, which is bound by the PI3-K products PtdIns-3,4-P2 and PtdIns-3,4,5-P3, is essential for activation of Akt by growth factors. Furthermore, phosphorylation of Thr^{308} (Thr^{309} in AKT2 and Thr^{305} in AKT3) and Ser^{473} (Ser^{474} in AKT2 and Ser^{472} in AKT3) is required for activation of the kinase. PDK-1 phosphorylates Akt on the Thr residue, whereas the identity of the $Ser^{473/474/472}$ kinase is still actively investigated. To date, three candidates have emerged: PDK-1, ILK, and MAP kinase-associated protein kinase-2 (MAPKAPK2) [53–55]. It is likely that each of these enzymes can phosphorylate $Ser^{473/474/472}$ residue of Akt under specific conditions. Akt activity is negatively regulated by *SHIP* [56, 57] and by *PTEN* [58, 59], a tumor suppressor that is mutated in several human cancers, including human ovarian carcinoma [60–62]. *PTEN* encodes a dual-specificity protein and lipid phosphatase that reduces PtdIns-3,4-P2 and PtdIns-3,4,5-P3 levels by converting them to PtdIns-4-P2 and PtdIns-4,5-P2, respectively, thereby inhibiting PI3K/Akt signaling [58, 59].

There are distinct differences in terms of biologic and physiologic function between the three Akt isoforms. *AKT1* expression is uniform in various normal organs, whereas high *AKT2* and *AKT3* mRNA are found in skeletal muscle, heart, placenta, and brain [18]. Furthermore, *AKT2* and *AKT3*, but not *AKT1*, are found upregulated in certain human cancers, such as carcinoma of the ovary, breast, and pancreas [63–67]. Moreover, Akt2- and Akt1-deficient mice display different phenotypes. $Akt2^{-/-}$ mice are born without apparent defects but develop peripheral insulin resistance and nonsuppressible hepatic glucose production, resulting in hyperglycemia accompanied by inadequate compensatory hyperinsulinemia [68]. These phenotypes cannot be rescued by the presence of Akt1 and Akt3, suggesting a high degree of substrate specificity between the three isoforms with respect to insulin-responsive tissues. By contrast, Akt1$^{-/-}$ mice do not display any diabetic phenotype [69, 70]. Akt1$^{-/-}$ mice are viable but display growth impairment. This suggests that there may be some Akt2 and Akt3 compensation for the lack of Akt1 in these mice.

PHYSIOLOGIC ROLE OF PI3-K/Akt SIGNALING

Several cell types have demonstrated that Akt promotes cell survival and suppresses apoptosis induced by a variety of stimuli. A major downstream target of Akt is Bad, a pro-apoptotic member of the *Bcl*-2 family of apoptotic regulators. Akt directly phosphorylates Bad on Ser^{136} [71–73]. Furthermore, Akt phosphorylates PAK1, which subsequently phosphorylates Bad at Ser^{112} [74]. The overall effect of Bad phosphorylation is its dissociation from the Bad-Bcl-$_{xL}$ complex and the prevention of mitochondrial cytochrome c (cyt c) release, thereby suppressing apoptosis mediated through the cyt c/Apaf-1/caspase-9 apoptosome.

Akt also phosphorylates and inactivates certain members of the Forkhead transcription factors [75–79] involved in the regulation of Fas ligand transcription, and IκB kinase α (IKKα) participating in the activation of the antiapoptotic NF-κB pathway [80]. Moreover, Akt promotes the movement of MDM2 from the cytoplasm to the nucleus, thus lowering the content and activity of the p53 tumor suppressor [81].

In addition to its role as an antiapoptotic regulator, Akt also promotes cell cycle progression and cell proliferation [80]. Akt phosphorylates glycogen synthase kinase-3β (GSK-3β) and ERα, resulting in upregulation of c-myc and cyclin D1 [80]. Furthermore, it phosphorylates p21, interfering with its function as a negative cell cycle regulator [82].

With its important role in the regulation of cell survival and proliferation, Akt has come under intense focus in cancer research, not only because of its role in tumor initiation and progression, but also more recently in chemoresistance. Current chemotherapeutic strategies rely in part on the ability of the cancer cell to undergo drug-induced apoptosis. Thus, while cell survival pathways (e.g., PI3K-Akt) may offer potential targets for chemotherapy, aberrant up- or downregulation of these pathways may also significantly influence the responsiveness of the tumor cells to chemotherapeutic agents.

PI3-K/Akt PATHWAY IN OVARIAN CANCER CHEMORESISTANCE

With the discovery of *PIK-3CA*, the gene encoding the catalytic subunit (p110α) of a class Ia PI3-K and an oncogene in ovarian cancer [63], the role of the PI3-K/Akt pathway in ovarian tumorigenesis and chemoresistance has been under intense investigation. Among the downstream mediators of PI3-K signaling, only Akt has been implicated in malignant transformation [83, 84]. Studies have demonstrated alterations of AKT2 at the DNA or mRNA levels in 15% to 20% of human ovarian cancers, as well as AKT2 activation (36%) and overexpression (46%) in 91 primary ovarian carcinomas [64]. In these studies, most of the tumors showing PI3-K/Akt alterations were high grade and late stage, indicating that PI3-K/Akt activation may be associated with cancer progression rather than with activation.

Recent evidence has suggested a role for PI3-K/Akt in resistance of cancer cells to a wide range of agents. HER-2/*neu* expression rendered tumor cells resistant to TNF-α—induced apoptosis, an effect mediated through Akt and NF-κB [85]. Furthermore, we and others have shown that ovarian cancer cells overexpressing a constitutively active Akt/*AKT1* or with amplified *AKT2* are resistant to paclitaxel and cisplatin, two primary agents for the treatment of ovarian cancer, compared to cells expressing low AKT levels [86]. A recent study has demonstrated that an ovarian cancer cell line expressing a constitutively active PI3-K catalytic subunit is more resistant to paclitaxel than its parental cells [87]. The paclitaxel resistance could be reversed with the PI3-K inhibitor LY294002. In the same study, mice carrying ovarian cancer xenografts were tested for the ability of paclitaxel, LY294002, or paclitaxel + LY294002 to reduce tumor burden. Although both paclitaxel and LY294002 significantly reduced tumor burden when given alone (by 51% and 38% reduction, respectively), the two agents together exerted a synergistic action (80% reduction), suggesting that the PI3-K/Akt pathway plays a role in maintaining cell viability even in the presence of antitumor agents. This study also raises the intriguing possibility of enhanced therapeutic advantages with combination therapy with inhibitors of the PI3-K/Akt pathway and traditional chemotherapeutic agents.

Our laboratory has previously demonstrated an involvement of XIAP in the development of chemoresistance in ovarian cancer, although information on the mechanism by which XIAP influences chemosensitivity in ovarian cancer cells has only begun to emerge. We have demonstrated that XIAP is involved in the upregulation of the PI3-K/Akt pathway, suggesting that XIAP-mediated chemoresistance may include a component of this antiapoptotic pathway.

REGULATION OF AKT SIGNALING BY XIAP

Our laboratory has recently shown that cisplatin treatment of cisplatin-sensitive ovarian cancer cells (A2780s) was associated with a downregulation of XIAP content and activation of procaspase-3 and -9 [36]. Moreover, incubation of whole cell lysates with human recombinant active caspase-3 induced Akt cleavage, an effect that was blocked by a specific caspase-3 inhibitor (Figure 37.3). Likewise, XIAP downregulation or cisplatin treatment of cultured ovarian cancer cells induced Akt cleavage and apoptosis, two responses attenuated by the presence of cell permeable caspase-3 inhibitors. These inhibitors also markedly reduced the ability of cisplatin to downregulate XIAP protein content. Taken together, these findings suggest that caspase-3-mediated apoptosis may be partly the result of modulation of the antiapoptotic effects of Akt.

We have previously demonstrated that overexpression of XIAP in cisplatin-sensitive ovarian cancer cells confers resistance of the cells to cisplatin [19, 35]. In addition, XIAP overexpression increases Akt phosphorylation and decreases apoptosis in these cancer cells (Figure 37.4) [36]. Total Akt content (phosphorylated + nonphosphorylated) was not altered, nor was the expression of the p85 subunit of PI3-K, suggesting that XIAP may elicit its antiapoptotic effects through Akt activation, but not PI3-K expression/degradation or upregulation of Akt content. In the presence of the PI3-K inhibitor LY294002, the ability of XIAP overexpression to increase phospho-Akt content or to block cisplatin-induced apoptosis was attenuated (Figure 37.5), suggesting that the site of XIAP action on the PI3-K/Akt pathway is proximal to Akt activation. It is not clear whether XIAP upregulates this pathway by turning on kinases such as PDK1 or ILK and/or by downregulating phosphatases such as PTEN or SHIP (Figure 37.6).

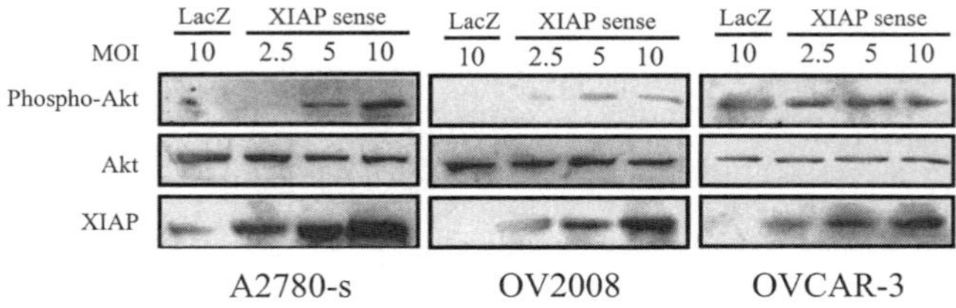

FIGURE 37.4 Overexpression of XIAP in human ovarian cancer cells. OV2008, OVCAR-3, and A2780-s cells were infected with adenoviral sense XIAP and LacZ vectors. Results demonstrate that XIAP overexpression increases Akt phosphorylation in human ovarian cancer cells. This phenomenon was observed in A2780-s and OV2008 cells, but not in OVCAR-3 cells, which express high basal levels of phospho-Akt. Total Akt is not affected by XIAP overexpression, suggesting that XIAP directly influences Akt phosphorylation, rather than Akt expression. (Taken from Asselin et al., 2001 [36] with permission).

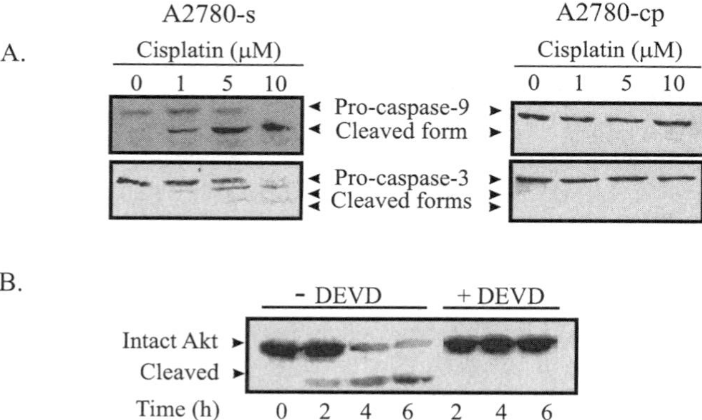

FIGURE 37.3 Akt cleavage during cisplatin treatment is caspase-3 dependent. **A,** A2780-s and A2780-cp cells were cultured in various concentrations of cisplatin. Results demonstrate a dose-dependent induction of Akt cleavage by cisplatin. **B,** A2780-s cell lysate was treated in vitro with human recombinant caspase-3 (10 μg) for 2, 4, and 6 hours in the absence or presence of the caspase-3 inhibitor DEVD (25 μM). Results demonstrate that Akt is a substrate for caspase-3 cleavage. (Taken from Asselin et al. 2001 [36] with permission).

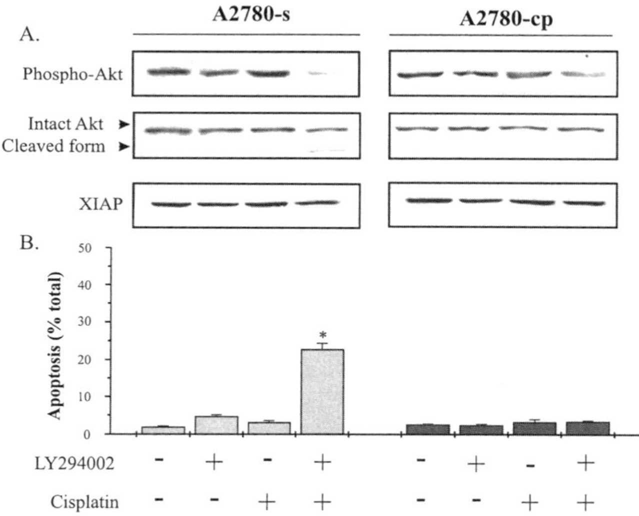

FIGURE 37.5 Ly294002 decreased phospho-Akt content and attenuated the protective effect of XIAP against cisplatin-induced apoptosis in ovarian cancer cells. A2780-s and A2780-cp cells were infected with adenoviral sense XIAP and subsequently treated with the PI3-K inhibitor LY294002 ± cisplatin. Although the LY294002 partially reversed XIAP-mediated chemoresistance in A2780-s cells (p53-wt), suggesting the possible involvement of the PI3-K pathway in chemoresistance, this effect was not seen in p53 mutant cells (A2780-cp), suggesting that p53 status may be an important determinant of chemoresistance. (Taken from Asselin et al., 2001 [36] with permission).

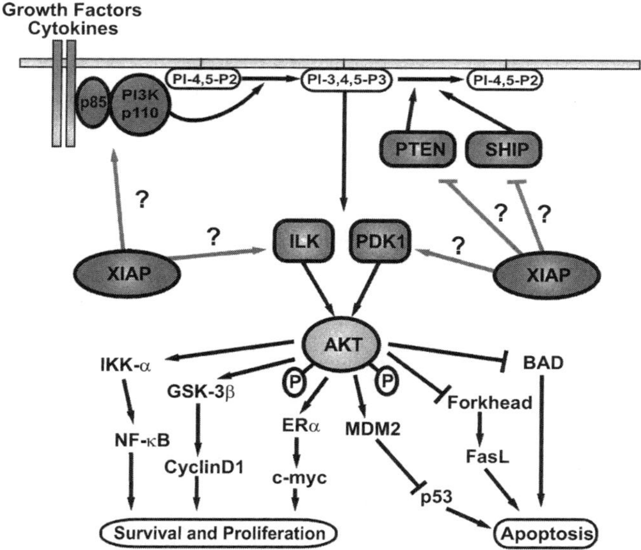

FIGURE 37.6 Interactions Between XIAP and the PI3-K/Akt Pathway. Activation of PI3-K by growth factors or cytokines leads to phosphorylation of specific membrane phospholipids (PI-4,5-P2 to PI-3,4,5-P3), which interact with the PH domain of downstream kinases (e.g., ILK, PDK1, Akt), leading to their recruitment to the membrane. ILK and PDK1 phosphorylate Akt, which then induces a multitude of downstream events associated with cell survival and proliferation. The system is opposed by the actions of PTEN and SHIP, which dephosphorylate PI-3,4,5-P3. Although overexpression of XIAP is known to increase Akt phosphorylation, whether it does so by turning on kinases or shutting off phosphatases is unknown.

Akt, p53, AND CHEMORESISTANCE

The tumor suppressor p53 is mutated or absent in a high percentage of human cancers [88]. Its central role is as a "guardian of the genome": it senses DNA damage, halts cell replication to permit DNA repair, and acts as a transcription factor to induce expression of several responsive genes involved in cell cycle arrest (e.g., $p21^{WAF1/CIP1}$) and apoptosis (e.g., Bax). Thus activation of p53 is associated with inhibition of cellular proliferation and, if the DNA damage is severe, the induction of cell death.

MDM2 is an oncoprotein that binds to p53 and sequesters the tumor suppressor in the cytosol. Moreover, MDM2 can catalyze p53 ubiquitination necessary for subsequent degradation in the 26S proteasome, thus regulating the basal levels of p53 within the cell. During apoptosis, MDM2 is cleaved, permitting p53 to accumulate and further promote the apoptotic response [89, 90]. Our data suggests that XIAP serves as an important regulator of MDM2 stability, and thus also of p53. XIAP downregulation is associated with MDM2 cleavage, p53 stabilization and accumulation, and apoptosis in p53 wild-type, cisplatin-resistant human ovarian cancer cells (C13*) [4].

In contrast to the cisplatin-resistant (C13*) cells, the chemoresistant p53-mutant (A2780cp) cells display striking differences in their apoptotic response to XIAP downregulation. Whereas C13* cells can be rendered cisplatin-sensitive by downregulation of XIAP, A2780cp cells do not display the same phenotypic characteristic; however, reconstitution of a wild-type p53 (via adenovirus) rendered the cells cisplatin-sensitive in response to XIAP downregulation, suggesting that the loss of functional p53 is an important determinant of XIAP-mediated chemoresistance [4].

Although XIAP overexpression increases phospho-Akt content in A2780s (cisplatin-sensitive) cells and the resulting cisplatin-resistance can be reversed by presence of a PI3-K inhibitor, the same is not true for the cisplatin-resistant p53 mutant (A2780cp), suggesting other factors may be operational in these cells. We hypothesized that p53 status is a critical determinant of cellular response to XIAP downregulation and that Akt mediates its actions through inhibition of p53-related responses. This hypothesis is supported by recent evidence suggesting Akt may modulate p53 content by phosphorylating and activating MDM2 [81].

Our recent studies indicate that while downregulation of Akt activity using an adenoviral vector containing a dominant-negative Akt (DN-Akt) in p53 wild-type human ovarian cancer cells (C13*) can reverse cisplatin-resistance, the same response is not evident in p53-mutant variant cells (A2780cp); however, expression of wild-type p53 in these cells sensitizes them to the pro-apoptotic actions of Akt downregulation, suggesting that the contribution of Akt to chemoresistance depends on its ability to modulate p53 content and function. This notion is consistent with our recent findings that the p53 inhibitor pifithrin-α (PFT) alone can attenuate the apoptotic response to Akt downregulation in p53 wild-type, but not mutant, ovarian cancer cells [81a].

Interestingly, it has been shown that cisplatin induces p53 phosphorylation, an effect mediated through activation of the MAP kinase family members ERK1 and ERK2 [91]. The phosphorylation was specific to Ser^{15} of p53, which maps to the MDM2 binding site. This suggests that cisplatin may regulate p53 content by interfering with MDM2-mediated degradation of the tumor suppressor, and emphasizes the importance of p53 in cisplatin sensitivity. Another study showed that mutation of Ser^{15} to Ala, with subsequent loss of phosphorylation, significantly reduced p53-mediated apoptotic activity [92], thus further implicating p53 phosphorylation in the apoptotic response. Moreover, replacement of p53 in glioma cells using an adenoviral vector in combination with the DNA-damaging agents cisplatin and BCNU showed synergistic increases in both apoptosis and p53 phosphorylation [93], suggesting that p53 gene therapy may enhance the effects of traditional chemotherapeutic agents.

It is clear that apoptosis induced by many of the current slate of chemotherapeutic agents is highly dependent on p53 status of their target cells. A further elucidation of the exact mechanisms of p53 activation by these agents, and of the subsequent downstream events, may revolutionize our thinking regarding chemoresistance in many types of human cancer.

THE FUTURE

Although the current understanding of the mechanisms that create chemoresistant ovarian cancer is relatively limited, there is intense focus on this problem in many laboratories, including our own. This research has permitted a much greater comprehension of this complex disease and is likely to continue to do so in the future. In the context of the now-well-established role of the PI3-K/Akt pathway in chemoresistance, several unanswered questions will provide the fuel for the next few years of research activities.

First, with both XIAP and the PI3-K/Akt pathway established as key determinants of cisplatin sensitivity in human ovarian cancer, what is the relationship between these two cell survival pathways? Although XIAP overexpression has already been shown to increase phospho-Akt content, the mechanism behind this phenomenon is unknown. Because XIAP overexpression does not affect total Akt content, it is believed that XIAP in some way directly influences Akt phosphorylation. Therefore, the enzymes that regulate Akt phosphorylation are currently under intense scrutiny to determine how, if at all, they interact with or are regulated by XIAP.

Second, the role of p53 in Akt- and XIAP-mediated chemoresistance remains unclear. Although the use of selective p53 inhibitors such as PFT may improve our understanding of the role of p53 in these processes, the information gained will only be indirect. In addition, the recent discovery of two novel genes displaying a high degree of homology to p53 has added a new level of complexity to the idea of "p53"-mediated apoptosis. Although these novel genes, named *p63* and *p73*, are structurally related to p53, they display marked differences in their physiologic function. For instance, whereas $p53^{-/-}$ mice display only slight developmental defects, the contrary is true in $p63^{-/-}$ mice, which die shortly after birth. Similarly, $p73^{-/-}$ mice suffer from other aberrations, including nervous system and respiratory tract dysfunction [94]. In addition, whereas p53 mutation has been implicated in cancer development, loss of p63 or p73 does not seem to predispose mice to cancer [95], although both p63 and p73 appeared to be required for p53-mediated apoptosis [96].

One study has shown that p63 is highly expressed in squamous cell and transitional cell carcinomas, but not in adenocarcinomas, suggesting that p63 may play a role in tumorigenesis in certain cancers [97]. Moreover, p73 can attenuate the effects of p53 in a human ovarian cancer cell line (A2780s) by competing with p53 for DNA binding sites on p53-responsive promoters [98], suggesting that this gene may be implicated in p53 inactivation, a phenomenon frequently observed in many cancers. Thus, while p53 status is an important determinant of the chemoresponsiveness of ovarian cancer cells, it will be of great value to understand the role of p63 and p73.

CONCLUSION

Our understanding of the processes underlying malignancy, although far more advanced than only a few years ago, remains mostly incomplete. Certainly, with respect to human ovarian cancer, the details of the fundamental causes of the disease are fuzzy at best. Compounding our relative inability to conquer the *causes* of ovarian cancer is the fact that chemoresistance remains a clinical problem that severely hampers our ability to eradicate ovarian cancer; however, the outlook for the future is encouraging. We have seen that several novel pathways have been linked to the onset and maintenance of chemoresistance in ovarian cancer. XIAP, for instance, is well established as a potent modulator of cisplatin sensitivity in human ovarian cancer cells. Its effects are known to range beyond (as its name suggests) direct inhibition of the apoptotic machinery. XIAP is not only an "inhibitor of apoptosis protein," but also a "stimulator of cell survival protein." In this context, the PI3-K/Akt pathway is implicated in chemoresistance in human ovarian cancer. Certainly, a better understanding of the complex interactions between these cell survival/death pathways will provide a clearer indication of precisely how PI3-K/Akt mediates chemoresistance.

Finally, we have detailed how the p53 family of proteins may be implicated in chemoresistance. This is not surprising, given the importance of p53 in apoptosis induced by several chemotherapeutic agents, including cisplatin; however, as with the PI3-K/Akt pathway, the exact role played by p53/p63/p73 within the ovarian cancer cell is not clear. Furthermore, the relationship between these proteins and XIAP has not been fully elucidated. Clearly, a complete characterization of the mechanisms at work will provide a better understanding of the tumor biology of chemoresistance, and most important, offer insight into novel strategies that may ultimately revolutionize our ability to successfully treat ovarian cancer.

ACKNOWLEDGMENTS

We would like to thank our current and past collaborators, Drs. E. Asselin, J. Q. Cheng, W. Faught, Q. Feng, M. Fung Kee Fung, X. Jiang, J.-M. Kim, R. G. Korneluk, F. Kotsuji, B. Leung, J. Li, M. Li, P. Liston, G. B. Mills, H. Sasaki, D. Schneiderman, M. Senterman, Y. L. Sheng, B. Vanderhyden, C. W. Xiao, and X. Yan, who contributed significantly to the research described in this review. Michael Fraser is the recipient of an Ontario Graduate Scholarship in Science and Technology, jointly funded by the Ontario Ministry of Education and the Ottawa Health Research Institute. This work was supported by the Canadian Institutes of Health Research (MOP-15691) and the National Cancer Institute of Canada (with funds from the Canadian Cancer Society; Grant 013335).

References

1. Rubin, S. C., and Sutton, G. P. (2001). *Ovarian Cancer*, 2nd ed. New York: Lippincott Williams & Wilkins.
2. *www.cancer.org/downloads/STT/F&F2001/pdf.*
3. Legros, M., Dauplat, J., Fleury, J., Cure, H., Suzanne, F., Chassagne, J., Bay, J. O., Sol, C., Canis, M., Condat, P., Choufi, B., Tavernier, F., Glenat, C., Chollet, P., and Plagne, R. (1997). High-dose chemotherapy with hematopoietic rescue in patients with stage III to IV ovarian cancer: long-term results. *J. Clin. Oncol.* 15, 1302–1308.
4. Sasaki, H., Sheng, Y., Kotsuji, F., and Tsang, B. K. (2000). Down-regulation of X-linked inhibitor of apoptosis protein induces apoptosis in chemoresistant human ovarian cancer cells. *Cancer Res.* 60, 5659–5666.
5. Gately, D. P., and Howell, S. B. (1993). Cellular accumulation of the anticancer agent cisplatin: A review. *Br. J. Cancer.* 67, 1171–1176.
6. Bose, R. N. (2002). Biomolecular targets for platinum antitumor drugs. *Mini. Rev. Med. Chem.* 2, 103–111.
7. Riordan, J. R., Deuchars, K., Kartner, N., Alon, N., Trent, J., and Ling, V. (1985). Amplification of P-glycoprotein genes in multidrug-resistant mammalian cell lines. *Nature* 316, 817–819.
8. Cole, S. P., and Deeley, R. G. (1993). Multidrug resistance-associated protein: Sequence correction. *Science* 260, 879.
9. Scheffer, G. L., Wijngaard, P. L., Flens, M. J., Izquierdo, M. A., Slovak, M. L., Pinedo, H. M., Meijer, C. J., Clevers, H. C., and Scheper, R. J. (1995). The drug resistance-related protein LRP is the human major vault protein. *Nat. Med.* 1, 578–582.
10. Ueda, K., Cardarelli, C., Gottesman, M. M., and Pastan, I. (1987). Expression of a full-length cDNA for the human "MDR1" gene confers resistance to colchicine, doxorubicin, and vinblastine. *Proc. Natl. Acad. Sci. USA* 84, 3004–3008.
11. Cole, S. P., Sparks, K. E., Fraser, K., Loe, D. W., Grant, C. E., Wilson, G. M., and Deeley, R. G. (1994). Pharmacological characterization of multidrug resistant MRP-transfected human tumor cells. *Cancer Res.* 54, 5902–5910.
12. Taniguchi, K., Wada, M., Kohno, K., Nakamura, T., Kawabe, T., Kawakami, M., Kagotani, K., Okumura, K., Akiyama, S., and Kuwano, M. (1996). A human canalicular multispecific organic anion transporter (cMOAT) gene is overexpressed in cisplatin-resistant human cancer cell lines with decreased drug accumulation. *Cancer Res.* 56, 4124–4129.
13. Kool, M., de Haas, M., Scheffer, G. L., Scheper, R. J., van Eijk, M. J., Juijn, J. A., Baas, F., and Borst, P. (1997). Analysis of expression of cMOAT (MRP2), MRP3, MRP4, and MRP5, homologues of the multidrug resistance-associated protein gene (MRP1), in human cancer cell lines. *Cancer Res.* 57, 3537–3547.
14. Izquierdo, M. A., Scheffer, G. L., Flens, M. J., Giaccone, G., Broxterman, H. J., Meijer, C. J., van der Valk, P., and Scheper, R. J. (1996). Broad distribution of the multidrug resistance-related vault lung resistance protein in normal human tissues and tumors. *Am. J. Pathol.* 148, 877–887.
15. Izquierdo, M. A., van der Zee, A. G., Vermorken, J. B., van der Valk, P., Belien, J. A., Giaccone, G., Scheffer, G. L., Flens, M. J., Pinedo, H. M., Kenemans, P., and et al. (1995). Drug resistance-associated marker Lrp for prediction of response to chemotherapy and prognoses in advanced ovarian carcinoma. *J. Natl. Cancer Inst.* 87, 1230–1237.
16. Komatsu, M., Sumizawa, T., Mutoh, M., Chen, Z. S., Terada, K., Furukawa, T., Yang, X. L., Gao, H., Miura, N., Sugiyama, T., and Akiyama, S. (2000). Copper-transporting P-type adenosine triphosphatase (ATP7B) is associated with cisplatin resistance. *Cancer Res.* 60, 1312–1316.
17. Nakayama, K., Kanzaki, A., Ogawa, K., Miyazaki, K., Neamati, N., and Takebayashi, Y. (2002). Copper-transporting P-type adenosine triphosphatase (ATP7B) as a cisplatin based chemoresistance marker in ovarian carcinoma: Comparative analysis with expression of MDR1, MRP1, MRP2, LRP and BCRP. *Intl. J. Cancer.* 101, 488–495.
18. Cheng, J. Q., Jiang, X., Fraser, M., Li, M., Dan, H. C., Sun, M., and Tsang, B. K. (2002). Role of X-linked inhibitor of apoptosis protein in chemoresistance in ovarian cancer: Possible involvement of the phosphoinositide-3 kinase/Akt pathway. *Drug Resist. Update* 5, 131–146.
19. Li, J., Sasaki, H., Sheng, Y. L., Schneiderman, D., Xiao, C. W., Kotsuji, F., and Tsang, B. K. (2000). Apoptosis and chemoresistance in human ovarian cancer: Is Xiap a determinant? *Biol. Signals Recept.* 9, 122–130.
20. Reed, E. (1998). Platinum-DNA adduct, nucleotide excision repair and platinum based anti-cancer chemotherapy. *Cancer Treat. Rev.* 24, 331–344.
21. Zamble, D. B., and Lippard, S. J. (1995). Cisplatin and DNA repair in cancer chemotherapy. *Trends Biochem. Sci.* 20, 435–439.
22. Eastman, A., and Schulte, N. (1988). Enhanced DNA repair as a mechanism of resistance to cis-diamminedichloroplatinum(II). *Biochemistry* 27, 4730–4734.
23. Parker, R. J., Eastman, A., Bostick-Bruton, F., and Reed, E. (1991). Acquired cisplatin resistance in human ovarian cancer cells is associated with enhanced repair of cisplatin-DNA lesions and reduced drug accumulation. *J. Clin. Invest.* 87, 772–777.
24. Sheibani, N., Jennerwein, M. M., and Eastman, A. (1989). DNA repair in cells sensitive and resistant to cis-

diamminedichloroplatinum(II): Host cell reactivation of damaged plasmid DNA. *Biochemistry* 28, 3120–3124.

25. Chu, G., and Chang, E. (1990). Cisplatin-resistant cells express increased levels of a factor that recognizes damaged DNA. *Proc. Natl. Acad. Sci. USA* 87, 3324–3328.
26. Zhen, W., Link, C. J., Jr., O'Connor, P. M., Reed, E., Parker, R., Howell, S. B., and Bohr, V. A. (1992). Increased gene-specific repair of cisplatin interstrand cross-links in cisplatin-resistant human ovarian cancer cell lines. *Mol. Cell. Biol.* 12, 3689–3698.
27. Dabholkar, M., Bostick-Bruton, F., Weber, C., Bohr, V. A., Egwuagu, C., and Reed, E. (1992). ERCC1 and ERCC2 expression in malignant tissues from ovarian cancer patients. *J. Natl. Cancer Inst.* 84, 1512–1517.
28. Sung, P., Bailly, V., Weber, C., Thompson, L. H., Prakash, L., and Prakash, S. (1993). Human xeroderma pigmentosum group D gene encodes a DNA helicase. *Nature* 365, 852–855.
29. Park, D. J., Stoehlmacher, J., Zhang, W., Tsao-Wei, D. D., Groshen, S., and Lenz, H. J. (2001). A Xeroderma pigmentosum group D gene polymorphism predicts clinical outcome to platinum-based chemotherapy in patients with advanced colorectal cancer. *Cancer Res.* 61, 8654–8658.
30. Liston, P., Roy, N., Tamai, K., Lefebvre, C., Baird, S., Cherton-Horvat, G., Farahani, R., McLean, M., Ikeda, J. E., MacKenzie, A., and Korneluk, R. G. (1996). Suppression of apoptosis in mammalian cells by NAIP and a related family of IAP genes. *Nature* 379, 349–353.
31. Rothe, M., Pan, M. G., Henzel, W. J., Ayres, T. M., and Goeddel, D. V. (1995). The TNFR2-TRAF signaling complex contains two novel proteins related to baculoviral inhibitor of apoptosis proteins. *Cell* 83, 1243–1252.
32. Deveraux, Q. L., Takahashi, R., Salvesen, G. S., and Reed, J. C. (1997). X-linked IAP is a direct inhibitor of cell-death proteases. *Nature* 388, 300–304.
33. Suzuki, Y., Nakabayashi, Y., and Takahashi, R. (2001). Ubiquitin-protein ligase activity of X-linked inhibitor of apoptosis protein promotes proteasomal degradation of caspase-3 and enhances its anti-apoptotic effect in Fas-induced cell death. *Proc. Natl. Acad. Sci. USA* 98, 8662–8667.
34. MacFarlane, M., Merrison, W., Bratton, S. B., and Cohen, G. M. (2002). Proteasome-mediated degradation of Smac during apoptosis: XIAP promotes Smac ubiquitination in vitro. *J. Biol. Chem.* 277, 36611–36616.
35. Li, J., Feng, Q., Kim, J. M., Schneiderman, D., Liston, P., Li, M., Vanderhyden, B., Faught, W., Fung, M. F., Senterman, M., Korneluk, R. G., and Tsang, B. K. (2001). Human ovarian cancer and cisplatin resistance: Possible role of inhibitor of apoptosis proteins. *Endocrinology* 142, 370–380.
36. Asselin, E., Mills, G. B., and Tsang, B. K. (2001). XIAP regulates Akt activity and caspase-3-dependent cleavage during cisplatin-induced apoptosis in human ovarian epithelial cancer cells. *Cancer Res.* 61, 1862–1868.
37. Birkey Reffey, S., Wurthner, J. U., Parks, W. T., Roberts, A. B., and Duckett, C. S. (2001). X-linked inhibitor of apoptosis protein functions as a cofactor in transforming growth factor-beta signaling. *J. Biol. Chem.* 276, 26542–26549.
38. Yamaguchi, K., Nagai, S., Ninomiya-Tsuji, J., Nishita, M., Tamai, K., Irie, K., Ueno, N., Nishida, E., Shibuya, H., and Matsumoto, K. (1999). XIAP, a cellular member of the inhibitor of apoptosis protein family, links the receptors to TAB1-TAK1 in the BMP signaling pathway. *Embo. J.* 18, 179–187.
39. Yamaguchi, A. (1995). Regulation of differentiation pathway of skeletal mesenchymal cells in cell lines by transform-ing growth factor-beta superfamily. *Semin. Cell. Biol.* 6, 165–173.
40. Sanna, M. G., Duckett, C. S., Richter, B. W., Thompson, C. B., and Ulevitch, R. J. (1998). Selective activation of JNK1 is necessary for the anti-apoptotic activity of hILP. *Proc. Natl. Acad. Sci. USA* 95, 6015–6020.
41. Sanna, M. G., da Silva Correia, J., Ducrey, O., Lee, J., Nomoto, K., Schrantz, N., Deveraux, Q. L., and Ulevitch, R. J. (2002). IAP suppression of apoptosis involves distinct mechanisms: the TAK1/JNK1 signaling cascade and caspase inhibition. *Mol. Cell. Biol.* 22, 1754–1766.
42. Sanna, M. G., da Silva Correia, J., Luo, Y., Chuang, B., Paulson, L. M., Nguyen, B., Deveraux, Q. L., and Ulevitch, R. J. (2002). ILPIP, a novel anti-apoptotic protein that enhances XIAP-mediated activation of JNK1 and protection against apoptosis. *J. Biol. Chem.* 277, 30454–30462.
43. Berchuck, A., Olt, G. J., Everitt, L., Soisson, A. P., Bast, R. C., Jr., and Boyer, C. M. (1990). The role of peptide growth factors in epithelial ovarian cancer. *Obstet. Gynecol.* 75, 255–262.
44. Berchuck, A., Rodriguez, G., Olt, G., Whitaker, R., Boente, M. P., Arrick, B. A., Clarke-Pearson, D. L., and Bast Jr., R. C. (1992). Regulation of growth of normal ovarian epithelial cells and ovarian cancer cell lines by transforming growth factor-beta. *Am. J. Obstet. Gynecol.* 166, 676–684.
45. Marth, C., Lang, T., Koza, A., Mayer, I., and Daxenbichler, G. (1990). Transforming growth factor-beta and ovarian carcinoma cells: Regulation of proliferation and surface antigen expression. *Cancer Lett.* 51, 221–225.
46. Bartlett, J. M., Rabiasz, G. J., Scott, W. N., Langdon, S. P., Smyth, J. F., and Miller, W. R. (1992). Transforming growth factor-beta mRNA expression and growth control of human ovarian carcinoma cells. *Br. J. Cancer.* 65, 655–660.
47. Jozan, S., Guerrin, M., Mazars, P., Dutaur, M., Monsarrat, B., Cheutin, F., Bugat, R., Martel, P., and Valette, A. (1992). Transforming growth factor beta 1 (TGF-beta 1) inhibits growth of a human ovarian carcinoma cell line (OVCCR1) and is expressed in human ovarian tumors. *Intl. J. Cancer.* 52, 766–770.
48. Rabiasz, G. J., Langdon, S. P., Bartlett, J. M., Crew, A. J., Miller, E. P., Scott, W. N., Smyth, J. F., and Miller, W. R. (1992). Growth control by epidermal growth factor and transforming growth factor-alpha in human lung squamous carcinoma cells. *Br. J. Cancer.* 66, 254–259.
49. Zhou, L., and Leung, B. S. (1992). Growth regulation of ovarian cancer cells by epidermal growth factor and transforming growth factors alpha and beta 1. *Biochim. Biophys. Acta.* 1180, 130–136.
50. Leevers, S. J., Vanhaesebroeck, B., and Waterfield, M. D. (1999). Signalling through phosphoinositide 3-kinases: The lipids take centre stage. *Curr. Opin. Cell. Biol.* 11, 219–225.
51. Cheng, J. Q., Godwin, A. K., Bellacosa, A., Taguchi, T., Franke, T. F., Hamilton, T. C., Tsichlis, P. N., and Testa, J. R. (1992). AKT2, a putative oncogene encoding a member of a

subfamily of protein-serine/threonine kinases, is amplified in human ovarian carcinomas. *Proc. Natl. Acad. Sci. USA* 89, 9267–9271.

52. Staal, S. P. (1987). Molecular cloning of the akt oncogene and its human homologues AKT1 and AKT2: Amplification of AKT1 in a primary human gastric adenocarcinoma. *Proc. Natl. Acad. Sci. USA* 84, 5034–5037.
53. Rane, M. J., Coxon, P. Y., Powell, D. W., Webster, R., Klein, J. B., Pierce, W., Ping, P., and McLeish, K. R. (2001). p38 Kinase-dependent MAPKAPK-2 activation functions as 3-phosphoinositide-dependent kinase-2 for Akt in human neutrophils. *J. Biol. Chem.* 276, 3517–3523.
54. Delcommenne, M., Tan, C., Gray, V., Rue, L., Woodgett, J., and Dedhar, S. (1998). Phosphoinositide-3-OH kinase-dependent regulation of glycogen synthase kinase 3 and protein kinase B/AKT by the integrin-linked kinase. *Proc. Natl. Acad. Sci. USA* 95, 11211–11216.
55. Balendran, A., Casamayor, A., Deak, M., Paterson, A., Gaffney, P., Currie, R., Downes, C. P., and Alessi, D. R. (1999). PDK1 acquires PDK2 activity in the presence of a synthetic peptide derived from the carboxyl terminus of PRK2. *Curr. Biol.* 9, 393–404.
56. Aman, M. J., Lamkin, T. D., Okada, H., Kurosaki, T., and Ravichandran, K. S. (1998). The inositol phosphatase SHIP inhibits Akt/PKB activation in B cells. *J. Biol. Chem.* 273, 33922–33928.
57. Liu, Q., Sasaki, T., Kozieradzki, I., Wakeham, A., Itie, A., Dumont, D. J., and Penninger, J. M. (1999). SHIP is a negative regulator of growth factor receptor-mediated PKB/Akt activation and myeloid cell survival. *Genes Dev.* 13, 786–791.
58. Stambolic, V., Suzuki, A., de la Pompa, J. L., Brothers, G. M., Mirtsos, C., Sasaki, T., Ruland, J., Penninger, J. M., Siderovski, D. P., and Mak, T. W. (1998). Negative regulation of PKB/Akt-dependent cell survival by the tumor suppressor PTEN. *Cell* 95, 29–39.
59. Li, J., Simpson, L., Takahashi, M., Miliaresis, C., Myers, M. P., Tonks, N., and Parsons, R. (1998). The PTEN/MMAC1 tumor suppressor induces cell death that is rescued by the AKT/protein kinase B oncogene. *Cancer Res.* 58, 5667–5672.
60. Saito, M., Okamoto, A., Kohno, T., Takakura, S., Shinozaki, H., Isonishi, S., Yasuhara, T., Yoshimura, T., Ohtake, Y., Ochiai, K., Yokota, J., and Tanaka, T. (2000). Allelic imbalance and mutations of the PTEN gene in ovarian cancer. *Intl. J. Cancer.* 85, 160–165.
61. Schondorf, T., Dostal, A., Grabmann, J., and Gohring, U. J. (2000). Single mutations of the PTEN gene in recurrent ovarian carcinomas. *J. Soc. Gynecol. Investig.* 7, 313–316.
62. Yokomizo, A., Tindall, D. J., Hartmann, L., Jenkins, R. B., Smith, D. I., and Liu, W. (1998). Mutation analysis of the putative tumor suppressor PTEN/MMAC1 in human ovarian cancer. *Intl. J. Oncol.* 13, 101–105.
63. Shayesteh, L., Lu, Y., Kuo, W. L., Baldocchi, R., Godfrey, T., Collins, C., Pinkel, D., Powell, B., Mills, G. B., and Gray, J. W. (1999). PIK3CA is implicated as an oncogene in ovarian cancer. *Nat Genet.* 21, 99–102.
64. Yuan, Z. Q., Sun, M., Feldman, R. I., Wang, G., Ma, X., Jiang, C., Coppola, D., Nicosia, S. V., and Cheng, J. Q. (2000). Frequent activation of AKT2 and induction of apoptosis by inhibition of phosphoinositide-3-OH kinase/Akt pathway in human ovarian cancer. *Oncogene* 19, 2324–2330.
65. Phillips, W. A., St Clair, F., Munday, A. D., Thomas, R. J., and Mitchell, C. A. (1998). Increased levels of phosphatidylinositol 3-kinase activity in colorectal tumors. *Cancer* 83, 41–47.
66. Moore, S. M., Rintoul, R. C., Walker, T. R., Chilvers, E. R., Haslett, C., and Sethi, T. (1998). The presence of a constitutively active phosphoinositide 3-kinase in small cell lung cancer cells mediates anchorage-independent proliferation via a protein kinase B and p70s6k-dependent pathway. *Cancer Res.* 58, 5239–5247.
67. Sun, M., Paciga, J. E., Feldman, R. I., Yuan, Z., Coppola, D., Lu, Y. Y., Shelley, S. A., Nicosia, S. V., and Cheng, J. Q. (2001). Phosphatidylinositol-3-OH Kinase (PI3K)/AKT2, activated in breast cancer, regulates and is induced by estrogen receptor alpha (ERalpha) via interaction between ERalpha and PI3K. *Cancer Res.* 61, 5985–5991.
68. Cho, H., Mu, J., Kim, J. K., Thorvaldsen, J. L., Chu, Q., Crenshaw, E. B., 3rd, Kaestner, K. H., Bartolomei, M. S., Shulman, G. I., and Birnbaum, M. J. (2001). Insulin resistance and a diabetes mellitus-like syndrome in mice lacking the protein kinase Akt2 (PKB beta). *Science* 292, 1728–1731.
69. Cho, H., Thorvaldsen, J. L., Chu, Q., Feng, F., and Birnbaum, M. J. (2001). Akt1/PKBalpha is required for normal growth but dispensable for maintenance of glucose homeostasis in mice. *J. Biol. Chem.* 276, 38349–38352.
70. Chen, W. S., Xu, P. Z., Gottlob, K., Chen, M. L., Sokol, K., Shiyanova, T., Roninson, I., Weng, W., Suzuki, R., Tobe, K., Kadowaki, T., and Hay, N. (2001). Growth retardation and increased apoptosis in mice with homozygous disruption of the Akt1 gene. *Genes Dev.* 15, 2203–2208.
71. Datta, S. R., Dudek, H., Tao, X., Masters, S., Fu, H., Gotoh, Y., and Greenberg, M. E. (1997). Akt phosphorylation of BAD couples survival signals to the cell-intrinsic death machinery. *Cell* 91, 231–241.
72. del Peso, L., Gonzalez-Garcia, M., Page, C., Herrera, R., and Nunez, G. (1997). Interleukin-3-induced phosphorylation of BAD through the protein kinase Akt. *Science* 278, 687–689.
73. Jiang, K., Coppola, D., Crespo, N. C., Nicosia, S. V., Hamilton, A. D., Sebti, S. M., and Cheng, J. Q. (2000). The phosphoinositide 3-OH kinase/AKT2 pathway as a critical target for farnesyltransferase inhibitor-induced apoptosis. *Mol. Cell. Biol.* 20, 139–148.
74. Tang, Y., Zhou, H., Chen, A., Pittman, R. N., and Field, J. (2000). The Akt proto-oncogene links Ras to Pak and cell survival signals. *J. Biol. Chem.* 275, 9106–9109.
75. Biggs III, W. H., Meisenhelder, J., Hunter, T., Cavenee, W. K., and Arden, K. C. (1999). Protein kinase B/Akt-mediated phosphorylation promotes nuclear exclusion of the winged helix transcription factor FKHR1. *Proc. Natl. Acad. Sci. USA* 96, 7421–7426.
76. Brunet, A., Bonni, A., Zigmond, M. J., Lin, M. Z., Juo, P., Hu, L. S., Anderson, M. J., Arden, K. C., Blenis, J., and Greenberg, M. E. (1999). Akt promotes cell survival by phosphorylating and inhibiting a Forkhead transcription factor. *Cell* 96, 857–868.
77. Brunet, A., Park, J., Tran, H., Hu, L. S., Hemmings, B. A., and Greenberg, M. E. (2001). Protein kinase SGK mediates survival signals by phosphorylating the forkhead transcription factor FKHRL1 (FOXO3a). *Mol. Cell. Biol.* 21, 952–965.

78. Kops, G. J., de Ruiter, N. D., De Vries-Smits, A. M., Powell, D. R., Bos, J. L., and Burgering, B. M. (1999). Direct control of the Forkhead transcription factor AFX by protein kinase B. *Nature* 398, 630–634.
79. Tang, E. D., Nunez, G., Barr, F. G., and Guan, K. L. (1999). Negative regulation of the forkhead transcription factor FKHR by Akt. *J. Biol. Chem.* 274, 16741–16746.
80. Datta, S. R., Brunet, A., and Greenberg, M. E. (1999). Cellular survival: A play in three Akts. *Genes Dev.* 13, 2905–2927.
81. Mayo, L. D., and Donner, D. B. (2001). A phosphatidylinositol 3-kinase/Akt pathway promotes translocation of Mdm2 from the cytoplasm to the nucleus. *Proc. Natl. Acad. Sci. USA* 98, 11598–11603.
81a. Fraser, M., Leung, B. M., Yan, X., Dan, H. C., Cheng, J. Q., and Tsang, B. K. (2003). p53 is a determinant of X-linked inhibitor of apoptosis protein/Akt-mediated chemoresistance in human ovarian cancer cells. *Cancer Res*. In Press.
82. Rossig, L., Jadidi, A. S., Urbich, C., Badorff, C., Zeiher, A. M., and Dimmeler, S. (2001). Akt-dependent phosphorylation of p21(Cip1) regulates PCNA binding and proliferation of endothelial cells. *Mol. Cell. Biol.* 21, 5644–5657.
83. Cheng, J. Q., Altomare, D. A., Klein, M. A., Lee, W. C., Kruh, G. D., Lissy, N. A., and Testa, J. R. (1997). Transforming activity and mitosis-related expression of the AKT2 oncogene: Evidence suggesting a link between cell cycle regulation and oncogenesis. *Oncogene* 14, 2793–2801.
84. Mende, I., Malstrom, S., Tsichlis, P. N., Vogt, P. K., and Aoki, M. (2001). Oncogenic transformation induced by membrane-targeted Akt2 and Akt3. *Oncogene* 20, 4419–4423.
85. Zhou, B. P., Hu, M. C., Miller, S. A., Yu, Z., Xia, W., Lin, S. Y., and Hung, M. C. (2000). HER-2/neu blocks tumor necrosis factor-induced apoptosis via the Akt/NF-kappaB pathway. *J. Biol. Chem.* 275, 8027–8031.
86. Page, C., Lin, H. J., Jin, Y., Castle, V. P., Nunez, G., Huang, M., and Lin, J. (2000). Overexpression of Akt/AKT can modulate chemotherapy-induced apoptosis. *Anticancer Res.* 20, 407–416.
87. Hu, L., Hofmann, J., Lu, Y., Mills, G. B., and Jaffe, R. B. (2002). Inhibition of phosphatidylinositol 3'-kinase increases efficacy of paclitaxel in in vitro and in vivo ovarian cancer models. *Cancer Res.* 62, 1087–1092.
88. Liu, M. C., and Gelmann, E. P. (2002). P53 gene mutations: case study of a clinical marker for solid tumors. *Semin. Oncol.* 29, 246–257.
89. Erhardt, P., Tomaselli, K. J., and Cooper, G. M. (1997). Identification of the MDM2 oncoprotein as a substrate for CPP32-like apoptotic proteases. *J. Biol. Chem.* 272, 15049–15052.
90. Chen, L., Marechal, V., Moreau, J., Levine, A. J., and Chen, J. (1997). Proteolytic cleavage of the mdm2 oncoprotein during apoptosis. *J. Biol. Chem.* 272, 22966–22973.
91. Persons, D. L., Yazlovitskaya, E. M., and Pelling, J. C. (2000). Effect of extracellular signal-regulated kinase on p53 accumulation in response to cisplatin. *J. Biol. Chem.* 275, 35778–35785.
92. Unger, T., Sionov, R. V., Moallem, E., Yee, C. L., Howley, P. M., Oren, M., and Haupt, Y. (1999). Mutations in serines 15 and 20 of human p53 impair its apoptotic activity. *Oncogene* 18, 3205–3212.
93. Shono, T., Tofilon, P. J., Schaefer, T. S., Parikh, D., Liu, T. J., and Lang, F. F. (2002). Apoptosis induced by adenovirus-mediated p53 gene transfer in human glioma correlates with site-specific phosphorylation. *Cancer Res.* 62, 1069–1076.
94. Yang, A., and McKeon, F. (2000). P63 and P73: P53 mimics, menaces and more. *Nat. Rev. Mol. Cell. Biol.* 1, 199–207.
95. Michael, D., and Oren, M. (2002). The p53 and Mdm2 families in cancer. *Curr. Opin. Genet. Dev.* 12, 53–59.
96. Flores, E. R., Tsai, K. Y., Crowley, D., Sengupta, S., Yang, A., McKeon, F., and Jacks, T. (2002). p63 and p73 are required for p53-dependent apoptosis in response to DNA damage. *Nature* 416, 560–564.
97. Di Como, C. J., Urist, M. J., Babayan, I., Drobnjak, M., Hedvat, C. V., Teruya-Feldstein, J., Pohar, K., Hoos, A., and Cordon-Cardo, C. (2002). p63 expression profiles in human normal and tumor tissues. *Clin. Cancer Res.* 8, 494–501.
98. Vikhanskaya, F., D'Incalci, M., and Broggini, M. (2000). p73 competes with p53 and attenuates its response in a human ovarian cancer cell line. *Nucleic Acids Res.* 28, 513–519.

CHAPTER **38**

Molecular Mechanisms of Pathogenesis and Progression of Epithelial Ovarian Cancer

ROBERT C. BAST, JR. AND GORDON B. MILLS

INTRODUCTION

Ovarian cancer is neither a common nor a rare disease. In the United States, a woman's lifetime risk of developing ovarian cancer is 1 in 70, and the annual incidence is 40 per 100,000 in a postmenopausal population. Approximately 85% of ovarian cancers exhibit epithelial histology. Of the epithelial ovarian cancers, 90% are sporadic and occur in the absence of a strong family history. Some 10% of cases are hereditary, with ovarian or breast cancers in multiple generations of each kindred. Most hereditary cancers result from mutations of *BRCA1* or *BRCA2*. Less commonly, hereditary ovarian cancers arise in families with Lynch type II syndrome (hereditary nonpolyposis colon cancer, HMPCC) related to germline mutations in mismatch repair genes. Very rarely, ovarian cancer can appear in Li-Fraumeni families that carry germline mutations of p53.

Epidemiologic studies have generally failed to demonstrate chemical carcinogens that contribute to the development of sporadic ovarian cancer. One possible exception to this generalization is an association of ovarian cancer with the use of talc products, although the literature contains conflicting reports [1, 2]. Cigarette smoking has been associated with increased risk for a minority of ovarian cancers with mucinous histology [3–5], although one cohort study suggests that smoking for 40 years or more is associated with a 2.5-fold increased risk for all histotypes [6]. Several observations point to the importance of ovulation as a co-factor in the development of ovarian cancer. Factors that increase the number of ovulatory cycles also increase the risk of ovarian cancer, including early menarche, late menopause, and nulliparity [7–9]. Conversely, factors that suppress ovulation—including multiple pregnancies and prolonged breastfeeding—decrease the risk of ovarian cancer [10, 11]. Whether or not fertility-stimulating drugs increase the risk of ovarian cancer is not clear, but use of oral contraceptives for as long as 5 years decreases the risk of ovarian cancer by 50% [12].

Over the last two decades, a great deal has been learned regarding the biology of ovarian cancers. To understand the origin and progression of ovarian cancer at the cellular and molecular levels, we must elucidate mechanisms that stimulate proliferation, block apoptosis, increase motility, enhance invasion, promote metastasis, and stimulate angiogenesis. Ultimately, we must define the molecular basis for the heterogeneity observed among ovarian cancers with regard to histotype, stage, grade, prognosis, and chemosensitivity, as well as the pathogenesis of borderline and invasive cancers.

CELL OF ORIGIN FOR HUMAN EPITHELIAL OVARIAN CANCERS

In cervical cancer, cytologic examination, culposcopy, and biopsy have been used to study the progression of dysplastic lesions to invasive cancers. Comparable studies of the origin of ovarian cancers have been limited by the inaccessibility of the ovaries. Consequently, controversy still surrounds the identity of the cell type(s) from which ovarian cancers arise. Most investigators believe that ovarian cancers develop from epithelial cells that cover the surface of the ovary or that line cysts immediately beneath the ovarian surface [13]. Inclusion cysts are thought to form through entrapment of ovarian surface epithelial cells during repair of ruptured follicles. Epithelial cells that line cysts can shed peptide or lipid growth factors into their lumens, achieving high ligand levels that mediate autocrine growth stimulation. Similarly, growth factors and integrins expressed by surrounding stromal cells could stimulate epithelial cells within cysts.

An alternate view has championed the secondary Müllerian system—endosalpingiosis, endometriosis, paraovarian cysts, and rete ovarii—as the site of origin for epithelial ovarian cancers [14]. Development of cells from rests that have already undergone Müllerian differentiation could explain the appearance of different ovarian epithelial cancer histotypes that resemble fallopian tube (serous), endometrium (endometrioid), endocervix (mucinous), and mesonephros (clear cell). The ovarian surface epithelium (OSE) arises from the coelomic epithelium, which is of mesodermal origin. If these cells are precursors of most ovarian cancers, flattened epithelial cells undergo metaplasia during malignant transformation to resemble the different histotypes.

At the time of conventional diagnosis, early-stage ovarian cancers can be found on the ovarian surface or confined within complex cysts. Nuclear and cellular atypia has been found in noncancerous tissue adjacent to primary stage I ovarian cancers [15]. Surface epithelial pseudostratification, surface papillomatosis, deep cortical invaginations, and epithelial inclusion cysts with papillary formations have been found in apparently normal ovaries from women with a strong family history of ovarian cancer [16], but these observations have not been confirmed consistently [17]. Microscopic occult cancers were found in 20 ovaries removed prophylactically from women with mutations of *BRCA1* or *BRCA2*. High-grade serous ovarian cancers were found within inclusion cysts in 19 of 20 specimens examined, suggesting that cancers might arise in cysts of these high-risk patients much more frequently than from the ovarian surface. This series may, however, have been biased by exclusion of ovaries with surface abnormalities or by the early metastasis of surface lesions. Other studies have suggested that low-grade "micropapillary" serous cancers might arise from the ovarian surface. A similarity in the pattern in mutations suggests that a fraction of endometrioid ovarian cancers may arise from deposits of endometriosis.

CLONAL ORIGIN OF EPITHELIAL OVARIAN CANCER

Of the epithelial ovarian cancers, some 90% are clonal neoplasms that arise from the progeny of a single cell [18–20]. Based on epidemiologic models, four to seven genetic events are required to transform normal ovarian epithelial cells. Genetic alterations can activate oncogenes, eliminate tumor suppressor function, or inhibit DNA repair. Activation of an oncogene can occur through amplification, translocation, or an activating mutation in the promoter or coding region. Loss of tumor suppressor gene function can result from an inactivating mutation, deletion, or promoter methylation. Mutations in DNA repair genes can increase genetic instability, contributing to the accumulation of aberrations in tumor suppressors and oncogenes. Defects in mismatch repair have been observed in HNPCC kindreds, but have also been detected in 25% to 39% of sporadic ovarian cancers with p53 mutations [21]. *BRCA1* and *BRCA2* appear to participate in a common pathway that is involved in the control of homologous recombination and in the maintenance of genomic integrity [22]. Heterozygous loss of *BRCA1* can impair the fidelity of DNA end-joining and compromise the ability of cells to repair double-strand DNA breaks [23].

ALTERATIONS IN CHROMOSOMAL DNA INVOLVING MULTIPLE GENES

Genomic abnormalities that affect chromosomal segments have been documented in human ovarian cancers using comparative genomic hybridization (CGH), spectral karyotyping (SKY), and fluorescence in situ hybridization (FISH). CGH utilizes DNA from cancer cells and from normal cells that have been labeled with different fluors. In early studies, labeled DNAs from both sources were coincubated with metaphase chromosome preparations. An excess or deficiency of binding of cancer DNA relative to normal DNA reflected the gain or loss of different chromosomal segments. More recent studies have produced higher resolution by hybridizing labeled DNAs with arrays from a series of bacterial artificial chromosomes (BACs) that span the entire human genome [24]. Increased or decreased copy number has been confirmed with FISH of cancer specimens using labeled BACs or labeled probes for genes that are included in the BACs.

Normal ovarian epithelial cells generally show normal copy numbers across the genome. Few abnormalities are observed in benign ovarian tumors, whereas cancers can exhibit multiple abnormalities with increases and decreases in copy number at different chromosomal sites. These abnormalities may arise from chromosomal fragmentation during telomeric crisis. With normal cells, two sites of hybridization are detected using FISH. When an increase in copy number is observed with CGH, more than two sites of hybridization are observed with FISH. A decrease in copy number is associated with only a single site of hybridization or loss of hybridization altogether.

Across different ovarian cancer histotypes, increased copy number is associated with portions of chromosomes 1q, 3q, 8q, 19p, 20p, and 20q [24]. Decreased copy number is found on portions of chromosomes 4q, 5q, 17p, 17q, Xp, and Xq [24]. Abnormalities are found both in early- and late-stage ovarian cancers. Abnormalities are, however, more frequent in high-grade, poorly differentiated ovarian cancers than in low-grade, well-differentiated cancers [25]. Among high-grade cancers, an increasing prevalence of copy number abnormalities appears to have adverse prognostic significance. As described below and on p. 5, amplification of material on chromosome 3q contains the PIK3CA, EEF1A2, and EVI-1 genes that may contribute to cancer growth and survival [26, 27].

ALTERATIONS IN GENE EXPRESSION

Oligonucleotide and complementaary DNA (cDNA) arrays can now measure simultaneous expression of more than 40,000 known genes and expressed sequence tags (ESTs). Upregulated genes have provided new candidates for tumor markers [28–30], including HE4 [31], kallikrein

10 [32], prostasin [33], mesothelin [33], and osteopontin [34]. Serial analysis of gene expression (SAGE) has also detected upregulation of several cell surface and shed proteins [35].

Alterations in gene expression have been correlated with histotype, grade, and stage. The pattern of gene expression can distinguish different histotypes with distinctive profiles in clear cell [36] and mucinous cancers [37]. Expression of 6,500 genes has been compared in low-grade (well-differentiated) and high-grade (poorly differentiated) serous ovarian cancers [38]. Levels of some 99 genes distinguished low- and high-grade lesions. A disproportionate number of genes on chromosome 20q13 were upregulated in high-grade cancers, including several centrosome-related genes. When early- and late-stage high-grade serous ovarian cancers were studied, the early-stage tumors exhibited profound alterations of gene expression, many of which were similar to those observed in late-stage disease. Differences in gene expression appeared quantitative rather than qualitative [39]. CGH analysis performed with DNA from the same cancers detected, however, substantial differences between early- and late-stage cancers.

Expression of genes can be coordinately regulated. Using 39 micro-dissected ovarian cancers, 13 genes were strongly upregulated [40]. Levels of STAT1 messenger RNA (mRNA) correlated with those of seven other genes across the different cancers. Overall, given the degree of coordinate regulation, four signaling pathways could account for most of the upregulation observed. One of the most intriguing analyses has compared gene expression in 18 ovarian cancers linked to *BRCA1* founder mutations, in 16 cases linked to *BRCA2* founder mutations, and in 27 cases negative for any founder mutation [41]. The largest contrast in gene expression was observed between the two BRCA-linked tumor groups, suggesting that transcriptional regulation is differentially altered by *BRCA1* and *BRCA2* germline mutations. BRCA1- and BRCA2-like expression profiles were also found in major subgroups of sporadic cancers, raising the possibility that sporadic and hereditary carcinogenic pathways might converge.

Gene expression profiles can predict the prognosis of ovarian cancer patients treated with a standard platinum-paclitaxel regimen [42]. Analysis of the expression levels of 30,000 genes identified 14 genes that correctly sorted 86% of 28 patients into those whose disease recurred in less than or greater than 23 months.

LOSS OF HETEROZYGOSITY AT DIFFERENT LOCI

Loss of heterozygosity (LOH) has been observed at several sites in sporadic ovarian cancers. Particularly frequent abnormalities (>50%) have been described on chromosomes 17p and 17q. A significant level of LOH (>30%) has been found at other sites, including 1p, 5q, 6p, 6q, 8g, 9p, 11p, 13q, 17p, 17q, 18g, 19p, 22q, and Xp. Candidate tumor suppressor genes have mapped to these sites on 1p, 5q, 6q, 13q, 16q, 17p, and 17q. Transfer of normal human chromosomes 2, 3, 7 and 22 has inhibited growth of some ovarian cancers, consistent with the restoration of tumor suppressor function.

TUMOR SUPPRESSOR GENES

Loss of several putative tumor suppressor genes has been described in ovarian cancers (Table 38.1). Several of these tumor suppressor genes were first discovered through studies of cancers that occurred at other sites. Over the last 10 years, however, several novel putative tumor suppressor genes have been discovered in ovarian epithelial cells. In subsequent studies, observations with ovarian cancers have been found relevant to cancers that arise from other organs. Taken together, putative suppressor genes expressed in normal ovarian epithelium have encoded matrix proteins, coupling molecules, G proteins, phosphatases, and transcription factors.

TP53

The most thoroughly studied of the tumor suppressor genes is p53. As discussed in greater detail on p. 632, damage to DNA can upregulate TP53, inducing cell cycle arrest and/or apoptosis. Among its many activities, wild-type p53 can repress the expression of survivin, a protein inhibitor of apoptosis that is overexpressed in most tumors [43]. Dysfunction of TP53 has also been associated with decreased levels of the angiogenesis inhibitor throm-

TABLE 38.1 Tumor Suppressor Genes in Epithelial Ovarian Cancer

Intact
RB 13q14
VHL 3p25
WT1 and WT2 11p13, 11p15
Loss of Function
BRCA1 17q21.1*
BRCA2 13q12*p53 17p13
NOEY2, 1p31
DOC2, 5p13
SPARC, 5q31
LOT-1, 6q25
OVCA1, 17p13
Semaphorin 3p21.3
PTEN 10q23.3
WWOX 16q23

*Germline in hereditary ovarian cancers.

bospondin-1 [44] and an increase in micro-vessel density within cancers [45].

Some 70% of ovarian cancers have lost TP53 function through missense or truncating mutations [46]. Missense mutations occur in approximately 50% of all ovarian cancers and exert a dominant negative effect where only one allele need be altered to eliminate TP53 activity. The dysfunctional mutant protein binds and inactivates wild-type TP53. Complexes are poorly degraded and accumulate in the cancer cell nucleus, creating overexpression on immunohistochemical staining. Truncating mutations occur in about 20% and require "two hits" with mutation or deletion of the contralateral allele. Missense mutation and consequent overexpression of TP53 protein has been associated with a metastatic phenotype. Only 15% of Stage IA and IB ovarian cancers overexpress TP53, whereas TP53 overexpression is observed in 44% to 50% of cancers in stages IC to IV [46]. Despite the statistical association with metastatic disease at the time of conventional diagnosis, TP53 overexpression has also been observed in epithelial inclusion cysts from apparently normal ovaries adjacent to serous carcinomas [47] and has been associated with microscopic primary cancers in ovaries removed prophylactically from patients with germline mutations of *BRCA1* or *BRCA2* [48], consistent with the possibility that some ovarian cancers have at least one of the genetic changes required for metastasis at a very early stage of development. Because ovarian cancers that contain somatic or germline mutations of *BRCA1* are generally associated with p53 dysfunction, this may, however, be a special circumstance that does not apply to cancers with intact *BRCA1*. In one study, p53 mutations were detected in 42 of 86 sporadic ovarian cancers compared with 13 of 15 cancers with somatic *BRCA1* mutations ($P = 0.007$) and 16 of 20 cancers with germline *BRCA1* mutations ($P = 0.01$) [49].

Mutations of p53 have been observed in some codons more frequently than in others, but no single mutation is characteristic of epithelial ovarian cancer. When the fraction of transitions, transversions, and deletions is considered, the profile of p53 mutations in ovarian cancer differs from that in lung, breast, and colon cancer, but resembles that of germline mutations in factor IX deficiency (hemophilia B), which have long been considered examples of spontaneous mutation [50].

The pattern of mutations in p53 is consistent with "wear and tear" produced by tissue repair following ovulation. OSE cells are ordinarily quiescent, but they proliferate in response to growth factors released from the follicle during ovulation, facilitating repair of the defect produced by release of an ovum. In addition to age and family history, the number of ovulatory cycles is an important factor in determining the epidemiologic risk of epithelial ovarian cancer. One study [51] suggests that women with ovarian cancers that overexpress p53 protein have a greater number of lifetime ovulatory cycles than women whose cancers do not overexpress p53 protein ($p = 0.0025$). Another similar trial found an association between increased ovulation and ovarian cancer risk, but could not confirm an association between p53 mutation and years of ovulation [52].

Mutations of p53 have correlated with prognosis in many [53, 54], but not all, studies [55]. Correlation with survival may relate to the biologic aggressiveness of cancers or, in part, to increased resistance to cisplatin chemotherapy in the presence of dysfunctional TP53 where overexpression of the protein has predicted a poor response to treatment [56, 57]. Loss of TP53 function has generally not increased resistance to taxanes [58].

Imprinted Tumor Suppressor Genes: ARH1 and Lot-1

Over the last decade, several putative tumor suppressor genes have been described in different epithelial ovarian cancers, including DOC-2 [59], SPARC [60], Lot-1 [61], OVCA 1 [62], and semaphorin [63]. Our own group has identified ARHI (NOEY2) as an imprinted putative tumor suppressor gene whose function is lost in ovarian and breast carcinomas [64]. ARHI was detected by differential display polymerase chain reaction, while seeking genes that are expressed in normal ovarian epithelial cells, but not in ovarian cancers. The nucleotide sequence of ARHI defines a 26 kD GTPase with 56% to 60% homology to RAS and RAP, but with a unique N-terminal extension [65]. ARHI is regularly expressed in normal ovarian and breast epithelial cells, but not in most ovarian and breast cancers. Re-expression of ARHI in cancer cells inhibits their growth. Growth inhibition is associated with induction of p21, downregulation of cyclin D1 promoter activity, inhibition of epidermal growth factor (EGF)-mediated signaling through *ras*/mitogen-activated protein (MAP), upregulation of Jun N-terminal kinase (JNK) activity, and the development of caspase-independent, calpain-dependent apoptosis [66].

When human ARHI is expressed in mice driven by a cytomegalovirus (CMV) promoter, the transgenic mice are small in size, infertile, and incapable of lactation. Defects in postpartum lactation are associated with a decrease in prolactin within the pituitary, plasma, and breast tissue, as well as reduced levels of tissue progesterone receptors and estrogen receptors [67]. To date, the mouse homolog of ARHI has not been isolated, although the gene is expressed in swine.

In humans, ARHI is monoallelically expressed and maternally imprinted [62]. Thus ARHI is one of some 40 known human genes that are silenced at the level of the sperm or ovum. In the case of ARHI, imprinting appears to be mediated by methylation of CpG islands in the promoter region and by condensation of adjacent chromatin through deacetylation. Normal cells exhibit methylation and silencing of the maternal allele, which can be reversed by treatment with 5-deoxy-azacytidine (5-AZA) and trichostatin A (TSA) [68]. As a consequence of imprinting, the maternal allele is silenced permanently in each normal cell, and only the paternal gene is active transcriptionally. In cancers, expression of ARHI can be lost through multiple mechanisms, including LOH in the functional allele, silencing of the functional allele by methylation of CpG islands, and transcriptional downregulation. ARHI maps to a locus on chromosome 1p31, where LOH has been observed in 40% of ovarian and breast cancers [69]. Among cases of LOH, the retained allele was methylated and silenced in 7 of 9 informative cases.

Hypermethylation of CpG islands, involving both the maternal and paternal alleles, has been observed in 4 of 9 breast cancer cell lines, but not in ovarian cancer cell lines. In the absence of LOH or hypermethylation, the ARHI promoter activity has been downregulated [70]. The most marked differences between normal and cancer cells are seen with a short 1800bp promoter segment [68]. Loss of ARHI function through multiple mechanisms suggests that this "G" protein may be particularly important in cell growth regulation.

The Lot-1 tumor suppressor gene is also imprinted [71], raising the interesting possibility that imprinted genes may be preferentially inactivated during ovarian oncogenesis. Lot-1 expression is regulated through the EGF-receptor and appears to regulate growth-promoting signals as a zinc-finger motif containing nuclear transcription factor [72]. If most mutations in ovarian epithelium occur through "spontaneous" mutation, rather than through the action of chemical carcinogens, then genes with only one functioning allele could be inactivated through a single genetic or epigenetic event. Putative tumor suppressor genes that map to the X chromosome might also be preferentially inactivated in ovarian cancer as one X-chromosome is inactivated during normal development.

WWOX

WWOX is a WW domain containing oxido-reductase that maps to 16q23 and that has been implicated as a putative tumor suppressor gene in ovarian cancer [73, 74]. This gene is located at the most common site of loss on chromosome 16, as indicated by CGH, and is also located at the FRA16D fragile site. Ectopic expression of WWOX in cells lacking WWOX results in decreased anchorage-independent growth in vitro and decreased growth as a xenograft in nude mice, compatible with a role as a tumor suppressor. The normal allele appears retained in most tumors, suggesting that it may be regulated by methylation.

ONCOGENES

PI3 Kinase Pathway

CGH has identified amplification of a region on chromosome 3q26 in most ovarian cancers [75]. Within this amplicon, the 110KD α-catalytic subunit of phosphatidylinositol-3-phosphate (PI3) kinase is encoded. PI3 kinase phosphorylates membrane phosphatidylinositols (PtdIns), generating 3-phosphorylation PtdIns, in particular PtdIns3,4,5P3. PtdIns3,4,5P3 recruits several proteins to the membrane through interaction with PH, C2, and FYVE domains, leading to the activation of a signaling cascade that includes a variety of kinases. Upregulation of the PI3 signaling pathway promotes tumor cell survival, increases neovascularization, enhances invasion, inhibits apoptosis, and increases resistance to cytotoxic drugs such as cisplatin and paclitaxel. Inhibition of PI3-K with LY294002 induces apoptosis in cells that overexpress p110. Somatic mutation of PIK3R1, which encodes the p85 regulatory subunit of PI3-K, has also been detected in ovarian cancer cell lines and in a minority of patient samples [76]. Introduction of mutant p85 increases PI3-K activity.

PI3 kinase activity is increased in most serous ovarian cancers, but not in endometrioid ovarian cancers [77]. The PTEN phosphatase dephosphorylates PtdIns3,4,5(P3) and truncates signaling through PI3-K and Akt. PTEN is mutated and inactivated in a large fraction of endometriod ovarian cancers, but much less commonly in serous tumors. Akt isoforms and particularly AKT2 are upregulated in a fraction of ovarian cancers [78, 100]. Upregulation of the PI3-K pathway renders ovarian cancer cells more sensitive to the effects of extracellular growth factors such as EGF or lysophatidic acid (LPA). Mutation of PTEN results in constitutive activation of the pathway. Taken together, however, the PI3-K/Akt pathway is critically important in ovarian cancer pathogenesis and represents a strong target for therapy. Indeed, inhibitors of PI3-K decrease the growth of ovarian cancer cells and sensitize the cells to taxol *in vitro* and *in vivo* [79, 80].

Tyrosine Kinase Growth Factor Receptors

Activation of several oncogenes has been observed in ovarian cancers (Table 38.2). Among these changes, overexpression of HER-2 has been observed in 11% to 30% of ovarian cancers [81–83]. Overexpression of HER-2 has been associated with a poor prognosis in many [79, 80], but not all, studies [84]. Several isoforms of heregulin (neuregulin) can bind to dimers of HER-2 with HER-3 or HER-4. In cell culture, heregulin increases the invasiveness of ovarian cancer cells that overexpress HER-2, associated with increased expression of matrix metalloproteinase-9 (MMP-9) [85]. Heregulin stimulates growth of cancer cells

TABLE 38.2 Oncogenes in Epithelial Ovarian Cancer

Amplification and overexpression of PIK3CA
Mutation of PIK3R1
Overexpression of wild-type HER-2
Continued expression of EGFR
Novel expression of FMS
Mutation or activation of *ras*
Activation of *src*
Amplification of STK/BTAK
Amplification and overexpression of EEF1A2 elongation factor
Amplification and overexpression of MYC
Amplification and overexpression of Evi-1

that express low ratios of HER-2 to HER-3, but inhibits growth of cells with high levels of HER-2 relative to HER-3 [83]. Consequently, the poor prognosis associated with overexpression of HER-2 may relate more to an increased ability to invade and metastasize than to a greater degree of proliferation. Different isoforms of the ligand neuregulin have been detected in 77% to 87% of ovarian cancers, consistent with the existence of an autocrine stimulatory loop in cells with low or moderate HER-2 expression [86]. HER-2 couples efficiently to the PI3-K pathway potentially linking these two processes.

Other tyrosine kinase growth factor receptors may contribute to ovarian oncogenesis. The *c-fms* proto-oncogene is upregulated in approximately half of ovarian cancers [87]. Normal ovarian epithelial cells produce only small amounts of macrophage colony–stimulating factor (M-CSF, CSF-1), whereas markedly elevated levels of M-CSF are produced by 70% of ovarian cancers [83, 88]. In addition to potential autocrine growth stimulation, M-CSF is a chemoattractant for macrophages that have been shown to produce paracrine growth factors that stimulate proliferation of ovarian cancers, including IL-1, IL-6, and TNF [89]. Ovarian cancers are associated with varying numbers of macrophages in solid and ascites tumors, and the presence of tumor-infiltrating mononuclear cells and T lymphocytes can correlate with patient outcome [90, 91].

Insulin-like growth factor 1 and 2 (IGF-1 and IGF-2) have been detected in epithelial ovarian cancers. In one study, each of seven ovarian cancers expressed IGF-1 mRNA [92]. Transfection of IGF-1 has transformed normal rabbit ovarian mesothelial cells, permitting anchorage-independent growth *in vitro* and growth as heterografts *in vivo*. Loss of imprinting of IGF-2 has been observed in 21% to 25% of ovarian cancers, and overexpression of IGF-2 protein has been observed in each of these cases [93, 94]. IGF-1 receptor (IGFR) mRNA has been found consistently in ovarian cancer cell lines and in clinical specimens [90]. IGF-2 can also bind to the insulin receptor and stimulate proliferation of insulin-responsive ovarian cancer cells. Consequently, IGF proteins may exert autocrine growth stimulation in ovarian cancers [95].

Ovarian cancers can also co-express the fibroblast growth factor (FGF)-1, FGF-7, and FGF-8 isoforms, as well as the FGR1-IIIc, FGR2-IIIb, FGR2-IIIc, and FGR4 receptors [96, 97]. Similarly, platelet-derived growth factor (PDGF) was detected in tumor cells from 33 of 45 ovarian cancers (73%), but in none of 20 benign tumors ($P < 0.001$) or 11 normal ovaries ($P < 0.001$) [98]. Cells in borderline tumors stained positive in 4 of 7 cases (57%). PDGF receptor (PDGFR)-α was detected in tumor cells in 16 of 45 malignant ovarian cancers (36%) and 1 of 7 borderline neoplasms (14%), but none was found in 16 benign tumors ($P = 0.002$) or in 10 normal ovaries ($P = 0.023$). Patients with ovarian cancer and PDGFR-α positive tumor cells demonstrated an overall shorter survival compared to those who had negatively stained tumors. Consequently, several receptor tyrosine kinases could mediate autocrine growth stimulation.

Normal OSE cells express stem cell factor (SCF), but not its receptor c-kit. Of 15 benign ovarian tumors and tumors of low malignant potential, 87% expressed c-kit and 92% of these co-expressed SCF, suggesting the possibility of autocrine growth regulation [99]. Of 35 malignant ovarian cancers, 71% expressed c-kit, and 92% co-expressed SCF with a trend for decreased c-kit expression in advanced disease stage. Paradoxically, patients whose tumors did not express c-kit have significantly shorter ($P < 0.05$) disease-free survival than patients who had c-kit–expressing tumors. Consequently, c-kit might mediate autocrine growth inhibition.

Ras Pathway

Early studies suggested that *ras* can be mutated and activated somatically in epithelial ovarian cancers [101]. In subsequent reports, it became apparent that *ras* is only occasionally mutated in high-grade serous ovarian cancers, but that *ras* mutations may contribute more frequently to the development of borderline serous, low-grade invasive serous, borderline mucinous, and invasive mucinous cancers [101]. Mutations in codon 12 or 13 of k-*ras* or of codon 599 of BRAF—a downstream mediator of *ras* signaling—were observed in 68% of 22 low-grade, invasive micropapillary serous carcinomas and 61% of 51 borderline serous tumors, but in none of 72 high-grade serous cancers [102]. In a second series, k-*ras* codon 12 mutations were observed in 5% of 38 serous ovarian cancers and 50% of 26 mucinous ovarian cancers ($P < 0.0001$) [103]. Conversely, p53 mutations are much more frequent in high-grade serous cancers than in borderline lesions [104].

Although *ras* is not frequently mutated in high-grade serous and undifferentiated ovarian cancers, it is physiologically activated in most cell lines [105, 106], consistent with (1) upstream activation of tyrosine kinase signaling pathways by ligand receptor interaction (EGF, TGF-α, heregulin, PDGF, FGF, IGF, IL-6) or receptor overexpression (HER-2); (2) cross talk from PI3 kinase; (3) loss of inhibitory docking molecules such as DOC-2; or (4) loss of inhibitory factors such as NF-1 [106].

Intracellular Tyrosine Kinases

Src is overexpressed and activated in most late-stage ovarian tumors, as well as in a panel of cultured malignant human ovarian epithelial cells, but not in normal ovarian epithelium or immortalized ovarian epithelial cells [107]. When the SKOv-3 cell line was transfected with an antisense c-*src* construct, no changes were observed in anchorage-dependent proliferation, adherence, density saturation, or wound migration; however, reduction in *src* activity was associated with altered cellular morphology, dramatically reduced anchorage-independent growth, and markedly decreased growth in nude mice [108]. Reduction of *src* activity was associated with reduced vascular endothelial growth factor (VEGF) mRNA expression *in vitro* and decreased micro-vessel density *in vivo*.

Serine-Threonine Kinases

The STK15/BTAK is an Aurora/Ipl-1–related serine/threonine kinase that is associated with centrosomes and that induces aneuploidy when overexpressed in mammalian cells, producing centrosome amplification and multipolar spindles [109]. Amplification of STK15/BTAK has been detected in 12% of primary breast cancers and in ovarian cancer cell lines [110]. How frequently the gene is amplified in primary ovarian cancers has not yet been reported.

CELL CYCLE REGULATION

One critical step in the pathogenesis of ovarian cancer is loss of the cell cycle control exerted by a complex interaction of cyclins, cyclin-dependent kinases (CDKs), and CDK inhibitors (CDKIs). In cancers that arise at other sites, upregulation of cyclins, loss of CDK inhibitor function, or mutation of CDKs to resist inhibition have been implicated in oncogenesis. In addition, abnormalities of Rb and p53 can affect cell cycle regulation.

Normal Cell Cycle Regulation

In normal cells, a series of cyclin proteins (A to H) are expressed sequentially during different phases of the cell cycle [111]. DNA synthesis and cell division are mediated by the formation of complexes between cyclins and CDKs that can phosphorylate regulatory proteins. Rb is a critical regulatory protein that prevents DNA synthesis in resting cells by binding the family of E2F proteins that are required for transcription of S-phase genes. Under the influence of growth stimulatory factors and adhesion molecules, cyclin D is upregulated. Complexes of cyclin D with CDK 4 or 6 partially phosphorylate Rb and stimulate transcription of cyclin E and of enzymes required for DNA synthesis, including dihydrofolate reductase, DNA polymerase-α, and thymidine kinase. Complexes of cyclin E with CDK2 further phosphorylate Rb and drive passage through the R (Restriction) checkpoint, committing the cell to divide. Two classes of CDK inhibitors have been described. One class includes the p16INK4a, p15INK4b, p18INK4c, and p19INK4d (p16, p15, p18, and p19) proteins that specifically inhibit activity of the complex formed between cyclin D and CDK4 or 6. The other class includes the p21CIP1, p27KIP1, and p57KIP2 (p21, p27, and p57) proteins that inhibit a variety of cyclin-CDK complexes, but may be particularly important for regulating cyclinE/CDK2 at the R checkpoint. In cells with moderate levels of DNA damage, elevated levels of p53 can upregulate p21 and arrest cells in G1, permitting time for repair. In this setting, levels of wild-type p53 may be upregulated by stabilization after phosphorylation by the ATM/ATR kinase that has been activated by DNA damage. Conversely, levels of p53 can be reduced in the presence of MDM2 protein that binds to p53 and targets the protein for degradation through the ubiquitin-proteasome pathway. Levels of MDM2 can, in turn, be downregulated by p19ARF. Consequently, forced expression of p19ARF can upregulate p53 and p21, producing G1 arrest.

Labeling Index

Invasive ovarian cancers exhibit a wide range of ^{3}H-thymidine or bromodeoxyuridine labeling indices measuring uptake by 0.4% to 79% of cancer cells, with a mean and median of 9% to 34% in different studies [112–114], depending on the stage and histology of cancer and the techniques utilized. In one report, low malignant potential and low-grade invasive cancers had a substantially lower mean labeling index (1.6% to 3.3%) than did high-grade invasive cancers (15%) [111]. In another study, invasive Stage I–II disease exhibited a labeling index of 13+/–15% and Stage III–IV disease had a growth fraction index of 40+/–17% [110]. Labeling indices have correlated with survival in some studies [112], but not in others [111].

Ki-67

Immunostaining of the Ki-67 antigen with the MIB-1 antibody has provided a convenient and more readily standardized test for cycling cells. The fraction of Ki-67–positive malignant cells ranges from 1% to 90% in different ovarian cancers, with mean values of 22% to 44% in different studies [115–117]. Ki-67 was expressed in a substantially smaller fraction of tumor cells in benign (1% to 6%) or borderline (5% to 12%) lesions than within high-grade invasive cancers (44%) [115, 118]. High Ki-67 expression has been correlated with spread to lymph nodes [119], but similar levels of Ki-67 positivity have been observed between primary invasive cancers and their metastases [114]. A low fraction of Ki-67 positive cells has been associated with a favorable prognosis in some studies [55, 120, 121], but not in others [115]. A decrease in the fraction of Ki-67–positive tumor cells between initial surgery and a second-look procedure has also correlated with improved survival [54].

TP53

A higher fraction of cycling cells has been observed in cancers that have lost TP53 function. As described previously, TP53 function is lost in some 70% of all advanced-stage ovarian cancers [122]. In the absence of functional p53, cancer cells with DNA damage can pass through the cell cycle, replicating abnormalities in structure or sequence, permanently altering the genome of damaged cells. Loss of TP53 function has been correlated with worsened survival in some reports [51], but not in others [53]. In one study, both TP53 and Ki-67 immunoreactivity correlated with a reduced overall survival, but the association was lost in multivariate analysis. However, patients with tumors that had both TP53 overexpression and a Ki-67 labeling index of more than 30% had significantly reduced overall survival in both univariate and multivariate analyses [113]. In those cancers that retain intact p53, dysfunction of other genes that affect growth regulation may obviate the need for inactivation of TP53. Thus, downregulation of RB, overexpression of cyclin D or E, or loss of relevant CDK inhibitors might permit more ready passage of cancer cells through the G1 checkpoint.

RB

In contrast to TP53, whose function is frequently lost, RB is rarely mutated or deleted in ovarian cancers [123, 124]. RB levels are decreased in many ovarian cancers, but function is usually not lost. In one series, RB has been detected immunohistochemically in 95% of borderline tumors and in 99% of invasive cancers [125]. The fraction of RB-positive cells, however, ranged from 1% to 90% between different tumors, with a median of 15% in invasive cancers and 10% in borderline cancers. Within invasive ovarian cancers, RB expression decreased with increasing grade, advancing stage, and greater bulk of residual disease. RB did not correlate with Ki-67 or with overall survival, but a low RB to Ki-67 ratio was an independent prognostic variable for poor overall survival in univariate and multivariate analyses [123].

Cyclins

Cyclin D1 is expressed at low levels in normal ovarian epithelial cells but upregulated in a fraction of ovarian cancers. When only nuclear localization is scored, cyclin D1 is upregulated in 26% to 30% of invasive ovarian cancers [126, 127], but if cytoplasmic staining is also considered, cyclin D1 overexpression is detected in up to 89% of cases [125]. Amplification of the cyclin D1 gene was found by polymerase chain reaction (PCR) in fewer than 5% of ovarian cancers [125, 128], but when fluorescence in situ hybridization (FISH) was carried out, 72% of 47 cases had an increased number of cyclin D1 gene copies [129]. When patients were stratified for residual tumor burden, an unfavorable outcome was associated with cancers that contained more than two copies of cyclin D1 per cell [127]. FISH did not correlate with immunohistochemistry. To date, expression of cyclin D1 at the level of mRNA or protein has not correlated with overall survival [121, 125]. Thus the role of increased cyclin D1 gene copy number in prognosis is unclear and could potentially reflect effects of amplification or rearrangement of nearby genes. The functional importance of cyclin D1 is suggested, however, by studies in cell culture where antisense oligonucleotides have decreased cyclin D1 in three ovarian cancer cell lines and markedly inhibited their growth [130]. In contrast to cyclin D1, neither cyclin D2 nor cyclin D3 appear to be amplified or upregulated in ovarian cancers [131, 132].

Relative to normal ovaries, cyclin E is overexpressed in 30% of ovarian cancers at the level of mRNA and in 40% to 54% at the level of protein [120, 133, 134]. Cyclin E is amplified in approximately 20% to 35% of ovarian cancers [132, 135]. Immunohistochemical analysis has demonstrated an increasing fraction of tumors, with more than 50% cyclin E expressing cells when comparing benign (9%), borderline (48%), and malignant ovarian tumors (70%) [136]. In a study that compared the characteristics of cancers from long-term (more than 5 years) and short-term (less than 2 years) survivors, cyclin E expression was marginally associated with shortened overall survival in univariate and multivariate analyses [137]. In a larger trial conducted using tissue from 139 ovarian cancer patients with advanced, suboptimally cytoreduced disease treated on the Gynecologic Oncology Group (GOG) Protocol 111, high cyclin E expression (more than 40% of cells) was associated with significantly shorter median survival (29+/–2 vs. 35+/–3 months) and worse overall survival ($P < 0.05$) [132]. Univariate and multivariate regression analysis revealed that high versus low expression of cyclin E was associated with a 40% to 50% increase in the risk of death.

Cyclin-Dependent Kinases

CDK2 is expressed by more than 10% of cells in 9% of benign tumors, 35% of borderline tumors, and 58% of invasive cancers [134]. CDK2 activity in malignant ovarian tumors is approximately twice that in benign neoplasms. Patients with cancers that overexpress CDK2 have lower overall survival than patients whose tumors have low CDK2 expression, but this finding fails to achieve statistical significance (P = 0.079). When the combined phenotypes of p27, cyclin E, and CDK2 were analyzed, the overall survival rate in patients with the p27-/cyclin E++/CDK2++ phenotype was significantly lower than that in patients with other phenotypes (P < 0.0001). CDK4 protein is expressed by all ovarian cancers and is strongly expressed by 87% [120]. CDK1 is not expressed in OSE and can be detected in fewer than 20% of cystadenomas, but is expressed at high levels in approximately 80% of ovarian cancers [138].

CDK Inhibitors

The p16 and p15 proteins inhibit the complex of cyclin D1 with CDK4/CDK6. Expression of p16 in ovarian cancer cells leads to downregulation of the expression of RB. Thus the CDKI and RB may be functionally linked [139]. Expression of p16 is frequently lost in ovarian cancer cell lines, but is less frequently deleted or mutated in DNA from freshly isolated ovarian cancer cells [120, 140, 141]. Methylation of the p16 promoter has silenced expression of the gene in cancers from other sites, but not in ovarian cancers [142, 143]. Levels of the p16 protein may, however, be regulated post-transcriptionally. In a particularly well-characterized series of tissues from GOG protocols 114 and 132, p16 protein could not be detected in 34% of 82 primary ovarian cancers, and loss of p16 was significantly more common in cases with wild-type p53 (14 of 28, 50%) compared to those with p53 mutations (14 of 54, 26%, P = 0.03) [120]. Overall, either loss of p16 or a p53 mutation was found in 83% of all ovarian cancers. Loss of p16 and the closely related p15 CDK inhibitors has had a negative impact on the survival of patients treated with platinum-based chemotherapy [144].

The p21, p27, and p57 proteins inhibit a variety of cyclin-CDK complexes, but they may be particularly important for regulating cyclin E/CDK2 at the R checkpoint. The p21 protein is expressed in 20% to 61% of ovarian cancers [145]. Within individual ovarian cancers, p21 could be detected in 7.3+/−12.5% of cells [141]. Expression of p21 is lost in 26% to 39% of cancers [143, 146]. High p21 expression is correlated with early stage and a lack of residual disease [143]. Conversely, low p21 labeling indices are associated with high grade, advanced stage, and residual tumor [141, 144]. In cell culture, overexpression of wild-type p53 can induce p21 expression, although p21 can also be regulated through p53-independent pathways. An inverse correlation has been noted between p21 and overexpression of mutant p53 in some studies [144, 147], but not in others [120, 143]. Low p21 is a predictor of poor disease-free and overall survival in univariate analysis, whereas p21−/p53+ cancers have a poor prognosis in multivariate analysis [144].

Even when both p16 and p21 are expressed, these proteins exhibit mean labeling indices of less than 10% within cancers, whereas p27 is expressed in 55% to 60% of cells in invasive cancers [141, 148] and by 90% of cells in borderline tumors or normal ovaries [146, 149]. When different cancers are examined, expression of p27 cannot be detected in 53% to 56% of cases [147, 150]. Decreased p27 expression is independently associated with poor survival when considered alone [148] or when combined with increased Ki-67 [146]. By contrast, decreases in expression of the related gene, p57, do not appear linked to prognosis [135]. Levels of p27 are regulated by catabolism through ubiquitination and proteasomal degradation. The p27 protein is recognized and targeted for ubiquitination by the Skp2 ligase, which has been shown to be upregulated in 47% of ovarian cancers [151]. Skp2 overexpression correlated with advanced stage and was not found in borderline tumors. In multivariate analysis, Skp2 overexpression (P = 0.0069) and clinical stage (P < 0.0001) remained significantly associated with overall survival, whereas age and histologic grade lost their significance.

p21 and p27 as well as mdm2 are direct targets of the Akt kinase. In each case, phosphorylation of the target results in altered subcellular distibution and interruption of the normal function of these cell cycle regulators. Furthermore, their phosphorylation and altered localization can result in increased proteosome-mediated degradation. Thus activation of the PI3-K/Akt pathway may contribute to the aberrations in expression and function of the CDK inhibitors in ovarian cancer.

In summary, the fraction of proliferating cells differs dramatically between borderline and invasive cancers, consistent with their different clinical behavior. Among invasive cancers, there is a wide range of growth fractions, almost certainly contributing to differences in prognosis. Loss of growth regulation depends on several alterations at a molecular level. Several changes relate to loss of inhibitory pathways. Some 70% of ovarian cancers have dysfunction of TP53, and an additional 13% have exhibited loss of p16 in the presence of wild-type p53. A substantial fraction of cancers exhibit loss of p21 (26% to 39%) and p27 (53% to 56%) independent of p53. Positive effects on ovarian cancer growth may be provided by increased expression of cyclin D1 (26% to 30%), cyclin E (40% to 54%), and CDK2 (55%), with the strongest prognostic correlation observed with cyclin E.

TELOMERASE

In ovarian cancers, increased proliferation is associated with avoidance of senescence and resistance to apoptosis (reviewed in Chapter 37). The life span of cells and senescence are regulated in part by telomeres, the oligonucleotide repeats that cap each chromosome. During each cell division, telomeres are progressively shortened. When the length of telomeres reaches a critical limit, chromosomes are destabilized and DNA damage occurs. At this point in their life cycle, most cells lose the ability to divide and become dormant or senesce, originally described in tissue culture as the Hayflick limit [152, 153].

Cells that have the ability to undergo multiple replicative cycles, such as germ cells and early embryo cells, have high levels of telomerase, a ribonucleoprotein enzyme complex, which adds new oligonucleotide repeats to the ends of chromosomes, maintaining telomere length. Telomerase consists of human telomerase RNA (hTR), telomerase-associated proteins (hTAPs), and the human telomerase catalytic subunit (hTERT) [152, 153]. Most cancer cells, including ovarian cancer cells, upregulate telomerase, which stabilizes telomeres and prevents senescence, resulting in an immortal phenotype. Although telomerase plays a critical role in immortalization, expression of telomerase alone is not sufficient for malignant transformation [154]. For transformation of normal ovarian epithelial cells, disruption of TP53 and RB with SV40 TAg and the activity of an oncogene such as *ras* are required in addition to the presence of telomerase [155, 156].

Normal OSE cells and most benign cysts contain low levels of telomerase activity [157–164]. Papillary cystadenomas and borderline tumors can express slightly higher levels of telomerase activity [155], but they do not attain the levels observed in 80% to 90% of invasive ovarian cancers. Normal ovarian epithelial cells, ovarian cysts, and borderline ovarian tumors express hTR and hTAPs, but exhibit only low levels of hTERT. Thus hTERT may provide the rate-limiting factor in telomerase activity [161, 162]. Although telomerase activity and hTert expression has been correlated with clinical stage [158] and lymph node involvement [159], telomerase activity has not been an independent predictor of outcome in multivariate analysis [159].

AUTOCRINE AND PARACRINE GROWTH REGULATION

Progression of ovarian cancer is driven not only by intrinsic alterations in oncogenes, tumor suppressor genes, cell cycle regulation, and telomerase, but also by interaction of autocrine and paracrine growth factors with receptors that are shared by normal cells and cancer cells. Growth factors can either stimulate or inhibit the proliferation, invasion, or metastasis of cancer cells.

Stimulatory Pathways

Autocrine or paracrine growth stimulation can occur through the epidermal growth factor receptor (EGFR). Ligands that bind to EGFR, including EGF, TGF-α, and amphiregulin and betacellulin have been detected in ovarian cancer cell lines, ovarian cancer tissues, cyst fluids, and ascites [165]. During malignant transformation, EGFR expression is lost by approximately 30% of ovarian cancers [166]. Loss of EGFR expression is associated with a better prognosis than is observed in patients whose tumors retain expression of EGFR, consistent with a contribution of signaling through EGFR to neoplastic growth [167]. Antibodies against TGF-α and antisense against the EGFR can inhibit growth of ovarian cancer cell lines [168]. When tissues are taken directly from patients, however, phosphorylation of EGFR is not commonly observed, raising questions regarding how frequently the receptor is activated *in vivo*.

Activation of EGFR can stimulate the *ras*/MAP pathway. Signaling through the *ras*/MAP pathway can affect proliferation, the expression of uPA, and the activation of MMPs. By upregulating *ets*, activated *ras* can stimulate expression of VGEF/VPF, IL-8, and basic FGF. As described previously, *ras* is mutated in only a fraction of borderline and low-grade ovarian cancers, but is physiologically activated in most high-grade cell lines.

Not all growth factors are peptides. Lipids can also be important. Lysophosphatidic acid (LPA) has been shown to interact with most ovarian cancers [169–171], enhancing phosphorylation of EGFR and HER-2, activating *ras*/MAP, increasing proliferation and blocking cell death, increasing motility and invasion, as well as increasing uPA, IL8, and VEGF secretion. LPA binds to seven times across the membrane G protein-linked receptors, including edg-2 (LPA1), edg-4 (LPA2), and edg-7 (LPA3). These edg receptors are expressed only at low levels in normal ovarian epithelial cells, but are upregulated in ovarian cancers. More than 90% of ascites fluids contain elevated levels of LPA, and this lipid molecule may serve as a marker for early detection of ovarian cancer. The enzymes producing and metabolizing LPA have been recently identified. Phospholipase D and secretory phospholipase A2 contribute to LPA production [172].

Both constitutive production and LPA-induced production of LPA are elevated in ovarian cancer cells when compared to normal OSE cells. Levels of LPA metabolizing enzymes—the lysophosphatidic acid phosphatases—are decreased in ovarian cancer, and re-expression of these enzymes decreases cell proliferation and increases cell death both *in vitro* and *in vivo* [174]. LPA production, action, and signaling may provide novel targets for detection and therapy of ovarian cancer.

Inhibitory Pathways

Incubation of normal OSE with exogenous TGF-β inhibits proliferation, but generally does not induce apoptosis [174]. By contrast, exogenous TGF-β can induce apoptosis in a fraction of ovarian cancers [174], although different cancer cell lines are resistant to growth inhibition or can even be stimulated by TGF-β [175]. Normal OSE cells express TGF-β 1, 2, and 3, consistent with the possible existence of an autocrine inhibitory loop [176]. TGF-β 1, 2, and 3 mRNAs were detected in 46%, 66%, and 66% of 96 primary ovarian cancers, respectively [177]. During malignant transformation, sensitivity to the growth inhibitory effect of TGF-β can be retained, but expression of TGF-β can be upregulated [178] or lost [175]. Depending on culture conditions *ex vivo*, TGF-β can regularly inhibit [179] or fail to inhibit [180] tumor explants and ascites tumor cells. Even when cancer cells have become resistant to growth inhibition, the TGF-β/Smad pathway generally remains intact [178, 181], although mutations of TGFR-I have been detected in as many as 33% of primary ovarian cancers [182]. In transformed cells, TGF-β can enhance invasion with upregulation of MMP2 [183]. TGF-β can be differentially regulated by steroid hormones, including progesterone and androgen [184, 185]. Both evi-1 and snon are located in the amplicon on chromosome 3q, interact with Smads, and alter TGF-β signaling, potentially contributing to the altered responses to TGF-β in ovarian cancer.

Factors That Inhibit or Stimulate Growth

As described previously, heregulin/neuregulin can stimulate or inhibit growth of ovarian cancers, depending on the level of HER-2 and HER-3 receptors present on the cells. Similarly, tumor necrosis factor-α (TNF-α) can inhibit, fail to affect, or stimulate tumor cell growth in culture. In certain ovarian cancer cell lines, TNF-α can induce apoptosis that is potentiated by inhibitors of protein synthesis [186]. TNF-α can stimulate proliferation in other cell lines and in 10% to 25% of tumor cells taken directly from patients [187]. Ovarian cancer cells express functional p55 and p75 receptors for TNF-α, suggesting that signaling distal to the receptor differs between cell lines [188]. Addition of TNF-α or IL1-α to ovarian cancer cells in culture can induce the expression of endogenous TNF-α and stimulate tumor cell proliferation. TNF-α expression is regulated transcriptionally and translationally through NF-kB. Although many cell lines have lost TNF-α expression, the cytokine has been detected in 16 of 20 ovarian cancers taken directly from patients [189]. When TNF-α has been injected intraperitoneally into mice with human ovarian cancers xenografts, nodule growth and invasion is increased associated with increased protease activity [190].

MOTILITY, ADHESION, AND INVASION

Pattern of Metastasis

Ovarian cancers exhibit a distinctive pattern of invasion and metastasis. A fraction of cancers arise from the ovarian surface, but many likely arise within cysts. To metastasize, cancer cells must first acquire the ability to invade across the cyst wall. Although ovarian cancer cells can metastasize hematogenously and through lymphatics, the most frequent route of spread is through the abdominal cavity. Cancer cells detach from the ovarian surface and form a myriad of small nodules on the peritoneum. Ovarian cancer cells are carried to the diaphragm, where they block lymphatics and impede the clearance of fluid from the peritoneal cavity. Most ovarian cancers express VEGF, a molecule that is identical to vascular permeability factor (VPF). VEGF/VPF levels are markedly elevated in ascites fluid [191].

VEGF/VPF enhances the permeability of tumor vessels and of normal vessels within the peritoneum, increasing the amount of fluid that accumulates within the abdomen. With increased production and decreased clearance of peritoneal fluid, many patients present with abdominal distension related to ascites.

Invasion

Proteinases in cancer cells and in surrounding stromal cells may contribute to enzymatic degradation of the extracellular matrix, local invasion of the ovary, entry into vessels and lymphatics, and implantation of peritoneal nodules. MMPs are zinc-dependent endopeptidases that digest collagen and other components of the extracellular matrix. Urokinase plasminogen activator (uPA) is a serine protease that catalyzes the activation of plasminogen to plasmin, activates MMPs, and digests laminin and fibronectin. MMP-2 [192], MMP-9 [192], Protease M [193], uPA [194], and uPA receptor [192] have all been detected in ovarian cancer cells in culture and have been found in ascites fluid. The predominant protease secreted by ovarian cancer cells in culture is MMP-2 [195]. Protein expression of pro-MMP-2 and pro-MMP-9, as well as antigen levels of uPA and PAI-1, are low in benign ovarian tumors but increase dramatically from low malignant potential tumors (LMP) to advanced ovarian cancers [196]. When human ovarian cancers were examined immuno-histochemically, levels of E-cadherin, MMP-2, and MMP-9 correlated with disease stage [197]. Multivariate analysis of overall survival showed that the MMP:E-cadherin ratio was a significant independent prognostic factor. UPA levels and MMP activity are increased by LPA consistent with LPA playing a role in protease activity in ovarian cancer [198].

Recent work has highlighted the upregulation, in parallel, of 7 of the 15 known kallikreins in ovarian cancer, including KLK 5, KLK 6, KLK7, KLK8, KLK10, KLK11, and KLK14 [199]. The kallikreins are serine proteases that are capable of degrading matrix. Elevated levels of hK6 (neurosin) [200], hK10 (NES1) [201], and hK11 (hippostasin) [202] have been detected in sera from ovarian cancer patients.

Proteomic spectra generated by surface-enhanced laser/desorption/ionization time-of-flight mass spectrometry (SELDI-TOF) have been reported to distinguish healthy women from patients with ovarian cancer with a high sensitivity and specificity [203]. Using SELDI-TOF, three proteins have been identified from among several thousand peaks that distinguish sera from normal individuals and sera from patients with Stage I ovarian cancer [204]. In combination with CA 125, these markers can achieve a sensitivity of 83% and a specificity of 94%. All three markers have been identified, and two are protease cleavage fragments of known serum proteins. Consequently, the proteases associated with ovarian cancers may generate a series of distinctive cleavage products that will prove useful in diagnosis and early detection.

Although many investigators have assumed that cancer cells contribute most of the protease activity, ovarian stromal cells may be an even more important source of several proteases [205]. Growth of human ovarian xenografts was markedly reduced in mice that lacked the gene for MMP-9 [206]. Microvessel density and macrophage infiltration were reduced relative to xenografts grown in mice that expressed MMP-9. Angiogenesis and tumor growth could be restored by infusing spleen cells from mice that expressed MMP-9. These observations suggest that host-derived MMP-9 expression, most likely in tumor-infiltrating macrophages, appears to play a critical role in growth of human ovarian cancer xenografts.

The invasiveness of tumor cells—judged by their ability to invade matrigel membranes—is increased by TGF-β [207], TNF-α [188], heregulin [208], and LPA [209]. Secretion of uPA is induced by several of these factors. Plasminogen activator inhibitor-2 (PAI-2) is expressed by 58% of primary tumors and 68% of metastases [210]. Expression of PAI-2 by ovarian cancer metastases is a strong predictor of prolonged disease-free and overall survival.

Ovarian cancer cell lines that expressed high to moderate levels of $\alpha(v)\beta(6)$ integrin demonstrate ligand-independent enhanced levels of high molecular weight uPA, pro-MMP-2, and pro-MMP-9 [211]. The $\alpha(v)$ integrins have also been shown to regulate proliferation in ovarian cancer cell lines by signaling through integrin-linked kinase (ILK) [212]. Endothelin-1 (ET-1) is present at high concentrations in ovarian ascites fluid and is overexpressed in primary and metastatic ovarian cancer. ET-1 upregulates the expression of MMP-1, -2, -9, -3, -7, and -13 and can induce cellular proliferation [213].

Adhesion

Molecular mechanisms have been sought for shedding of cancer cells from the ovarian surface, adhesion to peritoneal mesothelial cells, and invasion of the parietal and visceral peritoneum. Normal OSE cells bind to collagen and to laminin associated with the basement membrane [214]. Adhesion to collagen appears to be maintained during malignant transformation by ovarian cancer cells. Ovarian cancer cells bind preferentially to type I collagen utilizing $\alpha(2)\beta(1)$ integrin [215]. Interaction with laminin appears to be altered in ovarian cancer cells. Expression of a 37 kd laminin-binding protein is decreased in ovarian cancer cells, whereas the expression of a 67 kd laminin-binding protein is increased relative to normal ovarian epithelial cells [216]. Multiple integrins can bind laminin, including $\alpha(1)\beta(1)$, $\alpha(2)\beta(1)$, $\alpha(3)\beta(1)$, $\alpha(6)\beta(1)$, and $\alpha(6)\beta(4)$. The $\beta(1)$, $\alpha(2)$, and $\alpha(3)$ integrins are distributed over the entire surface of normal ovarian epithelial cells, whereas $\alpha(6)$ and $\beta(4)$ are found only on the basal surface of epithelial cells at sites of binding to basement membrane of the normal ovary.

Ovarian cancer cells within solid tumors express $\beta(1)$, $\alpha(2)$, and $\alpha(3)$ integrins over their entire surface, with only focal expression of $\alpha(6)$ and $\beta(4)$ [212]. Ascites tumor cells have a marked decrease in expression of $\alpha(6)$ and $\beta(4)$ integrin, possibly contributing to the lack of adherence to basement membranes for these free-floating cells [212]. $\alpha(v)\beta(6)$ integrin is not found in normal epithelium, but has been detected in each of 45 cancers, and expression has been correlated with grade. Ovarian cancer cell lines express $\beta(1)$ and $\alpha(v)\beta(3)$ integrins that mediate interaction with fibronectin [217]. Antibodies to $\beta(1)$ or $\alpha(v)\beta(3)$ integrins failed, however, to block binding of cancer cells to peritoneal mesothelial cells that are known to express fibronectin [215]. Cells transfected with AKT2 exhibit increased adhesion and invasion through collagen IV, mediated by upregulation of $\beta(1)$ integrins [218]. The interaction of integrins with the extracellular matrix can activate the FAK, ILK, and PI3 kinases. Once activated, these kinases play critical roles in determining whether cells undergo apoptosis or anoikis on dissociation from the substratum. In addition to changes in integrin profile, ovarian cancer cells are relatively deficient in E-cadherin when compared to normal OSE [219]. Expression of dipeptidyl peptidase on the ovarian cell surface can upregulate levels of E-cadherin, β-catenin, and tissue inhibitors of metalloproteinases 1 and 2 (TIMP 1 and 2) and downregulate levels of membrane MMP-1 and MMP-2 [220]. Consequently, this peptidase may downregulate the invasive properties of ovarian cancers.

Peritoneal mesothelial cells express hyaluronic acid. Normal ovarian epithelial cells express a standard form (CD44S) of the CD44 hyaluronic acid receptor, whereas some 70% of ovarian cancers exhibit a diverse mixture of CD44 splice variants [221]. Expression of CD44 is decreased in ascites tumor cells [222]. In heterograft models, anti-CD44 antibodies can partially block adhesion of ovarian cancer cells to peritoneal mesothelial cells [220] and can reduce the frequency of peritoneal metastases [223], suggesting that interaction of CD44 with hyaluronic acid may be important for tumor cell adhesion and formation of peritoneal implants.

ANGIOGENESIS

For metastatic tumors to grow beyond 1 mm in diameter, new blood vessels must be formed through the migration and proliferation of normal endothelial cells. Microvessel density correlates with the stage of disease and the presence of p53 mutation, particularly null mutations [224]. Ovarian cancers can produce multiple angiogenic and antiangiogenic factors. Among the angiogenic factors found in ovarian cancers are FGF-β, IL-6, gro-α, IL-8, and VEGF/VPF. As described previously, expression of VEGF/VPF is associated with ascites formation and angiogenesis. VEGF levels are increased in ascites, plasma, and urine [225–227]. Both Il-8 and VEGF levels are increased by LPA, which is present in high concentrations in ascites [228]. IL-8 correlates with aggressive tumor growth in immuno-suppressed mice. Production of Il-8 is increased by hypoxia and low pH, as well as by LPA [229].

CONCLUSION

A more fundamental understanding of the pathogenesis and progression of ovarian cancer suggests several potential therapeutic and diagnostic targets. Inhibitors of the PI3-K pathway are particularly attractive. In human ovarian cancer xenografts models, PI3-K inhibitors have blocked tumor growth, alone or in combination with cytotoxic chemotherapy. Only a small fraction of ovarian cancers overexpress HER-2, but trastuzumab is being evaluated for a few appropriate patients. Gene therapy with p53 gas has been tested, as has infection with a defective adenovirus, ONYX015, which can only grow in cancers with mutated p53. Gene therapy with ARHI has also inhibited growth of human tumor xenografts. Antiangiogenic strategies have included the use of anti-VEGF antibodies and of pegylated interferon, which downregulates expression of the angiogenic factors VEGF, IL-8, and basic FGF. LPA can serve both as therapeutic and a diagnostic target.

Over the next decade, our understanding of the pathogenesis and progression of ovarian cancer should develop even more rapidly. Progress will be facilitated by studying large groups of patients treated on uniform regimens. Evaluation of multiple molecules in the same tissue specimens should permit a more precise correlation of cellular and molecular alteration with cancer phenotype. Global, unbiased technologies that analyze genomic, epigenetic, transcriptional profiling, and proteomic patterns offer an opportunity to facilitate discovery research.

References

1. Cramer, D. W., Liberman, R. F., Titus-Ernstoff, L., Welch, W. R., Greenberg, E. R., Baron, J. A., and Harlow, B. L. (1999). Genital talc exposure and risk of ovarian cancer. *Intl. J. Cancer* 8, 351–356.
2. Wong, C., Hempling, R. E., Piver, M. S., Natarajan, N., and Mettlin, C. J. (1999). Perineal talc exposure and subsequent epithelial ovarian cancer: A case-control study. *Obstet. Gynecol* 93, 372–376.
3. Modugno, F., Ness, R. B., and Cottreau, C. M. (2002). Cigarette smoking and the risk of mucinous and nonmucinous epithelial ovarian cancer. *Epidemiology* 13, 467–471.
4. Green, A., Purdie, D., Bain, C., Siskind, V., and Webb, P. M. (2001). Cigarette smoking and risk of epithelal ovarian cancer. (Australia) *Cancer Causes Control* 12, 713–719.
5. Marchbanks, P. A., Wilson, H., Bastos, E., Cramer, D. W., Schildkraut, J. M., and Peterson, H. B. (2000). Cigarette smoking and epithelial ovarian cancer by histologic type. *Obstet. Gynecol* 95, 255–260.
6. Terry, P. D., Miller, A. B., Jones, J. G., and Rohan, T. E. (2003). Cigarette smoking and the risk of invasive epithelial ovarian cancer in a prospective cohort study. *Eur. J. Cancer* 39, 1157–1164.
7. Franceschi, S., La Vecchia, C., Booth, M. et al. (1991). Pooled analysis of three European case-control studies of epithelial ovarian cancer. II. Age at menarche and menopause. *Intl. J. Cancer* 49, 57–60.
8. Negri, E., Franceschi, S., Tzonou, A. et al. (1991). Pooled analysis of three European case-control studies of epithelial ovarian cancer: I. Reproductive factors and risk of epithelial ovarian cancer. *Intl. J. Cancer* 49, 50–56.
9. Fathalla, M. F. (1983). Incessant ovulation: A factor in ovarian neoplasia? *Lancet* 71, 717.
10. Centers for Disease Control Cancer and Steroid Hormone Study. (1983). Oral contraceptives and the risk of ovarian cancer. *JAMA* 249, 1596–1607.
11. Franceschi, S., Parazzini, F., Negri, E. et al. (1991). Pooled analysis of three European case control studies of epithelial ovarian cancer: III. Oral contraceptives use. *Intl. J. Cancer* 49, 61–65.
12. Stanford, J. L. (1991). Oral contraceptives and neoplasia of the ovary. *Contraception* 43, 543–556.
13. Auersperg, N., Edelson, M. I., Mok, S. C. et al. (1998). The biology of ovarian cancer. *Semin. Oncol.* 25, 281–304.
14. Dubeau, L. (1999). The cell of origin of ovarian epithelial tumors and the ovarian surface epithelium dogma: Does the emperor have no clothes? *Gynecol. Oncol.* 72, 437–442.
15. Plaxe, S. C., Deligdisch, L., Dottino, P. R., and Cohen, C. J. (1990). Ovarian intraepithelial neoplasia demonstrated in patients with stage I ovarian carcinoma. *Gynecol. Oncol.* 38, 367–372.
16. Salazar, H., Godwin, A. K., Daly, M. B., Laub, P. B., Hogan, W. M., Rosenblum, N., Boente, M. P., Lynch, H. T., and Hamilton, T. C. (1996). Microscopic benign and invasive malignant neoplasms and a cancer-prone phenotype in prophylactic oophorectomies. *J. Natl. Cancer Inst.* 88, 1810–1820.
17. Barakat, R. R., Federici, M. G., Saigo, P. E., Robson, M. E., Offit, K., and Boyd, J. (2000). Absence of premalignant histologic, molecular, or cell biologic alterations in prophylactic

oophorectomy specimens from BRCA1 heterozygotes. *Cancer* 89, 83–90.

18. Jacobs, I. J., Kohler, M. F., Wiseman, R. et al. (1992). Clonal origin of epithelial ovarian cancer: Analysis by loss of heterozygosity, p53 mutation and X chromosome inactivation. *J. Natl. Cancer Inst.* 84, 1793–1798.
19. Mok, C. H., Tsao, W. W., Knapp, R. C. et al. (1992). Unifocal origin of advanced human epithelial ovarian cancer. *Cancer Res.* 52, 5119–5122.
20. Li, S., Han, H., Resnik, E. et al. (1993). Advanced ovarian carcinoma: Molecular evidence of unifocal origin. *Gynecol. Oncol.* 51, 21–25.
21. Buller, R. E., Shahin, M. S., Holmes, R. W., Hatterman, M., Kirby, P. A., and Sood, A. K. (2001). P53 mutations and microsatellite instability in ovarian cancer: Yin and yang. *Am. J. Obstet. Gynecol.* 184, 891–902.
22. Scully, R. (2000). Role of BRCA gene dysfunction in breast and ovarian cancer predisposition. *Breast Cancer Res.* 2, 324–330.
23. Baldeyron, C., Jacquemin, E., Smith, J., Jacquemont, C., De Oliviera, I., Gad, S., Fenteun, J., Stoppa-Lyonnet, D., and Papadopoulo, D. (2002). A single mutated BRCA1 allele leads to impaired fidelity of double strand end-joining. *Oncogene* 21, 1401–1410.
24. Gray, J. W., Suzuki, S., Kuo, W. L., Polikoff, D., Deavers, M., Smith-McCune, K., Berchuck, A., Pinkel, D., Albertson, D., and Mills, G. B. (2003). Specific keynote: Genome copy number abnormalities in ovarian cancer. *Gynecol. Oncol.* 88, S16-S21.
25. Suzuki, S., Moore II, DH, Ginzinger, D. G., Godfrey, T. E., Barclay, J., Powell, B., Pinkel, D., Zaloudek, C., Lu, K., Mills, G., Berchuch, A., and Gray, J. W. (2000). An approach to analysis of large-scale correlations between genome changes and clinical endpoints in ovarian cancer. *Cancer Res.* 60, 5382–5385.
26. Mills, G. B., Fang, X., Lu, Y., Hasegawa, Y., Eder, A., Tanyi, J., Tabassam, F. H., Mao, M., Wang, H., Cheng, K. W., Nakayama, Y., Kuo, W., Erickson, J., Gershenson, D., Kohn, E. C., Jaffe, R., Bast Jr., R. C., and Gray, J. (2003). Molecular therapeutics in ovarian cancer. *Gynecol. Oncol.* 88, S88-S92.
27. Anand, N., Murthy, S., Amann, G., Wernick, M., Porter, L. A., Cukier, I. H., Collins, C., Gray, J. W., Diebold, J., Demetrick, D. J., and Lee, J. M. (2002). Protein elongation factor EEF1A2 is a putative oncogene in ovarian cancer. *Nat. Genet.* 3, 301–305.
28. Ismail, R. S., Baldwin, R. L., Fang, J., Browning, D., Karlan, B. Y., Gasson, J. C., and Chang, D. D. (2000). Differential gene expression between normal and tumor derived ovarian epithelial cells. *Cancer Res.* 60, 6744–6749.
29. Lu, K. H., Patterson, A., Atkinson, E. N., Baggerly, K., Marquez, R., Liu, J., Smith, D., Hartmann, L., Fishman, D., Berchuck, A., Whitaker, R., and Bast Jr., R. C. (2003). Selection of potential markers for epithelial ovarian cancer with gene expression array and recursive descent partition analysis. *Proc. Am. Assoc. Cancer Res.* 44, 573 (A#2520).
30. Welsh, J. B., Zarrinkar, P. P., Sapinoso, L. M., Kern, S. G., Behling, C. A., Monk, B. J., Lockhart, D. J., Burger, R. A., and Hampton, G. M. (2001). Analysis of gene expression profiles in normal and neoplastic ovarian tissue samples identifies candidate molecular markers of epithelial ovarian cancer. *Med. Sci.* 98, 1176–1181.
31. Schummer, M., Ng, W. V., Bumgarner, R. E., Nelson, P. S., Schummer, B., Bednarski, D. W., Hassell, L., Baldwin, R. L., Karlan, B. Y., and Hood, L. (1999). Comparative hybridization of an array of 21500 ovarian cDNAs for the discovery of genes overexpressed in ovarian carcinomas. *Gene* 238, 375–385.
32. Schvartsman, H. S., Lu, K. H., Lee, J., Lillie, J., Deavers, M., Clifford, S., Wolf, J., Bast Jr., R. C., Mills, G. B., Gershenson, D., and Schmandt, R. [2003]. Over-expression of kallikrein 10 in epithelial ovarian cancer. *Gynecol. Oncol.* 90, 44–50.
33. Mok, S. C., Chao, J., Skates, S., Wong, K., Yiu, G. K., Muto, M. G., Berkowitz, R. S., and Cramer, D. W. (2001). Prostasin, a potential serum marker for ovarian cancer: identification through microarray technology. *J. Natl. Cancer Inst.* 93, 1458–1464.
34. Kim, J. H., Skates, S. J., Uede, T., Wong, K. K., Schorge, J. O., Feltmate, C. M., Berkowitz, R. S., Cramer, D. W., and Mok, S. C. (2002). Osteopontin as a potential diagnostic biomarker for ovarian cancer. *JAMA* 287, 1671–1679.
35. Hough, C. D., Sherman-Baust, C. A., Pizer, E. S., Montz, F. J., Im, D. D., Rosenshein, N. B., Cho, K. R., Riggins, G. J., and Morin, P. J. (2000). Large-scale serial analysis of gene expression reveals genes differentially expressed in ovarian cancer. *Cancer Res.* 62, 6281–6287.
36. Schwartz, D. R., Kardia, S. L. R., Shedden, K. A., Kuick, R., Michailidis, G., Taylor, J. M. G., Misek, D. E., Wu, R., Zhai, Y., Darrah, D. M., Reed, H., Ellenson, L. H., Giordano, T. J., Rearon, E. R., Hanash, S. M., and Cho, K. R. (2002). Gene expression in ovarian cancer reflects both morphology and biological behavior, distinguishing clear cell from other poor-prognosis ovarian carcinomas. *Cancer Res.* 62, 4722–4729.
37. Marquez, R., Baggerly, K., Patterson, A., Frumuovitz, M., Atkinson, E. N., Liu, J., Smith, D., Hartmann, L., Fishman, D., Berchuck, A., Whitaker, R., Bast Jr., R. C., and Lu, K. H. (2003). Gene expression array analysis distinguishes different histotypes of epithelial ovarian cancer and suggests a distinct transcriptional program for mucinous cancers. *Proc. Am. Assoc. Cancer Res.* 44, 575 (A#2525).
38. Jazaeri, A. A., Lu, K., Schmandt, R., Harris, C. P., Rao, P. H., Sotiriou, C., Chandramouli, G. V., Gershenson, D. M., and Liu, E. T. (2003). Molecular determinants of tumor differentiation in papillary serous ovarian carcinoma. *Mol. Carcinog.* 36, 53–56.
39. Shridhar, V., Lee, J., Pandita, A., Iturria, S., Avula, R., Staub, J., Morrissey, M., Calhoun, E., Sen, A., Kalli, K., Kenney, G., Roche, P., Cliby, W., Lu, K., Schmandt, R., Mills, G. B., Bast Jr., R. C., James, D., Couch, F. J., Hartmann, L. C., Lillie, J., and Smith, D. I. (2001). Genetic analysis of early-versus late stage ovarian tumors. *Cancer Res.* 61, 5895–5904.
40. Hough, C. D., Cho, K. R., Zonderman, A. B., Schwartz, D. R., and Morin, P. J. (2001). Coordinately up-regulated genes in ovarian cancer. *Cancer Res.* 61, 3869–3876.
41. Jazaeri, A. A., Yee, C. J., Sotiriou, C., Brantley, K. R., Boyd, J., and Liu, E. T. (2002). Gene expression profiles of BRCA-linked and sporadic ovarian cancers. *Proc. Soc. Gynecol. Oncol.* Abstract #35.

42. Hartmann, L. C., Couch, F. J., Kaufmann, S. H., Cliby, W. A., Iturria, S. J., Kalli, K. R., Lu, K., Bast Jr., R. C., Lillie, J., Stec, J., Shridhar, V., Smith, D., and Clark, E. (2001). Chemoprediction in ovarian cancer? Genomic approaches. *Proc. Soc. Gynecol. Oncol.* Abstract #17.
43. Mirza, A., McGuirk, M., Hockenberry, T. N., Wu, Q., Ashar, H., Black, S., Wen, S. F., Wang, L., Kirschmeier, P., Bishop, W. R., Nielson, L. L., Pickett, C. B., and Liu, S. (2002). Human survivin is negatively regulated by wild-type p53 and participates in p53-dependent apoptotic pathway. *Oncogene* 21, 2613–2622.
44. Alvarez, A. A., Axelrod, J. R., Whitaker, R. S., Isner, P. D., Bentley, R. C., Dodge, R. K., and Rodriguez, G. C. (2001). Thrombospondin-1 expression in epithelial ovarian carcinoma: association with p53 status, tumor angiogenesis and survival in platinum-treated patients. *Gynecol. Oncol.* 82, 273–278.
45. Goodheart, M. J., Vasef, M. A., Sood, A. K., Davis, C. S., and Buller, R. E. (2002). Ovarian cancer p53 mutation is associated with tumor Microvessel density. *Gynecol. Oncol.* 86, 85–90.
46. Marks, J. R., Davidoff, A. M., Kerns, B. J. M. et al. (1991). Overexpression and mutation of p53 in epithelial ovarian cancer. *Cancer Res.* 51, 2975–2984.
47. Hutson, R., Ramsdale, J., and Wells, M. (1995). p53 protein expression in putative precursor lesions of epithelial ovarian cancer. *Histopathology* 27, 367–371.
48. Pothuri, B., Leitao, M., Barakat, R., Akram, M., Bogomolniy, F., Olvera, N., Lin, O., Soslow, R., Robson, M. E., Offit, K., and Boyd, J. (2001). Genetic analysis of ovarian carcinoma histogenesis. *Proc. Soc. Gynecol. Oncol.* Abstract #7.
49. Buller, R. E., Lallas, T. E., Shahin, M. S., Sood, A. K., Hatterman-Zogg, M., Anderson, B., Sorosky, J. I., and Kirby, P. A. (2001). The p53 mutational spectrum associated with BRCA1 mutant ovarian cancer. *Clin. Cancer Res.* 7, 831–838.
50. Kohler, M. F., Marks, J. R., Wiseman, R. W. et al. (1993). Spectrum of mutation and frequency of allelic deletion of the p53 gene in ovarian cancer. *J. Natl. Cancer Inst.* 85, 1513–1519.
51. Schildkraut, J., Bastos, E., and Berchuck, A. (1997). Relationship between lifetime ovulatory cycles and overexpression of mutant p53 in epithelial ovarian cancer. *J. Natl. Cancer. Inst.* 89, 932–938.
52. Webb, P. M., Green, A., Cummings, M. C., Purdie, D. M., Walsh, M. D., and Cenevix-Trench, G. (1999). Relationship between number of ovulatory cycles and accumulation of p53 in epithelial ovarian cancer. *Intl. J. Gynecol. Pathol.* 18, 29–41.
53. Henriksen, R., Strang, P., Wilander, E., Backstrom, T., Tribukait, B., and Oberg, K. (1994). p53 expression in epithelial ovarian neoplasms: Relationship to clinical and pathological parameters, Ki-67 expression and flow cytometry. *Gynecol. Oncol.* 53, 301–306.
54. Skirnisdottir, I., Seidal, T., Gerdin, E., and Sorbe, B. (2002). The prognostic importance of p53, bcl-2, and bax in early stage epithelial ovarian carcinoma treated with adjuvant chemotherapy. *Intl. J. Gynecol. Cancer* 12, 265–276.
55. Bosze, P., Bast Jr., R. C., Berchuck, A., Burke, H. B., Buller, R. E., Creasman, W. T., Dubeau, L., Fox, H., Geisler, H. E., Geisler, J. P., Henson, D. E., Rustin, C. J., Vermorken, J. B., Wells, M., and Wilbanks, G. D. (2000). Consensus statements on prognostic factors in epithelial ovarian carcinoma. Report of the Consensus Meeting organized by the European Society of Gynecolaecological Oncology, ESGO. *Eur. J. Gynecol. Oncol.* 2, 513–526.
56. Goff, B. A., Ries, J. A., Els, L. P., Coltrera, M. D., and Gown, A. M. (1998). Immunophenotype of ovarian cancer as predictor of clinical outcome: Evaluation at primary surgery and second-look procedure. *Gynecol. Oncol.* 70, 378–385.
57. Sengupta, P. S., McGown, A. T., Bajaj, V., Blackhall, F., Swindell, R., Bromley, M., Shanks, J. H., Ward, T., Buckley, C. H., Reynolds, K., Slade, R. J., and Jayson, G. C. (2000). P53 and related proteins in epithelial ovarian cancer. *Eur. J. Cancer* 36, 2317–2328.
58. Ranhtanen, V., Engblom, P., Raitanen, M., Hietanen, S., Haarala, M., Grenman, S., and Syrjanen, S. (2002). Mutations of TP53 do not correlate with the sensitivity to paclitaxel-a study using 27 gynecological cancer cell lines. *Eur. J. Cancer* 38, 1783–1791.
59. Mok, S. C., Wong, K. K., Chan, R. K. et al. (1994). Molecular cloning of differentially expressed genes in human epithelial ovarian cancer. *Gynecol. Oncol.* 52, 247–252.
60. Mok, S. C., Chan, W. Y., Wong, K. K. et al. (1996). SPARC, an extracellular matrix protein with tumor-suppressing activity in human ovarian epithelial cells. *Oncogene* 12, 1895–1901.
61. Abdollahi, A., Godwin, A. K., Miller, P. D. et al. (1997). Indentification of a gene containing zinc finger motifs based on lost expression in malignantly transformed rat ovarian surface epithelial cells. *Cancer Res.* 57, 2029–2034.
62. Schultz, D. C., Vandeweer, L., Berman, D. B. et al. (1996). Identification of two candidate tumor suppressor genes on chromosome 17p13.3. *Cancer Res.* 56, 1997–2002.
63. Tse, C., Xiang, R. H., Bracht, T., and Naylor, S. L. (2002). Human semaphorin 3B (SEMA3B) located at chromosome 3p21.3 suppresses tumor formation in an adenocarcinoma cell line. *Cancer Res.* 62, 542–546.
64. Yu, Y., Xu, F., Fang, X., Zhao, S., Li, Y., Cuevas, B., Kuo, W.-L., Gray, J. W., Siciliano, M., Mills, G., and Bast Jr., R. C. (1999). NOEY2 (ARHI), an imprinted putative tumor suppressor gene in ovarian and breast carcinomas. *Proc. Natl. Acad. Sci. USA* 96, 214–219.
65. Luo, R. Z., Fang, X., Marquez, R., Mills, G. B., Liao, W. S. L., Yu, Y., and Bast Jr., R. C. (2003). ARHI is a ras-related small G-protein with a novel N-terminal extension that inhibits growth of ovarian and breast cancers. *Oncogene.* 22, 2897–2909.
66. Bao, J., Le, X. F., Wang, R. Y., Yuan, J., Wang, L., LaPushin, R., Andreeff, M., Fang, B., Yu, Y., and Bast Jr., R. C. (2002). Re-expression of the tumor suppressor gene ARHI induces apoptosis in ovarian and breast cancer cells through a caspase-independent calpain-dependent pathway. *Cancer Res.* 62, 7264–7272.
67. Xu, F., Xia, W., Zhao, S., Peng, H., Luo, R. Z., Dai, J., Long, Y., Zhao, L., Le, W., Parlow, A. F., Hung, M., Bast Jr., R. C., and Yu, Y. (2000). *ARHI* acts as an inhibitor of growth and lactation in transgenic mice. *Cancer Res.* 60, 4913–4920.
68. Yu, Y., Fujii, S., Yuan, J., Luo, R. Z., Wang, L., Bao, J., Kadota, M., Oshimura, M., Dent, S. R., Issa, J.-P., and Bast Jr., R. C. (2003). Epigenetic regulation of ARHI in breast and ovarian cancer cells. *Ann. NY Acad. Sci.* 983, 268–277.

69. Peng, H. Q., Xu, F.-J., Pershad, R., Hogg, D., Gray, J. W., Berchuck, A., Bast Jr., R. C., and Yu, Y. H. (2000). ARHI is the center of allelic deletion on chromosome 1p31 in ovarian and breast cancers. *Intl. J. Cancer* 86, 690–694.
70. Luo, R., Peng, H. Q., Xu, F. J., Bao, J. J., Pershad, R., Issas, J. P. J., Liao, W. S. L., Auersperg, N., Bast Jr., R. C., and Yu, Y. H. (2001). Genomic structure and promoter characterization of an imprinted tumor suppressor gene *ARHI*. *Biochim. Biophys. Acta* 1519, 216–222.
71. Abdollahi, A., Pisarcik, D., Roberts, D., Weinstein, J., Cairns, P., and Hamilton, T. C. (2003). LOT1 (PLAGL1/ZAC1), the candidate tumor suppressor gene at chromosome 6q24–25, is epigenetically regulated in cancer. *J. Biol. Chem.* 278, 6041–6049.
72. Abdollahi, A., Bao, R., and Hamilton, T. C. (1999). LOT1 is a growth suppressor gene down-regulated by the epidermal growth factor receptor ligands and encodes a nuclear zinc-finger protein. *Oncogene* 18, 6477–6487.
73. Bednarek, A. K., Keck-Waggoner, C. L., Daniel, R. L., Laflin, K. J., Bergsagel, P. L., Kiguchi, K., Brenner, A. J., and Aldaz, C. M. (2001). WWOX, the FRA16D gene, behaves as a suppressor of tumor growth. *Cancer Res.* 15, 8068–8073.
74. Paige, A. J., Taylor, K. J., Taylor, C., Hillier, S. G., Farrington, S., Scott, D., Porteous, D. J., Smyth, J. F., Gabra, H., and Watson, J. E. (2001). WWOX: A candidate tumor suppressor gene involved in multiple tumor types. *Proc. Natl. Acc. USA*. 98, 1417–1422.
75. Shayesteh, L., Lu, Y., Kuo, W. L., Badocchi, R., Godfrey, T., Collins, C., Pinkel, D., Powell, B., Mills, G. B., and Gray, J. W. (1999). PIK3CA is implicated as an oncogene in ovarian cancer. *Nat. Genet.* 21, 99–102.
76. Philip, A. J., Campbell, I. G., Leet, C., Vincan, E., Rockman, S. P., Whitehead, R. H., Thomas, R., and Phillips, W. A. (2001). The phosphatidylinositol 3'-kinase p85x gene is an oncogene in human ovarian and colon tumors. *Cancer Res.* 61, 7426–7429.
77. Mills, G. B., Lu, Y., Fang, X., Wang, H., Eder, A., Mao, M., Swaby, R., Cheng, K. W., Stokoe, D., Siminovitch, K., Jaffe, R., and Gray, J. (2001). The role of genetic abnormalities of PTEN and the phosphatidylinositol 3-kinase pathway in breast and ovarian tumorigensis, prognosis, and therapy. *Semin. Oncol.* 28, 125–141.
78. Cheng, J. Q., Godwin, A. K., Bellacosa, A., Taguchi, T., Franke, T. F., Hamilton, T. C., Tsichlis, P. N., and Testa, J. R. (1992). AKT2, a putative oncogene encoding a member of a subfamily of protein-serine/threonine kinases, is amplified in human ovarian carcinomas. *Proc. Natl. Acad. Sci. USA* 899, 267–271.
79. Hu, L., Zaloudek, C., Mills, G. B., Gray, J., and Jaffe, R. B. (2000). In vivo and in vitro ovarian carcinoma growth inhibition by a phosphatidylinositol 3-kinase inhibitor. *Clin. Cancer Res.* 6, 880–886.
80. Hu, L., Hofmann, J., Lu, Y., Mills, G. B., and Jaffe, R. B. (2002). Inhibition of phosphatidylinositol 3'-kinase increases efficacy of Paclitaxel in in vitro and in vivo ovarian cancer models. *Cancer Res.* 62, 1087–1092.
81. Slamon, D. J., Godolphin, W., Jones, L. A. et al. (1989). Studies of the HER-2/neu protooncogene in human breast and ovarian cancer. *Science* 244, 707–712.
82. Berchuck, A., Kamel, A., Whitaker, R. et al. (1990). Overexpression of HER-2/*neu* is associated with poor survival in advanced epithelial ovarian cancer. *Cancer Res.* 50, 4087–4091.
83. Bookman, M. A., Darcy, K. M., Clarke-Pearson, D., Boothby, R. A., and Horowitz, I. R. (2003). Evaluation of monoclonal humanized anti-HER2 antibody, trastuzumab, in patients with recurrent or refractory ovarian or primary peritoneal carcinoma with overexpression of HER2: A phase II trial of the Gynecologic Oncology Group. *J. Clin. Oncol.* 21, 83–90.
84. Rubin, S. C., Finstad, C. L., Federici, M. G. et al. (1994). Prevalence and significance of HER-2/*neu* expression in early epithelial ovarian cancer. *Cancer* 73, 1456–1459.
85. Xu, F. J., Stack, S., Boyer, C., O'Briant, K., Whitaker, R., Mills, G. B., Yu, Y. H., and Bast Jr., R. C. (1997). Heregulin and agonistic anti-p185$^{c\text{-}erbB2}$ antibodies inhibit proliferation but increase invasiveness of breast cancer cells that overexpress p185$^{c\text{-}erbB2}$: Increased invasiveness may contribute to poor prognosis. *Clin. Cancer Res.* 3, 1629–1634.
86. Gilmour, L. M., Macleod, K. G., McCaig, A., Swewll, J. M., Gullick, W. J., Smyth, J. F., and Langdon, S. P. (2002). Neuregulin expression, function, and signaling in human ovarian cancer cells. *Clin. Cancer Res.* 8, 3933–3942.
87. Kacinski, B. M., Carter, D., Mittal, K. et al. (1990). Ovarian adenocarcinomas express fms-complementary transcripts and fms antigen, often with coexpression of CSF-1. *Am. J. Pathol.* 137, 135–147.
88. Lidor, Y. J., Xu, F. J., Martinez-Maza, O. et al. (1993). Constitutive production of macrophage colony stimulating factor and interleukin-6 by human ovarian surface epithelial cells. *Exp. Cell Res.* 207, 332–339.
89. Wu, S., Rodabaugh, K., Martinez-Maza, O., Watson, J. M., Silberstein, D. S., Boyer, C. M., Peters, W. P., Weinberg, J. B., Berek, J. S., and Bast Jr., R. C. (1992). Stimulation of ovarian tumor cell proliferation with monocyte products including interleukin-1, interleukin-6, and tumor necrosis factor-alpha. *Am. J. Obstet. Gynecol.* 166, 997–1007.
90. Zhang, L., Conejo-Garcia, J. R., Katsaros, D., Gimotty, P. A., Massobrio, M., Regnani, G., Makrigiannakis, A., Gray, H., Schlienger, K., Liebman, M. N., Rubin, S. C., and Coukos, G. (2003). Intratumoral T cells, recurrence, and survival in epithelial ovarian cancer. *N. Engl. J. Med.* 348, 203–213.
91. Eisenthal, A., Polyvkin, N., Bramante-Schreiber, L., Misonznik, F., Hassner, A., and Lifschitz-Mercer, B. (2001). Expression of dendritic cells in ovarian tumors correlates with clinical outcome in patients with ovarian cancer. *Hum. Pathol.* 32, 803–807.
92. Yee, D., Morales, F. R., Hamilton, T. R. C., and Von Hoff, D. D. (1991). Expression of insulin-like factor I, its binding proteins, and its receptor in ovarian cancer. *Cancer Res.* 51, 5107–5112.
93. Chen, C. L., Ip, S. M., Cheng, D., Wong, L. C., and Ngan, H. Y. (2000). Loss of imprinting of the IGF-II and H19 genes in epithelial ovarian cancer. *Clin. Cancer Res.* 6, 474–479.
94. Yaginuma, Y., Nishiwaki, K., Kitamura, S., Hayashi, H., Sengoku, K., and Ishikawa, M. (1997). Relaxation of insulin-like growth factor-II imprinting in human gynecologic tumors. *Oncology* 54, 502–507.

95. Kalli, K. R., Falowo, O. I., Bale, L. K., Zschunke, M. A., Roche, P. C., and Conover, C. A. (2002). Functional insulin receptors on human epithelial ovarian carcinoma cells: Implications for IGF-II mitongenic signaling. *Endocrinology* 143, 3259–3267.
96. Steele, I. A., Edmondson, R. J., Bulmer, J. N., Bolger, B. S., Leung, H. Y., and Davies, B. R. (2001). Induction of FGF receptor 2-IIIb expression and response to its ligands in epithelial ovarian cancer. *Oncogene* 20, 5878–5887.
97. Valve, E., Martikainen, P., Seppanen, J., Oksjoki, S., Hinkka, S., Anttila, L., Grenman, S., Klemi, P., and Harkonen, P. (2000). Expression of fibroblast growth factor (FGF)-8 isoforms and FGF receptors in human ovarian tumors. *Intl. J. Cancer* 88, 718–725.
98. Henriksen, R., Funa, K., Wilander, E., Backstrom, T., Ridderheim, M., and Oberg, K. (1993). Expression and prognostic significance of platelet-derived growth factor and its receptors in epithelial ovarian neoplasms. *Cancer Res.* 53, 4550–4554.
99. Tonary, A. M., Macdonald, E. A., Faught, W., Senterman, M. K., and Vanderhyden, B. C. (2000). Lack of expression of c-KIT in ovarian cancers is associated with poor prognosis. *Intl. J. Cancer* 20, 242–250.
100. Bellacosa, A., de Feo, D., Godwin, A. K. et al. (1995). Molecular alterations of the AKT2 oncogene in ovarian and breast carcinomas. *Intl. J. Cancer* 64, 280–285.
101. Enomoto, T., Inoue, M., Perantoni, A. O. et al. (1990). K-ras activation in neoplasms of the human female reproductive tract. *Cancer Res.* 50, 6139–6145.
102. Singer, G., Oldt III, R., Cohen, Y., Wang, B. G., Sidransky, D., Kurman, R. J., and Shih, L.-M. (2003). Mutations in BRAF and KRAS characterize the development of low-grade ovarian serous carcinomas. *J. Natl. Cancer Inst.* 95, 484–486.
103. Suzuki, M., Saito, S., Saga, Y., Ohwada, M., and Sato, I. (2000). Mutation of K-RAS protooncogene and loss of heterozygosity on 6q27 in serous and mucinous ovarian cancers. *Cancer Genet. Cytogenet.* 118, 132–135.
104. Caduff, R. F., Svaboda-Newman, S. M., Ferguson, A. W., Johnston, C. M., and Frank, T. S. (1999). Comparison of mutations of K-RAS and p53 immunoreactivity in borderline and malignant epithelial ovarian tumors. *Am. J. Surg. Pathol.* 23, 323–328.
105. Mok, S. C., Bell, D. A., Knapp, R. C. et al. (1993). Mutation of K-ras protooncogene in human ovarian epithelial tumors of borderline malignancy. *Cancer Res.* 53, 1489–1492.
106. Bast Jr., R. C., and Mills, G. B. (2001). The molecular pathogenesis of ovarian cancer. In *The Molecular Basis of Cancer*, 2nd ed., eds. J. Mendelsohn, P. Howley, M. Israel, and L. Liotta, 361–384. Philadelphia: W. B. Saunders Co.
107. Wiener, J. R., Windham, T. C., Estrella, V. C., Parikh, N. U., Thall, P. F., Deavers, M. T., Bast Jr., R. C., Mills, G. B., and Gallick, G. E. (2003). Activated SRC protein tyrosine kinase is overexpressed in late-stage human ovarian cancers. *Gynecol. Oncol.* 88, 73–79.
108. Wiener, J. R., Nakano, K., Kruzelock, R. P., Bucana, C. D., Bast Jr., R. C., and Gallick, G. E. (1999). Decreased Src tyrosine kinase activity inhibits malignant human ovarian cancer tumor growth in a nude mouse model. *Clin. Cancer Res.* 5, 2164–2170.
109. Stenoien, D. L., Sen, S., Mancini, M. A., and Brinkley, B. R. (2003). Dynamic association of a tumor amplified kinase, Aurora A with the centrosome and mitotic spindle. *Cell. Motil. Cytoskeleton* 55, 134–146.
110. Zhou, H., Kuang, J., Zhong, L., Kuo, W. L., Gray, J. W., Sahin, A., Brinkley, B. R., and Sen, S. (1998). Tumour amplified kinase STK15/BTAK induces centrosome amplification, aneuploidy and transformation. *Nat. Genet.* 20, 189–193.
111. Andreeff, M., Goodrich, D. W., and Pardee, A. B. (2003). Cell proliferation and differentiation. In *Cancer Medicine*, 6th ed., eds. Kufe, D., Pollock, R., Weichselbaum, R., Bast, R. C., Gansler, T., Holland, J., Frei, E. 27–39. BC Decker: Hamiton Ontario.
112. Vescio, R. A., Connors, K. M., Youngkin, T., Bordin, G. M., Robb, J. A., Umbreit, J. N., and Hoffman, R. M. (1990). Cancer biology for individualized therapy: Correlation of growth fraction index in native-state histoculture with tumor grade and stage. *Proc. Natl. Acad. Sci. USA* 87, 691–695.
113. Meyer, J. S., Gersell, D. J., and Yim, S. (2001). Cell proliferation in ovarian carcinoma: Superior accuracy of s-phase fraction (SPF) by DNA labeling index versus flow cytometric SPF, lack of independent prognostic power for SPF and DNA ploidy, and limited effect of SPF on tumor growth rate. *Gynecol. Oncol.* 81, 466–476.
114. Salihoglu, Y., Bilir, A., Aydiner, A., Erkan, M., Tuzlali, S., and Eralp, Y. (2001). Thymidine labeling index in epithelial ovarian cancer. *Intl. J. Gynecol. Obst.* 75, 171–176.
115. Viale, G., Maisonneuve, P., Bonoldi, E., DiBacco, A., Bevilacqua, P., Panizzoni, G. A., Radaelli, U., and Gasparini, G. (1997). The combined evaluation of p53 accumulation and of Ki-67 (M1B1) labelling index provides independent information on overall survival of ovarian carcinoma patients. *Ann. Oncol.* 8, 469–476.
116. Sakai, K., Kaku, T., Kamura, T., Kinukawa, N., Amada, S., Shigematsu, T., Hirakawa, T., Kobayashi, H., Ariyoshi, K., and Nakano, H. (1999). Comparison of p53, Ki-67, and CD44v6 expression between primary and matched metastatic lesions in ovarian cancer. *Gynecol. Oncol.* 72, 360–366.
117. Darai, E., Combrouze, F. W., Dauge-Geoffroy, M. C., Vincent, Y., Feldmann, G., Madelenat, P., and Scoazec, J. Y. (1998). Ki 67 expression in 35 borderline ovarian tumors: relations with clinicopathologic parameters and ploidy. *Eur. J. Obstet. Gynecol.* 76, 175–180.
118. Terlikowski, S., Sulkowski, S., Lenczewski, A., Musiatowicz, B., and Kulikowski, M. (1999). Study of borderline and invasive mucinous ovarian tumors using Ki-67 (MIB 1) antibodies and nucleolar organizer region (NOR) staining. *Arch. Gynecol. Obstet.* 263, 29–33.
119. Concin, N., Hefler, L., van Bavel, J., Mueller-Holzner, E., Zeimet, A., Daxenbichler, G., Speiser, P., Hacker, N., and Marth, C. (2003). Biological markers in pT1 and pT2 ovarian cancer with lymph node metastases. *Gynecol Oncol.* 89, 9–15.
120. Garzetti, G. G., Ciavattini, A., Goteri, G., De Nictolis, M., Stramazzotti, D., Lucarini, G., and Biagini, G. (1995). Ki67 antigen immunostaining (MIB 1 Monoclonal Antibody) in serous ovarian tumors: Index of proliferative activity with prognostic significance. *Gynecol. Oncol.* 56, 169–174.

121. Layfield, L. J., Saria, E. A., Berchuck, A., Dodge, R. K., Thompson, J. K., Conlon, D. H., and Kerns, B. J. M. (1997). Prognostic value of MIB-1 in advanced ovarian carcinoma as determined using automated immunohistochemistry and quantitative image analysis. *J. Surg. Oncol.* 66, 230–237.
122. Havrilesky, L. J., Alvarez, A. A., Whitaker, R. S., Marks, J. R., and Berchuck, A. (2002). Loss of expression of the p16 tumor suppressor gene is more frequent in advanced ovarian cancers lacking p53 mutations. *Gynecol. Oncol.* 83, 491–500.
123. Kim, T. M., Benedict, W. F., Xu, H. J. et al. (1994). Loss of heterozygosity on chromosome 13 is common only in the biologically more aggressive subtypes of ovarian epithelial tumors and is associated with normal retinoblastoma gene expression. *Cancer Res.* 54, 605–609.
124. Dodson, M. K., Cliby, W. A., Xu, H. J. et al. (1994). Evidence of functional RB protein in epithelial ovarian carcinomas despite loss of heterozygosity at the RB locus. *Cancer Res.* 54, 610–613.
125. Konstantinidou, A. E., Korkolopoulou, P., Vassilopoulos, I., Tsenga, A., Thymara, I., Agapitos, E., Patsouris, E., and Davaris, P. (2003). Reduced retinoblastoma gene protein to Ki-67 ratio is an adverse prognostic indicator for ovarian adenocarcinoma patients. *Gynecol. Oncol.* 88, 369–378.
126. Worsley, S. D., Ponder, B. A., and Davies, B. R. (1997). Overexpression of cyclin D1 in epithelial ovarian cancers. *Gynecol. Oncol.* 64, 189–195.
127. Dhar, K. K., Branigan, K., Parkes, J., Howells, R. E. J., Hand, P., Musgrove, C. D., Strange, R. C., Fryer, A. A., Redman, C. W. E., and Hoban, P. R. (1999). Expression and subcellular localization of cyclin D1 protein in epithelial ovarian tumour cells. *Brit. J. Cancer* 81, 1174–1181.
128. Masciullo, V., Scambia, G., Marone, M., Giannitelli, C., Ferrandina, G., Bellacosa, A., Benedetti, P., and Mancuso, S. (1997). Altered expression of cyclin D1 and CDK4 genes in ovarian carcinomas. *Intl. J. Cancer* 74, 390–395.
129. Diebold, J., Mosinger, K., Peiro, G., Pannekamp, U., Kaltz, C., Baretton, G., Meier, W., and Lohrs, U. (2000). 20q13 and cyclin D1 in ovarian carcinomas. Analysis by fluorescence in situ hybridization. *J. Pathol.* 190, 564–571.
130. Cagnoli, M., Barbieri, F., Bruzzo, C., and Alama, A. (1998). Control of cyclin D1 expression by antisense oligonucleotides in three ovarian cancer cell lines. *Gynecol. Oncol.* 70, 372–377.
131. Milde-Langosch, K., Hagen, M., Bamberger, A. M., and Loning, T. (2003). Expression and prognostic value of the cell-cycle regulatory proteins, Rb, p16MTS1, p21WAF1, p27KIP1, Cyclin E, and Cyclin D2, in ovarian cancer. *Intl. J. Gynecol. Pathol.* 22, 168–174.
132. Courjal, F., Louason, G., Speiser, P., Katsaros, D., Zeillinger, R., and Theillet, C. (1996). Cyclin gene amplification and overexpression in breast and ovarian cancers: Evidence for the selection of cyclin D1 in breast and cyclin E in ovarian tumors. *Intl. J. Cancer* 69, 247–253.
133. Sawasaki, T., Shigemasa, K., Shiroyama, Y., Kusuda, T., Fujii, T., Parmley, T. H., O'Brien, T. J., and Ohama, K. (2001). Cyclin E mRNA overexpression in epithelial ovarian cancers: inverse correlation with p53 protein accumulation. *J. Soc. Gynecol. Invest.* 8, 179–185.
134. Farley, J., Smith, L. M., Darcy, K. M., Sobel, E., O'Connor, D., Henderson, B., Morrison, L. E., and Birrer, M. J. (2003). Cyclin E expression is a significant predictor of survival in advanced, suboptimally debulked ovarian epithelial cancers: a gynecologic oncology group study. *Cancer Res.* 63, 1235–1241.
135. Marone, M., Scambia, G., Giannitelli, C., Ferrandina, G., Masciullo, V., Bellacosa, A., Benedetti-Panici, P., and Mancuso, S. (1998). Analysis of cyclin E and CDK2 in ovarian cancer: Gene amplification and RNA overexpression. *Intl. J. Cancer* 75, 34–39.
136. Sui, L., Dong, Y., Ohno, M., Sugimoto, K., Tai, Y., Hando, T., and Tokuda, M. (2001). Implication of malignancy and prognosis of p27kip1, cyclin E, and Cdk2 expression in epithelial ovarian tumors. *Gynecol. Oncol.* 83, 56–63.
137. Rosenberg, E., Demopoulos, R. I., Zeleniuch-Jacquotte, A., Yee, H., Sorich, J., Speyer, J., and Newcomb, E. W. (2001). Expression of cell cycle regulators p57ip2, cyclin D1, and cyclin E in epithelial ovarian tumors and survival. *Hum. Pathol.* 32, 808–813.
138. Barrette, B. A., Srivatsa, P. J., Cliby, W. A., Keeney, G. L. et al. (1997). Overexpression of p34cdc2 protein kinase in epithelial ovarian carcinoma. *Mayo Clin. Proc.* 72, 925–929.
139. Fang, X., Jin, X., Xu, H. J., Liu, L., Peng, H. Q., Hogg, D., Roth, J. A., Yu, Y., Xu, F., Bast Jr., R. C., and Mills, G. B. (1998). Expression of p16 induces transcriptional downregulation of the RB gene. *Oncogene* 16, 1–8.
140. Kanuma, T., Nishida, J., Gima, T., Barrett, J. C., and Wake, N. (1997). Alterations of the p16INK4A gene in human ovarian cancers. *Mol. Carcinogens* 18, 134–141.
141. Ichikawa, Y., Yoshida, S., Koyama, Y., Hirai, M., Ishikawa, T., Nishida, M., Tsunoda, H., Kubo, T., Kiwa, M., and Uchida, K. (1996). Inactivation of p16/CDKN2 and p15/MTS2 genes in different histological types and clinical stages of primary ovarian tumors. *Intl. J. Cancer* 69, 466–470.
142. Ryan, A., Al-Jehani, R. M., Mulligan, K. T., and Jacobs, I. J. (1998). No evidence exists for methylation inactivation of the p16 tumor suppressor gene in ovarian carcinogenesis. *Gynecol. Oncol.* 68, 14–17.
143. Saegusa, M., Machida, D., and Okayasu, I. (2001). Possible associations among expression of p14arf, p16ink4a, p21WAF1/CIP1, p27KIP1, and p53 accumulation and the balance of apoptosis and cell proliferation in ovarian carcinomas. *Cancer* 92, 1177–1189.
144. Kudoh, K., Ichikawa, Y., Yoshida, S., Hirai, M., Kikuchi, Y., Nagata, I., Miwa, M., and Uchida, K. (2002). Inactivation of p16/CDKN2 and p15/MTS2 is associated with prognosis and response to chemotherapy in ovarian cancer. *Intl. J. Cancer* 99, 579–582.
145. Schmider, A., Gee, C., Friedmann, W., Lukas, J. J., Press, M. F., Lichtenegger, W., and Reles, A. (2000). p21 (WAF1/CIP1) protein expression is associated with prolonged survival but not with p53 expression in epithelial ovarian carcinoma. *Gynecol. Oncol.* 77, 237–242.
146. Anttila, M. A., Kosma, V. M., Hongxiu, J., Puolakka, J., Juhola, M., Saarikoski, S., and Kyrjanen, K. (1999). p21/WAF1 expression as related to p53, cell proliferation and prognosis in epithelial ovarian cancer. *Brit. J. Cancer* 79, 1870–1878.
147. Elbendary, A. A., Cirisano, F. D., Evans Jr., A. C., Davis, P. L., Iglehart, J. D., Marks, J. R., and Berchuck, A. (1996). Relationship between p21 expression and mutation of the p53

tumor suppressor gene in normal and malignant ovarian epithelial cells. *Clin. Cancer Res.* 2, 1571–1575.

148. Korkolopoulou, P., Vassilopoulos, I., Konstantinidou, A. E., Zorzos, H., Patsouris, E., Agapitos, E., and Davaris, P. (2002). The combined evaluation of p27Kip1 and Ki-67 expression provides independent information on overall survival of ovarian carcinoma patients. *Gynecol. Oncol.* 85, 404–414.
149. Goff, B. A., Paley, P. J., Greer, B. E., and Grown, A. M. (2002). Evaluation of chemoresistance markers in women with epithelial ovarian carcinoma. *Gynecol. Oncol.* 81, 18–24.
150. Masciullo, V., Ferrandina, G., Pucci, B., Fanfani, F., Lovergine, S., Palazzo, J., Zannoni, G., Mancuso, S., Scambia, G., and Giordano, A. (2000). p27Kip1 expression is associated with clinical outcome in advanced epithelial ovarian cancer: multivariate analysis. *Clin. Cancer Res.* 6, 4816–4822.
151. Shigemasa, K., Gu, L., O'Brien, T. J., and Ohama, K. (2003). Skp2 Overexpression is a prognostic factor in patients with ovarian adenocarcinoma. *Clin. Cancer Res.* 9, 1756–1763.
152. Klingelhutz, A. J. (1999). The roles of telomeres and telomerase in cellular immortalization and the development of cancer. *Anticancer Res.* 19, 4823–4830.
153. Lichtsteiner, S. P., Lebkowski, J. S., and Vasserot, A. P. (1999). Telomerase. A target for anticancer therapy. *Ann. NY Acad. Sci.* 886, 1–11.
154. Gishi, T., Kigawa, J., Minagawa, Y., Shimada, M., Takahashi, M., and Terakawa, N. (1998). Alteration of telomerase activity associated with development and extension of epithelial ovarian cancer. *Obstet. Gynecol.* 91, 568–571.
155. Orsulic, S., Li, Y., Soslow, R. A., Vitale-Cross, L. A., Gutkind, S., and Varmus, H. E. (2002). Induction of ovarian cancer by defined multiple genetic changes in a mouse model system. *Cancer Cell* 1, 53–62.
156. Liu, J., Patterson, A., Thompson, J. A., Mills, G., Gray, J., and Bast Jr., R. C.(2003). Transformation targets of human ovarian surface epithelial cells by oncogenic H-rasV^{12} or K-rasV^{12} revealed by gene expression array. *Proc. Am. Assoc. Cancer Res.* 44, 270 (A#1182).
157. Wan, M., Li, W. Z., Duggan, B. D., Felix, J. C. et al. (1997). Telomerase activity in benign and malignant epithelial ovarian tumors. *J. Natl. Cancer Inst.* 89, 437–441.
158. Zheng, P. S., Iwasaka, T., Yamasaki, F., Ouchida, M. et al. (1997). Telomerase activity in gynecologic tumors. *Gynecol. Oncol.* 64, 171–175.
159. Kyo, S., Kanaya, T., Ishikawa, H., Ueno, H., and Inoue, M. (1996). Telomerase activity in gynecological tumors. *Clin. Cancer Res.* 2, 2023–2028.
160. Kyo, S., Takakura, M., Tanaka, M., Murakami, K. et al. (1998). Quantitative differences in telomerase activity among amalignant, premalignant, and benign ovarian lesions. *Clin. Cancer Res.* 4, 399–405.
161. Gishi, T., Kigawa, J., Minagawa, Y., Shimada, M., Takahashi, M., and Terakawa, N. (1998). Alteration of telomerase activity associated with development and extension of epithelial ovarian cancer. *Obstet. Gynecol.* 91, 568–571.
162. Kruk, P. A., Godwin, A. K., Hamilton, T. C., and Auersperg, N. (1999). Telomeric instability and reduced proliferative potential in ovarian surface epithelial cells from women with a family history of ovarian cancer. *Gynecol. Oncol.* 73, 229–236.
163. Kyo, S., Kanaya, T., Takakura, M., Tanaka, M. et al. (1999). Expression of human telomerase subunits in ovarian malignant, borderline and benign tumors. *Intl. J. Cancer* 80, 804–809.
164. Park, T. W., Riethdorf, S., Riethdorf, L., Loning, T., and Janicke, F. (1999). Differential telomerase activity, expression of the telomerase catalytic sub-unit and telomerase-RNA in ovarian tumors. *Intl. J. Cancer* 84. 426–431.
165. Stromberg, K., Johnson, G. R., O'Connor, D. M. et al. Frequent immunohistochemical detection of EGF supergene family members in ovarian carcinogenesis. (1994). *Intl. J. Gynecol. Pathol.* 13, 342–347.
166. Rodriguez, G. C., Berchuck, A., Whitaker, R. S., Schlossman, D., Clarke-Pearson, D. L., and Bast Jr., R. C. (1991). Epidermal growth factor receptor expression in normal ovarian epithelium and ovarian cancer. II. Relationship between receptor expression and response to epidermal growth factor. *Am. J. Obstet. Gynecol.* 164, 745–750.
167. Stromberg, K., Johnson, G. R., O'Connor, D. M. et al. (1994). Frequent immunohistochemical detection of EGF supergene family members in ovarian carcinogenesis. *Intl. J. Gynecol. Pathol.* 13, 342–347.
168. Stromberg, K., Collins, T. J., Gordon, A. W. et al. (1992). Transforming growth factor-alpha acts as an autocrine growth factor in ovarian cancer cell lines. *Cancer Res.* 52, 341–347.
169. Mills, G. B., May, C., McGill, M., Roifman, C., and Mellors, A. (1998). A putative new growth factor in ascitic fluid from ovarian cancer patients: Identification, characterization and mechanism of action. *Cancer Res.* 48, 1066–1071.
170. Mills, G. B., May, C., Hill, M., Campbell, S., Shaw, P., and Marks, A. (1990). Ascitic fluid from human ovarian cancer patients contains growth factors necessary for intraperitoneal growth of human ovarian cancer cells. *J. Clin. Invest.* 86, 851–855.
171. Xu, Y., Gaudette, D. C., Boynton, J. et al. (1994). Characterization of an ovarian cancer activating factor (OCAF) in ascites from ovarian cancer patients. *Clin. Cancer Res.* 1, 1223–1232.
172. Eder, A. M., Sasagawa, T., Mao, M., Aoki, J., and Mills, G. B. (2000). Constitutive and lysophosphatidic acid-induced LPA production: Role of phospholipase D and phospholipase A2. *Clin. Cancer Res.* 6, 2482–2491.
173. Tanyi, J. L., Morris, A. J., Wolf, J. K., Fang, X., Hasegawa, Y., Lapushin, R., Auersperg, N., Sigal, Y. J., Newman, R. A., Felix, E. A., Atkinson, E. N., and Mills, G. B. (2003). The human lipid phosphate phosphatase-3 decreases the growth, survival, and tumorigenesis of ovarian cancer cells: Validation of the lysophosphatidic acid signaling cascade as a target for therapy in ovarian cancer. *Cancer Res.* 63, 1073–1082.
174. Havrilesky, L. J., Hurteau, J. A., Whitaker, R. S., Elbendery, A., Wu, S., Rodriquez, G. C., Bast Jr., R. C., and Berchuck, A. (1995). Regulation of apoptosis in normal and malignant ovarian epithelial cells by TGFbeta. *Cancer Res.* 55, 944–948.
175. Berchuck, A., Rodriguez, G., Olt, G. J., Whitaker, R., Boente, M. P., Arrick, B. A., Clarke-Pearson, D. L., and Bast Jr., R. C. (1992). Regulation of growth of normal ovarian epithelial cells and ovarian cancer cell lines by transforming growth factor-β. *Am. J. Obstet. Gynecol.* 166, 676–684.

176. Nilsson, E. E., and Skinner, M. K. (2002). Role of transforming growth factor beta in ovarian surface epithelium biology and ovarian cancer. *Reprod. Biomed. Online* 5, 254–258.
177. Bartlett, J. M., Langdon, S. P., Scott, W. N., Love, S. B., Miller, E. P., Katsaros, D., Smyth, J. F., and Miller, W. R. (1997). Transforming growth factor-beta isoform expression in human ovarian tumours. *Eur. J. Cancer* 33, 2397–2403.
178. Bristow, R. E., Baldwin, R. L., Yamada, S. D., Korc, M., and Karlan, B. Y. (1999). Altered expression of transforming growth factor-beta ligands and receptors in primary and recurrent ovarian carcinoma. *Cancer* 85, 658–668.
179. Hurteau, J., Rodriguez, G. C., Whitaker, R. S., Shah, S., Mills, G., Bast Jr., R. C., and Berchuck, A. (1994). Transforming growth factor-ß inhibits proliferation of human ovarian cancer cells obtained from ascites. *Cancer* 74, 93–99.
180. Baldwin, R. L., Tran, H., and Karlan, B. Y. (2003). Loss of c-myc repression coincides with ovarian cancer resistance to transforming growth factor beta growth arrest independent of transforming growth factor beta/Smad signaling. *Cancer Res.* 63, 1413–1419.
181. Dunfield, L. D., Dwyer, E. J., and Nachtigal, M. W. (2002). TGF beta-induced Smad signaling remains intact in primary human ovarian cancer cells. *Endocrinology* 143, 1174–1181.
182. Chen, T., Triplett, J., Dehner, B., Hurst, B., Colligan, B., Pemberton, J., Graff, J. R., and Carter, J. H. (2001). Transforming growth factor-beta receptor type I gene is frequently mutated in ovarian carcinomas. *Cancer Res.* 61, 4679–4682.
183. Rodriguez, G. C., Haisley, C., Hurteau, J., Moser, T. L., Whitaker, R., Bast Jr., R. C. and Stack, M. S.. (2001). Regulation of invasion of epithelial ovarian cancer by transforming growth factor-beta. *Gynecol. Oncol.* 80, 245–253.
184. Rodriguez, G. C., Nagarsheth, N. P., Lee, K. L., Bentley, R. C., Walmer, D. K., Cline, M., Whitaker, R. S., Isner, P., Berchuck, A., Dodge, R. K., and Hughes, C. L. (2002). Progestin-induced apoptosis in the Macaque ovarian epithelium: differential regulation of transforming growth factor-beta. *J. Natl. Cancer Inst.* 94, 50–60.
185. Evangelou, A., Jindal, S. K., Brown, T. J., and Letarte, M. (2000). Down-regulation of transforming growth factor beta receptors by androgen in ovarian cancer cells. *Cancer Res.* 64, 929–935.
186. Mutch, D. G., Powell, C. B., Kao, M. S. et al. (1992). Resistance to cytolysis by tumor necrosis factor alpha in malignant gynecological cell lines is associated with the expression of protein(s) that prevent the activation of phospholipase A2 by tumor necrosis factor alpha. *Cancer Res.* 52, 866–872.
187. Wu, S., Boyer, C. M., Whitaker, R. S. et al. (1993). Tumor necrosis factor alpha as an autocrine and paracrine growth factor for ovarian cancer: Monokine induction of tumor cell proliferation and tumor necrosis factor alpha expression. *Cancer Res.* 53, 1939–1944.
188. Wu, S., Xu, F. J., Boyer, C. M., and Bast Jr., R. C. (1994). Proliferation and induction of NF-kappa B by tumor necrosis factor-α can be mediated through two distinct receptors in human ovarian cancer cells. *Proc. Am. Assoc. Cancer Res.* 35, 486 (A#2899).
189. Takeyama, H., Wakamiya, N., O'Hara, C. et al. (1991). Tumor necrosis factor expression by human ovarian carcinoma in vivo. *Cancer Res.* 51, 4476–4480.
190. Boyer, C. M., Wu, S., Xu, F.-J., et al. (1995). Stimulation of human ovarian cancer cell growth *in vivo* with TNFα or IL-1 in immunodeficient scid mice. *Proc. Am. Assoc. Cancer Res.* 36, 71(A#422).
191. Zebrowski, B. K., Liu, W., Ramirez, K., Akagi, M. D., Mills, G. B., Ellis, and L. M. (1999). Markedly elevated levels of vascular endothelial growth factor in malignant ascites. *Ann. Surg. Oncol.* 6, 373–378.
192. Moser, T. L., Young, T. N., Rodriguez, G. C. et al. (1994). Secretion of extracellular matrix-degrading proteinases is increased in epithelial ovarian carcinomas. *Intl. J. Cancer* 56, 552–559.
193. Mok, S. C., Wong, K. K., Chan, W. Y. et al. (1998). Changes in gene expression. In *Ovarian Cancer 5*, 25–33. Oxford, England: Isis Medical Media.
194. Young, T. N., Rodriguez, G. C., Moser, T. L. et al. (1994). Coordinate expression of urinary-type plasminogen activator and its receptor accompanies malignant transformation of the ovarian surface epithelium. *Am. J. Obstet. Gynecol.* 170, 1285–1296.
195. Fishman, D. A., Bafetti, L. M., Banionis, S., Lurain, J. R., and Stack, M. S. (1997). Analysis of proteinase production by primary human epithelial ovarian carcinoma cells derived from the ovary, ascites, and peritoneal metastases. *J. Soc. Gynecol. Invest.* 4, 119.
196. Schmalfeldt, B., Prechtel, D., Harting, K., Spathe, K., Rutke, S., Konik, E., Fridman, R., Berger, U., Schmitt, M., Kuhn, W., and Lengyel, E. (2001). Increased expression of matrix metalloproteinases (MMP)-2, MMP-9, and the urokinase-type plasminogen activator is associated with progression from benign to advanced ovarian cancer. *Clin. Cancer Res.* 7, 2396–2404.
197. Herrera, C. A., Xu, L., Bucana, D. C., el Silva, V. G., Hess, K. R., Gershenson, D. M., and Fidler, I. J. (2002). Expression of metastasis-related genes in human epithelial ovarian tumors. *Intl. J. Oncol.* 20, 5–13.
198. Fishman, D. A., Liu, Y., Ellerbroek, S. M., and Stack, M. S. (2001). Lysophosphatidic acid promotes matrix metalloproteinase (MMP) activation and MMP-dependent invasion in ovarian cancer cells. *Cancer Res.* 61, 3194–3199.
199. Yousef, G. M., Polymeris, M. E., Yacoub, G. M., Scorilas, A., Soosaipillai, A., Popalis, C., Fracchioli, S., Katsaros, D., and Diamandis, E. P. (2003). Parallel overexpression of seven kallikrein genes in ovarian cancer. *Cancer Res.* 63, 2223–2227.
200. Diamandis, E. P., Yousef, G. M., Soosaipillai, A. R., and Bunting, P. (2000). Human kallikrein 6 (zyme/protease M/neurosin): A new serum biomarker of ovarian carcinoma. *Clin. Biochem.* 33, 579–583.
201. Luo, L., Bunting, P., Scorilas, A., and Diamandis, E. P. (2001). Human kallikrein 10: A novel tumor marker for ovarian carcinoma? *Clin. Chim. Acta* 306, 111–118.
202. Diamandis, E. P., Okui, A., Mitsui, S., Luo, L. Y., Soosaipillai, A., Grass, L., Nakamura, T., Howarth, D. J., and Yamaguchi, N. (2002). Human kallikrein 11: A new biomarker of prostate and ovarian carcinoma. *Cancer Res.* 62, 295–300.
203. Petricoin III, E. F., Ardekani, A. M., Hitt, B. A., Levine, P. J., Fusaro, V. A., Steinberg, S. M., Mills, G. B., Simone, C., Fishman, D., Kohn, E. C., and Liotta, L. A. (2002). Use of proteanic patterns in serum to identify ovarian cancer. *Lancet* 359, 572–577.
204. Zhang, Z., Bast Jr., R. C., Fung, E. T., Yu, Y., Li, J.,

Rosenzweig, J., Cameron, B., Rai, A., Sokoll, L. J., Meng, X.-Y., Berchuck, A., van Haaften-Day, C., Hacker, N. F., de Bruijn, H. W. A., van der Zee, A. J. G., and Chan, D. W. (2003). A panel of three potential biomarkers discovered from serum proteomic profiling improves sensitivity of CA 125 in the detection of early stage ovarian cancer. A multi-institutional study. *Proc. Am. Assoc. Cancer Res.* 44, 1316 (A#5739).

205. Naylor, M. S., Burke, F., and Balwill, F. R. (1995). Cytokines and ovarian cancer. In *Ovarian Cancer 3*, eds F. Sharp, P. Mason, T. Blackett, and J. Berek, 89–97. London: Chapman and Hall Medical.
206. Huang, S., Van Arsdall, M., Tedjarati, S., McCarty, M., Wu, W., Langley, R., and Fidler, I. J. (2002). Contributions of stromal metalloproteinase 9 to angiogenesis and growth of human ovarian carcinoma in mice. *J. Natl. Cancer Inst.* 94, 1134–1142.
207. Rodriguez, G. C., Berchuck, A., Whitaker, R. et al. (1994). Regulation of invasion in ovarian cancer cell lines by transforming growth factor-β. 26th Annual Meeting Soc. *Gynecol. Oncol.*, 40.
208. Xu, F. J., Stack, S., Boyer, C. et al. (1997). Heregulin and agonistic anti-p185$^{c\text{-}erbB2}$ antibodies inhibit proliferation but increase invasiveness of breast cancer cells that overexpress p185$^{c\text{-}erbB2}$: Increased invasiveness may contribute to poor prognosis. *Clin. Cancer Res.* 3, 1629–1634.
209. Pustilnik, T., Bast Jr., R. C., and Mills, G. (1997). Lysophosphatidic acid induces urokinase secretion in ovarian cancer cells. *Proc. Am. Assoc. Cancer Res.* 38, 410 (A#2747).
210. Chambers, S. K., Ivins, C. M., and Carcangiu, M. L. (1997). Expression of plasminogen activator inhibitor-2 in epithelial ovarian cancer: A favorable prognostic factor related to the actions of CSF-1. *Intl. J. Cancer* 74, 571–575.
211. Ahmed, N., Riley, C., Rice, G. E., Quinn, M. A., and Baker, M. S. (2002). Alpha(v)beta(6) integrin—A marker for the malignant potential of epithelial ovarian cancer. *J. Histochem. Cytochem.* 50, 1371–1380.
212. Cruet-Hennequart, S., Maubant, S., Luis, J., Gauduchon, P., Staedel, C., and Dedhar, S. (2003). Alpha(v) integrins cell proliferation through integrin-linked kinase (ILK) in ovarian cancer cells. *Oncogene* 22, 1688–1702.
213. Rosano, L., Varmi, M., Salani, D., DiCastro, V., Spinella, F., Natali, P. G., and Bagnato, A. (2001). Endothelin-1 induces tumor prteinase activation and invasiveness of ovarian carcinoma cells. *Cancer Res.* 61, 8340–8346.
214. Skubitz, A. P. N., Bast Jr., R. C., Wayner, E. A. et al. (1996). Expression of α6 and β4 integrins in serous ovarian carcinoma correlates with expression of the basement membrane protein laminin. *Am. J. Pathol.* 148, 1445–1461.
215. Moser, T. L., Pizzo, S. V., Bafetti, L. M. et al. (1996). Evidence for preferential adhesion of ovarian epithelial carcinoma cells to type I collagen mediated by the alpha2beta1 integrin. *Intl. J. Cancer* 67, 695–701.
216. van den Brule, F. A., Berchuck, A., Bast Jr., R. C. et al. (1994). Differential expression of the 67-kD laminin receptor and 31-kD human laminin-binding protein in human ovarian carcinomas. *Eur. J. Cancer* 30A, 1096–1099.
217. Cannistra, S. A., Ottensmeier, C., Niloff, J. et al. (1995). Expression and function of beta1 and alpha v beta3 integrins in ovarian cancer. *Gynecol. Oncol.* 58, 216–225.
218. Arboleda, M. J., Lyons, J. F., Kabbinavar, F. F., Bray, M. R., Snow, B. E., Ayala, R., Danino, M., Karlan, B. Y., and Slamon, D. J. (2003). Overexpression of AKT2/protein kinase beta leads to upregulation of beta1 integrins, increased invasion, and metastasis of human breast and ovarian cancer cells. *Cancer Res.* 63, 196–206.
219. Risinger, J. I., Berchuck, A., Kohler, M. F., and Boyd, J. (1994). Mutations of the E-cadherin gene in human gynecologic cancers. *Nat. Genet.* 7, 98–102.
220. Kajiyama, K., Fumitaka, K., Khin, E., Shibata, K., Ino, K., and Mizutani, S. (2003). Dipeptidyl peptidase IV overexpression induces up-regulation of E-Cadherin and tissue inhibitors of matrix metalloproteinases, resulting in decreased invasive potential in ovarian carcinoma cells. *Cancer Res.* 63, 2278–2283.
221. Cannistra, S. A., Abu-Jawdeh, G., Niloff, J. et al. (1995). CD44 variant expression is a common feature of epithelial ovarian cancer: Lack of association with standard prognostic factors. *J. Clin. Oncol.* 13, 1912–1921.
222. Cannistra, S. A., Kansas, G. S., Niloff, J. et al. (1993). Binding of ovarian cancer cells to peritoneal mesothelium in vitro is partly mediated by CD44H. *Cancer Res.* 53, 3830–3838.
223. Strobel, T., Swanson, L., and Cannistra, S. A. (1997). In vivo inhibition of CD44 limits intra-abdominal spread of a human ovarian cancer xenograft in nude mice: A novel role for CD44 in the process of peritoneal implantation. *Cancer Res.* 57, 1228–1232.
224. Goodheart, M. J., Vasef, M. A., Sood, A. K., Davis, C. S., and Buller, R. E. (2002). Ovarian cancer p53 mutation is associated with tumor microvessel density. *Gynecol. Oncol.* 86, 85–90.
225. Senger, D. R., Galli, S. J., Dvorak, A. M. et al. (1983). Tumor cells secrete a vascular permeability factor that promotes accumulation of ascites fluid. *Science* 219, 983–985.
226. Zebrowski, B. K., Liu, W., Ramirez, K., Akagi, M. D., Mills, G. B., and Ellis, L. M. (1999). Markedly elevated levels of vascular endothelial growth factor in malignant ascites. *Ann. Surg. Oncol.* 6, 373–378.
227. Chen, C. A., Cheng, W. F., Lee, C. N. et al. (1999). Serum vascular endothelial growth factor in epithelial ovarian neoplasms: Correlation with patient survival. *Gynecol. Oncol.* 74, 235–240.
228. Hu, Y. L., Tee, M. K., Goetzl, E. J., Mills, G. B., Ferrara, N., and Jaffe, R. B. (2001). Induction of vascular endothelial growth factor expression by lysophosphatidic acid in normal and neoplastic human ovarian epithelial cells. *J. Natl. Cancer Inst.* 93, 734–735.
229. Xu, L., Xie, K., Mukaida, N. et al. (1999). Hypoxia-induced elevation in interleukin-8 expression by human ovarian carcinoma cells. *Cancer Res.* 59, 5822–5829.

Index

B

D

E

F

G

H

M